American Universities and Colleges

American Universities and Colleges

Nineteenth Edition

VOLUME 2

PRAEGER

AN IMPRINT OF ABC-CLIO, LLC
Santa Barbara, California • Denver, Colorado • Oxford, England

Library of Congress Cataloging-in-Publication Data

American universities and colleges, volume 1. -- Nineteenth ed.
v. 1-2 , p. cm.
Includes bibliographical references and indexes.
ISBN 978-0-313-36607-9 (hard copy : alk. paper) -- ISBN 978-0-313-36609-3 (hard copy : alk. paper) -- ISBN 978-0-313-36611-6 (hard copy : alk. paper) -- ISBN 978-0-313-36608-6 (e-book : alk. paper) -- ISBN 978-0-313-36610-9 (e-book : alk. paper) -- ISBN 978-0-313-36612-3 (e-book : alk. paper)
1. Universities and colleges--United States--Directories. 2. Education--United States--Directories.
LA226.A66 2010
378.73--dc22
2010006880

ISBN (Set): 978-0-313-36607-9

ISBN Vol. 1: 978-0-313-36609-3

ISBN Vol. 2: 978-0-313-36611-6

ABC-CLIO, LLC
130 Cremona Drive, P.O. Box 1911
Santa Barbara, California 93116-1911

This book is printed on acid-free paper ∞
Manufactured in the United States of America

Contents of Volume 2

Contents of Volume 1

Notes on Institutional Exhibits

Part III of this book includes more than 1,800 individual entries on degree-granting baccalaureate-or-above institutions and units thereof that are accredited or recognized candidates for accreditation by one of the eight regional agencies. Each institution's description also includes its regional, professional, and institutional accreditation. Those fields in which programs offering specific areas of the profession for accreditation are also indicated. For information on specialized professional accrediting agencies, see Part II of this book.

The information in Part III was prepared largely from data supplied by the institutions themselves in questionnaires sent to all degree-granting regionally accredited colleges and universities. In addition, information was gleaned from other available sources. The institutions which did not return questionnaires have exhibits prepared from data provided by the National Center for Education Statistics IPED Integrated Post-Secondary Education Database, college catalogs, and other institutional sources.

Unless noted, data are for the 2008-09 academic years. Changes in addresses, chief executive officers, and admissions officers up to 2008 are also reflected in the exhibits.

The material throughout Part III was prepared in as set a format as possible to augment comparison of data not only among exhibits in this edition but also to earlier editions of American Universities and Colleges. However, the variety of high education in America defies formulas, and the exhibits reflect diversity as well as similarity. Whenever possible, qualifications offered by the institutions appear (for example, estimates are so labeled). For the most part, negative information has been omitted. However, exhibits report if institutions conduct no summer sessions, offer no financial aid, especially for foreign students, have no campus housing, or do not permit cars on campus grounds.

Omission of sections from institutional descriptions may indicate negative information, data withheld, or unavailable or irrelevant material.

Institution Description. Institutions were asked to provide summary views—control, enrollment, degrees awarded, general relation to statewide coordinating bodies and governing boards, and membership in consortia oriented toward providing student services.

Accreditation. Regional, specialized, and institutional accreditation is noted.

History. Institutions were asked to provide brief histories followed, where available, by referrals to the best and most comprehensive institutional history available.

Institutional Structure. Institutions were asked to offer a summary view of their governing structure and composition. They were asked to list the number and type of members of the governing board and the number of administrators and faculty in the institution as well as the title of the academic governance body. Faculty represented by collective bargaining agents were so designated.

Calendar. This section indicates the institution's primary calendar system (semester, quarter, etc.) and whether or not summer session is available. It notes the months freshmen may enter and tells when degrees are offered and when commencement occurs.

Characteristics of Freshmen. Institutions were asked to offer information on the entering class (usually freshmen, but sometimes students at other levels in, for example, professional or upper-division-only schools). Institutions were further asked to specify average secondary school rank, SAT or ACT scores if appropriate, and to note number of Merit Scholars attending, number of applicants accepted, number of accepted applicants enrolling, number of freshmen graduating within five years.

Admission. Institutions were asked to describe both admission procedures and requirements. Procedures include the type of admission plan (rolling or standard) and the earliest and latest possible application dates, as well as information about the existence of early decision and early acceptance policies. Under the rolling admissions plan, applications are processed as received and the applicants notified when the processing is completed. Early decisions belong to the more traditional admissions plan and provide for a notification of acceptance for highly qualified students in advance of usual admissions notification date. Early acceptance pertains to a policy whereby such students may be admitted at the end of their junior year in high school. Institutions were asked to provide requirements common to their entering class (usually freshmen) as a whole. Requirements are distinguished from recommendations in information on number and distribution of secondary school units, secondary school class standing, GPA, and entrance examinations. Transfer student admission requirements could also be mentioned in this category.

Degree Requirements. Institutions were asked to indicate the levels of degrees for which they were reporting requirements and to list only common requirements. Special requirements often appear in the supplemental exhibits for complex institutions with separate units. Often credit, GPA, and residence requirements are reported as ranges rather than single figures. Institutions were asked to indicate whether students could fulfill requirements through achievement test, and whether exit examinations, chapel attendance, physical education , or ROTC were required. Finally, institutions were asked to describe their grading systems. In the case of regionally accredited graduate or professional schools, the degree requirements given, like the admission requirements, were those pertaining to programs entered directly following the baccalaureate.

Distinctive Educational Programs. Institutions were asked to report academic offerings such as work-experience programs, including cooperative education and internships; flexible meeting places and schedules, including off-campus centers, weekend and evening classes; accelerated degree plans; dual and joint degree programs involving two institutions and two degrees; double-degree programs where one institution awards two degrees; cooperative degree programs where two units or institutions offer one degree; external degree programs and continuing education curricula; special facilities for using telecommunications in the classroom; interdepartmental and interdisciplinary programs; study abroad; and many other programs.

ROTC. Institutions were asked to specify whether ROTC was available, whether it was required, and whether it was offered cooperatively with another institution.

Degrees Conferred. Institutions were asked to report degrees at the baccalaureate, master's, and doctoral degree levels in agriculture and natural resources, architecture and environmental design, area studies, biological sciences, business and management, communications, computer and information sciences, education, engineering, fine and applied arts, health professions, home economics, law, letters, library science, mathematics, military sciences, physical sciences, psychology, public affairs and services, social science, theology, interdisciplinary students, and other professions. Institutions listed in addition the number of degrees awarded at the associate level in arts and sciences; in science- or engineering-related organized occupational programs in data-processing, health services, and paramedical, mechanical and engineering, and natural science technologies, and in other occupational programs in business and commerce, and public service-related technologies. Finally, they were asked to report any intermediate degrees—formal recognitions for programs between master's and doctorates which are in essence the doctoral degree without the dissertation.

Fees and Other Expenses. Institutions were asked to provide tuition figures for 2008-09. They were also asked to provide information on fees and room and board.

Financial Aid. Institutions were asked to give the reasons for awarding their undergraduate scholarships, grants, and loans and their graduate fellowships (excluding first-professional awards). They were also asked to report figures on the number of recipients, the total funds awarded, and the range of awards for their undergraduate scholarships, grants, loans, and college-assigned jobs; and for their graduate fellowships (also excluding first-professional) and grants, teaching and research assistantships, and other college-assigned jobs. They were requested to provide similar information on federal and state aid received by their students.

Departments and Teaching Staff. Institutions were asked to list by department and rank those members of the teaching and research staff (including those with released time) who were employed on a full-time basis and whose major regular assignment was instruction. They were also asked to list part-time teachers who taught less than full time; however, that status was defined by the individual institutions. In complex institutions with separately defined units such as divisions, schools, or colleges, total faculty figures appear in the main exhibits, with the departmental breakdown available in the descriptions of the individual unit.

Enrollment. Institutions were asked to report their total student enrollment, divided into full-and part-time students at the undergraduate, first professional, and graduate levels. They were also asked to list unclassified students who take courses for credit but are not degree candidates, and numbers of transfer students.

Characteristics of Student Body. In this section, institutions were asked to provide data on ethnic/racial makeup of the student body as well as the age distribution.

International Students. In this section, institutions were asked to provide information on nonresident aliens in attendance as well as the number of students from various world areas. They were also requested to indicate the availability and extent of the programs, scholarships, fellowships, and loans especially designated for foreign students.

Student Life. Institutions were asked to indicate the presence and nature (particularly whether the dormitories were single-sex or coed) of institutionally provided housing and to describe the availability of married-student housing. They were asked to specify what kinds of intercollegiate athletics were available for men and women; and what kinds of student publications, radio, and television activities were possible. Institutions were asked whether their campus had special regulations regarding cars or residence halls hours. And they were asked to provide information about their medical services, campus transportation systems, and (if appropriate) learning resources centers. Finally, they were asked to characterize the surrounding community as to population and availability of mass transportation.

Publications. If appropriate, institutions were asked to provide information about their scholarly journals and university presses.

Library Collections. Institutions were asked to provide figures on their current collections of volumes, government document collections, microforms, audiovisual materials, and periodical subscriptions. They were also asked to describe their three most important special collections.

Buildings and Grounds. Institutions were asked to report their campus area, grounds, and equipment, the buildings completed since 1999, the buildings currently being constructed, and the number of buildings.

Chief Executive Officer. The chief executive and admissions officers are, whenever possible, those who held the position in 2008.

Accreditation in Higher Education

Accreditation is a system for recognizing educational institutions and professional programs affiliated with those institutions for a level of performance, integrity, and quality which entitles them to the confidence of the educational community and the public they serve. In the United States this recognition is extended primarily through nongovernmental, voluntary institutional or professional associates. These groups establish criteria for recognition, arrange site visits, and evaluate those institutions and professional programs that desire recognition status; they approve for recognition those which meet their criteria.

Institutional accreditation is granted by the accrediting commissions of associations of schools and colleges, which collectively serve most of the institutions chartered or licensed in the United Sates and its possessions. These commissions and associations accredit total operating units only.

Specialized accreditation of professional schools and programs is granted by commissions on accreditation set up by national professional organizations in such areas as business, dentistry, engineering, and law. Each of these groups has its distinctive definitions of eligibility, criteria for accreditation and operating procedures, but all have undertaken accreditation activities, primarily to provide quality assurances concerning the educational preparation of members of the profession.

USES OF ACCREDITATION

In most other countries the establishment and maintenance of educational standards are the responsibility of a central government bureau. In the United States, however, public authority in education is constitutionally reserved to the states. The system of voluntary nongovernmental evaluation called accreditation has evolved to promote both regional and national approaches to the determination of educational quality.

While accreditation is basically a private, nonvoluntary process, accrediting decisions are used as a consideration in many official actions: federal funding agencies consider accreditation as an important factor in determining eligibility for financial assistance; scholarship commissions and philanthropic foundations frequently limit their grants to accredited institutions or programs of study; employers rely on the accredited status of institutions when evaluating credentials; school counselors use the decisions in advising students about colleges and programs; college and university officials depend on them to assess and award academic credit; and potential students need them for assurance that a college or university has met minimum requirements for educational quality. In addition, these decisions are useful to faculty and staff in their efforts to develop comprehensive educational goals. In many professions, eligibility for certification or licensure is limited to graduates of accredited institutions. Finally, the public is protected from unqualified graduates who may have been inadequately prepared for professional practice.

The accrediting process is also useful in helping institutions maintain high educational standards and improve quality. The accrediting bodies provide counsel to both established and developing institutions and protect them from both external and internal encroachments that might jeopardize their educational effectiveness and academic freedom.

The accrediting process is continuously evolving. The trend has been from quantitative to qualitative criteria, from the early days of simple checklists to an increasing interest and emphasis on measuring the outcomes of educational experiences.

The process begins with the institutional or programmatic self-study, a comprehensive effort to measure progress according to previously accepted objected. The self-study considers the interests of a broad cross-section of constituencies—students, faculty administrators, alumni, trustees, and in some circumstances, the local community. The resulting report is reviewed by the appropriate accrediting commission and serves as the basis for evaluation by a site-visit team from the accrediting group. The site-visit team normally consists of professional educators (faculty and administrators), specialists selected according to the nature of the institution and members representing specific public interests. The visiting team considers the institution or program according to the dimensions of the self-study and adds judgments based on its own expertise and its external perspective. The evaluation team completes a report, which is reviewed by the institution or program for factual accuracy. The original self-study, the team report and any response the institution or program may wish to make are forwarded to an accreditation review committee. The review body uses these materials as the basis for action regarding the accreditation status of the institution or program. Negative actions may be appealed according to established procedures of the accrediting body.

Accrediting bodies reserve the right to review member institutions or programs at any time for cause. They also reserve the right to review any substantive changes, such as an expansion from undergraduate to graduate offerings. In this way accrediting bodies hold their member institutions and programs continually accountable to their educational peers, to the constituencies they serve, and to the public interest.

Historically and currently, accreditation at the postsecondary level may be said to foster excellence in postsecondary education through the development of uniform national criteria and guidelines for assessing educational effectiveness; to encourage improvement through continuous self-study and review; and to assure the educational community, the general public, and other agencies or organizations that an institution or program has clearly defined and appropriate objectives, maintains conditions under which their achievement can reasonably be expected, appears in fact to be accomplishing them substantially, and can be expected to continue to do so.

Accrediting bodies do not rank or grade institutions; they either accredit or decline to accredit them. Most commissions, however, do specify a definite term for which their accreditation is valid, five years usually being the maximum for initial accreditation and ten years for reaccredidation. Many accrediting bodies award candidate status to developing or newly applying institutions, which satisfy eligibility requirements and that present evidence of sound planning, adequate implementation resources, and potential for meeting stated goals within a reasonable period of time.

This status, designed for postsecondary institutions and programs that may or may not be fully operational, usually is granted for a two-year term. If progress is being made, candidacy can be extended for up to six years. Institutions or programs that show serious weakness in one or more areas, but which at the same time show firm potential for remedying the deficiencies, may be placed in a probationary status. Accreditation continues, but generally for a sharply reduced term, and an interim report or extra site visit is generally required.

ACCREDITING ORGANIZATIONS

Eight regional commissions in six geographic areas cover all parts of the nation and grant total institutional accreditations. These associations are: Commission on Higher Education, Middle States Association of Colleges and Schools, 3624 Market Street, Philadelphia, Pennsylvania 19104 (Delaware, District of Columbia, Maryland, New Jersey, New York, Pennsylvania, Puerto Rico, Virgin Islands), Commission on Institutions of Higher Education, New England Association of Schools and Colleges and Commission on Technical and Career Institutions, New England Association of Schools and Colleges, 209 Burlington Road, Bedford, Massachusetts 01730-1433 (Connecticut, Maine, Massachusetts, New Hampshire, Rhode Island, Vermont); Commission on Institutions of Higher Education, North Central Association of Colleges and Schools, 30 N. LaSalle Street, Suite 2400, Chicago, Illinois 60602 (Arizona, Arkansas, Colorado, Illinois, Indiana, Iowa, Kansas, Michigan, Minnesota, Missouri, Nebraska, New Mexico, North Dakota, Ohio, Oklahoma, South Dakota, West Virginia, Wisconsin, Wyoming); Commission on Colleges, Northwest Association of Schools and Colleges, 11130 NE 33rd Place, Suite 120, Bellevue, Washington 98004 (Alaska, Idaho, Montana, Nevada, Oregon, Utah, Washington); Commission on Colleges, Southern Association of Colleges and Schools, 1866 Southern Lane, Decatur, Georgia 30033-4097 (Alabama, Florida, Georgia, Kentucky, Louisiana, Mississippi, North Carolina, South Carolina, Tennessee, Texas, Virginia), Accrediting Commission for Senior Colleges and Universities, Western Association of Schools and Colleges, c/o Mills College, Box 9990, Oakland, California 94613 (American Samoa, California, Guam, Hawaii, Trust Territory of the Pacific); and Accrediting Commission for Community and Junior Colleges, Western Association of Schools and Colleges, 3402 Mendocino Avenue, Santa Rose, California 95403 (American Samoa, California, Guam, Hawaii, Trust Territory of the Pacific.)

Eight associations accredit total institutions on a national scale. These are: Commission on Accreditation, Accrediting Association of Bible Colleges, 5890 S. Semoran Boulevard, Orlando, FL 32822; Board of Commissioners, Accrediting Bureau of Health Education Schools, 2700 South Quincy Street, Suite 210, Arlington, VA 22206; Accrediting Commission for Career Schools/Colleges of Technology, 2101 Wilson Boulevard, Arlington, VA 22201; Accrediting Council for Independent Colleges and Schools, 750 First Street, NE, Suite 980, Washington, DC 20002; Accreditation Commission, Association of Advanced Rabbinical and Talmudic Schools, 175 Fifth Avenue, Suite 711, New York, NY 10010; Commission on Accrediting, The Association of Theological Schools in the United States and Canada, 10 Summit Park Drive, Pittsburgh, PA 15275-1103; Commission on Occupational Education, Council on Occupational Education, 41 Perimeter Center East, NE, Suite 640, Atlanta, GA 30346; and Accrediting Commission, Distance Education and Training Council, 1601 18th Street, NW, Washington, DC 20009.

Finally, forty-one national associations offer recognized specialized and professional accreditation for programs or other academic units within an institution, or for free-standing single purpose institutions. It is thus possible that a large number of accrediting bodies may be involved in a single institution, usually a university with a variety of professional programs. However, for most degree-granting institutions, the basic accreditation remains institutional (and usually regional) accreditation upon which virtually all other accreditation is built.

RELATIONSHIP OF ACCREDITATION TO THE STATES

Before the organization of voluntary accrediting associations, state departments of education and state universities were faced with the necessity of judging the quality of the educational programs of collegiate institutions within their state. The statutory responsibilities of the states for licensing public school teachers required the development of systems of state approval of teacher preparation institutions. The Board of Regents of the University of the State of New York was the first state agency to develop machinery for the approval of courses of study in teacher education, as well as in the liberal arts and many other specialized areas. The majority of the state agencies did not begin accrediting until after the first decade of the present century; and to a great extent, they have continued to limit their accrediting activities to approval of teacher education programs.

Accrediting activities by state universities in nearly every instance had their origin in relations with secondary schools. These accrediting activities related to the admissions of secondary school graduates to the universities on the basis of certification of the secondary schools rather than entrance examinations given to the applicants. Most of the state universities, however, have abandoned the practice of accrediting other institutions of higher education and now rely upon the accredited status given through the institutions accrediting associations.

THE RECOGNITION OF ACCREDITING BODIES

The Council for Higher Education Accreditation (CHEA) is the successor structure for the nongovernmental recognition of accrediting bodies. It replaces the Council on Postsecondary Accreditation (COPA), which dissolved on December 31, 1993, and its successor, the Commission on Recognition of Postsecondary Accreditation (CORPA) which dissolved on December 31, 1996.

The Council for Higher Education Accreditation (CHEA) is a nonprofit organization of colleges and universities. Established in 1996, CHEA serves as a national advocate for voluntary self-regulation through accreditation. CHEA serves students and their families, colleges and universities, sponsoring bodies, governments, and employers by promoting academic quality through formal recognition of higher education accrediting bodies. CHEA recognizes, coordinates, and periodically reviews the work of its recognized accrediting bodies and the appropriateness of existing or proposed accrediting bodies and their activities through its granting of recognition.

RELATIONSHIP OF ACCREDITATION WITH THE FEDERAL GOVERNMENT

Although the federal government does not accredit any educational activities, the Veterans Readjustment Act of 1952, which provided for federal assistance to veterans for their education, charged the former United States Commissioner of Education with the responsibility of publishing a list of nationally recognized accrediting agencies, which he determined to be reliable authorities for determining the quality of training offered by educational institutions. In 1968, the Accreditation and Institutional Eligibility Staff and an associated internal advisory committee were established in United States Office of Education to administer the commissioner's review process for accrediting agencies being used to establish institutional eligibility for several other educational acts.

Congressional authorization for federal involvement in nongovernmental accreditation has traditionally been limited to the establishment of an institution's eligibility to apply for funds from federal programs and the maintenance of records of accrediting status by the Secretary of Education to implement the processes of legislation.

THE TRIAD

As the system presently functions, there is a need for the federal government to establish eligibility for its funds, as there is a need for the states to charter educational institutions within their jurisdictions. The voluntary sector, represented by the accrediting organizations, serves as a bridge between the federal and state roles in education.

Thus, a three-part structure for accreditation has been created. This three-part structure has been termed a "triad" for eligibility. The triad consists of the states, which grant institutional charter of licenses to operate; the accrediting bodies, which provide an educational assessment of institutions and programs; and the federal government, which provides funding for some activities related to student aid and education.

REFERENCES

Astin, Alexander W., Bowen, Howard R., and Chambers, Charles M. *Evaluating Educational Quality.* Washington, DC: Council on Postsecondary Accreditation, 1979.

Casey, Robert J. and Harris, John W. *Accountability in Higher Education.* Washington, DC: Council on Postsecondary Accreditation, 1979.

Finkin, Matthew W. *Federal Reliance on Educational Accreditation: The Scope of Administrative Discretion.* Washington, DC: Council on Postsecondary Accreditation, 1978.

Fisk, Robert S. and Duryea, E.D. *Academic Collective Bargaining and Regional Accreditation.* Washington, DC: Council on Postsecondary Accreditation, 1980.

Harcleroad, Fred F. *Voluntary Organizations in America and the Development of Educational Accreditation.* Washington, DC: Council on Postsecondary Accreditation, 1980.

Kaplin, William A. *Accrediting Agencies' Legal Responsibilities: In Pursuit of the Public Interest.* Washington, DC: Council on Postsecondary Accreditation, 1981.

Kuhns, Eileen and Martorana, S.V. *Toward Academic Quality Off-Campus: Monitoring Requirements of Institutional Accrediting Bodies and the States for Off-Campus, Military Base, and Study Abroad Programs.* Washington, DC: Council on Postsecondary Accreditation, 1984.

Lenn, Marjorie Peace. "The US Accreditation System," *Quality Assurance in International Higher Education.* The Falmer Press, London and Washington, DC: 1992.

Selden, William K. and Porter, Harry V. *Accreditation: Its Purposes and Uses.* Washington, DC: Council on Postsecondary Accreditation, 1979.

Abbreviations and Definitions

The following sections define many of the terms and abbreviations that readers will encounter in Part III.

DEGREES

B.A.	Bachelor of Arts
B.D.	Bachelor of Divinity
B.F.A.	Bachelor of Fine Arts
B.S.	Bachelor of Science
D.B.	Bachelor of Divinity
D.C.	Doctor of Chiropractic
D.D.	Doctor of Divinity
D.D.S.	Doctor of Dental Science or Doctor of Dental Surgery
D.M.D.	Doctor of Dental Medicine
D.O.	Doctor of Osteopathy
D.P.	Doctor of Podiatry
D.Pharm.	Doctor of Pharmacy
D.V.M.	Doctor of Veterinary Medicine
J.D.	Doctor of Jurisprudence
L.H.D.	Doctor of Humanities
Litt.D.	Doctor of Letters
LL.B.	Bachelor of Laws
LL.D.	Doctor of Laws
M.A.	Master of Arts
M.B.A.	Master of Business Administration
M.D.	Doctor of Medicine
M.Div.	Master of Divinity
M.F.A.	Master of Fine Arts
M.S.	Master of Science
M.S.W.	Master of Social Work or Master of Social Welfare
O.D.	Doctor of Optometry
Ph.B.	Bachelor of Philosophy
Ph.D.	Doctor of Philosophy
Ph.G.	Graduate in Pharmacy

OTHER ABBREVIATIONS

AAC&U	Association of American Colleges and Universities
AACC	American Association of Community Colleges
AACN	American Association of Colleges of Nursing
AACRAO	American Association of Collegiate Registrars and Admissions Officers
AACTE	American Association of Colleges for Teacher Education
AAHE	American Association for Higher Education
AALS	Association of American Law Schools
AAMC	Association of American Medical Colleges
AARTS	Association of Advanced Rabbinical and Talmudic Schools
AASCU	American Association of State Colleges and Universities
AAU	Association of American Universities
AAUP	American Association of University Professors
ABHE	Association for Biblical Higher Education (formerly AABC)
ABHES	Accrediting Bureau of Health Education Schools
ACCSCT	Accrediting Commission for Career Schools/Colleges of Technology
ACCT	Association of Community College Trustees
ACCU	Association of Catholic Colleges and Universities
ACE	American Council on Education
ACICS	Accrediting Council for Independent Schools and Colleges
ACPA	American College Personnel Association
ACT	American College Testing
ADEA	American Dental Education Association
AGB	Association of Governing Boards of Universities and Colleges
AHC	Association of Academic Health Centers
AJCU	Association of Jesuit Colleges and Universities
APPA	Association of Higher Education Facilities Officers
ASEE	American Society for Engineering Education
ATS	Association of Theological Schools in the United States
CASE	Council for Advancement and Support of Education
CB	The College Board
CCA	Career College Association
CCCU	Council for Christian Colleges & Universities
CGS	Council of Graduate Schools
CHEA	Council for Higher Education Accreditation
CIC	Council for Independent Colleges
COE	Council for Opportunity in Education
COGR	The Council on Governmental Relations
CUPA-HR	College and University Professional Association for Human Resources
DELC	Distance Education and Learning Council
EDUCAUSE	EDUCAUSE
ETS	Educational Testing Service
HACU	Hispanic Association of Colleges and Universities
MSA	Middle States Association of Colleges and Schools
NACAC	National Association of College Admission Counseling
NACUA	National Association of College and University Attorneys
NACUBO	National Association of College and University Business Officers
NAFEO	National Association for Equal Opportunity in Higher Education
NAFSA	NAFSA: Association of International Educators
NAICU	National Association of Independent Colleges and Universities
NASFAA	National Association of Student Financial Aid Administrators
NASPA	National Association of Student Personnel Administrators

NASULGC	National Association of State Universities and Land-Grant Colleges
NAWE	NAWE: Advancing Women in Higher Education
NCA	North Central Association of Colleges and Schools
NCAA	National Collegiate Athletic Association
NCURA	National Council of University Research Administrators
NEASC	New England Association of Schools and Colleges
NWCCU	Northwest Commission of Colleges and Universities (formerly NASC)
SACS	Southern Association of Colleges and Schools
UCEA	University Continuing Education Association
UNCF	United Negro College Fund
WASC	Western Association of Schools and Colleges
WCC	Women's College Coalition
WHES	Business-Higher Education Forum

DEFINITIONS

Administrators—institutional staff members with administrative responsibilities who teach no more than one class per term and who have titles such as dean of instruction, academic dean, dean of faculty, dean of students, librarian, registrar, coach, etc.

Audiovisual Materials—teaching and learning aids that are neither books nor microforms, that are interpreted through hearing and/or sight, and that require special equipment to use. Audiovisual materials include motion pictures, records and tapes, filmstrips, slides, transparencies, videotapes, and the like.

Branch Campus—a relatively permanent unit of an institution that offers and organized program(s) of work requiring at least two years of study (as opposed to merely courses) located in a community beyond a reasonable commuting distance from the main campus or parent institution.

Calendar—the system by which an institution divides its year into periods for instruction. The most common systems include those based on semesters, trimesters, and quarters.

Cluster College—a group of institutions, located within close proximity to each other, that cooperate in providing educational programs and other facilities to students in all institutions forming the aggregate. Cluster colleges cooperate more closely than institutions in a consortium.

Continuing Education—instruction other than that offered in the regular campus academic program. Examples include evening or weekend colleges or correspondence courses. These programs often are designed to serve the special needs of learners such as part-time or fully employed students.

Cooperative Education—a program in which a student alternates between periods of full-time study and full-time employment in a related field. Typically, five years are required to complete a bachelor's degree under this plan.

Early Admission—the practice of admitting students who have not yet completed high school—usually students of exceptional ability who have completed their junior year.

External-Degree Program—a system of study that grants credit for courses at institutions other than that offering the degree; that often counts as extrainstitutional learning; and that often emphasizes off-campus, self-directed study.

First-Professional Degree—signifies completion of academic requirements for a selected profession based on a program requiring at least two academic years of postsecondary study. First-professional degrees include architecture; dentistry; medicine; optometry; osteopathic medicine; pharmacy; podiatry or podiatric medicine (including chiropody); veterinary medicine; chiropractic; law; general; theological professions, general.

4-1-4—a semester system that consists of two terms, each about 16 weeks long, divided by one-month term during which students participate in intensive short courses, independent study, employment, or other educational activities.

Free University—programs—usually operating without credit, grades, or attendance constraints—set up by students and faculty for discussion of issues and subjects not necessarily typical of those covered in other postsecondary courses.

Full-Time Instructional Faculty—those members of the instructional/research staff (including those with released time) who are employed on a full-time basis and whose major regular assignment is instruction. The group includes department heads (if they have no other administrative title and hold faculty rank) but does not include administrators with titles such as dean of instruction, academic dean, dean of faculty, dean of students, librarian, registrar, coach, etc., even though they may devote part of their time to classroom instruction.

Honors Program—any special program for highly capable students that offers the opportunity for educational enrichment, independent study, acceleration, or some combination of these activities.

Independent Study—an arrangement that allows students to complete some of their college program by studying on their own rather than by attending scheduled classes and completing standard assignments. Typically, students plan these programs in consultation with a faculty advisor or committee, who evaluates their progress.

Institutional System—a complex comprising two or more separately organized or independently complete postsecondary units under the control or supervision of a single administrative body (Compare **Multicampus Institution**.)

Intermediate Degree—a formal recognition (degree or certificate) for a program between the master's degree and the doctorate, which is essence is the terminal degree without the dissertation. Examples are Master of Philosophy, Candidate in Philosophy, etc.

Internships—short-term, supervised work experiences, usually related to a student's major field of study, for which the student earns academic credit.

Learning Resource Center—a specially designed study area where individual students or groups are provided with study supplies and equipment, usually including books, programmed materials, and audiovisual supplies.

Main Campus—the most important unit in an institution that is made up of one or more branch campuses. The main campus (sometimes called the parent institution) usually houses the core, primary, or most comprehensive program and is usually also the location of the central administrative office.

Microforms—books, periodicals, and other materials that have been photographically reduced in size for storage, protection, and inexpensive publication. These materials must be read with the aid of enlarging equipment.

Minority Group—Any racial, religious, ethnic, or social aggregation of people who have suffered some discrimination due to bias. IPEDS surveys (formerly HEGIS) suggest the following five racial/ethnic groups as minority categories: Black, non-Hispanic; American

Indian or Alaskan Native; Asian or Pacific Islander; Hispanic; and under the heading White, non-Hispanic, Middle Eastern. For purposes of this questionnaire, women are not considered a minority group.

Multicampus Institution—an organization that resembles an institutional system but is unequivocally designated as a single body organized according to one of the following specifications: (1) an institution having two or more administratively equal campuses responsible to a central governing structure (that may or may not be located on one of the campuses) or (2) an institution having a main campus with one or more branch campuses. (Compare **Institutional System.**)

Open Admissions—policy of admitting high school graduates and other adults generally without regard to conventional academic qualifications. Virtually all applicants with high school diplomas or the equivalent are accepted.

Organized Occupational Program—a course of study consisting of an integrated series of required and elective courses designed to prepare students for employment in a job or cluster of occupations. Programs are science- or engineering-related in areas of data processing technologies, health services and paramedical technologies, mechanical and engineering technologies, or natural science technologies. Other nonscience- and nonengineering related programs are in business and commerce technologies, and public service-related technologies. Completion requires at least one but less than four years of full-time attendance, or the equivalent in part-time attendance, and culminates in formal recognition that the student has completed an organized program.

Part-Time Instruction Faculty—those members of the instruction/research staff who are employed to teach less than—and are paid for less than—a full-time course level, however defined by the institution.

Post-Baccalaureate—graduate study beyond the bachelor's degree including that toward the first-professional (see definition), master's, intermediate (see definition), and doctoral awards.

Quarter—an academic calendar period of about 11 weeks. Each academic year is made up of four quarters, but students can make normal academic progress by attending three quarters annually.

Rolling Admissions Plan—an admissions procedure by which the college considers each student's application as soon as all required materials have been received and reviewed. Colleges following this practice usually notify applicants of admissions decisions continuously over several months in contrast to other institutions that announce all decisions simultaneously.

Semester—a period of about 17-18 weeks that makes up half of the usual academic year at institutions following this calendar system.

Sponsored Research—projects funded by extra-institutional financial sources, such as government or industry.

Student Services—systems and facilities provided to contribute to student well-being outside the context of formal academic instruction. Student services are provided by counseling centers, financial aid programs, student health systems (unless operated as a self-supporting enterprise), registrar's procedures, and admissions offices.

Telecourses—televised courses, taken for credit, that are broadcast on public or cable stations that can be viewed in the home or on campus.

Terminal Degree—one that represents the highest formal academic recognition or certificate available to an individual in a given field.

3-3—a calendar system in which the academic year is divided into three terms with students enrolled in three courses per term.

Trimester—an academic calendar period of about 15 weeks. Three trimesters make up each academic year, but students can make normal academic progress by attending two terms annually.

Unclassified Students—students who take courses for credit but are not candidates for a degree or other formal award.

Upper Division Only—Institution that has no freshman or sophomore postsecondary program. Students complete lower division studies at other institutions before entering the upper division institution to earn their bachelor's degree.

Weekend College—a program that allows students to take a complete course of study by attending classes only on weekends. These programs generally are restricted to a few areas of study and require more than the traditional number of years to complete.

II

Universities and Colleges: Institutional Exhibits

(continued)

New York

Adelphi University

1 South Avenue
Garden City, New York 11530-0701
Tel: (516) 877-3000 **E-mail:** admissions@adelphi.edu
Fax: (516) 877-3039 **Internet:** www.adelphi.edu

Institution Description: Adelphi University is a private, independent, nonprofit institution. *Enrollment:* 8,308. *Degrees awarded:* Associate, baccalaureate, master's, doctorate. Certificates also awarded.

Accreditation: *Regional:* MSA. *Professional*: audiology, business, clinical psychology, nursing, nursing education, social work, speech-language pathology

History: Established as Adelphi Academy 1863; chartered, changed name to Adelphi College, and offered first instruction at postsecondary level 1896; awarded first degree (baccalaureate) 1898; adopted present name 1963. *See* Chester Barrows, *Fifty Years at Adelphi* (Garden City: Adelphi College Press, 1946) for further information.

Institutional Structure: *Governing board:* Board of Trustees of Adelphi University. Representation 27 trustees. All voting. *Composition of institution:* Administrators 336. Academic affairs headed by provost. Management/personnel directed by vice president for administration; finances directed by university treasurer. Full-time instructional faculty 280. Academic governance body, Faculty Senate, meets 18 times per year. *Faculty representation:* Faculty served by collective bargaining agent affiliated with AAUP.

Calendar: Semesters (4-1-4 plan). Academic Aug. to May. Freshmen admitted Sept., Feb., June, July. Degrees conferred May, Aug., Feb. Formal commencements May, Feb. Summer session of 2 terms from early June to early Aug.

Characteristics of Freshmen: 6,865 applicants. 68% of applicants accepted. 21% of accepted applicants enrolled full-time.

74% (715 students) submitted SAT scores; 13% (120 students) submitted ACT scores. *25th percentile*: SAT Critical Reading 470, SAT Math 500, SAT Writing 470. ACT Composite 20, ACT English 20, ACT Math 20. *75th percentile*: SAT Critical Reading 590, SAT Math 580, SAT Writing 590; ACT Composite 26, ACT English 25, ACT Math 26.

60% of entering freshmen expected to graduate within 5 years. 92% of freshmen from New York. Freshmen from 24 states and 18 foreign countries.

Admission: *Requirements:* Either graduation from accredited secondary school or GED. Recommend 16 academic units, including 4 English, 2–3 foreign language, 3 mathematics, 3 science, 4 social studies. Minimum GPA 3.0 recommended. Lowest recommended secondary school class standing upper third. *Entrance tests:* College Board SAT or ACT composite. *For transfer students:* 2.5 minimum GPA; from 4-year accredited institution 90 semester hours maximum transfer credit; from 2-year accredited institution 64 hours.

College credit and advanced placement for postsecondary-level work completed in secondary school. College credit for extrainstitutional learning on basis of portfolio and faculty assessments.

Tutoring available. Noncredit remedial courses offered in summer session and regular academic year.

Degree Requirements: *For all associate degrees:* 60 semester hours. *For all baccalaureate degrees:* 120–127 hours; 2.0 GPA (2.0–2.8 GPA in major). *For all undergraduate degrees:* 2.0 GPA; last 30 credits in residence; distribution requirements. Prescribed curriculum for nursing program.

Fulfillment of some degree requirements and exemption from some beginning courses possible by passing College Board CLEP, AP. *Grading system:* A–F, withdraw (carries time limit).

Distinctive Educational Programs: Flexible meeting places and schedules; including off-campus centers (at Hauppauge and New York City, both less than 30 miles away from main institution), weekend and evening classes. Accelerated degree programs. Tutorials. Study abroad programs available in more than 30 countries including Spain, France, Denmark, England. *Other distinctive programs:* University College offering degree programs for adults returning to college. Seven-year joint programs in dentistry with Tufts University and in optometry with SUNY College of Optometry.

Degrees Conferred: 8 *associate;* 1,319 *baccalaureate*; 1,111 *master's*; 24 *doctorate*. Bachelor's degrees awarded in top five disciplines: health professions and related clinical sciences 232; business, management, marketing, and related support services 220; social sciences 139; visual and performing arts 75; education 61. Master's degrees awarded in top five disciplines: education 521; public administration and social services 280; business/marketing 132; psychology 95; health professions and related clinical sciences 95. Doctorates awarded: psychology 21; public administration and social services 2; health professions 1.

Fees and Other Expenses: *Full-time tuition per academic year 2008–09:* undergraduate $25,240; graduate varies by program. *Required fees:* $1,00. *Required fees:* $1,000. *Room and board per academic year:* $10,000. *Other expenses:* $2,300.

Financial Aid: Aid from institutionally generated funds is provided on the basis of academic merit, financial need, athletic ability, other criteria.

Financial aid to full-time, first-time undergraduate students: 80% received some form of aid. Average amount of aid received: federal grants $4,142; state/local grants $2,388; institutional grants $8,095; loans $3,101.

Departments and Teaching Staff: *Total instructional faculty:* 908 (280 full-time 628 part-time). 80% of faculty hold the doctorate, first-professional, or other terminal degree. Student/faculty ratio: 11:1.

Enrollment: Total enrollment 8,308. Undergraduate 5,137. Graduate 3,171. Undergraduate transfer-in students 574.

Characteristics of Student Body: *Ethnic/racial makeup:* number of Black non-Hispanic: 705; American Indian or Alaska Native: 6; Asian or Pacific Islander: 290; Hispanic: 392; White non-Hispanic: 2,325; unknown: 1,031. *Age distribution:* number under 18: 196; 18–19: 1,429; 20–21: 1,448; 22–24: 603; 25–29: 337; 30–34: 232; 35–39: 192; 40–49: 372; 50–64: 120;.

International Students: 267 nonresident aliens enrolled fall 2008. Students from Europe, Asia, Central and South America, Africa, Canada, Australia, Middle East. Programs available to aid students whose native language is not English: English as a Second Language Program. No financial aid specifically designated for international students.

Student Life: On-campus residence halls house 23% of undergraduate student body. *Intercollegiate athletics:* male: baseball, basketball, cross-country, golf, lacrosse, soccer, tennis, track; female: basketball, cross-country, lacrosse, soccer, softball, tennis, track, volleyball, co-ed: swimming. *Special regulations:* Registered cars permitted. *Special services:* Medical service, minibus service between university apartments and campus. *Student publications, radio:* Weekly newspaper, yearbook, web radio station. *Surrounding community:* Garden City population 25,000. New York City, 25 miles from campus, is nearest metropolitan area. Served by mass transit train system; airport 15 miles from campus; passenger rail service less than 1 mile from campus.

Library Collections: 667,500 volumes. Online catalog. Current serial subscriptions: 1,635 paper; 27,221 via electronic access. 28,497 audiovisual materials. 681 DVD discs; 1,194 CD-ROMs. Computer work stations available. Students have access to online information retrieval services and the Internet.

Most important special holdings include Americana Collection; William Cobbett Collection; William Blake Collection; Rare Books Collection.

Buildings and Grounds: Campus area 79 acres.

Chief Executive Officer: Dr. Robert A. Scott, President.

Address admission inquiries to Christine Murphy, Director of Admissions.

College of Arts and Sciences

Degree Programs Offered: *Baccalaureate* in American studies, anthropology, art, art history, biochemistry, biology, chemistry, communications, computer science, dance, design technology, earth sciences, education, English, environmental studies, foreign studies, French, German, history, Latin American studies, mathematics, music, philosophy, physics, political studies, pre-law, pre-medical, sociology, Spanish, theater; *master's* in art, biology, mathematics; *doctorate* in mathematics.

Distinctive Educational Programs: Dual-degree program in engineering with Columbia University and Polytechnic Institute of New York; dentistry with Tufts University; optometry with SUNY. Interdisciplinary programs in Afro-American studies, linguistics, women's studies. Facilities and programs for

ADELPHI UNIVERSITY—*cont'd*

independent research, including honors program in liberal studies, independent study. Washington (DC) internship semester.

School of Business and Money Management

Degree Programs Offered: *Baccalaureate, master's.*
Distinctive Educational Programs: Independent study.

School of Nursing

Degree Programs Offered: *Baccalaureate, master's, doctorate.*
Distinctive Educational Programs: Baccalaureate completion program for registered nurses.

School of Social Work

Degree Programs Offered: *Associate, baccalaureate, master's, doctorate.*
Distinctive Educational Programs: Independent Study. ANSWER, a baccalaureate completion program offered at off-campus centers on Long Island and in New York City for persons employed in social and community agencies.

Derner Institute of Advanced Psychological Studies

Degree Programs Offered: *Doctorate* in behavior research, clinical psychology. Postdoctoral certificate in psychotherapy also given.

School of Education

Degree Programs Offered: *Baccalaureate* in Art K-12, music K-12, early childhood/elementary education, secondary education, physical education, speech and hearing handicapped, health studies; *master's* in communication sciences and disorders, early childhood/elementary education, secondary education, reading, special education, TESOL:, bilingual education, health education; *doctorate* in communication disorders. Special certificate in exercise physiology.

Albany College of Pharmacy

106 New Scotland Avenue
Albany, New York 12208-3492
Tel: (518) 694-1200 **E-mail:** admissions@acp.edu
Fax: (518) 694-1202 **Internet:** www.acp.edu

Institution Description: Albany College of Pharmacy is a private, coeducational institution. *Enrollment:* 1,423. *Degrees awarded:* Baccalaureate, first-professional.

Accreditation: *Regional:* MSA. *Professional*: pharmacy

History: Founded in 1881 as the Department of Pharmacy of Union University. In 1981 the College constructed a new $4 million wing; in 1985, purchased an apartment building to act as first dormitory for non-commuting freshmen students.

Calendar: Semesters. Academic year Aug. to May. Degrees conferred and formal commencement May.

Characteristics of Freshmen: 1,186 applicants. 62% of applicants admitted. 39% of admitted students enrolled full-time.

97% (284 students) submitted SAT scores; 37% (109 students) submitted ACT scores. *25th percentile*: SAT Critical Reading 490, SAT Math 520, SAT Writing 490; ACT Composite 22. *75th percentile*: SAT Critical Reading 650, SAT Math 680, SAT Writing 630; ACT Composite 29.

80% of students from New York. Students from 20 states and 8 foreign countries.

Admission: Early decision deadline November 1 and regular decision deadline Feb. 1. Early decision applicants will be notified by mid-Dec. and regular decisions applicants in mid-March. *Requirements:* High school diploma with college-preparatory program. GED tests accepted in place of diploma. 17 units required, including English 4, mathematics 4 (including precalculus). Science 3, including chemistry, also required. *Entrance tests:* College Board SAT or ACT (SAT preferred). For foreign students TOEFL. *For transfer students:* must go through www.PharmCAS.org to apply for admission. Credit granted through Advanced Placement, college credit, or CLEP.

Degree Requirements: Doctor of Pharmacy 208 credit hours, 2.5 GPA; bachelor's degree 132 credit hours; 2.5 GPA.

Distinctive Educational Programs: 6-year Bachelor of Science in Pharmacy; 6-year B.S./Doctor of Philosophy. Joint B.S. in pharmacy/M.S. in health systems management. 2-year plus B.S. Doctor of Pharmacy program.

Degrees Conferred: 5 *bachelor's:* pharmacy; 193 *first-professional:* pharmacy.

Fees and Other Expenses: *Full-time tuition per academic year 2008–09:* $22,650. *Books and supplies:* $800. *Room and board per academic year:* $7,600. *Other expenses:* $2,504.

Financial Aid: Aid from institutionally generated funds is provided on the basis of academic merit, financial need. Institution has a Program Participation Agreement with the U.S. Department of Education for eligible students to receive Pell Grants and, depending upon the agreement, other federal aid.

Financial aid to full-time, first-time undergraduate students: 88% received some form of aid. Average amount of aid received: federal grants $4,546; state/local grants $1,869; institutional grants $3,074; loans $2,504.

Departments and Teaching Staff: *Total instructional faculty:* 84 (full-time 72, part-time 12). Student/faculty ratio: 14:1. 72% of faculty hold the doctorate, first-professional, or other terminal degree.

Enrollment: Total enrollment 1,423. Undergraduate 1,016. Graduate 467. Undergraduate transfer-in students 24.

Characteristics of Student Body: *Ethnic/racial makeup:* number of Black non-Hispanic: 13; Asian or Pacific Islander: 109. Hispanic: 7; White non-Hispanic: 687; unknown: 26. *Age distribution:* number under 18: 5; 18–19: 392; 20–21: 336; 22–24: 90; 25–29: 36; 30–34: 10; 35–39: 11; 40–49: 6; 50–64: 3.

International Students: 90 nonresident aliens enrolled fall 2008. Students from Asia, Africa, Middle East. English as a Second Language Program available. No financial aid specifically designated for international students.

Student Life: 95% of freshmen live in college housing (coed residence halls); 17% commute; 15% join fraternities/sororities. *Intercollegiate athletics:* basketball, soccer. *Special services:* employment service for undergraduates, placement services for graduates, services/facilities for handicapped, foreign student advisor. *Student publications: Alembic Pharmakon*, a yearbook; *Mortar and Pestle*, a newspaper.

Library Collections: 15,000 volumes. Online catalog. 25,500 microforms; 501 audiovisual materials; 175 current periodical subscriptions.

Most important special holdings include collections on pharmacy, history of pharmacy; Throop Pharmacy Museum.

Buildings and Grounds: Campus is comprised of 9 buildings including a Student Center and 4 residence facilities accommodating 900 students.

Chief Executive Officer: Dr. James Gozzo, President.

Address admission inquiries to Carly Connors, Director of Admissions.

Albany Law School of Union University

80 New Scotland Avenue
Albany, New York 12208
Tel: (518) 445-2326 **E-mail:** admissions@als.edu
Fax: (518) 445-2369 **Internet:** www.als.edu

Institution Description: Albany Law School of Union University is a private institution. *Enrollment:* 763. *Degrees awarded:* Master's, first-professional (law).

Accreditation: *National:* ABA. *Professional*: law

Institutional Structure: Full-time instructional faculty 46.

Calendar: Academic year Aug. to May.

Admission: Rolling admissions plan. *Requirements:* At least 90 undergraduate credits.

Degree Requirements: *For first-professional degrees:* Successful completion of 87 credits.

Distinctive Educational Programs: J.D.-M.B.A. program with Union College, College of St. Rose, and Rensselaer Polytechnic Institute. J.D.-M.P.A. program with State University of New York, Albany. International Commercial Lawyering, summer session at Montreal, Canada. J.D.-M.S.W. combined degree program with SUNY at Albany.

Degrees Conferred: 12 *master's*: law/legal studies; 212 *first-professional:* juris doctor.

Fees and Other Expenses: *Full-time tuition per academic year 2008–09:* contact the school for current tuition, fees, and housing costs.

Financial Aid: Aid from institutionally generated funds is provided on the basis of academic merit, financial need.

Departments and Teaching Staff: *Total instructional faculty:* 53. Total faculty with doctorate, first-professional, or other terminal degree: 53. Student/faculty ratio: 14:1.

Enrollment: Total enrollment 710.

Characteristics of Student Body: *Ethnic/racial makeup:* number of Black non-Hispanic: 36; American Indian or Alaska Native: 1; Asian or Pacific Islander: 48; Hispanic: 25; White non-Hispanic: 622; unknown: 9.

International Students: 14 nonresident aliens enrolled fall 2008. Students from Europe, Asia, Canada. No programs available to aid students whose native language is not English. Some financial aid available to international students.

Library Collections: 250,000 volumes. 1,200,000 microforms; 412 audiovisual materials; 1,477 current periodical subscriptions. Computer work stations available. Students have access to online information retrieval services and the Internet.

Most important special holdings include New York Court of Appeals Oral Arguments on videotape.

Chief Executive Officer: Thomas H. Guernsey, Dean and President.

Address admission inquiries to Gail Bensen, Director of Admissions.

Albany Medical College

47 New Scotland Avenue
Albany, New York 12208
Tel: (518) 262-5582 **E-mail:** admissions@amc.edu
Fax: (518) 262-6515 **Internet:** www.amc.edu

Institution Description: Albany Medical College is a private, independent institution. *Enrollment:* 762. *Degrees awarded:* First-professional (medicine), master's, doctorate.

Member of the consortium Hudson-Mohawk Association of Colleges and Universities.

Accreditation: *Regional:* MSA. *Professional*: cytotechnology, medicine, nurse anesthesia education, physician assisting, psychology internship

History: Established and chartered as Albany Medical College, offered first instruction at postsecondary level, awarded first degree (first-professional) 1839; Albany Medical College of Union University, 1873. *See* Andrew Van Vranken Raymond, *Union University - Its History, Influence, Characteristics and Equipment* (New York: Lewis Publishing Co., 1907) and Richard T. Beebe, M.D., SC.D., *Albany Medical College and Albany Hospital - A History 1839–1982* (Albany, New York: New Art Printing, 1983) for further information.

Institutional Structure: *Governing board:* Committee on College Affairs (Board of Trustees). 19 trustees. Extrainstitutional representation: dean of college, 1 alumnus. 11 voting. *Composition of institution:* Administrators 6. Academic affairs headed by vice dean. Management/business/finances directed by senior vice president for college operations. Full-time instructional faculty 521. Academic governance body, Committee on College Affairs (Board of Trustees) in consultation with the Academic Governing Council; the Board meets an average of 10 times per year; the Council meets 10 times per year.

Calendar: Semesters for years I-II; 12-month program for year III; 10-month program for year IV. Academic year Aug. to June. Entering students admitted Aug. Degrees conferred and formal commencement May. No summer session.

Admission: For fall admission, apply as early as June 1, but not later than Nov. 15. Application process begins with American Medical College Application Service (AMCAS). Students are notified of acceptance beginning Oct. *Requirements:* Minimum of 3 years of college work at an accredited institution, with 90 semester hours which must include 1 biology or zoology, 1 chemistry, 1 organic chemistry, 1 physics; proficiency in oral and written English required. *Entrance tests:* MCAT.

Degree Requirements: *First-professional:* Minimum age 21; minimum 4 years full-time enrollment; satisfactory completion of prescribed curriculum and examinations. *Grading system:* Honors; excellent; good; marginal; unsatisfactory; incomplete.

Distinctive Educational Programs: Combined degree programs. Seven-year baccalaureate-M.D. program with Rensselaer Polytechnic Institute and eight-year baccalaureate-M.D. program with Union College where students in this program earn a master's degree in health care administration. Eight-year program with Siena College with a special focus on community service and providing medical care to the under represented.

Degrees Conferred: 142 *first-professional:* medicine; 102, biomedical sciences 9; 55 *master's:* health professions and related clinical sciences; 9 *doctorate:* biological and biomedical sciences.

Fees and Other Expenses: *Full-time tuition per academic year 2008–09:* contact the college for current information regarding tuition/fees/housing costs.

Financial Aid: Aid from institutionally generated funds is provided on the basis of financial need. Institution has a Program Participation Agreement with the U.S. Department of Education for eligible students to receive Pell Grants and, depending upon the agreement, other federal aid.

Departments and Teaching Staff: *Total instructional faculty:* 372 FTE. Degrees held by full-time faculty: doctorate 25.9%, master's 8.7%, baccalaureate 1.2%$, professional 64.2%. 25.9% hold terminal degrees.

Enrollment: Total enrollment 762.

Characteristics of Student Body: *Ethnic/racial makeup:* Black non-Hispanic: 64.3%; American Indian or Alaska Native: .1%; Asian or Pacific Islander: 22.9%; Hispanic: 1.8%; White non-Hispanic: 64.3%; unknown: .1%.

International Students: 43 nonresident aliens enrolled fall 2008. Students from Europe, Asia, Latin America, Africa, Canada. No programs available to aid students whose native language is not English. No financial aid specifically designated for international students.

Student Life: No on-campus housing. *Special regulations:* Cars permitted without restrictions. *Special services:* Medical services, exercise room. *Student publications: Nexus*, a monthly newspaper; student directory; student handbook and academic planner. *Surrounding community:* Albany population 102,000. New York City is 180 miles from campus. Served by mass transit bus system; airport 10 miles from campus; passenger rail service 3 miles from campus.

Publications: *Center News, Legacy* (newsletter); Medical College Catalog, viewbook and brochure, graduate studies catalog.

Library Collections: 143,000 volumes. 610 microform titles; 2,400 audiovisual materials; 1,060 current periodical subscriptions. 3,095 recordings; 217 compact discs. Online catalog. Computer work stations available. Students have access to online information retrieval services and the Internet.

Most important special holdings include papers of Alden March, M.D., founder of the Albany Medical College; complete set of *Albany Medical Annals*.

Chief Executive Officer: Dr. Vincent P. Vandile, President.

First-professional students address admission inquiries to Director of Admissions; graduate inquiries to Associate Dean for Graduate Studies Program.

Alfred University

One Saxon Drive
Alfred, New York 14802-1205
Tel: (607) 871-2111 **E-mail:** admissions@alfred.edu
Fax: (607) 871-2373 **Internet:** www.alfred.edu

Institution Description: Alfred University is a private, independent, nonprofit institution that also administers the York State College of Ceramics, a statutory college of the State University of New York. *Enrollment:* 2,436. *Degrees awarded:* Baccalaureate, master's, doctorate.

Member of the consortium Rochester Area Colleges.

Accreditation: *Regional:* MSA. *Professional*: business, construction education, engineering

History: Established by Seventh Day Baptists as Alfred Select School 1836; changed name to Alfred Academy and chartered 1843; offered first instruction at postsecondary level 1856; adopted present name 1857; awarded first degree (baccalaureate) 1859. *See* John Nelson Norwood, *Fiat Lux: The Story of Alfred University* (Alfred: Alfred University, 1957) for further information.

Institutional Structure: *Governing board:* Alfred University Board of Trustees. Representation: 41 trustees, including 6 alumni, president of alumni association, president of university, president of parents association. 3 officio. All voting. *Composition of institution:* Academic affairs headed by provost. Management/business/finances directed by vice president for business and finance. Full-time instructional faculty 172. Academic governance body, Faculty Senate, meets an average of 9 times per year.

Calendar: Semesters. Academic year Aug. to May. Freshmen admitted Sept., Jan. Degrees conferred May, Aug., Jan. Formal commencement May. Summer session of 2 terms from mid-May to early Aug.

Characteristics of Freshmen: 2,551 applicants. 76% of applicants admitted. 26% of admitted students enrolled full-time.

96% (461 students) submitted SAT scores; 28% (142 students) submitted ACT scores. *25th percentile*: SAT Critical Reading 500, SAT Math 510; ACT Composite 21, ACT English 20, ACT Math 20. *75th percentile*: SAT Critical Reading 610, SAT Math 620; ACT Composite 26, ACT English 27, ACT Math 26.

65% of entering freshmen expected to graduate within 5 years. 69% freshmen from New York. Freshmen from 38 states and 11 foreign countries.

Admission: The Admissions Committee considers applications under two admission procedures: early decision and regular decision. Qualified students whose first choice is Alfred University may wish to resolve their college plans early in their senior year. Early decision candidates who meet the Dec. 1 deadline may expect notification by Dec. 15. Candidates accepted under this program must submit their acceptance deposit within two weeks after receipt of their financial aid notification.

Regular decision candidates should meet the Feb. 1 (priority) deadline; notification of admission decision by early Mar. Students applying after Feb. 1 will be considered on a space-available basis and will be reviewed on a rolling admission plan. Early admission is also available to students who wish to enter Alfred after completing their junior year of secondary school. *Requirements:* Graduation from accredited secondary school with 16 academic units. Normally the 16 units will consist of: 4 English, 4 social studies and history, 2–3 of college pre-

ALFRED UNIVERSITY—*cont'd*

paratory mathematics, 2–3 units of laboratory science. The remainder of the units should be earned in any of the above fields or in a foreign language. Art and design candidates must submit a portfolio. *Entrance tests:* Either ACT or SAT required. International students must submit TOEFL or show proficiency in English. *For transfer students:* 2.5 GPA required; maximum of 90 credit hours accepted in transfer.

College credit and advanced placement for postsecondary-level work completed in secondary school. In addition, credit granted for CLEP and institutional challenge examinations.

Degree Requirements: *Undergraduate:* 124–140 credit hours, 2.0 GPA; 2 semesters in residence; 2 different physical education activities.

Fulfillment of some degree requirements and exemption from some beginning courses possible by passing departmental examinations, College Board CLEP, AP, other standardized tests. *Grading system:* A–F, high pass—pass-fail; withdraw (carries time limit).

Distinctive Educational Programs: Cooperative education program with industry for engineering majors. Research facilities for graduate students include ASTEM, SIMS, X-ray diffraction, infrared and Raman spectroscopy. Educational Opportunity Program. Evening classes. Tutorials. Institutional sponsored study abroad: American Institute for Foreign Studies in Scotland, England, Ireland, Spain, France; Butler University's Institute for Study Abroad in Australia and United Kingdom; Beaver College Center for Education Abroad in Ireland and England; American University of Paris, France; other programs in Germany, Kenya, Nepal, Italy. Semester or year exchange through Visiting Student Program for Colleges and Universities in New York. Cross-registration through consortium and with Alfred State College (SUNY).

ROTC: Army in cooperation with St. Bonaventure University.

Degrees Conferred: 416 *baccalaureate*; 111 *master's*; 11 *doctorate*. Bachelor's degrees awarded in top five disciplines: visual and performing arts 110; engineering 61; business, management, marketing, and related support services 57; psychology 41; education 28. Master's degrees awarded: business/marketing 14; education 65; engineering 25; psychology 29; public administration and social service sciences 4; visual and performing arts 16. Doctorates awarded: psychology 7; engineering 4.

Fees and Other Expenses: *Full-time tuition per academic year 2008–09:* $24,278 undergraduate; contact the university for current graduate tuition/fees. *Room and board per academic year:* $10,796. *Books and supplies:* $899. *Other expenses:* $1,400.

Financial Aid: Aid from institutionally generated funds is provided on the basis of academic merit, financial need, other criteria. Institution has a Program Participation Agreement with the U.S. Department of Education for eligible students to receive Pell Grants and, depending upon the agreement, other federal aid.

Financial aid to full-time, first-time undergraduate students: 96% of students received some form of financial aid. Average amount of aid received: federal grants $4,039; state/local grants $2,749; institutional grants $11,529; loans $4,523.

Departments and Teaching Staff: *Total instructional faculty:* 172. Student/faculty ratio: 11:1.

Enrollment: Total enrollment 2,436. Undergraduate 2,030. Graduate 406. Undergraduate transfer-in students 90.

Characteristics of Student Body: *Ethnic/racial makeup:* Black non-Hispanic: 5%; American Indian or Alaska Native: 3.1%; Asian or Pacific Islander: 1.5%; Hispanic: 3.1%; White non-Hispanic: 70.1%; unknown: 17.6%.

International Students: 24 nonresident aliens enrolled fall 2008. Programs available to aid students whose native language is not English: social, cultural, financial. financial aid specifically designated for international students: variable number of scholarships available annually.

Student Life: On-campus residence halls house 65% of student body. Residence halls for both males and females constitute 100% of such space. 20% of males join and 11% live in fraternity housing; 10% of females join and 8% live in sorority housing. *Intercollegiate athletics:* male: basketball, football, lacrosse, soccer, swimming, tennis, track; female: basketball, soccer, swimming, tennis, volleyball; co-ed: equestrian, skiing. *Special regulations:* Cars permitted in designated parking areas. Quiet hours. *Special services:* Medical services. *Student publications, radio: Fiat Lux*, a biweekly newspaper; *Kanakadea*, a yearbook; *New Alfred Review*, an annual literary magazine. Radio station WALF broadcasts 133 hours per week. *Surrounding community:* Alfred population 4,665. Rochester, 60 miles from campus, is nearest metropolitan area. Served by mass transit bus system, airport 55 miles from campus.

Library Collections: 290,000 (Herrick Library). 10,508 paper, microform, and electronic serial subscriptions; 162,938 recordings, compact discs, CD-ROMs. Online and card catalogs. Computer work stations available. Students have access to online information retrieval services and the Internet.

Most important holdings include Openhym Collection (British literature and social history); Waid Collection (on Nazi Germany); Hostetler Collection (glass); Barringer Collection (ceramics); Howells-Frechette Collection.

Buildings and Grounds: Campus area 232 acres.

Chief Executive Officer: Dr. Charles M. Edmondson, President.

Address undergraduate admission inquiries to Jeremy C. Spenser, Director of Admissions; graduate inquiries to Kathleen Torrey, Graduate Studies.

College of Liberal Arts and Science

Degree Programs Offered: *Baccalaureate* in biology, chemistry, economics, elementary education, English, French, geology, history, mathematics, performing arts, philosophy, physics, political science, psychology, sociology, Spanish; *master's* in art education, coaching, college student development, community services administration, counselor education, elementary education, reading teacher, school psychology, secondary education.

Distinctive Educational Programs: Dual-degree program in engineering with Columbia University. Cooperative baccalaureate degree in medical laboratory technology with SUNY Agricultural and Technical College at Alfred. Interdisciplinary programs in computer science, criminal justice studies, environmental studies, communication studies, general science, gerontology, public administration, general studies. Individual majors.

College of Business and Administration

Degree Programs Offered: *Baccalaureate* in accounting, business administration, health planning and management, economics, finance, management, marketing.

Distinctive Educational Programs: Dual-degree program leading to M.B.A. awarded by Clarkson College of Technology. Cooperative baccalaureate program in health care administration with College of Nursing.

New York State College of Ceramics at Alfred University

Degree Programs Offered: *Baccalaureate, master's* in art and design, ceramic engineering, ceramic science, glass science; *doctorate* in ceramics.

Distinctive Educational Programs: Cooperative education program with industry for engineering majors. Research facilities for graduate students include scanning electron microscope, infrared and x-ray diffraction.

Bank Street College of Education

610 West 112th Street
New York, New York 10025
Tel: (212) 875-4400 **E-mail:** grad.courses@bankstreet.edu
Fax: (212) 875-4759 **Internet:** www.bankstreet.edu

Institution Description: Bank Street College of Education is a private, independent, nonprofit college. *Enrollment:* 1,032. *Degrees awarded:* Master's. Advanced certificates in special education, and supervision and administration also awarded.

Accreditation: *Regional:* MSA.

History: Established as Bureau of Educational Experiments 1916; chartered and offered first instruction at postsecondary level 1931; adopted present name 1950; awarded first degree (master's) 1952.

Institutional Structure: *Governing board:* Board of Trustees. Extrainstitutional representation: 26 trustees, 2 parents from Bank Street School for Children; institutional representation: president of the college, 2 full-time members of professional staff. 2 alumni. 1 ex officio. 25 voting. *Composition of institution:* Administrative leadership: president, dean of the graduate school, dean of children's programs, dean of continuing education, dean of external affairs, vice president for finance and administration. President serves as chief academic officer of the college. Vice president for finance and administration serves as chief fiscal officer. Instructional faculty: 68. Academic governance body: Administrative Advisory Committee.

Calendar: Semesters. Academic year Sept. to May. Entering students admitted Sept., Feb., July. Degrees conferred June, Aug. Formal commencement June. Two summer sessions, June or July.

Admission: Rolling admissions plan, but students who wish to begin courses and supervised field work in the fall should apply by Mar. 1. *Requirements:* Baccalaureate degree from accredited college or university with concentration in the liberal arts and sciences. An education background is appropriate for some programs. *Entrance tests:* Institutional examinations. For foreign students TOEFL. *For transfer students:* 3.0 minimum GPA; 6–9 semester hours maximum transfer credits.

Degree Requirements: 33–45 hours in residence; integrated independent study; core requirements. *Grading systems:* A–C-no credit; pass-no credit.

Distinctive Educational Programs: Emphasis on a learner-centered approach. Master's degree programs combining theory and practice in early childhood and elementary education, bilingual education, special education, museum education, and educational leadership. Program in supervision and administration with Parsons School of Design. Dual-degree program in special education with Columbia School of Social Work. Dual-degree program in infant and parent development and early intervention and in social work with Hunter College. Summer master's programs in early childhood leadership, leadership in mathematics education.

Degrees Conferred: 323 *master's:* education.

Fees and Other Expenses: *Tuition 2008–09:* charged per credit; contact the college for current rates.

Financial Aid: Aid from institutionally generated funds is provided on the basis of financial need, other considerations. Institution has a Program Participation Agreement with the U.S. Department of Education for eligible students to receive Pell Grants and, depending upon the agreement, other federal aid.

Departments and Teaching Staff: *Total instructional faculty:* 68. Degrees held by full-time faculty: doctorate 53%, master's 47%.

Enrollment: Total enrollment 1,032.

Characteristics of Student Body: *Ethnic/racial makeup:* Black non-Hispanic: 8.7%; American Indian or Alaska Native: 14.5%; Asian or Pacific Islander: 4.8%; Hispanic: 9.1%; White non-Hispanic: 62%.

International Students: 10 nonresident aliens enrolled fall 2008. No programs to aid students whose native language is not English. No financial aid specifically designated for international students.

Student Life: No on-campus housing. *Surrounding community:* New York City population over 7 million. Served by mass transit bus, rail systems; airport 10 miles from campus; passenger rail service 5 miles from campus.

Library Collections: 115,000 volumes. 305,000 microforms; 1,100 audiovisual materials; 455 current periodical subscriptions. Students have access to online information retrieval services and the Internet.

Most important holdings include collections on children's literature, early childhood, teacher education.

Chief Executive Officer: Augusta Souza Kappner, President.

Address admission inquiries to Ann Morgan, Director of Admissions.

Bard College

Annandale-on Hudson, New York 12504-5000

Tel: (845) 758-7472 **E-mail:** admission@bard.edu
Fax: (845) 758-5208 **Internet:** www.bard.edu

Institution Description: Bard College is a private, independent, nonprofit college. *Enrollment:* 2,109. *Degrees awarded:* Baccalaureate, master's.

Accreditation: *Regional:* MSA.

History: Established as St. Stephen's College, chartered, incorporated, and offered first instruction at postsecondary level 1860; awarded first degree (baccalaureate) 1861; became undergraduate college of Columbia University 1928; adopted present name 1933; became independent institution 1944.

Institutional Structure: *Governing board:* Bard College Board of Trustees. Extrainstitutional representation: 19 trustees; institutional representation: 1 administrator; 12alumni. 1 ex officio. 31 voting. *Composition of institution:* Administrators 15. Academic affairs headed by dean of the college. Management/business/finances directed by executive vice president. Full-time instructional faculty 104. Academic governance bodies, Executive Committee and Faculty Senate, each meet an average of 30 times per year. *Faculty representation:* Faculty served by collective bargaining agent affiliated with AAUP.

Calendar: Semesters. Academic year Aug. to May. Freshmen admitted Aug. Degrees conferred and formal commencement May. No summer session.

Characteristics of Freshmen: 4,828 applicants. 40% of applicants admitted. 27% of admitted students enrolled full-time.

Average secondary school rank of freshmen: 60% in top tenth of class.

65% of entering freshmen expected to graduate within 5 years. 24% of freshmen from New York. Freshmen from 48 states and 36 foreign countries.

Admission: For fall acceptance, apply no later than Jan. 15. Students may also apply at Immediate Decision Plan sessions held on campus in Nov. and Dec. and be notified of decision same day. *Requirements:* Either graduation from accredited secondary school with college preparatory curriculum or GED. Minimum GPA 3.0. *Entrance tests:* For foreign students minimum TOEFL score 600 (paper), 250 (computer). *For transfer students:* 2.5 minimum GPA; 64 hours maximum transfer credit.

College credit and advanced placement for postsecondary-level work completed in secondary school. Tutoring available.

Degree Requirements: *Undergraduate:* 124 semester hours; 4 semesters in residence; distribution requirements; freshman seminar and conference; individual evaluation for promotion to upper division; senior project.

Fulfillment of some degree requirements and exemption from some beginning courses possible by passing College Board AP (score of 4 or 5, depending on subject). *Grading system:* A–F; pass-fail withdraw (carries time limit; pass-fail appended to withdraw); incomplete.

Distinctive Educational Programs: Dual-degree programs in engineering with Columbia University, Washington University, and Dartmouth College; in forestry with Duke University; in social work with Adelphi University; in business administration with University of Rochester; in public administration with Syracuse University; in public health with Yale University. *Other distinctive programs:* Extensive study abroad programs. Independent Study Programs for adults. Bard College Center offering intergenerational seminars for undergraduates and community residents. Community focus program dealing with local issues. Distinguished Scientist Lecture Series. Hudson Valley Studies Program. Summer Institute on General Education.

Degrees Conferred: 117 *associate*; 324 *baccalaureate*; 115 *master's*; 2 *doctorates*. Bachelor's degrees awarded in top four disciplines: English language/literature 62; multidisciplinary studies 34; social studies 112; visual and performing arts 116. Master's degrees awarded: biomedical and biological sciences 14; education 21; visual and performing arts 80. Doctorates awarded: visual and performing arts 2.

Fees and Other Expenses: *Full-time tuition per academic year 2008–09:* contact the college for current costs. Variable tuition for graduate programs.

Financial Aid: Aid from institutionally generated funds is provided on the basis of academic merit, financial need. Institution has a Program Participation Agreement with the U.S. Department of Education for eligible students to receive Pell Grants and, depending upon the agreement, other federal aid.

Financial aid to full-time, first-time undergraduate students: 51% of students received some form of financial aid. Average amount of aid received: federal grants 43,650; state/local grants $2,718; institutional grants $18,545; loans $4,909.

Departments and Teaching Staff: *Total instructional faculty:* 161. Student/faculty ratio: 9:1. Degrees held by full-time faculty: 97% hold terminal degrees.

Enrollment: Total enrollment 2,109.

Characteristics of Student Body: *Ethnic/racial makeup:* Black non-Hispanic: 4%; American Indian or Alaska Native: .4%; Asian or Pacific Islander: 5.4%; Hispanic: 5.4%; White non-Hispanic. 67.4%; unknown: 10.4%.

International Students: 132 nonresident aliens enrolled fall 2008. Students from Europe, Asia, Central and South America, Africa, Canada. Programs available to aid students whose native language is not English: social, cultural. English as a Second Language Program. Financial aid programs specifically designated for international students: variable number of scholarships available annually.

Student Life: On-campus residence halls house 85% of student body. *Intercollegiate athletics:* male: basketball, cross-country running, fencing, soccer, squash, tennis, volleyball; female: basketball, cross-country running, fencing, soccer, squash, tennis, volleyball. *Special regulations:* Cars permitted without restrictions. Quiet hours. *Special services:* Medical services. *Student publications, radio: Bard Papers*, an annual magazine; *Bard Observer*, student newspaper; *The Bard Free Press*, student newspaper. Radio station WXBC broadcasts 15 hours per week. *Surrounding community:* Annandale, unincorporated, located in Dutchess County, population 246,000. New York City, 100 miles from campus, is nearest metropolitan area. Served by passenger rail service 8 miles from campus.

Library Collections: 200,000 volumes including bound books, serial backfiles, electronic documents, and government documents not in separate collections. Online catalog. Current serial subscriptions: 900 paper, 248 microform, 325 electronic. 2,500 recordings; 1,100 compact discs. Computer work stations available. Students have access to the Internet at no charge.

Most important holdings include personal libraries of 20th-century political philosopher Hannah Arendt, and 20th-century literary critic Marius Bewley; local history collection.

Buildings and Grounds: Campus area 600 acres.

Chief Executive Officer: Dr. Leon Botstein, President.

Undergraduates address admissions inquiries to Mary Backlund, Director of Admissions; graduate inquiries to Robert L. Martin, Dean of Graduate Studies.

Barnard College

3009 Broadway

New York, New York 10027-6598

Tel: (212) 854-5262 **E-mail:** admissions@barnard.edu
Fax: (212) 854-6220 **Internet:** www.barnard.edu

Institution Description: Barnard College is a private, independent, nonprofit college for women affiliated with Columbia University. *Enrollment:* 2,297. *Degrees awarded:* Baccalaureate.

BARNARD COLLEGE—*cont'd*

Accreditation: *Regional:* MSA.

History: Established as Barnard College, chartered, and offered first instruction at postsecondary level 1889; awarded first degree (baccalaureate) 1893; became affiliated with Columbia University 1900. *See: A History of Barnard College* (NY, privately printed, 1964) for further information.

Institutional Structure: *Governing board:* Barnard College Board of Trustees. Extrainstitutional representation: 26 trustees, including 4 alumnae; institutional representation: 8 administrators, 2 full-time instructional faculty representatives, 2 student representatives. 2 ex officio. 28 voting. *Composition of institution:* Administrators 139. Academic affairs headed by provost and vice president for finance and planning. Management/business/finances directed by vice president for finance and administration. Full-time instructional faculty 201. Academic governance body, the faculty, meets an average of 9 times per year.

Calendar: Semesters. Academic year Sept. to May. Freshmen admitted Sept., Jan. Degrees conferred May, Oct., Jan. Formal commencement May. No summer session.

Characteristics of Freshmen: 5,459 applicants. 25% of applicants accepted. 38% of accepted applicants enrolled full-time.

92% (514 students) submitted SAT scores; 27% (150 students) submitted ACT scores. *25th percentile*: SAT Critical Reading 640, STAT Math 640; ACT Composite 29, ACT English 29, ACT Math 28. *75th percentile*: SAT Critical Reading 740, SAT Math 710; ACT Composite 31, ACT English 34, ACT Math 31.

87% of entering freshmen expected to graduate within 5 years. 32% of freshmen from New York. Freshmen from 48 states and 36 foreign countries.

Admission: For fall acceptance, apply no later than Jan. 1. Students are notified of acceptance Apr. Apply by Nov. 15 for early decision; must limit application to Barnard. Early acceptance available. *Requirements:* Either graduation from accredited secondary school or GED. Recommend 4 units in English, 3-4 in a foreign language, 3 mathematics, 2 laboratory science, 1 history. Additional units in art, music recommended. Minimum GPA 3.0. *Entrance tests:* SAT or ACT with optional writing. For foreign students TOEFL. *For transfer students:* 3.0 minimum GPA; from 4- and 2-year accredited institutions 60 hours maximum transfer credit.

College credit and advanced placement for postsecondary-level work completed in secondary school.

Degree Requirements: 122 credit hours; 2.0 GPA; 4 semesters in residence; 2 terms physical education; general education and distribution requirements.

Fulfillment of some degree requirements and exemption from some beginning courses possible by passing departmental examinations, College Board AP. *Grading system:* A–F; pass-fail; withdraw (carries time limit).

Distinctive Educational Programs: Cluster colleges. Dual-degree programs in engineering and applied science, international affairs, law with Columbia University; in Hebrew literature with Jewish Theological Seminary of America. Interdepartmental programs in American studies, ancient studies, environmental science, foreign area studies, health and society, medieval and Renaissance studies, oriental studies, urban studies, women's studies. Facilities and programs for independent research, including honors programs, individual majors, tutorials. Cooperation with Columbia University, including cross-registration, shared faculty, facilities, library. Study abroad in England, France, Germany, Italy, Japan.

Degrees Conferred: 600 *baccalaureate* in various disciplines (architecture, area studies, biological sciences, computer and information sciences, English, foreign languages and literature, liberal arts, mathematics, natural resources/environmental science, physical sciences, psychology, social sciences and history, visual and performing arts).

Fees and Other Expenses: *Full-time tuition per academic year 2008–09:* \$38,374. *Room and board per academic year:* \$10,866. *Books and supplies:* \$860. *Other expenses:* \$1,150.

Financial Aid: Aid from institutionally generated funds is provided on the basis of financial need.

Financial aid to full-time, first-time undergraduate students: 71% received some form of aid. Average amount of aid received: federal grants \$4,012; state/local grants \$3,003; institutional grants \$19,232; loans \$4,884.

Departments and Teaching Staff: *Total instructional faculty:* 80% of faculty hold the doctorate, first-professional, or other terminal degree. Student/faculty ratio: 10:1.

Enrollment: Total enrollment 2,297. Undergraduate 2,036. Graduate 261. Undergraduate transfer-in students 39.

Characteristics of Student Body: *Ethnic/racial makeup:* Black non-Hispanic: 3%; American Indian or Alaska Native: 1%; Asian or Pacific Islander: 3%; Hispanic: 4%; White non-Hispanic: 69%; nonresident alien 9%. *Age distribution:* number under 18: 161; 18–19: 972; 20–21: 1,067; 22–24: 217; 25–29: 9; 30–34: 6.

International Students: 71 nonresident aliens enrolled fall 2008. Students from Europe. Asia, Central and South America, Africa, Canada, Australia, Middle East. No programs available to aid students whose native language is not English. No financial aid specifically designated for international students.

Student Life: On-campus residence halls house 90% of student body. *Intercollegiate athletics:* archery, basketball, crew, cross-country, fencing, field hockey, golf, lacrosse, soccer, softball, swimming and diving, tennis, indoor and outdoor track and field, volleyball. *Special regulations:* No parking on campus. *Special services:* Medical services, shuttle bus service to residence halls. *Student publications, radio:* A weekly newspaper, a biannual literary magazine, an annual art portfolio, a yearbook. Radio station broadcasts 10 hours per week. *Surrounding community:* New York City population over 7 million. Served by mass transit bus and subway system; airport 6 miles from campus; passenger rail service 4 miles from campus.

Library Collections: Library facilities shared with Columbia University. 205,912 volumes. Current periodical subscriptions: 459 paper; 17 microform; 47,852 via electronic access. 6,169 recordings; 5,490 compact discs. Computer work stations available. Students have access to online information retrieval services and the Internet.

Most important special holdings include the Barnard Archives; Overbury Collection (18th, 19th, and early 20th century first editions by American women authors).

Buildings and Grounds: Campus area 4 acres.

Chief Executive Officer: Judith R. Shapiro, President.

Address admission inquiries to Dean of Admissions.

Bernard M. Baruch College / CUNY

17 Lexington Avenue
New York, New York 10010
Tel: (646) 312-1000 **E-mail:** admissions@baruch.cuny.edu
Fax: (646) 312-2808 **Internet:** www.baruch.cuny.edu

Institution Description: *Enrollment:* 16,097. *Degrees awarded:* Baccalaureate, master's.

Accreditation: *Regional:* MSA. *Professional*: accounting, business, health services administration, public administration

History: Established as School of Business and Civil Administration of City College and offered first instruction at postsecondary level 1919; changed name to Bernard M. Baruch School of Business and Public Administration of the City College 1954; became independent college within university system and adopted present official name, Bernard M. Baruch College of the City University of New York, 1968.

Institutional Structure: *Composition of institution:* Administrators 34. Academic affairs headed by provost-vice president for academic affairs. Management/business/finances directed by vice president for administration. Full-time instructional faculty 405. Academic governance body, Faculty Senate, meets an average of 10 times per year.

Calendar: Semesters. Academic year Aug. to May. Freshmen admitted Sept., Jan. Degrees conferred June, Sept., Feb. Formal commencement June. Summer session of 2 terms from early June to late Aug.

Characteristics of Freshmen: 17,114 applicants. 26% of applicants accepted. 34% of accepted applicants admitted full-time.

25th percentile: SAT Critical Reading 490, SAT Math 550. *75th percentile*: SAT Critical Reading 580, SAT Math 650.

22% of entering freshmen expected to graduate within 5 years. 84% of freshmen from New York. Freshmen from 7 states.

Admission: For transfer students: 2.0 minimum GPA; maximum transfer credit limited only by residence requirement.

College credit and advanced placement for postsecondary-level work completed in secondary school. College credit for extrainstitutional learning on basis of faculty assessment.

Immersion Program offered in summer. Comprehensive Tutorial Center open all year.

Degree Requirements: *Undergraduate:* 124 semester hours for BBA; 2.0 GPA; 2 semesters in residence; competency examinations in writing and mathematics; 120 semester hours for BA and BS.

Fulfillment of some degree requirements and exemption from some beginning courses possible by passing College Board CLEP. *Grading system:* A–F, pass; withdraw (no penalty), unofficial withdrawal carries penalty.

Distinctive Educational Programs: Weekend and evening classes. Accelerated degree programs. Interdisciplinary programs in arts administration, business journalism. Management of Musical Enterprises. Facilities and programs for independent research, including honors programs, individual majors, tutorials. American Studies Program. Asian/American Studies Program. Honors Institute.

Degrees Conferred: 2,506 *baccalaureate*; 1,262 *master's*. Bachelor's degrees awarded in top five disciplines: business, management, marketing, and related support services 2,051; computer and information sciences 124; psychology 101; social sciences 89; English language/literature 57. Master's degrees awarded in top five disciplines: business/marketing 744; public administration and social service professions 133; education 88; communication, journalism and related programs 37; computer and information sciences 34.

Fees and Other Expenses: *Full-time tuition per academic year 2008–09:* undergraduate resident $4,570, nonresident $9,010. *Books and supplies:* $1,016. No on-campus housing.

Financial Aid: Aid from institutionally generated funds is provided on the basis of academic merit, financial need.

Financial aid to full-time, first-time undergraduate students: 82% of students received some form of financial aid. Average amount of aid received: federal grants $3,454; state/local grants $3,120; institutional grants $10,201; loans $2,129.

Departments and Teaching Staff: *Total instructional faculty:* 921. 75% of faculty hold the doctorate, first-professional, or other terminal degree. Student/faculty ratio: 13:1.

Enrollment: Total enrollment 16,097. Undergraduate 12,862. Graduate 3,234. Undergraduate transfer-in students 1,397.

Characteristics of Student Body: *Ethnic/racial makeup (undergraduate):* number of Black non-Hispanic: 1,745, American Indian or Alaska Native: 16; Asian or Pacific Islander: 3,396; Hispanic: 2,262; White non-Hispanic: 4,070. *Age distribution:* number under 18: 568; 18–19: 3,131; 20–21: 13,222; 22–24: 2,449; 25–29: 1,737; 30–34: 816; 35–39: 419; 40–49: 313; 50–64: 72; 65 and over: 2.

International Students: 1,374 undergraduate nonresident aliens enrolled fall 2008. Students from Europe, Asia, Central and South America, Africa,Canada. Programs available to aid students whose native language is not English: English as a Second Language Program. No financial aid specifically designated for international students.

Student Life: Housing available through an outside agency. *Intercollegiate athletics:* male: baseball, basketball, soccer, tennis, volleyball; female: basketball, cross-country, softball, tennis, volleyball. *Special services:* Medical services. *Student publications, radio: Ticker,* a weekly newspaper; *Dollars and Sense,* student publication. Radio station WBMB broadcasts 50 hours per week. *Surrounding community:* New York City population over 7 million. Served by mass transit bus and subway systems; 2 airports each less 5 miles from campus; passenger rail service 14 blocks from campus.

Publications: *Information Science Abstracts* (bimonthly) first published 1981; *Micropolitics* (quarterly) first published 1981; *Political Science Abstracts* (annually) first published 1980.

Library Collections: 426,000 volumes. Current serial subscriptions: 4,038 paper, 116 electronic. 500 compact discs; 490 CD-ROMs. 1,325 audiovisual materials. Computer work stations available. Students have access to online information retrieval services and the Internet.

Most important holdings include collection on business and economics; materials on bibliographic instruction.

Buildings and Grounds: Campus DVD available.

Chief Executive Officer: Dr. Kathleen Waldron, President.

Undergraduates address admission inquiries to Marybeth Murphy, Director of Admissions; graduate inquiries to Office of Graduate Admissions for School of Business or School of Public Affairs.

Boricua College

3755 Broadway
New York, New York 10032
Tel: (212) 694-1000
Fax: (212) 694-1015

Institution Description: Boricua College is a private, independent, nonprofit college with two campuses in Brooklyn and one in Manhattan. Offers bilingual instruction in English and Spanish. *Enrollment:* 1,058. *Degrees awarded:* Associate, baccalaureate, master's.

Accreditation: *Regional:* MSA.

History: Established 1974.

Institutional Structure: *Composition of institution:* Administrators 6. Management/business/finances directed dean of academic administration. Full-time instructional faculty 51.

Calendar: Trimesters. Academic year Sept. to June. Summer session of 1 term from mid-May to early July.

Characteristics of Freshmen: 826 applicants. 39% of applicants admitted. 69% of admitted students enrolled full-time. 100% of freshmen from New York.

Admission: Rolling admissions plan. For fall acceptance, apply no later than 1 week before beginning of term. *Requirements:* Either graduation from secondary school or the equivalent. Working knowledge of English and Spanish. Interview required. *Entrance tests:* Standardized examinations in English, mathematics, Spanish.

Degree Requirements: *For all associate degrees:* 64 credit hours. *For all baccalaureate degrees:* 128 credit hours. *For all undergraduate degrees:* Exit competency examinations in English, mathematics, Spanish. Required work (including internships) in applied studies, cultural studies, theoretical studies. *For master's degree:* 40 graduate credits.

Fulfillment of some degree requirements possible by passing College Board CLEP. *Grading system:* Credit-no grade.

Distinctive Educational Programs: Bilingual program with nontraditional curriculum designed to meet the needs of Puerto Ricans and other Spanish-speaking students. Internships. Evening classes. Tutorials. Facilities and programs for independent research, including tutorials, independent study, individualized curricula. Master of Arts in Latin American and Caribbean Studies; Master of Science in Human Services.

Degrees Conferred: 161 *associate:* liberal arts; 146 *baccalaureate:* business/marketing 21; education 22; liberal arts/general studies 39; public administration and services 106; 5 *master's:* public administration and services.

Fees and Other Expenses: *Full-time tuition per academic year 2008–09:* $9,000. undergraduate; contact the college for current graduate tuition and fees. *Books and supplies:* $400. No on-campus housing.

Financial Aid: Aid from institutionally generated funds is provided on the basis of academic merit, financial need, other criteria. Institution has a Program Participation Agreement with the U.S. Department of Education for eligible students to receive Pell Grants and, depending upon the agreement, other federal aid.

Financial aid to full-time, first-time undergraduate students: 952% of students received some form of financial aid. Average amount of aid received: federal grants $1,351; state/local grants $1,650.

Departments and Teaching Staff:
Total instructional faculty: 119 (full-time 53, part-time 66). 35% of faculty hold the doctorate, first-professional, or other terminal degree. Student/faculty ratio: 20:1.

Enrollment: Total enrollment 1,058. Undergraduate 1,004. Graduate 54. Undergraduate transfer-in students 54.

Characteristics of Student Body: *Ethnic/racial makeup:* Black non-Hispanic: 12%; Hispanic: 80%; White non-Hispanic: 3%. *Age distribution:* number 18–19: 22; 20–21: 97; 22–24: 190; 25–29: 197; 30–34: 170; 35–39: 153; 40–49: 221; 50–64: 72; 65 and over: 2. 50% of student body attend summer sessions.

International Students: Programs available to aid students whose native language is not English: social, cultural. No financial aid specifically designated for international students.

Student Life: No on-campus housing.

Publications: *Guaiza,* a triennial journal of contemporary Caribbean thought; *College Information Newsletter* (monthly); *Journal of Educational Facilitation.*

Library Collections: 129,000 volumes. 3,700 government documents; 40 microform titles; 3,000 audiovisual materials; 780 current periodical subscriptions.

Most important special holdings include Hon. Herman Badillo Congressional Papers Collection; Puerto Rican Diaspora Repository Papers; North American Congress of Latin America Archives.

Buildings and Grounds: Three campuses: 3755 Broadway (Manhattan); 186 North 6th Street and 9 Graham Avenue (Brooklyn).

Chief Executive Officer: Dr. Victor G. Alicea, President.

Address admission inquiries to Director of Student Services and Admissions.

Brooklyn College / CUNY

2900 Bedford Avenue
Brooklyn, New York 11210-2889
Tel: (718) 951-5000] **E-mail:** admingry@brooklyn.cuny.edu
Internet: www.brooklyn.cuny.edu

Institution Description: *Enrollment:* 16,037. *Degrees awarded:* Baccalaureate, master's. Certificates in accounting, computers and programming, film production, and advanced certificates in education also awarded.

Accreditation: *Regional:* MSA.*Professional*: dietetics, audiology, public health, speech-language pathology, teacher education

History: Established as Brooklyn College, chartered, and offered first instruction at postsecondary level 1930; awarded first degree (baccalaureate) 1932. *See* Murray Horowitz, *Brooklyn College—The First Half Century* (New York: Brooklyn College Press, 1981) for further information.

BROOKLYN COLLEGE / CUNY—*cont'd*

Institutional Structure: *Composition of institution:* Administrators 104. Academic affairs headed by provost and vice president for academic affairs. Management/business/finances directed by vice president for finance and administration. Full-time instructional faculty 515. Academic governance body, Faculty Council, meets an average of 10 times per year.

Calendar: Semesters. Academic year late Aug. to mid-May. Freshmen admitted Sept., Jan. Degrees conferred June, Sept., Feb. Formal commencement June. Summer session from mid-June to mid-Aug.

Characteristics of Freshmen: 14,754 applicants. 75% of applicants accepted. 44% of accepted applicants enrolled full-time. 100% (894 students) submitted SAT scores. *25th percentile*: SAT Critical Reading 450, SAT Math 490. *75th percentile*: SAT Critical Reading 560, SAT Math 590.

74% of entering freshmen expected to graduate within 5 years. 95% of freshmen from New York. Freshmen from 30 states and 98 foreign countries.

Admission: Rolling admissions plan. Students are encourage to apply by Mar. 15 for fall admission and Oct. 1 for spring admission. Students who apply during this period will be processed in phase 1 and will be considered for all programs offered at Brooklyn College. *Requirements:* Graduation from an accredited secondary school with the recommended high school units (4 English, 4 math, 3 science, 4 social studies/history, 3 foreign language); SAT scores, and a strong academic average. GED accepted based on a score of 300. *For transfer students:* Minimum GPA of 2.00 from an accredited institution. Students are eligible to transfer 60–90 credits from their previous accredited institution.

College credit for advanced placement courses and college level examination placement. College credit on basis of academic advisement; personal counseling. Tutoring, job placement, and ESL courses are offered to all students.

Degree Requirements: 120 semester hours; 2.0 GPA; 39 credits hours in residence; core curriculum; exit competency examinations in writing and mathematics.

Fulfillment of some degree requirements and exemption from some beginning courses possible by passing institutional examinations, College Board AP. *Grading system:* A–F; pass-fail; withdraw (carries penalty and time limit).

Distinctive Educational Programs: Honors Academy for academically superior students. Freshman Year College offers a coordinated program of advisement, support services, and specially designated course sections for first-time freshmen. Active internship programs with special professional and legislative internships available. Weekend and evening programs. Dual-degree programs in medicine offered with SUNY Health Sciences Center at Brooklyn. Joint engineering programs with CUNY, College of Staten Island, and Polytechnic University. B.A.-M.P.S. program in computer and information science and economics. Interdisciplinary programs in children's studies and environmental studies. Cooperative baccalaureate programs in health information management, occupational therapy, physical therapy, physician assistant training, and diagnostic medical imaging offered with SUNY Health Science Center at Brooklyn. Departmentally sponsored study abroad in Bulgaria, Caribbean, England, France, Ireland, Israel, Spain, Puerto Rico. *Other distinctive programs:* The Small College Program, a structured evening program in which adults may earn a baccalaureate in 4 or 5 years. Special Baccalaureate Program, part-time honors program for adults. Continuing Education program offers noncredit lifelong learning courses. Institute for Retired Professionals and Executives.

Degrees Conferred: 2,154 *baccalaureate*; 1,008 *master's*. Bachelor's degrees awarded in top five disciplines: business/marketing 547; psychology 236; education 209; social sciences 156; computer and information sciences 113. Master's degrees awarded in top five disciplines: education 846 (advanced certificates included); psychology 90 (advanced certificates included): visual and performing arts; social sciences 72; computer and information sciences 71.

Fees and Other Expenses: *Full-time tuition per academic year 2008–09:* undergraduate resident $4,431, nonresident $9,011; contact the college for current graduate tuition and fees. *Required fees:* $377. No on-campus housing.

Financial Aid: Aid from institutionally generated funds is provided on the basis of academic merit, financial need, other criteria (special talents in applied arts).

Financial aid to full-time, first-time undergraduate students:

Financial aid to full-time, first-time undergraduate students: 79% received some form of aid. Average amount of aid received: federal grants $3,386; state/local grants $3,127; institutional grants $4,158; loans $2,429.

Departments and Teaching Staff: *Total instructional faculty:* 1,134 (full-time 515, part-time 619). 55% of faculty hold the doctorate, first-professional, or other terminal degree. Student/faculty ratio: 16:1.

Enrollment: Total enrollment 16,087. Undergraduate 12,495. Graduate 3,592. Undergraduate transfer-in students 1,694.

Characteristics of Student Body: *Ethnic/racial makeup:* Black non-Hispanic: 28%; Asian or Pacific Islander: 13%; Hispanic: 12%; White non-Hispanic: 41%; nonresident alien 6%.

International Students: 963 undergraduate nonresident aliens enrolled fall 2008. Programs available to aid students whose native language is not English: social, cultural. English as a Second Language Program. Financial aid specifically designated for international students: scholarships available annually.

Student Life: No on-campus housing. *Intercollegiate athletics:* male: soccer; female: softball; both sexes: basketball, cross-country, swimming, tennis, track and field, volleyball. *Special regulations:* Limited parking available for disabled students and evening students; permit required. *Special services:* Learning Resources Center, medical services. *Student publications, radio: The English Majors Journal, Riverrun,* magazines published once or twice per year; *Excelsior* and *Kingsman,* weekly newspapers; *Night Call*, irregularly published newspaper. Radio station WBCR broadcasts on a regular schedule. *Surrounding community:* New York City population over 7 million. Served by mass transit bus and subway system; airport 5 miles from campus; passenger rail service 5 miles from campus.

Publications: *Institute for Studies in American Music* (biannually) first published in 1971; *Judaic Studies Network* (biannually) first published in 1987; *Studies on Society in Change* (more than 42 titles); *I.S.A.M.* Monograph Series (24 titles); special publications (4 titles); *Researches in American Music* (15 titles).

Library Collections: 1,330,000 volumes including bound books, serial backfiles, electronic documents, and government documents not in separate collections. Online catalog. 1,685,000 microforms; 23,500 audiovisual materials; 18,750 periodicals including via electronic access. Computer work stations available. Students have access to the Internet at no charge.

Most important holdings include Robert L. Hess Collection on Ethiopia and the Horn of Africa; William Alfred Papers; Sam Levenson Collection.

Buildings and Grounds: Campus area 26 acres.

Chief Executive Officer: Dr. Christopher M. Kimmich, President.

Address admission inquiries to Karen Alleyne-Piewrre, Director of Application services and Enrollment Communications.

Brooklyn Law School

250 Joralemon Street
Brooklyn, New York 11201
Tel: (718) 625-2200 **E-mail:** admissions@brooklaw.edu
Fax: (718) 625-0393 **Internet:** www.brooklaw.edu

Institution Description: The Brooklyn Law School is a private, independent graduate school. *Enrollment:* 1,496. *Degrees awarded:* First-professional.

Accreditation: *Regional:* Board of Regents of the State of New York. *Professional*: law

History: Established in 1901.

Calendar: Semesters. Academic year Aug. to May.

Admission: The entering class is admitted only in the fall semester. *Requirements:* Baccalaureate degree from an approved college or university. *Entrance tests:* LSAT. All applicants must register with LSDAS.

Degree Requirements: 86 credits.

Distinctive Educational Programs: Faculty-supervised clinical education courses. In the Federal Litigation Clinic, students function as attorneys on civil cases actually pending in federal district court. In the Big Apple Clinic, co-sponsored by the New York City Corporation Counsel, students represent the City in a variety of matters, including torts and civil rights actions. In the Judicial Clerkship Clinic, students are assigned to judges in the federal and state courts and to administrative law judges in the adjudicatory divisions of administrative agencies. In the Clinic for the Aging, students are placed with staff attorneys of the Senior Citizen Law Office, a provider of free civil legal services to the elderly in Manhattan. In the Landlord-Tenant Clinic, students represent clients on a variety of legal matters in Kings County Housing Court. In the Criminal Law Clinic, students work under the supervision of attorneys in prosecutor and defender offices such as the U.S. Attorney, the Manhattan, Kings and Bronx Counties District Attorney, and the Organized Crime Strike Force in Newark. In the Criminal Law/Capital Punishment Clinic, students work in a New York law firm representing defendants on death row. In the Civil Clinic, students are exposed to virtually every substantive area of the law through assignment to lawyers in a wide range of federal, state and city agencies. In the Dispute Resolution Clinic, students learn methods of alternate forms of dispute resolution and actually mediate cases in a local dispute center. In the Women's Rights Clinic, students work in one of several offices, such as the ACLU Reproductive Rights Project and the NOW Legal Defense and Education Fund, concerned with women's rights issues. The Discovery Workshop is a unique training program combining research at court and in law offices on how discovery is conducted and how it can be improved. The program is obtaining data needed to decide how pretrial practice should be controlled under current litigation conditions.

Degrees Conferred: 470 *first-professional:* law.

Fees and Other Expenses: *Tuition per academic year:* contact the school for current information.

Financial Aid: Aid from institutionally generated funds is provided on the basis of academic merit, financial need, other criteria. Institution has a Program Participation Agreement with the U.S. Department of Education for eligible students to receive Pell Grants and, depending upon the agreement, other federal aid.

Departments and Teaching Staff: *Total instructional faculty:* 71. 100% hold terminal degrees.

Enrollment: Total enrollment 1,496.

Characteristics of Student Body: *Ethnic/racial makeup:* Black non-Hispanic: 6%; Asian or Pacific Islander: 15%l Hispanic: 6%; White non-Hispanic: 62%; nonresident alien 1%.

International Students: 15 nonresident aliens enrolled fall 2008. Programs available to aid students whose native language is not English: Foreign Trained Lawyers Program. No financial aid specifically designated for international students.

Publications: *Law Review, Journal of International Law.*

Library Collections: 390,000 volumes; 188,000 microforms; 335 audiovisual materials; 4,200 current periodical subscriptions. Students have access to online information retrieval services and the Internet.

Most important special holdings include women and the law; international law; international business and trade law.

Chief Executive Officer: Joan G. Wesler, Dean.

Address admission inquiries to Myron B. Chaitovsky, Director of Admissions.

Canisius College

2001 Main Street
Buffalo, New York 14208-1098
Tel: (716) 883-7000 **E-mail:** admissions@canisius.edu
Fax: (716) 888-2125 **Internet:** www.canisius.edu

Institution Description: Canisius College is a private, independent, nonprofit college conducted in the Jesuit and Roman Catholic tradition. *Enrollment:* 4,984. *Degrees awarded:* Associate, baccalaureate, master's. Certificates also awarded.

Member of Western New York Consortium of Higher Education.

Accreditation: *Regional:* MSA. *Professional*: athletic training, audiology, business, teacher education

History: Established 1870; offered first instruction at postsecondary level 1876; chartered, incorporated, and first degree (baccalaureate) awarded 1883; became coeducational 1965. *See* Charles A. Brady, *The First Hundred Years: Canisius College 1870–1970* (Buffalo, N.Y.: Holling Press, Inc., 1970) for further information.

Institutional Structure: *Governing board:* Board of Trustees. Representation: 34 trustees, including 17 alumni, 8 Jesuits, president of the college. 2 ex officio. 1 emeritus. All voting. 11 consultants to Board of Trustees including 3 alumni, 1 Jesuit. *Composition of institution:* Administrators 145. Academic affairs headed by executive vice president for academic affairs. Management/business/finances directed by vice president for business and finance. Full-time instructional faculty 532. Academic Programs Board controls majors and policies. Council of Chairs advises academic vice president.

Calendar: Semesters. Academic year Aug. to May. Freshmen admitted Sept., Jan. Degrees conferred and formal commencement May. Summer session of 2 terms from June to Aug.

Characteristics of Freshmen: 3,847 applicants. 76% of applicants accepted. 28% of accepted applicants enrolled full-time.

96% (772 students) submitted SAT scores; 22% (179 students) submitted ACT scores. *25th percentile*: SAT Critical Reading 490, SAT Math 500; ACT Composite 22, ACT English 26, ACT Math 22. *75th percentile*: SAT Critical Reading 600, SAT Math 620; ACT Composite 27, ACT English 37, ACT Math 28.

88% of entering freshmen expected to graduate within 5 years. 89% of freshmen from New York. Freshmen from 32 states and 15 foreign countries.

Admission: Rolling admissions plan. For fall acceptance, apply as early as Sept. of previous year, but not later than July of year of enrollment. Early acceptance available. *Requirements:* Either graduation from accredited secondary school with 16 units which must include 4 English, 2 foreign language (preferably 1 language), 3 college preparatory mathematics, 2 social studies, 1 laboratory science, 4 academic electives; or GED. Additional requirements for some programs. *Entrance tests:* College Board SAT or ACT composite. For foreign students TOEFL. *For transfer students:* 2.0 minimum GPA from 4-year college; 2.0 minimum GPA from 2-year college; maximum transfer credit limited only by residence requirements.

College credit and advanced placement for postsecondary-level work completed in secondary school and for extrainstitutional learning (life experience) on basis of portfolio assessment. Tutoring available. Noncredit developmental/remedial courses offered during regular academic year.

Degree Requirements: *For all associate degrees:* 60 credit hours. *For all baccalaureate degrees:* 120 to 134 credit hours. *For all undergraduate degrees:* 2.0 GPA; last 30 hours in residence; distribution requirements.

Fulfillment of some degree requirements and exemption from some beginning courses possible by passing College Board CLEP, APP, other standardized tests. *Grading system:* A–F; pass-fail; withdraw (carries time limit); incomplete (deadline after which F is assigned).

Distinctive Educational Programs: *For undergraduates:* Work-experience programs. 5-year double-degree (baccalaureate and master's) program in business administration. Cooperative baccalaureates in medical technology with area hospitals. Interdisciplinary majors in biochemistry, international relations, urban studies. 2-year pre-engineering program; 2-year pre-environmental science and forestry leading to baccalaureate awarded by SUNY College of Environmental Science and Forestry at Syracuse. Joint degree BS/DDS with SUNY Buffalo. Early Assurance Programs with Upstate Medical and SUNY Buffalo Medical. Women's studies certificate. Programs for independent research, including honors programs, individualized majors. Semester internships in Washington (DC) and Albany (NY). *For graduates:* Internships. Cooperative master's program in reading instruction with Medaille College; in teaching of the hearing impaired with St. May's School for the Deaf. *Available to all students:* Evening classes. Special facilities for using telecommunications in the classroom. Programs for independent research, including tutorials, independent study. Cross-registration through consortium. *Other distinctive programs:* Degree-granting evening division primarily for adult learners; technical and liberal studies for students with previous training from approved professional or technical schools. One-year developmental/remedial program for persons seeking admission to full-time degree programs. Self-directed off-campus audio/video studies program. Semester orientation for women returning to the classroom. Noncredit institute for management development. Center for Entrepreneurship, ESL Program, Fine Arts Department; Fashion Merchandising with Fashion Institute in New York City, Hotel Management. Special orientation for nontraditional students. Study abroad programs in Australia, England, France, Germany, Japan, Mexico, Spain, Sweden, Switzerland.

ROTC: Army.

Degrees Conferred: 4 *associate;* 811 *baccalaureate*; 655 *master's*. Bachelor's degrees awarded in top five disciplines: business, management, marketing, and related support services 194; education 122; communication, journalism, and related programs 104; social sciences 61; biological/life sciences 48. Master's degrees awarded in top disciplines: business,management, marketing, and related support services 99; communications/journalism 8; education 410; engineering technologies 7; health professions and related clinical sciences 25; parks and recreation 12.

Fees and Other Expenses: *Full-time tuition per academic year 2008–09:* undergraduate $28,151; graduate tuition charged per credit (contact the college for current rate). *Room and board per academic year:* $10,150. *Books and supplies:* $700. *Other expenses:* $1,130.

Financial Aid: Aid from institutionally generated funds is provided on the basis of academic merit, financial need, athletic ability, other criteria. Institution has a Program Participation Agreement with the U.S. Department of Education for eligible students to receive Pell Grants and, depending upon the agreement, other federal aid.

Financial aid to full-time, first-time undergraduate students: 99% received some form of aid. Average amount of aid received: federal grants $3,779; state/local grants $2,485; institutional grants $12,856; loans $3,500.

Departments and Teaching Staff: *Total instructional faculty:* 532 (full-time 215, part-time 317). Student/faculty ratio: 12:1. Degrees held by full-time faculty: doctorates 90%, master's 100%, baccalaureates 100%. 90% hold terminal degrees.

Enrollment: Total enrollment 4,984. Undergraduate 3,490. Graduate 1,494. Undergraduate transfer-in students 169.

Characteristics of Student Body: *Ethnic/racial makeup:* Black non-Hispanic: 6%; Asian or Pacific Islander: 1%; Hispanic: 2%; White non-Hispanic: 86%; nonresident alien 4%.

International Students: 200 nonresident aliens enrolled fall 2008. Students from Europe, Asia, Central and South America, Africa, Canada, Middle East. Programs available to aid students whose native language is not English: social, cultural. English as a Second Language Program. Financial aid specifically designated for international students: scholarships available annually for qualifying students.

Student Life: On-campus residence halls house 32% of student body. *Intercollegiate athletics:* male: baseball, basketball, crew, cross-country, football, golf, hockey, lacrosse, rugby, soccer, tennis, track; female: basketball, crew, cross-country, lacrosse, soccer, softball, swimming, synchronized swimming,

CANISIUS COLLEGE—*cont'd*

tennis, track, volleyball; co-ed: rifle. *Special regulations:* Registered cars permitted on campus in designated areas only with vehicle permit. Quiet hours from 10pm to 10am Sun.–Thurs, midnight to noon Fri. and Sat. *Special services:* Learning Resources Center, student health center, counseling center, campus ministry, evening campus shuttle bus and escort service, disabled student services, Office of International Student Programs, Office of Multicultural Programs. *Student publications, radio: AZUWUR*, a yearbook; *Griffin*, a weekly newspaper; *Quadrangle*, a biannual literary magazine; *Viewbook*, admissions publication; *Canisius Commutes*, commuter newsletter; student handbooks. Radio Station WCCG-FM broadcasts 60 hours per week. *Surrounding community:* Buffalo surrounding area population 1.2 million. Served by mass transit bus and subway system; airport 6 miles from campus; passenger rail service 4 miles from campus.

Publications: *The Canisius College Magazine,* a quarterly alumni/ae magazine.

Library Collections: 348,000 volumes. 872,000 microforms; 10,000 audiovisual materials; 25,000 periodical subscriptions including via electronic access. Computer work stations available. Students have access to online information retrieval services and the Internet.

Most important holdings include 700 rare items, including some incunabula, pertaining to theology, philosophy, literature, history, letters, manuscripts, and other personal papers of literary author and critic Charles A. Brady; Canisius College Archives (1870–present); Shrub Oak Jesuit Seminary Collection (33,000 volumes); business.

Buildings and Grounds: Campus area 26 acres.

Chief Executive Officer: Rev. Vincent M. Cooke, S.J., President.

Address admission inquiries to Anne Marie Moslovic Director of Admissions.

Cazenovia College

22 Sullivan Street
Cazenovia, New York 13035
Tel: (800) 654-3210 **E-mail:** admission@cazcollege.edu
Fax: (315) 655-4860 **Internet:** www.cazcollege.edu

Institution Description: Cazenovia College is a private coeducational four-year college. *Enrollment:* 1,084. *Degrees awarded:* Associate, baccalaureate.

Accreditation: *Regional:* MSA.

History: The college traces its start to 1824 when it was founded as the Seminary of the Genessee Conference, the second Methodist seminary to be established in the United States; became Cazenovia Junior College 1942 and severed ties with the Methodist Conference; became Cazenovia College for Women 1961; again became coeducational 1983; awarded first baccalaureate degrees 1989.

Institutional Structure: *Governing board:* Cazenovia College Board of Trustees. Extrainstitutional representation: president of the college. 1 ex officio. All voting. *Composition of institution:* Administrators 9. Academic affairs headed by vice president for academic affairs and dean of the college. Management/business and finance directed by the vice president for business and chief financial officer. Full-time instructional faculty 52. College-wide governance body: the College Senate. Academic governance body: Council on Academic Affairs.

Calendar: Semesters. Academic year Aug. to May. Freshmen admitted Sept., Jan. Degrees conferred and formal commencement May. Summer session from July to Aug.

Characteristics of Freshmen: 2,330 applicants. 66% of applicants accepted. 19% of accepted applicants enrolled full-time.

84% of applicants submitted SAT scores; 24% submitted ACT scores. *25th percentile*: SAT Critical Reading 430, SAT Math 420; ACT Composite 18. *75th percentile*: SAT Critical Reading 540, SAT Math 530; ACT Composite 23.

39% of entering freshmen expected to graduate within 5 years. 80% of freshmen from New York. Freshmen from 24 states and 5 foreign countries.

Admission: Rolling admission plan. For fall acceptance apply as early as beginning of senior year in secondary school. Deadlines for freshmen: fall, Sept 1.; priority, Mar. 1; spring, rolling until Jan. 1. For transfers: fall, Sept. 1; spring, Jan. 1. Financial aid deadline: Apr. 15 recommended. *Requirements:* High school diploma with 4 units English, 2 units mathematics, 2 units science, 4 units social studies recommended; or GED. SAT or ACT recommended; some programs have special requirements. Students entering as juniors must have a college transcript; an associate degree; or have completed a minimum of 60 credits and taken all prerequisites.

Advanced placement for postsecondary-level work completed in secondary school, portfolio, and faculty assessment. Professional and peer tutoring available through the Center for Teaching and Learning.

Degree Requirements: *For all associate degrees:* 60–62 credit hours; 10 courses in residence. *For all baccalaureate degrees:* 120–126 credit hours; 15 courses in residence. *For all undergraduate degrees:* 2.0 GPA.

Fulfillment of some degree requirements and exemption from some beginning courses possible by passing College Board CLEP or AP. *Grading system:* A–F; withdraw pass; withdraw failing (carries time limit).

Distinctive Educational Programs: Internships, program in liberal and professional studies, specialization in fine and performing arts, literature and culture, interdisciplinary social sciences, and science and society, individualized studies, study abroad in England. Evening, weekend, and summer classes for adult students on campus and at remote locations.

ROTC: Army and Air Force offered in cooperation with Syracuse University.

Degrees Conferred: 6 *associate;* 176 *baccalaureate:* business/marketing 67; education 8; English language/literature 3; liberal arts/general studies 9; natural resources/environmental science 1; psychology 8; public administration and social services 13; social sciences 4; visual and performing arts 50.

Fees and Other Expenses: *Full-time tuition per academic year 2008–09:* $22,894. *Books and supplies:* $1,000. *Room and board per academic year:* $9,506. *Other expenses:* $1,200.

Financial Aid: Aid from institutionally generated funds is provided on the basis of academic merit, financial need. Institution has a Program Participation Agreement with the U.S. Department of Education for eligible students to receive Pell Grants and, depending upon the agreement, other federal aid.

Financial aid to full-time, first-time undergraduate students: 95% received some form of aid. Average amount of aid received: federal grants $1,976; state/local grants $2,628; institutional grants $6,864; loans $5,438.

Departments and Teaching Staff: *Total instructional faculty:* 141 (full-time 52, part-time 89).; 255 of faculty hold the doctorate, first-professional, or other terminal degree. Student/faculty ratio: 11:1.

Enrollment: Total enrollment 1,084. Undergraduate 1,084. Transfer-in students 52.

Characteristics of Student Body: *Ethnic/racial makeup:* Black non-Hispanic: 4%; American Indian or Alaska Native: 1%; Asian or Pacific Islander: 1%; Hispanic: 2%; White non-Hispanic: 71%; unknown: 20%.

International Students: 2 nonresident aliens enrolled fall 2008. Student from Asia, Canada. No programs available to aid students whose native language is not English. No financial aid specifically designated for international students.

Student Life: On-campus residence halls house 90% of student body. *Intercollegiate athletics:* male: basketball, soccer, tennis, baseball, golf; female: basketball, soccer, tennis, softball, volleyball; co-ed: equestrian team, crew. *Special regulations:* Cars permitted (parking fee applies). *Special services:* Health services, career development and placement. *Student publications, radio: The Quad*, a student newspaper; *Cazenovian*, a yearbook; *Images*, a student literary magazine; WITC, a student FM radio station. Student Government; creative an performing arts; special interest groups. *Surrounding community:* Cazenovia, population 2,500, is 12 miles southeast of Syracuse, its nearest metropolitan area.

Library Collections: 83,500 volumes. 14,700 microforms; 4,200 audiovisual titles. Current periodical subscription: 382 paper; 122 microform; others via electronic access. Online catalog. Students have access to online information retrieval services and the Internet. 43 computer work stations.

Most important special collection: Women's Studies (women's diaries on microfilm).

Buildings and Grounds: Campus area 27 acres.

Chief Executive Officer: Dr. Mark J. Tierno, President.

Address admissions inquiries to Robert A. Croot, Dean of Admissions and Financial Aid.

Christ the King Seminary

711 Knox Road
East Aurora, New York 14052
Tel: (716) 657-8900 **E-mail:** admissions@cks.edu
Fax: (716) 652-8903 **Internet:** www.cks.edu

Institution Description: Christ the King Seminary is a private graduate school of theology conducted by the Franciscans, Order of Friars Minor, Roman Catholic Church. *Enrollment:* 92. *Degrees awarded:* First-professional (master of divinity), master's.

Member of Western New York Consortium of Higher Education.

Accreditation: *Regional:* MSA. *National:* ATS. *Professional*: theology

History: Christ the King Seminary was founded by the Franciscan Friars in 1857 as a center for theological and pastoral education; adopted present name 1950; moved to present location, incorporated as independent seminary, and awarded first degree (master of divinity) 1974; in 1990 the Roman Catholic Diocese of Buffalo assumed the administration of the Seminary. The Diocese of Buffalo owns and maintains the property. While the Seminary is essentially oriented to the preparation of men for the Roman Catholic priesthood, men and women who qualify can pursue an advanced degree and/or prepare for ministries.

Institutional Structure: *Governing board:* Board of Trustees. Representation: 15 trustees, including 2 alumni; president of the college. 1 ex officio. All voting. *Composition of institution:* Administrators 9. Academic affairs headed by academic dean. Management/business/finances directed by treasurer-procurator. Full-time instructional faculty 14. Academic governance body, Faculty Council, meets an average of 20 times per year.

Calendar: Semesters. Academic year Aug. to May. Freshmen admitted Aug. Degrees conferred May, Dec. Formal commencement May. No summer session.

Admission: Rolling admissions plan. For fall acceptance apply no later than June 15. *Requirements:* Baccalaureate degree or equivalent from accredited college or university with minimum of 18 credit hours in philosophy. Minimum GPA 2.5. *For transfer students:* 2.5 minimum GPA; for master's programs, 6 hours maximum transfer credit from accredited institution.

Tutoring available. Developmental courses offered during regular regular academic year.

Degree Requirements: *For first-professional degree:* 110 semester hours; 2.0 GPA; 8 semesters in residence; core curriculum; theological field education. Chapel attendance expected for seminary students. *For master's degree:* 39 hours; 3.0 GPA; 24 hours in residence; distribution requirements. *For all students:* Exit competency examinations—written and oral comprehensives in individual fields of study. *Grading system:* A–F; pass-fail; withdraw (deadline after which pass-fail may be appended to withdraw).

Distinctive Educational Programs: Evening classes. Special facilities for using telecommunications in the classroom. Interdisciplinary program in personal and spiritual formation. Facilities and programs for independent research, including tutorials, independent study.

Degrees Conferred: 16 *master's:* theology; 4 *first-professional:* master of divinity.

Fees and Other Expenses: *Full-time tuition per academic year 2008–09:* contact the seminary for current tuition, fees, and housing costs.

Financial Aid: Aid from institutionally generated funds is provided on the basis of financial need. Institution has a Program Participation Agreement with the U.S. Department of Education for eligible students to receive Pell Grants and, depending upon the agreement, other federal aid.

Departments and Teaching Staff: *Total instructional faculty:* 20 (full-time 9, part-time 11). 80% of faculty hold the doctorate, first-professional, or other terminal degree.

Enrollment: Total enrollment 92. First-professional 92.

Characteristics of Student Body: *Ethnic/racial makeup:* Black non-Hispanic 7%; Asian or Pacific Islander 1%; White non-Hispanic 92%.

International Students: No programs available to aid students whose native language is not English. No financial aid specifically designated for international students.

Student Life: On-campus residence halls for males only house 2% of student body. *Special regulations:* Cars permitted without restrictions. *Surrounding community:* East Aurora population 7,000. Buffalo, 15 miles from campus, is nearest metropolitan area. Served by airport 15 miles from campus, passenger rail service 14 miles from campus.

Library Collections: 180,000 volumes. 3,500 microforms; 1,010 audiovisual materials; 430 current periodical subscriptions. Students have access to the Internet.

Most important holdings include Bray Collection (Niagara frontier and French Canadian history).

Buildings and Grounds: Campus area 132 acres.

Chief Executive Officer: Rev. Richard W. Siepka, President-Rector.

Address admission inquiries to Rev. Edward J. Sheedy, Academic Dean/Registrar.

City College / CUNY

160 Convent Avenue
New York, New York 10031-9101
Tel: (212) 650-7000 **E-mail:** admissions@ccny.cuny.edu
Fax: (212) 650-7680 **Internet:** www.ccny.cuny.edu

Institution Description: *Enrollment:* 14,392. *Degrees awarded:* Baccalaureate, master's.

Accreditation: *Regional:* MSA. *Professional*: clinical psychology, computer science, engineering, nursing, physical therapy, social work, teacher education

History: Established as the Free Academy, the first American tuition-free municipal college, 1847; offered first instruction at postsecondary level 1849; awarded first degree (baccalaureate) 1853; changed name to College of the City of New York 1866, to The City College 1929; adopted present name 1961. *See* S. Willis Rudy, *The College of the City of New York: A History 1847–1947* (New York: The City College Press, 1949) for further information.

Institutional Structure: *Composition of institution:* Administrators 88. Academic affairs headed by provost and vice president for academic affairs. Management/business/finances directed by vice president for administrative affairs. Academic governance body, Faculty Senate, meets an average of 9 times per year.

Calendar: Semesters. Academic year Aug. to June. Freshmen admitted Aug., Feb. Degrees conferred June, Aug., Jan. Formal commencement June. Summer session of 1 term from mid-June to early Aug.

Characteristics of Freshmen: 16,334 applicants (8,644 female, 7,690 male). 42% of applicants admitted. 26% of admitted students enrolled full-time.

99% (1,439 students) submitted SAT scores. *25th percentile*: SAT Critical Reading 410, SAT Math 440. *75th percentile*: SAT Critical Reading 550, SAT Math 580.

96% of freshmen from New York. Freshmen from 40 states and 60 foreign countries.

Admission: Rolling admissions plan. For fall acceptance, apply as early as Jan. 16, but not later than last day of registration. Students are notified of acceptance beginning March. *Requirements:* Either graduation from secondary school or GED. *For transfer students:* 2.0 minimum GPA; maximum transfer credit limited only by residence requirement.

College credit and advanced placement for postsecondary-level work completed in secondary school.

Tutoring available. Developmental and remedial courses offered in summer session and regular academic year.

Degree Requirements: *Undergraduate:* 128–136 semester hours; 2.0–2.5 GPA; 32 hours in residence; core requirements; exit competency examinations in writing and mathematics.

Fulfillment of some degree requirements and exemption from some beginning courses possible by passing departmental examinations, College Board AP. *Grading system:* A–F; pass-fail; withdraw (deadline after which pass-fail is appended to withdraw).

Distinctive Educational Programs: Work-experience programs. Flexible meeting places and schedules, including off-campus centers (at Long Island, Rockland County, Upper Westchester County; and other locations throughout New York City, each within 30 miles of main institution), evening classes. Accelerated degree programs. Interdisciplinary programs in labor studies, Latin American area studies, Puerto Rican studies, Russian studies, urban legal studies, women's studies. Facilities and programs for independent research, including honors programs, individual majors, tutorials. Institutionally arranged study abroad in China, Germany. *Other distinctive programs:* School of General Studies offers continuing education programs and programs of study leading to baccalaureate.

Degrees Conferred: 1,463 *baccalaureate*; 912 *master's*. Bachelor's degrees awarded in top five disciplines: liberal arts and sciences, general studies, and humanities 146; engineering 125; social sciences 115; psychology 105; visual and performing arts 100. Master's degrees awarded in top five disciplines: education 473; engineering 103; social sciences 48; computer and information sciences 39; visual and performing arts 34.

Fees and Other Expenses: *Full-time tuition per academic year 2008–09:* undergraduate resident $4,329, nonresident $8,969; contact the college for current graduate tuition/fees. *Books and supplies:* $1,016. *Room and board per academic year:* $12,736. *Other expenses:* $4,526.

Financial Aid: Aid from institutionally generated funds is provided on the basis of academic merit, financial need. Institution has a Program Participation Agreement with the U.S. Department of Education for eligible students to receive Pell Grants and, depending upon the agreement, other federal aid.

Financial aid to full-time, first-time undergraduate students: 83% of students received some form of financial aid. Average amount of aid received: federal grants $3,490; state/local grants $3,201; institutional grants $5,324; loans $2,502.

Departments and Teaching Staff: *Total instructional faculty:* 857. Student/faculty ratio: 18:1. Degrees held by full-time faculty: doctorate 86%, master's 2%, baccalaureate 2%, professional 11%. 90% hold terminal degrees.

Enrollment: Total enrollment 14,392. Undergraduate 11,181. Graduate 3,211. Undergraduate transfer-in students 1,196.

Characteristics of Student Body: *Ethnic/racial makeup:* Black non-Hispanic: 24%; Asian or Pacific Islander: 17%; Hispanic: 32%; White non-Hispanic: 17%; nonresident alien 11%.

International Students: 1,583 nonresident aliens enrolled fall 2008. Programs available to aid students whose native language is not English: social, cultural. No financial aid specifically designated for international students.

Student Life: *Intercollegiate athletics:* male: basketball, lacrosse, soccer, tennis, track, volleyball; female: basketball, fencing, volleyball. *Special regulations:* Limited on-campus parking. *Special services:* Learning Resources Center,

CITY COLLEGE / CUNY—*cont'd*

medical services, campus van service. *Student publications, radio: The Campus*, a weekly newspaper; *Fiction*, a biannual literary magazine; *Microcosm*, a yearbook; *The Paper*, a monthly newspaper. Radio stations WCCR-AM and WHCR-FM each broadcast 60 hours per week. *Surrounding community:* New York City population over 7 million. Served by mass transit bus and subway systems; airport 5 miles from campus; passenger rail service 2 miles from campus.

Library Collections: 1,500,000 volumes. 15,034 audiovisual materials; 2,547 current periodicals. 210 microform titles; 895 electronic titles. Computer work stations available. Online catalog. Students have access to online information retrieval services and the Internet.

Most important holdings include Russell Sage collection of materials on social welfare; Simon Newcomb collection of 17th- and 18th-century scientific books; 18th- and 19th-century English plays; Gershwin Music Library.

Buildings and Grounds: Campus area 35 acres.

Chief Executive Officer: Dr. Gregory H. Williams, President.

Address admission inquiries to Celia Lloyd, Director of Admissions.

College of Liberal Arts and Science

Degree Programs Offered: *Baccalaureate* in art, Asian studies, classical languages and Hebrew, communications, medieval and Renaissance studies, performing arts and other humanities fields; in ecology and environment, energy, history and philosophy of science and technology, oceanography, and other scientific fields; in anthropology, black studies, public policy and public service, and other fields; *master's* in art, creative writing, English, music, Romance languages, speech, theater, and other humanities fields; in biology, chemistry, mathematics, physics, and other scientific fields; in economics, history, international relations, psychology, sociology, and other fields.

Distinctive Educational Programs: Interdisciplinary program in international relations. Accelerated 4-year baccalaureate-master's programs in economics, English, mathematics, Romance languages. Preprofessional program in law.

School of Architecture and Environmental Studies

Degree Programs Offered: *Baccalaureate* in urban design, urban landscape; *master's* in urban planning.

Distinctive Educational Programs: 4- or 5-year combined degree program in architecture and landscape architecture. Architecture Center provides opportunities for specialized research and community-based architectural and design projects. Computer design workshop.

Sophie Davis School of Biomedical Education

Degree Programs Offered: *Baccalaureate*.

Distinctive Educational Programs: Physician's assistant program. Summer field experiences with approved health and social agencies. Preprofessional program in medicine.

School of Engineering

Degree Programs Offered: *Baccalaureate, master's* in biomedical engineering; *baccalaureate, master's, doctorate* in chemical engineering, civil engineering, computer sciences, electrical engineering, mechanical engineering, technology.

Distinctive Educational Programs: 4-year accelerated baccalaureate-master's in engineering and computer science. Cooperative education. Facilities for research, including digital communication laboratory, optical signal processing laboratory; turbomachinery and dynamics laboratories; and facilities for soil, fluids, and environmental engineering. Clean Fuels Institute. Institute of Applied Chemical Physics.

School of Education

Degree Programs Offered: *Baccalaureate* in industrial arts education, occupational education, physical education, secondary and continuing education, social and psychological foundations; *baccalaureate, master's* in bilingual education, early childhood education, elementary education, industrial education, school services (administration, guidance and counseling, school psychology, special education), secondary education; *master's* in adult and community education, health education, reading. Specialist certificates in administration and supervision, and school psychology also given.

School of Nursing

Degree Programs Offered: *Baccalaureate*.

Distinctive Educational Programs: Interdisciplinary programs in health care technology, occupational health nursing.

City University of New York

535 East 80th Street
New York, New York 10021
Tel: (212) 794-5555 **E-mail:** information@cuny.edu
Fax: (212) 794-5549 **Internet:** www.cuny.edu

Institution Description: The City University of New York (CUNY) is a state and city supported university system which includes nine senior colleges: Bernard M. Baruch College, Brooklyn College, City College, College of Staten Island, Hunter College, John Jay College of Criminal Justice, Herbert H. Lehman College, Queens College, York College; Graduate School and University Center; as well as seven community colleges: Borough of Manhattan Community College, Bronx Community College, Hostos Community College, Kingsborough Community College, La Guardia Community College, Medgar Evers College, Queensborough Community College, the New York City Technical College, and an affiliated professional school, the Mount Sinai School of Medicine. Eight of the senior colleges offer undergraduate and graduate study; York offers baccalaureate only. Graduate and first-professional degree study are offered at Mount Sinai; baccalaureate program in addition to offering graduate programs. Six of the community colleges offer associate degrees only. Medgar Evers also offers the baccalaureate.

Accreditation: *Regional:* MSA.

History: Municipal college system comprising City College of New York (established 1847 as The Free Academy) and Hunter College (established 1870) founded 1926 by state legislature; Brooklyn College established 1930, Queens College 1937, New York City Community College 1947, Staten Island Community College 1955, Bronx Community College 1957, and Queensborough Community College 1958; system designated City University of New York and Graduate School and University Center organized 1961; Borough of Manhattan Community College established 1963, John Jay College of Criminal Justice 1964, Richmond College 1965, York College 1966; Mount Sinai School of Medicine became affiliated with CUNY 1967; Medgar Evers College established 1968, Eugenio Maria de Hostos Community College 1968, Fiorello H. LaGuardia Community College 1968; Bernard M. Baruch College, formerly the School of Business and Public Administration at City College, became separate four-year college 1968; Herbert H. Lehman College, formerly a branch of Hunter College, became separate four-year college 1968; Richmond College and Staten Island Community College joined to become College of Staten Island 1976; City University of New York Law at Queens College opened in 1963; The Board of Trustees authorized the establishment of the Medical School 1984.

Institutional Structure: *Governing board:* Board of Trustees of the City University of New York. 15 appointed members (5 by mayor of New York City, 10 by governor of New York State), chairmen of faculty senate and student senate serve ex officio. 2 ex officio. 16 voting. *Faculty representation:* Faculty served by collective bargaining agent affiliated with AAUP/AFT.

Admission: Graduates of New York State secondary schools are guaranteed admission, but not necessarily to college or program of first choice.

Distinctive Educational Programs: SEEK program provides counseling, tutorial services, and financial aid to help secondary school graduates from city poverty areas succeed in college. Urban Centers, operated under contract with State University of New York in Harlem and Bedford-Stuyvesant and administered by Borough of Manhattan and New York City, offer career programs and courses for students preparing for secondary school equivalency examinations.

Fees and Other Expenses: *See* individual colleges.

Publications: *City University News*, published 3 times per year; *Freshman Admissions Guide*, published annually; *Success Book*, published annually.

Chief Executive Officer: Dr. Matthew Goldstein, Chancellor.

Address admission inquiries to Office of Admission Services, 101 West 31st Street, New York, New York 10001.

Clarkson University

Potsdam, New York 13699-5500
Tel: (315) 268-6400 **E-mail:** admissions@clarkson.edu
Fax: (315) 268-4475 **Internet:** www.clarkson

Institution Description: Clarkson University is a private, independent, nonprofit university. *Enrollment:* 2,949. *Degrees awarded:* Baccalaureate, master's, doctorate.

Member of the consortium Associated Colleges of the St. Lawrence Valley.

Accreditation: *Regional:* MSA. *Professional*: business, engineering, physical therapy

History: Established, chartered, and incorporated under present official name, Thomas S. Clarkson Memorial College of Technology, and offered first instruction at postsecondary level 1896; awarded first degree (baccalaureate) 1900; designated a university in 1984. *See* Bradford B. Broughton, *A Clarkson Mosaic* (Potsdam: Clarkson University, 1995) for further information.

Institutional Structure: *Governing board:* Board of Trustees of Clarkson University. Representation: 28 trustees, including 19 alumni, president of the university. 1 ex officio. All voting. *Composition of institution:* Administrators 67. Academic affairs directed by provost. Management/business/finances directed by senior vice president of finance and administration. Full-time instructional faculty 169. Academic governance body, Faculty Senate, meets an average of 9 times per year.

Calendar: Semesters. Academic year Aug. to May. Freshmen admitted Aug., Jan., June, July. Degrees conferred Dec. and May. Summer session of 2 terms from May to Aug.

Characteristics of Freshmen: 3,204 applicants. 79% of applicants accepted. 29% of accepted applicants enrolled full-time.

95% (699 students) submitted SAT scores; 38% (272 students) submitted ACT scores. *25th percentile*: SAT Critical Reading 500, SAT Math 550, SAT Writing 490; ACT Composite 24, ACT English 22, ACT Math 25. *75th percentile*: SAT Critical Reading 610, SAT Math 660, SAT Writing 590; ACT 26,ACT English 26, ACT Math 30.

66% of entering freshmen expected to graduate within 5 years. 72% of freshmen from New York. Freshmen from 41 states and 26 foreign countries.

Admission: For fall acceptance, apply as early as Oct. 1 of previous year, but not later than Jan. 15 of year of enrollment. Students are notified of acceptance beginning Feb. 15. Apply by Jan. 15 for early decision, with acceptance prior to Feb. 1. Apply by Jan. 15 for early decision II with acceptance prior to Feb. 1. *Requirements:* Either graduation from accredited secondary school with 16 units or GED. Recommend 4 units English, 4 mathematics, 3–4 laboratory science (including at least 1 chemistry or physics), 4–5 academic electives. Minimum GPA 3.0. *Entrance tests:* College Board SAT or ACT composite. College Board Achievement Tests recommended. All students entering as a first-year student must take the first-year seminar or an equivalent course that may be offered by the university. *For transfer students:* From 4-year accredited institution 2.75 preferred minimum GPA; from 2-year accredited institution 2.75 preferred GPA; 90 hours maximum transfer credit.

College credit and advanced placement for postsecondary-level work completed in secondary school.

Degree Requirements: *Undergraduate:* 120 credit hours; 2.00 GPA; 4 terms in residence; all entering first-year students must take first-year seminary or equivalent.

Fulfillment of some degree requirements and exemption from some beginning courses possible by passing College Board CLEP, APP, other standardized tests. *Grading system:* A–F; pass; withdraw (carries time limit); incomplete (carries time limit).

Distinctive Educational Programs: *For undergraduates:* Pre-professional advising; pre-dentistry, pre-law, pre-medicine, pre-physical therapy, pre-veterinary medicine. First-year options include business studies, engineering sciences, university studies. Four-year honors program for exceptional students majoring in any of the degree programs offered. More than 20 study abroad programs in 13 countries including Australia, England, France, Germany, Hong Kong, Korea, Mexico, Sweden. Co-op and internship programs offer students an opportunity to gain professional experience in their chosen field of interest.

ROTC: Army; Air Force.

Degrees Conferred: 609 *baccalaureate*; 111 *master's*; 37 *doctorate*. Bachelor's degrees awarded in top five disciplines: engineering 311; business/marketing 119; interdisciplinary studies 100; biological/life sciences 39; physical sciences 30. Master's degrees awarded: business/marketing 71; communications technologies 9; computer and information sciences 7; engineering 45; health professions and related sciences 5; mathematics 2; physical sciences 11. Doctorates awarded: engineering 23; mathematics 7; physical sciences 4.

Fees and Other Expenses: *Full-time tuition per academic year 2008–09:* undergraduate $31,010; graduate study charged per credit hour (vonctac the university for current rate). *Room and board per academic year:* $10,612. *Books and supplies:* $1,100. *Other expenses:* $2,078.

Financial Aid: The university offers a direct lending program. Aid from institutionally generated funds is provided on the basis of academic merit, financial need, athletic ability (hockey-Division I).

Financial aid to full-time, first-time undergraduate students: 96% received some form of aid. Average amount of aid received: federal grants $3,721; state/local grants $2,131; institutional grants $14,563; loans $8,594.

Departments and Teaching Staff: *Total instructional faculty:* 197 (full-time 173, part-time 24). 85% of faculty hold the doctorate, first-professional, or other terminal degree. Student/faculty ratio: 16:1.

Enrollment: Total enrollment 2,949. Undergraduate 2,540. Graduate 409. Undergraduate transfer-in students 91.

Characteristics of Student Body: *Ethnic/racial makeup:* Black non-Hispanic: 3%; Asian or Pacific Islander: 3%; Hispanic: 25; White non-Hispanic: 89%; nonresident alien 3%. *Age distribution:* number under 18: 102; 18–19: 1,078; 20–21: 1,091; 22–24: 215; 25–29: 27; 30–34: 15; 35–39: 7; 40–49: 7. 6% of student body attend summer sessions.

International Students: 90 nonresident aliens enrolled fall 2008. Students from Europe, Asia, Central and South Latin America, Africa, Canada, Australia, New Zealand, Middle East. Programs available to aid students whose native language is not English: English as a Second Language Program. Financial aid specifically designated for international students: scholarships available annually to qualifying students; 47 totaling $745,756 awarded 200^–07.

Student Life: On-campus residence halls house 80% of student body. 14% of males join and 4% live in fraternity housing; 16% of females join and 9% live in sorority housing. Limited housing available for married students. *Intercollegiate athletics:* male: baseball; female: volleyball; both sexes: basketball, cross-country, golf, hockey, lacrosse, skiing, soccer, swimming, *Special regulations:* Cars permitted without restrictions for all. Quiet hours set by dormitory residents. *Special services:* Learning Resources Center, medical services. *Student publications, radio, television: Clarksonian*, a yearbook; *Integrator*, a weekly newspaper; *Knight*, a magazine published annually. Radio stations WNTC and WTSC-FM each broadcast 140 hours per week. TV station WCKN broadcasts 4 hours per week. *Surrounding community:* Potsdam population 11,000. Montreal, 100 miles from campus, is nearest metropolitan area. Served by airport 20 miles from campus.

Library Collections: 593,412 volumes including bound books, serial backfiles, electronic documents, and government documents not in separate collections. Online catalog. 265,500 microforms; 2,100 audiovisual materials; Current serial subscriptions: 67 paper, 1,852 via electronic access. 635 audio/videotapes; 1,493 CD-ROMs. Computer work stations available. Students have access to the Internet at no charge.

Most important special collections include Energy collection (microfiche); corporate annual reports; NASA technical reports from 1970 to present; Clarkson University Archives.

Buildings and Grounds: Campus area 640 acres.

Chief Executive Officer: Dr. Anthony G. Collins, President.

Undergraduates address admission inquiries to Brian T. Grant, Director of Admissions; graduate inquiries Graduate School.

Colgate Rochester Crozer Divinity School

1100 South Goodman Street
Rochester, New York 14620
Tel: (585) 271-1320 **E-mail:** admissions@crcds.edu
Fax: (585) 271-8013 **Internet:** www.crcds.edu

Institution Description: Colgate Rochester Crozer Divinity School is a private interdenominational combined divinity school. *Enrollment:* 156. *Degrees awarded:* First-professional, master's, doctorate.

Accreditation: *National:* ATS. *Professional*: theology

History: Colgate Rochester Divinity School established 1817; united with Bexley Hall (founded 1824) in 1968; Crozer Theological Seminary joined to form current organization 1970; current name adopted 2000.

Calendar: Semesters. Academic year Aug. to May.

Admission: *Requirements:* Graduation from accredited college with a minimum cumulative grade point average of 2.5; physical and emotional health; maturity of character and purpose; religious commitment appropriate to the applicant's vocational objectives.

Degree Requirements: Completion of prescribed curriculum.

Degrees Conferred: 20 *master's:* theology; 5 *doctorate:* theology; 17 *first-professional:* master of divinity.

Fees and Other Expenses: *Full-time tuition per academic year 2008–09:* $7,140. *Required fees:* 155. *Housing per academic year:* $7,140.

Financial Aid: Aid from institutionally generated funds is provided on the basis of academic merit, financial need.

Departments and Teaching Staff: *Professors* 9, *part-time faculty* 10. *Total instructional faculty:* 19 (full-time 9, part-time 10). Total faculty with doctorate, first-professional, or other terminal degree: 18. Student/faculty ratio: 8:1.

Enrollment: Total enrollment 150. Undergraduate

Characteristics of Student Body: *Ethnic/racial makeup:* number of Black non-Hispanic: 38; Hispanic: 2; White non-Hispanic: 100; unknown: 2. Average age 44.

International Students: 8 nonresident aliens enrolled fall 2008. No programs available to aid students whose native language is not English. No financial aid specifically designated for international students.

Student Life: Residence hall accommodations available.

COLGATE ROCHESTER CROZER DIVINITY SCHOOL—*cont'd*

Library Collections: 300,000 volumes. 20,586 microforms; 2,870 audiovisual materials; 935 current periodical subscriptions. Computer work stations available.

Most important special collections include the J.A.W. Neander Library; Bishop Fulton J. Sheen Collection; Karpinsky Library of Reformation Resources.

Buildings and Grounds: Campus area 24 acres.

Chief Executive Officer: Dr. G. Thomas Halbrooks, President.

Address admission inquiries to Robert Jones, Vice President for Enrollment.

Colgate University

13 Oak Drive

Hamilton, New York 13346

Tel: (315) 228-7401 **E-mail:** admission@mail.colgate.edu
Fax: (315) 228-7544 **Internet:** www.colgate.edu

Institution Description: Colgate University is a private, independent, nonprofit institution. *Enrollment:* 2,841. *Degrees awarded:* Baccalaureate, master's.

Accreditation: *Regional:* MSA.

History: Established 1819; offered first instruction at postsecondary level 1820; awarded first degree (baccalaureate) 1822; chartered as Madison University 1846; adopted present name 1890. *See* Howard Williams, *A History of Colgate University 1819–1969* (New York: Van Nostrand Reinhold, 1969) for further information.

Institutional Structure: *Governing board:* The Colgate University Board of Trustees. Representation: 35 trustees. All voting. *Composition of institution:* Academic affairs headed by provost and dean of faculty. Management/business/finances directed by vice president for business and finance; treasurer. Full-time instructional faculty 271. Academic governance body, Academic Affairs Board, meets an average of 14 times per year.

Calendar: Semesters. Academic year Aug. to May. Degrees conferred and formal commencements May.

Characteristics of Freshmen: 9,415 applicants (5,102 female, 4,233 male). 24% of applicants admitted. 33% of admitted students enrolled full-time.

72% (549 students) submitted SAT scores; 28% (209 students) submitted ACT scores. *25th percentile*: SAT Critical Reading 630, SAT Math 640, SAT Writing 630; ACT Composite 29, ACT English 30, ACT Math 28. *75th percentile*: SAT Critical Reading 730, SAT Math 730, SAT Writing 720; ACT Composite 32, ACT English 34, ACT Math 33.

89% of entering freshmen expected to graduate within 5 years. 25% of freshmen from New York. Freshmen from 40 states and 34 foreign countries.

Admission: For fall acceptance, apply as early as Nov. 1 of previous year, but not later than Jan. 16 of year of enrollment. Students are notified of acceptance in Apr. Apply by Nov. 15 for early decision; need not limit application to Colgate, but must agree to enroll if accepted. Early acceptance available. *Requirements:* Either graduation from accredited secondary school or GED. Recommend 16 units from among English, foreign languages, and other humanities; biology and physical sciences; mathematics; social studies including history. *Entrance tests:* College Board SAT or ACT Composite. For foreign students TOEFL. *For transfer students:* 3.0 minimum GPA, 60 semester hours maximum transfer credit.

College credit and advanced placement for postsecondary-level work completed in secondary school. Tutoring available.

Degree Requirements: *Undergraduate:* Student must complete 32 course credits and requirements for general education, a concentration, language, and writing. Also required are 2 units of physical education and 7 terms in residence. A 2.0 minimum GPA is additionally needed.

Fulfillment of some degree requirements and exemption from some beginning courses possible by passing departmental examinations, College Board CLEP, AP. *Grading system:* A–F; withdraw (within a time limit); satisfactory/unsatisfactory grade option available.

Distinctive Educational Programs: Dual-degree programs in business administration and engineering with Columbia University, Cornell University, Rensselaer Polytechnic Institute, Carnegie-Mellon University (PA), Dartmouth College (NH). Comprehensive general education program includes freshmen seminary and four core courses. Special facilities for using telecommunications in the classroom. Interdisciplinary programs in Afro-American studies, astrogeophysics, astronomy-physics, East Asian studies, humanities, international relations, peace studies, philosophy and religion, Russian studies, social sciences, sociology and anthropology. Facilities and programs for independent research, including honors programs, individual majors, tutorials, independent study. Institutionally sponsored study abroad in Australia, China, Dominican Republic, England, France, Germany, India, Italy, Japan, Russia, Scotland, Spain, Switzerland, Wales, West Indies. Off-campus semester in U.S. in Los Angeles, Rocky Mountains of Wyoming, Washington (DC); during January interim through exchange programs with other universities and colleges; by individual arrangement. 12-week sea semester combines study of marine science at Woods Hole (MA) with study of sea in North Atlantic and Caribbean. *Other distinctive programs:* Higher Education Opportunity program and University Scholars provides academic and support services for economically and educationally disadvantaged students.

Degrees Conferred: 675 *baccalaureate*; 2 *master;s*. Bachelor's degrees awarded in top five disciplines: social sciences 221; English language/literature 82; biological/life sciences 54; philosophy and religious studies 48; history 46. *Master's*: education 2.

Fees and Other Expenses: *Full-time tuition per academic year 2008–09:* $39,545. *Room and board per academic year:* $9,625. *Books and supplies:* $1,000. *Other expenses:* $890.

Financial Aid: Financial assistance is available in the form of institutional grants, Pell Grants, College Work-Study, Veterans Administration Benefits, National Direct Student Loans, Supplemental Education Opportunity Grants (SEOG), Stafford Loans, other federal aid programs.

Financial aid to full-time, first-time undergraduate students:

Financial aid to full-time, first-time undergraduate students: 39% received some form of aid. Average amount of aid received: federal grants $4,513; state/local grants $3,902; institutional grants $27,997; loans $2,593.

Departments and Teaching Staff: *Total instructional faculty:* 322 (full-time 271, part-time 51). 98% of faculty hold the doctorate, first-professional, or other terminal degree. Student/faculty ratio: 10:1.

Enrollment: Total enrollment 2,841. Undergraduate 2,831. Graduate 10. Undergraduate transfer-in students 21.

Characteristics of Student Body: *Ethnic/racial makeup:* Black non-Hispanic: 5%; American Indian or Alaska Native: 1%; Asian or Pacific Islander: 8%; Hispanic: 5%; White non-Hispanic: 74%; unknown: 4%; nonresident alien 5%. *Age distribution:* number under 18: 106; 18–19: 1,343; 20–21: 1,208; 22–24: 114; 25–29: 5; 35–39: 1; 40–49: 3; unknown: 2.

International Students: 142 nonresident aliens enrolled fall 2008. Students from Europe, Asia, Central and South America, Africa, Canada, Middle East. No programs available to aid students whose native language is not English. No financial aid specifically designated for international students.

Student Life: On-campus residence halls house 51% of student body. 36% of student body housed on-campus in university owned apartment and theme houses. 29% of males join and 11% live in fraternity housing; 32% of female join and 7% live in sorority housing. *Intercollegiate athletics:* male: baseball, basketball, crew, football, golf, hockey, lacrosse, soccer, swimming, tennis, track, wrestling; female: basketball, crew, field hockey, ice hockey, lacrosse, softball, swimming, tennis, volleyball. *Special regulations:* Registered cars permitted for all students. *Special services:* Medical services. *Student publications, radio: Colgate Review*, an annual literary magazine, *Face of the Sage*, an annual literary magazine; *Harlequin*, a biannual literary magazine; *Like It Is*, an irregularly published newspaper; *Maroon News*, a weekly newspaper; *News*, a weekly newspaper; *Salmagundi*, a yearbook; *Tesseract*, an annual literary magazine. Radio station WRCU broadcasts 168 hours per week. *Surrounding community:* Hamilton population 2,500. Syracuse, 40 miles from campus, and Utica-Rome, 30 miles away, are nearest metropolitan areas. Served by airport and passenger rail service, each 20 miles from campus.

Publications: *Journal of the Sciences* (annually) first published in 1967; *Powys Newsletter*, (annually) first published 1970. *Publisher:* Colgate University Press.

Library Collections: 721,189 volumes plus 451,362 government documents. Online catalog. Current serial subscriptions: 1,698 paper, 179 microform, 29,632 via electronic access. 9,925 audio/videotapes; 1,487 DVD discs; 3,475 CD-ROMs. Computer work stations available. Students have access to the Internet at no charge.

Most important holdings include the Powys Family Papers, including letters, manuscripts and first editions; first editions, manuscripts and letters of Joseph Conrad; complete collection of Ernest Gann manuscripts; Chambers Collection; Richard Weiner Collection of the works of George Bernard Shaw.

Buildings and Grounds: Campus area 120 acres. *New buildings:* Case Library and Geyer Center for Information Technology completed 2007; Robert Ho Science Center 2007.

Chief Executive Officer: Dr. Rebecca Chopp, President.

Address admission inquiries to Gary Ross, Dean of Admission.

College of Mount Saint Vincent

6301 Riverdale Avenue
Riverdale, New York 10471-1093
Tel: (718) 405-3200 **E-mail:** admissions@cmsv.edu
Fax: (718) 601-6392 **Internet:** www.cmsv.edu

Institution Description: College of Mount Saint Vincent is a private, independent, coeducational liberal arts college in the Catholic tradition and the spirit of the Sisters of Charity. *Enrollment:* 1,810. *Degrees awarded:* Associate, baccalaureate, master's.

Accreditation: *Regional:* MSA. *Professional*: business, nursing

History: Established as Academy of Mount Saint Vincent, a school for women, 1847; chartered 1849; offered first instruction at postsecondary level 1895; awarded first degree (baccalaureate) 1913; became coeducational 1974. *See* Sr. Marie de Lourdes Walsh, *The Sisters of Charity of New York 1809–1959*, 3 vols. (New York: Fordham University Press, 1960).

Institutional Structure: *Governing board:* Board of Trustees. Extrainstitutional representation: 24 trustees; institutional representation: president of the college. 1 ex officio. All voting. *Composition of institution:* Administrators 63. Academic affairs headed by academic vice president. Vice president for student development is responsible for everything relating to student life. Chief financial officer manages and accounts for financial affairs. Full-time instructional faculty 71. Academic governance body, College Senate, meets monthly.

Calendar: Semesters. Academic year Aug. to May. Freshmen admitted Aug., Jan. Degrees conferred May, Jan. Formal commencement May. Summer session from mid-May to late July.

Characteristics of Freshmen: 2,224 applicants. 68.6% of applicants admitted. 26.2% of admitted students enrolled full-time.

100% (343 students) submitted SAT scores. *25th percentile*: SAT Critical Reading 460, SAT Math 450. *75th percentile*: SAT Critical Reading 550, SAT Math 530.

62% of entering freshmen expected to graduate within 5 years. 89% of freshmen from New York. Freshmen from 18 states and 4 foreign countries.

Admission: Rolling admissions plan. For fall acceptance, apply as early as June of previous year, but not later than Aug. 1 of year of enrollment. Apply by Nov. 1 for early decision; must limit application to College of Mount Saint Vincent. *Requirements:* Either graduation from accredited secondary school with 16 college preparatory units including 4 units English, 2 foreign language, 2 mathematics (3 mathematics for science or nursing majors), 1 U.S. history, 1 science (3 for science or nursing majors), 4–6 academic electives; or GED. Minimum GPA 80 on 100 scale. Lowest acceptable secondary school class standing 50th percentile. *Entrance tests:* SAT or ACT. *For transfer students:* 2.0 minimum GPA (2.5 for nursing students); from 4-year accredited institution 75 semester hours maximum transfer credit; from 2-year accredited institution 65 hours.

College credit and advanced placement for postsecondary-level work completed in secondary school. College credit for extrainstitutional learning on basis of portfolio and faculty assessments.

Degree Requirements: *For all associate degrees:* 62 credit hours. *For all baccalaureate degrees:* 120–126 credit hours. *For all undergraduate degrees:* 2.0 GPA; core curriculum requirements. *For all master's degrees:* 30–42 credits; 3.0 GPA.

Fulfillment of some degree requirements and exemption from some beginning courses possible by passing College Board CLEP, AP, other standardized tests. *Grading system:* A–F; pass-no credit, withdraw (deadline after which fail is appended to withdraw); incomplete (carries time limit).

Distinctive Educational Programs: Internships. Evening and weekend classes. Interdisciplinary programs in American studies, environmental studies, liberal arts. Facilities for independent research including individual majors, tutorials, independent study. Institutionally approved study abroad programs in Austria, England, France, Ireland, Italy, Spain. Semester or year exchange with College of Mount Saint Joseph (OH), College of St. Elizabeth (NJ), Elizabeth Seton College, Mount St. Vincent University (Nova Scotia, Canada), Seton Hill College (PA). Joint academic programs and activities with Manhattan College. *Other distinctive programs:* Degree-granting continuing education programs on campus and at the Malcolm-King Harlem College Extension (sponsored jointly with Fordham University and Marymount Manhattan College). Degree completion program for registered nurses. Higher Education Opportunity Program for academically promising, economically disadvantaged students.

ROTC: Air Force offered in cooperation with Manhattan College.

Degrees Conferred: 2 *associate;* 281 *baccalaureate*; 79 *master's*. Bachelor's degrees awarded in top five disciplines: health professions and related clinical sciences 62; business, management, marketing, and related support services 35; communication, journalism, and related programs 34; psychology 30; liberal arts and sciences, general studies, and humanities 24. Master's degrees awarded in various disciplines.

Fees and Other Expenses: *Full-time tuition per academic year 2008–09:* undergraduate $24,580l contact the college for current graduate tuition/fees. *Room and board per academic year:* $9,375. *Books and supplies:* $900. *Other expenses:* $1,100.

Financial Aid: Aid from institutionally generated funds is provided on the basis of academic merit, financial need. Institution has a Program Participation Agreement with the U.S. Department of Education for eligible students to receive Pell Grants and, depending upon the agreement, other federal aid.

Financial aid to full-time, first-time undergraduate students: 92% of students received some form of financial aid. Average amount of aid received: federal grants $2,988; state/local grants $2,730; institutional grants $9,900; loans $3,600.

Departments and Teaching Staff: *Total instructional faculty:* 82. Student/faculty ratio: 16:1. Degrees held by full-time faculty: doctorate 70%, master's 30%. 72% hold terminal degrees.

Enrollment: Total enrollment 1,810. Undergraduate 1,529. Graduate 281. Undergraduate transfer-in students 67.

Characteristics of Student Body: *Ethnic/racial makeup:* Black non-Hispanic: 11%; Asian or Pacific Islander: 11%; Hispanic: 29%; White non-Hispanic: 39%; unknown: 10%.

International Students: 15 nonresident aliens enrolled fall 2008. Students from Europe, Asia, Africa. No programs available to aid students whose native language is not English. No financial aid specifically designated for international students.

Student Life: On-campus residence halls house 60% of student body. *Intercollegiate athletics:* male: basketball, cross-country, tennis, golf, soccer, volleyball; female: basketball, tennis, cross-country, soccer volleyball. *Special regulations:* Student autos permitted on campus with restrictions. All resident students subject to visitation regulations with additional restrictions for first semester freshmen. *Special services:* Medical services, shuttle bus to and from Manhattan College, free use of Fitness Center, free cable TV in residence halls. *Student media:* tv station; radio station; publications: *Font Hill Dial*, an annual literary magazine; *MounTimes*, student newspaper; *Parapet*, a yearbook. *Surrounding community:* Riverdale is 20 minutes from mid-town Manhattan. New York City population over 7 million. Served by mass transit bus and subway systems; airport 15 miles from campus; passenger rail service ½ mile from campus.

Library Collections: 175,000 volumes. 6,300 microforms; 6,500 audiovisual materials; 615 current periodical subscriptions. Online catalog. Students have access to online information retrieval services and the Internet.

Most important holdings include Irish collection (450 items by Celtic authors on Celtic philosophy and genealogy, dating from the 15th century); Early American Collection (microfilmed copies of all American fiction published 1774–1900; 718 first editions, signed copies, and other items primarily by 19th-century authors); rare book collection (including Bibles, other religious literature dating from the 16th century); repository for the works of Joseph Tusiani, internationally known poet and translator of Italian classics.

Buildings and Grounds: Campus area 70 acres.

Chief Executive Officer: Dr. Charles L. Flynn, President.

Address admission inquiries to Timothy Nash, Director of Admissions.

College of New Rochelle

29 Castle Place
New Rochelle, New York 10805-2339
Tel: (914) 654-5000 **E-mail:** admissions@cnr.edu
Fax: (914) 654-5554 **Internet:** www.cnr.edu

Institution Description: College of New Rochelle is a private, independent, nonprofit college. *Enrollment:* 6,226. *Degrees awarded:* Baccalaureate, master's.

Member of Westchester Social Work Education Consortium.

Accreditation: *Regional:* MSA. *Professional*: nursing, social work

History: Established as College of St. Angela, chartered, and offered first instruction at postsecondary level 1904; awarded first degree (baccalaureate) 1908; adopted present name 1910.

Institutional Structure: *Governing board:* Board of Trustees. Extrainstitutional representation: 25 trustees; institutional representation: president of the college. 1 ex officio. All voting. *Composition of institution:* Administrators 123. Academic affairs headed by vice president for academic affairs. Management/business/finances directed by vice president for financial affairs. Full-time instructional faculty 62. Academic governance body, College Senate, meets an average of 10 times per year.

Calendar: Semesters. academic year Sept. to May. Freshmen admitted Sept., Jan., June. Degrees conferred May, Aug., Jan. Formal commencement May. Summer session from early June to early Aug.

COLLEGE OF NEW ROCHELLE—*cont'd*

Characteristics of Freshmen: 2,525 applicants. 64.7% of applicants accepted. 60.1% of accepted applicants enrolled.

90% (130 students) submitted SAT scores. *25th percentile*: SAT Critical Reading 430, SAT Math 420. *75th percentile*: SAT Critical Reading 530, SAT Math 480.

60% of entering freshmen expected to graduate within 5 years. 82% of freshmen from New York. Freshmen from 16 states and 9 foreign countries.

Admission: Rolling admissions plan. For fall acceptance, apply as early as beginning of senior year of secondary school, but not later than Aug. 15 of year of enrollment. Apply by Nov. 1 for early decision; must limit application to New Rochelle. Early acceptance available. *Requirements:* Graduation from accredited secondary school with 15 units. Recommend English, foreign language, social studies, and 3-unit sequences in mathematics and science. Additional requirements for nursing majors. Minimum GPA 3.0. Lowest acceptable secondary school class standing 50th percentile. *Entrance tests:* College Board SAT or ACT composite. For foreign students demonstrated proficiency in English. *For transfer students:* 2.0 minimum GPA; 68 semester hours maximum transfer credit. Students with 3.0 GPA may petition for 75 hours credit.

College credit and advanced placement for postsecondary-level work completed in secondary school. Tutoring available. Developmental and remedial courses offered in summer session and regular academic year.

Degree Requirements: *Undergraduate:* 120–123 semester hours; 2.0 GPA; 52–55 hours in residence; 4 physical education courses; general education requirements; demonstrated proficiency in writing; comprehensives in some fields of study.

Fulfillment of some degree requirements and exemption from some beginning courses possible by passing College Board CLEP, AP (score of 3). *Grading system:* A–F; pass-fail; withdraw (carries time limit).

Distinctive Educational Programs: Internships. Weekend and evening classes. Accelerated degree programs. Cooperative baccalaureate program in communication arts with Iona College. Special facilities for using telecommunications in the classroom. Interdisciplinary programs in American studies, comparative literature, international studies, native American studies, women's studies. Facilities and programs for independent research, including honors programs, individual majors, tutorials. Study abroad in Africa, Asia, and Europe available through programs sponsored by other institutions. Exchange program for 1 semester or 1 year through New York State Visiting Student Program. Cross-registration with Iona College. *Other distinctive programs:* Community Leadership Program assists economically and educationally disadvantaged students with academic potential. School of New Resources offers individualized degree programs for adults and emphasizes life experience and independent study.

Degrees Conferred: 976 *baccalaureate*; 409 *master's*. Bachelor's degrees awarded in top five disciplines: liberal arts and sciences, general studies, and humanities 798; health professions and related clinical sciences 150; psychology 32; biological and biomedical sciences 12; business, management, marketing, and related support service 11. Master's degrees awarded: communication, journalism, and related programs 12; education 375; health professions and related clinical sciences 34; public administration and social service professions 5; social sciences 7; visual and performing arts 17.

Fees and Other Expenses: *Full-time tuition per academic year 2008–09:* undergraduate $25,342; contact the college for current graduate tuition/fees. *Room and board per academic year:* $9,200. *Books and supplies:* $600. *Other expenses:* $4,000.

Financial Aid: Aid from institutionally generated funds is provided on the basis of academic merit, financial need. Institution has a Program Participation Agreement with the U.S. Department of Education for eligible students to receive Pell Grants and, depending upon the agreement, other federal aid.

Financial aid to full-time, first-time undergraduate students: 98% of students received some form of financial aid. Average amount of aid received: federal grants $3,167; state/local grants $3,300; institutional grants $8,136; loans $4,153.

Departments and Teaching Staff: *Total instructional faculty:* 90. Student/faculty ratio: 11:1. Degrees held by full-time faculty: doctorate 70%, master's 30%. 65% hold terminal degrees.

Enrollment: Total enrollment 6,226. Undergraduate 5,019. Graduate 1,207. Undergraduate transfer-in students 271.

Characteristics of Student Body: *Ethnic/racial makeup:* Black non-Hispanic: 51%; Asian or Pacific Islander: 6%; Hispanic: 11%; White 4%; unknown 32% *Age distribution:* 17–21: 30%; 22–24: 30%; 25–29: 15%; 30–34: 10%; 35–39: 10%; 50–59: 5%.

International Students: 21 nonresident aliens enrolled fall 2008. Students from Europe, Asia, Central and South America. No programs available to aid students whose native language is not English. No financial aid specifically designated for international students.

Student Life: On-campus residence halls for females house 57% of student body. *Intercollegiate athletics:* archery, basketball, diving, golf, swimming, tennis, volleyball. *Special regulations:* Registered cars with decals permitted. Curfews for first-semester freshmen only. *Special services:* Learning Resources Center, medical services, van service for students enrolled at Iona College, transportation for cultural events in New York City. *Student publication: Annales*, a yearbook; *CLP New Community*, a monthly newsletter; *Eos*, a monthly newsletter; *Grapevine*, a graduate school newsletter; *Phoenix*, an annual literary journal; *Tatler*, a biweekly newspaper. *Surrounding community:* New Rochelle population 70,000. New York City, 16 miles from campus, is nearest metropolitan area. Served by mass transit bus system, airport 10 miles from campus, passenger rail service 1 mile from campus.

Library Collections: 224,000 volumes. 305,000 microforms; 7,000 audiovisual materials; 1,500 current periodical subscriptions. Computer work stations available.

Most important holdings include Thomas More Collection of rare and original works; Ursuline Collections of Rare Books; James Joyce Collection of Rare Books.

Buildings and Grounds: Campus area 18 acres.

Chief Executive Officer: Dr. Stephen J. Sweeney, President. Undergraduates address admission inquiries to Stephanie Decker, Director of Admissions; graduate inquiries to Dr. Laura Ellis, Dean, Graduate Studies.

College of Saint Rose

432 Western Avenue
Albany, New York 12203-1490

Tel: (518) 454-5150 **E-mail:** admit@strose.edu
Fax: (518) 438-3293 **Internet:** www.strose.edu

Institution Description: College of Saint Rose is a private, independent, nonsectarian, nonprofit college. *Enrollment:* 4,949. *Degrees awarded:* Baccalaureate, master's.

Member of the consortium Hudson-Mohawk Association of Colleges and Universities.

Accreditation: *Regional:* MSA.

History: Established and offered first instruction at postsecondary level 1920; awarded first degree (baccalaureate) 1924; added graduate program 1949.

Institutional Structure: *Governing board:* Board of Trustees of the College of Saint Rose. Extrainstitutional representation: 34 trustees; institutional representation: president of the college. 2 ex officio. All voting. *Composition of institution:* Administrators 129. Academic affairs headed by vice president for academic affairs. Management/business/finances directed by vice president for administration and finance. Full-time instructional faculty 150. Academic governance body, the faculty, meets an average of once per month.

Calendar: Semesters. Academic year Sept. to May. Freshmen admitted Sept., Jan. Degrees conferred and formal commencement May. Summer session of 2 terms from May to Aug.

Characteristics of Freshmen: 4,835 applicants. 38% of applicants accepted. 31% of accepted applicants enrolled full-time.

97% (54 students) submitted SAT scores; 31% (177 students) submitted ACT scores. *25th percentile*: SAT Critical Reading 460, SAT Math 470, SAT Writing 460; ACT Composite 20. *75th percentile*: SAT Critical Reading 560, SAT Math 570, ACT Composite 25.

65% of entering freshmen expected to graduate within 5 years. 89% of freshmen from New York. Freshmen from 20 states and 10 foreign countries.

Admission: Rolling admissions plan. Early acceptance available. *Requirements:* Strongly recommend graduation from accredited secondary school with 16 college preparatory units. GED accepted. For music majors, ability to read music and perform on one instrument recommended. *Entrance tests:* College Board SAT preferred, ACT composite accepted. For foreign students TOEFL. *For transfer students:* 2.5 minimum GPA strongly recommended, maximum transfer credit limited only by residence requirement.

College credit and advanced placement for postsecondary-level work completed in secondary school. College credit for extrainstitutional learning on basis of *2006 Guide to the Evaluation of Educational Experiences in the Armed Services*; portfolio and faculty assessments; personal interview; proficiency examinations.

Tutoring available. Noncredit developmental courses offered in summer session and regular academic year.

Degree Requirements: *Undergraduate:* 122 credit hours; 2.0 GPA; 60 credit hours in residence; 2 physical education courses; core curriculum; distribution requirements.

Fulfillment of some degree requirements and exemption from some beginning courses possible by passing College Board CLEP or AP, or New York State College Proficiency Examinations. *Grading system:* A–F; pass-fail; withdraw; incomplete.

Distinctive Educational Programs: *Undergraduates:* Work-experience programs. Off-campus centers at varying locations by special arrangement. Cooperative programs in cytotechnology and electron microscopy with area hospitals. Interdepartmental and interdisciplinary programs in American studies, biology/chemistry, business/mathematics, communications and culture, fine arts, international studies, mathematics/physical science, political sociology, social sciences, sociology/business, urban studies. Study abroad programs: Center for Cross-Cultural Studies in Seville, Spain; Regents College in London, England. Double majors. Higher Education Opportunity Program for academically and culturally disadvantaged students. *For graduate students:* Interdepartmental and interdisciplinary program in liberal studies. *Available to all students:* Weekend and evening classes. Interdepartmental and interdisciplinary program in history-political science, including internships with the New York State Legislature. Facilities and programs for independent research, including individual majors, independent study. Internships in Albany community. Cross-registration through consortium and through Visiting Student Program for Colleges and Universities in the State of New York. *Other distinctive programs:* Tuition waivers and free admission to college events for senior citizens. Programs in Special Education, Applied Technology Education, Criminal Justice.

Degrees Conferred: 693 *baccalaureate*; 745 *master's*. Bachelor's degrees awarded in top five disciplines: education 331; business, management, marketing, and related support services 72; visual and performing arts 55; communication, journalism, and related programs 54; visual social sciences 31. Master's degrees awarded in top five disciplines: education 395; health professions and related clinical sciences 77; business/marketing 72; psychology 39; communications technologies 12.

Fees and Other Expenses: *Full-time tuition per academic year 2008–09:* undergraduate $21,972; graduate study charged per credit hour (contact the college for current rate). *Room and board per academic year:* $8,966. *Books and supplies:* $1,200. *Other expenses:* $2,100.

Financial Aid: Aid from institutionally generated funds is provided on the basis of academic merit, financial need, athletic ability, special talent. Institution has a Program Participation Agreement with the U.S. Department of Education for eligible students to receive Pell Grants and, depending upon the agreement, other federal aid.

Financial aid to full-time, first-time undergraduate students: 98% of students received some form of financial aid. Average amount of aid received: federal grants $1,437; state/local grants $2,048; institutional grants $8,009; loans $2,833.

Departments and Teaching Staff: *Total instructional faculty:* 204. Student/faculty ratio: 15:1. Degrees held by full-time faculty: doctorate 64%, master's 25%, professional 11%. 80% hold terminal degrees.

Enrollment: Total enrollment 4,949. Undergraduate 3,165. Graduate 1,784. Undergraduate transfer-in students 296.

Characteristics of Student Body: *Ethnic/racial makeup:* Black non-Hispanic: 35; Asian or Pacific Islander: 1%; Hispanic: 3%; White non-Hispanic: 79%; unknown: 12%; nonresident alien 1%.

International Students: 49 nonresident aliens enrolled fall 2008. Students from Europe, Asia, Central and South America, Africa, Canada. Programs available to aid students whose native language is not English: social, cultural. Financial aid specifically designated for international students: scholarships available annually.

Student Life: On-campus residence halls house 45% of student body. Residence halls for males constitute 33% of such space, for females 67%. *Intercollegiate athletics:* male: basketball, soccer; female basketball, softball, volleyball. *Special regulations:* Cars not permitted for freshmen. *Special services:* Learning Resources Center, disabled student services. *Student publications: Chronicle*, a bimonthly newspaper; *Sphere*, an annual literary magazine; a yearbook. *Surrounding community:* Albany population 103,000. New York City, approximately 145 miles from campus, is nearest metropolitan area. Served by mass transit bus system; airport 5 miles from campus; passenger rail service 12 miles from campus.

Library Collections: 207,000 volumes. 308,000 microforms; 1,580 audiovisual materials; 900 040 current periodical subscriptions. Online catalog. Students have access to online information retrieval services and the Internet.

Most important special collections include Curriculum Materials Center (teacher education); British Literature; College Archives.

Buildings and Grounds: Campus area 17 acres.

Chief Executive Officer: Dr. R. Mark Sullivan, President.

Undergraduates address admission inquiries to Mary M. Grondahl, Director of Admissions; graduate inquiries to Anne Tully, Dean of Graduate Studies.

College of Staten Island / CUNY

2800 Victory Boulevard
Staten Island, New York 10314
Tel: (718) 982-2000 **E-mail:** admissions@csi.cuny.edu
Fax: (718) 982-2500 **Internet:** www.csi.cuny.edu

Institution Description: *Enrollment:* 12,517. *Degrees awarded:* Associate, baccalaureate, master's, doctorate.

Accreditation: *Regional:* MSA. *Professional*: chemistry, computer science, engineering, nursing, physician assisting, physical therapy, teacher education

History: Founded 1976 through the union of Staten Island Community College (established 1955) and Richmond College (established 1965).

Institutional Structure: *Composition of institution:* Administrators 10. Academic affairs headed by vice-president for faculty and instruction. Management/business/finances directed by chief financial officer and business manager. Full-time instructional faculty 328.

Calendar: Semesters. Academic year from Aug. to June.

Characteristics of Freshmen: 7,956 applicants. 98% of applicants admitted. 32% of admitted applicants enrolled full-time.

99% (429 students) submitted SAT scores. *25th percentile*: SAT Critical Reading 450, SAT Math 460. *75th percentile*: SAT Critical Reading 530, SAT Math 560.

99% of freshmen from New York. Freshmen from 14 states and 69 foreign countries.

Admission: Rolling admissions plan. *Requirements:* Either graduation from accredited secondary school or GED.

Degree Requirements: *For all associate degrees:* 60 semester hours. *For all baccalaureate degrees:* 120 hours. *For all undergraduate degrees:* 2.0 GPA; 30 credits in residence including half the major requirement; 2 credits in physical education courses; distribution requirements including writing across the curriculum; foreign language requirement for BA degree. *Grading system:* A–F.

Distinctive Educational Programs: Study abroad in Florence, Italy (Italian civilization and culture, intensive Italian language, studio art and art history, film making); Rome, Italy (international business, Italian civilization and culture).

Degrees Conferred: 766 *associate;* 1m060 *baccalaureate*; 309 *master's*. Bachelor's degrees awarded in top five disciplines: business, management, marketing, and related support services 230; social sciences 187; psychology 103; liberal arts/general studies 100; computer and information sciences 56. Master's degrees awarded: biological/life sciences 3; computer and information sciences 11; education 259; English 9; health professions and related sciences 21; interdisciplinary studies 1; liberal arts/general studies 11; natural resources 1; visual and performing arts 6.

Fees and Other Expenses: *Full-time tuition per academic year 2008–09:* undergraduate resident $4,578, nonresident $9,018; contact the college for current graduate tuition. *Books and supplies:* $1,016. *Off-campus room and board per academic year:* $10,201. *Other expenses:* $4,526.

Financial Aid: Aid from institutionally generated funds is provided on the basis of academic merit, financial need. Institution has a Program Participation Agreement with the U.S. Department of Education for eligible students to receive Pell Grants and, depending upon the agreement, other federal aid.

Financial aid to full-time, first-time undergraduate students: 72% received some form of aid. Average amount of aid received: federal grants $3,112; state/local grants $2,339; institutional grants $4,165; loans $2,422.

Departments and Teaching Staff: *Total instructional faculty:* 851 (full-time 328, part-time 503). Student/faculty ratio: 17.9:1. Degrees held by full-time faculty: doctorate 60%, master's 90%, baccalaureate 100%, professional 8%. 74% hold terminal degrees.

Enrollment: Total enrollment 12,517. Undergraduate 11,588. Graduate 929. Undergraduate transfer-in students 1,175.

Characteristics of Student Body: *Ethnic/racial makeup:* Black non-Hispanic: 11%; Asian or Pacific Islander: 9%; Hispanic: 14%; White non-Hispanic: 62%; nonresident alien 4%. *Age distribution:* number under 18: 2,335; 18–19: 1,658; 20–21: 2,508; 22–24: 880; 25–29: 992; 30–34: 572; 35–39: 419; 40–49: 651; 50–64: 235; 65 and over: 5.

International Students: 501 nonresident aliens enrolled fall 2008.

Student Life: *Intercollegiate athletics:* male: basketball, soccer, baseball, tennis; female: basketball, softball, cross-country, softball, tennis. *Special services:* Childcare center. *Student publications: The College Voice*, a newspaper published every three weeks; *Dolphin*, a yearbook; *Serpentine*, an annual general literary magazine; *All Ways a Woman*, an annual feminist literary magazine. *Surrounding community:* Staten Island is one of the five boroughs of New York City. Served by mass transit, bus, train and ferry systems.

Library Collections: 229,000 volumes. 810,000 microforms; 11,118 audiovisual materials; 800 current periodical subscriptions. 12,000 audiovisual mate-

COLLEGE OF STATEN ISLAND / CUNY—*cont'd*

rials. Online catalog. Students have access to online information retrieval services. Total 3006–07 budget for books and materials: $500,000. *Special collections:* Staten Island History; papers of New York State Senator John Marchi; Willowbrook State School.

Buildings and Grounds: Campus area 204 acres.

Chief Executive Officer: Dr. Marlene Springer, President.

Address admission inquiries to Mary Beth Reilly, Director of Admissions.

Columbia University

2960 Broadway
New York, New York 10027
Tel: (212) 854-1754 **E-mail:** gsdegree@columbia.edu
Fax: (212) 749-0397 **Internet:** www.columbia.edu

Institution Description: Columbia University is a private, independent, nonprofit institution. *Enrollment:* 23,196. *Degrees awarded:* Baccalaureate, first-professional (dentistry, law, medicine), master's, doctorate.

Accreditation: *Regional:* MSA. *Professional*: architecture, business, dental hygiene, dentistry, engineering, health services administration, journalism, law, medicine, nursing, occupational therapy, physical therapy, public health, social work

History: Established by royal charter as King's College, incorporated, and offered first instruction at postsecondary level 1754; awarded first degree (baccalaureate) 1758; chartered by state as Columbia College 1784; rechartered 1810; present official name, Columbia University in the City of New York, adopted 1912. *See* Dwight C. Miner, ed., *The Bicentennial History of Columbia University* (New York: Columbia University Press, 1954) for further information.

Institutional Structure: *Governing board:* The Trustees of Columbia University in the City of New York. Extrainstitutional representation: 23 trustees, including 6 alumni; institutional representation: president of the university. All voting. *Composition of institution:* Administrators 31. Academic affairs headed by provosts. Management/business/finances directed by vice president for finance and treasurer. Total instructional faculty 2,287. Academic governance body, the faculty, meets an average of 2 times per year.

Calendar: Semesters. Academic year Sept. to May. Freshmen admitted Sept. (for Columbia College, School of Engineering and Applied Science); Sept., Jan, May (for School of General Studies). Degrees conferred Oct., Jan., May. Formal commencement May. Summer session of 7 terms from May to Aug.

Characteristics of Freshmen: 21,343 applicants. 11% of applicants admitted. 59% of of admitted students enrolled full-time.

25th percentile: SAT Critical Reading 660, SAT Math 670, SAT Writing 650; ACT Composite 28, ACT English 29, ACT Math 28. *75th percentile*: SAT Critical Reading 760, SAT Math 780, SAT Writing 760; ACT Composite 33, ACT English 34, ACT Math 34.

95% of entering freshmen expected to graduate within 5 years. 28% of freshmen from New York. Freshmen from 50 states and 100 foreign countries.

Admission: For fall acceptance, apply as early as Nov. of previous year, but no later than Jan. 15 for Columbia College (Feb. 1 for Engineering, July 15 for General Studies). Students are notified of acceptance Apr. for Columbia College and Engineering (Aug. for General Studies). Apply by Nov. 1 for early decision; must limit application to Columbia University (no early decision available for General Studies). Early acceptance available. *Requirements:* Recommend 4 years of English, 3 or 4 years of a foreign language, 3 or 4 years mathematics, 2 or 3 years laboratory science, 3 or 4 history; GED accepted. *Entrance tests:* College Board SAT, 3 Achievements. For foreign students TOEFL. *For transfer students:* 64 points maximum transfer credit.

College credit and advanced placement for postsecondary-level work completed in secondary school. Tutoring available. Developmental/remedial courses offered in summer session and regular academic year; credit given.

Degree Requirements: *Undergraduate:* 124 points; C- minimum average; 4 terms in residence; 2 semesters physical education courses (except for students in School of General Studies); core curriculum requirements (for Columbia College).

Fulfillment of some degree requirements and exemption from some beginning courses possible by passing College Board CLEP, AP, Achievement Tests. *Grading system:* A–F; high pass-pass-fail; pass-fail; pass; withdraw.

Distinctive Educational Programs: Evening classes. Facilities and programs for independent research, including honors programs, individual majors, tutorials. Study abroad in France at Columbia's Reid Hall.

Degrees Conferred: 1,824 *baccalaureate*; 5,401 *master's*; 497 *doctorate*; 721 *first-professional*. Bachelor;s degrees awarded in top five disciplines: social sciences 405; engineering 318; history 152; English language/literature 141; biological and biomedical sciences 91. Master's degrees awarded in top five disciplines: business, management, marketing, and related support services 1,063; public administration and social service professions 781; social sciences 464; health professions and related clinical sciences 447; engineering 343. Doctorates awarded in top five disciplines: biological and biomedical sciences 78; engineering 64; social sciences 64; physical sciences 63; health professions and related clinical sciences 47. First-professional degrees awarded: medicine 249; law 472.

Fees and Other Expenses: *Full-time tuition per academic year 2008–09:* undergraduate $39,326; contact the university for current graduate and first-professional tuition and fees. *Room and board per academic year:* $9,980. *Books and supplies:* $1,000. *Other expenses:* $1,100.

Financial Aid: Aid from institutionally generated funds is provided on the basis of financial need. Institution has a Program Participation Agreement with the U.S. Department of Education for eligible students to receive Pell Grants and, depending upon the agreement, other federal aid.

Financial aid to full-time, first-time undergraduate students: 51% of students received some form of financial aid. Average amount of aid received: federal grants $3,034; state/local grants $1,823; institutional grants $19,382; loans $2,021.

Departments and Teaching Staff: Humanities *faculty* 244, social science 159, natural sciences 158, School of Arts 21, architecture 23, business 103, engineering 109, journalism 24, law 56, library science 12, social work 42, special programs 22, health sciences 1,314.

Total instructional faculty: 2,240. Student/faculty ratio: 25:1. Degrees held by full-time faculty: Doctorate 90%.

Enrollment: Total enrollment 23,196. Undergraduate 7,495.

Characteristics of Student Body: *Ethnic/racial makeup (undergraduate):* Black non-Hispanic: 7.2%; American Indian or Alaska Native: .3%; Asian or Pacific Islander: 16%; Hispanic: 7.8%; White non-Hispanic: 46.6%; unknown: 7.4%.

International Students: 1,472 nonresident aliens enrolled fall 2008.

Student Life: On-campus residence halls, fraternities, and off-campus apartments owned by Columbia house 83% of student body. Some students live in residence halls shared with Barnard College students. Housing available for married students. *Intercollegiate athletics* male: baseball, basketball, crew, cross-country, fencing, football, soccer, swimming, tennis, track, wrestling; female: archery, basketball, crew, cross-country, fencing, soccer, swimming and diving, tennis, indoor and outdoor track and field; volleyball. *Special services:* Learning Resources Center, medical services. *Student publications, radio, television: Black Heights*, annually; *Columbia/Barnard Course Guide*, biannually; *Columbia Review*, biannually; *Columbia Spectator*, 5 days per week; *Jester*, quarterly; *Pulse*, bimonthly; *Sundial*, weekly; *Upstart*, annually. Radio station WKCR broadcasts 168 hours per week. TV station WCTV broadcasts approximately 12 hours per week. *Surrounding community:* New York population over 7 million. Served by mass transit bus and rail systems; airport 3 miles from campus; passenger rail service 2 miles from campus.

Publications: *Asian Journal* (annually) first published 1977, *Astronomical Journal* (monthly) first published 1949, *Career Development Bulletin* (quarterly) first published 1980, *Columbia Engineering Research* (biannually) first published 1970, *Columbia Human Rights Law Review* (biannually) first published 1968, *Columbia Journalism Review* (6 times per year) first published 1961, *Columbia Journal of Environmental Law* (biannually) first published 1974, *Columbia Journal of International Affairs* (biannually) first published 1946, *Columbia Journal of Law and Social Problems* (quarterly) first published 1980, *Columbia Journal of Transnational Law* (3 times per year) first published 1963, *Columbia Journal of World Business* (quarterly) first published 1965, *Columbia Law Review* (8 times per year) first published 1901, *Current Musicology* (biannually) first published 1965, *Japanese Economic Studies* (quarterly) first published 1981, *Johnsonian Newsletter* (quarterly) first published 1940, *Journal of Ideas* (biannually) first published 1976, *Journal of Philosophy* (monthly) first published 1904, *Proceedings of College of Physicians and Surgeons Biomedical Sciences Symposia* (annually) first published 1977, *Public Opinion Quarterly* first published 1937, *Renaissance Quarterly* first published 1948, *Research on International Change, Global Political Assessment* (biannually) first published 1972, *Values and Ethics in Health Care* (quarterly) first published 1975.

Library Collections: 8,000,000 volumes. 4,000,000 microforms; 18,000 audiovisual materials; 59,000 current periodical subscriptions. Online catalog. Students have access to the Internet and other online databases via computer work stations available campus-wide.

Most important holdings include Bakhmetoff Archives; George Plimpton Collection, including history of textbooks since manuscript period, and sections on calligraphy, mathematics, and English and Latin grammars; David Eugene Smith collection on mathematics.

Buildings and Grounds: Campus area 304 acres.

Chief Executive Officer: Lee C. Bollinger, President.

Address admission inquiries to Jessica Marinaciao, Director of Admissions.

Columbia College

Degree Programs Offered: *Baccalaureate* in anthropology, art history, astronomy, biology, chemistry, comparative literature, computer science, East Asian studies, economics, English, French, geography, geological sciences, German, Greek, history, Italian, Latin, linguistics, mathematics, Middle East studies, music, philosophy, physics, political science, psychology, religion, Russian, sociology, Spanish, statistics.

Distinctive Educational Programs: Interdepartmental programs in ancient studies, astrophysics, biochemistry, biology-psychology, biophysics, chemical physics, comparative literature, geochemistry, geophysics, history-sociology, philosophy-economics, regional studies and urban studies; and by individual arrangement. Joint baccalaureate and baccalaureate-master's programs with the School of the Arts, the School of Engineering and Applied Science, the School of International and Public Affairs (in international affairs, public administration).

School of Engineering and Applied Science

Degree Programs Offered: *Baccalaureate, master's* in applied chemistry, applied geophysics, applied mathematics, applied physics, bioengineering, chemical engineering, civil engineering, computer science, electrical engineering, engineering mechanics, industrial engineering, mechanical engineering, metallurgy and materials science, mineral engineering, nuclear engineering, operation research; *postbaccalaureate* in chemical, civil, electrical, industrial, mechanical, metallurgical, mineral, mining, and nuclear engineering; *doctorate* in engineering science; *Ph.D.* in cooperation with Graduate School of Arts and Sciences.

Distinctive Educational Programs: Dual-degree programs with Columbia, Barnard, and 83 other colleges and universities. Joint baccalaureate-J.D. with School of Law; joint master's-M.B.A. with Graduate School of Business.

School of Nursing

Degree Programs Offered: *Baccalaureate* in nursing; *master's* in adult nurse practitioner, gerontology, maternity nursing-nurse midwifery, nurse anesthesia, pediatric nursing (ambulatory care), pediatric nursing (pulmonary care), perinatal nursing, psychiatric-community mental health nursing, adult/child.

School of Dental and Oral Surgery

Degree Programs Offered: *Baccalaureate, master's* in dental hygiene; *first-professional* in dentistry. *Postdoctorate certificates* in endodontics, orthodontics, pedodontics, periodontics also given.

Admission: *For first-professional degree in dentistry:* Baccalaureate from accredited institution; personal interview by invitation; DAT.

Degree Requirements: *For first-professional degree:* 40 months in residence.

Distinctive Educational Programs: Dental clinic assists students in gaining experience in diagnosis and care of patients. Master's degree in cooperation with the School of Public Health.

School of Law

Degree Programs Offered: *First professional, master's* in civil procedure, commercial constitutional law, corporation law, government service, international law, labor law, legal history, legal philosophy, poverty law, property law, taxation, urban affairs, and others; *doctorate* in the science of law; *Ph.D.* in cooperation with Graduate School of Arts and Sciences.

Admission: *For first-professional degree in law:* Baccalaureate; LSAT.

Degree Requirements: *For first-professional degree:* 83 points, 3 years in residence. Moot court and legal writing requirements. Additional residency for joint program degrees.

Distinctive Educational Programs: J.D.-master's programs with the Parker School of Foreign and Comparative Law and the School of International and Public Affairs. Joint degrees also offered with Graduate School of Arts and Sciences, School of Business, School of Journalism. Summer study in Amsterdam and Leyden. Opportunities for research in areas including legislative drafting, law and economic studies, research and legal history, Chinese Communist law, inter-American law.

College of Physicians and Surgeons

Degree Programs Offered: *First-professional* in medicine; *master's* in occupational and physical therapy; *doctorate* in medical science; *Ph.D.* in cooperation with Graduate School of Arts and Sciences.

Admission: *For first-professional in medicine:* One year at the undergraduate level, in English, physics, biology, general chemistry, organic chemistry (with lab); MCAT.

Degree Requirements: *For first-professional degree:* Must successfully complete 4-year prescribed curriculum, National Board Examinations Parts I and II.

Distinctive Educational Programs: Joint M.D.-Ph.D. with the Graduate School of Arts and Sciences. Joint M.D.-master's in public health with the School of Public Health. Postgraduate courses for practicing physicians and specialists.

Graduate School of Arts and Sciences

Degree Programs Offered: *Master's, intermediate* (M.Phil.), and *doctorate* in anatomy, anthropology, applied chemistry, applied physics, archaeology, art history, astronomy, biochemistry, biological sciences, chemical engineering, chemistry, civil engineering, computer science, East Asian languages and cultures, economics, electrical engineering, engineering mechanics, French and Romance philosophy, Germanic languages, geological sciences, Greek, history, human genetics and development, industrial engineering, Italian, Latin, mathematical statistics, mathematics, mechanical engineering, metallurgical engineering, microbiology, Middle East languages and cultures, mineral engineering, microbiology, mining engineering, music, nuclear engineering, operations research, pathology, pharmacology, philosophy, physiology, physics, political science, psychology, religion, Slavic languages, sociology, Spanish and Portuguese, statistics; *doctorate* in biostatics, business, chemical physics, education, epidemiology, nutrition, sociomedical sciences, theater and film, Uralic studies, urban planning.

Distinctive Educational Programs: Part-time M.A. programs in anthropology, astronomy, English, French, geography, linguistics (Yiddish only), history, Italian, mathematical statistics, Middle Eastern languages and cultures, philosophy, and Spanish. *See* College of Physicians and Surgeons, School of Law.

Graduate School of Architecture, Planning and Preservation

Degree Programs Offered: *Master's* in architecture, architecture and building design, architecture and urban design, historic preservation, urban planning; *doctorate* offered through Graduate School of Arts and Sciences.

Distinctive Educational Programs: The Center for Advanced Research in Urban and Environmental Affairs allows students to undertake advanced research. Joint M.B.A.-master's with the Graduate School of Business, master's with School of Public Health, School of Social Work, J.D.-master's with School of Law.

School of the Arts

Degree Programs Offered: *Master's* in arts administration, film, painting, printmaking, sculpture, theater, writing; *doctorate* in music composition; *Ph.D.* in theater and film through the Graduate School of Arts and Sciences.

Distinctive Educational Programs: Columbia-Princeton Electronic Music Center offers instruction and studio facilities in electronic music for composition students. Center for Theater Studies, a combined effort of the School of the Arts, Teachers College, and the Graduate School of Arts and Sciences, sponsors productions, encourages basic research and conducts cooperative programs with theaters in New York City. Internships with the Shubert Organization in theater production and management available.

Columbia Business School

Degree Programs Offered: *Master's* in accounting, business economics and public policy, corporate relations and public affairs, finance, international business, management of organizations, management science, marketing, money and financial markets, operations management, public and nonprofit management; *doctorate* offered through Graduate School of Arts and Sciences.

Distinctive Educational Programs: Master's program offers young executives opportunity to broaden their knowledge and skills without interrupting their careers. Noncredit executive programs offered in areas including nonprofit management, commercial bank management, business strategy. *See* Graduate School of Architecture and Planning.

School of International and Public Affairs

Degree Programs Offered: *Master's* in economic and political development, international business, international economy, international finance and banking, international law and organization, international media and communications, international political economy, international security policy, public policy and administration, and in regional studies in Africa, East and South Asia, Latin America, the Middle East, Russia, Western and East Central Europe. Certificates also offered by regional institutes.

COLUMBIA UNIVERSITY—*cont'd*

Distinctive Educational Programs: Field work for all programs. Joint master's-M.B.A. with Graduate School of Business, master's in international affairs and urban planning with Graduate School of Business, master's in international affairs and urban planning with Graduate School of Architecture and Planning. *See* Graduate School of Journalism.

Graduate School of Journalism

Degree Programs Offered: *Master's.*

Distinctive Educational Programs: Joint M.S.-M.B.A. programs in media management with Graduate School of Business; M.S.-J.D. with School of Law. Cooperative programs with East Asian Institute, School of International and Public Affairs, Center for Advanced Study of Communication and Public Affairs.

School of Public Health

Degree Programs Offered: *Master's* in general public health, tropical medicine; *master's, doctorate* in biostatics, epidemiology, environmental science, health administration, parasitology, population and family health, sociomedical science.

Distinctive Educational Programs: Joint master's programs with Graduate School of Business, School of Nursing. *See* College of Physicians and Surgeons, School of Dental and Oral Surgery, School of Social Work.

School of Social Work

Degree Programs Offered: *Master's, doctorate* with field concentrations in practice, social work research, and social policy planning.

Distinctive Educational Programs: Field training. Joint master's programs with Graduate School of Business, Jewish Theological Seminary, School of Public Health, and the Graduate School of Architecture and Planning. Social Welfare Center, in cooperation with the School of Law, provides legal and social services to local members of the American Federation of State, County, and Municipal Employees.

School of General Studies

Degree Programs Offered: *Baccalaureate* in anthropology, applied mathematics, architecture, art history, biological sciences, chemistry, comparative literature, computer science, East Asian studies, economics, economics-mathematics, economics-philosophy, economics-statistics, English literature, film, French, geography, geological sciences, German, Greek, Greek and Latin, history, Hispanic studies, Italian, Latin, linguistics, mathematical statistics, mathematics, Middle East languages and cultures, music, philosophy, physics, political science, psychology, religion, Slavic languages (Polish, Russian), sociology, Spanish, theater arts, visual arts.

Admission: In addition to general requirements, applicant must be 19 years old for part-time study; 21 years old for full-time study. General Studies Aptitude Examination.

Distinctive Educational Programs: Interdepartmental programs in ancient studies, biology/psychology, and literature/writing. Preprofessional programs in dentistry, education, engineering, law, medicine; certain qualified degree candidates may fulfill major requirements with first year of work at the College of Physicians and Surgeons or another approved medical school, Graduate School of Architecture and Planning (in Architecture), School of Dental and Oral Surgery or Social Work. Joint baccalaureate-master's with the School of International and Public Affairs (including program in Public Administration), with Graduate School of Business, and with School of Engineering and Applied Science. Joint baccalaureate-J.D. program with School of Law. Cooperative programs in Hebrew literature with the Jewish Theological Seminary. The American Language Program offers full- and part-time noncredit instruction in English as a second language.

Concordia College

171 White Plains Road
Bronxville, New York 10708-1998
Tel: (914) 337-9300 **E-mail:** admission@concordia-ny.edu
Fax: (914) 395-4500 **Internet:** www.concordia-ny.edu

Institution Description: Concordia College is a private college affiliated with The Lutheran Church-Missouri Synod. *Enrollment:* 707. *Degrees awarded:* Associate, baccalaureate.

Accreditation: *Regional:* MSA. *Professional*: social work

History: Established as Concordia Collegiate Institute 1881; offered first instruction at postsecondary level 1907; chartered and first degree (associate) awarded 1936; changed name to Concordia Junior College 1966; adopted present name 1969. *See* Alan Steinberg, *We Will Remember. Concordia College: The First Century* (Bronxville: Concordia College, 1981) for further information.

Institutional Structure: *Governing board:* Board of Regents. Extrainstitutional representation: 8 trustees, including president of Atlantic District, The Lutheran Church-Missouri Synod; Institutional representation: president of the college. 1 ex officio. 8 voting. *Composition of institution:* Administrators 15. Academic affairs headed by dean of faculty. Management/business/finances directed by business manager. Full-time instructional faculty 29. Academic governance body, the faculty, meets an average of 10 times per year.

Calendar: Semesters. Academic year Sept. to May. Freshmen admitted Sept., Jan. Degrees conferred throughout the year. Formal commencement May. No summer session.

Characteristics of Freshmen: 720 applicants. 68% of applicants admitted. 22% of admitted students enrolled full-time.

87% (93 students) submitted SAT scores; 17% (18 students) submitted ACT scores. *25th percentile*: SAT Critical Reading 410, SAT Math 390, SAT Writing 400; ACT Composite 16, ACT English 15, ACT Math 16. *75th percentile*: SAT Critical Reading 490, SAT Math 490, SAT Writing 500; ACT Composite 19, ACT English 19, ACT Math 18.

66% of freshmen from New York. Freshmen from 27 states and 34 foreign countries.

Admission: Rolling admissions plan. For fall acceptance, apply by Mar. 15. Early acceptance available. *Requirements:* Either graduation from accredited secondary school with 4 units English, 2 in a foreign language, 3 mathematics, 2 social studies, 2 science. *Entrance tests:* College Board SAT or ACT composite required. *For transfer students:* 2.0 minimum GPA; from 4-year accredited minimum 2.0 GPA.

College credit and advanced placement for postsecondary-level work completed in secondary school and for extrainstitutional learning.

Tutoring available. Developmental courses offered during regular academic year; credit given.

Degree Requirements: *For all associate degrees:* 60–63 credit hours. *For all baccalaureate degrees:* 122–127 credit hours; recommendation by major department. *For all undergraduate degrees:* 2.0 GPA; 1 year in residence; 2 semester hours physical education; distribution requirements.

Fulfillment of some degree requirements and exemption from some beginning courses possible by passing College Board CLEP, AP, other standardized test. *Grading system:* A–F; pass-fail; withdraw (deadline after which pass-fail is appended to withdraw); incomplete (carries time limit).

Distinctive Educational Programs: Evening classes. Special facilities for using telecommunications in the classroom. Student-designed interdisciplinary majors. Preprofessional programs include pre-deaconess, pre-seminary, premed, pre-law, and pre-theology. Individual majors. Cross-registration through consortium. Study abroad at Oak Hill College, London, England.

Degrees Conferred: 5 *associate;* 123 *baccalaureate.* Bachelor's degrees awarded in top five disciplines: business, management, marketing, and related support services 37; education 21; social sciences 20; liberal arts and sciences, general studies, and humanities 14; biological and biomedical sciences 11.

Fees and Other Expenses: *Full-time tuition per academic year 2008=09:* $23,330. *Room and board per academic year:* $8,745. *Books and supplies:* $900. *Other expenses:* $2,000.

Financial Aid: Aid from institutionally generated funds is provided on the basis of academic merit, financial need, athletic ability, other criteria. Institution has a Program Participation Agreement with the U.S. Department of Education for eligible students to receive Pell Grants and, depending upon the agreement, other federal aid.

Financial aid to full-time, first-time undergraduate students: 91% of students received some form of financial aid. Average amount of aid received: federal grants $3,718; Pell grants $3,088; other federal grants $1,844; state/local grants $8,745; institutional grants $9,742.

Departments and Teaching Staff: *Total instructional faculty:* 46. Student/faculty ratio: 11:1. 79% hold terminal degrees.

Enrollment: Total enrollment 707 (undergraduate).

Characteristics of Student Body: *Ethnic/racial makeup:* Black non-Hispanic: 9.7%; American Indian or Alaska Native: ..3; Asian or Pacific Islander: 1.8%; Hispanic: 6.9%; White non-Hispanic: 57.3%; unknown: 20.8%.

International Students: 55 nonresident aliens enrolled fall 2008. Students form Europe, Asia, Central and South America, Africa, Canada. English as a Second Language Program available. No financial aid specifically designated for international students.

Student Life: On-campus residence halls house 65% of student body. Residence halls for males constitute 45% of such space, for females 55%. *Intercol-*

legiate athletics: male: baseball, basketball, soccer, tennis, volleyball; female: basketball, soccer, softball, tennis, volleyball. *Special regulations:* Registered cars permitted for upper classmen; freshmen by special permission. Residence hall visitation from 1pm to 11pm Sun.–Thurs., 1pm to 1am Fri.–Sat. *Special services:* Learning Resources Center, medical services. *Student publications: Chronicle*, student newspaper; *Concordia New-Yorker*, published 5 times per year. *Surrounding community:* Bronxville population 7,000. New York City, 15 miles from campus, is nearest metropolitan area. Served by mass transit bus and rail system, airport 15 miles from campus, passenger rail service 1 mile from campus.

Library Collections: 85,000 volumes. 25,000 microforms; 8,900 audiovisual materials; 350 current periodical subscriptions. Online catalog. Students have access to online information retrieval services and the Internet.

Most important holdings include Library of American Civilization (on microfiche); Library of English Literature, Vol. I (on microfiche); Library of Music (scores on microfiche).

Buildings and Grounds: Campus area 32 acres.

Chief Executive Officer: Dr. Viji D. George, President.

Address admission inquiries to Paul D. Grand Pre, Vice President for Enrollment Management.

Cooper Union for the Advancement of Science and Art

30 Cooper Square
New York, New York 10003-7120
Tel: (212) 353-4120 **E-mail:** admissions@cooper.edu
Fax: (212) 353-4342 **Internet:** www.cooper.edu

Institution Description: The Cooper Union is a private, independent, nonprofit institution. All students receive full tuition scholarship *Enrollment:* 957. *Degrees awarded:* Baccalaureate, master's.

Member of Research Library Consortium of Lower Manhattan.

Accreditation: *Regional:* MSA. *Professional*: architecture, art, engineering

History: Established and chartered under present official name, The Cooper Union for the Advancement of Science and Art, and offered first instruction at postsecondary level 1859; first degree (baccalaureate) awarded 1864; added master's program in engineering 1966, in architecture 2006.

Institutional Structure: *Governing board:* Board of Trustees. Extrainstitutional representation: 31 trustees, including 3 alumni. All voting. *Composition of institution:* Administrators 16. Academic affairs headed by the president. Management/business/finances directed by vice president for business affairs. Full-time instructional faculty 53. Academic governance body, Senate, meets an average of 8 times per year.

Calendar: Semesters. Academic year Sept. to May. Freshmen admitted Sept. Degrees conferred and formal commencement May.

Characteristics of Freshmen: 2,055. applicants. 9% of applicants accepted. 73% of admitted students enrolled full-time.

94% (194 students) submitted SAT scores; 5% (10 students) submitted ACT scores. *25th percentile*: SAT Critical Reading 620, SAT Math 640, SAT Writing 620; ACT Composite 27, ACT English 26, ACT Math 28. *75th percentile*: SAT Critical Reading 710, SAT Math 780, SAT Writing 710; ACT Composite 31, ACT English 30, ACT Math 31.

84% of entering freshmen expected to graduate within 5 years. 60% of freshmen from New York. Freshmen from 43 states and 21 foreign countries.

Admission: Apply as early as Sept. 1 of previous year. For schools of architecture and art apply no later than Jan. 1, for engineering program no later than Feb. 1. Students are notified of acceptance Mar. Early acceptance available. *Requirements:* Either graduation from approved secondary school with 16 units which must include 4 English, 2 history or social studies, 1 mathematics, 1 science; or GED. For architecture program, 2 additional mathematics. For engineering program, 1/2 additional mathematics, 1 chemistry, 1 physics. *Entrance tests:* College Board SAT. For architecture and art program, institutional art test. For engineering program, College Board Achievements in mathematics (level 1 or 2) and physics or chemistry. For foreign students TOEFL. *For transfer students:* For architecture program 100 hours maximum transfer credit; for art program 64 hours; for engineering program 67 hours.

College credit and advanced placement for postsecondary-level work completed in secondary school and for extrainstitutional learning on basis of portfolio and faculty assessments.

Tutoring available. Remedial courses offered during regular academic year; credit given.

Degree Requirements: *For all architecture degrees:* 160 credit hours. *For all art degrees:* 128 hours. *For all engineering degrees:* 135 hours. *For all undergraduate degrees:* 2.0 minimum GPA; 4 terms in residence; general studies curriculum.

Fulfillment of some degree requirements and exemption from some beginning courses possible by passing College Board CLEP, AP, other standardized tests. *Grading system:* A–F; pass-fail.

Distinctive Educational Programs: *For art students:* Off-campus programs in the U.S. and abroad, including study at Allgemeine Gewerbescherle, Switzerland; the Maryland Institute, College of Art; Massachusetts College of Art; Nova Scotia College of Art and Design; Otis Art Institute of Parsons School of Design (CA); Philadelphia College of Art; School of the Museum of Fine Arts; Tyler School of Art (PA); *For engineering students:* Dual-degree programs in various fields with New York University. Interdisciplinary programs. Synthesis of a Holistic Approach to Professional Education sponsored by the National Science Foundation and the National endowment for the Humanities, a competence-based program. *Available to all students:* Evening classes. Facilities and programs for independent research, including honors programs, individual majors. *Other distinctive programs:* Continuing education. For engineering students, exchange programs offered throughout the world.

Degrees Conferred: 215 *baccalaureate:*; 12 *master's*. Bachelor's degrees awarded in top three disciplines: architecture 31; engineering 111; visual arts 54. Master's degrees awarded: engineering 12.

Fees and Other Expenses: *Full-time tuition per academic year 2008–09:* $34,450. All students receive full-tuition scholarships. *Required fees:* $500. *Books and supplies:* $1,400. No on-campus housing.

Financial Aid: Financial aid to full-time, first-time undergraduate students:

Departments and Teaching Staff: *Total instructional faculty:* 211 (full-time 53, part-time 158) Student/faculty ratio: 7:1.

Enrollment: Total enrollment 951. Undergraduate 906. Graduate 51. Undergraduate transfer-in students 32.

Characteristics of Student Body: *Ethnic/racial makeup:* Black non-Hispanic: 5%; Asian or Pacific Islander: 17%; Hispanic: 8%; White non-Hispanic: 43%; unknown: 10%; nonresident alien 16%.

International Students: 153 nonresident aliens enrolled 2008. Students from Europe, Asia, Central and South America, Africa, Canada, New Zealand, Middle East. Programs available to aid students whose native language is not English: writing and language arts support. Financial aid specifically designated for international students: all students receive full-tuition scholarships.

Student Life: On-campus freshman residence hall. *Student publication: The Pioneer*, a monthly newspaper. *Surrounding community:* New York City population over 7 million. Served by mass transit bus, subway, commuter train systems; airport 3 miles from campus; passenger rail service 1 mile from campus.

Library Collections: 200,000 volumes. 3,268 microforms; 40,100 audiovisual materials; 370 current periodical subscriptions. Online catalog. Students have access to online information retrieval services and the Internet.

Most important holdings include published and unpublished materials relating to the founder of the institution, Peter Cooper, and his son-in-law Abram Hewitt.

Buildings and Grounds: Campus area 3 square blocks.

Chief Executive Officer: Dr. George Campbell, Jr., President.

Address admission inquiries to Mitchell L. Lipton, Director of Admissions.

Cornell University

Ithaca, New York 14853
Tel: (607) 255-2000 **E-mail:** admissions@cornell.edu
Fax: (607) 255-0659 **Internet:** www.cornell.edu

Institution Description: Cornell University is a private, not-for-profit, coeducational, nonsectarian institution of higher learning chartered and operated under Laws of the State of New York.

The academic programs are located principally at its main campus in Ithaca, New York, and in New York City. The privately funded schools and colleges in Ithaca are the College of Architecture, Art and Planning; College of Arts and Sciences; College of Engineering; School of Hotel Administration; Law School; and the Samuel Curtis Johnson Graduate School of Management (the "Endowed Colleges"). The endowed units in New York City are part of the New York Hospital-Cornell Medical Center and consist of the Cornell University Medical College and the Graduate School of Medical Sciences ("Medical Programs").

There are four State-supported colleges ("Contract Colleges") which are operated on behalf of the State pursuant to statute or contractual agreements under general supervision of the trustees of the State University of New York (SUNY). The Statutory Colleges are the College of Agriculture and Life Sciences; College of Human Ecology; School of Industrial and Labor Relations; and the College of Veterinary Medicine. The New York State Agricultural Experiment Station at Geneva is a unit of the College of Agriculture and Life Sciences and its departments are integral parts of the university.

Although a private institution, Cornell's Board of Trustees includes public representatives, consonant with its land grant status. As units of the State land grant institution, Cornell's four Statutory Colleges have been assigned by State

CORNELL UNIVERSITY—*cont'd*

legislation specific responsibilities in research and cooperative extension directed to State needs. These very specific statutory objectives in research and cooperative extension do not exist for other units of the State University of New York.

Enrollment: 19,800. *Degrees awarded:* Baccalaureate, first-professional (law, medicine, veterinary medicine), master's, professional master's, and doctorate.

Accreditation: *Regional:* MSA.*Professional*: architecture, business, dietetics, engineering, health services administration, interior design, landscape architecture, law, medicine, planning, veterinary medicine

History: Cornell was founded in 1865 by Ezra Cornell whose original endowment was augmented by a substantial land grant from the State of New York received under the Federal Land Grant (Morrill) Act of 1862. Offered first instruction at postsecondary level 1868; awarded first degree (baccalaureate) 1869. *See* Morris Bishop, *A History of Cornell* (Ithaca: Cornell University Press, 1962) for further information.

Institutional Structure: *Governance:* Cornell is governed by a 42-member Board of Trustees that meets four times a year. The Board includes: 21 members elected by the Board for staggered terms of 4 years each; 8 by alumni for staggered terms of 4 years each; 2 by faculty for terms of 4 years each; 2 by students for terms of 2 years each; and 1 by employees for a term of 4 years. There are four ex-officio trustees: The Governor of the State of New York, the Temporary President of the Senate, the Speaker of the Assembly and the President of the University who serve during their respective terms of office. In addition, the eldest lineal descendant of Ezra Cornell serves as trustee for life. *Administration:* The President of Cornell, as chief executive officer, is charged with the principal responsibility for administration of the University. The Board elects all executive officers. Provost is the President's first deputy officer and chief academic office and is responsible for overseeing all academic programs with the exception of those programs reporting to the Provost of Medical Affairs in New York City. Senior Vice President is the chief administrative officer and is responsible for the management of the non-academic (business) and support service operations. Vice President for Finance and Treasurer is the chief financial officer and responsible for overseeing the full range of financial operations including treasury, accounting, budget and audit functions.

Calendar: Semesters. Academic year Aug. to May. Freshmen admitted Sept., June. Degrees conferred Aug., Jan., May. Formal commencement end of May. Summer session of 3 terms from early June to mid-Aug.

Characteristics of Freshmen: 33,073 applicants. 21% of applicants admitted. 46% of admitted students enrolled full-time.

99% (3,122 students) submitted SAT scores; 30% (939 students) submitted ACT scores. *25th percentile*: SAT Critical Reading 630, SAT Math 670, SAT Writing 640; ACT Composite 29, ACT English 28, ACT Math 29. *75th percentile*: SAT Critical Reading 730, SAT Math 770, SAT Writing 730; ACT Composite 33, ACT English 34, ACT Math 34.

38% of freshmen from New York Freshmen from 50 states and 76 foreign countries.

Admission: Apply no later than Jan. 1 of year of enrollment. Students are notified of acceptance by mid-Apr. Apply by Nov. 1 for early decision; must limit application to Cornell. Early acceptance available. *Requirements:* 16 secondary school units or GED. Additional requirements vary according to program. *Entrance tests:* College Board SAT preferred, ACT composite accepted. College Board Achievements for some programs. For foreign students TOEFL.

College credit and advanced placement for postsecondary-level work completed in secondary school.

Degree Requirements: *Undergraduate:* 120 credit hours; 2 semesters physical education. Additional requirements for some programs. *See* below for specific graduate/professional school requirements.

Distinctive Educational Programs: Facilities and programs for independent research, including honors programs, individual major, tutorials. Africana Studies and Research Center offers course work to meet some distribution requirements. Center for International Studies coordinates programs in international and comparative studies. Qualified undergraduates may enter Johnson Graduate School of Management, or Medical College after junior year. *Other distinctive programs:* Adult university sponsors summer and weekend seminars. Credit and noncredit continuing education. Study Abroad in Africa, Australia, Belgium, China, Copenhagen, Denmark, Egypt, England, France, Germany, Ireland, Israel, Italy, Japan, Scotland, Spain, Sweden, and Switzerland.

ROTC: Navy.

Degrees Conferred: 3,431 *baccalaureate*; 1,757 *master's*; 465 *doctorate*; 287 *first-professional*. Bachelor's degrees awarded in top five disciplines: engineering 626; business, management, marketing, and related support services 449; biological and biomedical sciences 443; agriculture 408; social sciences 367. Master's degrees awarded in top five disciplines: business/marketing 461; computer and information sciences 123; engineering 372; physical sciences 81; social sciences 64. Doctorates awarded in top five disciplines: engineering 98; physical sciences 61; biological/biomedical sciences 60; agriculture 52; social sciences 5. First-professional degrees awarded: veterinary medicine 86; law 192; medicine 49.

Fees and Other Expenses: *Full-time tuition per academic year 2008–09:* $36,504; contact the university regarding tuition/fees for graduate and professional schools. *Room and board per academic year:* $11,640. *Books and supplies:* $740. *Other expenses:* $1,500.

Financial Aid: Aid from institutionally generated funds is provided on the basis of academic merit, financial need, other criteria. Institution has a Program Participation Agreement with the U.S. Department of Education for eligible students to receive Pell Grants and, depending upon the agreement, other federal aid.

Financial aid to full-time, first-time undergraduate students: 53% received some form of financial aid. Average amount of aid received: federal grants $2,903; state/local grants $2,819; institutional grants $19,653; loans $1,500.

Departments and Teaching Staff: *Total instructional faculty:* 1,869 (full-time 11,700, part-time 169). 95% of faculty hold the doctorate, first-professional, or other terminal degree. *Student/faculty ratio:* 9:1.

Enrollment: Total enrollment 19,800. Undergraduate 13,510. Graduate 6,290. Undergraduate transfer-in students: 547.

Characteristics of Student Body: *Ethnic/racial makeup:* Black non-Hispanic: 5%; American Indian or Alaska Native: 1%; Asian or Pacific Islander: 16%; Hispanic: 6%; White non-Hispanic: 50%; unknown: 15%; nonresident alien 8%. *Age distribution:* number under 18: 56; 18–19: 5,318; 20–21: 6,409; 22–24: 1,707; 25–29: 126; 30–34: 25; 35–39: 13; 40–49: 12; 50–64: 3.

International Students: 1,584 nonresident aliens enrolled fall 2008. Programs available to aid students whose native language is not English: social, cultural, financial. English as a Second Language Program. 10–15 undergraduate scholarships available annually.

Student Life: College operated residence halls for males, females, and co-ed. College operated apartments. Housing available for single, married and families. Cooperative housing for males and females. 45% undergraduate students live on campus. Freshmen are not required to live on campus. Assistance in locating off-campus housing (not affiliated with the college). Special interest housing available. *Intercollegiate athletics:* male: baseball, basketball, cross-country, football, golf, ice hockey, lacrosse, polo, rowing (crew), soccer, squash, swimming, tennis, track and field, water polo, wrestling; female: basketball, cross-country, equestrian, fencing, field hockey, gymnastics, ice hockey, lacrosse, polo, rowing (crew), soccer, softball, squash, swimming, tennis, track and field, volleyball. *Special regulations:* Registered cars permitted. *Special services:* aptitude testing; Career Counseling; employment service for undergraduates; freshman orientation program; Health Services; personal counseling; placement service for graduates; counselors for veterans, disabled, women's services, and psychological; services/facilities for the handicapped and students with learning disabilities. Microcomputers are available for general student use at various campus locations including residence halls, libraries, classrooms and computer centers. Microcomputers are available for lease or purchase at a discount. *Student activities:* Student Government; performing arts: choral groups, concert band, dance, drama, jazz band, marching band, music ensembles, musical theater, pep band, symphony orchestra. There are over 48 fraternities of which 28% of males are members and 22 sororities of which 22% of females are members. There are over 650 campus organizations. *Student publications:* magazine, radio, student newspaper, television, yearbook. *Surrounding community:* Ithaca population 30,000. Syracuse, 45 miles from campus, is nearest metropolitan area. Served by mass transit bus system; airport 3 miles from campus.

Publications: *Administrative Science Quarterly; Campus Guide; Campus Walks; Cornell Alumni News; Cornell Chronicle; Cornell Countryman; Cornell Daily Sun; Cornell Desk Book; Cornell Engineering News; Cornell Engineering Quarterly; Cornell Enterprise (JGSM); Cornell Hotel and Restaurant Administration Quarterly; Cornell in Perspective; Cornell International Law Journal; Cornell Law Forum; Cornell Law Review; Cornell Plantations; Cornell Reports; Cornell Veterinarian Quarterly; Cornellian; Epoch; Facts About Cornell; Farm Research Quarterly; Food Topics; Graduate School of Nutrition News; Human Ecology Forum; Industrial and Labor Relations Review; Introduction to Cornell; Library Journal Quarterly; Music at Cornell; Northeast Indian Quarterly; Philosophical Review; Sapsucker Woods;* and over 20 annual catalogs.

Library Collections: 19 million volumes. Online and card catalogs. Current serial subscriptions: paper 63,282. 115,765 audiovisual materials. Students have access to online information retrieval services and the Internet.

Most important holdings include Petrarch Collection; Wordsworth Collection; Icelandic Collection.

Buildings and Grounds: The academic programs of Cornell University are located principally at its main campus in Ithaca, New York, and in New York City. Extension services and research are carried out throughout New York State and there is a radio telescope facility in Arecibo, Puerto Rico. Cornell's land holdings for educational purposes comprise 10,936 acres in Tompkins County,

New York, and 5,577 acres in other areas of New York State. Cornell's main campus is situated on a hilltop overlooking downtown Ithaca and Cayuga Lake. The 745-acre site includes approximately 253 major buildings. The university occupies 11 buildings in New York City that house the Medical College. The university also owns 45 buildings at the Agricultural Experiment Station in Geneva, New York.

Chief Executive Officer: Dr. David Forton, President.

Undergraduates address admission inquiries to Jason Locke, Director of Undergraduate Admissions; first-professional and graduate inquiries contact appropriate college/school.

College of Arts and Sciences

Degree Programs Offered: *Baccalaureate* in American studies; anthropology; archaeology; Asian studies; astronomy; biological sciences; chemistry; classics (Latin); comparative literature; computer science; economics; English; geological sciences; German studies; government; history; history of art; mathematics; modern languages and linguistics (several including French, linguistics, Spanish); music; Near Eastern studies; philosophy; physics; psychology; romance studies (French, Italian, Spanish); Russian; sociology; special programs and interdisciplinary studies (Africana Studies and Research Center, agriculture, food and society concentration, American Indian Program, Asian American studies, biology and society, cognitive studies, East Asia, history and philosophy of science and technology, human biology, international relations, Jewish studies, Latin American studies, medieval studies, modern European studies, religious studies, Russian/Soviet and East European studies, science and technology studies, independent study, Society for the Humanities, South Asia Program, Southeast Asia Program, Statistics Center, women's studies); theatre arts (dance, film, theatre); and Writing Program.

Admission: *See* University admission requirements.

Degree Requirements: 2 freshman writing seminars; foreign language (4 courses to obtain qualification in 2 languages or proficiency in one); 4 approved sequences of 2 full-semester courses; declared major; 15 credits in electives; residency (8 full-time semesters); minimum number of courses (34 courses); 120 credit hours (100 must be taken in the College of Arts and Sciences); and 2 terms of physical education.

Distinctive Educational Programs: Accelerated degree programs. Double degree programs with College of Architecture, Art, and Planning; College of Engineering. Double registration with Law School and Medical College. Special-interest options include independent study; undergraduate research program; language study; prelaw study; and premedical study. Off-campus programs include study abroad (in more than 16 countries world-wide); summer residential programs in archaeology; marine science; Cornell-in-Washington; and fieldwork.

New York State College of Agriculture and Life Sciences

Degree Programs Offered: *Baccalaureate* in the major fields of agricultural and biological engineering; animal sciences; applied economics and business management; biological sciences; communication; education; entomology; food science; landscape architecture; natural resources; nutrition, food and agriculture; plant sciences; rural sociology; soil, crop and atmospheric sciences; statistics and biometry; and special agricultural studies.

Admission: *See* University admission requirements.

Degree Requirements: 120 minimum credit hours; resident (8 full-time semesters); 2 terms of physical education; GPA of 1.7 or above.

Distinctive Educational Programs: Off-campus students study in Sea education association, Shoals Marine Laboratory, Albany programs, Cornell-in-Washington, student teaching, clinical microbiology internships. Overseas academic programs include the countries of England, Ireland, Sweden, and Mexico. Joint enrollment agreement between Cornell and Ithaca College. Intercollege programs include the Colleges of Architecture, Art and Planning (landscape architecture); Veterinary Medicine (dual-registration); Engineering (agricultural and biological engineering); Human Ecology (nutritional sciences); program on science, technology and society; American Indian program (AIP); comparative and environmental toxicology program; and the Cornell laboratory of environmental applications of remote sensing (CLEARS). Experiment station in Geneva, New York. Animal Science Teaching Research Center.

College of Architecture, Art, and Planning

Degree Programs Offered: *Baccalaureate* in the major fields of architecture; city and regional planning; fine arts; history of architecture and urbanism; and urban and regional studies.

Admission: *Architecture:* portfolio, interview. *Art:* required to submit a slide portfolio and recommended to have a portfolio and interview review. *See* also University admission requirements.

Degree Requirements: *Bachelor of Architecture:* 177 minimum credit hours, 5 years residency. *Bachelor of Fine Arts:* 130 minimum credit hours, 4 years residency. *Bachelor of Science:* 120 minimum credit hours, 4 years residency.

Distinctive Educational Programs: Rome and Cornell-in-Washington programs. Dual-degree program. Joint registration with the College of Arts and Sciences.

College of Engineering

Degree Programs Offered: *Baccalaureate* in the major fields of agricultural engineering; chemical engineering; civil engineering; college program; computer science; electrical engineering; engineering physics; geological sciences; materials science and engineering; mechanical engineering; and operations research and engineering.

Admission: *See* University admission requirements.

Degree Requirements: 129–141 credit hours, which include 1 writing-intensive technical course, 1 computing applications course, and 2 terms of physical education.

Distinctive Educational Programs: Dual-degree program with the College of Arts and Sciences. Double major in Engineering. Engineering communications program offers instruction in written, oral and visual presentation. Engineering cooperative program provides an opportunity to gain practical experience in industry and other engineering-related enterprises.

School of Hotel Administration

Degree Programs Offered: *Baccalaureate.*

Admission: *See* University admission requirements.

Degree Requirements: 8 terms in residence; minimum cumulative GPA of 2.0, of 120 required and elective credits; 2 units of practice credit prior to the last term of residence; university requirement in physical education.

Distinctive Educational Programs: Independent research projects. Management-intern program in the Statler Hotel and J. Willard Marriott Executive Education Center. Study abroad to develop an awareness of the international component of the hospitality industry.

New York State College of Human Ecology

Degree Programs Offered: *Baccalaureate* in the major fields of biology and society; consumer economics and housing; design and environmental analysis; human development and family studies; human service studies; nutritional sciences; policy analysis; textiles and apparel; individual curriculum.

Admission: *See* University admission requirements.

Degree Requirements: Meet college credit and distribution requirements (120 credit hours minimum); complete requirements for a major; achieve a cumulative average of 1.7 (C-) or better; fulfill residency requirements (8 semesters); and complete 2 terms of physical education within the first 2 semesters.

Distinctive Educational Programs: Teacher certification in home economics. Human ecology field and international study. Africana studies and research center. Dual registration program with the Johnson Graduate School of Management, Law School and Cornell Medical College. Off-campus programs with New York State assembly internships, Ithaca College and Wells College.

New York State School of Industrial and Labor Relations

Degree Programs Offered: *Baccalaureate.* Certificates in labor studies also given.

Admission: *See* University admission requirements.

Degree Requirements: 120 credit hours, 55 of which are required courses. This requires 8 terms for an average of 30 credit hours a year, although some students accelerate their studies.

Distinctive Educational Programs: Accelerated baccalaureate-master's program with Johnson Graduate School of Management. Off-campus and study abroad semester programs provide experience in labor problem solving. Honors program: working for 2 semesters (for 3 credits each term) to research, write, and then defend a thesis.

Law School

Degree Programs Offered: *First-professional; Doctor of Law (JD).*

Admission: Baccalaureate in liberal arts or professional field from accredited college or university; LSAT; LSDAS.

Degree Requirements: 96 weeks of law study and 84 semester credit hours. 72 of the credit hours must be in professional law subjects. First-year courses are required. Second and third year students may not register for fewer than 12 hours or more than 16 hours in any term, or for fewer than 26 hours in any aca-

CORNELL UNIVERSITY—*cont'd*

demic year. Two special course requirements: writing and one of several courses dealing with issues of professional responsibility.

Distinctive Educational Programs: JD with specialization in International Legal Affairs. Second- and third-year students may take approved courses outside the law school. Some students admitted to program with specialization in international affairs. Joint degree programs with the Johnson Graduate School of Management (JD/MBA), the College of Arts and Sciences, the Department of City and Regional Planning (JD/MRP), the School of Industrial and Labor Relations (JD/MILR) and the graduate division in economics, history and philosophy (JD and PhD or MA in philosophy), as well as a special opportunity for highly qualified undergraduates in the College of Arts and Sciences to register in the Law School during their senior year.

New York State College of Veterinary Medicine

Degree Programs Offered: *First-professional; Doctor of Veterinary Medicine (DVM).*

Admission: Minimum of 3 years preveterinary curriculum at accredited college or university; animal practice requirement; GRE. Applications must be filed approximately one year before the proposed matriculation date.

Degree Requirements: Prescribed 4-year curriculum (approximately 171 credit hours); 1 year in residence.

Distinctive Educational Programs: Double registration with the College of Agriculture and Life Sciences and DVM/PhD programs provided in conjunction with the Graduate School. James A. Baker Institute for Animal Health; Feline Health Center; poultry disease and aquatic animal disease research programs; New York Mastitis Control Program; Equine Health Center; Bovine Research Center; and New York State Diagnostic Laboratory.

Graduate School

Degree Programs Offered: *Master's, doctorate, professional, master of professional studies* in fields in the Colleges of Agriculture and Life Sciences, Architecture, Art and Planning, Arts and Sciences, Engineering, Human Ecology, Veterinary Medicine, and the Schools of Hotel Administration, Industrial and Labor Relations, and the Law School. *Doctorate* also awarded in Johnson Graduate School of Management. There are over 20 different degree programs, some with an emphasis on scholarly research, others with an emphasis on education for a profession. There are 89 major fields of study and 12 minor fields of study.

Admission: Applicants must hold a baccalaureate degree or its equivalent, granted by a faculty or university of recognized standing; have adequate preparation for graduate study in the chosen field of instruction; have fluent command of the English language; present evidence of promise in advanced study and research; take the Graduate Record Examinations General Test for those fields that require the GREs. Applications for admission may be submitted at any time during the year. Many fields, however, require that applicants for fall admission submit their completed applications before January 10.

Degree Requirements: *For master's degree:* 2 residence units or 1 year. One final examination required. Thesis required for MA and MS. *For doctorate:* 6 residence units or 3 years. Two examinations required. Dissertation required. *For professional degree:* Course requirements applicable to specific fields.

Departments and Teaching Staff: Faculty drawn from other departments in university.

Distinctive Educational Programs: Master's of professional studies in African and Afro-American Studies (MPS-AAA); agriculture (MPS-Agr.); communication (MPS-Comm.); hotel administration (MPS-HAd.); human ecology (MPS-HuEd); and International Development (MPS-ID). Several interdisciplinary programs in various fields. Three-fourths of the graduate students are in the PhD program.

Samuel Curtis Johnson Graduate School of Management

Degree Programs Offered: *Master's* in business administration (MBA).

Admission: Bachelor's degree or its equivalent.

Degree Requirements: 60 credit hours, 4 semesters of residency and all core courses met.

Distinctive Educational Programs: Development program offers 4-week summer seminar for management executive training. Offers 1-week on-site customized programs. Student-faculty exchange program with Louvain and Leuven Universities (Belgium) and the London Business School. Japanese Business Program. Joint degree programs with other colleges on campus.

Medical College

1300 York Avenue
New York, NY 10021

Degree Programs Offered: *Doctorate:* Doctor of Medicine (M.D.)

Admission: Completed 4 years of college or satisfactory completion of at least 6 semester credit hours in each of the following subjects: English, physics, biology or zoology, general chemistry, and organic chemistry; at least 2 terms of biological science beyond introductory level; and the Medical College Admissions Test (MCAT).

Degree Requirements: 4 academic years of study of at least 32 weeks each; 21 years of age. 2 years in residence; prescribed curriculum; annual evaluation.

Distinctive Educational Programs: Summer fellowship program for minority students; M.D. with honors in research; Cornell scholars in biomedical sciences and clinical investigation; Tri-Institutional M.D./Ph.D. Program and the Ph.D./M.D. Program both in conjunction with the Graduate School of Medicine.

Graduate School of Medical Science

1300 York Avenue
New York, NY 10021

Degree Programs Offered: *Master's, doctorate* in one of the following 7 programs: biochemistry; cell biology and genetics; immunology; molecular biology; neuroscience; pharmacology; and physiology and biophysics.

Admission: Applicant must have a baccalaureate degree or the equivalent from a college or university of recognized standing; have adequate preparation in the chosen field of study; and show promise of ability to pursue advanced study and research, as judged by his/her previous record. Candidates may be admitted in September, February, or July, although places in the graduate program for February and July may not be available because of prior commitments to applicants for September admission. Applicants for February or July admission should correspond directly with the respective Program Director regarding the availability of places.

Degree Requirements: *For master's degree:* 4 years for completion and 2 units minimum in residency. *For doctorate:* maximum of 7 years for completion and 6 units minimum in residency.

Departments and Teaching Staff: Faculty drawn from the Medical College for the 7 departments/programs.

Distinctive Educational Programs: Tri-Institutional M.D./Ph.D. Program and the Ph.D./M.D. Program both in conjunction with the Medical College.

Culinary Institute of America

1946 Campus Drive
Hyde Park, New York 12538
Tel: (800) 285-4627 **E-mail:** admissions@culinary.edu
Fax: (845) 451-1068 **Internet:** www.ciachef.edu

Institution Description: The Culinary Institute of America is a private, nonprofit, educational institution providing professional culinary arts and science education. *Degrees awarded:* Associate, baccalaureate. *Enrollment:* 2,812.

Accreditation: *National:* ACCSCT. *Professional*: culinary education

History: The Culinary Institute began as the New Haven Restaurant Institute in 1946 in Connecticut; moved to a 40-room mansion near Yale University and renamed Restaurant Institute of Connecticut in 1947; adopted present name 1951; moved to Hyde Park location 1970. The Culinary Institute of America opened a West Coast campus in 1995 at Greystone, in the heart of the Napa Valley, north of San Francisco.

Institutional Structure: Governed by a board of trustees not compensated for its services, the institute benefits from the guidance of its board members who represent the hospitality field as well as the professional and educational communities.

Calendar: Continuous. 16 entry dates per academic year.

Characteristics of Freshmen: 1,115 applicants. 75% of applicants accepted. 89% of accepted applicants enrolled full-time.

Mean SAT scores male 490 verbal, 480 mathematical; female 510 verbal, 480 mathematical.

88% of entering freshmen expected to graduate within 5 years. 35% of freshmen from New York, Freshmen from 28 states and 22 foreign countries.

Admission: *Requirements:* Graduation from an accredited secondary school; 3 to 6 months of foodservice experience, including work in a professional kitchen; one letter of recommendation from foodservice professionals.

Degree Requirements: *For all associate degrees:* 69 credits for the baking and pastry arts program and for the culinary arts program; 2.00 GPA. *For bachelor's degree:* 63 credits beyond the associate degree for either the culinary arts program or the baking and pastry arts program; 2.00 GPA. *Grading system:* A–F.

Distinctive Educational Programs: Included in the curriculum for all students is an 18-week paid externship at an off-campus foodservice establishment. In addition, baccalaureate students complete a wine and food seminar in the California wine country.

Degrees Conferred: 1,085 *associate;* 266 *baccalaureate*: culinary arts.

Fees and Other Expenses: *Full-time tuition per academic year 2008–09:* $23,370. *Required fees:* $430. *Room and board per academic year:* $10,230. *Books and supplies:* $1,505. *Other expenses:* 5,000.

Financial Aid: Financial aid may be awarded through loans, grants, jobs, or a combination of two or three of these.

Financial aid to full-time, first-time undergraduate students: 89% of students received some form of financial aid. Average amount of aid received: federal grants $2,477; state/local grants $1,927; institutional grants 3,301; loans $10,163.

Departments and Teaching Staff: Instructors from 20 countries, including the largest concentration of American Culinary Federation-certified master chefs in the United States. Baking and pastry arts *professors* 2, *associate professors* 3, *assistant professors* 2, *instructors* 10, *part-time faculty* 1; business management 2, 6, 5, 3, 1; culinary arts 9, 20, 7, 14, 0; liberal arts 2, 3, 8, 1, 2; restaurant operations 6, 6, 4, 6, 0.

Total instructional faculty: 190 (full-time 131, part-time 59). *Student/faculty ratio:* 18:1. Degrees held by faculty: baccalaureate 19%, associate in culinary arts 37%, foreign culinary degree 20%, master's 9%, other 15%.

Enrollment: Total enrollment 2,812.

Characteristics of Student Body: *Ethnic/racial makeup:* Black non-Hispanic: 35; American Indian or Alaska Native: 1%; Asian or Pacific Islander: 5%; Hispanic: 6%; White non-Hispanic: 66%; unknown: 15%; nonresident alien 5%.

International Students: 141 nonresident aliens enrolled fall 2008. Students from Asia, Central and South America, Canada, Australia. No programs to aid students whose native language is not English. Financial aid specifically designated for international students: 9 scholarships available annually to qualifying students.

Student Life: Four residence halls on campus house 1,112 students. Recreational facilities include a 52,000 sq.ft. Student Recreation Center that opened in 1998. Intramural competitions in soccer, recreational ice hockey, basketball, tennis, softball, flag football, volleyball, racquetball, and indoor baseball. Various student organizations and clubs available for participation. Operated for the public are the St. Andrew's Cafe, Caterina de Medici Dining Room, Escoffier Restaurant, and American Bounty Restaurant. *Surrounding community:* Hyde Park, home of President Franklin D. Roosevelt, is located near the Hudson River, 1-½ hours north of New York City.

Library Collections: 72,000 volumes. 3,000 current periodical subscriptions; 2,300 videotapes. Computer work stations available. Students have access to online information retrieval services and the Internet.

The library houses one of the largest collections of specialized literature in the culinary field and a growing collection of liberal arts materials supporting the institute's associate and baccalaureate degree programs; Menu Collection; Video Collection.

Chief Executive Officer: L. Timothy Ryan, President.

Address admissions inquiries to Rachel Birchwood, Director of Admissions.

Daemen College

4380 Main Street
Amherst, New York 14226-3592
Tel: (716) 839-3600 **E-mail:** admissions@daemen.edu
Fax: (716) 839-8516 **Internet:** www.daemen.edu

Institution Description: Daemen College (Rosary Hill College until 1976) is a private, nonsectarian college. *Enrollment:* 2,716. *Degrees awarded:* Baccalaureate, master's. Post-master's certificate also awarded.

Accreditation: *Regional:* MSA. *Professional*: business, nursing, physical therapy, physician assisting, social work, teacher education

History: Established by the Order of St. Francis and chartered as Rosary Hill College, a women's college, 1947; adopted present name 1976.

Institutional Structure: *Governing board:* The Board of Trustees. Extrainstitutional representation: 24 trustees; Institutional representation: president of the college (ex officio), 1 faculty. *Composition of institution:* Administrators 98. Academic affairs headed by vice president for academic affairs. Management/business/finances directed by vice president for business affairs, treasurer. Full-time instructional faculty 85.

Calendar: Semesters. Academic year Aug. to May. Formal commencement May. Summer session of 2 terms from June to Aug.

Characteristics of Freshmen: 1,988 applicants 66% of applicants admitted. 31% of admitted students enrolled full-time.

79% (319 students) submitted SAT scores; 34% (137 students) submitted ACT scores. *25th percentile*: SAT Critical Reading 450, SAT Math 480, SAT Writing 440; ACT Composite 20. *75th percentile*: SAT Critical Reading 540, SAT Math 570, SAT Writing 530; ACT Composite 25.

46% of entering freshmen expected to graduate within 5 years. 96% of freshmen from New York. Freshmen from 16 states and 5 foreign countries.

Admission: For fall acceptance, apply as early as Nov. of previous year. Early acceptance available. *Requirements:* Graduation from accredited secondary school. GED accepted. Specific requirements vary with program. *Entrance tests:* College Board SAT or ACT composite. For foreign students TOEFL. *For transfer students:* 2.0 minimum GPA; good standing at institution previously attended.

College credit for USAFI and for extrainstitutional learning (life experience) on basis of faculty assessment.

Degree Requirements: *Undergraduate:* 120–176 semester hours; 2.0 GPA; 30 hours in residence; core requirements. For bachelor of arts, demonstrated proficiency in foreign language. *Graduate:* 34–40 semester hours. *Grading system:* A–F; pass-unsatisfactory; withdraw (carries penalty, deadline after which pass-fail appended to withdraw); FX (failure due to poor attendance).

Distinctive Educational Programs: Cooperative education, field experience, internships. Interdisciplinary programs in humanities, environmental studies. Directed study and research. Preprofessional programs in law, medicine. *Other distinctive programs:* Evening and weekend program; student designed major; entry-level master's program in physical therapy and physician assistant studies leading to a BS/MS degree (dual degree); accelerated MS degree in nursing; workshops and support services for nontraditional students through Extended Studies Program. Higher Education Opportunity Program for New York residents who lack credentials for regular admission but show potential. Spanish Language and Culture Program at Sevillo, Spain and Mexico.

ROTC: Army offered in cooperation with Canisius College.

Degrees Conferred: 263 *baccalaureate*; 353 *master's*; 50 *doctorate*. Bachelor's degrees awarded in top five disciplines: health professions and related clinical sciences 64; education 51; biological/life sciences 48; business, management, marketing, and related support services 35; visual and performing arts 30. Master's degrees awarded: business/marketing 5; education 284; health \ professions and related clinical sciences 30; interdisciplinary studies 9. Doctorates awarded: health professions 50.

Fees and Other Expenses: *Full-time tuition per academic year 2008–09:* undergraduate $19,870, graduate courses charged per credit. *Room and board per academic year:* $9,050. *Books and supplies:* $800. *Other expenses:* $1,500.

Financial Aid: Aid from institutionally generated funds is provided on the basis of academic merit, financial need, athletic ability. Institution has a Program Participation Agreement with the U.S. Department of Education for eligible students to receive Pell Grants and, depending upon the agreement, other federal aid.

Financial aid to full-time, first-time undergraduate students: 97% received some form of financial aid. Average amount of aid received: federal grants $1,511; state/local grants $2,004; institutional grants $4,119; loans $2,351.

Departments and Teaching Staff: *Total instructional faculty:* 269. Degrees held by full-time faculty: doctorate 63%, master's 28%, professional 4%. 42% of faculty hold the doctorate, first-professional, or other terminal degree. Student/faculty ratio: 14:1.

Enrollment: Total enrollment 2,716. Undergraduate 1,768. Graduate 948. Undergraduate transfer-in students 222.

Characteristics of Student Body: *Ethnic/racial makeup:* Black non-Hispanic: 36%; Hispanic: 36%; White non-Hispanic: 97%. *Age distribution:* number under 18: 298; 18–19: 302; 20–21: 432; 22–24: 188; 25–29: 51; 30–34: 15; 35–39: 14; 40–49: 11; 50–64: 5.

International Students: 315 nonresident aliens enrolled fall 2008. Students from Europe, Asia, Africa, Canada. No programs available to aid students whose native language is not English. No financial programs specifically designated for international students.

Student Life: On-campus residence halls. *Student publications: A Step Ascending*, a literary journal; *Summit*, a yearbook; *Ascent*, college student newspaper. *Surrounding community:* Amherst. Buffalo is nearest metropolitan area. Served by airport; passenger rail service; local, regional, and international bus service.

Publications: *Daemen Today*, a magazine for alumni and friends of Daemen College; *Daemen Dialogue*, a newsletter for campus administrators and faculty.

Library Collections: 152,000 volumes. Current periodical subscriptions: paper 189; microform 4; via electronic access 15,364. 1,874 audio/videotapes; 110 DVD discs; 8 CD-ROMs. Online catalog. Computer work stations available. Students have access to online information retrieval services and the Internet.

Most important special collections include books and periodicals in the allied health field; books written in French; English and American literature.

Buildings and Grounds: Campus area 35 acres.

Chief Executive Officer: Dr. Martin J. Anisman, President.

Address admission inquiries to Donna Shaffner, Director of Admissions.

Davis College

400 Riverside Drive
Johnson City, New York 13790
Tel: (607) 729-1581 **E-mail:** admissions@davisny.edu
Fax: (607) 729-2962 **Internet:** www.davisny.edu

Institution Description: Davis College, formerly named Practical Bible College, is a private, four-year college training men and women in bible/theology and ministry. *Enrollment:* 325. *Degrees awarded:* Associate, baccalaureate.

Accreditation: *Regional:* MSA. *National:* ABHE. *Professional*: theology

History: Established 1900 as a 3-year bible institute in Johnson City, New York (greater Binghamton area); became Practical Bible College 1993; adopted present name 2004.

Institutional Structure: *Governing board:* Representation: 21 members, all voting. Administrators 13. Academic affairs headed by vice president of academic affairs. Business affairs headed by vice president of business affairs.

Calendar: Semesters. Academic year Aug. to May. Formal commencement May. Summer session of two 2-week modules in May; two 1-week modules in June and July.

Characteristics of Freshmen: 51% of applicants admitted. 79% of admitted students enrolled full-time.

62% (28 students) submitted SAT scores; 33% (15 students) submitted ACT scores. *25th percentile*: SAT Critical Reading 411, SAT Math 404; ACT Composite 15, ACT English 14, ACT Math 14. *75th percentile*: SAT Critical Reading 595, SAT Math 561; ACT Composite 24, ACT English 37, ACT Math 25.

59% of entering freshmen expected to graduate within 5 years. 86% of freshmen from New York. Freshmen from 8 states and 8 foreign countries.

Admission: Rolling admissions. *Requirements:* High school graduate with minimum 2.00 GPA; ACT composite score minimum 15; application and medical form with 3 references. Minimum TOEFL score of 480 for international students whose native language is not English.

College credit and advanced placement for postsecondary-level work completed in secondary school and for extrainstitutional learning.

Developmental/remedial courses offered in summer session and regular academic year; credit given.

Degree Requirements: *For all associate degrees:* 64–66 credit hours; 30 hours in residence. *For all baccalaureate degrees:* 129–131 credit hours; 30 hours in residence. *Grading system:* A–F.

Distinctive Educational Programs: Senior internships completed by all graduates of Bachelor of Religious Education program.

Degrees Conferred: 9 *associate;* 38 *baccalaureate:* religious studies.

Fees and Other Expenses: *Full-time tuition per academic year 2008–09:* $12,901. *Room and board per academic year:* $6,000. *Books and supplies:* $800. *Other expenses:* $1,540.

Financial Aid: Aid from institutionally generated funds is provided on the basis of academic merit, financial need, other criteria.

Financial aid to full-time, first-time undergraduate students:

Financial aid to full-time, first-time undergraduate students: 98% received some form of aid. Average amount of aid received: federal grants $2,954; state/local grants $2,811; institutional grants $2,141.

Departments and Teaching Staff: *Total instructional faculty:* 17 (full-time 8, part-time 9). 62% of faculty hold the doctorate, first-professional, or other terminal degree. Student/faculty ratio: 24:1.

Enrollment: Total enrollment 325. Transfer-in students 32.

Characteristics of Student Body: *Ethnic/racial makeup:* number of Black non-Hispanic: 14; American Indian or Alaska Native: 1; Asian or Pacific Islander: 2; Hispanic: 4; White non-Hispanic: 252. *Age distribution:* number under 18: 33; 18–19: 72; 20–21: 59; 22–24: 40; 25–29: 32; 30–34: 8; 35–39: 15; 40–49: 22; 50–64: 4.

International Students: 14 nonresident aliens enrolled fall 2008. Students from Asia, Africa, Canada, Australia. Programs available to aid students whose native language is not English: English as a Second Language Program. Financial aid specifically designated for international students: 12 scholarships available annually for qualifying students.

Student Life: On-campus residence halls house 51% of full-time students; 3 apartment buildings house upperclassmen suites for married students and families. *Intermural athletics:* male and female: soccer, basketball, men: soccer. *Special services:* health services, counseling services. *Student publication: Touchstone*, quarterly newspaper. *Surrounding community:* Binghamton/Johnson City/Endicott located in the Southern Tier of New York State.

Library Collections: 88,500 volumes. Online catalog. 7,018 audiovisual materials; 140 current periodical subscriptions. Computer work stations available. Students have access to the Internet at no charge and online information retrieval services (fee-based). *Most important special collections:* theology; Bible; Ministry Studies.

Buildings and Grounds: Campus located on banks of Susquehanna river. 10 major buildings.

Chief Executive Officer: Dr. George Miller III, President.

Address admissions inquiries to West Ehret, Director of Admissions.

Dominican College of Blauvelt

470 Western Highway
Orangeburg, New York 10962
Tel: (845) 359-7800 **E-mail:** admissions@dc.edu
Fax: (845) 359-2313 **Internet:** www.dc.edu

Institution Description: Dominican College of Blauvelt is a private, independent, nonprofit college. *Enrollment:* 1,977. *Degrees awarded:* Associate, baccalaureate, master's, doctorate (physical therapy). Certificates also awarded.

Accreditation: *Regional:* MSA. *Professional*: athletic training, business, nursing, physical therapy, social work, occupational therapy, teacher education

History: Established as a 3-year institution. Dominican Junior College, chartered, and offered first instruction at postsecondary level 1952; awarded first degree (associate) 1954; became a 4-year institution and adopted present name 1959. *See* Sister M. Philomena Yonker, *Dominican College of Blauvelt: Genesis and Early Development* (Blauvelt, N.Y.: Convent of St. Dominic, 1972) for further information.

Institutional Structure: *Governing board:* Board of Trustees of Dominican College of Blauvelt. Extrainstitutional representation: 31 trustees; Institutional representation: chancellor of the college. 1 ex officio. All voting. *Composition of institution:* Administrators 66. Academic affairs headed by academic dean. Management/business/finances directed by director of fiscal affairs. Full-time instructional faculty 64. Academic governance body, the faculty, meets an average of 9 times per year.

Calendar: Semesters (4-1-4 plan). Academic year Sept. to May. Freshmen admitted Sept., June, July. Degrees conferred May, Jan. Formal commencement May. Summer session from June to Aug.

Characteristics of Freshmen: 1,247 applicants. 76% of applicants admitted. 30% of admitted applicants enrolled full-time.

95% (289 students) submitted SAT scores; 5% (15 students) submitted ACT scores. *25th percentile*: SAT Critical Reading 400, SAT Math 410, SAT Writing 400; ACT Composite 18, ACT English 16, ACT Math 16. *75th percentile*: SAT Critical Reading 490, SAT Math 480, SAT Writing 470; ACT Composite 23, ACT English 20, ACT Math 23.

50% of entering freshmen expected to graduate within 5 years. 75% of freshmen from New York. Freshmen from 16 states and 9 foreign countries.

Admission: Rolling admissions plan. Students must complete a secondary-school program or receive satisfactory scores in a high school equivalency examination. Recommended preparation includes 16 academic unit of study distributed among English, mathematics, natural sciences, and foreign languages.

College credit and advanced placement for postsecondary-level work completed in secondary school. College credit for extrainstitutional learning on basis of portfolio assessment.

Tutoring available. Developmental courses offered during regular academic year; credit given.

Degree Requirements: *For all associate degrees:* minimum 60 credit hours. *For all baccalaureate degrees:* maximum 120 credit hours. *For all degrees:* 2.0 GPA; general education requirements.

Fulfillment of some degree requirements and exemption from some beginning courses possible by passing College Board CLEP, AP, other standardized tests. *Grading system:* A–F; pass-fail; withdraw (carries time limit).

Distinctive Educational Programs: Weekend, evening, and accelerated evening classes. Honors Program. Tutorials. *Other distinctive programs:* 25% discount on tuition to senior citizens. Corporate Outreach Program offers courses/programs tailored to the needs of corporations either on-campus or at corporate facility. Combination online/in class courses offered.

Degrees Conferred: 304 *baccalaureate:*; 39 *master's*; 16 *doctorate*. Bachelor's degrees offered in top five disciplines: health professions and related clinical sciences 87; business/marketing 58; social sciences 30; education 24; computer and information sciences 17. Master's degrees awarded: education 17; health professions 9, other 13. Doctorates awarded: health professions 16.

Fees and Other Expenses: *Full-time tuition per academic year 2008–09* undergraduate $20,300; graduate study charged per credit hour (contact the college for current rate). *Room and board per academic year:* $9,730. *Books and supplies:* $1,800. *Other expenses:* $2,000.

Financial Aid: The college offers a direct lending program. Aid from institutionally generated funds is provided on the basis of academic merit, financial need, athletic ability.

Financial aid to full-time, first-time undergraduate students: 91% received some form of aid. Average amount of aid received: federal grants $4,144; state/local grants $2,769; institutional grants $8,198.

Departments and Teaching Staff: *Total instructional faculty:* 170 (full-time 66, part-time 104). 46% of faculty hold the doctorate, first-professional, or other terminal degree. Student/faculty ratio: 13:1.

Enrollment: Total enrollment 1,977. Undergraduate 1,675. Graduate 302. Undergraduate transfer-in students 165.

Characteristics of Student Body: *Ethnic/racial makeup:* number of Black non-Hispanic: 261; American Indian or Alaska Native: 4; Asian or Pacific Islander: 98; Hispanic: 219; White non-Hispanic: 788; unknown: 181. *Age distribution:* number 20–21: 602; 22–24: 196; 25–29: 154.

International Students: Programs available to aid students whose native language is not English: English as a Second Language Program. No financial aid specifically designated for international students.

Student Life: *Intercollegiate athletics:* male: baseball, basketball, cross-country, golf, lacrosse, soccer, track; female: basketball, cross-country, lacrosse, soccer, softball, volleyball. *Special regulations:*Cars must have college decal. *Student publications: Dominican Difference*, a student newspaper; *Cabachon*, a literary magazine. *Surrounding community:* Orangeburg, unincorporated, is 17 miles north of New York City in Rockland County; served by airports in Newark (NJ), New York City, Newburgh (NY).

Library Collections: 106,000 volumes. 17,000 microforms; 1,000 audiovisual materials; 10,500 periodicals including via electronic access. Online catalog. Computer work stations available.

Most important holdings include a Special Education collection; holdings in education, nursing, and social work.

Buildings and Grounds: Campus area 6 acres.

Chief Executive Officer: Sr. Mary Eileen O'Brien, O.P., President.

Address admission inquiries to Joyce Elbe, Director of Admissions.

Dowling College

150 Idle Hour Boulevard
Oakdale, New York 11769-1999
Tel: (800) 369-5464 **E-mail:** admissions@dowling.edu
Fax: (631) 563-3827 **Internet:** www.dowling.edu

Institution Description: Dowling College is a private, independent, comprehensive college. *Enrollment:* 5,706. *Degrees awarded:* Baccalaureate, master's, doctorate.

Accreditation: *Regional:* MSA.

History: Established as Adelphi Suffolk College of Adelphi University, chartered, and offered first instruction at postsecondary level 1959; awarded first degree (baccalaureate) 1962; adopted present name 1968.

Institutional Structure: *Governing board:* Board of Trustees. Extrainstitutional representation: 30 trustees; institutional representation: president of the college. 1 ex officio. 30 voting. *Composition of institution:* Administrators 44. Academic affairs headed by provost. Management/business/finances directed by vice president for business and finance. Full-time instructional faculty 117. Academic governance body, Faculty-Administrative Senate, meets an average of 30 times per year. *Faculty representation:* Faculty served by collective bargaining agent, New York State United Teachers, affiliated with AFT.

Calendar: Semesters. Academic year Sept. to May. Freshmen admitted Sept., Jan., Feb., June, July. Degrees conferred June, Aug., Feb. Formal commencement June. Summer session of 3 terms from early June to mid-Aug.

Characteristics of Freshmen: 2,866 applicants. 79% of applicants admitted. 29% of admitted students enrolled full-time. 53% (290 students) submitted SAT scores. *25th percentile*: SAT Critical Reading 410, SAT Math 410. *75th percentile*: SAT Critical Reading 500, SAT Math 540.

29% of entering freshmen expected to graduate within 5 years. 95% of freshmen from New York. Freshmen from 11 states and 17 countries.

Admission: Rolling admissions plan. For fall acceptance, apply as early as Sept. 1 of previous year, but not later than Aug. 30 of year of enrollment. *Requirements:* Either graduation from accredited secondary school or GED. Recommend 4 units English and 12 from among foreign language, history, mathematics, science, other academic electives. *Entrance tests:* College Board SAT or ACT composite. *For transfer students:* 2.0 minimum GPA; from 4-year accredited institution 90 credit hours maximum transfer credit; from 2-year accredited institution 60 hours.

College credit and advanced placement for postsecondary-level work completed in secondary school and for extrainstitutional learning on basis of faculty assessment.

Tutoring available. Noncredit developmental courses offered in summer session.

Degree Requirements: *Undergraduate:* 120 credit hours; 2.0 GPA; 2 terms in residence. Fulfillment of some degree requirements and exemption from some beginning courses possible by passing departmental examinations, College Board CLEP, AP, other standardized tests. *Grading system:* A–F; withdraw (deadline after which pass-fail is appended to withdraw).

Distinctive Educational Programs: *For undergraduates:* Preprofessional programs in law, medical science. Interdepartmental program in American studies. *Available to all students:* Weekend and evening classes. Facilities and programs for independent research, including individual majors.

ROTC: Air Force in cooperation with Manhattan College.

Degrees Conferred: 590 *baccalaureate*; 873 *master's*; 20 *doctorate*> Bachelor's degrees awarded in top five disciplines: business/marketing 183; education 134; liberal arts/general studies 48; social sciences 38; psychology 37. Master's degrees awarded: business/marketing 471; education 641; liberal arts 1; transportation and materials moving 1. Doctorates awarded: education 20.

Fees and Other Expenses: *Full-time tuition per academic year 2008–09:* undergraduate $20,310. *Room and board per academic year:* $9,200. *Books and supplies:* $1,000. *Other expenses:* $1,800.

Financial Aid: Aid from institutionally generated funds is provided on the basis of academic merit, financial need, athletic ability. Institution has a Program Participation Agreement with the U.S. Department of Education for eligible students to receive Pell Grants and, depending upon the agreement, other federal aid.

Financial aid to full-time, first-time undergraduate students: 80% received some form of aid. Average amount of aid received: 36% received federal grants; 35% Pell grants; 55% state/local grants; 78% institutional grants

Departments and Teaching Staff: *Total instructional faculty:* 407 (full-time 117, part-time 290). 96% of faculty hold the doctorate, first-professional, or other terminal degree. Student/faculty ratio: 15:1.

Enrollment: Total enrollment 5,706. Undergraduate 3,288. Graduate 2,418. Undergraduate transfer-in students 293.

Characteristics of Student Body: *Ethnic/racial makeup:* number of Black non-Hispanic: 346; American Indian or Alaska Native: 9; Asian or Pacific Islander: 40; Hispanic: 283; White non-Hispanic: 1,805; unknown: 412. *Age distribution:* number under 18: 195; 18–19: 765; 20–21: 690; 22–24: 600; 25–29: 340; 30–34: 174; 35–39: 146; 40–49: 229; 50–64: 92; 65 and over: 5.

International Students: 267 nonresident aliens enrolled fall 2008. Programs available to aid students whose native language is not English: English as a Second Language Program. No financial aid specifically designated for international students.

Student Life: On-campus residence halls house 7% of student body. *Intercollegiate athletics:* male: baseball, basketball, lacrosse, soccer, tennis; female: volleyball. *Special regulations:* Cars permitted without restrictions. *Special services:* Learning Resources Center, medical services. *Student publications, radio: Idle Hour*, a yearbook; *Lion's Voice*, a biweekly newspaper; *Riverrun*, a biannual literary magazine. *Surrounding community:* Oakdale, unincorporated, located in Suffolk County population 1,300,000. New York City, 50 miles from campus, is nearest metropolitan area. Served by mass transit bus and rail system; airport 8 miles from campus; passenger rail service 1 mile from campus.

Library Collections: 223,000 volumes. 11,500 government documents; 374,000 microforms; 2,900 audiovisual materials; 960 periodical subscriptions. Online catalog. Students have access to online information retrieval services and the Internet.

Most important holdings include Fogle Collection (19th-century British Romantic poetry); books and manuscripts dealing with Long Island history.

Buildings and Grounds: Campus area 157 acres. Campus DVD available.

Chief Executive Officer: Dr. Robert J. Gaffney, President.

Address admission inquiries to Diane Kazanecki Kempter, Vice President of Enrollment.

D'Youville College

320 Porter Avenue
Buffalo, New York 14201-1084
Tel: (716) 829-8000 **E-mail:** admissions@dyc.edu
Fax: (716) 829-7790 **Internet:** www.dyc.edu

Institution Description: D'Youville College is a private, independent, nonprofit college. *Enrollment:* 2,943. *Degrees awarded:* Baccalaureate, master's.

Accreditation: *Regional:* MSA. *Professional*: dietetics, nursing, nursing education, occupational therapy, physical therapy, physician assisting, social work, surgeon assisting

History: Established as a women's college and chartered 1865; offered first instruction at postsecondary level 1907; incorporated 1908; awarded first degree (baccalaureate) 1912; became coeducational 1971.

D'YOUVILLE COLLEGE—*cont'd*

Institutional Structure: *Governing board:* Board of Trustees. Extrainstitutional representation: 25 trustees; institutional representation: president of the college; 1 alumna. 2 ex officio. 19 voting. *Composition of institution:* Administrators 82. Academic affairs headed by jointly by deans of arts and science, professional studies, and health and human services. Management/business/finances directed by vice president for finance/treasurer. Full-time instructional faculty 90. Academic governance body, Academic Council, meets an average of 10 times per year. *Faculty representation:* Faculty served by collective bargaining agent, D'Youville College Faculty Association, affiliated with AAUP.

Calendar: Semesters. Academic year Aug. to May. Freshmen admitted Aug., Jan., June. Degrees conferred and formal commencement May. Summer session of 1 presession and 3 terms from mid-May to Aug.

Characteristics of Freshmen: 1,829 applicants. 84% of applicants accepted. 15% of accepted applicants enrolled full-time.

90% (204 students) submitted SAT scores; 34% (77 students) submitted ACT scores. *25th percentile*: SAT Critical Reading 440, SAT Math 450, SAT Writing 430; ACT Composite 20. *75th percentile*: SAT Critical Reading 530, SAT Math 550, SAT Writing 530; ACT Composite 24.

44% of freshmen expected to graduate within 5 years. 90% of freshmen from New York. Freshmen from 29 states and 44 foreign countries.

Admission: Rolling admissions plan. For fall acceptance, apply as early as Oct. of previous year, but not later than Aug. 15 of year of enrollment. Early acceptance available. *Requirements:* Either graduation from accredited secondary school with 16 units, or GED. Recommend 4 units English, foreign language, 3 units social studies, 2 mathematics, 3 science. Additional requirements for some programs. Minimum GPA 2.0. *Entrance tests:* College Board SAT or ACT composite. For foreign students minimum TOEFL score 500. *For transfer students:* Minimum grade average C; from 4-year accredited institution 98 hours maximum transfer credit; from 2-year accredited institution 64 hours.

College credit and advanced placement for postsecondary-level work completed in secondary school. College credit for extrainstitutional learning.

Tutoring available. Noncredit remedial courses offered in summer session and regular academic year.

Degree Requirements: 120–128 credit hours; 2.0 GPA; 30 hours in residence; core curriculum.

Fulfillment of some degree requirements and exemption from some beginning courses possible by passing departmental examinations, College Board CLEP, AP. *Grading system:* A–F; pass-fail; withdraw (deadline after which fail is appended to withdraw).

Distinctive Educational Programs: Weekend and evening classes. BS/MS in dietetics, occupational therapy, and physical therapy. Career Discovery Program for undecided majors. Post-baccalaureate programs in teacher certification and pre-medicine. programs. Business Management Program for adult learning (18 months in a modular format). Tutorials and mentor programs for all incoming freshmen. Cross-registration through consortium. Friday graduate nursing program.

Degrees Conferred: 290 *baccalaureate*; 449 *master's*; 25 *doctorate*. Bachelor's degrees awarded in top five disciplines: health professions and related clinical sciences 111; business, management, marketing, and related support services 40; liberal arts and sciences, general studies, and humanities 33; psychology 10; history 10. Master's degrees awarded: business/marketing 11; education 322; health professions 124. Doctorates awarded: health professions 22, education 3.

Fees and Other Expenses: *Full-time tuition per academic year 2008–09:* undergraduate $20,000; graduate study charged per credit hour (contact the college for current rate). *Room and board per academic year:* $9,300. *Gooks and supplies:* $1,200. *Other expenses:* $2,300.

Financial Aid: Aid from institutionally generated funds is provided on the basis of academic merit, financial need, athletic ability, other criteria. Institution has a Program Participation Agreement with the U.S. Department of Education for eligible students to receive Pell Grants and, depending upon the agreement, other federal aid.

Financial aid to full-time, first-time undergraduate students: 96% of students received some form of financial aid. Average amount of aid received: federal grants $3,917; Pell grants $3,089; Other federal grants $998; state/local grants $2,956; institutional grants $7,426.

Departments and Teaching Staff: *Total instructional faculty:* 166. Degrees held by full-time faculty: doctorate 67%, master's 100%, baccalaureate 100%. 67% hold terminal degrees.

Enrollment: Total enrollment 2,943. Undergraduate 1,748. Graduate 1,195. Undergraduate transfer-in students 230.

Characteristics of Student Body: *Ethnic/racial makeup:* Black non-Hispanic: 17.1%; American Indian or Alaska Native: .9%; Asian or Pacific Islander: 1.1%; Hispanic: 5.4%; White non-Hispanic: 60.5%; unknown: 3.3%.

International Students: 166 undergraduate nonresident aliens enrolled fall 2008. Students from Europe, Asia, Africa, Canada. Programs available to aid students whose native language is not English: English as a Second Language. No financial aid specifically designated for international students.

Student Life: On-campus residence halls house 15% of student body. Residence halls for males constitute 25% of such space, for females 75%. *Intercollegiate athletics:* male: basketball, bowling, tennis; female: basketball, bowling, tennis, volleyball. *Special regulations:* Cars permitted without restrictions. Quiet hours vary according to dormitory floor. Residence hall visitation from 1pm to midnight Sun.–Thurs., 1pm to 2am Fri. and Sat. *Special services:* Learning Resources Center, medical services. *Student publications: The Catalyst*, a monthly newspaper; *The D'Youvillian*, a yearbook. *Surrounding community:* Buffalo population 350,000. Served by mass transit bus system; airport 11 miles from campus; passenger rail service 10 miles from campus.

Library Collections: 105,000 volumes. 1450,000 microforms; 1,200 audiovisual materials; 719 current periodical subscriptions.

Buildings and Grounds: Campus area 2.5 square blocks.

Chief Executive Officer: Sr. Denise A. Roche, GNSH, Ph.D., President.

Address undergraduate admission inquiries to Ronald Dannecker, Director of Admissions; graduate inquiries to Joseph Syracuse, Dean of Graduate Studies.

Elmira College

One Park Place
Elmira, New York 14901

Tel: (607) 735-1800 **E-mail:** admissions@elmira.edu
Fax: (607) 735-1758 **Internet:** www.elmira.edu

Institution Description: Elmira College is a private, independent, nonprofit college. *Enrollment:* 1,639. *Degrees awarded:* Associate, baccalaureate, master's.

Member of College Center of the Finger Lakes and Spring Term Consortium.

Accreditation: *Regional:* MSA. *Professional*: nursing

History: Chartered as Elmira College 1853; offered first instruction at postsecondary level 1855; awarded first degree (baccalaureate) 1859. *See* Charles Barber, *Elmira College: The First 100 Years* (New York, N.Y.: McGraw Hill Publishing Co., Inc., 1955) for further information.

Institutional Structure: *Governing board:* Board of Trustees. Extrainstitutional representation: 15 trustees; institutional representation: president of the college; 5 alumni. 1 ex officio. 20 voting. *Composition of institution:* Administrators 82. Academic affairs headed by dean of faculty. Business/finances directed by financial vice president. Vice president for development and alumni relations; vice president for external affairs; vice president for student life. Full-time instructional faculty 71. Academic governance body, the faculty, meets an average of 9 times per year.

Calendar: Semesters. 4-1-4 plan (academic year of two 12-week terms and one 6-week term). Academic year early Sept. to late May. Freshmen admitted Sept., Jan., Apr., June. Degrees conferred and formal commencement June. Summer session from early June to early Aug.

Characteristics of Freshmen: 2,087 applicants. 78% of applicants accepted. 22% of accepted applicants enrolled full-time.

86% (273 students) submitted SAT scores; 35% (111 students) submitted ACT scores. *25th percentile*: SAT Critical Reading 500, SAT Math 490; ACT Composite 23, ACT English 22, ACT Math 23. *75th percentile*: SAT Critical Reading 620, SAT Math 610; ACT Composite 27, ACT English 28, ACT Math 27.

67% of entering freshmen expected to graduate within 5 years. 46% of freshmen form New York. Freshmen from 35 states and 24 foreign countries.

Admission: Rolling admissions. For fall admissions, apply anytime after the junior year in high school, but not later than May of the year of enrollment. Applicants are notified of decisions beginning Nov. 1. Early decision deadline Jan. 15 with decisions by Jan. 31. *Requirements:* Graduation from accredited secondary school or GED. Recommend 4 units English, 3 mathematics, 3 science, 3 social studies. Minimum grade average 80%. *Entrance tests:* College Board SAT or ACT required. *For transfer students:* 2.0 minimum GPA; from 4-year accredited institutions 90 credit hours maximum transfer credit; from 2-year accredited institutions 60 credit hours maximum transfer credit.

College credit and advanced placement for AP examinations and postsecondary-level work completed in secondary school may be given and for extrainstitutional learning (life experience) on basis of University of the State of New York Program on Noncollegiate Sponsored Instruction.

Tutoring available.

Degree Requirements: *For all associate degrees:* 60 semester hours. *For all baccalaureate degrees:* 120 semester hours; 2 physical education courses; career-related field experience, community service. *For all degrees:* 2.0 GPA; last 30 hours in residence; distribution requirements.

Fulfillment of some degree requirements and exemption from some beginning courses possible by passing departmental examinations, College Board CLEP subject or CLEP general examinations, AP, other standardized tests. *Grading system:* A–F; pass-fail; pass; withdraw (carries penalty); time limit (deadline after which pass/fail is appended to withdraw); incomplete (carries time limit).

Distinctive Educational Programs: Required interdisciplinary core program, freshman through junior years. Spring midterm with innovative courses. Study at the San Salvador (Bahamas) marine biology field station and other off-campus locations. Through Spring Term Consortium, study at a member college. Internships and credit-bearing community service experiences required of all students. Performing Arts Appreciation program. Accelerated degree programs. Honors programs. Individualized majors. Junior year abroad for qualified candidates. Baccalaureate program in medical technology with approved hospitals. Chemical Engineering with Clarkson University. MBA articulation agreements. Teaching fellows program for outstanding upper-division students. Facilities and programs for independent research, including tutorials.

ROTC: Army and Air Force offered in cooperation with Cornell University.

Degrees Conferred: 3 *associate;* 300 *baccalaureate*; 47 *master's*. Bachelor's degrees awarded in top five disciplines: education 71; business, management, marketing, and related support services 63; social sciences 30; health professions and related clinical sciences 27; psychology 25. Master's degrees awarded: education 49.

Fees and Other Expenses: *Full-time tuition per academic year 2008–09:* undergraduate $33,250; graduate tuition charged per credit (contact the college for current information). *Room and board per academic year:* $10,100. *Books and supplies:* $450. *Other expenses:* $550.

Financial Aid: Aid from institutionally generated funds is provided on the basis of academic merit, financial need, other criteria. Institution has a Program Participation Agreement with the U.S. Department of Education for eligible students to receive Pell Grants and, depending upon the agreement, other federal aid.

Financial aid to full-time, first-time undergraduate students: 98% received some form of financial aid. Average amount of aid received: federal grants $3,678; state/local grants $2,124; institutional grants $14,318; loans $5,687.

Departments and Teaching Staff: *Total instructional faculty:* 74 FTE. Student/faculty ratio: 12:1. Degrees held by full-time faculty: doctorate 61%, master's 100%, professional 25%. 98% hold terminal degrees.

Enrollment: Total enrollment 1,639. Undergraduate 1,386. Graduate 253 Undergraduate transfer-in students 126.

Characteristics of Student Body: *Ethnic/racial makeup:* Black non-Hispanic: 1.5%; American Indian or Alaska Native: .2%; Asian or Pacific Islander: .6%; Hispanic: .9%; White non-Hispanic: 75.1%; unknown: 17.4%.

International Students: 67 nonresident aliens enrolled fall 2008. Students from Europe, Asia, Central and South America, Africa, Canada. Programs available to aid students whose native language is not English: English as a Second Language Program. No financial aid specifically designated for international students.

Student Life: On-campus residence halls house 90% of student body. Residence halls for males constitute 23% of such space, for both sexes 77%. *Intercollegiate athletics:* male: basketball, golf, hockey, lacrosse, soccer, tennis; female: basketball, tennis, soccer, softball, tennis volleyball, field hockey, lacrosse. *Special regulations:* Registered cars permitted on campus in designated areas only. *Special services:* Tutorial Center, medical services, college-operated buses to sports complex. *Student publications, radio: Iris*, a yearbook; *Octagon*, a weekly newspaper; *Sibyl*, an annual literary magazine. Radio station WECW broadcasts 80 hours per week. *Surrounding community:* Elmira population 34,000. Syracuse, 90 miles from campus, is nearest metropolitan area. Served by mass transit bus system; airport 10 miles from campus.

Library Collections: 389,000 volumes. 1,320,000 microforms. 8,100 audiovisual materials. 860 current serial subscriptions. Computer work stations available. Students have access to the Internet at no charge.

Most important holdings include Mark Twain Collection, Women's History Collection; New York State Local History.

Buildings and Grounds: Campus area 498 acres.

Chief Executive Officer: Dr. Thomas K. Meier, President.

Address admission inquiries to Gary Fallis, Dean of Admissions.

Excelsior College

7 Columbia Circle
Albany, New York 12203-5159

Tel: (518) 464-8500 **E-mail:** admissions@excelsior.edu
Fax: (518) 464-8777 **Internet:** www.excelsior.edu

Institution Description: Excelsior College, formerly known as Regents College, is a distance education program granting degrees on the basis of proficiency examinations, college credit from regionally accredited institutions, and evaluated noncollegiate-sponsored instruction. *Enrollment:* 33,453. *Degrees awarded:* Associate, baccalaureate, master's.

Accreditation: *Regional:* MSA. *Professional*: engineering technology, nursing

History: Established 1970 and chartered 1998; awarded first degree (associate) 1972.

Institutional Structure: *Governing board:* Board of Trustees. Representation: 20 regents. All voting. *Composition of institution:* Administrators 22. Academic governance body, Excelsior College Faculty, meets an average of 3 times per year.

Calendar: Continuous enrollment. Students may apply and enroll at any time during the year. Degrees conferred monthly.

Characteristics of Freshmen: 100% of applicants accepted. 50% of entering students expected to graduate within 5 years. 9% of candidates from New York. Candidates from every state and 22 foreign countries.

Admission: *Requirements:* Open admissions. Admission to nursing program restricted to students with certain health care backgrounds. College credit for postsecondary-level work completed in secondary school, for various examinations, and for extrainstitutional learning on basis of New York Program on Noncollegiate Sponsored Instruction (NY-PONSI).

Degree Requirements: *For all associate degrees:* 60 credit hours. *For all baccalaureate degrees:* 120 credit hours. *For all undergraduate degrees:* 2.0 GPA.

Fulfillment of some degree requirements possible by passing College Board CLEP, AP, GRE, and other standardized tests, including Excelsior College Examinations. *Grading system:* A–F; pass-fail.

Distinctive Educational Programs: Credit also available for students currently enrolled in another college or university, for those seeking teacher certification, and by examination. No limit on transfer credits.

Degrees Conferred: 2,481 *associate* in arts and sciences, nursing; 2,714 *baccalaureate* in various disciplines; 72 *master's*: various disciplines.

Fees and Other Expenses: *Enrollment fee:* $895 associate, $995 baccalaureate; graduate $365 to $410 per credit. *Annual advisement and evaluation fee until graduation:* $450 associate, $515 baccalaureate.

Financial Aid: Aid from institutionally generated funds is provided on the basis of academic merit, financial need.

Departments and Teaching Staff: Faculty members from private and public institutions serve as governing faculty that sets degree policy.

Enrollment: Total enrollment 33,453. Undergraduate 32,457. Graduate 996. Undergraduate transfer-in students 32,133.

Characteristics of Student Body: *Ethnic/racial makeup:* Black non-Hispanic 17%; American Indian or Alaska Native 1%; Asian or Pacific Islander 4%; Hispanic 5%; White non-Hispanic 58%; unknown 14%. *Age distribution:* 22–24: 823; 25–29 3,822; 30–39; 9,723; 40–49 9,185; 50–59 3,703; 60–and over: 451.

International Students: 325 international students enrolled fall 2008. No programs available to aid students whose native language is not English. No financial aid specifically designated for international students.

Library Collections: Virtual library available to all students.

Chief Executive Officer: John F. Ebersole, President.

Address admission inquiries to Director of Admissions.

Farmingdale State University of New York

Route 110, Melville Road
Farmingdale, New York 11735-1021

Tel: (516) 420-2000 **E-mail:** admissions@farmingdale.edu
Fax: (516) 420-2693 **Internet:** www.farmingdale.edu

Institution Description: Farmingdale State University of New York, formerly named as the SUNY College of Technology at Farmingdale, is a public institution. *Enrollment:* 6,850. *Degrees awarded:* Associate, baccalaureate.

Accreditation: *Regional:* MSA. *Professional*: clinical lab technology, dental hygiene, engineering technology, nursing

History: Founded by the New York State Legislature 1912; became a unit of SUNY 1948; adopted present name 2006.

Calendar: Semesters. Academic year Sept. to May. 2 summer terms.

Characteristics of Freshmen: 4,643 applicants. 52% of applicants admitted. 43$ of admitted students enrolled full-time.

88% (900 students) submitted SAT scores. *25th percentile*: SAT Critical Reading 430, SAT Math 448, SAT Writing 420. *75th percentile*: SAT Critical Reading 570, SAT Math 549.

38% of entering freshmen expected to graduate within 5 years. 99% of freshmen from New York. Freshmen from 13 states and 30 foreign countries.

Admission: High school graduation or equivalent; individual programs have specific admissions requirements. Early admission, advanced placement avail-

FARMINGDALE STATE UNIVERSITY OF NEW YORK—*cont'd*

able. Admission to upper division baccalaureate programs requires an associate degree or equivalent.

Degree Requirements: Completion of prescribed curriculum; general distribution requirements.

Degrees Conferred: 523 *associate;* 544 *baccalaureate.* Bachelor's degrees awarded in top five disciplines: business, management, marketing, and related support services 165; engineering 77; computer and information sciences 67, communication, journalism, and related programs 66; transportation and materials moving 34.

Fees and Other Expenses: *Full-time tuition per academic year 2008–09:* resident $5,375, nonresident $11,635. *Books and supplies:* $1,186. *Room and board per academic year:* $10,844. *Other expenses:* $2,027.

Financial Aid: Aid from institutionally generated funds is provided on the basis of academic merit, other criteria. Institution has a Program Participation Agreement with the U.S. Department of Education for eligible students to receive Pell Grants and, depending upon the agreement, other federal aid.

Financial aid to full-time, first-time undergraduate students: 66% of students received some form of financial aid. Average amount of aid received: federal grants $4,297; Pell grants $,3067; other federal grants $1,554; state/local grants $2,902; institutional grants: $1,585.

Departments and Teaching Staff: *Total instructional faculty:* 318. Student/faculty ratio: 18:1.

Enrollment: *Total enrollment:* 6,850. Undergraduate 6,850. Transfer-in students 623.

Characteristics of Student Body: *Ethnic/racial makeup:* Black non-Hispanic: 11.9%; American Indian or Alaska Native: .2%; Asian or Pacific Islander: 5.2%; Hispanic: 8.6%; White non-Hispanic: 59.2%; unknown: 16.2%. *Age distribution:* 17–21: 46%; 22–24: 15%; 25–29: 14%; 30–34: 9%; 35–39: 7%; 40–49: 7%; 50–59: 1%; 60–up: 1%.

International Students: 45 nonresident aliens enrolled fall 2008. English as a Second Language Program available to aid students whose native language is not English. No financial aid specifically designated for international students.

Student Life: Residence halls available. *Surrounding community:* Farmingdale is located 30 miles east of New York City on Long Island.

Library Collections: 150,000 volumes. 144,000 government documents; 63,000 microforms; 18,000 audiovisual materials; 1,185 periodical subscriptions. Online catalog. Students have access to online information retrieval services.

Buildings and Grounds: Campus area 400 acres.

Chief Executive Officer: Dr. George P. Larosa, President.

Direct admission inquiries to James Hall, Director of Admissions.

Fashion Institute of Technology

227 West 27th Street
New York, New York 10001-5992
Tel: (212) 717-7999 **E-mail:** fitinfo@fitnyc.edu
Fax: (212) 594-7481 **Internet:** www.fitnyc.edu

Institution Description: The Fashion Institute of Technology is a specialized college under the supervision of the State University of New York. *Enrollment:* 10,065. *Degrees awarded:* Associate, baccalaureate, master's.

Accreditation: *Regional:* MSA. *Professional*: art, interior design

History: Established and offered first instruction at postsecondary level 1944; first degree awarded 1946.

Institutional Structure: *Composition of institution:* Administrators 16. Management/business/finances directed by treasurer and director of business affairs. Full-time instructional faculty 208. Academic governance body, Fashion Institute of Technology Faculty Association, meets an average of 10 times per year.

Calendar: Semesters. Academic year late Aug. to late May. Freshmen admitted Sept., Jan. Degrees conferred May, Dec. Formal commencement June. Summer session from early June to late July.

Characteristics of Freshmen: 3,913 applicants. 42% of applicants accepted. 66% accepted applicants enrolled full-time.

Average secondary school rank 60th percentile. Mean SAT scores 420 verbal, 400 mathematical. Mean ACT composite score 21.

40% of entering freshmen expected to graduate within 5 years. 63% of freshmen from New York. Freshmen from 50 states and 40 foreign countries.

Admission: Rolling admissions plan. For fall acceptance, apply no later than Mar. 15. *Requirements:* Either graduation from accredited secondary school with 15 units which must include 4 English, 2 mathematics; or GED. For art or design programs, portfolio review. Minimum grade average 75–78 on a 100-point scale. Lowest acceptable secondary school class standing 50th percentile. *Entrance tests:* College Board SAT or ACT composite. *For transfer students:* 2.5 minimum GPA; 60 semester hours maximum transfer credit.

College credit and advanced placement for postsecondary-level work completed in secondary school. Tutoring available. Developmental/remedial courses offered in summer session and regular academic year; credit given.

Degree Requirements: *For all associate degrees:* 65 semester hours; 2 terms in residence; 2 courses in physical education. *For all baccalaureate degrees:* 130 hours; 4 terms in residence. *Grading system:* A–F; pass-fail; withdraw (carries time limit).

Distinctive Educational Programs: Cooperative education. Flexible meeting places and schedules, including weekend and evening classes. Over 100 institutions have cooperative programs with Fashion Institute of Technology. Facilities and programs for independent research, including honors programs, individual majors, tutorials. Study abroad in England. *Other distinctive Programs:* Continuing education.

Degrees Conferred: 1,707 *associate;* 1,196 *baccalaureate*; 60 *master's.* Bachelor's degrees awarded: architecture and related services 45; business/marketing 382; education 13; engineering technologies 32; family and consumer sciences 24; visual and performing arts 371. Master's degrees awarded: business/marketing 33; multidisciplinary studies 3; visual and performing arts 24.

Fees and Other Expenses: *Full-time tuition per academic year 2008–09:* resident $3,854, nonresident $10,682. *Room and board per academic year:* $10,950. *Books and supplies:* $1,600. *Other expenses:* $2,100.

Financial Aid: Aid from institutionally generated funds is provided on the basis of academic merit. Institution has a Program Participation Agreement with the U.S. Department of Education for eligible students to receive Pell Grants and, depending upon the agreement, other federal aid.

Financial aid to full-time, first-time undergraduate students: 64% of students received some form of financial aid. Average amount of aid received: federal grants $3,027; Pell grants $3,198; other federal grants $975; state/local grants $1,743; institutional grants $607.

Departments and Teaching Staff: *Total instructional faculty:* 939. Student/faculty ratio: 32:1.

Enrollment: Total enrollment 10,065. Undergraduate 9,854. Graduate 211. Undergraduate transfer-in students 670.

Characteristics of Student Body: *Ethnic/racial makeup:* number of Black non-Hispanic: 780; American Indian or Alaska Native: 22; Asian or Pacific Islander: 1,349; Hispanic: 1,018; White non-Hispanic: 4,412; unknown: 1,977. *Age distribution:* number 18–19: 1,898; 20–21: 2,120; 22–24: 2,355; 25–29: 1,959; 30–34: 864; 35 and over: 118.

International Students: 775 nonresident aliens enrolled fall 2008. Students from Europe, Asia, Latin America, Africa, Canada, Australia. Programs available to aid students whose native language is not English: social and cultural. English as a Second Language Program. No financial aid specifically designated for international students.

Student Life: On-campus residence halls house 7% of student body. Residence halls for females constitute 42% of such space, for both sexes 58%. *Student publications, radio: Coloring Book*, an annual literary magazine; *Portfolio*, a yearbook; *Revelations*, a monthly newspaper. Radio station WFIT broadcasts 50 hours per week. *Surrounding community:* New York population over 7 million.

Library Collections: 177,000 volumes. 6,000 microforms; 3,900 audiovisual materials; 615 current periodical subscriptions. Students have access to online information retrieval services.

Most important special holdings include Berley Studio Sketches 1919–43; Lady Duff-Gordon Sketch Collection; Mainbocher Scrapbooks; Bergdorf Goodman Sketches.

Chief Executive Officer: Dr. Joyce F. Brown, President.

Address admission inquiries to Dolores Lombardi, Director of Admissions.

Five Towns College

305 North Service Road
Dix Hills, New York 11746
Tel: (631) 424-7000
Fax: (631) 656-2172

Institution Description: Five Towns College is a private institution. *Enrollment:* 1,173. *Degrees awarded:* Associate, baccalaureate, master's, doctorate.

Accreditation: *Regional:* MSA.

History: Founded in 1972, Five towns College was originally established to provide an alternative to the large university experience. The college became a baccalaureate institution in 1990. A teacher education program was established in 1991. The college moved to a new campus at Dix Hills in 1992. In 1998, the Bachelor of Fine Arts (BFA) was established in Theatre Arts; the BFA in Film/Video established in 2001.

Institutional Structure: *Governing board:* Representation: Five Towns College Board of Trustees. Extrainstitutional representation: 10 trustees; institutional representation: president of the college. 1 ex officio. All voting. *Composition of institution:* Academic affairs headed by vice president for academic affairs. Administrative affairs headed by dean of administration. Full-time instructional faculty 28. Academic governance body, College Counsel, meets monthly.

Calendar: Semesters. Academic year Aug. to May. Degrees conferred and formal commencement May. Summer session of 3 terms June to Aug.

Characteristics of Freshmen: 691 applicants. 79.3% of applicants admitted. 51.5% of admitted applicants enrolled full-time.

94% (2,66 students) submitted SAT scores. *25th percentile*: SAT Critical Reading 410, SAT Math 590, SAT Writing 410. *75th percentile*: SAT Critical Reading 500, SAT Math 510, SAT Writing 500.

Admission: Admissions are based upon a rolling policy. Applications processed in the order received and decisions communicated immediately to the applicant. All students are interviewed at the time of their placement tests prior to registration in order to assure class placements appropriate to their abilities. SAT required.

Developmental/remedial courses offered in summer session and regular academic year; credit given.

Degree Requirements: *For all associate degrees:* 60–64 credit hours. *For all baccalaureate degrees:* 120–128 credit hours. *For all undergraduate degrees:* Minimum cumulative GPA 2.0. *Grading system:* A–F.

Distinctive Educational Programs: The college awards the degrees of Bachelor of Music, Bachelor of Professional Studies, Bachelor of Fine Arts, Bachelor of Science in Elementary Teacher Education and Mass Communication. Associate in Art, Associate in Science, Associate in Applied Science.

Degrees Conferred: 8 *associate;* 281 *baccalaureate*; 21 *master's*. Bachelor's degrees awarded in top five disciplines: business, management, marketing, and related support services 122; education 18; liberal arts 2; visual and performing arts 59. Master's degrees awarded: education 13; visual and performing arts 8.

Fees and Other Expenses: *Full-time tuition per academic year 2008–09:* contact the college for current information regrading tuition, housing, and other costs.

Financial Aid: The college offers a direct lending program. Aid from institutionally generated funds is provided on the basis of academic merit, financial need, other considerations.

Financial aid to full-time, first-time undergraduate students: 86% received some form of financial aid. Average amount of aid received: federal grants $3,542; state/local grants $3,166; institutional grants $1,780; loans $5,080.

Departments and Teaching Staff: *Total instructional faculty:* 125 (full-time 58, part-time 67). Student/faculty ratio: 13:1. Degrees held by full-time faculty: doctorate 28%, master's 46%, baccalaureate 26%. 76% hold terminal degrees.

Enrollment: Total enrollment 1,173.

Characteristics of Student Body: *Ethnic/racial makeup:* number of Black non-Hispanic: 193; Asian or Pacific Islander: 30; Hispanic: 164; White non-Hispanic: 651; unknown: 61.

International Students: Programs available to aid students whose native language is not English: English as a Second Language Program. No financial aid specifically designated for international students.

Student Life: The student body is a diverse mix, with about 85% of the students between the ages of 17 and 21 and 15% older. The college is developing a diversified athletic program. *Special regulations:* Cars permitted without restrictions. *Special services:* College orientation, career placement center, academic advisement, housing, personal counseling, tutorial services, health services. *Student publications: The College Yearbook, The Record*, the college newspaper; *The Flyer*, a weekly newsletter; *The Bulletin*, issued several times a year to the student body and the community at large. A variety of clubs and organizations are available including student government, creative and performing arts, and special interest groups. *Surrounding community:* Dix Hills is in the town of Huntington on Long Island. New York City, with everything from Lincoln Center to Broadway, is just a train ride away and provides students with some of the best cultural advantages in the world.

Library Collections: 35,000 volumes. Online catalog. Current serial subscriptions: 650 paper, 50 microform. 8,500 recordings; 2,100 compact discs; 500 CD-ROMs. Computer work stations available. Students have access to the Internet at no charge.

Most important special holdings include jazz, swing, big band, guitar, and the music business.

Buildings and Grounds: Campus area 35 acres.

Chief Executive Officer: Dr. Stanley G. Cohen, President.

Address admissions inquiries to Sheldon Zuckoe, Director of Enrollment Services.

Fordham University

441 East Fordham Road
Bronx, New York 10458
Tel: (718) 817-1000 **E-mail:** admissions@fordham.edu
Fax: (212) 817-4925 **Internet:** www.fordham.edu

Institution Description: Fordham University is a private, independent, nonprofit institution with two main campuses, Rose Hill in the Bronx and Lincoln Center in Manhattan, and a branch campus in Tarrytown. *Enrollment:* 14,666. *Degrees awarded:* Baccalaureate, first-professional (law), master's, doctorate. Advanced certificate also awarded.

Member of the consortia American Academy in Rome, American School in Athens, Inter-University Doctoral Consortia.

Accreditation: *Regional:* MSA. *Professional*: business, clinical psychology, counseling psychology, law, school psychology, social work, teacher education

History: Established by Archbishop of New York as St. John's College 1841; offered first instruction at postsecondary level 1843; became chartered, transferred control to Society of Jesus, and awarded first degree (baccalaureate) 1846; adopted present name 1907; transferred control to lay board of trustees 1969. *See* Robert I. Gannon, S.J., *Up To the Present* (New York: Doubleday, 1967) for further information.

Institutional Structure: *Governing board:* Board of Trustees. Extrainstitutional representation: 39 trustees; institutional representation: president of the university; 1 ex officio; 40 voting. *Composition of institution:* Administrators 596. Academic affairs headed by vice president of academic affairs; vice presidents for administration, business, development, enrollment, finance, student affairs, Lincoln Center. Full-time instructional faculty 447, Faculty Senate meets 10 times per year.

Calendar: Semesters. Academic year Aug. to May. Freshmen admitted Sept., Jan. Degrees conferred May, Sept., Feb. Formal commencement May. Summer session of 2 terms: June and July.

Characteristics of Freshmen: 23,887 applicants. 47% of applicants admitted. 17% of admitted students enrolled full-time.

91% (1,725 students) submitted SAT scores; 29% (544 students) submitted ACT scores. *25th percentile*: SAT Critical Reading 560, SAT Math 570, SAT Writing 570; ACT Composite 25. *75th percentile*: SAT Critical Reading 660, SAT Math 660, SAT Writing 670; ACT Composite 29.

75% of entering freshmen expected to graduate within 5 years. 59% of freshmen from New York. Freshmen from 49 states and 51 foreign countries.

Admission: Rolling admissions plan. Apply by Nov. 1 for early decision; need not limit application to Fordham. Early acceptance available. *Requirements:* Either graduation from accredited secondary school with 16 units from among English, language, mathematics, science, social studies; or GED. For mathematics and science programs 4 years mathematics and 3–4 years science required. *Entrance tests:* College Board SAT or ACT composite. For foreign students TOEFL. *For transfer students:* Transfer credit varies.

Tutoring available. Developmental courses offered in summer session; credit given.

Degree Requirements: *Undergraduate liberal arts:* 124 credit hours; 2.0 GPA; 4 terms in residence; distribution requirements.

Fulfillment of some degree requirements possible by passing College Board CLEP, AP. *Grading system:* A–F; pass-fail.

Distinctive Educational Programs: Weekend and evening classes. Facilities and programs for independent research, including honors programs, individual majors, tutorials. All-University Center on Gerontology promotes curriculum development and research projects. *Other distinctive programs:* Hispanic Research Center; Louis Calder Conservation and Ecology Center; Third Age Center; National Center for Social Works and Education Collaboration. Students may elect to participate in an extensive array of internship programs. Study abroad in England, Ireland, Italy, Korea, Mexico. *See* individual college listings below for distinctive programs within each college.

ROTC: Army.

Degrees Conferred: 1,865 *baccalaureate*: 1,868 *master's*; 126 *doctorate*; 485 *first-professional*. Bachelor's degrees awarded in top five disciplines: business, management, marketing, and related support services 459; social sciences 331; communication, journalism, and related programs 228; English language/literature 100; psychology 107. Master's degrees awarded in top five disciplines: public administration and social service professions 550; education 546; business/marketing 467; social sciences 83; English language/literature 80. Doctoral degrees awarded: biological and biomedical sciences 3; education 49; English language 2; history 3; philosophy and religious studies 13; psychology 32; public administration and social service professions 4; social sciences 17, other 9. First-professional degrees awarded: law 485.

Fees and Other Expenses: *Full-time tuition per academic year 2008–09:* $35,251. undergraduate; contact the university for current graduate and first-pro-

FORDHAM UNIVERSITY—*cont'd*

fessional tuition and fees. *Room and board per academic year:* $12,980. *Books and supplies:*$840. *Other expenses:* $2,330.

Financial Aid: Aid from institutionally generated funds is provided on the basis of academic merit, financial need, athletic ability, other criteria. Institution has a Program Participation Agreement with the U.S. Department of Education for eligible students to receive Pell Grants and, depending upon the agreement, other federal aid.

Financial aid to full-time, first-time undergraduate students: 93% of students received some form of financial aid. Average amount of aid received: federal grants $4,653; Pell grants $3,453; other federal grants $15,670; state/local grants $3,853; institutional grants $13,041.

Departments and Teaching Staff: *Total instructional faculty:* 1,068. Student/faculty ratio: 15:1. Degrees held by full-time faculty: master's 2%, doctorate 95%, baccalaureate 1%, professional 1%. 98% hold terminal degrees.

Enrollment: Total enrollment 14,666. Undergraduate 7,994. Graduate 6,672. Undergraduate transfer-in students 331.

Characteristics of Student Body: *Ethnic/racial makeup:* Black non-Hispanic: 5.3%; American Indian or Native Alaskan: .2%; Asian or Pacific Islander: 1.1%; Hispanic: 11.3%; White non-Hispanic: 57.5%; unknown: 18.3%.

International Students: 98 nonresident aliens enrolled fall 2008. Students from Europe, Asia, Central and South America, Africa, Canada, Australia. Programs available to aid students whose native language is not English: English as a Second Language. No financial aid specifically designated for international students.

Student Life: On-campus residence halls house 65% of full-time undergraduates. *Intercollegiate athletics:* competition in 22 sports; male: baseball, basketball, cross-country, football, golf, soccer, squash, swimming and diving, tennis, indoor track, outdoor track, water polo; female: basketball, cheerleading, cross-country, softball, swimming and diving, tennis, indoor track, outdoor track, volleyball. *Special regulations:* Registered cars permitted; fee charged. *Special services:* Learning Resources Center, computer centers, campus-ministry program, health center, handicapped services, counseling center, commuter-student services, intercampus van service, credit unit. Lombardi Memorial Athletic Center offers variety of intramural, recreational, and lifetime sports activities. *Student publications, radio: The Observer, The Paper, and The Ram,* newspapers; *The Maroon,* a yearbook. Radio station WFUV-FM is affiliated with the American Public Radio Network and broadcasts 24 hours a day with 50,000 watts. The station publishes a monthly program guide, *The Folio.* Surrounding community: New York City population over 7 million. Served by mass transit bus, rail systems, airports; passenger rail service less than 1 mile from campus.

Publications: *International Philosophical Quarterly, Traditio* (annually).

Library Collections: 2,100,000 volumes. 363,227 government documents; 3,100,000 microforms; 19,300 audiovisual materials; 16,000 periodicals including electronic access. Online catalog. Students have access to online information retrieval services and the Internet.

Most important holdings include incunabula; Charles Allen Munn Collection of Revolutionary and Early Federal Americana; Jesuitica Collection; Sidney Rosenblatt Holocaust Collections; Joseph Givernaud Collection on the French revolution.

Buildings and Grounds: Campus area 92 acres.

Chief Executive Officer: Rev. Joseph M, McShane, S.J., President.

Undergraduates address admission inquiries to Peter Farrell, Director of Admissions; all others to Director of Admissions of the appropriate school.

Fordham College at Rose Hill

Degree Programs Offered: *Baccalaureate* in African and African-American studies, American studies, anthropology, art history, biological sciences, chemistry, classical civilization, classical languages, communications, computer science, economics, English, fine arts, general science, history, information science, Latin American studies, mathematics, mathematics-economics, medieval studies, Middle Eastern studies, modern languages, music, philosophy, physics, political science, political science-economics, psychology, sociology, Post-Soviet and East European studies, theology, urban studies, computer information sciences, peace and justice studies, women's studies, individualized majors.

Distinctive Educational Programs: Interdisciplinary programs in liberal arts, American studies, Latin American studies, medieval studies, Middle East studies, urban studies, women's studies, peace and justice studies, Soviet studies (Russia and the Commonwealth), and sciences. Honors programs. Junior year abroad. Student exchange program with University College Dublin and the University of San Francisco. Teacher Certification Program, Pre-Architecture, Pre-Dental, Pre-Law, Pre-Medical Advisory Program, 3/2 Engineering Program in association with Columbia and Case Western. Internship in Medical Ethics with Montefiore Hospital and Albert Einstein College of Medicine.

Fordham College at Lincoln Center

Degree Programs Offered: *Baccalaureate* in African American and African studies, anthropology, art history, bilingual bicultural studies, comparative literature, computational mathematics, computer science, economics, English, French, history, individualized major, information science, interdisciplinary economics and mathematics, international/intercultural studies, Italian, liberal arts theatre, media studies, Middle East studies, natural science, performance/production theatre, philosophy, political science, psychology, Puerto Rican and Latin American studies, religious studies, social science, sociology, Spanish, Spanish studies, theater, visual arts, women's studies.

Distinctive Educational Programs: Interdisciplinary programs. Business Administration and Pre-law Advising programs in conjunction with any liberal arts major. Pre-professional program in education (elementary and secondary school certifications) in cooperation with Graduate School of Education, Pre-Medical/Dental programs, Combined Plan in Engineering in affiliation with Columbia University, Combined Plan in Pharmacy in affiliation with Long Island University. *Other distinctive programs:* College at Sixty program for adults over the age of fifty; EXCEL, a program for adults pursuing a Bachelor of Arts degree; Gerontology Certificate; Higher Education Opportunity Program; internship and study abroad programs.

College of Business Administration

Degree Programs Offered: *Baccalaureate.*

Degree Requirements: *For Bachelor of Science in Business Administration:* 120 credits (40 courses). *For Bachelor of Science in Accounting:* 120 credits (40 courses).

Distinctive Educational Programs: G.L.O.B.E. program, an international business organization designed to prepare students for multinational careers. Five-year BS/MBA program, the CBA Honors Thesis, Legal and Ethical Studies specialization, liberal arts minors, internships (junior and senior year), CEO Breakfast Club (connecting students with top executives), evening program.

School of Law

Degree Programs Offered: *First-professional*: J.D., and LL.M.

Admission: *For J.D.:* graduation from an accredited four-year college or university, the Law School Admissions Test (LSAT) and subscription to the Law School Data Assembly Service (LSDAS). *For LL.M.:* J.D. degree from an ABA approved Law School or foreign equivalent.

Degree Requirements: *For J.D.:* 83 completed credits, a minimum GPA of 1.9 and 2 years in residence. *For LL.M.:* 24 completed credits and 1.7 minimum GPA.

Distinctive Educational Programs: Continuing Legal Education, Mediation Clinic, Litigation Skills Seminar, seminars in European Community Law, Clinical Externships, Research Fellowships, Travel Abroad Fellowships, Pro Bono Program, several student-run lecture series, Minority Enrichment Program and Moot Court Program.

Graduate School of Arts and Sciences

Degree Programs Offered: *Master's* in biological sciences, classical languages and literature, computer science, communications, economics, English language and literature, history, international political economy and development, liberal studies, medieval studies, philosophy, political science, psychology, sociology and anthropology, theology. *Doctorate* in biological sciences, classical languages and literature, economics, history, philosophy, political science, psychology (clinical, developmental, applied development, psychometrics), theology.

Distinctive Educational Programs: Cooperative programs in theology with Union Theological Seminary. Interdisciplinary programs in international political economy and development, medieval studies. Research opportunities at New York Botanical Gardens, Bronx Zoological Gardens, National Fish Health Research Laboratories, W. Alton Jones Cell Science Center. Cooperating institution of the American School of Classical Studies at Athens and a contributing institution to the American Academy at Rome. Member of the New York City Doctoral Consortium. Louis Calder Conservation and Ecology Center offers laboratory facilities, lake, and extensive forest, swamp and bay area. Hispanic Research Center specializes in interdisciplinary research on sociological needs of the Hispanic population in the U.S. and Puerto Rico.

Joseph A. Martino Graduate School of Business Administration

Degree Programs Offered: *Master's:* M.B.A.; M.S. in Taxation. Advanced certificates also awarded.

Distinctive Educational Programs: M.B.A. program offered at Tarrytown in Westchester County as well as Lincoln Center campus. Joint MBA/JD program in conjunction with the Fordham School of Law; Center for Communications; Center for Advanced Management Studies.

Graduate School of Education

Degree Programs Offered: The Fordham University Graduate School of Education offers programs at the master's, professional diploma, and doctoral levels in many specialties and subject areas in public and private education. The degrees awarded are the Master of Science in Education, Master of Arts in Teaching, Master of Science in Teaching, Master of Science in Adult Education, and a Master of Science in Human Resource Education. Professional diplomas are also offered in the fields of curriculum, administration, reading, reading administration, counseling, special education, educational psychology, administration and supervision, school psychology and bilingual education. Doctor of Education programs are available in the areas of educational administration and supervision. Doctor of Philosophy programs are offered in the areas of language, learning and literacy, educational psychology, counselor psychology, school psychology, educational administration and supervision and church leadership. Programs are offered at Tarrytown campus as well as Lincoln Center campus.

Distinctive Educational Programs: Doctorate in administration and supervision for church and school leaders with Fordham's Graduate School of Religion and Religious Education.

Graduate School of Religion and Religious Education

Degree Programs Offered: *Master's, post-master's* in religion and religious education. Professional diploma also awarded.

Graduate School of Social Service

Degree Programs Offered: *Master's, doctorate* in social work. Certificates also given. M.S.W. program available at Tarrytown in Westchester County as well as Lincoln Center campus. D.S.W. program is available at Lincoln Center only.

Degree Requirements: *M.S.W.:* 66 credit hours. *D.S.W.:* 48 credit hours (B average), passing written and oral comprehensive, and successful completion of oral defense of acceptable dissertation.

Distinctive Educational Programs: Center for Training and Research in Child Abuse and Family Violence; National Center for Social Work and Education Collaboration; The Ravazzin Center for Social Work Research on Aging; Fordham Institute for Innovation in Social Policy which publishes the annual Index of Social Health. Four-year M.S.W. program. Advanced Standing Program. Saturday courses.

Ignatius College

Degree Programs Offered: *Baccalaureate* in economics, English, fine arts, history, political science, psychology, social science, social work, sociology, biology, general science, computer science, individualized majors.

Admission: High school or equivalency diploma, interview; rolling admissions cycle for enrollment starting in fall, spring, or summer.

Degree Requirements: 120 credits, including the 54-credit common core curriculum required of all students. All courses offered evenings and Saturdays; full- or part-time enrollment optional.

Departments and Teaching Staff: Most faculty members drawn from liberal arts facilities on the Rose Hill campus.

Distinctive Educational Programs: Joint B.A./N.S.W. with Fordham's Graduate School of Social Service, pre-med and pre-health professions programs offered evenings for post-baccalaureate students, career-related certificate programs available. Approved as a National Testing Center for College Board CLEP Exams. All courses offered evenings and Saturdays; full- or part-time enrollment optional.

General Theological Seminary

175 Ninth Avenue
New York, New York 10011-4977
Tel: (212) 243-5150 **E-mail:** admissions@gts.edu
Fax: (212) 727-3907 **Internet:** www.gts.edu

Institution Description: General Theological Seminary is a private institution affiliated with The Episcopal Church. *Enrollment:* 146. *Degrees awarded:* First-professional (master of divinity), master's, doctorate.

Accreditation: *Regional:* MSA. *Professional*: ATS. theology

History: Established 1817.

Institutional Structure: *Governing board:* Board of Trustees has 42 members. institutional representation: 1 administrator, 2 full-time faculty members, 4 students. 1 ex officio. All voting. *Composition of institution:* Administrators 8. Academic affairs headed by academic dean. Management/business/finances directed by treasurer. Full-time instructional faculty 15.

Calendar: Semesters. Academic year Sept. to May.

Admission: Rolling admissions plan. *Requirements:* Baccalaureate from accredited university or college. *Entrance tests:* GRE.

Degree Requirements: *For first-professional degree:* 75 credit hours; field education. *For master's degree:* 40 credit hours; research paper. *For master's, first-professional degrees:* 3.0 GPA recommended; 1 year in residence required. *Grading system:* A–F.

Degrees Conferred: 41 *first-professional:* master of divinity; 2 *master's:* theology.

Fees and Other Expenses: *Full-time tuition per academic year 2008–09:* contact the seminary for current information.

Financial Aid: Aid from institutionally generated funds is provided on the basis of financial need. Institution has a Program Participation Agreement with the U.S. Department of Education for eligible students to receive Pell Grants and, depending upon the agreement, other federal aid.

Departments and Teaching Staff: *Total instructional faculty:* 22. Degrees held by full-time faculty: doctorate 99%, master's 100%.

Enrollment: Total enrollment 146.

Characteristics of Student Body: *Ethnic/racial makeup:* Black non-Hispanic: 6.8%; Asian or Pacific Islander: .7%; Hispanic: 3.4%; White non-Hispanic: 87%.

International Students: 2 nonresident alien enrolled fall 2008. No programs available to aid students whose native language is not English. No financial programs specifically designated for international students.

Student Life: 90% of student body live on campus. Married student housing available. *Surrounding community:* New York City population over 7 million. Served by mass transit system; airport 5 miles from campus; passenger rail service 2 miles from campus.

Library Collections: 243,000 volumes. 700 current periodical subscriptions. 200 recordings, 5 compact discs, 10 CD-ROMs. Computer work stations available, Students have access to the Internet.

Chief Executive Officer: V.Rev. Ward B. Ewing, President.

Address admission inquiries to Gladys Catalono, Registrar.

Graduate School and University Center / CUNY

365 Fifth Avenue
New York, New York 10016
Tel: (212) 817-7700 **E-mail:** admissions@gccuny.edu
Fax: (212) 817-1624 **Internet:** www.gc.cuny.edu

Institution Description: The Graduate School and University Center offers all doctoral programs and some master's programs for the City University of New York. It also administers the CUNY-wide baccalaureate program. *Enrollment:* 5,468. *Degrees awarded:* Baccalaureate, master's, doctorate.

Academic offering subject to approval by statewide coordinating bodies. Budget subject to approval by state governing boards. Member of Interuniversity Doctoral Consortium.

Accreditation: *Regional:* MSA.

History: Established and chartered as Division of Graduate Studies of the City University of New York 1961; offered first doctoral instruction 1962; awarded first degree (doctorate) 1965; adopted present name and assumed administrative responsibility for all doctoral education and for a number of university-wide activities 1972.

Institutional Structure: *Composition of institution:* Administrators include president, provost and senior vice president, vice president for finance and administration. Full-time instructional faculty 391. Academic governance body, Graduate Council, meets an average of 4 times per year.

Calendar: Semesters. Academic year mid-Sept. to late May. Entering students admitted Sept., Feb. Degrees conferred Oct., Feb., May. No summer session.

Admission: Rolling admissions plan. For fall acceptance, apply no later than April 15 for most programs. *Requirements:* For graduate programs, baccalaureate from accredited college or university. Additional requirements for some programs. *Entrance tests:* GRE. For foreign students TOEFL. *For transfer students:* 3.0 minimum GPA; for master's degree, 12 semester hours maximum transfer credit; for doctorate, 30 hours.

Degree Requirements: *For all master's degrees:* Minimum 30 semester hours; minimum 21 hours in residence; thesis. *For most doctoral degrees:* Min-

GRADUATE SCHOOL AND UNIVERSITY CENTER / CUNY—*cont'd*

imum 60 hours; minimum 30 hours in residence; language requirement; teaching, research, field work; dissertation. *Grading system:* A–C, F; withdraw.

Distinctive Educational Programs: Of the 32 doctoral programs offered, those in humanities and social sciences, mathematics, and speech and hearing sciences are offered at the Graduate Center in midtown Manhattan. Doctoral programs in professional areas such as criminal justice, engineering, business, biomedicine, and the sciences are located at the senior college campuses which have the appropriate undergraduate focus and laboratory resources. The Doctoral Faculty is drawn for the most part (more than 90%) from the senior CUNY colleges and over 750 teach each semester. The master's degree is offered in seven disciplines including an interdisciplinary master's program in liberal studies. The Graduate School and University Center administers the CUNY Baccalaureate Program through which undergraduate students pursue individually designed programs using the resources of any University campus. Special centers and facilities for research include: CUNY Data Service, Education (CASE), European Studies, Foreign Language Institute, Henri Peyre Institute for the Humanities, Human Environments, Logistics and Transportation, Policy Research, Ralph Bunche Institute on the United Nations, Speech and Hearing Sciences, Social Research, Theatre Arts (CASTA), Urban Policy Research, Women and Society.

Degrees Conferred: 195 *baccalaureate*; 55 *master;s*: liberal arts/general studies; 358 *doctorate*: liberal arts/general studies.

Fees and Other Expenses: *Full-time tuition per academic year:* contact the school for current tuition and fees.

Financial Aid: Aid from institutionally generated funds is provided on the basis of academic merit, financial need. Institution has a Program Participation Agreement with the U.S. Department of Education for eligible students to receive Pell Grants and, depending upon the agreement, other federal aid.

Departments and Teaching Staff: *Total instructional faculty:* 391. (1,775 doctoral faculty, of which 750 teach each semester). Degrees held by full-time faculty: doctorate 95%, master's 100%, baccalaureate 100%. 99% hold terminal degrees.

Enrollment: Total enrollment 5,468. Undergraduate 694. Graduate 4,774. Undergraduate transfer-in students 218.

Characteristics of Student Body: *Race/ethnicity:* Black non-Hispanic 37%; Asian or Pacific Islander: 5%; Hispanic: 37%; White non-Hispanic: 32%.

International Students: 786 nonresident aliens enrolled fall 2008. Students from Europe, Asia, and South America, Africa, Canada, Australia.

Student Life: Limited off-campus student housing. *Special services:* Special equipment for sight and hearing impaired students. *Surrounding community:* New York City population over 7 million. Served by mass transit bus and subway systems; 3 airports (Kennedy, LaGuardia, Newark); 2 passenger rail stations 3 blocks and 10 blocks from campus.

Publications: *The Journal of Comparative Politics* (quarterly) first published 1968, *RILM Abstracts* (quarterly) first published 1967.

Library Collections: 250,000 volumes. 478,000 microforms; 210,000 art slides; 1,580 current periodical subscriptions. Students have access to online information retrieval services. The New York Public Library is nearby and is available to all students.

Most important holdings include human relations area files; U.S. presidential papers; William H. and Gwynne V. Crouse Library for Publishing Arts.

Buildings and Grounds: The Graduate School and University Center moved in 1999 to 365 Fifth Avenue between 34th and 35th Streets, a renovated landmark building that was formerly the B. Altman department store.

Chief Executive Officer: Dr. Frances Degen Horowitz, President.

Address admission inquiries to Les Gribben, Director of Admissions.

Hamilton College

198 College Hill Road
Clinton, New York 13323

Tel: (315) 859-4421 **E-mail:** admission@hamilton.edu
Fax: (315) 859-4457 **Internet:** www.hamilton.edu

Institution Description: Hamilton College is a private, independent, nonprofit college and is the third oldest college in New York State. It is named in honor of U.S. statesman Alexander Hamilton. *Enrollment:* 1,872. *Degrees awarded:* Baccalaureate.

Accreditation: *Regional:* MSA.

History: Established as Hamilton-Oneida Academy 1793; adopted present name, received charter, and offered first instruction at postsecondary level 1812; awarded first degree (baccalaureate) 1814; merged with Kirkland College, an independent women's college, 1978. *See* Walter Pilkington, *Hamilton College: 1812–1962* (Clinton, NY: Hamilton College, 1962) for further information.

Institutional Structure: *Governing board:* Trustees of Hamilton College. Representation: 22 charter trustees, including 15 alumni, president of the college; 24 life trustees (21 are alumni) and 12 alumni trustees. All voting. *Composition of institution:* Administrators 106. Academic affairs headed by dean of the faculty. Management/business/finances directed by vice president, administration and finance. Full-time instructional faculty 173. Academic governance body, Academic Council, meets an average of 35 times per year.

Calendar: Semesters (two 15-week). Academic year Aug. to May. Freshmen admitted Aug. Degrees conferred and formal commencement May. No summer session.

Characteristics of Freshmen: 5,873 applicants. 28% of applicants accepted. 32% of accepted applicants enrolled full-time.

60% (277 students) submitted SAT scores; 16% (75 students) submitted ACT scores. *25th percentile*: SAT Critical Reading 650, SAT Math 655; ACT Composite 26. *75th percentile*: SAT Critical Reading 730, SAT Math 72; ACT Composite 31.

90% of entering freshmen expected to graduate within 5 years. 65% of freshmen from New York. Freshmen from 38 states and 30 foreign countries.

Admission: Deadline for applications Jan. 15 of year of enrollment. Dead lines for early decision/notification Nov. 15 and Jan. 15. Students are notified of acceptance Apr. 15. Transfer deadlines: for fall admission Mar. 15; for spring admission Dec. 1. *Requirements:* Graduation from a formal secondary school program with at least 16 units. Course distribution may vary, but 4 units in English, 3 mathematics, 3 in a single foreign language, 3 science, and 3 social studies are recommended. Personal interview recommended. *Entrance tests:* College Board SAT or ACT composite. Recommend 3 College Board Achievements. For foreign students TOEFL. Transfer students may not transfer more than two year's work from another institution.

Tutoring available. Higher Education Opportunity Program (HEOP) available to applicants who, because of educational and economic circumstances, would otherwise be unable to attend college. (HEOP summer session available for qualified incoming first-year students).

Degree Requirements: 32 units (1 unit equals 4 credit hours); average grade 72 on a scale of 100; 16 units, including last semester, in residence; two courses in each academic division (arts, humanities, science/mathematics, social science); 3 writing-intensive courses; at least two courses covering human diversity and ethical issues; senior project; physical education requirement.

Fulfillment of some degree requirements and exemption from some introductory courses possible with satisfactory scores on CEEB Advanced Placement exams. *Grading system:* A–F; credit-no credit; incomplete (carries time limit).

Distinctive Educational Programs: Dual-degree programs in engineering with Columbia University, Rensselaer Polytechnic Institute, University of Rochester, Washington University (MO); in law with Columbia University. Interdisciplinary programs in American studies, geoarchaeology, Asian studies, Latin American Studies, psychobiology, public policy, women's studies. Programs for independent research, including individual majors, independent study, senior fellowship program, and senior projects. Institutionally sponsored study abroad in China, France, Spain. Study abroad may also be individually arranged. Off-campus programs in the U.S. include Term in Washington Program, Williams College semester in American maritime studies at the Mystic Seaport Museum (CT); others by individual arrangement. Hamilton routinely sends at least one undergraduate each year to study and conduct research in Antarctica under the auspices of a NSF grant to a Hamilton professor. *Other distinctive programs:* Hamilton Horizons Program offers regular courses for nondegree credit to adults in the surrounding community.

ROTC: Army, Air Force. Offered in cooperation with Syracuse University.

Degrees Conferred: 442 *baccalaureate*. Bachelor's degrees awarded in top five disciplines: social sciences 171; English language/literature 50; foreign languages 48; visual and performing arts 39; psychology 31.

Fees and Other Expenses: *Full-time tuition per academic year 2008–09:* $38,600. *Room and board per academic year:* $9,810. *Books and supplies:* $51,300. *Other expenses:* $500.

Financial Aid: Aid from institutionally generated funds is provided on the basis of academic merit, financial need. Institution has a Program Participation Agreement with the U.S. Department of Education for eligible students to receive Pell Grants and, depending upon the agreement, other federal aid.

Financial aid for first-time, full-time undergraduate students: 54% received some form of financial aid. Average amount of aid received: federal grants $3,682; Pell grants $3,459; other federal grants $2,413; state/local grants $2,618; institutional grants $24,519.

Departments and Teaching Staff: *Total instructional faculty:* 205 (full-time 180, part-time 25). Student/faculty ratio: 9:1. Degrees held by full-time faculty: 98% hold terminal degrees.

Enrollment: Total enrollment 1,872 (undergraduate). Transfer-in students 14.

Characteristics of Student Body: *Ethnic/racial makeup:* number of Black non-Hispanic: 66; American Indian or Alaska Native: 13; Asian or Pacific Islander: 94; Hispanic: 64; White non-Hispanic: 1,360; unknown: 84.

International Students: 96 nonresident aliens enrolled fall 2008. No programs available to aid students whose native language is not English. Financial aid available to qualifying international students.

Student Life: On-campus residence halls house 95% of student body. Private societies (7 fraternities, 4 sororities, and one coed society) are now nonresidential. *Intercollegiate athletics:* male: baseball, basketball, cross-country, football, golf, ice hockey, lacrosse, soccer, squash, swimming, tennis, track; female: : basketball, cross-country, field hockey, ice hockey, lacrosse, soccer, softball, squash, swimming, tennis, track, volleyball. Club sports: bicycle co-op, cricket, equestrian club, male and female crew, fencing, female ice hockey, Outing Club, male and female rugby, sailing, self-defense, skiing, ultimate frisbee, male and female volleyball, water polo, female golf. *Special regulations:* All but first-year students may have cars on campus. Fee for parking permit. *Special services:* Study Skills Center, Reading/Writing Center, Quantitative Literacy Center, Health Center, Counseling and Psychological Services, Chaplaincy (Protestant, Roman Catholic, Jewish); Career Center; Office of Multicultural Affairs; Afro-Latin Cultural Center; Women's Center. *Student publications, radio: Spectator,* a weekly newspaper; *Red Weather,* a literary magazine; *Roots in the Glen,* a yearbook; *The Wag,* an annual humor magazine; *Discourse,* a journal of opinion. Radio station WHCL broadcasts 126 hours per week. Student-run television show "Panorama: Life on the Hill." *Surrounding community:* Clinton population 2,200. Syracuse, 45 miles from campus and Utica, 8 miles from campus, are nearest metropolitan areas. Served by airport and passenger rail service, each 10 miles from campus.

Library Collections: 318,000 volumes. 124,000 microforms; 2,500 audiovisual materials; 21,800 periodicals including via electronic access. Students have access to online information retrieval services.

Most important holdings include Ezra Pound Collection (3,200 items, including first editions, letters); McIntosh Collection (1,500 items dealing with the Women's Suffrage Movement, including rare books, first editions, manuscripts); Walter Beinecke, Jr., Collection (1,250 items dealing with prehistory and settlement of the Lesser Antilles, including rare books, maps, personal papers).

Buildings and Grounds: Campus area 350 acres.

Chief Executive Officer: Dr. Joan Hinde Stewart, President.

Address admission inquiries to Monica Inzer, Dean of Admissions and Financial Aid.

Hartwick College

One Hartwick Drive
Oneonta, New York 13820

Tel: (607) 431-4000 **E-mail:** admissions@hartwick.edu
Fax: (607) 431-4329 **Internet:** www.hartwick.edu

Institution Description: Hartwick College is a private, independent, nonprofit college. *Enrollment:* 1,493. *Degrees awarded:* Baccalaureate.

Accreditation: *Regional:* MSA. *Professional*: art, music, nursing

History: Established as Hartwick Seminary for men 1797; incorporated as Hartwick Seminary and Academy 1816; admitted first women 1851; became four-year college 1926; adopted present name 1927; awarded first degree (baccalaureate) 1932. *See* Henry Hardy Heins, *Throughout All the Years* (Oneonta: Board of Trustees of Hartwick College, 1946) for further information.

Institutional Structure: *Governing board:* Hartwick College Board of Trustees. Representation: 26 trustees; 7 alumni. All voting. *Composition of institution:* Administrators 42. Senior administrators include the president, vice president of academic affairs, vice president for finance, vice president for institutional advancement, dean of admissions, dean of student life, and chief information and planning officer. Full-time instructional faculty 127. Academic governance body, Faculty Council, meets an average of 40 times per year.

Calendar: Semesters (4-1-4 plan). Academic year Sept. to May. Freshmen admitted Sept., Jan., Feb. Degrees conferred and formal commencement May.

Characteristics of Freshmen: 2,533 applicants. 83% of applicants admitted. 21% of admitted applicants enrolled full-time.

60% (267 students) submitted SAT scores; 26% (114 students) submitted ACT scores. *25th percentile*: SAT Critical Reading 490, SAT Math 500, SAT Writing 480; ACT Composite 22. *75th percentile*: SAT Critical Reading 590, SAT Math 600, SAT Writing 580; ACT Composite 26.

54% of entering freshmen expected to graduate within 5 years. 65% freshmen from New York. Freshmen from 3 states and 30 foreign countries.

Admission: For fall acceptance, apply by Feb. 15. Decisions mailed mid-March. Early decision: two dates to apply—Dec. 1 and Jan. 15. *Requirements:* Either graduation from accredited secondary school with 4 units English, 2 in a foreign language, 3 mathematics, 2 history, 2 science; or GED. Additional requirements for some programs. *Entrance tests:* College Board SAT or ACT composite optional. For foreign students TOEFL. *For transfer students:* 2.0 minimum GPA; 18 courses maximum transfer credit.

College credit and advanced placement for postsecondary-level work completed in secondary school and for extrainstitutional learning (life experience) on basis of faculty assessment, personal interview.

Tutoring available. Remedial courses offered during regular academic year; credit given.

Degree Requirements: 120 credit hours; 2.0 GPA; 4 terms in residence; 4 half-unit courses in physical education; competency examinations in writing; distribution requirements.

Fulfillment of some degree requirements and exemption from some beginning courses possible by passing departmental examinations, College Board CLEP, APP, other standardized tests. *Grading system:* A–F; pass-not pass for physical education only; withdraw (carries time limit); incomplete (carries time limit).

Distinctive Educational Programs: Internships. Environmental campus center (at Pine Lake, 8 miles from main institution). Dual-degree programs in engineering with Clarkson College of Technology, Columbia University; 3+3 program with Albany Law School. Study abroad in Austria, France, Costa Rica, South Africa, Thailand, England, Ireland, Scotland, Germany, Russia. Interdisciplinary programs in education, environmental science and policy (minor), graphic communications (minor), Latin American and Caribbean studies (minor), ethnic studies (minor), women's studies (minor); interdisciplinary courses may also be arranged. Facilities for independent research, including honors programs, individual majors, tutorials, independent studies, directed studies.

Degrees Conferred: 297 *baccalaureate.* Bachelor's degrees awarded in top five disciplines: social sciences 60; business, management, marketing, and related support services 38; visual and performing arts 33; biomedical and biological sciences 24; health professions and related clinical sciences 20.

Fees and Other Expenses: *Full-time tuition per academic year 2008–09:* $31,900. *Room and board per academic year:* $8,635. *Books and supplies.* $700. *Other expenses:* $700.

Financial Aid: Aid from institutionally generated funds is provided on the basis of academic merit, financial need, athletic ability. Institution has a Program Participation Agreement with the U.S. Department of Education for eligible students to receive Pell Grants and, depending upon the agreement, other federal aid.

Financial aid to first-time, full-time undergraduate students: 99% received some for of financial aid. Average amount of aid received: federal grants $4,760; Pell grants $3,137; other federal grants $1,772; state/local grants $2,366; institutional grants $14,292.

Departments and Teaching Staff: *Total instructional faculty:* 154 (full-time 105, part-time 49). 92% of faculty hold the doctorate, first-professional, or other terminal degree. Student/faculty ratio: 11:1.

Enrollment: Total enrollment 1,493 (undergraduate). Transfer-in students 34.

Characteristics of Student Body: *Ethnic/racial makeup:* number of Black non-Hispanic: 11; American Indian or Alaska Native: 12; Asian or Pacific Islander: 19; Hispanic: 33; White non-Hispanic: 928; unknown: 345.

International Students: 59 nonresident aliens enrolled fall 2008. Students from Europe, Asia, Central and South America, Africa, Canada, New Zealand. No programs available to aid students whose native language is not English. Some financial aid specifically designated for qualifying international students.

Student Life: On-campus residence halls, townhouses, and special interest houses accommodate 84% of student body. Single sex housing available. 15% of males join and 8% live in fraternity housing; 17% of females join and 6% live in sorority housing. *Intercollegiate athletics:* male: baseball, basketball, cross-country, football, lacrosse, soccer, swimming, tennis, track; female: basketball, cross-country, equestrian, field hockey, lacrosse, soccer, softball, swimming, tennis, track, volleyball, water polo; both sexes: golf. *Special regulations:* Registered cars permitted in designated areas. *Special services:* Learning Resources Center, career planning and placement; internships; counseling and chemical dependency assessment; education and counseling program; medical services. *Student publications, radio, TV: Desideratum,* a quarterly literary magazine; *Hilltops,* a weekly newspaper; *Oyaron,* a yearbook. Radio station WRHO broadcasts 140–160 hours per week. TV station WICK-TV. *Surrounding community:* Oneonta population 14,000. Albany, 75 miles from campus, is nearest metropolitan area. Served by mass transit bus system.

Publications: Sources of information about Hartwick College include *The Wick,* an alumni magazine distributed to corporate and business leaders.

Library Collections: 318,000 volumes. 124,000 microforms; 2,500 audiovisual materials; 21,800 periodicals including via electronic access. Computer work stations available (library has wireless capability). Students have access to online information retrieval services and the Internet.

Most important holdings include 15,000 titles on North American Indians, including many first editions of early 19th century books; Hartwick Seminary Papers; William Cooper Papers.

Buildings and Grounds: Campus area 375 acres.

HARTWICK COLLEGE—*cont'd*

Chief Executive Officer: Dr. Richard P. Miller, Jr., President.

Address admission inquiries to Jacqueline Gregory, Director of Admissions.

Hebrew Union College - Jewish Institute of Religion

One West 4th Street
New York, New York 10012-1186
Tel: (212) 674-5300 **E-mail:** admissions@huc.edu
Fax: (212) 388-1720 **Internet:** www.huc.edu

Institution Description: Hebrew Union College - Jewish Institute of Religion is a branch campus of an institution with its main campus in Cincinnati, Ohio. *Enrollment:* 182. *Degrees awarded:* master's, doctorate, first-professional.

Accreditation: *Regional:* MSA.

History: Established as Jewish Institute of Religion and offered first instruction at postsecondary level 1922; first ordination 1926; merged with Hebrew Union College (founded Cincinnati 1875) 1950. *See* Michael Meyer, *Hebrew Union College - Jewish Institute of Religion at 100 years*, ed. Samuel Karff (Cincinnati: Hebrew Union College Press, 1976) for further information.

Institutional Structure: *Governing board:* Board of Governors. Extrainstitutional representation: 55 members. institutional representation: 4 administrators; 11 alumni. All voting. *Composition of institution:* Administrators 6. Academic affairs and management/business/finance directed by dean. Full-time instructional faculty 16. Academic governance body, Faculty, meets an average of 6 times per year.

Calendar: Semesters. Academic year Sept. to May. Entering students admitted Sept. Degrees conferred May. Formal commencement May. No summer session.

Characteristics of Freshmen: 52% of applicants accepted. 95% of accepted applicants enrolled. 95% of entering freshmen expected to graduate within 5 years. 35% of freshmen from New York. Freshmen from 12 states.

Admission: Rolling admissions plan. For fall acceptance, apply as early as Sept. of previous year, but not later than Jan. of year of enrollment. *Requirements:* For first-professional students, baccalaureate from accredited college or university; personal interview, including testing, to determine commitment to Reform Judaism, at least 1 year of college-level modern Hebrew. *Entrance tests:* GRE.

Degree Requirements: *For master's degree:* 120 semester hours; GPA of pass or equivalent of B or better; entire program in residence, with first year spent in Jerusalem for intensive study in Hebrew; rabbinic skills practica; thesis; sermon delivery requirement; demonstrated proficiency in speech; 2 additional years study for ordination as rabbi. *For all master's degrees:* 45 hours; 3.0 GPA; 1 year in residence; language requirement in Hebrew; thesis; distribution requirements. *Grading system:* A–F or pass-fail.

Distinctive Educational Programs: Work-experience programs, including field experience, in-service rabbinical training.

Degrees Conferred: 26 *master's:* theology; 4 *doctorate:* theology; 24 *first-professional:* rabbinic studies.

Fees and Other Expenses: *Full-time tuition per academic year 2008–09:* contact the institution for current information. Various fees may apply.

Financial Aid: Aid from institutionally generated funds is provided on the basis of academic merit, financial need. Institution has a Program Participation Agreement with the U.S. Department of Education for eligible students to receive Pell Grants and, depending upon the agreement, other federal aid.

Departments and Teaching Staff: School of Sacred Music *professors* 3, *part-time faculty* 16; Rabbinic 13, 25; Graduate Studies 11, 11.

Full-time instructional faculty: 19. *Total tenured faculty:* 14. *Degrees held by full-time faculty:* doctorate 93%. 100% hold terminal degrees.

Enrollment: Total enrollment 182.

Characteristics of Student Body: *Ethnic/racial makeup:* Black non-Hispanic .6%; Asian or Pacific Islander 1.2%; White non-Hispanic 89.9%.

International Students: 7 nonresident aliens enrolled fall 2008.

Student Life: No on-campus housing. *Special services:* Learning Resources Center. *Surrounding community:* New York City population over 7 million. Served by mass transit bus, subway systems; airport; passenger rail service.

Publications: *Publisher:* Hebrew Union College Press located at parent institution.

Library Collections: 140,000 volumes. 200 current periodical subscriptions.

Buildings and Grounds: Campus area 1 square block.

Chief Executive Officer: Dr. David Ellenson, President.

Address admission inquiries to Director of Admissions and Recruitment.

Hilbert College

5200 South Park Avenue
Hamburg, New York 14075-1597
Tel: (716) 649-7900 **E-mail:** admissions@hilbert.edu
Fax: (716) 649-0702 **Internet:** www.hilbert.edu

Institution Description: Hilbert College, founded in 1957, is an independent, coeducational, four-year institution of higher education with a Franciscan spirit. *Enrollment:* 996. *Degrees awarded:* Associate, baccalaureate.

Accreditation: *Regional:* MSA.

History: Hilbert College's origins are rooted in the Franciscan Sisters of St. Joseph who founded the college and who, as its sponsoring body, continue to support the mission of the college: to provide for the educational needs of those serviced s determined by the culture of the times and the circumstances that affect the people within that milieu.

Institutional Structure: *Governing board:* Board of Trustees charted by the Regents of the University of the State of New York.

Calendar: Semesters. Summer sessions.

Characteristics of Freshmen: 90% of applicants admitted. 35% of applicants admitted and enrolled.

57% (94 students) submitted SAT scores; 11% (11 students) submitted ACT scores. *25th percentile*: SAT Critical Reading 430, SAT Math 420; ACT Composite 19. *75th percentile*: SAT Critical Reading 500, SAT Math 550; ACT Composite 24.

57% of entering freshmen expected to graduate within 5 years. 970% of freshmen from New York. Freshmen from 4 states.

Admission: *Requirements:* Admission is based upon past academic performance, scholastic ability, and personal characteristics.

Degree Requirements: *For all baccalaureate degrees:* 120 semester hours; minimum of 93 credit hours distributed among the humanities, natural sciences and mathematics, and the social sciences, 39 hours of which are in the field of English. A minimum of 45 credit hours must be completed in the upper division. *For associate degree:* 60 credit hours primarily in liberal arts and sciences.

Distinctive Educational Programs: Accounting, business administration, communication studies, criminal justice, economic crime investigation, forensic science investigation, English, human services, liberal studies, paralegal studies, rehabilitation services, psychology.

Degrees Conferred: 31 *associate;* 221 *baccalaureate:* business/marketing 32; communications technologies 3; English 3; laws/legal studies 20; psychology 18; security and protective services 122; social sciences 19.

Fees and Other Expenses: *Full-time tuition per academic year 2008–09:* $17,350. *Required fees:* $600. *Room and board per academic year:* $6,950. *Books and supplies:* $600. *Other expenses:* $800.

Financial Aid: Aid from institutionally generated funds is provided on the basis of academic merit, financial need.

Financial aid to full-time, first-time undergraduate students: 100% received some form of financial aid.

Departments and Teaching Staff: *Total instructional faculty:* 119 (full-time 49, part-time 70). 56% of faculty hold the doctorate, first-professional, or other terminal degree. Student/faculty ratio: 11:1.

Enrollment: Total enrollment 996 (undergraduate). Transfer-in students 65.

Characteristics of Student Body: *Ethnic/racial makeup:* number of Black non-Hispanic: 32; American Indian or Alaska Native: 16; Asian or Pacific Islander: 3; Hispanic: 25; White non-Hispanic: 896; unknown: 91. *Age distribution:* number under 18: 29; 18–19: 280; 20–21: 266; 22–24: 182; 25–29: 100; 30–34: 49; 35–39: 47; 40–49: 80; 50–64: 22; 65 and over: 9.

International Students: 1 nonresident alien from New Zealand enrolled fall 2008. No programs available for students whose native language is not English. No financial aid specifically designated for international students.

Student Life: Annual activities include major concert, Quad Party, and Fall Fest. S Student activities are organized and sponsored by the student government, various clubs, and the resident students' association. Intercollegiate athletics include basketball, baseball, cross-country, golf, soccer, and volleyball for males; basketball, baseball cross-country, golf, soccer, and volleyball for females. Club sports include male hockey, lacrosse, and cheerleading.

Library Collections: 36,500 volumes including bound books, serial backfiles, electronic documents, and government documents not in separate collections. Online catalog. Current serial subscriptions: 340 paper; 25,000 via electronic access. 1,200 audio/videotapes; 180 DVD discs; 12 CD-ROMS. Computer work stations available. Students have access to the Internet at no charge.

Most important special collections include Law Collection; Children's Literature; College Archives.

Buildings and Grounds: Campus complex consists of 7 buildings.

Chief Executive Officer: Cynthia A. Lane, President.

Address admission inquiries to Timothy Lee, Director of Admissions.

Hobart and William Smith Colleges

337 Pulteney Street
Geneva, New York 14456
Tel: (315) 789-3000 **E-mail:** admissions@hws.edu
Fax: (315) 781-3400 **Internet:** www.hws.edu

Institution Description: Hobart and William Smith Colleges are private liberal arts colleges that share facilities, faculty, anc curriculum while maintaining distinct student governments, deans, athletic programs, and traditions for females and males. Hobart College is historically affiliated with the Episcopal Church. William Smith College is a nonsectarian college for women. *Enrollment:* 2,078. *Degrees awarded:* Baccalaureate, master's.

Member of the consortium Rochester Area Colleges.

Accreditation: *Regional:* MSA. *Professional*: teacher education

History: Hobart College established and offered first instruction at postsecondary level 1822; chartered 1825; awarded first degree (baccalaureate) 1826. William Smith College established and offered instruction at postsecondary level 1908; awarded first degree (baccalaureate) 1912. *See* Warren Hunting Smith, *Hobart and William Smith: The History of Two Colleges* (Geneva: Hobart and William Smith Colleges, 1972) for further information.

Institutional Structure: *Governing board:* Board of Trustees. Extrainstitutional representation: 42 trustees. 2 ex officio. All voting. *Composition of institution:* Administrators 197. Academic affairs headed by provost and dean of faculty. Management/business/finances directed by treasurer. Full-time instructional faculty 156.

Calendar: Semesters. Academic year Aug. to May. Freshmen admitted Aug. Degrees conferred and formal commencement May. No summer session.

Characteristics of Freshmen: 4,306 applicants. 54% of applicants admitted. 24% of applicants admitted and enrolled full-time.

95% (564 students) submitted SAT scores; 27% (161 students) submitted ACT scores. *25th percentile*: SAT Critical Reading 530, SAT Math 540; ACT Composite 23, ACT English 22, ACT Math 22. *75th percentile*: SAT Critical Reading 630, SAT Math 640; ACT Composite 27; ACT English 28; ACT Math 28.

46% of entering freshmen expected to graduate within 5 years. 49% of freshmen from New York. Freshmen from 40 states and 29 foreign countries.

Admission: Application deadlines: Nov. 15 and Jan 1. for early decisions I and II. Notification within 30 days after receipt of all credentials. Regular decision Feb. 1. Notification Apr. 1. Candidates' Reply Date May 1. Interview recommended. *Requirements:* High school transcript, 1 teacher recommendation. Credit given for score of 4 or 5 on AP Tests. *For transfer students:* 16 courses maximum transfer credit; transcripts; recommendations (1 professor, 1 academic dean).

Degree Requirements: 3 years in residence; pass 32 academic courses or equivalent with minimum 2.0 GPA; pass first-year seminary with C- or better; complete requirements for an academic major and minor or second major. general education requirements.

Fulfillment of some degree requirements and/or exemption from some beginning courses possible by passing College Board CLEP, AP (score of 4), other standardized tests. *Grading system:* A–C; credit.

Distinctive Educational Programs: Internships in architecture, health professions, urban studies. Accelerated degree programs. Dual-degree programs in engineering with Columbia University, Dartmouth College, Rensselaer Polytechnic Institute, and University of Rochester; in business administration with Clarkson College of Technology and Rochester Institute of Technology. Interdisciplinary programs in Africana and Latin American studies, architectural studies, biochemistry, environmental studies, American studies, Asian studies, comparative literature, urban, and women's studies. Facilities and programs for independent research, including honors programs, individual majors, independent study. Institutional and cooperative programs of study in 30 international locales. United Nations semester in cooperation with American University (Washington, DC). Cross-registration through consortium.

Degrees Conferred: 399 *baccalaureate:*; 9 *master's*. Bachelor's degrees awarded in top five disciplines: social sciences 113; psychology 38; public administration and social services 33; history 20; biological and biomedical sciences 22. Master's degrees awarded: education 9.

Fees and Other Expenses: *Full-time tuition per academic year 2008–09:* \$38,860. *Required fees:* \$958. *Room and board per academic year:* \$9,686. *Books and supplies:* \$1,309. *Other expenses:* \$1,040.

Financial Aid: Aid from institutionally generated funds is provided on the basis of academic merit, financial need.

Financial aid to full-time, first-time undergraduate students: 78% received some form of aid. Average amount of aid received: federal grants \$5,425; Pell grants \$2,951; other federal grants \$3,479; state/local grants \$2,915; institutional grants \$18,738.

Departments and Teaching Staff: *Total instructional faculty:* 188 (full-time 164, part-time 24). 97% of faculty hold the doctorate, first-professional, or other terminal degree. Student/faculty ratio: 11:1.

Enrollment: Total enrollment 2,078. Undergraduate 2,068. Graduate 9. Undergraduate transfer-in students 22.

Characteristics of Student Body: *Ethnic/racial makeup:* number of Black non-Hispanic: 68; American Indian or Alaska Native: 3; Asian or Pacific Islander: 40; Hispanic: 70; White non-Hispanic: 1,610; unknown: 33. *Age distribution:* number under 18: 60; 18–19: 448; 20–21: 855; 22–24: 479; 25–29: 7; 30–34: 4; 50–64: 2.

International Students: 32 nonresident aliens enrolled fall 2008. Students from Europe, Asia, Central and South America, Canada, Middle East. Programs available to aid students whose native language is not English: social, cultural. No financial aid specifically designated for international students.

Student Life: On-campus residence halls and cooperative facilities house 94% of student body. 20% of males join and 15% live in fraternity housing. *Intercollegiate sports:* Basketball, crew, cross-country, football, hockey, lacrosse, soccer, squash, swimming, tennis. *Special regulations:* Registered cars with decals permitted. *Special services:* Center for Teaching and Learning; health center; counseling center. *Student publications, radio: The Herald*, student newspaper; *Thel*, annual literary magazine; *Scry*, annual art magazine; *ECHO & PINE*, yearbook. Radio station WEOS broadcasts 105 hours per week. *Surrounding community:* Geneva population 15,000. Rochester, 45 miles from campus, is nearest metropolitan area.

Publications: *Seneca Review* (biannually) first published in 1970.

Library Collections: 393,000 volumes. Online catalog. Current periodical subscriptions: paper 1,014; 17,708 via electronic access. 7,375 audio/videotapes; 2,634 DVED discs; 384 CD-ROMs. Computer work stations available. Students have access to online information retrieval services and the Internet.

Most important holdings include The Geneva Local History Collection (4,700 monographs and 7,300 other items, including manuscripts, photographs, and journals pertaining to history of the colleges and the region, dating from the early 19th century; also 5,000 original issues of various Geneva newspapers published from 1806 to 1894—those from 1806 to 1839 are fully indexed); The Potter Historical Collection (287 monographs pertaining to France during the 17th and 18th centuries); The Douglas/Hale Collection (19th-century journals, manuscripts, correspondence, and other materials of a prominent Geneva family, including the only existing original sketches of bridges on the Erie Canal); Elizabeth Perry Asia Library (8,047 books related to Asian studies).

Buildings and Grounds: Campus area 180 acres.

Chief Executive Officer: Dr. Mark D. Gearan, President.

Address admission inquiries to John W. Young, Director of Admissions.

Hofstra University

100 Hofstra University
Hempstead, New York 11544
Tel: (516) 463-6600 **E-mail:** admitme@hofstra.edu
Fax: (516) 463-4848 **Internet:** www.hofstra.edu

Institution Description: Hofstra University is a private, independent, nonprofit institution. *Enrollment:* 12,333. *Degrees awarded:* Associate, baccalaureate, first-professional (law), master's, doctorate. Certificates also awarded.

Accreditation: *Regional:* MSA. *Professional*: accounting, athletic training, audiology, business, clinical psychology, engineering, engineering technology, law, psychology internship, rehabilitation counseling, speech-language pathology, teacher education

History: Established as Nassau College-Hofstra Memorial, an NYU Extension and offered first instruction at postsecondary level 1935; chartered 1937; awarded first degree (baccalaureate) and changed name to Hofstra College 1939; chartered as a University 1963.

Institutional Structure: *Governing board:* Board of Trustees. Board consists of 5 officers, including the president, 25 members of which 14 are alumni. *Composition of institution:* Administrators 469. Academic affairs headed by provost and senior vice president for academic affairs. Administrative affairs headed by the senior vice president for planning and administration. Management/business/finances directed by vice president of financial affairs and treasurer. Full-time instructional faculty 532. Academic governance body, University Senate, meets an average of 10 times per year. *Faculty representation:* Faculty served by collective bargaining agent affiliates with AAUP.

Calendar: Semesters (4-1-4). Academic year Sept. to May. Freshmen admitted Sept., Jan., May, July. Degrees conferred May, Aug., Dec. Formal commencements May, Dec. Summer session of 2 terms from May to Aug.

HOFSTRA UNIVERSITY—*cont'd*

Characteristics of Freshmen: 18,471 applicants. 54% of applicants admitted. 17% of admitted students enrolled full-time.

71% (1,219 students) submitted SAT scores; 16% (308 students) submitted ACT scores. *25th percentile*: SAT Critical Reading 540, SAT Math 550; ACT Composite 23. *75th percentile*: SAT Critical Reading 630, SAT Math 630; ACT Composite 26.

53% of entering freshmen expected to graduate within 5 years. 65% of freshmen from New York. Freshmen from 49 states and 51 foreign countries.

Admission: Rolling admissions plan. Apply by Nov. 15 for early action. Early acceptance available. *Requirements:* Either graduation from accredited secondary school with 16 units which must include 4 English, 2 foreign language, 3 social studies, 3 mathematics, 3 science (1 with laboratory), or GED with score of 300. Engineering major requires 4 math, 1 chemistry, 1 physics. *Entrance tests:* College Board SAT or ACT composite. *For transfer students:* From 4-year accredited institution 2.0 minimum GPA, 94 semester hours maximum transfer credit; from 2-year accredited institution 2.5 minimum GPA, 64 hours.

College credit for postsecondary-level work completed in secondary school. Tutoring available. Noncredit developmental courses offered in summer session and regular academic year.

Degree Requirements: *For all baccalaureate degrees:* 120–135 semester hours. *For all undergraduate degrees:* 2.0 GPA; 30 hours in residence; general education requirements.

Fulfillment of some degree requirements and exemption from some beginning courses possible by passing College Board CLEP. *Grading system:* A–F; pass-fail; withdraw; incomplete (deadline after which pass-fail is appended).

Distinctive Educational Programs: Work-experience programs. Evening classes. Accelerated degree programs. Dual-degree program in engineering with Columbia University. Interdisciplinary programs in African studies, Asian studies, creative studies, humanities, liberal arts, natural science, social science. Facilities and programs for independent research, including honors programs, individual majors, tutorials. Study abroad in France, Italy, England, Spain, Ireland, Mexico, Jamaica, Ecuador, Japan, Greece, Czech Republic. *Other distinctive programs:* Continuing education. Tuition discount for senior citizens.

ROTC: Army.

Degrees Conferred: 1,750 *baccalaureate*; 903 *master's*; 84 *doctorate*; 300 *first-professional*. Bachelor's degrees awarded in top five disciplines: business/marketing 619; communications/journalism 295; psychology 195; social sciences 115; English language/literature 89. Master's degrees awarded in top five disciplines: education 561; business/marketing 176; health professions and related clinical sciences 112; psychology 48; law/legal studies 10. Doctorates awarded: education 10; psychology 39, other 35. First-professional degrees awarded: law 300.

Fees and Other Expenses: *Full-time tuition per academic year 2008–09:* $28,630; contact the university for current graduate and first-professional tuition and fees. *Room and board per academic year:* $10,825. *Books and supplies:* $1,000. *Other expenses:* $2,715.

Financial Aid: Aid from institutionally generated funds is provided on the basis of academic merit, financial need, athletic ability. Institution has a Program Participation Agreement with the U.S. Department of Education for eligible students to receive Pell Grants and, depending upon the agreement, other federal aid.

Financial aid to full-time, first-time undergraduate students: 88% received some form of aid. Average amount of aid received: federal grants $4,104; Pell grants $3,066; other federal grants $1,368 state/local grants $2,632; institutional grants $12,857.

Departments and Teaching Staff: *Total instructional faculty:* 1,206 (full-time 532, part-time 674). 93% of faculty hold the doctorate, first-professional, or other terminal degree. Student/faculty ratio: 14:1.

Enrollment: Total enrollment 12,333. Undergraduate 8,320. Graduate 4,013. Undergraduate transfer-in students 571.

Characteristics of Student Body: *Ethnic/racial makeup:* number of Black non-Hispanic: 811; American Indian or Alaska Native: 40; Asian or Pacific Islander: 87; Hispanic: 655; White non-Hispanic: 5,531; unknown: 1,318. *Age distribution:* number under 18: 243; 18–19: 3,144; 20–21: 3,146; 22–24: 1,239; 25–29: 344; 30–34: 112; 35–39: 71; 40–49: 143; 50–64: 36; 65 and over: 4. 31% of student body attend summer sessions.

International Students: 238 nonresident aliens enrolled fall 2008. Students from Europe, Asia, Central and South Latin America, Africa, Canada, Australia, Middle East.

Programs available to aid students whose native language is not English: English as a Second Language Program. Financial aid specifically designated for international students: variable number of undergraduate scholarships available annually.

Student Life: On-campus residence halls house 51% of full-time undergraduate student body. *Intercollegiate athletics:* male: baseball, basketball, cross-country running, football, golf, lacrosse, soccer, tennis, wrestling; female: basketball, cross-country running, field hockey, lacrosse, soccer, softball, tennis, volleyball. *Special regulations:* Registered cars permitted in designated areas. *Special services:* Medical services, shuttle bus service. *Student publications, radio, television: The Chronicle* (weekly); *Conscience* (monthly); *Nonsense* 3 issues per semester; *Nexus* , a yearbook. Radio station WRHU-FM broadcasts regularly 365 days per year. The new Television Institute is one of the largest, most sophisticated, non-commercial TV facilities in the East. *Surrounding community:* Hempstead population 45,000. New York City, 25 miles from campus, is nearest metropolitan area. Served by mass transit bus system; passenger rail system 2 miles from campus; international airport 12 miles from campus.

Library Collections: 1,138,762 volumes. 234,152 government documents. Current periodical subscriptions: paper 1,793; via electronic access 19,612. Online catalog. 6,592 audio/videotapes; 1,0999 DVD discs. 59 computer work stations. Students have access to online information retrieval services and the Internet.

Most important holdings include Nassau County American Legion Memorial Library of New York State and Long Island History; Weingrow Fine Arts Collection; Nila Banton Smith Historical Collection in Reading; Kroul Collection of Nazi Culture and Propaganda.

Buildings and Grounds: Campus area 238 acres.

Chief Executive Officer: Dr. Stuart Rabinowitz, President.

Address admission inquiries to Jesslea Eads, Dean of Admissions and Financial Aid; graduate inquiries to Carol Drummer, Dean of Graduate Admissions.

New College

Degree Programs Offered: *Baccalaureate* in creative studies, humanities, interdisciplinary studies, natural sciences, social sciences; *master's* in interdisciplinary studies.

Degree Requirements: *See* General requirements. *For baccalaureate degree:* 120 credit hours, 1 year in residence.

Distinctive Educational Programs: Internships and apprenticeships. Interdisciplinary programs in creative studies, humanities, natural sciences, social sciences. Individual study.

School of Law

Degree Programs Offered: *First-professional, master of law.*

Admission: Baccalaureate from accredited institution, or equivalent; LSAT.

Degree Requirements: 87 credit hours, 2.0 GPA, 6 semesters in residence.

Houghton College

One Willard Avenue
Houghton, New York 14744
Tel: (585) 567-9353 **E-mail:** admissions@houghton.edu
Fax: (585) 567-9522 **Internet:** www.houghton.edu

Institution Description: Houghton College is a private, independent, nonprofit college affiliated with The Wesleyan Church. The college operates an extension campus at Buffalo. *Enrollment:* 1,415. *Degrees awarded:* Associate, baccalaureate, master's.

Member of Christian College Consortium; Western New York Consortium of Higher Education.

Accreditation: *Regional:* MSA. *Professional*: music

History: Chartered as Houghton Wesleyan Methodist Seminary, an elementary and secondary school, 1883; first instruction at postsecondary level 1889; became 4-year college and adopted present name 1923; awarded first degree (baccalaureate); merged with Buffalo Bible Institute 1969.

Institutional Structure: *Governing board:* Board of Trustees. Extrainstitutional representation: 30 trustees, including 15 alumni; institutional representation: president of the college. 1 ex officio. All voting. *Composition of institution:* Administrators 6. Academic affairs headed by academic dean. Business/finances directed by vice president for finance. Full-time instructional faculty 87. Academic governance body, the faculty, meets an average of 15 times per year.

Calendar: Semesters. Academic year Aug. to May. Freshmen admitted Aug., Jan., May, June. Degrees conferred and formal commencement May. Mayterm and summer session.

Characteristics of Freshmen: 972 applicants. 83% of applicants accepted. 41% of accepted applicants enrolled full-time.

80% (287 students) submitted SAT scores. 36% (117 students) submitted ACT scores. *25th percentile*: SAT Critical Reading 520, SAT Math 510, SAT Writing 500; ACT Composite 23, ACT English 22, ACT Math 21. *75th percentile*: SAT Critical Reading 650, SAT Math 620, SAT Writing 640; ACT Composite 29, ACT English 30, ACT Math 28.

70% of entering freshmen expected to graduate within 5 years. 52% of freshmen from New York. Freshmen from 32 states and 18 foreign countries.

Admission: Rolling admissions plan. *Requirements:* Either graduation from accredited secondary school with 16 units, including 3 English; or GED. Recommend 1 additional unit English, 2 foreign language, 3 history, 2 mathematics, 2 science. Lowest acceptable secondary school class standing 50th percentile. *Entrance tests:* College Board SAT or ACT composite. For foreign students TOEFL. *For transfer students:* 2.0 minimum GPA; from 4-year accredited institution 94 hours maximum transfer credit; from 2-year accredited institution 64 hours.

College credit and advanced placement for postsecondary-level work completed in secondary school. College credit for extrainstitutional learning.

Developmental courses offered during regular academic year; credit given.

Degree Requirements: *For all associate degrees:* 62 credit hours. *For all baccalaureate degrees:* 124–128 credit hours; minor requirement. *For all degrees:* 2.0 GPA; 2 terms in residence; chapel attendance 3 per week; 2 hours physical education; integrative studies.

Fulfillment of some degree requirements and exemption from some beginning courses possible by passing departmental examinations, College Board CLEP, AP, other standardized tests. *Grading system:* A–F; pass-fail; withdraw (carries time limit).

Distinctive Educational Programs: Evening classes. London First-Year Honors Program; East Meets West First-Year Honors Program. Cross-registration through consortia. Outstanding students accepted by professional schools after 3 years undergraduate study may earn baccalaureate degree in absentia.

ROTC: Army in cooperation with St. Bonaventure University.

Degrees Conferred: 7 *associate;* 355 *baccalaureate:*; 8 *master's.* Bachelor's degrees awarded in top five disciplines: business/marketing 106; English language and literature 41; philosophy and religious studies 38; visual and performing arts 31; biological and biomedical sciences 106. Master's degrees awarded: visual and performing arts 8.

Fees and Other Expenses: *Full-time tuition per academic year 2008–09:* $22,990. *Room and board per academic year:* $6,950. *Books and supplies:* $900. *Other expenses:* $2,200.

Financial Aid: Aid from institutionally generated funds is provided on the basis of academic merit, financial need, athletic ability, other criteria.

Financial aid to full-time, first-time undergraduate students: 98% received some form of aid. Average amount of aid received: federal grants $4,246; Pell grants $3,066; other federal grants $1,318 state/local grants $2,375; institutional grants: $9,137.

Departments and Teaching Staff: *Total instructional faculty:* 115 (full-time 87, part-time 28). Student/faculty ratio: 13:1. Degrees held by full-time faculty: doctorate 77%, master's 17%, baccalaureate 1%, professional 5%. 82% hold terminal degrees.

Enrollment: Total enrollment 1,415. Undergraduate 1,377. Graduate 38. Undergraduate transfer-in students 11.

Characteristics of Student Body: *Ethnic/racial makeup:* number of Black non-Hispanic: 36; American Indian or Alaska Native: 2; Asian or Pacific Islander: 21; Hispanic: 10; White non-Hispanic: 1,250; unknown: 40. *Age distribution:* number under 18: 29; 18–19: 529; 20–21: 1,124; 22–24: 123; 25–29: 40; 30–34: 36; 35–39: 35; 40–49: 60; 50–64: 21. 7% of student body attend summer sessions.

International Students: 47 nonresident aliens enrolled fall 2008. Students from Europe, Asia, Central and South America, Africa, Canada, New Zealand. Programs available to aid students whose native language is not English: social, cultural, financial. English as a Second Language Program.

Student Life: On-campus residence halls house 82f% of student body. Residence halls for males constitute 35% of such space, for females 65%. *Intercollegiate athletics:* male: basketball,soccer, track; female: basketball, field hockey, soccer, track, volleyball. *Special regulations:* Cars must be registered. *Special services:* Learning Resources Center, medical services. *Student publications, radio: Boulder,* a yearbook; *Info,* an annual student directory; *The Houghton Star,* a weekly newspaper; *Lanthorn,* a biannual literary magazine. *Surrounding community:* Houghton, unincorporated, located in Allegany County, population 6,000. Buffalo, 65 miles from campus, is nearest metropolitan area.

Publications: *For the Time Being,* a quarterly arts journal first published in 1979.

Library Collections: 260,000 volumes. 47,000 microforms; 12,000 audiovisual materials; 420 Current periodical subscriptions. Computer work stations avaialble. Students have access to online information retrieval services and the Internet.

Most important collections include Wesleyana Collection; Houghton College Archives.

Buildings and Grounds: Campus area 1,300 acres.

Chief Executive Officer: Dr. Shirley Mullen, President.

Address admission inquiries to Wayne MacBeth, Vice President for Enrollment Management.

Hunter College / CUNY

695 Park Avenue
New York, New York 10021-5085
Tel: (212) 772-4000 **E-mail:** admissions@hunter.cuny.edu
Internet: www.hunter.cuny.edu

Institution Description: *Enrollment:* 21,258. *Degrees awarded:* Baccalaureate, master's.

Accreditation: *Regional:* MSA. *Professional*: audiology, dietetics, nursing, nursing education, physical therapy, planning, public health, rehabilitation counseling, social work, speech-language pathology, teacher education

History: Established as Female Normal and High School 1870; chartered and offered first instruction at postsecondary level 1888; awarded first degree (baccalaureate) 1905; changed name to Hunter College 1914; became coeducational 1951; adopted present name 1961.

Institutional Structure: *Composition of institution:* Academic affairs headed by provost-vice president and deputy to president. Management/business/finances directed by vice president for administration. Full-time instructional faculty 552. Academic governance body, Senate, meets an average of 20 times per year.

Calendar: Semesters. Academic year Aug. to May. Freshmen admitted Aug., Feb., June. Degrees conferred and formal commencement May. Summer session of two terms from June to Aug.

Characteristics of Freshmen: 21,701 applicants. 30% of applicants admitted. 26% of admitted students enrolled full-time. 100% (1,698 students) submitted SAT scores.

25th percentile: SAT Critical Reading 480, SAT 500. *75th percentile*: SAT Critical Reading 580, SAT Math 600.

18% of entering freshmen expected to graduate within 5 years. 98% of freshmen from New York. Freshmen from 35 states and 100 foreign countries.

Admission: Rolling admissions plan. For fall acceptance, apply as early as Sept. of previous year, but not later than summer of year of enrollment. Early acceptance available. *Requirements:* High school graduation with at least an 80% average or place in the top one-third of class; or have a a total combined SAT score of 900; GED score of 300. *Entrance tests:* College Board SAT. *For transfer students:* 2.5 minimum GPA; from 4-year accredited institution 95 hours maximum transfer credit; from 2-year accredited institution 75 hours.

College credit and advanced placement for postsecondary-level work completed in secondary school. College credit for extrainstitutional learning on basis of faculty assessment.

Tutoring available. Developmental courses offered in summer session and regular academic year; credit given.

Degree Requirements: *Undergraduate:* 128 credit hours; 2.0 GPA; last 30 hours in residence; 1 credit physical education; general education requirements; exit competency examinations in writing, mathematics, reading.

Fulfillment of some degree requirements and exemption from some beginning courses possible by passing departmental examinations, College Board CLEP, AP. *Grading system:* A–F; pass-fail; withdraw (carries time limit).

Distinctive Educational Programs: Work-experience programs, including cooperative education, internships. Weekend and evening classes. Double-degree program in English, mathematics. Special facilities for using telecommunications in the classroom. Interdepartmental programs in archaeology, comparative literature, East Asian studies, English language arts, energy policy studies, environmental science studies, inter-American affairs, international affairs, Jewish social studies, religion, urban studies, women's studies. Facilities and programs for independent research, including honors programs, individual majors, tutorials. Study abroad through New York/Paris Exchange program (offers full-time students in all disciplines the opportunity to study at the University of Paris); University of Puerto Rico exchange program.

Degrees Conferred: 2,511 *baccalaureate*; 1,566 *master's.* Bachelor's degrees awarded in top five disciplines: social sciences 331; English 355; psychology 305; visual and performing arts 209; business, management, marketing, and related support services 186. Master's degrees awarded in top five disciplines: education 458; public administration and social service professions 294; health professions and related clinical sciences 186; social sciences 123; visual and performing arts 79.

Fees and Other Expenses: *Full-time tuition per academic year 2008–09:* resident undergraduate $4,399, nonresident $9,059. *Books and supplies:* $1,016. *Room and board per academic year:* $9,776. *Other expenses:* $4,526.

Financial Aid: Aid from institutionally generated funds is provided on the basis of academic merit, financial need.

HUNTER COLLEGE / CUNY—*cont'd*

Financial aid to full-time, 79% of students received some form of financial aid. Average amount of aid received: federal grants $3,972; Pell grants $3,520; other federal grants $671; state/local grants $2,757; institutional grants $4,227.

Departments and Teaching Staff: *Total instructional faculty:* 1,961. Student/faculty ratio: 15:1. Degrees held by full-time faculty: doctorate 80%, master's 85%, baccalaureate 100%. 80% hold terminal degrees.

Enrollment: Total enrollment 21,258. Undergraduate 15,698. Graduate 560. Undergraduate transfer-in students 1,470.

Characteristics of Student Body: *Ethnic/racial makeup (full-time):* number of Black non-Hispanic: 1,453; American Indian or Alaska Native: 20; Asian or Pacific Islander: 1,891; Hispanic: 1,112; White non-Hispanic: 4,089. *Age distribution:* number under 18: 950; 18–19: 2,646; 20–21: 3,205; 22–24: 390; 25–29: 272; 30–34: 1,189; 35–39: 610; 40–49: 627; 50–64: 306; 65 and over: 488.

International Students: 1,031 nonresident aliens enrolled fall 2008. Programs available to aid students whose native language is not English: social, cultural. English as a Second Language Program. No financial aid specifically designated for international students.

Student Life: On-campus residence halls house 2% of student body. Residence halls for males constitute 5% of such space, for females 15%, for both sexes 80%. *Intercollegiate athletics:* male: baseball, basketball, soccer, swimming, tennis, track, volleyball, wrestling; female: basketball, swimming, tennis, track, volleyball. *Special services:* Child care center for the children of students; women's center; academic computing services; counseling services; career counseling; tutoring; language laboratory; math learning center; writing center; teacher placement. *Student publications, radio: The Envoy,* student newspaper; *Pneuma,* newspaper; 3 literary magazines; returning women's news letter. Student radio station. *Surrounding community:* New York City population over 7 million. Served by mass transit bus, subway system; airport 3 miles from campus; passenger rail service 1 mile from campus.

Library Collections: 790,000 volumes. Current serial subscriptions: paper 6,282; microform 121,667. 13,487 recordings/tapes. Online catalog. Computer work stations. available. Students have access to online information retrieval services and the Internet.

Most important holdings include Stonehill Collection (English novels); collection of recent Cuban history; current elementary and high school textbooks; chemistry; social work.

Buildings and Grounds: Campus area 3 square blocks.

Chief Executive Officer: Dr. Jennifer J. Raab, President.

Address admission inquiries to William Zlata, Director of Admissions.

Iona College

715 North Avenue
New Rochelle, New York 10801-1890

Tel: (914) 633-2000 **E-mail:** icad@iona.edu
Fax: (914) 633-2642 **Internet:** www.iona.edu

Institution Description: Iona College is a private, independent, nonprofit college. *Enrollment:* 4,375. *Degrees awarded:* Associate, baccalaureate, master's, post-bachelors. post-master's.

Accreditation: *Regional:* MSA. *Professional*: business, computer science, nursing, social work, teacher education

History: Established and offered first instruction at postsecondary level 1940; awarded first degree (baccalaureate) 1944; chartered 1947; added master's program 1963; opened Rockland Branch Campus 1982.

Institutional Structure: *Governing board:* Iona College Board of Trustees. Extrainstitutional representation: 34 trustees, advisory trustees 12, trustees emeriti 10; institutional representation: administrators 7. 2 ex officio. All voting. *Composition of institution:* Administrators 10. Academic affairs headed by provost/vice president for academic affairs. Management/business/finances directed by vice president for finance and administration. Full-time instructional faculty 176. Academic governance body, College Council, meets an average of 6 times per year.

Calendar: Semester (trimester for some graduate programs). Academic year Sept. to May. Degrees conferred Feb., June, Aug. Formal commencement June. Summer session of 3 terms.

Characteristics of Freshmen: 6,009 applicants. 59% of applicants admitted. 26% of accepted applicants enrolled full-time.

95% (877 students) submitted SAT scores. *25th percentile*: SAT Critical Reading 540, SAT Math 550. *75th percentile*: SAT Critical Reading 640, SAT Math 660.

52% of entering freshmen expected to graduate within 5 years. 88% of freshmen from New York. Freshmen from 40 states and 33 foreign countries.

Admission: For fall acceptance, apply as early as Oct. 1 of senior year of secondary school, but not later than Aug. 1 of year of enrollment. Early acceptance available. Admission closing date Dec. 1. *Requirements:* Either graduation from accredited secondary school with 16 units which must include 4 English, 2 foreign language, 1 natural science, 3 mathematics, 1 American history, 1 social studies; or GED. *Entrance tests:* College Board SAT or ACT composite. For foreign students TOEFL. *For transfer students:* 2.0 GPA; from 4-year accredited institution 90 credit hours maximum transfer credit; from 2-year accredited institution 64 hours.

College credit and advanced placement for postsecondary-level work completed in secondary school. For extrainstitutional learning (life experience), college credit for continuing education students on basis of portfolio and faculty assessments, and personal interviews.

Tutoring available. Developmental courses offered in summer session and regular academic year; credit given.

Degree Requirements: *Undergraduate:* 120–126 credit hours; 2.0 GPA; 30 hours in residence; core and distribution requirements.

Fulfillment of some degree requirements possible by passing departmental examinations, College Board CLEP, AP. *Grading system:* A–F; pass-fail; withdraw (carries time limit).

Distinctive Educational Programs: Flexible meeting places and schedules, including branch campus for graduate programs (less than 30 miles away from main institution), and evening classes. Campus is wireless with special facilities for using telecommunications in the classroom. Preprofessional programs in health-related professions and law. Computer and art facilities. Graduate MBA program is regarded among the nation's best by the *Princeton Review* and *Business Week.* Interdisciplinary programs in American studies, science, urban studies, international studies, women's studies, peace and justice. Study abroad in England, Ireland, Italy, Mexico, Puerto Rico, Russia, Spain, and South American countries. *Other distinctive programs:* Continuing education, Bachelor of Professional Studies for Continuing Adult Education.

ROTC: Army, Navy, Air Force in cooperation with Fordham University.

Degrees Conferred: 787 *baccalaureate*; 255 *master's.*

Fees and Other Expenses: *Full-time tuition per academic year 2008–09:* undergraduate $26,206; contact the college for current graduate tuition and fees. *Required fees:* $1,700. *Room and board per academic year:* $10,800. *Books and supplies:* $1,500. *Other expenses:* $2,950.

Financial Aid: Aid from institutionally generated funds is provided on the basis of academic merit, financial need, athletic ability.

Financial aid to full-time, first-time undergraduate students: 98% received some form of aid. Average amount of aid received: federal grants $3,796; Pell grants $3,011; other federal grants $1,198; state/local grants $2,767; institutional grants $9,934.

Departments and Teaching Staff: *Total instructional faculty:* 382 (full-time 176, part-time 206). 80% of faculty hold the doctorate, first-professional, or other terminal degree. Student/faculty ratio: 14:1.

Enrollment: Total enrollment 4,375. Undergraduate 3,460. Graduate 915. Undergraduate transfer-in students 103.

Characteristics of Student Body: *Ethnic/racial makeup:* number of Black non-Hispanic: 233; American Indian or Alaska Native: 5; Asian or Pacific Islander: 60; Hispanic: 384; White non-Hispanic: 2,291; 357; unknown: 407.

International Students: 71 nonresident aliens enrolled fall 2008. Students from Europe, Asia, Central and South America, Africa, Canada, Australia. No programs available to aid students whose native language is not English. No financial aid specifically designated for international students.

Student Life: On-campus residence halls house 64% of freshmen and 30% of undergraduates. Residence halls for both sexes constitute 100% of such space. *Intercollegiate athletics:* male: baseball, basketball, crew, football, golf, soccer, swimming, tennis, track, water polo; female: basketball, crew, golf, soccer, swimming, tennis, volleyball. *Special services:* Learning Resources Center, Career Development Center, medical services. services. *Student publications: Ionian,* a weekly newspaper. *Surrounding community:* New Rochelle, population 71,000, is located within New York City metropolitan area. Served by mass transit bus system; airport 10 miles from campus; passenger rail service one mile from campus.

Publications: *The Journal of Pastoral Counseling* (biannually) first published in 1966.

Library Collections: 270,500 volumes. 510,000 microforms; 35,025 audiovisual materials; 750 serial subscriptions. Online catalog. Computer work stations available. Students have access to online information retrieval services.

Most important holdings include Irish collection; collection of rare books.

Buildings and Grounds: Campus area 35 acres.

Chief Executive Officer: Dr. James A. Liguori, C.F.C., President.

Address admission inquiries to Kevin Cavahagh, Assistant Vice President for College Admissions.

Ithaca College

953 Danby Road
Ithaca, New York 14850-7001
Tel: (607) 274-3124 **E-mail:** admission@ithaca.edu
Fax: (607) 274-1900 **Internet:** www.ithaca.edu

Institution Description: Ithaca College is a private, independent, nonprofit college. *Enrollment:* 6,448. *Degrees awarded:* Baccalaureate, master's, doctorate. Certificate program in gerontology.

Accreditation: *Regional:* MSA. *Professional*: athletic training, business, audiology, music, occupational therapy, physical therapy, recreation and leisure services, speech-language pathology, teacher education, theatre

History: Established as Ithaca College Conservatory of Music 1892; offered first instruction at postsecondary level 1893; awarded first degree (baccalaureate) 1897; chartered as Ithaca Conservatory and Affiliated Schools 1926; adopted present name 1931. *See* John Harcourt, *History of Ithaca College* (Ithaca: Ithaca College, 1981) for further information.

Institutional Structure: *Governing board:* Ithaca College Board of Trustees. Extrainstitutional representation: 21 trustees; 14 honorary trustees; 2 presidents emeriti; institutional representation: college president, 1 staff representative, 1 faculty member, 1 student. 25 voting. *Composition of institution:* Administrators 83. Academic affairs headed by provost/ vice president of academic affairs. Management/business/finances directed by vice president for business affairs, and vice president/treasurer. Full-time instructional faculty 442. Academic governance body, Faculty Council, meets 9 times per year.

Calendar: Semesters. Academic year June to May. Freshmen admitted Aug. and Jan. Degrees conferred May, Sept., Dec. Formal commencement May. Summer session of 2 terms.

Characteristics of Freshmen: 13,546 applicants. 59% of applicants accepted. 10% of accepted applicants enrolled full-time.

94% (1,356 students) submitted SAT scores; 34% (493 students) submitted ACT scores. *25th percentile*: SAT Critical Reading 540, SAT Math 550, SAT Writing 540; ACT Composite 23, ACT English 22, ACT Math 23. *75th percentile*: SAT Critical Reading 640, SAT Math 640, SAT Writing 640; ACT Composite 28, ACT English 29, ACT Math 28.

74% of entering freshmen expected to graduate within 5 years. 77% of freshmen from New York. Freshmen from 40 states and 53 foreign countries.

Admission: Rolling admissions plan. For fall acceptance, apply as early as end of junior year of secondary school, but not later than Feb. 1 of year of enrollment. Students are notified of acceptance between Jan. and Apr. Apply before Nov. 1 for early decision. Early acceptance available. *Requirements:* Graduation from secondary school, usually with college preparatory program. Students with nontraditional credentials also encouraged to apply. GED accepted. *Entrance tests:* College Board SAT or ACT. *See* specific schools for additional requirements. *For transfer students:* 2.5 GPA. Maximum transfer credit limited only by residence requirement.

College credit and advanced placement for postsecondary-level work completed in secondary school. Developmental courses offered during regular academic year; credit given.

Degree Requirements: *For all baccalaureate degrees:* 120–151.5 hours; 2.0 GPA; last 30 credits in residence. *For master's degrees:* 30–39 credit hours; some programs require a thesis or comprehensive exam. Some programs require students to finish within 6 years of matriculation dates.

Fulfillment of some degree requirements and exemption from some beginning courses possible by passing College Board CLEP, APP, other standardized tests, departmental examinations. *Grading system:* A–F; pass-fail (for courses not in major or1 minor field, up to 4 hours per semester to 20-hour maximum); withdraw (deadline after which penalty is appended to withdraw).

Distinctive Educational Programs: *Available to all students:* Evening classes. Facilities for using telecommunications in the classroom. Facilities and programs for independent research, including tutorials. Computing services and facilities as well as courses involving computers in every school. *For undergraduates:* Double majors, minors, and interdisciplinary programs involving such areas as biochemistry, computer science (with physics and mathematics), theatre arts management, recreation management, gerontology, musical theatre, philosophy-religion, applied psychology, and sports communication. Communication program in Los Angeles offers an abundance of internship opportunities with industry leaders in television, film and print media. Teacher education available in 17 major areas. Honors programs and individual majors. Writing Center offers individual and small group tutorials, testing and diagnosis, independent study, English for non-native speakers, and workshops. Study abroad in England at Ithaca College London Center. Exchange programs with University of Valencia (Spain), Masaryk University (Czech Republic), Griffith University (Australia), and Nanyang Technical Institute (Singapore). Study abroad programs in 53 additional countries through the Institute for American Universities, Institute for International Education of Students, and the School for International Training. Cross-registration with Cornell University and Wells College. See specific schools for other available programs.

ROTC: Army, Air Force offered in cooperation with Cornell University.

Degrees Conferred: 1,340 *baccalaureate*; 246 *master's*; 63 *doctorate*. Bachelor's degrees awarded in top five disciplines: communications/journalism 264; visual and performing arts 220; health professions and related clinical sciences 143; business/marketing 142; social sciences 132. Master;s degrees awarded: in top five disciplines: business/marketing 10; communications/journalism 14; education 19; parks and recreation 19; visual and performing arts. Doctorates awarded: health professions 63.

Fees and Other Expenses: *Full-time tuition and fees per academic year 2008–09:* undergraduate $30,606; contact the college for current graduate tuition and other fees. *Room and per academic year:* $11,162. *Books and supplies:* $1,130. *Other expenses:* $1,470.

Financial Aid: Aid from institutionally generated funds is provided on the basis of academic merit, financial need, other criteria.

Financial aid to full-time, first-time undergraduate students: 90% received some form of aid. Average amount of aid received: federal grants $4,797; Pell grants $3,085; other federal grants $2,015; state/local grants $2,537; institutional grants $13,407.

Departments and Teaching Staff: *Total instructional faculty:* 656. *Total tenured faculty:* 215. Student/faculty ratio: 12:1. Degrees held by full-time faculty: doctorate 77.6%, master's 30.8%, baccalaureate .9%, professional .7%. 91% hold terminal degrees.

Enrollment: Total enrollment 6,448. Undergraduate 6,031. Graduate 417. Undergraduate transfer-in students 124.

Characteristics of Student Body: *Ethnic/racial makeup:* number of Black non-Hispanic: 175; American Indian or Alaska Native: 27; Asian or Pacific Islander: 197; Hispanic: 225; White non-Hispanic: 4,935; unknown: 313. *Age distribution:* number under 18: 131; 18–19: 2,830; 20–21: 2,647; 22–24: 333; 25–29: 31; 30–34: 17; 35–39: 13; 40–49: 17; 50–64: 7; 65 and over: 2.

International Students: 176 nonresident aliens enrolled fall 2008. Students from Europe, Asia, South America, Africa, Canada, Australia, Middle East. Programs available to aid students whose native language is not English: social, cultural, financial. English as a Second Language Program. Financial aid available for qualifying international students.

Student Life: On-campus residence halls house 70% of student body. 1 residence hall specifically designated for females only, housing 1% of campus residents. 12% of the student body housed in college-operated apartments. *Intercollegiate athletics:* male: baseball, basketball, crew, cross-country, football, lacrosse, soccer, swimming, tennis, track (indoor and outdoor), wrestling; women only: basketball, crew, cross-country, field hockey, gymnastics, lacrosse, soccer, softball, swimming, tennis, track (indoor and outdoor), volleyball. *Special regulations:* Cars permitted with campus registration ($40 fee). *Special services:* Learning Resources Center, Student Health Service Center, Counseling Center, Career Planning and Placement Center, Office of Multicultural Affairs. *Student publications, radio, television: The Cayugan*, a yearbook; *The Ithacan*, a weekly newspaper; *Stillwater,* a annual literary magazine. Radio station VIC-AM/FM and WICB-FM, and cable television ICTV. *Surrounding community:* Ithaca population 30,000. Syracuse, 60 miles from campus, is nearest metropolitan area. Served by mass transit system; airport 5 miles from campus.

Publications: Sources of information about Ithaca College include *Ithaca College Admissions Prospectus*, an annual publication; *Ithaca College Quarterly*, a quarterly magazine; *Ithaca College News*, a biweekly newspaper.

Library Collections: 363,648 volumes. Online catalog. Current serial subscriptions: 2,590 paper; 15 microform; 38,200 via electronic access. 21,110 audiovisual materials. 8,624 DVD discs; 20 CD-ROMs. Computer work stations available. Students have access to the Internet at no charge.

Most important holdings include *Twilight Zone* film and screenplays; C. Hadley Smith Photographs Collection.

Buildings and Grounds: Campus area 757 acres.

Chief Executive Officer: Dr. Peggy R. Williams, President.

Address undergraduate inquires to Paula Mitchell, Director of College Admissions; graduate inquiries to Garry Woodward, Dean of Graduate Studies.

Division of Interdisciplinary and International Studies

Degree Programs Offered: *Baccalaureate*.

Admission: *See* general requirements above.

Distinctive Educational Programs: Office of International Programs; Washington Semester Program; majors in legal studies, cultural communications, gerontology, Center for Teacher Education; Center for the Study of culture, Race, and Ethnicity.

ITHACA COLLEGE—*cont'd*

School of Humanities and Sciences

Degree Programs Offered: *Baccalaureate* in the natural sciences, social sciences, humanities, and the fine and performing arts.

Admission: *See* general requirements above. *For theatre arts:* Audition. *For speech communication:* Interview.

Distinctive Educational Programs: Freshman seminars, strong science programs with student research orientation, theatre (including musical theatre), 3:2 program in engineering with Cornell University, 3:4 optometry program with Pennsylvania College of Optometry. London Center.

School of Allied Health Professions

Degree Programs Offered: Includes School of Health Sciences and Human Performance, and the School of Health, Physical Education, and Recreation. *Baccalaureate* in administration of health services, medical record administration, physical therapy, speech pathology and audiology, and teacher of the speech and hearing handicapped; *master's* in audiology, speech pathology, and teacher of the speech and hearing handicapped.

Admission: *See* general requirements above. *For physical therapy program:* active demonstration of interest in the field.

Degree Requirements: *See* general requirements. *For baccalaureate degrees:* 120–138 credit hours above. *For master's degrees:* 30 credit hours, 3.0 GPA.

Distinctive Educational Programs: *Administration of health services:* Includes gerontology minor with community agency affiliations; internships at over 70 affiliated hospitals in eastern U.S. *Medical record administration:* includes microcomputer laboratory, clinical rotations at numerous health care institutions. *Physical therapy:* includes well-equipped clinic, internship/clinical study at Albert Einstein College of Medicine at the Bronx Municipal Center. *Speech pathology and audiology:* includes well-equipped clinic, teacher certification field experiences, and clinical practice at health care institutions.

School of Business

Degree Programs Offered: *Baccalaureate* in accounting, finance, management, marketing, personnel and industrial relations.

Distinctive Educational Programs: Internships in finance, management, marketing. International business courses offered at Ithaca's London Center.]

Roy H. Park School of Communications

Degree Programs Offered: *Baccalaureate* in cinema and photography, telecommunications management, corporate/organizational media; *master's* in communications.

Admission: *See* general requirements above. *For master's in communications:* 30 credit hours, 3.0 GPA.

Distinctive Educational Programs: Internships in advertising, radio, television, film and photography. Courses in documentary and British television and internships at the London Center.

School of Music

Degree Programs Offered: *Baccalaureate, master's* in education, fine and performing arts.

Admission: In addition to general requirements above; audition.

Degree Requirements: *See* general requirements. *For all baccalaureate degrees:* 124 credit hours. *For all graduate degrees:* 30 credit hours, 3.0 GPA.

Distinctive Educational Programs: *For graduate students:* Music education degree with emphasis in Kodaly concepts through affiliation with Kodaly Center of America and Kodaly Musical Training Institute. Dalcroze certificate and license options for students pursuing degrees in music education or performance. *For undergraduates:* Jazz studies emphasis.

Jewish Theological Seminary of America

3080 Broadway
New York, New York 10027-4649
Tel: (212) 678-8000 **E-mail:** lcadmissions@jtsa.edu
Fax: (212) 678-8947 **Internet:** www.jtsa.edu

Institution Description: The Jewish Theological Seminary of America is a private institution affiliated with the Conservative Movement in Judaism. The seminary is coeducational. A coordinate institution, the University of Judaism in Los Angeles, serves as the seminary's West Coast branch. *Enrollment:* 544. *Degrees awarded:* Baccalaureate, first-professional (master of arts in rabbinics), master's, doctorate. Diplomas also awarded.

Accreditation: *Regional:* MSA.

History: Established as Jewish Theological Seminary Association and chartered 1886; offered first instruction at postsecondary level 1887; first ordination 1894; adopted present name 1901; organized graduate school 1902; established Teachers Institute 1909; awarded first baccalaureate 1914; established Cantors Institute 1952; ordained women rabbis in 1985.

Institutional Structure: *Governing board:* Board of Directors. Extrainstitutional representation: 32 directors, 12 honorary members. Executive Committee 25 members; institutional representation: 9 members. Academic affairs headed by provost. Full-time instructional faculty 62.

Calendar: Semesters. Academic year Sept. to May. Summer session of two terms from May to Aug.

Characteristics of Freshmen: 124 applicants. 60% of applicants accepted. 62% of accepted applicants enrolled full-time.

Admission: For fall acceptance, apply as early as Sept. of previous year, but not later than Feb. 1 of year of enrollment. Students are notified of acceptance Apr. Apply by Nov. 15 for early decision. Early acceptance available. *Requirements:* Graduation from secondary school; applicant must be 16 years of age or older. Recommend proficiency in Hebrew. *Entrance tests:* College Board SAT or ACT and EN or ESACH. For Cantors Institute, music aptitude test. *For transfer students:* 48 hours maximum transfer credit.

College credit and advanced placement for postsecondary-level work completed in secondary school. College credit for extrainstitutional learning (life experience) on basis of faculty assessment.

Tutoring available.

Degree Requirements: *Undergraduate:* 156 credit hours; 96 credits in residence; distribution requirements. *Grading system:* A–F; withdraw (carries time limit).

Distinctive Educational Programs: Dual-degree program leading to baccalaureates awarded by Columbia School of General Studies and Barnard College. Dual-degree program in cooperation with Columbia School of Social Work leading to master's degrees in Jewish studies and social work. Individual majors. Tutorials. Junior year abroad in Israel in cooperation with Hebrew University. Cross-registration with Union Theological Seminary for rabbinical students.

Degrees Conferred: 32 *baccalaureate:* ethnic and cultural studies; 74 *master's*: area and ethnic studies 44; Jewish education 30; 6 *doctorate*: Jewish education. 32 *first-professional.*

Fees and Other Expenses: *Full-time tuition per academic year 2008–09:* $15,000 undergraduate; contact the seminary for graduate costs. *Room and board per academic year:* $11,700. *Books and supplies:* $800. *Other expenses:* $4,000.

Financial Aid: Aid from institutionally generated funds is provided on the basis of academic merit, financial need. Institution has a Program Participation Agreement with the U.S. Department of Education for eligible students to receive Pell Grants and, depending upon the agreement, other federal aid.

Financial aid to full-time, first-time undergraduate students: 86% received institutional grants averaging $11,292.

Departments and Teaching Staff: *Total instructional faculty:* 121 (full-time 62,part-time 59), Student/faculty ratio: 6:1. Degrees held by full-time faculty: doctorate 90%, baccalaureate 100%.

Enrollment: Total enrollment 544. Undergraduate 190. Graduate 354.

Characteristics of Student Body: *Ethnic/racial makeup:* White non-Hispanic 538; Hispanic 8; Asian or Pacific Islander 2; unknown 73.

International Students: 1 nonresident alien enrolled fall 2008. No programs available to aid students whose native language is not English. No financial aid specifically designated for foreign students.

Student Life: On-campus residence halls house 100% of student body. Residence halls for males constitute 25% of such space, for both sexes 75%. Housing available for married students. 20% of married students request institutional housing; 15% are so housed. *Surrounding community:* New York City population over 7 million. Served by mass transit bus and subway system; airport 5 miles from campus; passenger rail service 4 miles from campus.

Publications: *Moreshet (Heritage)* (annually) first published in 1975.

Library Collections: 275,000 volumes. 9,100 microforms; 5,250 recordings/tapes; 720 current periodical subscriptions. Online catalog. Students have access to online information retrieval services and the Internet.

Most important holdings include Cairo Genizah Manuscript fragments; Hebrew incunabula; medieval Hebrew manuscripts.

Buildings and Grounds: Campus area 1 square block.

Chief Executive Officer: Dr. Arnold Eisen, Chancellor.

Address admission inquiries to Director of Admission.

John Jay College of Criminal Justice / CUNY

445 West 59th Street
New York, New York 10019
Tel: (212) 237-8000 **E-mail:** admiss@jjay.cuny.edu
Fax: (212) 237-8742 **Internet:** www.jjay.cuny.edu

Institution Description: *Enrollment:* 14,844. *Degrees awarded:* Associate, baccalaureate, master's.

Accreditation: *Regional:* MSA.

History: Established as College of Police Science and chartered 1964; offered first instruction 1965; awarded first degree (baccalaureate) and adopted present name 1966. *See: John Jay College of Criminal Justice: The 15th Anniversary Commemorative Service* (New York: John Jay College of Criminal Justice, 1979) for further information.

Institutional Structure: *Composition of institution:* Administrators 15. Academic affairs headed by vice president for academic affairs and provost. Management/business/finances directed by vice president for administration. Full-time instructional faculty 322. Academic governance body, College Council, meets an average of 8 times per year.

Calendar: Semesters. Academic year Aug. to May. Freshmen admitted Aug., Jan. Degrees conferred June, Feb., Aug. Formal commencement June. Summer session from early June to late July.

Characteristics of Freshmen: 9,394 applicants. 77% of applicants admitted. 39% of applicants admitted and enrolled full-time.

37 (1,016 students) submitted SAT scores. *25th percentile*: SAT Critical Reading 410, SAT Math 410. *75th percentile*: SAT Critical Reading 510, SAT Math 520.

95% of freshmen from New York. Freshmen from 4 states and 6 foreign countries.

Admission: Modified rolling admissions plan. For fall acceptance, apply no later than Sept. of year of enrollment. Students are notified of acceptance beginning in Feb. Early acceptance available. *Requirements:* Effective September 2000, admission to the baccalaureate program for recent graduates of domestic high schools will be determined using an index that weights specific performance indicators. The indicators weighted include college admission average, number of academic courses completed in high school, and SAT or ACT scores, SAT or ACT scores are required for admission to the baccalaureate program. Applicants to the baccalaureate program who are not recent graduates of domestic high schools must have a high school academic average of at least 80 and a minimum of 16 academic units with a combined total of 4 units of English and Math, with at least one unit in each discipline, or SAT score of at least 1020. Applicants who do not meet the above criteria may be admitted to the associate degree program provided that they have an SAT score of at lest 900 or a minimum high school academic average of 72, or a GED score of at least 300.

College credit and advanced placement for postsecondary-level work completed in secondary school. College credit for extrainstitutional learning (life experience) on basis of portfolio and faculty assessments, personal interviews.

Tutoring available. Developmental/remedial courses offered during regular academic year; credit given.

Degree Requirements: Candidates for the baccalaureate degree must complete 120 credits comprised of the general education requirements, major, and electives. The associate degree requires a minimum of 60 credits with a maximum of 90 credits as detailed in the college's *Bulletin*. For all undergraduate degrees, at least half of the major credit requirements must be completed at John Jay College; minimum GPA of 2.00 with a 30-credit residence requirement.

Fulfillment of some degree requirements and exemption from some beginning courses possible by passing departmental examinations, College Board CLEP. *Grading system:* A–F; pass-fail; pass; withdraw (carries time limit).

Distinctive Educational Programs: Internships. Flexible meeting places and schedules, including an off-campus center (at U.S. Military Academy at West Point), weekend and evening classes. Joint baccalaureate-master's program. Interdepartmental programs, including cross-listed courses and thematic studies. Facilities and programs for independent research, including honors programs and tutorials. Study abroad in England and Ireland.

Degrees Conferred: 186 *associate;* 1,717 *baccalaureate*; 526 *master's.* Bachelor's degrees awarded: computer and information sciences 30; legal professions 108; psychology 62; public administration and social service professions 62; security and protective services 722; social sciences 209. Master's degrees awarded: computer and information sciences 3; psychology 222; public administration and social service professions 139; security and protective services 148.

Fees and Other Expenses: *Full-time tuition per academic year 2008–09:* undergraduate resident $4,329, nonresident $8,969; contact the college for current graduate tuition and fees. *Books and supplies:* $1,016. *Other expenses:* $4,526. No on-campus housing.

Financial Aid: The college offers a direct lending program. Aid from institutionally generated funds is provided on the basis of academic merit.

Financial aid to full-time, first-time undergraduate students: 80% of students received some form of financial aid. Average amount of aid received: federal grants $3,167; state/local grants $2,858; loans $2,456.

Departments and Teaching Staff: *Total instructional faculty:* 913 (full-time 322, part-time 591). Degrees held by full-time faculty: doctorate 78.2%, master's 16.9%, baccalaureate 4%, professional .9%.

Enrollment: Total enrollment 14,844. Undergraduate 12,943. Graduate 901. Undergraduate transfer-in students 1,207.

Characteristics of Student Body: *Ethnic/racial makeup:* number of Black non-Hispanic: 3,298; American Indian or Alaska Native: 21; Asian or Pacific Islander: 720; Hispanic: 4,494; White non-Hispanic: 3,444. *Age distribution:* number under 18: 111; 18–19: 1,416; 20–21: 2,523; 22–24: 1,908; 25–29: 1,110; 30–34: 541; 35–39: 383; 40–49: 351; 50–64: 92; 65 and over: 4.

International Students: 460 nonresident aliens enrolled fall 2008. Students from Europe, Asia, Central and South America, Africa, Canada. Programs available to aid students whose native language is not English: social, cultural, financial. English as a Second Language Program.

Student Life: No on-campus housing. *Intercollegiate athletics:* male: baseball, basketball, tennis; female: baseball, basketball, tennis; both sexes: cross-country, judo, karate, rifle. *Student publications:* newspaper published 6 times per year. *Surrounding community:* New York City population over 7 million. Served by mass transit bus and rail system; airport 3 miles from campus; passenger rail service 1 mile from campus.

Publications: *Law Enforcement News* (semimonthly) first published in 1975; *Journal of Criminal Justice Ethics.*

Library Collections: 243,262 volumes. 200,427 microforms. Current serial subscriptions include 3,193 paper, 300 microform, 3,860 electronic. 100 CD-ROMs. Computer work stations available. Students have access to online information retrieval services.

Most important holdings include Court of General Sessions trial transcripts, 1883–1927; Annual Report Collection of criminal justice agencies; Warden Lewis E. Lawes papers (Sing Sing warden, 1920–1941); Flora R. Schreiber Personal papers; NYC Police Department Blotter, 1920–1933.

Chief Executive Officer: Dr. Jeremy Travis, President.

Address admission inquiries Sandra Palleja, Director of Admissions.

Keuka College

136 Central Avenue
Keuka Park, New York 14478
Tel: (315) 279-5000 **E-mail:** admissions@keuka.edu
Fax: (315) 536-5386 **Internet:** www.keuka.edu

Institution Description: Keuka College is a private, independent, nonprofit coeducational college affiliated with the American Baptist Church. *Enrollment:* 1,521. *Degrees awarded:* Baccalaureate.

Member of the consortium Rochester Area Colleges, Inc. and the College Consortium of the Finger Lakes.

Accreditation: *Regional:* MSA. *Professional*: business, nursing, occupational therapy, social work

History: Established by Rev. George Ball of Free Will Baptists as coeducational academy and college and offered first instruction at postsecondary level 1890; awarded first degree 1893; closed 1915; reestablished as women's institution 1919; chartered 1924; returned to coeducation fall 1984. *See* Philip A. Africa, *Keuka College: A History* (Valley Forge, Pa.: Judson Press, 1974) for further information.

Institutional Structure: *Governing board:* Keuka College Board of Trustees. Extrainstitutional representation: 35 trustees, including 9 alumni; institutional representation: 2 students. All voting. *Composition of institution:* Administrators 54. Academic affairs headed by academic dean. Management/business/finances directed by treasurer and business manager. Full-time instructional faculty 57. Academic governance body, Keuka College faculty, meets an average of 10 times per year.

Calendar: Semesters. Academic year Aug. to May. Freshmen admitted Aug., Feb. Degrees conferred and formal commencement May.

Characteristics of Freshmen: 93% of applicants accepted. 25% of accepted applicants enrolled.

8% (204 students) submitted SAT scores; 56% (83 students) submitted ACT scores. *25th percentile*: SAT Critical Reading 410, SAT Math 425. *75th percentile*: SAT Critical Reading 520, SAT Math 540.

35% of entering freshmen expected to graduate within 5 years. 89% of freshmen from New York. Freshmen from 13 states and 1 foreign country.

Admission: Rolling admissions plan. Apply no later than Aug. 15. Early acceptance available. Fall application days allow same day decision. *Require-*

KEUKA COLLEGE—*cont'd*

ments: Graduation from accredited secondary school and possession of a minimum of 16 college preparatory units. GED considered on individual basis. Special admission offered in individual cases with special conditions. Education transfer students must have a 2.5 GPA. *For transfer students:* 2.0 GPA; 90 hours maximum transfer credit.

College credit and advanced placement for postsecondary-level work completed in high school.

Personal and computer-assisted tutoring available.

Degree Requirements: 120 credit hours; 2.0 GPA; completion of the last 30 credits, including one field period at Keuka College; core curriculum; participation in field period during each year of enrollment (maximum of four); additional requirements for some majors.

Fulfillment of some degree requirements and exemption from some beginning courses possible by passing departmental examinations, College Board CLEP, APP, or other standardized tests. *Grading system:* A–F; withdraw; incomplete; satisfactory and unsatisfactory (field period only).

Distinctive Educational Programs: Five-week Field Period program for academic credit that integrates classroom and experiential learning. Required of every student every year. In consultation with faculty, students develop a proposal that includes focused learning objectives, activities, and evaluation strategies. Distinctive programs include occupational therapy, nursing, education (unified elementary/special education, unified secondary/special education), criminal justice, organizational communication, food, hotel and resort management. Cooperative baccalaureate programs in medical technology and chiropractic. Honors Program that combines coursework and co-curricular learning. Study abroad through group Field Periods. Washington DC semester program. Albany legislative semester. Cross-registration through Rochester Area Colleges Consortium. Exchange program in China with Honk Kong Baptist University.

Degrees Conferred: 362 *baccalaureate*; 5 *master's*. Bachelor's degrees awarded in top five disciplines: business, management, marketing, and related support services 104; health professions and related clinical sciences 99; education 65; public administration and social services 41; social sciences 17. Master's degrees awarded: business/marketing 41; health professions and related clinical sciences 16.

Fees and Other Expenses: *Full-time tuition per academic year 2008–09:* contact the college for current information regarding tuition, fees, and housing costs.

Financial Aid: Aid from institutionally generated funds is provided on the basis of academic merit, financial need. Institution has a Program Participation Agreement with the U.S. Department of Education for eligible students to receive Pell Grants and, depending upon the agreement, other federal aid.

Financial aid to full-time, first-time undergraduate students: 43% received federal grants averaging $3,098; 76% state/local grants averaging $2,319; 100% institutional grants averaging $8,106; 99% received loans averaging $5,034.

Departments and Teaching Staff: *Total instructional faculty:* 63. Student/faculty ratio: 14:1. Degrees held by full-time faculty: doctorates 58%, master's 100%. 62% hold terminal degrees.

Enrollment: Total enrollment 1.526.

Characteristics of Student Body: *Ethnic/racial makeup:* Black non-Hispanic: 103; American Indian or Alaska Native: 15; Asian or Pacific Islander: 11; Hispanic: 30; White non-Hispanic: 1,289; unknown: 69.

International Students: 4 nonresident aliens enrolled fall 2008. No programs available to aid students whose native language is not English. No financial aid specifically designated for international students.

Student Life: All students live either on campus or with their families. On-campus residence halls house 87% of student body. *Intercollegiate athletics:* basketball, swimming, tennis, volleyball. *Special regulations:* Cars permitted without restrictions. *Special services:* Learning Resources Center, medical services, Multicultural Affairs Office. *Student publications, radio: Keukonian*, a biweekly newspaper; *Kiondaga*, a yearbook; *Red Jacket*, a quarterly literary publication. Radio station WKCS broadcasts 10 hours per week. *Surrounding community:* Keuka Park population 1,200. Rochester, 50 miles from campus, is nearest metropolitan area.

Library Collections: 123,000 volumes. Online catalog. Current serial subscriptions: paper 384. 4,537 microforms; 1,939 audiovisual materials; 73 CD-ROMs. Computer work stations available. Students have access to the Internet and online information retrieval services.

Most important special collections include women's history; local Baptist Church and other local religions (Jemima Wilkinson); Penn Yan and Yates County history.

Buildings and Grounds: Campus area 165 acres.

Chief Executive Officer: Dr. Joseph G. Burke, President.

Address admission inquiries to Claudine Ninestine, Dean of Admissions.

Laboratory Institute of Merchandising

12 East 53rd Street
New York, New York 10022
Tel: (212) 752-1530 **E-mail:** admissions@limcollege.edu
Fax: (212) 421-4341 **Internet:** www.limcollege.edu

Institution Description: The Laboratory Institute of Merchandising is a private, independent institution. *Enrollment:* 1,295. *Degrees awarded:* Associate, baccalaureate.

Accreditation: *Regional:* MSA.

History: Founded 1939.

Institutional Structure: *Composition of institution:* Six divisions, each with a chairperson. *Full-time instructional staff:* 16.

Calendar: Semesters (4-1-4 plan). Academic year Aug. to July. Students admitted Aug., Jan. Degrees conferred and formal commencement May.

Characteristics of Freshmen: 1,063 applicants. 51% of applicants admitted. 54% of applicants admitted and enrolled full-time.

96% (232 students) submitted SAT scores; 4% (19 students) submitted ACT scores. *25th percentile*: SAT Critical Reading 430, SAT Math 419, ACT Composite 17, ACT English, ACT Math 15. *75th percentile*: SAT Critical Reading 520, SAT Math 510; ACT Composite 20,ACT English 21, ACT Math 20.

67% of entering freshmen expected to graduate within 5 years. 423% of freshmen from New York. Freshmen from 37 states and 15 foreign countries.

Admission: Rolling admissions plan. *Requirements:* Graduation from accredited secondary school; interview; letter of recommendation strongly encouraged. Applicants to the upper division must hold an associate degree or have 60 acceptable credits; interview; 2 letters of recommendation (1 faculty, 1 employer) required for all applicants. *Entrance tests:* SAT or ACT.

Degree Requirements: *For all associate degrees:* 64 credits; 2.0 GPA. *For all baccalaureate degrees:* 126 credits; 2.0 GPA. *For all degrees:* co-op and/or work projects required of all students.

Distinctive Educational Programs: Work-study abroad programs in London and Paris.

Degrees Conferred: 27 *associate;* 212 *baccalaureate:* fashion merchandising and marketing.

Fees and Other Expenses: *Full-time tuition and fees per academic year 2008–09:* $19,825. *Required fees:* $450. *Room and board per academic year:* $18,750. *Books and supplies:* $1,100. *Other expenses:* $3,200.

Financial Aid: Aid from institutionally generated funds is provided on the basis of academic merit, financial need.

Financial aid to full-time, first-time undergraduate students:

Departments and Teaching Staff: *Total instructional faculty:* 119 (full-time 16, part-time 103). Student/faculty ratio: 17:1. Degrees held by full-time faculty: doctorate 17%, master's 40%, baccalaureate 40%. 17% hold terminal degrees.

Enrollment: Total enrollment 1,295 (undergraduate). Transfer-in students 201.

Characteristics of Student Body: *Ethnic/racial makeup:* number of Black non-Hispanic: 72; American Indian or Alaska Native: 4; Asian or Pacific Islander: 61; Hispanic: 145; White non-Hispanic: 674. *Age distribution:* number under 18: 56; 18–19: 353; 20–21: 346; 22–24: 171; 25–29: 41; 30–34: 3. 20% of student body attend summer sessions.

International Students: 14 nonresident aliens enrolled fall 2008. Students from Europe, Asia, Central and South America, Canada. No programs available to aid students whose native language is not English. No financial programs specifically designated for international students.

Student Life: *Special services:* Student government, fashion club, marketing club, fashion styling club, professional career development club, film club, Sigma Beta Delta. *Student publications:* Yearbook; *Fashionista: Student Newsletter.*

Library Collections: 12,000 volumes. Online catalog. 400 audiovisual materials; 105 current periodical subscriptions. Computer work stations available. Students have access to the Internet at no charge.

Most important special holdings include B. Earl Puckett Fund for Retail Education; 1950s–1960s bound *Harper's Bazaar* and *Vogue* magazines.

Chief Executive Officer: Elizabeth Marcuse, President.

Address admission inquiries to Kristina Gibson, Director of Admissions.

Le Moyne College

1419 Salt Springs Road
Syracuse, New York 13214-1301
Tel: (315) 445-4100 **E-mail:** admissions@lemoyne.edu
Fax: (315) 445-4540 **Internet:** www.lemoyne.edu

Institution Description: Le Moyne College is a private, independent, nonprofit college in the Jesuit tradition. *Enrollment:* 3,479. *Degrees awarded:* Baccalaureate, master's.

Member of Syracuse Consortium for the Cultural Foundations of Medicine.

Accreditation: *Regional:* MSA. *Professional*: chemistry, physician assisting

History: Adopted present name 1945; established, chartered, and offered first instruction at postsecondary level 1946; awarded first degree (baccalaureate) 1951. *See* John W. Langdon, *Against the Sky; The First Fifty Years of Le Moyne College* (1996) for further information.

Institutional Structure: *Governing board:* Le Moyne College Board of Trustees. 39 trustees including 2 ex officio (College President and Chair, Board of Regents) and 20 alumni. All voting. *Composition of institution:* Administrators 133. Academic affairs headed by provost and vice president for academic affairs. Management/business/finances directed by vice president for finance and administration. Full-time instructional faculty 161. Academic governance body, Faculty Senate, meets an average of 8 times per year.

Calendar: Semesters. Academic year Aug. to May. Freshmen admitted Aug. and Jan. Degrees conferred and formal commencement May. Summer session of 3 terms from May to Aug.

Characteristics of Freshmen: 4,212 applicants. 61% of applicants accepted. 21% of accepted applicants enrolled full-time.

87% (472 students) submitted SAT scores; 44% (239 students) submitted ACT scores. *25th percentile*: SAT Critical Reading 480, SAT Math 500; ACT Composite 21, ACT English 19, ACT Math 21. *75th percentile*: SAT Critical Reading 580, SAT Math 590; ACT Composite 25, ACT English 25, ACT Math 26.

66% of entering freshmen expected to graduate within 5 years. 98% of freshmen from New York. Freshmen from 23 states and 15 foreign countries.

Admission: Rolling admission plan with a priority deadline of Feb. 1. Apply by Dec. 1 for early action. Early admission also available. *Requirements:* Graduation from accredited secondary school with 4 units in English, 3 foreign language, 3 mathematics, 4 social studies, 3 science; 3.0 GPA. Lowest acceptable secondary school class standing 50th percentile. *Entrance tests:* SAT or ACT. *For transfer students:* 2.6 minimum GPA; from 4-year accredited institution 90 credits; from 2-year accredited institution 60 credits.

College credit and advanced placement for postsecondary-level work completed in secondary school.

Academic Resource Center available.

Degree Requirements: 120 credit hours minimum; at least 30 must be completed at Le Moyne. 2.0 GPA overall in major. Complete at least one course in residency at Le Moyne in each of the four disciplines of the Core (English, history, philosophy, religion). Complete at least half the major requirements at Le Moyne. Fulfillment of some degree requirements and exemption from some beginning courses possible by passing College Board CLEP, APP, other standardized tests. *Grading system:* A–F; pass-fail; withdraw (carries time limit); incomplete (carries time limit).

Distinctive Educational Programs: Center for Advancement of Values Education, Integral Honors Program, Internship program, and Physician Assistant Program. Dual-degree programs in engineering with Manhattan College, Clarkson University, and the University of Detroit; in dentistry with SUNY Buffalo, co-op programs in environmental science and forestry with SUNY College of Environmental Science and Forestry in Syracuse; and in medicine, physical therapy, medical technology, and cytotechnology at the SUNY Health Science Center at Syracuse.

ROTC: Army, Air Force offered in cooperation with Syracuse University.

Degrees Conferred: 526 *baccalaureate*; 300 *master's*. Bachelor's degrees awarded in top five disciplines: business/marketing 192; psychology 129; social sciences 68; biological/life sciences 57; English 18. Masters's degrees awarded: business/marketing 52; education 278.

Fees and Other Expenses: *Full-time tuition per academic year 2008–09:* $25,000; graduate programs vary (contact the college for current rates). *Room and board per academic year:* $9,490. *Books and supplies:* $700. *Other expenses:* $1,710.

Financial Aid: Aid from institutionally generated funds is provided on the basis of academic merit, financial need, athletic ability, other criteria.

Financial aid to full-time, first-time undergraduate students: 98% received some form of aid. Average amount of aid received: federal grants $3,947; Pell grants $2,845; other federal grants $11,140; state/local grants $2,859; institutional grants $12,054.

Departments and Teaching Staff: *Total instructional faculty:* 338 (full-time 161, part-time 177). 92% of faculty hold the doctorate, first-professional, or other terminal degree. Student/faculty ratio: 13:1.

Enrollment: Total enrollment 3,479. Undergraduate 2,761. Graduate 718. Undergraduate transfer-in students 192.

Characteristics of Student Body: *Ethnic/racial makeup:* number of Black non-Hispanic: 161; American Indian or Alaska Native: 20; Asian or Pacific Islander: 61; Hispanic: 110; White non-Hispanic: 2,875; unknown: 332. *Age distribution:* number under 18: 96; 18–19: 1,007; 20–21: 948; 22–24: 317; 25–29: 131; 30–34: 75; 35–39: 61; 40–49: 85; 50–64: 28; 65 and over: 6.

International Students: 23 nonresident aliens enrolled fall 2008. Student from Europe, Asia, Central and South America, Africa, Canada, Middle East. No programs available to aid students whose native language is not English. No financial aid specifically designated for international students.

Student Life: On-campus residence halls house 60% of student body. Residences for males constitute 13% of such space, for females 14%, for both sexes 73%. *Intercollegiate athletics:* male: baseball, basketball, cross-country, golf, lacrosse, soccer, tennis, swimming and diving; female: basketball, cross-country, lacrosse, soccer, softball, tennis, volleyball, swimming and diving. Club sports for males only: rugby, ice hockey, volleyball. Club sports for females only: rugby, field hockey. *Special regulations:* Registered cars permitted; fee charged. *Special services:* Academic Resource Center, health services. *Student publications, radio: The Black Robe*, a yearbook; *The Dolphin*, a weekly newspaper; literary publications. Radio station WLMU broadcasts on campus 35 hours per week. *Surrounding community:* Syracuse metropolitan area population 732,177. Served by mass transit bus system; airport 10 miles from campus; passenger rail service 5 miles from campus.

Library Collections: 274,000 volumes. Current periodical subscriptions: paper 1,180; microform 98; via electronic access 34,152. 5,683 audiovisual materials. 1,102 DVD discs; 665 CD-ROMs. Online catalog. Access to online information retrieval services.

Most important holdings include The Reverend William Noon, S.J. Irish Literature Collection (300 volumes, with emphasis on James Joyce and the Irish Renaissance); Jesuitica. Subject strengths include English literature (American and English); industrial relations; philosophy and religious studies; Danny Biasone Syracuse National Basketball Collection.

Buildings and Grounds: Campus area 161 acres.

Chief Executive Officer: Rev. Charles J. Beirne, S.J., President.

Address admission inquiries to Dennis J. Nicholson, Director of Admission; graduate inquiries to Kristen P. Trapasso, Director of Graduate Admission.

Lehman College / CUNY

250 Bedford Park Boulevard West
Bronx, New York 10468
Tel: (718) 960-8000 **E-mail:** admissions@lehman/cuny
Fax: (718) 960-8712 **Internet:** www.lehman.edu

Institution Description: Lehman College (officially Herbert H. Lehman College) is a public institution offering both undergraduate and graduate instruction in liberal arts and sciences and certain professional areas. *Enrollment:* 11,860. *Degrees awarded:* Baccalaureate, master's.

Accreditation: *Regional:* MSA. *Professional*: accounting, chemistry, nursing, dietetics, health services administration, social work, speech-language pathology, teacher education

History: Established as Hunter College in the Bronx 1931; offered first instruction at postsecondary level 1932; became coeducational 1951; offered first instruction at upper division level and awarded first degree (baccalaureate) 1955; became an independent college within the City University of New York and changed name to Herbert H. Lehman College 1968; adopted present name recently.

Institutional Structure: *Composition of institution:* Administrators 30. Academic affairs headed by provost and vice president for academic affairs. Management/business/finances directed by vice president for administration. Full-time instructional faculty 337. Academic governance body, Lehman College Senate, meets an average of 8 times per year.

Calendar: Semesters. Academic year Sept. to May. Freshmen admitted Sept., Jan., June. Degrees conferred June, Sept., Jan. Formal commencement June. Summer session of 1 term from late June to early Aug.

Characteristics of Freshmen: 12,408 applicants. 31% of applicants admitted. 23% of applicants admitted and enrolled full-time.

97% (539 students) submitted SAT scores. *25th percentile*: SAT Critical Reading 400, SAT Math 400. *75th percentile*: SAT Critical Reading 490, SAT Math 500.

LEHMAN COLLEGE / CUNY—*cont'd*

29% of entering freshmen expected to graduate within 5 years. 99% of freshmen from New York. Freshmen from 2 states and 69 foreign countries.

Admission: Rolling admissions plan. For fall acceptance, apply as early as Aug. 1 of previous year, but not later than Aug. 31 of year of enrollment. Early acceptance available. *Requirements:* Either graduation from accredited secondary school with GPA of 80 or secondary school rank in top 35% or GED with minimum score of 300. *For transfer students:* 2.0 minimum GPA; from 4-year accredited institution 90 credit hours maximum transfer credit; from 2-year accredited institution 64 hours.

College credit and advanced placement for postsecondary-level work completed in secondary school. Advanced placement on basis of portfolio and faculty assessment.

Tutoring available. Credit development and noncredit remedial courses offered during regular academic year.

Degree Requirements: *Undergraduate:* 128 semester hours; 2.0 GPA; senior year in residence; foundation course in physical education; foreign language requirement; core curriculum requirement; exit competency examinations in writing and mathematics.

Fulfillment of some degree requirements and exemption from some beginning courses possible by passing College Board CLEP. *Grading system:* A–F; pass-fail; withdraw (carries time limit).

Distinctive Educational Programs: Adult degree program; weekend and evening classes; program for deaf and hearing impaired; work-experience programs; accelerated degree programs; interdepartmental programs in Latin American and Caribbean studies, American studies, ancient civilizations of the Mediterranean and Near East, bioanthropology, biology-biochemistry, city and humanities, comparative literature, Italian-American studies, physical anthropology. Facilities and programs for independent research, including honors programs, individual majors, tutorials. Study abroad through New York/Paris Exchange; Summer Study/Travel Program (Nantes, France; London, Spain exchanges).

ROTC: Army in cooperation with Fordham University.

Degrees Conferred: 1,383 *baccalaureate*; 654 *master's*. Bachelor's degrees awarded in top five disciplines: health professions and related clinical sciences 275; social sciences 244; business/marketing 195; public administration and social services 128; computer and information sciences 85. Master's degrees awarded: biological/life sciences 8; business/marketing 13; computer and information sciences 23; education 517; English 14; family and consumer sciences 281; history 6; visual and performing arts 7.

Fees and Other Expenses: *Full-time tuition per academic year 2008–09:* resident $4,340, nonresident $8,980. *Required fees:* $290. No on-campus housing. *Books and supplies* $1,016. *Other expenses:* $4,526.

Financial Aid: Aid from institutionally generated funds is provided on the basis of academic merit, financial need.

Financial aid to full-time, first-time undergraduate students:

Financial aid to full-time, first-time undergraduate students: 89% received some form of aid. Average amount of aid received: federal grants $4,340; Pell grants $3,692; other federal grants $613; state/local grants $3,508; institutional grants $5,269.

Departments and Teaching Staff: *Total instructional faculty:* 898 (full-time 337, part-time 561). Student/faculty ratio: 15:1. 405 of faculty hold the doctorate, first-professional, or other terminal degree.

Enrollment: Total enrollment 11,860. Undergraduate 9,569. Graduate 2,291. Undergraduate transfer-in students 1,209.

Characteristics of Student Body: *Ethnic/racial makeup:* number of Black non-Hispanic: 1,849; American Indian or Alaska Native: 5; Asian or Pacific Islander: 373; Hispanic: 4,186; White non-Hispanic: 905. *Age distribution:* number under 136: 18–19: 1,436; 20–21: 1,973; 22–24: 1,677; 25–29: 1,467; 30–34: 857; 35–39: 597; 40–49: 824; 50–64: 319; 65 and over: 68.

International Students: 489 nonresident aliens enrolled fall 2008. Students from Europe, Asia, Central and South America, Africa, Canada, Middle East. Programs available to aid students whose native language is not English: social, cultural, financial. English as a Second Language Program.

Student Life: No on-campus housing. *Intercollegiate athletics:* male: baseball, basketball, soccer, track, volleyball; female: basketball, track, softball, volleyball; both sexes: swimming, tennis. *Special regulations:* Cars permitted without restrictions. *Student publications, radio: Examiner*, a quarterly science newsletter; *Footnotes*, a quarterly literary magazine; *Meridian*, a weekly newspaper; *Quatros*, a yearbook. Radio station WHLC broadcasts 30 hours per week. *Surrounding community:* New York City population over 7 million. Served by mass transit bus and train systems; airports 3 and 5 miles from campus; passenger rail service less than 1 mile from campus.

Publications: *Lehman Letter, Lehman Report, Herbert H. Lehman Memorial Lectures, Undergraduate and Graduate Bulletins. Publisher:* Lehman College Press.

Library Collections: 572,000 volumes. Online catalog. 45,618 government documents; 500,000 microforms; 418,547 audiovisual materials; 13,451 current periodical subscriptions. Students have access to online information retrieval services and the Internet.

Most important holdings include collection on Bronx history; Fordham Manor Church Records; Riverdale Neighborhood House Records.

Buildings and Grounds: Campus area 37 acres.

Chief Executive Officer: Dr. Ricardo r. Fernandez, President.

Address admission inquiries to Clarence Wilkes, Director of Admissions.

Long Island University - Brooklyn Campus

One University Plaza
Brooklyn, New York 11201-9926

Tel: (718) 488-1011 **E-mail:** admissions@liu.edu
Fax: (718) 797-2399 **Internet:** www.liu.edu

Institution Description: *Enrollment:* 8,051. *Degrees awarded:* Associate, baccalaureate, first-professional (pharmacy), master's, doctorate.

Accreditation: *Regional:* MSA. *Professional*: nursing, pharmacy, physical therapy, physician assisting, psychology internship, public administration, respiratory therapy, speech-language pathology

History: Established and provisionally chartered as Long Island University College of Arts and Sciences; offered first instruction at postsecondary level 1927; officially chartered and awarded first degree (baccalaureate) 1931; adopted present name 1969.

Institutional Structure: *Governing board:* Board of Trustees of Long Island University. Extrainstitutional representation: 45 trustees; institutional representation: president; president ex officio. *Composition of institution:* Administrators 202. Academic affairs headed by vice president for academic affairs. Management/business/finances directed by vice president for finance. Full-time instructional faculty: 320.

Calendar: Semesters. Academic year Sept. to May. Freshmen admitted Sept., Feb., June. Degrees conferred and formal commencement June. Summer session from early June to early Aug.

Characteristics of Freshmen: 5,307 applicants 60% of applicants accepted. 37% of accepted applicants enrolled full-time.

50% (644 students) submitted SAT scores; 37% (31 students) submitted ACT scores. *25th percentile*: SAT Critical Reading 400, SAT Math 410, SAT Writing 400. *75th percentile*: SAT Critical Reading 500, SAT Math 550; ACT Composite 500.

Admission: Rolling admissions plan. Early acceptance available. *Requirements:* Either graduation from accredited secondary school or GED. Minimum grade average 80 on 100-point scale. *Entrance tests:* College Board SAT recommended. For foreign students TOEFL. *For transfer students:* 2.0 minimum GPA; maximum transfer credit limited only by residence requirement. Higher minimum GPA required for some programs.

College credit and advanced placement for postsecondary-level work completed in secondary school.

Tutoring available. Noncredit developmental/remedial courses available.

Degree Requirements: *For all associate degrees:* 64 semester hours. *For all baccalaureate degrees:* 128–165 hours. *For all undergraduate degrees:* 2.0 GPA; 32 hours in residence; core curriculum. For baccalaureate in pharmacy, 3 years in residence. *Grading system:* A–F; pass-fail; withdraw; withdrew failing.

Degrees Conferred: 26 *associate;* 580 *baccalaureate:* 815 *master's*; 26 *doctorate*. Bachelor's degrees awarded in top five disciplines: health professions and related sciences 114; business and management 85; communications 53; computer and information sciences 51; psychology 44. 200 *first-professional:* pharmacy.

Fees and Other Expenses: *Full-time tuition per academic year 2008–09:* $25,574 undergraduate; contact the institution for current graduate and first-professional tuition, fees, and other costs.

Financial Aid: Institution has a Program Participation Agreement with the U.S. Department of Education for eligible students to receive Pell Grants and, depending upon the agreement, other federal aid.

Departments and Teaching Staff: *Total instructional faculty:* 320. Student/faculty ratio: 17:1.

Enrollment: Total enrollment 8,051. Undergraduate 3,958. Graduate 4,113. Undergraduate transfer-in students 24.

Characteristics of Student Body: *Ethnic/racial makeup:* number of Black non-Hispanic: 3,223; American Indian or Alaska Native: 17; Asian or Pacific Islander: 1,062; Hispanic: 947; White non-Hispanic: 1,827; unknown: 592. *Age distribution:* number under 18: 65; 18–19: 1,268; 20–21: 1,133; 22–24: 1,044; 25–29: 756; 30–34: 388; 35–39: 263; 40–49: 269; 50–64: 89; 65 and over: 2.

International Students: 295 nonresident aliens enrolled 2008. Programs available to aid students whose native language is not English: noncredit English language institute.

Student Life: On-campus residence halls and apartments available. *Intercollegiate athletics:* male: baseball, basketball, cross-country, golf, soccer, tennis; track (indoor/outdoor); female: basketball, cross-country, softball, tennis, track (indoor/outdoor). *Special services:* Learning Resources Center, medical services. *Student publications, radio: Seawanhaka*, a weekly newspaper; *Sound*, a yearbook. Radio station WLIU. *Surrounding community:* New York City population over 7 million. Served by mass transit bus and rail systems; airport 15 miles from campus; passenger rail service 1 block from campus.

Library Collections: 2,200,000 volumes. 814,000 microforms; 8,000 recordings/tapes; 8,000 periodicals. Online catalog. Students have access to online information retrieval services and the Internet.

Buildings and Grounds: Campus area 22 acres.

Chief Executive Officer: Dr. David J. Steinberg, President.

Address admission inquiries to Dean of Admissions.

Long Island University - C. W. Post Campus

720 Northern Boulevard
Brookville, New York 11548-1300
Tel: (516) 299-2000 **E-mail:** enroll@cwpost.liu.edu
Fax: (516) 299-3829 **Internet:** www.cwpost.liu.edu

Institution Description: *Enrollment:* 8,421. *Degrees awarded:* Associate, baccalaureate, first-professional, master's.

Accreditation: *Regional:* MSA. *Professional*: business, clinical lab scientist, counseling, librarianship, medical record administration, nursing, psychology internship, public administration, radiography

History: Established 1954; offered first instruction at postsecondary level 1955; awarded first degree (baccalaureate) 1958.

Institutional Structure: *Governing board:* Board of Trustees of Long Island University. Extrainstitutional representation: 43 trustees; institutional representation: chancellor of the university. 1 ex officio. 27 voting. *Composition of institution:* Academic affairs headed by vice president for academic affairs. Management/business/finances directed by vice president for administration. Full-time instructional faculty 328. Academic governance body, Faculty Council, meets an average of 8 times per year. *Faculty representation:* Faculty served by collective bargaining agent, New York State United Teachers, affiliated with AFT.

Calendar: Semesters. Academic year Sept. to May. Freshmen admitted Sept. Jan., May, June, July. Degrees conferred May, Jan., Oct. Formal commencement May. Summer session from mid-May to late Aug.

Characteristics of Freshmen: 75% of applicants accepted. 29% of accepted applicants enrolled.

91% (540 students) submitted SAT scores; 10% (102 students) submitted ACT scores. *25th percentile*: SAT Critical Reading 450, SAT Math 450; ACT Composite 18. *75th percentile*: SAT Critical Reading 540, SAT Math 550; ACT Composite 23.

87% of entering freshmen expected to graduate within 5 years. 91% of freshmen from New York. Freshmen from 32 states and 47 foreign countries.

Admission: Rolling admissions plan. For fall acceptance, apply as early as July 1, but not later than Sept. 15 of year of enrollment. Early acceptance available. *Requirements:* Either graduation from accredited secondary school with 4 units English, 2 foreign language, 2 mathematics, 1 laboratory science, 3 social studies, 4 in electives; or GED. Minimum grade average 75. Lowest acceptable secondary school class standing 45th percentile. *Entrance tests:* College Board SAT or ACT composite. For foreign students TOEFL. *For transfer students:* 2.0 minimum GPA; from 4-year accredited institution 96 hours maximum transfer credit; from 2-year accredited institution 64 hours.

College credit and advanced placement for postsecondary-level work completed in secondary school. College credit for extrainstitutional learning on basis of portfolio and faculty assessments.

Tutoring available. Remedial courses offered during regular academic year; credit given.

Degree Requirements: *For all associate degrees:* 64 semester hours; complete program in residence; courses in English. *For all baccalaureate degrees:* 128 hours; 2.0 GPA (higher for some programs); 2 terms in residence; core curriculum requirements. *For all undergraduate degrees:* Exit competency examinations in writing and mathematics; demonstrated competency in oral English, library usage, and computer literacy.

Fulfillment of some degree requirements and exemption from some beginning courses possible by passing departmental examinations, College Board CLEP, AP. *Grading system:* A–F; pass-fail, withdraw.

Distinctive Educational Programs: Work-experience programs. Flexible meeting places and schedules, including off-campus centers (in Brentwood and Orangeburg), weekend and evening classes. Accelerated degree programs. Special facilities for using telecommunications in the classroom. Interdepartmental and interdisciplinary programs in area studies, environmental studies, international affairs; individually designed majors. Facilities and programs for independent research, including honors programs, individual majors, tutorials. Independent study. Cross-registration with various Long Island colleges. *Other distinctive programs:* Degree-granting evening and weekend college for nontraditional students. Continuing education programs for community groups, individuals, and businesses on a credit and noncredit basis.

ROTC: Army in cooperation with Hofstra University.

Degrees Conferred: 2 *associate;* 101 *baccalaureate*; 1,527 *master's*; 28 *doctorate*. Bachelor's degrees awarded in top five disciplines: education 369; business/marketing 162; visual and performing arts 91; protective services/public administration 76; psychology 60.

Fees and Other Expenses: *Full-time tuition per academic year 2008–09:* contact the institution for current tuition, fees, and housing costs.

Financial Aid: The university offers a direct lending program. Aid from institutionally generated funds is provided on the basis of academic merit, financial need, athletic ability. Institution has a Program Participation Agreement with the U.S. Department of Education for eligible students to receive Pell Grants and, depending upon the agreement, other federal aid.

Departments and Teaching Staff: *Total instructional faculty:* 328. Student/faculty ratio: 15:1. Degrees held by full-time faculty: doctorate 77%, master's 15%, baccalaureate 5%, professional 3%. 77% hold terminal degrees.

Enrollment: Total enrollment 8,421.

Characteristics of Student Body: *Ethnic/racial makeup:* number of Black non-Hispanic: 430; American Indian or Alaska Native: 16; Asian or Pacific Islander: 122; Hispanic: 345; White non-Hispanic: 2,267; unknown: 1,565. *Age distribution:* number under 18: 117; 18–19: 1,608; 20–21: 1,389; 22–24: 980; 25–29: 333; 30–34: 117; 35–39: 92; 40–49: 158; 50–64: 79; 65 and over: 4.

International Students: Students from Europe, Asia, Central and South America, Australia, New Zealand. Programs available to aid students whose native language is not English: social, cultural. English as a Second Language Program. Financial aid specifically designated fop international students: variable number of scholarships available.

Student Life: On-campus residence halls house 30% of undergraduates; graduate student housing available. *Intercollegiate athletics:* male: baseball, basketball, football, lacrosse, soccer, tennis, track, indoor track, cross-country, wrestling; female: basketball, field hockey, softball, tennis, volleyball, track, cross country, indoor track. *Special regulations:* Cars with parking permit allowed on campus. *Special services:* Learning Resources Center, Co-op program, student health and counseling center, career services, campus bus system, medical services, *Student publications, radio: Loomings*, a biannual literary magazine; *Opticon*, a yearbook; *Pioneer*, a weekly newspaper. Radio station WCWP-FM broadcasts 123 hours per week. *Surrounding community:* Brookville. New York City, 25 miles from campus, is nearest metropolitan area. Served by mass transit bus and rail systems; airport 19 miles from campus; passenger rail service 4 miles from campus.

Library Collections: The B. Davis Schwartz Memorial Library has a large and diverse collection with over 1 million volumes and more than 5,000 periodicals and newspaper subscriptions in its various public service departments. Online catalog. The collections of all Long Island University's libraries are linked LIUCAT, a computerized network (housed at C.W. Post) makes all resources available to students and faculty.

Most important holdings include Eugene and Carlotta O'Neill private collection, Theodore Roosevelt Association Collection, Center for Business Research, William Randolph Hearst Collection of Photographs and Objects d'Art.

Buildings and Grounds: Campus area 400 acres.

Chief Executive Officer: Dr. David J. Steinberg, President.

Address admission inquiries to Gary R. Bergman, Associate Provost for Enrollment.

Manhattan College

Manhattan College Parkway
Riverdale, New York 10471-4098
Tel: (718) 862-7200 **E-mail:** admit@manhattan.edu
Fax: (718) 862-8019 **Internet:** www.manhattan.ecu

Institution Description: Manhattan College is a private, independent, nonprofit institution. *Enrollment:* 3,441. *Degrees awarded:* Associate, baccalaureate, master's.

Accreditation: *Regional:* MSA. *Professional*: chemistry, engineering

History: Established as Academy of the Holy Infancy (for men) 1853; offered first instruction at postsecondary level 1861; chartered as Manhattan College 1863; awarded first degree (baccalaureate) 1866; became coeducational 1973.

MANHATTAN COLLEGE—*cont'd*

See Gabriel Costello, F.S.C., *The Arches of the Years* (Riverdale: Manhattan College, 1980) for further information.

Institutional Structure: *Governing board:* Board of Trustees. Extrainstitutional representation: 36 trustees; institutional representation: president of the college; 6 alumni. 2 ex officio. All voting. *Composition of institution:* Administrators 32. Academic affairs headed by president. Management/business/finances directed by vice president for administrative services. Full-time instructional faculty 167. Academic governance body, Council of Academic Administrators, meets an average of 14 times per year.

Calendar: Semesters. Academic year early Sept. to early May. Freshmen admitted Jan., Sept. Degrees conferred May, Sept., Jan. Formal commencement May. Summer session of 4 terms.

Characteristics of Freshmen: 5,513 applicants. 51% of applicants accepted. 26% of accepted applicants enrolled full-time.

97% (702 students) submitted SAT scores; 13% (89 students) submitted ACT scores. *25th percentile*: SAT Critical Reading 580, SAT Math 510, SAT Writing 500; ACT Composite 22. *75th percentile*: SAT Critical Reading 590, SAT Math 615, SAT Writing 590; ACT Composite 26.

75% of entering freshmen expected to graduate within 5 years. 70% of freshmen from New York. Freshmen from 32 states and 10 foreign countries.

Admission: Rolling admissions plan. For fall acceptance, apply as early as fall of senior year of secondary school, but not later than Mar. 1 of year of enrollment. Early acceptance available. *Requirements:* Graduation from accredited secondary school with 4 units in English, 2 in a modern or classical foreign language, 3 mathematics, 3 social studies, 2 science, 2 electives; or GED. *Entrance tests:* College Board SAT or ACT composite. For foreign students TOEFL. *For transfer students:* 2.5 minimum GPA; from 4- and 2-year accredited institutions 66 hours maximum transfer credit.

College credit and advanced placement for postsecondary-level work completed in secondary school. College credit for extrainstitutional learning.

Tutoring available.

Degree Requirements: *For all baccalaureate degrees:* 120–133 credit hours; 4 terms in residence. *For all undergraduate degrees:* 2.0 GPA; general education requirements.

Fulfillment of some degree requirements and exemption from some beginning courses possible by passing College Board CLEP, other standardized tests. *Grading system:* A–F; withdraw.

Distinctive Educational Programs: Cooperative education. Flexible meeting places and schedules, including weekend and evening classes. Cross-registration with the College of Mount Saint Vincent in English, fine arts, modern languages, physical education, psychology, religious studies, and sociology; joint departmental programs in biology, chemistry, physics, mathematics and computer science. Special computer facilities. Interdisciplinary programs in peace studies, international studies, urban studies. Preprofessional programs in dentistry, veterinary medicine. Facilities and programs for independent research, including honors programs, tutorials, directed independent study. Study abroad in Austria, Canada, England, France, Ireland, Italy, Mexico, Spain, Germany.

ROTC: Air Force.

Degrees Conferred: 658 *baccalaureate*; 121 *master's*. Bachelor's degrees awarded in top five disciplines: business, management, marketing, and related support services 231; engineering 128; education 127; communication, journalism, and related programs 83; psychology 49. Master's degrees awarded: education 68; engineering 69.

Fees and Other Expenses: *Full-time tuition per academic year 2008–09:* undergraduate $23,130; contact the college for current graduate tuition and fees. *Books and supplies:* $1,100. *Room and board per academic year:*$9,770. *Other expenses:* $1,800.

Financial Aid: Aid from institutionally generated funds is provided on the basis of academic merit, financial need, athletic ability, other criteria. Institution has a Program Participation Agreement with the U.S. Department of Education for eligible students to receive Pell Grants and, depending upon the agreement, other federal aid.

Financial aid to first-time, full-time undergraduate students: 82% of students received some form of financial aid: federal grants 16%; Pell grants 16% other federal grants 13%; state/local grants 34%; institutional grants 72%.

Departments and Teaching Staff: *Total instructional faculty:* 176. Total tenured faculty: 124. Student/faculty ratio: 14:1. Degrees held by full-time faculty: doctorate 90.7%, master's 7.5%, baccalaureate .6%. 91% hold terminal degrees.

Enrollment: Total enrollment 3,441. Undergraduate 3,022.

Characteristics of Student Body: *Ethnic/racial makeup:* number of Black non-Hispanic: 131; American Indian or Alaska Native: 1; Asian or Pacific Islander: 111; Hispanic: 318; White non-Hispanic: 1,947; unknown: 284. *Age distribution:* number under 18: 8; 18–19: 557; 20–21: 1,327; 22–24: 836; 25–29: 92; 30–34: 27; 35–39: 20; 40–49: 19; 50–64: 17; 65 and over: 1.

International Students: 30 nonresident aliens enrolled fall 2008. Students from Europe, Asia, Central and South America, Africa, Australia. Programs available to aid students whose native language is not English: social and cultural. ASPECT Language School on campus. No financial aid specifically designated for international students.

Student Life: On-campus residence halls house 40% of student body. Residence halls for males and females constitute 100% of such space. *Intercollegiate athletics:* male: baseball, basketball, crew, football, golf, hockey, soccer, swimming, tennis track; female: basketball, softball, swimming, tennis, volleyball. *Special regulations:* Registered cars with decals permitted in designated parking areas. *Special services:* Learning Resources Center, medical services, bus service between campus and College of Mount Saint Vincent. *Student publications, radio: Chalk Dust*, a journal; *Manhattan College Humanist*, a semiannual literary magazine; *Manhattan College Manhattanite*, a yearbook; *The Quadrangle*, a student newspaper. Radio station WRCM broadcasts 82 hours per week. *Surrounding community:* New York City population over 7 million. Served by mass transit bus and subway systems; airport 12 miles from campus; passenger and rail service 2 miles from campus.

Library Collections: 220,000 volumes. 541,850 microforms; 3,680 audiovisual materials; 1,390 current periodical subscriptions. Online catalog. 746 recordings, 41 compact discs; 23 CD-ROMs. Students have access to online information retrieval services and the Internet.

Most important holdings include Slattery Dante collection; De Coursey Fales collection of English and American literature; Thomas More collection.

Buildings and Grounds: Campus area 50 acres.

Chief Executive Officer: Bro. Thomas J. Scanlan, F.S.C., President.

Address admission inquiries to Kevin P. Cavanaugh, Director of Admissions.

School of Arts

Degree Programs Offered: *Baccalaureate* in communications, economics, English, fine arts, government, history, international studies, government, history, modern foreign languages, peace studies, peace studies, philosophy, psychology, religious studies, sociology, urban affairs.

Distinctive Educational Programs: Clusters in law, American studies, Pan-African studies, Latin-American and Caribbean area studies, women's studies, Roman Catholic studies.

School of Science

Degree Programs Offered: *Baccalaureate* in biology, biochemistry, chemistry, computer science, mathematics, physics.

Distinctive Educational Programs: Early Assurance Program School of Medicine, SUNY at Buffalo; cooperative programs with New York Chiropractic College, New York University College of Dentistry, New York College of Podiatric Medicine, SUNY State University of Optometry.

School of Business

Degree Programs Offered: *Baccalaureate* in accounting, computer information systems, economics, finance, managerial sciences, marketing.

Degree Requirements: 129 credits.

Distinctive Educational Programs: International Field Study each January intersession whereby students tour one European nation as part of a marketing course. Accounting internship programs. Small business management seminary offers assistance to small business community through student counseling teams.

School of Engineering

Degree Programs Offered: *Baccalaureate* in engineering (chemical, civil, computer, electrical, environmental, mechanical).

Distinctive Educational Programs: Fire engineering program, developed with assistance of New York City Fire Department. Particulate Solids Research Institute. Cooperative 3-2 program with several liberal arts colleges. Seamless master's degree program.

School of Education

Degree Programs Offered: *Baccalaureate* in secondary education, elementary education, special education, physical education, exercise science and sports medicine, radiological and health sciences.

Distinctive Educational Programs: Project CHAMP. Project SPORT.

Graduate Division

Degree Programs Offered: *Master's* in business administration, engineering (chemical, civil, computer, electrical, environmental, mechanical), counseling, special education, school administration and supervision, biotechnology program. Professional diploma in school counselor, school administration and supervision, advanced leadership studies.

Departments and Teaching Staff: Faculty drawn from other schools within Manhattan College.

Manhattan School of Music

120 Claremont Avenue
New York, New York 10027
Tel: (212) 749-2801 **E-mail:** admission@msmnyc.edu
Fax: (212) 749-5471 **Internet:** www.msmnyc.edu

Institution Description: Manhattan School of Music is a private, independent, nonprofit institution. *Enrollment:* 967. *Degrees awarded:* Baccalaureate, master's, doctorate. Diplomas also awarded.

Accreditation: *Regional:* MSA. *Professional*: music

History: Established as Neighborhood Music School 1917; incorporated 1920; adopted present name 1938; offered first instruction at postsecondary level 1943; awarded first degree (baccalaureate) 1944; awarded first master of music degree 1948; awarded first doctor of musical arts degree 1976. *See* Janet D. Schenck, *Adventure in Music, A Reminiscence* (New York: American Printing Co., 1961) for further information.

Institutional Structure: *Governing board:* Board of Trustees. Representation: 14 trustees plus 4 honorary trustees and nonvoting trustees. *Composition of institution:* Administrators 18. Academic affairs headed by vice president. Management/business/finances directed by chief financial officer. Full-time Instructional faculty 75. Academic governance body, Committee for Academic and Student Affairs, meets irregularly.

Calendar: Semesters. Academic year Sept. to May. Freshmen admitted Sept. Degrees conferred and formal commencement May.

Characteristics of Freshmen: 2,751 applicants. 39% of applicants accepted. 41% of accepted applicants enrolled full-time.

32% of freshmen from New York.

Admission: Deadlines correspond to specific audition periods: Dec. 1 for Mar. auditions. *Requirements:* Either graduation from accredited secondary school with 16 academic units, or GED. Audition required. *Entrance tests:* Institutional examinations in English, music theory, and keyboard skills. For international students minimum TOEFL score 550. *For transfer students:* 3.0 minimum GPA; audition; maximum 60 credits for transfer.

College credit and advanced placement for postsecondary-level work completed in secondary school. Tutoring available. Noncredit remedial courses offered during regular academic year.

Degree Requirements: *Undergraduate:* 122 semester hours; 1 year in resident. For brass, guitar, harp, jazz, piano, string, voice and woodwind majors, public solo recital; for all other majors, faculty jury examination. *For graduate (master's) students:* 60 semester hours; 2 years in residence. All majors, except orchestral performance, composition and percussion, public solo recital. Other majors, faculty jury examination. *Doctoral:* 59–61 semester hours; 2 years in residence. Two solo recitals, one chamber recital Concerto performance (guitar and piano only). Orchestral Excerpts Jury Examination for all orchestral instrument majors. Comprehensive examination. Thesis examination.

Fulfillment of some degree requirements and exemption from some beginning courses possible by passing departmental examinations, College Board CLEP, other standardized tests. *Grading system:* A–F; pass; withdraw (carries time limit).

Distinctive Educational Programs: *Available to all students:* Evening classes. *Other distinctive programs:* Bachelor of Music and Master of Music programs in jazz performance. Two symphony orchestras; professional-level opera theater; three jazz big bands; chamber orchestra; recording studio; Master of Music degree in orchestral performance (first such degree offered in the United States).

Degrees Conferred: 95 *baccalaureate:* visual and performing arts; 135 *master's:* visual and performing arts; 10 *doctorate:* visual and performing arts.

Fees and Other Expenses: *Full-time tuition per academic year 2008–09:* undergraduate and graduate $30,450. *Required fees:* $460. *Other fees:* $4,600. *Room and board per academic year:* $13,755.

Financial Aid: Aid from institutionally generated funds is provided on the basis of academic merit, financial need.

Financial aid to full-time, first-time undergraduate students:

Departments and Teaching Staff: Faculty members are engaged on the basis of professional achievement. *Total instruction faculty:* 380 (full-time 75, part-time 305). 405 of faculty hold the doctorate, first-professional, or other terminal degree.

Enrollment: Total enrollment 967. Undergraduate 420. Graduate 547. Undergraduate transfer-in students 30.

Characteristics of Student Body: *Ethnic/racial makeup:* number of Black non-Hispanic: 28; American Indian or Alaska Native: 2; Asian or Pacific Islander: 26; Hispanic: 37; White non-Hispanic: 315; unknown: 102. *Age distribution:* number under 18: 5; 18–19: 144; 20–21: 151; 22–24: 80; 25–29: 31; 30–34: 3; 35–39: 1.

International Students: 273 nonresident aliens enrolled fall 2008. Students from Europe, Asia, Central and south America, Africa, Canada, Australia, New Zealand, Middle East. Programs available to aid students whose native language is not English: social, financial.

Student Life: Institution-sponsored housing accommodates 400 students. *Special services:* Health clinic, personal/psychological counseling. New student orientation program at the beginning of each semester. *Surrounding community:* New York population over 7 million. Served by mass transit bus and rail systems; airport 5 miles from campus; passenger rail service 5 miles from campus.

Library Collections: 110,000 volumes. Online catalog. 19,000 audiovisual materials. 180 current periodical subscriptions. 30,000 recordings. 6 computer work stations. Total 2008–09 budget for books and materials: $100,000.

Most important special holdings include the school's student performances (recordings/videos); school archives.

Buildings and Grounds: Campus area ½ square block.

Chief Executive Officer: Robert Sirota, President.

Address admission inquiries to Amy A. Anderson, Assistant Dean for Enrollment Management.

Manhattanville College

2900 Purchase Street
Purchase, New York 10577-2132
Tel: (914) 694-2200 **E-mail:** admissions@mville.edu
Fax: (914) 694-6234 **Internet:** www.mville.edu

Institution Description: Manhattanville College is a private, independent, nonprofit college. *Enrollment:* 2,823. *Degrees awarded:* Baccalaureate, master's.

Member of Westchester Consortium for International Studies.

Accreditation: *Regional:* MSA.

History: Established as Manhattanville Academy 1841; changed name to Manhattanville Seminary 1851; offered first instruction at postsecondary level 1914; chartered and changed name to College of the Sacred Heart 1917; awarded first degree (baccalaureate) 1918; change name to Manhattanville College of the Sacred Heart 1937; became independent and adopted present name 1966; became coeducational 1971.

Institutional Structure: *Governing board:* Board of Trustees. Extrainstitutional representation: 29 members, 1 institutional representative, 14 alumni. 29 voting. *Composition of institution:* Administrators 48. Academic affairs headed by provost and dean of faculty. Management/business/finances directed by vice president for finance and treasurer. Full-time instructional faculty 94. Academic governance body, the faculty, meets an average of 9 times per year.

Calendar: Semesters. Academic year Sept. to May. Degrees conferred May, Aug., Jan. Formal commencement May. Two five-week summer sessions. January intersession.

Characteristics of Freshmen: 4,556 applicants. 52% of applicants accepted. 24% of accepted applicants enrolled full-time.

87% (432 students) submitted SAT scores; 23% (114 students) submitted ACT scores. *25th percentile*: SAT Critical Reading 500, SAT Math 490, SAT Writing 500; ACT Composite 21. *75th percentile*: SAT Critical Reading 610, SAT Math 610, SAT Writing 610; ACT Composite 24.

60% of entering freshmen expected to graduate within 5 years. 55% of freshmen from New York. Freshmen from 39 states and 60 foreign countries.

Admission: Rolling admissions plan. For fall acceptance, apply no later than Mar. 1. Students are notified beginning Feb. 1. Manhattanville participates in Common Application Program. Early decision available. Early decision candidates must apply by Dec. 1. *Requirements:* 4 secondary school units in English. 3–4 years each in foreign language, history, mathematics, and science recommended. GED accepted. Additional requirements for some programs. Minimum GPA 3.0. Lowest acceptable secondary school class standing 50th percentile. *Entrance tests:* College Board SAT or ACT composite. Alternate application procedure available. *For transfer students:* 2.5 minimum GPA; 60 credits maximum may be transferred.

College credit and advanced placement for extrainstitutional learning (life experience) on basis of faculty assessment; CLEP, AP, A-levels, 1B high-level exams.

Tutoring available. Noncredit developmental/remedial courses offered during regular academic year.

Degree Requirements: *Undergraduate:* 120 credit hours; 2.0 GPA; 4 terms in residence; faculty committee approval of portfolio representing student's

MANHATTANVILLE COLLEGE—*cont'd*

work during 4 years of college. Some degree requirements can be met and exemption from some beginning courses possible by passing College Board CLEP or other achievement tests. Some major programs (education, music and dance/theater) exceed 120 credits. *Grading system:* A–F; pass-fail; withdraw (must be approved before midsemester); descriptive reports in small-enrollment courses.

Distinctive Educational Programs: *For undergraduates:* Accelerated degree programs. Joint degree programs. BA/MAT or BA/MPS with Manhattanville's Graduate School of Education, BA/MS in physical therapy with New York Medical College, BA/MS in computer science with Brooklyn Polytechnic. Interdisciplinary programs in American studies, Asian studies, biochemistry, classics, international studies, and Romance languages. Facilities and programs for independent research. College Honors Program, as well as departmental honors programs. Semester abroad through cooperative programs in Washington (DC), California, Oxford, Berlin, Galway, Paris, Rome, Florence, Seville, Madrid, Tokyo, and Osaka. Cross-registration with SUNY at Purchase. *Available to all students:* Evening classes. Tutorials. *For graduate students:* MA in liberal studies, writing. MAT and MPS in education. MS in leadership/strategic management/human resource development.

Degrees Conferred: 394 *baccalaureate*; 375 *master's*. Bachelor's degrees awarded in top five disciplines: business/marketing 97; psychology 60; visual and performing arts 46; social sciences 37; history 36. Master's degrees awarded: business/marketing 33; education 267; English 17; liberal arts 5.

Fees and Other Expenses: *Full-time tuition per academic year 2008=09:* $31,620. *Required fees:* $1,140. *Room and board per academic year:* $13,040. *Books and supplies:* $1,100.

Financial Aid: Aid from institutionally generated funds is provided on the basis of academic merit, financial need. Institution has a Program Participation Agreement with the U.S. Department of Education for eligible students to receive Pell Grants and, depending upon the agreement, other federal aid.

Financial aid to full-time, first-time undergraduate students: 92% received some form of aid. Average amount of aid received: federal grants $2,038; Pell grants $2,843; other federal grants $929; state/local grants $2,380; institutional grants $17,118.

Departments and Teaching Staff: *Total instructional faculty:* 1,288 (full-time 94, part-time 194). Student/faculty ratio: 12:1.

Enrollment: Total enrollment 2,823. Undergraduate 1,792. Graduate 1,031. Undergraduate transfer-in students 67.

Characteristics of Student Body: *Ethnic/racial makeup:* number of Black non-Hispanic: 185; American Indian or Alaska Native: 13; Asian or Pacific Islander: 50; Hispanic: 273; White non-Hispanic: 1,045; unknown: 167. *Age distribution:* number under 18: 3; 18–19: 722; 20–21: 719; 22–24: 275; 25–29: 41; 30–34: 2; 35–39: 4; 40–49: 6.

International Students: 150 nonresident aliens enrolled fall 2008. Students from Europe, Asia, Central and South America, Africa, Canada, New Zealand, Middle East. Programs available to aid students whose native language is not English: social, cultural. English as a Second Language Program. Financial aid specifically designated for international students.

Student Life: On-campus residence halls house 60% of student body. *Intercollegiate athletics:* male: baseball, basketball, golf, ice hockey, lacrosse, soccer, tennis; female: basketball, cheerleading, field hockey, ice hockey, lacrosse, soccer, softball, swimming, tennis, volleyball. Wellness Program. 50 student-run organizations on campus. *Special regulations:* Quiet hours in certain areas. *Special services:* Learning Resources Center, medical services. *Student publications, radio: Touchstone*, a newspaper published weekly; annual literary magazine. Radio station WMVL. *Surrounding community:* Purchase (incorporated). New York City, 30 miles from campus, is nearest metropolitan area. Served by mass transit bus system; airport 5 miles from campus; rail service 3 miles from campus.

Library Collections: 259,000 volumes including bound books, serial backfiles, electronic documents, and government documents not in separate collections. Online catalog. Current serial subscriptions: 369 paper, 18,930 via electronic access. 3,921 audiovisual volumes. Computer work stations available. Students have access to the Internet at no charge.

Most important holdings include Zigmund Cerbu Collection (Hinduism, Buddhism); Allain Biography Collection; Alexander Stephens Collection (letters); Victor Young Collection.

Buildings and Grounds: Campus area 100 acres. *New buildings:* Environmental Park dedicated September 2006.

Chief Executive Officer: Dr. Richard A. Berman, President.

Address admission inquiries to Jose Flores, Vice President for Enrollment Management.

Marist College

3390 North Road
Poughkeepsie, New York 12601
Tel: (845) 575-3000 **E-mail:** admissions@marist.edu
Fax: (845) 471-6213 **Internet:** www.marist.edu

Institution Description: Marist College is a private, independent, nonprofit college. *Enrollment:* 5,828. *Degrees awarded:* Baccalaureate, master's.

Member of the consortium Association of Colleges in the Mid-Hudson Area.

Accreditation: *Regional:* MSA. *Professional*: clinical lab scientist, social work

History: Established as Marist Training School and offered first instruction at postsecondary level 1930; chartered as Marist College 1946; awarded first degree (baccalaureate) 1948; present name adopted 1960.

Institutional Structure: *Governing board:* Marist College Board of Trustees. Extrainstitutional representation: 19 trustees; institutional representation: president of the college; 6 alumni. 1 ex officio. 25 voting. *Composition of institution:* Administrators 119. Academic affairs headed by academic vice president. Management/business/finances directed by vice president for administration and finance. Full-time instructional faculty 130. Academic governance body, the faculty, meets an average of 2 times per year.

Calendar: Semesters. Academic year Sept. to May. Freshmen admitted Sept., Jan., June. Degrees conferred May, Aug., Jan. Formal commencement May.

Characteristics of Freshmen: 9,198 applicants. 38% of applicants accepted. 30% of accepted applicants enrolled full-time.

91% (934 students) submitted SAT scores; 30% (302 students) submitted ACT scores. *25th percentile*: SAT Critical Reading 530, SAT Math 540, SAT Writing 540; ACT Composite 23. *75th percentile*: SAT Critical Reading 620, SAT Math 630, SAT Writing 620; ACT Composite 27.

59% of freshmen from New York. Freshmen from 39 states and 10 foreign countries.

Admission: Rolling admissions begins Feb. 15 and continues until class is filled. Deadline for freshmen is Mar. 1. Early decision/early action deadline is Dec. 1 with notification by Dec. 20. *Requirements:* Graduation from secondary school or GED. Recommend college prep curriculum. *Entrance tests:* College Board SAT or ACT. *For transfer students:* 2.5 minimum GPA; from 4-year accredited institution 90 hours maximum transfer credit; from 2-year accredited institution 60 hours.

College credit and advanced placement for postsecondary-level work completed in secondary school, for USAFI-DANTES, and for extrainstitutional learning on basis of portfolio and faculty assessments.

Tutoring available. Developmental courses offered during regular academic year; credit given.

Degree Requirements: *Undergraduate:* 120 credit hours; 2.0 GPA (overall and in major field); last 30 hours in residence; general education requirements; writing proficiency requirement. For criminal justice degree, physical education requirement.

Fulfillment of some degree requirements and exemption from some beginning courses possible by passing College Board CLEP, APP, other standardized tests. *Grading system:* A–F; pass-fail; pass-no credit; withdraw (deadline after which pass-fail is appended to withdraw); incomplete (carries time limit); satisfactory.

Distinctive Educational Programs: *For undergraduates:* Flexible meeting places and schedules, including off-campus center (at Otisville, less than 30 miles away from main institution) and weekend classes. Dual-degree program in engineering with University of Detroit. Special facilities for using telecommunications in the classroom. Interdisciplinary programs in bilingual education, science of man. Facilities for independent research, including honors programs, independent study. Marist Abroad Program in Ireland (Galway, Dublin), England (Oxford, Leeds, Lancaster), France (Strasbourg, Paris), Italy (Florence, Milan). *For graduate students:* Off-campus center (at Middletown, less than 30 miles away from main institution). Interdisciplinary program in public administration. *Available to all students:* Internships. Evening classes. Accelerated degree programs. Cross-registration through consortium. Higher Education Opportunity Program for disadvantaged students offers 6-week summer session for freshmen and other support services. Student exchange program with other New York colleges and universities. *Other distinctive programs:* Continuing education program. Center for Estuarine and environmental studies research on Hudson River. Franklin D. Roosevelt Summer Institute in cooperation with Franklin D. Roosevelt Library. Marist Institute of administration and management for local government officials. Upward Bound program.

Degrees Conferred: 1,155 *baccalaureate*; 320 *master's*. Bachelor's degrees awarded in top five disciplines: business, management, marketing, and related support services 267; communication, journalism, and related programs 256; education 147; liberal arts and sciences, general studies, and humanities 101; psychology 82. Master's degrees awarded in top five disciplines: business/marketing 43; computer and information sciences 48; education 14; psychology 91; public administration and social service professions 91.

Fees and Other Expenses: *Full-time tuition per academic year 2008–09:* $25,596. *Room and board per academic year:* $10,730. *Books and supplies:* $1,300. *Other expenses:* $1,825.

Financial Aid: Aid from institutionally generated funds is provided on the basis of academic merit, financial need, athletic ability, other criteria. Institution has a Program Participation Agreement with the U.S. Department of Education for eligible students to receive Pell Grants and, depending upon the agreement, other federal aid.

Financial aid to full-time, first-time undergraduate students: 91% received some form of financial aid. Average amount of aid received: federal grants $9,279; Pell grants $2,894; other federal grants $14,740; state/local grants $2,657; institutional grants $9,305.

Departments and Teaching Staff: *Total instructional faculty:* 265. Student/faculty ratio: 15:1. Degrees held by full-time faculty: doctorate 72%, master's 24%, baccalaureate 4%. 78% hold terminal degrees.

Enrollment: Total enrollment 5,828. Undergraduate 5,031. Graduate 797. Undergraduate transfer-in students 312.

Characteristics of Student Body: *Ethnic/racial makeup:* Black non-Hispanic: 3.4%; American Indian or Alaska Native: .3%; Asian or Pacific Islander: 2.1%; Hispanic: 5.7%; White non-Hispanic: 77.8%; unknown: 10.4%.

International Students: 147 undergraduate nonresident aliens enrolled fall 2008. Programs available to aid students whose native language is not English: English as a Second Language Program. No financial aid specifically designated for international students.

Student Life: On-campus residence halls house 45% of student body. Residence halls for males constitute 55% of such space, for females 45%. 5% of student body live off campus in dormitory, motel rented by Marist. *Intercollegiate athletics:* male: basketball, crew, football, lacrosse, soccer, tennis, track; female: basketball, tennis, volleyball; both sexes: swimming. *Special regulations:* Registered cars permitted for sophomores, juniors, and seniors; by special permission for freshmen. Curfews, quiet hours and visitation regulations vary according to residence hall. *Special services:* Learning Resources Center, medical services. *Student publications, radio: The Circle*, a weekly newspaper; *The Mosaic*, an annual literary magazine; *Reynard*, a yearbook. Radio station WMCR broadcasts 105 hours per week. *Surrounding community:* Poughkeepsie population 30,000. New York, 82 miles from campus, is nearest metropolitan area. Served by mass transit bus system; airport 9 miles from campus; passenger rail service 1 mile from campus.

Publications: Sources of information about Marist include *Marist Today*, a magazine, and *Update*, a newsletter, both distributed to the public. *Mid-Hudson Language Studies* (annually) first published in 1978.

Library Collections: 208,000 volumes. 252,000 microforms; 5,600 audiovisual materials; 1,825 periodical subscriptions. Online catalog. Students have access to online information retrieval services and the Internet.

Most important holdings include a local history collection containing material by and about the Marist Brothers; historical documents and annals of St. Anne's Hermitage (first Marist house of studies in U.S.); material about Duchess County and the 6 surrounding counties, including county annuals, legislative proceedings, and rare books; Lowell Thomas Collection; Whitesell Collection of Rhythm and Blues Recordings.

Buildings and Grounds: Campus area 120 acres.

Chief Executive Officer: Dr. Dennis J. Murray, President.

Address admission inquiries to Georia Schmitt, Director of Admissions.

Marymount College of Fordham University

100 Marymount Avenue
Tarrytown, New York 10591-3796
Tel: (914) 631-3200 **E-mail:** admiss@marymt.edu
Fax: (914) 332-4956 **Internet:** www.marymt.edu

Institution Description: Marymount College is a private women's college founded by the Religious of the Sacred Heart of Mary, Roman Catholic Church and is under the aegis of Fordham University. *Enrollment:* 949. Men admitted to continuing education and weekend college. *Degrees awarded:* Associate (weekend college), baccalaureate.

Accreditation: *Regional:* MSA. *Professional*: social work

History: Established 1907; chartered and offered first instruction at postsecondary level 1919; awarded first degree (baccalaureate) 1924.

Institutional Structure: *Governing board:* Board of Trustees. Extrainstitutional representation: 24 trustees; institutional representation: president of the college, ex officio. All voting. *Composition of institution:* Academic affairs headed by vice president for academic affairs. Management/business/finances directed by vice president for finance. Full-time instructional faculty 59. Academic governance body, Educational Policies Committee, meets an average of 12 times per year. *Faculty representation:* Faculty served by collective bargaining agent affiliated with AAUP.

Calendar: Semesters. Academic year Aug. to May. Freshmen admitted Aug., Jan. Degrees conferred May, Aug., Dec. Formal commencement May. Summer session of 1 term from May to Aug.

Characteristics of Freshmen: 85% of applicants accepted. 32% of accepted applicants enrolled.

Average secondary school rank of freshmen 62nd percentile. Mean SAT scores 469 verbal, 477 mathematical.

57% of entering freshmen expected to graduate within 5 years. 64% of freshmen from New York. Freshmen from 20 states and 2 foreign countries.

Admission: Rolling admissions plan. For fall acceptance, apply as early as Oct. of previous year. Early acceptance available. *Requirements:* Either graduation from accredited secondary school with 16 academic units; or GED; essay. Minimum recommended GPA 2.5. Lowest acceptable secondary school class standing 50th percentile. *Entrance tests:* College Board SAT or ACT. For foreign students TOEFL. *For transfer students:* 2.0 minimum GPA; 75 hours maximum transfer credit.

College credit and advanced placement for postsecondary-level work completed in secondary school. College credit for extrainstitutional learning on basis of portfolio assessment.

Tutoring available. Developmental courses offered in summer session and regular academic year; credit given.

Degree Requirements: 120 credit hours; 2.0 GPA; 3 terms in residence; 2 terms physical education; demonstrated English, computational, and analytical reasoning skills; demonstrated foreign language skills.

Fulfillment of some degree requirements and exemption from some beginning courses possible by passing College Board CLEP, AP, other standardized tests. *Grading system:* A–D-no credit; pass-no credit; withdraw (carries time limit); incomplete (deadline after which no credit is given).

Distinctive Educational Programs: Work-experience programs, including internships. Accelerated master's degree programs in physical therapy with Touro College, computer science with New York Polytechnic University, Articulation with physical assistant program at Touro College (B.A./B.S.). Interdisciplinary programs in American studies, fashion design, fashion merchandising, interior design, women's studies, and by individual arrangement. Preprofessional programs in medical technology and nursing. Facilities and programs for independent research, including honors programs, individual majors, tutorials; independent study. Institutionally sponsored study abroad in England, Scotland, and Australia; also through American Institute for Foreign Study. Off-campus study in the U.S. may be individually arranged. *Other distinctive programs:* Community Leadership Program for educationally disadvantaged women from New York. Continuing education evening program and degree-granting weekend college for adults.

Degrees Conferred: 1 *associate*; 218 *baccalaureate*. Bachelor's degrees awarded in top five disciplines: business, management, marketing, and related support services 66 education 33; visual and performing arts 27; psychology 26; family and consumer sciences 12.

Fees and Other Expenses: *Full-time tuition per academic year 2008–09:* contact the college for current information regarding tuition, fees, and other costs.

Financial Aid: Aid from institutionally generated funds is provided on the basis of academic merit, financial need. Institution has a Program Participation agreement with the U.S. Department of Education for eligible students to receive Pell Grants and, depending upon the agreement, other federal aid.

Financial aid to full-time, first-time undergraduate students: 99% received some form of financial aid. Average amount of aid received: federal grants $3,676; state/local grants $3,091; institutional grants $7,989; loans $5,643.

Departments and Teaching Staff: *Total instructional faculty:* 156. Student/faculty ratio: 9:1. Degrees held by full-time faculty: doctorate 73%, master's 10%, professional 17%. 98% hold terminal degrees.

Enrollment: Total enrollment 949.

Characteristics of Student Body: *Ethnic/racial makeup:* lack non-Hispanic: 17.9%; Asian or Pacific Islander: 6%; Hispanic: 39.2%; White non-Hispanic: 39.4%; unknown: 21.5%.

International Students: 10 undergraduate nonresident aliens enrolled fall 2008. Programs available to aid students whose native language is not English: Social, cultural. English as a Second Language Program. Limited financial aid available for qualifying international students.

Student Life: On-campus residence halls house 65% of student body. Student organizations include clubs related to major programs, Black Student Union, Patinas Unidas, Gay/Straight Alliance, Sisters of Universal Light (gospel choir), Student Government Association, Campus Activities Board, international and commuter students' associations. *Intercollegiate athletics:* Basketball, softball, tennis, volleyball, swimming, equestrian team. *Special regulations:* Cars permitted without restrictions. For first semester freshmen, visitation permitted Sun.–

MARYMOUNT COLLEGE OF FORDHAM UNIVERSITY—*cont'd*

Thurs., 11am to 11pm and Fri.–Sat. 11am to 1:30am. Quiet hours set by dormitory residents. *Special services:* Learning Resources Center, Wellness Center, Health and Counseling Services, computer laboratory, math laboratory, writing center. *Student publications: Cormont*, a bimonthly newspaper; *Elan*, a yearbook; *Inside the Dome,* literary magazine. *Surrounding community:* Tarrytown population 11,000. New York City, 20 miles from campus, is nearest metropolitan area. Served by mass transit bus and rail system; airport 30 miles from campus, passenger rail service 1 mile from campus.

Publications: Sources of information about Marymount College include a viewbook, catalogue, and a variety of newsletters and brochures.

Library Collections: 105,000 volumes including bound books, serial backfiles, electronic documents, and government documents not in separate collections. Online catalog. Current serial subscriptions: 349 paper, 37 microform, 5 electronic. 32 compact discs; 32 CD-ROMs. Computer work stations available. Students have access to the Internet and online information retrieval services.

Most important holdings include Mussolini Papers (personal papers and official records on 316 reels of microfilm); *Catholic News* (collection of the publication of the Archdiocese of New York 1888–1965); Thomas More Collection (books by and about More, including incunabula, first editions); Early American Newspapers (16 reels of microfilm).

Buildings and Grounds: Campus area 23 acres.

Chief Executive Officer: Dr. Anne M. Slattery, President.

Address admission inquiries to Daneila Esposito, Director of Admissions.

Marymount Manhattan College

221 East 71st Street New York
New York 10021-4597
Tel: (212) 517-0400 **E-mail:** admissions@mmm.edu
Fax: (212) 517-0451 **Internet:** www.mmm.edu

Institution Description: Marymount Manhattan College is a private, independent, nonprofit college founded by the Religious of the Sacred Heart of Mary, Roman Catholic Church. *Enrollment:* 1,988. *Degrees awarded:* Associate, baccalaureate.

Accreditation: *Regional:* MSA.

History: Established 1936 as the New York City campus of Marymount College, Tarrytown; chartered as an independent four-year institution 1961.

Institutional Structure: *Governing board:* Marymount Manhattan College Board of Trustees. Extrainstitutional representation: 30 trustees; institutional representation: president of the college. 1 ex officio. All voting. *Composition of institution:* Senior administration: 8, Academic affairs headed by vice president of academic affairs. Management/business/finances directed by vice president for administration and finance. Full-time instructional faculty 72. Academic governance body, Faculty Council, meets an average of 9 times per year.

Calendar: Semesters. Academic year early Sept. to May. Freshmen admitted Sept., Jan., Feb., June, July. Degrees conferred June, Sept., Dec. Formal commencement June. Summer session from late May to July. early Aug.

Characteristics of Freshmen: 2,565 applicants. 74% of applicants accepted. 26% of applicants accepted and enrolled full-time.

90% (439 students) submitted SAT scores; 6% (28 students) submitted ACT scores. *25th percentile*: SAT Critical Reading 490, SAT Math 470; ACT Composite 21. *75th percentile*: SAT Critical Reading 600, SAT Math 570; ACT Composite 25.

43% of entering freshmen expected to graduate within 5 years. 50% of freshmen from New York. Freshmen from 44 states and 27 foreign countries.

Admission: Rolling admissions. For fall acceptance, apply by Mar. 15. Early acceptance available. *Requirements:* Either graduation from official secondary school with 16 academic units, including 4 English, 2 language, 2 mathematics, 2 science, 2 social studies; or GED. 4 additional units recommended. Minimum GPA 3.0. SAT scores required for degree seeking students who graduated high school within 5 years of application date. *For transfer students:* 2.0 minimum GPA; 90 hours maximum transfer credit.

College credit and advanced placement for postsecondary-level work completed in secondary school. College credit for extrainstitutional learning (life experience) according to school guidelines. Select degree and certificate programs can be completed during weekend, evening, or day courses.

Tutoring available. Developmental courses offered in summer session and regular academic year.

Degree Requirements: 120 credit hours; 2.0 GPA; 30 credits in residence. Fulfillment of some degree requirements and exemption from some beginning courses possible by passing College Board CLEP, AP, other standardized tests. *Grading system:* A–F; pass-fail; withdraw (carries time limit and penalty) incomplete (carries time limit).

Distinctive Educational Programs: Baccalaureate programs in accounting, art, theatre and dance, speech pathology and audiology, international studies, communication (media study), and studio art. Programs in creative writing, public policy, teaching certification in education of the deaf and special education. Internships opportunities in the arts, sciences, communication, and business management. Study abroad by individual arrangement.

Degrees Conferred: 5 *associate;* 375 *baccalaureate.* Bachelor's degrees awarded in top five disciplines: visual and performing arts 153; communication, journalism, and related programs 82; social sciences 25; business, management, marketing, and related support services 34; psychology 35.

Fees and Other Expenses: *Full-time tuition per academic year 2008–09:* $21,792. *Books and supplies:* $1,000. *Room and board per academic year:* $12,660. *Other expenses:* $3,000.

Financial Aid: Aid from institutionally generated funds is provided on the basis of academic merit, financial need.

Financial aid to full-time, first-time undergraduate students: 89% of students received some form of financial aid. Average amount of aid received: federal grants $4,170; Pell grants 3,109; other federal grants $11,710; state/local grants $2,917; institutional grants $6,843.

Departments and Teaching Staff: *Total instructional faculty:* 317 (full-time 83, part-time 234). 85% of faculty hold the doctorate, first-professional, or other terminal degree. Student/faculty ratio: 12:1.

Enrollment: Total enrollment 1,988 (undergraduate). Transfer in students 149.

Characteristics of Student Body: *Ethnic/racial makeup:* number of Black non-Hispanic: 307; American Indian or Alaska Native: 7; Asian or Pacific Islander: 881 Hispanic: 258; White non-Hispanic: 1,355. *Age distribution:* number under 18: 20; 18–19: 697; 20–21: 621; 22–24: 288; 25–29: 132; 30–34: 38; 35–39: 67; 40–49: 101; 50–64: 61; 65 and over: 12; unknown: 20.

International Students: 50 nonresident aliens enrolled fall 2008. Students from Europe, Asia, Africa, Canada, Australia. Programs available to aid students whose native language is not English: English as a Second Language Program. No financial aid specifically designated for international students.

Student Life: Four college-operated residence halls. 500 students live in college housing. The college offers a broad range of student activities: Student Government, over 25 student-run clubs and organizations. *Special services:* Learning Resources Center, medical services. *Surrounding community:* New York population over 7 million. Served by mass transit bus, rail, and subway systems; airport 10 miles from campus; passenger rail service less than 1 mile from campus.

Library Collections: 102,000 volumes (including bound periodicals); 70,000 microforms; 4,000 audiovisual materials; 2,750 current periodical subscriptions: Online catalog. Computer work stations available. Students have access to online information retrieval services and the Internet.

Most important special holdings include Social Aspects of Business; Women's Studies; Geraldine A. Ferraro Papers.

Buildings and Grounds: Campus area 2 buildings.

Chief Executive Officer: Dr. Judson R. Shaver, President.

Address admission inquiries to James Rogers, Dean of Admissions.

Medaille College

18 Agassiz Circle
Buffalo, New York 14214-2695
Tel: (716) 880-2000 **E-mail:** sdesing@medaille.edu
Fax: (716) 884-0291 **Internet:** www.medaille.edu

Institution Description: Medaille College is a private, independent, nonprofit, nonsectarian, coeducational, four-year liberal arts college. *Enrollment:* 2,883. *Degrees awarded:* Associate, baccalaureate, master's.

Member of Western New York Consortium of Higher Education.

Accreditation: *Regional:* MSA.

History: Established as Sisters of Saint Joseph Institute for Teachers, affiliated with the Roman Catholic Church, and offered first instruction at postsecondary level 1875; changed name to Mount St. Joseph Normal School 1925; chartered as Mount St. Joseph Teachers College 1937; awarded first degree (baccalaureate) 1938; changed name to Mount St. Joseph College 1964; became nonsectarian and adopted present name 1968.

Institutional Structure: *Governing board:* Board of Trustees of Medaille College. Extrainstitutional representation: 19 trustees (including 12 directors of executive committee); institutional representation: president of the college. 1 ex officio. 16 voting. *Composition of institution:* Administrators 42. vice president for academic affairs. Management/business/finances directed by business officer. Full-time instructional faculty 98. Academic governance body, Curriculum Committee, meets an average of 10 times per year.

Calendar: Semesters. Academic year July to June. Freshmen admitted fall, spring, and summer semesters. Degrees conferred and formal commencement May. Summer session from May to Aug.

Characteristics of Freshmen: 1,317 applicants. 71% of applicants accepted. 43% of accepted students enrolled full-time.

90% (362 students) submitted SAT scores; 23% (94 students) submitted ACT scores. *25th percentile*: SAT Critical Reading 420, SAT Math 400; ACT Composite 17. *75th percentile*: SAT Critical Reading 510, SAT Math 490; ACT Composite 22.

36% of entering freshmen expected to graduate within 5 years. 96% of freshmen from New York. Freshmen from 4 states and 3 foreign countries.

Admission: Rolling admissions plan. For fall acceptance, apply as early as Nov. 1 of previous year, but not later than May 15 of year of enrollment. Early acceptance available. *Requirements:* Either graduation from accredited secondary school or GED (minimum score of 225); SAT1 or ACT required; SAT1 preferred. *For transfer students:* 2.0 minimum GPA; from 4-year accredited institution 90 hours maximum transfer credit; from 2-year accredited institution 72 hours.

College credit and advanced placement for postsecondary-level work completed in secondary school. College credit for extrainstitutional learning (life experience) on basis of portfolio assessment.

Tutoring available.

Degree Requirements: *For all associate degrees:* 60 semester hours and a 2.0 GPA with the exception of Veterinary Technology which requires 72 semester hours and a 2.5 GPA. *For all baccalaureate degrees:* 120 semester hours and a 2.0 GPA with the exception of Elementary Education which requires 125 semester hours and a 2.5 GPA. *For all degrees:* general education component.

Fulfillment of some degree requirements and exemption from some beginning courses possible by passing College Board CLEP, AP, or college credit earned in secondary school. *Grading system:* A–F; pass-fail; withdraw.

Distinctive Educational Programs: Internship program. Off-campus centers. Evening classes. Facilities and programs for independent research, including honors programs, individual majors. Independent study. Study abroad in England. Cross-registration through consortium. Weekend college program. Accelerated programs in business administration leading to A.S., B.B.A., and M.B.A. degrees offered at Amherst Branch Campus.

ROTC: Army in cooperation with Canisius College.

Degrees Conferred: 74 *associate;* 318 *baccalaureate*; 203 *master's*. Bachelor's degrees awarded in top five disciplines: business/marketing 112; education 46; liberal arts 18; public administration and social services 16; parks and recreation 16. Master's degrees awarded: business/marketing 104; education 91; health professions and related sciences 7; psychology 1.

Fees and Other Expenses: *Full-time tuition per academic year 2008–09:* undergraduate $17,420; contact the college for current graduate tuition and fees. *Room and board per academic year:* $8,845. *Books and supplies:* $1,100. *Other expenses:* $3,100.

Financial Aid: Aid from institutionally generated funds is provided on the basis of academic merit, financial need.

Financial aid to full-time, first-time undergraduate students: 100% received some form of aid. 50% received federal grants; 27% Pell grants; 23% other federal grants; 61% state/local grants; 100% institutional grants

Departments and Teaching Staff: *Total instructional faculty:* 411 (full-time 98, part-time 313). 74% of faculty hold the doctorate, first-professional, or other terminal degree. Student/faculty ratio: 15:1.

Enrollment: Total enrollment 2,883. Undergraduate 1,691. Graduate 1,192. Undergraduate transfer-in students 191.

Characteristics of Student Body: *Ethnic/racial makeup:* number of Black non-Hispanic: 247; American Indian or Alaska Native: 2; Asian or Pacific Islander: 16; Hispanic: 38; White non-Hispanic: 1,275; unknown: '106. 25% of student body attend summer sessions.

International Students: 23 nonresident aliens enrolled fall 2008. Students from Europe, Canada. No programs available to aid students whose native language is not English. No financial aid specifically designated for international students.

Student Life: The college purchased five houses adjacent to the main campus which have been converted into student residence halls. *Special services:* Academic Support Center, Career Planning and Placement, Health and Multicultural Services. *Athletics and recreations:* Intramural flag football, volleyball, basketball, softball, golf; intercollegiate sports include male and female basketball, lacrosse, soccer, volleyball; female cross-country, softball; male baseball, golf. *Student publications, radio, television:* newspaper and yearbook. Radio station WMCB broadcasts 25 hours per week. 18 organizations including clubs related to majors. *Surrounding community:* Buffalo population 1.2 million. Served by bus and light-rail system; airport and passenger rail service, each 10 miles from campus.

Library Collections: 57,000 volumes including bound books, serial backfiles, electronic documents, and government documents not in separate collections. Online catalog. Current serial subscriptions: 225 paper, 200 microform, 11,000 via electronic access. 300 audio/videotapes; 35 DVD discs; 50 CD-ROMs. Computer work stations available. Students have access to the Internet at no charge.

Most important special collections include veterinary technology; Buffalo History; elementary education.

Buildings and Grounds: Campus area 13 acres.

Chief Executive Officer: Dr. Richard K.Davis, President.

Address admission inquiries to Gregory Florczak, Director, Undergraduate Admissions; graduate inquiries to Jacqueline S. Matheny, Director, Graduate Admissions.

Medgar Evers College / CUNY

1650 Bedford Avenue
Brooklyn, New York 11225
Tel: (718) 270-4900 **E-mail:** admissions@mec.cuny.edu
Fax: (718) 270-6171 **Internet:** www.mec.cuny.edu

Institution Description: Medgar Evers College of CUNY is a four-year, coeducational institution that was established to meet the educational and social needs of the community. *Enrollment:* 6,036. *Degrees awarded.* Associate, baccalaureate.

Accreditation: *Regional:* MSA. *Professional*: accounting, business, nursing, teacher education

History: Established 1967 as a two-year community college; became a four-year college 1969; adopted present name 1970.

Institutional Structure: *Composition of institution:* Administrators 37. Academic affairs headed by senior vice president/provost. Management/business/finances directed by vice president. Full-time instructional faculty 150.

Calendar: Semesters. Academic year Sept. to May. Summer session of 1 term from late June to early Aug.

Characteristics of Freshmen: 4,831 applicants. 96% of applicants admitted; 19% of accepted applicants enrolled full time.

Admission: *Requirements:* Either graduation from accredited secondary school with an average of 80 or above for a baccalaureate degree or below for an associate degree; or GED (minimum score of 225). *For transfer students:* 2.0 minimum GPA (lower GPA accepted on probation).

Degree Requirements: *For all associate degrees:* 60 credits with a 2.0 GPA. *For all baccalaureate degrees:* 120 credits with a minimum GPA of 2.0.

Fulfillment of some degree requirements by passing institutional examinations, College Board CLEP, other standardized tests. *Grading system:* A–F; pass-fail; withdraw (deadline after which fail is appended to withdraw).

Distinctive Educational Programs: *Other distinctive programs:* Honors Program; Freshman Year Program; Worker Education Program.

Degrees Conferred: 390 *associate;* 225 *baccalaureate:* biological/life sciences 20; business/marketing 106; computer and information sciences 1; education 24; English 8; health professions and related sciences 16; mathematics 1; natural and environmental sciences 4; psychology 37; public administration and social services professions 8.

Fees and Other Expenses: *Full-time tuition per academic year 2008–09:* resident $4,302, nonresident $8,942. *Books and supplies:* $1,016. *Other expenses:* $4,526. No on-campus housing.

Financial Aid: Aid from institutionally generated funds is provided on the basis of financial need.

Financial aid to full-time, first-time undergraduate students: 82% of students received some form of financial aid. Average amount of aid received: federal grants $3,615; Pell grants $3,364; other federal grants $6,040; state/local grants $27,765.

Departments and Teaching Staff: *Total instructional faculty:* 339 (full-time 150, part-time 189). Degrees held full-time faculty: doctorate 65%, master's 34%. Student/faculty ratio: 17:1.

Enrollment: Total enrollment 6,036 (undergraduate). Transfer-in students 643.

Characteristics of Student Body: *Ethnic/racial makeup:* number of Black non-Hispanic: 4,529; American Indian or Alaska Native: 5; Asian or Pacific Islander: 48; Hispanic: 217; White non-Hispanic: 39; unknown: 106. *Age distribution:* number 18–19: 769; 20–21: 609; 22–24: 778; 25–29: 866; 30–34: 657; 35–39: 495; 40–49: 753; 50–64: 239; 65 and over: 5.

International Students: 646 nonresident aliens enrolled fall 2008. No programs available to aid students whose native language is not English. No financial aid specifically designated for international students.

Student Life: No on-campus housing. *Intercollegiate athletics:* male: basketball, cross-country, soccer, track; female: volleyball. *Special services:* Learning

MEDGAR EVERS COLLEGE / CUNY—*cont'd*

Resources Center, medical services. *Surrounding community:* New York City population over 7 million. Served by mass transit bus and rail systems.

Library Collections: 120,000 volumes. 42,200 microforms; 6,000 audiovisual materials; 36,300 periodicals including via electronic access. Online catalog. Students have access to online information retrieval services.

Most important holdings include: Schomburg collection for research in African American Studies; Southern African Collection; Porter Black Bibliography of the African American Experience.

Chief Executive Officer: Dr. Edison O. Jackson, President.

Address admission inquiries to Rose Banton, Director of Admissions.

Mercy College

555 Broadway
Dobbs Ferry, New York 10522
Tel: (914) 693-4500 **E-mail:** admissions@mercy.edu
Fax: (914) 693-9455 **Internet:** www.mercy.edu

Institution Description: Mercy College is a private, independent, nonprofit college with branch campuses at Yorktown Heights, Peekskill, White Plains, Yonkers, and the Bronx. *Enrollment:* 9,043. *Degrees awarded:* Associate, baccalaureate, master's.

Member of Westchester Consortium for Teacher Education.

Accreditation: *Regional:* MSA. *Professional*: nursing, social work.

History: Established as Mercy Junior College and offered first instruction at postsecondary level 1950; chartered and incorporated 1952; adopted present name 1961; awarded first degree (baccalaureate) 1965; became coeducational 1969; branch campus status granted to the Bronx, Peekskill, White Plains, and Yonkers campuses 1986.

Institutional Structure: *Governing board:* Board of Trustees of Mercy College. Extrainstitutional representation: 25 trustees; institutional representation: president of the college. All voting. *Composition of institution:* Academic affairs headed by provost/vice president for academic affairs; vice president for administration responsible for administrative operations, computer operations, and other college operations. Treasurer/vice president for financial affairs is chief financial officer. Full-time instructional faculty 125. Academic governance body, the faculty, meets 6 times per year.

Calendar: Semesters. Academic year early Sept. to late May. Freshmen admitted Sept., Oct., Jan., Feb., Mar., June. Degrees conferred May, Aug. Jan. Formal commencement May, Jan. Summer session from early June to mid-Aug.

Characteristics of Freshmen: 2,547 applicants. 35% of applicants accepted. 67% of accepted applicants enrolled.

99% of freshmen from New York. Freshmen from 4 states and 10 foreign countries.

Admission: Rolling admissions plan. Early acceptance available. *Requirements:* Either graduation from accredited secondary school with 16 units; or GED. Minimum 2.0 GPA. *Entrance tests:* College Board SAT or ACT composite. *For transfer students:* 2.0 minimum GPA; 90 hours maximum transfer credit.

College credit and advanced placement for postsecondary-level work completed in secondary school and for extrainstitutional learning. Noncredit remedial courses offered in summer session and regular academic year.

Degree Requirements: *For all associate degrees:* 60 semester hours; 1 term in residence. *For all baccalaureate degrees:* 120 hours; 2 terms in residence. *For all degrees:* 2.0 GPA; distribution requirements.

Fulfillment of some degree requirements possible by passing departmental examinations, College Board CLEP, AP, other standardized tests. *Grading system:* A–F; pass-fail; withdraw (carries time limit).

Distinctive Educational Programs: Flexible scheduling at six convenient campuses. Day, evening, and weekend classes. Dual-degree programs in accounting and business and cooperative baccalaureate in pharmacy with Long Island University Center. Interdisciplinary programs by individual arrangement. Facilities for independent research, including honors programs, individual majors, tutorials. Institutionally sponsored study abroad in various countries. *Other distinctive programs:* Degree-granting continuing education program.

ROTC: Air Force offered in cooperation with Manhattan College.

Degrees Conferred: 95 *associate*; 1,037 *baccalaureate*; 1,603 *master's*; 14 *doctorate*. Bachelor's degrees awarded in top five disciplines: social sciences 306; business, management, marketing, and related support services 265; health professions and related clinical sciences 172; psychology 145; computer and information sciences 53. Master's degrees awarded: business/marketing 199; English language/literature 3; education 1,093; health professions 192; psychology 1. Doctorates awarded: health professions 14.

Fees and Other Expenses: *Full-time tuition per academic year 2008–09:* $15,470 undergraduate; contact the college for current graduate tuition. *Books and supplies:* $1,260. *Room and board per academic year:* $10,588. *Other expenses:* $2,218.

Financial Aid: Aid from institutionally generated funds is provided on the basis of academic merit, financial need. Institution has a Program Participation Agreement with the U.S. Department of Education for eligible students to receive Pell Grants and, depending upon the agreement, other federal aid.

Financial aid to full-time, first-time undergraduate students: 81% of students received some form of financial aid. Average amount of aid received: federal grants $3,575; Pell grants $3,254; other federal grants $496; state/local grants $3,377; institutional grants $4,276.

Departments and Teaching Staff: *Total instructional faculty:* 219. Student/faculty ratio: 16:1. 76% hold terminal degrees.

Enrollment: Total enrollment 9,043. Undergraduate 5,390. Graduate 3,653. Undergraduate transfer-in students 896.

Characteristics of Student Body: *Ethnic/racial makeup:* Black non-Hispanic: 30.2%; American Indian or Alaska Native: .3%; Asian or Pacific Islander: 3.4%; Hispanic: 36.9%; White non-Hispanic: 31.7%.

International Students: 90 undergraduate nonresident aliens enrolled fall 2008.

Student Life: *Intercollegiate athletics:* male: baseball, basketball, soccer, tennis; female: basketball, softball, volleyball. *Special regulations:* Cars with decals permitted; fee charged. *Special services:* Learning Resources Center, medical services. *Student publications: Wickers Creek*, honors program magazine; *Latent Image*, photography club magazine; *Reporter's Impact*, a biweekly newspaper; *Spoken Wheel*, an annual literary magazine; a yearbook. *Surrounding community:* Dobbs Ferry, population 10,000, is located in New York City metropolitan area. Served by mass transit and rail systems; airport 15 miles from campus; passenger rail service less than 1 mile from campus.

Library Collections: 325,000 volumes. 44,500 government documents; 18,200 microforms; 8,500 recordings/tapes; 1,765 periodical subscriptions. Online catalog. Students have access to online information retrieval services and the Internet.

Most important special collections include Millbrook Hunt Collection (equestrian arts); Peter Goldmark Record Collection; Vander Peel Art Print Collection.

Buildings and Grounds: Campus area 77 acres.

Chief Executive Officer: Dr. Louise Faroe, President.

Address admission inquiries to Jeffrey Cutting, Director of Admissions.

Molloy College

1000 Hempstead Avenue
P.O. Box 5002
Rockville Centre, New York 11571-5002
Tel: (516) 678-5000 **E-mail:** admissions@molloy.edu
Fax: (516) 256-2232 **Internet:** www.molloy.edu

Institution Description: Molloy College (Molloy Catholic College For Women until 1971) is a private, independent, nonprofit coeducational college. *Enrollment:* 3,879. Men are admitted to all programs, evening, and weekend courses. *Degrees awarded:* Associate, baccalaureate, master's.

Member of the consortium Long Island Regional Advisory Council on Higher Education.

Accreditation: *Regional:* MSA. *Professional*: health information technician, nuclear medicine technology, nursing, respiratory therapy, social work

History: Established as Molloy Catholic College for Women and offered first instruction at postsecondary level 1955; awarded first degree (baccalaureate) 1959; chartered 1960; adopted present name 1971.

Institutional Structure: *Governing board:* Molloy College Board of Trustees. Extrainstitutional representation: 23 trustees; institutional representation: president of the college. All voting. *Composition of institution:* Administrators 31. Academic affairs headed by vice president for academic affairs. Management/business/finances directed by vice president for finance and treasurer. Full-time instructional faculty 157. Molloy governance body by committees meets regularly.

Calendar: Semesters (4-1-4 plan). Academic year Sept. to May. Freshmen admitted Sept., Jan. Degrees conferred May, Aug., Dec., Jan. Formal commencement May. Summer session of 5 terms from late May through Aug.

Characteristics of Freshmen: 1,664 applicants. 56% of applicants accepted. 43% of accepted applicants enrolled full-time.

95% (353 students) submitted SAT scores. *25th percentile*: SAT Critical Reading 460, SAT Math 450. *75th percentile*: SAT Critical Reading 565, SAT Math 600.

61% of entering freshmen expected to graduate within 5 years. 100% of freshmen from New York.

Admission: Rolling admissions plan. For fall acceptance, apply as early as Sept. of previous year, but not later than Sept. of year of enrollment. Apply by

Nov. 1 for early action; must limit application to Molloy. Early acceptance available. *Requirements:* Either graduation from accredited secondary school with 16 units which must include 4 English, 2 foreign language, 3 social studies, 2 mathematics, 2 science; or GED. Additional recommendations for some programs. Minimum 2.0 GPA. Lowest acceptable secondary school class standing 40th percentile. *Entrance tests:* College Board SAT or ACT composite. *For transfer students:* 2.0 minimum GPA; from 4-year accredited institution 98 hours maximum transfer credit; from 2-year accredited institution 64 hours

College credit and advanced placement for postsecondary-level work completed in secondary school and for extrainstitutional learning on basis of portfolio assessment. >

Tutoring available. Noncredit developmental and remedial courses offered in summer session and regular academic year; may be available during interim.

Degree Requirements: *For all associate degrees:* minimum 64 credit hours; 33 hours, including last 12, in residence. *For all baccalaureate degrees:* minimum 128 credit hours; last 30 hours in residence. *For all undergraduate degrees:* 2.0 GPA; 1 credit physical education; distribution requirements.

Fulfillment of some degree requirements and exemption from some beginning courses possible by passing College Board CLEP, APP, other standardized tests. *Grading system:* A–F; pass-fail; pass; withdraw; incomplete (carries time limit).

Distinctive Educational Programs: Work-experience programs. Weekend and evening classes. Accelerated degree programs. Special facilities for using telecommunications in the classroom. Facilities and programs for independent research, including individual majors, tutorials. Study abroad in Africa, Austria, Belgium, France, Greece, India, Italy, Japan, Mexico, Spain, Thailand. Cross-registration through consortium. *Other distinctive programs:* Higher Education Opportunity Program in cooperation with state education department offers financial and academic support to disadvantaged students. Continuing education.

ROTC: Army offered in cooperation with Hofstra University; Air Force in cooperation with the New York Institute of Technology. Navy (nursing program only) in cooperation with SUNY Maritime College.

Degrees Conferred: 44 *associate;* 572 *baccalaureate*; 221 *master's*. Bachelor's degrees awarded in top five disciplines: health professions and related clinical sciences 182; education 70; business/marketing 35; psychology 35; visual and performing arts 29. Master's degrees awarded: business/marketing 21; education 169; health professions and related clinical sciences 58.

Fees and Other Expenses: *Full-time tuition per academic year 2008–09:* $19,450 undergraduate; graduate study charged per credit hour (contact the college for current rate). *Other fees:* $930. *Books and supplies:* $1,000. No on campus housing.

Financial Aid: Aid from institutionally generated funds is provided on the basis of academic merit, financial need, athletic ability, other considerations.

Financial aid to full-time, first-time undergraduate students: 94% received some form of aid. Average amount of aid received: federal grants $4,571; Pell grants #3,133; other federal aid $2,853; state/local grants $2,520; institutional grants $7,185.

Departments and Teaching Staff: *Total instructional faculty:* 493. Student/faculty ratio: 10:1. Degrees held by full-time faculty: doctorate 51%, master's 46%, baccalaureate 100%. 52% hold terminal degrees.

Enrollment: Total enrollment 3,879. Undergraduate 2,916. Graduate 963. Undergraduate transfer-in students 280.

Characteristics of Student Body: *Age distribution:* number under 18: 6; 18–19: 531; 20–21: 619; 22–24: 519; 25–29: 347; 30–34: 172; 35–39: 142; 40–49: 231; 50–64: 100; 65 and over: 3.

International Students: 3 nonresident aliens from Europe enrolled fall 2008. Programs available to aid students whose native language is not English: English as a Second Language Program. No financial aid specifically designated for international students.

Student Life: No on-campus housing. *Intercollegiate athletics:* basketball, cross-country, lacrosse, soccer, softball, tennis, volleyball, baseball, equestrian. *Special regulations:* Cars permitted without restrictions. *Special services:* Writing Lab; health services, personal counseling, career services, Academic Enrichment Program; Disability Support Services. *Student publications: Molloy Forum*, a student newspaper; *Curiouser & Curiouser*; *Chrysalis*, a yearbook. *Surrounding community:* Rockville Centre population 25,000. New York City, 25 miles from campus, is nearest metropolitan area. Served by mass transit bus and rail systems; airport 15 miles from campus.

Library Collections: 115,000 volumes including bound books, serial backfiles, electronic documents, and government documents not in separate collections. Online catalog. Current serial subscriptions: 600 paper, 500 microform. 50 via electronic access. 660 recordings; 20CD-ROMs. Computer work stations available. Students have access to the Internet at no charge.

Most important special holdings include Microbook of English Literature; American Academic Encyclopedia.

Buildings and Grounds: Campus area 30 acres.

Chief Executive Officer: Dr. Drew Bogned, President.
Address admission inquiries to Marguerite Lane, Director of Admissions.

Morrisville State College

P.O. Box 901
Morrisville, New York 13408
Tel: (800) 258-0111 **E-mail:** admissions@morrisville.edu
Fax: (315) 654-6427 **Internet:** www.morrisville.edu

Institution Description: Morrisville State College was formerly known as State University of New York College of Agriculture and Technology at Morrisville. The college has recently expanded its offerings beyond the associate degree level. *Enrollment:* 3,338. *Degrees awarded:* Associate, baccalaureate.

Academic offerings subject to approval by statewide coordinating bodies. Member of the consortium Rochester Area Colleges.

Accreditation: *Regional:* MSA. *Professional*: business, engineering, nursing

History: The college was founded in 1908 as an agricultural school. In 1948 the New York State Agricultural and Technical Institute at Morrisville became part of the State University of New York; in 1987 the school was named the State University of New York College of Agriculture and Technology at Morrisville. The present name, Morrisville State College, was adopted 2003.

Institutional Structure: *Composition of institution:* SUNY Board of Trustees, Morrisville State College Council, as well as the Morrisville College Foundation, Inc. and the Alumni Board of Directors.

Calendar: Semesters. Academic year Aug. to May. Freshmen and transfer student admitted Aug., Jan. Degrees conferred May. Formal commencement May. Summer session from May to early Aug.

Characteristics of Freshmen: 4,085 applicants. 71% of applicants admitted. 38% of admitted applicants enrolled full-time.

56% (1,864 students) submitted SAT scores' 14% (189 students) submitted ACT scores. *25th percentile*: SAT Critical Reading 420, SAT Math 430; ACT Composite 18. *75th percentile*: SAT Critical Reading 520, SAT Math 550; ACT Composite 23.

43% of freshmen from New York. Freshmen from 26 states and 8 foreign countries.

Admission: Rolling admissions plan. Students are admitted to specific curricula rather than to a general freshman program. Candidates must be high school graduates or equivalent with grades acceptable to the major for which admissions is sought. SAT/ACT scores are required for bachelor degree candidates. Review of applications begins Nov. 1.

Degree Requirements: Student must complete all specific coursework within the program chosen and must meet the minimum total number o semester hours for appropriate degrees; 2.0 GPA in all coursework.

Distinctive Educational Programs: The college offers 13 bachelor degrees and a wide variety of associate degrees with transfer options. Academics integrate computers into teaching and learning environment that allows students access to technology from any place at any time.

Degrees Conferred: 453 *associate*; 132 *baccalaureate*: agriculture 23; computer and information sciences 26; mechanic and repair technologies 1; natural resources/environmental sciences 5; various other disciplines 77.

Fees and Other Expenses: *Full-time tuition per academic year 2008–09:* undergraduate resident $5,771, nonresident $8,631. *Required fees:* $925. *Room and board per academic year:* $8,570. *Books and supplies* $1,200. *Other expenses:* $2,160.

Financial Aid: Aid from institutionally generated funds is provided on the basis of academic merit, financial need.

Financial aid to full-time, first-time undergraduate students: 90% received some form of aid. Average amount of aid received: federal grants $1,511; state/local grants $2,004; institutional grants $4,119; loans $2,351.

Departments and Teaching Staff: *Total instructional faculty:* 260 (full-time 131, part-time 129). 25% of faculty hold the doctorate, first-professional, or other terminal degree. Student/faculty ratio: 19:1.

Enrollment: Total enrollment 3,338 (undergraduate). Transfer-in students 195.

Characteristics of Student Body: *Ethnic/racial makeup:* number of Black non-Hispanic: 332; American Indian or Alaska Native: 19; Asian or Pacific Islander: 23; Hispanic: 129; White non-Hispanic: 2,307; unknown: 373. *Age distribution:* number under 18: 16; 18–19: 1,629; 20–21: 875; 22–24: 178; 25–29: 189; 30–34: 120; 35–39: 207; 40–49: 82; 50–64: 20; 65 and over: 8.

International Students: 38 nonresident aliens enrolled fall 2008. Students from Europe, Asia, Africa, Canada. Programs available to aid students whose native language is not English: English as a Second Language Program. No financial aid specifically designated for international students.

Student Life: Ten on-campus residence halls house 1,800 students. Each resident student is issued a Nextel cell phone for their use while living on campus.

MORRISVILLE STATE COLLEGE—*cont'd*

Intercollegiate athletics available that includes 26 varsity sports, open recreation, and club sports. Over 40 social clubs and organizations; many majors of study have their own clubs as well. *Special services:* career counseling; academic support; health center; international student's office; services for students with disabilities. *Publications: The Chimes*, student newspaper; *Arcadia*, yearbook. Student run radio station called *The Vortex*. *Surrounding community:* The college is located in Morrisville and the nearest metropolitan ares are Utica (25 minutes away) and Syracuse (45 minutes away). Both cities are served by mass transit (train and bus). The nearest airport is located in Syracuse.

Library Collections: 100,000 volumes including bound books, serial backfiles, electronic documents, and government documents not in separate collections. Online catalog. Current serial subscriptions: paper 350; via electronic access 2,000. 1,600 recordings. 100 DVD discs. Computer work stations available. Students have access to the Internet at no charge.

Most important special holdings include local history; Lee Brown Cove Collection; Morrisville State College History and Images.

Buildings and Grounds: Campus area 150 acres.

Chief Executive Officer: Dr. Raymond W. Cross, President. Address admission inquiries to Timothy S. Williams, Dean of Admissions.

Mount Saint Mary College

330 Powell Avenue
Newburgh, New York 12550-3494
Tel: (845) 561-0800 **E-mail:** admissions@msmc.edu
Fax: (815) 562-6762 **Internet:** www.msmc.edu

Institution Description: Mount Saint Mary College is a private, independent, nonprofit college. *Enrollment:* 2,629. *Degrees awarded:* Baccalaureate, master's. Member of the consortium Associated Colleges of the Mid-Hudson Area.

Accreditation: *Regional:* MSA. *Professional*: nursing, teacher education

History: Established as Mount Saint Mary Normal School for teacher training by the Dominican Sisters in 1930; chartered as 4-year college 1959; awarded first degree (baccalaureate) 1963; awarded first master's degree 1986.

Institutional Structure: *Governing board:* Extrainstitutional representation: 21 trustees. All voting. *Composition of institution:* Administrators 65. Academic affairs headed by vice president for academic affairs. Management/business/finances directed by vice president for finance and administration. Full-time instructional faculty 73. Academic governance body, Faculty Senate, meets an average of 10 times per year.

Calendar: Semesters. Academic year Sept. to May. Freshmen admitted Sept., Jan., May, June. Degrees conferred Dec., May, Aug. Formal commencement May. Summer session of 2 terms from May to July.

Characteristics of Freshmen: 1,878 applicants. 77% of applicants admitted. 30% of admitted students enrolled full-time.

90% (396 students) submitted SAT scores; 24% (106 students) submitted ACT scores. *25th percentile*: SAT Critical Reading 450, SAT Math 450, SAT Writing 450; ACT Composite 18, ACT English 16, ACT Math 17. *75th percentile*: SAT Critical Reading 550, SAT math 540, SAT Writing 540; ACT Composite 23, ACT English 22, ACT Math 23.

53% of entering freshmen expected to graduate within 5 years. 88% of freshmen from New York. Freshmen from 13 states and 3 foreign countries.

Admission: Rolling admissions plan. Early acceptance available. *Requirements:* Either graduation from accredited secondary school with program that normally includes 4 units English, 3 foreign language, 4 history or social studies, 3 mathematics, 3 science, 3.5 electives; or GED. *Entrance tests:* College Board SAT or ACT composite. *For transfer students:* 2.0 minimum GPA; from 4-year accredited institution 90 hours maximum transfer credit; from 2-year accredited institution 60 hours; correspondence/extension students, credit evaluated individually.

College credit and advanced placement for postsecondary-level work completed in secondary school. College credit for extrainstitutional learning (life experience) on basis of portfolio assessment.

Tutoring available. Noncredit developmental courses offered in summer session, regular academic year, and January interim.

Degree Requirements: *For most baccalaureate degrees:* 120 credit hours (medical technology 128 credit hours; nursing 124 credit hours); 2.0 GPA; 30 credits in residence; distribution requirements. *For master's degrees:* 33 credit hours (at least 24 in residence); 3.0 GPA.

Fulfillment of some degree requirements and exemption from some beginning courses possible by passing departmental examinations, College Board CLEP, AP, other standardized tests. *Grading system:* A–F; pass-fail; withdraw (carries time limit); incomplete (carries time limit).

Distinctive Educational Programs: Accelerated weekend and evening classes. Special facilities for using telecommunications in the classroom. Facilities and programs for independent research, including honors programs and individual majors. Individually arranged study abroad in Europe and Central America. Special consideration program for in-coming freshmen.

Degrees Conferred: 437 *baccalaureate*; 179 *master's*. Bachelor's degrees awarded in top five disciplines: business/marketing 109; English 59; psychology 52; history 47; health professions and related clinical sciences 40. Master's degrees awarded: business/marketing 35; education 131; health professions and related clinical sciences 6.

Fees and Other Expenses: *Full-time tuition per academic year 2008–09:* undergraduate $20,745; contact the college for current graduate tuition. *Required fees:* $560. *Room and board per academic year:* $11,030.

Financial Aid: Aid from institutionally generated funds is provided on the basis of academic merit, financial need.

Financial aid to full-time, first-time undergraduate students: 83% received some form of aid. Average amount of aid received: federal grants $3,610; Pell grants $2,979; other federal grants $996; state/local grants $2,883; institutional grants $6,290.

Departments and Teaching Staff: *Total instructional faculty:* 215 (full-time 73, part-time 142). 73% of faculty hold the doctorate, first-professional, or other terminal degree:. Student/faculty ratio: 17:1.

Enrollment: Total enrollment 2,629. Undergraduate 2,109. Graduate 520. Undergraduate transfer-in students 204.

Characteristics of Student Body: *Ethnic/racial makeup:* number of Black non-Hispanic: 214; American Indian or Alaska Native: 5; Asian or Pacific Islander: 60; Hispanic: 182; White non-Hispanic: 1,572; unknown: 6. *Age distribution:* number under 18: 56; 18–19: 626; 20–21: 553; 22–24: 316; 25–29: 162; 30–34: 92; 35–39: 96; 40–49: 114; 50–64: 21; 65 and over: 3. 175 of student body attend summer sessions.

International Students: No programs available to aid students whose native language is not English. No financial aid specifically designated for international students.

Student Life: On-campus residence halls house 42% of student body. Housing for males constitute 26% of such space, for females 76%. *Intercollegiate athletics:* male: baseball, basketball, soccer, swimming, tennis; female: basketball, volleyball, soccer, softball, swimming, tennis. *Special regulations:* Freshmen curfews; all students visitation regulations. *Special services:* Learning Resources Center, tutoring, medical services. *Student publications: The Clarion*, a biweekly newspaper; *Thyme*, a yearbook. *Surrounding community:* Newburgh population 28,259. New York City, 60 miles from campus, is nearest metropolitan area. Served by passenger rail service 10 miles from campus; Interstate Highway 84 and New York Thruway minutes from campus.

Publications: Undergraduate catalog, graduate catalog, viewbook, annual report, speakers bureau directory, class schedules; *Happenings*, a quarterly magazine.

Library Collections: 118,000 volumes including bound books, serial backfiles, electronic documents, and government documents not in separate collections. Online catalog. 716,000 microforms, 7,000 audiovisual materials; 330 periodical subscriptions. Online catalog. Computer work stations available. Students have access to the Internet at no charge.

Most important special collections include Monihan Collection (Newburgh and local history); Desmond Collection; Curriculum Materials Center (materials for teacher education program).

Buildings and Grounds: Campus area 72 acres.

Chief Executive Officer: Sr. Ann Sakac, President.

Address admission inquiries to J. Randall Ogribene, Director of Admissions.

Mount Sinai School of Medicine

One Gustave L. Levy Place
New York, New York 10029
Tel: (212) 241-6696 **E-mail:** admissions@mssm.edu
Fax: (212) 369-6013 **Internet:** www.mssm.edu

Institution Description: The Mount Sinai School of Medicine is a private medical school affiliated with the City University of New York. *Enrollment:* 902. *Degrees awarded:* First-professional, doctorate.

Accreditation: *Regional:* MSA. *Professional* medicine

Institutional Structure: *Governing board:* Board of Trustees. Although affiliated with the City University of New York, the school is financially autonomous and self-supporting.

Calendar: Semesters. Academic year Aug. to June.

Admission: *Requirements:* Minimum 3 years undergraduate work in an accredited college or university; 1 year each of inorganic chemistry, organic chemistry, biology, college-level mathematics, English, physics. *Entrance tests:* MCAT.

Degree Requirements: Completion of prescribed curriculum.

Distinctive Educational Programs: M.D./Ph.D. program.

Degrees Conferred: First-professional: medicine 111; master's: biomedical sciences 9; doctorates: health professions 11.

Fees and Other Expenses: *Full-time tuition per academic year 2008–09:* contact the school for current information regarding tuition, fees, housing costs.

Financial Aid: Aid from institutionally generated funds is provided on the basis of financial need. Institution has a Program Participation Agreement with the U.S. Department of Education for eligible students to receive Pell Grants and, depending upon the agreement, other federal aid.

Departments and Teaching Staff: *Total instructional faculty:* 1,478 FTE.

Enrollment: Total enrollment 902.

Characteristics of Student Body: *Ethnic/racial makeup:* Black non-Hispanic: 4.9%; American Indian or Alaska Native: 1.4%; Asian or Pacific Islander: 17.2%; Hispanic: 13.2%; White non-Hispanic: 51.7%; unknown: .8%.

International Students: 70 nonresident aliens enrolled. No programs available to aid students whose native language is not English. No financial aid specifically designated for international students.

Library Collections: 155,000 volumes. 2,500 audiovisual materials; 2,500 current periodical subscriptions.

Buildings and Grounds: Urban campus.

Chief Executive Officer: Dr. John W. Rowe, President.

Address admission inquiries to Director of Admissions.

Nazareth College of Rochester

4245 East Avenue
Rochester, New York 14618-3790
Tel: (585) 389-2525 **E-mail:** admissions@naz.edu
Fax: (585) 389-2452 **Internet:** www.@naz.edu

Institution Description: Nazareth College of Rochester is a private, independent, nonprofit, liberal arts college. *Enrollment:* 3,250. *Degrees awarded:* Baccalaureate, master's.

Member of consortium Rochester Area Colleges, Inc.

Accreditation: *Regional:* MSA. *Professional*: business, music, nursing, social work, physical therapy, speech-language pathology

History: Established as institution for women and offered first instruction at postsecondary level 1924; chartered and incorporated 1925; awarded first degree (baccalaureate) 1928; became coeducational 1973.

Institutional Structure: *Governing board:* Nazareth College Board of Trustees. Representation: 32 trustees, including president of the college and one designated alumni trustee. All voting. *Composition of institution:* Academic affairs headed by vice president for academic affairs. Management/business/finances directed by vice president for finance and treasurer. Full-time instructional faculty 140. Academic governance body, Faculty, meets an average of 8 times per year.

Calendar: Semesters. Academic year Aug. to May. Freshmen admitted Aug., Jan. Degrees conferred and formal commencement May. Summer session of 2 terms.

Characteristics of Freshmen: 2,181 applicants, 74% of applicants accepted. 29% of accepted applicants enrolled full-time.

100% (2,001 students) submitted SAT scores; 41% (205 students) submitted ACT scores. *25th percentile*: SAT Critical Reading 510, SAT Math 510, SAT Writing 500; ACT Composite 22. *75th percentile*: SAT Critical Reading 610, SAT Math 610, SAT Writing 500; ACT Composite 26.

73% of entering freshmen expected to graduate within 5 years. 95% of freshmen from New York. Freshmen from 25 states and 20 foreign countries.

Admission: Application deadline for fall is Feb. 5 (Jan. 15 for physical therapy). Nov. 15 deadline for early decision (notification begins Dec. 15). Regular decision notification begins Feb. 1. *Requirements:* Either graduation from accredited secondary school with 17 units recommended to include 4 English, 3 in a foreign language, 4 social studies, 3 mathematics, 3 science; or GED (with 2 units in a foreign language, 2 mathematics, 2 sciences from a secondary school). *Entrance tests:* College Board SAT or ACT composite. For foreign students TOEFL. *For transfer students:* 2.5 minimum GPA; from 4-year accredited institution 90 hours maximum transfer credit; from 2-year accredited institution 60 hours.

College credit and advanced placement for postsecondary-level work completed in secondary school. College credit for extrainstitutional learning (life experience).

Tutoring available. Noncredit developmental courses offered during regular academic year.

Degree Requirements: 120 credit hours; 2.0 GPA (2.5 in major field); 30 hours in residence; 2 semesters physical education; distribution requirements; exit competency examinations in individual fields of study.

Fulfillment of some degree requirements and exemption from some beginning courses possible by passing departmental examinations, College Board CLEP, AP, standardized tests. *Grading system:* A–F; pass-fail; withdraw (carries time limit).

Distinctive Educational Programs: *For undergraduates:* Interdisciplinary programs in American studies, international studies, multicultural studies, and women's studies. Facilities and programs for independent research, including individual majors, tutorials. Institutionally sponsored study abroad in Rennes, France; Valencia, Spain; Pescara, Italy. Individually arranged study in Germany and other countries; study at other New York institutions through Visiting Student Program. Cross-registration through consortium. *Available to all students:* Evening classes. *Other distinctive programs:* Honors program.

Degrees Conferred: 516 *baccalaureate*; 413 *master's*. Bachelor's degrees awarded in top five disciplines: health professions and related clinical sciences 85; business, management, marketing, and related support services 80; psychology 51; social sciences 48; English language/literature 42. Master's degrees awarded: business/marketing 18; education 316; health professions 47; liberal arts 16; public administration and social service professions 16.

Fees and Other Expenses: *Full-time tuition per academic year 2008–09:* undergraduate $24,076; contact the college for graduate tuition and fees. *Room and board per academic year:* $9,916. *Books and supplies:* $1,000. *Other expenses:* $1,100.

Financial Aid: Aid from institutionally generated funds is provided on the basis of academic merit, financial need. Institution has a Program Participation Agreement with the U.S. Department of Education for eligible students to receive Pell Grants and, depending upon the agreement, other federal aid.

Financial aid to full-time, first-time undergraduate students: 100% received some form of financial aid. Average amount of aid received: federal grants $3,961; Pell grants $2,822; other federal grants $1,249; state/local grants $2,442; institutional grants $9,117.

Departments and Teaching Staff: *Total instructional faculty:* 294 (full-time 134, part-time 160). 97% of faculty hold the doctorate, first-professional, or other terminal degree. Student/faculty ratio: 13:1.

Enrollment: Total enrollment 3,250. Undergraduate 2,188. Graduate 1,062. Undergraduate transfer-in students 166.

Characteristics of Student Body: *Ethnic/racial makeup:* number of Black non-Hispanic: 98; American Indian or Alaska Native: 9; Asian or Pacific Islander: 52; Hispanic: 34; White non-Hispanic: 1,744, unknown: 96.

International Students: 10 nonresident aliens enrolled fall 2008. Students from Europe, Asia, Africa, Canada. No programs available to aid students whose native language is not English. No financial aid specifically designated for international students.

Student Life: On-campus residence halls house 64% of student body. 85% of residence halls are co-ed; 15% females only. *Intercollegiate athletics:* male: basketball, golf, lacrosse, swimming, soccer, tennis; female: basketball, field hockey, swimming, tennis, volleyball. *Special regulations:* Cars with permits allowed in designated parking areas. Residence hall visitation from noon to midnight Sun.–Thurs., noon to 1:30am Fri. and Sat. *Special services:* Medical services, transportation between campus and St. John Fisher College; community service projects; computer labs. *Student publications: The Gleaner*, a bimonthly newspaper; *Sigillum*, a yearbook; *Verity*, an annual literary magazine. *Surrounding community:* The town of Pittsford is located in the Rochester metropolitan area. Served by mass transit system; airport 10 miles from campus; passenger rail service 10 miles from campus.

Library Collections: 283,500 volumes including bound books, serial backfiles, electronic documents, and government documents not in separate collections. Online catalog. 460,200 microforms; 12,400 audiovisual materials; 1,420 Current serial subscriptions. Computer work stations available. Students have access to the Internet at no charge.

Most important special holdings include G.K. Chesterton Collection; Thomas Merton Collection; Belloc Collection.

Buildings and Grounds: Campus area 149 acres.

Chief Executive Officer: Dr. Dean Braveman, President.

Undergraduates address admission inquiries to Thomas R. Darin, Director of Admissions; graduate inquiries to Dr. Kay Marshman, Dean, Graduate Studies.

New School

66 West 12th Street
New York, New York 10011
Tel: (212) 229-5600 **E-mail:** admissions@newschool.edu
Fax: (212) 989-3887 **Internet:** www.newschool.edu

Institution Description: The New School, formerly named New School for Social Research, is a private, independent, nonprofit institution; it includes the Graduate Faculty of Political and Social Science, Parsons School of Design,

NEW SCHOOL—*cont'd*

Eugene Lang College, Mannes School of Music, Milano Graduate School in Management and Urban Policy, The New School, School of Dramatic Arts/The Actors' Studio, Jazz and Contemporary Music Program, *Enrollment:* 9,825. *Degrees awarded:* Associate, baccalaureate, master's, doctorate. Diplomas also awarded.

Academic offerings subject to approval by New York State Education Department. Member of Interuniversity Doctoral Consortia, Research Library Consortium of Lower Manhattan.

Accreditation: *Regional:* MSA. *Professional*: architecture, art, music, psychology internship, public administration

History: Established in 1919 as America's first university for adults and as an informal center for exchange of ideas; chartered, established Graduate Faculty of Political and Social Science, and offered first instruction at postsecondary level 1934; awarded first degree (master's) 1936; began undergraduate program 1944; established Graduate School of Management and Urban Policy in 1964; affiliated with Parsons School of Design 1970; added media studies program 1975; established Eugene Lang College in 1985; Jazz and Contemporary Music Program 1986; affiliated with Mannes College of Music 1989; DIAL (Distance Learning) added in 1994; founded School of Dramatic Arts/The Actors' Studio in 1995.

Institutional Structure: *Governing board:* Board of Trustees. Extrainstitutional representation: 51 trustees. institutional representation: president of the institution. All voting. *Composition of institution:* Seven academic divisions, each headed by a dean; 13 university officers 18 administrators. Academic affairs headed by office of the provost. Facilities, business operations, and financed directed by office of the executive vice president. Instructional faculty 1,769.

Calendar: Semesters. Academic year Sept. to May. Freshmen admitted Sept., Jan. Degrees conferred May, Jan. Formal commencement May. Summer session of 1 term from early June to late July.

Characteristics of Freshmen: 5,692 applicants. 51% of applicants accepted. 37% of accepted applicants enrolled full-time.

68% (734 students) submitted SAT scores; 14% (150 students) submitted ACT scores. *25th percentile*: SAT Critical Reading 500, SAT Math 490, SAT Writing 510; ACT Composite 22, ACT English 21, ACT Math 20. *75th percentile*: SAT Critical Reading 620, SAT Math 620, SAT Writing 630; ACT Composite 26, ACT English 28, ACT Math 26.

40% of freshmen from New York. Freshmen from 49 states and 36 foreign countries.

Admission: Applicants must enroll in individual schools according to school deadlines and requirements.

Degree Requirements: 120 credit hours; 2.0 GPA; 30 credits in residence. Fulfillment of some degree requirements and exemption from some beginning courses possible by passing College Board CLEP, AP, other standardized tests. *Grading system:* A–F; withdraw (carries time limit).

Distinctive Educational Programs: Flexible meeting places and schedules; weekend and evening classes. Interdisciplinary master's in liberal studies program. Facilities and programs for independent research, including individual majors, tutorials. Human Relations Center. Center for New York City Affairs.

Degrees Conferred: 413 *associate*; 1,014 *baccalaureate;* 880 *master's;* 63 *doctorate*. Bachelor's degrees awarded: architecture 20; business/marketing 106; liberal arts/general studies 347; visual and performing arts 541.

Fees and Other Expenses: *Full-time tuition per academic year 2008–09:* $33,700. *Room and board per academic year:* $13,071. *Books and supplies:* $1,104. *Other expenses:* $3,412.

Financial Aid: Financial aid available for those who qualify. Institution has a Program Participation Agreement with the U.S. Department of Education for eligible students to receive Pell Grants and, depending upon the agreement, other federal aid.

Financial aid to first-time, full-time undergraduate students: 78% received some form of financial aid. Average amount of aid received: federal grants $3,706; state/local grants $3,705; institutional grants $10,147; loans $8,928.

Departments and Teaching Staff: *Total instructional faculty:* 1,773.

Enrollment: Total enrollment 9,825. Undergraduate 6,375. Graduate 3,450. Undergraduate transfer-in students 1,145.

Characteristics of Student Body: 189 nonresident aliens enrolled fall 2008. Programs available to aid students whose native language is not English: English as a Second Language Program. Financial aid specifically designated for international students; graduate student fellowships available annually.

Student Life: On-campus residence halls house less than 1% of student body. *Student publications: Newsletter*, weekly; *Outlook*, a biannual literary magazine. *Surrounding community:* New York City population over 7 million. Served by mass transit bus and subway system; airport 10 miles from campus; passenger rail service 1 mile from campus.

Publications: *Social Research Quarterly* first published 1934; *Graduate Faculty Philosophy Journal,* first published 1972; *World Policy Journal.*

Library Collections: 465,086 volumes including books, bound periodicals, music scores; microforms. 900 current periodical subscriptions including electronic indices. Access to online information retrieval services. Participation in city-wide library consortium allows student access to thousands of additional materials.

Buildings and Grounds: Urban campus.

Chief Executive Officer: Robert Kerrey, President.

Address admission inquiries to Christy Kalan, Director of Enrollment Management.

Eugene Lang College

Degree Programs Offered: *Baccalaureate* in liberal arts.

Departments and Teaching Staff: Faculty members drawn from the Graduate Faculty of Social and Political Science; also part-time teachers utilized.

Distinctive Educational Programs: Accelerated baccalaureate-master's programs in economics and political economy, health services administration, human resources, media studies, urban affairs. Special freshman curriculum in liberal studies, also open to students not regularly enrolled in institution.

Graduate Faculty of Political and Social Science

Degree Programs Offered: *Master's* in anthropology, clinical psychology, economics, experimental psychology, liberal studies, personality-social psychology, philosophy, political science, sociology; *doctorate:* in anthropology, clinical psychology, economics, experimental psychology, psychology, social-personality psychology.

Distinctive Educational Programs: Joint baccalaureate-master's degree in liberal arts.

Milano Graduate School of Management and Urban Policy

Degree Programs Offered: *Master's* in urban policy analysis and management, nonprofit management, health services management and policy, human resources management; *doctorate* in public and urban policy.

Distinctive Educational Programs: Joint baccalaureate-master's program with the Undergraduate Division.

New School

Degree Programs Offered: *Degree programs:* Bachelor of Arts, Master of Arts in Media Studies, Master of Fine Arts in Creative Writing; nondegree and noncredit courses available including culinary arts. MA/MS in international affairs.

School of Dramatic Arts, the Actors' Studio

Degree Programs Offered: *Master of Fine Arts* in acting, directing, and playwriting.

Admission: *Requirements:* Baccalaureate degree from an accredited institution; statement of purpose, resume, headshot, transcript, letters of recommendation; auditions are required of action program applicants; writing samples are required of playwriting program applicants.

Jazz and Contemporary Music Program

Degree Programs Offered: *Degree programs:* Bachelor of Fine Arts.

Admission: *Requirements:* Audition required of students within 200 mile radius; personal statement; high school graduation or equivalent; transfer credit and advanced placement are considered.

Mannes College of Music

Degree Programs Offered: *Baccalaureate, master's, diploma.*

Admission: *Requirements:* Graduation from accredited secondary school; in-person or taped audition. *Entrance tests:* Written music examination.

Degree Requirements: Completion of prescribed curriculum.

Parsons School of Design

Degree Programs Offered: *Associate, baccalaureate, master's*

Admission: *Requirements:* Either graduation from secondary or GED; portfolio.

Degree Requirements: *For all associate degrees:* 65 credit hours; 30 credits in residence. *For all baccalaureate degrees:* 134 credit hours; 2 years in residence. *For all undergraduate degrees:* 2.0 GPA.

Distinctive Educational Programs: Cooperative baccalaureate program in art education with Bank Street College of Education. Facilities and programs for independent research, including individual majors, tutorials. Study abroad in England, France. Exchange programs with Otis Art Institute of Parsons School of Design (CA), School of the Art Institute of Chicago (IL), and consortium members. Summer program for high school and college students.

New York Chiropractic College

2360 State Route 89
P.O. Box 800
Seneca Falls, New York 13148-0800
Tel: (315) 568-3000 **E-mail:** enrollnow@nycc.edu
Fax: (315) 568-3012 **Internet:** www.nycc.edu

Institution Description: New York Chiropractic College is a private, independent, nonprofit professional school. *Enrollment:* 842. *Degrees awarded:* First-professional.

Accreditation: *Regional:* MSA. *Professional*: chiropractic education

History: Established as Columbia Institute of Chiropractic 1919; adopted present name 1977.

Calendar: Trimesters. Terms begin Sept., Jan., May. New students admitted Sept., Jan., May. Degrees conferred all terms.

Characteristics of Freshmen: 79% of applicants admitted. 50% of admitted students enrolled full-time.

Admission: Rolling admissions. Applications should be filled approximately one year in advance of the desired entrance date to ensure full consideration of the desired term. *Requirements:* 2 or more years college including biology, physics, general and organic chemistry, English, psychology, humanities.

Degree Requirements: Completion of 211-credit hour program with 2.5 minimum GPA, including completion of 4-trimester internship.

Distinctive Educational Programs: Postgraduate/continuing education programs for chiropractors. Graduate program for acupuncture and oriental medicine.

Degrees Conferred: 164 *first-professional:* chiropractic.

Fees and Other Expenses: Contact the college for current tuition, fees, and housing costs.

Financial Aid: Aid from institutionally generated funds is provided on the basis of academic merit, financial need. Institution has a Program Participation Agreement with the U.S. Department of Education for eligible students to receive Pell Grants and, depending upon the agreement, other federal aid. *Graduate aid:* 131 students received $52,000 in federal and state-funded fellowships/grants; 660 received $18,000,000 in federal and state-funded loans; 172 students held work-study jobs worth $175,000.

Departments and Teaching Staff: *Total instructional faculty:* 79 (full-time 51, part-time 28). 100% of faculty hold the doctorate, first-professional, or other terminal degree. Student/faculty ratio: 9:1.

Enrollment: Total enrollment 842.

Characteristics of Student Body: *Ethnic/racial makeup:* number of Black non-Hispanic: 16; American Indian or Alaska Native: 5; Asian or Pacific Islander: 29; Hispanic: 33; White non-Hispanic: 334; unknown: 30. *Age distribution:* number 20–21: 22; 22–24: 265; 25–29: 289; 30–34: 58; 35–39: 24; 40–49: 17; 50–64: 3.

International Students: 100 nonresident aliens enrolled fall 2008. Students from Europe, Asia, Central and South America, Canada. No programs available to aid students whose native language is not English. No financial aid specifically designated for international students.

Student Life: *Student publications: Impulse*, a newsletter; *C.N.S.*, Student Government publication. *Student services:* College Chaplain, Residence Life, Leadership Education and Activities Programming; Career Development Center, Recreational Services and Special Events.

Publications: *Transitions*, quarterly magazine; *The Dean;s Chronicle*, quarterly newsletter.

Library Collections: 36,000 volumes including bound books, serial backfiles, electronic documents, and government documents not in separate collections. Card catalog. Current serial subscriptions: 300 paper, 18,700 microform. Computer work stations available. Students have access to the Internet at no charge.

Most important special holdings include Palmer Series; collections on sacro-occipital technique, applied kinesiology; Chiropractic Archival Books.

Buildings and Grounds: Campus area 286 acres.

Chief Executive Officer: Dr. Frank J. Nicchi, President.

Address admission inquiries to Michael Lynch, Director of Admissions.

New York City College of Technology / CUNY

300 Jay Street
Brooklyn, New York 11201
Tel: (718) 260-5000 **E-mail:** admissions@citytech.cuny.edu
Fax: (718) 260-5198 **Internet:** www.cityech.cuny.edu

Institution Description: New York City College of Technology, formerly named New York City Technical College, is a public, urban technical college within the City University of New York system. It offers career-oriented degree programs. *Enrollment:* 14,268. *Degrees awarded:* associate, baccalaureate. Certificates also awarded.

Accreditation: *Regional:* MSA. *Professional*: dental hygiene, dental laboratory technology, engineering technology, radiography.

History: Established as new York State Institute of Applied Arts and Sciences 1946; became a unit of the State University of New York 1948; became a New York City Community College sponsored by New York City Board of Estimate 1953; became a part of the City University of New York 1964; adopted present name 1980.

Institutional Structure: *Composition of institution:* President and chief executive officer. Academic affairs headed by provost and vice president for academic affairs. Vice presidents for finance, planning, management; student affairs; administration. Full-time instructional faculty 304.

Calendar: Semesters. Academic year Sept to June. Freshmen admitted Sept. Feb. Degrees conferred Oct., Feb., June. Formal commencement June. Summer session of 6 weeks.

Characteristics of Freshmen: 11,618 applicants. 88% of accepted applicants enrolled. 26% of accepted applicants enrolled full-time. 99% of freshmen from New York. Freshmen from 14 states and 1 foreign country.

Admission: Open admissions. All applicants must possess high school of General Equivalency Diploma. All applicants must take CUNY Skills Assessment Tests in reading, writing, mathematics. Students may apply through City University Application Processing Center or directly through College's Admissions Office. Transfer credit awarded.

Degree Requirements: *For all associate degrees:* 64–74 credits. *For all baccalaureate degrees:* 128 credits. *For all degrees:* students must have passed CUNY Skills Assessment Tests.

Distinctive Educational Programs: Evening classes. Weekend College. Dual enrollment of high school students. Independent study, internships. Study abroad in Hotel and Restaurant Management program. Bridge program to higher education or careers in engineering technology. Alternate Format program for students out of high school for five years with or without diploma.

Degrees Conferred: 875 *associate;* 559 *baccalaureate*. Bachelor's degrees awarded in top five disciplines: computer and information sciences 146; public administration and social service professions 68; business, management, marketing, and related support services 59; visual nd performing arts 48; engineering technologies 47.

Fees and Other Expenses: *Full-time tuition per academic year 2008–09:* resident $4,339, nonresident $8,979. *Books and supplies:* $1,016. No on-campus housing. *Other expenses:* $4,526.

Financial Aid: Aid from institutionally generated funds is provided on the basis of academic merit, financial need, other criteria.

Financial aid to full-time, first-time undergraduate students: 81% of students received some form of financial aid. Average amount of aid received: federal grants $3,489; Pell grants $3,290; other federal grants $512; state/local grants $2,698.

Departments and Teaching Staff: *Total full-time instructional faculty:* 304.

Enrollment: Total enrollment: 14,268 (undergraduate). Transfer-in students 1,093.

Characteristics of Student Body: *Ethnic/racial makeup:* number of Black non-Hispanic: 39.2%; American Indian or Alaska Native: .2%; Asian or Pacific Islander: 12%; Hispanic: 24.5%; White non-Hispanic: 12.3%.

International Students: 1,604 nonresident aliens enrolled 2008. Programs available to aid students whose native language is not English: social, cultural. English as a Second Language Program. No financial aid specifically designated for international students.

Student Life: *Special services:* Counseling, placement, health services, day care. *Student publications:* Magazine, newspaper, yearbook. *Surrounding community:* Downtown Brooklyn; New York City population over 7 million.

Library Collections: 183,000 volumes. 14,000 microforms; 6,200 audiovisual materials; 8,000 periodicals including via electronic access. Students have access to online information retrieval services and the Internet.

Most important special holdings include menu collection.

Chief Executive Officer: Dr. Russell Hotzler, President.

NEW YORK CITY COLLEGE OF TECHNOLOGY / CUNY—*cont'd*

Address admission inquiries to Alexis Chaconis, Director of Admissions.

New York College of Podiatric Medicine

1800 Park Avenue
New York, New York 10035
Tel: (212) 410-8053 **E-mail:** admissions@nycpm.edu
Fax: (212) 722-4918 **Internet:** www.nycpm.edu

Institution Description: New York College of Podiatric Medicine is a privately supported professional school. *Enrollment:* 344. *Degrees awarded:* First-professional.

Accreditation: *Professional*: podiatry

History: Founded in 1912 as New York School of Chiropody.

Calendar: Semesters.

Admission: *Requirements:* Minimum of 3 years of college study at an accredited college or university with at least 6 semester hours in English, 8 each in biology or zoology, physics, general chemistry, organic chemistry. *Entrance tests:* MCAT.

Degree Requirements: Completion of prescribed curriculum.

Degrees Conferred: 60 *first-professional:* podiatric medicine. 4 *honorary degree awarded 2006:* Doctor of Humane Letters.

Fees and Other Expenses: *Full-time tuition per academic year 2008–09:* $23,100. *Required fees:* $2,716.

Financial Aid: Aid from institutionally generated funds is provided on the basis of academic merit, financial need, other criteria. *Graduate aid:* 40 students received $48,313 in federal and state-funded fellowships/grants; 298 received $10,169,553 in federal and state-funded loans; 139 received $282,049 for work-study jobs.

Departments and Teaching Staff: *Total instructional faculty:* 62 (full-time 21, part-time 41). Total faculty with doctorate, first-professional, or other terminal degree: 62. Student/faculty ratio: 4.33:1.

Enrollment: Total enrollment 344.

Characteristics of Student Body: *Ethnic/racial makeup:* number of Black non-Hispanic: 72; Asian or Pacific Islander: 40; Hispanic: 29; White non-Hispanic: 136; unknown: 10. *Age distribution:* number 20–21: 3; 22–24: 107; 25–29: 137; 30–34: 20; 35–39: 9; 40–49: 15; 50–64: 1.

International Students: 8 nonresident aliens enrolled fall 2008. Students from Asia, Latin America, Canada, Middle East. No financial aid specifically designated for international students.

Library Collections: 15,000 volumes. 340 microform titles; 2,100 audiovisual materials; 160 current periodical subscriptions. Students have access to online information retrieval services and the Internet.

Major strengths of the library collection are in the fields of podiatry, orthopedics, and dermatology.

Buildings and Grounds: Urban campus.

Chief Executive Officer: Dr. Louis L. Levine, President.

Address admission inquiries to Lisa K. Lee, Assistant Dean, Admissions and Student Services.

New York Institute of Technology

Wheatley Road
P.O. Box 8000
Old Westbury, New York 11568
Tel: (800) 345-NYIT **E-mail:** admissions@nyit.edu
Fax: (516) 636-7o13 **Internet:** www.nyit.edu

Institution Description: New York Institute of Technology is a private, independent, nonprofit institution with branch campuses in New York City and Central Islip. *Enrollment:* 9,073. *Degrees awarded:* Associate, baccalaureate, first-professional (osteopathic medicine), master's.

Academic offerings subject to approval by statewide coordinating bodies. Member of the consortium Long Island Regional Advisory Council on Higher Education.

Accreditation: *Regional:* MSA. *Professional*: architecture, culinary education, engineering, engineering technology, interior design, occupational therapy, osteopathy

History: Established, chartered, incorporated, and offered first instruction at postsecondary level 1955; awarded first degree (associate) 1957; became 4-year college 1960.

Institutional Structure: *Governing board:* New York Institute of Technology Board of Trustees. Extrainstitutional representation: 17 trustees; institutional representation: 1 administrator. 17 voting. *Composition of institution:* Administrators 126. Academic affairs headed by vice president for academic affairs. Management/business/finances directed by treasurer. Full-time instructional faculty 279. Academic governance body, Faculty Senate, meets an average of 4 times per year. *Faculty representation:* Faculty served by collective bargaining agent affiliated with AAUP.

Calendar: Semesters; trimesters for New York College of Osteopathic Medicine. Academic year Sept. to May. Freshmen admitted Sept., Jan., June. Degrees conferred May, Aug., Dec. Formal commencement May. Summer session from mid-June to mid-Aug.

Characteristics of Freshmen: 2,671 applicants 78% of applicants admitted. 35% of applicants admitted and enrolled full-time.

89% (641 students) submitted SAT scores; 13% (95 students) submitted ACT scores. *25th percentile*: SAT Critical Reading 420, SAT Math 470; ACT Composite 20. *75th percentile*: SAT Critical Reading 550, SAT Math 590; ACT Composite 26.

59% of entering freshmen expected to graduate within 5 years. 55% of freshmen from New York. Freshmen from 45 states and 75 foreign countries.

Admission: Rolling admissions plan except for Feb. 1 nursing, BS/DO, physical therapy, physician assisting, and occupational therapy. Early acceptance available. *Requirements:* Either graduation from accredited secondary school or equivalency except for architecture, engineering, physical therapy, occupational therapy, nursing, BS/DO, and premedical science. Portfolio for fine arts students. Recommended freehand drawing for architecture students, additional mathematics for sciences and engineering. *Entrance exams:* College Board SAT or ACT composite. For foreign students TOEFL. *For transfer students:* 99 hours maximum transfer credit.

College credit and advanced placement for postsecondary-level work completed in secondary school and for state program in noncollegiate-sponsored instruction. For extrainstitutional learning college credit on basis of portfolio and faculty assessments; personal interviews.

Tutoring available. Developmental courses offered in summer session and regular academic year; credit given.

Degree Requirements: *For all associate degrees:* 64 credit hours; 30 credits must be completed in residency at NYIT. *For all baccalaureate degrees:* 120–169 credit hours; 2–4 terms in residence. *For all undergraduate degrees:* 2.0 GPA.

Fulfillment of some degree requirements possible by passing departmental examinations, College Board CLEP. *Grading system:* A–F; withdraw (carries time limit); incomplete (carries time limit).

Distinctive Educational Programs: Work-experience programs. Flexible meeting places and schedules, including off-campus centers (at various locations on Long Island and in the boroughs of Brooklyn, Manhattan, and Queens, all less than 30 miles away from main institution); in Florida at Lynn University (Boca Raton) and Keiser College (Fort Lauderdale). Weekend and evening classes. Accelerated degree programs. Multidisciplinary curricula, including fine arts, design graphics, interior design, biomedical engineering technology, environmental biology, industrial design. Preprofessional program in health sciences. Facilities and programs for independent research, including honors programs, tutorials. Summer study-travel abroad in England, Italy. Cross-registration through consortium. Higher education opportunity program provides academic and other support services for economically and educationally disadvantaged students. *Other distinctive programs:* Continuing education.

ROTC: Air Force, Army.

Degrees Conferred: 11 *associate;* 639 *baccalaureate*; 985 *master's*; 30 *doctorate*. Bachelor's degrees awarded in top five disciplines: business/marketing 290; health professions and related clinical sciences 199; liberal arts 185; architecture 240; visual and performing arts 75. Master's degrees awarded: architecture 19; business/marketing 458; communication technologies 153; computer and information sciences 94; education 99; engineering 98; family and consumer sciences 39; health professions and related sciences 25.

Fees and Other Expenses: *Full-time tuition per academic year 2008–09:* $22,780 undergraduate; contact the institute for current graduate tuition and fees. *Books and supplies:* $800. *Room and board per academic year:* $10,250. *Other expenses:* $2,550.

Financial Aid: Aid from institutionally generated funds is provided on the basis of academic merit, financial need, athletic ability, other criteria.

Financial aid to full-time, first-time undergraduate students: 97% received some form of aid. Average amount of aid received: federal grants $4,466; Pell grants $3,236; other federal grants $2,456; state/local grants $947; institutional grants $8,491.

Departments and Teaching Staff: *Total instructional faculty:* 849 (full-time 279, part-time 570). 90% of faculty hold the doctorate, first-professional, or other terminal degree: Student/faculty ratio: 24:1.

Enrollment: Total enrollment 9,073. Undergraduate 5,643. Graduate 3,430. Undergraduate transfer-in students 318.

Characteristics of Student Body: *Ethnic/racial makeup:* number of Black non-Hispanic: 777; American Indian or Alaska Native: 24; Asian or Pacific Islander: 595; Hispanic: 604; White non-Hispanic: 2,447; unknown: 2,039.

International Students: 1,475 nonresidents aliens enrolled fall 2008. Programs available to aid students whose native language is not English: Financial. English as a Second Language Program.

Student Life: Campus housing on central Islip campus. *Intercollegiate athletics:* male: baseball, basketball, cross-country, football,soccer, tennis, track; female: basketball, cross-country, soccer, softball, track and field, volleyball. *Special regulations:* Cars permitted on campus in designated areas only. *Special services:* Learning Resources Center, medical services, bus service. *Student publications, radio:* Newspaper. Radio station WNYT broadcasts 168 hours per week. *Surrounding community:* Old Westbury population 4,000. New York City, 30 miles from campus, is nearest metropolitan area. Served by mass transit bus and rail systems; airport; passenger rail service 2 miles from campus.

Library Collections: 185,500 volumes. Current periodical subscriptions: 2,259 paper; 888,929 microforms, 11,568 via electronic access. Online catalog. Students have access to online information retrieval services.

Most important holdings include collections on art and architecture, culinary arts, Center for Prejudice Reduction.

Buildings and Grounds: Campus area 700 acres.

Chief Executive Officer: Dr. Edward Giuliano, President.

Address admission inquiries to Jacquelyn Nealon, Dean of Admissions.

New York College of Osteopathic Medicine

Degree Programs Offered: *First-professional.*

Admission: Baccalaureate or 90 semester hours (135 quarter hours) from accredited university or college with 8 hours English, 8 each (including 2 in laboratory) in biology, general chemistry, organic chemistry, physics; MCAT.

Degree Requirements: 2,848 clock hours in first 8 trimesters; 2 trimesters each prescribed and elective clinical clerkships, 2 preceptorships; 2.0 GPA in all courses.

New York Law School

57 Worth Street
New York, New York 10013-2960
Tel: (212) 431-2100 **E-mail:** admissions@nyls.edu
Fax: (212) 343-2137 **Internet:** www.nyls.edu

Institution Description: New York Law School is a private institution offering professional study leading to the juris doctor degree. *Enrollment:* 1,655. *Degrees awarded:* First-professional, master's.

Accreditation: *National:* American Bar Association. *Professional*: law

History: Founded in 1891, New York Law School is one of the oldest independent law schools in the United States.

Calendar: Semesters. Academic year Aug. to May.

Admission: *Requirements:* Bachelor's degree from an accredited college or university. *Entrance tests:* LSAT.

Degree Requirements: Completion of prescribed curriculum.

Distinctive Educational Programs: Center for International Law; Center for New York City Law; Communications Media Law Center.

Degrees Conferred: 40 *master's:* legal professions; 407 *first-professional:* law.

Fees and Other Expenses: *Full-time tuition per academic year:* contact the school for current information regarding tuition and other costs.

Financial Aid: Aid from institutionally generated funds is provided on the basis of academic merit, financial need. Institution has a Program Participation Agreement with the U.S. Department of Education for eligible students to receive Pell Grants and, depending upon the agreement, other federal aid.

Departments and Teaching Staff: *Total instructional faculty:* 135. Total tenured faculty: 53. Student/faculty ratio: 22.4:1. Degrees held by full-time faculty: professional 100%.

Enrollment: Total enrollment 1,655.

Characteristics of Student Body: *Ethnic/racial makeup:* Black non-Hispanic: 7.3%; American Indian or Alaska Native: .4%; Asian or Pacific Islander: 6.8%; Hispanic: 5%; White non-Hispanic: 74.9%; unknown: 3.9%.

International Students: 27 nonresident aliens enrolled fall 2008.

Student Life: Located in Manhattan's TriBeCa district and within walking distance of the Civic Center and Wall Street.

Publications: *New York Law School Law Review; New York Law School Journal of International and Comparative Law; New York Law School Journal of Human Rights; City Law.*

Library Collections: 465,000 volumes.

Chief Executive Officer: Matasar A. Richard, Dean.

Address admission inquiries to Perez Williams, Assistant Dean Admissions.

New York Medical College

Sunshine Cottage
Valhalla, New York 10595
Tel: (914) 594-4000 **E-mail:** admissions@nymc.edu
Fax: (914) 594-4479 **Internet:** www.nymc.edu

Institution Description: New York Medical College is a private health sciences university with three schools: School of Medicine, Graduate School of Basic Medical Sciences, School of Public Health. The college includes a major medical school research center with grants and awards for research, research training, medical education and health services from federal and state agencies, foundations, and voluntary health organizations, commercial sponsors, and private donors. *Enrollment:* 1,414. *Degrees awarded:* Master's, doctorate, first-professional.

Accreditation: *Regional:* MSA. *Professional*: dentistry, medicine, physical therapy, public health, speech-language pathology

History: Founded 1860.

Institutional Structure: *Governing board:* Board of Trustees. Extrainstitutional representation: 22 trustees. *Composition of institution:* Academic affairs headed by provost/dean. *Full-time and part-time instructional faculty:* 1,689. Academic governance body, Faculty Senate, meets an average of 4 times per year. Student Senate meets monthly.

Calendar: Semesters. Academic year July to June. Formal commencement May.

Admission: Highly competitive admissions standards with only 190 students accepted from over 10,000 applicants. Objective academic criteria and subjective assessments of motivation, maturity, stability, integrity, etc. are evaluated. *Requirements:* Baccalaureate degree including specific science courses with substantial laboratory work. All applicants are required to take the New Medical College Admissions test recommended by the Association of American Medical Colleges. Additional information for admissions available at www.nymc.edu.a

Degree Requirements: Medical School: Three standing faculty committees on student promotions periodically review the academic records of all students which reflect performance in all aspects of coursework, including the results of examinations. A student who has successfully completed all courses, and who otherwise is in good standing, will be recommended for graduation. School of Public Health: MS degree requires 36 credits; MPH degree requires 45 credits; Physical Therapy 120 credits including clinical training. Graduate School of Basic Medical Sciences: MS degree requires 30 to 32 degrees; PH.D. requires 60 credits including 15 research including 15 research credits.

Distinctive Educational Programs: Innovative 6-year curriculum in primary care. M.P.H. and M.S. degrees offered in biostatistics, correctional health, developmental disabilities, emergency medical services, environmental health, epidemiology, general public health (including health promotion and maternal and child health), gerontology, health services management and policy, international health, and nutrition. Combined MD/MPH and MD/PhD programs.

Degrees Conferred: 119 *master's:* biological sciences 36; health professions 83; 10 *doctorate:* biological sciences 9; health professions 1. 192 *first-professional:* medicine.

Fees and Other Expenses: *Full-time tuition per academic year 2008–09:* contact the college for current tuition, fees, and other costs.

Financial Aid: Aid from institutionally generated funds is provided on the basis of academic merit, financial need. *Graduate aid:* 91 students received $229,574 in federal and state-funded fellowships/grants; 902 received $28,376,776 in federal and state-funded loans; 66 received $103,470 for work-study jobs; 236 received $2,356,954 for other fellowships/grants; 56 students held research assistantships worth $1,288,000.

Departments and Teaching Staff: *Total instructional faculty:* 1,689 (full-time 1,394, part-time 295). 100% of faculty hold the doctorate, first-professional, or other terminal degree.

Enrollment: Total enrollment 1,414.

International Students: 68 nonresident aliens enrolled fall 2008. No financial aid specifically designated for international students.

Student Life: On-campus residence hall, nearby residence facilities and a limited number of on-campus, one- and two-bedroom garden apartments as well as a new apartment complex in Manhattan. *Special services:* Alpha Omega Alpha, the national honor medical society, maintains a chapter at the college with election to membership based on scholarship. A chapter of the American Med-

NEW YORK MEDICAL COLLEGE—*cont'd*

ical Student Association (AMSA) enables student representatives to participate in national and regional conventions where subjects such as national health legislation and medical school curricula are discussed. *Student publications:* student yearbook. *Surrounding community:* Westchester County. New York City is 35 minutes from campus. Served by mass transit bus system; local and 3 metropolitan New York area airports; nearby passenger rail system.

Library Collections: 205,000 volumes. Current periodical subscriptions: paper 927; microform 71; via electronic access 11,546. 851 audio/videotapes. 22 DVD discs; 437 CD-ROMs. Students have access to online information retrieval services and the Internet.

Most important special holdings include history of medicine; disaster medicine, pharmacology, homeopathy.

Buildings and Grounds: Campus is located in the center of Westchester County in Valhalla, New York. The largest campus building, the Basic Sciences Building, occupies 4.5 acres and consists of multidisciplinary teaching laboratories, library, lecture halls, bookstore, cafeteria and student lounge. Medical Education Center containing 3 floors of classrooms, module, and laboratories plus a large lecture hall (completed 2001). Sharing the campus is Westchester County Medical Center, a tertiary care university teaching hospital. Additional university hospitals are located in New York City, including the boroughs of Manhattan and the Bronx.

Chief Executive Officer: Dr. Ralph A. O'Connell, M.D., President.

Address admission inquiries for the Medical School to Associate Dean for Admissions; inquiries for the School of Public Health should be addressed to the Assistant Dean of Admissions; for the Graduate School of Basic Medical Sciences to student's admission counselors.

New York School of Interior Design

170 East 70th Street
New York, New York 10021-5110
Tel: (212) 472-1500 **E-mail:** admissions@nysid.edu
Fax: (212) 472-1867 **Internet:** www.nysid.edu

Institution Description: The New York School of Interior Design is a private institution. *Enrollment:* 628. *Degrees awarded:* Associate, baccalaureate, master's. Diplomas are also awarded.

Accreditation: *National:* NASAD. *Professional*: interior design

Calendar: Semesters. Academic year from June to May.

Characteristics of Freshmen: 75% of applicants admitted. 66% of accepted applicants enrolled.

70% of freshmen expected to graduate within 5 years. 44% of freshmen from New York. Freshmen from 17states and 20 foreign countries.

Admission: High school graduation.

Degree Requirements: Completion of prescribed curriculum.

Degrees Conferred: 78 *associate;* 29 *baccalaureate:* interior design; 9 *master's:* interior design.

Fees and Other Expenses: *Full-time tuition per academic year 2008–09:* undergraduate $15,890; contact the school for current graduate tuition/fees. *Books and supplies:* $1,000. No on-campus housing.

Financial Aid: Aid from institutionally generated funds is provided on the basis of financial need.

Financial aid to full-time, first-time undergraduate students: 79% of students received some form of financial aid.

Departments and Teaching Staff: *Total instructional faculty* 79 (full-time 2, part-time 77). 61% of faculty hold the doctorate, first-professional, or other terminal degree. Student/faculty ratio: 12:1.

Enrollment: Total enrollment 628. Undergraduate 612. Graduate 16. Undergraduate transfer-in students 20.

Characteristics of Student Body: *Ethnic/racial makeup:* Black non-Hispanic: 4.3%; Asian or Pacific Islander: 6.7%; Hispanic: 6.6%; White non-Hispanic: 73.2%; nonresident alien 7.2%.

International Students: 52 nonresident aliens enrolled fall 2008. Students from Europe, Asia, Central and South America, Africa, Canada, Australia. Programs available to aid students whose native language is not English: cultural. English as a Second Language Program. Financial aid designated for international students: 5 scholarships available annually for international graduate students.

Library Collections: 11,000 volumes. 1,850 slides; 70 current periodical subscriptions. Students have access to online information retrieval services.

Most important holdings include works on interior design, architecture, and design.

Chief Executive Officer: Inge Heckel, President.

Address admission inquiries to David Sprouls, Director of Admissions.

New York Theological Seminary

475 Riverside Drive
Suite 500
New York, New York 10115
Tel: (212) 870-1211 **E-mail:** admissions@nyts.edu
Fax: (212) 870-1236 **Internet:** www.nyts.edu

Institution Description: New York Theological Seminary is a private, multicultural, interdenominational institution offering graduate professional training. *Enrollment:* 342. *Degrees awarded:* First professional, master's, doctorate.

Accreditation: *National:* ATS. *Professional*: theology

History: The Seminary was founded in 1900.

Calendar: Semesters. Academic year from July to June.

Admission: Rolling admissions. *Requirements:* BA degree.

Degree Requirements: Completion of prescribed curriculum.

Degrees Conferred: 26 *master's*: master of professional studies; 51 *doctorate:* ministerial studies; 37 *first-professional:* master of divinity.

Fees and Other Expenses: *Full-time tuition per academic year 2008–09:* contact the seminary for current tuition, fees, and housing costs.

Financial Aid: Aid from institutionally generated funds is provided on the basis of financial need. Federally funded aid available.

Departments and Teaching Staff: *Total instructional faculty:* 40 (full-time 13, part-time 27). 96% of faculty hold the doctorate, first-professional, or other terminal degree. Student/faculty ratio: 8:1.

Enrollment: Total enrollment 342. First-professional 342.

International Students: 49 nonresident aliens enrolled fall 2008. Students from Europe, Asia, Africa. Programs available to aid students whose native language is not English: English as a Second Language program. No financial aid specifically designated for international students.

Library Collections: 25,000 volumes. 700 microforms, 800 audiovisual materials; 41 current periodical subscriptions.

Most important special collections include biblical/theological books in Korean and Spanish.

Chief Executive Officer: Dr. Dale T. Irvin, President.

Address admission inquiries to Yen Su Kang, Registrar.

New York University

22 Washington Square South
New York, New York 10012
Tel: (212) 998-1212 **E-mail:** admissions@nyu.edu
Fax: (212) 995-4902 **Internet:** www.nyu.edu

Institution Description: New York University is a private, independent, nonprofit institution. *Enrollment:* 42,189. *Degrees awarded:* Associate, baccalaureate, first-professional (dentistry, medicine, law), master's, doctorate.

Member of Inter-University Doctoral Consortia.

Accreditation: *Regional:* MSA. *Professional*: accounting, business, community health/preventive medicine, clinical psychology, counseling psychology, dance, dentistry, dental assisting, dental hygiene, dietetics, diagnostic medical sonography, endodontics, health services administration, journalism, law, medicine, nursing, nursing-midwifery, occupational therapy, oral and maxillofacial surgery, orthodontics, pediatric dentistry, periodontics, physical therapy, psychology internship, prosthodontics, public administration, rehabilitation counseling, respiratory therapy, school psychology, social work, speech-language pathology, teacher education

History: Established and chartered as University of the City of New York 1831; offered first instruction at postsecondary level 1832; awarded first degree (baccalaureate) 1834; adopted present name 1896. *See* Theodore Francis Jones, *New York University: 1831–1932* (New York: New York University Press, 1933) for further information.

Institutional Structure: *Governing board:* New York University Board of Trustees. Extrainstitutional representation: 67 trustees; institutional representation: 1 administrator, 1 ex officio, 50 voting. *Composition of institution:* Academic affairs headed by provost. Business/finance directed by executive vice president. Full-time instructional faculty 2,152. Academic governance body, University Senate, meets an average of 6 times per year.

Calendar: Semesters. Academic year Sept. to May. Freshmen admitted Sept., Jan., June. Degrees conferred June, Oct., Feb. Formal commencement May. Summer session of 2 terms from May to Aug.

Characteristics of Freshmen: 37,245 applicants. 32% of applicants admitted. 37% of admitted students enrolled full-time.

87% (3,859 students) submitted SAT scores; 13 (592 students) submitted ACT scores. *25th percentile*: SAT Critical Reading 630, SAT Math 620, SAT Writing 630; ACT Composite 28. *75th percentile*: SAT Critical Reading 720, SAT Math 720, SAT Writing 720. ACT Composite 31.

83% of freshmen expected to graduate within 5 years. 39% of freshmen from New York. Freshmen from 50 states and 94 foreign countries.

Admission: For fall acceptance, apply as early as Sept. of previous year, but not later than Jan. 15 of year of enrollment. Students are notified of acceptance Apr. 1. Apply by Nov. 15 for early decision; must withdraw applications from other college(s) if admitted to New York University. Early acceptance available. *Requirements:* Either graduation from accredited secondary school with 4 units English, 3 mathematics, 2 foreign language, 4 history; or GED. Additional requirements for some programs. *Entrance tests:* College Board SAT or ACT (with writing component) required; two SAT subject tests recommended. *For transfer students:* Admitted in fall, spring, and summer terms. Maximum transfer credit from 4-year regionally accredited institutions: 96 credits; maximum transfer credit from 2-year regionally accredited institution: 64 credits.

College credit and advanced placement for postsecondary-level work completed in secondary school and for extrainstitutional learning on basis of portfolio assessment.

Tutoring available.

Degree Requirements: *For all associate degrees:* 60–78 credit hours. *For all baccalaureate degrees:* 120–134 credit hours; *For all undergraduate degrees:* 2.0 GPA; final 32 credits must be earned in residence.

Fulfillment of some degree requirements possible by passing departmental examinations. *Grading system:* A–F; pass-fail; withdraw.

Distinctive Educational Programs: Evening classes. Facilities and programs for independent research. Gallatin School for Individualized Study offers flexible scheduling, extensive internships, and independent study. The College of Arts and Science offers a joint BS/BE with Stevens Institute of Technology, Hoboken, N.J. Study abroad programs in Florence, London, Paris, Madrid, Salamanca, Milan, Prague, Cracow, Venice, Amsterdam, Israel, and other countries. International student exchanges with institutions in The Netherlands, Denmark, Germany, Italy, Ghana, Sweden, Czech Republic, Bratislava, Korea, Chile, and Mexico.

ROTC: Army and Navy offered in cooperation with Fordham University.

Degrees Conferred: 454 *associate;* 5,086 *baccalaureate;* 6,006 *master's;* 415 *doctorate,* 906 *first-professional.* Bachelor's degrees awarded in top five disciplines: business/marketing 1,140; visual and performing arts 978; social sciences 868; communications/journalism 474; psychology 298. Master's degrees awarded in top five disciplines: business/marketing 414; parks administration and social services 679; visual and performing arts 668; education 499; law/legal studies 472. Doctorates awarded in top five disciplines: social sciences 54; health professions 50; visual and performing arts 44; biological/life sciences 42; psychology 37. First-professional degrees awarded: dentistry 288; law 465; medicine 153. *Honorary degrees awarded 2005–06:* Doctor of Fine Arts 1, Doctor of Commercial Science 2, Doctor of Letters 1, Doctor of Humane Letters 2.

Fees and Other Expenses: *Full-time tuition per academic year 2008–09:* undergraduate $37,372; Graduate tuition/fees vary; contact the school of interest for current information. *Room and board per academic year:* $12,910. *Required fees:* $1,886. *Books and supplies:* $800. *Other expenses:* $1,000.

Financial Aid: Aid from institutionally generated funds is provided on the basis of academic merit, financial need.

Financial aid to full-time, first-time undergraduate students: 72% received some form of aid. Average amount of aid received: federal grants $5,394; Pell grants $3,246; other federal grants $2,337; state/local grants $3,466; institutional grants $12,192.

Departments and Teaching Staff: *Total instructional faculty:* 5,005 (full-time 1,823, part-time 3) 555 of faculty hold the doctorate, first-professional, or other terminal degree: 2,196. Student/faculty ratio: 11:1.

Enrollment: Total enrollment 42,189. Undergraduate 21,269. Graduate 20,920.

Characteristics of Student Body: *Ethnic/racial makeup (undergraduate):* number of Black non-Hispanic: 975; American Indian or Alaska Native: 46; Asian or Pacific Islander: 3,585; Hispanic: 1,599; White non-Hispanic: 10,336; unknown: 3,446. *Age distribution:* number under 18: 107; 18–19: 8,107; 20–21: 9,069; 22–24: 1,887; 25–29: 736; 30–34: 407; 35–39: 258; 40–49: 300; 50–64: 85; 65 and over: 9.

International Students: 4,305 nonresident aliens enrolled fall 2008. Students from Europe, Central and South America, Africa, Canada, Australia, New Zealand, Middle East, Caribbean. Programs available to aid students whose native language is not English: social, cultural. English as a Second Language Program. Financial aid specifically designated for international students: scholarships available annually

Student Life: On-campus residence halls house 51% of undergraduate student body. Residence halls for both sexes constitute 100% of such space. 15% of fraternity and sorority members live in Greek housing. There are 230 clubs and organizations. *Intercollegiate athletics:* male: basketball, cross-country, diving, fencing, golf, soccer, swimming, tennis, track, volleyball, wrestling; female: basketball, cross-country, diving, fencing, swimming, tennis, track, volleyball. Member NCAA Division III, University Athletic Association. *Special services:* Learning Resources Center, medical services. Office for African-American Student Services, Center for Students with Disabilities. *Student publications, radio: Washington Square News,* a student-run daily newspaper produced once a semester; *Brownstone,* an African-American magazine; *Expressions of Dread,* a magazine devoted to terror; *F-Stop,* photography magazine; *Hype,* a music-related newspaper; *L'Image,* French literary publication; *Minetta Review* and *New Ink,* literary magazines; *The Plague,* a humorous magazine; *The Hotline,* a bimonthly magazine of college events. WNYU-AM/FM broadcasts 45 hours per week. *Surrounding community:* New York City population over 7 million. Served by mass transit bus, subway, commuter railroad systems.

Publications: *Annual Survey of American Law* (quarterly) first published in 1961, *Artibus Asiae* (semi-annually), first published in 1925; *The Entrepreneurialship Forum* (annually), first published 1984; *Financial Markets, Institutions and Instruments* (quarterly), first published in 1992; *Journal of International Law and Politics* (quarterly), first published in 1968; *Moot Court Casebook* (annually), first published in 1977; *Monograph Series in Finance and Economics* (quarterly), first published in 1966; *New York University Environmental Law Journal* (six issues a year), first published in 1992; *New York University Law Review* (six issues a year), first published in 1924; *New York University Review of Law and Social Change* (quarterly), first published in 1969; *Peqoid Literary Journal* (biannually), first published in 1976; *Revue* (biannual), a bilingual academic journal, first published in 1991; *Ross Institute of NYU Journal of Accounting, Auditing and Finance* (quarterly), first published in 1978; *TDR: a journal of performance studies* (quarterly), first published in 1955; *Women & Performance* (biannually), first published in 1983; *The Working Paper Series* publishes 55–60 economic research reports a year.

Library Collections: 5,624,000 volumes. Current serial subscriptions: 31,492 paper and electronic. 854,989 audiovisual materials; 56,781 recordings and compact discs. Online catalog. Computer work stations available campus-wide. Students have access to online information retrieval services.

Most important special holdings include Fales Library of 19th and 20th Century English and American Literature; Tamiment Library of American Radical History; Wagner Labor Archives; Alfred C. Berol Collection of Lewis Carroll Materials; Richard Maars Collection of Westchester and New York State.

Buildings and Grounds: Campus area 230 acres. Campus DVD available.

Chief Executive Officer: Dr. John Sexton, President.

Undergraduates address admission Director of Admissions; graduate inquiries to appropriate school.

College of Arts and Science

Degree Programs Offered: *Baccalaureate.*

Distinctive Educational Programs: Preprofessional programs in dentistry, education, engineering, law, medicine, social work. Metropolitan Studies program offers multidisciplinary study on the problems and processes of city life; including public lectures, summer institutes, intensive seminars. Russian Area Studies program provides comprehensive background in Slavic studies to prepare students for graduate research. Majors in classical civilization and Hellenic studies, women's studies. Honors programs in anthropology, biology, economics, English, fine arts, French, German, history, music, philosophy, psychology, politics, Slavic languages, medieval and Renaissance studies. Coordinated liberal studies comprising half of baccalaureate requirements is offered through college for its students and for those in all other undergraduate schools or divisions of the university. Accelerated B.A.-M.B.A. or B.A.-M.S. in quantitative analysis with Graduate School of Business Administration; B.A.-Master of Public Administration with Graduate School of Public Administration; B.A.-D.D.S. with College of Dentistry. Dual-degree program in engineering with Stevens Institute of Technology.

Tisch School of the Arts

Degree Programs Offered: *Baccalaureate, master's* in cinema studies, dance, drama, dramatic writing, film and television, photography, theatrical design; *master's* in cinema studies, interactive telecommunications, film, musical theater, performance studies; *doctorate* in cinema studies, performance studies. Certificates also given in some programs.

Distinctive Educational Programs: The Institute of Performing Arts offers professional training programs in acting, dance, theatrical design, technical theatre, and musical theater. The Institute of Film and Television offers programs in cinema studies, film, television, radio, animation, dramatic writing, photography and interactive telecommunications. All programs require an audition or creative portfolio in addition to meeting academic criteria. The undergraduate programs combine professional training and the liberal arts. Evening classes. Facilities and programs for independent research. Study abroad programs in

NEW YORK UNIVERSITY—*cont'd*

Florence, London, Paris, Madrid, Salamanca, Milan, Prague, Cracow, Venice, Amsterdam, and Israel. International student exchanges with institutions in The Netherlands, Denmark, Germany, Italy, Ghana, Sweden, Czech Republic, Bratislava, Korea, Chile, and Mexico.

Leonard N. Stern School of Business

Degree Programs Offered: *Baccalaureate, master's, doctorate.*

Admission: High school GPA of 3.2 or 1200; transfer students 3.0 GPA from 4-year college, 3.3 GPA from community college; baccalaureate degree for graduate programs.

Distinctive Educational Programs: Internships. Professional business certificate program for students with baccalaureate degrees. Joint baccalaureate-master's of business administration with Graduate School of Business Administration. University Scholar Program for qualified freshmen subsidizes professional, social, and cultural activities and an annual trip to Europe. Study abroad programs in Florence, London, Paris, Madrid, Salamanca, Milan, Prague, Cracow, Venice, Amsterdam, and Israel. International student exchanges with institutions in The Netherlands, Denmark, Germany, Italy, Ghana, Sweden, Czech Republic, Bratislava, Korea, Chile, and Mexico.

School of Education

Degree Programs Offered: *Baccalaureate* (B.S., B.M.), *master's* (M.A., M.M., M.S., M.P.H.), *certificate of advanced study* (6th year certificate), *doctorate* (D.A. Ed.D., Ph.D., Psy.D.).

Distinctive Educational Programs: University and Future Educators Scholars Programs for qualified freshmen subsidizes international travel and professional and cultural activities. Community College Transfer Opportunity Program provides scholarship support to qualified transfer students from 10 area community colleges. Special scholarship initiatives for under-represented graduate students, prospective master's students in teacher education, and part-time master's students. B.S. in applied psychological studies four semesters of intensive fieldwork in different settings. M.A. in studio art offers special emphasis on computer art, joint program in photography with International Center for Photography. Graduate programs in visual and performing arts administration. Dual B.S. degree in special education/elementary education. Special course sequence in Educational Administration and Supervision for M.A. and advanced certificate students in School of Business Administration. Master's training in clinical nutrition. Special undergraduate programs in nursing for registered nurses (2 years) and college graduates seeking a second degree (accelerated 11-month program). New master's level tracks in nursing in adult acute care and clinical nursing. More than 12 Study Abroad programs for graduate students in education, health and the arts. Metropolitan Center for Research and Development supports research and training in urban school reform, drop-out prevention. National Arts Education Research Center supports research and training. Nordoff-Robbins Music Therapy Clinic. Para-Educator Center trains learning disabled young adults. Study abroad programs in Florence, London, Paris, Madrid, Salamanca, Milan, Prague, Cracow, Venice, Amsterdam, and Israel. International student exchanges with institutions in The Netherlands, Denmark, Germany, Italy, Ghana, Sweden, Czech Republic, Bratislava, Korea, Chile, and Mexico.

Gallatin School for Individualized Study

Degree Programs Offered: *Baccalaureate, master's.*

Distinctive Educational Programs: Working closely with faculty advisors, students design their own programs of study. Emphasizing the history of ideas and significant texts in the humanities, social sciences, and sciences, Gallatin provides a diverse, flexible, and individualized approach to education.

Shirley M. Ehrenkranz School of Social Work

Degree Programs Offered: *Baccalaureate, master's, doctorate.*

Distinctive Educational Programs: Undergraduate program prepares for beginning social work practice. M.S.W. and Ph.D. programs offer a concentration in clinical social work.

School of Continuing and Professional Studies

Degree Programs Offered: *Associate, baccalaureate, master's; advanced professional certificates; professional diploma programs.*

Distinctive Educational Programs: 2-year interdisciplinary liberal arts programs designed to meet the liberal educational requirements for all NYU bachelor degree programs. A full-time, daytime program for traditional aged undergraduate students.

New York University College of Dentistry

Degree Programs Offered: *First-professional.*

Admission: Recommend baccalaureate degree from accredited college or university. Minimum 3 years from accredited college or university with 6 semester hours English, 6–8 biology and physics, 3–12 inorganic chemistry including analytical chemistry, 6–8 organic chemistry; DAT; personal interview.

Degree Requirements: Prescribed curriculum; passing grade in every course.

Distinctive Educational Programs: Joint master's of science-dental certificate program with Graduate School of Arts and Sciences. Postgraduate certificate programs in endodontics, pediatric dentistry prosthodontics, periodontics, oral and maxillofacial surgery, orthodontics. Continuing dental education program. 1-year dental assisting program. Dental Auxiliary Utilization Program enables student to develop skills of chairside assistant. Institute for Foreign Trained Dentists. Institute for Dental Research. Hospital Dentistry program. David B. Kriser Oro-Facial Pain Center. David B. Kriser Institute for the Rehabilitation of Disabled Dentists. Outreach program provides oral health care directly to the public.

New York University School of Law

Degree Programs Offered: *First-professional* in law; *master's* in comparative jurisprudence, law, taxation; *doctorate.*

Admission: *For first-professional students:* Baccalaureate from accredited college or university, LSAT, LSDAS.

Distinctive Educational Programs: Extensive clinical programs, including a mandatory first-year Lawyering Course. Extensive interdisciplinary work including Law and Philosophy, Law and History, Law and Economics, Law and Social Theory, and International Law. Dual degree in public administration with Princeton University (NJ). Joint first-professional MBA with Graduate School of Business Administration, master of public administration or urban planning with Graduate School of Public Administration, master of arts with Graduate School of Arts and Sciences. Center for International Studies, Arthur Garfield Hays Civil Liberties Program, Center for Research in Crime and Justice, Institute of Judicial Administration. Root-Tilden Scholarship Program supports students committed to public interest practice.

New York University School of Medicine

Degree Programs Offered: *First-professional.*

Admission: 3 years from accredited college or university which must include 1 year of biology, 1 inorganic chemistry, 1 organic chemistry, 1 physics, 1 English.

Degree Requirements: 2 years in residence, 4 years prescribed courses.

Distinctive Educational Programs: 6-year M.D.-Ph.D program with Graduate School of Arts and Sciences. Honors program permits students to do laboratory work under guidance of senior faculty member or in-depth study of branch of basic science. Honors summer research fellowship at Woods Hole, Will Rogers Memorial Hospital, other institutes. Medical Science Year Fellowship offers alternative 5-year curriculum, including 1 year of laboratory study. Graduate certificate courses available in forensic medicine, neurology, otorhinolaryngology, psychiatry.

Graduate School of Arts and Science

Degree Programs Offered: *Master's* in dental materials science, European studies, journalism, Latin American and Caribbean studies, liberal studies, museum studies, Near Eastern Studies, philosophy, religious studies and Slavic languages and literatures; *doctorate* in basic medical sciences, ergonomics, and biomechanics; *master's* and *doctorate* in American civilization, anthropology, applied science, biology, chemistry, cinema studies, classics, comparative literature, computer science, economics, English, environmental health sciences, fine arts (history of art and archaeology), French, French studies, German, Hebrew and Judaic studies, history, Italian, linguistics, mathematics, music, neural science, Near Eastern languages and literatures, performance studies, physics, politics, psychology, sociology, and Spanish and Portuguese.

Distinctive Educational Programs: Joint degrees with the Law School, Graduate School of Business Administration and Medical School in certain departments. Concentration in history and historical anthropology at the doctoral level. Certificate in ethnographic film. Master's with a concentration in creative writing (fiction or poetry). Master's in science and environmental reporting. Joint master's in journalism and Near Eastern studies and biomedical journalism. Joint master's and doctorate in French studies and anthropology, history, politics and sociology. Cooperative program in Near Eastern studies with Princeton University. Consortium in Latin American and Caribbean studies with Columbia, doctoral consortium with the Graduate Schools of Arts and Science at Columbia University, City University of New York (Graduate Center), Fordham and New School of Social Research. NYU in France and NYU in Spain programs.

Robert F. Wagner Graduate School of Public Service

Degree Programs Offered: *Master's, doctorate.*

Admission: Baccalaureate from a regionally accredited college or university.

Degree Requirements: For MPA or MUP: 60 credits (15 courses); for Ph.D.: 72 credits.

Distinctive Educational Programs: 2-year Master of Public Administration degree with programs in public administration, and health policy and management. Concentrations in management for public and nonprofit organizations, financial management and public finance, information management, public policy analysis, development administration, international administration, health services management, health policy analysis, financial management of health organizations. 2-year Master of Urban Planning program. 1 year Master of Science program with concentration in management. Joint degree programs with Washington Square and University College of Arts and Science, College of Business and Public Administration, School of Social Work, School of Law. Advanced professional certificates in public administration, health, and urban planning.

Niagara University

Niagara University, New York 14109-9999
Tel: (716) 286-8700 **E-mail:** admissions@niagara.edu
Fax: (716) 286-8710 **Internet:** www.niagara.edu

Institution Description: Niagara University is a four-year, private, coeducational institution with a Vincentian tradition. *Enrollment:* 4,254. *Degrees awarded:* Associate, baccalaureate, master's. Certificates also awarded.

Member of Western New York Consortium of Higher Education.

Accreditation: *Regional:* MSA. *Professional*: business, nursing, social work, teacher education

History: Established as College and Seminary of Our Lady of Angels 1856; chartered as a seminary, offered first instruction at postsecondary level and awarded first degree (baccalaureate) 1863; chartered as a university and adopted present name 1883.

Institutional Structure: *Governing board:* Niagara University Board of Trustees. Extrainstitutional representation: 19 trustees (17 elected, 2 ex officio). institutional representation: president of the university. 6 alumni. All voting. *Composition of institution:* Administrators 46. Academic affairs headed by executive vice president for academic affairs. Management/business/finances directed by vice president for business affairs. Full-time instructional faculty 145. Academic governance body, Academic Senate, meets 8 times per year. *Faculty representation:* Faculty served by independent collective bargaining agent.

Calendar: Semesters. Academic year Aug. to May. Freshmen admitted Aug., Jan., June. Degrees conferred and formal commencement May. Summer session of 3 terms for undergraduates and 2 terms for graduates.

Characteristics of Freshmen: 3,268 applicants. 74% of applicants admitted. 31% of admitted students enrolled full-time.

94% (594 students) submitted SAT scores; 42% (312 student) submitted ACT scores. *25th percentile*: SAT Critical Reading 450, SAT Math 470; ACT Composite 19. *75th percentile*: SAT Critical Reading 590, SAT Math 570; ACT Composite 24.

61% of entering freshmen expected to graduate within 5 years. 81 of freshmen from New York. Freshmen from 31 states and 11 foreign countries.

Admission: Rolling admissions plan. For fall acceptance, apply as early as Sept. 1 of previous year, but not later than Aug. 1 of year of enrollment. *Requirements:* Either graduation from accredited secondary school with 16 units which must include 4 English, 2 in a foreign language (for all but business students), 2–3 college preparatory mathematics, 2-3 science, 2 history; or GED. *Entrance tests:* College Board SAT or ACT composite. *For transfer students:* 2.0 minimum GPA except for nursing which requires a 2.3 minimum GPA and education which requires a 2.5 minimum GPA; from 4-year accredited institution 90 hours maximum transfer credit; from 2-year accredited institution 60 hours.

College credit and advanced placement for postsecondary-level work completed in secondary school and for extrainstitutional learning on basis of portfolio assessment.

Tutoring available. Noncredit developmental/remedial courses offered in summer session and regular academic year.

Degree Requirements: *For all associate degrees:* 60–63 credit hours; 2.0 GPA; 30 hours in residence. *For all baccalaureate degrees:* 120–126 credit hours; 2.0–2.5 GPA; last 30 hours in residence. *For all undergraduate degrees:* general education requirements.

Fulfillment of some degree requirements and exemption from some beginning courses possible by passing departmental examinations, College Board AP, other standardized tests. *Grading system:* A–F; satisfactory-unsatisfactory; withdraw (deadline after which pass-fail is appended to withdraw).

Distinctive Educational Programs: Internships. Evening classes. Accelerated degree programs. Honors programs. Special facilities for using telecommunications in the classroom. Independent study. Study abroad in Angers, France; Seville, Spain; Engelberg, Switzerland; Strasbourg, France. Cross-registration through consortium. Higher education opportunity program provides academic and support services for economically and educationally disadvantaged students. Castellani Art Museum. Cooperative education program available in 26 different majors. *Other distinctive programs:* Degree-granting evening division primarily for adults. Credit and enrichment continuing education. Secondary school seniors may enroll in college courses for credit.

ROTC: Army.

Degrees Conferred: 683 *baccalaureate*; 448 *master's*. Bachelor's degrees awarded in top five disciplines: business/marketing 162; education 127; security and protective services 55; social sciences 45; visual nd performing arts 34. Master's degrees awarded: business/marketing 41; education 381; security and protective services 26.

Fees and Other Expenses: *Full-time tuition per academic year 2008–09:* $23,450. *Required fees:* $840. *Room and board per academic year:* $9,750. *Books and supplies:* $900. *Other expenses:* $1,450.

Financial Aid: Aid from institutionally generated funds is provided on the basis of academic merit, financial need, athletic ability, other criteria.

Financial aid to full-time, first-time undergraduate students: 98% received some form of aid.

Departments and Teaching Staff: *Total instructional faculty:* 341 (full-time 145, part-time 196). 885 of faculty hold the doctorate, first-professional, or other terminal degree. Student/faculty ratio: 15:1.

Enrollment: Total enrollment 4,254. Undergraduate 3,325. Graduate 928. Undergraduate transfer-in students 200.

Characteristics of Student Body: *Ethnic/racial makeup:* number of Black non-Hispanic: 112; American Indian or Alaska Native: 21; Asian or Pacific Islander: 36; Hispanic: 44; White non-Hispanic: 2,358; unknown: 239.

International Students: 157 undergraduate nonresident aliens enrolled fall 2008. Programs available to aid students whose native language is not English: social, cultural. English as a Second Language Program. No financial aid specifically designated for international students.

Student Life: On-campus residence halls house 53% of student body. *Intercollegiate athletics:* male: baseball, basketball, hockey, soccer, swimming, tennis, track; female: basketball, hockey, lacrosse, softball, swimming, tennis, track, volleyball. *Special regulations:* Cars permitted for all students. *Special services:* Learning Resources Center, medical services. *Student publications, radio: Aquila*, an annual literary magazine; *The Index*, a weekly newspaper; *Niagaran*, a yearbook; Radio station WRNU. *Surrounding community:* Niagara Falls population 66,000. Buffalo, 25 miles from campus, is nearest metropolitan area. Served by mass transit bus system; airport 30 miles from campus; passenger rail service 2 miles from campus.

Library Collections: 274,000 volumes. 80,000 microforms; 770 audiovisual materials. Current periodical subscriptions: paper 8,600; microform 76,187. Students have access to online information retrieval services.

Most important special holdings include collections on St. Vincent DePaul; 15th–17th century religious materials.

Buildings and Grounds: Campus area 160 acres.

Chief Executive Officer: Fr. Joseph L. Lejesque, C.M., President.

Address admission inquiries to Harry Gono, Director of Admissions.

College of Arts and Sciences

Degree Programs Offered: *Associate* in arts; *baccalaureate* in art, fine arts, science; *master's* in science.

Distinctive Educational Programs: Interdepartmental programs in liberal arts and social sciences. Internships, study abroad, honors programs.

College of Business Administration

Degree Programs Offered: *Baccalaureate* in accounting, economics, human resources, management, marketing, transportation and logistics management; *master's* in business administration.

Distinctive Educational Programs: Cooperative education.

School of Education

Degree Programs Offered: *Baccalaureate, master's* in teacher education, foundations in teaching, counseling, administration/supervision. Certificate in advanced studies also given.

Distinctive Educational Programs: M.S. in Ed in Teacher Education/elementary/secondary/education, M.S. in Ed, Foundations and Teaching, Counsel-

NIAGARA UNIVERSITY—*cont'd*

ing and Administration/Supervision. Off-campus centers in Ontario, Canada, offering graduate programs in education (at Hamilton, 70 miles away from main institution; at Toronto, 90 miles away; Scarborough, 110 miles away; Burlington, 80 miles away; and Mississauga, 85 miles away).

School of Nursing

Degree Programs Offered: *Baccalaureate.*

Distinctive Educational Programs: Baccalaureate completion program for registered nurses.

Institute of Travel/Hotel and Restaurant Administration

Degree Programs Offered: *Baccalaureate, master's.*

Division of General Academic Studies

Distinctive Educational Programs: Freshman Seminar assists all students in adjusting to college life. The Academic Exploration Program guides students who wish to explore various disciplines before choosing a major. The Center for Continuing Studies offers both undergraduate and graduate evening courses, seminars, and conferences and life experience credit. The Summer Sessions provide opportunities to students to satisfy requirements during the summer months. The Senior High School Program and the Niagara University Senior Term Enrichment Program extend the collegiate learning experience to qualified high school students.

Nyack College

One South Boulevard
Nyack, New York 10960-3698
Tel: (845) 358-1710 **E-mail:** admissions@nyack.edu
Fax: (845) 358-3047 **Internet:** www.nyack.edu

Institution Description: Nyack College is a private college affiliated with The Christian and Missionary Alliance. Extensions located in New York City, Puerto Rico, Washington (D.C.), Dayton (OH), and Kiev (Ukraine). *Enrollment:* 3,041. *Degrees awarded:* Associate, baccalaureate. Alliance Theological Seminary, Nyack's graduate and professional school, offers first-professional (master of divinity) and master's degrees.

Accreditation: *Regional:* MSA. *National:* ATS. *Professional*: music, theology

History: Established as the Missionary Training Institute and offered first instruction at postsecondary level 1882; chartered 1944; awarded first degree (baccalaureate) 1946; changed name to Nyack Missionary College 1956; adopted present name 1972.

Institutional Structure: *Governing board:* Board of Trustees. Full-time instructional faculty 107.

Calendar: Semesters (trimesters at Manhattan extension center). Academic year Aug. to May. Freshmen admitted all terms, including summer. Degrees conferred at formal commencement in May. Summer sessions.

Characteristics of Freshmen: 522 applicants. 93% of applicants accepted. 40% of accepted applicants enrolled full-time.

79% (155 students) submitted SAT scores; 18% (37 students) submitted ACT scores. *25th percentile*: SAT Critical Reading 400, SAT Math 480; ACT Composite 17. *75th percentile*: SAT Critical Reading 540, SAT Math 530; ACT Composite 22.

381% of entering freshmen expected to graduate within 5 years. 67% of freshmen from New York.

Admission: Rolling admissions plan. *Required:* school transcript, SAT or ACT scores for some; recommendations, evidence of Christian faith experience. TOEFL or CELT score for students whose primary language is not English. Recommended secondary level coursework: 4 units English, 2 foreign language, 3 math and/or science, 3 history/social science. *For transfer students:* only courses with grade of C- or above will be considered for transfer credit.

Developmental courses offered; credit given for some courses.

Degree Requirements: *For all associate degrees:* 60 credit hours (27 credits core curriculum; 8 hours Bible). *For all baccalaureate degrees:* 120–130 credit hours depending on major; 54 credits core curriculum courses (includes 17 hours Bible). For music majors: recital.

Fulfillment of some degree requirements and exemption from some beginning courses possible by passing departmental examinations, College Board CLEP, AP. *Grading system:* A–F; pass-fail; withdraw (carries time limit).

Distinctive Educational Programs: *For undergraduates:* Mentored (independent study). Honors Program. Overseas and off-campus study programs. Limited online courses. Adult Degree Completion Program allows students to earn up to 28 credits based on prior work/life experience.

Degrees Conferred: 12 *associate;* 516 *baccalaureate*; 185 *master's.* Bachelor's degrees awarded in top five disciplines: business, management, marketing, and related support services 20; liberal arts 65; psychology 43; education 42; theology and ministerial studies 31. Master's degrees awarded: business/marketing 74; education 6; health professions and related clinical sciences 54; philosophy and religious studies 30; theology and ministerial studies 21.

Fees and Other Expenses: *Full-time tuition per academic year 2008–09:* \$18,300. *Books and supplies:* \$750. *Room and board per academic year:* \$7,800. *Other expenses:* \$2,610.

Financial Aid: Aid from institutionally generated funds is provided on the basis of academic merit, athletic ability, financial need, other criteria.

Financial aid to full-time, first-time undergraduate students: 99% received some form of financial aid. Average amount of aid received: federal grants \$4,197; Pell grants \$3,318; other federal grants \$1,466; state/local grants \$3,980; institutional grants \$7,897.

Departments and Teaching Staff: *Total instructional faculty:* 288 (full-time 107, part-time 181). 64% of faculty hold the doctorate, first-professional, or other terminal degree. Student/faculty ratio: 21:1.

Enrollment: Total enrollment 3,041. Undergraduate 1,917. Graduate 1,124. Undergraduate transfer-in students 972.

Characteristics of Student Body: *Ethnic/racial makeup:* number of Black non-Hispanic: 122; American Indian or Alaska Native: 2; Asian or Pacific Islander: 115; Hispanic: 429; White non-Hispanic: 615; unknown: 68.

International Students: 99 nonresident aliens enrolled fall 2008. Programs available to aid students whose native language is not English: English as a Second Language Program. No financial aid specifically designated for international students.

Student Life: On-campus residence halls house 75% of student body. *Intercollegiate athletics:* NCAA, NCCAA. Competition includes male baseball, basketball, cross-country, golf, soccer; female basketball, cross-country, soccer, softball, volleyball. *Student publications: Forum*, a monthly news publication; *Missionarian*, a yearbook; *The Fine Print*, the Nyack College Journal of Literature and Art. *Surrounding community:* Nyack population 6,500. New York City, 25 miles from campus, is nearest metropolitan area. Served by mass transit bus system; 3 major airports within 50 minutes of campus.

Library Collections: 182,000 volumes. Online catalog. 875 current periodical subscriptions. Computer work stations available. Students have access to the Internet at no charge.

Buildings and Grounds: Campus area 102 acres.

Chief Executive Officer: Dr. Michael G. Scales, President.

Address admission inquiries to Miguel Sanchez, Director of Admissions.

Alliance Theological Seminary

Degree Programs Offered: *First-professional* in divinity; *master's* in ministerial leadership and theological areas.

Admission: *For first-professional, master's* degrees: Baccalaureate degree from accredited institution; other requirements vary by program.

Degree Requirements: *All degrees:* Successful completion of required credit hours which may vary by program. Other requirements may include: approved internship, residence requirement, comprehensive exam and/or thesis, Bible proficiency exam.

Pace University

One Pace Plaza
New York, New York 10038
Tel: (212) 346-1200 **E-mail:** infoctr@pace.edu
Fax: (212) 346-1821 **Internet:** www.pace.edu

Institution Description: Pace University is a private, independent institution with branch campuses in White Plains and Pleasantville. *Enrollment:* 12,704. *Degrees awarded:* Associate, baccalaureate, master's, first-professional, doctorate. Certificates also awarded.

Accreditation: *Regional:* MSA. *Professional*: computer science, psychology internship

History: Established 1906 as Pace Institute; became Pace College 1942; adopted present name during expansion under leadership of Dr. Edward J. Mortola.

Institutional Structure: *Governing board:* Board of Trustees. Total instructional faculty 1,384 (university-wide). Academic governance body, Pace University Senate, meets regularly.

Calendar: Semesters. Academic year Sept. to May. Optional May term. Freshmen admitted Sept., Jan., Feb., June. Degrees conferred May, Sept., Feb. Formal commencement May.

Characteristics of Freshmen: 7,444 applicants. 78% of applicants admitted. 27% of admitted students enrolled full-time.

96% (1,445 students) submitted SAT scores. *25th percentile*: SAT Critical Reading 480, SAT Math 490. *75th percentile*: SAT Critical Reading 580, SAT Math 590;

65% of freshmen from New York. Freshmen from 40 states and 30 foreign countries.

Admission: Early decision available, apply before Nov. 1 and notification of acceptance by Dec. 15. *Requirements:* Graduation from accredited secondary school; recommendation from high school counselor and/or teachers; personal statement; achievement tests in English, mathematics, science. *Entrance tests:* SAT or ACT. For foreign students TOEFL. *For transfer students:* from 4-year accredited institution hours 96 maximum transfer credit; from 2-year accredited institution 68 hours maximum.

College credit and advanced placement for postsecondary work completed in secondary school through CLEP, APP, CPEP. College credit for extrainstitutional learning (life experience) on basis of portfolio assessments.

Tutoring available. Remedial courses offering during regular academic year; credit given.

Degree Requirements: QPA 2.0; completion of at least 32 credits at Pace University; 128–133 credits (baccalaureate), 60-66 credits (associate).

Distinctive Educational Programs: Work-experience programs, including internships, cooperative education. Weekend and evening classes. Accelerated degree programs. Baccalaureate-M.B.A. programs, including program in public accounting. Cooperative baccalaureate program in medical technology with approved hospitals. Special facilities for using telecommunications in the classroom. Interdisciplinary New York City Humanities minor. Facilities and programs for independent research, including honors programs, individual majors, tutorials, independent study. InterFuture Scholars program to Europe or third world country. Other study abroad in England, France, Spain, Mexico, Switzerland, Brazil. *Other distinctive programs:* Challenge to Achievement at Pace Program provides 1-year day school program for recent high school graduates who do not meet university admissions requirements. Continuing education.

ROTC: Air Force.

Degrees Conferred: 99 *associate;* 1,635 *baccalaureate*; 1,495 *master's*; 3 *doctorate*; 219 *first-professional*. Bachelor's degrees awarded in top five disciplines: business, management, marketing, and related support services 773; communication/journalism and related programs 173; health professions and related clinical sciences 193; computer and information sciences and support services 181; psychology 100. Masters's degrees awarded: business/marketing 508; communication, journalism, and related programs 37; computer and information sciences 211; education 571; engineering 3; health professions 86; natural resources and conservation 1; psychology 40; security and protective services 5; social sciences 14; visual and performing arts 1. Doctorates awarded: busiess/marketing 7; computer and information sciences 8; psychology 12. First-professional: law 219.

Fees and Other Expenses: *Full-time tuition per academic year 2008–09:* undergraduate $31,351; graduate study charged per credit (contact the university for current rate). *Books and supplies:* $800. *Room and board per academic year:* $11,180. *Other expenses:* $1,848.

Financial Aid: Aid from institutionally generated funds is provided on the basis of academic merit, financial need, athletic ability, other criteria. Institution has a Program Participation Agreement with the U.S. Department of Education for eligible students to receive Pell Grants and, depending upon the agreement, other federal aid.

Financial aid to full-time, first-time undergraduate students: 93% of students received some form of financial aid. Average amount of aid received: federal grants $3,968; Pell grants #3,081; other federal grants $1,431; state/local grants $2,997; institutional grants $13,782.

Departments and Teaching Staff: *Total instructional faculty:* 1,384 FTE. Student/faculty ratio: 15:1. Degrees held by full-time faculty: doctorate 60%, master's 27%, baccalaureate 2%.

Enrollment: Total enrollment 12,704. Undergraduate 7,807. Graduate 4,817. Undergraduate transfer-in students 394.

Characteristics of Student Body: *Ethnic/racial makeup:* Black non-Hispanic: 10.1%; American Indian or Alaska Native: .3%; Asian or Pacific Islander: 10.4%; Hispanic: 11.1%; White non-Hispanic: 43.8%; unknown: 19.4%.

International Students: 285 undergraduate nonresident aliens enrolled fall 2008. Programs available to aid students whose native language is not English: social, cultural. No financial aid specifically designated for international students.

Student Life: On-campus residence halls house 2% of student body. Residence halls for males constitute 44% of such space; for females 64%. *Intercollegiate athletics:* male: basketball. *Special regulations:* Quiet hours. *Special services:* medical services, intercampus shuttle bus. *Student publications, radio: Aphros*, an annual literary magazine; *The Legend*, a yearbook; *The Pace University Press*, a weekly newspaper; *The Exchange*, a Lubin graduate student newspaper. Radio station WPUB broadcasts 46 hours per week. *Surrounding community:* New York City population over 7 million. Served by mass transit bus, subway, and train systems; airport 8 miles from campus; passenger rail service 4 miles from campus.

Library Collections: 793,000 volumes. 75,300 microforms; 2,400 audiovisual materials; 33,000 periodicals including via electronic access. Online catalog. Students have access to online information retrieval services and the Internet.

Chief Executive Officer: Dr. David A. Caputo, President.

Address admission inquiries to Joanna Broda, Director of Admissions.

Polytechnic University

6 Metrotech Center
Brooklyn, New York 11201-2999
Tel: (718) 260-3600 **E-mail:** uadmit@poly.edu
Fax: (718) 260-3446 **Internet:** www.poly.edu

Institution Description: Polytechnic University (formerly Polytechnic Institute of New York) is a private, independent, nonprofit college with a branch campus on Long Island in Farmingdale. *Enrollment:* 3,983. *Degrees awarded:* Baccalaureate, master's, doctorate.

Member of the consortium Long Island Regional Advisory Council on Higher Education.

Accreditation: *Regional:* MSA. *Professional*: engineering

History: Established and chartered as Brooklyn Collegiate and Polytechnic Institute, a preparatory school and junior college, 1854; offered first instruction at postsecondary level 1855; became 4-year college 1869; awarded first degree (baccalaureate) 1871; changed name to Polytechnic Institute of Brooklyn 1889; merged with New York University School of Engineering and Science (established 1855) and changed to Polytechnic Institute of Brooklyn 1973; name changed to Polytechnic University 1983.

Institutional Structure: *Governing board:* The Corporation. Extrainstitutional representation: 40 trustees; institutional representation: president of the university; 3 alumni. 1 ex officio. All voting. *Composition of institution:* Administrators 17. Academic affairs headed by provost. Management/business/ finances directed by vice president for administration and finance. Full-time instructional faculty 138. Academic governance body, Faculty Senate, meets an average of 9 times per year.

Calendar: Semesters. academic year Sept. to May. Freshmen admitted Sept., Jan., June. Degrees conferred formal commencement June. Session May to Aug.

Characteristics of Freshmen: 1,482 applicants. 73% of applicants admitted. 31% of admitted students enrolled full-time.

95% (315 students) submitted SAT scores. *25th percentile*: SAT Critical Reading 470, SAT Math 560. *75th percentile*: SAT Critical Reading 600, SAT Math 675.

74% of entering freshmen expected to graduate within 5 years. 88% of freshmen from New York. Freshmen from 22 states and 31 foreign countries.

Admission: Rolling admission. For fall acceptance, apply as early as beginning of senior year, but not later than Feb. 1 of year of enrollment. Students are notified of acceptance Mar. Apply by Nov. 1 for early decision; must limit application Polytechnic University. Early acceptance available. *Requirements:* Graduation from accredited secondary school with 16 units including 4 English, 3 college preparatory mathematics, 3 science (with laboratory). 2 units history recommended. *Entrance tests:* College Board SAT or ACT; For foreign students TOEFL. *For transfer students:* 2.5 minimum GPA; maximum transfer credit limited only by residence requirement.

College credit and advanced placement for postsecondary-level work completed in secondary school. Tutoring available. Developmental courses offered in summer session and regular academic year.

Degree Requirements: *For all undergraduate degrees:* 120–131 credit hours; 2.0 GPA; 1 continuous year in residence as full-time student; 4 semesters physical education courses; distribution requirements.

Fulfillment of some degree requirements and exemption from some beginning courses possible by passing College Board AP. *Grading system:* A–F; pass-fail; withdraw (carries time limit).

Distinctive Educational Programs: Cooperative education. Evening classes. Telecommunications management. Academic and other support services for economically and educationally disadvantaged students through Higher Education Opportunity Program (HEOP). Research centers and institutes, including Center for Digital Systems, Institute for Imaging Science, Weber Research Institute, Polymer Research Institute, Transportation Training and Research Center. Qualified secondary school seniors may take college courses for credit.

POLYTECHNIC UNIVERSITY—*cont'd*

Degrees Conferred: 259 *baccalaureate*; 540 *master's*; 29 *doctorate*. Bachelor's degrees awarded in top five disciplines: engineering 186; computer and information sciences 74; business, management, marketing, and related support services 26; liberal arts/general studies 14; physical sciences 7. Master's degrees awarded: business/marketing 95; computer and information sciences 89; engineering 243; liberal arts/general studies 11; mathematics 1; physical sciences 8. Doctorates awarded: computer and information sciences 6; engineering 15; physical sciences 4. Doctorates awarded: various disciplines 29.

Fees and Other Expenses: *Full-time tuition per academic year 2008–09:* $32,644; contact the university for current graduate tuition. *Books and supplies:* $1,000. *Required fees:* $1,044. *Room and board per academic year:* $8,721. *Other expenses:* $1,575.

Financial Aid: Aid from institutionally generated funds is provided on the basis of academic merit. Institution has a Program Participation Agreement with the U.S. Department of Education for eligible students to receive Pell Grants and, depending upon the agreement, other federal aid.

Financial aid to full-time, first-time undergraduate students: 99% received some form of aid. Average amount of aid received: federal grants $4,845; Pell grants $3,488; other federal grants $1,786; state/local grants $3,429; institutional grants $15,812.

Departments and Teaching Staff: *Total instructional faculty:* 273 (full-time 138, part-time 135). Student/faculty ratio: 17:1. Degrees held by full-time faculty: doctorates 84%, master's 13%, baccalaureate 3%.

Enrollment: Total enrollment 3,983. Undergraduate 1,541. Graduate 2,442. Undergraduate transfer-in students 96.

Characteristics of Student Body: *Ethnic/racial makeup:* number of Black non-Hispanic: 161; American Indian or Alaska Native: 2; Asian or Pacific Islander: 454; Hispanic: 77; White non-Hispanic: 437; unknown: 100. *Age distribution:* number under 18: 334; 18–19: 545; 20–21: 379; 22–24: 90; 25–29: 37; 30–34: 9; 35–49: 4; 50–64: 3; 65 and over: 1.

International Students: 165 undergraduate nonresident aliens enrolled fall 2008. Students from Europe, Asia, Central and South America, Africa, Canada, Middle East. No programs available to aid students whose native language is not English. No financial aid specifically designated for international students.

Student Life: Institutional housing available at Long Island campus; local area housing at Brooklyn campus. 5% of males join and less than 1% live in fraternity housing. *Intercollegiate athletics:* baseball, basketball, cross-country, lacrosse, soccer, tennis. *Student publications, radio: The Polytechnic Reporter*, a biweekly newspaper; *Polywog*, a yearbook. *Surrounding community:* New York City population over 7 million. Served by mass transit system; airport 5 miles from campus; passenger rail service 5 miles from campus.

Library Collections: 212m599 volumes. 2,000 microform titles; 185 audiovisual materials; 1,300 current periodical subscriptions. Students have access to online information retrieval services.

Buildings and Grounds: Campus area 3 acres.

Chief Executive Officer: Dr. Jerry McArthur Fulton, President.

Address admission inquiries to Joy Wexler, Director of Admissions; graduate inquiries to Sunil Kumar, Associate Provost for Graduate School.

Pratt Institute

200 Willoughby Avenue
Brooklyn, New York 11025
Tel: (718) 636-3600 **E-mail:** admissions@pratt.edu
Fax: (718) 636-3670 **Internet:** www.pratt.edu

Institution Description: Pratt Institute is a private, independent, nonprofit coeducational institution. *Enrollment:* 4,946. *Degrees awarded:* Associate, baccalaureate, master's, first-professional.

Member of the consortium Student Mobility Programs.

Accreditation: *Regional:* MSA. *Professional*: architecture, art, engineering, interior design, librarianship

History: Established; chartered; and offered first instruction at postsecondary level 1887; awarded first degree (baccalaureate) 1938.

Institutional Structure: *Governing board:* Board of Trustees. Extrainstitutional representation: 13 trustees; institutional representation: 1 full-time instructional faculty member, 1 student, 11 alumni. 1 ex officio. All voting. Management/business/finances directed by the provost. Full-time instructional faculty 94. Academic governance body, Dean's Council and Academic Senate. *Faculty representation:* Faculty served by collective bargaining agent, United Federation of College Teachers, affiliated with AFT.

Calendar: Semesters (4-1-4 plan). Academic year Sept. to May. Freshmen admitted Sept., Jan., May. Degrees conferred June, Oct., Feb. Formal commencement June. Summer session of 2 terms from late May to mid-Aug.

Characteristics of Freshmen: 4,341 applicants. 43% of applicants admitted. 31% of admitted students enrolled full-time.

80% (470 students) submitted SAT scores; 14% (80 students) submitted ACT scores. *25th percentile*: SAT Critical Reading 510, SAT Math 520; ACT Composite 22. *75th percentile*: SAT Critical Reading 640, SAT Math 630; ACT Composite 27.

47% of entering freshmen expected to graduate within 5 years. 43% of freshmen from New York. Freshmen from 49 states and 62 foreign countries.

Admission: Rolling admissions plan. For fall acceptance, apply no later than March 15; for spring, Nov. 15. Early decision applications due Nov. 1; early action applications due Feb. 1. *Requirements:* Either graduation from accredited secondary school with 4 units English, 1–4 mathematics, 1–2 science, 1–2 social studies, 5–6 electives; or GED. High school GPA of 2.8 required. Portfolio required for fine arts-design and architecture programs. *Entrance tests:* SAT or ACT. Achievements are recommended for some programs. *For transfer students:* 2.0 minimum GPA; maximum transfer credit limited only by residence requirement. Portfolio required for studio credit transfer.

Degree Requirements: *For all associate degrees:* 66 semester hours; ⅓ of required credits and last 12 credits in residence. *For all baccalaureate degrees:* 132–202 hours; 48 credits, including last 32, in residence. *For all undergraduate degrees:* 2.0 GPA; liberal arts distribution requirements.

Fulfillment of some degree requirements and exemption from some beginning courses possible by passing College Board CLEP, APP, other standardized tests. *Grading system:* A–F; pass-fail; withdraw (carries time limit).

Distinctive Educational Programs: Undergraduate and graduate programs in the Schools of Architecture and Art and Design; graduate program in the School of Information and Library Science. Liberal arts core for all professional programs. Study abroad in Denmark, France, and Italy.

ROTC: Army in cooperation with Fordham University, St. John's University, and Polytechnic University.

Degrees Conferred: 49 *associate;* 686 *baccalaureate*; 701 *master's*. Bachelor's degrees awarded in top five disciplines: visual and performing arts 383; architecture 67; communication technologies 20; education 7; English language/literature 5. Master's degrees awarded: various disciplines 701.

Fees and Other Expenses: *Full-time tuition per academic year 2008–09:* undergraduate $32,990; contact the institute for current graduate tuition/fees. *Room and board per academic year:* $9,476. *Books and supplies:* $3,000. *Other expenses:* $650.

Financial Aid: Aid from institutionally generated funds is provided on the basis of academic merit, financial need. Institution has a Program Participation Agreement with the U.S. Department of Education for eligible students to receive Pell Grants and, depending upon the agreement, other federal aid.

Financial aid to full-time, first-time undergraduate students: 88% of students received some form of financial aid. Average mount of aid received: federal grants $2,311; Pell grants $2,921; other federal grants $1,082; state/local grants $2,575; institutional grants $10,017.

Departments and Teaching Staff: *Total instructional faculty:* 473. Student/faculty ratio: 11:1. Degrees held by full-time faculty: baccalaureate 18%, master's 51%, doctorate 28%. 89% hold terminal degrees.

Enrollment: Total enrollment 4,946. Undergraduate 3,307. Graduate 1,639. Undergraduate transfer-in students 791.

Characteristics of Student Body: *Ethnic/racial makeup:* Black non-Hispanic 7.4%; American Indian or Native Alaskan: .4%; Asian or Pacific Islander: 12%; Hispanic: 8.4%; White non-Hispanic: 62.3%; unknown: .1%.

International Students: 310 undergraduate nonresident aliens enrolled fall 2008. Programs available to aid students whose native language is not English: social, cultural, financial. English as a Second Language Program.

Student Life: On-campus residence halls house 78% of student body. All residence halls are coed. Housing available for married graduate students. *Intercollegiate athletics:* male and female soccer, tennis, track and field, cross-country running; male basketball; female volleyball. *Special services:* Over 55 student-run activities including honors societies and clubs, student publications, radio station, films, plays, gallery openings and lectures; career services and internship offices; counseling and health services; international student affairs office; interdenominational chapel. *Student publications, radio: Prattler*, a monthly newspaper; *Prattonia,* a yearbook. Radio station WPIR broadcasts 40 hours per week. *Surrounding community:* New York City population over 7 million. Served by mass transit system, airport, passenger rail service.

Library Collections: 387,000 volumes. 8,100 government documents; 320,000 000 microforms; 10,500 audiovisual materials; 44,700 periodicals including via electronic access. Online catalog. Students have access to online information retrieval services and the Internet.

Most important special holdings include collections on art and architecture, information/reference; library and information science.

Buildings and Grounds: Campus area 25 acres.

Chief Executive Officer: Dr. Thomas F. Schutte, President.

Address undergraduate admission inquiries to Judith Aaron, Vice President Enrollment Management; graduate inquiries to Director of Graduate Admissions.

Queens College / CUNY

63-30 Kissena Boulevard
Flushing, New York 11367-1597
Tel: (718) 997-5000 **E-mail:** applyto@uapc.cuny.edu
Fax: (718) 997-5000 **Internet:** www.qc.cuny.edu

Institution Description: *Enrollment:* 19,572. *Degrees awarded:* Baccalaureate, first-professional, master's. Certificates also awarded.

Accreditation: *Regional:* MSA. *Professional*: audiology, librarianship, speech-language pathology, teacher education

History: Established as Queens College of the City of New York and offered first instruction at postsecondary level 1937; awarded first degree (baccalaureate) 1941; became part of CUNY system and adopted present name 1961.

Institutional Structure: *Composition of institution:* Administrators 209. Academic affairs headed by provost. Management/business/finances directed by vice president for finance and business. Full-time instructional faculty 552. Academic governance body, Academic Senate, meets an average of 12 times per year.

Calendar: Semesters. Academic year early Aug. to May. Freshmen admitted Sept., Feb. Degrees conferred June, Sept., Feb. Formal commencement June. Summer session from June to Aug.

Characteristics of Freshmen: 14,436 applicants (8,215 female, male 6,221). 40% of applicants admitted. 30% of admitted students enrolled full-time.

100 (1,1,377 students) submitted SAT scores. *25th percentile*: SAT Critical Reading 452, SAT Math 480. *75th percentile*: SAT Critical Reading 550, SAT Math 580.

45% of entering freshmen expected to graduate within 5 years. 99% of freshmen from New York. Freshmen from 15 states and 117 foreign countries.

Admission: Rolling admissions plan. Applications accepted beginning Dec. 1, notification begins Feb. 1. *Requirements:* High school diploma required; GED accepted. Equivalent of 16 Carnegie units required, 18 units recommended. SAT required, minimum GPA 85 on 100 point scale. TOEFL minimum score 500. Both transfer and freshman accepted for fall and spring semesters. For transfer students, college transcript, minimum high school GPA 3.0; minimum college GPA 2.5; 75 credits maxim may be transferred in.

College credit and advanced placement for postsecondary-level work completed in secondary school. Tutoring available. Developmental/remedial courses offered on a limited basis.

Degree Requirements: 120 credit hours; 2.0 GPA; 45 credits in residence; 1 physical education course; distribution requirements.

Exemption from some beginning courses possible by passing College Board CLEP, AP, other standardized tests. *Grading system:* A+–F, P/NC.

Distinctive Educational Programs: Evening classes. Dual-degree programs in engineering with local universities. Interdisciplinary programs in Africana studies, American area studies, East Asian studies, film studies, Jewish studies, Latin America area studies. Facilities and programs for independent research, including honors programs, individual majors, tutorials. Study abroad in France, Israel, Italy. *Other distinctive programs:* Continuing education offers noncredit workshops, lectures, and seminars for adults. Adult Collegiate Education Program offered through the School of General Studies provides accelerated baccalaureate program for motivated adults. Bachelor degree in labor studies, master of arts in liberal studies, master of arts in applied linguistics. Environmental studies major. National Endowment for the Humanities Visiting Scholars Program.

ROTC: Army, Navy in cooperation with St. John's University.

Degrees Conferred: 2,433 *baccalaureate*; 1,238 *master's.* Bachelor's degrees awarded in top five disciplines: business/marketing 428; social sciences 486; psychology 320; education 259; English language/literature 168 Master's degrees awarded in top five disciplines: education 170; library science 126; social sciences 117; psychology 64; visual and performing arts 45.

Fees and Other Expenses: *Full-time tuition per academic year 2008–09:* $4,447 resident, $9,081 nonresident; contact the college for graduate tuition. *Required fees:* $377. No on-campus housing.

Financial Aid: Aid from institutionally generated funds is provided on the basis of academic merit, financial need, athletic ability.

Financial aid to full-time, first-time undergraduate students: 77% received some form of aid. Average amount of aid received: federal grants $3,992; Pell grants $3,603; other federal grants $638; state/local grants $2,884; institutional grants $3,964.

Departments and Teaching Staff: *Total instructional faculty:* 1,260 (full-time 577, part-time 683). 70% of faculty hold the doctorate, first-professional, or other terminal degree. Student/faculty ratio: 16:1.

Enrollment: Total enrollment 19,572. Undergraduate 15,262 (60% female, 50% male); 71% full-time. Graduate 4,310. Undergraduate transfer-in students 2,081.

Characteristics of Student Body: *Ethnic/racial makeup:* Black non-Hispanic: 9%; Asian or Pacific Islander: 22%; 18%; White non-Hispanic: 45%. *Age distribution:* number under 18: 39; 18–19: 2,817; 20–21: 3,092; 22–24: 2,960; 25–29: 1,723; 30–34: 799; 35–39: 547; 40–49: 768; 50–64: 260; 65 and over: 13.

International Students: 1,206 nonresident aliens enrolled fall 2008. Students from Europe, Asia, Central and South America, Africa, Canada, Middle East. Programs available to aid students whose native language is not English: social, cultural. English as a Second Language Program. No financial aid specifically designated for international students.

Student Life: No on-campus housing. Athletics activities include basketball, baseball, cross-country, equestrian, golf, indoor tack, soccer, softball, swimming, tennis, track and field, volleyball, water polo. *Special regulations:* Parking permit required; limited number available. *Special services:* Learning Resources Center, Office of Career Development and Internships, Minority student Affairs and Preprofessional Advisement, Student Government, Disabled Student Services, Concert Band, Jazz Band, choral groups. *Publications, radio: The Quad*, an undergraduate paper. *Surrounding community:* New York population over 7 million. Served by mass transit bus, subway system; airport and passenger rail service each 5 miles from campus.

Library Collections: 1,674,594 volumes. Current serial subscriptions: paper 2,689; microform 951,449; via electronic access 3,532. 27,000 recordings. 217 computer work stations. Students have access to online information retrieval services.

Most important holdings include collections of theater programs and memorabilia; colonial newspapers in micro format; historical documents of New York County-Queens Country through mid-1880s; Louis Armstrong paper; Karol Rathaus Papers; Benjamin Rosenthal Paper; Saul Luprin Papers.

Buildings and Grounds: Campus area 76 acres.

Chief Executive Officer: Dr. James L. Muyskens, President.

Address admission inquiries to Dr. Vincent J. Angrisani, Director of Admissions; graduate inquiries to Mario Caruso, Director of Graduate Admissions.

Rensselaer Polytechnic Institute

110 Eighth Street
Troy, New York 12180-3590
Tel: (518) 276-6000 **E-mail:** admissions@rpi.edu
Fax: N/A **Internet:** www.rpi.edu

Institution Description: Rensselaer Polytechnic Institute is a private, independent, nonprofit institution. *Enrollment:* 6,777. *Degrees awarded:* Baccalaureate, master's, doctorate.

Member of the consortium Hudson-Mohawk Association of Colleges and Universities.

Accreditation: *Regional:* MSA. *Professional*: architecture, business, chemistry, engineering

History: Established as Rensselaer School 1824; incorporated, offered first instruction at postsecondary level, and awarded first degree (baccalaureate) 1826; changed name to Rensselaer Institute 1832; adopted adopted present name 1851. *See* Samuel Rezneck, *Education for a Technological Society* (Troy: Rensselaer Polytechnic Institute, 1968) for further information.

Institutional Structure: *Governing board:* Board of Trustees of Rensselaer Polytechnic Institute. Extrainstitutional representation: 32 trustees, mayor of Troy; institutional representation: president of the institute. 32 voting. *Composition of institution:* Administrators 13. Administrative management affairs directed by vice president for administration; financial affairs directed by vice president for finance. Full-time instructional faculty 400.

Calendar: Semesters. Academic year Aug. to May. Freshmen admitted Sept., Jan. Degrees conferred and formal commencement May. Summer session of 2 terms from mid-May to mid-Aug.

Characteristics of Freshmen: 11,249 applicants (3,171 female, 8,098 male). 44% of applicants accepted. 27% of accepted applicants enrolled full-time.

72% (974 students) submitted SAT scores; 29% (382 students) submitted ACT scores. *25th percentile*: SAT Critical Reading 680, SAT Math 650, SAT Writing 580; ACT Composite 24. *75th percentile*: SAT Critical Reading 690, SAT Math 730, SAT Writing 680; ACT Composite 29.

81% of freshmen expected to graduate within 5 years. Freshmen from 49 states and 62 foreign countries.

Admission: For fall acceptance, apply no later than Jan. 1. Students are notified of acceptance Apr. Apply by Nov. 1 for early decision. Early acceptance

RENSSELAER POLYTECHNIC INSTITUTE—*cont'd*

available. *Requirements:* Graduation from accredited secondary school. Applicants best suited for Rensselaer will have completed 4 years of English, 4 years of mathematics through pre-calculus, 3 years of science, and 2 years of social studies and/or history. *Entrance tests:* College Board SAT, or ACT composite may be substituted for SAT in some programs. *For transfer students:* 3.0 minimum GPA; maximum transfer credit institution hours.

College credit and advanced placement for postsecondary-level work completed in secondary school.

Tutoring available. Developmental courses offered in summer session and regular academic year; credit given.

Degree Requirements: *For all undergraduate degrees:* 124–131 credit hours; 1.8 GPA; 4 terms, including final term, in residence; minimum 24 credit hours in physical, life, and engineering sciences, including at least 8 credit hours in mathematics; minimum of 24 credit hours in humanities and social sciences; required to successfully complete a writing course or a writing intensive course.

Fulfillment of some degree requirements and exemption from some beginning courses possible by passing department examinations, College Board AP. *Grading system:* A–F; pass-fail.

Distinctive Educational Programs: Undergraduate research; Archer Center for Student Leadership Development; Rensselaer Incubator Program; Rensselaer Technology Park; Office of the First-Year Experience; Cooperative Education; Honors Program; Accelerated medical and law program; double degrees; interdisciplinary courses cut across all 5 academic schools. Cooperative education; accelerated degree programs. Honors programs; double degrees. Interdisciplinary courses. Available to all students: special facilities for using communications in the classroom; tutorials; cross-registration through the consortium. Roman Studies and India and China Studies for architecture students.

ROTC: Army, Navy, Air Force.

Degrees Conferred: 1,144 *baccalaureate*; 384 *master's*; 158 *doctorate*. Bachelor's degrees awarded in top five disciplines: engineering 550; computer and information sciences 190; business, management, marketing, and related support services 75; communication, journalism, and related programs 37; architecture and related services 34. Master's degrees awarded in top five disciplines: business/marketing 319; engineering 249; computer and information sciences 71; mathematics 22; physical science 22. Doctorates awarded: biological/biomedical sciences 2; business/marketing 5; computer and information sciences 15; engineering 86; interdisciplinary studies 7; mathematics 11; physical sciences 14.

Fees and Other Expenses: *Full-time tuition per academic year 2008–09:* undergraduate $37,490; contact the institute for current graduate rates. *Room and board per academic year:* $10,730. *Required fees:* $896. *Books and supplies:* $1,000. *Other expenses:* $815.

Financial Aid: Aid from institutionally generated funds is provided on the basis of academic merit, financial need, athletic ability.

Financial aid to full-time, first-time undergraduate students:

Financial aid to full-time, first-time undergraduate students: 99% received some form of aid. Average amount of aid received: federal grants $6,215; Pell grants $3,050; other federal grants $3,584; state/local grants $1,805; institutional grants $16,999.

Departments and Teaching Staff: *Total instructional faculty:* 481 (full-time 400, part-time 81). Student/faculty ratio: 15:1. Degrees held by full-time faculty: baccalaureate 100%, master's 100%, doctorate 94%. 99% hold terminal degrees.

Enrollment: Total enrollment 6,777. Undergraduate 5,394. Graduate 1,383. Undergraduate transfer-in students 112.

Characteristics of Student Body: *Ethnic/racial makeup:* number of Black non-Hispanic: 208; American Indian or Alaska Native: 116; Asian or Pacific Islander: 566; Hispanic: 291; White non-Hispanic: 3,797; unknown: 122. *Age distribution:* number under 18: 144; 18–19: 2,307; 20–21: 2,062; 22–24: 25–29: 486; 30–34: 28; 35–39: 12; 40–49: 5; 50–64: 1.

International Students: 682 nonresident aliens enrolled fall 2008. Students from Europe, Asia, Central and South America, Africa, Canada, Australia, Middle East. Programs available to aid students whose native language is not English: English as a Second Language Program. Some financial aid designated for international students.

Student Life: On-campus housing is guaranteed for first-year students. Housing available for married students. 72% of students live on campus. *Intercollegiate athletics:* male: baseball, basketball, cross-country, football, golf, hockey, lacrosse, soccer, swimming, tennis, track; female: basketball, ice hockey, lacrosse, softball, tennis, track, field hockey, soccer, swimming, cross-country. *Special regulations:* Cars permitted in designated areas. *Special services:* Student Health Center; Counseling Center; health education and wellness programs. *Student publications, radio: Engineer*, a magazine published 4 times per year; *The Gorgon*, a literary magazine; *Statler & Waldorf*, monthly humor magazine; *The Polytechnic*, a weekly newspaper; *Transit*, a yearbook. Radio station WRPI broadcasts 140 hours per week. *Surrounding community:* Troy, population 55,000, is located within the Albany-Schenectady-Troy metropolitan area. Served by mass transit bus system; airport 8 miles from campus; passenger rail service 5 miles from campus.

Library Collections: 525,508 volumes. Current periodical subscriptions: paper 717; microform 10, via electronic access 36,165. 4,593 recordings; 1,494 compact discs; 1,694 CD-ROMs. Computer work stations available. Online catalog. Students have access to online information retrieval services and the Internet.

Most important holdings include correspondence and books from the mid-1800s by and about the inventor, chemist, botanist Eben N. Horsford; John A. Roebling collection of books, manuscripts, and original drawings (c. 1840–1880) from the designer of the Brooklyn Bridge; Stephen Van Rensselaer materials. School of Architecture Library collection of 30,000 print titles and over 10,000 slides is housed in the Greene Building.

Buildings and Grounds: Campus area 260 acres.

Chief Executive Officer: Dr. Shirley Ann Jackson, President.

Address admission inquiries to James G. Nondorf, Vice President for Enrollment.

Roberts Wesleyan College

2301 Westside Drive
Rochester, New York 14624-1997

Tel: (585) 594-6000 **E-mail:** admissions@roberts.edu
Fax: (585) 594-6371 **Internet:** www.roberts.edu

Institution Description: Roberts Wesleyan College is a private college affiliated with the Free Methodist Church. *Enrollment:* 1,902. *Degrees awarded:* Associate, baccalaureate, master's.

Accreditation: *Regional:* MSA. *Professional*: art, business, music, nursing, social work

History: Established as Chili Seminary, an academy, and offered first instruction at postsecondary level 1866; chartered 1869; changed name to Chesbrough Seminary 1885; became junior college 1921; changed name to Roberts Junior College 1945; adopted present name 1949; awarded first baccalaureate degree 1951.

Institutional Structure: *Governing board:* Board of Trustees. Extrainstitutional representation: 31 trustees; institutional representation: president of the college; 1 alumnus. 30 voting. *Composition of institution:* Administrators 7. Academic affairs headed by provost. Business/finances directed by vice president and treasurer. Full-time instructional faculty 76. Academic governance body, Faculty Senate, meets an average of 8 times per year.

Calendar: Semesters. Academic year Aug. to May. Freshmen admitted fall and spring semesters. Degrees conferred May, Aug., Dec. Formal commencement May. Summer sessions of 3 terms from mid-May to mid-Aug.

Characteristics of Freshmen: 1,501 applicants (1,074 female, 426 male). 65% of applicants admitted. 24% of applicants admitted and enrolled full-time.

83% (195 students) submitted SAT scores; 33% (78 students) submitted ACT scores. *25th percentile*: SAT Critical Reading 470, SAT Math 460, SAT Writing 450; ACT Composite 20, ACT English 20, ACT Math 20. *75th percentile*: SAT Critical Reading 590, SAT Math 580, SAT Writing 570; ACT Composite 27, ACT English 27, ACT Math 27.

55% of entering freshmen expected to graduate within 5 years. 88% of freshmen from New York. Freshmen from 20 states and 18 foreign countries.

Admission: Rolling admissions plan. For fall acceptance, priority is given to applications received by Feb. 1. Early acceptance available. *Requirements:* Graduation from accredited secondary school or GED. Recommend courses in English, mathematics, science. Lowest recommended secondary school class standing top three-fifths. *Entrance tests:* College Board SAT or ACT composite. *For transfer students:* 2.0 minimum GPA; from 4-year accredited institution 90 hours maximum transfer credit; from 2-year accredited institution 72 hours.

College credit and advanced placement for postsecondary-level work completed in secondary school and for extrainstitutional learning.

Tutoring available. Noncredit developmental/remedial courses offered during regular academic year. *For all associate degrees:* 62 credit hours; 2 hours physical education. *For all baccalaureate degrees:* 124 credit hours; 3 hours physical education; demonstrated proficiency in a foreign language, mathematics. *For all associate and baccalaureate degrees:* 2.0 GPA; 30 hours in residence; weekly chapel attendance. *For master's degree:* M.S.M and M.Ed. 36 credit hours; for M.S.W. 60 credit hours; advance standing M.S.W. 30 credit hours. 3.0 GPA; 24 hours in residence.

Fulfillment of some degree requirements possible by passing College Board CLEP. *Grading system:* A–F; withdraw (deadline after which pass-fail is appended to withdraw).

Distinctive Educational Programs: Communications, gerontology, criminal justice, continuing education. Dual-degree program in engineering with Clarkson College of Technology, Rochester Institute of Technology, and Rensselaer Polytechnic Institute. Preprofessional program in pharmacy leading to degree awarded by State University of New York at Buffalo. Interdisciplinary programs in Christian ministries, communication, comprehensive science, comprehensive social studies, humanities, religion-philosophy. Tutorials. Overseas study for some courses. *Other distinctive programs:* Management of Human Resources (an adult degree completion program). Organizational Management and Nursing RN (adult degree completion programs). Master of Science in Management (adult program). Study abroad programs at Jerusalem University College (Jerusalem); England, Latin American Studies in Costa Rica; Middle East Studies (Egypt); Russian Studies (Novgorad).

ROTC: Cooperative ROTC program with Rochester Institute of Technology.

Degrees Conferred: 390 *baccalaureate:*; 296 *master's*. Bachelor's degrees awarded in top five disciplines: business, management, marketing, and related support services 104; education 87; health professions and related clinical sciences 71; public administration and social service professions 25; visual and performing arts 14. Master's degrees awarded: education 197; psychology 25; public administration 48.

Fees and Other Expenses: *Full-time tuition per academic year:* 2008–09: undergraduate $22,598; graduate courses charged per credit hour (contact the college for current rate). *Room and board per academic year: $8,228. Books and supplies:* $1,000. *Other expenses:* $2,484.

Financial Aid: The college offers a direct lending program. Aid from institutionally generated funds is provided on the basis of academic merit, financial need, athletic ability, other criteria.

Financial aid to full-time, first-time undergraduate students: 96% received some form of financial aid. Average amount of aid received: federal grants $4,445; Pell grants $2,536; other federal grants $2,048; state/local grants $2,136; institutional grants $8,255.

Departments and Teaching Staff: *Total instructional faculty:* 101 (full-time 91, part-time 10). *Student/faculty ratio:* 13:1. Degrees held by full-time faculty: doctorate 47%, master's 50%. 47% hold terminal degrees.

Enrollment: Total enrollment 1,902. Undergraduate 1,359. Graduate 543. Undergraduate transfer-in students 115.

Characteristics of Student Body: *Ethnic/racial makeup:* number of Black non-Hispanic: 142; American Indian or Alaska Native: 7; Asian or Pacific Islander: 23; Hispanic: 46; White non-Hispanic: 1,472; unknown: 193.

International Students: 34 nonresident aliens enrolled fall 2008. Students from Europe, Central and South America, Africa, Canada. Programs available to aid students whose native language is not English: social, cultural. Financial aid available for international students: variable number of scholarships available annually to qualifying students.

Student Life: On-campus residence halls house 70% of student body. Residence halls for males constitute 38% of such space, for females 62%. Limited housing available for married students. *Intercollegiate athletics:* male: basketball, cross-country, soccer, track; female: basketball, cross-country, softball, track, volleyball. *Special services:* Medical services. *Student publications: The Beacon*, a biweekly newspaper; *The Chesbronian*, a yearbook. *Surrounding community:* Rochester population 250,000. Served by mass transit bus system; airport 7 miles from campus; passenger rail service 8 miles from campus.

Library Collections: 124,000 volumes including bound books, serial backfiles, electronic documents, and government documents not in separate collections. Online catalog. Current serial subscriptions: 875 paper, 44 microform; 157 via electronic access. 1,345 compact discs; 8 CD-ROMs. Computer work stations available. Students have access to the Internet at no charge.

Most important special holdings include Benjamin Titus Roberts Collection (founder of Free Methodist Church).

Buildings and Grounds: Campus area 70 acres.

Chief Executive Officer: Dr. John A. Martin, President.

Address admission inquiries to Linda E. Kurtz-Hoffman, Vice President for Admissions.

Rochester Institute of Technology

One Lomb Memorial Drive
Rochester, New York 14623-5603
Tel: (585) 475-2411 **E-mail:** admissions@rit.edu
Fax: (585) 475-7424 **Internet:** www.rit.edu

Institution Description: Rochester Institute of Technology is a private, independent, nonprofit institution. *Enrollment:* 15,055. *Degrees awarded:* Associate, baccalaureate, master's, doctorate.

Member of the consortium Rochester Area Colleges.

Accreditation: *Regional:* MSA. *Professional*: art, business, chemistry, computer science, dietetics, engineering, engineering technology, physician assisting

History: Established as Rochester Athenaeum 1829; chartered 1830; merged with Mechanics Institute (established 1885) 1891; offered first instruction at postsecondary level 1912; adopted present name 1944; awarded first degree (baccalaureate) 1955.

Institutional Structure: *Governing board:* Board of Trustees. Extrainstitutional representation: 53 trustees; institutional representation: president of the institute; 23 alumni. All voting. *Composition of institution:* Academic affairs headed by provost and vice president, academic affairs. Management/business/finances directed by vice president, finance and administration. Full-time instructional faculty 788. Academic governance body, Institute Council, meets an average of 9 times per year.

Calendar: Quarters. Academic year early Sept. to late May. Freshmen admitted Sept. through June. Degrees conferred May., Aug. Formal commencement May. Summer session from early June to mid-Aug.

Characteristics of Freshmen: 12,725 applicants (4,186 female, 8,539 male). 60% of applicants admitted. 34% of applicants admitted and enrolled full-time.

74% (1,934 students) submitted SAT scores. 25% (653 students) submitted ACT scores. *25th percentile*: SAT Critical Reading 540, SAT Math 560, SAT Writing 530; ACT Composite 24. *75th percentile*: SAT Critical Reading 630, SAT math 670, SAT Writing 610; ACT Composite 29.

62% of entering freshmen expected to graduate within 5 years. 55% of freshmen from New York. Freshmen from 50 states and 96 foreign countries.

Admission: Rolling admissions plan. Regular decision plan: Feb. 1. deadline. Early decision plan deadline Dec. 1. *Requirements:* Either graduation from accredited secondary school with 3–4 units English, 2–4 mathematics, 2–4 science, 2–3 social studies; or GED. Additional units in science and mathematics recommended. Minimum 2.5 GPA. Lowest acceptable secondary school class standing varies by college. *Entrance tests:* College Board SAT or ACT composite. For foreign students TOEFL. *For transfer students:* 2.5 minimum GPA; from 4-year and 2-year accredited institutions maximum transfer credit limited only by residence requirement.

College credit and advanced placement for postsecondary-level work completed in secondary school and for extrainstitutional learning on basis of portfolio and faculty assessments.

Tutoring available. Noncredit developmental courses offered in summer session, during regular academic year, and by individual arrangement.

Degree Requirements: *For all associate degrees:* 90 quarter hours; 2 quarters physical education courses. *For all baccalaureate degrees:* 180 quarter hours; 3 quarters physical education; exit competency examination in writing. *For all undergraduate degrees:* 2.0 GPA; 3 terms in residence; general education and core requirement.

Fulfillment of some degree requirements and exemption from some beginning courses possible by passing College Board CLEP, AP, IB, other standardized tests. *Grading system:* A–F; withdraw (carries time limit).

Distinctive Educational Programs: Cooperative education; internships; undergraduate research; honors; dual degrees; double majors; online courses; off-campus centers. Weekend and evening classes. Special facilities for using telecommunications in the classroom. Independent study. Study abroad in mathematics and science programs at Oxford University (England) and business management programs at Sheffield University (England); Engineering and technologies at Kanazawa Institute of Technology (Japan). Additional study abroad programs offered in cooperation with Syracuse University.

ROTC: Air Force, Army.

Degrees Conferred: 172 *associate;* 2,266 *baccalaureate*; 829 *master's*; 19 *doctorate*. Bachelor's degrees awarded in top five disciplines: visual and performing arts 380; communications/journalism 320; business/marketing 248; computer and information sciences 201; interdisciplinary studies 200. Master's degrees awarded in top five disciplines: business/marketing 234; engineering 158; communication/journalism 99; computer and information sciences 69; visual and performing arts 62. Doctorates awarded: engineering 10 physical sciences 9.

Fees and Other Expenses: *Full-time tuition per academic year 2008–09:* undergraduate $28,035; contact the institute for current graduate tuition. *Required fees:* $384. *Room and board per academic year:* $9,381. *Books and supplies:* $900. *Other expenses:* $1,025.

Financial Aid: Aid from institutionally generated funds is awarded on the basis of academic merit, financial need.

Financial aid to full-time, first-time undergraduate students:

Financial aid to full-time, first-time undergraduate students: 92% received some form of aid. average amount of aid received: federal grants $4,132; Pell grants $2,918; other federal grants $1,563; state/local grants $2,450; institutional grants $1,500.

Departments and Teaching Staff: *Total instructional faculty:* 1,230 (full-time 788, part-time 442). Student/faculty ratio: 13:1. Degrees held by full-time faculty: 80% hold terminal degrees.

Enrollment: Total enrollment 15,055. Undergraduate 12,689. Graduate 2,366. Undergraduate transfer-in students 626.

ROCHESTER INSTITUTE OF TECHNOLOGY—*cont'd*

Characteristics of Student Body: *Ethnic/racial makeup:* number of Black non-Hispanic: 553; American Indian or Alaska Native: 44; Asian or Pacific Islander: 751; Hispanic: 466; White non-Hispanic: 8,725, unknown: 1,119. *Age distribution:* number under 18: 214; 18–19: 3,983; 20–21: 4,407; 22–24: 2,814; 25–29: 744; 30–34: 282; 35–39: 201; 40–49: 353; 50–64: 117; 65 and over: 8. 29% of student body attend summer sessions.

International Students: 1,213 nonresident aliens enrolled fall 2008. Students from Europe, Asia, Central and South America, Africa, Canada, Australia, Middle East. Programs available to aid students whose native language is not English: social, cultural, financial. English as a Second Language Program. Scholarships specifically designated for undergraduate international students; 160 totaling $1 million awarded 2008–09.

Student Life: On-campus residence halls (including space for fraternities and sororities) house 42% of student body. On-campus apartments house 21% of student body. Housing available for married students. *Intercollegiate athletics:* male: baseball, basketball, crew, cross-country, hockey, lacrosse, soccer, swimming, tennis, track, wrestling; female: : basketball, crew, cross-country, ice hockey, lacrosse, soccer, softball, swimming, tennis, track, volleyball. *Special regulations:* Registered cars permitted. *Special services:* Academic Support Center, Student Health Center, Counseling Center, Women's Resource Center, Margaret House Child Center; on-campus child care is available to students at a reduced rate with a child care tuition assistance program in place; English Language Center; bus service between off-campus residences and campus. *Student publications, radio: The Reporter*, a weekly student news magazine. Radio station WITR-FM broadcasts 24/7. *Surrounding community:* Rochester population 212,481.

Library Collections: 474,300 volumes including bound books, serial backfiles, electronic documents, and government documents not in separate collections. Online catalog. Current serial subscriptions: 2,087 paper, 401 microform; 19,068 via electronic access. 1,869 audiovisual materials; 506 DVDs; 205 CD-ROMs. Computer work stations available. Students have access to the Internet at no charge.

Most important special holdings include collection of materials on the deaf; Cary Collection covering printing, publishing, typography; Frederick W. Goudy-Howard Coggeshall Memorial Workshop Collection.

Buildings and Grounds: Campus area 1,300 acres.

Chief Executive Officer: Dr. Albert J. Simone, President.

Address admission inquiries to Daniel Shelley, Director of Admissions.

College of Applied Science and Technology

Degree Programs Offered: *Baccalaureate* in technologies: electrical engineering, computer engineering, telecommunications engineering, mechanical engineering, electrical/mechanical engineering, civil engineering, packaging science, environmental management and safety, hospitality and service management, nutrition management. *Master's* in packaging science, human resource development, training and instructional design, service management, hospitality-tourism management, health systems administration, telecommunication engineering, environmental health and safety management, cross-disciplinary professional studies, manufacturing and mechanical systems integration.

Kate Gleason College of Engineering

Degree Programs Offered: *Associate* in engineering science; *baccalaureate* in computer, electrical, industrial, mechanical and microelectronic engineering; *master's* in electrical and mechanical engineering. A master's in material science and engineering is offered jointly with the College of Science.

College of Imaging Arts and Sciences

Degree Programs Offered: *Associate, baccalaureate* in new media design and imaging, graphic design, industrial design, new media publishing, graphic communications, newspaper operations management, printing and computer science, film/video/animation, advertising photography, photojournalism, fine art photography, biomedical photographic communications, imaging and photographic technology, imaging systems management, illustration, medical illustration, fine arts studio, ceramics and ceramic sculpture, glass and glass sculpture, metals and jewelry design, woodworking and furniture design; *master's* in photography, computer animation, ceramic and ceramic sculpture, computer graphics design, medical illustration, metals/jewelry design, woodworking and furniture design, graphic design, graphic arts systems, graphic arts publishing, printing technology.

College of Science

Degree Programs Offered: *Baccalaureate* in biology, biochemistry, chemistry, polymer chemistry, applied mathematics, applied statistics, computational mathematics, environmental science, physics, medical technology, nuclear medicine technology, diagnostic medical sonography, biomedical computing, physician assistant, imaging science, premedical studies; *master's* in chemistry, clinical chemistry, environmental science, color science, imaging science, materials science and engineering (offered jointly with the College of Engineering); *doctorate* in imaging science.

National Institute for the Deaf

Degree Programs Offered: *Associate* in art and computer design, applied computer technology, accounting technology, administrative support, business, American Sign Language and English interpretation, digital imaging and publishing, computer aided drafting, automation technology, computer integrated machining, applied optical technology, laboratory science; *baccalaureate* in American Sign Language and English interpretation; *master's* in education for secondary teachers of the deaf and hard of hearing.

Admission: In addition to general requirements, students must have a hearing loss of 70 decibels, demonstrate overall 8th grade achievement level through standardized tests. Students may be admitted prior to graduation from secondary school if school authorities certify student will benefit more from NTID program than from another year in secondary school.

Distinctive Educational Programs: Cross-registration with other R.I.T. colleges for qualified students. Summer Vestibule Program helps entering students make the transition from secondary school.

College of Business

Degree Programs Offered: *Baccalaureate* in business administration with 7 major fields; *master's* in finance, manufacturing management and leadership, product development; MBA.

Distinctive Educational Programs: 4 + 1 agreements held with RIT colleges and many other universities. Dual admission to BS/MBA option available to qualified students.

College of Computing and Information Sciences

Degree Programs Offered: *Associate* in computer sciences and information technology; *baccalaureate* in computer science, information technology, software engineering, applied networking and system administration, new media information technology, and medical informatics; *master's* in computer science, information technology, software development and management, computer security and information assurance; *advanced certificate* in interactive multimedia development.

College of Liberal Arts

Degree Programs Offered: *Baccalaureate* in criminal justice, social work, economics, technical and professional communications, advertising and public relations, international studies, psychology, public policy; *master's* in school psychology, communication and media technologies, public policy.

Russell Sage College

45 Ferry Street
Troy, New York 12180
Tel: (518) 244-2217 **E-mail:** rscadm@sage.edu
Fax: (518) 244-6880 **Internet:** www.sage.edu

Institution Description: Russell Sage College is a private, independent, nonprofit college for women. It is part of The Sage Colleges which consists of four institutions: Russell Sage College, Sage Junior College at Albany, Sage Graduate School, Sage Evening College. *Enrollment:* 699. *Degrees awarded:* Baccalaureate, master's.

Member of the consortium Hudson-Mohawk Association of Colleges and Universities.

Accreditation: *Regional:* MSA. *Professional*: nursing, occupational therapy, physical therapy

History: Established and offered first instruction at postsecondary level 1916; awarded first degree (baccalaureate) 1920; chartered 1928; added coeducational division in Albany 1949; recharted with other components as The Sage Colleges 1995.

Institutional Structure: *Governing board:* The Sate Colleges Board of Trustees. Extrainstitutional representation: 21 trustees, including 9 alumnae/i. institutional representation: 1 trustee, president of the college, *Composition of*

institution: Administrators 112. Academic affairs headed by vice president of academic affairs. Management/business/finances directed by vice president of finance and administration. Full-time instructional faculty 58. Academic governance body, the faculty, meets an average of 9 times per year.

Calendar: Semesters. Academic year Aug. to May. Freshmen admitted Aug., Jan., Feb. Degrees conferred and formal commencement May. Summer sessions from mid-May to mid-Aug.

Characteristics of Freshmen: 377 applicants (377 female). 75% of applicants accepted. 44% of accepted applicants enrolled full-time.

79% (97 students) submitted SAT scores; 28% (34 students) submitted ACT scores. *25th percentile*: SAT Critical Reading 540, SAT Math 510; ACT Composite 22. *75th percentile*: SAT Critical Reading 610, SAT Math 570; ACT Composite 25.

46% of entering freshmen expected to graduate within 5 years. 92% of freshmen from New York. Freshmen from 13 states and 3 foreign countries.

Admission: Rolling admissions plan. For fall acceptance, apply as early as end of junior year, but not later than Sept. of year of enrollment. Apply by Dec. 1 for early decision. Early acceptance available. *Requirements:* Either graduation from accredited secondary school with 16 units in academic subjects which should include English, foreign language, mathematics, natural science, social studies; or GED. Minimum GPA 2.5. Lowest acceptable secondary school class standing 50th percentile. *Entrance tests:* College Board SAT I or ACT. *For transfer students:* 2.5 minimum GPA; from 4-year accredited institution 75 hours maximum transfer credit; from 2-year accredited institution 60 hours.

College credit and advanced placement for postsecondary-level work completed in secondary school. Tutoring available. Developmental courses offered in summer session and regular academic year; credit given.

Degree Requirements: *For all baccalaureate degrees:* 120 credit hours; 2.0 GPA; final 45 hours in residence; one half of the major must be taken in residence; 1 year physical education, 6 hours interim coursework; cumulative GPA 2.0; complete general education program of 36 credits; complete 90 credits of liberal arts for a B.A.; complete 60 credits of liberal arts for B.S.; must maintain appropriate GPA defined by major of study.

Fulfillment of some degree requirements possible by passing College Board CLEP and AP. *Grading system:* A–F; pass-fail; withdraw.

Distinctive Educational Programs: Internships. Dual-degree program in engineering with Rensselaer Polytechnic Institute. Interdisciplinary majors by individual arrangement. Facilities for independent research, including majors, tutorials. Study abroad in England, France, Spain, Australia; program with Oxford University (England), University of Puerto Rico, University de Seville (Spain). Cross-registration with Rensselaer Polytechnic Institute and through consortium. Evening division offers undergraduate and graduate study at both campuses and at extension centers, and an experiential learning program which grants credit for life experience. *Other distinctive programs:* Degree-granting continuing education program for women.

Degrees Conferred: 197 *baccalaureate.* Bachelor's degrees awarded in top five disciplines: health professions and related clinical sciences 46; education 27; psychology 19; multidisciplinary studies 15; social sciences 16.

Fees and Other Expenses: *Full-time tuition per academic year 2008–09:* $26,540. *Books and supplies:* $1,000. *Room and board per academic year:* $9,200. *Other expenses:* $2,060.

Financial Aid: Aid from institutionally generated funds is provided on the basis of academic merit, financial need. Institution has a Program Participation Agreement with the U.S. Department of Education for eligible students to receive Pell Grants and, depending upon the agreement, other federal aid.

Financial aid to full-time, first-time undergraduate students: 100% received some form of financial aid. Average amount of aid received: federal grants $3,919; Pell grants $3,113; other federal grants $1,612; state/local grants $2,363; institutional grants $9,688.

Departments and Teaching Staff: *Total instructional faculty:* 97.5 FTE. Student/faculty ratio: 13:1. *Total tenured faculty:* 52. Degrees held by full-time faculty: doctorate 59%, master's 99%, baccalaureate 100%. 74% hold terminal degrees.

Enrollment: Total enrollment 699 (undergraduate). Transfer-in students 122.

Characteristics of Student Body: *Ethnic/racial makeup:* Black non-Hispanic: 4.6%; Asian or Pacific Islander: 2.4%; Hispanic: 2.9%; White non-Hispanic: 74.6%; unknown: 15.%.

International Students: 16 nonresident aliens enrolled fall 2008 No programs to aid students whose native language is not English. No financial aid specifically designated for international students.

Student Life: On-campus residence halls house 52% of student body. Residence halls for females constitute 100% of such space. *Intercollegiate athletics:* female: basketball, soccer, softball, tennis, volleyball. *Special regulations:* Registered cars permitted on campus for commuters, senior student teachers, and students with special permission. *Special services:* Medical services. *Student publications: Sage Horizons*, magazine of the Sage Colleges; *The Quill*, an independent student-run newspaper; *Sage Leaves*, a yearbook; *Russell Sage Connection*, an alumnae publication. *Surrounding community:* Troy population 55,500. New York, 300 miles from campus, is nearest metropolitan area. Served by mass transit bus system; airport and passenger rail service, each 10 miles from campus.

Library Collections: 360,000 volumes including bound books, serial backfiles, electronic documents, and government documents not in separate collections. Online catalog. Current serial subscriptions: 1,221 paper, 3,575 microform, 1,422 electronic. 30 CD-ROMs. Computer work stations available. Students have access to the Internet at no charge.

Most important special holdings in the fields of allied health, fine arts, 20th-century poetry, women's studies.

Buildings and Grounds: 26-acre campus (2 locations).

Chief Executive Officer: Dr. Jeanne H. Neff, President (Sage Colleges).

Address admission inquiries Kathy Rusch, Director of Admissions.

Sage College of Albany

140 New Scotland Avenue
Albany, New York 12208
Tel: (518) 292-1717 **E-mail:** admissions@sage.edu
Fax: (518) 292-1728 **Internet:** www.sage.edu

Institution Description: Sage College of Albany, a coeducational college of applied studies, prepares students for life's commitments and work in a changing world. The college offers associate and baccalaureate degrees. Sage Graduate School preparesmales and females for leadership roles by combining theoretical preparation with professional practice. *Enrollment:* 2,070. *Degrees awarded:* Associate, baccalaureate, master's.

Accreditation: *Regional:* MSA.

Institutional Structure: *Governing board:* The Sate Colleges Board of Trustees. Extrainstitutional representation: 21 trustees, including 9 alumnae/i. institutional representation: 1 trustee, president of the college, *Composition of institution:* Administrators 112. Academic affairs headed by vice president of academic affairs. Management/business/finances directed by vice president of finance and administration. Full-time instructional faculty 162. Academic governance body, the faculty, meets an average of 9 times per year.

Calendar: Semesters. Academic year Aug. to May. Freshmen admitted Aug., Jan., Feb. Degrees conferred and formal commencement May. Summer sessions from mid-May to mid-Aug.

Characteristics of Freshmen: 372 applicants (280 female, 92 male). 63% of applicants admitted. 45% of admitted students enrolled full-time.

73% (77 students) submitted SAT scores; 25% (26 students) submitted ACT scores. *25th percentile*: SAT Critical Reading 440, SAT Math 430; ACT Composite 18. *75th percentile*: SAT Critical Reading 540, SAT Math 530, ACT Composite 22.

Admission: Rolling admissions plan. For fall acceptance, apply as early as end of junior year, but not later than Sept. of year of enrollment. Apply by Dec. 1 for early decision. Early acceptance available. *Requirements:* Either graduation from accredited secondary school with 16 units in academic subjects which should include English, foreign language, mathematics, natural science, social studies; or GED. Minimum GPA 2.5. Lowest acceptable secondary school class standing 50th percentile. *Entrance tests:* College Board SAT I or ACT. *For transfer students:* 2.5 minimum GPA; from 4-year accredited institution 75 hours maximum transfer credit; from 2-year accredited institution 60 hours.

College credit and advanced placement for postsecondary-level work completed in secondary school. Tutoring available. Developmental courses offered in summer session and regular academic year; credit given.

Degree Requirements: *For all baccalaureate degrees:* 120 credit hours; 2.0 GPA; final 45 hours in residence; one half of the major must be taken in residence; 1 year physical education, 6 hours interim coursework; cumulative GPA 2.0; complete general education program of 36 credits; complete 90 credits of liberal arts for a B.A.; complete 60 credits of liberal arts for B.S.; must maintain appropriate GPA defined by major of study.

Fulfillment of some degree requirements possible by passing College Board CLEP and AP. *Grading system:* A–F; pass-fail; withdraw.

Degrees Conferred: 71 *associate*; 201 *baccalaureate*; 332 *master's*. Bachelor's degrees awarded in top five disciplines: business, management, marketing, and related support services 57; liberal arts 28; visual and performing arts 28; legal professions and studies 25; education 21. Master's degrees awarded: business, management, marketing, and related support services 23; education 187; health professions and related clinical sciences 89; psychology 30; public administration and social service professions 3.

Fees and Other Expenses: *Full-time tuition per academic year 2008–09:* contact the college for current information regarding tuition, fees, and housing costs.

SAGE COLLEGE OF ALBANY—*cont'd*

Financial Aid: Aid from institutionally generated funds is provided on the basis of academic merit, financial need. Institution has a Program Participation Agreement with the U.S. Department of Education for eligible students to receive Pell Grants and, depending upon the agreement, other federal aid.

Financial aid to full-time, first-time undergraduate students: 97% of students received some form of financial aid. Average amount of aid received: federal grants $3,190; state/local grants $3,382; institutional grants $6,886; loans $6,922.

Enrollment: Total enrollment 2,070. Undergraduate 1,031.

Characteristics of Student Body: *Ethnic/racial makeup:* Black non-Hispanic: 8.2%; Asian or Pacific Islander: 1.8%; Hispanic: 2.1%; White non-Hispanic: 69.8%; unknown: 18.5%.

International Students: 2 undergraduate nonresident aliens enrolled fall 2008. No programs to aid students whose native language is not English. No financial aid specifically designated for international students.

Library Collections: Online catalog. Computer work stations available. Students have access to the Internet at no charge.

Chief Executive Officer: Dr. James H. Neff, President (Sage Colleges).

Address admission inquiries to Amanda Langue, Director of Admissions.

St. Bonaventure University

Route 417
St. Bonaventure, New York 14778
Tel: (716) 375-2000 **E-mail:** admissions@sbu.edu
Fax: (716) 375-2005 **Internet:** www.sbu.edu

Institution Description: St. Bonaventure University is a private, independent, nonprofit institution. *Enrollment:* 2,406. *Degrees awarded:* Baccalaureate, master's.

Member of Western New York Consortium of Higher Education.

Accreditation: *Regional:* MSA.

History: Established as St. Bonaventure College and offered first instruction at postsecondary level 1858; awarded first degree (baccalaureate) 1860; chartered 1875; incorporated 1883; adopted present name 1950. *See* Mark Angelo, *A History of St. Bonaventure University* (St. Bonaventure: Franciscan Institute Publications, 1961) for further information.

Institutional Structure: *Governing board:* Board of Trustees. Extrainstitutional representation: 23 trustees; institutional representation: 1 administrator; 1 alumnus. 2 ex officio. All voting. *Composition of institution:* Administrators 19. Academic affairs headed by vice president for academic affairs. Management/business/finances directed by executive vice president. Full-time instructional faculty 115. Academic governance body, Faculty Senate, meets an average of 10 times per year.

Calendar: Semesters. Academic year late Aug. to mid-May. Freshmen admitted Sept., Jan., June, July. Degrees conferred May, Aug. Formal commencement May. Summer session from mid-May to late July.

Characteristics of Freshmen: 1,731 applicants (959 female, 772 male). 91% of applicants admitted. 36% of admitted students enrolled full-time.

95% (535 students) submitted SAT scores; 41% (283 students) submitted ACT scores. *25th percentile*: SAT Critical Reading 460, SAT Math 465; ACT Composite 20, ACT English 19, ACT Math 19. *75th percentile*: SAT Critical Reading 580, SAT Math 590; ACT Composite 26, ACT English 26, ACT Math 26.

64% of entering freshmen expected to graduate within 5 years. 77% of freshmen from New York. Freshmen from 38 states and 7 foreign countries.

Admission: Rolling admissions plan. For fall acceptance, apply as early as Sept. 1 of previous year, but not later than Aug. 1 of year of enrollment. Early acceptance available. *Requirements:* Either graduation from approved secondary school with 14 academic units or GED. Recommend 16–19 units, including 4 English, 2–3 foreign language, 4 social studies, 3–4 mathematics, 3–4 science. *Entrance tests:* College Board SAT or ACT composite. *For transfer students:* 2.0 minimum GPA; 90 hours maximum transfer credit.

College credit and advanced placement for postsecondary-level work completed in secondary school. College credit for extrainstitutional learning.

Tutoring available. Noncredit developmental/remedial courses offered in summer session and regular academic year.

Degree Requirements: 120 credit hours; 2.0 GPA; 2 terms in residence; core curriculum; distribution requirements; demonstrated proficiency in individual fields of study.

Fulfillment of some degree requirements and exemption from some beginning courses possible by passing departmental examinations, College Board CLEP, APP, other standardized tests. *Grading system:* A–F; pass-fail; withdraw (deadline after which pass-fail is appended to withdraw); H (honors course).

Distinctive Educational Programs: *For undergraduates:* Cooperative baccalaureate program in engineering with degree awarded by University of Detroit; in medical technology with WCA Hospital. Interdepartmental/interdisciplinary programs. Preprofessional programs in business, law. Honors programs. Study abroad in Rome through Loyola University of Chicago; elsewhere by individual arrangement. Off-campus study through New York State Visiting Student Program. *For graduate students:* Off-campus center (at Buffalo Center located on Hilbert College campus, 75 miles away from main institution). Franciscan Institute offering opportunities for research and a program leading to a master's degree in Franciscan studies. *Available to all students:* Work-experience programs. Evening classes. Accelerated degree programs. Tutorials. *Other distinctive programs:* Tuition waiver for senior citizens. Operation Giant Step enables qualified secondary school students to enroll in college courses; scholarships available.

ROTC: Army.

Degrees Conferred: 463 *baccalaureate*; 271 *master's*. Bachelor's degrees awarded in top five disciplines: business, management, marketing, and related support services 149; communication, journalism, and related programs 80; education 79; social sciences 55; history 21. Master's degrees awarded: business/marketing 110; communication, journalism and related programs 15; education 113; foreign languages 12; philosophy and religious studies 10; theology and ministerial studies 1.

Fees and Other Expenses: *Full-time tuition per academic year 2008–09:* undergraduate $24,785; graduate study charged per credit (contact the university for current rates). *Books and supplies:* <$700. *Room and board per academic year:* $9,195. *Other expenses:* $1,050.

Financial Aid: Aid from institutionally generated funds is provided on the basis of academic merit, financial need, athletic ability. Institution has a Program Participation Agreement with the U.S. Department of Education for eligible students to receive Pell Grants and, depending upon the agreement, other federal aid.

99% of students received some form of financial aid. Average amount of aid received: federal grants $5,950; Pell grants $2,984; other federal grants $3,202; state/local grants $2,886; institutional grants $13,226.

Departments and Teaching Staff: *Total instructional faculty:* 173.67 FTE. Degrees held by full-time faculty: doctorate 83%, master's 17%. 85% hold terminal degrees.

Enrollment: Total enrollment 2,406. Undergraduate 1,932. Graduate 474. Undergraduate transfer-in students 57.

Characteristics of Student Body: *Ethnic/racial makeup:* Black non-Hispanic: 2.8%; American Indian or Alaska Native: .4%; Asian or Pacific Islander: .7%; Hispanic: 1.6%; White non-Hispanic: 59.2%; unknown: 38.4%.

International Students: 39 nonresident aliens enrolled fall 2008. Students from Europe, Asia, Central and South America, Africa, Canada. No programs available to aid students whose native language is not English. No financial aid specifically designated for international students.

Student Life: On-campus residence halls and apartments house 67% of student body. 50%. *Intercollegiate athletics:* male: baseball, basketball, cross-country, golf, soccer, swimming, tennis; female: basketball, cross-country, lacrosse, soccer, softball, swimming, tennis. *Special regulations:* Cars permitted in designated parking areas. Quiet hours vary according to dormitory. Residence hall visitation from 2pm to 2am. *Special services:* Learning Resources Center, medical services. *Student publications, radio: The Bona Venture*, a newspaper; *The Laurel*, a campus literary magazine. Radio station WSBU broadcasts 50 hours per week. *Surrounding community:* St. Bonaventure, unincorporated, located in Cattaraugus County, population 52,000. Buffalo, approximately 70 miles from campus, is nearest metropolitan area. Served by airport 25 miles from campus.

Publications: *Bonalumnus*, university's alumni magazine.

Library Collections: 270,000 volumes. 150,000 government documents; 690,000 microforms; 8,000 audiovisual materials; 1,533 current periodical subscriptions. Students have access to online information retrieval services and the Internet.

Most important special holdings include Franciscan Collection (books by Franciscans and others on theology and church history, including incunabula and rare books); Gutenberg-Ruppel Collection (books, articles, pamphlets, and other items on the history of printing from the personal library of Gutenberg scholar Aloys Ruppel); Thomas Merton Collection (books by and about Merton, including first editions; also notebooks, journals, letters, photographs, memorabilia).

Buildings and Grounds: Campus area 589 acres.

Chief Executive Officer: Dr. Margaret Carney, O.S.F., President.

Undergraduates address admission inquiries to James M. Dirisio, Director of Admission Services; graduate inquiries to Dean of Graduate School.

St. Francis College

180 Remsen Street
Brooklyn Heights, New York 11201
Tel: (718) 522-2300 **E-mail:** admissions@stfranciscollege.edu
Fax: (718) 522-1274 **Internet:** www.stfranciscollege.edu

Institution Description: St. Francis College is a private, nonsectarian, nonprofit college. *Enrollment:* 2,425. *Degrees awarded:* Associate, baccalaureate.

Member of the consortia The Brooklyn Educational and Cultural Alliance and Academic Libraries of Brooklyn.

Accreditation: *Regional:* MSA.

History: Established as St. Francis Academy 1858; incorporated as The St. Francis Monastery of the City of Brooklyn 1868; offered first instruction at postsecondary level and adopted present name 1884; awarded first degree (baccalaureate) 1885; became coeducational 1969.

Institutional Structure: *Governing board:* Board of Trustees. Representation: 20 trustees. All voting. *Composition of institution:* Administrators 45. Student affairs headed by vice president for student affairs/dean of students. Management/business/finances directed by vice president for financial affairs. Full-time instructional faculty 58.

Calendar: Semesters. Academic year Sept. to May. Freshmen admitted admitted Sept., Jan., June. Degrees conferred May, Sept., Feb. Formal commencement May. Summer session of 2 terms.

Characteristics of Freshmen: 1,707 applicants (1,041 female, 666 male). 75% of applicants accepted. 46% of accepted applicants enrolled.

98 (560 students) submitted SAT scores. *25th percentile*: SAT Critical Reading 410, SAT Math 410, SAT Writing 410. *75th percentile*: SAT Critical Reading 520, SAT Math 520, SAT Writing 510.

35% of entering freshmen expected to graduate within 5 years. 98% of freshmen from New York. Freshmen from 5 states and 22 foreign countries.

Admission: Rolling admissions plan. For fall acceptance, apply as early as October of previous year, but not later than August of year of enrollment. Early acceptance available. *Requirements:* Either graduation from accredited secondary school with 16 units which must include 4 in English. The remaining 12 units should include a 3-year sequence and a 2-year sequence in language, mathematics, science, social studies, or business. GED accepted. Additional unites in mathematics required for some programs. Minimum GPA 2.0. *Entrance tests:* College Board SAT required. For foreign students TOEFL. *For transfer students:* 2.0 minimum GPA; from 4-year accredited institution 96 semester hours maximum transfer credit; from 2-year accredited institution 60 semester hours.

College credit and advanced placement for postsecondary-level work completed in secondary school, USAFI-DANTES, and for extrainstitutional learning on basis of portfolio and faculty assessments.

Degree Requirements: *For all associate degrees:* 63 semester hours. *For all baccalaureate degrees:* 128 semester hours (130 semester hours for accounting majors); core curriculum; comprehensive examinations or projects in individual fields of study. *For all degrees:* 2.0 GPA; 30 semester hours in residence.

Fulfillment of some degree requirements and exemption from some beginning courses possible by passing College Board CLEP, AP, other standardized tests. *Grading system:* A–F; pass-fail; withdraw.

Distinctive Educational Programs: Flexible meeting places and schedules, including weekend and evening classes. Dual-degree program in podiatric medicine with New York College of Podiatric Medicine and in dentistry with New York University College of Dentistry; affiliation with SUNY Health Sciences Center at Brooklyn leading to B.S. degrees in nursing, occupational therapy, radiologic science and technology, medical sonography, and medical records administration. Facilities and programs for independent research, including honors programs, individual majors. Study abroad in various locations. Experiential learning program.

ROTC: Army in cooperation with Polytechnic Institute of New York; Air Force in cooperation with Manhattan College.

Degrees Conferred: 18 *associate;* 443 *baccalaureate*; 8 *master's*. Bachelor's degrees awarded in top five disciplines; business/marketing 101; liberal arts/general studies 80; psychology 42; communications, journalism, and related support services 39; computer and information sciences 34. Master's degrees awarded: business/marketing 8.

Fees and Other Expenses: *Full-time tuition per academic year 2008–09* \$15,720. *Required fees:* \$360. *Books and supplies:* \$1,000. Off-campus housing only.

Financial Aid: Aid from institutionally generated funds is provided on the basis of academic merit, financial need, athletic ability. Institution has a Program Participation Agreement with the U.S. Department of Education for eligible students to receive Pell Grants and, depending upon the agreement, other federal aid.

Financial aid to full-time, first-time undergraduate students: 91% received some form of aid. Average amount of aid received: federal grants \$3,444; Pell grants \$3,144; other federal grants \$989; state/local grants \$2,931; institutional grants \$6,630.

Departments and Teaching Staff: Total instructional faculty: 211. Student/faculty ratio: 18:1. Degrees held by full-time faculty: doctorates 67%, master's 100. 71% hold terminal degrees.

Enrollment: Total enrollment 2,425. Undergraduate2,407. Graduate 18. Undergraduate transfer-in students 454.

Characteristics of Student Body: *Ethnic/racial makeup:* number of Black non-Hispanic: 446; American Indian or Alaska Native: 2; Asian or Pacific Islander: 50; Hispanic: 360; White non-Hispanic: 1,064; unknown: 111.

International Students: 203 undergraduate nonresident aliens enrolled fall 2008. Students from Europe, Asia, Central and South America, Africa, Canada. No programs available to aid students whose native language is not English. No financial aid specifically designated for international students.

Student Life: No on-campus housing. *Intercollegiate athletics:* male: baseball, basketball, soccer, swimming, water polo; female: basketball, swimming, volleyball; both sexes: cross-country, tennis, track. *Special services:* medical services. *Student publications: The Franciscan*, a yearbook; *Montage*, an annual literary magazine; *The Voice*, a bimonthly newspaper. *Surrounding community:* Served by mass transit bus, rail, and subway systems; airport 5 miles from campus; passenger rail service 2 miles from campus.

Library Collections: 140,000 volumes. 10,500 microforms; 2,100 audiovisual materials; 570 current periodical subscriptions. Online catalog. Students have access to online information retrieval services and the Internet.

Most important special collections include Franciscan literature, philosophy and religion, education; Kennedy Collection; Curriculum Library.

Buildings and Grounds: Campus area consists of five interconnected buildings.

Chief Executive Officer: Dr. Frank J. Macchiarola, President.

Address admission inquiries to Steven Bogart, Director of Enrollment Management.

St. John Fisher College

3690 East Avenue
Rochester, New York 14618
Tel: (585) 385-8064 **E-mail:** admissions@sjfc.edu
Fax: (585) 385-8386 **Internet:** www.sjfc.edu

Institution Description: St. John Fisher College is a coeducational, private, college in the Catholic tradition. *Enrollment:* 3,832. *Degrees awarded:* Baccalaureate, master's.

Member of the consortium Rochester Area Colleges.

Accreditation: *Regional:* MSA. *Professional*: business, chemistry, nursing, pharmacy

History: Established 1948; chartered and offered first instruction at postsecondary level 1951; awarded first degree (baccalaureate) 1955; became coeducational 1971; offered first graduate program 1983.

Institutional Structure: *Governing board:* Board of Trustees of St. John Fisher College. Extrainstitutional representation: 33 trustees, including 11 alumni, 3 Basilican priests, 1 faculty member; institutional representation: president of the college, vice chair of faculty, assembly president of student government. All voting. *Composition of institution:* Administrators 70. Academic affairs headed by dean of the college. Management/business/finances directed by vice president for finance. Full-time instructional faculty 167.

Calendar: Semesters. Academic year Sept. to May. Freshmen admitted Sept., Jan., June. Degrees conferred May, Aug., Dec. Formal commencement May. Summer session of 3 terms from mid-May to mid-Aug.

Characteristics of Freshmen: 3,231 applicants (1,774 female, 1,457 male). 62% of applicants admitted. 28% of admitted students enrolled full-time.

95% (543 386 students) submitted SAT scores; 50% (282 students) submitted ACT scores. *25th percentile*: SAT Critical Reading 480, SAT Math 570, SAt Writing 470; ACT Composite 22, ACT English 21, ACT Math 21. *75th percentile*: SAT Critical Reading 570, SAT Math 600, SAT Writing 560; ACT Composite 26, ACT English 25, ACT Math 26.

63% of entering freshmen expected to graduate within 5 years. 98% of freshmen from New York. Freshmen from 20 states and 7 foreign countries.

Admission: Rolling admissions plan. For fall acceptance, apply as early as Oct. of previous year, but not later than Aug. of year of enrollment. Early acceptance available. *Requirements:* Graduation from accredited secondary school with 16 units which must include 4 in English. *Entrance tests:* College Board SAT or ACT. For foreign students TOEFL. *For transfer students:* 2.0 minimum GPA; from 4-year accredited institution no limit on hours of transfer credit; from 2-year accredited institution 66 semester hours.

ST. JOHN FISHER COLLEGE—*cont'd*

College credit and/or advanced placement for postsecondary-level work completed in secondary school; Advanced Placement tests; international baccalaureate; Excelsior College examinations; CLEP subject tests; USAFI-DANTES, departmental examinations.

Degree Requirements: *For baccalaureate degrees:* 120 credit hours; core curriculum; comprehensive examinations or projects in individual fields of study. *For all degrees:* 2.0 GPA; 30 hours in residence.

Fulfillment of some degree requirements and exemption from some beginning courses possible by passing College Board CLEP, AP, other standardized tests. *Grading system:* A–F; pass-fail; withdraw.

Distinctive Educational Programs: Cooperative programs in Far Eastern languages with University of Rochester; in engineering with Clarkson University, Columbia University, Manhattan College; SUNY at Buffalo, and University of Detroit; in optometry with Pennsylvania College of Optometry; 2+2 program with SUNY College of Environmental Science and Forestry; one-year intensive Executive MBA program. Doctorate in pharmacy; doctorate in education (educational leadership).

ROTC: Army and Air Force in cooperation with Rochester Institute of Technology.

Degrees Conferred: 695 *baccalaureate*; 344 *master's*. Bachelor's degrees awarded in top five disciplines: business/marketing 168; education 144; social sciences 75; communications/journalism 66; psychology 46. Master's degrees awarded: business/marketing 61; education 232; health professions and related clinical sciences 27; public administration and social services 3; social sciences 11.

Fees and Other Expenses: *Full-time tuition per academic year 2008–09:* undergraduate $23,390; graduate charged per credit (varies by program). *Room and board per academic year:* $10,040. *Required fees:* $260. *Books and supplies:* $900. *Other expenses:* $900.

Financial Aid: Aid from institutionally generated funds is provided on the basis of academic merit, financial need.

Financial aid to full-time, first-time undergraduate students:

Financial aid to full-time, first-time undergraduate students: 98% received some form of aid. Average amount of aid received: federal grants $3,976; Pell grants $2,816; other federal grants 41,192; state/local grants $2,292; institutional grants $1,063.

Departments and Teaching Staff: *Total instructional faculty:* 395 (full-time 167, part-time 178). 91% of faculty hold the doctorate, first-professional, or other terminal degree. Student/faculty ratio: 14:1.

Enrollment: Total enrollment 3,832. Undergraduate 2,878. Graduate 954. Undergraduate transfer-in students 291.

Characteristics of Student Body: *Ethnic/racial makeup:* number of Black non-Hispanic: 112; American Indian or Alaska Native: 10; Asian or Pacific Islander: 46; Hispanic: 74; White non-Hispanic: 2,427; unknown: 114. *Age distribution:* number under 18: 25; 18–19: 1,054; 20–21: 1,059; 22–24: 544; 25–29: 151; 30–34: 59; 35–39: 46; 40–49: 53.

International Students: No programs available to aid students whose native language is not English. Some financial aid specifically designated for international students.

Student Life: On-campus residence halls house 55% of student body. *Intercollegiate athletics:* male: baseball, basketball, football, golf, soccer, tennis; female: basketball, cheerleading, cross-country, soccer, softball, tennis, volleyball. *Special regulations:* Registered cars permitted for all except freshmen. Residence hall visitation. *Special services:* Learning Resources Center, medical services, intra-city van and bus transportation. *Student publications, radio: The Angle*, an annual literary magazine; *Jo Roffs*, a yearbook. *Surrounding community:* Rochester metropolitan population one million. Served by mass transit bus system; airport 8 miles from campus; passenger rail service 5 miles from campus.

Library Collections: 215,000 volumes. 210,000 microform titles; 6,900 audiovisual materials; 22,500 periodicals including via electronic access. Computer work stations available. Students have access to online information retrieval services and the Internet.

Most important special holdings include The Reverend Alexander Stewart Collection of papers, books, original correspondence, and documents about 17th-century Jesuit Missionaries' contact with the Indians of western New York; Grand Army of the Republic collection of correspondence by and published materials and films about local Union Army veterans and their families from 1866–1945; documents of George Decker, the Rochester lawyer who represented the 6 nations of Iroquois Confederacy in the early 1900s; Frederick Douglas Papers.

Buildings and Grounds: Campus area 140 acres.

Chief Executive Officer: Dr. Donald L. Boin, President.

Address undergraduate admission inquiries to Stacy Lederman, Director of Freshman Admissions; graduate inquiries to Shannon Cleverley, Director of Graduate Admissions.

St. John's University

8000 Utopia Parkway
Jamaica, New York 11439
Tel: (718) 990-6161 **E-mail:** admissions@stjohns.edu
Fax: (718) 990-5723 **Internet:** www.stjohns.edu

Institution Description: St. John's University is a private, nonprofit institution affiliated with the Roman Catholic Church, Congregation of the Mission (Vincentian Community). The university operates a branch campus on Staten Island, Manhattan, eastern Long Island, and a graduate center in Rome, Italy. *Enrollment:* 20,109. *Degrees awarded:* Associate, baccalaureate, first-professional (divinity, law, pharmacy), master's, doctorate. Advanced certificates also awarded.

Accreditation: *Regional:* MSA. *Professional*: audiology, business, chemistry, clinical psychology, law, librarianship, pharmacy, school psychology, speech-language pathology

History: Established as St. John's College and offered first instruction at postsecondary level 1870; chartered 1871; awarded first degree (baccalaureate) 1881; changed name to St. John's University, Brooklyn, 1933; adopted present official name, St. John's University, New York, 1954; assumed control of Notre Dame College of Staten Island (established 1931) 1971; established a graduate center in Rome, Italy 1995; opened Oakdale, Eastern Long Island campus 1999; merged with the College of Insurance to create Manhattan campus 2001.

Institutional Structure: *Governing board:* Board of Trustees. Extrainstitutional representation: 28 trustees; institutional representation: 1 administrator ex officio, 12 members emeritus. All voting. *Composition of institution:* Full-time administrators 726. Academic affairs headed by provost. Management/business/finances directed by executive vice president and chief operating officer. Full-time instructional faculty 648. Academic governance body, University Senate. Faculty represented by collective bargaining agent affiliated with AAUP and the faculty association.

Calendar: Semesters. Academic year Sept. to May. Freshmen admitted Sept., Jan., May, June, July. Degrees conferred May, June, July, Sept., Jan. Formal commencements May, June, July, Jan. Summer session of 5 terms.

Characteristics of Freshmen: 27m754 applicants (16,384 female, 11,370 male). 56% of applicants admitted. 21% of applicants admitted and enrolled full-time.

97% (3,069 students) submitted SAT scores. *25th percentile*: SAT Critical Reading 480, SAT Math 480. *75th percentile*: SAT Critical Reading 580, SAT Math 600.

51% of entering freshmen expected to graduate within 5 years. 89% of freshmen from New York. Freshmen from 43 states and 104 foreign countries.

Admission: Rolling admissions plan (except for pharmacy which has a Feb. 1 deadline for admission of freshmen in fall). For fall acceptance, apply no later than Mar. 1. Early acceptance available. *Requirements:* Graduation from accredited secondary school with 16 units which must include 4 English, 2 mathematics; 1 science; 2 foreign language; 1 history; 6 academic electives. Additional units may be required of some majors. For art majors, portfolio. GED accepted. *Entrance tests:* College Board SAT or ACT composite. For foreign students TOEFL. *For transfer students:* minimum GPA varies with program of study; transfer credit package guarantees 62 transferable credits for students who completed an AA or AS degree and intend to transfer into a baccalaureate program in liberal arts and sciences.

College credit and advanced placement may be accepted for credit. For some programs, college credit for extrainstitutional learning (life experience) on basis of portfolio and faculty assessments; personal interviews.

Tutoring available. Noncredit developmental courses offered in summer session and regular academic year.

Degree Requirements: *For all associate degrees:* 60–64 credit hours. *For all baccalaureate degrees:* minimum of 126 credit hours. *For all undergraduate degrees:* 2.0 GPA; 2 semesters in residence; core curriculum. Other requirements vary by program.

Fulfillment of some degree requirements and exemption from some beginning courses possible by passing College Board CLEP, AP (score of 3), other standardized tests. *Grading system:* A–F; pass-fail; withdraw (carries time limit).

Distinctive Educational Programs: Work-experience programs, including internships, field work. Flexible meeting places and schedules, including off-campus centers (at various locations throughout metropolitan New York), weekend and evening classes. A 6-year Doctor of Pharmacy program for incoming freshmen. Accelerated degree programs. Combined degree programs including B.A./J.D.; B.S./J.D.; B.S./M.S.; B.S./M.S. Dual-degree program in engineering with Polytechnic Institute of New York and Pratt Institute. Cooperative baccalaureate programs in fine arts (photography) with the International Center of Photography; funeral service administration with the American Academy McAllister Institute; in medical technology, pathologist's assistant, or physician's assistant in cooperation with affiliated hospitals; in dentistry with Columbia University; in optometry with SUNY-Optometry; in pediatric medicine with the New York College of Pediatric Medicine; in biomedical engineering with Polytechnic University. Special facilities for using telecommunications in the classroom. Interdisciplinary majors in American studies, Asian studies, environmental studies, liberal arts, social science. Facilities and programs for independent research, including honors programs, tutorials. Some courses area available online. A semester-long study abroad program, entitled College Europa, is designed for undergraduate students and based in Budapest, Hungary with a three-week travel component. Study abroad also available in Ireland, Italy, and Japan as well as to the countries of Argentina, Brazil, Australia, Belgium, Chile, Cost Rica, Czech Republic, Ghana, Indonesia, Netherlands, Spain, England, France, Peoples Republic of China, Poland, South Africa, Thailand, and Tunisia through the Council on International Education Exchange Study Abroad. *Other distinctive programs:* Qualified students in selected area secondary schools may enroll in university courses for audit.

ROTC: Army.

Degrees Conferred: 46 *associate;* 2,117 *baccalaureate;* 1,115 *master's;* 72 *doctorate;* 528 *first-professional.* Bachelor's degrees awarded in top five disciplines: business, management, marketing, and related support services 523; communication, journalism, and related programs 239; education 196; security and protective services; psychology 144. Master's degrees awarded in top five disciplines: education 204; business/marketing 300; health professions 86; social sciences 70; security and protective services 50. Doctorates awarded: biological/life sciences 6; education 21; English 2; health professions 3; history 4; psychology 36. First-professional degrees awarded: pharmacy 200; law 328.

Fees and Other Expenses: *Full-time tuition per academic year 2008–09:* undergraduate $28,790; contact the university for graduate and first-professional tuition/fees. *Room and board per academic year:* $13,570. *Required fees:* $570. *Books and supplies:* $1,000. *Other expenses:* $3,800.

Financial Aid: Aid from institutionally generated funds is provided on the basis of academic merit, financial need, athletic ability, other criteria. Institution has a Program Participation Agreement with the U.S. Department of Education for eligible students to receive Pell Grants and, depending upon the agreement, other federal aid.

Financial aid to full-time, first-time undergraduate students: 99% received some form of aid. Average amount of aid received: federal grants $1,511; state/local grants $2,004; institutional grants $4,119; loans $2,351.

Departments and Teaching Staff:

Total instructional faculty: 1,486 (full-time 627, part-time 859). Student/faculty ratio: 18:1. Degrees held by full-time faculty: doctorate 76%, master's 12%, professional 12%. 88% hold terminal degrees.

Enrollment: Total enrollment 20,109. Undergraduate 14,816. Graduate 5,293. Undergraduate transfer-in students 490.

Characteristics of Student Body: *Ethnic/racial makeup:* number of Black non-Hispanic: 2,112; American Indian or Alaska Native: 22; Asian or Pacific Islander: 2,229; Hispanic1 2,072; White non-Hispanic: 6,553; unknown: 1,535.

International Students: 1,066 undergraduate nonresident aliens enrolled fall 2008. Students from Europe, Asia, Central and South America, Africa, Canada, Australia, Middle East. Programs available to aid students whose native language is not English: social, cultural. English as a Second Language Program. No financial aid specifically designated for international students.

Student Life: On-campus housing. *Intercollegiate athletics:* male: baseball, basketball, fencing, football, golf, soccer, swimming, tennis, track; female: basketball, fencing, golf, soccer, softball, swimming, tennis, track, volleyball. *Special regulations:* Cars with permits allowed. *Special services:* Learning Resources Center. *Student publications, radio:* Annual literary magazine, weekly newspaper, yearbook. Radio station WSJU broadcasts 60 hours per week. *Surrounding community:* Located in the Borough of Queens; New York City population over 7 million. Served by mass transit bus and subway systems; airport 7 miles from campus; passenger rail service 11 miles from campus.

Library Collections: 1,250,000 volumes. 120,000 government documents. Current serial subscriptions: paper 3,306; microform 279; via electronic access 49,776. 6,916 audio/videotapes; 53 DVDs; 504 CD-ROMs. Computer work stations available. Students have access to online information retrieval services and the Internet.

Most important special collections include Baxter Collection; William M. Fischer Lawn Tennis Collection; Governor Hugh Carey Collection; Myer Collection of 16th–19th-century books on accounting and bookkeeping.

Buildings and Grounds: Queens campus area 95 acres; Staten Island campus 16.5 acres; Oakdale Campus 175 acres.

Chief Executive Officer: Rev. Donald J. Harrington, C.M., President.

Address admission inquiries to Andrew Ippolitto, Associate Director of Admission; graduate inquiries to Wayne Jones, Associate Director of Admission; School of Law inquiries to Gloria Rivera, Assistant Dean.

St. Joseph's College

245 Clinton Avenue
Brooklyn, New York 11205-3688
Tel: (718) 636-6800 **E-mail:** admissions@sjcny.edu
Fax: (718) 636-7242 **Internet:** www.sjcny.edu

Institution Description: St. Joseph's College is a private, nonsectarian, nonprofit college. Its Suffolk Campus is located in Patchogue, Long Island. *Enrollment:* 1,246. *Degrees awarded:* Baccalaureate.

Accreditation: *Regional:* MSA. *Professional*: nursing, teacher education

History: Established and chartered as St. Joseph's College for Women, and offered first instruction at postsecondary level 1916; awarded first degree (baccalaureate) 1920; adopted present name 1970; became coeducational 1970. Established campus in Suffolk County 1971; Branch Campus is now located in Patchogue, Suffolk County, Long Island. Developed the Division of General Studies for adult and non-traditional students 1974.

Institutional Structure: *Governing board:* Board of Trustees, St. Joseph's College, New York. Representation: 23 trustees (including president of the college). All voting. *Composition of institution:* Administrators 11. Academic affairs headed by academic vice president. Finances directed by Chief Business Officer. Full-time instructional faculty 44. Academic governance body, faculty (committee of the whole), meets 6 times per year.

Calendar: Semesters. Academic year Sept. to June. Freshmen admitted Sept., Jan. Degrees conferred June, Aug., Jan. Formal commencement June. Summer session of 2 terms from late May to late July.

Characteristics of Freshmen: Brooklyn campus: 825 applicants (617 female, 208 male). 74% of applicants admitted. 21% of admitted students enrolled full-time.

89% (128 students) submitted SAT scores, 5% (23 students) submitted ACT scores. *25th percentile*: SAT Critical Reading 410, SAT Math 430, SAT Writing 300. *75th percentile*: SAT Critical Reading 500, SAT Math 540, SAT Writing 510. 57% of entering freshmen expected to graduate within 5 years. 99% of freshmen from New York. Freshmen from 5 states and 1 foreign country.

Admission: Rolling admissions plan. For fall acceptance, apply no later than Aug. 15 of year of enrollment. *Requirements:* Either graduation from accredited secondary school with 4 units English, 2 in a foreign language, 2 mathematics, 1 American history, 1 science, 6 electives; or GED. Additional requirements for mathematics, science, business, and accounting programs. Interview recommended. Minimum GPA 2.0. *Entrance tests:* College Board SAT. For foreign students TOEFL. *For transfer students:* 2.0 minimum GPA; from 4-year accredited institution 80 hours maximum transfer credit; from 2-year accredited institution 64 hours.

College credit and advanced placement for postsecondary-level work completed in secondary school. College credit for extrainstitutional learning on basis of portfolio and faculty assessments; life experience seminar in Division of General Studies (for adults).

Tutoring available.

Degree Requirements: 128 credit hours; 2.0 GPA; 3 terms in residence; distribution requirements; demonstrated competency in English composition.

Fulfillment of some degree requirements and exemption from some beginning courses possible by passing College Board CLEP, AP. *Grading system:* A–F; pass-no credit; withdraw (carries time limit); incomplete (carries time limit).

Distinctive Educational Programs: Internships available. Senior research/thesis in major field. *Brooklyn Campus:* Honors Program; Dillon Child Study Center, laboratory pre-school (100 children, 3–6 years of age) for prospective teachers. *Suffolk Campus:* Clare Rose Playhouse, repertory theatre and teaching facility for theatre courses. *Division of General Studies:* (both campuses) flexible schedules on campus and at off-campus sites for adults, faculty who are professionals in their fields and adult-centered in their teaching.

Degrees Conferred: *Brooklyn Campus:* 236 *baccalaureate*; 60 *master's.* Bachelor's degrees awarded in top five disciplines: health professions and related clinical sciences 107; business/marketing 58; education 44; computer and information sciences 14; social sciences 8. Master's degrees awarded: business/marketing 63. *Suffolk Campus:* Bachelor's degrees awarded in top five disciplines: education 467; business/marketing 138; health professions and related sciences 78; psychology 54; social sciences 51. Master's degrees awarded: business/marketing 51; education 25.

Fees and Other Expenses: *Full-time tuition per academic year 2008–09:* contact the college for current information regarding tuition, fees, and housing costs.

ST. JOSEPH'S COLLEGE—*cont'd*

Financial Aid: Institution has a Program Participation Agreement with the U.S. Department of Education for eligible students to receive Pell Grants and, depending upon the agreement, other federal aid.

Financial aid to full-time, first-time undergraduate students: 96% received some form of aid. Average amount of aid received: federal grants $1,511; state/local grants $2,004; institutional grants $4,119; loans $2,351.

Departments and Teaching Staff: *Total instructional faculty:* 534 (full-time 154, part-time 380). Student/faculty ratio: 12:1. Degrees held by full-time faculty: master's 45%, doctorate 49%, professional 6%. 51% hold terminal degrees.

Enrollment: Total enrollment 5,350 (1,246 Brooklyn Campus, 4,104 Suffolk Campus). Undergraduate 1,033 (Brooklyn campus). Graduate 213. Undergraduate transfer-in students 113.

Characteristics of Student Body: *Ethnic/racial makeup Brooklyn and Suffolk Campuses:* number of Black non-Hispanic: 706; American Indian or Native Alaskan:7; Asian or Pacific Islander: 142; Hispanic: 377; White non-Hispanic: 3,959; unknown 82. *Age distribution:* number under 18: 125; 18–19: 1,092; 20–21: 1,246; 22–24: 733; 25–29: 470; 30–34: 310; 35–39: 311; 40–49: 105; 50–64: 330; 65 and over: 7. 28% of student body attend summer sessions.

International Students: 168 nonresident aliens enrolled 2007. Students from Europe, Asia, Central and South America; Africa, Canada, Middle East. No programs available to aid students whose native language is not English. Some financial aid specifically designated for international students.

Student Life: *Intercollegiate athletics:* male: (Brooklyn Campus) basketball; female: softball; (Suffolk Campus) male: baseball, basketball, bowling, soccer, tennis; female: bowling, tennis, softball, volleyball, equestrian. *Special regulations:* Parking permits are for sale at both campuses. *Student publication:* (Brooklyn Campus) *Footprints,* Arts and Sciences yearbook; *Achievements,* General Studies yearbook; *Happenings,* a weekly newsletter; *The Spirit,* newspaper; (Suffolk Campus) *Horizons,* yearbook; *Jotter,* weekly newsletter; *Callipe,* literary magazine; *Talon,* newspaper. *Surrounding community:* New York City population over 7 million. Both campuses served by mass transit bus and rail systems.

Library Collections: 152,000 volumes. 6,200 government documents collections; 4,400 microforms; 4,500 audiovisual materials; 435 current periodical subscriptions. Online catalog. Students have access to online information retrieval services and the Internet.

Most important holdings include Long Island History (Nassau and Suffolk) collection; Brooklyn history; journals in special education.

Buildings and Grounds: Brooklyn Campus area 3 acres. Suffolk Campus area 25 acres.

Chief Executive Officer: Sr. Elizabeth A. Hill, President.

Address admission inquiries to Teresa L. Meyer, Director of Admissions.

St. Joseph's Seminary

201 Seminary Avenue
Yonkers, New York 10704

Tel: (914) 968-6200 **E-mail:** admissions@dunwoodie.edu
Fax: (914) 376-2019 **Internet:** www.dunwoodie.edu

Institution Description: St. Joseph's Seminary is a private institution affiliated with the Archbishopric of New York. *Enrollment:* 115. *Degrees awarded:* First-professional (master of divinity), master's. Institute of Religious Studies, a separate institution established under the seminary's charter, offers a master's degree in religious studies and a post-master's certificate.

Accreditation: *Regional:* MSA. *National*: ATS. *Professional*: theology

History: Established, chartered, and incorporated under present official name, St. Joseph's Seminary and College, and offered first instruction at postsecondary level 1896; awarded first degree (baccalaureate) 1898.

Institutional Structure: *Governing board:* Board of Trustees. Extrainstitutional representation: 14 trustees, archbishop of New York, 2 vicars general of archdiocese of New York; institutional representation: rector of the seminary. 3 ex officio. 18 voting. *Composition of institution:* Administrators 15. Academic affairs headed by academic dean. Full-time instructional faculty 13. Academic governance body, resident faculty, meets an average of 16 times per year.

Calendar: Semesters. Academic year Aug. to May. Entering students admitted Aug. Degrees conferred May. Ordination to priesthood May. No summer session.

Admission: Students are sponsored by a priest and/or Bishop. Students are notified of acceptance during the early summer. *Requirements:* Baccalaureate from accredited institution which normally includes 18 credits in philosophy.

Tutoring available.

Degree Requirements: 120 credit hours; daily chapel attendance; prescribed curriculum; written and oral comprehensive exams. *Grading system:* A–F; pass-fail.

Distinctive Educational Programs: Pastoral field education programs, including adult education and other ministries. Weekend classes. Telecommunications available. Seminar in communication with the deaf. *Other distinctive programs:* Pastoral Life Conference extension program for priests and nuns working in the archdiocese of New York. Permanent Diaconate Program to prepare men to become deacons in the archdiocese of New York.

Degrees Conferred: 21 *first-professional:* master of divinity 8; theology and religious vocations 13. .

Fees and Other Expenses: Archdiocese of New York seminarians attend tuition and room and board free.

Departments and Teaching Staff: *Total instructional faculty:* 30. Degrees held by full-time faculty: doctorate 60%, master's 36%, professional 4%. 90% of faculty hold terminal degrees.

Enrollment: Total enrollment 115.

Characteristics of Student Body: *Age distribution:* 17–21: 2%; 22–24: 15%; 25–29: 245%; 30–34: 24%; 35–39: 15%; 40–49: 15; 50–59: 5%.

International Students: 11 nonresident aliens enrolled. Students from Europe, Asia, Latin America, Canada. No programs available to aid students whose native language is not English. No financial aid specifically designated for international students.

Student Life: On-campus residence halls house 100% of student body. *Special regulations:* Clerical garb required. Registered cars permitted. Curfews. Quiet hours. *Surrounding community:* Yonkers, population 192,000, is located within New York City metropolitan area.

Library Collections: 102,000 volumes. 7,864 microforms; 288 current periodical subscriptions. Computer work stations available. Students have access to online information retrieval services and the Internet.

Most important holdings include libraries of Archbishop Michael Corrigan, Francis Cardinal Spellman, and the Rev. Patrick J. Brady; archives of archdiocese of New York and the Liturgical Research Center.

Buildings and Grounds: Campus area 44 acres.

Chief Executive Officer: Rev. Msgr. Peter G. Finn, Rector/President.

Address admission inquiries to Rev. Joseph R. Giandurco, Dean of Admissions.

Institute of Religious Studies

Degree Programs Offered: *Master's* in religious studies. Post-graduate certificates in scripture, systematic theology, and ecclesial history.

Admission: Baccalaureate or equivalent from accredited institution with 18 credits philosophy or theology.

Degree Requirements: 30 credit hours; 3.0 GPA, 24 credits in residence, comprehensive examination.

St. Lawrence University

23 Romoda Drive
Canton, New York 13617-1445

Tel: (800) 285-1856 **E-mail:** admissions@stlawu.edu
Fax: (315) 229-5818 **Internet:** www.stlawu.edu

Institution Description: St. Lawrence University is a private, independent, nonprofit institution. *Enrollment:* 1,715. *Degrees awarded:* Baccalaureate, master's.

Member of the consortium Associated Colleges of the Saint Lawrence Valley.

Accreditation: *Regional:* MSA.

History: Established and chartered 1856; offered first instruction at postsecondary level 1859; awarded first degree (baccalaureate) 1863. *See* Louis H. Pink and Rutherford E. Delmage, *Candle in the Wilderness* (New York: Appleton-Century-Crofts, Inc., 1957) for further information.

Institutional Structure: *Governing board:* Board of Trustees. Representation: 38 trustees, including 1 alumni, 2 faculty delegates,2 student delegates. president of the college; 12 trustees emeriti. *Composition of institution:* Academic affairs headed by vice president of the university and dean of academic affairs. Management/business/finances directed by vice president finance. Academic governance body, Faculty Council, meets an average of 24 time per year.

Calendar: Semesters. Academic year Aug. to May. Freshmen admitted Aug., Jan. Degrees conferred May, Aug. Formal commencement May. Summer session of 2 terms from June to Aug.

Characteristics of Freshmen: 2,801 applicants (2,182 female, 619 male). 44% of applicants admitted. 29% of admitted students enrolled full-time.

53% (324 students) submitted SAT scores; 17% (104 students) submitted ACT scores. *25th percentile*: SAT Critical Reading 550, SAT Math 550; . *75th percentile*: SAT Critical Reading 640, SAT Math 640.

69% of entering freshmen expected to graduate within 5 years. 42% of freshmen from New York. Freshmen from 31 states and 15 foreign countries.

Admission: For fall acceptance, apply as early as Sept. 1 of senior year in secondary school, but not later than Feb. 1. Students are notified of acceptance Mar. Regular decision deadline Feb. 15. Apply by Nov. 15 or Jan. 15 for early decision; must limit application to St. Lawrence. Early acceptance available. *Requirements:* Either graduation from accredited secondary school or GED. Strongly recommend 4 units English, 3–4 foreign language, 4 social studies, 3–4 mathematics, 3–4 science; additional units also recommended. Interviews encouraged. *Entrance tests:* College Board SAT or ACT optional. *For transfer students:* 3.0 minimum GPA; maximum transfer credit limited only by residence requirements.

College credit and advanced placement for postsecondary-level work completed in secondary school. Tutoring available.

Degree Requirements: *For undergraduate degrees:* 33.5 units; 2.0 GPA; 2 years, including 1 semester, in residence; distribution and activity requirements.

Fulfillment of some degree requirements and exemption from some beginning courses possible by passing College Board CLEP, AP, other standardized tests. *Grading system:* 4.0 scale; pass-fail; withdraw (carries time limit); incomplete (carries time limit).

Distinctive Educational Programs: *For undergraduates:* Dual-degree programs in business with Clarkson University; in engineering with Clarkson University, Columbia University, Rensselaer Polytechnic Institute, University of Rochester, University of Southern California, Washington University (MO), Worcester Polytechnic Institute (MA). Interdepartmental programs in environmental studies, Asian studies, Canadian studies. Facilities for independent research, including individual majors. Institutionally sponsored study abroad in Denmark, Japan, Austria (University of Vienna), Australia, Canada. China, England, Costa Rica, France, India, Kenya, Spain. Tabago, Trinidad. *For graduate students:* Evening classes. *Available to all students:* Work-experience programs including internships, practicums. New global studies major; Adirondack Semester Program. Special facilities for using telecommunications in the classroom.

ROTC: Army, Air Force in cooperation with Clarkson University.

Degrees Conferred: 303 *baccalaureate*; 131 *master's*. Bachelor's degrees awarded in top five disciplines: social studies social sciences 98; psychology 75; English language and literature 74; law/legal studies 64; visual and performing arts 55. Master's degrees awarded: education 131.

Fees and Other Expenses: *Tuition per academic year 2008–09:* undergraduate $40,350. *Required fees:* $220. *Room and board per academic year:* $8,630. *Books and supplies:* $600. *Other expenses:* $800.

Financial Aid: Aid from institutionally generated funds is provided on the basis of financial need, academic merit, athletic ability (men's ice hockey). Institution has a Program Participation Agreement with the U.S. Department of Education for eligible students to receive Pell Grants and, depending upon the agreement, other federal aid.

Financial aid to full-time, first-time undergraduate students: 80% received some form of aid. Average percentage of aid received: federal grants 155; Pell grants 15%; other federal grants $44; state/local grants 9%; institutional grants46%.

Departments and Teaching Staff: *Total instructional faculty:* 189. Student/faculty ratio: 9:1. Degrees held by full-time faculty: 92% hold a doctorate and highest terminal degree.

Enrollment: Total enrollment 1,715. Undergraduate 1,309. Graduate 325. Undergraduate transfer-in students 38.

Characteristics of Student Body: *Ethnic/racial makeup:* number of Black non-Hispanic: 55; American Indian or Native Alaskan: 15; Asian or Pacific Islander: 52; Hispanic: 58; White non-Hispanic: 1,521; unknown: 290.

International Students: 109 nonresident aliens enrolled fall 2008. No programs available to aid students whose native language is not English. No financial aid specifically designated for international students.

Student Life: On-campus residence halls, fraternity and sorority houses serve 95% of student body. Housing for males constitute 20% of such space, for females 20%, for both sexes 60%. 3% of males join fraternities; 20% of females join and 10% live in sorority housing. 15% of student body live on campus in university-owned and -operated cottages. 90% of students live on campus. *Intercollegiate athletics:* male: baseball, basketball, crew, golf, football, ice hockey, horseback riding, lacrosse, soccer, softball, squash, swimming, tennis, track; female: basketball, field hockey, ice hockey, horseback riding, lacrosse, soccer, swimming, tennis, volleyball. *Special services:* Learning Resources Center, medical services. *Student publications, radio: Gridiron*, a yearbook; *Hill News*, a weekly newspaper; *Laurentian*, a biannual literary magazine; *Northern Light*, an irregularly published newspaper. Radio station KSLU broadcasts 85 hours per week. *Surrounding community:* Canton population 7,000. Montreal (Canada), 125 miles from campus, is nearest metropolitan area. Served by mass transit bus system; airport 20 miles from campus.

Library Collections: 587,000 volumes. Online catalog. Current serial subscriptions: 1,899 paper, 593,581 microforms, 20,000 via electronic access. Computer work stations available campus-wide. Students have access to online information retrieval services and the Internet.

Most important special collections include works by Nathaniel Hawthorne; books and correspondence of Frederic Remington, American painter, sculptor, and author; Adirondack history and culture; poetry of Robert Frost; William Rose Benet Collection of American Poetry.

Buildings and Grounds: Campus area 1,000 acres.

Chief Executive Officer: Dr. Daniel F. Sullivan, President.

Address undergraduate admission inquiries to Teresa E. Cowdrey, Dean of Admissions and Financial Aid; graduate inquiries to James Schuman, Associate Professor of Education.

Saint Thomas Aquinas College

125 Route 340
Sparkill, New York 10976-1050

Tel: (845) 398-4100 **E-mail:** admissions@stac.edu
Fax: (845) 398-4114 **Internet:** www.stac.edu

Institution Description: Saint Thomas Aquinas College is a private, independent, nonprofit college. *Enrollment:* 2,100, *Degrees awarded:* Associate, baccalaureate, master's.

Accreditation: *Regional:* MSA.

History: Established by Dominican Sisters of Sparkill; chartered, offered first instruction at postsecondary level 1952; awarded first degree (baccalaureate) 1958; admitted men as full-time students 1969.

Institutional Structure: *Governing board:* St. Thomas Aquinas College Board of Trustees. Extrainstitutional representation: 25 trustees; institutional representation: president of the college. All voting. *Composition of institution:* Administrators 33. Academic affairs headed by vice president. Management/business/finances directed by vice president of financial affairs. Full-time instructional faculty 76. Academic governance body, Faculty-At-Large, meets an average of 6 times per year.

Calendar: Semesters. Freshmen admitted Sept., Jan., June. Degrees conferred May, Jan. Formal commencement May. Summer session of 3 terms.

Characteristics of Freshmen: 1,443 applicants (863 female, 580 male). 79% of applicants admitted. 31% of admitted students enrolled full-time.

95% (335 students) submitted SAT scores; 18% (65 students) submitted ACT scores. *25th percentile*: SAT Critical Reading 420, SAT Math 400, SAT Writing 410; ACT Composite 16. *75th percentile*: SAT Critical Reading 510, SAT Math 530, SAT Writing 510; ACT Composite 20. 75% of entering freshmen expected to graduate within 5 years. 75% of freshmen from New York. Freshmen from 6 states and 9 foreign countries.

Admission: Rolling admissions plan. For fall acceptance, apply as early as Sept. of previous year, but not later than Aug. 15. Early acceptance available. *Requirements:* Either graduation from accredited secondary school or GED. Recommend 4 units English, 2 in a foreign language, 2 mathematics, 1 American history, 1 science. 3-4 additional units recommended. Minimum recommended GPA 2.3. *Entrance tests:* College Board SAT preferred; ACT composite accepted. *For transfer students:* 2.0 minimum GPA; from 4-year accredited institution 90 hours maximum transfer credit; from 2-year accredited institution 64 hours.

College credit and advanced placement for postsecondary-level work completed in secondary school and for extrainstitutional learning on basis of portfolio and faculty assessments; personal interview.

Tutoring available. Developmental courses offered during regular academic year; credit given.

Degree Requirements: 120 credit hours; distribution requirements; 2.0 GPA; last 30 hours in residence; distribution requirements; comprehensives in individual fields of study (URE, GRE, or approved professional examination). *Grading system:* A–F; pass-fail; withdraw (deadline after which pass-fail is appended to withdraw).

Distinctive Educational Programs: Work-experience programs. Flexible meeting places and schedules, including weekend and evening classes. Accelerated degree programs. Dual-degree program in engineering with George Washington University (DC) and Manhattan College (NY). Independent study. Study abroad programs in Hungary, Italy, Ireland, Spain, Nova Scotia. Exchange programs with Aquinas College (MI), Barry University (FL), Dominican College of San Rafael (CA). *Other distinctive programs:* HEOP. Program for learning disabled students. Honors Program with scholarships. New degree program offered in computer and information science.

ROTC: Air Force in cooperation with Manhattan College.

SAINT THOMAS AQUINAS COLLEGE—*cont'd*

Degrees Conferred: 8 *associate;* 294 *baccalaureate*; 76 *master's*. Bachelor's degrees awarded in top five disciplines: business, management, marketing, and related support services 72; social sciences 48; education 45; psychology 35; communication, journalism, and related programs 21. Master's degrees awarded: education 59; business/marketing 17.

Fees and Other Expenses: *Full-time tuition per academic year 2008–09:* $20,000. *Room and board per academic year:* $10,330. *Books and supplies*: $750. *Other expenses:* $1,750.

Financial Aid: Aid from institutionally generated funds is provided on the basis of academic merit, financial need, athletic ability.

Financial aid to full-time, first-time undergraduate students: 86% received some form of financial aid. Average amount of aid received: federal grants $3,416; Pell grants $3,033; other federal grants $958; state/local grants $3,089; institutional grants $7,020.

Departments and Teaching Staff: *Total instructional faculty:* 79. Degrees held by full-time faculty: doctorate 89%, master's 100%. 94% hold terminal degrees.

Enrollment: Total enrollment 2,100. Undergraduate 1,884. Graduate 216. Undergraduate transfer-in students 162.

Characteristics of Student Body: *Ethnic/racial makeup:* number of Black non-Hispanic: 91; American Indian or Native Alaskan: 3; Asian or Pacific Islander: 58; Hispanic: 171; White non-Hispanic: 1,592.

International Students: 22 nonresident aliens enrolled fall 2008. Programs available to aid students whose native language is not English: remedial courses in English available. No financial aid specifically designated for international students.

Student Life: On-campus residence halls house 30% of student body. 3% of student body live off campus in college-subsidized apartments. *Intercollegiate athletics:* male: baseball, basketball, golf, cross-country; female: basketball, volleyball, softball. *Special regulations:* Cars permitted without restriction. *Special services:* Learning Resources Center, medical services. *Student publications, radio: Thoma*, a bimonthly newspaper; *Thomist*, a yearbook; *Private Moments*, an annual literary magazine. Radio station WTAC broadcasts approximately 32 hours per week. *Surrounding community:* Sparkill, unincorporated, is located in Rockland County. New York City, 16 miles from campus, is nearest metropolitan area. Served by bus system; passenger rail service 10 miles from campus.

Library Collections: 105,000 volumes. 46,000 microforms. 110 periodical subscriptions.

Buildings and Grounds: Campus area 43 acres.

Chief Executive Officer: Dr. Margaret M. Fitzpatrick, S.C., President.
Address admission inquiries to Mildred Alexiou, Registrar.

St. Vladimir's Orthodox Theological Seminary

575 Scarsdale Road
Crestwood, New York 10707
Tel: (914) 961-8313 **E-mail:** admissions@svots.edu
Fax: (914) 961-4507 **Internet:** www,svits.edu

Institution Description: St. Vladimir's Orthodox Theological Seminary prepares candidates for the priesthood in the Orthodox Church in America (formerly the Russian Orthodox Greek Catholic Church of North America). *Enrollment:* 88. *Degrees awarded:* First-professional, master's.

Accreditation: *National:* ATS. *Professional*: theology

Calendar: Semesters. Academic year Sept. to May.

Admission: *Requirements:* Bachelor's degree from an accredited college or university for the master of divinity program; graduation from an approved theological school for postgraduate program.

Degree Requirements: Completion of prescribed curriculum.

Degrees Conferred: 2 *first-professional:* theology; 22 *master's:* theology; 2 *doctorate:* theology.

Fees and Other Expenses: *Full-time tuition per academic year 2008–09:* contact the seminary for current tuition, fees, and housing costs.

Departments and Teaching Staff: *Total instructional faculty:* 20.

Enrollment: Total enrollment 105. First-professional

Characteristics of Student Body: *Ethnic/racial makeup:* number of Back non Hispanic: 2; Asian or Pacific Islander: 1; White non-Hispanic: 80. *Age distribution:* 17–21: 1%; 22–24: 13%; 25–29: 32%; 30–34: 27%; 35–39: 7%; 40–49: 16%; 50–59: 8%; 60–up: 1%.

International Students: No programs available to aid students whose native language is not English. No financial aid specifically designated for international students.

Chief Executive Officer: Metropolitan Theodosius, President.
Address admission inquiries to Director of Admissions.

Sarah Lawrence College

One Mead Way
Bronxville, New York 10708
Tel: (914) 337-0700 **E-mail:** slcadmit@slc.edu
Fax: (914) 395-2515 **Internet:** www.slc.edu

Institution Description: Sarah Lawrence College is a private, independent, nonprofit college. *Enrollment:* 1,715. *Degrees awarded:* Baccalaureate, master's.

Accreditation: *Regional:* MSA.

History: Established as Sarah Lawrence College for Women 1926; offered first instruction at postsecondary level 1928; chartered and awarded first degree (baccalaureate) 1929; adopted present name 1947; became coeducational 1968.

Institutional Structure: *Governing board:* The Board of Trustees of Sarah Lawrence College. 32 trustees, 2 alumnae/i, 1 faculty member, 1 administrator, 2 ex officio. All voting. *Composition of institution:* Administrators 101. Academic affairs headed by dean of the college. Management/business/finances directed by vice president for finance and planning. Full-time instructional faculty 163. Academic governance body, the faculty, meets an average of 9 times per year.

Calendar: Semesters. Academic year Sept. to May. Freshmen admitted Sept., Jan. Degrees conferred and formal commencements Dec., May.

Characteristics of Freshmen: 2,801 applicants (2,182 female, 619 male). 44% of applicants admitted. 29% of applicants admitted and enrolled full-time. 78% of entering freshmen expected to graduate within 5 years. 19% freshmen from New York. Freshmen from 46 states and 26 foreign countries.

Admission: For fall acceptance, apply by Jan. 1. Early decision I, apply by Jan. 1. Early admission available. *Requirements:* Either 16 secondary school units in academic subjects or GED. *For transfer students:* 60 hours maximum transfer credit.

College credit and advanced placement for postsecondary-level work completed in secondary school and for "A" level, Baccalaureate, and International Baccalaureate examinations, or College Board CLEP and AP.

Degree Requirements: 120 hours; 4 terms in residence; 1 year physical education; freshman studies. *Grading system: written evaluations;* A–F; pass (by special permission).

Distinctive Educational Programs: *Available to all students:* Seminar/tutorial system. Most coursework consists of two parts: the seminar limited to 15 students, and the conference, a private biweekly meeting with the seminar professor. *For undergraduates:* Individualized programs of study designed by students and their dons. No formal majors. Study abroad programs in Paris, Florence, Havana, London, Oxford. *Other distinctive programs:* Master's programs include creative writing, child development, the art of teaching, health advocacy, human genetics, dance, theatre, and women's history. Summer writers program offered.

Degrees Conferred: 303 *baccalaureate:* liberal arts 303; 131 *master's:* education 13; English (writing program) 68; health professions and related sciences 24; social sciences 9; visual and performing arts 13; other 27.

Fees and Other Expenses: *Full-time tuition per academic year 2008–09: $40,350 undergraduate; contact the college for current graduate tuition. fees:* %$800. *Room and board per academic year:* $13,104.

Financial Aid: Aid from institutionally generated funds is provided on the basis of financial need.

Financial aid to full-time, first-time undergraduate students:

Financial aid to full-time, first-time undergraduate students: 80% received some form of aid. Average amount of aid received: federal grants $1,511; state/local grants $2,004; institutional grants $4,119; loans $2,351.

Departments and Teaching Staff: *Total instructional faculty:* 236 (full-time 199, part-time 37). 98% of faculty hold the doctorate, first-professional, or other terminal degree. Student/faculty ratio: 9:1.

Enrollment: Total enrollment 1,715. Undergraduate 1,389. Graduate 326. Undergraduate transfer-in students 38.

Characteristics of Student Body: *Ethnic/racial makeup:* number of Black non-Hispanic: 73; American Indian or Alaska Native: 9; Asian or Pacific Islander: 66; Hispanic: 64; White non-Hispanic: 962; unknown: 188. *Age distribution:* number under 18: 5; 18–19: 582; 20–21: 1,578; 22–24: 129; 25–29: 25; 30–34: 14; 35–39: 13; 40–49: 14; 50–64: 19; 65 and over: 4.

International Students: 49 nonresident aliens enrolled fall 2008. Students from Europe, Asia, Central and South America, Africa, Canada, Australia, New Zealand. No programs available to aid students whose native language is not English. No financial aid specifically designated for international students.

Student Life: On-campus residence halls house 85% of student body. Most students live in single rooms after their first year. *Intercollegiate athletics:* female: volleyball; both sexes: crew, cross-country, tennis, equestrian. *Special regulations:* Cars permitted after freshmen year. *Special services:* Writing Center, medical services. *Student publications: Sarah Lawrence College Literary Review*, an annual publication; *The Phoenix*, student newspaper; *Dark Phases*, literature journal for students, faculty and staff of color; *Lumina*, an annual literary journal produced by graduate students. *Surrounding community:* Suburban Westchester County, 15 miles north of midtown Manhattan in New York City.

Library Collections: 299,000 volumes. 54,000 government documents; 240,000 microforms; 108,000 audiovisual materials; 920 current periodical subscriptions. Computer work stations available. Students have access to online information retrieval services and the Internet.

Most important special holdings include Sarah Lawrence College Archives; Bessie Schoenberg Dance Photography Collection; Women's History Collection.

Buildings and Grounds: Campus area 35 acres.

Chief Executive Officer: Dr. Michele Tolela Myers, President.

Undergraduates address admission inquiries to Thyra Briggs, Dean Enrollment; graduate inquiries to Dean of Graduate Studies.

School of Visual Arts

209 East Twenty-third Street
New York, New York 10010
Tel: (212) 592-2000 **E-mail:** admissions@schoolofvisualarts.edu
Fax: (212) 592-2116 **Internet:** www.schoolofvisualarts.edu

Institution Description: School of Visual Arts is a private, profit-making college. *Enrollment:* 3,988. *Degrees awarded:* Baccalaureate, master's.

Accreditation: *Regional:* MSA. *Professional*: art, design technology

History: Established as Cartoonists and Illustrators School; incorporated and offered first instruction at postsecondary level 1947; adopted present name 1956; awarded first degree (baccalaureate) 1973; conferred first master of fine arts 1985.

Institutional Structure: *Governing board:* Board of Directors. Extrainstitutional representation: 5 directors; institutional representation: 2 administrators (including president of the college), 1 part-time instructional faculty member; 1 alumna. All voting. *Composition of institution:* Administrators 101. Full-time instructional faculty 102. Board of Directors meets an average of 2 times per year.

Calendar: Semesters. Winter workshop courses January. Academic year Sept. to May. Freshmen admitted Sept., Jan. Degrees conferred and formal commencement May. Summer session: day classes June to July; evening classes June to Aug.

Characteristics of Freshmen: 2,565 applicants (1,592 female, 973 male). 72% of applicants admitted. 36% of admitted students enrolled full-time.

86% (517 students) submitted SAT scores; 14% (83 students) submitted ACT scores. *25th percentile*: SAT Critical Reading 460, SAT Math 440, SAT Writing 460; ACT Composite 19. *75th percentile*: SAT Critical Reading 580, SAT Math 590, SAT Writing 580; ACT Composite 24.

65% of entering freshmen expected to graduate within 5 years. 45% of freshmen from New York. Freshmen from 47 states and 46 foreign countries.

Admission: Rolling admissions plan. *Requirements:* Either graduation from accredited secondary school or GED; minimum GPA 2.5. *Entrance tests:* SAT. For foreign students TOEFL. *For transfer students:* 2.0 minimum GPA; 64 hours maximum transfer credit.

College credit and advanced placement for postsecondary-level work completed in secondary school. For extrainstitutional learning, college credit on basis of portfolio assessment; faculty assessment; personal interviews.

Remedial courses offered during regular academic year; credit given.

Degree Requirements: 120 credit hours; 2.0 GPA; 64 hours in residence; 70–84 hours in studio art; 32–46 hours in humanities including 12–15 hours in art history; senior thesis. For visual arts majors, B average in major studio art courses. *For master of fine arts:* 60 credit hours; 48 hours in residence; acceptance of thesis/project. For MPS degree requirements: successful completion of 60 credits including all required courses. For MAT degree requirements: 36 credits including all required courses.

Fulfillment of some degree requirements and exemption from some beginning courses possible by passing College Board CLEP Subject Examinations, AP. *Grading system:* A–F; pass-fail; withdraw (may carry penalty).

Distinctive Educational Programs: Internships. Weekend and evening classes. Individual majors. Institutionally sponsored summer study abroad in Barcelona, Spain (painting); Greece (art and archaeology). Public Advertising System provides professional advertising by students and faculty for nonprofit community organizations. Visual Arts Museum and Visual Arts Gallery for student and professional exhibitions; 6 other student-run art galleries. Specialized graduate programs in computer art, illustration, fine arts, and photography. *Other distinctive programs:* Continuing education evening school offers credit and enrichment courses.

Degrees Conferred: 614 *baccalaureate:* visual and performing arts; 187 *master's*: visual and performing arts.

Fees and Other Expenses: *Full-time tuition per academic year 2008–09:* $25,000 undergraduate; graduate tuition/fees vary. *Books and supplies:* $3,150. *Room and board per academic year:* $15,000. *Other expenses:* $4,100.

Financial Aid: Aid from institutionally generated funds is provided on the basis of academic merit, financial need.

Financial aid to full-time, first-time undergraduate students: 77% received some form of aid. Average amount of aid received: federal grants $1,511; state/local grants $2,004; institutional grants $4,119; loans $2,351.

Departments and Teaching Staff: *Total instructional faculty:* 830 (full-time 102, part-time 728) Student/faculty ratio: 9:1. Degrees held by full-time faculty: doctorate 12%, master's 47%, baccalaureate 28%. 36% hold terminal degrees.

Enrollment: Total enrollment 3m988. Undergraduate 3,539. Graduate 449. Undergraduate transfer-in students 449.

Characteristics of Student Body: *Ethnic/racial makeup:* number of Black non-Hispanic: 117; American Indian or Alaska Native: 11; Asian or Pacific Islander: 400' Hispanic: 305; White non-Hispanic: 1,723; unknown: 115.

International Students: 586 nonresident aliens enrolled fall 2008. Students from Europe, Asia, Central and South America, Africa, Canada, Australia, Middle East. Programs available to aid students whose native language is not English: social. English as a Second Language Program. Financial aid specifically designated for international students: scholarships available annually to qualifying students.

Student Life: On-campus dormitory accommodations for 1000. *Special services:* medical services. *Student publications, radio station: Kartunz*, an irregularly published magazine; *Off-Beat*, a semiannual magazine; *VASA Newsletter*, a weekly tabloid; *Words*, a semiannual literary magazine. Student radio station WSVA. *Surrounding community:* New York City population over 7 million. Served by mass transit bus and rail systems; airport 10 miles from campus; passenger rail service less than 1 mile from campus.

Publications: *Publisher:* School of Visual Arts Press, Ltd.

Library Collections: 70,000 volumes. 1,000 microforms; 1,586 audiovisual materials; 300 current periodical subscriptions. Computer work stations available. Students have access to online information retrieval services and the Internet.

Most important special collections in graphic design, fine arts, photography.

Buildings and Grounds: Campus area 5 square blocks.

Chief Executive Officer: Dr. David Rhodes, President.

Address admission inquiries to Alan Rogers, Director of Admissions.

Seminary of the Immaculate Conception

440 West Neck Road
Huntington, New York 11743
Tel: (631) 423-0483 **E-mail:** info@iseminary.edu
Fax: (631) 423-2346 **Internet:** www.iseminary..edu

Institution Description: Seminary of the Immaculate Conception is a private, independent, nonprofit institution affiliated with the Roman Catholic Church. *Enrollment:* 150. Women are admitted as students to the master's program. *Degrees awarded:* First-professional (master of divinity); master's, doctorate.

Accreditation: *Regional:* MSA. *National:* ATS. *Professional*: theology

History: Established in 1926; offered first instruction at postsecondary level 1930; awarded first degree (baccalaureate) 1934; discontinued baccalaureate and began graduate program 1967; chartered 1973. *See* Rev. Michael J. Cantley, *A City With Foundations* (Huntington: Seminary of the Immaculate Conception, 1980) for further information.

Institutional Structure: *Governing board:* Board of Governors. Extrainstitutional representation: 19 members; institutional representation: rector-president of the seminary. 9 ex officio. All voting. *Composition of institution:* Administrators 7. Academic affairs headed by academic dean. Management/business/finances directed by business officer. Full-time instructional faculty 8. Academic governance body, Board of Governors, meets an average of 3 times per year.

Calendar: Semesters. Academic year Sept. to May. Entering students admitted Sept. Degrees conferred May, Dec. Formal commencement Dec. Summer session June to July.

Admission: Rolling admissions plan. *Requirements:* Baccalaureate from an accredited institution. For first-professional students, 30 credit hours in philosophy and 12 credits in theology. Minimum grade average B. From accredited institution, transfer credit limited to 6 credits.

SEMINARY OF THE IMMACULATE CONCEPTION—*cont'd*

Tutoring available. Noncredit developmental courses offered during regular academic year.

Degree Requirements: *For first-professional degree:* 126 credit hours; 2.0 GPA on a 4.0 scale; daily chapel attendance; pastoral internship. *For master's degree:* 39 credit hours; 3.0 GPA on a 4.0 scale; *Grading system:* A–F; incomplete (carries time limit).

Distinctive Educational Programs: Weekend and evening classes. Tutorials. *Other distinctive programs:* Nondegree continuing education for priests.

Degrees Conferred: 307 *master's:* theology; 6 *first-professional:* master of divinity; 7 *doctorate:* doctor of ministry.

Fees and Other Expenses: *Tuition per academic year 2008–09:* contact the seminary for current information.

Financial Aid: Aid from institutionally generated funds is provided on the basis of financial need.

Departments and Teaching Staff: Total faculty with doctorate, first-professional, or other terminal degree: 16. Student/faculty ratio: 7:1.

Enrollment: Total enrollment 150 (first-professional).

Student Life: On-campus residence halls for males house 27% of student body. *Special regulations:* Cars permitted without restrictions. Clerical garb required at Sunday services for seminarians. *Surrounding community:* Huntington Township population 190,000. New York City is 35 miles from campus. Served by passenger rail service 5 miles from campus.

Library Collections: 48,000 volumes. 280 periodical subscriptions. 900 recordings. 4 computer work stations. Students have access to the Internet and online information retrieval services.

Most important special holdings include a collection on Canon Law.

Buildings and Grounds: Campus area 216 acres.

Chief Executive Officer: Msgr. James M. McDonald, J.C.D., Rector.

Address admission inquiries to Rev. Jerome M. Vereb, C.J., Associate Dean and Director of Graduate Studies.

Siena College

515 Loudon Road
Loudonville, New York 12211-1462
Tel: (518) 783-2423 **E-mail:** admit@siena.edu
Fax: (518) 783-2436 **Internet:** www.siena.edu

Institution Description: Siena College is a coeducational, independent, liberal arts college with a Franciscan and Catholic tradition. *Enrollment:* 3,305. *Degrees awarded:* Baccalaureate. Certificates also awarded.

Member of consortium Hudson-Mohawk Association of Colleges and Universities.

Accreditation: *Regional:* MSA. *Professional*: chemistry, social work, teacher education

History: Established as St. Bernardine of Siena College, an institution for men; offered first instruction at postsecondary level 1937; chartered 1938; awarded first degree (baccalaureate) 1940; adopted present name 1968; became coeducational 1969.

Institutional Structure: *Governing board:* The Board of Trustees. Extrainstitutional representation: 32 trustees; institutional representation: 1 administrator. All voting. *Composition of institution:* Administrators 192. Academic affairs headed by vice president for academic affairs. Management/business/finances directed by vice president for finance. Full-time instructional faculty 180.

Calendar: Semesters. Academic year Sept. to May. Freshmen admitted Sept., Jan., June. Degrees conferred and formal commencement May. Summer session of 2 terms from May to June and June to July.

Characteristics of Freshmen: 6,440 applicants (3,841 female, 2,649 male). 56% of applicants admitted. 23% of applicants admitted and enrolled full-time.

77% (641 students) submitted SAT scores; 32% (268 students) submitted ACT scores. *25th percentile*: SAT Critical Reading 500, SAT Math 530; ACT Composite 23. *75th percentile*: SAT Critical Reading 590, SAT Math 630; ACT Composite 27.

77% of entering freshmen expected to graduate within 5 years. 32% of freshmen from New York. Freshmen from 44 states and 42 foreign countries.

Admission: For fall acceptance, apply as early as Sept. 1 of previous year, but not later than Mar. 1. Students are notified of acceptance Mar. Apply by Dec. 1 for early decision; need not limit application to Siena. Early acceptance available. *Requirements:* Either graduation from accredited secondary school or GED. 3 units in college preparatory mathematics for business program and 4 for science and computer science. Recommend 4 units in English, 3 foreign language, and 4 college preparatory mathematics. Lowest recommended secondary school class standing 75th percentile. *Entrance tests:* College Board SAT or ACT composite. *For transfer students:* From 4-year accredited institution 90 hours maximum transfer credit; from 2-year accredited institution 66 hours.

College credit and advanced placement for postsecondary-level work completed in secondary school and for extrainstitutional learning.

Tutoring available.

Degree Requirements: 120 credit hours; core requirements. 2.0 GPA and earn at least a C- in every major field course used to satisfy the credit hours requirement of the major; at least half of the major field must be earned at Siena.

Fulfillment of some degree requirements and exemption from some beginning courses possible by passing College Board CLEP, AP, other standardized tests. *Grading system:* A–F; pass-fail; withdraw (carries time limit); U (for failure due to excessive absence).

Distinctive Educational Programs: Internships. Weekend and evening classes. Dual-degree program in engineering with RPI, Catholic University, SUNY Binghamton, Western New England, Clarkson College of Technology, Manhattan College. Cooperative baccalaureate program in environmental science and forestry with degree awarded by Syracuse University. Interdepartmental programs, including American studies and a program in international studies, foreign language and business; Peace Studies Program. Cooperative business management program with Clarkson University enabling students to earn undergraduate degree and MBA in 5 years. Facilities and programs for independent research, including honors programs, individual majors, tutorials. Institutionally sponsored individualized program of study abroad in various countries. Cross-registration through consortium. Opportunity Program that assists academically and economically disadvantaged students with counseling and remedial work, as well as financial support. Program includes 6-week summer session prior to freshman year. Certificate programs (to augment major) in health studies, theatre, environmental studies. *Other distinctive programs:* Siena/Albany Medical College 8-year program of medical education. Siena/Georgetown Cooperative dental program (time shortened doctoral degree in dentistry). Washington Semester study program through Siena and American University.

ROTC: Army. Air Force through cross-registration with Rensselaer Polytechnic Institute.

Degrees Conferred: 769 *baccalaureate*. Bachelor's degrees awarded in top five disciplines: business/marketing 300; psychology 80; social sciences 75; English 71; history 45.

Fees and Other Expenses: *Full-time tuition per academic year 2008–09:* $23,950. *Required fees:* $175. *Room and board per academic year:* $9,414. *Other expenses:* $1,520.

Financial Aid: Aid from institutionally generated funds is provided on the basis of academic merit, financial need, athletic ability, other criteria.

Financial aid to full-time, first-time undergraduate students: 94% received some form of aid. Average amount of aid received: federal grants $1,511; state/local grants $2,004; institutional grants $4,119; loans $2,351.

Departments and Teaching Staff: *Total instructional faculty:* 307 (full-time 180, part-time 127). 83% of faculty hold the doctorate, first-professional, or other terminal degree. Student/faculty ratio: 14:1.

Enrollment: Total enrollment 3,305 (undergraduate). Transfer-in students 167.

Characteristics of Student Body: *Ethnic/racial makeup:* number of Black non-Hispanic: 67; American Indian or Alaska Native: 4; Asian or Pacific Islander: 112; Hispanic: 111; White non-Hispanic: 2,693; unknown: 151. *Age distribution:* number 18–19: 1,387; 20–21: 1,369; 22–24: 181; 25–29: 37; 30–34: 9; 35–39: 2; 40–49: 7.

International Students: 18 nonresident aliens enrolled fall 2008. Students from Europe, Central and South America, Canada, Australia. No programs available to aid students whose native language is not English. No financial aid specifically designated for international students.

Student Life: On-campus residence halls house 80% of student body. 28% of students live in townhouses. *Intercollegiate athletics:* male: baseball, basketball, cross-country, golf, lacrosse, soccer, tennis; female: basketball, cross-country, golf, lacrosse, tennis, soccer, softball, swimming, volleyball. *Special regulations:* Freshmen are not permitted to have cars on campus. Quiet hours Sun. through Thurs, from 10pm to 7am; weekends midnight to 7:30am. *Special services:* Medical services; Multicultural Affairs; Sr. Thea Bowman Center for Women; Counseling Center; Support Services-Students with Disabilities. . *Student publications, radio: The Prometheon*, a campus newspaper; *Saga*, a yearbook; *Pen-Dragon*, a literary magazine; *X-Po-Ze*. Radio station WVCR-FM; SCTV-Siena College Television. *Surrounding community:* Loudonville, unincorporated, located in Albany-Schenectady-Troy metropolitan area. Served by mass transit bus system; airport 5 miles from campus; passenger rail service 8 miles from campus.

Publications: *Greyfrair: Siena Studies in Literature* (annually) first published in 1958; *Siena News*, quarterly, first published 1997.

Library Collections: 426,000 volumes. Current serial subscriptions: paper 900; microform 8; via electronic access 5,562. 3,153 audio/videotapes; 3,881

DVDs; 73 CD-ROMs. Computer work stations available. Students have access to online information retrieval services and the Internet.

Most important special holdings include Franciscana; Convivium (medieval and early modern history); T.E. Lawrence Collection.

Buildings and Grounds: Campus area 164.

Chief Executive Officer: Fr. Kevin E. Mackin, O.F.M., President.

Address admission inquiries to Heather Renault, Director of Admissions.

Skidmore College

815 North Broadway
Saratoga Springs, New York 12866-1832
Tel: (518) 580-5570 **E-mail:** admissions@skidmore.edu
Fax: (518) 580-5584 **Internet:** www.skidmore.edu

Institution Description: Skidmore College is a private, independent, nonprofit college. *Enrollment:* 2,777. *Degrees awarded:* Baccalaureate, master's.

Member of the consortium Hudson-Mohawk Association of Colleges and Universities.

Accreditation: *Regional:* MSA. *Professional*: art, business, social work

History: Founded in 1903 as Young Women's Industrial Club of Saratoga; became Skidmore School of Arts and offered first instruction at postsecondary level 1911; chartered and awarded first degree (baccalaureate) 1922; became coeducational 1971. For further information, *see* Mary C. Lynn, "Make No Small Plans: A History of Skidmore College."

Institutional Structure: *Governing board:* Skidmore College Board of Trustees. Extrainstitutional representation: 30 trustees; institutional representation: president of the college; president of the alumni association; 4 alumni. 2 ex officio. All voting. *Composition of institution:* Administrators 49. Academic affairs headed by vice president for academic affairs. Management/business/finances directed by vice president for business affairs and treasurer. Full-time instructional faculty 241. Academic governance body, the faculty, meets an average of 10 times per year.

Calendar: Semesters. Academic year Sept. to May. Freshmen admitted Sept., Feb. Degrees conferred and formal commencement May. Summer session of 2 terms from late May to early Aug.

Characteristics of Freshmen: 7,318 applicants (4,868 female, 2,448 male). 30% of applicants accepted. 30% of accepted applicants enrolled full-time.

89% (580 students) submitted SAT scores; 30% (198 students) submitted ACT scores. *25th percentile*: SAT Critical Reading 580, SAT Math 590, SAT Writing 590; ACT Composite 26, ACT English 26, ACT Math 25. *75th percentile*: SAT Critical Reading 680, SAT Math 670, SAT Writing 690; ACT Composite 29, ACT English 32, ACT Math 29.

80% of entering freshmen expected to graduate within 5 years. 32% of freshmen from New York. Freshmen from 44 states and 42 foreign countries.

Admission: For fall acceptance, apply as early as possible in the senior year, but not later than Jan. 15 of year of enrollment. Students notified of acceptance in early April. Apply by Nov. 15 for Round I early decision or Jan. 15 for Round II early decision; must agree to enroll if accepted. Early acceptance available. *Requirements:* Graduation from accredited secondary school with 206 units which normally include 4 English, 3 foreign languages, 4 mathematics, 3 social studies, 4 science (2 laboratory science). *Entrance tests:* College Board SAT or ACT accepted. With the SAT, 2 achievements are recommended, including English composition. *For transfer students:* 2.7 minimum GPA; maximum transfer credit limited only by residence requirements.

College credit for postsecondary-level work completed in secondary school (AP test score of 4 or 5). College credit for extrainstitutional learning (life experience) awarded in Skidmore University Without Walls on basis of faculty assessment.

Tutoring available. Noncredit developmental courses offered in summer session and regular academic year.

Degree Requirements: 120 credit hours; 2.0 GPA; minimum 60 hours, including senior year, in residence; required courses in expository writing, quantitative reasoning, cultural diversity sequence, laboratory science, foreign language, arts, and non-Western culture.

Fulfillment of some degree requirements and exemption from some beginning courses possible by passing College Board CLEP, AP (score of 4). *Grading system:* A–F; pass-fail; withdraw (carries time limit).

Distinctive Educational Programs: Dual degree programs in engineering with Dartmouth College and Clarkson University; dual degree program in business administration with Clarkson University; MAT with Union College; institutionally sponsored study abroad in Australia, China, England, France, Greece, India, Israel, Italy, Russia, Spain. Associated programs with Institute for European and Asian Studies (IES/IAS) and Washington Semester at American University. *Other distinctive programs:* Skidmore University Without Walls program allows students to design degree plans and earn credits through a nonresidential, nontraditional learning process. State-funded Higher Education Opportunity Program assists academically and economically disadvantaged New York State residents.

ROTC: Programs available off-campus through the Hudson-Mohawk Consortium of Colleges and Universities.

Degrees Conferred: 638 *baccalaureate*; 13 *master's*. Bachelor's degrees awarded in top five disciplines: social sciences 106; visual and performing arts 103; business, management, marketing, and related support services 92; psychology 57; liberal arts and sciences, general studies 52. Master's degrees awarded: liberal arts 13.

Fees and Other Expenses: *Full-time tuition per academic year 2008–09:* \$35,888. *Required fees:* \$470. *Room and board per academic year:* \$10,378. *Books and supplies* \$1,085. *Other expenses:* \$1,150.

Financial Aid: Aid from institutionally generated funds is provided on the basis of financial need. Institution has a Program Participation Agreement with the U.S. Department of Education for eligible students to receive Pell Grants and, depending upon the agreement, other federal aid.

Financial aid to full-time, first-time undergraduate students: 41% of students received some form of financial aid.

Departments and Teaching Staff: *Total instructional faculty:* 329 (full-time 232, part-time 97). Student/faculty ratio: 10:1. Degrees held by full-time faculty: baccalaureate .37%, master's 12%, doctorate 84%. 85% hold terminal degrees.

Enrollment: Total enrollment 2,777. Undergraduate 2,719. Graduate 60. Undergraduate transfer-in students 32.

Characteristics of Student Body: *Ethnic/racial makeup:* number of Black non-Hispanic: 68; American Indian or Alaska Native: 17; Asian or Pacific Islander: 179; Hispanic: 107; White non-Hispanic: 1,899; unknown: 422. *Age distribution:* number under 18: 44; 18–19: 1,206; 22–24: 133; 25–29: 6; 30–39: 1; 40–49: 1.

International Students: 34 nonresident aliens enrolled fall 2008. Students from Europe, Asia, Central and South America, Africa, Canada.

Student Life: On-campus residence halls and college-owned residence halls house 82% of student body. *Intercollegiate athletics:* male: basketball, baseball, crew, golf, ice hockey, lacrosse, skiing, soccer, tennis, polo; female: basketball, crew, field hockey, lacrosse, polo, riding, skiing, soccer, softball, swimming and diving, volleyball. *Special regulations:* Registered cars permitted on campus in designated areas. Quiet hours vary according to residence hall. *Special services:* medical services; bus service to and from downtown Saratoga Springs. *Student publications, radio: Eromdiks*, a yearbook; *Folio*, an art and literary journal; *Skidmore News,* weekly newspaper; *Politeia*, an annual journal of social sciences and humanities; *Student Handbook*, published annually. Radio station WSPN broadcasts 24 hours daily. *Surrounding community:* Saratoga Springs population 35,000. Albany, 30 miles from campus, is nearest major metropolitan area. Served by airport 25 miles from campus; passenger rail service 1 mile from campus.

Publications: *Salmagundi* (literary quarterly) first published 1969; *Skidmore Scope*, tabloid format, published 6 times annually.

Library Collections: 430,000 volumes. 90,000 government documents; 136,000 microforms; 100,000 audiovisual materials; 4,700 current periodical subscriptions. Computer work stations available. Students have access to online information retrieval services and the Internet.

Most important special collections include the Frances E. Steloff Collection of autographs and first editions; Edna St. Vincent Millay Collection; Hannah M. Adler Collection.

Buildings and Grounds: Campus area 700 acres.

Chief Executive Officer: Dr. Philip A. Glotzbach, President.

Address admission inquiries to Mary Lou Bates, Director of Admissions.

State University of New York at Albany

1400 Washington Avenue
Albany, New York 12222-0001
Tel: (518) 442-3300 **E-mail:** ugadmissions@albany.edu
Fax: (518) 442-4909 **Internet:** www.albany.edu

Institution Description: *Enrollment:* 18,204. *Degrees awarded:* Baccalaureate, master's, doctorate. Certificates also awarded.

Member of the consortium Hudson-Mohawk Association of Colleges and Universities.

Accreditation: *Regional:* MSA. *Professional*: accounting, business, clinical psychology, counseling psychology, librarianship, planning, public administration, public health, rehabilitation counseling, school psychology, social work

History: The University at Albany is one of four university centers in the SUNY system. Founded in 1844 as the first state institution in New York to train teachers and the fourth such school in the nation, it was the first state college to award the baccalaureate in 1908. The mission for the Normal College, as it was first known, was changed to a liberal arts college for teachers in 1905. It was the

STATE UNIVERSITY OF NEW YORK AT ALBANY—*cont'd*

first such conversion of a normal school in the country. Albany was also the oldest state-supported campus to enter the SUNY system in 1948. Its original purpose was expanded in 1962 to include a baccalaureate for those students not wishing to pursue a teaching career. Awarding its first doctoral degree in 1963, Albany was named a university center in 1964.

Institutional Structure: *Composition of institution:* Academic affairs headed by vice president for academic affairs and provost. Vice presidential areas for student affairs, management/business/finance, research and graduate studies, and university advancement. Full-time instructional faculty 590. Academic governance body, University Senate, meets an average of 8 times per year.

Calendar: Semesters. Academic year Sept. to May. Freshmen admitted Sept., Jan., June. Degrees conferred May, Aug., Dec. Formal commencement May. Summer session composed of two 6-week sessions, three 3-week sessions, and two 3-week science modules from early June through late Aug.

Characteristics of Freshmen: 20,249 applicants (10,785 female, 9,514 male). 52% of applicants admitted. 24% of admitted students enrolled full-time.

97% (2,450 students) submitted SAT scores; 22% (554 students) submitted ACT scores. *25th percentile*: SAT Critical Reading 500, SAT Math 510; ACT Composite 22. *75th percentile*: SAT Critical Reading 590, SAT Math 610; ACT Composite 26.

62% of entering freshmen expected to graduate within 5 years. 91% of freshmen from New York. Freshmen from 23 states and 11 foreign countries.

Admission: Modified rolling admissions plan. For fall acceptance, apply as early as Sept. 1 of previous year, but not later than Mar. 1 of year of enrollment. Students are notified of acceptance beginning in Jan. Early acceptance available. *Requirements:* Graduation from accredited secondary school with 18 units which must include 4 English, 2 mathematics, 2 science, 3 social studies, 5 academic electives. Recommend additional units in above fields. *Entrance tests:* College Board SAT or ACT. *For transfer students:* From 4-year or 2-year institution, 90 hours maximum transfer credit.

College credit and advanced placement for postsecondary-level work completed in secondary school. Tutoring available. Noncredit developmental courses offered in summer session and regular academic year.

Degree Requirements: *For undergraduate degrees:* 120 credit hours; 30 credits in residence; distribution requirements.

Fulfillment of some degree requirements possible by passing College Board CLEP, other standardized tests. *Grading system:* A–E; pass-fail.

Distinctive Educational Programs: *For undergraduates:* Work-experience programs. Evening classes. Accelerated degree programs. Dual-degree program in law with Union University. Honors College. 3/2 engineering program with Rensselaer Polytechnic Institute, Clarkson, SUNY Binghamton. Project Renaissance for freshmen.Interdisciplinary programs. Combined baccalaureate-master's programs. Facilities and programs for independent research, including honors programs, individual majors. Tutorials. Study abroad in Brazil, China, Costa Rica, Denmark, Dominican Republic, Finland, France, Germany, Ghana, Hungary, Iceland, Ireland, Israel, Japan, Korea, the Netherlands, Norway, Puerto Rico, Russia, Singapore, South Africa, Spain, Sweden, United Kingdom, Yugoslavia. Cross-registration through Hudson-Mohawk consortium.

ROTC: Army; Air Force in cooperation with Rensselaer Polytechnic Institute.

Degrees Conferred: 2,734 *baccalaureate*; 1,362 *master's*; 151 *doctorate*. Bachelor's degrees awarded in top five disciplines: social sciences 670; English 428; business/marketing 394; public administration and social services 369; biological/life sciences 207. Master's degrees awarded in top five disciplines: education 399; business/marketing 216; public administration and social services 197; computer and information sciences 123; security and protective services 9. Doctorates awarded in top five disciplines: psychology 27; social sciences 27; public administration and social services 17; biological/life sciences 17; education 14.

Fees and Other Expenses: *Full-time tuition per academic year 2008–09:* undergraduate resident $6,978, nonresident $12,338; contact the university for current graduate tuition. *Required fees:* $1,589. *Room and board per academic year:* $9,778. *Books and supplies:* $1,000. *Other expenses:* $1,792.

Financial Aid: Aid from institutionally generated funds is awarded on the basis of academic merit, financial need, athletic ability.

Financial aid to full-time, first-time undergraduate students:

Financial aid to full-time, first-time undergraduate students: 80% received some form of aid. Average amount of aid received: federal grants $4,145; Pell grants $3,284; other federal grants $958; state/local grants $2,418; institutional grants $4,194.

Departments and Teaching Staff: *Total instructional faculty:* 1,161 (full-time 631, part-time 530). 95% of faculty hold the doctorate, first-professional, or other terminal degree. Student/faculty ratio: 21:1.

Enrollment: Total enrollment 18,204. Undergraduate 13,248. Graduate 4,956. Undergraduate transfer-in students 1,490.

Characteristics of Student Body: *Ethnic/racial makeup:* number of Black non-Hispanic: 960; American Indian or Alaska Native: 28; Asian or Pacific Islander: 663; Hispanic: 867; White non-Hispanic: 7,031; unknown: 1,920.

International Students: 912 nonresident aliens enrolled fall 2008. Programs available to aid students whose native language is not English: social, cultural. English as a Second Language Program. No financial aid specifically designated for international students.

Student Life: On-campus residence halls house 60% of undergraduate student body. *Intercollegiate athletics:* male: baseball, basketball, cross-country, football, lacrosse, soccer, track. female: basketball, cross-country, field hockey, golf, lacrosse, softball, tennis, track, volleyball. *Special regulations:* Freshmen not permitted cars on campus. *Special services:* Learning Resources Center, medical services, campus transportation system. There are over 160 student organizations, clubs, fraternities, and sororities. *Student publications, radio: ASP,* a biweekly newspaper. Radio station WCDB broadcasts 168 hours per week. *Surrounding community:* Albany population 100,000.

Publications: More than 160 faculty members annually produce approximately 300 scholarly works of distinction, including books, journal articles, peer-reviewed conference volumes, and journals. These include *Journal of Computing Machiners, Atomic and Nuclear Data Tables, Behavior Therapy, Journal of Biomolecular Structure & Dynamics, Bulletin of Sung-Yuan Studies, Journal of Comparative Psychology, Continuing Social Work Education, Criminal Law Bulletin, Diogenes, Film Literature Index, The Gerontologist, Group and Organizational Studies, Humor in Life & Letters/Series, International Journal of Research in Mother Tongue Education, Justice System Journal, The Little Magazine, Man and the Northeast, Modern Jewish Literature and Culture/Series, Monthly Weather Review, Reference Librarian, ReReading, Research in Crime and Delinquency, Research on Teaching/English, Social Science Record, Sociological Forum, South Asia Bulletin, Systems Dynamics Review, 13th Moon,* and *The American Sociologist.*

Library Collections: 2,100,000 volumes. Online catalog. 96,982 audiovisual materials; 2,714,891 microform units. 500 computer work stations campus-wide. Students have access to online information retrieval services and the Internet.

Most important holdings include German Intellectual Emigre Collection; University Archives; Capital District Labor History Archive; Miriam Snow Mathes Historical Children's Literature Collection.

Buildings and Grounds: Uptown and downtown campuses comprise 506 acres. *New buildings:* University Hall Administration Building opened 2006.

Chief Executive Officer: Dr. Susan V,. Herbst, President.

Undergraduates address admission inquiries to Robert Andrea, Director of Undergraduate Admissions; graduate inquiries to Michael DeRensis, Director of Graduate Admissions.

State University of New York at Binghamton

P.O. Box 6000

Binghamton, New York 13902-6000

Tel: (607) 777-2171 **E-mail:** admit@binghamton.edu
Fax: (607) 777-4445 **Internet:** www.binghamton.edu

Institution Description: *Enrollment:* 14,382. *Degrees awarded:* Baccalaureate, master's, doctorate. Certificates also awarded.

Member of the consortia Center for Research Libraries, Research Libraries Group, South Central Regional Library Council; Coalition for Networked Information, Northeast Research Libraries; West Chester Academic Library Directors Organization.

Accreditation: *Regional:* MSA. *Professional*: business, computer science, engineering, music, nursing, psychology, public administration, social work, teacher education

History: Established as Triple Cities College and offered first instruction at postsecondary level 1946; changed name to Harpur College 1950; awarded first degree (baccalaureate) 1951; adopted present name 1965. *See* Stephen McIntire, *Harpur College in the Bartle Era* (Binghamton: Privately printed, 1975) for further information.

Institutional Structure: *Composition of institution:* Academic affairs headed by provost and vice president for academic affairs. Management/business/finances directed by vice president for administration. Full-time instructional faculty 551. Academic governance body is Faculty Senate.

Calendar: Semesters. Academic year Aug. to May. Freshmen admitted Sept., Feb. Degrees conferred and formal commencement May. Winter session in January. Summer session of 3 terms from May to Aug.

Characteristics of Freshmen: 25,252 applicants (13,286 female, 11,956 male). 39% of applicants admitted. 24% of applicants admitted and enrolled full-time.

92% (2,117 students) submitted SAT scores; 18% (124 students) submitted ACT scores. *25th percentile*: SAT Critical Reading 570, SAT Math 610; ACT Composite 25. *75th percentile*: SAT Critical Reading 660, SAT Math 690; ACT Composite 29.

77% of entering freshmen expected to graduate within 5 years. 93% of freshmen from New York. Freshmen from 40 states and 67 foreign countries.

Admission: Modified rolling admissions plan. For fall acceptance, apply as early as Sept. of previous year, but not later than Jan. 15 of year of enrollment. Students are notified of acceptance beginning March 15. Early acceptance available. *Requirements:* Graduation from accredited secondary school with 4 units in English, 3 mathematics (including intermediate algebra, geometry), 2 science, 2 social science. For nursing program, 1 unit chemistry; for liberal arts programs 2 units each in two languages or 3 in one language. *Entrance tests:* College Board SAT or ACT composite.

College credit given for postsecondary-level work completed in secondary school (Advanced Placement) and for CLEP and RCEP on the basis of ACE score recommendations.

Tutoring available. Developmental courses offered in summer session and regular academic year; credit given.

Degree Requirements: 120–128 credit hours; 2.0 GPA; 1 year in residence; 2 credit hours physical education courses; all students (except transfers) required to complete university-wide general education requirement; distribution requirements.

Fulfillment of some degree requirements possible by passing College Board CLEP. *Grading system:* A–F; pass-fail.

Distinctive Educational Programs: Evening classes. Combined degree programs in business administration and arts, arts administration, history, music. Interdisciplinary programs. Harpur College: Africana studies, Judaic studies, Latin American and Caribbean area studies, philosophy/politics and law; medieval studies, modern drama and theater, Russian and East European studies, Middle Eastern and North African studies, women's studies; School of Education and Human Development: American studies, criminal justice, health and society, human services, leadership and organizational studies, peace and social justice; School of Management: East Asian and Management studies. Facilities and programs for independent research, including honors programs, individual majors, tutorials. Study abroad programs available in Australia, Austria, Belize, Costa Rica, England, Germany, Italy, Morocco, Northern Ireland, Scotland, Senegal, Turkey, plus access to over 100 other SUNY sponsored programs. Research centers include Institute of Biomedical Technology, Center for Computing Technologies, Center for Cognitive and Psycholinguistic Sciences, Center for Developmental Psychobiology, Center for Leadership Studies, Institute for Materials Research, Center for Medieval and Early Renaissance Studies, Center for the Historical Study of Women and Gender, Center for Nursing Research, Center for Research in Translation, Center for the Study of Natural Hazards, Fernand Braudel Center for the Study of Economies, Historical Systems, and Civilizations, Institute for Research in Electronics Packaging, Institute for Global Cultural Studies. 3-2 program in engineering, education. Emphasis on living/learning environment through a system of residential colleges. Extensive integration of computing throughout the curriculum.

ROTC: Air Force in cooperation with Cornell University.

Degrees Conferred: 2,821 *baccalaureate*; 636 *master's*l 116 *doctorate*. Bachelor's degrees awarded in top five disciplines: social sciences 592; business/marketing 374; psychology 316; English 224; health professions 223. Master's degrees awarded in top five disciplines: social sciences 113; business/marketing 108; education 102; public administration 56; computer and information sciences 34. Doctorates awarded in top five disciplines: social sciences 23; psychology 15; engineering 13; English language/literature 11; physical sciences 10.

Fees and Other Expenses: *Full-time tuition per academic year 2008–09:* undergraduate resident $6,072, nonresident $12,332; contact the university for current graduate tuition. *Required fees:* $1,560. *Room and board per academic year:* $9,774. *Books and supplies:* $800. *Other expenses:* $1,000.

Financial Aid: Aid from institutionally generated funds is provided on the basis of academic merit, financial need athletic ability.

Financial aid to full-time, first-time undergraduate students: 70% received some form of aid. Average amount of aid received: federal grants $4,153; Pell grants $3,443; other federal grants $837; state/local grants $534; institutional grants $2,748.

Departments and Teaching Staff: *Total instructional faculty:* 889 (full-time 551, part-time 338). 95% of faculty hold the doctorate, first-professional, or other terminal degree. Student/faculty ratio: 20:1.

Enrollment: Total enrollment 14,882. Undergraduate 11,805. Graduate 3,077. Undergraduate transfer-in students 775.

Characteristics of Student Body: *Ethnic/racial makeup:* number of Black non-Hispanic: 575; American Indian or Alaska Native: 18; Asian or Pacific Islander: 622; Hispanic: 757; White non-Hispanic: 5,420; unknown: 2,292. *Age distribution:* number under 18: 448; 18–19: 4,412; 20–21: 4,798; 22–24: 1,192; 25–29: 328; 30–34: 94; 35–39: 67; 40–49: 91; 50–64: 16; 65 and over: 7. 18% of student body attend summer sessions.

International Students: 1,643 nonresident aliens enrolled fall 2008. Students from Europe, Asia, Central and South America, Africa, Canada, Australia, New Zealand, Middle East. Programs available to aid students whose native language is not English: social, cultural. English as a Second Language Program. No financial aid specifically designated for international students.

Student Life: University residential halls and apartment complexes house 56% of undergraduate population. University housing provides space for males and females in coeducational settings. *Intercollegiate athletics:* male: baseball, basketball, cross-country, golf, ice hockey, lacrosse, soccer, swimming, tennis, track and field, wrestling; female: basketball, cross-country, lacrosse, soccer, softball, swimming, tennis, track and field, volleyball. *Special regulations:* Cars must be registered, requiring registration and parking fees. *Special services:* Extensive computer support, tutorial assistance, medical services, buses to and from local community, services for students with disabilities. *Student publications, radio: Clarendon*, an annual literary magazine; *Pipe Dream*, a semi-weekly newspaper. Radio station WHRW-FM. *Surrounding community:* Binghamton population 200,000.

Publications: *The International Journal of African Studies; International Studies in Philosophy; Harpur Palate; Stirrings Still; Bernardo Lectures 1990–2002; Mediaevalia.*

Library Collections: 2,347,000 volumes. 1,869,000 microforms; 122,000 audiovisual materials; 62,000 periodicals including via electronic access. Computer work stations available. Students have access to online information retrieval services and the Internet.

Most important special holdings include Max Reinhardt Archive; William J. Haggerty Collection of French Colonial History; Edwin Link Papers; Conole Archives of Recorded Sound.

Buildings and Grounds: Campus area 606 acres.

Chief Executive Officer: Dr. Lois B. DeFleur, President.

Address undergraduate admission inquiries to Cheryl Brown, Director of Admissions; graduate inquiries to Graduate School.

Harpur College of Arts and Sciences

Degree Programs Offered: *Baccalaureate, master's, doctorate* in various fields.

School Education and Human Development

Degree Programs Offered: *Baccalaureate, master's.*

School of Management

Degree Programs Offered: *Baccalaureate, master's, doctorate.*

Decker School of Nursing

Degree Programs Offered: *Baccalaureate, master's, doctorate.*

Thomas J. Watson School of Engineering and Applied Science

Degree Programs Offered: *Baccalaureate, master's, doctorate.*

State University of New York at Buffalo

501 Capen Hall
Buffalo, New York 14260-1600

Tel: (716) 645-2000 **E-mail:** admissions@buffalo.edu
Fax: N/A **Internet:** www.buffalo.edu

Institution Description: The State University at Buffalo is New York's premier public center for graduate and professional education and largest and most comprehensive public university. The university is the home of SUNY's only Schools of Law, Pharmacy, and Architecture and the state's only comprehensive public School of Engineering. *Enrollment:* 28,192. *Degrees awarded:* Associate, baccalaureate, first-professional (dentistry, law, medicine, pharmacy), master's, doctorate. Post-master's certificates also awarded.

Member of the Western New York Consortium of Higher Education.

Accreditation: *Regional:* MSA. *Professional*: accounting, art, audiology, clinical psychology, dental assisting, dentistry, endodontics, engineering, English language education, law, librarianship, medicine, nurse anesthesia education, nursing, nursing education, occupational therapy, oral and maxillofacial

STATE UNIVERSITY OF NEW YORK AT BUFFALO—*cont'd*

pathology, oral and maxillofacial surgery, orthodontics, pediatric dentistry, periodontics, pharmacy, physical therapy, planning, psychology internship, rehabilitation counseling, social work, speech-language pathology, teacher education

History: Established as the University of Buffalo 1846; awarded first degree (Medical School) 1847; merged with the State University of New York and became State University of New York at Buffalo 1962. *See* Robert T. Marlett, "This University These Restless Men," Office of University Publications, SUNY at Buffalo, for further information.

Institutional Structure: *Composition of institution:* Administrators 172. Academic affairs headed by provost. Management/business/finances directed by senior vice president of university services. Full-time and instructional faculty 1,241. Academic governance body, Faculty Senate, meets an average of 10 times per year.

Calendar: Semesters. Academic year Aug. to May. Freshmen admitted Sept., Jan. Degrees conferred May, Sept., Feb. Formal commencement May. Summer session of 3 terms from May to Aug.

Characteristics of Freshmen: 19,831 applicants (9,800 female, 10,031 male). 52% of applicants admitted. 32% of admitted students enrolled full-time.

93% (3,034 students) submitted SAT scores; 27% (895 students) submitted ACT scores. *25th percentile*: SAT Critical Reading 500, SAT Math 540; ACT Composite 23. *75th percentile*: SAT Critical Reading 610, SAT Math 550; ACT Composite 27.

51% of entering freshmen expected to graduate within 5 years. 99% of freshmen from New York. Freshmen from 34 states and 15 foreign countries.

Admission: Applicants for fall freshman admission should file in early November; first offers in late Dec. Early decision applications must be filed by Nov. 1. *Requirements:* Present 3 year high school average and class rank. Recommend college preparatory program of 4 years English, 4 years social studies, 3 years of college preparatory math and science, and 3 years of a second language. Also require SAT or ACT scores. Audition and portfolio requirement for music and art applicants. Special talent admission process for some applicants. Early admission program for high school juniors. Spring freshman admission on a space available basis. *For transfer students:* Minimum of 24 semester hours completed with 2.0 GPA. A.A. and A.S. degree holders will be deemed to have completed all General Education requirements. Entry at junior level requires higher GPA for some programs. Maximum transfer credit only limited by residency requirement.

Credit awarded for military experience and other non-traditional sources. Summer session is open enrollment for all high school graduates (for credit, non-degree study).

Degree Requirements: 120 credit hours; 2.0 GPA; 30 hours in residence; distribution requirements; for arts and sciences majors additional requirements of courses in World Civilization, American Pluralism, lab science and foreign language. Additional requirements depending on program.

Fulfillment of some degree requirements and exemption from some beginning courses possible by passing College Board CLEP, AP, International Baccalaureate. *Grading system:* A–F plus, minus; satisfactory-unsatisfactory available but there is a limit on the number of courses.

Distinctive Educational Programs: University Honors Program for freshmen and transfer students. Minority Academic Achievement Program. Joint baccalaureate/professional programs (e.g. liberal arts and law; sociology and social work); Early Medical Assurance Program; shortened degree programs. Special Major (individualized degree program); professional and interdisciplinary minors. Study abroad and exchange programs for academic year in France (Grenoble, Toulouse, Provence); International Christian University, Tokyo, Japan; Beijing, China; Aarhus, Denmark (graduate architecture); University of Kent at Canterbury, England; Sheffield, England; Wolverhampton, England (art); Montpellier, France (management); Darmstadt, Germany; Kanazawa, Japan; Meisei University, Tokyo, Japan; Tokyo University of Agriculture and Technology (engineering or natural sciences); Monterey, Mexico (management); Madrid, Spain; University of Latvia and Riga Technical University, Riga, Latvia; Wurzburg, Germany. Summer study abroad and exchange programs offered in: Krakow, Poland; Salamanca, Spain; International Christian University, Tokyo, Japan; Miyagi Prefectural Government Internship, Sendai, Japan (management); Costa Rica (graduate architecture); Monterey, Mexico (management); Barcelona, Spain (graduate architecture). Evening classes through Millard Fillmore College.

ROTC: Army in cooperation with Canisius College.

Degrees Conferred: 3,966 *baccalaureate*; 1,973 *master's*; 150 *doctorate*; 555 *first-professional*: dentistry 89; law 234; medicine 142; pharmacy 90. Bachelor's degrees awarded in top five disciplines: business, management, marketing, and related support services 621; engineering/engineering technologies 416; psychology 374; communication, journalism, and related programs 368; liberal arts 298. Master's degrees awarded in top five disciplines: education 416; business/marketing 288; engineering 220; health professions and related clinical sciences 146; library science 139. Doctorate degrees awarded in top five disciplines: health professions 58; biological and biomedical sciences 45; engineering 40; education 38; physical sciences 29.

Fees and Other Expenses: *Full-time tuition per academic year 2008–09:* undergraduate resident $6,285, nonresident $12,545; contact the university for current graduate and professional school tuition. *Books and supplies* $947. *Room and board per academic year:* $9,552. *Other expenses:* $1,274.

Financial Aid: The university offers a direct lending program. Aid from institutionally generated funds is provided on the basis of academic merit, financial need, athletic ability.

Financial aid to full-time, first-time undergraduate students: 80% received some form of financial aid. Average amount of aid received: federal grants $4,179; Pell grants $3,529; other federal grants $9,520; state/local grants $2,042; institutional grants $4,110.

Departments and Teaching Staff: *Total instructional faculty:* 1,746 (full-time 1,142, part-time 604). 98% of faculty hold the doctorate, first-professional, or other terminal degree. Student/faculty ratio: 15:1.

Enrollment: Total enrollment 28,972. Undergraduate 19,022. Graduate 9,170. Undergraduate transfer-in students 1,917.

Characteristics of Student Body: *Ethnic/racial makeup:* number of Black non-Hispanic: 1,248; American Indian or Alaska Native: 75; Asian or Pacific Islander: 1,520; Hispanic: 627; White non-Hispanic: 11,504; unknown: 1,756. *Age distribution:* number under 18: 2,676; 18–19: 6,554; 20–21: 5,117; 22–24: 1,911; 25–29: 767; 30–34: 310; 35–39: 194; 40–49: 83; 50–64: 65 and over: 3.

International Students: 1,290 nonresident aliens enrolled fall 2008. Students from Europe, Asia, Central and South America, Africa, Canada, Australia, New Zealand. Programs available to aid students whose language is not English: social, cultural. English as a Second Language Program. Some financial aid specifically designated for qualifying international students,

Student Life: On-campus residence halls house 20% of student body. Residence halls for both sexes constitute 100% of such space. *Intercollegiate athletics:* male and female basketball, swimming, diving, cross-country, soccer, tennis, indoor and outdoor track and field; male football and wrestling; female: volleyball. *Special regulations:* Cars permitted without restrictions; no alcohol served on campus except at catered events. *Special services:* Buses to and from the 2 campuses. *Student publications, radio: Spectrum,* a triweekly newspaper; *Generation,* a weekly magazine. Radio station WBFO. *Surrounding community:* Southern campus located on the northern tip of the City of Buffalo. Northern campus located in the Town of Amherst, a suburban community a few miles north of the city.

Library Collections: 3,360,036 volumes. Online catalog. 5,354,000 microforms. 186,500 audiovisual materials. Access to 32,500 periodicals. Computer work stations available. Students have access to information retrieval services and the Internet.

Most important special holdings include collections on poetry (20th century English language), also James Joyce and Frank Lloyd Wright manuscripts; History of Medicine Collection; Polish Collection.

Buildings and Grounds: The university has 2 major campuses. The 150-acre Main Street Campus is on the northern edge of the city of Buffalo and has undergone major construction and renovation to provide expanded and modernized facilities for the University's Health Sciences divisions (linked to downtown via rapid transit). The 1,200-acre suburban Amherst Campus is 3 miles from the Main Street site.

Chief Executive Officer: Dr. John B. Simpson, President.

Address admission inquiries to Marcia G. Armstrong, Director of Admissions; graduate/professional school inquiries to the area of interest.

College of Arts and Science

Degree Programs Offered: *Baccalaureate, master's, doctorate.*

Departments and Teaching Staff: *See* Departments and Teaching Staff above.

Distinctive Educational Programs: Interdisciplinary programs in American Studies, comparative literature. Special facilities including Center for the Psychological Study of the Arts, Middle East Filmmakers Project. Study abroad in France, Spain, Germany. Practicum in Field Archaeology in Israel. Studio Art Program in Italy. Semester in New York. Summer Shakespeare in the Park.

School of Architecture and Planning

Degree Programs Offered: *Baccalaureate, master's.*

Departments and Teaching Staff: See *Departments and Teaching Staff above.*

Distinctive Educational Programs: School of Architecture is organized into e departments: Architecture, Environmental Design and Planning, Design Studies. Joint M. Arch.-M.B.A. program with School of Management, M. Arch.-

master's in civil engineering with School of Engineering and Applied Sciences. Center associated with Buffalo Organization for Social and Technological Innovation, Center for Comparative Studies in Development, Center for Integrative Studies, Community Planning Assistance Center, Community Research and Development.

School of Engineering and Applied Sciences

Degree Programs Offered: *Baccalaureate, master's, doctorate.*

Departments and Teaching Staff: *See* Departments and Teaching Staff above.

School of Management

Degree Programs Offered: *Baccalaureate, master's, doctorate.*

Departments and Teaching Staff: *See* Departments and Teaching Staff above.

Distinctive Educational Programs: Special programs through Bank Management Institute, Center for Management Development, Human Resources Center, International Executive Program in Management and English Language, Regional Economic Assistance Center. *See* also Faculty of Law and Jurisprudence.

School of Law

Degree Programs Offered: *First-professional.*

Admission: *For first-professional:* 3 years of study at college or university; LSAT.

Degree Requirements: *For first-professional:* 2 years in residence, satisfactory completion of first year core curriculum.

Distinctive Educational Programs: Joint J.D.-Ph.D. programs with departments of economics, history, philosophy, political science; Center for Policy Studies; School of Management. Baldy Center provides interdisciplinary research.

Graduate School of Education

Degree Programs Offered: *Master's, doctorate.* Certificates also awarded.

School of Informatics

Degree Programs Offered: *Bachelor's, master's, doctorate.* Certificates also awarded.

Distinctive Educational Programs: Informatics interdisciplinary degree programs; doctorate in communication with cognate in informatics; school media specialty in library degree program.

School of Social Work

Degree Programs Offered: *Master's, doctorate.*

Departments and Teaching Staff: *See* Departments and Teaching Staff above.

Distinctive Educational Programs: Joint degree program with School of Law and interdisciplinary program with Department of Social Sciences.

School of Dental Medicine

Degree Programs Offered: *First-professional, master's, doctorate, certificates.*

Admission: *For first-professional:* Graduation from accredited college or university with 1 year English, 1 year biology with labs, 1 year general chemistry with lab, 1 year organic chemistry with lab, 1 year physics with lab, DAT scores, college and high school transcripts along with application.

Degree Requirements: *For first-professional:* Satisfactory completion of 2 years core curriculum and 2 years clinical study.

Departments and Teaching Staff: *See* Departments and Teaching Staff above.

Distinctive Educational Programs: Combined D.D.S.-Ph.D. program. Federal Grant Training programs in neuromuscular research in clinical dentistry, periodontal disease clinical research. Cultural exchange program with programs, faculty and students in 8 foreign countries.

School of Health Related Professions

Degree Programs Offered: *Baccalaureate, master's, doctorate.*

Departments and Teaching Staff: *See* Departments and Teaching Staff above.

School of Medicine and Biomedical Sciences

Degree Programs Offered: *Baccalaureate, first-professional, master's, doctorate.*

Admission: *For first-professional:* 1 year biology with lab, 1 physics, 1 chemistry with lab, 1 English, 1/2 organic chemistry with lab; MCAT.

Degree Requirements: *For first-professional:* Satisfactory completion of 2 years core curriculum and 2 years of clinical study.

Departments and Teaching Staff: *See* Departments and Teaching Staff above.

Distinctive Educational Programs: Facilities include Center for Immunology.

School of Nursing

Degree Programs Offered: *Baccalaureate, master's, doctorate.*

Departments and Teaching Staff: *See* Departments and Teaching Staff above.

School of Pharmacy and Pharmaceutical Sciences

Degree Programs Offered: *Baccalaureate, first-professional, master's, doctorate.*

Admission: *For first-professional:* B.S. degree in pharmacy from an ACPE accredited institution with 3.0 GPA.

Degree Requirements: Vary; based on degree program.

Departments and Teaching Staff: *See* Departments and Teaching Staff above.

Roswell Park Graduate Division

Degree Programs Offered: *Master's, doctorate.*

State University of New York at New Paltz

1 Hawk Drive
New Paltz, New York 12561-2443

Tel: (845) 257-1869 **E-mail:** admissions@newpaltz.edu
Fax: (845) 257-3209 **Internet:** www.newpaltz.edu

Institution Description: *Enrollment:* 8,205. *Degrees awarded:* Baccalaureate, master's, Certificate of Advanced Study also awarded.

Accreditation: *Regional:* MSA. *Professional*: art, audiology, computer science, engineering, music, nursing, speech-language pathology, teacher education, theatre

History: Founded as School of Learning of Classics 1828.

Institutional Structure: *Composition of institution:* Administrators 50. Academic affairs headed by provost. Management/business/finances directed by vice president for administration. Full-time instructional faculty 305. Academic governance body, Academic Senate, meets an average of 15 times per year.

Calendar: Semesters. Academic year Aug. to May. Freshmen admitted Sept., Jan. Degrees conferred May, Aug., Dec. Summer session of 2 terms from late May to early Aug.

Characteristics of Freshmen: 12,843 applicants (7,900 female, 4,643 male). 36% of applicants admitted. 21% of admitted students enrolled full-time.

92% (869 students) submitted SAT scores. *25th percentile*: SAT Critical Reading 520, SAT Math 510. *75th percentile*: SAT Critical Reading 600, SAT Math 600.

23% of entering freshmen expected to graduate within 5 years. 92% of freshmen from New York. Freshmen from 14 states and 10 foreign countries.

Admission: Rolling admissions plan. For fall acceptance, apply no later than May 1 of year of enrollment. *Requirements:* Either graduation from accredited secondary school or GED. Required 4 units in English, 3 foreign language, 3 mathematics, 3 science, 3 social studies. For Fine Arts programs, portfolio is required for placement, for Music and Theatre programs, audition is required for placement. Recommend B/B+ academic average. *Entrance tests:* College Board SAT or ACT. *For transfer students:* 2.5 minimum GPA; from 4-year accredited institution, maximum transfer credit of 90 credits; from 2-year accredited institution, 70 credits.

College credit and advanced placement for postsecondary-level work completed in secondary school and for extrainstitutional learning on basis of portfolio, and faculty assessments.

Degree Requirements: *For all undergraduate degrees:* 120 credit hours; 2.0 GPA; 30 credits in residence, completion of general education program; completion of minimum liberal arts credit appropriate to degree; 45 upper division credits; demonstrated proficiency in English composition and mathematics.

STATE UNIVERSITY OF NEW YORK AT NEW PALTZ—*cont'd*

Distinctive Educational Programs: Cross-registration program with other colleges in the area. English as a Second Language Program, Honors Program, Study Abroad Program; Educational Opportunity Program; Foreign Language Immersion Program; Archeological Field School; Cooperative Education and Internships; Albany Legislative Intern Program; Legislative Gazette Program; Model UN Program. Academic year/summer abroad programs in China, United Kingdom, France, Spain, Italy, Germany, The Netherlands, Israel, Russia, New Zealand, Greece, Japan.

Degrees Conferred: 1,592 *baccalaureate*; 230 *master's*. Bachelor's degrees awarded in top five disciplines: education 320; business, management, marketing, and related support services 208; visual and performing arts 183; social sciences 148; communications/journalism 123. Master's degrees awarded in top five disciplines: education 365; business/marketing 49; visual and performing arts 30; computer and information sciences 24; English language/literature 21.

Fees and Other Expenses: *Full-time tuition per academic year 2008–09:* resident $5,419, nonresident $11,679; contact the university for current graduate tuition/fee. *Books and supplies:* $1,250. *Room and board per academic year:* $8,690. *Required fees:* $990.

Financial Aid: Aid from institutionally generated funds is provided on the basis of academic merit. Institution has a Program Participation Agreement with the U.S. Department of Education for eligible students to receive Pell Grants and, depending upon the agreement, other federal aid.

Financial aid to full-time, first-time undergraduate students: 75% received some form of aid. Average amount of aid received: federal grants $1,511; state/local grants $2,004; institutional grants $4,119; loans $2,351.

Departments and Teaching Staff: *Total instructional faculty:* 703. 84% of faculty hold the doctorate, first-professional, or other terminal degree.

Enrollment: Total enrollment 8,205. Undergraduate 6,701. Graduate 1,498. Undergraduate transfer-in students 469.

Characteristics of Student Body: *Ethnic/racial makeup:* number of Black non-Hispanic: 439; American Indian or Alaska Native: 15; Asian or Pacific Islander: 212; Hispanic: 595; White non-Hispanic: 3,719; unknown: 1,056. *Age distribution:* number under 18: 1418–19: 1,813; 20–21: 2,059; 22–24: 1,377; 25–29: 409; 30–34: 156; 35–39: 148; 40–49: 217; 50–64: 68; 65 and over: 1.

International Students: 399 nonresident aliens enrolled fall 2008. Students from Europe, Asia, Central and South America, Canada, Middle East. Programs available to aid students whose native language is not English: social. English as a Second Language Program. No financial aid specifically designated for international students.

Student Life: On-campus residence halls house over 50% of the full-time student body. *Intercollegiate athletics:* basketball, diving, soccer, swimming, softball, baseball, tennis, golf, volleyball. Club sports include rugby, ice hockey, lacrosse and fencing. *Special services:* Learning Resource Center, Health Center, Counseling Center, International and Disabled Student Services. *Student publications, radio, television: Oracle, Fahari*, and *Hermanos Latinos*, newspapers. Radio station WRNP-FM; TV station WNPC. *Student organizations:* Student Association, Residence Hall Student Association, 13 fraternities, 9 sororities, 11 hall governments and 89 clubs. *Surrounding community:* Town of New Paltz, population 11,000. Easy access to New York City (90 miles from campus) and Albany (65 miles from campus).

Library Collections: 583,000 volumes. 238,000 government documents. Current serial subscriptions: paper 1,441; microform 74; via electronic access 29,704. 1,486 audio/videotapes 1,586; 536 DVDs; 1,928 CD-ROMs. Online catalog. Computer work stations available. Students have access to online information retrieval services and the Internet.

Most important special collections include Art Collection; non-Western material (Asian, African); Sojourner Truth Collection.

Buildings and Grounds: Campus area 220 acres.

Chief Executive Officer: Dr. Steven G. Poskanzer, President.

Address admission inquiries to Kimberly Loavoie, Director of Admissions.

State University of New York at Stony Brook

Nicholls Road
Stony Brook, New York 11794-1401
Tel: (631) 632-6868 **E-mail:** enroll@stonybrook.edu
Fax: (631) 632-9027 **Internet:** www.stonybrook.edu

Institution Description: *Enrollment:* 23,991. SUNY at Stony BroOk is also known as Stoy Brook University. *Degrees awarded:* Baccalaureate, first-professional (dentistry, medicine), master's, doctorate. Advanced certificates also awarded.

Member of the consortium Long Island Regional Advisory Council for Higher Education.

Accreditation: *Regional:* MSA. *Professional*: clinical lab scientist, clinical psychology, cytotechnology, dentistry, dietetics, endodontics, engineering, medicine, nursing, nursing education, nursing-midwifery, occupational therapy, orthodontic and dentofacial orthopedics, periodontics, physical therapy, physician assisting, psychology internship, radiation therapy technology, respiratory therapy, social work, surgeon assisting,

History: Established as State University College on Long Island and offered first instruction at postsecondary level 1957; awarded first degree (baccalaureate) 1961; adopted present name 1962. Campuses also located in Southampton, and New York City.

Institutional Structure: *Composition of institution:* Academic affairs headed by provost. Other senior administrators: vice presidents for advancement, economic development, facilities, finance, research and student affairs, executive dean for the health sciences, dean of medicine, chief executive office of the Medical Center, dean of the Southampton Campus. Full-time instructional faculty 822. Academic governance body, University Senate, meets an average of 10 times per year.

Calendar: Semesters. Academic year Sept. to May. Freshmen admitted Sept., Jan., June. Degrees conferred May, Aug., Dec. Formal commencement May. Summer session of 2 terms from early June to mid-Aug.

Characteristics of Freshmen: 25,590 applicants (13,715 female, 11,875 male). 43% of applicants accepted. 67% of accepted applicants enrolled full-time. 96% (2,769 students) submitted SAT scores; 18% (527 students) submitted ACT scores. *25th percentile*: SAT Critical Reading 520, SAT Math 570, SAT Writing 510; ACT Composite 24, ACT English 21, ACT Math 24. *75th percentile*: SAT Critical Reading 610, AT Math 660, SAT Writing 610; ACT Composite 28, ACT English 26, ACT Math 29.

59% of entering freshmen expected to graduate within 5 years. 87% of freshmen from New York. Freshmen from 35 states and 28 foreign countries.

Admission: Rolling admissions plan. Early acceptance available. *Requirements:* High school diploma preferably with Regents designation; high school average of 85 with 3–4 units math, 4 units English, 4 units social studies, 3 units science (4 required for engineering),, 2–3 units foreign language; standardized test scores that indicate the promise of success in a rigorous undergraduate course of study. *Entrance tests:* College Board SAT or ACT composite. *For transfer students:* Maximum transfer credit limited only by residence requirement. From 4-year accredited institution 2.5 minimum GPA.

College credit and advanced placement for postsecondary-level work completed in secondary school and for extrainstitutional learning.

Tutoring available. Remedial courses offered regular academic year; credit given.

Degree Requirements: 120–128 credit hours; 2.0 GPA (after achieving upper division status); beginning with 58th credit, 36 credits in residence; distribution requirements; demonstrated proficiency in English composition, mathematics, foreign language.

Fulfillment of some degree requirements and exemption from some beginning courses possible by passing College Board CLEP, other standardized tests. *Grading system:* A–F; withdraw; pass-no credit.

Distinctive Educational Programs: Evening programs. Accelerated degree programs. Interdisciplinary programs. Internship programs. National Student Exchange Program and Honors College. Study abroad.

ROTC: Air Force offered in cooperation with New York Institute of Technology (Old Westbury NY); Army in cooperation with Hofstra University (Uniondale NY).

Degrees Conferred: 3,671 *baccalaureate*; 1,716 *master's*; 355 *doctorate*. Bachelor's degrees awarded in top five disciplines: social sciences 506; psychology 370; biological/life sciences 320; business/marketing 243; engineering 182. First-professional degrees awarded: dentistry 40; medicine 118; other 497.

Fees and Other Expenses: *Full-time tuition per academic year 2008–09:* undergraduate resident $5,810, nonresident $12,070; contact the university for current graduate and first-professional tuition. *Room and board per academic year:* $9,132. *Books and supplies:* $900. *Other expenses:* $3,842.

Financial Aid: Aid from institutionally generated funds is provided on the basis of academic merit, athletic ability.

Financial aid to full-time, first-time undergraduate students: 79% received some form of aid. Average amount of aid received: federal grants $4,449; Pell grants $3,641; other federal grants $9,670; grants $2,908; institutional grants $1,241.

Departments and Teaching Staff: *Total instructional faculty:* 2,009 (full-time 909, part-time 480). 90% of faculty hold the doctorate, first-professional, or other terminal degree. Student/faculty ratio: 19:1.

Enrollment: Total enrollment 23,991. Undergraduate 15,921. Graduate 8,070. Undergraduate transfer-in students 1,481.

Characteristics of Student Body: *Ethnic/racial makeup:* number of Black non-Hispanic: 1,307; American Indian or Alaska Native: 24; Asian or Pacific Islander: 3,249; Hispanic: 1,309; White non-Hispanic: 5,150. unknown: 2,924.

Age distribution: number under 18: 128; 18–19: 5,004; 20–21: 5,196; 22–24. 2,934; 25–29: 887; 30–34: 260; 35–39: 164; 40–49: 202; 50–64: 68; 65 and over: 4.

International Students: 2,345 nonresident aliens enrolled fall 2008. Programs available to aid students whose native language is not English: social, cultural. English as a Second Language Program. No financial aid specifically designated for international students.

Student Life: On-campus housing available for single and married students. *Athletics:* Intercollegiate Sports Division I, NCAA. *Special services:* Medical services, campus bus system. *Student publications, radio: Fortnight*, a magazine; *Specula*, a yearbook. Radio station WUSB. *Surrounding community:* Stony Brook, population 16,500, is located on eastern Long Island. New York City is nearest metropolitan area.

Publications: *Anthropology, Archives of Sexual Behavior, Art Criticism, Biological Psychiatry, Bulletin of Research in the Humanities, Circuits, Systems and Signal Processing, Evolution, Gradiva, Heat Transfer-Japanese Research, Journal of Applied Behavior Analysis, Journal of College Science Teaching, Journal of Educational Technology Systems, Journal of Symbolic Interaction, Journal of Urban Analysis, Marine Biology Letters, Mental Retardation and Development Disabilities, Physics and Chemistry of Minerals, The Physics Teacher, Previews of Heat and Mass Transfer, Quarterly Review of Biology, Socioeconomic Planning Sciences, Transplantation Proceedings.*

Library Collections: 1,936,000 volumes. 235,000 government documents; 2,500,000 microform units; 34,000 audiovisual materials. Current serial subscriptions: 7,430 paper; 85 microform; 29,275 via electronic access. Online catalog. Students have access to online information retrieval services and the Internet.

Most important special holdings include Yeats Collection; Senator Jacob Javits Collection.

Buildings and Grounds: Campus area 1,086

Chief Executive Officer: Dr. Shirley Strum Kenny, President.

Undergraduates address admission inquiries to Judith Burke-Berhannon, Director of Admissions; graduate inquiries to Dr. Lawrence Martin, Dean, Graduate School; for Health Science Center programs contact the various schools.

Health Science Center

Degree Programs Offered: *Baccalaureate* in various fields; *first-professional* in dentistry, medicine; *master's, doctorate* in various fields.

Admission: *For first-professional in dentistry:* From accredited college or university 1 year each behavioral science, biology or zoology, inorganic chemistry, organic chemistry, physics, social science, all with laboratory; 1 mathematics (calculus preferred, statistics accepted). DAT. *For first-professional in medicine:* Premedical course work with laboratory from accredited college or university, including 1 year each biology, general chemistry, organic chemistry, physics. MCAT. 1 year calculus recommended. *For both programs:* 2 years course work from accredited college or university. Baccalaureate strongly recommended.

Fees and Other Expenses: Contact the school for current information.

State University of New York College at Brockport

350 New Campus Drive
Brockport, New York 14420-2919
Tel: (585) 395-2211 **E-mail:** admit@.brockport.edu
Fax: (585) 395-5452 **Internet:** www.brockport.edu

Institution Description: *Enrollment:* 8,275. *Degrees awarded:* Baccalaureate, master's. Post-master's certificates of advanced study also awarded.

Member of the consortium Rochester Area Colleges.

Accreditation: *Regional:* MSA. *Professional*: business, computer science, counseling, dance, nursing, nursing education, public administration, recreation and leisure services, social work

History: Established as Brockport Normal School and offered first instruction at postsecondary level 1867; changed name to Brockport State Teachers College 1942; adopted present name 1948. *See* W. Wayne Dedman, *Cherishing This Heritage* (New York: Appleton-Century-Crofts, 1969) for further information.

Institutional Structure: *Composition of institution:* Administrators 46. Academic affairs headed by vice president for academic affairs. Management/business/finances directed by vice president for administrative services. Total instructional faculty 597. Academic governance body, Faculty Senate, meets an average of 15 times per year.

Calendar: Semesters. Academic year Ayg. to May. Freshmen admitted Sept., Jan. Degrees conferred May, Aug., Dec. Formal commencement May. Summer session of two 2-week sessions and five 5-week sessions from the end of May to the end of Aug.

Characteristics of Freshmen: 8,545 applicants (4,718 female, 3,827 male). 44% of applicants admitted. 26% of admitted applicants enrolled full-time.

100% (991 students) submitted SAT scores; 40% (401 students) submitted ACT scores. *25th percentile*: SAT Critical Reading 480, SAT Math 500; ACT Composite 21. *75th percentile*: SAT Critical Reading 580, SAT Math 590; ACT Composite 27.

53% of entering freshmen expected to graduate within 5 years. 99% of freshmen from New York. Freshmen from 26 states and 21 foreign countries.

Admission: Preference is given to students who have completed a strong college preparatory program (generally regents courses for state residents) including a minimum of 18 academic units in English, mathematics, science, social studies, foreign languages and fine arts. Additional information considered includes: an essay, letters of recommendation, and extracurricular activities. Preference is given to transfers with an A.A. or A.S. degree. Transfers must identify their intended academic major at the time of application. A minimum 2.25 cumulative grade point average is required for admission to most programs. Admission to a growing number of majors now requires a GPA of 2.5 or higher due to high demand and limited space. These programs include all teacher certification programs plus majors in accounting, business administration, communication, criminal justice, nursing, physical education, social work, and sport management.

Degree Requirements: Completion of 120 semester hours in an approved program with a minimum earned academic average of 2.0 and a minimum average of 2.0 in all courses taken in the major discipline. Completion of general education requirements. Residency requirement of 24 of last 30 hours on the Brockport campus. *Grading system:* A–E; pass-fail; withdraw; satisfactory-unsatisfactory; incomplete.

Distinctive Educational Programs: Honors program; cooperative education program. Engineering-Liberal Arts Five-Year Program with SUNY Buffalo, Case Western Reserve University, Clarkson University, or Syracuse University. Experiential education. Industrial and Labor Relations Program with Cornell University. Study abroad in England, Brazil, Mexico, Canada, Japan, France. Washington and Albany off-campus semesters. Interdisciplinary minors in applied social research, communications meteorology, film studies, gerontology, scientific writing, and Latin American studies. Flexible meeting places and schedules including off-campus locations and weekend and evening classes. Accelerated degree programs through Delta College. Interdisciplinary Arts for Children. International business and liberal studies. Independent study opportunities.

ROTC: Army in cooperation with Rochester Institute of Technology; Navy with University of Rochester.

Degrees Conferred: 1,610 *baccalaureate*; 437 *master's*. Bachelor's degrees awarded in top five disciplines: business, management, marketing, and related support services 227; education 175; health professions and related clinical sciences 160; psychology 130; security and protective services 129.

Fees and Other Expenses: *Full-time tuition per academic year 2008–09:* undergraduate resident $45,444, nonresident $11,704; contact the college for current graduate tuition/fees. *Books and supplies:* $1,000. *Room and board per academic year:* $8,615. *Other expenses:* $2,021.

Financial Aid: The university offers a direct lending program. Aid from institutionally generated funds is provided on the basis of academic merit, financial need.

Financial aid to full-time, first-time undergraduate students: 90% received some form of aid. Average amount of aid received: federal grants $1,511; state/local grants $2,004; institutional grants $4,119; loans $2,351.

Departments and Teaching Staff: *Total instructional faculty:* 615 (full-time 321, part-time 294). *Student/faculty ratio:* 17:1. Degrees held by full-time faculty: doctorate 88%, master's 10%, baccalaureate 2%. 90% hold terminal degrees.

Enrollment: Total enrollment 8,275. Undergraduate 6,970; Graduate 1,305. Undergraduate transfer-in students 919.

Characteristics of Student Body: *Ethnic/racial makeup:* number of Black non-Hispanic: 383; American Indian or Alaska Native: 30; Asian or Pacific Islander: 82%; Hispanic: 208; White non-Hispanic: 5,188; unknown: 900. *Age distribution:* number under 18: 60; 18–19: 1,736; 20–21: 2,402; 22–24: 1,549; 25–29: 507; 30–34: 193; 35–39: 147; 40–49: 2111 50–64: 60; 65 and over: 1.

International Students: 66 undergraduate nonresident aliens enrolled fall 2008. Programs available to aid students whose native language is not English: social, cultural. Some financial aid designated for international students.

Student Life: On-campus residence halls house 45% of full-time undergraduate student body, 35% of all undergraduates. Housing in campus apartments is available for graduate and married students. *Intercollegiate athletics:* Baseball, basketball, cross-country, field hockey, football, gymnastics, ice hockey, lacrosse, soccer, softball, swimming and diving, tennis, track and field, volleyball, wrestling. *Special regulations:* Cars permitted for all students. *Special ser-*

STATE UNIVERSITY OF NEW YORK COLLEGE AT BROCKPORT—*cont'd*

vices: Academic Computing Services, Educational Communications Services, Learning Skills Center, Health Center, Counseling Center, Career Development and Placement Center, Handicapped Student Services, Regional Transit Bus Service to and from Rochester. *Student publications, radio: The Stylus*, a weekly newspaper; *Saga*, the student yearbook; *The Brockport Handbook*, a biannual catalog. Radio station WBSU AM and FM. *Surrounding community:* Brockport population 10,000.

Library Collections: 473,000 volumes including bound books, serial backfiles, electronic documents, and government documents not in separate collections. Online catalog. Current serial subscriptions: 1,400 paper, 30 microform, 1,300 electronic. Students have access to the Internet at no charge.

Most important special holdings include D.S. Morgan Company Records.

Buildings and Grounds: Campus area 435 acres.

Chief Executive Officer: Dr. John B. Clark, President.

Address admission inquiries to Bernie Valento, Director of Admissions.

State University of New York College at Buffalo

1300 Elmwood Avenue
Buffalo, New York 14222-1095

Tel: (716) 878-4000 **E-mail:** admission@buffalostate.edu
Fax: (716) 878-6000 **Internet:** www.buffalostate.edu

Institution Description: SUNY College at Buffalo is also known as Buffalo State College. *Enrollment:* 11,254. *Degrees awarded:* baccalaureate, master's. Certificates also awarded.

Accreditation: *Regional:* MSA.*Professional*: audiology, dietetics, engineering, engineering technology, industrial technology, social work, speech-language pathology, teacher education

History: Established 1867; offered first instruction at postsecondary level 1871; awarded first degree 1873.

Institutional Structure: *Composition of institution:* Administrators 17. Academic affairs headed by vice president for academic affairs. Management/business/finances directed by vice president for administration. Full-time instructional faculty 263. Academic governance body, College Senate, meets an average of 10 times per year.

Calendar: Semesters. Academic year Aug. to May. Freshmen admitted Aug., Jan., June. Degrees conferred Dec., May, Aug. Formal commencement May. Summer sessions from early June to late Aug.

Characteristics of Freshmen: 10,388 applicants (5,954 female, 4,434 male). 45% of applicants admitted. 33% of applicants admitted and enrolled full-time.

94% (1,224 students) submitted SAT scores. *25th percentile*: SAT Critical Reading 450, SAT Math 460, SAT Writing 430. *75th percentile*: SAT Critical Reading 530, SAT Math 550, SAT Writing 520.

36% of entering freshmen expected to graduate within 5 years. 99% of freshmen from New York. Freshmen from 29 states and 15 foreign countries.

Admission: Rolling admissions plan. For fall acceptance, apply as early as Oct. of previous year, but not later than Aug. of year of enrollment. All applicants must possess or be a candidate for a high school diploma. A State High School Equivalency Diploma is also acceptable. High school preparation should be broad and balanced with study in the areas of social science, English, natural science, mathematics, and foreign language. Admission decisions are based on a combination of high school grades, rank in class, scores on standardized examinations such as the SAT or ACT, and high school recommendation.

College credit and advanced placement for postsecondary-level work completed in secondary school. Remedial courses offered.

Degree Requirements: 123 credit hours; 2.0 GPA; minimum of 32 hours, including the last 16, must be completed at the college; foreign language requirement, where appropriate, must be fulfilled; 2 hours physical education courses; 60 hours in the general education area. Fulfillment of some degree requirements and exemption from some beginning courses possible by passing College Board CLEP, AP, other standardized test. *Grading system:* A–F; pass-fail; withdraw (carries time limit).

Distinctive Educational Programs: Weekend and evening classes. Numerous evening degree programs. Special facilities for using telecommunications in the classroom. Interdepartmental-interdisciplinary programs. Facilities and programs for independent research, individual majors and tutorials. Departmentally-based and all-college honors programs. Study abroad in Australia, Italy, Japan, Netherlands, Spain, United Kingdom. The college participates in international student exchange and national student exchange programs. Internship opportunities in the community and the NYS Intern Program (Albany); NYS Senate Session Assistant Program (Albany). Cross-registration with other western New York colleges.

ROTC: Army in cooperation with Canisius College.

Degrees Conferred: 1,767 *baccalaureate*; 757 *master's*. Bachelor's degrees awarded in top five disciplines: education 559; business/marketing 151; social sciences 129; communications/journalism 128; visual and performing arts 115. Master's degrees awarded in top five disciplines: education 334; interdisciplinary studies 174; visual and performing arts 50; English 10; security and protective services 8.

Fees and Other Expenses: *Full-time tuition per academic year 2008–09:* undergraduate resident $5,575, nonresident $12,610; contact the university for current graduate tuition/fees. *Other fees:* $935. *Room and board per academic year:* $9,064. *Books and supplies:* $900. *Other expenses:* $2,200.

Financial Aid: The university offers a direct lending program. Aid from institutionally generated funds is provided on the basis of academic merit, financial need.

Financial aid to full-time, first-time undergraduate students: need-based scholarships/grants totaling $21,035,157, self-help $19,100,370; non-need-based scholarships/grants totaling $1,302,772, self-help $11,284,250, parent loans $1,635,326.

Departments and Teaching Staff: *Total instructional faculty:* 715 (full-time 393, part-time 322). Student/faculty ratio: 17:1. Degrees held by full-time faculty: 89% hold terminal degrees.

Enrollment: Total enrollment 11,234. Undergraduate 9,371. Graduate 1,803. Undergraduate transfer-in student 1,103.

Characteristics of Student Body: *Ethnic/racial makeup:* number of Black non-Hispanic: 1,261; American Indian or Alaska Native: 50; Asian or Pacific Islander: 149; Hispanic: 387; White non-Hispanic: 6,164; unknown: 1,266. *Age distribution:* number under 18: 39; 18–19: 2,330; 20–21: 2,640; 22–24: 2,353; 25–29: 989; 30–34: 362; 35–39: 231; 40–49: 272; 50–64: 881; 65 and over: 2.

International Students: 49 nonresident aliens enrolled fall 2008. Students from Europe, Central and South America, Africa, Canada, Middle East. Programs available to students whose native language is not English: social, cultural. No financial aid specifically designated for international students.

Student Life: On-campus residence halls house 17% of student body (nearly 1,800 students live in their choice of 9 residence halls). *Intercollegiate athletics:* NCAA Div. III tennis, cross-country, soccer, basketball, swimming, track and field (male and female) football (male), volleyball and softball (female). *Special services:* Career Development Center, Counseling Health Center, Academic Skills Center, dental clinic, day care center, sexuality center. *Student publications, radio: The Record*, a student newspaper. Radio station WBNY. *Surrounding community:* Buffalo population 328,000. Campus is near Delaware Park and across from the Albright-Knox Art Gallery. Close to Niagara Falls and Toronto, Canada.

Library Collections: 478,000 volumes including bound books, serial backfiles, electronic documents, and government documents not in separate collections. Online catalog. Current serial subscriptions: 2,858 paper, 291 microform, 234 electronic. 7,758 recordings; 133 compact discs. 51 computer work stations. Students have access to the Internet at no charge.

Most important special holdings include Courier Express Collection; Lois Lenski Collection; Selig-Adler Jewish Archives of Greater Buffalo; Francis E. Froncsak Collection; E.H. Butler family correspondence.

Buildings and Grounds: Campus area 115 acres.

Chief Executive Officer: Dr. Muriel A. Howard, President.

Address undergraduate admission inquiries to Lesa Loritts, Director of Admissions; graduate inquiries to Thomas Kinsey, Dean of Graduate Studies and Research.

State University of New York College at Cortland

Graham Avenue
P.O. Box 2000
Cortland, New York 130450900

Tel: (607) 753-2011 **E-mail:** admissions@cortland.edu
Fax: (607) 753-5998 **Internet:** www.cortland.edu

Institution Description: *Enrollment:* 7,234. *Degrees awarded:* Baccalaureate, master's. Certificates also awarded.

Accreditation: *Regional:* MSA. *Professional*: teacher education

History: Established 1866; chartered as Cortland State Normal School 1868; offered first instruction at postsecondary level 1869; awarded first degree (baccalaureate) and changed name to Cortland State Teachers College 1941; became part of state university system 1948; changed name to State University College of Education 1959; adopted present name 1961. *See* Bessie L. Park, *Cortland—*

Our Alma Mater (Ithaca: Cayuga Press, 1960) and Leonard F. Ralston, *Cortland College, An Illustrated History* (1991) for further information.

Institutional Structure: *Composition of institution:* Administrators 35. Academic affairs headed by provost. Management/business/finances directed by vice president of finance and management. Full-time instructional faculty 237. Academic governance body, Faculty Senate, meets biweekly.

Calendar: Semesters. Academic year Aug. to May. Freshmen admitted Sept., Jan., June. Degrees conferred May, Jan. Formal commencement May. Summer session of 2 terms from mid-June to mid-Aug.

Characteristics of Freshmen: 11,562 applicants (5,151 female, 6,405 male). 41% OF applicants accepted. 25% of accepted applicants enrolled full-time. *25th percentile*: SAT Critical Reading 500, SAT Math 486; ACT Composite 20. *75th percentile:* SAT Critical Reading 590, SAT Math 550; ACT Composite 24.

55% of entering freshmen expected to graduate within 5 years. 98% of freshmen from New York. Freshmen from 8 states and 2 foreign countries.

Admission: Rolling admissions after Feb. 1. Early admission; early decision. Regular admission deadline Dec. 1. Decisions sent between Jan. 21 and March 15. Rolling admissions for transfer students. *Requirements:* Either graduation from accredited secondary school or GED. Minimum 2.0 GPA. *Entrance tests:* ACT or SAT required. *For transfer students:* 2.5 minimum GPA; from 4-year accredited institution 75 semester hours maximum transfer credit; from 2-year accredited institution 64 semester hours.

College credit and advanced placement for postsecondary-level work completed in secondary school. Tutoring available.

Degree Requirements: 124–132 semester hours; 2.0 GPA; 45 hours in residence; core requirements; exit competency examinations in writing. Fulfillment of some degree requirements possible by passing College Board CLEP. *Grading system:* A–F; pass-fail; withdraw (deadline after which pass-fail is appended to withdraw).

Distinctive Educational Programs: Work-experience programs. Accelerated degree programs. Dual-degree programs with other institutions. Interdisciplinary programs. Facilities and programs for independent research, including honors programs, tutorials. Study abroad programs in 11 countries.

ROTC: Army and Air Force in cooperation with Cornell University.

Degrees Conferred: 1,275 *baccalaureate*; 379 *master's*. Bachelor's degrees awarded in top five disciplines: education 659; social sciences 156; parks and recreation 109; psychology 58; communication, journalism, and related programs 58. Master's degrees awarded in various disciplines.

Fees and Other Expenses: *Full-time tuition per academic year 2008–09:* undergraduate resident $5,450, nonresident $11,400; contact the college for current graduate tuition. *Books and supplies:* $800. *Room and board per academic year:* $9,350. *Other expenses:* $2,300.

Financial Aid: Aid from institutionally generated funds is provided on the basis of academic merit, financial need, leadership.

Financial aid to full-time, first-time undergraduate students: 84% received some form of financial aid.

Departments and Teaching Staff: <*Total instructional faculty:* 481. Student/faculty ratio: 22:1. Degrees held by full-time faculty: 87% hold terminal degrees.

Enrollment: Total enrollment 7,234. Undergraduate 6,199. Graduate 1,035. Undergraduate transfer-in students 601.

Characteristics of Student Body: *Ethnic/racial makeup:* Black non-Hispanic: 6.6%; American Indian or Alaska Native: .4%; Asian or Pacific Islander: 1.2%; Hispanic: 3.7%; White non-Hispanic: 81%; unknown: 10.6%.

International Students: 36 undergraduate nonresident aliens enrolled fall 2006. Programs available to aid students whose native language is not English: English as a Second Language Program. No financial aid specifically designated for international students.

Student Life: On-campus student housing available. *Intercollegiate athletics:* male: baseball, basketball, cross-country, football, gymnastics, hockey, soccer, swimming, tennis, track; female: basketball, cross-country, gymnastics, hockey, soccer, swimming, tennis, track, volleyball. *Special services:* Learning Resources Center, medical services, bus service to and from parking lots and off-campus dormitory. *Student publications, radio: Press*, a weekly newspaper. Radio station WSUC. *Surrounding community:* Cortland population 19,500. Syracuse, 35 miles from campus, is nearest metropolitan area.

Library Collections: 410,000 volumes including bound books, serial backfiles, electronic documents, and government documents not in separate collections. Online catalog. Current serial subscriptions: 2,943 paper, microform, electronic. Computer work stations available. Students have access to the Internet at no charge.

Most important special collections include the Teaching Materials Center.

Buildings and Grounds: Campus area 191 acres.

Chief Executive Officer: Dr. Erik J. Bitterbaum, President.

Address admission inquiries to Mark Yakavone, Director of Admissions.

State University of New York College at Fredonia

Central Avenue
Fredonia, New York 14063-1136
Tel: (716) 673-3111 **E-mail:** admissions@fredonia.edu
Fax: (716) 673-3325 **Internet:** www.fredonia.edu

Institution Description: *Enrollment:* 5,573. *Degrees awarded:* Baccalaureate, master's. Certificates also awarded.

Accreditation: *Regional:* MSA *Professional*: audiology, music, speech-language pathology, theatre

History: Established as Fredonia Academy 1826; chartered as one of the first six State Normal Schools and offered first instruction at postsecondary level 1867; named a New York State Teachers College 1942; became a part of the State University of New York system as State University of New York College at Fredonia 1948.

Institutional Structure: *Composition of institution:* Administrators 38. Academic affairs headed by vice president for academic affairs. Management/business/finances directed by vice president of finance and personnel. Full-time instructional faculty 230. Academic governance body, College Senate, meets an average of 8 times per year.

Calendar: Semesters. Academic year Aug. to May. Freshmen admitted Aug., Jan. Degrees conferred Aug., Dec., May. Formal commencement May. Summer session of 2 terms from May to July.

Characteristics of Freshmen: 5,893 applicants (3,428 female, 2,475 male). 56% of applicants admitted. 32% of admitted students enrolled full-time.

84% (891 students) submitted SAT scores; 22% (233 students) submitted ACT scores. *25th percentile*: SAT Critical Reading 500, SAT Math 510; ACT Composite 21. *75th percentile*: SAT Critical Reading 590, SAT Math 600; ACT Composite 26.

61% of entering freshmen expected to graduate within 5 years. 97% of freshmen from New York. Freshmen from 21 states and 10 foreign countries.

Admission: Rolling admissions plan. For fall acceptance, apply as early as Sept. 1 of previous year, but not later than July 1 of year of enrollment. Students are notified of acceptance beginning Nov. *Requirements:* Either graduation from accredited secondary school with 4 units English, 4 social studies, 3 mathematics, 3 science; or GED. For bachelor of arts degree, 2 units in foreign languages recommended. For bachelor of science, 4 mathematics required. Minimum 2.5 GPA (80 HSA). *Entrance tests:* College Board SAT or ACT composite. *For transfer students:* 2.0 minimum GPA (2.5 GPA for students in education and speech pathology); from 4-year and 2-year accredited institutions 75 semester hours maximum transfer credit. The college offers a special admissions program for talented and educationally/economically disadvantaged students.

College credit for postsecondary-level work completed in secondary school and for extrainstitutional learning on basis of portfolio and faculty assessments.

Tutoring available. Developmental/remedial courses offered in regular academic year; credit given.

Degree Requirements: 120 credit hours; 2.0 GPA; 45 hours in residence. Fulfillment of some degree requirements and exemption from some beginning courses possible by passing College Board CLEP, AP. *Grading system:* A–F; pass-fail; withdraw (deadline after which pass-fail is appended to withdraw).

Distinctive Educational Programs: Work-experience program. Evening classes. Accelerated degree programs. Cooperative program in engineering with various institutions, including Case Western Reserve University, Clarkson College of Technology, Syracuse University. Interdepartmental-interdisciplinary programs in special studies. Individual majors. Programs in music, speech pathology, gene technology, media arts, sound recording.

Degrees Conferred: 1,124 *baccalaureate*; 199 *master's*. Bachelor's degrees awarded in top five disciplines: business, management, marketing, and related support services 122; communication, journalism, and related programs 106; social sciences 90; visual and performing arts 71; psychology 71. Master's degrees awarded: biological/life sciences 7; business/marketing 1; education 142; health professions 29; interdisciplinary studies 7; physical sciences 1; visual and performing arts 12.

Fees and Other Expenses: *Full-time tuition per academic year 2008–09:* undergraduate resident $5,585, nonresident $11,845; contact the college for current graduate tuition/fees. *Required fees:* $1,091. *Books and supplies:* $1,000. *Room and board per academic year:* $9,140. *Other expenses:* $1,125.

Financial Aid: Aid from institutionally generated funds is provided on the basis of academic merit, financial need.

Financial aid to full-time, first-time undergraduate students: 91% received some form of aid. Average amount of aid received: federal grants $3,453; Pell grants $2,815; other federal grants $9,170; state/local grants $1,945; institutional grants $1,702.

STATE UNIVERSITY OF NEW YORK COLLEGE AT FREDONIA—*cont'd*

Departments and Teaching Staff: *Total instructional faculty*: 444. Student/faculty ratio: 16:1. Degrees held by full-time faculty: master's 5%, doctorate 90%, professional 5%. 98% hold terminal degrees.

Enrollment: Total enrollment 5,573. Undergraduate 5,178. Graduate 395. Undergraduate transfer-in students 443.

Characteristics of Student Body: *Ethnic/racial makeup:* number of Black non-Hispanic: 106; American Indian or Alaska Native: 31; Asian or Pacific Islander:104; Hispanic: 129; White non-Hispanic: 424; unknown: 449.

International Students: 88 nonresident aliens enrolled fall 2008. Students from Europe, Asia, Central and South America, Africa, Canada. Programs available to aid students whose native language is not English: English as a Second Language Program. No financial aid specifically designated for international students.

Student Life: On-campus residence halls house 45% of student body. *Intercollegiate athletics:* male: baseball, basketball, cross-country, soccer, tennis, ice hockey, indoor and outdoor track and field; female: soccer, softball, cross-country, lacrosse, volleyball, tennis, basketball, indoor and outdoor track and field. *Special regulations:* Cars permitted without restrictions. *Special services:* Learning Center, medical services, campus transportation system. There are over 100 active clubs and organizations on campus. *Student publications, radio, television: The Fig*, a literary magazine; *The Leader*, a weekly newspaper. Radio station WCVF-AM broadcasts 133 hours per week following fall and spring schedules; radio station WCVF-FM broadcast 133 hours per week, 365 days per year. Television station WNYF (6 cable) broadcasts 35 hours per week following fall and spring academic schedules. *Surrounding community:* Fredonia population 10,500.

Publications: *Nineteenth Century French Studies* (quarterly); *The Third Decade*.

Library Collections: 1,507,000 volumes including bound books, serial backfiles, electronic documents, and government documents not in separate collections. Online catalog. Current serial subscriptions: 797 paper, 4 microform, 5,000 via electronic access. 20,382 recordings; 170 DVDs. 28 computer work stations. Students have access to the Internet at no charge.

Most important special holdings include music collection (scores and recordings); Stefan Zweig Collection (print and manuscript materials); Seneca Nation of Indians Collection; Holland Land Company Collection.

Buildings and Grounds: Campus area 245 acres.

Chief Executive Officer: Dr. Dennis L. Hefner, President. Direct admission inquiries to Michael Bleechner, Director of Admissions.

State University of New York College at Geneseo

1 College Circle
Geneseo, New York 14454
Tel: (585) 245-5211 **E-mail:** admissions@geneseo.edu
Fax: (585) 245-5005 **Internet:** www.geneseo.edu

Institution Description: *Enrollment:* 5,585. *Degrees awarded:* Baccalaureate, master's.

Academic offerings subject to approval by statewide coordinating bodies. Member of the consortium Rochester Area Colleges.

Accreditation: *Regional:* MSA. *Professional*: business, chemistry, speech-language pathology

History: Established as Geneseo Normal and Training School 1867; offered first instruction at postsecondary level 1871; awarded first degree 1872; became 4-year college 1938; changed name to Geneseo Teachers College 1942; became part of state university system and changed name to State University Teachers College of Education 1959; adopted present name 1962. *See* Rosalind R. Fisher, *The Stone Strength of the Past* (Buffalo, New York: William J. Keller, Inc., 1971) for further information.

Institutional Structure: *Composition of institution:* Administrators 94. Academic affairs headed by Provost. Management/business/finances directed by vice president for administration. Full-time instructional faculty 245. Academic governance body, Faculty Senate, meets an average of 10 times per year.

Calendar: Semesters. Academic year Aug. to May. Freshmen admitted Sept., Jan., June, July, Aug. Degrees conferred Dec., May. Formal commencement May. Summer session of 3 terms.

Characteristics of Freshmen: 10,435 applicants. 35% of applicants admitted. 29% of applicants admitted and enrolled full-time.

68% (736 students) submitted SAT scores; 30% (324 students) submitted ACT scores. *25th percentile*: SAT Critical Reading 610, SAT Math 620; ACT Composite 287. *75th percentile*: SAT Critical Reading 690, SAT Math 690; ACT Composite 30.

79% of entering freshmen expected to graduate within 5 years. 96% of freshmen from New York. Freshmen from 24 states and 35 foreign countries.

Admission: For fall acceptance, apply as early as Oct. of previous year, but not later than Apr. of year of enrollment. Early acceptance available. *Requirements:* Either graduation from accredited secondary school or GED. *Entrance tests:* College Board SAT or ACT composite. *For transfer students:* 2.5 minimum GPA; from 4-year accredited institution 92 semester hours maximum transfer credit; from 2-year accredited institution 62 semester hours.

College credit for military education experiences.

Tutoring available. Developmental/remedial courses offered in summer session and regular academic year; credit given.

Degree Requirements: 120 semester hours; 2.0 GPA; 2 semesters (32 hours) in residence; core curriculum; demonstration of proficiency in writing. Additional requirements for some programs.

Fulfillment of some degree requirements and exemption from some beginning courses possible by passing College Board CLEP, AP, other standardized tests. *Grading system:* A–E; pass-fail; withdraw.

Distinctive Educational Programs: Work-experience programs. Evening classes. Accelerated degree programs. Dual-degree programs in business administration with SUNY Buffalo; in engineering with Alfred University, Clarkson College of Technology, Columbia University, Rochester Institute of Technology, University of Rochester, SUNY Binghamton, SUNY Buffalo, Case Western Reserve University (OH), Ohio State University, Syracuse University; in forestry with SUNY College of Environmental Science and Forestry. Special facilities for using telecommunications in the classroom. Interdisciplinary programs in American civilization, environmental study, linguistics, musical theater, public relations women's studies. Tutorials. Students have access to the entire State University of New York Study Abroad System.

ROTC: Army and Air Force in cooperation with Rochester Institute of Technology.

Degrees Conferred: 1,132 *baccalaureate*; 87 *master's*. Bachelors' degrees awarded in top five disciplines: education 230; business/marketing 177; social sciences 144; psychology 114; biological/life sciences 103. Master's degrees awarded: biological/life sciences 1; business/marketing 4; education 64; English 2; foreign languages and literature 1; health professions and related clinical sciences 9; mathematics 6.

Fees and Other Expenses: *Full-time tuition per academic year 2008–09:* undergraduate resident $5,658, nonresident $11,918; contact the university for current graduate tuition/fees. *Required fees:* $1,210. *Room and board per academic year:* $9,070. *Books and supplies:* $800. *Other expenses:* $1,600.

Financial Aid: Aid from institutionally generated funds is provided on the basis of academic merit.

Financial aid to full-time, first-time undergraduate students: 60% received some form of aid. Average amount of aid received: federal grants $1,511; state/local grants $2,004; institutional grants $4,119; loans $2,351.

Departments and Teaching Staff: *Total instructional faculty:* 329 (full-time 245, part-time 84). 87% of faculty hold the doctorate, first-professional, or other terminal degree. Student/faculty ratio: 19:1.

Enrollment: Total enrollment 5,585. Undergraduate 5,451. Graduate 134. Undergraduate transfer-in students 341.

Characteristics of Student Body: *Ethnic/racial makeup:* number of Black non-Hispanic: 108; American Indian or Alaska Native: 20; Asian or Pacific Islander: 305; Hispanic: 166; White non-Hispanic: 4,084; unknown: 538. *Age distribution:* number under 18: 210; 18–19: 2,218; 20–21: 2,257; 22–24: 508; 25–29: 92; 30–34: 30; 35–39: 16; 40–49: 17; 50–64: 10.

International Students: 129 nonresident aliens enrolled fall 2008. Students from Europe, Asia, Central and South America, Africa, Canada, Middle East. Programs available to aid students whose native language is not English: English as a Second Language Program. Financial aid specifically designated for qualifying international students.

Student Life: On-campus residence halls house 55% of student body. Dormitories for females only constitute 28% of such space, for both males and females 72%.*Intercollegiate athletics:* male: lacrosse, soccer, swimming, hockey, basketball, track, cross-country; female: soccer, swimming, softball, basketball, equestrian, volleyball, track, cross-country. *Special regulations:* Cars permitted in designated areas. *Special services:* Learning Resources Center, medical services. *Student publications, radio, television: Lamron*, a weekly newspaper; *Review*, an annual literary magazine. Radio stations WGBC-AM, WGSU-FM. TV station GSTV. *Surrounding community:* Geneseo population 8,500.

Publications: *EnCompass*, an online version of the college campus newspaper.

Library Collections: 647,000 volumes including bound books, serial backfiles, electronic documents, and government documents not in separate collections. Online catalog. 853,000 microforms; 28,000 audiovisual materials; 4,235 current serial subscriptions. Computer work stations available. Students have access to the Internet at no charge.

Most important special holdings include Genesee Valley Historical Collection; Wadsworth Family Papers; Carl Schmidt Collection on Local Architecture.

Chief Executive Officer: Dr. Christopher C. Dahl, President.

Address admission inquiries to Kris Shay, Director of Admissions.

State University of New York College at Old Westbury

223 Store Hill Road
Box 210
Old Westbury, New York 11568
Tel: (516) 876-3000 **E-mail:** enroll@oldwestbury.edu
Fax: (516) 876-3307 **Internet:** www.oldwestbury.edu

Institution Description: *Enrollment:* 3,505. *Degrees awarded:* Baccalaureate, master's.

Accreditation: *Regional:* MSA. *Professional*: chemistry

History: Established 1965; offered first instruction at postsecondary level 1968; awarded first degree 1969.

Institutional Structure: *Composition of institution:* Administrators 8. Academic affairs headed by provost/vice president of academic affairs. Business/finances directed by chief financial officer. Full-time instructional faculty 133, Academic governance body, Faculty Senate, meets an average of 18 times per year.

Calendar: Semesters. Academic year Sept. to May. Freshmen admitted Sept., Feb. Degrees conferred and formal commencement May. Summer session of 3 terms from May to Aug.

Characteristics of Freshmen: 3,651 applicants. 45% of applicants admitted. 21% of applicants admitted and enrolled full-time.

98% (334 students) submitted SAT scores. 65 (21 students) submitted ACT scores. *25th percentile*: SAT Critical Reading 445, SAT Math 460, SAT Writing 420; ACT Composite 19. *75th percentile*: SAT Critical Reading 535, SAT Math 575, SAT Writing 510; ACT Composite 22.

97% of freshmen from New York. Freshmen from 7 states and 5 foreign countries.

Admission: Rolling admissions plan. For fall acceptance, apply as early as Nov. 1 of previous year. Students are notified of acceptance beginning in Feb. Early acceptance available. *Requirements:* Either graduation from accredited secondary school or GED. Applicants are evaluated on 1 or more of 4 qualifying categories: (1) academic achievement; (2) special knowledge and creative ability; (3) paid work experience; (4) social or personal experience. *For transfer students:* From accredited institutions 72 hours maximum transfer credit.

College credit and advanced placement for postsecondary-level work completed in secondary school and for extrainstitutional learning on basis of portfolio assessment.

Tutoring available. Developmental/remedial courses offered during regular academic year.

Degree Requirements: 120 credit hours; 3 terms in residence; distribution requirements; demonstrated mastery of American English language skills and computational skills. General education program requirements. *Grading system:* A–F; pass-fail; withdraw.

Distinctive Educational Programs: Facilities and programs for independent research. Study abroad in China, Cuba, Kenya, Korea, Mexico, Puerto Rico, Spain.

ROTC: Air Force in cooperation with Manhattan College; Army in cooperation with Hofstra University.

Degrees Conferred: 630 *baccalaureate*; 13 *master's*. Bachelor's degrees awarded in top five disciplines: business/marketing 223; education 106; social sciences 99; psychology 74; computer and information sciences 48. Master's degrees awarded: business/marketing 13.

Fees and Other Expenses: *Full-time tuition per academic year 2008–09:* undergraduate resident $5,177, nonresident $11,437; contact the college for current graduate tuition/fees. *Required fees:* 726. *Room and board per academic year:* $9,032. *Books and supplies:* $800. *Other expenses:* $1,960.

Financial Aid: Aid from institutionally generated funds is provided on the basis of academic merit, financial need.

Financial aid to full-time, first-time undergraduate students: 83% received some form of aid. Average amount of aid received: federal grants $1,511; state/local grants $2,004; institutional grants $4,119; loans $2,351.

Departments and Teaching Staff: *Total instructional faculty:* 264 (full-time 133, part-time 131). 45% of faculty hold the doctorate, first-professional, or other terminal degree. Student/faculty ratio: 18:1.

Enrollment: Total enrollment 3,505. Undergraduate 3,457. Graduate 48. Undergraduate transfer-in students 459.

Characteristics of Student Body: *Ethnic/racial makeup:* number of Black non-Hispanic: 1,077; American Indian or Alaska Native: 6; Asian or Pacific Islander: 297; Hispanic: 645; White non-Hispanic: 1,295; unknown: 818. *Age distribution:* number under 18: 15; 18–19: 792; 20–21: 935; 22–24: 1,099; 25–29: 641; 30–34: 227; 35–39: 174; 40–49: 257; 50–64: 88; 65 and over: 2. 25% of student body attend summer sessions.

International Students: 66 nonresident aliens enrolled fall 2008. Students from Europe, Asia, Central and South America, Africa, Canada, Middle East. Programs available to aid students whose native language is not English: English as a Second Language Program. No financial aid specifically designated for international students.

Student Life: On-campus residence halls available for males and females. *Intercollegiate athletics:* male: baseball, soccer; female: softball, volleyball; coed: basketball, cross-country, tennis. *Student services:* Counseling and career planning; financial aid; Educational Opportunity Program; student health services; disabled student services; orientation. Student government; clubs and organizations. *Student publications: Catalyst*, a biweekly newspaper; *Voices / Voces*, a biannual literary magazine; a yearbook. *Surrounding community:* Old Westbury population 4,000.

Library Collections: 252,000 volumes. 570,000 microforms; 2,500 audiovisual materials. 4,000 periodicals subscriptions. Students have access to online information retrieval services and the Internet.

Most important special holdings include collections on women's studies, contemporary African/American playwrights; Black history and literature.

Buildings and Grounds: Campus area 605 acres.

Chief Executive Officer: Dr. Calvin O. Butts, III, President.

Address admission inquiries to Office of Enrollment Services.

State University of New York College at Oneonta

Ravine Parkway
Oneonta, New York 13820-4015
Tel: (607) 436-3500 **E-mail:** admissions@oneonta.edu
Fax: (607) 436-3089 **Internet:** www.oneonta.edu

Institution Description: *Enrollment:* 5,757. *Degrees awarded:* Baccalaureate, master's. Certificate of Advanced Study in School Counseling and Counselor Education (post-master's) and Certificate in Adolescence Education (post-baccalaureate) also awarded.

Accreditation: *Regional:* MSA. *Professional*: chemistry, dietetics, music, teacher education

History: Established 1887; chartered as Oneonta State Normal School and offered first instruction at postsecondary level 1889; awarded first degree 1890; changed name to State Teachers College 1942, to State University Teachers College 1948, to State University College of Education 1959; adopted present name 1961.

Institutional Structure: *Composition of institution:* Administrators 53. Academic affairs headed by provost/vice president for academic affairs. Management/business/finances directed by vice president for administration. Full-time instructional faculty 259. Academic governance body, College Senate, meets biweekly.

Calendar: Semesters. Academic year Aug. to May. Freshmen admitted Aug., Jan.. Degrees conferred May, Aug., Dec. Formal commencement May. Summer session of 2 terms from May to Aug.

Characteristics of Freshmen: 12,540 applicants (7,415 female, 5,125 male). 38% of applicants accepted. 24% of accepted applicants enrolled full-time.

95% (1,134 students) submitted SAT scores; 22% (263 students) submitted ACT scores. *25th percentile*: SAT Critical Reading 510, SAT Math 530; ACT Composite 22. *75th percentile*: SAT Critical Reading 590, SAT Math 610; ACT 25.

54% of entering freshmen expected to graduate within 5 years. 95% of freshmen from New York. Freshmen from 64 states and 23 foreign countries.

Admission: Rolling admissions plan. For fall acceptance, apply as early as Sept. 1 of previous year. Early action available. *Requirements:* Either graduation from accredited secondary school or GED. Recommend 4 units English; 8 from among foreign language, mathematics, science; 4 social studies. *Entrance tests:* College Board SAT or ACT composite. *For transfer students:* From 4-year accredited institution 77 semester hours maximum transfer credit; from 2-year accredited institution 66 semester hours. Recommend minimum 2.8 GPA for education majors; 2.5 GPA for others.

College credit and advanced placement for postsecondary-level work completed in secondary school and for extrainstitutional learning on basis of portfolio assessment, CLEP, experiential learning.

STATE UNIVERSITY OF NEW YORK COLLEGE AT ONEONTA—*cont'd*

Developmental courses offered in summer session and regular academic year.

Degree Requirements: 122–128 semester hours; 2.0 GPA; 45 hours, including 30 of the last 60, in residence; basic curriculum requirements. *Grading system:* A–E; pass-fail; withdraw (carries time limit).

Distinctive Educational Programs: College-wide emphases on teaching and learning with technology and communications, service-learning, and experiential learning; largest elementary education major in the SUNY system; distinctive programs in business, music industry, human ecology, psychology, environmental sciences, and computer art; wide range of majors and minors in the liberal arts, sciences, and social sciences; preprofessional programs in dentistry, law, medicine, and veterinary; cooperative 2-2, 3-1, and 4-1 programs with various institutions in accounting, business, computer art, engineering, fashion, and a range of health-related fields. Study abroad England, Greece, India, Italy, Russia, Wales.

Degrees Conferred: 1,315 *baccalaureate*; 52 *master's*. Bachelor's degrees awarded in top five disciplines: education 253; visual and performing arts 199; English 151; family and consumer sciences 117; business/marketing 101. Master's degrees awarded: various disciplines 52.

Fees and Other Expenses: *Full-time tuition per academic year 2008–09:* undergraduate resident $5,502, nonresident $22,762; contact the college for current graduate tuition/fees. *Fees:* $1,062. *Room and board per academic year:* $8,880. *Books and supplies:*$1,000. *Other expenses:* $2,119.

Financial Aid: The university offers a direct lending program. Aid from institutionally generated funds is provided on the basis of academic merit, financial need, athletic ability.

Financial aid to full-time, first-time undergraduate students: 84% received some form of aid. Average amount of aid received:federal grants $3,971; Pell grants $3,021; other federal grants $9,570; state/local grants $2,670; institutional grants $1,195.

Departments and Teaching Staff: *Total instructional faculty:* 475 (full-time 259, part-time 216). 71% of faculty hold the doctorate, first-professional, or other terminal degree. Student/faculty ratio: 18:1.

Enrollment: Total enrollment 5,757. Undergraduate 5,578. Graduate 179. Undergraduate transfer-in students 535.

Characteristics of Student Body: *Ethnic/racial makeup:* number of Black non-Hispanic: 169; American Indian or Alaska Native: 13; Asian or Pacific Islander: 100; Hispanic: 248; White non-Hispanic: 4,632; unknown: 332, *Age distribution:* number under 18: 17; 18–19: 1,063; 20–21: 2,305; 22–24: 943; 25–29: 153; 30–34: 41; 35–39: 18; 40–49: 39; 50–64: 17.

International Students: 102 nonresident aliens enrolled fall 2008. Students from Europe, Asia, Central and South America, Africa, Middle East. Programs available to aid students whose native language is not English: social, cultural, financial. English as a Second Language Program. Financial aid specifically designated for international students.

Student Life: On-campus residence halls house 58% of student body. Residence halls for males and females constitute 100% of such space. *Intercollegiate athletics:* male: baseball, basketball, cross-country, lacrosse, soccer, swimming, tennis, track and field, wrestling; female: basketball, cross-country, field hockey, lacrosse, soccer, softball, swimming, tennis, track and field, volleyball. Extensive intramural program; some club sports. *Special regulations:* Cars permitted for upper division and graduate students only. *Special services:* Medical services. *Student publications, radio: The State Times*, weekly newspaper; *Art and Scope*, literary magazine; quarterly alumni magazine. Radio station WONY. *Surrounding community:* Oneonta population 14,500.

Library Collections: 558,000 volumes including bound books, serial backfiles, electronic documents, and government documents not in separate collections. Online catalog. 1,960,000 microforms; 26,000 audiovisual materials; 25,400 serials including via electronic access. Computer work stations available. Students have access to the Internet at no charge.

Most important special holdings include collections on early educational theory; collection of early educational textbooks; popular fiction (late 19th and 20th centuries) collection; Environmental Collection.

Chief Executive Officer: Dr. Alan B. Donovan, President.

Undergraduates address admission inquiries to Karen A. Brown, Director of Admissions; graduate inquiries to Dr. Alfred M. Lubell, Dean of Graduate Studies.

State University of New York College at Oswego

7060 Star Route 104
Oswego, New York 13126-3599
Tel: (315) 341-2500 **E-mail:** admiss@oswego.edu
Fax: (315) 341-5438 **Internet:** www.oswego.edu

Institution Description: SUNY at Oswego i a comprehensive public college with 140 years of history and tradition. *Enrollment:* 8,909. *Degrees awarded:* Baccalaureate, master's. Certificates also awarded.

Accreditation: *Regional:* MSA. *Professional*: business, chemistry, counseling psychology, music, school psychology, teacher education

History: Established as Oswego Normal School and offered first instruction at postsecondary level 1861; awarded first degree (baccalaureate) 1940; changed name to Oswego State Teachers College 1942; became part of state university system 1948; changed name to State University College of Education 1959; adopted present name 1962. *See* Dorothy Rogers, *Oswego Fountainhead of Teacher Education* (New York: Appleton-Century-Crofts, 1961) for further information.

Institutional Structure: *Composition of institution:* Administrators 57. Academic affairs headed by Vice President/Provost; budget and finance by Vice President for Budget and Finance; enrollment and development by Vice President for Enrollment, Marketing, and Development; students by Vice President for Student Services. Full-time instructional faculty 312. Academic governance body, Faculty Assembly, meet an average of 17 times per year.

Calendar: Semesters. Academic year Aug. to May. Freshmen admitted Aug., Jan. Degrees conferred May, Aug., Dec. Formal commencement May. Summer session of 4 terms from May to Aug.

Characteristics of Freshmen: 9,965 applicants (5,451 female, 4,504 male). 47% of applicants admitted. 31% of applicants admitted and enrolled full-time.

97% (1,417 students) submitted SAT scores; 34% (490 students) submitted ACT scores. *25th percentile*: SAT Critical Reading 500, SAT Math 520; ACT Composite 21. *75th percentile*: SAT Critical Reading 580, SAT Math 580; ACT Composite 25.

53% of entering freshmen expected to graduate within 5 years. 95% of freshmen from New York. Freshmen from 13 states and 7 foreign countries.

Admission: Rolling admissions plan. For fall acceptance, apply as early as Oct. of previous year, but not later than May 1 of year of enrollment. Students are notified of acceptance beginning Jan. 1. *Requirements:* Either graduation from accredited secondary school with units in English, mathematics, modern languages, science, social studies; or GED. Combined total of 7 units mathematics and science highly recommended. *Entrance tests:* College Board SAT or ACT composite. *For transfer students:* 2.3 or higher generally required. The average GPA of incoming transfer students is 2.9. Some programs may be more selective. From 4-year accredited institution, 92 semester hours maximum transfer credit; from 2-year accredited institution, 62 semester hours.

College credit and advanced placement for postsecondary-level work completed in secondary school and for extrainstitutional learning on basis of portfolio assessment. Tutoring available. Developmental courses offered during regular academic year; credit given.

Degree Requirements: 122–127 credit hours; 2.0 GPA; 30 semester hours, including ½ of major requirements, in residence; general education requirements.

Fulfillment of some degree requirements and exemption from some beginning courses possible by passing College Board CLEP, AP, other standardized tests. *Grading system:* A–F; pass-fail; withdraw (carries time limit); satisfactory-unsatisfactory.

Distinctive Educational Programs: Honors program. Work-experience programs, including cooperative education, internships. Evening classes. Dual-degree programs in engineering with Case Western Reserve, Clarkson College of Technology, and SUNY Binghamton. Interdepartmental-interdisciplinary programs in African-Afro-American studies, American studies, applied mathematical economics, Asian studies, European medieval studies, forensic science, geochemistry, Industrial Training Program, international studies, Latin American area studies, management science, Native American studies, philosophy/psychology, public justice, Russian and East European studies, women's studies. Study abroad in Australia, England, France, Germany, Ireland, Italy, Mexico, Spain, Scotland, Wales. Unique degree programs in technology management, wellness management, women's studies, public relations, cognitive sciences, human computer interaction program, information science, technology education, zoology, meteorology.

ROTC: Army in cooperation with Syracuse University.

Degrees Conferred: 1,440 *baccalaureate*; 347 *master's*. Bachelor's degrees awarded in top five disciplines: education 405; business/marketing 300; social sciences 177; communications/journalism 147; psychology 137. Master's degrees awarded: various disciplines 347.

Fees and Other Expenses: *Full-time tuition per academic year 2008–09:* undergraduate resident $6,031, nonresident $12,291; contact the college for current graduate tuition/fees. *Required fees:* $1,010. *Room and board per academic year:* $10,170. *Books and supplies:* $800. *Other expenses:* $1,600.

Financial Aid: Aid from institutionally generated funds is provided on the basis of academic merit, other criteria.

Financial aid to full-time, first-time undergraduate students: 89% received some form of financial aid. Average amount of aid received: federal grants $3,654; Pell grants $2,966; other federal grants $797; state/local grants $2,436; institutional grants $2,658.

Departments and Teaching Staff: *Total instructional faculty:* 507 (full-time 319, part-time 188). 73% of faculty hold the doctorate, first-professional, or other terminal degree. Student/faculty ratio: 19:1.

Enrollment: Total enrollment 8,909. Undergraduate 7,971. Graduate 938. Undergraduate transfer-in students 688.

Characteristics of Student Body: *Ethnic/racial makeup:* number of Black non-Hispanic: 256; American Indian or Alaska Native: 35; Asian or Pacific Islander: 122; Hispanic: 242; White non-Hispanic: 5,813. *Age distribution:* number under 18: 10; 18–19: 2,258; 20–21: 2,598; 22–24: 1,405; 25–29: 374; 30–34: 136; 35–39: 113; 40–49: 149; 50–64: 53.

International Students: 143 nonresident aliens enrolled fall 2008. Students from Europe, Asia, Central and South Latin America, Africa, Canada, Middle East. No programs available to aid students whose native language is not English. No financial aid specifically designated for international students.

Student Life: On-campus residence halls house 58% of full-time undergraduate student body. The campus has more than 120 extracurricular organizations covering social, academic, cultural and intellectual interests. Intercollegiate athletics includes 21 varsity teams: basketball, cross-country, golf, field hockey, ice hockey, lacrosse, soccer, softball, swimming and diving, tennis, track and field, wrestling. *Special regulations:* Cars permitted in designated areas. *Special services:* Learning Resources Center, medical services, free campus bus system. *Student publications, radio: Ontarian*, a yearbook; *Oswegonian*, a weekly newspaper. Radio stations WNYO and WRVO broadcast 126 and 133 hours per week, respectively. *Surrounding community:* Oswego population 18,096.

Library Collections: 475,000 volumes including bound books, serial backfiles, electronic documents, and government documents not in separate collections. Online catalog. Current serial subscriptions: 182,305 via electronic access. 32,359 audiovisual materials. Computer work stations available. Students have access to the Internet at no charge.

Most important special holdings include Millard Fillmore Papers; college archives and local history.

Buildings and Grounds: Campus area 641 acres.

Chief Executive Officer: Dr. Deborah F. Stanley, President.

Undergraduates address admission inquiries to Dr. Joseph Grant, Vice President for Student Affairs and Enrollment Management; graduate inquiries to Dr. David King, Dean of Graduate Studies.

State University of New York College at Plattsburgh

101 Broad Street
Plattsburgh, New York 12901-2681
Tel: (518) 564-2000 **E-mail:** admissions@plattsburgh.edu
Fax: (518) 564-2045 **Internet:** www.plattsburgh.edu

Institution Description: *Enrollment:* 6,358. *Degrees offered:* Baccalaureate, master's. Certificates also awarded.

Accreditation: *Regional:* MSA. *Professional*: computer science, nursing, teacher education

History: Established as Plattsburgh State Normal School 1889; offered first instruction at postsecondary level 1890; awarded first degree 1892; changed name to State Teachers College of Education 1959; adopted present name 1961.

Institutional Structure: *Composition of institution:* Administrators 41. Academic affairs headed by provost/vice president for academic affairs. Management/business/finances directed by senior business officer. Full-time instructional faculty 263. Academic governance body, Faculty Senate, meets an average of 10 times per year.

Calendar: Semesters. Academic year Aug. to May. Freshmen admitted Aug., Jan. Degrees conferred May, Dec. Formal commencement May. Summer session from late May to mid-Aug.

Characteristics of Freshmen: 6,909 applicants (3949 female, 29,60 male). 49% of applicants admitted. 30% of applicants admitted and enrolled full-time.

98% (1,009 students) submitted SAT scores; 29 (300 students) submitted ACT scores. *25th percentile*: SAT Critical Reading 480, SAT Math 490; ACT Composite 20, ACT English 19, ACT Math 19. *75th percentile*: SAT Critical Reading 560, SAT Math 580; ACT Composite 25, ACT English 24, ACT Math 25.

62% of entering freshmen expected to graduate within 5 years. 89% of freshmen from New York. Freshmen from 32 states and 21 foreign countries.

Admission: Rolling admissions plan. For fall acceptance, apply as early as Sept. of previous year, but not later than June of year of enrollment. Early acceptance available. *Requirements:* Either graduation from accredited secondary school with 4 units English, 6 mathematics/science, 2 history, 2 social studies; or GED. Recommend 2 units foreign language, 3 additional units mathematics, 3 additional science. Minimum 3.0 GPA. *Entrance tests:* College Board SAT or ACT. *For transfer students:* 2.0 minimum GPA; from 4-year accredited institution 89 hours maximum transfer credit; from 2-year accredited institution 72 semester hours.

College credit and advanced placement for postsecondary-level work completed in secondary school and for extrainstitutional learning (life experience).

Tutoring available. Noncredit Developmental-remedial courses offered during regular academic year.

Degree Requirements: 120 semester hours; 2.0 GPA; 36 semester hours in residence; academic major requirements; general education requirements. Fulfillment of some degree requirements and exemption from some beginning courses possible by passing College Board CLEP. *Grading system:* A–F; pass-fail; withdraw (carries time limit).

Distinctive Educational Programs: Evening classes. Accelerated degree programs. Dual-degree programs in engineering with Clarkson College of Technology, State University of New York Colleges at Binghamton, Buffalo, Stony Brook. Interdisciplinary programs in Asian studies, Canadian studies, Latin American studies, international business, speech and hearing services, master of science in teaching, minority studies, women's studies. Five-year BA-MS programs in French Adolescence and Spanish Adolescence added; also added were programs in mental health, counseling, global supply chain management and ecology. Facilities and programs for independent research, including honors programs, individual majors. Study abroad programs in Argentina, Australia, Chile, Uruguay, England, and Canada.

Degrees Conferred: 1,103 *baccalaureate:*; 277 *master's*. Bachelors' degrees awarded in top five disciplines: business, management, marketing, and related support services 231; education 190; communications/journalism 103; health professions and related clinical sciences 84; security and protective services 79. Master's degrees awarded: education 221; health professions 12; liberal arts/general studies 26; psychology 11.

Fees and Other Expenses: *Full-time tuition per academic year 2008–09:* undergraduate resident $5,429, nonresident $11,689; contact the college for current graduate tuition. *Required fees:* $987. *Room and board per academic year:* $8,250. *Books and supplies:* $950. *Other expenses:* $1,981.

Financial Aid: Aid from institutionally generated funds is provided on the basis of academic merit, financial need.

Financial aid to full-time, first-time undergraduate students: 90% received some form of financial aid. Average amount of aid received: federal grants $1,511; state/local grants $2,004; institutional grants $4,119; loans $2,351.

Departments and Teaching Staff: *Total instructional faculty:* 487 (full-time 263, part-time 224). Student/faculty ratio: 16:1. Degrees held by full-time faculty: doctorate 94%, master's 6%, 55% hold terminal degrees.

Enrollment: Total enrollment 6,358. Undergraduate 5,736. Graduate 622. Undergraduate transfer-in students 592.

Characteristics of Student Body: *Ethnic/racial makeup:* number of Black non-Hispanic 274; American Indian or Native Alaskan 24; Asian or Pacific Islander 111; Hispanic 228; White non-Hispanic 4,115; unknown 463. *Age distribution:* number under 18: 23; 18–19: 1,809; 20–21: 1,899; 22–24: 1,184; 25–29: 334; 30–34: 109; 35–39: 72; 40–49: 108; 50–64: 27; 65 and over: 2.

International Students: 363 nonresident aliens enrolled fall 2008. Students from Europe, Asia, Central and South America, Africa, Canada, Australia, Middle East. Programs available to aid students whose native language is not English: social, cultural. English as a Second Language Program. Some financial aid specifically designated for international students.

Student Life: On-campus residence halls house 50% of student body. *Intercollegiate athletics:* Basketball, cross-country, hockey, soccer, swimming, tennis, track, volleyball. *Special regulations:* Registered cars permitted in designated areas. *Special services:* Learning Center, medical services. *Student publications, radio, television: Cardinal Points*, a newspaper. Radio station WPLT broadcasts 193 hours per week. TV station PSTV broadcasts 20 hours per week. *Surrounding community:* Plattsburgh population 21,500. Montreal (Canada), 60 miles from campus, is nearest metropolitan area. Served by airport 3 miles from campus; passenger rail service 2 miles from campus.

Library Collections: 300,000 volumes. 307,409 government documents; 926,800 microforms; 24,200 audiovisual materials; 1,450 periodical subscriptions. Computer work stations available. Students have access to online information retrieval services.

Buildings and Grounds: Campus area 264 acres.

STATE UNIVERSITY OF NEW YORK COLLEGE AT PLATTSBURGH—*cont'd*

Chief Executive Officer: Dr. John Ettling, President.

Address undergraduate admission inquiries to Richard Higgins, Director of Admissions; graduate inquiries to Sharon Derr, Assistant Director of Graduate Admission.

State University of New York College at Potsdam

44 Pierrepont Avenue
Potsdam, New York 13676-2294
Tel: (315) 267-2000 **E-mail:** admissions@potsdam.edu
Fax: (315) 267-2163 **Internet:** www.potsdam.edu

Institution Description: *Enrollment:* 4,328. *Degrees awarded:* Baccalaureate, master's.

Member of the consortium Associated Colleges of the St. Lawrence Valley.

Accreditation: *Regional:* MSA. *Professional*: business, music, teacher education

History: Established as St. Lawrence Academy 1816; changed name to Potsdam Normal School and offered first instruction at postsecondary level 1869; awarded awarded first degree 1871; changed name to State Teacher's College 1942; adopted present name 1948. *See* W. Charles Lahey, *The Potsdam Tradition* (New York: Meredith Publishing Company, 1966) for further information.

Institutional Structure: *Composition of institution:* Administrators 147. Academic affairs headed by provost. Business/finances directed by vice president for business affairs. Full-time instructional faculty 217. Academic governance body, Faculty Assembly, meets an average of 10 times per year.

Calendar: Semesters. Academic year Aug. to May. Freshmen admitted Aug., Jan., July. Degrees conferred May, Aug., Dec. Formal commencement May.

Characteristics of Freshmen: 3,539 applicants (1,914 female, 1,625 male). 71% of applicants accepted. 30% of accepted applicants enrolled.

92% (692 students) submitted SAT scores. *25th percentile*: SAT Critical Reading 470, SAT Math 480. *75th percentile*: SAT Critical Reading 580, SAT Math 590.

96% of freshmen from New York. Freshmen from 10 states and 7 foreign countries.

Admission: Rolling admissions plan. For fall acceptance, apply as early as Sept. of previous year but not later than Feb. 15 of year of enrollment. Students are notified of acceptance immediately upon completion of application reviewed. Early acceptance available. *Requirements:* Either graduation from accredited secondary school with 17 units from among English, foreign languages, mathematics, science, social studies; or GED. For music program, an audition is required; for art program, portfolio recommended. Lowest acceptable secondary school class standing 50th percentile. *Entrance tests:* College Board SAT or ACT composite. *For transfer students:* 2.0 minimum GPA; from 4-year accredited institution 90 semester hours maximum transfer credit; from 2-year accredited institution 75 semester hours; correspondence/extension students 60 semester hours.

College credit and advanced placement for postsecondary-level work completed in secondary school and for extrainstitutional learning on basis of faculty assessment.

Tutoring available.

Degree Requirements: Completion of 120 credit hours (not including 4 credit hours of physical education courses). Completion of 90 hours of liberal arts credit for B.A. students; 75 hours for B.S. students, and 36 hours (exclusive of music) for B.M. students. *Grading system:* 0=4; pass-fail; withdraw (carries time limit).

Distinctive Educational Programs: Student internships and service learning experiences are available. First-year Experience Program. Study abroad and National Student Exchange opportunities are available. Honors programs, individual majors, tutorials.

ROTC: Army and Air Force in cooperation with Clarkson University.

Degrees Conferred: 679 *baccalaureate*; 420 *master's*. Bachelor's degrees awarded in top five disciplines: education 177; visual and performing arts 89; social sciences 72; business, management, marketing, and related support services 72; psychology 62. Master's degrees awarded: computer and information sciences 10; education 401; mathematics and statistics 1; visual and performing arts 5.

Fees and Other Expenses: *Full-time tuition per academic year 2008–09:* undergraduate resident $5,429, nonresident $11,689; contact the university for current graduate tuition. *Required fees:* $950. *Room and board per academic year:* $8,250. *Books and supplies:* $950. *Other expenses:* $1,980..

Financial Aid: The university offers a direct lending program. Aid from institutionally generated funds is provided on the basis of academic merit, financial need.

Financial aid to full-time, first-time undergraduate students: 93% received some form of financial aid. Average amount of aid received: federal grants $3,084; state/local grants $2,057; institutional grants $2,951; loans $4,570.

Departments and Teaching Staff: *Total instructional faculty:* 327 (full-time 237, part-time 90). 63% of faculty hold the doctorate, first-professional, or other terminal degree:. Student/faculty ratio: 15:1.

Enrollment: Total enrollment 4,329. Undergraduate 3,619.

Characteristics of Student Body: *Ethnic/racial makeup:* number of Black non-Hispanic: 63; American Indian or Alaska Native: 66; Asian or Pacific Islander: 48; Hispanic: 58; White non-Hispanic: 2,771; unknown: 411. *Age distribution (undergraduate):* number under 18: 10; 18–19: 1,193; 20–21: 1,222; 22–24: 712; 25–29: 184; 30–34: 84; 35–39: 51; 40–49: 62; 50–64: 19; 65 and over: 2.

International Students: 123 nonresident aliens enrolled fall 2008. Programs available to aid international students: variable number of scholarships available annually for both graduate and undergraduate international students.

Student Life: On-campus residence halls house 520% of student body. Students can choose from among five modern residence halls. All student rooms have a computer network connection for each student. *Intercollegiate athletics:* male: basketball, ice hockey, lacrosse, soccer, swimming, tennis; female: basketball, field hockey, ice hockey, swimming, tennis, volleyball; both genders: horseback riding. 80 clubs and organizations. *Special regulations:* Cars with permits allowed in designated areas. *Special services:* Learning Resources Center, medical services. *Student publications: Perspectives*, an annual literary magazine; *Pioneer*, a yearbook; *Raquette*, a weekly newspaper. *Surrounding community:* Potsdam population 10,500.

Library Collections: 467,000 volumes, serial backfiles, electronic documents, and government documents. Current serial subscriptions 933 paper, 12 microform, 15,556 via electronic access. 15,570 recordings. Students have access to online information retrieval services.

Most important special holdings include Bertrand Snell Papers; Julia Crane Papers; Helen Hosmer Papers.

Buildings and Grounds: Campus area 240 acres.

Chief Executive Officer: Dr. John F. Schwaller, President.

Address undergraduate admission inquiries to Thomas W. Nesbitt, Director of Admissions; graduate inquiries to Dr. William J. Amoriell, Dean, School of Education and Professional Studies.

State University of New York at Purchase College

735 Anderson Hill Road
Purchase, New York 10577
Tel: (914) 251-6000 **E-mail:** admissions@brick.purchase.edu
Fax: (914) 251-6314 **Internet:** www.purchase.edu

Institution Description: *Enrollment:* 4,251. *Degrees awarded:* Baccalaureate, master's.

Accreditation: *Regional:* MSA.

History: Established 1967; offered first instruction at postsecondary level 1969; awarded first degree 1973.

Institutional Structure: *Composition of institution:* Three academic units (College of Letters and Science, School of the Arts, Continuing Education program) under the direction of the senior vice president for academic affairs; vice presidents for student affairs and external affairs and development. Full-time instructional faculty 120. Academic governance body, All College Senate, meets an average of 8 times per year.

Calendar: Semesters. Academic year Aug. to May. Freshmen admitted Aug., Jan. Degrees conferred May, Jan. Formal commencement May. Summer session of 1 term from mid-June to late July.

Characteristics of Freshmen: 8,906 applicants (5,409 female, 3,496 male). 24% of applicants admitted 33% of admitted students enrolled full-time.

91% (643 students) submitted SAT scores. 22% (159 students) submitted ACT scores. *25th percentile*: SAT Critical Reading 520, SAT Math 490; ACt Composite 22, ACT English 21, ACT Math 19. *75th percentile*: SAT Critical Reading 620, SAT Math 590; ACT Composite 26, ACT English 27, ACT Math 26.

82% of freshmen from New York. Freshmen from 39 states and 24 foreign countries.

Admission: Rolling admissions plan. For fall entry, apply no later than March 1 for the School of the Arts, July 1 for the College of Letters and Science. Fall decisions for the College of Letters and Science are released beginning Dec. 1 of the prior year; for the School of the Arts decisions are released as required audition, slide review, and interview results become available. *Requirements:* Secondary school diploma with minimum 16 units: 4 in English, 3 in foreign language, 4 in mathematics, 3 in natural sciences, 3 in social sciences, and 2 academic electives. A solid B average in the aforementioned areas. A GED is an acceptable substitute; minimum score 280 with no subject below 55. *Entrance tests:* SAT or ACT accepted. *For transfer students:* 2.0 minimum GPA; good academic standing at previous institution with no incomplete grades unresolved. Maximum transfer credit is 90 semester hours, 75 for junior college transfers.

College credit and advanced placement for postsecondary-level work completed in secondary school. Tutoring available. Developmental/remedial courses offered; credit given.

Degree Requirements: 120 semester hours; 4 semesters in residence. Additional requirements for some programs. *Grading system:* A–F; high pass/pass-no credit; withdraw (carries time limit).

Distinctive Educational Programs: Day and evening classes. Full-time and part-time degree programs. Individualized and interdisciplinary programs. Students in the arts programs may study abroad in Amsterdam.

Degrees Conferred: 743 *baccalaureate*; 46 *master's*. Bachelor's degrees awarded in top five disciplines: visual and performing arts 291; liberal arts and sciences, general studies, and humanities 178; social sciences 56; English language/literature 49; psychology 38. Master's degrees awarded: visual and performing arts 46.

Fees and Other Expenses: *Full-time tuition per academic year 2008–09:* \$5,801 resident, \$12,061 nonresident. *Books and supplies:* \$1,100. *Room and board per academic year:* \$9,908. *Other expenses:* \$1,200.

Financial Aid: Aid from institutionally generated funds is provided on the basis of academic merit, financial need. Institution has a Program Participation Agreement with the U.S. Department of Education for eligible students to receive Pell Grants and, depending upon the agreement, other federal aid.

Financial aid to full-time, first-time undergraduate students: 80% received some form of financial aid. Average amount of aid received: federal grants \$3,859, Pell grants \$3,136; other federal grants \$849; state/local grants \$2,263; institutional grants \$2,834.

Departments and Teaching Staff: *Total instructional faculty:* 263. Student/faculty ratio: 22:1. 100% of faculty hold the doctorate, first-professional, or other terminal degree.

Enrollment: Total enrollment 4,251. Undergraduate 4,106. Graduate 145. Undergraduate transfer-in students 327.

Characteristics of Student Body: *Ethnic/racial makeup:* Black non-Hispanic: 8%; American Indian or Alaska Native: .4%; Asian or Pacific Islander: 3.6%; Hispanic: 9.4%; White non-Hispanic: 54.8%; unknown: 22.7%.

International Students: 51 undergraduate nonresident aliens enrolled fall 2008. Programs available to aid students whose native language is not English: English as a Second Language Program. No financial aid specifically designated for international students.

Student Life: 70% of the matriculated students live on campus in coed and single-sex residence environments. *Intercollegiate athletics:* male: tennis, soccer (females permitted), fencing (female permitted); female: tennis, volleyball. Full intramural and open recreation program available. Sports clubs include: ultimate frisbee, hiking, running, weight lifting, and archery. *Special regulations:* Cars permitted without restrictions. *Special services:* Medical services, campus transportation system, Academic Resource Center. *Student publications, radio: The Load*, a newspaper; radio station WPUR. *Surrounding community:* Purchase, located in Westchester County, is 45 minutes by car from midtown Manhattan.

Library Collections: 275,000 volumes including bound books, serial backfiles, electronic documents, and government documents not in separate collections. Online catalog. 1,400 current periodical subscriptions. 16,700 audiovisual materials. 253,000 microforms. Computer work stations available. Students have access to the Internet at no charge.

Most important special holdings include Noah Greenberg-New York Pro Musica Antiqua Collection; Gerald McDonald Collection on Cinema; Peter Pauper Press editions.

Buildings and Grounds: Campus area 500 acres.

Chief Executive Officer: Dr. Thomas J. Schwarz, President.

Address admission inquiries to Dennis Craig, Vice President for Admissions.

State University of New York College of Agriculture and Technology at Cobleskill

Cobleskill, New York 12043

Tel: (518) 255-5523 **E-mail:** admissions@cobleskill.edu
Fax: (518) 255-5333 **Internet:** www.cobleskill.edu

Institution Description: The SUNY College of Agriculture and Technology at Cobleskill is a public institution. *Enrollment:* 2,615. *Degrees awarded:* Associate, baccalaureate.

Accreditation: *Regional:* MSA. *Professional*: histologic technology

History: Founded 1916.

Institutional Structure: Semesters. Academic year Aug. to May.

Calendar: 3m713 applicants (1,808 female, 1,905 male). 79% of applicants admitted. 89% of admitted students enrolled full-time.

84% (334 students) submitted SAT scores; 18% (89 students) submitted ACT scores. *25th percentile*: SAT Critical Reading 460, SAT Math 480; ACT Composite 19. *75th percentile*: SAT Critical Reading 550, SAT Math 550; ACT Composite 23.

20% of entering freshmen expected to graduate within 5 years. 90% of freshmen from New York. Freshmen from 15 states and 16 foreign countries.

Admission: Graduation from an accredited secondary school or GED; college preparatory course in high school recommended.

Degree Requirements: *For baccalaureate degrees:* 126 credit hours; 2.0 GPA. *For associate degrees:* 66 credit hours; 2.0 GPA.

Degrees Conferred: 361 *associate;* 203 *baccalaureate:* agriculture 98; business/marketing 25; computer and information sciences 26; family and consumer science 9; natural resources and environmental science 2; other 51.

Fees and Other Expenses: *Full-time tuition per academic year 2008–09:* resident \$5.611. nonresident \$11.871. *Books and supplies* \$1,200. *Room and board per academic year:* \$9,010. *Other expenses:* \$2,092.

Financial Aid: Aid from institutionally generated funds is provided on the basis of academic merit, financial need, other criteria.

Financial aid to full-time, first-time undergraduate students: 81% received some form of financial aid. Average amount of aid received: federal grants \$2,510; state/local grants \$2,130; institutional grants \$1,352; loans \$3,002.

Departments and Teaching Staff: *Total instructional faculty:* 146. Student/faculty ratio: 18.4:1. Degrees held by full-time faculty: doctorate 35%, master's 63%, baccalaureate 2%.

Enrollment: *Total enrollment:* 2,615. Transfer-in students 188.

International Students: 64 nonresident aliens enrolled fall 2008. Programs available to aid students whose native language is not English: English as a Second Language. No financial aid specifically designated for international students.

Student Life: On-campus housing available for 80% of student body. Cars permitted without restriction. *Student activities:* Various organizations and groups. *Surrounding community:* Cobleskill is located 35 miles west of Albany in a rural area.

Library Collections: 125,000 volumes. Online catalog. 56,000 audiovisual materials; 12,882 microform units. 1,000 current periodical subscriptions. Computer work stations available. Students have access to the Internet at no charge.

Buildings and Grounds: Campus area 750 acres.

Chief Executive Officer: Dr. Thomas J. Haas, President.

Address admission inquiries to Christopher L. Tacea, Director of Admissions.

State University of New York College of Agriculture and Technology at Farmingdale

SEE Farmingdale State University of New York

State University of New York College of Agriculture and Technology at Morrisville

SEE Morrisville State College

State University of New York College of Environmental Science and Forestry

1 Forestry Drive
Syracuse, New York 13210
Tel: (315) 470-6500 **E-mail:** admissions@esf.edu
Fax: (315) 470-6779 **Internet:** www.esf.edu

Institution Description: State University of New York College of Environmental Science and Forestry offers primarily upper division baccalaureate and graduate study. *Enrollment:* 2,523. *Degrees awarded:* Associate, baccalaureate, master's, doctorate.

Accreditation: *Regional:* MSA. *Professional*: construction education, engineering, forestry, landscape architecture

History: Established as a state college and offered first instruction at postsecondary level 1911; awarded first degree 1913; adopted present name 1972. *See* George R. Armstrong, *Forestry College 1911–1961* (Syracuse: Alumni Association, 1961) for further information.

Institutional Structure: *Composition of institution:* Administrators 23. Academic affairs headed by vice president of academic affairs/provost. Management/business/finances directed by vice president of administration. Student affairs directed by vice president of student affairs and institutional advancement. Full-time instructional faculty 123. Academic governance body, the faculty, meets an average of 6 times per year.

Calendar: Semesters. Academic year Aug. to May. Degrees conferred May, Aug., Dec. Formal commencement May. Summer session from June to July.

Characteristics of Freshmen: 1,545 applicants (667 female, 878 male). 49% of applicants admitted. 41% of admitted applicants enrolled full-time.

100% (209 students) submitted SAT scores; 38% (118 students) submitted ACT scores. *25th percentile*: SAT Critical Reading 520, SAT Math 540; ACT Composite 21. *75th percentile*: SAT Critical Reading 610, SAT Math 630; ACT Composite 27.

78% of entering freshmen expected to graduate within 5 years. 89% of freshmen from New York. Freshmen from 24 states and 8 foreign countries.

Admission: Selective admissions. High school seniors who have a minimum of 4 years of mathematics, science (including chemistry) and English are encouraged to apply for freshman entry. This option is available for all majors except the Forest Technology Program. High school seniors with three years of mathematics or science are encouraged to apply for the Guaranteed Transfer Admissions option. Applicants accepted under this option are given a guarantee of admissions for either the college sophomore or junior year of college. In addition, the college encourages students from other colleges who desire a degree to apply as transfer students. Those transfer students who have been following the lower division course requirements outlined the college catalog and possess a high GPA will be given first consideration. Freshmen are encouraged to have their applications completed by Jan. of the year they wish to enter. Transfer students should have their applications completed by May 1.

Degree Requirements: *For all associate degrees:* 76 credit hours; 2 terms in residence. *For all baccalaureate degrees:* 124–160 credit hours; 2.0 GPA; 24 of the last 30 credit hours in residence. *For all undergraduate degrees:* 2.0 GPA.

Some degree requirements may be fulfilled by passing College Board CLEP. *Grading system:* A–F.

Distinctive Educational Programs: Concurrent degree programs with Syracuse University. Special facilities for using telecommunications in the classroom. Interdisciplinary majors in environmental science. Honors programs. Tutorials. Study abroad program in landscape architecture.

ROTC: Army and Air Force offered in cooperation with Syracuse University.

Degrees Conferred: 38 *associate*; 265 *baccalaureate*; 97 *master's*; 22 *doctorate*. Bachelor's degrees awarded: architecture 41; biological and biomedical sciences 32; construction trades 18; engineering 22; natural resources and environmental sciences 89; physical sciences 10. Master's degrees awarded: architecture 16; biological and biomedical sciences 26; engineering 18; natural resources 34; physical sciences 3. Doctorates awarded: biological and biomedical sciences 2; engineering 7; natural resources 9; physical sciences 4.

Fees and Other Expenses: *Full-time tuition per academic year 2008–09:* $5,209 resident, nonresident $11,469. *Books and supplies:* $1,200. *Room and board per academic year:* $11,920. *Other expenses:* $1,050.

Financial Aid: Aid from institutionally generated funds is provided on the basis of academic merit, financial need, other criteria. Institution has a Program Participation Agreement with the U.S. Department of Education for eligible students to receive Pell Grants and, depending upon the agreement, other federal aid.

Financial aid to full-time, first-time undergraduate students: 93% received some form of financial aid. Average amount of aid received: federal grants $2,813; Pell grants $2,875; other federal grants $2,000; state/local grants $1,540; institutional grants $1,620.

Departments and Teaching Staff: *Total instructional faculty:* 140. Student/faculty ratio: 10:1. 95% of faculty hold the doctorate, first-professional, or other terminal degree.

Enrollment: Total enrollment 2,523. Undergraduate 2,014. Graduate 509. Undergraduate transfer-in students 165.

Characteristics of Student Body: *Ethnic/racial makeup:* number of Black non-Hispanic: 1%; American Indian or Alaska Native: .6%; Asian or Pacific Islander: 2.1%; Hispanic: 2.7%; White non-Hispanic: 12.6%.

International Students: 18 nonresident aliens enrolled fall 2008. Students from Europe, Asia, Central and south America, Africa, Canada. Programs available to aid students whose native language is not English: social, cultural. No financial aid specifically designated for international students.

Student Life: Residence halls available through Syracuse University. *Special regulations:* Cars permitted with restrictions. *Special services:* Learning Resources Center, medical services available through Syracuse University. *Student publications:* daily newspaper. *Surrounding community:* Syracuse population 165,000.

Library Collections: 135,500 volumes. 200,000 microforms; 1,200 audiovisual materials; 2,000 current periodical subscriptions. Online catalog. Students have access to online information retrieval services.

Most important special holdings include Fletcher Steele collection on landscape architecture; Thomas Cook collection on paper making.

Buildings and Grounds: Urban campus.

Chief Executive Officer: Dr. Cornelius B. Murphy, Jr., President.

Address admission inquiries to Susan H. Sanford, Director of Admissions.

State University of New York College of Optometry

33 West 42nd Street
New York, New York 10036
Tel: (212) 780-5100 **E-mail:** admissions@sunyopt.edu
Fax: (212) 780-5104 **Internet:** www.sunyopt.edu

Institution Description: *Enrollment:* 303. *Degrees awarded:* First-professional (optometry), master's, doctorate.

Accreditation: *Regional:* MSA. *Professional*: optometry

History: Established by New York State Legislature 1971; established Schnurmacher Institute for Vision Research.

Institutional Structure: *Composition of institution:* Administrators 12. Management/business/finances directed by vice president for business affairs. Full-time instructional faculty 79.

Calendar: Quarters. Academic year Aug. to May.

Admission: Modified rolling admissions plan. For fall acceptance, apply as early as Sept. 1 of previous year, but not later than Feb. 15 of year of enrollment. Students are notified of acceptance beginning Dec. 15. *Requirements:* For first-professional students, a minimum of 3 years college-level study which must include 1 year each in English composition and literature, organic chemistry, social science, general biology, general chemistry, general physics, 1 semester each of calculus (differential) general psychology, statistics. *Entrance tests:* OAT.

Degree Requirements: *For first-professional degree:* 4-year prescribed curriculum, including clinical work.

Degrees Conferred: 3 *master's:* health professions; 2 *doctorate:* health professions; 78 *first-professional:* optometry.

Fees and Other Expenses: *Full-time tuition per academic year 2008–09:* contact the college for current information regarding tuition, fees, housing, and other costs.

Financial Aid: Aid from institutionally generated funds is provided on the basis of academic merit, financial need. Institution has a Program Participation Agreement with the U.S. Department of Education for eligible students to receive Pell Grants and, depending upon the agreement, other federal aid.

Departments and Teaching Staff: *Total instructional faculty:* 123 (full-time 84, part-time 39). 100% of faculty hold the doctorate, first-professional, or other terminal degree. Student/faculty ratio: 4:1.

Enrollment: Total enrollment 303.

International Students: 23 nonresident aliens enrolled fall 2008. Students from Asia, Canada. No programs available to aid students whose native language is not English. Some financial aid specifically designated for qualifying international students.

Student Life: Some off-campus housing available. *Special services:* Tutorials, counseling, career planning and placement, National Optometric Student

Organization. *Student publications: Afterimages*, a yearbook. *Surrounding community:* New York City population over 7 million.

Library Collections: 40,000 volumes. 5,000 microforms; 2,175 audiovisual materials; 425 current periodical subscriptions. Students have access to online information retrieval services and the Internet.

Most important special holdings include collections on optometry/ophthalmology; learning disabilities; visual perception.

Chief Executive Officer: Dr. Alden N. Haffner, President. Address admission inquiries to Dr. Edward Johnston, Director of Admissions.

State University of New York College of Technology at Alfred

10 Upper College Drive
Alfred, New York 14802-1196
Tel: (607) 587-4215 **E-mail:** admissions@alfredstate.edu
Fax: (607) 587-4299 **Internet:** www.alfredstate.edu

Institution Description: The State University of New York College of Technology at Alfred is a public institution. *Enrollment:* 3,216. *Degrees awarded:* Associate, baccalaureate. Certificates also awarded.

Accreditation: *Regional:* MSA. *Professional*: clinical lab technology, engineering technology, medical record technology, nursing

History: SUNY College of Technology at Alfred was established in 1908.

Institutional Structure: Full-time instructional faculty 132.

Calendar: Semesters. Academic year Aug. to May.

Admission: College credit and advanced placement for postsecondary-level work completed in secondary school and for extrainstitutional learning.

Developmental/remedial courses offered in summer session and regular academic year; credit given.

Degree Requirements: Completion of prescribed curriculum. *Grading system:* A–F.

Degrees Conferred: 691 *associate*; 186 *baccalaureate:* business, management, marketing, and support services 47; computer and information sciences 44; construction trades 15, engineering technologies 80.

Fees and Other Expenses: *Full-time tuition per academic year 2008–09:* resident $5,498, nonresident $8,358. *Required fees:* $901. *Room and board per academic year:*$8,660. *Books and supplies:* $1,200. *Other expenses:* $2,550.

Financial Aid: Aid from institutionally generated funds is provided on the basis of academic merit, financial need, athletic ability, other criteria.

Financial aid to full-time, first-time undergraduate students: 92% received some form of financial aid. Average amount of aid received: federal grants $2,726; state/local grants $2,103; institutional grants $2,124; loans $4,817.

Departments and Teaching Staff: *Total instructional faculty:* 132. *Total tenured faculty:* 117. Student/faculty ratio: 18:1.

Enrollment: Total enrollment 3,276 (undergraduate). Transfer-in students 233.

International Students: 46 nonresident aliens enrolled fall 2008. No programs available to aid students whose native language is not English. No financial aid specifically designated for international students.

Library Collections: 72,000 volumes. Online catalog. 600 microform titles. 8,200 audiovisual materials. 450 current serial subscriptions. Students have access to online information retrieval services and the Internet.

Most important special holdings include Western New York Historical Collection.

Buildings and Grounds: Campus area 175 acres.

Chief Executive Officer: Dr. John B. Clark, President.

Address admissions inquiries to Valerie B. Noxon, Vice President for Enrollment Management.

State University College of Technology at Canton

34 Cornell Drive
Canton, New York 13617
Tel: (315) 386-7011 **E-mail:** admissions@canton.edu
Fax: (315) 386-7929 **Internet:** www.canton.edu

Institution Description: The college is a member institution of the State University of New York system. *Enrollment:* 2,970. *Degrees awarded:* Associate, baccalaureate.

Accreditation: *Regional:* MSA. *Professional*: engineering, mortuary science, nursing, occupational therapy, physical therapy assisting, veterinary medicine.

History: Founded in 1906 as the School of Agriculture at St. Lawrence University, SUNY Canton was the first postsecondary, two-year college in New York. in 1987 the college was given the present designation as State University of New York at Canton. Baccalaureate programs were inaugurated in 1997.

Institutional Structure: *Governing board:* SUNY Board of Regents. Academic affairs headed by provost. Institutional advancement, administrative services, and student affairs directed by separate vice presidents. Academic governance body, the Faculty Assembly, meets once per month.

Calendar: Semesters. Academic year Aug. to May.

Characteristics of Freshmen: 2,125 applicants (1,078 female, 1,055 male). 91% of applicants admitted. 39% of applicants admitted and enrolled full-time.

43% (334 students) submitted SAT scores; 14% (107 students) submitted ACT scores. *25th percentile*: SAT Critical Reading 390, SAT Math 400; ACT Composite 17. *75th percentile*: SAT Critical Reading 483, SAT Math 520; ACT Composite 21.

56% of freshmen expected to graduate within 5 years. 975 of freshmen from New York, Freshmen from 9 states and 4 foreign countries.

Admission: Rolling admissions. *Requirements:* Graduation from an accredited secondary school or GED. *SEE* website: www.canton,edu/admissions for further information.

Degree Requirements: *For all associate and baccalaureate degrees:* Completion of prescribed curricular programs.

Distinctive Educational Programs: SUNY Canton specializes in delivering a hands-on education for in-demand careers. Newly designed bachelor's degrees in Alternative and Renewable Energy Applications and Emergency and Disaster Management are tow examples of this innovative approach.

Degrees Conferred: 467 *associate*; 85 *baccalaureate<:* business, management, marketing, and related support services 22; computer and information sciences 10. health professions and related clinical sciences 14; security and protective services 39.

Fees and Other Expenses: *Full time tuition per academic year 2008–09:* resident $5,624, resident; $8,484 nonresident. *Required fees:* $1,145. *Books and supplies:* $1,200. *Room and board per academic year:* $8,970.

Financial Aid: Aid from institutionally generated funds is provided on the basis of academic merit, financial need. Institution has a Program Participation Agreement with the U.S. Department of Education for eligible students to receive Pell Grants and, depending upon the agreement, other federal aid.

Financial aid to full-time, first-time undergraduate students: 94% received some form of aid. Average amount of aid received: federal grants $1,511; state/local grants $2,004; institutional grants $4,119; loans $2,351.

Departments and Teaching Staff: *Total instructional faculty:* 168 (full-time 100, part-time 68). Student/faculty ratio: 20:1. Degrees held by full-time faculty: doctorate 21%, master's 47%, baccalaureate 20%, professional 4%. 30% hold terminal degrees.

Enrollment: Total enrollment 2,970 (undergraduate). Transfer-in students 260.

Characteristics of Student Body: *Ethnic/racial makeup:* number of Black non-Hispanic: 206; American Indian or Alaska Native: 44; Asian or Pacific Islander: 27; Hispanic: 86; White non-Hispanic: 2,201. *Age distribution:* number under 18: 67; 18–19: 1,003; 22–24: 660; 25–29: 228; 30–34: 110; 35–39: 90; 40–49: 110; 50–64: 26; 65 and over: 1. 15% of students attend summer sessions.

International Students: 20 nonresident aliens enrolled fall 2008. Students from Europe, Asia, Africa, Canada, Russia. Programs available to aid students whose native language is not English: social, cultural, financial.

Student Life: College-owned residence halls for 850 students are available. Students services include personal counseling, career advisement, educational planning, job placement assistance, legal services, handicapped services, health center, housing office. Yearbook, newspaper. A wide variety of student activities available. Intercollegiate male and female sports programs (basketball, soccer, softball, volleyball).

Library Collections: 68,000 volumes including bound books, serial backfiles, electronic documents, and govern documents not in separate collections. Online catalog. Current serial subscriptions: 237, 6 microform. 1,652 audio/videotapes; 89 DVD discs; 44 CD-ROMs. Computer work stations available. Students have access to online information retrieval services and the Internet.

Most import special collections include nursing and allied health, criminal justice, mortuary science.

Buildings and Grounds: Campus area 555 acres.

Chief Executive Officer: Dr. Joseph L. Kennedy, President.

Address admissions inquiries to Jodi Revill, Director of Admissions.

State University College of Technology at Delhi

2 Main Street
Delhi, New York 13753-1100
Tel: (607) 746-4000 **E-mail:** admissions@delhi.edu
Fax: (607) 746-4208 **Internet:** www.delhi.edu

Institution Description: The college is a member institution of the State University of New York system. *Enrollment:* 2,971. *Degrees awarded:* Associate, baccalaureate.

Accreditation: *Regional:* MSA. *Professional*: construction education, nursing, veterinary technology

History: Founded in 1911, the college is one of New York State's pioneers in the two-year concept of higher education. It began as the State School for Agriculture and Domestic Science and as served as an integral part of the SUNY system since 1948. Baccalaureate programs were inaugurated in 1995.

Institutional Structure: *Governing board:* SUNY Board of Regents.

Calendar: Semesters. Academic year Aug. to May.

Admission: *Requirements:* Graduation from an accredited secondary school or GED.

Degree Requirements: *For all associate and baccalaureate degrees:* Completion of prescribed curricular programs.

Distinctive Educational Programs: *For undergraduates:* Baccalaureate programs in golf course management and hospitality management. Associate in Applied Science program in veterinary science technology.

Degrees Conferred: 460 *associate*; 111 *baccalaureate*<: business, management, marketing, and related support services 101; computer and information sciences 10.

Fees and Other Expenses: *Full-time tuition per academic year 2008–09:* resident $3,605, nonresident $8,465. *Books and supplies:* $1,300. *Room and board per academic year:* $9,024. *Other expenses:* $1,436.

Financial Aid: Aid from institutionally generated funds is provided on the basis of academic merit, financial need. Institution has a Program Participation Agreement with the U.S. Department of Education for eligible students to receive Pell Grants and, depending upon the agreement, other federal aid.

Financial aid to full-time, first-time undergraduate students: 83% received some form of financial aid. Average amount of aid received: federal grants $2,874; state/local grants $2,588; institutional grants $1,586; loans $4,203.

Departments and Teaching Staff: *Total instructional faculty:* 117. Student/faculty ratio: 18:1. Degrees held by full-time faculty: doctorate 21%, master's 47%, baccalaureate 20%, professional 4%. 25% hold terminal degrees.

Enrollment: Total enrollment 2,971 (undergraduate). Transfer-in students 270.

Characteristics of Student Body: *Ethnic/racial makeup:* Black non-Hispanic: 12%; American Indian or Alaska Native: .2%; Asian or Pacific Islander: 1.5%; Hispanic: 6.2%; White non-Hispanic: 71.4%; unknown: 6.7%.

International Students: 51 nonresident aliens enrolled fall 2008. Students from Asia, Australia, Caribbean. Programs available to aid students whose native language is not English: social, cultural, financial.

Student Life: College-owned residence halls available. Students services include personal counseling, career advisement, educational planning, job placement assistance, legal services, handicapped services, health center, housing office. Yearbook, newspaper. A wide variety of student activities available. Intramural male and female sports program.

Library Collections: 70,000 volumes including bound books, serial backfiles, electronic documents, and govern documents not in separate collections. Online catalog. Current serial subscriptions: 375 paper, 37 microform, 14 electronic. 566 recordings. 42 computer work stations. Students have access to online information retrieval services and the Internet.

Most import special collections include turf and golf management collection; Delaware County and Regional History Collection; federal documents collection.

Buildings and Grounds: Campus area 625 acres.

Chief Executive Officer: Dr. Candace S. Vancko, President.

Address admissions inquiries to Robert Mazzel, Director of Admissions.

State University of New York Empire State College

2 Union Avenue
Saratoga Springs, New York 12866
Tel: (800) 847-3000 **E-mail:** admissions@esc.edu
Fax: (518) 587-5592 **Internet:** www.esc.edu

Institution Description: Empire State College is the external degree-granting branch of the State University of New York, with 7 regional centers and 35 locations in New York State. *Enrollment:* 13,614. *Degrees awarded:* Associate, baccalaureate, master's.

Member of the consortium Hudson-Mohawk Association of Colleges and Universities.

Accreditation: *Regional:* MSA.

History: Established, chartered, and offered first instruction at postsecondary level 1971; awarded first degree 1972.

Institutional Structure: *Composition of institution:* Administrators 24. Academic affairs headed by vice president for academic affairs. Management/business/finances directed by vice president for administration. Full-time instructional faculty 135.

Calendar: Beginning in fall 2008, the college implemented a five-term academic calendar, consisting of four 15-week terms that begin in September, November, January, and March. A fifth term beginning in May includes both an 8-week session and a 15-week sessions. In the past, the college offered 48 different study start-dates and term reporting was based on the aggregation of start dates.

Admission: Rolling admissions plan. *Requirements:* Either graduation from secondary school, its equivalent, or the ability to benefit from college study as evidenced by acceptable score on SAT, ACT, or other acceptable examination. *For transfer students:* 2.0 minimum GPA; from 4-year accredited institution maximum transfer credit limited only by residence requirement; from 2-year accredited institution 64 hours.

College credit for extrainstitutional learning (life experience) on basis of portfolio assessment.

Degree Requirements: *For all associate degrees:* 64 credit hours; 24 credits in residence; must include 30 credits across seven of the ten education knowledge and skill areas. *For all baccalaureate degrees:* 128 credit hours; 32 credits in residence; minimum of 45 advanced level credits with a minimum of 24 in the concentration. *For all degrees:* liberal studies requirements.

Fulfillment of some degree requirements possible by passing College Board CLEP, other standardized tests, college-evaluated experiential learning. *Grading system:* A–F; Descriptive reports only.

Distinctive Educational Programs: The college provides students with choices regarding how best to earn credit toward a degree. A number of flexible education options are offered such as: guided independent study; distance learning; study groups, residencies, internships, and cross-registration. Students may also request academic credit for life learning that is college-level.

In addition, the FORUM Management Education program is offered as a bachelor's degree program designed for experienced business professionals looking for an accelerated path to a degree. Other programs include: Harry Van Arsdale Jr. Center for Labor Studies; International Programs; Verizon Corporate College Program; Studio Semester Program; Photojournalism Program; a combined bachelor's/master's degree in business; Master of Arts Teaching Program.

Degrees Conferred: 618 *associate;* 2,181 *baccalaureate*; 123 *master's*<. Bachelor's degrees awarded in top five disciplines: business/marketing 1,133; public administration and social services 142; interdisciplinary studies 291; physical sciences 144; psychology 142. Master's degrees awarded: business/marketing 54; liberal arts/general studies 35; social sciences 34.

Fees and Other Expenses: *Full-time tuition per academic year 2008–09:* undergraduate resident $4,575, nonresident $10,835. *Required fees:* $225. No housing necessary as courses are by distance learning.

Financial Aid: Aid from institutionally generated funds is provided on the basis of academic merit, financial need.

Financial aid to full-time, first-time undergraduate students: 72% received some form of financial aid.

Departments and Teaching Staff: *Total instructional faculty:* 1,118 (full-time 155, part-time 903). Total faculty with doctorate, first-professional, or other terminal degree: 149. Student/faculty ratio: 11:1.

Enrollment: Total enrollment 13,614. Undergraduate 12,766. Graduate 848. Undergraduate transfer-in students 3,095.

Characteristics of Student Body: *Ethnic/racial makeup:* number of Black non-Hispanic: 833; American Indian or Alaska Native: 85; Asian or Pacific Islander: 219; Hispanic: 915; White non-Hispanic: 9,262, unknown: 2,097. *Age distribution:* number under 18: 13; 18–19: 173; 20–21: 623; 22–24: 1,776; 25–

29: 2,542; 30–34: 2,132; 35–39: 2,132; 40–49: 3,799; 50–64: 1,811; 65 and over: 39.

International Students: 747 international students enrolled fall 2008. Students from Europe, Asia, Central and South America, Canada, Middle East. No programs available to aid students whose native language is not English. No financial aid specifically designated for international students.

Library Collections: Students use State University of New York and community libraries. The college maintains web-based online library resources at www.esc.edu/library.

Chief Executive Officer: Dr. Joseph B. Moore, President.

Address admission inquiries to Jennifer Riley, Assistant Director of Admissions.

State University of New York Health Science Center at Brooklyn

450 Clarkson Avenue
Brooklyn, New York 11203-2098
Tel: (718) 270-1000 **E-mail:** admissions@downstate..edu
Fax: (718) 270-7592 **Internet:** www.downstate.edu

Institution Description: State University of New York Health Science Center at Brooklyn, formerly Downstate Medical Center, is a state institution offering upper division baccalaureate and first-professional degrees. Graduate degrees offered through School of Graduate Studies. Total enrollment: 1,613. *Degrees awarded:* Baccalaureate, first-professional (medicine), master's, doctorate. Certificates also awarded.

Accreditation: *Regional:* MSA. *Professional*: diagnostic medical sonography, medical record administration, medicine, nuclear medicine technology, nursing, occupational therapy, physical therapy

History: Established as teaching division of Long Island College Hospital 1858; offered first instruction at postsecondary level 1860; awarded first degree (first-professional) 1862; changed name to Long Island College of Medicine 1930; merged with the State University of New York and changed name to Downstate Medical Center 1950; College of Health Related Professions and School of Graduate Studies established 1966; College of Nursing established 1967; adopted present name 1986. *See* Evelyn Goodwin, *Medical Education in Brooklyn—The First Hundred Years* (New York: Downstate Medical Center Public Relations Office, n.d.) for further information.

Institutional Structure: *Composition of institution:* President; vice presidents for academic affairs, administration/finance, university affairs; executive director of hospital. 13 administrative offices, 16 clinical departments, 6 basic science departments in academic affairs division; 12 administrative offices in administration/finance division. Full-time instructional faculty 134.

Calendar: Semesters. Academic year early Sept. to mid-June. No summer session.

Admission: Rolling admissions plan. For fall acceptance, apply as early as Sept. of previous year, but not later than Aug. of year of enrollment. *Requirements:* 60 semester credits from accredited college or university. Specific course and credit requirements vary with program. Minimum 2.0 GPA. *Entrance tests:* College Board SAT. *For transfer students:* 2.0 minimum GPA; from 4-year and 2-year accredited institutions 60 semester hours maximum transfer credit.

College credit and advanced placement for postsecondary-level work completed in secondary school and for extrainstitutional learning.

Degree Requirements: *For undergraduate degrees:* 2.0 GPA; core requirements. Additional requirements vary with program. *Grading system:* A–F; withdraw (deadline after which pass-fail is appended to withdraw).

Distinctive Educational Programs: Honors program. Medical Scientist Training Program awarding M.D.-Ph.D. Dual-degree programs in nursing with Brooklyn College, State University College at Old Westbury.

Degrees Conferred: 189 *baccalaureate*; 125 *master's;*; 16 *doctorate*; 198 *first-professional*.

Fees and Other Expenses: *Full-time tuition per academic year 2008–09:* contact the center for current tuition, fees, and expenses.

Financial Aid: Aid from institutionally generated funds is provided on the basis of academic merit, financial need. Institution has a Program Participation Agreement with the U.S. Department of Education for eligible students to receive Pell Grants and, depending upon the agreement, other federal aid.

Departments and Teaching Staff: *Total instructional faculty:* 134. Degrees held by full-time faculty: doctorate 17%, master's 12%, baccalaureate 5%, professional 66%. 76% hold terminal degrees.

Enrollment: *Total enrollment:* 1,613. Undergraduate 324. Graduate 1,289. Undergraduate transfer-in students 89.

Characteristics of Student Body: *Ethnic/racial makeup:* Black non-Hispanic: 50%; Asian or Pacific Islander: 7%; Hispanic: 7%; White non-Hispanic: 32%; unknown: 4%. *Age distribution:* 17–21: 8.1%; 22–24: 41.4%; 25–29: 31.4%; 30–34: 11.5%; 35–39: 3.3%; 40–49: 3.5%; 50–59: 6%; 60–up: 0.2%.

International Students: 5 undergraduate nonresident aliens enrolled fall 2008. No programs available to aid students whose native language is not English. No financial aid specifically designated for international students.

Student Life: On-campus residence halls house 400 students. *Special regulations:* Cars are permitted without restrictions. *Special services:* Student health service, student center. *Surrounding community:* New York City population over 7 million.

Library Collections: 258,000 volumes. 1,660 current periodical subscriptions. Online catalog. Students have access to online information retrieval services and the Internet.

Most important special holdings include Gamble-Curran medical history collection; Brooklyn medical archives.

Buildings and Grounds: Campus area 14 square acres, including 372-bed teaching hospital.

Chief Executive Officer: Dr. John C. Larosa, President.

Address admission inquiries to Thomas S. Sabia, Director of Admissions.

State University of New York Health Science Center at Syracuse

750 East Adams Street
Syracuse, New York 13210
Tel: (315) 464-5540 **E-mail:** admiss@hscsyr.edu
Fax: (315) 464-8823 **Internet:** www.hscsyr.edu

Institution Description: State University of New York Health Science Center at Syracuse, formerly Upstate Medical Center, is a state institution. *Enrollment:* 1,374. *Degrees awarded:* Baccalaureate, first-professional (medicine), master's, doctorate.

Accreditation: *Regional:* MSA. *Professional*: blood bank technology, cytotechnology, medicine, nursing, perfusion, physical therapy, psychology internship, radiography, respiratory therapy

History: Established 1834; offered first instruction at postsecondary level and awarded first degree 1835.

Institutional Structure: *Composition of institution:* Administrators 79. Academic affairs headed by provost. Management/business/finances directed by directed by vice president for finance and management. Full-time instructional faculty 551.

Calendar: Semesters. Dates of academic year vary by program. Degrees conferred Jan., May, Aug. Formal commencement May. Summer session of 1 term from mid-May to mid-Aug.

Admission: Rolling admissions plan. For fall acceptance, apply as early as July 1 of previous year. Early acceptance available. *Requirements:* Primarily an upper-division college requiring 60–70 semester hours of previous college work. Prerequisites vary by major. Medical school admission requires 6–8 college credits each in English, biology, physics with laboratory, 4–6 credits in each of inorganic and organic chemistry with laboratory. *Entrance tests:* College Board SAT or ACT composite. *For transfer students:* 2.0 minimum GPA; 30 hours maximum transfer credit.

College credit and advanced placement for postsecondary-level work completed in secondary school. College credit for extrainstitutional learning on basis of faculty assessment.

Degree Requirements: Credit requirements vary by degree and program. *For all undergraduate degrees:* 2.0 GPA; residency requirement.

Fulfillment of some degree requirements possible by passing College Board CLEP. *Grading system:* A–F; withdraw. Medical School grading system is modified pass/fail.

Distinctive Educational Programs: Tutorials.

Degrees Conferred: 94 *baccalaureate:* health professions; 33 *master's;* health professions; 40 *doctorate:* health professions; 157 *first-professional:* medicine.

Fees and Other Expenses: *Full-time tuition per academic year 2008–09:* contact the Center for current tuition, fees, and housing costs.

Financial Aid: Aid from institutionally generated funds is provided on the basis of academic merit, financial need. Institution has a Program Participation Agreement with the U.S. Department of Education for eligible students to receive Pell Grants and, depending upon the agreement, other federal aid.

Departments and Teaching Staff: *Total instructional faculty:* 773 (full-time 564, part-time 209). Degrees held by full-time faculty: doctorate 30%, master's 1%, professional 69%. 30% hold terminal degrees.

Enrollment: Total enrollment 1,374. Undergraduate 284. Graduate 1,090. Undergraduate transfer-in students 128.

STATE UNIVERSITY OF NEW YORK HEALTH SCIENCE CENTER AT SYRACUSE—*cont'd*

Characteristics of Student Body: *Ethnic/racial makeup:* number of Black non-Hispanic: 9; American Indian or Alaska Native: 1; Asian or Pacific Islander: 7; Hispanic: 4; White non-Hispanic: 230. *Age distribution:* number 20–21: 31; 22–24: 67; 25–29: 47; 30–34: 24; 35–39: 28; 40–49: 46; 50–64: 17.

International Students: 8 nonresident aliens enrolled fall 2008. Students from Europe, Asia, Central and South America. No programs available to aid students whose native language is not English. No financial aid specifically designated for international students.

Student Life: On-campus residence halls house 40% of student body. *Special regulations:* Cars permitted without restrictions. *Special services:* Medical services. *Surrounding community:* Syracuse population 165,000.

Library Collections: 178,000 volumes. 6,000 microforms; 29,600 audiovisual materials; 1,800 periodical subscriptions. Online catalog. Students have access to online information retrieval services.

Most important special holdings include Geneva Medical College; Stephen Smith Collection; Arthur Ecker Collection.

Buildings and Grounds: Urban campus.

Chief Executive Officer: Dr. David R. Smith, President.

Address admission inquiries to Jennifer C. Welsh, Director of Admissions.

College of Medicine

Degree Programs Offered: *First-professional.*

Admission: Minimum 3 years undergraduate study with 90 semester hours which must include 6–8 in each of English, biology or zoology with lab, inorganic chemistry with lab, organic chemistry with lab, physics with lab; MCAT; AMCAS.

Degree Requirements: 4 years in residence; 2.0 GPA; satisfactory completion of core curriculum and electives.

College of Graduate Studies

Degree Programs Offered: *Master's, doctorate.*

Distinctive Educational Programs: Joint first-professional-doctorate program.

College of Health Professions

Degree Programs Offered: *Bachelor's, bachelor of professional studies, master's, doctor of physical therapy.*

Admission: Vary by program.

College of Nursing

Degree Programs Offered: *Bachelor's, master's, psot master's, advanced certificate.*

Admission: Preadmission advisement 10 to 12 months prior to the date of anticipated matriculation.

State University of New York Institute of Technology at Utica/Rome

Horatio Street
P.O. Box 3050
Utica, New York 13504-3050
Tel: (315) 792-7100 **E-mail:** admissions@sunyit.edu
Fax: (315) 792-7837 **Internet:** www.sunyit.edu

Institution Description: State University of New York Institute of Technology offers upper division baccalaureate and graduate study only. *Enrollment:* 2,590. *Degrees awarded:* Baccalaureate, master's.

Accreditation: *Regional:* MSA. *Professional*: engineering, medical record administration, nursing

History: Established 1966; offered first instruction at postsecondary level 1969; awarded first degree 1975.

Institutional Structure: *Composition of institution:* Administrators 30. Academic affairs headed by vice president for academic affairs. Management/business/finances directed by vice president for administration. Full-time instructional faculty 83. Academic governance body, Faculty Assembly, meets an average of 9 times per year.

Calendar: Semesters. Academic year Sept. to May. Entering students admitted Sept., Jan. Degrees conferred May, Aug., Dec. Formal commencement May. Summer session of 4 terms from June to Aug.

Characteristics of Freshmen: 1,201 applicants (302 female, 899 male). 40% of applicants admitted. 28% of admitted students enrolled full-time.

95% (124 students) submitted SAT scores; 5% (7 students) submitted ACT scores. *25th percentile*: SAT Critical Reading 448, SAT Math 480; ACT Composite 22, ACT English 20, ACT Math 24. *75th percentile*: SAT Critical Reading 625, SAT Math 652; ACT Composite 27, ACT English 26, ACT Math 27.

Admission: Rolling admissions plan. *Requirements for transfer students:* 56 semester hours from an accredited college or university; minimum 2.0 GPA; maximum credit transfer of 64 semester hours from lower division studies. A total, not exceeding 100 semester hours, is the maximum credit transfer of both lower and upper division credit to the College of Technology.

College credit for extrainstitutional learning. Tutoring available.

Degree Requirements: *For undergraduate degrees:* 124–128 credit hours; 2.0 GPA. Some degree requirements may be fulfilled by passing College Board CLEP. *Grading system:* A–F; pass-fail; withdraw (carries penalty; carries time limit).

Distinctive Educational Programs: Work-experience programs. Off-campus centers (at Syracuse, 50 miles away from main institution; Albany, 90 miles away). Weekend and evening classes. Accelerated degree programs. Tutorials.

Degrees Conferred: 425 *baccalaureate*; 147 *master's*. Bachelor's degrees awarded in top five disciplines: business, management, marketing, and related support services 101; engineering 86; health professions and related clinical sciences 85; computer and information sciences 52; psychology 30. Master's degrees awarded: business/marketing 63; communication, journalism, and related programs 20; computer and information sciences 24; health professions and related clinical sciences 29; science technologies 2; visual and preforming arts 9.

Fees and Other Expenses: *Full-time tuition per academic year 2008–09:* contact the institute for current information regarding tuition, fees, housing, and other costs.

Financial Aid: Aid from institutionally generated funds is provided on the basis of academic merit, financial need. Institution has a Program Participation Agreement with the U.S. Department of Education for eligible students to receive Pell Grants and, depending upon the agreement, other federal aid.

Financial aid to full-time, first-time undergraduate students: 68% received some form of financial aid. Average amount of aid received: federal grants $1,371; state/local grants $1,213; institutional grants $3,421; loans $984.

Departments and Teaching Staff: *Total instructional faculty:* 157. Student/faculty ratio: 27:1. Degrees held by full-time faculty: baccalaureate 1%, master's 28.8%, doctorate 66.7%, professional 3.5%. 71% hold terminal degrees.

Enrollment: Total enrollment 2,390 (undergraduate).

Characteristics of Student Body: Ethnic/racial makeup: American Indian or Alaska Native: .6%; Asian or Pacific Islander: 2.5%; Hispanic: 2.5; White non-Hispanic: 86.5%; unknown: .7%.

International Students: 20 undergraduate nonresident aliens enrolled fall 2008. Students from Europe, Asia, Central and South America, Africa. No programs available to aid students whose native language is not English. No financial aid specifically designated for international students.

Student Life: Two residence halls accommodating over 575 students. *Intercollegiate athletics:* male: basketball, soccer; female: basketball, softball, volleyball. *Special regulations:* Cars with decals permitted. *Special services:* Learning Resources Center, medical services. *Surrounding community:* Utica population 75,000.

Library Collections: 195,000 volumes. 45,000 government documents; 176,266 microforms; 2,936 audiovisual materials; 975 current periodical subscriptions. Online catalog. Students have access to online information retrieval services and the Internet.

Most important special holdings include collections on business, health care, computers and technology.

Buildings and Grounds: Campus area 800 acres.

Chief Executive Officer: Dr. Peter Spina, President.

Address admission inquiries to Mary Beth Lyons, Director of Admissions.

State University of New York Maritime College

Fort Schuyler
6 Pennyfield Avenue
Throgs Neck, New York 10465
Tel: (718) 409-7220 **E-mail:** admissions@sunymaritime.edu
Fax: (718) 409-7465 **Internet:** www.sunymaritime

Institution Description: State University of New York Maritime College prepares cadets for licensure as officers in the merchant marine while they earn baccalaureate degrees. A Master of Science in transportation is also offered. *Enrollment:* 1,630. *Degrees awarded:* Associate, baccalaureate, master's.

Accreditation: *Regional:* MSA. *Professional*: engineering

History: Established 1874; awarded first degree 1947.

Institutional Structure: *Composition of institution:* Specialized college of SUNY system. Academic affairs headed by vice president of academic affairs. Business/finances directed by vice president of finance/administration. Total instructional faculty 82. Academic governance body, the faculty, meets at least 4 times per year.

Calendar: Semesters. Academic year Sept. to MAY. Freshmen admitted Sept. Degrees conferred May, Aug., Jan. Formal commencement May.

Characteristics of Freshmen: 1,345 applicants (173 female, 1,172 male). 69% of applicants admitted. 43% of admitted students enrolled full-time.

93% (372 students) submitted SAT scores; 30% (119 students) submitted ACT scores. *25th percentile*: SAT Critical Reading 460, SAT Math 490; ACT Composite 19. *75th percentile*: SAT Critical Reading 560, SAT Math 590; ACT Composite 23.

47% of entering freshmen expected to graduate within 5 years. 72% of freshmen from New York. Freshmen from 24 states and 15 foreign countries.

Admission: Early acceptance available. *Requirements:* Either graduation from accredited secondary school with 16 units or GED. Preparation must include 4 units English; 1 each in elementary algebra, plane geometry, physics or chemistry; 1/2 each in intermediate algebra, plane trigonometry. Recommend additional units in foreign language, mathematics, science. *Entrance tests:* College Board SAT or ACT composite. For foreign students TOEFL. *For transfer students:* 2.0 minimum GPA.

Degree Requirements: *For undergraduate degrees:* 153–160 credit hours; 2.0 GPA; three years in residence.

Fulfillment of some degree requirements and exemption from some beginning courses possible by passing College Board CLEP, AP, other standardized tests. *Grading system:* A–F; withdraw (deadline after which fail is appended to withdraw).

Distinctive Educational Programs: Non-license master's program in transportation management. Weekend and evening classes for graduate students. Tutorials. Undergraduate program includes 2 months at sea on ocean-going training ship Empire State making various ports of call. *Other distinctive programs:* Continuing education. Three summers semesters at sea preparing for the U.S. Merchant Marine Officer's License.

ROTC: Navy and Merchant Marine Reserve (USNR-MMR).

Degrees Conferred: 4 *associate*; 218 *baccalaureate*; 46 *master's*. Bachelor's degrees awarded: business, management, marketing, and related support services 65; engineering 76; physical sciences 11, other 66. Master's degrees awarded: business/management 46.

Fees and Other Expenses: *Full-time tuition per academic year 2008–09:* undergraduate resident $5,426, nonresident $11,686; 5,695; contact the college for current graduate tuition. *Room and board per academic year:* $9,500. *Books and supplies:* $1,200. *Other expenses:* $2,710.

Financial Aid: Institution has a Program Participation Agreement with the U.S. Department of Education for eligible students to receive Pell Grants and, depending upon the agreement, other federal aid.

Financial aid to full-time, first-time undergraduate students: 87% of students received some form of financial aid. Average amount of aid received: federal grants $3,518; Pell grants $3,016; other federal grants $665; state/local grants $2,743.

Departments and Teaching Staff: *Total instructional faculty:* 82. Student/faculty ratio: 17:1.

Enrollment: Total enrollment 1,630. U*undergraduate 1,446. Graduate 184. Undergraduate transfer-in students 64.

Characteristics of Student Body: *Ethnic/racial makeup:* Black non-Hispanic: 6.3%; American Indian or Alaska Native: .3%; Asian or Pacific Islander: 5.3%; Hispanic: 9%; White non-Hispanic: 73.5%. *Age distribution:* 17–21: 77%; 22–24: 17%; 25–29: 4%; 30–34: 2%.

International Students: 40 undergraduate nonresident aliens enrolled fall 2008. Students from Europe, Asia, Central and South America, Africa. Programs available to aid students whose native language is not English: English as a Second Language Program. No financial aid specifically designated for international students.

Student Life: On-campus housing available. *Surrounding community:* Throgs Neck is located in The Bronx, a Borough of New York City (population over 7 million).

Library Collections: 82,000. Online catalog. 27,000 government documents. 350 current serial subscriptions. 13,000 microforms. 5,000 audiovisual materials. Computer work stations available. Students have access to the Internet at no charge.

Most important special holdings include collections of maritime research journals/technical reports; Luce Maritime History Collection; Sailor's Snug Harbor Archives (1833-); Sandy Hook Pilots Archives (1845-); Marine Society Archives (1797-).

Buildings and Grounds: Campus area 52 acres.

Chief Executive Officer: Vice Admiral John W. Craine, President.

Address admission inquiries to Carol Roth, Registrar.

Syracuse University

Syracuse, New York 13244

Tel: (315) 443-1870 **E-mail:** admissions@syr.edu
Fax: (315) 443-4226 **Internet:** www.syr.edu

Institution Description: Syracuse University is a private, independent, nonprofit institution. *Enrollment:* 19,366. *Degrees awarded:* Associate, baccalaureate, first-professional (law), master's, doctorate. Certificates of Advanced Study in arts and sciences, citizenship and public affairs, computer science, education, human services, and information studies.

Accreditation: *Regional:* MSA. *Professional*: architecture, art, audiology, business, chemistry, dietetics, engineering, interior design, journalism, landscape architecture, law, librarianship, music, nursing, rehabilitation counseling, psychology internship, social work, speech-language pathology, teacher education

History: Established and offered first instruction at postsecondary level 1870; awarded first degree 1875.

Institutional Structure: *Governing board:* Syracuse University Board of Trustees. Extrainstitutional representation: 87 trustees; institutional representation: president of the university. 3 ex officio. 46 voting. *Composition of institution:* Chancellor and president; vice chancellor for academic affairs; school and college deans; senior vice president for university relations; vice president for student affairs; senior vice president for business/finance/administrative services; senior vice president for human resources and government relations; vice presidents for research and computing, undergraduate studies, enrollment management, continuing education. Full-time instructional faculty 865. Academic governance body, University Senate, meets an average of 11 times per year.

Calendar: Semesters. Academic year Aug to May. Freshmen admitted Sept., Jan., May, June. Degrees conferred May, June, Aug., Dec. Formal commencement May. Summer session of 2 terms from May to Aug.

Characteristics of Freshmen: 22,079 applicants (12,123 female, 9,956 male). 53% of applicants admitted. 27% of admitted students enrolled full-time.

90% (2,838 students) submitted SAT scores; 34% (1,079 students) submitted ACT scores. *25th percentile*: SAT Critical Reading 520, 530, SAT Math 550, SAT Writing 530; ACT Composite 23, ACT English 23, ACT Math 23. *75th percentile*: SAT Critical Reading 620, SAT Math 650, SAT Writing 630; ACT Composite 28, ACT English 26, ACT Math 29.

78% of entering freshmen expected to graduate within 5 years. 47% of freshmen from New York. Freshmen from 50 states and 63 foreign countries.

Admission: For fall acceptance, apply by Jan. 15. After that date, applications are accepted on a rolling basis. *Requirements:* Graduation from accredited secondary school with a minimum of 15 units in college preparatory curriculum (4 years English, 3 mathematics, 3 lab science, 3 social studies, and a minimum of 3 years of a spoken foreign language). Portfolio for Art and Architecture; audition required for Music and Drama. *Entrance tests:* College Board SAT I or ACT composite. For foreign students TOEFL. *For transfer students:* From 4-year accredited institution 90 hours maximum transfer credit; from 2-year accredited institution 60 hours.

College credit for postsecondary-level work completed in secondary school.

Degree Requirements: *For all baccalaureate degrees:* minimum 120 credit hours. *For all undergraduate degrees:* 2.0 GPA; 2 terms in residence.

Fulfillment of some degree requirements by achieving certain scores on College Board CLEP. *Grading system:* A–F, plus-minus; pass-fail; withdraw with restrictions.

Distinctive Educational Programs: Accelerated programs, cooperative plan programs, double majors, dual enrollment, English as a second language, honors program, independent study, internships, liberal arts/career combination, student-designed majors, undergraduate research program, preprofessional programs. Study abroad programs in over 35 countries worldwide.

ROTC: Army, Air Force.

Degrees Conferred: 7 *associate*; 2,886 *baccalaureate*; 1,648 *master's*; 81 *doctorate*; 309 *first-professional*. Bachelor's degrees awarded in top five disciplines: business, management, marketing, and related support services 436; visual and performing arts 350; socials sciences 331; communications/journalism 277; psychology 180. Master's degrees awarded in top five disciplines: public administration and social services 360; engineering 223; communications/journalism 240; engineering 223; computer and information sciences 240. Doctorates awarded: biological/life sciences 6; business/marketing 9; communications/journalism 2; computer and information sciences 7; education 32; engineering 18; English 3; foamily and consumer sciences 4; history 5; mathematics

SYRACUSE UNIVERSITY—*cont'd*

3; philosophy and religious studies 12; psychology 11; public administration and social services 7; social sciences 28. First—professional degrees awarded: law 109.

Fees and Other Expenses: *Full-time tuition per academic year 2008–09:* $33,440 undergraduate; contact the university for graduate and first-professional program tuition. *Room and board per academic year:* $11,656. *Books and supplies:* $1,268. *Other expenses:* $1,456.

Financial Aid: Aid from institutionally generated funds is provided on the basis of academic merit, financial need, athletic ability, other criteria. Institution has a Program Participation Agreement with the U.S. Department of Education for eligible students to receive Pell Grants and, depending upon the agreement, other federal aid.

Financial aid to full-time, first-time undergraduate students: 79% received some form of financial aid. Average amount of aid received: federal grants $3,249; Pell grants $3,249; other federal grants $2,218; state/local grants $3,509; institutional grants $18,179.

Departments and Teaching Staff: *Total instructional faculty:* 1,391 (full-time 165, part-time 526). Student/faculty ratio: 15:1. Degrees held by full-time faculty: master's 10%, doctorate 75%, professional 11%. 86% hold terminal degrees.

Enrollment: Total enrollment 19,366. Undergraduate 13,651. Graduate 5,715. Undergraduate transfer-in students 336.

Characteristics of Student Body: *Ethnic/racial makeup (undergraduate):* number of Black non-Hispanic: 854; American Indian or Alaska Native: 81; Asian or Pacific Islander: 889; Hispanic: 639; White non-Hispanic: 8,355; unknown: 1,943. *Age distribution:* number under 18: 438; 18–19: 3,666; 20–21: 5,411; 22–24: 944; 25–29: 208; 30–34: 99; 35–39: 79; 40–49: 176; 50–64: 89; 65 and over: 6; unknown: 40.

International Students: 1,813 undergraduate nonresident aliens enrolled fall 2008. Students from Europe, Asia,, Central and South America, Africa, Canada, Australia, New Zealand, Middle East. Programs available to aid students whose native language is not English: social, cultural. English as a Second Language Program. No financial aid specifically designated for international students.

Student Life: Approximately 65% of undergraduates live on campus, 5% commute, 30% reside in off-campus apartments. Undergraduates guaranteed on-campus housing 4 years. Freshmen and sophomores are required to live in university housing. 15% of males join fraternity housing; 25% of females join sororities. Freshmen are not permitted to join fraternities/sororities until their second semester. There are more than 300 extracurricular clubs and organizations on campus (social, academic, religious, political, sports/recreation, ethics, social-service oriented). *Intercollegiate athletics:* male: basketball, crew, cross-country, football, gymnastics, indoor track and field, lacrosse, outdoor track and field, soccer, swimming and diving; female: basketball, crew, cross country, field hockey, indoor track and field, lacrosse, swimming and diving, tennis, volleyball. More than 50 intramural and club sports also available. *Special regulations:* Cars permitted for all but resident freshmen. *Special services:* Health services, counseling services, campus ministries/chaplains, Center for Career Services, services for the learning disabled, parents liaison office, shuttle bus. *Student radio, television:* WAER-FM, WJPZ-FM. *The Daily Orange,* a student newspaper. There are more than 300 extracurricular clubs and organizations on campus (social, academic, religious, political, sports/recreation, ethnics, social-service oriented). *Surrounding community:* Syracuse metropolitan area population over 500,000. Served by mass transit bus system, airport, and passenger rail service.

Publications: *Syracuse Record*, weekly newspaper published during the academic year by the Office of News and Publications; *Syracuse University Magazine*, alumni news magazine published quarterly.

Library Collections: 3,181,000 volumes. 288,000 government documents; 7,402,000 microforms; 435,000 audiovisual materials; 22,900 current serials including via electronic access. Online catalog. Students have access to online information retrieval services and the Internet.

Most important special holdings include Stephen Crane manuscripts; Joyce Carol Oates manuscripts; Leopold von Ranke Library; Margaret Bourke-White Collection; Gerrit Smith Papers.

Buildings and Grounds: Campus area 200 acres.

Chief Executive Officer: Dr. Nancy Cantor, President. Address all admission inquiries to Susan E. Donovan, Dean of Admissions.

School of Architecture

Degree Programs Offered: *Baccalaureate, master's.*

College of Arts and Sciences

Degree Programs Offered: *Baccalaureate* in African-American studies, American studies, anthropology, biology, biochemistry, chemistry, classical civilization, classics, economics, English and textual studies, European literature, fine French, geography, geology, German, history, history of architecture, Italian, international relations, Latin American studies, linguistics, mathematics, Medieval and Renaissance studies, modern foreign language, nonviolent conflict and change, philosophy, physics, political philosophy, political science, policy studies, psychology, religion, Russian, Russian studies, sociology, Spanish, women's studies. *Masters, doctorate* in various fields.

L.C. Smith College of Engineering and Computer Science

Degree Programs Offered: *Baccalaureate:* Aerospace engineering, bioengineering, chemical engineering, civil engineering, computer engineering, computer science, electrical engineering, engineering physics, environmental engineering, mechanical engineering, systems and information science. *Master's, doctorate* in various fields.

School of Education

Degree Programs Offered: *Baccalaureate:* Inclusive elementary and special education, secondary education, art education, communication sciences and disorders, English education, health and exercise science, mathematics education, music education, physical education, science education, social studies education. *Master's, doctorate* in various fields.

College for Human Development

Degree Programs Offered: *Baccalaureate:* Child and family studies, clinical nutrition, consumer studies, environmental design (interiors), fashion design, nutrition, nutrition science, restaurant and foodservice management, retailing, textile design. *Master's, doctorate* in various fields.

School of Information Studies

Degree Programs Offered: *Baccalaureate* in information management and technology. *Master's, doctorate* in various fields.

S.I. Newhouse School of Public Communications

Degree Programs Offered: *Baccalaureate:* Advertising, broadcast journalism, graphic arts, magazine, newspaper, photography, public relations, television/radio/film. *Master's* in various fields; *doctorate* in mass communications.

College of Visual and Performing Arts

Degree Programs Offered: *Baccalaureate:* Advertising design, art education, art photography, art video, ceramics, communications design, computer graphics, design/technical theater, drama, fiber arts, film (art or drama emphasis), art history, illustration, industrial design (five-year program), interior design, metalsmithing, music composition, music education, music industry, music performance (organ, percussion, piano, string instruments, voice, wind instruments), musical theater, painting, printmaking, sculpture, speech communication, surface pattern design. *Master's* in various fields.

College of Law

Degree Programs Offered: *First-professional.*

Admission: Baccalaureate from accredited college or university; LSAT.

Distinctive Educational Programs: Joint first-professional-master's of public administration with Maxwell School of Citizenship and Public Affairs; first-professional-master of library science with School of Information Studies; first-professional-master of business administration with the School of Management.

Maxwell School of Citizenship and Public Affairs

Degree Programs Offered: *Master's, doctorate* in anthropology, economics, geography, history, international relations, political science, public administration, sociology. *Doctorate* in social science.

University College

Degree Programs Offered: *Baccalaureate* in applied computer technology, legal studies, organizational leadership, professional communications.

Whitman School of Management

Degree Programs Offered: *Baccalaureate:* Accounting, finance, marketing, entrepreneurship and emerging enterprises, general management studies, supply chain management. *Master's, doctorate* in various fields.

Teachers College at Columbia University

525 West 120th Street
New York, New York 10027-6413
Tel: (212) 678-3000 **E-mail:** admissions@tc.columbia.edu
Internet: www.tc.columbia.edu

Institution Description: Teachers College is a private, independent, nonprofit graduate school affiliated with Columbia University. *Enrollment:* 5,040. *Degrees awarded:* Master's, doctorate.

Accreditation: *Regional:* MSA. *Professional*: audiology, community health, nursing, psychology internship, speech-language pathology, teacher education

History: Established and offered first instruction at postsecondary level 1887; chartered 1892; became affiliated with Columbia University 1898. *See* Lawrence A. Cremin et al., *A History of Teacher's College, Columbia University* (New York: Columbia University Press, 1954) for further information.

Institutional Structure: *Governing board:* Trustees of Teachers College. Representation: 26 trustees (all voting members), including 5 alumni, president of the college, president of the university. 2 ex officio. *Composition of institution:* Administrators 16. Academic affairs headed by president. Management/business/finances directed by vice president for finance and administration. Total instructional faculty 130. Academic governance body, College Policy Committee, meets an average of 11 times per year.

Calendar: Semesters. Academic year Sept. to May. Entering students admitted Sept., Jan., May, July. Degrees conferred and formal commencement May. Summer session of 2 terms from late May to late Aug.

Admission: Rolling admissions plan. For Fall acceptance, apply no later than July 15 of year of enrollment; for Spring acceptance, apply no later than Dec. 15. For Summer A session, apply by Apr. 1. For Summer B session, apply by May 1. *Requirements:* vary by program; general requirements for all programs—transcripts from other institutions attended, 2 letters of reference, personal statement.

Degree Requirements: *For all master's degrees:* 30–32 points; 18–20 points in residence; 12 points in major essay or project. Additional requirements for master of education. *For all doctoral degrees:* 75–90 points; 30–45 points in residence; departmental certification examinations; preparation and defense of dissertation. For doctor of philosophy, foreign language examinations. Additional requirements for some programs. *Grading system:* A–F; pass; withdraw (carries time limit).

Distinctive Educational Programs: Internships in supervision of student teachers and school interns, internships for prospective college teachers; research internships also available. Weekend and evening classes. Accelerated degree programs. Joint doctorate-M.B.A. program with Columbia University Graduate School of Business. Cooperative doctoral program with Union Theological Seminary. Cooperative master's and doctoral programs in international education with Columbia University School of International and Public Affairs. Interdisciplinary programs by individual arrangement. Individual majors.

Degrees Conferred: Master's degrees awarded: 1,565; doctorates awarded: 214.

Fees and Other Expenses: *Full-time tuition per academic year:* contact the college for current information regarding tuition, fees, room and board.

Financial Aid: Institution has a Program Participation Agreement with the U.S. Department of Education for eligible students to receive Pell Grants and, depending upon the agreement, other federal aid.

Departments and Teaching Staff: *Total instructional faculty:* 139.

Enrollment: Total enrollment 5,040.

Characteristics of Student Body: *Ethnic/racial makeup:* Black non-Hispanic: 9.1%; American Indian or Alaska Native: .2%; Asian or Pacific Islander: 11.7%; Hispanic: 6.1%; White non-Hispanic: 51%; unknown: 11.4%.

International Students: 534 nonresident aliens enrolled fall 2008. Programs available to aid students whose native language is not English: social, cultural, financial. English as a Second Language Program. Financial aid specifically designated for international students: variable number of scholarships available annually.

Student Life: On-campus residence halls available. Traditional and nontraditional family housing available. *Student publications: Teachers College Advocate*, a monthly newspaper. *Surrounding community:* New York City population over 7 million.

Publications: *Teachers College Record* (quarterly) first published 1900. *Publisher:* Teachers College Press.

Library Collections: 540,000. volumes. 420,000 microforms; 11,000 audiovisual materials; 1,974 current periodicals. Online catalog. Students have Access to online information retrieval services and the Internet.

Most important holdings include records of the Board of Education of the City of New York; nursing archives; Harvey Darton Collection (including pre-1850 children's English books).

Buildings and Grounds: Campus area 1 square block.

Chief Executive Officer: Dr. Susan H. Fuhrman, President.

Address admission inquiries to Thomas Rock, Director of Admissions.

Touro College

27 West 23rd Street
New York, New York 10110
Tel: (212) 463-0400 **E-mail:** admissions@touro.edu
Fax: (212) 779-2344 **Internet:** www.touro.edu

Institution Description: Touro College is a private, independent, nonprofit college. *Enrollment:* 17,321. *Degrees awarded:* Associate, baccalaureate, master's, first-professional.

Accreditation: *Regional:* MSA. *Professional*: law, medical record administration, physical therapy, physician assisting

History: Established and chartered 1970; offered first instruction at postsecondary level 1971.

Institutional Structure: *Governing board:* Board of Trustees. Extrainstitutional representation:15 trustees; institutional representation: 1 administrator. 1 ex officio. *Composition of institution:* Administrators 12. Academic affairs headed by dean of planning and review. Management/business/finances directed by director of fiscal affairs. Full-time instructional faculty 250.

Calendar: Semesters. Freshmen admitted Sept., Jan., June. Summer session of 1 term.

Characteristics of Freshmen: 4m899 applicants (3,232 female, 1,667 male). 57% of applicants admitted. 75% of admitted students enrolled full-time.

Admission: Rolling admissions plan. Early acceptance available. *Requirements:* Either graduation from accredited secondary school with 16 units in college preparatory subjects, or GED. *Entrance tests:* College Board SAT or ACT composite. For foreign students TOEFL. *For transfer students:* 2.0 minimum GPA; maximum transfer credit limited only by residence requirement.

College credit and advanced placement for postsecondary-level work completed in secondary school. College credit for extrainstitutional learning.

Tutoring available. Developmental courses offered in summer session and regular academic year; credit given.

Degree Requirements: *For all baccalaureate degrees:* 120 credit hours; 2.0 GPA; 30 credits in residence; general education requirements; senior thesis or project; exit competency examination in writing.

Degrees Conferred: 795 *associate*; 1,526 *baccalaureate*; 2,391 *master's*; 46 *doctorate*; 389 *first-professional*. Bachelor's degrees awarded in top five disciplines: business, management, marketing, and related support services 614; health professions and related clinical sciences 485; liberal arts and sciences, general studies, and humanities 293; psychology 162; public administration 119. Master's degrees awarded in top five disciplines: education 1,984; business/marketing 623; health professions and related clinical sciences 406; area, ethnic, cultural, and gender studies 277; psychology 32. Doctorates awarded: business/marketing 14; education 6; health professions 62. First-professional degrees awarded: medicine 190; law 199..

Fees and Other Expenses: *Full-time tuition per academic year 2008–09:* $14,200 undergraduate; contact the college for current graduate and professional tuition. *Room and board per academic year:* $6,250. *Books and supplies:* $900. *Other expenses:* $2,820.

Departments and Teaching Staff: *Total instructional faculty:* 810 (full-time 240). Student/faculty ratio: 23:1.

Enrollment: Total enrollment 17,327. Undergraduate 7,915. Graduate 9,412. Undergraduate transfer-in students 9.

Characteristics of Student Body: *Ethnic/racial makeup:* Black non-Hispanic: 17.7%; American Indian or Alaska Native: .5%; Asian or Pacific Islander: 3.6%; Hispanic: 11.2%; White non-Hispanic: 54.2%.

International Students: Programs available to aid students whose native language is not English: social, cultural.

Library Collections: 535,000 volumes. 4,700 periodicals. Students have access to online information retrieval services and the Internet.

Chief Executive Officer: Dr. Bernard Lander, President.

Address admission inquiries to Ira Tyszler, Dean of Enrollment Management.

Unification Theological Seminary

30 Seminary Drive
Barrytown, New York 12507
Tel: (845) 752-3000 **E-mail:** admissions@uts.edu
Fax: (845) 758-2156 **Internet:** www.uts.edu

Institution Description: Unification Theological Seminary is a private graduate seminary affiliated with the Unification Church. *Enrollment:* 173. *Degrees awarded:* Master's, doctorate, first-professional.

Accreditation: *Regional:* MSA.

History: The seminary was established in 1975.

Institutional Structure: *Governing board:* Board of Trustees.

Calendar: Trimesters. Academic year Sept. to June.

Admission: *Requirements:* Baccalaureate degree from an accredited four-year college or university. TOEFL score of 550 for non-native English speakers.

Degree Requirements: *For Master of Religious Education:* 72 credits; 2.5 minimum GPA; mid-program review; religious education project, spring term in residence prior to graduation. *For Master of Divinity:* 111 credits; 2.5 minimum GPA, mid-program review, divinity thesis, spring term residence prior to graduation. of Divinity degree: 111 credits.

Degrees Conferred: 35 *aster's*: theology. 9 *first-professional*: master of divinity.

Fees and Other Expenses: *Full-time tuition per academic year 2008–09:* contact the for current information.

Financial Aid: Aid from institutionally generated funds is provided on the basis of academic merit, financial need, other criteria.

Departments and Teaching Staff: *Total instructional faculty:* 39 (full-time 7, part-time 32).

Enrollment: Total enrollment 173.

International Students: 53 nonresident aliens enrolled fall 2008. Programs available to aid students whose native language is not English: English as a Second Language Program. No financial aid specifically designated for international students.

Student Life: The majority of full-time students live on-campus. Limited family housing available.

Library Collections: 56,000 volumes including bound books, serial backfiles, electronic documents, and govern documents not in separate collections. Online catalog. 75 current serial subscriptions. 750 recordings. 8 computer work stations. Students have access to the Internet at no charge.

Most import special collections include Unification Church-related materials.

Buildings and Grounds: Campus area 350 acres.

Chief Executive Officer: Dr. Tyler O. Hendricks, President.

Address admission inquiries to Henry Christopher, Director of Admissions.

Union College

807 Union Street
Schenectady, New York 12308
Tel: (518) 388-6112 **E-mail:** admissions@union.edu
Fax: (518) 388-6986 **Internet:** www.union.edu

Institution Description: Union College is a private, independent, college of liberal arts and engineering. *Enrollment:* 2,240. *Degrees awarded:* Baccalaureate.

Member of consortium Hudson-Mohawk Association of Colleges and Universities.

Accreditation: *Regional:* MSA.*Professional*: engineering

History: Established as Schenectady Academy 1795; chartered under present name and offered first instruction at postsecondary level 1795; awarded first degree (baccalaureate) 1797. *See* Dixon Ryan Fox, *Union College - An Unfinished History* (Schenectady: Graduate Council, Union College, 1945) for further information.

Institutional Structure: *Governing board:* The Trustees of Union College of the Town of Schenectady in the State of New York. 32 trustees, including governor of New York, president of the college, 2 full-time instructional faculty members, 2 students, 4 alumni; all voting members. *Composition of institution:* Administrators 100. Academic affairs headed by president. Business and finance directed by vice president for finance. Full-time instructional faculty 184. Academic governance body, General Faculty, meets an average of 6 times per year.

Calendar: Trimesters (3 ten-week terms). Academic year Sept. to June. Degrees conferred and formal commencement June. Limited summer session of 1 six-week term.

Characteristics of Freshmen: 43% of applicants accepted. 30% of applicants enrolled.

<94% (535 students) submitted SAT scores; 25% (39 students) submitted ACT scores. *25th percentile*: SAT Critical Reading 550, SAT Math 580; ACT Composite 24. *75th percentile*: SAT Critical Reading 650, SAT Math 670; ACT Composite 29.

85% of entering freshmen expected to graduate within 5 years. 40% of freshmen from New York. Freshmen from 37 states and 27 foreign countries.

Admission: For fall acceptance, apply as early as July 1 of previous year, but not later than Jan. 15 of year of enrollment. Students are notified of acceptance by Apr. 15. Apply by Nov. 15 for Early Decision I for a decision by Dec. 15; for Early Decision II, apply by Jan. 15 for a decision by Feb. 1. Early admission available. *Requirements:* minimum requirements include certain fundamentals as English, foreign language, mathematics, social studies, and science. *Entrance tests:* Testing is optional except for combined programs. Applicants for the Leadership in Medicine and Law and Public Policy programs are required to submit the SAT I and SAT II tests and must complete the necessary tests no later than December of the senior year. For foreign students TOEFL. *For transfer students:* 60 hours maximum transfer credit.

College credit and advanced placement possible for postsecondary-level work completed in secondary school.

Degree Requirements: Generally a minimum of 36 term courses; 1.8 GPA (2.0 in major); 2 years in residency; general education requirements; comprehensive sin many individual fields of study.

Fulfillment of some degree requirements and exemption from some beginning courses possible by passing AP exams. *Grading system:* A–F; pass-fail; withdraw.

Distinctive Educational Programs: Dual-degree programs with Albany Law School and with Albany Medical College. Interdepartmental programs and majors in comparative studies, environmental studies, health-related science studies, industrial economics, Latin American studies, East Asian studies, women's studies. Facilities and programs for independent research, individualized majors. Union College offers formal resident-study abroad programs. Terms of study area available in various countries. A term of marine studies in Bermuda, Woods Hole, and Newfoundland are also offered. In addition, a summer semester program offered in which students examine the national health programs of Canada, England, and Holland.

ROTC: Army in cooperation with Siena College; Air Force and Navy with Rensselaer Polytechnic Institute.

Degrees Conferred: 473 *baccalaureate*. Bachelor's degrees offered in top five disciplines: social sciences 144; engineering 64; biological/life sciences 50; psychology 46; liberal arts/general studies 42. *Honorary degrees awarded 2005–06:* Doctor of Laws 1; Doctor of Letters 1.

Fees and Other Expenses: *Full-time tuition per academic year 2008–09:* $44,043 comprehensive tuition/fees/room and board.

Financial Aid: Aid from institutionally generated funds is provided on the basis of financial need.

Financial aid to full-time, first-time undergraduate students: 67% received some form of aid. Average amount of aid received: federal grants $1,511; state/local grants $2,004; institutional grants $4,119; loans $2,351.

Departments and Teaching Staff: *Total instructional faculty:* 223 (full-time 184, part-time 39). Student/faculty ratio: 10:1. Degrees held by full-time faculty: doctorate 92%, master's 3%, baccalaureate 2%. 3% hold terminal degrees.

Enrollment: Total enrollment 2,240 (undergraduate). Transfer-in students 33.

Characteristics of Student Body: *Ethnic/racial makeup:* number of Black non-Hispanic: 63; American Indian or alaska Native 2; Asian or Pacific Islander: 129; Hispanic: 95; White non-Hispanic: 1,809; unknown: 9. *Age distribution:* number under 18: 41: 20–21: 1,036; 22–24: 123; 25–29: 3; 30–34: 1; 35–39: unknown: 3.

International Students: 47 nonresident aliens enrolled fall 2008. Students from Europe, Asia, Central and South America, Africa, Canada. Programs available to aid students whose native language is not English: English as a Second Language program. No financial aid specifically designated for international students.

Student Life: On-campus residence halls house 89% of student body. Housing for males constitute 20% of such space, for females 20%, coed 57%, theme housing 10%. Approximately 28% of the student body joins the Greek fraternity/sorority system. *Intercollegiate athletics:* male: baseball, basketball, cross-country, football, ice hockey, lacrosse, soccer, swimming, tennis, indoor track, outdoor track; female: basketball, cross-country, field hockey, lacrosse, soccer, softball, swimming, tennis, indoor track, outdoor track, volleyball. *Special regulations:* Freshmen are not permitted to have cars on campus. *Special services:* Medical services. *Student publications: Concordiensis*, a weekly newspaper; *Garnet*, a yearbook; *Idol*, a literary magazine; *Sentinel*, a political magazine. *Surrounding community:* Schenectady population 62,000. Served by mass transit bus system; airport 10 miles from campus; passenger rail service 1 mile from campus.

Library Collections: 694,000 volumes. Online catalog. Current serial subscriptions: paper 1,820; microform 55; 2,578 via electronic access. 11,190 recordings; 906 DVD discs; 778 CD-ROMs. Computer work stations available. Students have access to online information retrieval services and the Internet.

Most important special holdings include the Elephant Folio Edition of *Audubon's Birds of America*; Bailey Collection of American Wit and Humor; John Bigelow Collection and John Bigelow Papers.

Buildings and Grounds: Campus area 100 acres.

Chief Executive Officer: Dr. Stephen C. Ainlay, President.

Address admission inquiries to Grant Hall, Dean of Admissions.

Union Theological Seminary

3041 Broadway

New York, New York 10027-5710

Tel: (212) 662-7100 **E-mail:** admissions@uts.columbia.edu

Fax: (212) 280-1416 **Internet:** www.uts.columbia.edu

Institution Description: Union Theological Seminary is a private, interdenominational, Christian institution. *Enrollment:* 245. *Degrees awarded:* First-professional (master of divinity), master's, doctorate.

Accreditation: *Regional:* MSA. *National:* ATS. *Professional*: theology

History: Established and offered first instruction at postsecondary level 1836; chartered 1839.

Institutional Structure: *Governing board:* Board of Trustees. Directors. Extrainstitutional representation: 40 directors; institutional representation: president of the seminary. *Composition of institution:* Academic affairs headed by academic dean. Management/business/finances directed by executive vice president. Full-time instructional faculty 17.

Calendar: Semesters. Academic year Sept. to May.

Admission: Master of Divinity and Master of Arts application no later than July 15. S.T.M. and Ph.D. applications no later than Jan. 6. Students are notified of acceptance beginning Mar. 15. *Requirements:* Graduation from an accredited college or university.

Degree Requirements: *For first-professional degree:* 78 points; thesis. *For master of arts degree:* 51 points; thesis. *For doctorate:* 40 points in residence; field exams; dissertation. *Grading system:* Credit-no credit; written evaluations.

Distinctive Educational Programs: Work-experience programs, including clinical training, internships, summer ministries. Cooperative master's and doctorate programs, and joint first-professional/master of science in social work with Columbia University. Tutorials. Study abroad in Costa Rica, other nations. Cross-registration with General Theological Seminary, New York Theological Seminary, Jewish Theological Seminary, City University of New York. *Other distinctive programs:* Cooperative continuing education programs with Auburn Seminary.

Degrees Conferred: 24 *master's:* theology; 4 *doctorate:* theology; 58 *first-professional:* master of divinity.

Fees and Other Expenses: *Full-time tuition per academic year:* contact the seminary for current information regarding tuition, fees, and housing costs.

Departments and Teaching Staff: Biblical *professors* 2, *associate professors* 0, *assistant professors* 1, *part-time faculty* 6; historical 3, 0, 0, 5; theological 5, 1, 0, 2; practical 4, 1, 0, 13.

Full-time instructional faculty: 43.

Enrollment: Total enrollment 245.

International Students: 10 nonresident aliens enrolled. Students from Europe, Asia, Africa, Canada. No programs available to aid students whose native language is not English. Some scholarships available to international students.

Publications: *Union Seminary Quarterly Review; Union News.*

Library Collections: 605,000 volumes. 163,000 microforms; 1,700 audiovisual materials; 1,500 current periodical subscriptions.

Most important special collections include the McAlpin Collection of British History and Theology, 1501–1640; Missionary Research Library; Van Ess Collection (early printed books and manuscripts, particularly in liturgical and biblical studies).

Chief Executive Officer: Dr. Joseph C. Hough, Jr., President.

Address admission inquiries to Director of Admissions.

United States Merchant Marine Academy

300 Steamboat Road

Kings Point, New York 11024-1699

Tel: (516) 773-5000 **E-mail:** admissions@usmma.edu

Fax: (516) 773-5390 **Internet:** www.usmma.edu

Institution Description: United States Merchant Marine Academy is a federal institution. *Enrollment:* 986. *Degrees awarded:* Baccalaureate.

Accreditation: *Regional:* MSA. *Professional*: engineering

History: Authorized by act of Congress 1936; chartered 1938; offered first instruction at postsecondary level 1943; awarded first degree (baccalaureate) 1950. *See* C. Bradford Mitchell, *We'll Deliver* (Kings Point: U.S.M.M.A. Alumni Association, 1977) for further information.

Institutional Structure: *Governing board:* Maritime Administration of Department of Transportation. Representation: Advisory board (7 members) appointed by secretary of transportation for 3-year terms. *Composition of institution:* Administrators 7. Academic affairs headed by academic dean. Management/business/finances directed by assistant superintendent. Full-time instructional faculty 85. Academic governance body, Academic Board, meets an average of 52 times per year. *Faculty representation:* Faculty served by collective bargaining agent, Faculty Union, affiliated with American Federation of Government Employees.

Calendar: Trimesters. Academic year July to mid-June. Freshmen admitted July. Degrees conferred and formal commencement June.

Characteristics of Freshmen: 28% of applicants admitted. 17% of admitted students enrolled.

82% (221 students) submitted SAT scores; 46% (24 students) submitted ACT scores. *25th percentile*: SAT Critical Reading 540, SAT Math 594; ACT Composite 25, ACT English 23, ACT Math 26. *75th percentile*: SAT Critical Reading 640, SAT Math 659; ACT Composite 29, ACT English 29, ACT Math 29.

70% of entering freshmen expected to graduate within 5 years. 12% of freshmen from New York.

Admission: For fall acceptance, apply as early as July of previous year, but not later than Mar. 1 of year of enrollment. Students notified of acceptance by Apr. 15. *Requirements:* Either graduation from accredited secondary school with 16 units which must include 4 English, 3 mathematics (algebra, geometry, and trigonometry), 1 chemistry or physics with laboratory; or GED. Foreign language, drafting recommended. Candidates must be 17 to 25 years of age; a Congressional nomination is required for admission. *Entrance tests:* College Board SAT or ACT.

Tutoring available.

Degree Requirements: 174 semester hours; 2.0 GPA; 9 trimesters in residence; 3 semesters at sea; 4 years military training; physical education requirements; general education and technical core requirements; exit competency examinations in writing, mathematics; U.S. Coast Guard License examination. Must apply for and, if offered, accept a commission in the U.S. Naval Reserve. *Grading system:* A–F.

Distinctive Educational Programs: All students participate in shipboard training program, spending half of second and third years aboard commercial vessels engaged in domestic and foreign travel. Special facilities for using telecommunications in the classroom. Facilities for independent research and study.

Degrees Conferred: 211 *baccalaureate:* engineering 109; marine transportation 102

Fees and Other Expenses: *Full-time tuition per academic year 2008–09:* Tuition, room, board, textbooks, uniforms are borne by the U.S. government. $3,000 mandatory deposit for entering freshmen.

Financial Aid: Financial aid to full-time, first-time undergraduate students: 88% received financial aid.

Departments and Teaching Staff: *Total instructional faculty:* 85. Student/faculty ratio: 11:1. Degrees held by full-time faculty: 49% hold terminal degrees.

Enrollment: Total enrollment 986,

Characteristics of Student Body: *Ethnic/racial makeup:* number of Black non-Hispanic: 21; American Indian or Alaska Native: 2; Asian or Pacific Islander: 42; Hispanic: 57; White non-Hispanic: 838. *Age distribution:* number under 18: 8; 18–19: 400; 20–21: 427; 22–24: 112; 25–29: 2.

International Students: 18 nonresident aliens enrolled fall 2008. Student from Asia, Central and South America. No programs available to aid students whose native language is not English. No financial aid specifically designated for international

Student Life: On-campus residence halls house 100% of student body. Residence halls for males constitute 85% of such space, for females 15%. *Athletics:* cross-country, indoor/outdoor tack, pistol, swimming, diving, sailing, crew, golf, tennis, basketball; male: wrestling, baseball, lacrosse, football; female: softball, volleyball. Student newspaper: (*Hear This*); Yearbook: (*Midships*); Faculty

UNITED STATES MERCHANT MARINE ACADEMY—*cont'd*

newsletter: (*Academy Sports News*). *Special regulations:* Cars permitted for seniors. Military uniforms required on campus. Curfews. Quiet hours. Residence hall visitation hours vary according to class. *Special services:* Learning Resources Center, medical services. *Surrounding community:* Kings Point population 5,500. New York City, 20 miles from campus, is nearest metropolitan area. Served by mass transit bus system; airport 21 miles from campus; passenger rail service 4 miles from campus.

Library Collections: 203,000 volumes. Current serial subscriptions: paper 958; 19,000 via electronic access. 918 audio/videotapes; 200 DVD discs; 41 CD-ROMs. Computer work stations available. Online catalog. Students have access to online information retrieval services.

Most important special collections include Maritime Transportation Information System; Nuclear Ship Savannah Collection; Captain John F. Campbell Collections; ships clippings vertical files; rare books (maritime-related).

Buildings and Grounds: Campus area 75 acres.

Chief Executive Officer: Vice Admiral Joseph D. Stewart, Superintendent.

Address admission inquiries to Captain Robert E. Johnson, Director of Admissions.

United States Military Academy

West Point, New York 10996

Tel: (845) 938-4200 **E-mail:** admissions@usma.edu
Fax: (984) 938-3021 **Internet:** www.usma.edu

Institution Description: The United States Military Academy is a federal institution. *Enrollment:* 4,448. *Degrees awarded:* Baccalaureate.

Accreditation: *Regional:* MSA.

History: Established, chartered, and offered first instruction at postsecondary level 1802; awarded first degree (baccalaureate) 1933.

Institutional Structure: *Governing board:* Board of Visitors of the United States Military Academy. Extrainstitutional representation: 6 members appointed by the president of the United States; 4 members, including 2 members of the House Appropriations Committee, including 2 members of the Senate Appropriations Committee, designated by the vice president of the United States; 1 member designated by the chairman of the Senate Armed Services Committee; 1 designated by the chairman of the House Armed Services Committee. All voting. *Composition of institution:* Administrators 232. Academic affairs headed by dean of the academic board. Full-time instructional faculty 529. Academic governance body, Academic Board, meets an average of 35 times per year.

Calendar: Semesters. Academic year Aug. to May. Freshmen admitted July. Degrees conferred May, June, July, Dec. Formal commencement May, Dec. Summer session from late May to late July.

Characteristics of Freshmen: 13% of applicants accepted. 73% of accepted applicants enrolled.

Average secondary school rank 73rd percentile. Mean SAT class scores men 559 verbal, 648 mathematical. Mean ACT composite class score 27.

71% of entering freshmen expected to graduate within 5 years. Freshmen from 50 states, District of Columbia, and 20 foreign countries.

Admission: Rolling admissions plan. For fall acceptance, apply as early as Oct. of previous year, but not later than Mar. 1 of year of enrollment. Apply by Oct. for early decision; must limit application to Military Academy. *Requirements:* Recommend 4 secondary school units English, 2 in a foreign language, 4 mathematics, 1 chemistry, 1 physics, 1 U.S. history. Nomination to Military Academy by specified official source. Candidate must be 17–22 years of age on July 1 of year of admission; a U.S. citizen except for specified exceptions; trustworthy, emotionally stable and motivated; unmarried, with no dependent children. *Entrance tests:* College Board SAT or ACT English, Mathematics, and Natural Science; medical and physical aptitude examinations. *For transfer students:* All transfer students enter as freshmen.

College credit and advanced placement for postsecondary-level work completed in secondary school. Tutoring available. Developmental courses offered in summer session and regular academic year.

Degree Requirements: 43 courses; 2.0 GPA; 4 years in residence; 4 years military training; 7 credit hours physical education, core curriculum; commitment to 5 years military service.

Fulfillment of some degree requirements and exemption from some beginning courses possible by passing departmental examinations, College Board CLEP, AP. *Grading system:* A–F; pass-fail; withdraw.

Distinctive Educational Programs: Weekend classes. Special facilities for using telecommunications in the classroom. Interdisciplinary programs in basic sciences, foreign area studies, humanities, national security, and public affairs. Tutorials. Interservice exchange program with United States Air Force, Coast Guard, and Naval Academies.

Degrees Conferred: 960 *baccalaureate*. Bachelor's degrees awarded in top five disciplines: social sciences 279; engineering 220; foreign language 64; legal/law studies 63; business, management, marketing, and related support services 62.

Fees and Other Expenses: $2,400 deposit from freshmen for uniforms/equipment. Cadets receive a salary of $10,148 a year. Room and board, dental and medical care are provided free.

Departments and Teaching Staff: *Total instructional faculty:* 119. Degrees held by full-time faculty: doctorate 34%, master's 66%.

Enrollment: Total enrollment 4,448.

Characteristics of Student Body: *Ethnic/racial makeup:* Black non-Hispanic: 6.1%; American Indian or Alaska Native: .8%; Asian or Pacific Islander: 7.1; Hispanic: 6.1%; White non-Hispanic: 77.5%; unknown: 1.4%.

International Students: 46 nonresident aliens enrolled fall 2008. No programs available to aid students whose native language is not English.

Student Life: On-campus residence halls house 100% of student body. Residence halls for both sexes constitute 100% of such space. *Intercollegiate athletics:* male: baseball, basketball, cross-country, football and 150-pound football, golf, gymnastics, hockey, lacrosse, pistol, rifle, soccer, squash, swimming, tennis, track, wrestling; female: basketball, cross-country, softball, swimming, tennis, track, volleyball. *Special regulations:* Cars permitted for seniors only. Military uniforms are worn daily. Curfews from midnight to 5:30am. Quiet hours and residence hall visitation from 8:15pm to midnight. *Special services:* Medical services, shuttle bus on base. *Student publications, radio: Bugle Notes*, an annual freshmen fact book; *Howitzer*, a yearbook; *Pointer*, a humor magazine. Radio Station WKDT broadcasts 168 hours per week. *Surrounding community:* West Point population 8,000. New York City, 45 miles from campus, is nearest metropolitan area. Served by airport 45 miles from campus; passenger rail service 25 miles from campus.

Library Collections: 443m999 volumes. 748,500 microforms; 12,400 audiovisual materials; 1,970 current periodicals. Online catalog. Cadets have access to online information retrieval services and the Internet.

Most important holdings include Thayer Collection (1,000 books purchased for the academy 1815–17); Schley Collection (works on military art and engineering); William Faulkner collection (816 volumes, including first editions, periodicals).

Buildings and Grounds: Campus area 16,080 acres.

Chief Executive Officer: Lt. Gen. Daniel W. Christman, Superintendent.

Address admission inquiries to Col. Michael L. Jones, Director of Admissions.

University of Rochester

River Station
Rochester, New York 14627

Tel: (585) 275-2121 **E-mail:** admit@admissions.rochester.edu
Fax: (585) 275-0359 **Internet:** www.rochester.edu

Institution Description: University of Rochester is a private, independent, nonprofit institution with 3 local branch campuses. *Enrollment:* 9,735. *Degrees awarded:* Baccalaureate, first-professional (medicine), master's, doctorate.

Accreditation: *Regional:* MSA. *Professional*: business, clinical pastoral education, computer science, counseling, dentistry, diagnostic medical sonography, dietetics, engineering, engineering technology, interior design, marriage and family therapy, medicine, music, nuclear medicine technology, nursing, physician assisting, psychology internship, public health, social work, surgeon assisting, teacher education

History: Established as men's college, chartered, and offered first instruction at postsecondary level 1850; awarded first degree (baccalaureate) 1851; became coeducational 1900.

Institutional Structure: *Governing board:* University of Rochester Board of Trustees. Representation: 37 voting (appointed trustees and the president of the university), 46 life trustees, 10 senior trustees. *Composition of institution:* academic affairs headed by provost. Full-time instructional faculty 1,258. Academic governance body, Faculty Senate, meets 8 times per year. Management/business/fiances directed by senior vice president for administration and finance/chief financial officer. Full-time executive, administrative, managerial staff 1,183.

Calendar: Semesters. Academic year Sept. to May. Freshmen admitted Sept., Jan. Degrees conferred Oct., Mar., May. Formal commencement May. Summer sessions from May to Aug.

Characteristics of Freshmen: 12,677 applicants (6,389 female, 6,288 male). 41% of applicants accepted. 25% of accepted applicants enrolled full-time.

80% (931 students) submitted SAT scores; 37% (433 students) submitted ACT scores. *25th percentile*: SAT Critical Reading 600, SAT Math 630; ACT

Composite 27, ACT English 26, ACT Math 27. *75th percentile*: SAT Critical Reading 690, SAT math 720; ACT Composite 31, ACT English 32; ACT math 32.

81% of entering freshmen expected to graduate within 5 years. 47% of freshmen from New York. Freshmen from 50 states and 55 foreign countries.

Admission: Rochester accepts the Common Application with a supplemental form. The regular decision deadline is Jan. 15. Students are notified of admissions decisions by April 1. Early decision notification will be made in mid-December for applicants who apply before Nov. 15. Enrolling students are expected to make formal acceptance and pay the $400 enrollment deposit by Jan. 15 for early decision and May 1 for regular decision applicants. *Requirements:* Recommend 4 units English, 2–3 in a foreign language, 4 history, 3–4 laboratory sciences, 3–4 mathematics. *Entrance tests:* College Board SAT or ACT. *For transfer students:* Maximum transfer credit limited only by residence requirement.

College credit and advanced placement for postsecondary-level work completed in secondary school on basis of College Board AP or International Baccalaureate higher-level examinations. Tutoring available.

Degree Requirements: *For undergraduate degrees:* minimum of 128 credit hours; 2.0 GPA; 2 semesters in residence. Rochester does not have general education requirements. Beginning in 1996, a new and distinctive curricular structure called the College Program, replaced the previous set of distribution requirements. Courses in the college are divided into the three classic division of learning: humanities and arts; social science, natural science, mathematics, and engineering. Students are expected to complete a cluster of three related courses in each of the two divisions outside their major. These divisional clusters give students the opportunity for sustained and integrated study in diverse fields of their own choosing and the chance to participate in three communities of learning. The M.B.A. degree requires 67 hours of study and a 3.0 GPA. Other program requirements vary. *Grading system:* A–F; satisfactory-fail; withdrawal.

Distinctive Educational Programs: The Take Five Scholars Program, Kauffman Entrepreneurial Year Program,, and the Courses in the Quest Program are available to qualifying students (see www.rochester.edu for specific details). Study abroad programs in England, Egypt, Israel, Germany, Chile, China, France, Ghana, Russia; Institute of European and Asian Study Program; Internships in Europe (Belgium, England, France, Germany, Spain). Other programs in Italy and Sweden. Summer and winter program in Israel (archeological dig), England, France, Germany, Italy, Peru, Romania, Russia, Mexico.

ROTC: University programs available to prepare students seeking commissions in the U.S. Navy or the U.S. Marine Corps. Students may choose training for the U.S. Army or the U.S. Air Force through a cooperative program with Rochester Institute of Technology.

Degrees Conferred: 1,232 *baccalaureate*; 913 *master's*; 271 *doctorate*; 99 *first-professional*. Bachelor's degrees awarded in top five disciplines: social sciences 259; visual and performing arts 154; biological/life sciences 144; psychology 137; health professions and related clinical sciences 86. Master's degrees awarded in top five disciplines: business/marketing 286; visual and performing arts 103; education 93; health professions and related clinical sciences 87; physical sciences 49. Doctorate degrees awarded in top five disciplines: biological/life sciences 89; visual and performing arts 39; physical sciences 28; social sciences 17; education 15. First-professional degrees awarded: medicine 99. *Honorary degrees awarded 2005–06:* Doctor of Laws 6; Doctor of Humane Letters 1; Master of Humane Letters 1.

Fees and Other Expenses: *Full-time tuition per academic year 2008–09:* $32,650. *Required fees:* $776. *Room per academic year:* $5,940. *Board per academic year:* $4,612. Contact the university for graduate and professional school tuition and fees.

Financial Aid: Aid from institutionally generated funds is provided on the basis of academic merit, financial need, music talent at Eastman School of Music.

Financial aid to full-time, first-time undergraduate students: 92% received some form of aid. Average amount of aid received: federal grants $1,511; state/local grants $2,004; institutional grants $4,119; loans $2,351.

Departments and Teaching Staff: *Total instructional faculty:* 1,542. Student/faculty ratio: 9.2:1. Degrees held by full-time instructional faculty: doctorate 56%, master's 4%, baccalaureate 2%, professional 100%.

Enrollment: Total enrollment 9,735. Undergraduate 5,378. Graduate 4,351. Undergraduate transfer-in students 108.

Characteristics of Student Body: *Ethnic/racial makeup (undergraduate):* number of Black non-Hispanic: 224; American Indian or Alaska Native: 12; Asian or Pacific Islander: 482; Hispanic: 200; White non-Hispanic: 3,010; unknown: 748. *Age distribution:* number under 18: 48; 18–19: 2,013; 20–21: 2,016; 22–24: 503; 25–29: 125; 30–34: 66; 35–39: 46; 40–49: 53; 50–64: 31; unknown: 3.

International Students: 228 nonresident aliens enrolled 2008. Students from Europe, Asia, Central and South America, Africa, Canada, Australia, New Zealand, Caribbean, Middle East. Financial aid available for qualifying international students.

Student Life: 85% of students live in on-campus residence halls and fraternities. 100% of freshmen and sophomores live on campus. Housing is available for graduate students and families. *Intercollegiate athletics:* male: baseball, basketball, cross-country, football, golf, soccer, squash, swimming and diving, tennis, track and field; female: basketball, cross-country, field hockey, lacrosse, soccer, swimming and diving, tennis, track and field, volleyball. *Special regulations:* Cars permitted after freshman year; fee fee charged. *Special services:* University Health Service; shuttle bus; international student services; office of University Disability Services; ResNet; cable TV; campus wireless; online music service. *Student publications, radio:* WRUR radio; *Campus Times*, newspaper published once a week; *Interpres*, a yearbook; *Logos*, a literary magazine published twice per semester; *The Norm,* a satire magazine. *Surrounding community:* Rochester population 250,000. Served by mass transit bus system; airport and passenger rail service, each 3 miles from campus.

Library Collections: 3,608,000 volumes. 43,509 government documents; 5,104,000 microforms; 113,500 audiovisual materials; 26,000 periodicals including via electronic access. Online catalog. Computer work stations available. Students have access to online information retrieval services and the Internet.

Most important special holdings include Frederick Douglass Collection; Susan B. Anthony Collection; William Henry Seward Collection.

Buildings and Grounds: Main campus area 154 acres. *New buildings:* Medical Research Annex; Biomedical Engineering and Optics; Cancer Center.

Chief Executive Officer: Dr. Joel Seligman, President.

Address undergraduate admission inquiries to Jonathan Burdick Dean of Admissions and Financial Aid; graduate inquiries to various professional schools below.

The College of Arts, Sciences, Engineering

Degree Programs Offered: *Baccalaureate* in anthropology, applied mathematics, art history, biological sciences (specialties in biochemistry, cell and developmental biology, biomedical engineering), brain and cognitive sciences, chemical engineering, environmental studies, environmental science, Japanese, mathematics, mechanical engineering, optics, physics, physics and astronomy, political science, psychology, religion, computer sciences, film and media studies, health and society, women's studies, chemistry, economics, English, French, geology, geomechanics, German, history, interdepartmental studies, linguistics, mathematics-statistics, music, philosophy, Russian, Russian studies, Spanish, visual and cultural studies, interdepartmental studies; *doctorate* in biology, biomedical engineering, brain and cognitive sciences, chemical engineering, chemistry, clinical psychology, computer science, departmental psychology, economics, electrical engineering, English, mechanical engineering, optics, physics, physics and astronomy, political science, social-personality psychology, visual and cultural studies. *Certificates* also given in conjunction with baccalaureate degree in actuarial studies, Asian studies, biotechnology, Citation for Achievement in College Leadership, international relations, management studies, mathematical modeling, in political science and economics, Polish and Central European Studies.

Degree Requirements: Beginning with the Class of 2000, undergraduate students complete a major from one of three academic divisions plus a cluster of related courses from each of the other two, as well as primary and upper-level writing requirements. Graduate degree requirements vary by level and program.

Distinctive Educational Programs: The College designed the Rochester Curriculum to allow students' interests to drive their learning. In this curriculum there are no required subjects. Students pursue at least a major in one of the three divisions of learning (humanities, social science, natural science) and take at least a cluster in each of the other two areas. The choice of subject matter and level of concentration (major, minor, or cluster) in each division is theirs. Independent Study, Internships, "Quest" Courses, Study Abroad, "Take Five" Scholars, Certificate Programs, Undergraduate Research.

Eastman School of Music

Degree Programs Offered: *Baccalaureate* in applied music, jazz studies and contemporary media, music composition, music education, music history, music theory, musical arts; *master's* in conducting, ethnomusicology, jazz studies and contemporary media, music composition, music education, music theory, musicology, opera, performance and literature, piano accompanying; *doctorate* in conducting, jazz studies and contemporary media, music composition, music education, music theory, musicology, performance and literature, piano accompanying.

Admission: Admissions deadline Dec. 1 for enrollment in BM programs the following September. Auditions and interviews, depending on major focus.

Degree Requirements: Vary by program.

UNIVERSITY OF ROCHESTER—*cont'd*

Distinctive Educational Programs: Community education division, including summer study program, for students of precollege age and for adults pursuing study outside regular program. Summer session, workshops, and institutes of special interest, including annual workshops in computer music techniques. Performer's Certificate and Artist's Diploma programs. Many ensembles and other performance groups, including InterMusica (chamber music), Eastman Opera Theater, Musica Nova (contemporary chamber music, modern music), several jazz ensembles. Institute of American Music. The Sibley Music Library, an outstanding music research library, offers listening and public services facilities. The Hanson Institute of American Music, promotes the commissioning, recording, performance study, and preservation of works of American composers.

Margaret Warner Graduate School of Education and Human Development

Degree Programs Offered: Master's and doctoral degree programs in teaching and curriculum; counseling; human development; school administration; higher education. *Master's* in art of teaching. *Doctorate* in education. Certificates also awarded.

Admission: Applicants must have a bachelor's degree from an accredited institution or equivalent by the time they enter the program, with the exception of those applying for early admission programs. Applicants must have the ability to do graduate work as demonstrated by their past academic performance and their academic writing skills; sufficient communication and interpersonal skills; additional criteria may be established for individual programs.

Degree Requirements: Doctor programs: 90 credits (96 for Counseling); master's and master's with certification: credits vary.

Distinctive Educational Programs: Master's and doctoral degrees as well as non-degree programs for certification or advanced study in teaching and curriculum, counseling and human development, educational leadership, higher education, and educational policy.

William E. Simon Graduate School of Business Administration

Degree Programs Offered: *Master's* in accountancy; *master's, doctorate* in business administration.

Admission: Form, essays, official transcripts, letter of recommendation, resume, official scores reported by Pewarson VUE from the GMAT, and by ETS from TOEFL for international applicants who are non-native English speakers.

Degree Requirements: The M.B.A. degree requires 67 hours of study and a 3.0 GPA. Other program requirements vary.

Distinctive Educational Programs: The school emphasizes group work, allowing each student to benefit from quality and the diverse cultural and business backgrounds of classmates.

School of Medicine and Dentistry

Degree Programs Offered: *First-professional* in medicine; *master's* in clinical investigation, dental science, medical statistics, microbiology-medical, public health; *master's, doctorate* in neurology and anatomy, biochemistry, biophysics, genetics, microbiology and immunology, neuroscience, pathology, pharmacology, physiology, statistics, toxicology; *doctorate* in microbiology and immunology.

Admission: Master's and Ph.D. applicants: online application, required documents. First-professional: 3 years at approved university or college with 2 units chemistry, 1 biology, 1 English, 1 physics. Recommend integral calculus and statistics.

Degree Requirements: *For all first-professional degrees:* Prescribed 4-year program. Graduate education in biomedical sciences programs organized into interest areas, or clusters; requirements vary.

Distinctive Educational Programs: The Double Helix Curriculum captures the integrated strands of basic science and clinical medicine as they are woven throughout the four-year curriculum. Joint-degree programs; post-graduate program certificates in dentistry.

School of Nursing

Degree Programs Offered: *Baccalaureate, master's, doctorate.* Clinical specialty area for master's include acute care, adult, care of children and families, family, gerontological, psychiatric-mental heath, pediatric-psychiatric-mental health. *Master's* in leadership in health care systems.

Admission: Criteria vary by program.

Degree Requirements: Criteria vary by program.

Distinctive Educational Programs: Programs blend nursing practice and research into educational programs. Baccalaureate, master's, and doctoral programs; Leadership in Health Care Systems Master's Program; Nurse Practitioner Master's Program; MS/Ph.D. dual degree accelerated program; post master's program; RN to BS program; RN to BS to MS program; accelerated bachelor's program for non-nurses; accelerated master's program for non-nurses.

Utica College

1600 Burrstone Road
Utica, New York 13502-4892
Tel: (315) 792-3111 **E-mail:** admiss@utica.edu
Fax: (315) 792-3292 **Internet:** www.utica.edu

Institution Description: Utica College, formerly named Utica College of Syracuse University, is a private, nonprofit institution. *Enrollment:* 3,082. *Degrees awarded:* Baccalaureate, master's, first-professional.

Academic offerings subject to approval by statewide coordinating bodies.

Accreditation: *Regional:* MSA. *Professional*: nursing, occupational therapy, physical therapy

History: Founded by Syracuse University, Utica College established, chartered, and offered first instruction at postsecondary level 1946; independently chartered 1995; awarded its first graduate Utica College degree 2001.

Institutional Structure: *Governing board:* Utica College Board of Trustees. Extrainstitutional representation: 45 trustees; ex officio representation President of the college (voting) and Chancellor of Syracuse University (nonvoting). *Composition of institution:* Administrators 171. Academic affairs headed by vice president and dean of faculty management. Management/business/finances directed by vice president and treasurer. Student affairs headed by vice president and dean of students. Full-time instructional faculty 123. Academic governance body, Utica Faculty Senate, meets an average of 9 times per year. *Faculty representation:* Faculty served by collective bargaining agent, Utica College Chapter of AAUP.

Calendar: Semesters. Academic year late Aug. 28 to mid-May. Freshmen admitted Sept., Jan., June. Degrees conferred May, Aug., Dec. Formal commencement May. Summer session of 4 terms.

Characteristics of Freshmen: 2,898 applicants (1,528 female, 1,370 male). 74% of applicants admitted. 27% of applicants admitted and enrolled full-time. 75% (371 students) submitted SAT scores; 17% (80 students) submitted ACT scores. *25th percentile*: SAT Critical Reading 420, SAT Math 430; ACT Composite 19, ACT English 17, ACT Math 18. *75th percentile*: SAT Critical Reading 530, SAT Math 540; ACT Composite 23, ACT English 23, ACT Math 24.

44% of entering freshmen expected to graduate within 5 years. 83% of freshmen from New York. Freshmen from 39 states and 13 foreign countries.

Admission: General admission rolling: Jan. 15 for applicants for merit scholarship; the combined medical, physical therapy, and occupational therapy programs; Feb. 15 for nursing program. *Requirements:* graduation from accredited secondary school with 16 academic units (or GED). *For transfer students:* 2.5 minimum GPA; limited to 90–98 hours from accredited 4-year institution; from 2-year accredited institution 60–64 hours.

College credit awarded for postsecondary-level work completed in secondary school and for extrainstitutional learning on basis of departmental assessment.

Tutoring available. Developmental courses offered in summer session and regular academic year; credit given.

Degree Requirements: *For all baccalaureate degrees:* 120–128 credit hours; 30 hours in residence. 2.0 GPA; courses in liberal arts and sciences. *For all graduate degrees:* 33–35 credit hours in residence; 3.0 GPA; degree completion within 6 years,as well as the completion of a thesis, research project, and/or a comprehensive exam.

Fulfillment of some degree requirements and exemption from some beginning courses possible by passing College Board CLEP. *Grading system:* A–F; pass-fail; withdraw (carries time limit).

Distinctive Educational Programs: Academic programs: weekend occupational therapy; economic crime investigation/criminal justice child life/psychology, and public relations. Combined admission with professional medical and dental schools. Study abroad in China, Italy, Poland, and Wales in addition to Syracuse University sites. All graduates receive a Syracuse University degree.

ROTC: Army in cooperation with Syracuse University.

Degrees Conferred: 487 *baccalaureate*; 145 *master's*; 49 *doctorate*. Bachelor's degrees awarded in top five disciplines: health professions and related clinical sciences 82; security and protective services 81; psychology 71; business/marketing 71; communications/journalism 40. Master's degrees awarded: business/marketing 3; education 74; health professions and related sciences 31; liberal arts 1; security and protective services 13.

Fees and Other Expenses: *Full-time tuition per academic year 2008–09:* $26,058 undergraduate; contact the college for current graduate tuition.

Required fees: $210. *Books and supplies:* $946. *Room and board per academic year:* $10,706. *Other expenses:* $1,590.

Financial Aid: Aid from institutionally generated funds is provided on the basis of academic merit, financial need.

Financial aid to full-time, first-time undergraduate students: 97% received some form of aid. Average amount of aid received: federal grants $1,511; state/local grants $2,004; institutional grants $4,119; loans $2,351.

Departments and Teaching Staff: *Total instructional faculty:* 290 (full-time 123, part-time 107). Total faculty with doctorate, first-professional, or other terminal degree: 137. Student/faculty ratio: 17:1. Degrees held by full-time faculty: doctorate 59%, master's 37%, baccalaureate 4%.

Enrollment: Total enrollment 3,082. Undergraduate 2,502. Graduate 580. Undergraduate transfer-in students 257.

Characteristics of Student Body: *Ethnic/racial makeup:* number of Black non-Hispanic: 230; American Indian or Alaska Native: 10; Asian or Pacific Islander: 46; Hispanic: 79; White non-Hispanic: 1,522; unknown: 502. *Age distribution:* number under 18: 6; 18–19: 781; 20–21: 722; 22–24: 336; 25–29: 156; 30–34: 100; 35–39: 97; 40–49: 117; 50–64: 41; 65 and over: 3.

International Students: 48 nonresident aliens enrolled fall 2008. Students from Europe, Asia, Central and South America, Africa, Canada. No programs available to aid students whose native language is not English. Some scholarships specifically available for qualifying international students; 20 totaling $174,660 awarded 1006–07.

Student Life: On-campus residence halls house 45% of full-time student body. Utica offers a variety of options in campus residence, including single-sex floors and co-ed floors. There is a wide variety of social, cultural, and educational activities often planned by students that complement the academic program. *Intercollegiate athletics:* male: baseball, basketball, soccer, swimming, tennis; female: basketball, soccer, swimming, tennis, volleyball. There is also a wide variety of club sports, including fencing, lacrosse, volleyball and karate. Over two-thirds of the students participate in intramural and/or intercollegiate athletic activities. *Special regulations:* Cars permitted without restrictions. Quiet hours. *Special services:* Academic Support Services; medical services. *Student publications, radio: Tangerine*, a weekly newspaper; *Annales*, student yearbook; *Ampersand,* a student literary magazine. Radio station WPNR-FM broadcasts 150 hours per week. *Surrounding community:* Utica population 60,000. Syracuse, 55 miles from campus, is nearest metropolitan area. Served by mass transit bus system; Hancock International Airport, located in Syracuse, 55 miles from campus; passenger rail service 3.5 miles from campus.

Library Collections: 186,000 volumes. Online catalog. 39,000 microforms; 9,900 audiovisual materials; 2,000 Current serial subscriptions. Computer work stations available. Students have access to online information retrieval services.

Most important special holdings include Welsh Collection; Upstate New York fiction.

Buildings and Grounds: Campus area 128 acres.

Chief Executive Officer: Dr. Todd Hutton, President.

Address undergraduate admission inquiries to Patrick Quinn, Vice President for Enrollment Management; graduate inquiries to John d. Rowe, Director of Graduate Admissions.

Vassar College

124 Raymond Avenue
Poughkeepsie, New York 12604-0002

Tel: (845) 437-7000 **E-mail:** admissions@vassar.edu
Fax: (845) 437-7063 **Internet:** www.vassar.edu

Institution Description: Vassar College is a private, independent, nonprofit college. *Enrollment:* 2,389. *Degrees awarded:* Baccalaureate.

Member of Consortium Twelve College Exchange.

Accreditation: *Regional:* MSA.

History: Established and chartered as Vassar Female College 1861; offered first instruction at postsecondary level 1865; awarded first degree (baccalaureate) and adopted present name 1867; became coeducational 1969. *See* Dorothy Plum and George Dowdell, *The Magnificent Enterprise: A Chronicle of Vassar College* (Poughkeepsie, N.Y.: Vassar College, 1961) for further information.

Institutional Structure: *Governing board:* The Board of Trustees of Vassar College. Extrainstitutional representation: 30 trustees, alumni; institutional representation: president of the college. 1 ex officio. 29 voting. *Composition of institution:* Administrators 214. Academic affairs headed by dean of the faculty. Management/business/finances directed by chief financial officer. Full-time instructional faculty 277. Academic governance body, the faculty, meets an average of 9 times per year.

Calendar: Semesters. Academic year Sept. to May. Freshmen admitted Sept. Degrees conferred and formal commencement May. No summer session.

Characteristics of Freshmen: 7,361 applicants (5,104 female, 2,251 male). 25% of applicants admitted. 35% of admitted students enrolled full-time.

87% (589 students) submitted SAT scores; 27% (187 students) submitted ACT scores. *25th percentile*: SAT Critical Reading 660, SAT Math 640, SAT Writing 650; ACT Composite 29, ACT English 29, ACT math 29. *75th percentile*: SAT Critical Reading 750, SAT Math 710, SAT Writing 740; ACT Composite 32, ACT English 32, ACT Math 32.

90% of entering freshmen expected to graduate within 5 years. 26% of freshmen from New York. Freshmen from 50 states and 52 foreign countries.

Admission: For fall acceptance, apply as early as Sept. of previous year, but not later than Jan. 1. Students are notified of acceptance Apr. Apply by Jan. 1 for early decision; must commit to enroll if accepted. *Requirements:* Either graduation from secondary school or GED. Recommend 4 units in English, 3 in a foreign language (or 2 in two languages), 4 mathematics, 3 laboratory science, 3 history, with inclusion of honors courses and/or advanced placement work whenever possible. *Entrance tests:* College Board SAT, SAT IIs, or ACT. *For transfer students:* 3.0 minimum GPA; from 4-year and 2-year accredited institutions 17 units maximum transfer credit.

College credit and advanced placement for postsecondary-level work completed in secondary school.

Tutoring available. Noncredit remedial courses offered during regular academic year.

Degree Requirements: 34 units; 2.0 GPA; 4 terms in residence; senior project and additional requirements for some majors.

Fulfillment of some degree requirements and exemption from some beginning courses possible by passing departmental examinations, College Board AP (score of 4). *Grading system:* A–F; non-recorded option; withdraw (carries time limit).

Distinctive Educational Programs: *For undergraduates:* Accelerated baccalaureate-master's program in chemistry. Multidisciplinary program in African studies; Asian studies; science, technology, and society; cognitive science; environmental studies, Jewish studies; Latin American and Latino/a studies; media studies; urban studies international studies; women's studies; American culture; individual majors. Institutionally sponsored study abroad in Germany. England, Spain, Italy, Morocco, Russia. New York State Assembly Intern Program. Off-campus study for one semester or year through consortium and with Fisk University (TN), Morehouse and Spelman Colleges (GA). *Available to all students:* Work-experience programs. Evening classes. Art gallery containing over 10,000 paintings, sculptures, prints, drawings and photographs of European and American art.

Degrees Conferred: 638 *baccalaureate.* Bachelor's degrees awarded in top five disciplines: social sciences 165; visual and performing arts 109; foreign languages and literature 74; English language/literature 71; psychology 53.

Fees and Other Expenses: *Full-time tuition per academic year 2008–09:* $40,210. *Required fees:* $570. *Books and supplies* $860. *Room and board per academic year:* $9,040. *Other expenses:* $1,260.

Financial Aid: Aid from institutionally generated funds is provided on the basis of financial need.

Financial aid to full-time, first-time undergraduate students: 71% received some form of aid. Average amount of aid received: federal grants $1,511; state/local grants $2,004; institutional grants $4,119; loans $2,351.

Departments and Teaching Staff: *Total instructional faculty:* 318 (full-time 281, part-time 37). Total faculty with doctorate, first-professional, or other terminal degree: 273. Student/faculty ratio: 8:1.

Enrollment: Total enrollment 2,389 (undergraduate). Transfer-in students 11.

Characteristics of Student Body: *Ethnic/racial makeup:* number of Black non-Hispanic: 117; American Indian or Alaska Native: 7; Asian or Pacific Islander: 223; Hispanic: 146; White non-Hispanic: 1,799. *Age distribution:* number under 18: 10; 18–19: 1,124; 20–21: 1,054; 22–24: 180; 25–29: 5; 30–34: 3; 35–49: 2.

International Students: 131 nonresident aliens enrolled fall 2008. Students from Europe, Asia, Central and south America, Africa, Canada, Australia, New Zealand. English. Some need-based financial aid specifically designated for international students.

Student Life: On-campus residence halls house 95% of student body. Some students live in married student apartments. *Athletics:* 25 varsity sports and 14 intercollegiate teams. *Special regulations:* Restricted student parking areas during college business hours. *Special services:* Teaching and Learning Center. *Student publications, radio: Miscellany News*, a weekly newspaper; *Vassarion*, a yearbook; *Vassar Review,* literary magazine published each semester. Radio station WKVR broadcasts 140 hours per week. *Surrounding community:* Poughkeepsie population 30,500. New York City, 75 miles from campus, is nearest metropolitan area. Served by mass transit bus system; airport 5 miles from campus; passenger rail service 3 miles from campus.

Library Collections: 886,000 volumes. 611,000 microforms; 7,953 sound recordings; 2,781 videocassettes; Current serial subscriptions: paper 1,904; microform 34; 2,610 via electronic access. 24,000 audiovisual materials; 3,403

VASSAR COLLEGE—*cont'd*

DVD discs; 76 CD-ROMs. Online catalog. Computer work stations. available. Students have access to on-line information retrieval services and the Internet.

Most important special holdings include Jean Webster McKinney family papers (includes correspondence and manuscripts of Mark Twain); Mary McCarthy Papers; Elizabeth Bishop Papers.

Buildings and Grounds: Campus area 1,020 acres.

Chief Executive Officer: Dr. Catharine B. Hill, President.

Address admission inquiries to David Borus, Dean of Admission and Financial Aid.

Vaughn College of Aeronautics and Technology

86-01 23rd Avenue
Flushing, New York 11369
Tel: (718) 429-6600 **E-mail:** admissions@vaughn.edu
Fax: (718) 429-0256 **Internet:** www.vaughn.edu

Institution Description: Vaughn College of Aeronautics and Technology is a private college offering programs in aviation technology. *Enrollment:* 1,097. *Degrees awarded:* Associate, baccalaureate.

Accreditation: *Regional:* MSA. *Professional*: engineering

History: Founded 1932;students may enroll in associate and bachelor's degree programs in five primary areas: flight, maintenance, computer technologies, pre-engineering, and avionics.

Institutional Structure: Trimesters. Academic year Aug. to May.

Calendar: 96% of applicants accepted. 52% of accepted applicants enrolled.
Mean SAT scores 480 verbal, 480 mathematical.
98% of freshmen from New York.

Admission: Open enrollment. Early admissions plan available. *Requirements:* Graduation from an accredited secondary school with rank in upper 75% of graduating class; completion of 18 units including 4 English, 3 mathematics, 2 science, 4 social science. *Entrance tests:* SAT with score of 400 on both verbal and mathematical.

Degree Requirements: Completion of prescribed curriculum with 2.0 GPA; fulfillment of appropriate licensing requirements.

Distinctive Educational Programs: Cross-registration with New York Institute of Technology.

Degrees Conferred: 117 *associate*; 114 *baccalaureate:* engineering-related technologies.

Fees and Other Expenses: *Full-time tuition per academic year 2008–09:* $15,900. *Books and supplies:* $1,320. *Required fees:* $140. No on-campus housing.

Financial Aid: Aid from institutionally generated funds is provided on the basis of academic merit, financial need. Institution has a Program Participation Agreement with the U.S. Department of Education for eligible students to receive Pell Grants and, depending upon the agreement, other federal aid.

Financial aid to full-time, first-time undergraduate students: 92% received federal grants averaging $4,050; 74% state/local grants averaging $5,000; 86% institutional grants averaging $750; 74% received loans averaging $2,625.

Departments and Teaching Staff: *Total instructional faculty:* 95 (full-time 33, part-time 32). Student/faculty ratio: 20:1. Degrees held by full-time faculty: doctorate 10%, master's 92%, baccalaureate 100%, professional 80%.

Enrollment: *Total enrollment:* 1,097 (undergraduate). Transfer-in students 115.

Characteristics of Student Body: *Ethnic/racial makeup:* number of Black non-Hispanic: 218; Asian or Pacific Islander: 136; Hispanic: 368; White non-Hispanic: 208; unknown: 133. *Age distribution:* number under 18: 12; 18–19: 204; 20–21: 263; 22–24: 152; 25–29: 202; 30–34: 51; 35–39: 29; 40–49: 58; 50–64: 14.

International Students: 34 nonresident aliens enrolled fall 2008. Students from Europe, Asia, Central and south America, Africa, Australia. English as a Second Language Program available. No financial aid specifically designated for international students.

Student Life: No residence halls. Assistance in finding local living accommodations. *Student activities:* Various student organizations including Flying Club. Campus is located at LaGuardia Airport in the borough of Queens. Bus transportation from subway and local stops directly to campus.

Library Collections: 73,400 volumes. 138 serial subscriptions Online catalog. 1,249 audio/videotapes; 954 DVDs; 285 CD-ROMs. Computer work stations available. Students have access to online information retrieval services and the Internet. *Most important special holdings:* World War II Aircraft/Engine Technical Orders; aviation rare books; aviation videos.

Buildings and Grounds: Campus area 6 acres.

Chief Executive Officer: Dr. John C. Fitzpatrick, President.

Address admission inquiries to Vincent Papandrea, Director of Admissions.

Wagner College

One Campus Road
Staten Island, New York 10301-4495
Tel: (718) 390-3100 **E-mail:** adm@wagner.edu
Fax: (718) 390-3467 **Internet:** www.wagner.edu

Institution Description: Wagner College is a private college supported by the Metropolitan and Upper New York Synods of the Lutheran Church in America. *Enrollment:* 2,294. *Degrees awarded:* Baccalaureate, master's.

Accreditation: *Regional:* MSA. *Professional*: nursing

History: Established 1833; chartered and incorporated as Rochester Lutheran Proseminary in Rochester 1885; changed name to Wagner Memorial Lutheran College 1886; moved to Staten Island 1918; offered first instruction at postsecondary level 1925; awarded first degree (baccalaureate) 1928; changed name to Wagner Lutheran College 1952; adopted present name 1959.

Institutional Structure: *Governing board:* Wagner College Board of Trustees. Extrainstitutional representation: President of the College, 22 alumni, 3 ex officio, 31 voting. *Composition of institution:* Administrators 73. Academic affairs headed by Academic Vice President. Management/business/finances directed by Vice President for Finance/Administration. Full-time instructional faculty 98. Academic governance body, Wagner College Faculty, meets an average of 5 times per year.

Calendar: Semesters. Academic year Sept. to May. Freshmen admitted Sept., Jan. Degrees conferred Aug., Dec., May. 4- and 5-week summer sessions.

Characteristics of Freshmen: 3,012 applicants (1,841 female, 1,171 male). 61% of applicants accepted. 26% of accepted applicants enrolled full-time.

87% (415 students) submitted SAT scores; 13% (62 students) submitted ACT scores. *25th percentile*: SAT Critical Reading 530, SAT Math 530. SAT Writing 520; ACT Composite 23, ACT English 23. ACT Math 24. *75th percentile*: SAT Critical Reading 640, SAT Math 630, SAT Writing 650; ACT Composite 28, ACT English 29, ACT Math 28.

70% of entering freshmen expected to graduate within 5 years. 48% of freshmen from New York. Freshmen from 40 states and 14 foreign countries.

Admission: Rolling admissions plan. Apply by Dec. 1 for early decision; must limit application to Wagner College. Early acceptance available. *Requirements:* Either graduation from accredited secondary school with 16 units which must include 4 English, 2 foreign language, 3 history, 3 mathematics, 1 laboratory science, 1 other science; or GED. Recommend units in art, foreign language, mathematics, music, natural science, and social studies. Minimum GPA 2.5. Lowest acceptable secondary school class standing 50th percentile. *Entrance tests:* College Board SAT or ACT composite. *For transfer students:* 2.5 minimum GPA; from 4-year accredited institution maximum transfer credit 90 semester hours; from 2-year accredited institution 64 hours.

College credit and advanced placement for postsecondary-level work completed in secondary school. College credit for extrainstitutional learning on basis of portfolio assessment. Tutoring available.

Degree Requirements: *For all undergraduate degrees:* 128 credit hours; 2.0 GPA; senior year in residence; prescribed courses and distribution requirement. Fulfillment of some degree requirements and exemption from some beginning courses possible by passing College Board CLEP, AP. *Grading system:* A–F; pass-fail; withdraw (may carry penalty, carries time limit).

Distinctive Educational Programs: *For undergraduates:* Interdisciplinary program in art administration; Preprofessional programs in dentistry and medicine; physician's assistant program; special 3:4 program with NYU in dentistry (D.D.S.). Honors Program; facilities for independent research. *Available to all students:* Evening classes. *Other distinctive programs:* Nondegree continuing education program.

ROTC: Army offered in cooperation with St. John's University; Air Force in cooperation with Rutgers, The State University of New Jersey.

Degrees Conferred: 384 *baccalaureate*; 165 *master's.* Bachelor's degrees awarded in top five disciplines: business, management, marketing, and related support services 103; visual and performing arts 61; psychology 49; health professions and related clinical sciences 39; social sciences 32.

Fees and Other Expenses: *Full-time tuition per academic year 2008–09:* $31,050; graduate study charged per credit (contact the college for current rate). *Books and supplies:* $725. *Room and board per academic year:* $9,250. *Other expenses:* $1,985.

Financial Aid: Aid from institutionally generated funds is provided on the basis of academic merit, financial need, athletic ability. Institution has a Program Participation Agreement with the U.S. Department of Education for eligible students to receive Pell Grants and, depending upon the agreement, other federal aid.

Financial aid to full-time, first-time undergraduate students: 99% received some form of aid. Average amount of aid received: federal grants $1,511; state/local grants $2,004; institutional grants $4,119; loans $2,351.

Departments and Teaching Staff: *Total instructional faculty:* 231 (full-time 98, part-time 133). Student/faculty ratio: 19:1. Degrees held by full-time faculty: master's 97%, doctorate 70%. 85% hold terminal degrees.

Enrollment: Total enrollment 2,294. Undergraduate 1,924. Graduate 270. Undergraduate transfer-in students 15.

Characteristics of Student Body: *Ethnic/racial makeup:* number of Black non-Hispanic:22; American Indian or Alaska Native: 4; Asian or Pacific Islander: 44; Hispanic: 97; ; White non-Hispanic: 399; unknown: 177.

International Students: 11 undergraduate nonresident aliens enrolled fall 2008. Students from Europe, Asia, Latin America. Programs available to aid students whose native language is not English: English as a Second Language Program. No financial aid specifically designated for international students.

Student Life: On-campus residence halls house 50% of student body. Rooms for males constitute 40% of such space, for females 60%. *Intercollegiate athletics:* male: baseball, basketball, football, golf, hockey, tennis; female: volleyball, basketball, softball, tennis; both sexes: track. *Special regulations:* Registered cars permitted in designated areas. Quiet hours 10pm to 10am Sun.–Thurs., 1am to noon Fri. and Sat. *Special services:* Academic counseling, medical services, mental health counseling. *Student publications: Kallista*, the school yearbook; *Nimbus*, the literary magazine; *Wagnerian*, a biweekly newspaper. *Surrounding community:* Staten Island population 380,000. New York metropolitan population over 7 million. Served by mass transit bus system; airport and passenger rail service each 15 miles from campus.

Publications: *Markham Review* (quarterly).

Library Collections: 390,000 volumes. 47,500 government documents; 361,200 microforms; 1,000 periodical subscriptions. Online catalog. Students have access to online information retrieval services and the Internet.

Most important holdings include the Edward Markham Collection of 10,000 volumes and 25,000 items (including manuscripts, letters, and rare books) by and about the American poet, the Thomas Harris Collection (1,000 volumes, including many rare books, from the library of the American man of letters); Eric collection.

Buildings and Grounds: Campus area 105 acres.

Chief Executive Officer: Dr. Richard Guarasci, President.

Address admission inquiries to Angelo Araimo, Dean of Admissions.

Webb Institute

298 Crescent Beach Road
Glen Cove, New York 11542-1398
Tel: (516) 671-2213 **E-mail:** admissions@webb-institute.edu
Fax: (516) 674-9838 **Internet:** www.webb-institute.edu

Institution Description: Webb Institute, formerly known as the Webb Institute of Naval Architecture is a private, independent, nonprofit institution. *Enrollment:* 90. *Degrees awarded:* Baccalaureate.

Accreditation: *Regional:* MSA. *Professional*: engineering

History: Established as Webb's Academy, a 3-year institution, and chartered 1889; offered first instruction at postsecondary level 1894; became 4-year institution 1909; became Webb Institute of Naval Architecture 1920; awarded first degree (baccalaureate) 1933; adopted present name 1994.

Institutional Structure: *Governing board:* Board of Trustees of Webb Institute. Extrainstitutional representation: 21 trustees; institutional representation: president of the college; 8 alumni. All voting. *Composition of institution:* Administrators 22. Academic affairs headed by headed by dean of the college. Management/business/finances directed by the president. Full-time instructional faculty 8. Academic governance body, the faculty, meets an average of 9 times per year.

Calendar: Semesters with 8-week winter work period. Academic year late Aug. to late June. Freshmen admitted Aug. Degrees conferred and formal commencement June.

Characteristics of Freshmen: 90 applicants (16 female, 74 male). 34% of applicants accepted. 77% of accepted applicants enrolled.

100% (224 students) submitted SAT scores. *25th percentile*: SAT Critical Reading 600, SAT Math 700, SAT Writing 630. *75th percentile*: SAT Critical Reading 700, SAT Math 770, SAT Writing 690.

74% entering freshmen expected to graduate within 5 years. 24% of freshmen from New York. Freshmen from 22 states and 1 foreign country.

Admission: Apply no later than Feb. 15. Students are notified of acceptance Mar. and Apr. *Requirements:* Graduation from accredited secondary school with 4 units English, 4 mathematics, 2 history, 1 chemistry, 1 physics, 4 electives, including foreign language. Recommend additional units in calculus and drafting. Minimum 3.2 GPA. U.S. citizenship. Students must be physically capable of performing required work. *Entrance tests:* College Board SAT and 3 Achievements (English composition, mathematics, physics or chemistry). *For transfer students:* minimum 3.2 GPA. Transfer students enter as freshmen.

Degree Requirements: *For baccalaureate degree:* 146 credit hours; entire program in residence; prescribed curriculum; senior thesis; 8 weeks per year of work in course-related industries. *Grading system:* 100-point scale.

Distinctive Educational Programs: Every student is required to work in the marine industry during January and February each academic year. The Haeberle Laboratory provides facilities and equipment for the study of marine engineering and mechanical systems, material testing, and structural systems, electrical engineering and measurements, and fluids. Other facilities include 93-foot model testing basin.

Degrees Conferred: 34 *engineering*.

Fees and Other Expenses: *Full-time tuition per academic year 2008–09:* None. *Room and board per academic year:* $9,500. *Books and supplies:* $800. *Other expenses:* $800.

Financial Aid: Aid from institutionally generated funds is provided on the basis of financial need. Institution has a Program Participation Agreement with the U.S. Department of Education for eligible students to receive Pell Grants and, depending upon the agreement, other federal aid.

Financial aid for first-time, full-time students: 81% received some form of financial aid. Average amount of aid received: 36% received state/local grants; 8% institutional grants; 8% loans.

Departments and Teaching Staff: *Total instructional faculty:* 14. Student/faculty ratio: 101. Degrees held by full-time faculty: doctorate 60%, master's 100%. 60% hold terminal degrees.

Enrollment: Total enrollment 90.

Characteristics of Student Body: *Ethnic/racial makeup:* Black non-Hispanic: 1.3%; Asian or Pacific Islander: 2.5%; Hispanic: 1.3%;White non-Hispanic: 95%.

International Students: No programs available to aid students whose native language is not English. No financial aid specifically designated for international students.

Student Life: On-campus residence halls house 99% of student body. Residence halls for males constitute 81% of such space, for females 7%, for both sexes 12%. *Intercollegiate athletics:* baseball, basketball, cross-country, sailing, soccer, tennis, volleyball. *Special regulations:* All students must live on campus; exceptions made only by president of the institute. Cars permitted on campus in designated areas. Residence hall visitation until midnight Sun.–Thurs., 2am Fri. and Sat. *Special services:* Medical services. *Student publication: The Binnacle*, a biannual magazine. *Surrounding community:* Glen Cove population 25,000. New York City, 30 miles from campus, is nearest metropolitan area. Served by passenger rail service 2 miles from campus.

Library Collections: 51,000 volumes. 1,640 microforms; 1,850 audiovisual materials; 270 current periodical subscriptions. Online catalog. Computer work stations available. Students have access to online information retrieval services.

Most important special holdings include collections on American and European naval architecture; marine engineering; naval and shipbuilding history.

Buildings and Grounds: Campus area 26 acres.

Chief Executive Officer: R. Adm. Robert C. Olson, Jr., President.

Address admission inquiries to Stephen Ostendorff, Director of Admissions.

Wells College

Route 170
P.O. Box 500
Aurora, New York 13026-0500
Tel: (315) 364-3266 **E-mail:** admissions@wells.edu
Fax: (315) 364-3227 **Internet:** www.wells.edu

Institution Description: Wells College is a private, independent, nonprofit, coeducational college. *Enrollment:* 481. *Degrees awarded:* Baccalaureate.

Accreditation: *Regional:* MSA.

History: Established as Wells Seminary 1866; chartered and offered first instruction at postsecondary level 1868; awarded first degree (baccalaureate) 1869; adopted present name 1870; became co-ed 2005.

Institutional Structure: *Governing board:* Wells College Board of Trustees. Extrainstitutional representation: 25 trustees; institutional representation: 1 administrator; 3 alumnae. 1 ex officio. 23 voting. *Composition of institution:* Administrators 7. Academic affairs headed by vice president of academic affairs/dean of the college. Management/business/finances directed by vice president and treasurer. Full-time instructional faculty 47. Academic governance body, the faculty, meets an average of 9 times per year.

WELLS COLLEGE—*cont'd*

Calendar: Semesters. Academic year Aug. to May. No summer session. Degrees conferred and formal commencement in May.

Characteristics of Freshmen: 21% of applicants accepted. 16% of accepted applicants enrolled.

90% (151 students) submitted SAT scores; 32% (31 students) submitted ACT scores. *25th percentile*: SAT Critical Reading 520, SAT Math 490; ACT Composite 20. *75th percentile*: SAT Critical Reading 610; SAT Math 590; ACT Composite 26.

60% of entering freshmen expected to graduate within 5 years. 59% of freshmen from New York. Freshmen from 22 states and 6 foreign countries.

Admission: For fall acceptance, apply as early as July of previous year, but not later than Aug. of year of enrollment. Students are notified of acceptance April. *Requirements:* 4 secondary school units English (including grammar, composition, literature), 3 years foreign language, 3 mathematics, 2 history, 2 laboratory science recommended; GED accepted. Upper half secondary school class standing recommended. *Entrance tests:* College Board SAT or ACT composite. *For transfer students:* 2.5 minimum GPA; 2 years maximum transfer credit.

College credit and advanced placement for postsecondary-level work completed in secondary school and for extrainstitutional learning (life experience) specifically related to courses offered at Wells, with evaluation based on portfolio and faculty assessments.

Degree Requirements: *For undergraduate degrees:* 120 credit hours; 2.0 GPA; 60 semester hours in residence; comprehensives in major field of study. Fulfillment of some degree requirements possible by passing College Board or CLEP examination. Core requirements, breadth expectations, physical education requirement. *Grading system:* A–F; S/U/; P/F (restrictions apply).

Distinctive Educational Programs: Work-experience programs. Extensive experiential program. Dual-degree programs in engineering with Columbia University and Washington University (MO), in business and in community health with University of Rochester. Interdisciplinary minors in communications; elementary education, social and criminal justice; indigenous studies, science, health and values; secondary education, women's studies. Preprofessional programs in dentistry, law, medicine, veterinary medicine. Facilities and programs for independent research. Individualized majors. Study abroad in Chile, Costa Rica, Dominican Republic, France, Germany, Ireland, Italy, Spain, United Kingdom, Denmark, Japan, Mexico, Senegal. Washington (DC) semester at American University. Cornell University and Ithaca College Exchange Programs. Study at other colleges arranged through off-campus study committee. Internships available during January term.

ROTC: Air Force and Army in cooperation with Cornell University.

Degrees Conferred: 89 *baccalaureate:* biological/life sciences 5; business/marketing 3; computer and information sciences 1; English 4; foreign language 5; history 4; interdisciplinary studies 1; mathematics 3; natural resources/environmental science 4; philosophy/religious studies 4; physical sciences 1; psychology 16; public administration and social services 4; social sciences 19; visual and performing arts 8.

Fees and Other Expenses: Full-time tuition per academic year 2008–09: contact the college for current information regarding tuition, fees, and housing.

Financial Aid: Aid from institutionally generated funds is provided on the basis of academic merit and financial need.

Financial aid to full-time, first-time undergraduate students: need-based scholarships/grants totaling $4,424,151, self-help $1,7171,740, tuition waivers $23,300; non-need-based scholarships/grants totaling $308,645, self-help $536,223, parent loans $718,744, tuition waivers $46,940.

Departments and Teaching Staff: *Total instructional faculty:* 69 (full-time 47, part-time 12). Student/faculty ratio: 8:1. Degrees held by full-time faculty: doctorate 89%, master's 11%. 15%. 100% hold terminal degrees.

Enrollment: Total enrollment 481 (undergraduate). Transfer-in students: 85.

Characteristics of Student Body: *Ethnic/racial makeup:* number of Black non-Hispanic: 31; American Indian or Alaska Native: 3; Asian or Pacific Islander: 10; Hispanic: 18; White non-Hispanic: 313; unknown: 98. *Age distribution:* number under 18: 16; 18–19: 148; 20–21: 153; 22–24: 33; 25–29: 14, 30–34: 6; 35–39: 7; 40–49: 12; 50–64: 8.

International Students: 8 nonresident aliens enrolled fall 2008. Students from Asia, Africa, Canada. Programs available to aid students whose native language is not English: English as a Second Language Program. No financial aid specifically designated for international students.

Student Life: On-campus residence halls and college-owned apartments house over 90% of student body. *Intercollegiate athletics:* cross-country, field hockey, lacrosse, soccer, softball, swimming, tennis. *Special regulations:*Cars permitted if registered with school. Visitation hours voted upon by individual residence halls. *Special services:* medical services, campus shuttle service to Ithaca. *Student publications: Onyx*, a monthly newspaper; *Cardinal*, a yearbook; *Chronicle*, an annual literary magazine; *Surrounding community:* Aurora Village population 500. Syracuse, 45 miles from campus, is nearest metropolitan area. Airport 26 miles from campus; passenger rail service 52 miles from campus.

Publications: *News at Wells*, a weekly newsletter for the campus community; *Campus Calendar of Events*, published by the Student Activities Office.

Library Collections: 210,550 volumes. 888 audiovisual items. Current periodical subscriptions: paper 382; 3 microform. Online catalog. Computer work stations available. Students have access to online information retrieval services and the Internet.

Most important holdings include collection of memorabilia, documents, and correspondence pertaining to early express companies such as Wells Fargo; Pierce W. Gaines Collection of Americana, including pamphlets and broadsides of the late 18th and 19th centuries; papers of Emily Howland (1827–1929), early feminist and close friend of Susan B. Anthony.

Buildings and Grounds: Campus area 360 acres. *New buildings:* Science Facility completed 2007.

Chief Executive Officer: Dr. Lisa Marsh Ryerson, President.

Address admission inquiries to Susan Sloan, Director of Admissions.

Yeshiva University

500 West 185th Street
New York, New York 10033-3299
Tel: (212) 960-5285 **E-mail:** yuadmit@mail.yu.edu
Fax: (212) 960-0043 **Internet:** www.yu.edu

Institution Description: Yeshiva University is an independent, nonprofit institution offering undergraduate and graduate study programs. It is comprised of 4 campus, The Main, Midtown, and Brookdale Centers in Manhattan and the Bronx Center. *Enrollment:* 6,292. *Degrees awarded:* Associate, baccalaureate, first-professional (law, medicine), master's, doctorate.

Accreditation: *Regional:* MSA. *Professional*: law, medicine, nuclear medicine technology, psychology internship, social work

History: Established as Yeshiva Eitz Chaim 1886; Rabbi Isaac Elchanan Seminary founded at same location 1896; the 2 institutions merged under the name of the latter 1915; changed name to Yeshiva College and offered first instruction at postsecondary level 1928; awarded first degree (baccalaureate) 1931; adopted present name 1945; centennial celebration 1991–92. *See* Gilbert Klaperman, *The Story of Yeshiva University* (London: Macmillan Company, 1969) for further information.

Institutional Structure: *Governing board:* Board of Trustees. Representation: 48 trustees (including 1 honorary member). 47 voting. *Composition of institution:* Academic affairs headed by president. Management/business/finances directed by vice president for business affairs. Full-time instructional faculty 188 (and 1,137 full-time faculty members at the College of Medicine). Each school has its own faculty governing body which meets about 2 times per year.

Calendar: Semesters. Academic year early Sept. to late May. Freshmen admitted Sept., Feb. Degrees conferred June, Sept., Jan. Formal commencement May. Summer session from early June to mid-Aug.

Characteristics of Freshmen: 2,108 applicants (991 female, 1,117 male). 67% of applicants admitted. 70% of admitted applicants enrolled full-time.

84% (817 students) submitted SAT scores. 19% (189 students) submitted ACT scores. *25th percentile*: SAT Critical Reading 540, SAT Math 540; ACT Composite 23. *75th percentile*: SAT Critical Reading 670, SAT Math 670; ACT Composite 28.

45% of entering freshmen expected to graduate within 5 years. 48% of freshmen from New York. Freshmen from 31 states and 17 foreign countries.

Admission: Rolling admissions plan. For fall acceptance, apply as early as Oct. 1 of previous year, but not later than Sept. 1 of year of enrollment. Early acceptance available. *Requirements:* Either graduation from accredited secondary school with 16 units which must include 4 units English, 2 foreign language, 2 mathematics, 2 science, 2 social studies; or GED. Interview. *Entrance tests:* College Board SAT. For foreign students TOEFL. *For transfer students:* 2.6 minimum GPA; 70 hours maximum transfer credit.

College credit and advanced placement for postsecondary-level work completed in secondary school.

Noncredit remedial courses offered during regular academic year.

Degree Requirements: *For all baccalaureate degrees:* 128 credit hours; 4 semesters in residence; exit competency examinations for some programs; comprehensives in individual fields of study. *For all undergraduate degrees:* 2.0 GPA; 1 credit hour physical education; general education requirements, including courses in Hebrew literature, language, and culture.

Fulfillment of some degree requirements and exemption from some beginning courses possible by passing departmental examinations, College Board CLEP, AP, other standardized tests. *Grading system:* A–F; pass-no credit.

Distinctive Educational Programs: Evening classes in some programs. Dual-degree programs in engineering with Columbia University and with Polytechnic University of New York, in nursing with Columbia University, in occupational therapy with Columbia University and New York University, in podiatry with New York College of Podiatric Medicine. Interdisciplinary program in Jewish studies. Preprofessional programs in engineering, law, and health sciences. Facilities and programs for independent research, including honors programs, individual majors, tutorials. Institutionally sponsored study abroad in Israel.

Degrees Conferred: 292 *associate*; 646 *baccalaureate*; 412 *master's*; 113 *doctorate*; 536 *first-professional*. Bachelor's degrees awarded in top five disciplines: business, management, marketing, and related support services 169; psychology 88; social sciences 61; philosophy and religious studies 46; English language and literature 42. Master's degrees awarded: biological and biomedical sciences 56; education 44; legal professions 65; multidisciplinary studies 11; philosophy and religious studies 9; psychology 50; public administration 154; theology and religious studies 3. Doctorates awarded: biological and biomedical studies 39; education 1; health professions 5; philosophy and religious studies 1; psychology 82; social sciences 13. First-professional degrees awarded: medicine 146; law 360.

Fees and Other Expenses: *Full-time tuition per academic year 2008–09:* $32,094 undergraduate; contact the university for current graduate and first-professional tuition and any other applicable program fees. *Books and supplies:* $1,100. *Room and board per academic year:* $9,880. *Other expenses:* $1,125.

Financial Aid: Institution has a Program Participation Agreement with the U.S. Department of Education for eligible students to receive Pell Grants and, depending upon the agreement, other federal aid.

Financial aid to full-time, first-time undergraduate students: 85% received some form of financial aid. Average amount of aid received: federal grants $3,631; state/local grants $2,563; institutional grants $313; loans $5,274.

Departments and Teaching Staff: *Total instructional faculty:* 1,802. Student/faculty ratio: 19:1. Degrees held by full-time faculty: doctorate 54%, master's 22%, baccalaureate 7%, professional 17%. 71% hold terminal degrees.

Enrollment: Total enrollment 6,292. Undergraduate 3,044. Graduate 3,248. Undergraduate transfer-in students 85.

Characteristics of Student Body: *Ethnic/racial makeup:* White non-Hispanic: 93.3%; unknown .7%.

International Students: 140 undergraduate nonresident aliens enrolled fall 2008. No programs available to aid students whose native language is not English. No financial aid specifically designated for international students.

Student Life: On-campus residence halls house 89% of student body. Residence halls for males constitute 57% of such space, for females 43%. *Intercollegiate athletics:* male: basketball, bowling, cross-country, fencing, riflery, soccer, tennis, wrestling; female: basketball, bowling. *Special services:* Medical services, shuttle van to subway and between Main and Midtown centers. *Student publications, radio: The Commentator*, a biweekly Main Center newspaper; *Hamevaser*, a monthly Main Center newspaper; *Kochaviah*, a senior yearbook at Midtown Center; *Masmid*, a senior yearbook at Main Center; *The Observer*, a biweekly Midtown Center newspaper. Radio station WYUR broadcasts 40 hours per week. *Surrounding community:* New York City population over 7 million. Served by mass transit bus, train, subway systems; airport 8 miles from campus; passenger rail service 7 miles from campus.

Library Collections: 900,000 volumes. 26,000 government documents; 760,000 microforms; 980 audiovisual materials. 7,800 periodical subscriptions. Online catalog. Students have access to online information retrieval services and the Internet.

Most important special holdings include Rare Book Room Collection; Strauss Collection of Hebraica; archives of the Central Relief Committee and the Vaad Hatzalah.

Buildings and Grounds: Campus area 26 acres.

Chief Executive Officer: Dr. Richard M. Joel, President.

Address admission inquiries to Dr. John B. Fisher, Director of Enrollment Management.

Albert Einstein College of Medicine

1300 Morris Park Avenue
Bronx, New York 10461
Tel: (212) 960-5285

Degree Programs Offered: *First-professional:* M.D.

Admission: 3 years of college, including 1 year each of biology, general chemistry, organic chemistry, physics, mathematics, English; MCAT; AMCAS.

Degree Requirements: 4-year prescribed curriculum.

Benjamin N. Cardozo School of Law

55 Fifth Avenue
New York, New York 10003
Tel: (212) 790-0200

Degree Programs Offered: *First-professional:* J.D.

Admission: Baccalaureate from accredited college or university, LSAT, LSDAS.

Degree Requirements: 84 credit hours, 2.0 GPA, 20 months in residence.

Bernard Revel Graduate School and Harry Fischel School for Higher Jewish Studies

500 West 185th Street
New York, New York 10033
Tel: (212) 960-5253

Degree Programs Offered: *Master's, doctorate* in Jewish studies.

Admission: Baccalaureate from accredited college or university; promise of meeting standards of the school and demands of particular program; GRE General test.

Degree Requirements: 30 credit hours for master's degree, an additional 45 for doctorate; research project for some master's, dissertation for doctorate; 3.0 GPA; 24 credits in residence for master's, 30 for doctorate.

David J. Azrieli Graduate Institute of Jewish Education and Administration

245 Lexington Avenue
New York, New York 10016
Tel: (212) 340-7705

Degree Programs Offered: *Master's, doctorate*, and *specialist certificate* in Jewish elementary and secondary education.

Admission: Baccalaureate from accredited college or university; advanced background in Jewish studies; competence in Hebrew; GRE General test; 2 letters of recommendation.

Degree Requirements: *For master's:* 30 credits; 150 hours student teaching, comprehensive examination, 3.0 GPA, 24 credits in residence; *for specialist certificate:* additional 30 credits, 300 hours teaching internship, 3.0 GPA, 24 credits in residence; *for doctorate:* additional 45 credits, 300 hours teaching internship, dissertation; 36 credits in residence plus all research.

Ferkauf Graduate School of Psychology

55 Fifth Avenue
New York, New York 10003
Tel: (212) 430-4204

Degree Programs Offered: *Master's, doctorate* in psychology.

Admission: Baccalaureate degree from accredited college or university, including 12 credits in psychology; GRE General test; 2 letters of recommendation; interview.

Degree Requirements: *For master's:* 36 credits; comprehensive examination. *For Ph.D.:* 72-84 credits; doctoral certifying examination; predoctoral research; 2 foreign language examinations; doctoral comprehensive examination; dissertation; oral defense; internship. *For Psy.D.:* 96 credits; internships; comprehensive examination; 2 research projects; oral examination.

Isaac Breuer College of Hebraic Studies

500 West 185th Street
New York, New York 10033
Tel: (212) 960-5347

Degree Programs Offered: *Associate, baccalaureate* in Jewish studies; Hebrew Teacher's Diploma.

Admission: In addition to general requirements, graduation from Jewish all-day high school or equivalent work, Isaac Breuer College Entrance Examination.

Degree Requirements: *See* general requirements.

Departments and Teaching Staff: Faculty drawn from Division of Jewish Studies.

James Striar School of General Jewish Studies

500 West 185th Street
New York, New York 10033
Tel: (212) 960-5225

Degree Programs Offered: *Associate* in Jewish studies.

Admission: *See* general requirements.

YESHIVA UNIVERSITY—*cont'd*

Departments and Teaching Staff: Faculty drawn from Division of Jewish Studies.

Distinctive Educational Programs: 4-year program in Hebrew language and literature, and Jewish culture and civilization for men who enter Yeshiva with little background in Jewish studies. Prior or simultaneous receipt of baccalaureate from Yeshiva required for associate from James Striar.

Stern College for Women

245 Lexington Avenue
New York, New York 10016
Tel: (212) 960-5225

Degree Programs Offered: *Baccalaureate* in accounting, biology, business, chemistry, computer sciences, economics, education, English-communications, English literature, Hebrew studies, history, Jewish studies, mathematics, physics, political science, pre-engineering, pre-health sciences, psychology, sociology, speech and drama, speech-communication disorders, Shaped Major (designed by student).

Admission: *See* general requirements.

Degree Requirements: *See* general requirements.

Sue Golding Graduate Division of Medical Sciences

1300 Morris Park Avenue
Bronx, New York 10461
Tel: (212) 430-2345

Degree Programs Offered: *Master's, doctorate* in biological sciences.

Admission: Baccalaureate degree from accredited college or university; courses in biology, general chemistry, organic chemistry, calculus, physics; GRE General and subject.

Degree Requirements: *For doctorate:* 90 credits (at least 60 in residence), qualifying examination, dissertation, oral defense. Some departments require a foreign language.

Departments and Teaching Staff: Faculty drawn from Albert Einstein College of Medicine.

Wurzweiler School of Social Work

55 Fifth Avenue
New York, New York 10003
Tel: (212) 960-0820

Degree Programs Offered: *Master's, doctorate* in social work. Post-Master's Certificate in Gerontology.

Admission: *For master's:* Baccalaureate degree from accredited college or university; demonstrated capacity for performing graduate work satisfactorily; personality suitable for the social work profession. *For doctorate:* Master's degree in social work from accredited college or university (applicants without this degree may be required to complete specified work at the master's level before admission to doctoral candidacy); intellectual competence, evidenced by previous academic performance; at least 3 years' professional social work experience (pre-M.S.W. social work experience evaluated on individual basis); attributes suitable for scholarship, including conceptual and writing skills. *For Post-Master's Certificate in Gerontology:* Master's degree in social work or a related field.

Degree Requirements: *For master's:* 64 credits (36 classwork, 28 in field instruction); integrative essay. *For doctorate:* 66 credits (32 in lecture courses, 12 field study, 22 tutorial/dissertation); oral and written comprehensive examination; dissertation; oral defense. *For Post-Master's Certificate in Gerontology:* 12 credits.

Yeshiva College

500 West 185th Street
New York, New York 10033
Tel: (212) 960-5214

Degree Programs Offered: *Baccalaureate* in accounting, biology, chemistry, classical languages, computer sciences, economics, English, French, Hebrew, history, Jewish studies, mathematics, music, philosophy, physics, political science, pre-engineering, pre-health sciences, psychology, sociology, speech and drama.

Admission: *See* general requirements.

Degree Requirements: *See* general requirements.

Yeshiva Program / Mazer School of Talmudic Studies

500 West 185th Street
New York, New York 10033
Tel: (212) 960-5344

Admission: In addition to general requirements, graduation from Jewish all-day high school or equivalent work, Yeshiva Program Entrance Examination.

Distinctive Educational Programs: Traditional course of study for those with advanced background in Jewish studies; emphasizes intensive analysis of Talmudic texts and commentaries in the original Aramaic and Hebrew.

York College / CUNY

94-20 Guy R. Brewer Boulevard
Jamaica, New York 11451
Tel: (718) 262-2000 **E-mail:** admissions@york.cuny.edu
Fax: (718) 262-2786 **Internet:** www.york.cuny.edu

Institution Description: *Enrollment:* 7,157. *Degrees awarded:* Baccalaureate.

Accreditation: *Regional:* MSA.

History: Established under official name, York College of the City University of New York, and chartered 1966; offered first instruction at postsecondary level 1967; awarded first degree (baccalaureate) 1970; moved to new campus 1986.

Institutional Structure: *Composition of institution:* Administrators 9. Academic affairs headed by vice president for academic affairs. Management/business/finances directed by vice president for administrative affairs. Full-time instructional faculty 180. Academic governance body, York College Senate, meets an average of 6 times per year.

Calendar: Semesters. Academic year Aug. to May. Freshmen admitted Sept., Feb., June. Degrees conferred June, Sept., Feb. Formal commencement June. Summer session of in June and July.

Characteristics of Freshmen: 8,329 applicants (5,275 female, 3,054 male). 48% of applicants admitted. 25% of admitted students enrolled full-time.

93% (548 students) submitted SAT scores. *25th percentile*: SAT Critical Reading 370, SAT Math 390. *75th percentile*: SAT Critical Reading 460, SAT Math 470.

96.5% of freshmen from New York.

Admission: Rolling admissions plan. For fall acceptance, apply as early as Sept. of previous year, but not later than August of year of registration. Early acceptance available. *Requirements:* Either graduation from accredited secondary school or GED. *For transfer students:* 2.0 minimum GPA; from 4-year 80 credits will be accepted in transfer, 68 credits from a 2-year college.

College credit and advanced placement for postsecondary-level work completed in secondary school. College credit for extrainstitutional learning on basis of faculty assessment.

Tutoring available. Developmental courses offered in summer session and regular academic year; credit given.

Degree Requirements: 120 credit hours; 2.0 GPA; 2 terms in residence; 1 physical education course; exit competency examination in writing; distribution requirements.

Fulfillment of some degree requirements and exemption from some beginning courses possible by passing College Board CLEP, other standardized tests. *Grading system:* A–F; pass-fail; pass-no credit; withdraw (carries time limit; may carry penalty).

Distinctive Educational Programs: Cooperative education. Weekend and evening classes. Interdisciplinary programs in Afro-American studies, gerontology. Honors programs. Individual majors. Community Professional degree program designed for adults who will be granted credit for community service. Credit and noncredit continuing education. Study abroad through CUNY/University of Paris.

Degrees Conferred: 746 *baccalaureate*; 17 *master's*.Bachelor's degrees awarded in top five disciplines: business, management, marketing, and related support services 233; psychology 115; education 67; public administration and social service professions 65; social sciences 56. Master's degrees awarded: occupational therapy 17.

Fees and Other Expenses: *Full-time tuition per academic year 2008–09:* resident $4,312, nonresident $8,952. *Books and supplies:* $1,016. No on-campus housing. *Other expenses:* $4,526.

Financial Aid: Aid from institutionally generated funds is provided on the basis of academic merit, financial need. Institution has a Program Participation Agreement with the U.S. Department of Education for eligible students to receive Pell Grants and, depending upon the agreement, other federal aid.

Financial aid to full-time, first-time undergraduate students: 82% of students received some form of financial aid. Average amount of aid received: federal grants $3,309; state/local grants $3,192; loans $1,808.

Departments and Teaching Staff: *Total instructional faculty:* 378. Student/ faculty ratio: 18:1. Degrees held by full-time faculty: doctorate 70%, master's 28%, baccalaureate 2%. 70% hold terminal degrees.

Enrollment: Total enrollment 7,157. Undergraduate 7,111. Graduate 46. Undergraduate transfer-in students 697.

Characteristics of Student Body: *Ethnic/racial makeup:* Black non-Hispanic: 55%; American Indian or Alaska Native: .4%; Asian or Pacific Islander:10%; Hispanic: 15.8%; White non-Hispanic: 6.5%.

International Students: 723 nonresident aliens enrolled fall 2008. Students from Europe, Asia, Central and South America, Africa. Programs available to aid students whose native language is not English: English as a Second Language Program. No financial aid specifically designated for international students.

Student Life: No on-campus housing. *Intercollegiate athletics:* male: baseball, basketball, soccer, tennis; female: basketball, cross-country, track and field, volleyball. *Special regulations:* Cars permitted in designated area; fee charged. *Special services:* Learning Resources Center, medical services. *Student publications, radio: El Casique*, a monthly Hispanic publication; *Haitian Perspectives*, an annual publication; *Pandora's Box*, a bimonthly newspaper; *Sholom*, an annual Jewish publication; *Spirit Magazine*, a quarterly Black student publication. Radio station WYCR broadcasts 38 hours per week. *Surrounding community:* New York City population over 7 million. Served by mass transit bus and rail systems; airport 7 miles from campus; passenger rail service ¼ mile from campus.

Library Collections: 180,000 volumes. 8,900 government documents; 154,000 microforms; 4,600 audiovisual materials. 1,100 current periodical subscriptions. Online catalog. Computer work stations. available. Students have access to the Internet.

Most important special holdings include curriculum materials collection; Library of American Civilization (19,000 volumes on microform); American and foreign newspapers; Human Relations Area File.

Buildings and Grounds: Campus area 28 acres.

Chief Executive Officer: Dr. Marcia V. Keizs, President.

Address admission inquiries to Richard Starkhardt, Director of Admissions.

North Carolina

Appalachian State University

Boone, North Carolina 28608

Tel: (828) 262-2000 **E-mail:** admissions@appstate.edu

Fax: (828) 262-3296 **Internet:** www.appstate.edu

Institution Description: *Enrollment:* 16,610. *Degrees awarded:* Baccalaureate, master's.

Accreditation: *Regional:* SACS-Comm. on Coll. *Professional*: business, chemistry, computer science, counseling, dietetics, music, speech-language pathology, teacher education

History: Established as Watauga Academy 1899; offered first instruction at postsecondary level 1903; changed name to Appalachian State Normal School 1925; changed name to Appalachian State Teachers' College 1929; awarded first degree (baccalaureate) 1931; adopted present name 1967; became part of University of North Carolina system 1971.

Institutional Structure: *Governing board:* Appalachian State University Board of Trustees. Representation: 16 trustees (including 1 student), 6 honorary trustees. Academic affairs headed by provost and executive vice chancellor. Management/business/finances directed by vice chancellor for business affairs. Full-time instructional faculty 703.

Calendar: Semesters. Academic year Aug. to May. Summer session from May to Aug.

Characteristics of Freshmen: 11,468 applicants (6,031 female, 5,451 male). 65% of applicants admitted. 37% of applicants admitted and enrolled full-time. 96% (2,670 students) submitted SAT scores; 21% (364 students) submitted ACT scores. *25th percentile*: SAT Critical Reading 510, SAT Math 53-. SAT Writing 490; ACT Composite 21, ACT English 20, ACT Math 21. *75th percentile*: SAT Critical Reading 600, SAT Math 610, SAT Writing 540; ACT Composite 26, ACT English 26, ACT Math 26.

58% of entering freshmen expected to graduate within 5 years. 92% of freshmen from North Carolina. Freshmen from 48 states and 30 foreign countries.

Admission: Rolling admissions plan. *Requirements:* Graduation from accredited secondary school and must meet minimum admission requirements of the University of North Carolina system: 4 units of English, 3 units of mathematics, 3 units of science, and 2 units of social studies; or GED. 2 course units one foreign language recommended. *Entrance tests:* College Board SAT (SAT Writing required for ACT composite). For foreign students TOEFL. *For transfer students:* 2.0 minimum GPA; good standing at institution previously attended.

College credit and advanced placement for postsecondary-level work completed in secondary school.

Degree Requirements: 122 credit hours; 2.0 GPA; 30 hours in residence; general education requirements.

Fulfillment of some degree requirements and exemption from some beginning courses possible by passing College Board AP. *Grading system:* A–F; pass-fail; satisfactory-unsatisfactory; withdraw (carries time limit, deadline after which fail is appended to withdraw); incomplete (carries time limit).

Distinctive Educational Programs: Interdisciplinary programs in American studies, Appalachian studies, Black studies, environmental policy and planning, gerontology, international studies, liberal studies, sustainable development, urban studies, women's studies. Independent study, dual-degree engineering program with Auburn University, Honors Program, pre-professional programs. *Other distinctive programs:* Continuing education. Appalachian Regional Bureau of Government, Mathematics and Science Education Center, National Center for Developmental Education, Center for Appalachian Studies, Center for Management Development, Bureau of Economic and Business Research. Semester/year study programs in Sweden, Holland, England, China, Germany, Mexico. Summer study in Barbados (anthropology), England (business, English), France (business), Germany (foreign language), Honduras (interdisciplinary studies, anthropology), Switzerland (art, human development and psychological counseling), Spain (foreign language), Hawaii (hospitality management).

ROTC: Army.

Degrees Conferred: 2,634 *baccalaureate*; 652 *master's*; 15 *doctorate*. Bachelor's degrees awarded in top five disciplines: business/marketing 520; education 433; social sciences 210; communications/communication 216; visual and performing arts 152. Master's degrees: biological/life sciences 8; business/marketing 43; computer and information sciences 3; education 308; engineering technologies 8; English 8; family and consumer sciences 7; foreign languages 9; health professions 43; history 6; interdisciplinary studies 5; library science 51; mathematics 2; parks and recreation 10; physical sciences 8; psychology 24; public administration and social services 15; social sciences 9; visual and performing arts 8. Doctorates awarded: education 15.

Fees and Other Expenses: *Full-time tuition per academic year 2008–09:* undergraduate resident $4,333, nonresident $14,392; contact the university for current graduate tuition. *Room and board per academic year:* $6,160. *Books and supplies:* $700. *Other expenses:* $2,500.

Financial Aid: Aid from institutionally generated funds is provided on the basis of academic merit, financial need, athletic ability, other criteria.

Financial aid to full-time, first-time undergraduate students: 56% received some form of aid. Average amount of aid received: federal grants $3,803; Pell grants $2,791; other federal grants $1,214; state/local grants $3,153; institutional grants $1,678.

Departments and Teaching Staff: *Total instructional faculty:* 998 (full-time 703, part-time 295). *Student/faculty ratio:* 19:1. Degrees held by full-time faculty: baccalaureate 1%, master's 13.7%, doctorate and professional 85.2%. 85% hold terminal degrees.

Enrollment: Total enrollment 16,610. Undergraduate 14,561 (51% female, 49% male).

Characteristics of Student Body: *Ethnic/racial makeup:* Black non-Hispanic: 3%; Asian or Pacific Islander: 15%; Hispanic: 2%; White non-Hispanic: 69%; unknown: 4%; nonresident alien 1%. *Age distribution:* number under 18: 45; 18–19: 486; 20–21: 5,023; 22–24: 2,334; 25–29: 527; 30–34: 212 35–39: 152 40–49: 194 50–64: 89; 65 and over: 5. 42% of student body attend summer sessions..

International Students: 166 nonresident aliens enrolled fall 2008. Students from Europe, Asia, Central and south America, Africa, Canada, Australia, New Zealand, Middle East. Programs available to aid students whose native language is not English: social, cultural. English as a Second Language Program. No financial aid specifically designated for international students.

Student Life: On-campus residence halls and apartments available. *Intercollegiate athletics:* cheerleading; male: baseball, basketball, cross-country, football, golf, soccer, tennis, track, wrestling; female: basketball, cross-country, field hockey, golf, tennis, track, volleyball. *Special regulations:* Registered cars permitted. *Special services:* Over 200 clubs/organizations;co-curricular social, cultural, and recreational programs; Counseling and Psychological Services Center; career planning and employment; health services. Student publications, radio. Intramural and club sports, three fitness facilities. *Surrounding community:* Boone population 13,500. Winston-Salem, 100 miles from campus, is nearest metropolitan area.

Library Collections: 871,500 volumes. Online catalog. 1,532,000 microforms; 39,300 audiovisual materials; 40,275 periodicals including via electronic access. Computer work stations available. Students have access to online information retrieval services and the Internet.

Most important special holdings include W.L. Eury Appalachian Collection; Music Library; Justice-Query Instructional Materials Center.

Buildings and Grounds: Campus area 255 acres.

Chief Executive Officer: Dr. Kenneth E. Peacock, Chancellor.

Undergraduates address admission inquiries to Director of Admissions; graduate inquiries to Dean of Graduate School.

Barber-Scotia College

145 Cabarrus Avenue
Concord, North Carolina 28025-5143
Tel: (704) 789-2900 **E-mail:** admissions@b-sc.edu
Fax: (704) 789-3817 **Internet:** www.b-sc.edu

Institution Description: Barber-Scotia College is a private college affiliated with The United Presbyterian Church in the United States. *Enrollment:* 488. *Degrees awarded:* Baccalaureate.

Accreditation: *Regional:* SACS-Comm. on Coll. *Professional*: nursing

History: Established as Scotia Seminary, a women's institution, 1867; chartered 1870; name changed to Scotia Women's College 1916; merged with Barber Memorial College and adopted present name 1930; offered first instruction at postsecondary level 1941; awarded first degree (baccalaureate) 1945; became coeducational 1954.

Institutional Structure: *Governing board:* Board of Trustees. Extrainstitutional representation: 25 trustees; institutional representation: 1 administrator. 1 ex officio. 25 voting. *Composition of institution:* Administrators 6. Academic affairs headed by dean of the college. Management/business/finances directed by business manager. Full-time instructional faculty 22.

Calendar: Semesters. Academic year Aug. to May.

Characteristics of Freshmen:

64% of applicants accepted. 30% of accepted applicants enrolled.

48% of freshmen from North Carolina. Freshmen from 21 states.

Admission: Rolling admissions plan. *Requirements:* Either graduation from accredited secondary school with 16 units which must include 4 English, 2 mathematics, 2 science (including biology), 2 social studies (including U.S. history); or GED. Minimum GPA 2.0. *Entrance tests:* College Board SAT or ACT composite.

Degree Requirements: 125 semester hours; 2.0–2.5 GPA; last year in residence; general education requirements.

Degrees Conferred: 36 *baccalaureate*. Bachelor's degrees awarded in top five disciplines: business, management, marketing, and related support services 15; social sciences 9; psychology 3; biomedical/biological sciences 3; communication, journalism, and related programs 3.

Fees and Other Expenses: *Full-time tuition per academic year 2008–09:* contact the college for current tuition, fees, and other costs.

Financial Aid: Financial assistance is available in the form of Pell Grants, College Work-Study, Veterans Administration Benefits, National Direct Student Loans, Supplemental Education Opportunity Grants (SEOG), Higher Education Assistance Loans (HEAL), Stafford Loans, other federal aid programs.

Departments and Teaching Staff: *Total instructional faculty:* 28. Student/faculty ratio: 14:1. Degrees held by full-time faculty: doctorate 50%, master's 50%, baccalaureate 100%. 50% hold terminal degrees.

Enrollment: Total enrollment 488.

Characteristics of Student Body: *Ethnic/racial makeup:* Black non-Hispanic: 98%; Asian or Pacific Islander: 1%; Hispanic: 1%; White non-Hispanic: 1%.

International Students: 2 nonresident aliens enrolled. No programs available to aid students whose native language is not English. No financial aid specifically designated for international students.

Library Collections: 26,000 volumes including bound books, serial backfiles, electronic documents, and government documents not in separate collections. 195 current serial subscriptions.

Buildings and Grounds: Campus area 23 acres.

Chief Executive Officer: Dr. Sammie Potts, President.

Address admission inquiries to Director of Admissions.

Barton College

College Station
P.O. Box 5000
Wilson, North Carolina 27893-7000
Tel: (252) 399-6300 **E-mail:** enroll@barton.edu
Fax: (252) 399-6572 **Internet:** www.barton.edu

Institution Description: Barton College is a private, 4-year, coeducational institution affiliated with the Christian Church (Disciples of Christ). *Enrollment:* 1,152. *Degrees awarded:* Baccalaureate.

Accreditation: *Regional:* SACS-Comm. on Coll. *Professional*: nursing, social work, teacher education

History: Established, incorporated and offered first instruction at postsecondary level 1902; awarded first degree (baccalaureate) 1903. *See* William Jerry MacLean, *Barton College: Our Century* (Wislon, NC, Barton College, 2002) for further information. In 1990, the official name of the college was changed from Atlantic Christian College to Barton College in honor of Barton W. Stone, a principal founder of the Christian Church (Disciples of Christ).

Institutional Structure: *Governing board:* Barton College Board of Trustees. Extrainstitutional representation: 36 trustees, including 3 ministers and 2 trustees emeriti; institutional representation: 5 administrators, 1 full-time instructional faculty member, 1 student; 3 alumni. 6 ex officio. *Composition of institution:* Administrators 22. Academic affairs headed by vice-president for academic affairs and dean of the college. Management/business/finances directed by vice president for administration and finance. Full-time instructional faculty 74. Academic governance body, Faculty/Staff Assembly, meets 4 times per year.

Calendar: Semesters. Academic year Aug. to May. Freshmen admitted June, July, Aug., Jan. Degrees conferred May, Aug. Formal commencement May. Summer session from late May to early Aug.

Characteristics of Freshmen: 2,468 applicants (1,570 female, 898 male). 46% of applicants admitted. 21% of applicants admitted and enrolled full-time.

92% (229 students) submitted SAT scores; 23% (58 students) submitted ACT scores. *25th percentile*: SAT Critical Reading 393, SAT Math 397, SAT Writing 381; ACT Composite 16, ACT English 13, ACT Math 17. *75th percentile*: SAT Critical Reading 565, SAT Math 568; SAT Writing 543; ACT Composite 24, ACT English 24, ACT Math 25.

62% of entering freshmen expected to graduate within 5 years. 81% of freshmen from North Carolina. Freshmen from 26 states and 9 foreign countries.

Admission: Rolling admissions plan. For fall acceptance, apply as early as summer of previous year, but not later than Aug. of year of enrollment. Early acceptance available. *Requirements:* Either 20 secondary school units which must include 13 college preparatory; or GED. *Entrance tests:* College Board SAT or ACT accepted. *For transfer students:* 1.8 minimum GPA; from 2-year accredited institution 64 maximum transferable hours; from 4-year accredited institution, no maximum of transferable hours; for credit by exam, 30 hours.

College credit for postsecondary-level work completed in secondary school.

Tutoring available. Noncredit developmental cures offered during the regular academic year.

Degree Requirements: 126 semester hours; 2.0 GPA; 45 hours in residence, of these the last 30 hours must be in upper division level of major; general education requirements.

Fulfillment of some degree requirements and exemption from some beginning courses possible by passing College Board CLEP, AP, departmental examinations, and correspondence / extension courses. *Grading system:* A–F; withdraw (carries time limit, deadline after which pass-fail is appended to withdraw).

Distinctive Educational Programs: Evening classes. Weekend College Program through the Office of Lifelong and Extended Programs. Accelerated degree programs. Facilities for independent research, including honors programs and individual majors. Preprofessional programs in dentistry, medicine, engineering, optometry, physical therapy, pharmacy, and veterinary medicine. Study abroad by exchange agreements in England, Japan, and Switzerland as well as agreements with Australian and Central College Study Abroad.

Degrees Conferred: 210 *baccalaureate*. Bachelor's degrees awarded in top five disciplines: business/marketing 62; education 35; health professions and related clinical sciences; public administration and social services 28; biological/life sciences 13.

Fees and Other Expenses: *Full-time tuition per academic year 2008–09:* $19,935. *Room and board per academic year:* $6,780. *Books and supplies:* $1,100. *Other expenses:* $3,994.

Financial Aid: Aid from institutionally generated funds is provided on the basis of academic merit, financial need, athletic ability, other criteria.

Financial aid to full-time, first-time undergraduate students: 99% received some form of aid. Average amount of aid received: federal grants $4,214, Pell grants $3,072; other federal aid $1,383; state/local grants $4,'176; institutional grants $7,220.

Departments and Teaching Staff: *Total instructional faculty:* 111 (full-time 71, part-time 40). 73% of faculty hold the doctorate, first-professional, or other terminal degree. Student/faculty ratio: 12:1.

Enrollment: Total enrollment 1,155. Undergraduate 1,155 (70% female, 30% male).

Characteristics of Student Body: *Ethnic/racial makeup:* Black non-Hispanic: 24%; American Indian or Alaska Native: 1%; Asian or Pacific Islander: 1%; Hispanic: 3%; White non-Hispanic: 64%; unknown: 5%; nonresident alien 2%. *Age distribution:* number under 18: 17; 18–19: 363; 20–21: 291; 22–24: 252; 25–29: 85; 30–34: 75; 35–39: 47; 40–49: 75; 50–64: 26; 65 and over: 1.

International Students: 24 nonresident aliens enrolled fall 2008. Students from Europe, Asia, Central and South America, Africa, Canada, Australia. No programs available to aid students whose native language is not English. Financial aid specifically designated for international students: variable number of scholarships available annually.

BARTON COLLEGE—*cont'd*

Student Life: On-campus residence halls house 52% of full-time students. 12% of males join fraternities; 19% of females join sororities. *Intercollegiate athletics:* male: soccer, basketball, baseball, golf, tennis; female: volleyball, basketball, soccer, softball, tennis. *Special regulations:* Cars permitted with campus registration; open parking. Visitation hours from 9am to 12 midnight Mon.-Tues and 9am to 2am Fri. and Sat. *Special services:* Writing Center, Math Lab, Counseling Services, medical services. *Student publications: The Collegiate*, a bimonthly newspaper. *Surrounding community:* Wilson population 44,000. Greenville. 30 miles from campus, is nearest metropolitan area. Served by mass transit bus system; airport 45 miles from campus; passenger rail service 1 mile from campus.

Library Collections: 183,600 volumes including bound books, serial backfiles, electronic documents, and government documents not in separate collections. Online catalog. Current serial subscriptions: 246 paper, 673 microform; 16,527 via electronic access. 2,028 audio/videotapes; 68 DVD discs; 1,481 CD-ROMs. Computer work stations available. Students have access to the Internet at no charge.

Most important special holdings include Deaf Education Book; Fore-Edged Printing; Religion.

Buildings and Grounds: Campus area 76 acres.

Chief Executive Officer: Dr. Norval C. Kneten, President.

Address admission inquiries to Amanda Humphrey, Director of Admissions.

Belmont Abbey College

100 Belmont-Mt. Holly Road
Belmont, North Carolina 28012-1802
Tel: (704) 825-6700 **E-mail:** admissions@bac.edu
Fax: (704) 825-6727 **Internet:** www.bac.edu

Institution Description: Belmont Abbey College is a private college affiliated with the Benedictine monks of the Roman Catholic Church. *Enrollment:* 1,497. *Degrees awarded:* Baccalaureate.

Member of Charlotte Area Educational Consortium.

Accreditation: *Regional:* SACS-Comm. on Coll.

History: Established as St. Mary's College (for men) 1986; offered first instruction at postsecondary level 1878; chartered and awarded first degree (associate) 1886; adopted present name 1913; reorganized as associate-level institution 1928; again awarded baccalaureates 1952; became coeducational 1972. *See* John P. Bradley, *The First Hundred Years: Belmont Abbey College, 1876–1976* (Belmont, N.C.: Belmont Abbey College, Inc., 1976) for further information.

Institutional Structure: *Governing board:* Board of Trustees of Belmont Abbey College. Extrainstitutional representation: 26 trustees; institutional representation: Abbot of Belmont Abbey, 7 monks of Belmont Abbey. 1 ex officio. 33 voting. *Composition of institution:* Administrators 16. Academic affairs headed by vice president for academic affairs. Management/business/finances directed by vice president for business affairs. Full-time instructional faculty 39. Academic governance body, Faculty Assembly of Belmont Abbey College, meets at least 4 times per year.

Calendar: Semesters. Academic year Aug. to May. Freshmen admitted Aug., Jan. Degrees conferred May, Dec. Formal commencement May. 2 summer sessions.

Characteristics of Freshmen: 1,628 applicants (860 female, 768 male). 63% of applicants admitted. 28% of applicants admitted and enrolled full-time.

80% (239 students) submitted SAT scores; 29% (84 students) submitted ACT scores. *25th percentile*: SAT Critical Reading 450, SAT Math 460; ACT English 18, ACT Math 23. *75th percentile*: SAT Critical Reading 570, SAT Math 570; ACT English 25, ACT 25.

41% of entering freshmen expected to graduate within 5 years. 67% of freshmen from North Carolina. Freshmen from 36 states and 15 foreign countries.

Admission: Rolling admissions plan. For fall acceptance, apply as early as Sept. of previous year, but not later than Aug. of year of enrollment. Early acceptance available. *Requirements:* 16 secondary school units which must include 4 English, 3 mathematics, 1 history, 1 science, 2 science. *Entrance tests:* College Board SAT or ACT Composite. For foreign students TOEFL (500 minimum). *For transfer students:* 2.0 minimum GPA; good standing at institution previously attended; from 4-year accredited institution hours maximum transfer credit; from 2-year accredited institution 65 hours. Students from nonaccredited institutions admitted provisionally; credits evaluated individually.

College credit and advanced placement for postsecondary-level work completed in secondary school.

Degree Requirements: 120 credit hours; 2.0 GPA; 2 semesters in residence; comprehensives in individual fields of study or completion of equivalent project as defined by major department.

Fulfillment of some degree requirements and exemption from some beginning courses possible by passing College Board CLEP, advanced placement, or departmental examinations. *Grading system:* A–F; pass-fail; withdraw (deadline after which pass-fail is appended to withdraw); incomplete.

Distinctive Educational Programs: Full-semester, 12-credit internship programs available to qualified seniors. Evening classes. Facilities and programs for independent research, including honors programs and tutorials. Study abroad in England, France, and Spain. Cross-registration through Charlotte Area Educational Consortium. Study abroad in England, France, Spain.

ROTC: Air Force, Army, Navy offered in cooperation with UNC Charlotte.

Degrees Conferred: 155 *baccalaureate:* biological/life sciences 11; business/marketing 85; computer and information sciences 7; education 44; English 2; health professions 1; history 7; liberal arts/general studies 8; philosophy/religion/theology 5; psychology 6; social sciences 7 16.

Fees and Other Expenses: *Full-time tuition per academic year 2008–09:* $21,039. *Required fees:* $858. *Room per academic year:* $9,866. *Books and supplies:* $900. *Other expenses:* $4,000.

Financial Aid: The college offers a direct lending program. Aid from institutionally generated funds is provided on the basis of academic merit, athletic ability, financial need, leadership.

Financial aid to full-time, first-time undergraduate students: 96% received some form of aid. Average amount of aid received: federal grants $3,144; Pell grants $3,555; other federal aid $4,399; state/local grants $4,448; institutional grants $12,592.

Departments and Teaching Staff: *Total instructional faculty:* 84 (full-time 53, part-time 31). Student/faculty ratio: 17:1. 49% of faculty hold the doctorate, first-professional, or other terminal degree.

Enrollment: Total enrollment 1,100. Undergraduate 1,497 (63% female, 37% male). Transfer-in students 191.

Characteristics of Student Body: *Ethnic/racial makeup:* Black non-Hispanic: 23%; American Indian or Alaska Native: 1%; Asian or Pacific Islander: 2%; Hispanic: 4%; White non-Hispanic: 59%; unknown: 7%; nonresident alien 45. *Age distribution:* number under 18: 10 18–19: 375; 20–21: 231; 22–24: 126; 25–29: 97; 30–34: 68; 35–39: 69; 40–49: 103; 50–64: 30; 60 and over: 1.

International Students: 60 nonresident aliens enrolled fall 2008. Students from Europe, Asia, Central and south Latin America, Africa, Canada, Australia, No programs available to aid students whose native language is not English. No financial aid specifically designated for international students.

Student Life: On-campus residence halls house 66% of traditional student body. Residence halls for males constitute 57% of such space, for female 43%. *Intercollegiate athletics:* male: basketball, golf, soccer, tennis; female: basketball, volleyball. *Special regulations:* Registered cars permitted without restrictions. Residence hall visitation permitted between 2pm and midnight Fri. and Sat., 2pm and 8pm Sun. *Special services:* Medical services. *Student publications, radio: The Crusader*, a monthly student newspaper; Radio station WABY broadcasts 40 hours per week. *Surrounding community:* Belmont population 5,000. Charlotte-Gastonia, 10 miles from campus, is nearest metropolitan area. Served by airport 7 miles from campus; passenger rail service 10 miles from campus.

Publications: Sources of information about Belmont include *Crossroads*, a bimonthly newspaper for friends of Belmont Abbey.

Library Collections: 118,800 volumes including bound books, serial backfiles, electronic documents, and government documents not in separate collections. Online catalog. Current serial subscriptions: 275 paper; 22 microform; 7,000 via electronic access. 3,337 audio/videotapes; 374 DVDs; 1,698 CD-ROMs. Computer work stations available. Students have access to the Internet at no charge.

Most important holdings include Napoleon Collection; Benedictine Collection; Carolina Collection; Rare Books Collection.

Buildings and Grounds: Campus area 200 acres.

Chief Executive Officer: Dr. William K, Thierfielder, President.

Address admission inquiries to Roger L. Jones, Director of Admissions.

Bennett College for Women

900 East Washington Street
Greensboro, North Carolina 27401-3239
Tel: (336) 273-4431 **E-mail:** admissions@bennett.edu
Fax: (336) 273-8653 **Internet:** www.bennett.edu

Institution Description: Bennett College for Women is a private liberal arts college affiliated with the United Methodist Church. *Enrollment:* 689. *Degrees awarded:* Baccalaureate.

Member of Greensboro Regional Consortium, Inc.; Piedmont Independent College Association.

Accreditation: *Regional:* SACS-Comm. on Coll. *Professional*: social work, teacher education

History: Established as coeducational institution 1873; offered first instruction at postsecondary level 1879; awarded first degree (baccalaureate) 1885; incorporated 1889; reorganized as women's college 1926.

Institutional Structure: *Governing board:* Board of Trustees. Representation: 28 trustees. All voting. *Composition of institution:* Administrators 7. Academic affairs headed by vice president for academic affairs. Management/business/finances directed by vice president of fiscal affairs. Development and fundraising by vice president for institutional advancement. Student development affairs by vice president for student development. Full-time instructional faculty 52. Academic governance body, the faculty, meets 9 times per year.

Calendar: Semesters. Academic year Aug. to May. Freshmen admitted Aug., Jan. Degrees conferred and formal commencement May. No summer session.

Characteristics of Freshmen: 1,293 applicants (1,293 female). 48% of applicants accepted. 36% of accepted applicants enrolled full-time.

73% (163 students) submitted SAT scores; 25% (56 students) submitted ACT scores. *25th percentile*: SAT Critical Reading 360, SAT Math 350; ACT Composite 15, ACT English 14, ACT math 15. *75th percentile*: SAT Critical Reading 450, SAT Math 440; ACT Composite 18, ACT English 19, ACT Math 17.

28% of entering freshmen expected to graduate within 5 years. 24% of freshmen from North Carolina. Freshmen from 34 states and 6 foreign countries.

Admission: Rolling admissions plan. For fall acceptance, apply as early as Oct. of previous year; applications accepted until class is full. *Requirements:* Either 16 secondary school units (12 units in academic subjects) which should include 4 English, 2 mathematics, 2 foreign language, 2 natural science, 2 social studies, 5 academic electives; or GED. 4 additional units recommended. Minimum 2.0 GPA. *Entrance tests:* College Board SAT or ACT optional but required for scholarship consideration. *For transfer students:* 2.0 minimum GPA; from 4-year accredited institution 92 hours maximum transfer credit; from 2-year accredited institution 64 hours.

College credit and advanced placement for postsecondary-level work completed in secondary school with a grade of C or better. Academic credit also granted for students who have scored at least a 3 on the Advanced Placement Test. >r<Tutoring available. Noncredit developmental courses offered during regular academic year.

Degree Requirements: 124 credit hours; 2.0 GPA; 1 year in residence; 24 of last 36 hours must be taken at the college with the exception of those students in special degree programs officially arranged by Bennett College; 4 hours physical education; general education requirements; successful passage of English Comprehensive and Mathematics Comprehensive Examinations; exit competency examination in communication skills.

Fulfillment of some degree requirements and exemption from some beginning courses possible by passing College Board CLEP, AP. *Grading system:* A–F; withdraw (deadline after which pass-fail is appended to withdraw); incomplete (carries time limit).

Distinctive Educational Programs: Work-experience programs, including internships and externships, cooperative education. Cluster colleges. Accelerated degree programs. Dual-degree program in engineering with North Carolina Agricultural and Technical State University; in nursing with North Carolina A&T State University. Cooperative baccalaureate programs in medical technology with the Bowman Gray School of Medicine, Washington (DC) Hospital Center. Interdisciplinary programs including communications media and public relations, women's studies. Facilities and programs for independent research including honors programs, individual majors, academic advising, tutorials, freshman studies, learning resources center and special services for academic underachievers. Cross-registration and cooperative majors through the consortium.

ROTC: Army, Air Force offered in cooperation with North Carolina Agricultural and Technical State University.

Degrees Conferred: 108 *baccalaureate:* degrees awarded in top five disciplines: biological/life sciences 16; psychology 11; social work 8; public administration and social services 8.

Fees and Other Expenses: *Full-time tuition per academic year 2008–09:* $14,648. *Required fees:* $1,836. *Room and board per academic year:* $6,478. *Books and supplies:* $1,200. *Other expenses:* $3,000.

Financial Aid: Aid from institutionally generated funds is provided on the basis of academic merit, other criteria.

Financial aid to full-time, first-time undergraduate students: 93% received some form of aid. Average amount of aid received: federal grants $3,540; Pell grants $3,397; other federal aid $864; state/local grants $1,761; institutional grants $7,459.

Departments and Teaching Staff: *Total instructional faculty:* 70 (full-time 49, part-time 21). 58% of faculty hold the doctorate, first-professional, or other terminal degree. Student/faculty ratio: 11:1.

Enrollment: Total enrollment 688. Undergraduate 689 (100% female). Transfer-in students 13.

Characteristics of Student Body: *Ethnic/racial makeup:* Black non-Hispanic: 98%; Hispanic 1%; unknown 1%. *Age distribution:* number under 18: 51; 18–19: 276; 20–21: 3751; 22–24: 77; 25–29: 14; 30–34: 4; 35–39: 3; 40–49: 4; 50–64: 2; 65 and over: 1.

International Students: 7 nonresident aliens enrolled fall 2008. Students from Central and South America, Africa, Canada. Programs available to aid students whose native language is not English: social, cultural. No financial aid specifically designated for international students.

Student Life: On-campus residence halls house 80% of student body. *Intercollegiate athletics:* baseball. *Special regulations:* Cars permitted for junior and seniors only. Curfews begin 11pm for freshmen, 2am for upperclass students. Quiet hours from 7pm to 7am. *Special services:* Learning Resources Center, medical services. 3 national Greek sororities, departmental clubs, performing arts, dance company and touring choir. Student government association. Lyceum Cultural Series. *Student publications, radio: Bennett Banner*, a student newspaper; *Bennett College Annual*. *Surrounding community:* Greensboro metropolitan area population 155,000. Served by airport 15 miles from campus; passenger rail service 2 miles from campus.

Publications: *The Belle Ringer*, an alumni publication published 2 times a year, and *Alumnae Directory*, published every 5 years. College catalog published every 2 years. Calendar of Events published every semester.

Library Collections: 98,000 volumes. Online catalog. Current serial publications: paper 79; microform. 848 audiovisual materials; 42 DVDs; 94 CD-ROMs. Students have access to online information retrieval services and the Internet.

Most important special holdings include Afro-American Women's Collection (letters, rare first editions); Norris Wright Cuney Collection (diaries, logbooks, newspaper clippings from Reconstruction); Bennett College archives.

Buildings and Grounds: Campus area 55 acres.

Chief Executive Officer: Dr. Johnetta B. Cole, President.

Address admission inquiries Linda Torrence, Association Director for Enrollment Management.

Cabarrus College of Health Sciences

431 Copperfield Boulevard N.E.
Concord, North Carolina 28025-2405

Tel: (704) 783-1555 **E-mail:** admissions@cabaruscollege.edu
Fax: (704) 783-2077 **Internet:** www.cabaruscollege.edu

Institution Description: Cabarrus College of Health Sciences is a private institution. *Degrees awarded:* Associate, baccalaureate. *Enrollment:* 372.

Accreditation: *Regional:* SACS-Comm. on Coll. *Professional*: nursing, medical assisting, occupational therapy, surgeon assisting, social work

History: Founded in 1942 as Cabarrus Memorial Hospital School of Nursing; assumed present name 1996.

Institutional Structure: *Governing board:* Cabarrus College of Health Sciences governing board. Representation: 10 members. Administrators 5. Total faculty 47.

Calendar: Semesters. Academic year Aug. to May. Freshmen admitted Aug., Jan. Summer terms from May to July.

Characteristics of Freshmen: 140 applicants (131 female, 9 male). 46% of applicants accepted. 39% of accepted applicants enrolled. full-time.

88% (22 students) submitted SAT scores; 28% (7 students) submitted ACT scores. *25th percentile*: SAT Critical Reading 440, SAT Math 440; ACT Composite 19, ACT English 18, ACT Math 21. *75th percentile*: SAT Critical Reading 520, SAT Math 560; ACT Composite 24, ACT English 23, ACT Math 25.

60% of entering freshmen expected to graduate within 5 years. 100% of freshmen from North Carolina.

Admission: Official transcript showing evidence of high school graduation or equivalent; evidence of all immunizations and/or health information required by the college.

Degree Requirements: For diplomas: minimum of 38 semester hours; for associate degrees: minimum of 64 semester hours; for all baccalaureate degrees: 120 semester hours.

Degrees Conferred: 93 *associate*: 13 *baccalaureate*: health sciences.

Fees and Other Expenses: *Full-time tuition per academic year 2008–09:* $9,450. *Books and supplies:* $1,300. *Off-campus room and board per academic year:* $7,680. *Other expenses:* $5,280.

Financial Aid: Aid from institutionally generated funds is provided on the basis of academic merit, other criteria. Institution has a Program Participation Agreement with the U.S. Department of Education for eligible students to receive Pell Grants and, depending upon the agreement, other federal aid.

Financial aid to full-time, first-time undergraduate students: 99% received some form of aid. Average amount of aid received: federal grants $1,511; state/local grants $2,004; institutional grants $4,119; loans $2,351.

CABARRUS COLLEGE OF HEALTH SCIENCES—*cont'd*

Departments and Teaching Staff: *Total instructional faculty:* 46. Total faculty with doctorate, first-professional, or other terminal degree: 5. Student/faculty ratio: 22:1.

Enrollment: Total enrollment 372. Undergraduate372 (90% female, 10% male).

Characteristics of Student Body: *Ethnic/racial makeup:* Black non-Hispanic: 6%; American Indian or Alaskan Native 1%; Asian or Pacific Islander: 2%; White non-Hispanic: 89%. *Age distribution:* number 18–19: 58; 20–21: 65; 22–24: 62; 25–29: 44; 30–34: 27; 35–39: 15; 40–49: 25.

International Students: 17 nonresident aliens enrolled fall 2008.

Student Life: No college housing available. Clubs and student publication opportunities for students. Honor societies. *Student services:* academic advising; career services; personal and group counseling available. *Surrounding community:* Concord population 56,000. Charlotte, 25 miles from campus, is the nearest metropolitan area.

Library Collections: 12,000 volumes. Online catalog. 84 current periodical subscriptions. 775 recordings. Computer work stations available. Students have access to the Internet at no charge.

<Most important special holdings include Management Development Collection; Duncan Calder Collection; History of Medicine Collection.

Chief Executive Officer: Anita A. Brown, Chancellor.

Address admissions inquiries to: Mark A. Ellison, Director of Admissions.

Campbell University

P.O. Box 97
Buie's Creek, North Carolina 27506-0127
Tel: (910) 893-1291 **E-mail:** adm@mailcenter.campbell
Fax: (910) 893-1288 **Internet:** www.campbell.edu

Institution Description: Campbell University (Campbell College until 1979) is a private institution affiliated with the Baptist State Convention of North Carolina. *Enrollment:* 8,033. *Degrees awarded:* Associate, baccalaureate, master's, doctorate, first-professional.

Accreditation: *Regional:* SACS-Comm. on Coll. *Professional*: law, pharmacy, teacher education

History: Established as Buie's Creek Academy in 1887, the school became Campbell University in June 1979. The Campbell University School of Law was founded in 1979 and has been renamed the Norman Adrian Wiggins School of Law. The Lundy-Fetterman School of Business was begun in 1983, and the Schools of Pharmacy and Education were established in 1985. *See* J. Winston Pearce, *Campbell College (1887–1974)* (Nashville, TN: Broadman Press, 1976) for further information.

Institutional Structure: *Governing board:* Campbell University Board of Trustees. Representation: 48 trustees. All voting. *Composition of institution:* Administrators 33. Academic affairs headed by vice president for academic affairs and provost. Management/business/finances directed by vice president for business and treasurer. Full-time instructional faculty 172. Academic governance body, Faculty Senate, meets an average of 10 times per year.

Calendar: Semesters. Academic year Aug. to May. Freshmen admitted Aug., Jan., May. Degrees conferred May, Aug., Dec. Formal commencement May. Summer session of 2 terms from May to July.

Characteristics of Freshmen: 3,440 applicants (1,856 female, 1,584 male). 60% of applicants admitted. 40% of admitted applicants enrolled full-time.

84% (687 applicants) submitted SAT scores; 8% of applicants submitted ACT scores. *25th percentile*: SAT Critical Reading 518, SAT Math 510; ACT Composite 22. *75th percentile*: SAT Critical Reading 642, SAT Math 654; ACT Composite 29.

54% of entering freshmen expected to graduate within 5 years. 77% of freshmen from North Carolina. Freshmen from 50 states and 43 foreign countries.

Admission: Rolling admissions plan. For fall acceptance, apply as early as Sept. 1 of previous year, but not later than end of late registration period. *Requirements:* Either graduation from accredited secondary school with 13 units or GED. Require 4 units English, 2 foreign language, 2 history, 3 mathematics, 2 science. Minimum GPA 2.0. *Entrance tests:* College Board SAT or ACT. *For transfer students:* 2.0 minimum GPA; from 4-year accredited institution maximum transfer credit limited only by residence requirements; from 2-year accredited institution 64 hours maximum transfer credit.

College credit and advanced placement for postsecondary-level work completed in secondary school.

Developmental courses offered in summer session and regular academic year; credit given.

Degree Requirements: *For all associate degrees:* 64 credit hours. *For all baccalaureate degrees:* 128 credit hours. *For all undergraduate degrees:* 2.0 GPA; 32 hours in residence. Up to 4 semesters of attendance is required for Cultural Enrichment Programs. 3 hours physical education; general education requirements for some programs.

Fulfillment of some degree requirements and exemption from some beginning courses possible by passing College Board CLEP, AP. *Grading system:* A–F; withdraw (deadline after which pass-fail is appended to withdraw).

Distinctive Educational Programs: Internships. Flexible meeting places and schedules, including off-campus centers at Camp Lejeune, Ft. Bragg, and Pope AFB; off-campus programs at Raleigh, Rocky Mount, and Seymour Johnson AFB. Evening and weekend classes. Special facilities for using telecommunications in the classroom. Facilities and programs for independent research, individual majors, tutorials. Study abroad at South Wales Baptist College in Cardiff, Wales. *Other distinctive programs:* Baccalaureate program in applied science at Tunku Abdul Rahman College in Kuala Lumpur, Malaysia. Master of Divinity and Master of Arts degree programs added 1996.

ROTC: Army.

Degrees Conferred: 122 *associate*; 888 *baccalaureate*; 181 *master's*; 214 *doctorate*. Bachelor's degrees awarded in top five disciplines: business, management, marketing, and related support services 319; psychology 98; social sciences 80; health professions and related clinical sciences 67; education 38. 214 *first-professional:* pharmacy 95, law 111, theology 8.

Fees and Other Expenses: *Full-time tuition per academic year 2008–09:* $20,350 undergraduate; contact the university for graduate and professional schools tuition and fees. *Room and board per academic year:* $6,830. *Books and supplies:* $1,500. *Other expenses:* $4,384.

Financial Aid: Aid from institutionally generated funds is provided on the basis of academic merit, financial need, athletic ability.

Financial aid to full-time, first-time undergraduate students: 94% received some form of aid. Average amount of aid received: federal grants $4,664; Pell grants $2,979; other federal aid $2,424; state/local grants $3,981; institutional grants $8,430.

Departments and Teaching Staff: *Total instructional faculty:* 434. Student/faculty ratio: 18:1. Degrees held by full-time faculty: baccalaureate 2%, master's 12%, doctorate 87%. 89% hold terminal degrees.

Enrollment: Total enrollment 8,033 (31% female, 49% male). Transfer-in students 543.

Characteristics of Student Body: *Ethnic/racial makeup (undergraduate):* Black non-Hispanic: 17%; American Indian or Alaska Native: 1%; Hispanic: 4%; White non-Hispanic: 68%; unknown: 6%; nonresident alien 3%.

International Students: 241 nonresident aliens enrolled fall 2008. Students from Europe, Asia, Latin America, Canada, Australia. Programs available to aid students whose native language is not English: social, cultural. No financial aid specifically designated for international students.

Student Life: On-campus residence halls available. *Intercollegiate athletics:* NCAA Division I for males: baseball, basketball, golf, soccer, tennis, track and field, wrestling, cross-country; females: basketball, soccer, tennis, volleyball, softball, golf, cross-country, track and field. *Special regulations:* Cars with stickers permitted in designated parking area; fee charged. Quiet hours. *Special services:* Learning Resources Center, medical services. *Student publications, radio: The Campbell Times,* a weekly newspaper; *Pine Burr,* a yearbook; *Campbell Law Review,* annual law school publication; *The Lyricist,* annual literary magazine; *Prospect,* quarterly alumni paper. Student radio station WCCE broadcasts 133 hours per week. *Surrounding community:* Buie's Creek population 2,000. Raleigh (NC), 30 miles from campus, is nearest metropolitan area. Served by mass transit bus system; airport 30 miles from campus; passenger rail service 35 miles from campus.

Publications: *The Campbell Law Observer* (monthly) first published 1980. *Publisher:* The Campbell University Press, Incorporated.

Library Collections: 332,000 volumes including bound books, serial backfiles, electronic documents, and government documents not in separate collections. Online catalog. 750,000 microforms; 4,300 audiovisual materials. Current serial subscriptions: 4,400. Computer work stations available. Students have access to the Internet at no charge.

Most important holdings include Southern Baptist Convention Papers; J. A. and Leslie Campbell Papers; Gilbert Stephenson Papers.

Buildings and Grounds: Campus area 864 acres.

Chief Executive Officer: Dr. Jerry M. Wallace, President.

Undergraduates address admission inquiries to Herbert V. Kerner, Jr., Dean of Admissions; first-professional students to Alan Woodlief, Law School; Dr. Dan Teat, Pharmacy School; Jim Farthing, School of Education.

Norman Adrian Wiggins School of Law

Degree Programs Offered: *First-professional.*

Admission: Baccalaureate from accredited college or university, LSAT, personal interview.

Degree Requirements: 90 credit hours, 72 GPA on 100 scale, 27 months in residence.

Campbell University Pharmacy School

Degree Programs Offered: *Pharm. D.*

Admission: Prerequisite minimum of 2 years of pre-pharmacy work. Formal interview. 3 letters of recommendation and PCAT (Pharmacy College Admissions Test).

Degree Requirements: 4 years of professional study after the 2 years of prepharmacy.

Lundy-Fetterman School of Business

Degree Programs Offered: *Bachelor of Business Administration, Master of Business Administration.*

Admission: *For graduate program:* Bachelor's degree from an accredited institution. GMAT score of 450.

Degree Requirements: 30 semester hours of required graduate courses with a GPA of 3.0.

Distinctive Educational Programs: In its 31st year, the Southeastern Trust School serves professional bankers from across the U.S. for its 2-week summer program, which is accredited by American Bankers Association's National Graduate Trust School. Campbell University is the only university in the state whose graduates are eligible to sit for the Certified Financial Planners Exam.

Campbell University School of Education

Degree Programs Offered: *Bachelor of Science* in elementary education; *master's* in middle grades education.

Admission: *For graduate program:* Satisfactory scores on MAT (Miller Analogy Test), 3 letters of recommendation/

Degree Requirements: Satisfactory GPA (varies with program).

Campbell University Divinity School

Degree Programs Offered: *Master of Arts, Master of Divinity.*

Admission: *For graduate program:* Accredited baccalaureate degree; 2.5 or above GPA; 3 letters of reference; church approval.

Catawba College

2300 West Innes Street
Salisbury, North Carolina 28144
Tel: (704) 637-4111 **E-mail:** admission@catawba.edu
Fax: (704) 637-4754 **Internet:** www.catawba.edu

Institution Description: Catawba College is a private college affiliated with the United Church of Christ. *Enrollment:* 1,261. *Degrees awarded:* Baccalaureate, master's.

Accreditation: *Regional:* SACS-Comm. on Coll. *Professional*: teacher education

History: Established and chartered as a men's institution and offered first instruction at postsecondary level 1851; awarded first degree (baccalaureate) 1889; became coeducational 1890. *See* Banks Peeler, *A Story of the Southern Synod of the Evangelical and Reformed Church* (Salisbury, N.C.: The Reformed Church, 1968) for further information. *See also* Francis B. Dedmond, *Catawba: The Story of a College* (1989).

Institutional Structure: *Governing board:* Catawba College Board of Trustees. Representation: 40 trustees, all voting, meet twice a year; board is self-perpetuating. *Composition of institution:* 7 administrative officers including president, chief academic office and dean of the college, senior vice president and chaplain, chief financial officer, chief communications officer, chief enrollment officer. 73 full-time instructional faculty provide for academic governance through standing committees; the full faculty meets an average of 9 times a year.

Calendar: Semesters. Academic year Aug. to Aug. New students admitted Aug., Jan., May, June. Formal commencement May. Summer session of 2 terms from May to June.

Characteristics of Freshmen: 992 applicants (460 female, 532 male). 61% of applicants accepted. 41% of accepted applicants enrolled full-time.

81% (202 students) submitted SAT scores; 21% (52 students) submitted ACT scores. *25th percentile*: SAT Critical Reading 460, SAT Math 490; ACT Composite 19, ACT English 17, ACT Math 19. *75th percentile*: SAT Critical Reading 580, SAT Math 590; ACT Composite 25, ACT English 25, ACT Math 26.

48% of entering freshmen expected to graduate within 5 years. 74% of freshmen from North Carolina. Freshmen from 29 states and 18 foreign countries.

Admission: Rolling admissions plan. For fall acceptance, apply as early as summer following junior year, but not later than end of registration. Apply by Oct. 1 for early decision; need not limit application to Catawba. Early acceptance available. *Requirements:* Each student must present a minimum of 16 high school units of which 12 must be academic subjects. It is recommended that each student successfully complete the following courses in high school: 4 units English, 2 units mathematics (Algebra I or above), 2 units science, 2 units social science, 2 units foreign language (highly recommended). GED accepted. *Entrance tests:* College Board SAT preferred; ACT composite accepted. *For transfer students:* 2.0 minimum GPA; maximum transfer credit limited only by residency requirement; from 2-year accredited institution 64 hours maximum transfer credit.

Advanced placement for postsecondary-level work completed in secondary school. College credit for extrainstitutional learning (life experience) on basis of portfolio and faculty assessments, College Board CLEP.

Degree Requirements: 120 credit hours; 2.0 GPA; last 30 hours in residence; distribution requirements.

Fulfillment of some degree requirements and exemption from some beginning courses possible by passing College Board AP. *Grading system:* A–F; withdraw (carries time limit, deadline after which pass-fail is appended to withdraw).

Distinctive Educational Programs: Work-experience programs. Cooperative program in medical technology with Bowman-Gray School of Medicine of Wake Forest University. Facilities and programs for independent research, including honors programs, individual majors, tutorials. Study abroad at Harlaxton College, Lincolnshire, England.

ROTC: Army in cooperation with University of North Carolina-Charlotte.

Degrees Conferred: 281 *baccalaureate*; 3 *master's*. Bachelor's degrees awarded in top five disciplines: business/marketing 123; education 27; parks and recreation 20; visual and performing arts 16; health professions and related clinical sciences 16. Master's degrees awarded: education 5.

Fees and Other Expenses: *Full-time tuition per academic year 2008–09:* $22,240. *Room and board per academic year:* $7,700. *Books and supplies:* $1,200. *Other expenses:* #2,400.

Financial Aid: Aid from institutionally generated funds is provided on the basis of academic merit, financial need.

Financial aid to full-time, first-time undergraduate students: 1005 received some form of aid. Average amount of aid received: federal grants $1,511; state/local grants $2,004; institutional grants $4,119; loans $2,351.

Departments and Teaching Staff: *Total instructional faculty:* 100 (full-time 73, part-time 27). 67% of faculty hold the doctorate, first-professional, or other terminal degree.Student/faculty ratio: 17:1.

Enrollment: Total enrollment 1,261. Undergraduate 1,225 (53% female, 47% male). Graduate 36. Transfer-in students 126.

Characteristics of Student Body: *Ethnic/racial makeup:* Black non-Hispanic: 15%; Hispanic: 1%; White non-Hispanic: 80%; unknown 1%; nonresident alien 2%. *Age distribution:* number under 18: 1; 18–19: 363; 20–21: 377; 22–24: 193; 25–29: 103; 30–34: 74; 35–39: 67; 40–49: 71; 50–64: 20.

International Students: 24 nonresident aliens enrolled fall 2008. Students from Europe, Asia, Central and South America, Africa, Canada, New Zealand. No programs available to aid students whose native language is not English. No financial aid specifically designated for international students.

Student Life: On-campus residence halls house 63% of student body. *Intercollegiate athletics:* male: baseball, basketball, cross-country, football, golf, lacrosse, soccer, tennis; female: basketball, cross-country, field hockey, golf, softball, swimming, tennis, volleyball. *Special regulations:* Cars permitted without restrictions. Quiet hours from 11pm to 9am Sun.–Thurs. and 1am to 9am Fri. and Sat. Residence hall visitation from 1pm to 11pm Sun. through Thurs. and 1pm to 1:30am Fri. and Sat. *Special services:* medical services. *Student publications: Arrowhead*, a biannual literary magazine; *The Pioneer*, a monthly newspaper; *The Sayakini*, a yearbook; *The Tom Tom*, an annual handbook. *Surrounding community:* Salisbury population 23,000. Charlotte (NC), 40 miles from campus, is the nearest metropolitan area. Served by mass transit bus system; airport 45 minutes from campus; passenger rail service 2 miles from campus.

Library Collections: 188,000 volumes including bound books, serial backfiles, electronic documents, and government documents not in separate collections. Online catalog. 632,000 microforms; 8,000 audiovisual materials; current serial subscriptions: 75 paper, 386 microform, 7,421 via electronic access. Computer work stations campus-wide. Students have access to the Internet at no charge.

Most important special collection is Historical Collection of United Church of Christ, Southern Conference.

Buildings and Grounds: Campus area 210 acres.

Chief Executive Officer: Dr. Robert E. Knott, President.

CATAWBA COLLEGE—*cont'd*

Address admission inquiries to Dr. Russell Water, Vice President and Dean of Admissions; graduate inquiries to Dr. Lou Ann Kasias, Graduate Program Director.

Chowan University

One University Place
Murfreesboro, North Carolina 27855
Tel: (252) 398-6500 **E-mail:** admissions@chowan.edu
Fax: (252) 398-3401 **Internet:** www.chowan.edu

Institution Description: Chowan College is an independent Baptist four-year college. *Enrollment:* 952. *Degrees awarded:* Associate, baccalaureate.

Accreditation: *Regional:* SACS-Comm. on Colleges.

History: Founded 1848.

Calendar: Semesters. Academic year Aug. to May.

Characteristics of Freshmen: 3,240 applicants (1,659 female, 1,581 male). 33% of applicants accepted/ 19% of accepted applicants enrolled full-time.

Average secondary school rank of freshmen men 53rd percentile, women 39th percentile, class 48th percentile. Mean ACT composite score 20.

33% of freshmen from North Carolina. Freshmen from 20 states and 3 foreign countries.

Admission: *Requirements:* High school transcript; SAT I or ACT; recommended 2.0 GPA, 3 years of high school mathematics and science; foreign language.

College credit and advanced placement for postsecondary-level work completed in secondary school.

Developmental/remedial courses offered in summer session and regular academic year; credit given.

Degree Requirements: *For baccalaureate degree:* minimum 122 semester hours; minimum 1 math course; computer course; internship and senior project required for some majors. *Grading system:* A–F.

Degrees Conferred: 9 *associate;* 93 *baccalaureate:* degrees awarded in top five disciplines: health professions and related clinical sciences 23; business/marketing 19; protective services/public administration 19; communications/communication technologies 10; biological/life sciences 8.

Fees and Other Expenses: *Full-time tuition per academic year 2008–09:* $18,120. *Room and board per academic year:* $7,210. *Books and supplies:* $864. *Other expenses:* $240.

Financial Aid: Aid from institutionally generated funds is provided on the basis of academic merit, financial need. Institution has a Program Participation Agreement with the U.S. Department of Education for eligible students to receive Pell Grants and, depending upon the agreement, other federal aid.

Departments and Teaching Staff: *Total instructional faculty:* 73. *Student/faculty ratio:* 13:1. Degrees held by full-time faculty: master's 50%, doctorate 50%. 55% hold terminal degrees.

Enrollment: Total enrollment 952. Undergraduate 952 (49% female, 51% male).

Characteristics of Student Body: *Ethnic/racial makeup:* Black non-Hispanic: 49%; American Indian or Native Alaskan: 1%; Hispanic: 2%; White non-Hispanic: 43%; unknown 4%.

International Students: 6 nonresident aliens enrolled fall 2008. Student from Europe, Asia, Africa. No programs available to aid students whose native language is not English. No financial aid specifically designated for international students.

Student Life: *Intercollegiate athletics:* member NCAA Division III. Intramural sports program. Over 40 organizations available for student participation.

Library Collections: 97,000 volumes. 27,000 microforms; 4,000 audiovisual materials; 925 current periodical subscriptions. Online catalog. Students have access to online information retrieval services and the Internet.

Most important special holdings include Daniel Hall Music Library; Instructional Materials Center; McDowell Collection of Archives/Antiquities.

Buildings and Grounds: Campus area 286 acres.

Chief Executive Officer: Dr. Christopher White, President.

Address admissions inquiries to Vice President for Enrollment Management.

Davidson College

Main Street
P.O. Box 5000
Davidson, North Carolina 28035-5000
Tel: (704) 894-2000 **E-mail:** admissions@davidson.edu
Fax: (704) 894-2005 **Internet:** www.davidson.edu

Institution Description: Davidson College is a private college affiliated with The Presbyterian Church (U.S.A.). *Enrollment:* 1,688. *Degrees awarded:* Baccalaureate.

Member of Charlotte Area Educational Consortium.

Accreditation: *Regional:* SACS-Comm. on Coll.

History: Established as Davidson College for men, chartered and offered first instruction at postsecondary level 1837; awarded first degree (baccalaureate) 1840; admitted women 1972.

Institutional Structure: *Governing board:* Board of Trustees. Representation: 49 trustees elected as follows: 12 at-large by the Board; 8 by the National Alumni Association; 16 by Presbyteries in North Carolina and Florida. 5 trustees are ex-officio and non-voting. *Composition of institution:* Administrators 42. Academic affairs headed by vice president for academic affairs and dean of the faculty. Management/business/finances directed by vice president for business and finance. Full-time instructional faculty 1628. Academic governance body, the faculty, meets an average of 9 times per year.

Calendar: Semesters. Academic year Aug. to May. Freshmen admitted Aug. Degrees conferred and formal commencement May. No summer session.

Characteristics of Freshmen: 4,412 applicants (2,351 female, 2,055 male). 28% of applicants admitted. 43% of applicants admitted and enrolled full-time.

90% (434 students) submitted SAT scores; 45% (219 students) submitted ACT scores. *25th percentile*: SAT Critical Reading 630, SAT Math 640; ACT Composite 28. *75th percentile*: SAT Critical Reading 730, SAT Math 730; ACT Composite 32.

12% of entering freshmen expected to graduate within 5 years. 19% of freshmen from North Carolina. Freshmen from 59 states and 37 foreign countries.

Admission: For fall acceptance, application deadline Jan. 1 of year of enrollment. Apply by Nov. 15 for early decision; must limit application to Davidson. Students are notified of acceptance Apr. 1. *Requirements:* Graduation from accredited secondary school with 16 units which must include 4 English, 2 same foreign language, 3 mathematics, 2 social science or history, 6 academic electives. Additional units in science, history, mathematics recommended. *Entrance tests:* SAT or ACT required; 3 Achievements recommended. *For transfer students:* 2.0 minimum GPA; maximum transfer of 18 courses or 2 years' equivalent.

Advanced placement available to students presenting results of 4 or 5 on the Advanced Placement Examinations.

Degree Requirements: 32 courses (2.0 GPA); 16 courses in residence; 4 physical education courses (not included in the 32 courses); distribution requirements; foreign language proficiency.

Fulfillment of some degree requirements and exemption from some beginning courses possible by passing College Board APP. *Grading system:* A–F; pass-fail.

Distinctive Educational Programs: Accelerated degree programs. Facilities for independent research, including individual majors, independent study. Institutionally sponsored study abroad in France, Germany, India, Spain, Mexico, Greece, Italy, Great Britain. Off-campus programs include Junior Year Abroad/Fall Semester/Spring Semester in France, Germany, India, Italy, Greece, England. Summer Archaeological Dig in Cyprus.

ROTC: Air Force, Army offered in cooperation with UNC-Charlotte.

Degrees Conferred: 432 *baccalaureate*. Bachelor's degrees awarded in top five disciplines: social sciences 132; English 65; history 55; biological/life sciences 47; psychology 39.

Fees and Other Expenses: *Full-time tuition per academic year 2008–09:* $33,479. *Required fees:* $1,075. *Room and board per academic year:* $9,471. *Books and supplies:* $1,000. *Other expenses:* 1,775.

Financial Aid: Aid from institutionally generated funds is provided on the basis of academic merit, financial need, athletic ability, other criteria. Institution has a Program Participation Agreement with the U.S. Department of Education for eligible students to receive

Financial aid to full-time, first-time undergraduate students: 66% received some form of aid. Average amount of aid received: federal grants $4,100; Pell grants $2,719; other federal aid $1,429 state/local grants $3,250; institutional grants $2,154.

Departments and Teaching Staff: *Total instructional faculty:* 172 (full-time 162, part-time 120). Student/faculty ratio: 10:1. Degrees held by full-time faculty: 98% hold terminal degrees.

Enrollment: Total enrollment 1,699. Undergraduate 1,688 (51% female, 49% male). Transfer-in students 10.

Characteristics of Student Body: *Ethnic/racial makeup:* Black non-Hispanic: 6%; American Indian or Alaska Native: 1%; Asian or Pacific Islander: 4%; Hispanic: 6%; White non-Hispanic: 74%; unknown: 7%; nonresident alien 4%. *Age distribution:* number under 18: 13; 18–19: 821; 20–21: 735; 22–24: 97.

International Students: 68 nonresident aliens enrolled fall 2008. Students from Europe, Asia, Central and south America, Africa, Canada, Middle East.

Programs available to aid students whose native language is not English: social, cultural, financial.

Student Life: On-campus residence halls house 91% of student body. Residence halls for males constitute 6% of such space, for females 7%, for both sexes 87%. 6% of student body housed on campus in perimeter and eating houses. 48% of males join fraternities; a majority of sophomores, juniors and seniors belong to a fraternity, female's eating house, or coed eating house. *Intercollegiate athletics:* male: baseball, basketball, cross-country, football, golf, soccer, tennis, indoor track, outdoor track, wrestling; female: cross-country, field hockey, golf, tennis, indoor track, outdoor track, volleyball. *Special regulations:* Cars permitted without restriction, but parking is limited and policy is currently under study. *Special services:* Careers Office, medical services including Infirmary and Davidson College Emergency Rescue Service. *Student publications, radio: The Davidsonian*, a weekly newspaper; *Hubert Park* and *The Davidson Miscellany*, literary magazines; *Quips and Cranks*, a yearbook. Radio station WALT radio station. *Surrounding community:* Davidson population 7,500. Charlotte, 20 miles from campus, is nearest metropolitan area with population surpassing 1 million. Served by airport 20 miles from campus and passenger rail 20 miles from campus.

Publications: *Annual Report; The Crier*, a weekly newsletter for College faculty and staff; catalogue; *Davidson Journal*, a quarterly magazine for alumni and friends; *Oak Row Report*, a newsletter of college events for the community; *Soundings*, a listening guide for WALT; *>rack of the Cat*, sports newsletter for alumni and friends.

Library Collections: 630,500 including bound books, serial backfiles, electronic documents, and government documents not in separate collections. Online catalog. 525,500 microforms; 15,200 audiovisual materials; current serial subscriptions: 2,899 paper and microform, 1,993 via electronic access. Computer work stations available. Students have access to the Internet at no charge.

Most important holdings include first edition of *Diderot's l'Encyclopedia;* collection of books about Davidson student Woodrow Wilson; William Patterson Cumming Map Collection; Marvin Collection of 20th century printing, including first and rare editions; Peter Stuart Ney Collection.

Buildings and Grounds: Campus area 450 acres.

Chief Executive Officer: Dr. Robert F. Vagt, President.

Address admission inquiries to Christopher J. Gruber, Director of Admissions.

Duke University

103 Allen Building
Durham, North Carolina 27708
Tel: (919) 684-3914 **E-mail:** askduke@duke.edu
Fax: (919) 684-9941 **Internet:** www.duke.edu

Institution Description: Duke University is a private, independent, nonsectarian institution associated with the United Methodist Church. *Enrollment:* 14,060. *Degrees awarded:* Baccalaureate, master's, doctorate, first-professional.

Member of Consortium on Financing Higher Education and Organization of Tropical Studies.

Accreditation: *Regional:* SACS-Comm. on Coll. *Professional*: business, chemistry, clinical pastoral education, cytotechnology, engineering, forestry, law, medicine, nuclear medicine technology, nursing, physical therapy, physician assisting, psychology internship, radiation therapy technology, teacher education, theology

History: Established as Brown's Schoolhouse 1838; changed name to Union Institute 1839; chartered 1841; changed name to Normal College and offered first instruction at postsecondary level 1851; awarded first degree (baccalaureate) 1853; changed name to Trinity College 1859; adopted present name and incorporated 1924.

Institutional Structure: *Governing board:* Board of Trustees of Duke University. Extrainstitutional representation: 37 trustees; institutional representation: 3 students. All voting. *Composition of institution:* Administrators 18. Academic affairs headed by provost. Management/business/finances directed by executive vice president for administration. Full-time instructional faculty 1,226. Academic governance body, Academic Council, meets an average of 9 times per year.

Calendar: Semesters. Academic year Sept. to May. Freshmen admitted Sept., Jan. Degrees conferred May, Sept., Dec. Formal commencement May. Summer session of 2 terms from May to Aug.

Characteristics of Freshmen: 17,748 applicants (9,081 female, 8,667 male). 23% of applicants accepted. 42% of accepted applicants enrolled full-time.

93% (1,574 students) submitted SAT scores; 42% (608 students) submitted ACT scores. *25th percentile*: SAT Critical Reading 660, SAT Math 680, SAT Writing 680; ACT Composite 29, ACT English 30, ACT Math 29. *75th percentile*: SAT Critical Reading 780, SAT Math 790, SAT Writing 760; ACT Composite 34, ACT English 34, ACT Math 36. 14% of freshmen from North Carolina. Freshmen from 48 states and 396 foreign countries.

Admission: There are 2 admissions programs: Early Decision (binding) and April Decision. At this time, Duke uses a 2-part application. For Early Decision, Part 1 is due by Oct. 1, and Part 2 is due by Nov. 1. Students are notified of the decision by December 15. For April Decision, students should submit Part 1 by Dec. 1, and the completed application must be submitted by Jan. 2. Students will receive decisions by April 15. *Requirements:* Solid program of college preparatory work (normally including 4 years of English, at least 3 of mathematics, natural science, and a foreign language, and 2 years of history). Advanced level work encouraged. *Entrance tests:* College Board SAT with 3 Achievement Tests (one achievement test must be English Comp., and, if applying for engineering, English Comp. plus Math I or II are required). TOEFL for students whose first language is not English.

Some college credit and advanced placement may be awarded for AP work or postsecondary-level work completed in secondary school.

Degree Requirements: *For undergraduate degrees:* 34 course credits; no more than 2 grades of D; 17 courses in residence (including the senior year); at least 21 outside the major department; no more than 17 within the Major Course of Study for a Bachelor of Arts; no more than 19 within the major Course of Study for a Bachelor of Science; at least 12 courses at or above the 100 level; no more than 2 half-credit activity courses (e.g., physical education, dance), 2 credits for house courses, 4 in military science, and 6 from professional schools. Before reaching junior status: at least 1 full course designated as a seminar, tutorial, or independent study; or a combination of 2 preceptorials or discussion sections. During the junior and senior years: at least 2 full courses designated as seminars, tutorials, independent study, or a thesis. *Grading system:* A–F; pass-fail; withdraw (deadline after which pass-fail is appended to withdraw).

Distinctive Educational Programs: Flexible meeting places and schedules, including off-campus center (at Beaufort, 180 miles away from main institution) and evening classes. Accelerated degree programs. Facilities for independent research, including honors programs, individual majors, tutorials, cross-registration with North Carolina Central University, North Carolina State University at Raleigh, University of North Carolina at Chapel Hill. Off-campus study at Duke Marine Laboratory. Study abroad in Austria; Britain; Montreal, Canada; China; Cairo, Egypt; Oxford, England; Paris, France; Berlin, Germany; Madras, India; Bologna/Florence, Italy; Rome, Italy; Tokyo, Japan; Glasgow, Scotland; Spain. Summer Programs in Belgium/Netherlands, British Isles/England (Cambridge, Durham, London, Oxford), Canada, France, Germany (Erlangen/Nurnberg), Greece, India, Israel, Italy (Rome), Japan, Morocco, the Netherlands (Amsterdam), Poland, Soviet Union, Spain, Switzerland, Taiwan, and Zimbabwe/Botswana. *Other distinctive programs:* School of the Environment, Science Resource Initiative, Certificate Program in Markets and Management. Focus programs for first-year students include the Twentieth Century America program; Science, Technology and Modern Culture; Evolution and Humankind; and Twentieth Century Non-Western Culture. Continuing education.

ROTC: Army, Air Force, Navy.

Degrees Conferred: 1,505 *baccalaureate*; 1,423 *master's*; 271 *doctorate*; 434 *first-professional* (law, medicine, theology). Bachelor's degrees awarded in top five disciplines: social sciences 433; engineering 221; public administration 153; psychology 143; biomedical/biological sciences 101.

Fees and Other Expenses: *Tuition per academic year 2008–09:* $37,295 undergraduate. *Books and supplies:* $1,105. *Room and board per academic year:* $10,690. *Other expenses:* $1,835. Contact the university for current graduate and professional schools tuition and fees.

Financial Aid: Aid from institutionally generated funds is provided on the basis of academic merit, financial need, other criteria. Institution has a Program Participation Agreement with the U.S. Department of Education for eligible students to receive Pell Grants and, depending upon the agreement, other federal aid.

Financial aid to full-time, first-time undergraduate students: 59% received some form of financial aid. Average amount of aid received: federal grants $5,261; Pell grants $3,026; other federal aid $2,386; state/local grants $1,754; institutional grants $24,779.

Departments and Teaching Staff: *Total instructional faculty:* 1,579. Student/faculty ratio: 10:1. Degrees held by full-time faculty: baccalaureate .38%, master's 2.47%, doctorate 48.89%, professional 48.26%. 97% hold terminal degrees.

DUKE UNIVERSITY—*cont'd*

Enrollment: Total enrollment 14,060. Undergraduate 6,496 (49% female, 515 male). Graduate 7,564 (full-time 95%).

Characteristics of Student Body: *Ethnic/racial makeup:* Black non-Hispanic: 10%; Asian or Pacific Islander: 21%; Hispanic: 6%; White non-Hispanic: 51%. unknown: 6%; nonresident alien 6%.

International Students: 316 nonresident aliens enrolled fall 2008. Students from Europe, Asia, Latin America, Africa, Canada, Australia, New Zealand. Programs available to aid students whose native language is not English: social, cultural. English as a Second Language Program. No financial aid specifically designated for international students.

Student Life: On-campus residence halls house 70% of student body. 13% of undergraduate student body live in campus-owned apartments. Housing available for married students. *Special regulations:* Cars permitted without restrictions. *Special services:* Medical services, campus bus service between institutional living areas and university buildings. *Student publications, radio, television: The Archive*, a biannual literary magazine; *Chanticleer*, a yearbook; *The Chronicle*, a newspaper published 5 times per week; *Jabberwocky,* a biannual humor publication; *Teacher Course Evaluation*, annual; *Tobacco Road*, a bimonthly feature magazine. Radio station WDUK broadcasts 24 hours per week. TV station Cable 13 broadcasts 28 hours per week; offers student affairs programs. *Surrounding community:* Durham population 200,000. Charlotte, 140 miles from campus, is nearest metropolitan area. Served by mass transit bus system; airport 14 miles from campus; passenger rail service 25 miles from campus.

Publications: *American Literature* (quarterly) first published in 1934; *Hispanic American Historical Review* (quarterly) first published 1921, *History of Political Economy* (quarterly) first published 1961, *Journal of Health, Politics, Policy and Law* (quarterly) first published 1977, *Journal of Medieval and Renaissance Studies* (biannually) first published 1971, *Journal of Personality* (quarterly) first published 1932, *Law and Contemporary Problems* (quarterly) first published 1936, *South Atlantic Quarterly* first published 1902.

Library Collections: 5,472,000 volumes. 1,300,000 government documents; 4,257,000 microforms; 38,000 periodicals. 77,000 audiovisual materials. Online catalog. Students have access to online information retrieval services and the Internet. >p<Most important special holdings include Flowers Collection (Southern Americana); Trent Collection (History of Medicine); Frank Baker Collection of Wesleyan and British Methodism.

Buildings and Grounds: Campus area 9,700 acres.

Chief Executive Officer: Dr. Richard H. Brodhead, President.

Address undergraduate admission inquiries to Christoph G. Guttentag, Director of Admissions; graduate/first-professional inquiries to the school of interest.

Trinity College of Arts and Sciences

Degree Programs Offered: *Baccalaureate, master's, doctorate* in various fields.

Distinctive Educational Programs: Interdisciplinary majors in Afro-American studies, comparative area studies (Africa, Asia, Latin America), comparative literature, Medieval and Renaissance studies; concentrations in biomathematics, microbiology, oceanography. Study abroad programs. Membership in Triangle Computation Center in Research Triangle Park. Joint baccalaureate-first-professional program in medicine for selected undergraduates. Dual master's-first-professional programs in law and health administration, public policy sciences with School of Law. *See also* Divinity School, School of Law. *Other distinctive programs:* Performances and courses through American Dance Festival.

Divinity School

Degree Programs Offered: *First-professional, master's.*

Admission: Baccalaureate degree from an accredited college with 2.65 GPA; commitment to ordained or lay ministry.

Degree Requirements: *For first-professional:* 24 courses, 6 semesters in residence, 2.0 GPA, 2 units field education.

Distinctive Educational Programs: Degree programs, courses, and internships in pastoral psychology. *Other distinctive programs:* Continuing education residence programs and summer clinics for ministers.

School of Engineering

Degree Programs Offered: *Baccalaureate, master's, doctorate* offered through Trinity College of Arts and Sciences.

Distinctive Educational Programs: Double-major in public policy studies and various engineering fields.

School of Nursing

Degree Programs Offered: *Master's.*

Law School

Degree Programs Offered: *First-professional, master's.*

Admission: *For first-professional:* Normally graduation from 4-year accredited college; LSAT; applications must be processed through LSDAS.

Degree Requirements: *For first-professional:* 86 credit hours, 1.8 GPA, 90 academic weeks in residence.

Distinctive Educational Programs: Joint M.D.-J.D. program with School of Law. Master's and doctorate available, primarily for international students and with special permission of faculty. *See* Trinity College of Arts and Sciences and J.B. Fuqua School of Business.

School of Medicine

Degree Programs Offered: *Baccalaureate, first-professional.*

Admission: *For first-professional:* 60 semester hours from approved college which must include 1 course in English, 3 natural sciences, 3 social science, 1 humanities.

Degree Requirements: *For first-professional:* 155 credit hours, 36 months in residence.

Distinctive Educational Programs: Clinical psychology internship. Training programs in audiology and speech pathology, cytotechnology, hospital technology, nuclear medicine, pastoral care and counseling. Master's programs in health administration, physical therapy with Trinity College of Arts and Sciences. Academic programs in cooperation with East Carolina University, University of North Carolina at Chapel Hill. *See also* School of Law.

Fuqua School of Business

Degree Programs Offered: *Master's, doctorate.*

Distinctive Educational Programs: Joint MBA-JD program with School of Law. Degree and nondegree executive development programs. Ph.D. program. MBA-MS in Engineering; MBA-MF and MBA-MEM (School of Environment); MBA-AM in Policy Science.

School of the Environment

Degree Programs Offered: *Baccalaureate, master's, doctorate.*

Degree Requirements: *For master's:* From 60 to 48 credit hours, or 30 hours with an accredited BSF, or a strong undergraduate background in environmental studies.

Distinctive Educational Programs: Dual-degree programs in cooperation with numerous undergraduate schools.

East Carolina University

East Fifth Street
Greenville, North Carolina 27858-4353

Tel: (252) 328-6131 **E-mail:** admis@mail.ecu.edu
Fax: (252) 328-6945 **Internet:** www.ecu.edu

Institution Description: *Enrollment:* 22,767. *Degrees awarded:* Baccalaureate, master's, first-professional, doctorate. Specialist certificates also awarded.

Accreditation: *Regional:* SACS-Comm. on Coll. *Professional*: art, athletic training, business, chemistry, clinical lab technology, cytotechnology, dietetics, environmental health, health information administration, marriage and family therapy, medicine, music, nursing, occupational therapy, physical therapy, rehabilitation counseling, physician assisting, recreation and leisure services, marriage and family therapy, social work, speech-language pathology, teacher education

History: Established and chartered as East Carolina Teacher Training School 1907; offered first instruction at postsecondary level 1909; awarded first degree (baccalaureate) 1911; changed name to East Carolina Teachers College 1921, to East Carolina College 1951, adopted present name 1967.

Institutional Structure: *Governing board:* East Carolina University Board of Trustees. 13 trustees, including 9 alumni, 1 student ex officio. All voting. *Composition of institution:* Administrators 301. Academic affairs headed by vice chancellor; management/business/finances directed by vice chancellor for business affairs. Full-time instructional faculty 1,077. Academic governance body, Faculty Senate, meets an average of 9 times per year.

Calendar: Semesters. Academic year Aug. to May. Freshmen admitted Aug., Jan., May, June. Degrees conferred Dec., May, Aug. Formal commencement May. Summer session of 2 terms from May to Aug.

Characteristics of Freshmen: 76% of applicants admitted. 37% of applicants admitted and enrolled.

91% (3,184 students) submitted SAT scores; 7% 256 (585 students) submitted ACT scores. *25th percentile*: SAT Critical Reading 450, SAT Math 470; ACT Composite 17, ACT English 16, ACT Math 17. *75th percentile*: SAT Critical Reading 540, SAT Math 560; ACT Composite 22, ACT English 22, ACT 23.

48% of entering freshmen ' expected to graduate within 5 years. 83% of freshmen from North Carolina. Freshmen from 32 states and 19 foreign countries.

Admission: Rolling admissions plan. Deadline for summer of fall admission is March 15; deadline for spring admission is Nov. 1. *Requirements:* Graduation from accredited secondary school with at least 13 units, including 4 English, 3 math (algebra I and II and either geometry or a course for which Algebra II is a prerequisite); 2 social studies (including U.S. history); and 3 science (including at least 1 biological and 1 physical science). Audition requirement for direct admission of music majors. *Entrance tests:* SAT or ACT composite. For foreign students TOEFL. *For transfer students:* Good standing at college previously attended, same high school units as freshman, 30 semester hours of college credits. One-half of credits in the major and at least 30 semester hours must be completed at East Carolina, and one-half of the degree credits must be earned at an accredited 4-year institution. Correspondence/extension courses limited to 15% of degree credits.

College credit and advanced placement given for postsecondary-level work completed while in high school. College credit for extrainstitutional learning on basis of CLEP and by credit examinations.

Tutoring available. Limited developmental/remedial courses offered; institutional (non-degree) credit only.

Degree Requirements: *For all undergraduate degrees:* Typically 120–127 semester hours; 2.0 GPA; 30 hours in residence; 42 hours general education requirements. Additional requirements for some majors.

Fulfillment of some degree requirements and exemption from some beginning courses possible by passing departmental examinations. *Grading system:* A–F; withdraw (deadline after which pass-fail is appended to withdraw).

Distinctive Educational Programs: *For undergraduates:* Cooperative education. Flexible meeting places and schedules, including off-campus centers (at Elizabeth City, 95 miles from main institution, Jacksonville, 65 miles away; Fayetteville, 120 miles away), weekend and evening classes. Interdisciplinary honors seminars, programs in area studies, coastal studies. Facilities for independent research, including honors programs, tutorials. Study abroad in Australia, Canada, Ecuador, England, Finland, France, Germany, Poland, Spain, Sweden. Off-campus coastal and marine study at Pamlico Estuarine Laboratory. *Other distinctive programs:* Credit and enrichment continuing education. Student internships and community service through speech and hearing clinic.

ROTC: Air Force, Army.

Degrees Conferred: 3,237 *baccalaureate*; 1,359 *master's*; 121 *doctorate*; 69 *first-professional*. Bachelor's degrees awarded in top five disciplines: business/marketing 522; education 426; health professions and related clinical sciences 484; communications technologies 476; engineering technologies 267. Master's degrees awarded in top five disciplines: education 412; health professions and related clinical sciences 244; business/marketing 185; public administration and social services 124; library science 63. Doctorates awarded: biological/life sciences 10; education 24; English 1; health professions 80; interdisciplinary studies 6. First-professional degrees awarded: medicine 69.

Fees and Other Expenses: *Full-time tuition per academic year 2008–09:* contact the university for current information regarding tuition, fees, housing, and other costs.

Financial Aid: Aid from institutionally generated funds is provided on the basis of academic merit, athletic ability, other criteria.

Financial aid to full-time, first-time undergraduate students:

Departments and Teaching Staff: *Total instructional faculty:* 1,1,290 (full-time 1,185, part-time 105). Student/faculty ratio: 18:1. Degrees held by full-time faculty: baccalaureate 1%, master's 25%, doctorate 55.%, professional 19%. 1,036 faculty members hold terminal degrees.

Enrollment: Total enrollment 22,767. Undergraduate 15,736.

Characteristics of Student Body: *Ethnic/racial makeup:* number of Black non-Hispanic: 2,669; American Indian or Alaska Native: 124; Asian or Pacific Islander: 396; Hispanic: 274; White non-Hispanic: 1,365; unknown: 202. *Age distribution:* number under 18: 96;18–19: 6,015; 20–21: 5,731; 22–24: 3,220; 25–29: 1,000; 30–34: 499; 35–39: 373; 40–49: 445; 50–64: 124; 65 and over: 7.

International Students: No programs available to aid students whose native language is not English. No financial aid specifically designated for international students.

Student Life: On-campus residence halls accommodate 29% of undergraduate students. Of this residence hall space, 9% is for males, 20% for females, 71% co-ed. 8% of males belong to fraternities and 3% live in fraternity houses. 61% of females belong to sororities and 3.2% live in sorority houses. *Intercollegiate athletics:* male: baseball, basketball, football, golf, soccer, cross-country, swimming, tennis, track; female: basketball, softball, swimming, tennis, track, volleyball, cross-country. Club sport teams: crew, disc golf, fencing, female frisbee, male frisbee, lacrosse, kayaking, Goju Shoring Karate, rugby; male soccer, Tae Kwon do, underwater hockey, volleyball, and water skiing. *Special regulations:* Registered cars permitted in designated ares. Residence hall visitation hours from noon to 1am Sun.–Thurs., noon to 2am Fri. and Sat. *Special services:* Career Services, Counseling Services, Services for Students with Disabilities; Minority, International programs; non-traditional; Program for Hearing Impaired, Student Health Services, transportation system, Reading Center, Writing Center, computer labs and math lab. *Student publications, radio: The East Carolinian,* a newspaper published Tuesday and Thursday during regular academic year and weekly during summer; *Expressions,* a minority newspaper published twice per semester; *Rebel,* an art and literary magazine published annually; *Buccaneer,* a yearbook. Radio station WZMB-FM broadcasts 24 hours per day. *Surrounding community:* Greenville population 45,000. Raleigh, 90 miles from campus, is nearest metropolitan area. Greenville served by mass transit bus system, airport 5 miles from campus.

Library Collections: Joyner Library: 4,213,205 volumes. 820,462 government documents; 1,662,032 microforms; 30,527 audiovisual materials; 7,138 current periodical subscriptions. Students have access to online information retrieval services and the Internet.

Most important special collections include The Hoover Collection on International Communism; Maritime History Collection.

Lampus Health Science Library: 158,173 volumes. Most important special holdings include the Karel B. Absolon History of Medicine Library - European Themes; rare books from the History of Health Care - American and European; oral history interviews with local health care providers.

Buildings and Grounds: Campus area 1,367 acres.

Chief Executive Officer: Dr. Steve Ballard, Chancellor.

Undergraduates address admission inquiries to Carol Nichols McElfresh, Director of Admissions; graduate inquiries to Dr. Paul Tschetter, Dean of the Graduate School; medical school inquiries to Dr. James G. Peden, Jr., Associate Dean for Admissions.

Elizabeth City State University

1704 Weeksville Road
Elizabeth City, North Carolina 27909
Tel: (252) 335-3400 **E-mail:** admissions@ecsu.edu
Fax: (252) 335-3731 **Internet:** ecsu.edu

Institution Description: *Enrollment:* 3,104. *Degrees awarded:* Baccalaureate, master's.

Accreditation: *Regional:* SACS-Comm. on Coll.

History: Established as Elizabeth State Colored Normal School 1891; offered first instruction at postsecondary level 1937; changed name to Elizabeth City State Teachers College and awarded first degree (baccalaureate) 1939; changed name to Elizabeth City State College 1963; adopted present name 1969.

Institutional Structure: *Governing board:* Board of Trustees for Elizabeth City State University. Representation: 12 trustees. Institutional representation: student government association president. 1 ex officio. 13 voting. *Composition of institution:* \Administrators 17. Academic affairs headed by vice chancellor for academic affairs. Management/business/finances directed by vice chancellor for fiscal affairs. Full-time instructional faculty 105. Academic governance body, Faculty Council, meets an average of 4 times per year.

Calendar: Semesters. Academic year Aug. to May. Freshmen admitted Aug., Jan. Degrees conferred and formal commencement May. Summer session.

Characteristics of Freshmen: 1,807 applicants (1,031 female, 726 male). 80% of applicants admitted. 45% of admitted students enrolled full-time.

94% (807 students) submitted SAT scores; 13% (82 students) submitted ACT scores. *25th percentile*: SAT Critical Reading 370, SAT Math 380, SAT Writing 360; ACT Composite 14, ACT English 12, ACT Math 15. *75th percentile*: SAT Critical Reading 460, SAT Math 470, SAT Writing 450; ACT Composite 18, ACT English 18, ACT Math 18.

Admission: Rolling admissions plan. Early acceptance available. *Requirements:* Either graduation from accredited secondary school or GED. *Entrance tests:* College Board SAT. *For transfer students:* 2.0 minimum GPA; 60 hours maximum transfer credit.

Advanced placement for postsecondary-level work completed in secondary school. Tutoring available. Noncredit courses offered.

Degree Requirements: 124–130 credit hours; 2.0 GPA; 2 physical education courses; general education requirements; for teacher education fields, exit competency examination.

Exemption from some beginning courses possible by passing departmental examinations, College Board CLEP, APP. *Grading system:* A–F; withdraw (carries time limit).

ELIZABETH CITY STATE UNIVERSITY—*cont'd*

Distinctive Educational Programs: Work experience programs. Evening classes. Interdisciplinary programs in arts, humanities, social sciences. Honors programs.

ROTC: Army in cooperation with Norfolk State University (VA), North Carolina State University.

Degrees Conferred: 389 *baccalaureate*; 22*master's*. Bachelor's degrees awarded in top five disciplines: business, management, marketing, and related support services 91; security and protective services 42; public administration and social services 26; social sciences 22; psychology 18.

Fees and Other Expenses: *Full-time tuition per academic year 2008–09:* resident $3,164, nonresident $11,936. *Books and supplies:* $600. *Room and board per academic year:* $5,300. *Other expenses:* $1,000.

Financial Aid: Aid from institutionally generated funds is provided on the basis of academic merit, financial need, other criteria. Institution has a Program Participation Agreement with the U.S. Department of Education for eligible students to receive Pell Grants and, depending upon the agreement, other federal aid.

Financial aid to full-time, first-time undergraduate students: 95% received some form of financial aid. Average amount of aid received: federal grants $3,588; state/local grants #2,866; institutional grants $1,142; loans $3,310.

Departments and Teaching Staff: *Total instructional faculty:* 105. Student/faculty ratio: 16:1.

Enrollment: Total enrollment 3,104. Undergraduate 3,021 (62% female, 38% male). Graduate 83 (full-time 10%). Undergraduate transfer-in students 83.

Characteristics of Student Body: *Ethnic/racial makeup:* Black non-Hispanic: 80%; Hispanic 1%; white non-Hispanic 14%; unknown 3%; nonresident alien 1%.

International Students: 31 nonresident aliens enrolled fall 2008. No programs to aid students whose native language is not English. No financial aid specifically designated for international students.

Student Life: On-campus residence halls house 50% of student body. *Intercollegiate athletics:* male: basketball, football, wrestling; female: basketball, softball; both sexes, tennis, track. *Student publications, Compass*, a quarterly newspaper; *The Viking*, a yearbook. *Surrounding community:* Elizabeth City population 14,000. Served by airport 50 miles from campus.

Library Collections: 175,000 volumes. 1,700 serial subscriptions. 457,000 microforms. 12,300 audiovisual materials. Online catalog. Students have access to online information retrieval services and the Internet.

Buildings and Grounds: Campus area 640 acres.

Chief Executive Officer: Dr. Mickey L. Burnim, Chancellor.

Address admission inquiries to Bridget Golham, Director of Admissions.

Elon University

100 Campus Drive
Elon College, North Carolina 27244-2010
Tel: (800) 334-8448 **E-mail:** admissions@elon.edu
Fax: (336) 278-7699 **Internet:** www.elon.edu

Institution Description: Elon University is a private institution affiliated with the Southern Conference of United Church of Christ. *Enrollment:* 5,628. *Degrees awarded:* Baccalaureate, master's.

Accreditation: *Regional:* SACS-Comm. on Coll.

History: Established and chartered 1889; offered first instruction at postsecondary level 1890; awarded first degree (baccalaureate) 1891.

Institutional Structure: *Governing board:* Elon College Board of Trustees. Extrainstitutional representation: 41 trustees; institutional representation: president of the college. 3 ex officio. 38 voting. *Composition of institution:* Administrators 18. Academic affairs headed by vice president for academic affairs and dean of faculty. Management/business/finances directed by vice president for business and finance. Full-time instructional faculty 261. Academic governance body, Academic Council, meets an average of 11 times per year.

Calendar: Semesters (4-1-4 plan). Academic year Aug. to May. Freshmen admitted Aug., Jan., and Feb. Degrees conferred and formal commencement May. Summer session of 2 terms from June to Aug.

Characteristics of Freshmen: 9,434 applicants (6,133 female, 3,301 male). 42% of applicants accepted. 32% of accepted applicants enrolled full-time.

100% (1,291 students) submitted SAT scores; 41% (528 students) submitted ACT scores. *25th percentile*: SAT Critical Reading 560, SAT Math 570, SAT Writing 570; ACT Composite 24. *75th percentile*: SAT Critical Reading 650, SAT Math 660, SAT Writing 660; ACT Composite 28.

64% of entering freshmen expected to graduate within 5 years. 29% of freshmen from North Carolina. Freshmen from 46 states and 46 foreign countries.

Admission: For fall acceptance, apply by Jan. 1. Closing date Jan. 10. Early decision/early action available. *Requirements:* Either graduation from accredited secondary school with 16 academic units which must include 4 English, 2 foreign language, 3 college preparatory mathematics; recommend 1 social studies, 3 science; 3 electives; or GED. *Entrance tests:* College Board SAT, or ACT composite. *For transfer students:* 2.5 minimum GPA; from 4-year accredited maximum transfer credit 99 credit hours; from 2-year accredited institution 65 hours.

College credit for postsecondary-level work completed in secondary school. Advanced placement for extrainstitutional learning (life experience) on basis of assessment of dean.

Tutoring available. Remedial courses offered during regular academic year; credit given.

Degree Requirements: *For all baccalaureate degrees:* 132 hours; distribution requirements; 2.0 GPA; 2 terms, including last term, in residence.

Fulfillment of some degree requirements and exemption from some beginning courses possible by passing departmental examinations, College Board CLEP, AP. *Grading system:* A–F; pass-fail; withdraw (deadline after which pass/fail is appended to withdrawal); incomplete (carries time limit).

Distinctive Educational Programs: Work-experience programs, including cooperative education and internships. Evening classes. Facilities and programs for independent research, including honors programs, individual majors, tutorials. Semester study abroad in England; Exchange program with Japanese colleges; Summer study in China and India; Winter programs in London, Costa Rica, and Mexico. Elon Experiences: study abroad, leadership, internships,/coops, volunteer service.

ROTC: Army in cooperation with North Carolina Agricultural and Technical State University.

Degrees Conferred: 1,104 *baccalaureate*; 66 *master's*; 33 *doctorates*.

Fees and Other Expenses: *Full-time tuition per academic year 2008–09:* $24,076. Contact the college for graduate tuition and fees. *Required fees:* $245. *Books and supplies:* $900. *Room and board per academic year:* $7,770. *Other expenses:* $2,600.

Financial Aid: Aid from institutionally generated funds is provided on the basis of academic need, financial need, athletic ability, other criteria.

Financial aid to full-time, first-time undergraduate students: 74% received some form of financial aid. Average amount of aid received: federal grants $4,142; Pell grants $2,796; other federal aid $1,492; state/local grants $4,140; institutional grants $7,102.

Departments and Teaching Staff: *Total instructional faculty:* 335 (full-time 261, part-time 74). Student/faculty ratio: 17:1. Degrees held by full-time faculty: doctorate 75%, master's 25%. 83% hold terminal degrees.

Enrollment: Total enrollment 5,628. Undergraduate 4,992 (59% female, 41% male). Graduate 636. Undergraduate transfer-in students 82.

Characteristics of Student Body: *Ethnic/racial makeup:* Black non-Hispanic: 6%; Asian or Pacific Islander: 1%; Hispanic: 2%; White non-Hispanic: 81%; unknown: 7%; nonresident alien 2%.

International Students: 112 nonresident aliens enrolled fall 2008. Students from Europe, Asia, Central and South America, Africa, Canada, New Zealand. Programs available to aid students whose native language is not English: social, cultural. Some financial aid designated for qualifying international students.

Student Life: On-campus residence halls house 60% of student body. 25% of males join fraternities; 44% of females join sororities. *Intercollegiate athletics:* male: football, baseball, basketball, golf, soccer, tennis; female: basketball, volleyball, softball, tennis, soccer; both sexes: track. Lacrosse is played as a club sport. *Special services:* Learning Resources Center, medical services, personal counseling. *Student publications, radio: Elon Colonnades*, an annual literary magazine; *The Pendulum*, a weekly newspaper; *Phi Psi Chi*, a yearbook. Radio station WSOE broadcasts 96 hours per week. *Surrounding community:* Adjacent to Burlington; population 50,000. 15 miles east of Greensboro; 64 miles west of Raleigh. Accessible to airlines in both cities.

Library Collections: 278,500 volumes. Online catalog. 79,959 government documents; 944,000 microforms; 23,800 audiovisual materials; 25,700 periodicals including via electronic access. Students have access to online information retrieval services and the Internet.

Most important special collections include Church History Collection (archives of the Southern Conference of the United Church of Christ); Elon College Archival History Collection; McClendon Collection of Civil War Materials.

Buildings and Grounds: Campus area 575 acres.

Chief Executive Officer: Dr. Leo M. Lambert, President.

Address admission inquiries to Susan C. Klopman, Dean of Admissions and Financial Planning.

Fayetteville State University

1200 Murchinson Road
Newbold Station
Fayetteville, North Carolina 28301-4732
Tel: (910) 486-1371 **E-mail:** admissions@uncfsu.edu
Fax: (910) 436-1423 **Internet:** www.uncfsu.edu

Institution Description: *Enrollment:* 6,217. *Degrees awarded:* Associate, baccalaureate, master's, doctorate.

Academic offerings subject to approval by statewide coordinating bodies.

Accreditation: *Regional:* SACS-Comm. on Coll. *Professional*: teacher education

History: Established as Howard School 1867; chartered as State Colored Normal School 1877; changed name to State Colored Normal and Industrial School 1916; offered first instruction at postsecondary level and changed name to State Normal School for the Negro Race 1921, to State Normal School 1926, to Fayetteville State Teachers College 1939; awarded first degree (baccalaureate) 1943; changed name to Fayetteville State College 1963; adopted present name 1969. *See* Mildred P. Jones, *Fayetteville State College* (Fayetteville: Fayetteville State College Print Shop, 1969) for further information.

Institutional Structure: *Governing board:* Board of Trustees. Representation: 12 trustees, including 2 alumni; 1 student. 1 ex officio. 12 voting. *Composition of institution:* Administrators 36. Academic affairs headed by provost and vice chancellor of academic affairs. Management/business/finances directed by vice chancellor of fiscal affairs. Full-time instructional faculty 200. Academic governance body, Academic Affairs Council, meets an average of 3 times per year.

Calendar: Semesters. Academic year Aug. to May. Freshmen admitted Aug., Jan., June. Degrees conferred and formal commencement May. Summer session of 2 terms from mid-May to mid-Aug.

Characteristics of Freshmen: 2,454 applicants (1,582 female, 872 male). 78% of applicants admitted. 49% of admitted applicants enrolled full-time.

94% (885 students) submitted SAT scores; 13% (127 students) submitted ACT scores. *25th percentile*: SAT Critical Reading 370, SAT Math 380, SAT Writing 360; ACT Composite 15, ACT Wnglihs 13, ACT Math 16. *75th percentile*: SAT Critical Reading 456, SAT Math 470, SAT Writing 440; ACT Composite 18, ACT English 17, ACT Math 19.

40% of entering freshmen expected to graduate within 5 years. 90% of freshmen from North Carolina. Freshmen from 16 states and 5 foreign countries.

Admission: Rolling admissions plan. Apply as early as second semester of junior year of secondary school, but not later than July 1 of year of enrollment. Apply by Dec. for early decision; need not limit application to Fayetteville State. Early acceptance available. *Requirements:* Either graduation from accredited secondary school with 16 academic units which must include 4 English, 2 science, 2 social studies; or GED. Minimum GPA 2.0. Lowest acceptable secondary school class standing 33rd percentile. *Entrance tests:* College Board SAT. For foreign students TOEFL. *For transfer students:* 2.0 minimum GPA; 60 semester hours maximum transfer credit.

College credit and advanced placement for postsecondary-level work completed in secondary school. Tutoring available. Noncredit Developmental courses offered in summer session and regular academic year.

Degree Requirements: *For all associate degrees:* 60 semester hours. *For all baccalaureate degrees:* 120 hours; 30 hours and final year in residence; 3 credit hours of physical education courses; exit competency examinations in reading, writing; comprehensives in individual fields of study. *For all degrees:* 2.0 GPA; general education requirements.

Fulfillment of some degree requirements and exemption from some beginning courses possible by passing College Board CLEP. *Grading system:* A–F; withdraw.

Distinctive Educational Programs: Work-experience programs, including internships, cooperative education. Flexible meeting places and schedules, including off-campus centers (at Fort Bragg-Pope Air Force Base, less than 30 miles away from main institution), weekend and evening classes. Cooperative baccalaureate program in engineering with North Carolina State University at Raleigh; in medical technology with approved hospitals. Interdisciplinary programs in black studies, environmental studies. Preprofessional programs in dentistry, medicine, veterinary medicine. Facilities and programs for independent research, including honors programs, individual majors, tutorials. Institutionally sponsored study abroad in China, Taiwan. *Other distinctive programs:* Continuing education. Servicemembers Opportunity College.

ROTC: Air Force.

Degrees Conferred: 775 *baccalaureate*; 160 *master's*; 13 *doctorates*. Bachelor's degrees awarded in top five disciplines: business and management 130, education 64, protective services 84, psychology 80, social sciences and history 98; master's awarded: various disciplines 160; doctorates awarded: education 13.

Fees and Other Expenses: *Full-time tuition per academic year 2008–09:* $3,703 resident, $13,805 nonresident; contact the university for current graduate tuition and fees. *Room and board per academic year:* $5,010. *Books and supplies:* $500. *Other expenses:* $4,300.

Financial Aid: Aid from institutionally generated funds is provided on the basis of academic merit, financial need, other criteria. Financial assistance is available in the form of Pell Grants, College Work-Study, Veterans Administration Benefits, National Direct Student Loans, Supplemental Education Opportunity Grants (SEOG), Stafford Loans, other federal aid programs.

Financial aid for first-time, full-time undergraduate students: 93% received some form of financial aid. Average amount of aid received: federal grants $3,083; state/local grants $1,366; institutional grants $2,415; loans $3,134.

Departments and Teaching Staff: *Total instructional faculty:* 202. *Degrees held by full-time faculty:* 53% hold terminal degrees.

Enrollment: Total enrollment 6,217. Undergraduate 5,602 (68% female, 32% male). Graduate 615 (full-time 37%). Undergraduate transfer-in students 567.

Characteristics of Student Body: *Ethnic/racial makeup:* Black non-Hispanic 74%; American Indian or Native Alaskan 1%; Asian or Pacific Islander 1%, Hispanic 4%; White non-Hispanic 15%; unknown 5%.

International Students: No programs available to aid students whose native language is not English. No financial aid specifically designated for international students.

Student Life: On-campus residence halls house 48% of student body. Residence halls for males constitute 55% of such space, for females 25%, for both sexes 20%. *Intercollegiate athletics:* male: basketball, football, golf, tennis, track; female: basketball, softball, tennis, volleyball. *Special regulations:* Cars with decals permitted in designated areas. Curfews. Quiet hours. Residence hall visitation from 6am to midnight. *Special services:* Learning Resources Center, medical services, bus service to and from athletic and cultural activities. *Student publications, radio: The Voice*, a monthly newspaper. Radio station WFSS broadcasts 84 hours per week. *Surrounding community:* Fayetteville population 60,000. Raleigh-Durham, 50 miles from campus, is nearest metropolitan area. Served by mass transit bus system; airport 8 miles from campus; passenger rail service 4 miles from campus.

Library Collections: 241,000 volumes. 936,000 microforms; 6,700 audiovisual materials. 1,363 current periodical subscriptions. Online catalog. Students have access to online information retrieval services and the Internet.

Buildings and Grounds: Campus area 156 acres.

Chief Executive Officer: Dr. T. J. Bryan, Chancellor.

Address admission inquiries to Charles Darlington, Director of Enrollment Management.

Gardner-Webb University

Main Street
Boiling Springs, North Carolina 28017
Tel: (704) 406-4264 **E-mail:** admissions@gardner-webb.edu
Fax: (704) 406-4261 **Internet:** www.gardner-webb.edu

Institution Description: Gardner-Webb University is a private coeducational residential university affiliated with the Baptist State Convention of North Carolina. *Enrollment:* 4,070. *Degrees awarded:* Associate, baccalaureate, master's.

Accreditation: *Regional:* SACS-Comm. on Coll. *Professional*; business, music, nursing, psychology, teacher education

History: Established and chartered as Boiling Springs High School 1905; changed name to Gardner-Webb Junior College and offered first instruction at postsecondary level 1928; awarded first degree (baccalaureate) 1930; adopted present name 1942; incorporated as senior college 1969; implemented master's program in education 1980; became university 1993. *See* Francis B. Dedmond, *Lengthened Shadows* (Boiling Springs: Gardner-Webb College, 1957) for further information.

Institutional Structure: *Governing board:* Board of Trustees. Representation: 36 trustees. All voting. *Composition of institution:* Senior staff consisting of President, Provost and Senior Vice President; six vice presidents; 2 associate provosts; chair of faculty. Full-time instructional faculty 127.

Calendar: Semesters. Academic year Aug. to May. Freshmen admitted Aug., Jan., June, July. Degrees conferred and formal commencement May, Aug. Summer session from May to Aug.

Characteristics of Freshmen: 2,696 applicants (1,473 female, 1,220 male). 64% of applicants accepted. 26% of applicants admitted and enrolled full-time.

85% (378 students) submitted SAT scores; 30% (136 students) submitted ACT scores. *25th percentile*: SAT Critical Reading 450, SAT Math 440, SAT Writing 430; ACT Composite 17. *75th percentile*: SAT Critical Reading 580, SAT Math 550, SAT Writing 550; ACT Composite 23.

GARDNER-WEBB UNIVERSITY—*cont'd*

53% of entering freshmen expected to graduate within 5 years. 78% of freshmen from North Carolina. Freshmen from 36 states and 4 foreign countries.

Admission: Rolling admissions plan. For fall acceptance, apply as early as end of junior year but not later than 1 week prior to beginning of semester. Early acceptance available. *Requirements:* Either graduation from accredited secondary school or GED. Recommend 4 units English, 2 in a foreign language, 2 algebra, 2 social studies, 1 geometry, 1 natural science, and 4 electives. *Entrance tests:* College Board SAT or ACT composite. *For transfer students:* From 4-year accredited institution 2.0 GPA, 90 semester hours maximum transfer credit; from 2-year accredited institution 1.5 GPA, 64 hours.

College credit for postsecondary-level work completed in secondary school. Developmental courses offered during regular academic year; credit given.

Degree Requirements: *For all associate degrees:* 64 credit hours. *For all baccalaureate degrees:* 128 credit hours. *For all undergraduate degrees:* 2.0 GPA; 2 terms in residence; weekly chapel attendance; 2 semester hours of physical education; distribution requirements. Fulfillment of some degree requirements and exemption from some beginning courses possible by passing College Board CLEP, APP. *Grading system:* A–F; withdraw (deadline after which pass-fail is appended to withdraw); incomplete.

Distinctive Educational Programs: *For undergraduates:* Dual-degree program in engineering with Auburn University (AL). Cooperative programs in medical technology with the Bowman Gray School of Medicine of Wake Forest University and Charlotte Memorial Hospital. Independent study. Institutionally sponsored travel and study in Europe, Israel, and Latin America. Greater Opportunity for Adult Learners, for students with associate degrees desiring to earn baccalaureates in select areas. Servicemembers Opportunity College. Facilities and programs for the deaf and blind. *Available to all students:* Evening classes. Several study abroad programs available through the Consortium for Global Education of the Association of Southern Baptist Colleges and Schools.

Degrees Conferred: 65 *associate;* 689 *baccalaureate*; 334 *master's*; 15 *first-professional*: theology. Bachelor's degrees awarded in top five disciplines: business/marketing 251; social sciences 168; health professions and related sciences 44; philosophy and religious studies 41; parks and recreation 31. Master's degrees awarded: business/marketing 138; education 54; English 4; health professions and related sciences 29; parks and recreation 5; psychology 4.

Fees and Other Expenses: *Full-time tuition per academic year 2008–09:* \$20,160; contact the university for current information regarding graduate and professional tuition. *Books and supplies:* \$1,100. *Other expenses:* \$750.

Financial Aid: Aid from institutionally generated funds is provided on the basis of academic merit, financial need, athletic ability, other criteria. Institution has a Program Participation Agreement with the U.S. Department of Education for eligible students to receive Pell Grants and, depending upon the agreement, other federal aid.

Financial aid to full-time, first-time undergraduate students: 96% received some form of aid. Average amount of aid received: federal grants \$4,167; Pell grants \$2,049; other federal aid \$1,478; state/local grants \$5,153; institutional grants \$9,125.

Departments and Teaching Staff: *Total instructional faculty:* 127. 76% of faculty hold the doctorate, first-professional, or other terminal degree. Student-to=faculty ratio: 15:1.

Enrollment: Total enrollment 4,070. Undergraduate 2,704 (68% female, 345 male). Graduate 1,366 (full-time 23%). Undergraduate transfer-in students 397.

Characteristics of Student Body: *Ethnic/racial makeup:* Black non-Hispanic: 17%; Asian or Pacific Islander: 1%; Hispanic: 2%; White non-Hispanic: 73%; unknown: 6%. *Age distribution:* number under 18: 15; 18–19: 518; 20–21: 527; 22–24: 274; 25–29: 173; 30–34: 143; 35–39: 118; 40–49: 169; 50–64: 43.

International Students: 63 nonresident aliens enrolled fall 2008. Students from Europe, Asia, Central and South America, Africa, Canada, Australia, Niddle East. No programs available to aid students whose native language is not English. No financial aid specifically designated for international students.

Student Life: On-campus residence halls house 68% of on-campus undergraduates. Residence halls for males constitute 46% of such space, for females 54%. *Intercollegiate athletics:* male: baseball, basketball, football, golf, soccer, cross-country, tennis, wrestling; female: basketball, soccer, cross-country, softball, tennis, volleyball; both sexes: cheerleading, athletic training. *Special regulations:* Registered cars permitted on campus in designated areas only. Quiet hours from 8pm to 8am. Visitation is limited to lobbies. *Student development programs:* Counseling, career counseling, campus ministry, residence life, student activities, student entertainment association, international students program. *Special services:* Campus Security. *Student publications, radio: The Pilot*, a monthly newspaper; *Reflections*, an annual literary magazine; *The Web*, a yearbook. Radio station WGWG-FM broadcasts 88 hours per week; programs are of a Christian educational nature. *Surrounding community:* Boiling Springs population 2,500. Charlotte, 50 miles from campus, is nearest metropolitan area.

Publications: Alumni publication *The Web*, a quarterly magazine.

Library Collections: 239,000 volumes including bound books, serial backfiles, electronic documents, and government documents not in separate collections. Online catalog. 650,000 microforms; 10,500 audiovisual materials; 15,000 periodicals including via electronic access. Computer work stations available. Students have access to the Internet at no charge.

Most important special holdings include writings and personal library of Thomas R. Dixon, noted minister, playwright, maker of *Birth of a Nation*; correspondence, diaries, scrapbooks of Fay Webb Gardner, wife of O. Max Gardner, former North Carolina governor, advisor to F.D. Roosevelt, ambassador to Court of St. James.

Buildings and Grounds: Campus area over 200 acres.

Chief Executive Officer: Dr. Frank Bonner, President.

Address admission inquiries to Nathan Alexander, Director of Undergraduate Admissions; graduate inquiries to Jack Buchanan, Vice President for Enrollment Management.

Greensboro College

815 West Market Street
Greensboro, North Carolina 27401-1875
Tel: (336) 271-7102 **E-mail:** admissions@gborocollege.edu
Fax: (336) 271-6634 **Internet:** www.gborocollege.edu

Institution Description: Greensboro College is a four-year coeducational liberal arts college affiliated with the United Methodist Church. *Enrollment:* 1,279. *Degrees awarded:* Baccalaureate, master's.

Member of the Greensboro Regional Consortium and the Piedmont Independent College Association.

Accreditation: *Regional:* SACS-Comm. on Coll. *Professional*: teacher education

History: Greensborough Female College founded 1838; awarded first degree (baccalaureate) and changed name to Greensboro College for Women 1913; adopted present name 1921; became coeducational 1954; awarded first master's degree 2004.

Institutional Structure: *Governing board:* Board of Trustees. Extrainstitutional representation: 30 voting. *Composition of institution:* Academic affairs headed by Vice President for Academic Affairs. Management/business/finances directed by Vice President for Business and Finance/Treasurer. Full-time instructional faculty 61. Academic governance body, the Faculty, meets an average of 9 times per year.

Calendar: Semesters. Academic year Aug. to May. Degrees conferred and formal commencement May. Summer session of two terms May to Aug.

Characteristics of Freshmen: 1,058 applicants (479 female, 579 male). 64% of applicants admitted. 30% of applicants admitted and enrolled full-time.

91% (186 students) submitted SAT scores; 26% (52 students) submitted ACT scores. *25th percentile*: SAT Critical Reading 410, SAT Math 410, SAT Writing 410; ACT Composite 16, ACT English 15, ACT Math 16. *75th percentile*: SAT Critical Reading 530, SAT Math 550, SAT Writing 520; ACT Composite 21, ACT English 20, ACT Math 23.

43% of entering freshmen expected to graduate within 5 years. 71% of freshmen from North Carolina. Freshmen from 30 states and 15 foreign countries.

Admission: Rolling admissions plan. Apply by mid-Dec. of senior year of secondary school for early action. Early acceptance available. *Requirements:* Either graduation from accredited secondary school with 4 English, 2 foreign language, 3 mathematics, 2 science, 2 social studies; or GED. Additional requirements for some programs. *Entrance tests:* College Board SAT or ACT composite. *For transfer students:* from 4-year accredited institution unlimited transfer credit; from 2-year accredited institution 72 semester hours.

College credit and advanced placement for postsecondary-level work completed in secondary school. College credit for extrainstitutional learning (life experience) on basis of CLEP, DANTES, AP, challenge exams, portfolio.

Tutoring available. Remedial courses offered during regular academic year; credit given.

Degree Requirements: 124 credit hours; 2.0 GPA; 31 semester hours in residence; 2 semester hours physical education; distribution requirements; demonstrated proficiency in written English. Additional requirements for some programs.

Fulfillment of some degree requirements and exemption from some beginning courses possible by passing departmental examinations, College Board CLEP, AP. *Grading system:* A–F; pass-fail withdraw (carries time limit).

Distinctive Educational Programs: Adult Education Program for adult students with evening and weekend classes. Internship opportunities for all students. Honors degree program for superior students; recommended freshman seminar course for all first-semester freshmen. Writing Across the Curriculum and Ethics Across the Curriculum available. Study abroad: North Carolina Semester in Paris; academic courses abroad rotated during the summer sessions (e.g., Kenya, France, England). Other programs available by contacting Study Abroad Advisor for information.

ROTC: Army, Air Force in cooperation with North Carolina Agricultural and Technical State University.

Degrees Conferred: 151 *baccalaureate*; 16 *master's*. Bachelor's degrees awarded: biological/life sciences 15, business/marketing 36; education 14; English 10; foreign languages and literature 5; interdisciplinary studies 3; mathematics 7; parks and recreation 24; philosophy/religion/theology 9; psychology 10; social sciences and history 19; visual and performing arts 14; master's degrees awarded: education 16.

Fees and Other Expenses: *Full-time tuition per academic year 2008–09:* $22,480. *Required fees:* $270. *Room and board per academic year:* $8,420. *Books and supplies:* $900. *Other expenses:* $1,200.

Financial Aid: Aid from institutionally generated funds is provided on the basis of academic merit, financial need, other criteria.

Financial aid to full-time, first-time undergraduate students: 100% received some form of financial aid. Average amount of aid received: federal grants $2,042, state/local grants $1,900; institutional grants $1,401; loans $2,104.

Departments and Teaching Staff: *Total instructional faculty:* 125 (full-time 61, part-time 64). 82% of faculty hold the doctorate, first-professional, or other terminal degree. Student/faculty ratio: 13:1.

Enrollment: Total enrollment 1,279. Undergraduate 1,194. Graduate 85 (full-time 42%).

Characteristics of Student Body: *Ethnic/racial makeup:* number of Black non-Hispanic: 177; American Indian or Alaska Native: 3; Asian or Pacific Islander: 9; Hispanic: 8; White non-Hispanic: 710; unknown: 11. *Age distribution:* number under 18: 46; 18–19: 399; 20–21: 302; 22–24: 153; 25–29: 82; 30–34: 43; 35–39: 37; 40–49: 70; 50–64: 32; 65 and over: 1. 40% of student body attend summer sessions.

International Students: No programs to aid students whose native language is not English. No financial aid specifically designated for international students.

Student Life: On-campus residence halls house 50% of student body. *Intercollegiate athletics:* male: baseball, basketball, cross-country, football, golf, lacrosse, soccer, tennis; female: basketball, cross-country, lacrosse, soccer, swimming, tennis, volleyball. *Special services:* medical services; tutorial services. *Student publications: Collegian*, campus newspaper; *The Lyre*, literary magazine; *Echo,* a yearbook. *Surrounding community:* Greensboro population 185,000. Served by mass transit bus system; airport 10 miles from campus.

Publications: *The Magazine,* alumni news.

Library Collections: 110,000 volumes; 3,000 microforms; 28700 audiovisual materials; 490 current periodical subscriptions. Students have access to online information retrieval services and the Internet.

Most important special collections include Greensboro College Archives; Rare Books Collection.

Buildings and Grounds: Campus area 46 acres.

Chief Executive Officer: Dr. Steven E. Williams, President.

Address admission inquiries to Timothy Jackson, Director of Admissions; graduate inquiries to Judy Cheatham, Director of Adult Education and Graduate Studies.

Guilford College

5800 West Friendly Avenue
Greensboro, North Carolina 27410

Tel: (336) 316-2000 **E-mail:** admission@guilford.edu
Fax: (336) 316-2954 **Internet:** www.guilford.edu

Institution Description: Guilford College is a private liberal arts college affiliated with the Religious Society of Friends. *Enrollment:* 2,641.

Accreditation: *Regional:* SACS-Comm. on Coll.

History: Chartered 1834; established as New Garden Board School 1837; offered first instruction at postsecondary level, awarded first degree (baccalaureate), and adopted present name 1889.

Institutional Structure: *Governing board:* Board of Trustees. *Representation:* 24–32 trustees. All voting. *Composition of institution:* Administrative Council 19 faculty,staff, and student members. President serves as chief executive officer. Academic Affairs headed by Academic Dean. Finances/business directed by vice President for finance and administration; development/alumni/public relations directed by vice president for Institutional Advancement. Full-time instructional faculty 98.

Calendar: Semesters. Academic year Aug. to May. Formal commencement May. Summer sessions include 2 five-week day sessions and a ten-week evening session. Freshmen admitted June, Aug., Jan. Degrees conferred May, July.

Characteristics of Freshmen: 3,352 applicants (1,837 female, 1,715 male). 60% of applicants accepted. 19% of accepted applicants enrolled full-time.

86% (348 students) submitted SAT scores; 25% (100 students) submitted ACT scores. *25th percentile*: SAT Critical Reading 500, SAT Math 500, SAT Writing 480; ACT Composite 21. *75th percentile*: SAT Critical Reading 620, SAT Math 600, SAT Writing 610; ACT Composite 26.

58% of entering freshmen expected to graduate within 5 years. 64% of freshmen from North Carolina. Freshmen from 45 states and 16 foreign countries.

Admission: Deadline and notification: early decision Dec. 1, notification Dec. 15; regular decision Feb. 1, notification Apr. 1; after March: rolling admission depending on space available. *Requirements:* Either graduation from accredited secondary school or GED. *Entrance tests:* College Board SAT or ACT composite. For foreign students TOEFL. *For transfer students:* minimum grade of C in courses bearing some relationship to Guilford's liberal arts curriculum; from 2-year college maximum of 64 credits (up to 48 credits from two-year technical college).

Degree Requirements: *For all baccalaureate degrees:* 128 credit hours; 2.0 GPA; 2 semesters in residence; core curriculum. *Grading system:* A–F.

Distinctive Educational Programs: 3-2 liberal arts career programs for undergraduates: Forestry and Environmental Studies - Duke University (NC); Law - any A.B.A.-approved law school; Medical Technology and Physician's Assistant - Bowman Gray School of Medicine, Wake Forest University (NC). Study abroad - semester in Brunnenberg, China, London, Paris, Munich, Guadalajara. Year-long program in Japan; semester at Washington Center for Learning Alternatives. Honors Program; internships in all fields. Accelerated program for bachelor's degree in 3 years. Advanced placement - maximum credit 16 with a minimum score 4. Quaker Leadership Scholars Program for interested Quaker students; Corella and Bertram F. Bonner Scholars Program combines academic and community service. First-Year Seminar program as extended orientation.

Degrees Conferred: 521 *baccalaureate:* degrees awarded in top five disciplines: business/marketing 94; security and protective services 66; biological/life sciences 43; psychology 42; computer and information sciences 29.

Fees and Other Expenses: *Full-time tuition per academic year 2008–09:* $26,031. *Mandatory fees:* $330. *Room and board per academic year:* $7,140. *Books and supplies:* $1,000. *Other expenses:* $1,650.

Financial Aid: Aid from institutionally generated funds is provided on the basis of academic merit, financial need, other considerations.

Financial aid to full-time, first-time undergraduate students: 98% received some form of aid. Average amount of aid received: federal grants $2,145; Pell grants $3,269; other federal aid $1,514; state/local grants $1,867; institutional grants $10,366.

Departments and Teaching Staff: *Total instructional faculty:* 205 (full-time 133, part-time 92). 89% of faculty hold the doctorate, first-professional, or other terminal degree. Student/faculty ratio: 15:1.

Enrollment: Total enrollment 2,641 (undergraduate). Transfer-in students 338.

Characteristics of Student Body: *Ethnic/racial makeup:* number of Black non-Hispanic: 531; American Indian or Alaska Native: 22; Asian or Pacific Islander: 41; Hispanic: 51; White non-Hispanic: 1,828; unknown: 91. *Age distribution:* number under 18: 113; 18–19: 706; 20–21: 514; 22–24: 204; 25–29: 381; 30–34: 257; 35–39: 210; 40–49: 214; 50–64: 87; 65 and over: 1.

International Students: 23 nonresident aliens enrolled fall 2008. Students from Europe, Asia, Central and South America, Africa. Programs available to aid students whose native language is not English: social and cultural. English as a Second Language Program. No financial aid specifically designated for international students.

Student Life: The college is primarily a residential campus. On-campus residence halls for males, females, and co-ed. *Intercollegiate athletics:* male: baseball, basketball, football, golf, lacrosse, soccer, tennis; female: basketball, lacrosse, soccer, swimming, tennis, volleyball. *Special regulations:* Cars permitted on campus if properly registered and parked in designated parking area. *Special services:* Student health service; campus ministry, leadership development. *Student publications: The Guilfordian*, student newspaper; *The Quaker*, the college yearbook; *the lighthouse*, features original poetry, prose, and graphics. WQFS-FM 90.9 is student-run radio station. 43 clubs and organizations; several community service organizations. *Surrounding community:* Greensboro has a population of 200,000. The Greensboro/High Point/Winston-Salem Regional Airport 3 miles west of the city serves the area.

Library Collections: 256,500 volumes. 21,200 microforms; 4,400 audiovisual materials; 17,600 periodicals including via electronic access. Online catalog. Students have access to online information retrieval services and the Internet.

Most important special collection: Friends Historical Collection.

Buildings and Grounds: Campus area 340 acres.

Chief Executive Officer: Dr. Kent John Chabotar, President.

Address admission inquiries to Randy Doss, Vice President for Enrollment and Campus Life.

High Point University

833 Montlieu Avenue
High Point, North Carolina 27262-3598
Tel: (336) 841-9000 **E-mail:** admiss@highpoint.edu
Fax: (336) 841-4599 **Internet:** www.highpoint.edu

Institution Description: High Point University is a private institution affiliated with the United Methodist Church. *Enrollment:* 3,409. *Degrees awarded:* Baccalaureate, master's.

Member of Greater Greensboro Consortium.

Accreditation: *Regional:* SACS-Comm. on Coll. *Professional*: business, teacher education

History: Established and offered first instruction at postsecondary level 1924; awarded first degree (baccalaureate) 1927; awarded first master's degree 1995. *See* William R. Locke, *No Easy Task* (Greensboro, NC.: Piedmont Press, 1975); Bernard B. McCaslin, "Remembered by Thy blessings: High Point University, The College Years—1924-1991 (High Point, NC, High Point University Press, 1995) for further information.

Institutional Structure: *Governing board:* Trustees of High Point University. Representation: 27–36 trustees including 4 ex officio trustees; 5 administrative areas headed by 5 presidents: academic affairs, institutional advancement, enrollment, community relations, and information services. Divisions: day, evening, graduate. Departments: 12 departments offer 36 majors.

Calendar: Semesters. Academic year Aug. to May. Freshmen admitted Aug., Jan., June, July. Degrees conferred and formal commencement May. Summer session of 3 terms: May, June, July.

Characteristics of Freshmen: 3,428 applicants (2,185 female, 1,243 male). 74% of applicants accepted. 35% of accepted applicants enrolled full-time.

91% (805 students) submitted SAT scores; 35% (311 students) submitted ACT scores. *25th percentile*: SAT Critical Reading 480, SAT Math 480, SAT Writing 480; ACT Composite 20, ACT English 20, ACT Math 19. *75th percentile*: SAT Critical Reading 570, SAT Math 580, SAT Writing 570; ACT Composite 24, ACT English 25, ACT Math 25.

53% of entering freshmen expected to graduate within 5 years. 37% of freshmen from North Carolina. Freshmen from 44 states and 41 foreign countries.

Admission: Rolling admissions plan. Students admitted for terms beginning in Aug., Jan., May, June, July. *Requirements:* High school graduation with 4 units English, 1–2 foreign language, 2 mathematics, 1 history, 1 science, 5–6 electives; or GED. *Entrance tests:* SAT or ACT. Non-citizens TOEFL, SAT, or ACT required, except that varsity athletes must take ACT or SAT. *For transfer students:* 2.0 or higher GPA; from 2-year accredited institution 64 semester hours maximum transfer credit; from 4-year institution 93 semester hours. Advanced standing options: AP, CLEP, International Baccalaureate.

College credit and advanced placement for postsecondary-level work completed in secondary school. College credit for extrainstitutional learning (life experience).

Developmental/remedial courses offered during regular academic year; credit given.

Degree Requirements: 124 semester hours; 2.0 GPA; last 31 hours must be earned in residence, except that students who have earned at lest 90 hours at High Point must complete the last 31 hours in residence. Also required: general education courses; major with 2.0 average or higher; electives.

Fulfillment of some degree requirements and exemption from some beginning courses possible by passing departmental examinations, College Board CLEP, AP. *Grading system:* A–F.

Distinctive Educational Programs: Experiential learning; Honors; internships. student research, evening classes; academic enrichment, cross-registration with institutions of the Greater Greensboro consortium. Dual-degree programs in forestry/environmental studies with Duke University; medical technology with Bowman Gray School of Medicine, Wake Forest. Unique majors: home furnishings marketing, home furnishings management. Interdisciplinary majors: behavioral science, chemistry-business, communications, human relations, international business. Summer study abroad in China, England, France, Italy, Mexico, Latin America, Spain.

ROTC: Air Force through the Greater Greensboro Consortium.

Degrees Conferred: 479 *baccalaureate*; 102 *master's*. Bachelor's degrees awarded in top five disciplines: business/marketing 275; computer and information sciences 96; education 39; health professions and related sciences 38; psychology 38. Master's degrees awarded: business/marketing 70; education 11; health professions and related sciences 21.

Fees and Other Expenses: *Full-time tuition per academic year 2008=09:* $18,000 undergraduate; $472 per credit for graduate study. *Room and board per academic year:* $7,960. *Required fees:* $1,850.

Financial Aid: Aid from institutionally generated funds is provided on the basis of academic merit, financial need, athletic ability. Financial assistance is available in the form of Pell Grants, College Work-Study, Veterans Administration Benefits, National Direct Student Loans, Supplemental Education Opportunity Grants (SEOG), Stafford Loans, other federal aid programs.

Financial aid to full-time, first-time undergraduate students: 91% received some form of aid. Average amount of aid received: federal grants $1,511; state/local grants $2,004; institutional grants $4,119; loans $2,351.

Departments and Teaching Staff: *Total instructional faculty:* 267 (full-time 127, part-time 140). Degrees held by full-time faculty: doctorate 67%, master's 33%. 122 faculty members hold terminal degrees.

Enrollment: Total enrollment 3,409. Undergraduate 3,059. Graduate 350. Undergraduate transfer-in students 350.

Characteristics of Student Body: *Ethnic/racial makeup:* number of Black non-Hispanic: 520; American Indian or Alaska Native 12; Asian or Pacific Islander: 65; Hispanic: 52; White non-Hispanic: 1,829.

International Students: 86 nonresident aliens enrolled fall 2008. Students from Europe, Asia, Central and South America, Africa, Canada, Middle East. Programs available to aid students whose native language is not English: social. English as a Second Language Program. No financial aid specifically designated for international students.

Student Life: Campus-based programs: NCAA athletics for males and females. Greek organizations. 4 national fraternities, 4 national sororities. 4 service organizations. 4 religious organizations. 2 literary magazines; campus newspaper. 8 honor societies. 10 professional organizations. Publications: *The Lamplighter, The Apogee, Campus Chronicle, Zenith* (yearbook). *Surrounding community:* High Point population 95,400. Served by mass transit system, airport, passenger rail service.

Library Collections: 204,500 volumes. 8,000 audiovisual materials. Current periodical subscriptions: paper 650; microform 83,692 units; via electronic access 23,100. Online catalog. Students have access to online information retrieval services and the Internet.

Most important special collections include Furniture Market Collection; Archives of Western North Carolina Methodist Church; Business Collection.

Buildings and Grounds: Campus area 130 acres.

Chief Executive Officer: Dr. Nido R, Qubein, President.

Address undergraduate admission inquiries to Jessie McMcIlrath Carter, Director of Admissions; graduate inquiries to Dr. Alberta Herron, Dean of the Graduate School.

John Wesley College

2314 North Centennial Street
High Point, North Carolina 27265-3197
Tel: (336) 889-2262 **E-mail:** admissions@johnwesley.edu
Fax: (336) 889-2261 **Internet:** johnwesley.edu

Institution Description: John Wesley College is an interdenominational Bible college that provides training of students as missionaries, pastors, evangelists, and other fields of Christian service. *Enrollment:* 102. *Degrees awarded:* Baccalaureate.

Accreditation: *National:* ABHE.

History: Founded 1932.

Institutional Structure: *Governing board:* Board of Trustees. Academic affairs headed by president. Management/business/finances directed by business manager. Full-time instructional faculty 6.

Calendar: Semesters. Academic year Aug. to May. Freshmen admitted Aug. Degrees conferred and formal commencement May. Summer session of 2 terms.

Characteristics of Freshmen: 46 applicants (22 female, 24 male). 76% of applicants accepted. 60% of accepted applicants enrolled full-time.

69% of entering students expected to graduate within 5 years. 92% of freshmen from North Carolina. Students from 2 states.

Admission: *Requirements:* Either graduation from accredited secondary school or GED and satisfactory scores on placement test.

Degree Requirements: *For baccalaureate degree:* 128 semester hours; 2.0 GPA.

Distinctive Educational Programs: Majors available in Bible/theology, Christian counseling, Christian education, elementary Christian school teacher education, missions, pastoral ministries, pre-seminary, management and ethics; minors in missions and music.

Degrees Conferred: 39 *baccalaureate:* philosophy/religion/theology.

Fees and Other Expenses: *Full-time tuition per academic year 2008–09:* $10,750. *Required fees:* $478. *Room and board per academic year:* $4,676. *Books and supplies:* $1,200. *Other expenses:* $2,700. >

Financial Aid: Aid from institutionally generated funds is provided on the basis of academic merit, financial need.

Financial aid to full-time, first-time undergraduate students: need-based scholarships/grants totaling $245,943, self-help $396,637; non-need-based scholarships/grants totaling $41,449, self-help $227,496, parent loans $29,008, tuition waivers $18,500.

Departments and Teaching Staff: *Total instructional faculty:* 21 (full-time 3, part-time 18). Total faculty with doctorate, first-professional, or other terminal degree: 10. Student/faculty ratio: 18:1. Degrees held by full-time faculty: master's 20%, doctorate 80%. 80% hold terminal degrees.

Enrollment: Total enrollment 102.

Characteristics of Student Body: *Ethnic/racial makeup:* number of Black non-Hispanic: 54; American Indian or Alaska Native: 1; Asian or Pacific Islander: 1; Hispanic: 3; White non-Hispanic: 111. *Age distribution:* number under 18: 1; 18–19: 10; 20–21: 17; 22–24: 22; 25–29: 18; 30–34: 20; 35–39: 29; 40–49: 38; 50–64: 15.

International Students: No programs available to aid students whose native language is not English. No financial aid specifically designated for international students.

Student Life: One 12-unit apartment complex designed for both single and married housing.

Publications: *The Crusader*, published quarterly.

Library Collections: 36,000 volumes. 95 microform titles; 2,900 audiovisual materials; 110 current periodical subscriptions. 10 computer work stations. Students have access to online information retrieval services and the Internet.

Most important special holdings include John Wesley Collection; Bible/Theology Collection; Pastoral Counseling Collection.

Chief Executive Officer: Dr. Brian C. Donley, President.

Address admission inquiries to Greg Workman, Director of Admissions.

Johnson C. Smith University

100 Beatties Ford Road
Charlotte, North Carolina 28216
Tel: (704) 378-1000 **E-mail:** admissions@jcsu.edu
Fax: (704) 378-1242 **Internet:** www.jcsu.edu

Institution Description: Johnson C. Smith University is a private institution affiliated with the Presbyterian Church in the United States of America. *Enrollment:* 1,571. *Degrees awarded:* Baccalaureate.

Accreditation: *Regional:* SACS-Comm. on Coll. *Professional*: business, social work, teacher education

History: Established as The Biddle Memorial Institute, a men's college, 1867; chartered 1869; awarded first degree (baccalaureate) 1872; changed name to Biddle University 1876; adopted present name 1923; women first admitted 1932.

Institutional Structure: *Governing board:* Board of Trustees. Representation: 22 trustees, 15 trustees emeriti. *Composition of institution:* 8 administrators. Academic affairs headed by vice president for academic affairs. Management/business/finances directed by vice president for financial affairs. Full-time instructional faculty 83.

Calendar: Semesters. Academic year July to June. Formal commencements May, Aug. Summer session from early June to early Aug.

Characteristics of Freshmen: 5,290 applicants (3,474 female, 1,825 male). 21% of accepted applicants enrolled.

86% (432 students) submitted SAT scores; 14% (70 students) submitted ACT scores. *25th percentile*: SAT Critical Reasoning 434, SAT Math 436; ACT Composite 19. *75th percentile*: SAT Critical Reading 504, SAT Math 506; ACT Composite 27.

40% of entering freshmen expected to graduate within 5 years. 30% of freshmen from North Carolina. Freshmen from 35 states and 6 foreign countries.

Admission: Rolling admissions plan. Apply no later than 2 months prior to enrollment. *Requirements:* Graduation from accredited secondary school with 16 units, including 4 English, 2 mathematics, 1 laboratory science, 2 social science. *Entrance tests:* College Board SAT or ACT composite. For foreign students TOEFL. *For transfer students:* 2.0 minimum GPA; from 2-year accredited institution 64 semester hours maximum transfer credit; from 4-year accredited institution 90 semester hours.

Degree Requirements: 122 credit hours; 2.0 GPA; last 32 hours in residence; 2 hours physical education; general education requirements; demonstrated proficiency in English; demonstrated competence in mathematics.

Grading system: A–F; P; withdraw.

Distinctive Educational Programs: Honors College; joint degree engineering program with the University of North Carolina, Charlotte; Banking and Finance Center; Minority Biomedical Research Support Program; Minority Access to Research Careers Program; cooperative pharmacy program with Howard University; Transfer Articulation Program with Central Piedmont Community College. Study abroad in Australia, Japan, Morocco, Russia.

ROTC: Air Force, Army in cooperation with UNC-Charlotte.

Degrees Conferred: 213 *baccalaureate*. Bachelor's degrees awarded in top five disciplines: computer and information sciences 43; business/marketing 39; communications/journalism 38; liberal arts/general studies 21; interdisciplinary studies 16.

Fees and Other Expenses: *Full-time tuition per academic year 2008–09:* $15,754. *Required fees:* $2,279. *Room and board per academic year:* $6,132. *Books and supplies:* $1,500. *Other expenses:* $2,000.

Financial Aid: Aid from institutionally generated funds is provided on the basis of academic merit, financial need, athletic ability.

Financial aid to full-time, first-time undergraduate students: 81% received some form of aid. Average amount of aid received: federal grants $3,758; Pell grants $3,150; other federal aid $1,501; state/local grants $2,902; institutional grants $6,945.

Departments and Teaching Staff: *Total instructional faculty:* 132 (full-time 105, part-time 27). 78% of faculty hold the doctorate, first-professional, or other terminal degree. Student/faculty ratio: 13:1.

Enrollment: Total enrollment 1,571 (undergraduate). Transfer-in students 50.

Characteristics of Student Body: *Ethnic/racial makeup:* number of Black non-Hispanic: 1,470. *Age distribution:* number under 18: 44; 18–19: 603; 20–21: 470; 22–24: 191; 25–29: 29; 30–34: 8; 35–39: 8; unknown: 132.

Student Life: On-campus housing available. In addition to the Student Government, there are over 60 registered student organizations and clubs. *Student publications, radio: The Bull*, a yearbook; *The University Student*, a newspaper. Radio station WJCS. *Surrounding community:* Charlotte metropolitan area population 650,000.

Library Collections: 101,000 volumes. 42,430 microforms; 1,995 audiovisual materials; Current serial subscriptions: paper 222; microform 144; via electronic access 14. Online catalog. Students have access to online information retrieval services and the Internet.

Most important special holdings include Earl A. Johnson Collection (Black studies and Judaica and art); Calvin Hoover Collection (history and governmental biography).

Buildings and Grounds: Campus area 105 acres.

Chief Executive Officer: Dr. Dorothy Cowser Yancy, President.

Address admission inquiries to Jeffrey A. Smith, Director of Admissions.

Lees-McRae College

275 College Drive
Banner Elk, North Carolina 28604-0128
Tel: (828) 898-5241 **E-mail:** admissions@lmc.edu
Fax: (828) 898-8814 **Internet:** www.lmc.edu

Institution Description: Lees-McRae College is a private, coeducational, independent nonprofit college affiliated with the Presbyterian Church (U.S.A.). *Enrollment:* 889, *Degrees awarded:* Baccalaureate.

Accreditation: *Regional:* SACS-Comm. on Coll. *Professional*; teacher education

History: Established 1900 as a school for girls; chartered by the state in 1907 as Lees-McRae Institute; 1927 became coeducational; became Lees-McRae College in 1931 (junior college); approved as a senior college in 1988.

Institutional Structure: *Governing board:* Lees-McRae College Board of Trustees. *Composition of institution:* Administrators: 22. Full-time instructional faculty 45. Academic Affairs headed by Provost/Dean of the College. Management/Business directed by Vice President for Institutional Advancement/Business Affairs.

Calendar: Semesters. Academic year Aug. to May. Freshmen admitted Aug., Jan. Degrees conferred May, July, Aug., Dec. Formal commencement May. Summer session of 2 terms from early June to early Aug.

Characteristics of Freshmen: 806 applicants. 75.8% of applicants admitted. 39.6% of admitted students enrolled full-time.

76% (190 students) submitted SAT scores; 59.6% of admitted students enrolled full-time. *25th percentile*: SAT Critical Reading 410, SAT I Math 450; ACT Composite 18, ACT English 17; ACT Math 17. *75th percentile*: SAT Critical Reading 550, SAT math 540; ACT Composite 24, ACT English 23, ACT Math 21.

61% of freshmen from North Carolina. Freshmen from 30 states and 15 foreign countries.

Admission: Rolling admissions plan. For fall acceptance apply as early as Aug. of previous year, but not later than Aug. 1 of year of enrollment. Early acceptance available. *Requirements:* Graduation from an accredited high school is required. A GED certificate will be considered. A "certificate of attendance" is not acceptable in considering an individual for acceptance. An applicant must submit certification of high school graduation. This must be noted on the high school transcript. The high school curriculum should consist of 4 units English,

LEES-MCRAE COLLEGE—*cont'd*

2 algebra, 1 U.S. history, 1 biology, as well as other units which meet requirements for high school graduation. *Entrance tests:* College Board SAT or ACT composite. Minimum GPA 2.00 and SAT combined score 930 or ACT score of 19. If a student falls below the requirements listed for unconditional acceptance, he may be accepted if he shows promise for success as a college student. *For transfer students:* Suggested 2.0 GPA on work completed prior to entering Lees-McRae; student must be eligible to return to previous college attended. *Transfer credit:* From 4-year accredited institution 96 semester hours maximum; from 2-year accredited institution 68 semester hours maximum.

College credit and advanced placement for postsecondary-level work are considered for transfer, extra-institutional learning (life experience). Tutoring available.

Degree Requirements: *For all associate degrees:* 66 semester hours credit; 2.00 overall GPA, including last 12 hours in residence. *For all baccalaureate degrees:* 124 semester hours credit; overall 2.00 GPA, the last 30 hours earned at Lees-McRae.

Grading system: A–F; withdraw (W). Incomplete grades noted with the F grade until the work has been completed.

Distinctive Educational Programs: The Teacher Education Program promotes positive mentoring and a sound course of study for each certification program. Committed to a mentoring model, as a viable educational concept, the faculty serves as model teachers, counsel wisely, and devote many hours to advising education students about their course work and their progress as growing professionals. The Study Abroad Program consists of Lees-McRae belonging to the Cooperative Center for Study in Great Britain (CCSB). CCSB is a consortium of colleges under the central directorship of the University of Kentucky. CCSB provides students the opportunity to take classes in London or Ireland during the summer or during January and to receive academic credit for these classes.

ROTC: Army offered in conjunction with Appalachia State University.

Degrees Conferred: 134 *baccalaureate*. Bachelor's degrees awarded in top five disciplines: education 58; health professions and related clinical sciences 26; business, management, marketing, and related support services 17; social sciences 13; communication, journalism, and related programs 7.

Fees and Other Expenses: *Full-time tuition per academic year 2008–09:* contact the college for current information.

Financial Aid: Aid from institutionally generated funds is provided on the basis of academic merit, financial need, athletic ability. Institution has a Program Participation Agreement with the U.S. Department of Education for eligible students to receive Pell Grants and, depending upon the agreement, other federal aid.

Financial aid to full-time, first-time undergraduate students: 97% received some form of financial aid. Average amount of aid received: federal grants $3,165, state/local grants 3,065; institutional grants $8,200; loans $4,213.

Departments and Teaching Staff: *Total instructional faculty:* 51. Student/faculty ratio: 12:1. Degrees held by full-time faculty: doctorate 63%, master's 37%. 77% hold terminal degrees.

Enrollment: Total enrollment 889.

Characteristics of Student Body: *Ethnic/racial makeup:* Black non-Hispanic: 5%; American Indian or Alaska Native: 1%; Asian or Pacific Islander:1%; Hispanic: 2%; White non-Hispanic: 56%; unknown: 32%.

International Students: 27 nonresident aliens enrolled fall 2008. Programs available to aid students whose native language is not English: English as a Second Language Program. Some financial aid designated for international students.

Student Life: Students are required to live on campus unless 21, junior, commuting from parents' home, married, veteran or have earned 60 semester hours of credit. 714 bed spaces available on campus. *Intercollegiate athletics:* male: basketball, cross-country, soccer, tennis, lacrosse, skiing, golf; females: soccer, cross-country, tennis, volleyball, softball, basketball, skiing. *Special regulations:* Cars permitted for all students; no alcohol allowed. *Special services:* Center for Academic Advancement (tutoring services), Computer Lab, Math Lab, Business Center, Health Services. *Student publications: Ontaroga,* a student yearbook. *Surrounding community:* Banner Elk 1,000; 2 major snow skiing resorts, located in the Blue Ridge Mountains of Western North Carolina.

Library Collections: 97,000 volumes. 257,000 microforms; 12,200 audiovisual materials; 345 current periodical subscriptions. Students have access to online information retrieval services and the Internet.

Most important holdings include Stirling Collection of Southern Appalachian History.

Buildings and Grounds: Campus area 400 acres.

Chief Executive Officer: Dr. David W. Bushman, President.

Address admission inquiries to Wendy Jackson, Registrar.

Lenoir-Rhyne College

625 7th Avenue N.E.
Hickory, North Carolina 28603
Tel: (828) 328-1741 **E-mail:** admissions@lrc.edu
Fax: (828) 328-7338 **Internet:** www.lrc.edu

Institution Description: Lenoir-Rhyne College is a private college affiliated with the North Carolina Synod of the Lutheran Church in America. *Enrollment:* 1,540. *Degrees awarded:* Baccalaureate, master's. Certificates also awarded.

Accreditation: *Regional:* SACS-Comm. on Coll. *Professional*: audiology, nursing, occupational therapy, teacher education

History: Established as Highland College and offered first instruction at postsecondary level 1891; chartered as Lenoir College and awarded first degree (baccalaureate) 1892; adopted present name 1923.

Institutional Structure: *Governing board:* Lenoir-Rhyne College Board of Trustees. Extrainstitutional representation: 29 trustees, bishop of North Carolina Synod; institutional representation: president of the college. 2 ex officio. 29 voting. *Composition of institution:* Administrators 11. Academic affairs headed by vice president and dean of academic affairs. Management/business/finances directed by vice president for administration and finance. Full-time instructional faculty 107. Academic governance body, Faculty Assembly, meets an average of 9 times per year.

Calendar: Semesters. Academic year Aug. to May. Freshmen admitted Aug., Jan., June. Degrees conferred and formal commencement May, Aug. Summer session of 2 terms from June to Aug.; Evening College offered in five 8-week sessions during the year.

Characteristics of Freshmen: 2,251 applicants (1,333 female, 918 male). 81% of applicants admitted. 19% of admitted students enrolled full-time.

98% (391 students) submitted SAT scores; 22% (76 students) submitted ACT scores. *25th percentile*: SAT Critical Reading 440, SAT Math 460; ACT Composite 15, ACT English 16, ACT Math 18. *75th percentile*: SAT Critical Reading 550, SAT Math 580; ACT Composite 23, ACT English 23, ACT math 25.

70% of freshmen from North Carolina. Freshmen from 29 states and 10 foreign countries.

Admission: Rolling admissions plan. For fall acceptance, apply as early as completion of junior year in secondary school, but not later than 2 weeks prior to commencement of classes. Early acceptance available. *Requirements:* Either graduation from accredited secondary school with 12-16 units which must include 4 English, 2 algebra, 1 geometry, 1 laboratory science, 1 history, and no more than 2 in vocational subjects; or GED. Additional requirements for nursing program. Lowest acceptable secondary school class standing 50th percentile. *Entrance tests:* College Board SAT or ACT composite. *For transfer students:* 2.0 minimum GPA; from 4-year accredited institution 96 semester hours maximum transfer credit; from 2-year accredited institution 64 semester hours.

College credit and advanced placement for postsecondary-level work completed in secondary school.

Tutoring available. Developmental/remedial courses offered in summer session and regular academic year; credit given.

Degree Requirements: 128 semester hours; 2.0 GPA; 2 years in residence; 1 physical education course; core curriculum requirements (53 semester hours).

Fulfillment of some degree requirements and exemption from some beginning courses possible by passing departmental examinations, College Board CLEP, AP. *Grading system:* A–F; pass-fail; withdraw (deadline after which pass-fail is appended to withdraw).

Distinctive Educational Programs: Internships. Flexible meeting places and schedules, including off-campus centers, evening classes. Accelerated degree programs. Dual-degree programs in engineering with Georgia Institute of Technology and North Carolina State University; in forestry or environmental management with Duke University. Cooperative baccalaureate in medical technology with approved hospitals. Cooperative physicians' assistant program with Wake Forest University; in prepharmacy with University of North Carolina at Chapel Hill. Preprofessional programs in law and medical science. Facilities for independent research, including honors programs, individual majors, tutorials. Independent study. International baccalaureate program. Study abroad in England (Harlaxton College, College Consortium for International Studies Program) and France. The Lutheran College Washington Semester. Academic support services for hearing-impaired students.

ROTC: Army in cooperation with Davidson College; Air Force in cooperation with Catawba Valley Community College and University of North Carolina.

Degrees Conferred: 284 *baccalaureate*; 36 *master's*. Bachelor's degrees awarded in top five disciplines: business, management, marketing, and related support services 64; health professions and related clinical sciences 46; social sciences 33; psychology 22; education 21.

Fees and Other Expenses: *Full-time tuition per academic year 2008–09* $23,070. graduate study charged per credit hour. *Books and supplies:* $1,100. *Room and board per academic year:* $6,150. *Other expenses:* $2,750.

Financial Aid: Aid from institutionally generated funds is provided on the basis of academic merit, financial need, athletic ability, other criteria. Institution has a Program Participation Agreement with the U.S. Department of Education for eligible students to receive Pell Grants and, depending upon the agreement, other federal aid.

Financial aid to full-time, first-time undergraduate students: 98% received some form of financial aid. Average amount of aid received: federal grants $3,671; state/local grants $2,513; institutional grants $6,877; loans $3,769.

Departments and Teaching Staff: *Total full-time instructional faculty:* 107. Student/faculty ratio: 12:1. Degrees held by full-time faculty: doctorate 70%, master's 28%, baccalaureate 1%. 73% hold terminal degrees.

Enrollment: Total enrollment 1,540. Undergraduate 1,381. Graduate 139. Undergraduate transfer-in students 307.

Characteristics of Student Body: *Ethnic/racial makeup* Black non-Hispanic: 8%; Asian or Pacific Islander: 2%; Hispanic: 1%; White non-Hispanic: 83%; unknown: 5%.

International Students: Programs available to aid students whose native language is not English: social, cultural. English as a Second Language Program. No financial aid specifically designated for international students.

Student Life: On-campus residence halls house 55% of student body. *Intercollegiate athletics:* male: baseball, basketball, cross-country, football, golf, soccer, tennis, track; female: basketball, cross-country, soccer, softball, tennis, volleyball. *Special regulations:* Registered cars permitted in designated areas. *Special services:* Learning Resources Center, medical services. *Student publications, radio:* A yearbook; *Lenoir-Rhynean*, a weekly newspaper; *Carnival*, a literary publication. Radio station WLRC broadcasts 40 hours per week. *Surrounding community:* Hickory population 28,000. Charlotte, 60 miles from campus, is nearest metropolitan area. Served by airport 5 miles from campus.

Publications: *Comm Talk*, (5 per year) a publication by the Department of Art/Theatre Arts/Communication; *Profile* (quarterly), an alumni publication.

Library Collections: 146,000 volumes. 463,000 microforms; 91,000 audiovisual materials; 5,400 current periodicals (including electronic access). Students have access to online information retrieval services and the Internet.

Most important special holdings include Martin Luther Works (Wiemar Edition); Quetzalcoate Collection; Lutherans in Catawba County.

Buildings and Grounds: Campus area 100 acres.

Chief Executive Officer: Dr. Wayne Powell, President.

Address admission inquiries to Kathy Hahn, Registrar.

Livingstone College

701 West Monroe Street
Salisbury, North Carolina 28144-5213
Tel: (704) 216-6000 **E-mail:** admissions@livingstone.edu
Fax: (704) 216-6217 **Internet:** www.livingstone.edu

Institution Description: Livingstone College is a private college affiliated with the African Methodist Episcopal Zion Church. *Enrollment:* 994. *Degrees awarded:* Baccalaureate, master's, first-professional.

Accreditation: *Regional:* SACS-Comm. on Coll. *Professional*: social work, teacher education

History: Established as Zion Wesley Institute and incorporated 1879; offered first instruction at postsecondary level 1880; chartered and changed name to Zion Wesley College 1885; awarded first degree (baccalaureate) and adopted present name 1887.

Institutional Structure: *Governing board:* Board of Trustees. Representation: 21 trustees (including 12 alumni; president of the college), 9 associate trustees, 1 faculty representative, 2 student representatives. 24 voting. *Composition of institution:* Administrators 8. Academic affairs headed by academic dean. Management/business/finances directed by business manager. Full-time instructional faculty 51. Academic governance body, College Faculty, meets an average of 12 times per year.

Calendar: Semesters. Academic year Aug. to May. Freshmen admitted Aug., Jan., June. Degrees conferred and formal commencement May. No summer session.

Characteristics of Freshmen: 1,979 applicants (1,071 female, 708 male). 57% of applicants accepted. 30% of accepted applicants enrolled full-time.

70% (238 students) submitted SAT scores; 16% (55 students) submitted ACT scores. *25th percentile*: SAT Critical Reading 320, SAT Math 310, SAT Writing 300; ACT Composite 13, ACT English 11, ACT Math 15. *75th percentile*: SAT Critical Reading 420, SAT math 420, SAT Writing 400; ACT Composite 16, ACT English 16, ACT Math 17.

26% of entering freshmen expected to graduate within 5 years. 55% of freshmen from North Carolina. Freshmen from 22 states and 7 foreign countries.

Admission: Rolling admissions plan. *Requirements:* Either graduation from accredited secondary school with 20 credits which must include 4 English, 2 math, 2 science, 2 social studies, 2 foreign language; or GED. *Entrance tests:* College Board SAT or ACT.

Advanced placement for postsecondary-level work completed in secondary school. Tutoring available. Remedial courses offered during and regular academic year; credit given.

Degree Requirements: 125 semester hours minimum; 2.5 GPA; general education requirements; minimum of 24 credit hours in major field and a maximum of 73 credit hours; last 30 hours in residence; complete 80 hours of community service. *Grading system:* A–F; withdraw (deadline after which pass-fail is appended to withdraw).

Distinctive Educational Programs: Work-experience programs and internships. Evening classes. Dual-degree program in engineering at North Carolina Agricultural and Technical College. Facilities and programs for independent research, including honors programs, individual majors, tutorials.

ROTC: Army in cooperation with UNC-Charlotte.

Degrees Conferred: 118 *baccalaureate:* biological/life sciences 9; business/marketing 32; computer and information sciences 19; education 4; English 1; history 4; mathematics 1; parks and recreation 9; philosophy and religious studies 5; physical sciences 1; psychology 9; public administration and social services 2; security and protective services 15; social sciences 13; visual and performing arts 5.

Fees and Other Expenses: *Full-time tuition per academic year 2008–09:* $12,174. *room and board per academic year:* $5,641. *Books and supplies:* $1,300. *Other expenses:* $2,000.

Financial Aid: The college offers a direct lending program. Aid from institutionally generated funds is provided on the basis of academic merit, athletic ability, financial need, other criteria.

Financial aid to full-time, first-time undergraduate students:

Departments and Teaching Staff: *Total instructional faculty:* 53 (full-time 52, part-time 1). 64% of faculty hold the doctorate, first-professional, or other terminal degree. Student/faculty ratio: 17:1.

Enrollment: Total enrollment 994 (undergraduate). Transfer-in students 63.

Characteristics of Student Body: *Ethnic/racial makeup:* number of Black non-Hispanic: 844; American Indian or Alaska Native: 2; Asian or Pacific Islander 2; Hispanic: 2; White non-Hispanic: 7; unknown 32. *Age distribution:* number under 18: 4; 18–19: 236;20–21: 294; 22–24: 239; 25–29: 62; 30–34: 9; 35–39: 7; 40–49: 16; 50–64: 28.

International Students: 10 nonresident aliens enrolled fall 2008. No programs available to aid students whose native language is not English. No financial aid specifically designated for international students.

Student Life: On-campus residence halls house 63% of student body. *Intercollegiate athletics:* male: basketball, football, golf, softball, wrestling; female: basketball, track. *Special services:* Learning Resources Center, medical services, campus transportation system. *Student publications, Arts Magazine*, an annual publication; *The Bear's Tale*, a literary magazine; *Living Stone*, a monthly publication; *Livingstonian*, a yearbook. *Surrounding community:* Salisbury population 27,800. Charlotte, 60 miles from campus, is nearest metropolitan area. Served by airport 50 miles from campus.

Library Collections: 80,500 volumes. 6,400 microforms; 1,600 audiovisual materials. Current periodical subscriptions: paper 15; via electronic access 120. Computer work stations available. Students have access to the Internet and online information retrieval services.

Most important holdings include Black studies collection.

Buildings and Grounds: Campus area 272 acres.

Chief Executive Officer: Dr. Jimmy R. Jenkins, Sr. President.

Address admission inquiries to Rolanda Burney, Associate Vice President for Enrollment Management.

Mars Hill College

100 Athletic Street
Mars Hill, North Carolina 28787
Tel: (828) 689-1201 **E-mail:** cholt@mhc.edu
Fax: (828) 689-1473 **Internet:** www.mhc.edu

Institution Description: Mars Hill College is a private college affiliated with the North Carolina Southern Baptist Convention. *Enrollment:* 1,245. *Degrees awarded:* Baccalaureate.

Member of Appalachian Consortium.

Accreditation: *Regional:* SACS-Comm. on Coll. *Professional*: music, social work, teacher education, theatre

MARS HILL COLLEGE—*cont'd*

History: Established as French Broad Baptist Institute 1856; adopted present name and chartered 1859; became junior college and offered first instruction at postsecondary level 1921; awarded first degree (associate) 1922; added baccalaureate program 1963. *See* John Angus McLeod, *From These Stones* (Mars Hill: Mars Hill College, 1968) for further information.

Institutional Structure: *Governing board:* Board of Trustees. Extrainstitutional representation: 36 trustees. All voting. *Composition of institution:* Administrators 18. Academic affairs headed by vice president for academic affairs. Management/business/finances directed by vice president. Full-time instructional faculty 80. Academic governance body, the faculty, meets an average of 10 times per year.

Calendar: Semesters. Academic year Aug. to May. Freshmen admitted Aug., Jan., July. Degrees conferred and formal commencement May. Summer session of 2 terms from early June to early Aug.

Characteristics of Freshmen: 1,523 applicants (762 female, 761 male). 69% of applicants admitted. 30% of applicants admitted and enrolled full-time.

77% (289 students) submitted SAT scores. *25th percentile*: SAT Critical Reading 410, SAT Math 420. *75th percentile*: SAT Critical Reading 530, SAT Math 550.

37% of entering freshmen expected to graduate within 5 years. 60% of freshmen from North Carolina. Freshmen from 19 states and 21 foreign countries.

Admission: Rolling admissions plan. For fall acceptance, apply no later than Aug. of year of enrollment. Early acceptance available. *Requirements:* Either graduation from accredited secondary school with 18 units which normally include 4 English, 3 mathematics (including algebra), 2 history, 2 natural science; or GED. Minimum 2.0 GPA. Lowest acceptable secondary school class standing 20th percentile. *Entrance tests:* College Board SAT or ACT composite. *For transfer students:* From 4-year accredited institution hours maximum transfer credit limited only by residence requirement; from 2-year accredited institution 68 hours maximum toward 128 graduation minimum.

College credit and advanced placement for postsecondary-level work completed in secondary school and for extrainstitutional learning (life experience) on basis of portfolio and faculty assessments, personal interview.

Tutoring available. Developmental courses offered in during regular academic year; credit given.

Degree Requirements: *For all baccalaureate degrees:* 128 credit hours; last 2 semesters in residence; 3 hours physical education; general education requirements.

Fulfillment of some degree requirements and exemption from some beginning courses possible by passing departmental examinations, College Board CLEP, APP. *Grading system:* A–F; pass-fail; withdraw (carries time limit); incomplete (carries time limit).

Distinctive Educational Programs: Internships. Flexible meeting places and schedules, including off-campus centers (at Brevard, Hendersonville, Marion, all within 50 miles of main institution) and evening classes. Accelerated degree programs. Facilities and programs for independent research, including individual majors, independent study, directed reading, experimental education (tutoring, student teaching, social work practicums). Institutionally sponsored study abroad in Great Britain, Honduras, Israel, Mexico. *Other distinctive programs:* Continuing education.

Degrees Conferred: 214 *baccalaureate:* biological/life sciences 3; business/marketing 43; computer and information sciences 6; education 56; English 8; foreign languages 3; health professions and related sciences 3; history 5; mathematics 4; parks and recreation 7; philosophy/religious studies 4; physical sciences 2; psychology 16; public administration and social services 12; social sciences 15; visual and performing arts 21.

Fees and Other Expenses: *Full-time tuition per academic year 2008–09:* $19,894. *Required fees:* $1,706. *Room and board per academic year:* $7,250. *Books and supplies:* $1,250. *Other expenses:* $1,900.

Financial Aid: Aid from institutionally generated funds is provided on the basis of academic merit, financial need, athletic ability, other criteria. Institution has a Program Participation Agreement with the U.S. Department of Education for eligible students to receive Pell Grants and, depending upon the agreement, other federal aid.

Financial aid to full-time, first-time undergraduate students: 93% received some form of aid. Average amount of aid received: federal grants $3,518; Pell grants $2,858; other federal aid $829; state/local grants $4,125; institutional grants $8,209.

Departments and Teaching Staff: *Total instructional faculty:* 83 (full-time 80, part-time 3). 65% of faculty hold the doctorate, first-professional, or other terminal degree. Student/faculty ratio: 12:1.

Enrollment: Total enrollment 1,245 (undergraduate). Transfer-in students 106.

Characteristics of Student Body: *Ethnic/racial makeup:* number of Black non-Hispanic: 174; American Indian or Alaska Native: 8; Asian or Pacific Islander: 11; Hispanic: 20; White non-Hispanic: 993; unknown: 10. *Age distribution:* number under 18: 7; 18–19: 400; 20–21: 389; 22–24: 178; 25–29: 66; 30–34: 51; 35–39: 58; 40–49: 70; 50–64: 30; 65 and over: 1.

International Students: 34 nonresident aliens enrolled fall 2008. Students from Europe, Asia, Latin America, Africa, Canada. Programs available to aid students whose native language is not English: English as a Second Language Program. No financial aid specifically designated for international students.

Student Life: On-campus residence halls house 63% of student body. Residence halls for males constitute 50% of such space, for females 50%. 50% of married students request institutional housing; 2% are so housed. *Intercollegiate athletics:* male: baseball, basketball, football, lacrosse, tennis, track; female: basketball, softball, swimming, tennis, volleyball. *Special regulations:* Cars permitted without restrictions. Quiet hours from 7pm to 7am. *Special services:* Learning Resources Center, medical services, transportation to and from airport and bus station. *Student publications, radio: Cadenza*, an annual literary magazine; *The Hilltop*, a biweekly newspaper; *Laurel*, a yearbook. Radio station WVMH broadcasts 126 hours per week. *Surrounding community:* Mars Hill population 2,500. Atlanta (GA), 200 miles from campus, is nearest metropolitan area. Served by airport 30 miles from campus; passenger rail service 80 miles from campus.

Library Collections: 98,000 volumes. 76,500 microforms; 6,200 audiovisual materials; 650 current periodical subscriptions. Students have access to online information retrieval services and the Internet.

Most important special holdings include Bascomb Lamar Lundsford Folk Music collection (scrapbooks, pictures, sound recordings, memorabilia); Long Collection of Baptist Records (including association minutes, church histories, college archives); Robert L. Moore collection (including papers of this former Mars Hill president and Baptist minister).

Buildings and Grounds: Campus area 180 acres.

Chief Executive Officer: Dr. Dan Lansford, President.

Address admission inquiries to Robert McLendon, Vice President for Admissions and Enrollment.

Meredith College

3800 Hillsborough Street
Raleigh, North Carolina 27607-5298
Tel: (919) 760-8600 **E-mail:** admissions@meredith.edu
Fax: (919) 760-2828 **Internet:** www.meredith.edu

Institution Description: Meredith College is a private college affiliated with the North Carolina Baptist State Convention. *Enrollment:* 2,250. Men enrolled in other colleges that participate in the Cooperating Raleigh Colleges Consortium may take classes on Meredith's campus. *Degrees awarded:* Baccalaureate, master's. Postbaccalaureate certificate also awarded.

Member of the Cooperating Raleigh Colleges Consortium.

Accreditation: *Regional:* SACS-Comm. on Coll. *Professional*: dietetics, interior design, music, social work, teacher education

History: Established 1889; chartered as Baptist Female University 1891; offered first instruction at postsecondary level 1899; awarded first degree 1902; changed name to Baptist University for Women 1905; adopted present name 1909.

Institutional Structure: *Governing board:* Board of Trustees. Representation: 36 trustees. All voting. *Composition of institution:* Administrators with faculty status 33. Academic Division headed by senior vice president and vice president for academic affairs. Seventeen academic departments housed in six schools that are headed by deans. Full-time instructional faculty 131. Academic Council, Faculty Affairs Committee, Faculty of the Whole meets an average of 5 times per year.

Calendar: Semesters. Academic year Aug. to May. Freshmen admitted Aug., Jan., May. Degrees conferred and formal commencements May, Aug., Dec. Summer session of 3 terms from early May to late July.

Characteristics of Freshmen: 1,557 applicants (female 1,557). 69% of applicants admitted. 37% of applicants admitted and enrolled full-time.

95% (379 students) submitted SAT scores; 25% (100 students) submitted ACT scores. *25th percentile*: SAT Critical Reading 470, SAT Math 470; ACT Composite 19, ACT English 19, ACT Math 18. *75th percentile*: SAT Critical Reading 560, SAT Math 570; ACT Composite 24, ACT English 24, ACT Math 24.

66% of entering freshmen expected to graduate within 5 years. 80% of freshmen from North Carolina. Freshmen from 31 states and 15 foreign countries.

Admission: Rolling admissions plan beginning Nov. 1. Recommended deadline Feb. 15. Early decision available with Oct. 1 deadline and Oct. 15 notification. *Requirements:* Graduation from accredited secondary school with 16 units which must include 4 English, 2 foreign language, 3 mathematics, 3 history/social studies, 3 science, 1 elective. GED acceptable for 23+ Program candidates and some transfer students. Class rank expected to be top half of class. Minimum

2.0 GPA. *Entrance tests:* College Board SAT I or ACT composite. For foreign students TOEFL. *For transfer students:* 2.0 minimum GPA; if less than 30 transferable hours of credit, student must also meet freshman admission requirements.

College credit and advanced placement for postsecondary-level work completed in secondary school based on AP, CLEP, IB, and Commonwealth Advanced Level examinations.

Noncredit review courses in English composition and mathematics offered in regular academic year. Tutor available in writing center.

Degree Requirements: *For all baccalaureate degrees:* 124 hours; 2.0 GPA; general education requirements; at least 58 hours must be earned in a 4-year college setting; at least 31 credit hours must be completed at Meredith.

Grading system: A–F; pass-fail; withdraw (deadline after which pass-fail is appended to withdraw); descriptive reports.

Distinctive Educational Programs: Honors Program; North Carolina Teaching Fellows Program. Dual-degree programs in engineering with North Carolina State University at Raleigh. Exchange agreements with Universitas Nebrissensis (Madrid, Spain), Universite Catholique de l'Ouest (Angers, France), Dongebi University (People's Republic of China). Summer abroad program in England, Italy, and the Czech Republic. Facilities and programs for independent research and contractual majors. Double majors; student-designed majors, minors; independent study; accelerated study; dual enrollment. Civic engagement through Service Learning and Volunteer Programs; Center for Women in the Arta.

ROTC: Army, Air Force in cooperation with North Carolina State University.

Degrees Conferred: 349 *baccalaureate*; 37 *master's*; 80 *doctorate*. Bachelors degrees awarded: area and ethnic studies 1; biological/life sciences 7; business/marketing 109; communications/communication technologies 24; computer and information sciences 7; education 6; English 17; foreign languages and literature 9; health professions and related sciences 28; home economics and vocational home economics 27; interdisciplinary studies 6; mathematics 7; parks and recreation 5; philosophy/religion/theology 4; physical sciences 3; protective services/public administration 10; psychology 43; social sciences and history 37; visual and performing arts 77. Master's degrees awarded: business/marketing 29; education 5; home economics 2; visual and performing arts 2.

Fees and Other Expenses: *Full-time tuition per academic year 2008–09:* \$23,550 undergraduate; graduate tuition charged per credit hour (contact the college for the current rate). *Required fees:* \$50. *Room and board per academic year:* \$6,740. *Books and supplies:* \$750. *Other expenses:* \$1,800.

Financial Aid: Aid from institutionally generated funds is provided on the basis of academic merit, financial need, other criteria.

Financial aid to full-time, first-time undergraduate students: 99% received some form of financial aid. Average amount of aid received: federal grants \$3,588; Pell grants \$2,644; other federal aid \$1,035; state/local grants \$3,789; institutional grants \$6,408.

Departments and Teaching Staff: *Total instructional faculty:* 262 (full-time 128, part-time 134). Student/faculty ratio: 10:1. Degrees held by full-time faculty: master's 20%, doctorate 78%. 79% hold terminal degrees.

Enrollment: Total enrollment 2,250. Undergraduate 2,001. Graduate 249. Undergraduate transfer-in students 93.

Characteristics of Student Body: *Ethnic/racial makeup:* number of Black non-Hispanic: 190; American Indian or Alaska Native: 7; Asian or Pacific Islander: 33; Hispanic: 45; White non-Hispanic: 1,623; unknown: 87. *Age distribution:* number under 18: 57; 18–19: 658; 20–21: 698; 22–24: 220; 25–29: 166; 30–34: 87; 35–39: 72; 40–49: 32; 50–64: 21; 65 and over: 1; unknown 2. 27% of student body attend summer sessions.

International Students: 20 nonresident aliens enrolled fall 2008. Students from Europe, Asia, Central and South America, Africa. Programs available to aid students whose native language is not English: social, cultural. Financial aid specifically designated for qualifying international students: variable number of scholarships available annually.

Student Life: On-campus residence halls house 46% of student body and over 90% of entering freshmen. All buildings are non-smoking. Alcohol and illegal drugs are not permitted on campus. *Intercollegiate athletics:* female: basketball, fast-pitch softball, soccer, tennis, volleyball. *Special regulations:* Male guests may visit residence hall lounges only except during six open house weekends each semester. *Special services:* Health Center; Counseling Center; Campus Minister; Learning Center. *Student publications: The Meredith Herald,* a weekly newspaper; *The Colton Review*, a literary magazine published once a year; *Oak Leaves*, a yearbook. *Surrounding community:* Raleigh population 260,000 . Served by mass transit bus system, airport 8 miles from campus.

Library Collections: 186,000 volumes including bound books, serial backfiles, electronic documents, and government documents not in separate collections. Online catalog. Current serial subscriptions: 669 paper, 61 microform, 4,877 electronic. 12,947 recordings. 30 computer work stations. Students have access to the Internet at no charge.

Most important holdings include Women's Studies Collection; Meredith College History; Clyde Edgerton Collection.

Buildings and Grounds: Campus area 225 acres.

Chief Executive Officer: Dr. Maureen A. Hartford, President.

Undergraduates address admission inquiries to Heidi L. Fletcher, Director of Admissions; graduate inquiries to Director of Graduate Studies.

Methodist University

5400 Ramsey Street
Fayetteville, North Carolina 28311-1420
Tel: (910) 630-7000 **E-mail:** admissions@methodist.edu
Fax: (910) 630-7285 **Internet:** www.methodist.edu

Institution Description: Methodist University, formerly Methodist College, is a private college affiliated with the United Methodist Church. *Enrollment:* 2,190. *Degrees awarded:* Associate, baccalaureate, master's.

Member of North Carolina Southeastern Consortium for International Education.

Accreditation: *Regional:* SACS-Comm. on Coll.

History: Established and chartered 1956; offered first instruction at postsecondary level 1960; awarded first degree (baccalaureate) 1964; achieved university status 2006.

Institutional Structure: *Governing board:* Methodist University Board of Trustees. Representation: 35 voting members. *Composition of institution:* Administrators 40. Academic affairs headed by Vice President for Academic Affairs and Dean of the College. Management/business/finances directed by Vice President for Business Affairs. Full-time instructional faculty 101. Academic governance body, the faculty, meets an average of 10 times per year.

Calendar: Semesters. Academic year Aug. to May. Interim term in Jan. Freshmen admitted Aug., Jan., May. Degrees conferred and formal commencements May, Aug., Dec. Summer term May to Aug. Evening college consists of 5 8-week terms from Aug. to July.

Characteristics of Freshmen: 2,484 applicants (876 female, 1,608 male). 73% of applicants admitted. 24% of admitted students enrolled full-time.

75% (319 students) submitted SAT scores; 32% (136 students) submitted ACT scores. *25th percentile*: SAT Critical Reading 430, SAT Math 450, SAT Writing 460; ACT Composite 18, ACT English 15, ACT Math 17. *75th percentile*: SAT Critical Reading 530, SAT Math 570, SAT Writing 520; ACT Composite 23, ACT English 22, ACT Math 24.

30% of entering freshmen expected to graduate within 5 years. 58% of freshmen from North Carolina. Freshmen from 44 states and 32 foreign countries.

Admission: Rolling admissions plan. For fall acceptance, apply as early as Sept. 1 of previous year, but not later than Aug. 29 of year of enrollment. Early acceptance available. *Requirements:* Either graduation from accredited secondary school with 18 units which must include 4 English, 2 mathematics, 2 history, 2 science; or GED. Minimum 2.0 GPA. *Entrance tests:* College Board SAT or ACT composite. For foreign students TOEFL. *For transfer students:* 2.0 minimum GPA; from 4-year accredited institution 98 hours maximum transfer credit; from 2-year accredited institution 64 hours; correspondence/extension students 64 hours.

College credit and advanced placement for postsecondary-level work completed in secondary school.

Tutoring available. Noncredit developmental courses offered in summer session and regular academic year.

Degree Requirements: *For all associate degrees:* minimum 62 to 64 semester hours; 15 semester hours in residence. *For all baccalaureate degrees:* 124 semester hours; minimum 30 semester hours in residence, of which 24 hours must be at the upper-level (300/400 level courses). Additionally, 50% of major must be taken in residency at upper level. Must have 12 semester hours at upper level (300/400 level courses) outside of major area. (Not required in residency). *For all undergraduate degrees:* 2.0 GPA; 2 semester hours physical education; general education requirements.

Fulfillment of some degree requirements and exemption from some beginning courses possible by passing College Board CLEP, AP. *Grading system:* A–F; pass-fail; withdraw (deadline after which pass-fail is appended to withdraw); descriptive reports.

Distinctive Educational Programs: Flexible schedules to include day, evening, interim, and summer semesters or terms. Professional Golf Management and Professional Tennis Management programs. Honors program. Bachelor of Applied Science Program. Mentor Program. Dual-degree programs in engineering with North Carolina State University at Raleigh, NC (pending reaffiliation) and Georgia Institute of Technology. All entering students must take English Placement Examination. Study abroad in England, France.

ROTC: Army in cooperation with Campbell University.

Degrees Conferred: 15 *associate*; 324 *baccalaureate*; 48 *master's*. Bachelor's degrees awarded in to five disciplines: business, management, marketing, and related support services 110; social sciences 25; parks and recreation 20; biomedical/biological sciences 16; education 15.

METHODIST UNIVERSITY—*cont'd*

Fees and Other Expenses: *Full-time tuition per academic year 2008–09:* $21,520. *Books and supplies:* $1,200. *Room and board per academic year:* $7,990; *Other expenses:* %6,625.

Financial Aid: Aid from institutionally generated funds is provided on the basis of academic merit, financial need. Institution has a Program Participation Agreement with the U.S. Department of Education for eligible students to receive Pell Grants and, depending upon the agreement, other federal aid.

Financial aid to full-time, first-time undergraduate students: 98% received some form of financial aid. Average amount of aid received: federal grants $4,461; Pell grants $2,881; other federal aid $2,065; state/local grants $3,832; institutional grants $7,689.

Departments and Teaching Staff: *Total instructional faculty:* 118. Student/faculty ratio: 16:1. Degrees held by full-time faculty: doctorate 50%, master's 100%. 50% hold terminal degrees.

Enrollment: Total enrollment 2,190. Undergraduate 2,032. Graduate 158. Undergraduate transfer-in students 208.

Characteristics of Student Body: *Ethnic racial makeup:* Hispanic 6%; Black non-Hispanic 18%; 76% White non-Hispanic.

International Students: 85 nonresident aliens enrolled fall 2008. Students from Europe, Asia, Central and South America, Canada. Programs available to aid students whose native language is not English: social, cultural. English as a Second Language Program. No financial aid specifically designated for international students.

Student Life: On-campus residence halls house 50% of student body. Dormitories for males constitute 65% of such space, for females 35%. Housing available for married students. *Intercollegiate athletics:* male: baseball, football, basketball, cross-country, golf, soccer, track, tennis; female: basketball, softball, tennis, soccer, volleyball. *Special regulations:* Registered cars with decals permitted. Quiet hours. *Special services:* Learning Resources Center, medical services and Mentor Program. *Student publications: Carillon*, a yearbook, *Small Talk*, a biweekly newspaper; *Tapestry*, an annual literary magazine. *Surrounding community:* Fayetteville population 76,000. Raleigh/Durham, 60 miles from campus, is nearest metropolitan area served by mass transit bus system; airport 15 miles from campus; passenger rail service 7 miles from campus.

Library Collections: 182,000 volumes. 58,000 microforms; 590 current periodical subscriptions. 13,500 audiovisual materials. Access to online information retrieval services and the Internet.

Most important special collections include Marquis de Lafayette Collection; Allen Lee Bible Collection; North Carolina Collection.

Buildings and Grounds: Campus area 600 acres.

Chief Executive Officer: Dr. M. Elton Hendricks, President.

Address admission inquiries to James Legg, Director of Admissions.

Montreat College

310 Gaither Circle
Montreat, North Carolina 28757-1267
Tel: (828) 669-8011 **E-mail:** admissions@montreat.edu
Fax: (828) 669-0120 **Internet:** www.montreat.edu

Institution Description: Montreat College, formerly known as Montreat-Anderson College, is a private, 4-year liberal arts college affiliated with the Presbyterian Church (U.S.A.). *Enrollment:* 1,113. *Degrees awarded:* Associate, baccalaureate, master's.

Accreditation: *Regional:* SACS-Comm. on Coll.

History: Established as Montreat Normal School in 1916. Became a junior college in 1933; from 1945 to 1959 was a 4-year college for women. In 1959 the institution was renamed Montreat-Anderson College. Baccalaureate degrees were again offered beginning in 1986. In 1955 the institution name was changed back to Montreat College. Graduate degrees were first offered beginning 1996.

Institutional Structure: *Governing board:* Montreat-Anderson College Board of Trustees. Extrainstitutional representation: 34 trustees. *Composition of institution:* President. Academic affairs headed by Vice President/Dean of the college. Business affairs handled by Business Manager/Treasurer. Full-time instructional faculty 32.

Calendar: Semesters. Academic year Aug. to May. Freshmen admitted Aug., Jan. Degrees conferred May, Dec. Formal commencement May.

Characteristics of Freshmen: 425 applicants (240 female, 183 male). 61% of applicants admitted. 49% of admitted students enrolled full-time.

71% (186 students) submitted SAT scores. *25th percentile*: SAT Critical Reading 440, SAT Math 430, SAT Writing 420; ACT Composite 18. *75th percentile*: SAT Critical Reading 550, SAT Math 560, SAT Writing 540; ACT Composite 24.

79% of freshmen from North Carolina. Freshmen from 21 states and 12 foreign countries.

Degrees Conferred: 45 *associate;* 151 *baccalaureate*; 33 *master's*. Bachelor's degrees awarded in top five disciplines: business, management, marketing, and related support services 153; philosophy/religion 14; parks and recreation 13; education 9; public administration. Doctorates awarded: business/marketing 33.

Fees and Other Expenses: *Full-time tuition per academic year 2008–09:* $19,080. *Room and board per academic year:* $6,000. *Books and supplies:* $1,000. *Other expenses:* $3,300.

Financial Aid: Aid from institutionally generated funds is provided on the basis of academic merit, financial need, athletic ability. Institution has a Program Participation Agreement with the U.S. Department of Education for eligible students to receive Pell Grants and, depending upon the agreement, other federal aid.

Financial aid to full-time, first-time undergraduate students: 84% received some form of financial aid. Average amount of aid received: federal grants $3,390; Pell grants $2,522; other federal aid $910; state/local grants $3,651; institutional grants $6,691.

Departments and Teaching Staff: *Total instructional faculty:* 49. Student/faculty ratio: 12:1. Degrees held by full-time faculty: baccalaureate 100%, master's 43%, doctorate 57%. 67% hold terminal degrees.

Enrollment: Total enrollment 1,113. Undergraduate 943. Graduate 170. Undergraduate transfer-in students 47.

Characteristics of Student Body: *Ethnic/racial makeup:* Black non-Hispanic: 23%; American Indian or Alaska Native: 6%; Asian or Pacific Islander: 1%; Hispanic: 3%; White non-Hispanic: 62%; unknown: 4%.

International Students: 19 nonresident aliens enrolled fall 2008. Students from Europe, Asia, Central and South America, Africa. Programs available to aid students whose native language is not English: social, cultural, financial. English as a Second Language Program.

Student Life: On-campus housing in residence halls. *Intercollegiate athletics:* male and female: basketball, golf, soccer, tennis; male: baseball; female: volleyball, softball. *Special services:* Counseling, placement and health services provided. *Student publications:* Biweekly newspaper, college annual, literary magazine. *Surrounding community:* Montreat, a Presbyterian conference center. Asheville, 15 miles from campus, is nearest city and airport.

Library Collections: 79,200 volumes. 117,200 microforms; 3,300 audiovisual materials; 485 current periodical subscriptions. Online catalog. Students have access to online information retrieval services and the Internet.

Most important special holdings include Crosby Adams Music Collection; L. Nelson Bell Memorabilia.

Chief Executive Officer: Dr. Dan W. Struble, President.

Address admission inquiries to Anita F. Darby, Director of Admissions.

Mount Olive College

634 Henderson Street
Mount Olive, North Carolina 28365
Tel: (919) 658-2502 **E-mail:** admissions@moc.edu
Fax: (919) 658-7180 **Internet:** www.moc.edu

Institution Description: Mount Olive College is a private, coeducational, liberal arts college founded by the Original Free Will Baptist Church. *Enrollment:* 3,390. *Degrees awarded:* Associate, baccalaureate.

Accreditation: *Regional:* SACS.

History: The institution was chartered in 1951 and opened in 1952 at Cragmont Assembly as Mount Allen Junior College. In September 1953, the college was moved to Mount Olive. In 1956, the college name was changed to Mount Olive Junior College. In September 1970, the school's name was officially changed to Mount Olive College. The junior year was added in 1984 and the senior year in 1985. The college was officially accredited as a 4-year institution in 1986.

Institutional Structure: Board of Trustees, 30 members and 3 honorary members. Administrators 10. full-time faculty 40. Academic affairs headed by Academic Dean. Business/Finance directed by Vice President-Finance and Treasurer.

Calendar: Semesters. Academic year Aug. to May. Degrees conferred and formal commencement May. 2 summer sessions. Modular programs begin at different times throughout the year at 4 locations.

Characteristics of Freshmen: 617 applicants. 74% of applicants admitted. 55% of admitted students enrolled full-time.

61% (153 students) submitted SAT scores; 18% (31 students) submitted ACT scores. *25th percentile*: SAT Critical Reading 410, SAT Math 420, ACT Composite 15. *75th percentile*: SAT Critical Reading 540, SAT Math 530; ACT Composite 20.

23% of entering freshmen expected to graduate within 5 years. 59% of freshmen from North Carolina. Freshmen from 19 states and 4 foreign countries.

Admission: Rolling admissions plan. Early admissions available. *Requirements:* Completed application form with application fee, an official high school transcript, GED scores or State High School Equivalency Certificate or evidence of graduation from an accredited high school or equivalent thereof. SAT or ACT scores. TOEFL scores of 500 minimum if English is not the native language. *Transfer students:* Dean's Evaluation from the last college or institution attended, an official transcript from all colleges attended, and a financial aid transcript (if applicable).

Degree Requirements: *For all associate degrees:* Minimum of 64 semester hours with an overall cumulative grade point average of at least 2.00 on all studies at Mount Olive College and a minimum of 18 semester hours in residence. *For all baccalaureate degrees:* minimum of 126 semester hours with an overall cumulative grade point average of at least 2.00 on all studies at Mount Olive College and a minimum of 32 in residence.

Fulfillment of some degree requirements and exemption from some courses possible by passing College Board CLEP. *Grading system:* A–F, Withdraw Passing, Withdraw Failing, Incomplete (carries time limit).

Distinctive Educational Programs: Work experience programs, cooperative education programs, evening classes. Accelerated degree program. 2 on-campus computer labs. Tutoring services in math and English available. Internships available. Internships available for Recreation, Psychology, and Business programs.

Degrees Conferred: 206 *associate;* 627 . Bachelor's degrees awarded in top five disciplines: business, management, marketing, and related support services 343; security and protective services 66; computer and information sciences and support services 25; theology and ministerial studies 16; park, recreation, leisure, and fitness studies 11.

Fees and Other Expenses: *Full-time tuition per academic year 2008–09:* $13,776. *Books and supplies:* $1,240. *Room and board per academic year:* $5,540. *Other expenses:* $3,570.

Financial Aid: Aid from institutionally generated funds is provided on the basis of academic merit, financial need, athletic ability, other criteria.

Financial aid to full-time, first time undergraduate students: 100% received some form of financial aid. Average amount of aid received: federal grants $2,955, state/local grants $2,803; institutional grants $4,770; loans $4,341.

Departments and Teaching Staff: *Total instructional faculty:* 199 (full-time 66, part-time 133). 63% of faculty hold the doctorate, first-professional, or other terminal degree. Student/faculty ratio: 19:1.

Enrollment: Total enrollment 3,390 (undergraduate). Transfer-in students 496.

Characteristics of Student Body: *Ethnic/racial makeup:* number of Black non-Hispanic: 722; American Indian or Alaska Native: 7; Asian or Pacific Islander: 16; Hispanic: 56; White non-Hispanic: 1,540; unknown: 231.

International Students: No programs available to aid students whose native language is not English. No financial aid specifically designated for international students.

Student Life: On-campus housing available in residence halls and apartments. *Intercollegiate athletics:* male: basketball, baseball, cross country, soccer, tennis, golf; female: basketball, softball, soccer, tennis, cross-country, volleyball. *Special services:* Student Health Services, Career Planning and Placement. *Student publications:* Student newspaper. *Surrounding community:* Rural campus in a small town. Located 13 miles from Goldsboro.

Library Collections: 78,000 volumes including bound books, serial backfiles, electronic documents, and government documents not in separate collections. Online and card catalogs. Current serial subscriptions: 5,980 paper, 48,740 microform units; 3,276 electronic. 2,000 audiovisual materials. Computer work stations available. Students have access to the Internet at no charge.

Most important special holdings include the Free Will Baptist Historical Collection; language and literature; art and music.

Buildings and Grounds: Campus area 138 acres.

Chief Executive Officer: Dr. J. William Byrd, President.

Address admission inquiries to Timothy Woodard, Director of Admissions.

North Carolina Agricultural and Technical State University

1601 East Market Street
Greensboro, North Carolina 27411
Tel: (336) 334-7500 **E-mail:** admissions@ncat.edu
Fax: (336) 334-7082 **Internet:** www.ncat.edu

Institution Description: *Enrollment:* 10,388. *Degrees awarded:* Baccalaureate, master's.

Member of Greensboro Regional Consortium, Inc. Academic offerings subject to approval by statewide coordinating bodies.

Accreditation: *Regional:* SACS-Comm. on Coll. *Professional*: accounting, business, chemistry, engineering, industrial technology, nursing, social work, teacher education

History: Chartered 1890; established as A and M College for the Colored Race 1891; offered first instruction in Raleigh as annex of Shaw University 1890; moved to present location 1893; awarded first degree (baccalaureate) 1896; changed name to Agricultural and Technical College of North Carolina 1915; adopted present name 1967; became part of state system 1972. *See* Warmoth T. Gibbs, *History of the North Carolina Agricultural and Technical College* (Dubuque, Iowa: W.M.C. Brown Book Company, 1966) for further information.

Institutional Structure: *Governing board:* Board of Trustees. Representation: 13 trustees. All voting. *Composition of institution:* Administrators 24. Academic affairs headed by vice chancellor for academic affairs. Management/business/finances directed by vice chancellor for business and finance. Full-time instructional faculty 374. Academic governance body, University Senate, meets an average of 10 times per year.

Calendar: Semesters. Academic year Aug. to May. Freshmen admitted May, Aug., Jan. Degrees conferred and formal commencement May. Summer session of 2 terms from mid-May to early Aug.

Characteristics of Freshmen: 5,598 applicants (3,053 female, 2,545 male). 56% of applicants admitted. 51% of admitted students enrolled full-time.

93% (1m487 students) submitted SAT scores; 19% (299 students) submitted ACT scores. *25th percentile*: SAT Critical Reading 390, SAT Math 400, SAT Writing 380; ACT Composite 16, ACT English 14, ACT Math 16. *75th percentile*: SAT Critical Reading 480, SAT Math 500, SAT Writing 460; ACT Composite 21, ACT English 21, ACT Math 21.

82% of freshmen from North Carolina. Freshmen from 39 states and 25 foreign countries.

Admission: Rolling admissions plan. Early acceptance available. *Requirements:* For admission to all undergraduate programs, the applicant must present 16 units of high school credit in the following academic fields: 4 English (emphasizing grammar, composition and literature), 3 mathematics (including algebra I, algebra II, and geometry, or a higher level mathematics course for which algebra II is a prerequisite); 2 social studies (including 1 unit in U.S. history), 3 science (at least 1 unit in a life or biological science; at least 1 unit in physical science; at least 1 laboratory course). In addition, it is recommended that prospective students complete at least 2 units in 1 foreign language, and take 1 foreign language course unit and 1 mathematics course unit in the twelfth grade. Students who plan to major in engineering, mathematics, chemistry and physics must present an additional unit beyond algebra II, e.g., trigonometry, math analysis, etc. No more than 2 units in vocational subjects and 2 units in the disciplines of music and physical education. Some academic schools and majors in the College of Arts and Science have higher standards. *Entrance tests:* College Board SAT with a combined score of 750 or higher, or a cumulative GPA of B or better. *For transfer students:* 2.0 minimum GPA; from 4-year accredited institution 90 hours maximum transfer credit; from 2-year accredited institution 64 hours.

College credit and advanced placement for postsecondary-level work completed in secondary school. College credit for extrainstitutional learning on basis of faculty assessment. Tutoring available. Developmental/remedial courses offered in summer session and regular academic year.

Degree Requirements: 124 credit hours; 2.0 GPA; 3 semesters in residence; 2 semesters physical education; core requirements.

Fulfillment of some degree requirements and exemption from some beginning courses possible by passing College Board CLEP, AP. *Grading system:* A–F; withdraw.

Distinctive Educational Programs: Cooperative education. Weekend and evening classes. Special facilities for using telecommunications in the classroom. Facilities for independent research, including honors programs, individual majors, tutorials. Study abroad at University of Grenoble, France; Oxford Polytechnical, England; Cuauhnahuac: Instituto Colectivo Mexico. *Other distinctive programs:* Continuing education.

ROTC: Army, Air Force in cooperation with Elon College.

Degrees Conferred: 1,172 *baccalaureate*; 437 *master's*; 32 *doctorate*. Bachelor's degrees awarded in top five disciplines: engineering 161, business, management, marketing, and related support services 153; engineering technologies 93; visual and performing arts 68; health professions and related clinical sciences 65.

Fees and Other Expenses: *Full-time tuition per academic year 2008–09:* $4,040 resident, $12m482 nonresident; contact the university for current graduate tuition and fees. *Books and supplies:* $1,054. *Room and board per academic year:* $6,390. *Other expenses:* $2,800.

Financial Aid: Aid from institutionally generated funds is provided on the basis of academic merit, financial need, athletic ability. Institution has a Program Participation Agreement with the U.S. Department of Education for eligible stu-

NORTH CAROLINA AGRICULTURAL AND TECHNICAL STATE UNIVERSITY—*cont'd*

dents to receive Pell Grants and, depending upon the agreement, other federal aid.

Financial aid to full-time, first-time undergraduate students: 91% received some form of financial aid. Average amount of aid received: federal grants $4,092; Pell grants $3,279; other federal aid $963; state/local grants $2,907; institutional grants $1,776.

Departments and Teaching Staff: *Total instructional faculty:* 374. Student/faculty ratio: 14:1. Degrees held by full-time faculty: baccalaureate 6%, master's 36%, doctorate 58%. 61% hold terminal degrees.

Enrollment: Total enrollment 10,388. Undergraduate 8,829. Graduate 1,559. Undergraduate transfer-in students 265.

Characteristics of Student Body: *Ethnic/racial makeup (undergraduate):* Black non-Hispanic: 91%; Asian or Pacific Islander: 1%; Hispanic: 1%; White non-Hispanic: 4%; unknown 3%.

International Students: 52 nonresident aliens enrolled. Students from Asia, Central and South America, Africa. Programs available to aid students whose native language is not English: social, cultural. English as a Second Language Program. No financial aid specifically designated for international students.

Student Life: On-campus residence halls house 51% of student body. Residence halls for males constitute 54% of such space, for females 46%. *Intercollegiate athletics:* male: baseball, basketball, football, tennis, track; female: basketball, softball, tennis, track, volleyball. *Special regulations:* Cars permitted in designated parking areas. Residence hall visitation hours specified. *Special services:* Learning Resources Center, medical services. *Student publications, radio: The Register,* a biweekly newspaper. Radio station WNAA broadcasts 119 hours per week. *Surrounding community:* Greensboro population 156,000. Served by mass transit bus system; airport 12 miles from campus; passenger rail service 5 miles from campus.

Publications: *Undergraduate Bulletin.*

Library Collections: 507,000 volumes. 223,013 government documents; 1,400,000 microforms; 34,000 audiovisual materials; 5,500 periodicals (including electronic access). Online catalog. Students have access to online information retrieval services and the Internet.

Most important special collections include personal papers of North Carolina A&T State University presidents.

Buildings and Grounds: Campus area 798 acres.

Chief Executive Officer: Dr. Lloyd V. Mackley, Chancellor.

Address admission inquiries to John Smith, Director of Admissions.

North Carolina Central University

1801 Fayetteville Street
Durham, North Carolina 27707

Tel: (919) 560-6367 **E-mail:** admissions@nccu.edu
Fax: (919) 560-7973 **Internet:** www.nccu.edu

Institution Description: *Enrollment:* 8,035. *Degrees awarded:* Baccalaureate, first-professional (law), master's.

Accreditation: *Regional:* SACS-Comm. on Coll. *Professional*: law, librarianship, nursing, teacher education

History: Established and chartered as National Religious Training School and Chatauga, a private institution, 1909; offered first instruction at postsecondary level 1910; sold and reorganized as National Training School 1915; became state institution and changed name to Durham State Normal School 1923; changed name to North Carolina College for Negroes 1925; awarded first degree (baccalaureate) 1929; changed name to North Carolina College at Durham 1947; adopted present name 1969; became part of University of North Carolina System 1972. For further information, see: *A History of North Carolina College for Negroes* (Durham: Duke University Press, 1941).

Institutional Structure: *Governing board:* Board of Trustees of North Carolina Central University. Extrainstitutional representation: 12 trustees, including 4 alumni; institutional representation: 1 student. 1 ex officio. All voting. *Composition of institution:* Administrators 62. Academic affairs headed by vice chancellor for academic affairs. Management/business/finances directed by vice chancellor for financial affairs. Full-time instructional faculty 248. Academic governance body, Faculty Senate, meets an average of 11 times per year.

Calendar: Semesters. Academic year Aug. to May. Freshmen admitted Aug., Jan., May. Degrees conferred and formal commencement May. Summer session from late May to early Aug.

Characteristics of Freshmen: 3,513 applicants (2,154 female, 1,359 male). 74% of applicants admitted. 49% of admitted students enrolled full-time.

89% (1,120 students) submitted SAT scores; 18% (223 students) submitted ACT scores. *25th percentile*: SAT Critical Reading 370, SAT Math 370, SAT Writing 360; ACT Composite 14, ACT English 12, ACT Math 15. *75th percentile*: SAT Critical Reading 460, SAT Math 480, SAT Writing 450; ACT Composite 18, ACT English 17, ACT Math 18.

41% of entering freshmen expected to graduate within 5 years. 89% of freshmen from North Carolina. Freshmen from 40 states and 18 foreign countries.

Admission: Rolling admissions plan. *Requirements:* Either graduation from accredited secondary school with 16 units which must include 4 English, 2 in a foreign language, 2 mathematics (algebra and geometry), 1 social science; or GED. *Entrance tests:* College Board SAT or ACT composite. *For transfer students:* 2.0 minimum GPA.

College credit and advanced placement for postsecondary-level work completed in secondary school.

Tutoring available. Developmental/remedial courses offered in summer session and regular academic year; credit given.

Degree Requirements: *For all undergraduate degrees:* 124 credit hours; 2.0 GPA; one year or 36 weeks summer school in residence; 1 or 2 physical education courses; general education requirements.

Fulfillment of some degree requirements possible by passing departmental examinations, College Board CLEP. *Grading system:* A–F; withdraw (deadline after which pass-fail is appended to withdraw); incomplete; satisfactory progress.

Distinctive Educational Programs: Work-experience programs. Weekend and evening classes. Dual-degree programs in cooperation with Georgia Institute of Technology. Special facilities for using telecommunications in the classroom.Honors programs. Individual majors. RN to BSN in Wake, Vance, and Granville Counties. School of Education: communications disorders, visual impairment program through distance learning. Evening degree program offered by School of Law. *Other distinctive programs:* Continuing education.

ROTC: Air Force in cooperation with Duke University.

Degrees Conferred: 854 *baccalaureate*; 390 *master's*; 141 *first-professional*. Bachelor's degrees awarded in top five disciplines: business, management, marketing, and related support services 128; education 83; social sciences 65; security and protective services 61; health professions and related clinical sciences 57.

Fees and Other Expenses: *Full-time tuition per academic year 2008–09:* undergraduate resident $4,360, nonresident $4,104; contact the university for graduate and first-professional (law school) tuition. *Room and board per academic year:* $7,616. *Books and supplies:* $1,500. *Other expenses:* $2,310.

Financial Aid: Aid from institutionally generated funds is provided on the basis of academic merit, athletic ability. Institution has a Program Participation Agreement with the U.S. Department of Education for eligible students to receive Pell Grants and, depending upon the agreement, other federal aid.

Financial aid to full-time, first-time undergraduate students: 93% received some form of financial aid. Average amount of aid received: federal grants $4,642; Pell grants $3,417; other federal aid $1,553; state/local grants $2,431; institutional grants $1,773.

Departments and Teaching Staff: *Total instructional faculty:* 467. Student/faculty ratio: 13:1. Degrees held by full-time faculty: 75% hold terminal degrees.

Enrollment: Total enrollment 8,035. Undergraduate 5,978. Graduate 2057. Undergraduate transfer-in students 308.

Characteristics of Student Body: *Ethnic/racial makeup:* Black non-Hispanic: 85%; Asian or Pacific Islander: 1%; Hispanic: 2%; White non-Hispanic: 7%; unknown: 4%.

International Students: 30 nonresident aliens enrolled fall 2008. No programs available to aid students whose native language is not English. No financial aid specifically designated for international students.

Student Life: On-campus residence halls house 38% of student body. Residence halls for males constitute 22% of such space, for females 78%. Housing available for married students. *Intercollegiate athletics:* male: baseball, basketball, football, golf, tennis, track; female: baseball, basketball, tennis, volleyball; both sexes: bowling, swimming. *Special regulations:* Cars must have parking stickers. Visitation hours vary according to residence hall. *Special services:* Learning Resources Center, medical services. *Student publications*, weekly student newspaper; *Ex Umbra*, a bimonthly literary magazine. *Surrounding community:* Durham, population 178,000, is located in Raleigh-Durham, metropolitan area. Served by mass transit system; airport 10 miles from campus; passenger rail service 20 miles from campus.

Library Collections: 802,000 volumes including bound books, serial backfiles, electronic documents, government documents. Online and card catalogs. Current serial subscriptions: 6,290 paper and microform, 270 electronic. Computer work stations available. Students have access to the Internet and information retrieval services (fee-based).

Most important special collections include Martin Collection on Black History and Literature; Tucker Collection of Children's Books by Black Authors; McKissick Collection on Civil Rights.

Buildings and Grounds: Campus area 103 acres.

Chief Executive Officer: Dr. James H. Ammons, Chancellor.
Address admission inquiries to Jocelyn L. Foy, Director of Admissions.

College of Arts and Sciences

Degree Programs Offered: *Baccalaureate* in fine and applied arts, foreign languages, health professions; *master's* in physical sciences; *baccalaureate, master's* in biological sciences, education, home economics, letters, mathematics, psychology, public affairs and services, social sciences.

School of Business

Degree Programs Offered: *Baccalaureate, master's* in accounting, business education, economics and finance, and management and marketing.

School of Education

Degree Programs Offered: *Baccalaureate* in elementary education, middle grades education; *master's, doctorate* in curriculum and instruction, special education, counselor education, educational technology, communication disorders.

Admission: 2.5 overall GPA; 3.0 GPA in the undergraduate majors.

Degree Requirements: 33 to 48 credit hours.

School of Library Science

Degree Programs Offered: *Master's.*

Distinctive Educational Programs: Advanced students in the School of Arts and Sciences are admitted to library science program upon approval of the Dean.

School of Law

Degree Programs Offered: *First-professional.*

Admission: Baccalaureate from accredited college or university.

Degree Requirements: 88 credit hours, 2.0 GPA; 3 years in residence.

North Carolina School of the Arts

1533 South Main Street
Winston-Salem, North Carolina 27117-2738
Tel: (336) 770-3399 **E-mail:** admissions@ncarts.edu
Fax: (336) 770-3375 **Internet:** www.ncarts.edu

Institution Description: *Enrollment:* 879. *Degrees awarded:* Baccalaureate, master's. Diplomas also awarded.

Accreditation: *Regional:* SACS-Comm. on Coll.

History: Established 1963; chartered and offered first instruction at postsecondary level 1965; awarded first degree (baccalaureate) 1968; became part of the University of North Carolina system 1972.

Institutional Structure: *Governing board:* North Carolina School of the Arts Board of Trustees. Extrainstitutional representation: 12 trustees, 1 secretary, 1 conductor; institutional representation: 1 student. 4 ex officio. 12 voting. *Composition of institution:* Administrators 15. Academic affairs headed chief academic officer. Management/business/finances directed by vice chancellor for finance and administration. Full-time instructional faculty 129. Academic governance body, Faculty Council, meets an average of 9 times per year.

Calendar: Trimesters. Academic year Sept. to May. Freshmen admitted Sept., Jan., Mar. Degrees conferred May, Dec., Mar. Formal commencement May. Summer session of 1 term from June to July.

Characteristics of Freshmen: 682 applicants (female 347, male 335). 44% of applicants accepted. 47% of accepted applicants enrolled full-time.

78% (145 students) submitted SAT scores; 25% (47 students) submitted ACT scores. *25th percentile*: SAT Critical Reading 500, SAT Math 470, SAT Writing 470; ACT Composite 19, ACT English 18, ACT Math 17. *75th percentile*: Sat Critical Reading 620, SAT Math 610, SAT Writing 600; ACT Composite 27, ACT 27, ACT Math 25.

47% of entering freshmen expected to graduate within 4 years. 50 of freshmen from North Carolina. Freshmen from 44 states and 29 foreign countries.

Admission: Rolling admissions plan. Early acceptance available. *Requirements:* Either graduation from accredited secondary school or GED. Audition. *Entrance tests:* College Board SAT. *For transfer students:* 2.0 minimum GPA; from 4-year and 2-year accredited institutions maximum transfer credit limited only by residence requirement.

Advanced placement for postsecondary-level work completed in secondary school and for extrainstitutional learning (life experience) on basis of portfolio and faculty assessment.

Tutoring available. Noncredit developmental courses offered during academic year.

Degree Requirements: 155-172 credit hours; 2.0 GPA; 2 semesters in residence; prescribed curriculum; general education requirements.

Fulfillment of some degree requirements and exemption from some beginning courses possible by passing College Board CLEP, AP, other standardized tests. *Grading system:* A–F; pass-fail; withdraw; incomplete.

Distinctive Educational Programs: International programs in dance and music for summer study and performance abroad. Adult Center for Arts Enrichment: evening classes for community.

Degrees Conferred: 119 *baccalaureate*: visual and performing arts; 39 *master's*: visual and performing arts .

Fees and Other Expenses: *Full-time tuition per academic year 2008–09:* resident $5,647, nonresident $17,527. *Other fees:* $1,605. *Room and board per academic year:* $6,831. *Books and supplies:* $1,050. *Other expenses:* $2,630.

Financial Aid: Aid from institutionally generated funds is provided on the basis of financial need, artistic ability. Institution has a Program Participation Agreement with the U.S. Department of Education for eligible students to receive Pell Grants and, depending upon the agreement, other federal aid.

Departments and Teaching Staff: *Total instructional faculty:* 139. *Student/faculty ratio:* 8:1. Degrees held by full-time faculty: baccalaureate 18%, master's 51%, doctorate 13%, professional artists 18%.

Enrollment: Total enrollment 879. Undergraduate 765. Graduate 114 (2% full-time). Undergraduate transfer-in students 54.

Characteristics of Student Body: *Ethnic/racial makeup:* number of Black non-Hispanic: 66; American Indian or Alaska Native: 2; Asian or Pacific Islander: 22; Hispanic: 24; White non-Hispanic: 650; unknown: 15. *Age distribution:* number under 18: 125; 18–19: 131; 20–21: 151; 22–24: 277; 25–41: 99; 41–64: 5.

International Students: 31 nonresident aliens enrolled fall 2008. No programs available to aid students whose native language is not English. No financial aid specifically designated for international students.

Student Life: On-campus residence halls house 68.9% of student body. Residence halls for males constitute 5.3% of such space, for females 5.3%; both sexes 89.3%. *Special regulations:* Cars permitted without restriction. *Special services:* medical services, including physical therapy and counseling services. *Surrounding community:* Winston-Salem metropolitan area population 855,000. Served by mass transit bus system; airport 17 miles from campus.

Library Collections: 114,000 volumes. 25,000 microforms; 73,000 audiovisual materials; 490 current periodical subscriptions. Students have access to information retrieval services and the Internet.

Most important holdings include music collection (scores, books, recordings), school archives, and Giannini score collection.

Buildings and Grounds: Campus area 67 acres.

Chief Executive Officer: Dr. John Maucen, Chancellor.
Address admission inquiries to Sheeler Lawson, Director of Admissions.

North Carolina State University at Raleigh

P.O. Box 7001
Raleigh, North Carolina 27695-7001
Tel: (919) 515-2011 **E-mail:** admissions@ncsu.edu
Fax: (919) 515-5039 **Internet:** www.ncsu.edu

Institution Description: *Enrollment:* 32,872. *Degrees awarded:* Associate, baccalaureate, first-professional (veterinary medicine), master's, doctorate. Postbaccalaureate programs in engineering also awarded.

Member of the consortia Cooperating Raleigh Colleges and Oak Ridge Associated Universities.

Accreditation: *Regional:* SACS-Comm. on Coll. *Professional*: architecture, chemistry, computer science, engineering, forestry, landscape architecture, public administration, recreation and leisure services, social work, teacher education, veterinary medicine

History: Established by the State General Assembly 1887; became North Carolina College of Agriculture and Mechanic Arts and offered first instruction at postsecondary level 1889; awarded first degree (baccalaureate) 1893; changed name to North Carolina College of Agriculture and Engineering 1917; adopted present name 1965; added school of veterinary medicine 1898. *See* David A. Lockmiller, *History of the N.C. State College of Agriculture and Engineering of the University of North Carolina, 1889–1939* (Raleigh: NCSU Alumni Association, 1939) for further information.

Institutional Structure: *Governing board:* The North Carolina State University Board of Trustees. Extrainstitutional representation: 13 trustees; institutional representation: student government president. 1 ex officio. 13 voting. *Composition of institution:* Administrators 155. Academic affairs headed by provost and vice chancellor. Management/business/finances directed by vice

NORTH CAROLINA STATE UNIVERSITY AT RALEIGH—*cont'd*

chancellor for finance and business. Full-time instructional faculty 1,652. Academic governance body, Administrative Council, meets an average of 11 times per year.

Calendar: Semesters. Academic year July to June. Freshmen admitted Aug., Jan., May, July. Degrees conferred May, June, Aug., Dec. Formal commencement Dec. and May. Summer session of 2 terms from May to Aug.

Characteristics of Freshmen: 16,553 applicants (female 7,780, male 8,773). 60% of applicants admitted. 49% of applicants admitted and enrolled full-time.

96% (4,708 students) submitted SAT scores; 19% (939 students) submitted ACT scores. *25th percentile*: SAT Critical Reading 520, SAT Math 550, SAT Writing 510; ACT Composite 22, ACT English 21, ACT Math 23. *75th percentile*: SAT Critical Reading 610, SAT Math 650, SAT Writing 610; ACT Composite 26, ACT English 27, ACT Math 28.

65% of entering freshmen expected to graduate within 5 years. 90% of freshmen from North Carolina. Freshmen from 50 states and 54 foreign countries.

Admission: Rolling admissions plan. For fall acceptance, apply as early as early as summer following junior year of secondary school, but not later than February of year of enrollment. *Requirements:* Either graduation from accredited secondary school or GED with 4 units English, 2 algebra, 1 geometry, 3 science, 2 social studies (one must be U.S. history), 2 foreign language. Physics, advanced mathematics recommended. For School of Design, applications must be submitted by Dec. 15, on-campus interview, and portfolio or other evidence of creativity required. *Entrance tests:* SAT or ACT. For foreign students TOEFL. *For transfer students:* 2.0 minimum GPA (higher for most programs); maximum transfer credit limited only by residence requirements.

Tutoring available. Developmental courses offered in summer session and regular academic year; nondegree credit given.

Degree Requirements: *For all associate degrees:* 64 credit hours; last 30 hours in residence; 2 credits physical education. *For all baccalaureate degrees:* 124-139 credit hours; last 30 hours in residence; 2-4 credits physical education. For School of Forest Resources, summer internship, practicum, camp, or work experience. *For all undergraduate degrees:* Minimum grade point average of 2.0 for all courses taken at N.C. State; core requirements.

Fulfillment of some degree requirements and exemption from some beginning courses possible by passing College Board CLEP, Achievement Tests, APP, other standardized tests. *Grading system:* A–NC; limited pass-fail; withdraw (deadline after which pass-fail is appended to withdraw).

Distinctive Educational Programs: Evening classes. Special facilities for using telecommunications in the classroom. Multi-disciplinary programs in contemporary issues. Classes offered via the Internet. Facilities and programs for independent research, including honors programs, individual majors, tutorials. Study abroad summer programs in England, Mexico, Austria, Germany; year-round programs in Spain, Japan, England, France, Costa Rica; elsewhere through International Student Exchange Program (34 countries). *Other distinctive programs:* Credit and noncredit evening classes for adults, independent study, and summer sessions through Division of Continuing Education.

ROTC: Air Force, Army, Navy.

Degrees Conferred: 132 *associate;* 4,535 *baccalaureate*; 1,307 *master's*; 369 *doctorate*; 75 *first-professional*: veterinary medicine. Bachelor's degrees awarded in top five professions: engineering 959; business/marketing 600; biological and biomedical sciences 491; social sciences 375; communications/journalism 309. Master's degrees awarded in top five disciplines: engineering 373; education 230; business/marketing 176; social sciences 75; mathematics and statistics 60. Doctorates awarded in top five disciplines: engineering 114; education 55; biological and biomedical sciences 60; multi/interdisciplinary studies 2; social sciences 25.

Fees and Other Expenses: *Full-time tuition per academic year 2007–08:* undergraduate resident $4,708, nonresident $17,584; contact the university for current graduate and first-professional tuition. *Required fees:* $1,357. *Room and board per academic year:* $7,982. *Books and supplies:* $930. *Other expenses:* $1,830.

Financial Aid: Aid from institutionally generated funds is provided on the basis of academic merit, financial need, athletic ability, other criteria.

Financial aid to full-time, first-time undergraduate students: 58% received some form of aid. Average amount of aid received: federal grants $4,198; Pell grants $2,843; other federal aid $1,847; state/local grants $3,347; institutional grants $4,222.

Departments and Teaching Staff: *Total instructional faculty:* 1,645 (full time 1,652, part-time 193). Student/faculty ratio: 16:1. Degrees held by full-time faculty: baccalaureate 1.6%, master's 11.9%, doctorate 82.3%, professional 4.2%. 90% hold terminal degrees.

Enrollment: Total enrollment 32,872. Undergraduate 24,471. Graduate 8,131. Undergraduate transfer-in students 1,093.

Characteristics of Student Body: *Ethnic/racial makeup:* number of Black non-Hispanic: 2,214; American Indian or Alaska Native: 155; Asian or Pacific Islander: 1,200; Hispanic: 580; White non-Hispanic: 18,885; unknown: 913. *Age distribution:* number under 18: 237; 18–19: 8,569; 20–21: 8,098; 22–24: 5,911; 25–29: 3,954; 30–34: 1,828; 35–39: 1,046; 40–49: 1,022; 50–64: 431; 65 and over: 34. 335 of student body attend summer sessions.

International Students: 1,891 nonresident aliens enrolled fall 2008. Students from Europe, Asia, Central and South America, Africa, Canada, Australia, New Zealand, Middle East. Programs available to aid students whose native language is not English: social, cultural, financial. English as a Second Language Program. Financial aid specifically designated for international graduate students: scholarships available annually.

Student Life: On-campus residence halls house 23% of student body. Residence halls for males constitute 34% of such space, for females 13%, for both sexes 53%. 26 fraternities; 14 sororities. *Intercollegiate athletics:* male: baseball, basketball, cross-country, diving, football, golf, soccer, swimming, tennis, indoor and outdoor track, wrestling; female: basketball, cross-country, gymnastics, soccer, swimming, tennis, indoor and outdoor track, volleyball; for both sexes: cheerleading, rifle. *Special regulations:* Cars with parking permits allowed for all but freshmen dormitory residents and others living within 1 mile of center of campus; fee charged. Quiet hours Sun.–Thurs. 8pm to 8am. Residence halls visitation from 9am to 1am Sun.–Thurs., 9am to 2am Fri. and Sat. *Special services:* Learning Resources Center, medical services, campus transportation system. Over 300 clubs and organizations, including visual and performing arts, intramural sports, 24 fraternities and 10 sororities. *Student publications, radio: Agromeck*, a yearbook; *Technician*, a newspaper published 5 times per week; *the Nubian Message*, African American newspaper; *Graduate Student News*, a graduate student newspaper; *Windhover*, an annual literary magazine. Radio station WKNC-FM broadcasts 168 hours per week. *Surrounding community:* Raleigh metropolitan area near one millinon; Raleigh population 300,000. Served by mass transit bus system; airport 15 miles from campus; passenger rail service 2 miles from campus.

Library Collections: 3,688,000 volumes. 5,433,200 microforms; 117,739 audiovisual materials; 15,818 current periodicals; access to 35,466 via electronic access. Online catalog. Students have Access to on-line information retrieval services and the Internet.

Most important special holdings include Tipman Collection in entomology; Metcalf Collection in entomology; Greenways Archives; architectural and golf course design drawings.

Buildings and Grounds: NCSU has a campus of 1,736 acres that includes a central campus and a nearby satellite campus for the College of Veterinary Medicine with 166 acres and a new campus that adjoins the main campus called "Centennial Campus." In addition, the University has 88,000 acres throughout the state. This includes a 78,000-acre research forest, research farms and facilities, nurseries for genetics, horticulture and floriculture research, biology and ecology sites, a football stadium, extension offices in all of the state's 100 counties and the Cherokee Indian Reservation.

Chief Executive Officer: Dr. James L. Oblinger, Chancellor.

Undergraduates address admission inquiries to Thomas Griffin, Director of Admissions; graduate inquiries to Dean of Graduate School.

College of Humanities and Social Sciences

Degree Programs Offered: *Baccalaureate* in accounting, business management, communication, criminal justice, economics, English, French, history, multidisciplinary studies, philosophy, political science, psychology, social work, sociology, Spanish, writing-editing; *master's* in economics, English, history, management, political science, public affairs; *doctorate* in economics, psychology, sociology.

Departments and Teaching Staff: *Total instructional faculty:* 416.

Distinctive Educational Programs: Cooperative education. Accelerated double degree program with College of Agriculture and Life Sciences, College of Engineering, College of Textiles; evening degree programs; off-campus degree programs; Administrative Officers Management Program. *Other distinctive programs:* Intensive English for foreign students through 6-week summer institute, Humanities Extension; Instructional Telecommunication courses; Study Abroad programs.

College of Agriculture and Life Sciences

Degree Programs Offered: *Associate, baccalaureate, master's, doctorate.*

Departments and Teaching Staff: *Total faculty:* 435.

Distinctive Educational Programs: 2-year associate degree programs are offered in agribusiness management; agricultural pest control; field crops technology; food processing, distribution and service; general agriculture; livestock management and technology; ornamental and landscape technology; turfgrass management. Undergraduate programs in agricultural business management, agricultural and extension education, agricultural and environmental technology, agronomy, animal science, applied sociology, biochemistry, biological engineering, environmental sciences, microbiology, natural resources, biological sciences, botany, conservation, fisheries and wildlife sciences, food science, horticultural science, medical technology, poultry science and zoology. Preprofessional programs in dentistry, medicine, optometry, and preveterinary medicine. Undergraduate minors in agricultural business management, agricultural economics, animal science, applied sociology, biological sciences, botany, entomology, food science, genetics, horticultural science, microbiology, nutrition, poultry science, soil science and zoology. Graduate programs in agriculture, agricultural economics, agricultural education, animal science, biochemistry, biological and agricultural engineering, botany, crop science, ecology, economics, entomology, food science, genetics, horticultural science, immunology, life sciences, management, microbiology, nutrition, physiology, plant pathology, plant physiology, poultry science, rural sociology, sociology, soil science, toxicology, wildlife biology, zoology. The College of Agriculture and Life Sciences is well equipped and provides extensive facilities for laboratory and field research. Included are sophisticated computing facilities; a 180-acre Biology Field Laboratory with a 20-acre pond and modern laboratories; a Center for Electron Microscopy; a biotechnology 500- and 360-MHz NMR facility; a circular dichroism facility; molecular graphics; hybridoma and DNA synthesis facilities; the Highlands Biological Station; a Pesticide Residue Research Laboratory; a Reproductive Physiology Research Laboratory; a Phytotron, maintained in cooperation with the Southeastern Plan Environmental Laboratories; and 16 outlying research facilities distributed throughout the state. Animal research facilities for cattle, swine, sheep, and poultry are outstanding and include capabilities for intensive metabolism studies; laboratory animal facilities are being expanded. In addition, a variety of resources are made available through the University's participation in the Organization for Tropical Studies.

College of Design

Degree Programs Offered: *Baccalaureate, master's, doctorate.*
Departments and Teaching Staff: *Total instructional faculty:* 57.

College of Education

Degree Programs Offered: *Baccalaureate, master's, doctorate.*
Departments and Teaching Staff: *Total instructional faculty:* 88.
Distinctive Educational Programs: Facilities include curriculum materials center, instructional materials production center, computer facility, teaching laboratories, children's playroom with observation area. Human resources development combines field experiences and campus study for undergraduate psychology students. Multidisciplinary graduate programs in educational administration and supervision. *Other distinctive programs:* Public school sixth-year certification programs.

College of Engineering

Degree Programs Offered: *Baccalaureate, master's, doctorate.*
Departments and Teaching Staff: *Total instructional faculty:* 255.
Distinctive Educational Programs: Cooperative education. Independent study. Dual-degree (2+2 and 3+2) programs with other North Carolina state universities. Multidisciplinary graduate programs in cooperation with North Carolina Institute for Transportation Research and Education, North Carolina Sea Grant Program, Water Resources Institution. Postbaccalaureates in transportation and city and regional planning in cooperation with University of North Carolina at Chapel Hill. Industrial Extension Service. Facilities include 1-megawatt PULSTAR nuclear reactor and Minerals Industrial Research Laboratories (in Asheville).

College of Management

Degree Programs Offered: *Baccalaureate, master's, doctorate.*
Departments and Teaching Staff: *Total instructional faculty:* 90.

College of Natural Resources

Degree Programs Offered: *Associate, baccalaureate, master's, doctorate.*
Departments and Teaching Staff: *Total instructional faculty:* 88.
Distinctive Educational Programs: Baccalaureate degrees in natural resources; environmental sciences; forest management; parks/recreation/tourism management; pulp and paper science and technology; and wood products. Double-degree programs in cooperation with other departments at NCSU, including pulp and paper and chemical engineering. Wildlife degrees offered in cooperation with Department of Zoology. Cooperative education opportunities in all departments. Facilities include Hodges Wood Products Laboratory, Robertson Laboratory for pulp and paper studies, geographic information systems laboratory, computer teaching lab, school forests totaling over 80,000 acres and biotechnology labs. Department of Forestry has numerous cooperative research programs, including international gene conservation, tree improvement, forest nutrition and hardwood management. Department of Parks, Recreation, and Tourism Management has Recreation Resources Service supporting state and local recreation departments. Extension programs serve the public, government, and industry.

College of Physical and Mathematical Sciences

Degree Programs Offered: *Baccalaureate, master's, doctorate.*
Departments and Teaching Staff: *Total instructional faculty:* 212.
Distinctive Educational Programs: Each department in the college utilizes a number of highly specialized research facilities. These range from highly specialized laboratories such as those in sold state physics or nuclear magnetic resonance spectroscopy to state-of-the-art instruments such as X-ray diffractometers and electron spin resonance spectometers. These laboratories are routinely utilized by advanced undergraduates taking part in research programs. In addition, each department maintains up-to-date computer laboratories and each has access to the CRAY YMP super computer in the Research Triangle Park. These facilities are utilized not only for graduate research but for undergraduate research and instruction. A detailed list of specialized equipment is available upon request for each department.

College of Textiles

Degree Programs Offered: *Baccalaureate, master's, doctorate.*
Departments and Teaching Staff: *Total instructional faculty:* 40,
Distinctive Educational Programs: Work-experience programs may be individually arranged. *Other distinctive programs:* Extension and continuing education programs. 1-year baccalaureate program in textiles for student with other baccalaureate degree. Located on Centennial Campus, a unique research/educational campus adjacent to North and South Campus.

College of Veterinary Medicine

Degree Programs Offered: *Master's (M.S.), doctorate (Ph.D), Doctor of Veterinary Medicine (D.V.M.).*
Admission: 2 units English, 4 mathematics, 3 chemistry, 2 biochemistry, 2 physics, 2 zoology, 1 animal or poultry science, 1 biology, 1 genetics, 1 statistics.
Degree Requirements: 150 credit hours, 2.0 GPA, entire program in residence.
Departments and Teaching Staff: *Total instructional faculty:* 125.

North Carolina Wesleyan College

3400 North Wesleyan Boulevard
Rocky Mount, North Carolina 27804-9906
Tel: (252) 985-5100 **E-mail:** adm@ncwc.edu
Fax: (252) 977-5295 **Internet:** www.ncwc.edu

Institution Description: North Carolina Wesleyan College is a private college affiliated with the United Methodist Church. *Enrollment:* 1,506. *Degrees awarded:* Baccalaureate.
Accreditation: *Regional:* SACS-Comm. on Coll.
History: Established and chartered 1956; offered first instruction at postsecondary level 1960; awarded first degree (baccalaureate) 1964.
Institutional Structure: *Governing board:* Board of Trustees. Extrainstitutional representation: 26 trustees; institutional representation: president of the college. 6 ex officio. 26 voting. *Composition of institution:* Administrators 7. Academic affairs headed by academic vice president. Management/business/finances directed by director of administration. Full-time instructional faculty 43. Academic governance body, the faculty, meets an average of 9 times per year.
Calendar: Semesters. Academic year June to July. Freshmen admitted Aug., Jan., May, July. Degrees conferred and formal commencement May. Summer session of 2 terms from May to Aug.
Characteristics of Freshmen: 1,659 applicants (female 703, male 936). 21% of applicants admitted. 92% of admitted applicants enrolled full-time.
5% (196 students) submitted SAT scores; 29% (82 students) submitted ACT scores. *25th percentile*: SAT Critical Reading 370, SAT Math 415, SAT Writing 415; ACT Composite 15, ACT English 15, ACT 15. *75th percentile*: SAT Critical Reading 480, SAT math 500, SAT Writing 490; ACT Composite 18, ACT English 17, ACT Math 19.
34% of freshmen from North Carolina. Freshmen from 24 states and 9 foreign countries.
Admission: Rolling admissions plan. For fall acceptance, apply as early as end of junior year of secondary school, but not later than July 15. Early accep-

NORTH CAROLINA WESLEYAN COLLEGE—*cont'd*

tance available. *Requirements:* It is strongly recommended that the applicant have a minimum of 16 academic courses at the secondary school level, including 4 in English, 2 social studies, 2 foreign language, 3 mathematics, 2 lab sciences. The GED is recognized for non-traditional students. Letters of recommendation and essays are optional. Most students rank in the upper half of their graduating classes. *Entrance tests:* Students should take the SAT or ACT. SAT average combined scores range from 800 to 1000. *For transfer students:* The student must be in good academic standing and should have a cumulative GPA of 2.0 on a 4.0 scale. The maximum credit accepted from 2-year institutions is 64 semester hours (96 quarter hours); however, additional credit may be awarded from 4-year baccalaureate degree-granting institutions.

Credit obtained through standardized testing programs (College Level Examination Program, Defense Activities for Non-Traditional Education Support, or American Testing Program) and formal professional or military training as recognized by the American Council on Education will also be reviewed and considered for transfer credit.

Tutoring available. Developmental courses offered in summer session and regular academic year; credit given.

Degree Requirements: 124 credit hours; 2.0 GPA; 30 semester hours in residence. Fulfillment of some degree requirements and exemption from some beginning courses possible by passing departmental examinations, College Board CLEP, AP, other standardized tests. *Grading system:* A–F and with approval, credit only; pass/fail; withdraw and incomplete carry time limit.

Distinctive Educational Programs: Flexible meeting places and schedules, including off-campus centers (at Goldsboro, 59 miles away from main institution; Raleigh, 68 miles away) and evening classes. Accelerated degree program. Interdepartmental majors in behavioral studies, environmental science, fish and wildlife management, politics, sociology and anthropology; interdisciplinary programs in humanities, western man. Programs for independent research, including individual majors, individualized study. *Other distinctive programs:* Degree-granting continuing education program. Study abroad at the Sorbonne, Paris, France, during the summer includes history, language, architecture, art and French.

Degrees Conferred: 386 *baccalaureate*.

Fees and Other Expenses: *Full-time tuition per academic year 2008–09:* $20,190. *Required fees:* $1,264. *Room and board per academic year:* $7,380. *Books and supplies:* $1,000. *Other expenses:* $1,500.

Financial Aid: Aid from institutionally generated funds is provided on the basis of academic merit, financial need.

Financial aid to full-time, first-time undergraduate students: 98% received some form of financial aid. Average amount of aid received: federal grants $2,532; state/local grants $4,313; institutional grants $6,670; loans $5,406.

Departments and Teaching Staff: *Total instructional faculty:* 177 (full-time 51, part-time 126). Student/faculty ratio: 17:1. Degrees held by full-time faculty: master's 12%, doctorate 31%. 72% hold terminal degrees.

Enrollment: Total enrollment 1,506 (undergraduate). Transfer-in students 111.

Characteristics of Student Body: *Ethnic/racial makeup:* number of Black non-Hispanic: 744; American Indian or Alaska Native: 14; Asian or Pacific Islander: 13; Hispanic: 36; White non-Hispanic: 818; unknown: 147.

International Students: 88 nonresident aliens enrolled fall 2008. Programs available to aid students whose native language is not English: social. No financial aid specifically designated for international students.

Student Life: On-campus residence halls will accommodate 591 students. Space is divided equally between males and females. 2 of the 4 halls are coed and 1 is devoted to freshmen as part of the Freshman Experience. *Intercollegiate athletics:* Member, Dixie Intercollegiate Athletic Conference and Division III of the NCAA. Male: baseball, basketball, golf, soccer; female: soccer, softball, basketball, volleyball. Intramural and club sports include badminton, basketball, flag football, skeet, soccer, softball, table tennis, tennis, and beach volleyball. *Special regulations:* Cars permitted without restrictions. *Special services:* Student Services Center (pre-major advising, career planning, career placement, cooperative education and peer tutoring, learning disabled consultation, new student orientation, student referral program, and graduate school entrance assistance). Tutor's Crossing, located in the Center, provides a variety of academic support services including help with the fundamentals of reading, writing and mathematics, assignments in specific courses, and use of several state-of-the-art computers. A registered nurse, counselor, and a certified clinical psychologist hold convenient office hours. A staff of 5 medical doctors is on call 24 hours a day. *Student publications: The Decree,* a student newspaper; *The Dissenter,* a yearbook. *Surrounding community:* Rocky Mount population 50,000. Raleigh-Durham is approximately 60 miles east. The campus is served by a regional airport and passenger rail (Amtrak).

Library Collections: 94,000 volumes. Online catalog. Current serial subscriptions: paper 475; microform 34,227. 2,161 recordings. Computer work stations available. Students have access to online information retrieval services and the Internet.

Most important special collections include Black Mountain Collection (by and about alumni/teachers); Methodist Church Journals.

Buildings and Grounds: Campus area 200 acres.

Chief Executive Officer: Dr.Ian Newbould, President.

Address admission inquiries to Cecelia Summers, Director of Admissions.

Pfeiffer University

48380 Highway 52 North
P.O. Box 960
Misenheimer, North Carolina 28109-0960
Tel: (704) 463-1360 **E-mail:** admiss@pfeiffer.edu
Fax: (704) 463-1363 **Internet:** www.pfeiffer.edu

Institution Description: Pfeiffer University, formerly Pfeiffer College, is a private institution affiliated with the United Methodist Church. *Enrollment:* 2,019. *Degrees awarded:* Baccalaureate, master's.

Accreditation: *Regional:* SACS-Comm. on Coll. *Professional*: music, teacher education

History: Established near Lenoir as Oberlin Home and School 1885; control passed to Methodist Episcopal Church and name changed to Mitchell Home School 1903; moved to present location 1910; changed name to Mitchell Junior College and offered first instruction at postsecondary level 1928; awarded first degree (associate) 1930; changed name to Pfeiffer Junior College 1935; incorporated 1937; became Pfeiffer College 1954; achieved university status 1996.

Institutional Structure: *Governing board:* Pfeiffer University Board of Trustees. Representation: up to 50 regular members, 50% of whom must be Methodist; includes 2 alumni; student and faculty representatives are ex officio. *Composition of institution:* Administrators 15. Academic affairs headed by vice president for academic affairs. Management/business/finances directed by vice president for finance. Full-time instructional faculty 67. Academic governance body, Faculty Assembly, meets an average of 7 times per year.

Calendar: Semesters. Freshmen admitted Aug., Jan., June, July. Degrees conferred May, Aug., Dec. Formal commencement May, Aug. Multiple summer sessions.

Characteristics of Freshmen: 1,127 applicants (female 529, male 598). 71% of applicants admitted. 73% of applicants admitted and enrolled full-time.

94% of applicants submitted SAT scores; 21% ACT scores. *25th percentile*: SAT Critical Reading 420, SAT Math 430, SAT Writing 530; ACT Composite 22. *75th percentile*: SAT Critical Reading 520, SAT Math 550, SAT Writing 530; ACT Composite 22.

45% of entering freshmen expected to graduate within 5 years. 76% of freshmen from North Carolina. Freshmen from 31 states and 11 foreign countries.

Admission: Rolling admissions plan. Apply at any time. *Requirements:* Either graduation from accredited secondary school with 4 units English; or GED. Recommend 3 units algebra. *Entrance tests:* College Board SAT or ACT, English proficiency examination. *For transfer students:* 2.0 minimum GPA.

College credit and advanced placement for postsecondary-level work completed in secondary school. CLEP exams accepted. Students who have completed a GED examination may also be considered for admission.

Tutoring available. Developmental courses offered during regular academic year; credit given.

Degree Requirements: 120 semester hours and 4 activity courses and 60 cultural units; general education and distribution requirements; exit competency examinations in English and computer competency. *Grading system:* A–F; withdraw (deadline after which pass-fail is appended to withdraw); incomplete (carries time limit).

Distinctive Educational Programs: Off-campus center at Charlotte (45 miles away from main institution) offers upper-division baccalaureate study in business administration, criminal justice; health care management, liberal arts and management information systems; MBA, MBA/MHA, and MSOM are also offered. Evening classes. Dual-degree program in engineering with Auburn University (AL). Interdisciplinary programs in arts administration, Christian education-music, chemistry-business, Christian education-business, mathematics-computer information systems, mathematics-economics, and religion-business. Facilities and programs for independent research, including honors programs, independent and directed study. Institutionally sponsored study abroad in Europe and Israel during winter and summer vacations.

ROTC: Army offered in cooperation with the University of North Carolina at Charlotte.

Degrees Conferred: 234 *baccalaureate*; 407 *master's*. Bachelor's degrees awarded in top five disciplines: business/marketing 98; education 37; security and protective services 23; parks and recreation 20; parks administration and social services 14. Master's degrees awarded: business/marketing 257; education 28; health professions and related sciences 92; theology and religious vocations 14.

Fees and Other Expenses: *Full-time tuition and fees per academic year 2008–09:* $18,570 undergraduate; contact the university for current graduate tuition. *Room and board per academic year:* $7,480. *Books and supplies:* $1,300. *Other expenses:* $2,380.

Financial Aid: Aid from institutionally generated funds is provided on the basis of academic merit, financial need, athletic ability.

Financial aid to full-time, first-time undergraduate students: 98% received some form of aid. Average amount of aid received: federal grants $3,750; Pell grants $2,657; other federal aid $1,249; state/local grants $1,870; institutional grants $3,872.

Departments and Teaching Staff: *Total instructional faculty:* 157 (full-time 67, par-time 90). Student/faculty ratio: 13:1. Degrees held by full-time faculty: doctorate 69.5%, master's 27.1%, professional 3.4%. 73% hold terminal degrees.

Enrollment: Total enrollment 2,019. Undergraduate 1,089. Graduate 930 (18% full-time). Undergraduate transfer-in students 90.

Characteristics of Student Body: *Ethnic/racial makeup:* number of Black non-Hispanic: 259; American Indian or Alaska Native: 6; Asian or Pacific Islander: 9; Hispanic: 35; White non-Hispanic: 771; unknown: 5. *Age distribution:* number 18–19: 29; 20–21: 317; 22–24: 249; 25–29: 130; 30–34: 94; 35–39: 81; 40–49: 100; 50–64: 18; 65 and over: 1.

International Students: 46 nonresident aliens enrolled fall 2008. Students from Europe, Asia, Central and South America, Canada, Australia, Middle East. Programs available to aid students whose native language is not English: social, cultural. No financial aid specifically designated for international students.

Student Life: On-campus residence halls house 63% of student body. Residence halls for males constitute 26% of such space, for females 20%; co-ed 54%. Housing available for married students. 1% of married students request and live in institutional housing. *Intercollegiate athletics:* male: baseball, basketball, cross-country, cycling, golf, lacrosse, soccer, tennis; female: basketball, cross-country, cycling, golf, lacrosse, soccer, softball, swimming, tennis, volleyball. *Special regulations:* Registered cars permitted without restrictions. Quiet hours vary according to residence hall. Residence hall visitation from 5pm to 9pm Mon.–Thurs., 1pm to 1am Fri.–Sun. *Special services:* Medical services, transportation to and from airports, bus terminals, train stations. *Student publications: Chimes; Pfeiffer News*, a biweekly newspaper; *Pfeiffer Review*, an annual literary magazine. *Surrounding community:* Misenheimer, incorporated, located in Stanly County, population 59,000. Charlotte, 40 miles from campus, is nearest metropolitan area. Served by airport 50 miles from campus; passenger rail service 18 miles from campus.

Library Collections: 161,500 volumes including bound books, serial backfiles, electronic documents, and government documents not in separate collections. Online catalog. Current serial subscriptions: 300. 3,084 CD-ROMs. Computer work stations available. Students have access to the Internet at no charge.

Most important special collections include Representative Hefner Legislative Collection; North Carolina Political Archives; Mineral and Artifact Collection.

Buildings and Grounds: Campus area 300 acres.

Chief Executive Officer: Dr. Charles M. Ambrose, President.

Address admission inquiries to Steve Cumming, Director of Admissions.

Piedmont Baptist College

716 Franklin Street
Winston-Salem, North Carolina 27101-5133
Tel: (336) 725-8344 **E-mail:** admissions@pbc.edu
Fax: (336) 725-5522 **Internet:** www.pbc.edu

Institution Description: Piedmont Baptist College, formerly named Piedmont Bible College, is a Baptist institution offering a four- and five-year curriculum. *Enrollment:* 393. *Degrees awarded:* Associate, baccalaureate, master's.

Accreditation: *Nonregional:* Transnational Association of Christian Colleges and Schools.

History: Established 1945.

Calendar: Semesters. Academic year Aug. to May.

Characteristics of Freshmen: 72% of applicants admitted. 77% of applicants admitted and enrolled.

100% (47 students) submitted ACT scores. *25th percentile*: ACT Composite 16. *75th percentile*: ACT Composite 24.

30% of entering freshmen expected to graduate within 5 years. 52$ of freshmen from North Carolina. Freshmen from 23 states and 12 foreign countries.

Admission: *Requirements:* Graduation from accredited secondary school or GED; completion of 10 units with 4 English, 1 science, 1 mathematics, 2 social science, 2 foreign language recommended but not required. *Entrance tests:* SAT or ACT.

Degree Requirements: Completion of prescribed curriculum.

Distinctive Educational Programs: Five-year bachelor of science in missionary aviation.

Degrees Conferred: 7 *associate;* 46 *baccalaureate:* education 9, missionary aviation 3; philosophy/religion/theology 24. 4 *master's:* theology.

Fees and Other Expenses: *Full-time tuition per academic year 2008–09:* $10,750; contact the college for current graduate tuition and fees. *Books and supplies:* $550. *Room and board per academic year:* $5,600. *Other expenses:* $4,675.

Financial Aid: Aid from institutionally generated funds is provided on the basis of academic merit, financial need, other criteria. Institution has a Program Participation Agreement with the U.S. Department of Education for eligible students to receive Pell Grants and, depending upon the agreement, other federal aid.

Financial aid to full-time, first-time undergraduate students: 94% received some form of financial aid. Average amount of aid received: federal grants $2,975; institutional grants $2,689; loans $2,992.

Departments and Teaching Staff: *Total instructional faculty:* 39 (full-time 27, part-time 2). 25% of faculty hold the doctorate, first-professional, or other terminal degree. Student/faculty ratio: 8:1.

Enrollment: Total enrollment 393. Undergraduate 264. Graduate 129 (full-time 16%). Undergraduate transfer-in students 129.

Characteristics of Student Body: *Ethnic/racial makeup:* number of Black non-Hispanic: 12; Asian or Pacific Islander: 22; Hispanic: 3; White non-Hispanic: 272.

International Students: 3 nonresident aliens enrolled fall 2008. No programs available to aid students whose native language is not English. No financial aid specifically designated for international students.

Library Collections: 52,000 volumes including bound books, serial backfiles, electronic documents, and government documents not in separate collections. Online catalog. Current serial subscriptions: 219 paper, 5 microform. 3,722 recordings. Computer work stations available. Students have access to the Internet at no charge.

Chief Executive Officer: Dr. Charles Petitt, President.

Address admission inquiries to Ronnie Mathis, Director of Admissions.

Queens University of Charlotte

1900 Selwyn Avenue
Charlotte, North Carolina 28274
Tel: (704) 337-2200 **E-mail:** admissions@queens.edu
Fax: (704) 337-2403 **Internet:** www.queens.edu

Institution Description: Queens University of Charlotte is a private, urban-based, diversified liberal arts institution with close ties to the Presbyterian Church (USA). Queens serves a variety of learners through its 3 colleges: the College of Arts and Sciences, a coeducational undergraduate program that emphasizes the traditional liberal arts; the New College at Queens, for working men and women who want to earn undergraduate degrees in evening or Saturday classes; and The Graduate School, offering mostly evening and Saturday courses leading to the master's degree in business or education. *Enrollment:* 2,302. *Degrees awarded:* Baccalaureate, master's.

Member of Charlotte Area Educational Consortium.

Accreditation: *Regional:* SACS-Comm. on Coll.

History: Queens was founded in 1957 as the Charlotte Female Institute in downtown Charlotte. In 1891 it became the Seminary for Girls and in 1896 the name was changed to the Presbyterian College for Women. In 1912, anticipating the move to its present campus in the Myers Park residential area in 1914, it became Queens College. Coeducational evening programs were begun in 1948, and the first graduate programs, also coeducational, started in 1980. Queens became fully coeducational in 1987 and achieved university status in 2002.

Institutional Structure: *Governing board:* Board of Trustees comprising 34 extra-institutional trustees (4 elected by the alumni association), 16 non-voting advisory trustees, and the president of the college, ex officio. *Composition of institution:* Administrators 22. Academic affairs headed by vice president for academic affairs. Management/business/finances directed by vice president for finance and planning. Full-time instructional faculty 65. Academic governance body, Educational Programs and Curriculum Committee, meets an average of 25 times per year.

Calendar: Semesters (4-1-4 plan). Academic year Aug. to May. First-year students admitted Aug., Jan. Degrees conferred and formal commencement May. Summer session May to July.

Characteristics of Freshmen: 2,099 applicants (female 1,610, male 489). 57% of applicants admitted. 27% of admitted students enrolled full-time.

QUEENS UNIVERSITY OF CHARLOTTE—*cont'd*

93% (290 students) submitted SAT scores; 31% (90 students) submitted ACT scores. *25th percentile*: SAT Critical Reading 470, SAT Math 480, SAT Writing 470; ACT Composite 20, ACT English 18, ACT Math 19. *75th percentile*: SAT Critical Reading 580, SAT Math 580, SAT Writing 570; ACT Composite 24, ACT English 24, ACT Math 25.

55% of entering freshmen expected to graduate within 5 years. 72% of freshmen from North Carolina. Freshmen from 34 states and 19 foreign countries.

Admission: Rolling admissions plan. *Requirements:* Graduation from accredited secondary school with academic units which should include 4 English, 2 foreign language, 3 mathematics, 2 social studies, 1 laboratory science. *Entrance tests:* College Board SAT or ACT required. For foreign students TOEFL. *For transfer students:* 2.0 minimum GPA; maximum transfer credit limited by residence requirement.

College credit and/or advanced placement for College Board Advanced Placement exams.

Tutoring available.

Degree Requirements: 122 credit hours, including 26 hours in Queens' nationally recognized core curriculum, the Foundations of Liberal Learning; 2.0 GPA; 60 hours, including last 30, in residence; at least 36 semester hours in courses at the 300 level or above; competency in a foreign language through the 102 level; at least 4 credit hours of laboratory science; 2 physical education courses; attendance at three annual college convocations.

Fulfillment of some degree requirements and exemption from some beginning courses possible by passing College Board CLEP, AP. *Grading system:* A–F; pass-no record; withdraw; pass-fail; incomplete (carries time limit).

Distinctive Educational Programs: Foundations of Liberal Learning Program, an interdisciplinary, team-taught core curriculum; extensive opportunities for internships; evening classes; programs in European studies, business/foreign language.

Degrees Conferred: 124 *associate*; 253 *baccalaureate*; 155 *master's*. Bachelor's degrees awarded in top five disciplines: business, management, marketing, and related support services 74; communication, journalism, and related programs 36; health professions and related clinical sciences 26; psychology 15; English language/literature 14.

Fees and Other Expenses: *Full-time tuition per academic year 2008–09:* $22,068 undergraduate; graduate study charged per credit. *Room and Board per academic year:* $7,882. *Books and supplies:* $800. *Other expenses:* $1,800.

Financial Aid: Aid from institutionally generated funds is provided on the basis of academic merit, financial need, athletic ability. Institution has a Program Participation Agreement with the U.S. Department of Education for eligible students to receive Pell Grants and, depending upon the agreement, other federal aid.

Financial aid to full-time, first-time undergraduate students: 95% received some form of financial aid. Average amount of aid received: federal grants $3,137; state/local grants $4,436; institutional grants $8,165; loans $4,177.

Departments and Teaching Staff: *Total instructional faculty:* 80.67 FTE. Student/faculty ratio: 13:1. Degrees held by full-time faculty: master's 37%, doctorate 59%, professional 4%. 83% hold terminal degrees.

Enrollment: Total enrollment 2,118. Undergraduate

Characteristics of Student Body: *Ethnic/racial makeup:* Black non-Hispanic: 19%; American Indian or Alaska Native: 1%; Asian or Pacific Islander: 2%; Hispanic: 45; White non-Hispanic: 66^; unknown: 3%.

International Students: 83 nonresident aliens enrolled fall 2008.

Student Life: On-campus residence halls house 61% of full-time students. Residence halls for females constitute 60% of such space. *Intercollegiate athletics:* male: basketball, golf, soccer, tennis; female: basketball, soccer, tennis, volleyball. *Special regulations:* Cars permitted without restrictions. Quiet hours. *Special services:* Career Development Center, Student Counseling Center, medical services, chaplain, computer terminals available in residence halls. *Student publications: Arete*, a yearbook; *Queens Current,* a monthly newspaper; *Signet*, an annual literary review. *Surrounding community:* Charlotte population 425,000. Metropolitan Statistical Area 1,210,000. Served by mass transit bus system; AMTRAK station 3 miles, airport 5 miles from campus.

Library Collections: 142,500 volumes. 4,500 government documents; 88,000 microforms; 1,640 audiovisual materials; 520 current periodical subscriptions. Online catalog. Students have access to online information retrieval services and the Internet.

Most important special collections include Queens University of Charlotte archives; local history materials relating to university history; materials relating to history of the Presbyterian Church in this area.

Buildings and Grounds: Campus area 25 acres.

Chief Executive Officer: Dr. Pamela L. Davies, President.

Address admission inquiries to William Lee, Director of Admissions.

Roanoke Bible College

715 North Poindexter Street
Elizabeth City, North Carolina 27909-4054
Tel: (252) 334-2000 **E-mail:** admissions@roanokebible.edu
Fax: (252) 334-2071 **Internet:** www.roanokebible.edu

Institution Description: Roanoke Bible College is a private, nondenominational, nonprofit institution affiliated with the Christian Churches and Churches of Christ. *Enrollment:* 153. *Degrees awarded:* Associate, baccalaureate.

Accreditation: *Regional:* SACS. *National:* ABHE.

History: Established 1948 as a ministerial training school.

Institutional Structure: *Governing board:* Board of Trustees. Extrainstitutional representation: 20 trustees. *Composition of institution:* president, 4 administrative divisions headed by vice presidents of academic affairs, development, finance, and student development. Full-time instructional faculty 11.

Calendar: Semesters. Academic year Aug. to May. Freshmen admitted Aug, Jan. Degrees conferred and formal commencement May.

Characteristics of Freshmen: 100% of applicants admitted. 53% of admitted applicants enrolled.

84% (21 students) submitted SAT scores; 16% (3 students) submitted ACT scores. *25th percentile*: SAT Critical reading 400, SAT Math 330; ACT Composite 14, ACT English 19, ACT Math 18. *75th percentile*: SAT Critical Reading 580, SAT Math 590; ACT Composite 21, ACT English 24, ACT Math 25.

44% of entering freshmen expected to graduate within 5 years. 29% of freshmen from North Carolina. Freshmen from 4 states.

Admission: Students are admitted who exhibit good Christian character and fulfill all other requirements for admission. *Requirements:* Graduation from high school or GED; biographical sketch; church and school references. *Entrance tests:* College Board SAT or ACT.

Degree Requirements: *For all associate degrees:* 64 semester hours. *For all baccalaureate degrees:* 128 semester hours.

Distinctive Educational Programs: Baccalaureate programs with Bible/theology major and professional studies minors in Christian education, counseling, cross-cultural ministry, elementary education, preaching ministry, youth ministry. State teacher certification co-op program with local university. Associate programs in Bible/theology, (interpreting), worship and music, and early childhood education. Dual-enrollment option with local community college in business, nursing, and other programs. Dual-enrollment option with local state university in various programs. Cross-cultural ministry semester abroad.

Degrees Conferred: 6 *associate;* 19 *baccalaureate:* philosophy and religious studies.

Fees and Other Expenses: *Full-time tuition per academic year 2008–09:* $9,740. *Required fees:* $930. *Room and board per academic year:* $5,810. *Other expenses:* $4,150.

Financial Aid: Aid from institutionally generated funds is provided on the basis of academic merit, financial need. 100% of students received some for of financial aid.

Departments and Teaching Staff: *Total instructional faculty:* 28 (full-time 11, part-time 17). Student/faculty ratio: 9:1. Degrees held by full-time faculty: doctorate 28%, master's 64%, baccalaureate 8%. 21% hold terminal degrees.

Enrollment: Total enrollment 153 (undergraduate). Transfer-in students 25.

Characteristics of Student Body: *Ethnic/racial makeup:* number of Black non-Hispanic: 9; American Indian or Alaska Native: 1; Asian or Pacific Islander: 1; Hispanic 3; White non-Hispanic: 142. *Age distribution:* number under 18: 6; 18–19: 40; 20–21: 45; 22–24: 22; 25–29: 12; 30–34: 5; 35–39: 6, 40–49: 13, 50–64: 5. 65 and over: 1.

International Students: No programs available to aid students whose native language is not English. Some financial aid specifically designated for international students.

Student Life: On-campus residence halls house 67% of student body. All residence halls are fully carpeted and air conditioned and are equipped with lobbies, kitchens, snack areas and sun-deck. Most classes are over by 3pm every day. Daily chapel. *Intercollegiate athletics:* basketball, volleyball. *Special regulations:* All students permitted to have cars. *Student publications:* yearbook. *Surrounding community:* Campus is 45 minutes from the beaches of Nags Head (NC) and the city of Norfolk (VA).

Library Collections: 30,000 volumes. 9,876 microforms; 6,531 audiovisual materials; 214 current periodical subscriptions. Computer work stations available. Students have access to online information retrieval services and the Internet.

Most important special holdings include collections on creation science, the deaf, the mentally retarded, Discipliana.

Buildings and Grounds: Campus area 20 waterfront acres.

Chief Executive Officer: Dr. D. Clay Perkins, President.

Address admission inquiries to Andrea Stamper, Director of Admissions and Financial Aid.

St. Andrews Presbyterian College

1700 Dogwood Mile
Laurinburg, North Carolina 28352
Tel: (910) 277-5000 **E-mail:** admissions@sapc.edu
Fax: (910) 277-5087 **Internet:** www.sapc.edu

Institution Description: St. Andrews Presbyterian College is a private college affiliated with the Synod of North Carolina, Presbyterian Church in the U.S. Branch college at Pinehurst, North Carolina (junior/senior level). *Enrollment:* 623. *Degrees awarded:* Baccalaureate.

Accreditation: *Regional:* SACS-Comm. on Coll.

History: Established as Consolidated Presbyterian College 1955 through merger of Flora Macdonald College (established 1896) and Presbyterian Junior College for Men (established 1928); chartered 1958; adopted present name 1960 offered first instruction at postsecondary level 1961; awarded first degree (baccalaureate) 1962.

Institutional Structure: *Governing board:* Board of Trustees. Representation 36 trustees. All voting. *Composition of institution:* Administrators 8. Academic affairs headed by vice president for academic affairs. Management/business/finances directed by vice president for administration and finance. Full-time instructional faculty 42. Academic governance body, the faculty, meets an average of 8 times per year.

Calendar: Semesters. Academic year Aug. to May. Freshmen admitted Sept., Jan., Feb., June, July. Degrees conferred and formal commencement May. Summer session of 2 terms from late June to early Aug.

Characteristics of Freshmen: 76% of applicants accepted. 21 of accepted applicants enrolled.

96% (188 students) submitted SAT scores; 31% (58 students) submitted ACT scores; *25th percentile*: SAT Critical Reading 560, SAT Math 560. *75th percentile*: SAT Critical Reading 440, SAT Math 450.

65% of entering freshmen expected to graduate within 5 years. 39% of freshmen from North Carolina. Freshmen from 34 states and 14 foreign countries.

Admission: Rolling admissions plan. Apply no later than first week of classes. Early acceptance available. *Requirements:* Either graduation from accredited secondary school or GED. Recommend 15 units including 4 English, 2 in a foreign language, 3 mathematics, 3 science. 2 social science. *Entrance tests:* College Board SAT or ACT composite. *For transfer students:* from 4-year accredited institution 90 semester hours maximum transfer credit; from 2-year accredited institution 65 hours; correspondence / extension students 6 hours.

Degree Requirements: 120 semester hours; 2.0 GPA; 2 terms in residence; 1 physical education course; general education requirements.

Fulfillment of some degree requirements and exemption from some beginning courses possible by passing College Board CLEP, APP. *Grading system:* A–F; pass-fail; withdraw (carries time limit); incomplete (carries time limit).

Distinctive Educational Programs: Internships. Evening classes. Accelerated degree programs. Facilities for independent research, including honors programs, individual majors, tutorials. Study abroad at Brunnenburg Castle, Northern Italy; Ecuador Exchange Program in Cuenca, Ecuador; study Chinese language and culture in Beijing, China; additional opportunities through several other exchange programs.

Degrees Conferred: 171 *baccalaureate*: biological/life sciences 6; business/marketing 34; communications/journalism 3; education 17; English 12; health professions and related sciences 4; history 1; law/legal studies 1; liberal arts/general studies 7; mathematics 1; parks and recreation 8; philosophy and religious studies 3; physical sciences 3; psychology 6; social sciences 12; visual and performing arts 1.

Fees and Other Expenses: *Full-time tuition per academic year 2008–09:* $20,375. *Room and board per academic year:* $6,425. *Books and supplies:* $1,200. *Other expenses:* $4,500.

Financial Aid: Aid from institutionally generated funds is provided on the basis of academic merit, financial need, athletic ability, other criteria.

Financial aid to full-time, first-time undergraduate students: 90% of student body received some form of financial aid.

Departments and Teaching Staff: *Total instructional faculty:* 84 (full-time 42, part-time 42). 885 of faculty hold the doctorate, first-professional, or other terminal degree.

Enrollment: Total enrollment 625 (undergraduate).

Characteristics of Student Body: *Ethnic/racial makeup:* number of Black non-Hispanic: 72; American Indian or Alaska Native: 6; Asian or Pacific Islander: 9; Hispanic: 24; White non-Hispanic: 672. *Age distribution:* number 18–19: 290; 20–21: 273; 22–24: 135; 25–29: 31; 30–34: 20; 35–39: 20; 40–49: 24; 50–64: 12; unknown: 3.

International Students: 25 nonresident aliens enrolled fall 2008. Students from Europe, Central and South America, Africa, Canada. No programs available to aid students whose native language is not English. No financial aid specifically designated for international students.

Student Life: On-campus residence halls house 80% of student body. Residence halls for males constitute 30% of such space, for females 29%, for both sexes 41%. *Intercollegiate athletics:* male: baseball, basketball, cross-county, golf, lacrosse, soccer, swimming, tennis, track, wrestling; female: basketball, lacrosse, soccer, softball, swimming, tennis, volleyball. *Special regulations:* Cars permitted without restrictions. Quiet hours begin 9pm Sun.–Thurs. *Special services:* Learning Resources Center, medical services. *Student publications, radio: The Cairn*, an annual literary magazine; *The Lamp and Shield*, a yearbook; *The Lance*, a weekly newspaper. Radio station WASP broadcasts irregular hours. *Surrounding community:* Laurinburg population 12,000. Charlotte, 100 miles from campus, is nearest metropolitan area. Served by airport 40 miles from campus; passenger rail service 10 miles from campus.

Library Collections: 134,000 volumes. Current periodical subscriptions: paper 187; microform 124; 13,972 via electronic access. 931 recordings; 12 compact discs; 28 CD-ROMs. Online catalog. Students have access to online information retrieval services and the Internet.

Most important special holdings include Scottish Collection; Rare Books Collection; St. Andrews Collection.

Buildings and Grounds: Campus area 600 acres.

Chief Executive Officer: Dr. John Deegan, Jr., President.

Address admission inquiries to Glen Batten, Vice President for Enrollment.

Saint Augustine's College

1315 Oakwood Avenue
Raleigh, North Carolina 27612-2298
Tel: (919) 516-4000 **E-mail:** admissions@st-aug.edu
Fax: (919) 516-4415 **Internet:** www.st-aug.edu

Institution Description: Saint Augustine's College is a private college affiliated with the Episcopal Church. *Enrollment:* 1,451. *Degrees awarded:* Baccalaureate.

Member of the consortium Raleigh Cooperating Colleges.

Accreditation: *Regional:* SACS-Comm. on Coll.

History: Established as Saint Augustine's Normal School and Collegiate Institute 1867; changed name to Saint Augustine's School 1893; offered first instruction at postsecondary level and changed name to Saint Augustine's Junior College 1919; became 4-year institution 1927; adopted present name 1928; awarded first degree (baccalaureate) 1931. *See* C. D. Halliburton, *A History of Saint Augustine's College* (Raleigh: Broughton Press, 1937) for further information.

Institutional Structure: *Governing board:* Board of Trustees. Representation: 34 trustees, including 6 alumni, president of the college, 2 students. All voting. *Composition of institution:* Administrators 6. Academic affairs headed by dean of academic affairs. Management/business/finances directed by vice president for financial affairs. Full-time instructional faculty 94. Academic governance body, Curriculum Council, meets at least twice each semester.

Calendar: Semesters. Academic year Aug. to May. Freshmen admitted Aug., Jan. Degrees conferred and formal commencement May. Summer session of 1 term from early June to mid-July.

Characteristics of Freshmen: 3,488 applicants (female 1,962, male 1,526). 44% of applicants admitted. 27% of admitted students enrolled full-time.

76% (315 students) submitted SAT scores; 24% (98 students) submitted ACT scores. *25th percentile*: SAT Critical Reading 310, SAT Math 310; ACT Composite 12, ACT English 11, ACT Math 12. *75th percentile*: SAT Critical Reading 460, SAT Math 420; ACT Composite 19, ACT English 16, ACT Math 20.

31% of freshmen expected to graduate within 5 years. 51% of freshmen from North Carolina. Freshmen from 34 states and 17 foreign countries.

Admission: Rolling admissions plan. For fall acceptance, apply no later than July 1. *Requirements:* Either graduation from accredited secondary school with 16 units which must include 4 English. 2 science, 2 social studies, 1 mathematics; or GED. Minimum GPA 2.0. *Entrance tests:* College Board SAT. *For transfer students:* 2.0 minimum GPA, maximum transfer credit limited only by residence requirement.

College credit and advanced placement for postsecondary-level work completed in secondary school.

Tutoring available. Developmental courses offered in summer session and regular academic year; credit given.

Degree Requirements: 120 credit hours; 2.0 GPA; 30 hours in residence; 2 hours physical education; core requirements; undergraduate assessment program tests; comprehensives in individual fields of study. *Grading system:* A–F; withdraw (carries penalty); incomplete (carries time limit).

SAINT AUGUSTINE'S COLLEGE—*cont'd*

Distinctive Educational Programs: Cooperative education, internships. Weekend and evening classes. Accelerated degree programs. Cooperative baccalaureates in engineering with North Carolina State University, African American studies and international studies. Study abroad in the Bahamas and England.

ROTC: Army.

Degrees Conferred: 168 *baccalaureate*. Degrees awarded in top five disciplines: business/marketing 86; social sciences 26; computer and information sciences 25; security and protective services 22; communication, journalism, and related programs 15.

Fees and Other Expenses: *Full-time tuition per academic year* $14,124. *Room and board per academic year:* $6,652. *Books and supplies:* $1,470. *Other expenses:* $3,213.

Financial Aid: Aid from institutionally generated funds is provided on the basis of academic merit, athletic ability, financial need, other criteria. Institution has a Program Participation Agreement with the U.S. Department of Education for eligible students to receive Pell Grants and, depending upon the agreement, other federal aid.

Financial aid to full-time, first-time undergraduate students: 99% of students received some form of financial aid. Average amount of aid received: federal grants $5,905; state/local grants $3,006; institutional grants $8,054; loans $7,093.

Departments and Teaching Staff: *Total instructional faculty:* 114. Student/faculty ratio: 16:1. Degrees held by full-time faculty: doctorate 45%, master's 52%, baccalaureate 1%, professional 25. 47% hold terminal degrees.

Enrollment: Total enrollment 1,451 (undergraduate). Transfer-in students 47.

Characteristics of Student Body: *Ethnic/racial makeup:* number of Black non-Hispanic: 92%; Hispanic: 1%; other 7%.

International Students: 62 nonresident aliens enrolled fall 2008.

Student Life: On-campus residence halls house 70% of student body. *Intercollegiate athletics:* male: baseball, fencing, golf, soccer, tennis, track; female: basketball, softball, tennis, track, volleyball. *Special regulations:* Registered cars permitted without restrictions. Residence hall visitation from 5pm to 11pm. *Special services:* Learning Resources Center, medical services. *Student publications, The Falcon,* a yearbook; *The Pen,* a monthly newspaper. *Surrounding community:* Raleigh, population 240,000. is located in Raleigh-Durham metropolitan area. Served by airport 14 miles from campus; passenger rail service 1 mile from campus.

Publications: *The Faculty Research Journal* (annually) first published in 1963.

Library Collections: 159,500 volumes. 500 microforms; 760 current periodical subscriptions. Online catalog. Students have access to online information retrieval services and the Internet.

Buildings and Grounds: Campus area 110 acres.

Chief Executive Officer: Dr. Dianne Broadley Suber, President.

Address admission inquiries to Timothy Chapman, Director of Admissions.

Salem College

601 South Church Street
Winston-Salem, North Carolina 27101
Tel: (336) 721-2600 **E-mail:** admissions@salem.edu
Fax: (336) 724-7102 **Internet:** www.salem.edu

Institution Description: Salem College is a private college for women affiliated with the Moravian Church. *Enrollment:* 939. *Degrees awarded:* Baccalaureate, master's.

Accreditation: *Regional:* SACS-Comm. on Coll. *Professional* music, teacher education

History: Established as Salem Female Academy 1772; incorporated 1866; offered first instruction at postsecondary level 1877; awarded first degree (baccalaureate) 1890; adopted present name 1897. *See* Frances Griffen, *Less Time for Meddling* (Winston-Salem, N.C.: John F. Blair, 1980) for further information.

Institutional Structure: *Governing board:* Salem Academy and College Board of Trustees. Extrainstitutional representation: 28 trustees; 12 alumnae. All voting. *Composition of institution:* Administrators 10. Academic affairs headed by Dean of the College. Management/business/finances directed by Chief Business Officer. Full-time instructional faculty 61. Academic governance body, Salem College Faculty, meets an average of 9 times per year.

Calendar: Semesters (4-1-4 plan). Academic year Aug. to May. Freshmen admitted Aug., Jan., Feb. Degrees conferred and formal commencement May. Summer session of two terms.

Characteristics of Freshmen: 438 applicants (female 438). 59% of applicants admitted. 49% of admitted applicants enrolled full-time.

88% (108 students) submitted SAT scores; 26% (32 students) submitted ACT scores. *25th percentile*: SAT Critical Reading 480, SAT Math 470; ACT Composite 22, SAT English 24, SAT Math 18. *75th percentile*: SAT Critical Reading 610, SAT Math 580; ACT Composite 28; ACT English 30,ACT Math 26. >pt<54% of entering freshmen expected to graduate within 5 years. 51% of freshmen from North Carolina. Freshmen from 23 states and 18 foreign countries.

Admission: Rolling admissions plan. For fall acceptance, apply no later than 2 weeks prior to enrollment. Early acceptance available. *Requirements:* Either graduation from accredited secondary school or GED. Recommend 16 units, including 4 English, 2 in a foreign language, 3 mathematics, 2 history, 1 laboratory science, 4 academic electives. *Entrance tests:* College Board SAT or ACT composite. *For transfer students:* 2.0 minimum GPA; 27 courses maximum transfer credit; from 2-year accredited institution 20 courses maximum.

College credit and advanced placement for postsecondary-level work completed in secondary school.

Degree Requirements: 36 courses; 2.0 GPA; 2 terms in residence; 2 years physical education. Fulfillment of some degree requirements and exemption from some beginning courses possible by passing departmental examinations, College Board AP. *Grading system:* A–F; pass-fail; withdraw (deadline after which pass-fail is appended to withdraw); incomplete (carries time limit).

Distinctive Educational Programs: Cooperative baccalaureate program in medical technology with approved medical schools. Interdepartmental/interdisciplinary programs in American studies, arts management, fine arts, foreign language management, interior design, international relations. Facilities and programs for independent research, including honors courses, student designed majors, and independent study. Study abroad through programs in France and Mexico, and at St. Peter's College, University of Oxford, England. Off-campus study in U.S. includes Washington (DC) semester at American University; United nations semester through Drew University (NJ). Cross-registration with Wake Forest University. *Other distinctive programs:* Affiliation with Bowman Gray School of Medicine for physician assistant program; affiliation with Duke University and Vanderbilt University for pre-engineering program. Continuing education.

Degrees Conferred: 157 *baccalaureate*; 44 *master's*. Bachelor's degrees awarded in top five disciplines: social sciences 35; visual and performing arts 26, psychology 24, English 22; business, management, marketing, and related support services 21. Master's degrees awarded: education 44.

Fees and Other Expenses: *Full-time tuition per academic year 2008–09:* $20,415. *Books and supplies:* $950. *Room and board per academic year:* $10,705. *Other expenses:* $3,540.

Financial Aid: Aid from institutionally generated funds is provided on the basis of academic merit, financial need. Institution has a Program Participation Agreement with the U.S. Department of Education for eligible students to receive Pell Grants and, depending upon the agreement, other federal aid.

Financial aid to full-time, first-time undergraduate students: 100% of student body received some form of financial aid.

Departments and Teaching Staff: *Total instructional faculty:* 103 (full-time 61, part-time 42). Student/faculty ratio: 13:1. Degrees held by full-time faculty: baccalaureate 100%, master's 100%, doctorate 80%. 92% hold terminal degrees.

Enrollment: Total enrollment 939. Undergraduate 735. Graduate 204 (full-time 9%). Undergraduate transfer-in students 99.

Characteristics of Student Body: *Ethnic/racial makeup:* number of Black non-Hispanic: 136; American Indian or Alaska Native: 2; Asian or Pacific Islander: 9; Hispanic: 28; White non-Hispanic: 556; unknown: 54. *Age distribution:* number under 18: 33; 18–19: 212; 20–21: 336; 22–24: 71; 25–29: 92; 30–34: 47; 35–39: 55; 40–49: 74; 50–64: 42.

International Students: 96 nonresident aliens enrolled fall 2008. Students from Europe, Asia, Central and South America, Africa, Canada. No programs available to aid students whose native language is not English. *Financial aid specifically designated for undergraduate international students:* One scholarships available annually.

Student Life: On-campus residence halls house 36% of student body. Residence halls for females only constitute 100% of such space. *Intercollegiate athletics:* female: tennis, field hockey, horseback riding, soccer, volleyball. *Special regulations:* Registered cars permitted; fee charged. Quiet hours from 7pm to 10pm and 10:30pm to 8am. Sun.–Thurs. Residence hall visitation Sun. through Thurs. from noon to 11:45pm and 11am to 1:45am Fri. and Sat. *Special services:* medical services. *Student publications, Incunabula,* a semiannual literary magazine; the *Salemite*, a monthly newspaper; *Sights and Insights*, a yearbook. *Surrounding community:* Greensboro/Winston-Salem/High Point metropolitan area population 830,000. Served by mass transit bus system; airport 20 miles from campus; passenger rail service 30 miles from campus.

Library Collections: 152,000 olumes. 303,000 microforms; 13,600 audiovisual materials; 15,000 periodicals including via electronic access. Online catalog. Students have access to online information retrieval services and the Internet.

Most important special collections include North Carolina and Moravian History; Samuel Johnson/James Boswell Collection; U.S. Slavery Debate; Southern Women Writers.

Buildings and Grounds: Campus area 57 acres.

Chief Executive Officer: Dr. Susan Pauly, President.

Address admission inquiries to Donna E. Evans, Dean of Admissions.

Shaw University

118 East South Street
Raleigh, North Carolina 27601
Tel: (919) 546-8200 **E-mail:** admissions@shawu.edu
Fax: (919) 546-8271 **Internet:** www.shawu.edu

Institution Description: Shaw University is a private independent institution. *Enrollment:* 2,882. *Degrees awarded:* Associate, baccalaureate.

Member of the consortium Cooperating Raleigh Colleges.

Accreditation: *Regional:* SACS-Comm. on Coll. *National:* ATS. *Professional*: teacher education, theology

History: Established as Raleigh Institute 1865; changed name to Shaw Collegiate Institute 1870; offered first instruction at postsecondary level 1874; adopted present name 1875; awarded first degree (baccalaureate) 1878. *See* Wilmoth A. Carter, *Shaw's Universe* (Rockville, MD: D.C. National Publishing, Inc., 1973) for further information.

Institutional Structure: *Governing board:* Trustee Board. Extrainstitutional representation: 39 trustees, including 1 honorary trustees, 1 student, 4 ex officio. 38 voting. *Composition of institution:* 9 senior administrators. Academic affairs headed by vice president of academic affairs and research. Management/business/finances directed by business manager. Full-time instructional faculty 85. Academic governance body, Faculty Senate, meets 8 times per year.

Calendar: Semesters. Academic year Aug. to July. Freshmen admitted Aug., Jan. Degrees conferred and formal commencement May. No summer session.

Characteristics of Freshmen: 4,226 applicants. 65% of applicants accepted. 21% of accepted applicants enrolled.

61% (366 students) submitted SAT scores; 19% (118 students) submitted ACT scores.

25th percentile: SAT Critical Reading 330, SAT Math 320; ACT Composite 12, ACT English 9, ACT Math 13. *75th percentile*: SAT Critical Reading 430, SAT Math 430; ACT Composite 16, ACT English 15, ACT Math 16.

29% of entering freshmen expected to graduate within 5 years. 73% of freshmen from North Carolina. Freshmen from 32 states and 10 foreign countries.

Admission: Rolling admissions plan. Application deadline Aug. 30 for fall; Nov. 30 for spring. Apply no later than day of registration. Apply by fall of senior year for early decision. *Requirements:* Either graduation from accredited secondary school with 18 units which must include 3 English, 2 mathematics, 2 natural sciences, 2 social sciences, 9 electives. GED accepted. *For transfer students:* Minimum grade average C; from 4 year accredited institution 90 semester hours maximum transfer credit; from 2-year accredited institution 70 hours.

College credit for extrainstitutional learning on basis of portfolio assessment. Tutoring available.

Degree Requirements: 120 credit hours; 2.0 GPA on 4.0 scale; 30 semester hours in residence; completion of all major and university core requirements; English and mathematics proficiency by examination. *Grading system:* A–F.

Distinctive Educational Programs: Off-campus centers (at Charleston, SC; Fayetteville; High Point). Evening classes. Honors program. Dual-degree programs in pre-engineering, with North Carolina State University at Raleigh. Study abroad, usually in Middle Eastern countries.

ROTC: Army offered in cooperation with Saint Augustine's College; Air Force with North Carolina State University at Raleigh.

Degrees Conferred: 7 *associate*; 435 *baccalaureate*: 6 *master's*; 21 *first-professional:* theology. Bachelor's degrees awarded: biological/life sciences 3; business/marketing 121; communications/communication technologies 18; computer and information sciences 24; education 1; English 5; health professions and related sciences 2; liberal arts/general studies 20; mathematics 3; natural resources/environmental science 3; parks and recreation 11; philosophy/religion/theology 38; physical sciences 2; protective services/public administration 104; psychology 17; social sciences and history 37; visual and performing arts 4.

Fees and Other Expenses: *Full-time tuition per academic year 2008–09:* contact the university for current information.

Financial Aid: The university offers a direct lending program. Aid from institutionally generated funds is provided on the basis of academic merit, athletic ability, other criteria.

Financial aid to full-time, first-time undergraduate students: 95% received some form of financial aid. Average amount of aid received: federal grants $3,604; state/local grants $2,245; institutional grants $2,572; loans $5,482.

Departments and Teaching Staff: *Total instructional faculty:* 265 (full-time 105, part-time 160). Student/faculty ratio: 16:1. Degrees held by full-time faculty: doctorate 55%, master's 29%, professional 1%. 68% hold terminal degrees.

Enrollment: Total enrollment 2,882.

Characteristics of Student Body: *Ethnic/racial makeup:* number of Black non-Hispanic: 2,239; American Indian or Alaska Native: 1; Asian or Pacific Islander: 1; Hispanic: 5; White non-Hispanic: 42; unknown: 176. *Age distribution:* number under 18: 4; 18–19: 462; 20–21: 469; 22–24: 419; 25–29: 246; 30–34: 218; 35–39: 180; 40–49: 284; 50–64: 146; 65 and over: 3. 16% of student body attend summer sessions. Correspondence courses offered for credit.

International Students: 27 nonresident aliens enrolled fall 2008. No programs available to aid students whose native language is not English. No financial aid specifically designated for international students.

Student Life: On-campus residence halls house 55% of student body. *Intercollegiate athletics:* male: baseball, basketball, cross-country, indoor/outdoor track, golf, tennis; female: basketball, bowling, cross-country, indoor/outdoor track, softball, tennis, volleyball. Student government, fraternities and sororities, intramural sports, academic and social clubs, choir, jazz band, marching band, cheerleading, dance club, theater group. *Special regulations:* Cars permitted without restrictions. *Special services:* Learning Resources Center, medical services. *Student publications, radio: The University Yearbook.* Radio station WSHA broadcasts 168 hours per week. *Surrounding community:* Raleigh population 150,000. Served by airport 15 miles from campus; passenger rail service 10 blocks from campus.

Library Collections: 153,000 volumes. 2,497 paper and microform serial subscriptions.] 16,050 audiovisual materials. Online catalog. Computer work stations available. Students have access to online information retrieval services and the Internet.

Most important special collections include African American Collection; John Fleming Collection; Large Print Collection.

Buildings and Grounds: Campus area 30 acres.

Chief Executive Officer: Dr. Clarence G. Newsome, President.

Address admission inquiries to Cassandra Clifton, Director of Admissions.

Southeastern Baptist Theological Seminary

120 South Wingate
P.O. Box 1889
Wake Forest, North Carolina 27588-1889
Tel: (919) 556-3101 **E-mail:** admissions@sebts.edu
Fax: (919) 556-0998 **Internet:** www.sebts.edu

Institution Description: Southeastern Baptist Theological Seminary is a private institution affiliated with the Southern Baptist Convention. *Enrollment:* 2,109. *Degrees awarded:* First-professional (master of divinity), master's, doctorate. Associate of divinity awarded through program for students over 30 years of age.

Accreditation: *Regional:* SACS-Comm. on Coll. *National:* ATS. *Professional*: theology

History: Established and chartered 1950; offered first instruction at postsecondary level 1951; awarded first degree (first-professional) 1954.

Institutional Structure: *Governing board:* Board of Trustees of Southern Baptist Theological Seminary. Extrainstitutional representation: 30 trustees. All voting. *Composition of institution:* Academic affairs headed by dean of the faculty. Management/business/finances directed by assistant to the president for business affairs. Full-time instructional faculty 33. Academic governance body, Academic Policy and Procedure Committee, meets an average of 9 times per year.

Calendar: Semesters. Academic year Aug. to May. Students admitted Aug., Jan., June, July. Degrees conferred and formal commencement May, Dec. Summer session of 2 terms from mid-June to early Aug.

Admission: Rolling admissions plan. For fall acceptance, apply as early as 1 year prior to enrollment, but not later than 30 days prior to beginning of semester (60 days for master's students). *Requirements:* Either baccalaureate in liberal arts from accredited college or university, or 112 semester hours undergraduate coursework with 75 hours in liberal arts. *For transfer students:* 2.0 minimum GPA; maximum transfer credit limited only by residence requirement.

Noncredit remedial courses offered during regular academic year for associate degree program only.

Degree Requirements: *For first-professional degree:* 88 semester hours; 1.0 GPA on a 3.0 scale. *For master of arts in Christian education and master of arts in church music* 64 hours. *For all degrees:* 26 hours in residence; core courses in scripture, theology, and the Christian tradition; supervised ministries. *Grading system:* A–F; withdraw (deadline after which pass-fail is appended to withdraw).

Distinctive Educational Programs: Interdisciplinary course in library resources in theological education and in ministry; interdisciplinary colloquia in

UNIVERSITY OF NORTH CAROLINA AT CHARLOTTE—*cont'd*

Admission: Applicants are admitted to the nursing major at the upper division only. Nursing students must present biology and chemistry. Minimum criteria: GPA 2.5 or better in all college coursework; minimum of C in all required prerequisites.

Degree Requirements: Bachelor of Science in nursing requires 120 semester hours; last 30 semester hours must be earned in residence. Contact the college for current requirements for the master's degree program.

University of North Carolina at Greensboro

1000 Spring Garden Street
Greensboro, North Carolina 27403
Tel: (336) 334-5000 **E-mail:** admissions@uncg.edu
Fax: (336) 334-5946 **Internet:** www.uncg.edu

Institution Description: *Enrollment:* 19,976. *Degrees awarded:* Baccalaureate, master's, doctorate. Education Specialist and Certificate of Advanced Study also awarded. Member of Greensboro Regional Consortium of Higher Education.

Accreditation: *Regional:* SACS-Comm. on Coll. *Professional*: business, chemistry, clinical psychology, counseling, audiology, dietetics, interior design, librarianship, music, nursing, recreation and leisure services, social work, teacher education

History: Established and incorporated as State Normal and Industrial School for Women 1891; offered first instruction at postsecondary level 1892; changed name to State Normal and Industrial College 1897; awarded first degree (baccalaureate) 1903; changed name to North Carolina College for Women 1918, to Women's College of The University of North Carolina 1932; adopted present name 1963; became coeducational 1967. *See* Elizabeth Ann Bowles, *A Good Beginning: The First Four Decades of The University of North Carolina at Greensboro* (Chapel Hill, NC: University of North Carolina Press, 1967) for further information.

Institutional Structure: *Governing board:* Board of Trustees. Extrainstitutional representation: 13 trustees; 8 elected by the Board of Governors of the University System; 4 appointed by governor of North Carolina; 1 student body president ex officio. *Composition of institution:* Administrators 67. Academic affairs headed by provost. Management/business/finances directed by vice chancellor for business affairs. Full-time instructional faculty 746. Academic governance body, Faculty Senate, meets not less than 4 times per year.

Calendar: Semesters. Academic year Aug. to May. Freshmen admitted Aug., Jan., May. Degrees conferred May, Aug., Dec. Formal commencement May. Summer session from May to Aug.

Characteristics of Freshmen: 8,856 applicants (female 8,076, male 2,780). 71% of applicants accepted. 39% of accepted applicants enrolled full-time.

97% (2,377 students) submitted SAT scores; 12% (283 students) submitted ACT scores. *25th percentile*: SAT Critical Reading 460, SAT Math 470, SAt Writing 450; ACT Composite 19, ACT English 18, ACT Math 18. *75th percentile*: SAT Critical Reading 570, SAT Math 570, SAT Writing 550; ACT Composite 23, ACT English 23, ACT Math 24.

48% of freshmen expected to graduate within 5 years. Freshmen from 49 states and 28 foreign countries.

Admission: Rolling admissions plan. For fall acceptance, apply no later than Aug. 1. *Requirements:* Either graduation from accredited secondary school with 15 units which must include 4 English, 2 in a foreign language, 3 college preparatory mathematics, 2 social studies, 3 science; or GED. Provisional admission possible for graduates from nonaccredited secondary school. Additional requirements for music applicants. Lowest acceptable secondary school class standing 50th percentile. *Entrance tests:* College Board SAT or ACT composite. For foreign students TOEFL. *For transfer students:* 2.0 minimum GPA; from 4-year accredited institution unlimited transfer credit; from 2-year accredited institution and for correspondence/extension students 64 hours.

College credit and advanced placement for postsecondary-level work completed in secondary school. Tutoring available.

Degree Requirements: *For undergraduate degrees:* 122 semester hours; 2.0 GPA; 30 hours in residence; general education requirements; core course requirements. Additional requirements for some schools. *Grading system:* A–F; withdraw (deadline after which pass-fail is appended to withdraw).

Distinctive Educational Programs: Accelerated degree program. Challenge exams for registered nurses; special examinations. Honors Program. Graduation with honors. Cooperative education program. Combined bachelor's/graduate program. External degree program. Advanced placement. College-Level Examination Program. Junior Year Abroad; summer study and travel abroad in Australia, Costa Rica, Finland, France, Germany, Spain, Sweden, Poland, United Kingdom. *Other distinctive programs:* Plan II allows students to design their own course of study. Interdepartmental studies; international studies. Cross-registration through Greater Greensboro Consortium. Residential College. Special Services Program. Nontraditional studies program.

ROTC: Army, Air Force in cooperation with North Carolina Agricultural and Technical State University.

Degrees Conferred: 2,388 *baccalaureate*; 807 *master's*; 93 *doctorate*. Bachelor's degrees awarded in top five disciplines: business, management, marketing, and related support services 339; education 293; health professions and related sciences 217; social sciences 166; English language/literature 157. Master's degrees awarded in top five disciplines: business/marketing 173; education 171; health professions 145; library science 92; visual and performing arts 58, Doctorates awarded: education 46; English 6; interdisciplinary studies 3; parks and recreation 7; psychology 9; visual and performing arts 26.

Fees and Other Expenses: *Full-time tuition per academic year 2008–09:* resident undergraduate $4,135, nonresident $15,629; contact the university for current graduate tuition/fees. *Books and supplies:* $1,730. *Room and board per academic year:* $6,288. *Other expenses:* $2,440.

Financial Aid: Aid from institutionally generated funds is provided on the basis of academic merit, financial need, athletic ability, other criteria.

Financial aid to full-time, first-time undergraduate students: 89% received some form of aid. Average amount of aid received: federal grants $3,668; Pell grants $2,383; other federal aid $897; state/local grants $3,001; institutional grants $2,507.

Departments and Teaching Staff:
Total instructional faculty: 989 (full-time 746, part-time 243). 94% of faculty hold the doctorate, first-professional, or other terminal degree. Student/faculty ratio: 16:1.

Enrollment: Total enrollment 19,976. Undergraduate 16,194. Graduate 3,782 (full-time 34%). Undergraduate transfer-in students 1,495.

Characteristics of Student Body: *Ethnic/racial makeup (undergraduate):* number of Black non-Hispanic: 2,604; American Indian or Alaska Native: 58; Asian or Pacific Islander: 436; Hispanic: 300; White non-Hispanic: 8,839, unknown: 587. *Age distribution:* number under 18: 472; 18–19: 4,332; 20–21: 3,767; 22–24: 1,994; 25–29: 265; 30–34: 98; 35–39: 265; 40–49: 357; 50–64: 98; 65 and over: 235.

International Students: 297 undergraduate nonresident aliens enrolled fall 2008. No programs available to aid students whose native language is not English. No financial aid specifically designated for international students.

Student Life: On-campus residence halls house nearly 4,000 students in both single-sex and co-ed halls; apartment-style housing is available. Approximately 80% of freshmen live on campus. Elliott University Center provides space for many campus groups and activities, including over 150 student organizations. State-of-the-art Student Recreation Facility provides basketball courts, running track, handball/squash courts, fitness equipment, aerobics and dance classrooms for individual, informal group and intramural activities. Swimming pool available in HHP Building next door. Renovated dining facility provides 3 different eating areas with a variety of meal plans and cash options; 10 different food areas on the campus: pizza, deli. bakery, ice cream shop, soda shop, grill, in addition to board cafeteria and restaurants. *Intercollegiate athletics:* The campus competes in NCAA Division I athletics in 14 sports: male and female soccer, basketball, tennis, and golf; female cross-country, volleyball, softball; male baseball, cross-country, wrestling. *Special regulations:* Cars must be registered. *Special services:* Disabled Student Services including learning disabilities; Student Health Center; Counseling and Testing Center; Special Services. *Student publications, radio: Carolinian*, a newspaper; *Coraddi*, a quarterly literary magazine; *Pine Needles*, a print yearbook; *Kaleidoscope,* a video yearbook; student-run radio station WUAG. *Surrounding community:* The campus is located near the center of Greensboro, the state's third largest city. Greensboro population 238,440, is part of the Piedmont Triad (High Point and Winston-Salem). Served by mass transit bus system; airport 10 miles from campus; Amtrak 2 miles from campus.

Publications: *Greensboro Review* (biannually) first published in 1966; *North Carolina Review of Business and Economics,* (quarterly) first published 1974.

Library Collections: 3,400,000 volumes. 640,000 government documents; 1,000,000 microforms; 59,000 audiovisual materials; 8,700 periodical subscriptions including via electronic access. Online catalog. Students have access to online information retrieval services and the Internet.

Most important special holdings include Luigi Silva cello music collection; Randall Jarrell Collection; Women's Studies Collection.

Buildings and Grounds: Campus area 210 acres.

Chief Executive Officer: Dr. Patricia A. Sullivan, Chancellor.

Undergraduates address admission inquiries to Lee Keller, Director of Undergraduate Admissions; graduate inquiries to James Peterson, Dean of Graduate School.

College of Arts and Sciences

Degree Programs Offered: *Baccalaureate* in anthropology, art, biology, chemistry, communication and theater, drama, earth science, education of the deaf, English, French, geography, Germany, Greek, history, Latin, Latin American studies, mathematics, philosophy, physics, political science, psychology, religious studies, social work, sociology, Spanish, speech pathology and audiology; *master's* in biology, chemistry, communication, computer science, theatre, drama, English, French, history, mathematics, political science, psychology, sociology, Spanish; *doctorate* in English, history, psychology.

Distinctive Educational Programs: Residential College program allows lower division students who take a common core interdisciplinary program to live in the same dormitory. Weatherspoon Art Gallery provides showcase for student art. Parkway Summer Playhouse offers summer stock experience for theater students.

School of Business and Economics

Degree Programs Offered: *Baccalaureate* in accounting, business education, business education/information processing, economics, financial management, human resources, management, management information systems, marketing education, marketing, merchandising management, office systems administration, operations management, risk management and insurance; *master's* in accounting, business administration, business education, economics, information systems and operations management; *doctorate* in accounting, information systems.

School of Education

Degree Programs Offered: *Baccalaureate* in education of deaf, elementary education, middle grades education; *master's* in curriculum and instruction, library and information sciences.

Admission: 3.0 GPA for elementary education and middle grades education (undergraduates).

Distinctive Educational Programs: Field-based educational programs in cooperation with Agricultural and Technical State University and a local secondary school.

School of Health and Human Performance

Degree Programs Offered: *Baccalaureate* in dance, dance education, health education, physical education, recreation; *master's* in dance, health education, physical education; *doctorate* in physical education.

Distinctive Educational Programs: Center for Environmental and Outdoor Education provides research, service, and internship opportunities. Piney Lake Field Campus offers instruction, research, and recreation programs in outdoor laboratories. Rosenthal Human Performance Laboratory for research in physical education. Social and Motor Behavior Laboratory for research in teacher and pupil behavior and mainstreaming of the disabled.

School of Human Environmental Sciences

Degree Programs Offered: *Baccalaureate* in child development; nutrition; social work; *master's, doctorate* in child development and family relations; food, nutrition, and food service management; home economics education.

Distinctive Educational Programs: Cooperative bachelor's degree program in social work with North Carolina Agricultural and Technical State University; cooperative agreement with Egerton University of summer experience in Kenya; graduate internationalist program with Peace Corps in home economics education and nutrition; undergraduate majors in textile products marketing and design; master's degree program for preschool handicapped.

School of Music

Degree Programs Offered: *Baccalaureate, master's, doctorate.* Certificate of Advanced Study in music education also offered.

Degree Requirements: 122-132 hours.

School of Nursing

Degree Programs Offered: *Baccalaureate; master's* in: nursing; health management.

University of North Carolina at Pembroke

One University Drive
P.O. Box 1510
Pembroke, North Carolina 28372-1510
Tel: (010) 521-6000 **E-mail:** admissions@uncp.edu
Fax: (910) 521-6497 **Internet:** www.uncp.edu

Institution Description: The University of North Carolina at Pembroke was formerly known as Pembroke State University. *Enrollment:* 5,027. *Degrees awarded:* Baccalaureate, master's.

Member of North Carolina Southeastern Consortium for International Education.

Accreditation: *Regional:* SACS-Comm. on Coll. *Professional*: music, nursing, social work, teacher education

History: Established as Croatan Normal School and chartered 1887; changed name to Indian Normal School of Robeson Country 1911; offered first instruction at postsecondary level 1926; awarded first degree (baccalaureate) 1940; changed name to Pembroke State University for Indians 1941, to Pembroke State College 1949; to Pembroke State University 1969; became a part of University of North Carolina system 1972; adopted present name 1996. *See* Clifton Oxendine, *Pembroke State College for Indians* (Raleigh: North Carolina Historical Review, Division of Archives and History, Jan., 1945, pp. 22–23).

Institutional Structure: *Governing board:* University of North Carolina at Pembroke Board of Trustees. Extrainstitutional representation: 13 trustees; institutional representation: 1 student ex officio. 13 voting. *Composition of institution:* Administrators 31. Academic affairs headed by provost and vice chancellor of academic affairs. Management/business/finances directed by vice chancellor for business affairs. Full-time instructional faculty 146. Academic governance body, faculty senate, meets an average of 8 times per year.

Calendar: Semesters. Academic year Aug. to May. Freshmen admitted Aug., Jan., June, July. Degrees conferred and formal commencement May. Summer session of 2 terms from late May to early Aug.

Characteristics of Freshmen: 84% of applicants admitted. 45% of applicants admitted and enrolled.

95% (911 students) submitted SAT scores; 9% (90 students) submitted ACT scores. *25th percentile*: SAT Critical Reading 500, SAT Math 520; ACT Composite 16, ACT English 14, ACT Math 16. *75th percentile*: SAT Critical Reading 410, SAT Math 520; ACT Composite 20, ACT English 20, ACT Math 20.

34% of entering freshmen expected to graduate within 5 years. 95% of freshmen from North Carolina. Freshmen from 31 states and 21 foreign countries.

Admission: Rolling admissions plan. For fall acceptance, apply as early as completion of junior year of secondary school, but not later than July 15 of year of enrollment; by Dec. 1 for spring. *Requirements:* Graduation from accredited secondary school or GED. Required 4 units English, 3 units mathematics (including algebra I, algebra II, geometry); 3 units science (with 1 lab), 2 units social studies. Recommended 2 units foreign language. Minimum GPA 2.0. *Entrance tests:* College Board SAT or ACT composite. For foreign students TOEFL. *For transfer students:* 2.0 minimum GPA. From 4-year accredited institution unlimited transfer credit accepted. From 2-year accredited institution 64 hours maximum transfer credit; no student with junior status will be allowed to transfer credit for any college work completed after that time in a 2-year institution. A 30 hour residency is required. Correspondence / extension students 12 maximum transfer credit.

College credit and advanced placement for postsecondary-level work completed in secondary school.

Tutoring available. Noncredit Developmental courses offered in summer session and regular academic year.

Degree Requirements: *For all undergraduate degrees:* Minimum of 128 semester hours of course work; 2.0 GPA; 30 hours in residence.

Fulfillment of some degree requirements and exemption from some beginning courses possible by passing College Board CLEP, AP. *Grading system:* A–F; pass-fail; withdraw (deadline after which pass-fail is appended to withdraw).

Distinctive Educational Programs: Internships available. Evening classes. American Indian Studies Program. Honors Program. Teaching Fellows Program. *Other distinctive programs:* Continuing education.

ROTC: Army in cooperation with Campbell University;

Degrees Conferred: 555 *baccalaureate*; 110 *master's*. Bachelor's degrees awarded in top five disciplines: business/marketing 89; education 76; social sciences 57; public administration and social services 31; biological/biomedical sciences 49. Master's degrees awarded: business/marketing 5; education 72; public administration and social services 33.

Fees and Other Expenses: *Full-time tuition per academic year 2008–09:* contact the university for current information regarding tuition, fees, housing, and other expenses.

UNIVERSITY OF NORTH CAROLINA AT PEMBROKE—*cont'd*

Financial Aid: Aid from institutionally generated funds is provided on the basis of academic merit, financial need, athletic ability.

Departments and Teaching Staff: *Total instructional faculty:* 355 (full-time 226, part-time 129). 78% of faculty hold the doctorate, first-professional, or other terminal degree. Student/faculty ratio: 15:1.

Enrollment: Total enrollment 5,827.

Characteristics of Student Body: *Ethnic/racial makeup:* number of Black non-Hispanic: 1,207; American Indian or Alaska Native: 1,070; Asian or Pacific Islander: 92; Hispanic: 142; White non-Hispanic: 2,345; unknown: 73. *Age distribution:* number under 18: 27; 18–19: 1,425; 20–21: 971; 22–24: 748; 25–29: 651; 30–34: 369; 35–39: 258; 40–49: 384; 50–64: 128; 65 and over: 2.

International Students: 70 nonresident aliens enrolled fall 2008. Students from Europe, Canada, Australia. No programs available to aid students whose native language is not English. No financial aid specifically designated for international students.

Student Life: On-campus residence halls house 25% of student body. 46% of students living in dormitories are female, 54% are male. *Intercollegiate athletics:* male: baseball, golf, soccer, track/field, wrestling; female: softball, volleyball;male and female basketball, cross-country running, tennis. *Special regulations:* Cars must be registered. Residence hall visitation from noon to midnight Sun. through Thurs., noon to 1am Fri. through Sat. *Special services:* Learning Resources Center, medical services. *Student publications:* Indian-*head*, a yearbook; *Pine Needle*, a newspaper published every 2 weeks. *Surrounding community:* Pembroke. Fayetteville (NC) 43 miles from campus; Raleigh (NC) 105 miles from campus.

Publications: *Pembroke Magazine* (annually) first published in 1969.

Library Collections: 350,000 volumes. Current periodical subscriptions: 1,300 paper; 13,823 via electronic access. Access to online information retrieval services.

Most important special holdings include Native American Archives; Lumbee History collection; North Carolina history collection; Congressman Charlie Rose's government papers.

Buildings and Grounds: Campus area 152 acres.

Chief Executive Officer: Dr. Allen C. Meaders, Chancellor.

Undergraduates address admission inquiries to Lela Clark, Director of Admissions; graduate inquiries to Kathleen Hilton, Dean, School of Graduate Studies.

University of North Carolina at Wilmington

601 South College Road
Wilmington, North Carolina 28403-5963
Tel: (910) 962-3000 **E-mail:** admissions@uncw.edu
Fax: (910) 962-3038 **Internet:** www.uncw.edu

Institution Description: *Enrollment:* 12,643. *Degrees awarded:* Baccalaureate, master's, doctorate.

Accreditation: *Regional:* SACS-Comm. on Coll. *Professional*: business, chemistry, nursing, teacher education

History: Established as Wilmington College, chartered, and offered first instruction at postsecondary level 1947; awarded first degree (associate) 1949; added baccalaureate program 1963; adopted present name and became a campus of University of North Carolina 1969; added graduate program 1977.

Institutional Structure: *Governing board:* Board of Trustees of The University of North Carolina at Wilmington. Extrainstitutional representation: 15 trustees; institutional representation: 1 student. 1 ex officio. *Composition of institution:* Administrators 267. Academic affairs headed by vice chancellor for academic affairs. Management/business/finances directed by vice chancellor for business affairs. Full-time instructional faculty 515. Academic governance body, Faculty Senate, meets an average of 9 times per year.

Calendar: Semesters. academic year Aug. to May. Freshmen admitted Aug., Jan., May, July. Degrees conferred May, Aug., Dec. Formal commencement Dec. and May. Summer session from late May to late July.

Characteristics of Freshmen: 8,740 applicants (female 5,427, male 3,313). 58% of applicants admitted. 38% of applicants admitted and enrolled full-time.

84% (1,613 students) submitted SAT scores; 28% (547 students) submitted ACT scores. *25th percentile:* SAT Critical Reading 530, SAT Math 540, SAT Writing 510; ACT Composite 21, ACT English 21, ACT Math 20. *75th percentile*: SAT Critical Reading 610, SAT Math 630, SAT Writing 600; ACT Composite 26, ACT English 26, ACT Math 26.

62% entering freshmen expected to graduate within 5 years. 87% of freshmen from North Carolina. Freshmen from 40 states and 37 foreign countries.

Admission: Early applications are encouraged. For fall acceptance, apply as early as 1 year prior to enrollment; closing date Feb 1. priority date Nov. 1. *Requirements:* Either graduation from approved secondary school with 4 units in English, 2 in a foreign language, 4 mathematics (algebra I and II, geometry), 2 social studies, 3 science; or GED. 5 additional units recommended. Minimum 2.5 GPA. *Entrance tests:* College Board SAT. *For transfer students:* 2.5 minimum GPA; from 4-year accredited institution 93 hours maximum transfer credit; from 2-year accredited institution 64 hours. Students offering fewer than 24 hours must meet freshman admission requirements.

College credit and advanced placement for postsecondary-level work completed in secondary school.

Noncredit developmental courses offered during regular academic year.

Degree Requirements: *For all baccalaureate degrees:* 124 hours; 31 hours in residence; 2 semesters physical education; basic studies courses. *For all undergraduate degrees:* 2.0 GPA.

Fulfillment of some degree requirements and exemption from some beginning courses possible by passing College Board CLEP, AP (score of 3). *Grading system:* A–F; withdraw (carries time limit).

Distinctive Educational Programs: Cooperative baccalaureate in engineering operations with North Carolina State University at Raleigh, in clinical research with affiliated hospitals. Interdisciplinary program in environmental studies. Honors programs. Preprofessional program in engineering. Marine sciences curriculum and research. Center for Marine Science Research at Wrightsville Beach. Summer field program in various tropical areas of the world. *Other distinctive programs:* Continuing education programs for business, social service and government agencies, civic groups, and others.

Degrees Conferred: 2,451 *baccalaureate*; 398 *master's*; 1 *doctorate*. Bachelor's degrees awarded in top five disciplines: business/marketing 566; education 219; psychology 166; visual and performing arts 145; social sciences 122. Master's degrees awarded in top five disciplines: business/marketing 104; education 84; English 42; liberal arts/general studies 29; physical sciences 25. Doctorates awarded: biological/life sciences 1.

Fees and Other Expenses: *Full-time tuition per academic year 2008–09:* undergraduate resident $4,528, nonresident $14,695; contact the university for current graduate tuition/fees. *Required fees:* $1,939. *Room and board per academic year:* $7,280. *Books and supplies:* $934. *Other expenses:* $2,510.

Financial Aid: The university sponsors the William D. Ford Federal Direct Loan Program. Aid from institutionally generated funds is provided on the basis of academic merit, financial need, athletic ability, special talent.

Financial aid to full-time, first-time undergraduate students: 57% received some form of aid. Average amount of aid received: federal grants $3,654; Pell grants $2,730; other federal aid $1,174; state/local grants $2,485; institutional grants $2,863.

Departments and Teaching Staff: *Total instructional faculty:* 492. 65% of faculty hold the doctorate, first-professional, or other terminal degree. Student/faculty ratio: 19:1.

Enrollment: Total enrollment 12,643. Undergraduate 11,311. Graduate 1,332 (full-time 38%). Undergraduate transfer-in students 1,279.

Characteristics of Student Body: *Ethnic/racial makeup:* Black non-Hispanic: 5%; Hispanic 1%; White non-Hispanic: 94%. *Age distribution:* number under 18: 50; 18–19: 3,519; 20–21: 3,857; 22–24: 2,838; 25–29: 787; 787; 30–34: 201; 35–39: 99; 40–49: 155; 50–64: 48; 65 and over: 5.

International Students: 39 nonresident aliens enrolled fall 2008. Students from Europe, Asia, Central and South America, Africa,Canada, Australia, Middle East. Program available to aid students whose native language is not English: social, cultural, English as a Second language Program. Some financial aid specifically designated for international students.

Student Life: On-campus residence halls and apartment buildings house 27% of student body. *Intercollegiate athletics:* male: soccer, basketball, tennis, golf, baseball, swimming, cross-country; female: volleyball, basketball, tennis, golf, softball, swimming, cross-country. *Special regulations:* Residence hall visitation until 11am to 11pm Sun.–Thurs; 11am to 2am Fri.–Sat. *Special services:* On-campus dining facilities, health and wellness center for all students, and services for disabled students. *Student publications, radio: The Atlantis*, a biannual literary magazine; *The Seahawk*, a weekly newspaper. Radio station WLOZ. *Surrounding community:* Wilmington population 94,300. Served by mass transit bus system; airport 10 miles from campus.

Library Collections: 553,000 volumes including bound books, serial backfiles, electronic documents, and government documents not in separate collections. Online catalog. Current serial subscriptions: 22,218 (paper, microform, electronic access). 44,525 recordings, compact discs, CD=ROMs. Students have access to online information retrieval services and the Internet.

Most important special holdings include collections on marine biology, education, and business administration.

Buildings and Grounds: Campus area 650 acres. *New buildings:* Fisher Student Center; Cultural Arts Building.

Chief Executive Officer: Dr. Rosemary DePaolo, Chancellor.

Address admission inquiries to Dr. Terrence M. Curran, Associate Provost; graduate inquiries to Robert Roer, Dean of Graduate School.

Wake Forest University

P.O. Box 7305
Reynolda Station
Winston-Salem, North Carolina 27109-7305
Tel: (336) 759-5201 **E-mail:** admissions@wfu.edu
Fax: (336) 759-6074 **Internet:** www.wfu.edu

Institution Description: Wake Forest University is a private institution. *Enrollment:* 6,862. *Degrees awarded:* Baccalaureate, first-professional (law, medicine), master's, doctorate.

Accreditation: *Regional:* SACS-Comm. on Coll. *Professional*: chemistry, cytotechnology, law, medicine, physician assisting, teacher education

History: Founded in 1834 as Wake Forest Institute in Wake Forest (NC) by the Baptist State Convention of North Carolina; relocated to Winston-Salem in 1956; present name adopted in 1967; established autonomous Board of Trustees 1986; hosted presidential debates 1988 and 2000. *See* George Pascal, *History of Wake Forest College* (Raleigh, NC: Edwards and Broughton Co., 1943) for further information.

Institutional Structure: *Governing board:* Wake Forest Board of Trustees. 40 trustees, including 1 student trustee. All voting. *Composition of institution:* Academic affairs headed by provost. Management/business/finances directed by vice president and treasurer. Full-time instructional faculty 1280. Faculty service on executive, advisory, and special committees, as well as joint committees with members of the administration.

Calendar: Semesters. Academic year Aug. to May. Freshmen admitted Aug., Jan., May. Degrees conferred May, Aug., Dec. Formal commencement May. Summer session of 2 terms from May to Aug.

Characteristics of Freshmen: 9,050 applicants (female 4,725, male 4,325). 38% of applicants accepted. 35% of accepted applicants enrolled full-time.

72% (861 students) submitted SAT scores; 28% (341 students) submitted ACT scores. *25th percentile*: SAT Critical Reading 610, SAT Math 630; ACT Composite 27. *75th percentile*: SAT Critical Reading 690, SAT Math 710; ACT Composite 31.

85% of entering freshmen expected to graduate within 5 years. 25% of freshmen from North Carolina. Freshmen from 49 states and 22 foreign countries.

Admission: For fall acceptance, students should apply by Jan. 15. Students are notified of acceptance Apr. 1. Apply by Nov. 15 for early decision. Early acceptance available. *Requirements:* Either graduation from accredited secondary school with 16 academic units which normally include 4 English, 2 in a foreign language, 3 mathematics, 2 history and social studies, 2 in a single foreign language, 1 in natural science; or GED. Additional courses in those areas recommended. *Entrance tests:* College Board SAT. For foreign students TOEFL. *For transfer students:* 2.0 minimum GPA; 69 semester hours maximum transfer credit.

College credit and advanced placement for postsecondary-level work completed in secondary school.

Degree Requirements: *For undergraduate degrees:* Minimum 2.0 GPA and 120 credits required for graduation. At lest 60 credits must be completed in the undergraduate schools. In addition to work within a major, students must complete a core curriculum of division requirements, a first-year seminar, a writing seminar, a foreign language literature course, and two health and exercise science courses.

Grading system: A–F; pass-fail; withdraw (carries time limit).

Distinctive Educational Programs: Honors programs. The university offers opportunities for study abroad in Wake Forest-owned residential study centers in Vienna (Austria) London (England), and Venice (Italy). Institutionally sponsored study abroad in Dijon, France; Salamanca, Spain; Venice, Italy; London, UK; Tokai, Japan; Moscow, Soviet Union; Freiburg, Germany; Vienna, Austria; Beijing, China. Launched in 1996, first-year undergraduates at Wake Forest follow the Undergraduate Plan, a carefully drawn blueprint for advancing higher education to a new level. Students gain from an intensified commitment to individualized instruction, small classes and personal mentoring by senior faculty. As part of the plan, five-year students receive laptop computers and color printers. Computers are upgraded after two years and become the property of the student upon graduation. Students also participate in first-year seminars to help develop analytical and critical-thinking skills.

ROTC: Army.

Degrees Conferred: 1,020 *baccalaureate* (B); 531 *master's* (M); 56 *doctorate*(D). Biological sciences 64 (B), 15 (M), 24 (D); business/marketing 201 (B), 353 (M); communications/communication technologies 101 (B), 13 (M); computer and information sciences 11 (B), 12 (M); education 18 (B), 49 (M); engineering and engineering technologies 3 (D); English 71 (B), 5 (M); foreign languages and literature 23 (B); health professions and related sciences 1 (B), 47 (M); interdisciplinary studies 4 (D); law/legal studies 13 (M); liberal arts/general studies 9 (M); mathematics 25 (B), 4 (M); parks and recreation 40 (B), 7 (M); philosophy/religion/theology 26 (B), 3 (M); physical sciences 36 (B), 5 (M), 8 (D); protective services/public administration 94 (B); psychology 12 (M); social sciences and history 258 (B); visual and performing arts 31 (B). 311 *first-professional*: law, medicine, theology.

Fees and Other Expenses: *Full-time tuition per academic year 2008–09:* $30,210. *Books and supplies:* $850. *Required fees:* $100. *Room and board per academic year:* $8,800. Contact the university for graduate and professional school tuition and fees.

Financial Aid: Aid from institutionally generated funds is provided on the basis of academic merit, financial need, athletic ability.

Financial aid to full-time, first-time undergraduate students: 75% of students received some form of financial aid. Average amount of aid received: federal grants $5,977; state/local grants $3,110; institutional grants $18,111; loans $5,561.

Departments and Teaching Staff: *Total instructional faculty:* 428. Student/faculty ratio: 10:1. Degrees held by full-time faculty: 85% hold terminal degrees.

Enrollment: Total enrollment 6,062. Undergraduate 4,476. Graduate 2,386 (full-time 97%). Undergraduate transfer in students 36.

Characteristics of Student Body: *Ethnic/racial makeup:* Black non-Hispanic: 249; American Indian or Alaska Native: 14; Asian or Pacific Islander: 159; Hispanic: 87; White non-Hispanic: 3,568.

International Students: 64 nonresident aliens enrolled fall 2008. Students from Europe, Asia, Central and South America, Africa, Canada, Australia. No programs available to aid students whose native language is not English. No financial aid specifically designated for international students.

Student Life: On-campus residence halls house 78% of undergraduate student body. *Intercollegiate athletics:* baseball, basketball, cross-country, field hockey, football, golf, soccer, tennis, track, volleyball. *Special regulations:* Registered cars permitted. *Special services:* Student Health Service. *Student publications, radio:* yearbook, newspaper, online magazine, online radio station, and campus television station. *Surrounding community:* Winston-Salem, population 186,000, is located in Greensboro-Winston-Salem-High Point metropolitan area. Served by airport 30 miles from campus.

Library Collections: 2,080,000 volumes (entire university libraries). 15,899 serials subscriptions (paper, microform, electronic). 7,560 recordings. Computer work stations available. Students have access to online information retrieval services and the Internet.

Most important special holdings include collections on Mark Twain, Gertrude Stein, Ethel Taylor Crittendon (Baptist History); Maya Angelou's personal papers; William Butler Yeats Book Collection; Dolmen Press publishing archives.

Buildings and Grounds: Campus area 340 acres.

Chief Executive Officer: Dr. Nathan D. Hatch, President.

Address admission inquiries to Martha B. Allman, Director of Undergraduate Admissions. Graduate and professional school inquiries to the area of interest.

Wake Forest School of Law

Degree Programs Offered: *First-professional.*

Admission: Baccalaureate from accredited institution, LSAT.

Degree Requirements: 89 credit hours, minimum 73 GPA on scale of 100.

Wake Forest School of Medicine

Degree Programs Offered: *First-professional* in medicine; *doctorate* in anatomy, biochemistry, comparative medicine, microbiology-immunology, pathology, pharmacology, physiology.

Admission: 90 semester hours of college-level work with 8 hours each in biology, general chemistry, organic chemistry, physics, MCAT. Graduate requirements vary according to program.

Degree Requirements: *For first-professional degree:* 2.0 GPA, 32 months in residence, exit competency examination—National Board of Medical Examiners Examinations, Parts I and II. Graduation requirements may vary.

Babcock Graduate School of Management

Degree Programs Offered: *Master's* in business administration; JD/MBA with Wake Forest School of Law. MD/MBA with Wake Forest School of Medicine. MS/MBA; MBA/PhD.

Admission: Baccalaureate from accredited institution, GMAT.

WAKE FOREST UNIVERSITY—*cont'd*

Divinity School

Degree Programs Offered: *Master of Divinity.*

Admission: Baccalaureate degree from an accredited institution.

Degree Requirements: 90 hours of coursework; 3.0 GPA; successful completion of program in vocational development.

Warren Wilson College

701 Warren Wilson Road
Swannanoa, North Carolina 28778-2099
Tel: (828) 771-2000 **E-mail:** admissions@warren-wilson.edu
Fax: (800) 934-3536 **Internet:** www.warren-wilson.edu

Institution Description: Warren Wilson College is a private college affiliated with the Presbyterian Church (U.S.A.). *Enrollment:* 1,002. *Degrees awarded:* Baccalaureate, master's.

Member of the Appalachian Consortium.

Accreditation: *Regional:* SACS-Comm. on Coll.

History: Established as Asheville Farm School 1894; merged with Dorland Bell School (established 1893), became junior college, offered first instruction at postsecondary level and changed name to Warren H. Wilson Vocational Junior College 1942; became 4-year institution and adopted present name 1965; awarded first degree (baccalaureate) 1969.

Institutional Structure: *Governing board:* Board of Trustees-Warren Wilson College. Extrainstitutional representation: 36 trustees; 1 representative to Synod of Mid Atlantic, President of the college, 1 alumni representative, chairs of the Board of Visitors and Board of Church Visitors, all 5 ex-officio voting. *Composition of institution:* Administrators 8. Academic affairs headed by dean. Management/business/finances directed by chief financial officer. Full-time instructional faculty 54. Academic governance body, academic staff, meets an average of 10 times per year.

Calendar: Semesters. Academic year Aug. to May. Freshmen admitted Aug., Jan. Degrees conferred and formal commencement May.

Characteristics of Freshmen: 904 applicants (female 542, male 362). 77% of applicants admitted. 36% of admitted students enrolled full-time.

78% (194 students) submitted SAT scores. *25th percentile*: SAT Critical Reading 540, SAT Math 500, SAT Writing 520. *75th percentile*: SAT Critical Reading 660, SAT Math 610, SAT Writing 630.

39% of entering freshmen expected to graduate within 5 years. 17% of freshmen from North Carolina. Freshmen from 44 states and 15 foreign countries.

Admission: For fall acceptance, apply as early as Sept. 1 of previous year, but not later than Mar. 15 of year of enrollment. Early decision available. *Requirements:* Either graduation from accredited secondary school with 12 units which normally include 4 English, 2 algebra, 2 science, 1 geometry, 1 history; or GED; minimum GPA 2.5. *Entrance tests:* College Board SAT or ACT composite. For foreign students TOEFL. *For transfer students:* minimum 2.0 GPA; from 4-year accredited institution 104 hours maximum transfer credit; from 2-year accredited institution 64 hours.

College credit and advanced placement for postsecondary-level work completed in secondary school.

Degree Requirements: 128 semester hours; 2.0 GPA; 1 year in residence; core curriculum; writing competency, service project (20 hours per year). All students help maintain college facilities by participating 15 hours per week in Work Program.

Fulfillment of some degree requirements and exemption from some beginning courses possible by passing College Board CLEP, AP. *Grading system:* A–F; pass-fail.

Distinctive Educational Programs: *For undergraduates:* Interdisciplinary programs in environmental studies, intercultural studies, humanities, integrative studies. Honors programs in English, natural sciences. Special programs in outdoor leadership, Appalachian studies, peace studies, pre-veterinary medicine. Institutionally sponsored study and service abroad. *For graduate students:* Low residency Master of Fine Arts Program for writers: Poetry and Fiction.

Degrees Conferred: 177 *baccalaureate*; 32 *master's*. Bachelor's degrees awarded in top five disciplines: social sciences 39; natural science and environmental studies 34; multidisciplinary studies 18; English language/literature 14; history 11. Master's degrees awarded: English language and literature 32.

Fees and Other Expenses: *Full-time tuition per academic year 2008–09:* $22,666. *Books and supplies:* $900. *Room and board per academic year:* $7,116. *Books and supplies:* $900. *Other expenses:* $3,018.

Financial Aid: Aid from institutionally generated funds is provided on the basis of academic merit, financial need. Institution has a Program Participation Agreement with the U.S. Department of Education for eligible students to receive Pell Grants and, depending upon the agreement, other federal aid.

Financial aid to full-time, first-time undergraduate students: 81% received some form of financial aid. Average amount of aid received: federal grants $3,193; Pell grants $2,397; other federal aid $1,137; state/local grants $3,201; institutional grants $7,190.

Departments and Teaching Staff: *Total instructional faculty:* 73. Student/faculty ratio: 12:1. Degrees held by full-time faculty: master's 100%, doctorate 55%. 76% hold terminal degrees.

Enrollment: Total enrollment 1,002. Undergraduate 927. Graduate 75 (full-time 100%). Undergraduate transfer-in students 74.

Characteristics of Student Body: *Ethnic/racial makeup:* Black non-Hispanic: 1%; Asian or Pacific Islander: 1%; Hispanic: 1; White non-Hispanic: 92%; unknown: 2%.

International Students: 25 nonresident aliens enrolled fall 2008. Students from Europe, Asia, Central and South America, Africa. Unlimited number of scholarships available for qualifying undergraduate international students.

Student Life: On-campus residence halls house 90% of student body. Males constitute 43% of the student body population, females 57%. Limited housing available for married students. *Intercollegiate athletics:* male and female: basketball, cross-country, soccer, swimming. Club sports: male and female swim teams, male and female indoor soccer, co-ed volleyball, whitewater, ultimate frisbee. *Special services:* Personal and pastoral counseling, career counseling, medical services, extensive leadership opportunities, outing club (climbing, hiking, camping, etc.). *Special regulations:* Cars permitted for all students. Quiet hours. *Student publications:* biweekly newspaper, annual literary magazine, yearbook. *Surrounding community:* Asheville population 100,000. Greenville/Spartanburg (SC), nearest metropolitan area, 60 miles from campus. Served by airport 22 miles from campus.

Library Collections: 111,000 volumes. 52,000 microforms; 3,500 audiovisual materials; 11,000 periodicals including via electronic access. Online catalog. Students have access to online information retrieval services and the Internet.

Most important holdings include collections of art books and exhibition catalogs, college archives, Jamie Clarke Papers, mountain music.

Buildings and Grounds: Campus area 1,100 acres.

Chief Executive Officer: Dr. William S. Pfeiffer, President.

Address admission inquiries to Richard L. Blomgren, Dean of Admissions.

Western Carolina University

One University Drive
Cullowhee, North Carolina 28723
Tel: (828) 227-7211 **E-mail:** admiss@email.wcu.edu
Fax: (828) 227-7176 **Internet:** www.wcu.edu

Institution Description: *Enrollment:* 9,050. *Degrees awarded:* Baccalaureate, master's, doctorate. Specialist in education; graduate certificate in psychology also awarded.

Member of Appalachian Consortium.

Accreditation: *Regional:* SACS-Comm. on Coll. *Professional*: business, chemistry, clinical lab scientist, engineering technology, dietetics, environmental health, interior design, medical record administration, music, nursing, physical therapy, social work, teacher education

History: Established and chartered as Cullowhee High School 1889; changed name to Cullowhee Normal and Industrial School 1905; offered first instruction at postsecondary level, added junior college program, and discontinued secondary school level 1912; changed name to Western Carolina Teachers College and became 4-year institution 1929; changed name to Western Carolina College 1953; adopted present name 1967; became part of the University of North Carolina 1972. *See* William Ernest Bird, *The History of Western Carolina College* (Chapel Hill, NC: University of North Carolina Press, 1963) for further information.

Institutional Structure: *Governing board:* Board of Trustees of Western Carolina University. Extrainstitutional representation: 12 trustees; institutional representation: 1 full-time instructional faculty member, 1 student; 1 alumnus. 1 ex officio. 12 voting. *Composition of institution:* Administrators 73. Academic affairs headed by provost. . Management/business/finances directed by vice chancellor for business affairs. Full-time instructional faculty 374. Academic governance body, Faculty Senate, meets an average of 8 times per year.

Calendar: Semesters. Academic year Aug. to May. Freshmen and transfers admitted Aug., Jan., May, July. Degrees conferred and formal commencements May, Aug., Dec.

Characteristics of Freshmen: 4,792 applicants (female 2,528, male 2,264). 68% of applicants admitted. 39% of applicants admitted and enrolled full-time. 94% (1,184 students) submitted SAT scores; 19% (242 students) submitted ACT scores. *25th percentile*: SAT Critical Reading 450, SAT Math 470, SAT Writing 430; ACT Composite 18, ACT English 16, ACT Math 18. *75th percentile*: SAT Critical Reading 550, SAT Math 560, SAT Writing 530; ACT Composite 23, ACT English 22, ACT Math 23.

42% of entering freshmen expected to graduate within 5 years. 92% of freshmen from North Carolina. Freshmen from 34 states and 12 foreign countries.

Admission: Admission to Western Carolina University and placement into courses and programs are based upon a variety of factors including courses taken in high school, rank in class, SAT scores, recommendations from school counselors, principals, and/or teachers, and placement tests at Western. Applicants must be graduates of accredited high schools. Home-schooled applicants must meet standards equivalent to those used for applicants from approved secondary schools. Graduates of unaccredited high schools may satisfy entrance requirements by examination. The university reserves the right to require any conditions deemed necessary. Applications also are considered for admission from prospective students who have achieved high school graduation equivalency by means of Tests of General Education Development (GED tests). *Requirements:* Students must have successfully completed 14 units of college preparatory courses in high school: 4 units English; 2 units algebra; 1 unit geometry or advanced math; 3 units science (including 1 unit of a life or biological science and 1 unit of a physical science); 2 units social studies (including 1 unit in U.S. history). Also, it is highly recommended that students complete at least 2 years of a foreign language in high school. Effective in the fall of 2006, 1 additional unit of mathematics beyond algebra II will be required. *Entrance tests:* Freshman applicants must take the SAT. The achievement test in subject-matter fields is not required.

Degree Requirements: 120–128 semester hours including a l;liberal studies program, a major as prescribed by one of the departments, a minor, second major, concentration, or other approved program as specified by the appropriate college and department, and 4 elective courses; 2.0 GPA; 30 hours, including 12 hours upper division work, in residence; 50% or more of the credits in the major presented for graduation on the junior-senior level enrollment at Western is the intended semester of graduation. The 42-hour Liberal Studies component includes courses in writing, mathematics, oral communication, wellness, physical and biological sciences with at least on lab course required; a fist-year seminar, upper-level courses in social sciences, history, humanities, fine and performing arts, and world cultures. Recitals are required for music majors. >p<Fulfillment of some degree requirements and exemption from some beginning courses possible by passing departmental examinations, College Board CLEP, APP, SAT, other standardized tests. *Grading system:* A–F; satisfactory-unsatisfactory; withdraw (carries time limit).

Distinctive Educational Programs: Work-experience programs. Flexible meeting places and schedules, including off-campus centers (at Cherokee, less than 30 miles away from main institution; Asheville, 50 miles away) and evening classes. Cooperative baccalaureate programs in agriculture, engineering, forestry, life sciences with North Carolina State University at Raleigh. Cooperative agreement between School of Technology and Applied Science and statewide technical and community colleges. Interdisciplinary majors in computer science, environmental health, industrial chemistry, international business, parks and recreation management, science education, social sciences; minors in American studies, Cherokee studies. Internships in American schools are arranged on demand in various locations in Latin America, including Columbia, Central America, and the West Indies. A liberal arts program is offered in London, and an archeological program is offered in Yucatan. Other programs are announced each year. Master's degree program in physical therapy. *Other distinctive programs:* Off-campus degree-granting programs for employed individuals offered through Community Oriented Regional Education Program and in-service program. Continuing education offering noncredit and extension credit courses and programs for adults. Summer music camp for junior and senior secondary school students. Summer school for gifted children sponsored by School of Education and Psychology. B.S. degree in Electrical Engineering as a joint offering between Western and UNC-Charlotte based on the Cullowhee campus.

Degrees Conferred: 1,525 *baccalaureate*; 471 *master's*; 15 *doctorate*. Bachelor's degrees awarded: biological/life sciences 20; business/marketing 252; communications/communication technologies 66; computer and information sciences 10; education 272; engineering and engineering technologies 36; English 31; foreign languages and literature 4; health professions and related sciences 121; home economics and vocational home economics 2; liberal arts/general studies 21; mathematics 8; natural resources/environmental science 11; parks and recreation 52; philosophy/religion/theology 5; physical sciences 23; protective services/public administration 108; psychology 26; social sciences and history 63; visual and performing arts 45;.

Fees and Other Expenses: *Full-time tuition per academic year 2008–09:* resident undergraduate $4,19, nonresident $13,779; contact the university for current graduate tuition, fees, and other costs. *Required fees:* $1,622. *Books and supplies:* $2,005. *Room and board per academic year:* $5,626. *Other expenses:* $2,150.

Financial Aid: The university offers a direct lending program. Aid from institutionally generated funds is provided on the basis of academic merit, athletic ability, financial need.

Financial aid to full-time, first-time undergraduate students: 74% received some form of financial aid. Average amount of aid received: federal grants $3,588; Pell grants $2,931; other federal aid $942; state/local grants $3,171; institutional grants $1,441.

Departments and Teaching Staff: 80% of faculty hold the doctorate, first-professional, or other terminal degree. Student/faculty ratio: 8:1.

Enrollment: Total enrollment 9,050. Undergraduate 7,130. Graduate 1,920 (full-time 31%). Undergraduate transfer-in students 742.

Characteristics of Student Body: *Ethnic/racial makeup:* number of Black non-Hispanic: 361; American Indian or Alaska Native: 117; Asian or Pacific Islander: 47; Hispanic: 81; White non-Hispanic: 5,858, unknown: 100. *Age distribution:* number under 18: 20; 18–19: 2,602; 20–21: 1,853; 22–24: 1,060; 25–29: 476; 30–34: 260; 35–39: 176; 40–49: 251; 50–64: 82.

International Students: 71 nonresident aliens enrolled fall 2008. Programs available to aid students whose native language is not English: social, cultural. English as a Second Language Program. No financial aid specifically designated for international students.

Student Life: On-campus residence halls house 20% of full-time male students, 20% of full-time female students. 3 residence halls house only males; 1 residence hall houses only females; 8 residence halls, that are living/learning center for honors students, are co-ed. *Intercollegiate athletics:* male: baseball, basketball, cross-country, football, golf, tennis, indoor track; female: basketball, tennis, volleyball, cross-country, indoor track. *Special regulations:* Cars permitted without restrictions. *Special services:* Advising Center, Cooperative Education; Counseling, Testing, Psychological Services, Reading Center, Student Infirmary, Writing Center. *Student publications, radio: Catamount*, a yearbook; *Nomad*, an annual literary publication; *Western Carolinian*, a weekly newspaper. Radio station WWCU broadcasts 126 hours per week. *Surrounding community:* The university is located in western North Carolina between the Blue Ridge and Great Smoky Mountains; 50 miles from Asheville (NC), 120 miles from Knoxville (TN), 155 miles from Atlanta (GA). Nearest commercial airport 55 miles from campus.

Library Collections: 644,500 books, serial book files, and government documents. Online catalog. 1,512,000 microforms; 18,000 audiovisual materials; 36,400 periodicals including via electronic access. Computer work stations available. Students have access to online information retrieval services.

Most important holdings include Horace Kepart Papers and Books; Cherokee Documents and Foreign Archives; William Holland Thomas Papers; Sue Ellen Bridgers Collection.

Buildings and Grounds: Campus area 227 acres plus 38.2 acres at the North Carolina Center for the Advancement of Teaching.

Chief Executive Officer: Dr. John W. Bardo, Chancellor.

Undergraduates address admission inquiries to Alan Kines, Director of Admissions; graduate inquiries to Dean, Research and Graduate Studies.

Wingate University

315 East Wilson Street
Wingate, North Carolina 28174-0159
Tel: (800) 755-5550 **E-mail:** admit@wingate.edu
Fax: (704) 233-8192 **Internet:** www.wingate.edu

Institution Description: Wingate University is a private college affiliated with the Baptist State Convention of North Carolina. *Enrollment:* 2,128. *Degrees awarded:* Baccalaureate, master's.

Member of Charlotte Area Educational Consortium.

Accreditation: *Regional:* SACS-Comm. on Coll. *Professional*: athletic training, business, music, teacher education

History: Established as Wingate School 1896; offered first instruction at postsecondary level and adopted present name 1923; awarded first degree (associate) 1925; began baccalaureate program 1977; began offering graduate work 1985; became Wingate University 1996.

Institutional Structure: *Governing board:* Wingate University Board of Trustees. Extrainstitutional representation: 36 trustees. All voting. *Composition of institution:* Administrators 39. Academic affairs headed by vice president for academic affairs. Management/business/finances directed by executive vice president and chief financial officer. Full-time instructional faculty 105. Academic governance body, Faculty Assembly, meets an average of 9 times per year.

Calendar: Semesters. Academic year Aug. to May. Freshmen admitted Sept., Jan., June, July. Degrees conferred May, Aug. Formal commencement May,. Summer session from June to July.

Characteristics of Freshmen: 3,897 applicants (female 2,026, male 1,871). 55% of applicants admitted. 20% of applicants admitted and enrolled full-time.

WINGATE UNIVERSITY—*cont'd*

91% (393 students) submitted SAT scores; 18% (77 students) submitted ACT scores. *25th percentile*: SAT Critical Reading 440, SAT Math 470, SAT Writing 440; ACT Composite 19. *75th percentile*: SAT Critical Reading 550, SAT Math 580, SAt Writing 540; ACT Composite 24.

47% of entering freshmen expected to graduate within 5 years. 66% of freshmen from North Carolina. Freshmen from 31 states and 14 foreign countries.

Admission: Rolling admissions plan. For fall acceptance, apply as early as 1 year prior to enrollment, but not later than Aug. 1 of year of enrollment. Early acceptance available. *Requirements:* Recommend 16 units from accredited secondary school including 4 English, 3 mathematics, 2 foreign language, 2 history, 2 science. GED accepted. Interview recommended. Minimum 2.5 GPA. *Entrance tests:* College Board SAT or ACT Composite. For foreign students TOEFL score 550. *For transfer students:* 2.0 minimum GPA; from 4-year accredited institution 95 hours maximum transfer credit; from 2-year accredited institution 64 hours; good standing at institution previously attended.

College credit and advanced placement for postsecondary-level work completed in secondary school and for USAFI. Tutoring available.

Degree Requirements: *For all baccalaureate degrees:* 125 credit hours. *For all undergraduate degrees:* 2.0 GPA; last 30 hours in residence; 3 hours physical education; distribution requirements.

Fulfillment of some degree requirements and exemption from some beginning courses possible by passing departmental examinations, College Board CLEP, AP. *Grading system:* A–F; withdraw-withdraw failing; incomplete (carries time limit).

Distinctive Educational Programs: Work-experience programs, including practicums, field experience, internships. Flexible meeting places and schedules, including off-campus center (at Matthews, 25 miles away from main institution) and evening classes. Interdepartmental/interdisciplinary programs in American studies, communication studies, human services, religious studies, social studies. Facilities for independent research, including honors programs, independent study. Institutionally sponsored study abroad in England, other western European countries, and Hong Kong. Cross-registration through consortium.

ROTC: Army and Air Force coordinated through University of North Carolina-Charlotte.

Degrees Conferred: 278 *baccalaureate*; 79 *master's*, 61 *doctorate*. Bachelor's degrees awarded in top five disciplines: business/marketing 61; communications/journalism; parks and recreation 29; education 28; biological/life sciences 20. Master's degrees awarded: business/marketing 20; education 17.

Fees and Other Expenses: *Tuition per academic year 2008–09:* $19,350. *Other fees:* $1,050. *books and supplies:* $1,000. *Other expenses:* $1,300.

Financial Aid: Aid from institutionally generated funds is provided on the basis of academic merit, financial need, athletic ability, music/art.

Financial aid to full-time, first-time undergraduate students: 99% received some form of aid. Average amount of aid received: federal grants $4,747; Pell grants $1,770; other federal aid $1,770; state/local grants $4,247; institutional grants $9,340.

Departments and Teaching Staff: *Total instructional faculty:* 162 (full-time 105, part-time 57). 80% of faculty hold the doctorate, first-professional, or other terminal degree. Student/faculty ratio: 14:1.

Enrollment: Total enrollment 2,128. Undergraduate 1,445. Graduate 683 (full-time 42%). Undergraduate transfer-in students 89.

Characteristics of Student Body: *Ethnic/racial makeup:* Black non-Hispanic: 17; American Indian or Alaska native: 10; Asian or Pacific Islander: 16; Hispanic 22: White non-Hispanic: 933; unknown: 259. *Age distribution:* number under 18: 7; 18–19: 563; 20–21: 507; 22–24: 166; 25–29: 31; 30–34: 15; 35–39: 12; 40–49: 91 50–64: 13; 65 and over: 1.

International Students: 33 nonresident aliens enrolled fall 2008. Students from Europe, Asia, Central and South America, Africa, Canada, Caribbean, Australia. No programs available to aid students whose native language is not English. No financial aid specifically designated for international students.

Student Life: On-campus residence halls and apartments house 81% of student body. *Intercollegiate athletics:* male: baseball, basketball, lacrosse, golf, cross-country, football, soccer, tennis; female: basketball, cross-country, golf, swimming, soccer, softball, tennis, volleyball. *Special regulations:* Registered cars permitted without restrictions. *Special services:* Medical services. *Student publications: Counterpoint*, an annual literary magazine; *The Gate*, a yearbook; *The Triangle*, a weekly newspaper. *Surrounding community:* Wingate population 3,000. Charlotte, 28 miles from campus, is nearest metropolitan area. Served by airport 36 miles from campus.

Library Collections: 110,500 volumes. 6,830 microforms; 8,500 audiovisual materials. Current periodical subscriptions: paper 180; microform 7,732. Students have access to online information retrieval services and the Internet.

Most important special holdings include collections on Wingate University Archives; Barnett Music Recording Collection.

Buildings and Grounds: Campus area 300 acres.

Chief Executive Officer: Dr. Jerry E. McGee, President.

Address admission inquiries to Rhett Brown, Dean of Enrollment Management.

Winston-Salem State University

601 Martin Luther King, Jr. Drive
Winston-Salem, North Carolina 27'101
Tel: (336) 750-2000 **E-mail:** admissions@.edu
Fax: (336) 771-7097 **Internet:** www.wssu.edu

Institution Description: *Enrollment:* 6,442. *Degrees awarded:* Baccalaureate, master's.

Accreditation: *Regional:* SACS-Comm. on Coll. *Professional*: business, music, nursing, teacher education

History: Established as Slater Industrial Academy 1892; chartered 1897; offered first instruction at postsecondary level and changed name to Winston-Salem Teachers College 1925; awarded first degree (baccalaureate) 1927; changed name to Winston-Salem State College 1963; adopted present name 1969.

Institutional Structure: *Governing board:* Board of Trustees. Extrainstitutional representation: 11 trustees; institutional representation: 1 student; 1 alumnus. 1 ex officio. All voting. *Composition of institution:* Administrators 17. Academic affairs headed by provost and vice chancellor for academic affairs. Management/business/finances directed by vice chancellor for finance and administration. Full-time instructional faculty 275. Academic governance body, Educational Council, meets an average of 11 times per year.

Calendar: Semesters. Academic year Aug. to May. Freshmen admitted Aug., Jan., June. Degrees conferred and formal commencement May. Summer session of 2 terms from late May to mid-July.

Characteristics of Freshmen: 3,345 applicants (female 2,251, male 1,094). 68% of applicants admitted. 43% of applicants admitted and enrolled full-time.

90% (876 students) submitted SAT scores; 16% (597 students) submitted ACT scores. *25th percentile*: SAT Critical Reading 390, SAT Math 400, SAT Writing 380; ACT Composite 15, ACT English 14, ACT Math 16. *75th percentile*: SAT Critical Reading 470, SAT Math 480, SAT Writing 460; ACT Composite 19, ACT English 19, ACT Math 19.

40% of entering freshmen expected to graduate within 5 years. 92% of freshmen from North Carolina. Freshmen from 26 states and 8 foreign countries.

Admission: Rolling admissions plan. *Requirements:* Either graduation from accredited secondary school with 4 units English, 2 social studies, 1 mathematics, 1 science, 8 electives; or GED. Minimum 2.0 GPA. Lowest acceptable secondary school class standing 60th percentile. *Entrance tests:* College Board SAT preferred; ACT composite accepted. *For transfer students:* 2.0 minimum GPA; from 4-year accredited institution 96 hours maximum transfer credit; from 2-year accredited institution 64 hours.

Advanced placement for postsecondary-level work completed in secondary school.

Tutoring available. Developmental courses offered during regular academic year.

Degree Requirements: 127 credit hours; 2.0 GPA; 30 hours in residence; 2 physical activity courses and 1 personal hygiene course; core program.

Fulfillment of some degree requirements possible by passing College Board CLEP. *Grading system:* A–F; pass-fail; withdraw.

Distinctive Educational Programs: Internships. Evening classes. Cooperative baccalaureate program in medical technology with affiliated hospitals. Interdisciplinary programs in Black studies, environmental science, natural sciences, social sciences, urban affairs.

ROTC: Army in cooperation with Wake Forest University.

Degrees Conferred: 867 *baccalaureate*; 131 *master's*. Bachelor's degrees awarded in top five disciplines: health professions and related sciences 390; business/marketing 66; social sciences 50; computer and information sciences 36; psychology 33. Master's degrees awarded: business/marketing 13; computer and information sciences 4; education 9; health professions and related sciences 35; various other disciplines 70.

Fees and Other Expenses: *Full-time tuition per academic year 2008=09:* resident undergraduate $3,389, nonresident $12,029; contact the university for current graduate tuition/fees. *Required fees:* $1,458. *Room and board per academic year:* $5,742. *Books and supplies:* $2,000. *Other expenses:* $2,750.

Financial Aid: Aid from institutionally generated funds is provided on the basis of academic merit, financial need, athletic ability, other criteria.

Financial aid to full-time, first-time undergraduate students: 88% received some form of aid. Average amount of aid received: federal grants $3,970; Pell grants $3,371; other federal aid $1,446; state/local grants $2,722; institutional grants $5,732.

Departments and Teaching Staff: *Total instructional faculty:* 400 (full-time 275, part-time 125). 50% of faculty hold the doctorate, first-professional, or other terminal degree. Student/faculty ratio: 16:1.

Enrollment: Total enrollment 6,442. Undergraduate 5,975. Graduate 467 (full-time 53%). Undergraduate transfer-in students 557.

Characteristics of Student Body: *Ethnic/racial makeup:* Black non-Hispanic: 83%; Hispanic 1%; White non-Hispanic 12%; unknown 4%. *Age distribution:* number under 18: 45; 18–19: 1,694; 20–21: 1,318; 22–24: 1,829; 50–64 426; 65 and over: 5.

International Students: 16 nonresident alien enrolled fall 2008. No programs available to aid students whose native language is not English. No financial aid specifically designated for international students.

Student Life: On-campus residence halls house 39% of student body. *Intercollegiate athletics:* male: basketball, football; female: basketball. *Special regulations:* Cars must be registered with university security office. *Special services:* Learning Resources Center, medical services. *Student publications: News Argus*, a monthly newspaper. *Surrounding community:* Winston-Salem metropolitan area population 826,500. Served by mass transit bus system, airport.

Publications: *Social Science Journal* (annually).

Library Collections: 223,500 volumes including bound books, serial backfiles, electronic documents, and government documents not in separate collections. Online catalog. 348,000 microforms; 5,300 audiovisual aids; 28,200 periodicals including via electronic access. Students have access to the Internet at no charge.

Buildings and Grounds: Campus area 85.5 acres. Campus DVD available.

Chief Executive Officer: Dr. Michelle Howard-Vital, Chancellor.

Address admission inquiries to Tomikia LeGrande, Director of Admissions.

North Dakota

Dickinson State University

291 Campus Drive
Dickinson, North Dakota 58601-4896
Tel: (701) 483-2787 **E-mail:** admissions@dickinsonstate.edu
Fax: (701) 483-2025 **Internet:** www.dickinsonstate.edu

Institution Description: Dickinson State University is a regional four-year institution within the North Dakota University System. *Enrollment:* 2,730. *Degrees awarded:* Associate, baccalaureate.

Academic offerings subject to approval by statewide coordinating bodies. Budget subject to approval by state governing boards. Member of Northern Plains Consortium for Education, Inc.

Accreditation: *Regional:* NCA. *Professional*: nursing, teacher education

History: Established as Dickinson State Normal School and offered first instruction at postsecondary level 1918; awarded first degree (baccalaureate) and changed name to Dickinson State Teachers College 1931; became Dickinson State College 1963; became State University of North Dakota—Dickinson 1986; adopted present name 1987.

Institutional Structure: *Governing board:* Board of Higher Education. Representation: 8 members (including 1 student) appointed by governor of North Dakota. *Composition of institution:* Administrators 8. Academic affairs headed by vice president for academic affairs. Management/business/finances directed by director of vice president of business affairs. Full-time instructional faculty 89. Academic governance body, Academic Policies Council, meets periodically.

Calendar: Semesters. Academic year Aug. to May. Freshmen admitted Aug., Jan., May. Formal commencement Apr. Summer session of 1 term from May to June.

Characteristics of Freshmen: 30% of freshmen expected to graduate in five years. 66% of freshmen from North Dakota. Freshmen from 36 states and 28 foreign countries.

Admission: Rolling admissions plan. *Requirements:* Either graduation from accredited secondary school or GED. For out-of-state students, recommend secondary school class standing 50th percentile. *Entrance tests:* ACT composite or SAT (m/v). *For transfer students:* 2.0 minimum GPA; from 4-year accredited institution 96 semester hours maximum transfer credit; from 2-year accredited institution 64 semester hours; correspondence/extension students 24 semester hours.

College credit and advanced placement for postsecondary-level work completed in secondary school. Tutoring available.

Degree Requirements: *For all associate degrees:* 64 semester hours. *For all baccalaureate degrees:* 128 semester hours; general studies requirements. *For all undergraduate degrees:* 2.0 GPA; 2 semesters in residence; 2 credit hours of physical education courses, including swimming. Additional requirements for some majors.

Fulfillment of some degree requirements and exemption from some beginning courses possible by passing departmental examinations, College Board CLEP, AP. *Grading system:* A–F; pass-fail; withdraw (carries time limit).

Distinctive Educational Programs: Internships. Cooperative baccalaureate program in medical technology with approved schools. Interdisciplinary program in environmental science. Preprofessional programs in social work leading to baccalaureate awarded by University of North Dakota; other programs include agriculture, dentistry, engineering, health sciences, medicine, mortuary science. Facilities and programs for independent research, including honors programs, individual majors, independent and directed study. *Other distinctive programs:* Credit and noncredit continuing education. Student and faculty exchange agreements with universities in China, Russia, and Ukraine.

Degrees Conferred: 48 *associate*; 386 *baccalaureate*. Bachelor's degrees awarded in top five disciplines: business, management, marketing, and related support services 98; education 97; liberal arts and sciences, general studies, and humanities 35; health professions and related sciences 26; psychology 15.

Fees and Other Expenses: *Full-time tuition per academic year 2008–09:* North Dakota resident $5,084, out-of-state $11,795. *Required fees:* $825. *Room and board per academic year:* $4,276. *Books and supplies:* $1,000. *Other expenses:* $3,200.

Financial Aid: Aid from institutionally generated funds is provided on the basis of academic merit, financial need, athletic ability, other criteria. Institution has a Program Participation Agreement with the U.S. Department of Education for eligible students to receive Pell Grants and, depending upon the agreement, other federal aid.

Financial aid to full-time, first-time undergraduate students: 90% received federal grants averaging $1,926; Pell grants $2,790; other federal aid $754; state/local grants $758; institutional grants $2,783.

Departments and Teaching Staff: *Total instructional faculty:* 175 (full-time 89, part-time 86). Student/faculty ratio: 19:1.

Enrollment: Total enrollment 2,572 (undergraduate). Transfer-in students

Characteristics of Student Body: *Ethnic/racial makeup:* Black non-Hispanic: 2%; American Indian or Alaska Native: 2%; Asian or Pacific Islander 1%; Hispanic 2%; White non-Hispanic: 67%; unknown 11%; nonresident alien 16%.

International Students: 167 nonresident aliens enrolled fall 2008. Students from Europe, Asia, Central and South America, Africa, Canada, Australia. No programs available to aid students whose native language is not English. Financial aid specifically designated for international students: scholarships available annually to qualifying students.

Student Life: On-campus residence halls house 26% of student body. Residence halls for males constitute 50% of such space, for females 50%. Housing available for married students. *Intercollegiate athletics:* male: baseball, basketball, cross-country, football, track, golf, tennis, wrestling, rodeo; female: basketball, cross-country, tennis, track, softball, rodeo, volleyball. *Special regulations:* Cars permitted without restrictions. *Special services:* Student Support Services, peer tutoring, medical services. *Student publications: Prairie Smoke*, a yearbook; *The Western Concept*, a bimonthly newspaper. *Surrounding community:* Dickinson population 17,000. Minneapolis-St. Paul (MN), 550 miles from campus, is nearest metropolitan area. Served by airport 5 miles from campus.

Library Collections: 158,000 volumes. 25,420 government documents; 9,000 microforms; 5,500 audiovisual materials; 1,750 periodical subscriptions. Students have access to online information retrieval services and the Internet.

Most important special holdings include Theodore Roosevelt Collection.

Buildings and Grounds: Campus area 100 acres.

Chief Executive Officer: Dr. Lee A. Vickers, President.

Address admission inquiries to Steve Glasser, Director of Enrollment Services.

Jamestown College

6000 College Lane
Jamestown, North Dakota 58405
Tel: (701) 252-3467 **E-mail:** admissions@jc.edu
Fax: (701) 253-4318 **Internet:** www.jc.edu

Institution Description: Jamestown College is a private college affiliated with the United Presbyterian Church in the U.S.A. *Enrollment:* 1,025. *Degrees awarded:* Baccalaureate.

Accreditation: *Regional:* NCA. *Professional*: nursing, teacher education

History: Established, chartered, and incorporated 1883; offered first instruction at postsecondary level 1886; awarded first degree (baccalaureate) 1913.

Institutional Structure: *Governing board:* Jamestown College Board of Trustees. Representation: 29 trustees plus the president of the college and 5 ex officio. All voting. *Composition of institution:* Academic affairs headed by vice president/dean of academic affairs. Student affairs headed by dean of students. Management/business/finances directed by business manager. Full-time instructional faculty 57. Academic governance body, Academic Council, meets an average of 15 times per year.

Calendar: Semesters. Academic year Aug. to May. Freshmen admitted Sept., Jan., May. Degrees conferred May. Summer session May to July.

Characteristics of Freshmen: 883 applicants (323 female, 560 male). 67% of applicants admitted. 46% of admitted students enrolled full-time.

14% (36 students) submitted SAT scores; 86% (223 students) submitted ACT scores. *25th percentile*: SAT Critical Reading 420, SAT Math 440; ACT Composite 20, ACT English 18, ACT Math 19. *75th percentile*: SAT Critical Reading 530, SAT Math 540; ACT Composite 25. ACT English 24, ACT Math 25.

42% of entering freshmen expected to graduate within 5 years. 58% of freshmen from North Dakota. Freshmen from 23 states and 11 foreign countries.

Admission: Rolling admissions plan. For fall acceptance, apply no later than July 1 of year of enrollment. Early acceptance available. *Requirements:* Graduation from accredited secondary school with 17 units or GED. Minimum grade average C. Lowest acceptable secondary school class standing 50th percentile.(exceptions possible). *Entrance tests:* Recommend ACT composite or College Board SAT. ACT composite preferred. *For transfer students:* 2.0 minimum GPA; from 4-year accredited institution 93 semester hours maximum transfer credit; from 2-year accredited institution 64 hours; correspondence/extension students 8 hours.

College credit and advanced placement for postsecondary-level work completed in secondary school. College credit for extrainstitutional learning on basis of portfolio and faculty assessment.

Tutoring available. Developmental courses offered during regular academic year; nondegree credit given.

Degree Requirements: 128 semester hours; 2.0 GPA; 35 credits, including final semester in residence; general education requirements; distribution requirements. Fulfillment of some degree requirements and exemption from some beginning courses possible by passing departmental examinations, College Board CLEP, AP. *Grading system:* A–F; pass-fail; withdraw.

Distinctive Educational Programs: Cooperative education. Evening classes. For engineering students, dual-degree programs with and preprofessional programs leading to baccalaureate from North Dakota State University (Fargo), South Dakota State University, University of North Dakota (Grand Forks). Cooperative baccalaureate program in medical technology with area hospitals. Preprofessional program in pharmacy leading to baccalaureate awarded by North Dakota State University. Facilities and programs for independent research, including honors programs, individual majors, tutorials. Customized degree program for working adults.

Degrees Conferred: 166 *baccalaureate:* biological/life sciences 6; business and management 41; computer and information sciences 8; education 26; English 8; health professions 68; history 15, mathematics 8; philosophy/religion/theology 2; physical sciences 1, psychology 9; security and protective services 13; visual and performing arts 6.

Fees and Other Expenses: *Full-time tuition per academic year 2008–09:* $15,035. *Room and board per academic year:* $4,850. *Books and supplies:* $1,000. *Other expenses:* $2,800.

Financial Aid: Aid from institutionally generated funds is provided on the basis of academic merit, athletic ability.

Financial aid to full-time, first-time undergraduate students: 99% received some form of aid. Average amount of aid received:federal grants $3,020; Pell grants $2,643; other federal aid $1,250; state/local grants $858; institutional grants $4,879.

Departments and Teaching Staff: *Total instructional faculty:* 77 (full-time 57, part-time 20). 555 of faculty hold the doctorate, first-professional, or other terminal degree: Student/faculty ratio: 15:1.

Enrollment: Total enrollment 1,025 (undergraduate).

Characteristics of Student Body: *Ethnic/racial makeup:* Black non-Hispanic: 2%; American Indian or Alaska Native: 1%; Asian or Pacific Islander: 2%; Hispanic: 2%; White non-Hispanic: 89%; nonresident alien 55. *Age distribution:* number under 18: 21; 18–19: 403; 20–21: 333; 22–24: 142; 25–29: 26; 30–34: 16; 35–39: 5; 40–49: 23; 50–64: 10; 65 and over: 1. 15% of student body attend summer sessions.

International Students: 51 nonresident aliens enrolled fall 2008. Students from Europe, Asia, Africa, Canada, Middle East. No programs available to aid students whose native language is not English. No financial aid specifically designated for international students.

Student Life: On-campus residence halls house 70% of student body. *Intercollegiate athletics:* male: baseball, basketball, cross-country, football, golf, soccer, track, wrestling; female: basketball, cross-country, golf, soccer, softball, track, volleyball. *Special services:* Career Center, Chaplain's Office, Tutoring Center. *Student publications: The Collegian*, a bimonthly newspaper; *Hea Kan*, a yearbook; *Plainsong,* publishes the work of Jamestown College students. *Surrounding community:* Jamestown population 17,000. Minneapolis (MN), 300 miles from campus, is nearest metropolitan area. Served by airport 2 miles from campus.

Library Collections: 112,200 volumes including bound books, serial backfiles, electronic documents, and government documents not in separate collections. Online catalog. 9,000 microforms; 5,500 audiovisual materials; 18,600 periodicals including via electronic access. Computer work stations available. Students have access to the Internet at no charge.

Most important special holdings include Louis L'Amour Collection; Curriculum Library; Presbyterian history/religion; College Archives.

Buildings and Grounds: Campus area 87 acres.

Chief Executive Officer: Dr. Robert Bodal, President.

Address admission inquiries to Judy Erickson, Director of Admission.

Mayville State University

330 Third Street N.E.
Mayville, North Dakota 58257-1299

Tel: (800) 437-4101 **E-mail:** admit@mayvillestate.edu
Fax: (701) 788-4748 **Internet:** www.mayvillestate.edu

Institution Description: Mayville State University is a member of the North Dakota University System. *Enrollment:* 789. *Degrees awarded:* Associate, baccalaureate.

Academic offerings subject to approval by statewide coordinating bodies. Budget subject to approval by state governing boards. Member of Northern Plains Consortium for Education, Inc.

Accreditation: *Regional:* NCA. *Professional*: teacher education

History: Established and chartered as Mayville Normal School 1889; offered first instruction at postsecondary level 1890; first certificate awarded 1895; changed name to Mayville State Teachers College 1925; awarded first degree (baccalaureate) 1927; became Mayville State College 1963; adopted present name 1995. *See* James W. Neilson, *The School of Personal Service* (Grand Forks, N.D.: Washburn, 1979) for further information.

Institutional Structure: *Governing board:* North Dakota State Board of Higher Education. Extrainstitutional representation: 7 directors. All voting. *Composition of institution:* Administrators 10. Academic affairs headed by dean of the college. Management/business/finances directed by director of business affairs. Full-time instructional faculty 36. Academic governance body, Mayville State College Faculty Association, meets an average of 8 times per year.

Calendar: Semesters. Academic year Aug. to May. Freshmen admitted Aug., Jan., June. Degrees conferred May, July, Dec. Formal commencement May. Summer session from June to July.

Characteristics of Freshmen: 68% of applicants admitted. 47% of applicants admitted and enrolled.

81(116 students) submitted ACT scores. *25th percentile*: ACT Composite 16.9, ACT English 15.1, ACT Math 13.1. *75th percentile*: ACT Composite 21.7, ACT English 21, ACT Math 22.3.

31% of entering freshmen expected to graduate within 5 years. 69% of freshmen from North Dakota. Freshmen from 32 states and 5 foreign countries.

Admission: Rolling admissions plan. For fall acceptance, apply as early as beginning of senior year in secondary school, but not later than last day of registration. Students are notified of acceptance upon completion of application. Early acceptance available. *Requirements:* Open admissions. Graduate from accredited high school must meet minimum high school core courses including: 4 credits English, 3 mathematics (algebra I or higher), 3 science (including 2 credits in a laboratory science), 3 social science. GED also accepted. . *Entrance tests:* ACT Composite or SAT. *For transfer students:* 2.0 minimum GPA; from 4-year accredited institution 86 semester hours maximum transfer credit; from 2-year accredited institution 86 semester hours.

Advanced placement for postsecondary-level work completed in secondary school. College credit and advanced placement for College Board CLEP and departmental examinations, and for extrainstitutional learning.

Tutoring available. Developmental courses offered in summer session and regular academic year; credit given.

Degree Requirements: *For all associate degrees:* 64 credit hours; 30 credits in residence. *For all baccalaureate degrees:* 120 semester hours; 60 credits in residence. *For all undergraduate degrees:* 2.0 GPA. For degrees in Education: 2.75 GPA.

For baccalaureate candidates, fulfillment of some degree requirements and exemption from some beginning courses possible by passing College Board CLEP. *Grading system:* A–F; pass-fail; withdraw (carries time limit).

Distinctive Educational Programs: Computers across the curriculum program (notebook computers issued to all students). Work-experience programs. Accelerated degree programs. Internet access for all students. Facilities for using telecommunications in the classroom. New major in applied psychology; new minors in educational technology and electronic commerce.

Degrees Conferred: 2 *associate;* 106 *baccalaureate:* business/marketing 26; computer and information sciences 11; education 52; English 1; mathematics 2; philosophy and religious studies 7; physical sciences 3; psychology 2; social sciences 2.

Fees and Other Expenses: *Full-time tuition per academic year 2008=09:* resident $5,654, nonresident $7,646. *Required fees:* $1,643. *Room and board per academic year:* $4,212. *Books and supplies:* $800. *Other expenses:* $2,800.

MAYVILLE STATE UNIVERSITY—*cont'd*

Financial Aid: Aid from institutionally generated funds is provided on the basis of academic merit, financial need, athletic ability.

Financial aid to full-time, first-time undergraduate students: 98% received some form of aid. Average amount of aid received: federal grants $3,001; Pell grants $2,339; other federal aid $871; state/local grants $685; institutional grants $1,080.

Departments and Teaching Staff: *Total instructional faculty:* 74 (full-time 36, part-time 38). Student/faculty ratio: 15:1. Degrees held by full-time faculty: doctorate 50%, master's 40%, baccalaureate 10%. 50% hold terminal degrees.

Enrollment: Total enrollment 789 (undergraduate). Transfer-in students 22.

Characteristics of Student Body: *Ethnic/racial makeup:* Black non-Hispanic: 3%; American Indian or Alaska Native: 3%; Asian or Pacific Islander: 1%; Hispanic: 2%; White non-Hispanic: 85%; unknown 1%; nonresident alien 3%. *Age distribution:* number under 18: 57;18–21 231; 22–24: 199; 22–24: 177; 25–29: 70; 30–34: 31; 35–39: 20; 50–49: 34; 50–64: 13.

International Students: 24 nonresident aliens enrolled fall 2008. Students from Europe, Asia, Central and south America, Canada. No programs available to aid students whose native language is not English. Some financial aid specifically designated for international students; 5 scholarships available annually. 3 totaling $18,250 awarded 2008–09.

Student Life: On-campus residence halls house 60% of student body. Residence halls for males constitute 45% of such space, for females 55%. Housing available for students with families. *Intercollegiate athletics:* male: football, basketball, baseball, soccer; female: basketball, soccer, softball, volleyball. *Special regulations:* Cars permitted without restrictions. Quiet hours from 9pm to noon. Residence hall visitation from noon to 11pm Sunday through Thursday and 24 hours on Friday and Saturday. *Special services:* medical services. *Student publications: The Mill*, a yearbook; *Flash*, monthly newspaper; *MaSU Handbook*, an annual publication. *Surrounding community:* Mayville population 3,000. Fargo, ND/Moorehead MN, 56 miles from campus, is nearest large metropolitan area; Grand Forks with population of 50,000 is 40 miles away.

Library Collections: 106,000 volumes. Online catalog. 15,200 microforms; 9,000 audiovisual materials; 500 current periodical subscriptions. All students have laptop computers and access to the Internet.

North Dakota Collection is most important special collection.

Buildings and Grounds: Campus area 55 acres. Campus DVD available.

Chief Executive Officer: Dr. Gary Hagen, President.

Address admission inquiries to Vice President for Enrollment Management.

Minot State University

500 University Avenue, West
Minot, North Dakota 58707
Tel: (701) 858-3000 **E-mail:** askmsu@nodak.edu
Fax: (701) 858-3386 **Internet:** www.misu.nodak.edu

Institution Description: Minot State University is a member of the North Dakota University System. *Enrollment:* 3,432. *Degrees awarded:* Associate, baccalaureate, master's. Specialist certificates also awarded.

Accreditation: *Regional:* NCA. *Professional*: audiology, music, nursing, school psychology, social work, speech-language pathology, teacher education

History: Chartered as Northwestern Normal School and offered first instruction at postsecondary level 1913; changed name to Minot State Teachers College 1924; awarded first degree (baccalaureate) 1928; became Minot State College 1964; adopted present name 1995.

Institutional Structure: *Governing board:* North Dakota State Board of Higher Education. Representation: 7 trustees (appointed by governor of North Dakota), 1 student, 1 faculty (appointed by Council of College Faculties). *Composition of institution:* Administrators 11. Full-time instructional faculty 174.

Calendar: Semesters. Academic year Aug. to May. Summer session.

Characteristics of Freshmen: 643 applicants (405 female, 238 male). 72%students admitted. 95% of admitted students enrolled full-time.

11% (52 students) submitted SAT scores; 83% (363 students) submitted ACT scores. *25th percentile*: SAT Critical Reading 440, SAT math 430, SAT Writing 390; ACT Composite 19, ACT English 18, ACT Math 18. *75th percentile*: SAT Critical Reading 530, SAT Math 520, SAT 510; ACT Composite 24, ACT English 23, ACT Math 24.

39% of entering freshmen expected to graduate within 5 years. 83% of freshmen from North Dakota. Freshmen from 14 states and 19 foreign countries.

Admission: Early acceptance available. *Requirements:* Either graduation from accredited secondary school with 4 units English, 3 social studies, 3 laboratory science, 3 mathematics (algebra I or greater); or GED. For student without these requirements, lowest acceptable secondary school GPA is 2.75 or ACT composite score of 19. *Entrance tests:* College Board SAT or ACT composite. *For transfer students:* From 4-year accredited institution maximum transfer credit limited only by residence requirement; from 2-year institution, in order to be awarded a degree, a student must earn a minimum of 60 semester credits at a four-year institution, 30 of which must be earned in residence at Minot State University.

College credit for extrainstitutional learning.

Degree Requirements: *For all associate degrees:* 60 semester hours; 30 hours in residence. *For all baccalaureate degrees:* 128 semester hours; 30 semester hours in residence; 60 semester hours from a 4-year institution. *For all undergraduate degrees:* 2.0 cumulative GPA; general education requirements.

Fulfillment of some degree requirements possible by passing institutional examinations, College Board CLEP. *Grading system:* A–F; pass-fail, pass; withdraw (carries time limit); satisfactory-unsatisfactory; noncredit.

Distinctive Educational Programs: Continuing education program offering correspondence and extension courses for community residents and military personnel.

Degrees Conferred: 477 *baccalaureate*; 90 *master's*. Bachelor's degrees awarded in top five disciplines: business, management, marketing, and related support services 126; education 115 health professions and related clinical sciences 81; security and protective services 52; liberal arts and sciences, general studies, and humanities 29. Master's degrees awarded: various disciplines 90.

Fees and Other Expenses: *Full-time tuition per academic year 2008–09:* resident undergraduate $5,043, nonresident $12,022; contact the university for current graduate tuition/fees. *Required fees:* $702. *Room and board per academic year:* $5,670. *Books and supplies:* $900. *Other expenses:* $3,100.

Financial Aid: Aid from institutionally generated funds is provided on the basis of academic merit, financial need, athletic ability. Institution has a Program Participation Agreement with the U.S. Department of Education for eligible students to receive Pell Grants and, depending upon the agreement, other federal aid.

Financial aid to full-time, first-time undergraduate students: 84% received some form of aid. Average amount of aid received: federal grants $2,369; Pell grants $2,624; other federal aid: $2,222; state/local grants $871; institutional grants $1,136.

Departments and Teaching Staff: *Total instructional faculty:* 264 (full-time 174, part-time 40). Student/faculty ratio: 14:1. Degrees held by full-time faculty: baccalaureate 100%, master's 100%, doctorate 60%. 64% hold terminal degrees.

Enrollment: Total enrollment 3,436. Undergraduate 3,172. Graduate 260 (full-time 43%). Undergraduate transfer in-students 270.

Characteristics of Student Body: *Ethnic/racial makeup:* Black non-Hispanic: 3%; American Indian or Alaska Native: 4%; Asian or Pacific Islander: 1%; Hispanic: 3%; White non-Hispanic: 79%; unknown 1%; nonresident alien 9%. *Age distribution:* number under 18: 60; 18–19: 665; 0–21: 1,810; 22–24: 807; 25–29: 462; 30–34: 44; 35–39: 1449; 40–49: 173; 50–64: 50; 65 and over: 2

International Students: 288 nonresident aliens enrolled fall 2008. Students from Europe, Asia, Central and South America, Canada. No programs available to aid students whose native language is not English. No financial aid specifically designated for international students.

Student Life: On-campus housing for single and married students available. *Intercollegiate athletics:* male: baseball, basketball, cross-country, football, golf, tennis, track; female: basketball, cross-country, golf, track, volleyball. *Special regulations:* Cars with permits allowed. *Student publications: The Beaver*, a yearbook; *The Coup*, an annual literary magazine; *The Red and Green*, a weekly newspaper. *Surrounding community:* Minot population 35,000.

Library Collections: 437,000 volumes including bound books, serial backfiles, electronic documents, and government documents not in separate collections. Online catalog. 688,000 microforms; 15,000 audiovisual materials; 800 current serial subscriptions. Computer work stations available. Students have access to the Internet at no charge.

Most important holdings include collection on Indians of North Central North America; children's literature recordings, filmstrips, and curriculum materials; U.S. Representative Brynhild Haugland Papers. Library serves as depository for U.S. and state government documents.

Buildings and Grounds: Campus area 103 acres.

Chief Executive Officer: Dr. David Fuller, President.

Address admission inquiries to Alexis Hendricks, Director of Enrollment Services.

North Dakota State University of Agriculture and Applied Science

1301 Twelfth Avenue North
Fargo, North Dakota 58105
Tel: (701) 231-8011 **E-mail:** ndsuadmiss@ndsu.edu
Fax: (701) 231-8802 **Internet:** www.ndsu.edu

Institution Description: North Dakota State University of Agriculture and Applied Science is a state institution and land-grant college. *Enrollment:* 13,230. *Degrees awarded:* Associate, baccalaureate, first-professional (pharmacy), master's, doctorate.

Academic offerings subject to approval by statewide coordinating bodies. Budget subject to approval by state governing boards.

Accreditation: *Regional:* NCA. *Professional*: architecture, business, chemistry, dietetics, engineering, family and consumer science, music, nursing, pharmacy, teacher education

History: Established and chartered as North Dakota Agricultural College 1890; offered first instruction at postsecondary level 1891; awarded first degree (baccalaureate) 1895; adopted present name 1960. *See* William C. Hunter, *Beacon Across the Prairie* (Minneapolis, MN: The Lund Press, Inc., 1961) for further information.

Institutional Structure: *Governing board:* North Dakota Board of Higher Education. Representation: 7 members appointed by governor of North Dakota, 1 student. 1 faculty representative. 8 voting. *Composition of institution:* Administrators 13. Academic affairs headed by vice president for academic affairs. Management/business/finances directed by vice president for business and finance. Full-time instructional faculty 541. Academic governance body, Faculty Senate, meets an average of 9 times per year.

Calendar: Semesters. Academic year Sept. to May. Freshmen admitted Sept., Nov., Mar., June, July. Degrees conferred May, July, Aug., Nov., Mar. Formal commencement May. Summer session of 2 terms from early June to late Aug.

Characteristics of Freshmen: 5,678 applicants (2,705 female, 2,973male). 80% of applicants admitted. 59% of admitted applicants enrolled full-time. 3% (87 students) submitted SAT scores; 97% (2,568 students) submitted ACT scores. *25th percentile*: SAT Critical Reading 480, SAT Math 570; ACT Composite 20, ACT English 19, ACT Math 20. *75th percentile*: SAT Critical Reading 660, SAT Math 670; ACT Composite 25, ACT English 25, ACT Math 26.

25% of entering freshmen expected to graduate within 5 years. 60% of freshmen from North Dakota. Freshmen from 36 states and 63 foreign countries.

Admission: Rolling admissions plan. For fall acceptance, apply as early as 1 year, but not later than 1 month, prior to enrollment. Early acceptance available. *Requirements:* Either graduation from accredited secondary school with 13 units which must include 4 English, 3 mathematics, 3 lab science, 3 social science; or GED. Additional requirements for some programs. *Entrance tests:* College Board SAT, or ACT composite. *For transfer students:* minimum 2.0 GPA.

College credit for postsecondary-level work completed in secondary school would include advanced placement on basis of faculty assessment.

Tutoring available. Noncredit remedial courses offered in summer session and regular academic year.

Degree Requirements: *For all baccalaureate degrees:* minimum 122 semester hours; 2.0 GPA; last 30 semester credits in residence. *For all undergraduate degrees:* general education requirements.

Fulfillment of some degree requirements and exemption from some beginning courses possible by passing departmental examination, College Board CLEP, AP, other standardized tests. *Grading system:* A–F; pass-fail; withdraw; satisfactory, incomplete.

Distinctive Educational Programs: Evening classes. Special facilities for using telecommunications in the classroom. Interdisciplinary programs available. Facilities and programs for independent research, including honors programs, individual majors, independent study. Cross registration and shared degree programs through consortium.

ROTC: Air Force, Army.

Degrees Conferred: 1,770 *baccalaureate*; 390 *master's*; 59 *doctorate*; 65 *first-professional*. Bachelor's degrees awarded in top five disciplines: business/marketing 239; engineering 211; health professions and related clinical sciences 177; agriculture 118; architecture 116. Master's degrees awarded in various disciplines. First-professional degrees awarded: pharmacy 65.

Fees and Other Expenses: *Full-time tuition per academic year 2008–09:* undergraduate resident $6,326, nonresident $15,025; contact the university for current graduate and first-professional tuition/fees. *Required fees:* $948. *Room and board per academic year:* $6,220. *Books and supplies:* $100. *Other expenses:* $2,600.

Financial Aid: Aid from institutionally generated funds is provided on the basis of academic merit, athletic ability, financial need.

Financial aid to full-time, first-time undergraduate students: 86% received some form of aid. Average amount of aid received: federal grants $3,871; Pell grants $2,651; other federal aid $1,423; state/local grants $1,249; institutional grants $2,405.

Departments and Teaching Staff: *Total instructional faculty:* 630 (full-time 541, part-time 89). 70% of faculty hold the doctorate, first-professional, or other terminal degree. Student/faculty ratio: 19:1.

Enrollment: Total enrollment 13,230. Undergraduate 11,062. Graduate 2,168 (full-time 44%). Undergraduate transfer-in students 717.

Characteristics of Student Body: *Ethnic/racial makeup:* Black non-Hispanic: 2%; American Indian or Alaska Native: 1%; Asian or Pacific Islander: 1%; Hispanic: 1%; White non-Hispanic: 90%; unknown 1%; nonresident alien 4%. *Age distribution:* number under 18: 7; 18–19: 2,949; 20–21: 3,475; 22–24: 2,320; 25–29: 328; 30–34: 116; 35–39: 55; 40–49: 16; 50–64: 7.

International Students: 528 nonresident aliens enrolled fall 2008. Students from Europe, Asia, Central and South America, Africa, Canada, Australia. Programs available to aid students whose native language is not English: social, cultural. English as a Second Language Program. Financial aid specifically designated for undergraduate international students: scholarships available annually;

Student Life: On-campus residence halls house 32% of student body. Residence halls for males constitute 40% of such space, for females 40%, for both sexes 20%. 9% of males join and 8% live in fraternity housing; 7% of females join and 2% live in sorority housing. 4% of student body live off-campus in college-owned and college-operated residence halls. 40% of married students request institutional housing; 29% are so housed. *Intercollegiate athletics:* male: baseball, basketball, cross-country, football, golf, outdoor track and field, wrestling; female: basketball, cross-country, golf, outdoor track and field, soccer, softball, volleyball. *Special regulations:* Cars must have parking permits. Quiet hours. *Special services:* Learning Resources Center, medical services. *Student publications, radio: Spectrum*, a biweekly newspaper. *Surrounding community:* Fargo population 93,000. Minneapolis-St.Paul, 225 miles from campus, is nearest metropolitan area. Served by mass transit bus system; airport 1 mile from campus; passenger rail service 2 miles from campus.

Library Collections: 917,000 volumes. 445,000 microforms; 51,300 audiovisual materials; 5,100 current serial subscriptions. Online catalog. Computer work stations available. Students have access to online information retrieval services and the Internet.

Most important special collections include Polymers and Coatings Collection; Agricultural Collection; Germans from Russia Collection.

Buildings and Grounds: Campus area 286 acres. >

Chief Executive Officer: Dr. Joseph A. Chapman, President.

Address admission inquiries to Dr. Kate Haugen, Dean of of Enrollment Management; graduate inquiries to Dr.David Wittrock, Dean of Graduate School.

Trinity Bible College

50 South 6th Avenue
Ellendale, North Dakota 58436-7150
Tel: (888) 822-2329 **E-mail:** info@trinitybibc.edu
Fax: (701) 349-5786 **Internet:** www.trinitybc.edu

Institution Description: Trinity Bible College is a private institution affiliated with the Assembly of God. *Enrollment:* 216. *Degrees awarded:* Associate, baccalaureate.

Accreditation: *Regional:* NCA. *National:* ABHE. *Professional*: teacher education

Calendar: Semesters. Academic year Aug. to May.

Characteristics of Freshmen: 99% of applicants accepted. 57% of accepted applicants enrolled.

Mean ACT Composite score 19.

29% of freshmen expected to graduate within 5 years. Freshmen from 28 states and 2 foreign countries.

Admission: Open admission.

Degree Requirements: Completion of prescribed curriculum.

Degrees Conferred: 8 *associate;* 34 *baccalaureate:* philosophy and religious studies.

Fees and Other Expenses: *Full-time tuition per academic year 2008–09:* $12,940. *Room and board per academic year:* $4,590. *Books and supplies:* $880. *Other expenses:* $4,200.

Financial Aid: Aid from institutionally generated funds is provided on the basis of academic merit, other criteria.

Financial aid to full-time, first-time undergraduate students: 100% received some form of financial aid. Average amount of aid received: federal grants $3,404; Pell grants $2,681; other federal aid $955; institutional grants $5,018.

TRINITY BIBLE COLLEGE—*cont'd*

Departments and Teaching Staff: *Total instructional faculty:* 24. Student/faculty ratio: 12:1. Degrees held by full-time faculty: baccalaureate 29%, master's 42%, doctorate 29%. 29% hold terminal degrees.

Enrollment: Total enrollment 296 (undergraduate).

Characteristics of Student Body: *Ethnic/racial makeup:* number of Black non-Hispanic: 9; American Indian or Alaska Native: 13; Asian or Pacific Islander: 2; Hispanic: 7; White non-Hispanic: 279, unknown: 1. *Age distribution:* number under 18: 3; 18–19: 71; 20–21: 109; 22–24: 61; 25–29: 26; 30–34: 10; 35–39: 7; 40–49: 81 50–64: 6.

International Students: No programs available to aid students whose native language is not English. No financial aid specifically designated for international students.

Student Life: *Special services:* Center for Personalized Instruction. Radio station KTBC broadcasts on campus.

Library Collections: 82,000 volumes. 5,873 microforms; 3,657 audiovisual materials; 174 current periodical subscriptions; access to 14,575 via electronic access. Online catalog. Computer work stations available. Students have access to online information retrieval services and the Internet.

Most important special holdings include books on the history of the Assemblies of God; turn-of-the-century books on North Dakota history.

Chief Executive Officer: Dr. Dennis Niles, President.

Address admission inquiries to Steve Tvedf, Vice President of College Relations.

University of Mary

7500 University Drive
Bismarck, North Dakota 58504
Tel: (701) 255-7500 **E-mail:** admissions@umary.edu
Fax: (701) 255-7687 **Internet:** www.umary.edu

Institution Description: University of Mary is a private, independent, nonprofit institution owned by the Benedictine Sisters of Annunciation Priory of the Roman *Degrees awarded:* Associate, baccalaureate, master's. doctorate. Enrollment: 2,862.

Accreditation: *Regional:* NCA. *Professional*: nursing, occupational therapy, physical therapy, social work

History: Established by the Benedictine Sisters of Annunciation Priory, Roman Catholic Church, and offered first instruction at postsecondary level 1955; incorporated and added 4-year curriculum 1959; awarded first degree (baccalaureate) 1960; renamed University of Mary (from Mary College) 1986.

Institutional Structure: *Governing board:* University of Mary Board of Trustees. Extrainstitutional representation: 9 trustees. 1 ex officio. All voting. *Composition of institution:* Administrators 21. Academic affairs headed by vice president for academic affairs. Management/business/finances directed by vice president for financial affairs. Full-time instructional faculty 101. Academic governance body, University Senate, meets an average of 8 times per year.

Calendar: Semesters (4-4-1 plan). Academic year Aug. to May. Freshmen admitted Aug., Jan., May, June, July. Degrees conferred Apr., May, June. Formal commencement Apr. Summer session of 2 terms from June to July.

Characteristics of Freshmen: 1,020 applicants (557 female, 463 male). 81% of applicants admitted. 46% of admitted applicants enrolled full-time.

11% (39 students) submitted SAT scores; 90% (318 students) submitted ACT scores. *25th percentile*: ACT Composite 20, ACT English 18, ACT Math 18. *75th percentile*: ACT Composite 25, ACT English 24, ACT Math 25.

52% of entering freshmen expected to graduate within 5 years. 70% of freshmen from North Dakota. Freshmen from 33 states and 24 foreign countries.

Admission: Rolling admissions plan. For fall acceptance, apply as early as 1 year prior to registration, but not later than registration day. Early acceptance available. *Requirements:* Either graduation from accredited secondary school or GED. *Entrance tests:* ACT strongly recommended. *For transfer students:* 2.0 minimum GPA.

College credit and advanced placement for postsecondary-level work completed in secondary school. College credit for extrainstitutional learning on basis of portfolio and faculty assessments; personal interviews.

Tutoring available. Remedial courses offered during regular academic year; credit given.

Degree Requirements: *For all associate degrees:* 64 credit hours. *For all baccalaureate degrees:* 128 credit hours. *For all undergraduate degrees:* 2.0 GPA; 2 terms in residence; 2.0 GPA in major.

Fulfillment of some degree requirements and exemption from some beginning courses possible by passing College Board CLEP, APP, other standardized examinations, and departmental examinations. *Grading system:* A–F; pass-fail; withdraw (not recorded on transcript).

Distinctive Educational Programs: Evening classes. Facilities and programs for independent study. Credit for experiential learning. Accelerated degree completion program. Leadership development program involving all students.

Degrees Conferred: 540 *baccalaureate*; 361 *master's*; 25 *doctorate*. Bachelor's degrees awarded in top five disciplines: business, management, marketing, and related support services 222; health professions and related clinical sciences 103; computer and liberal arts/general studies 24; biological/life sciences 20. Master's degrees awarded: business/marketing 295; education 17; health professions 34. Doctorates awarded: health professions 25.

Fees and Other Expenses: *Full-time tuition per semester 2008–09:* undergraduate $12,190. *Required fees:* $224. *Books and supplies:* $900. *Room and board per academic year:* $4,820. *Other expenses:* $2,000.

Financial Aid: Aid from institutionally generated funds is provided on the basis of academic merit, financial need, athletic ability, other criteria.

Financial aid to full-time, first-time undergraduate students: 99% received some form of aid. Average amount of aid received: federal grants $4,810, Pell grants $3,032; other federal aid $1,291; state/local grants $1,160; institutional grants $3,452.

Departments and Teaching Staff: *Total instructional faculty:* 313 (full-time 101, part-time 212). Student/faculty ratio: 15:1. Degrees held by full-time faculty: baccalaureate 7%, master's 63%, doctorate 30%. 37% hold terminal degrees.

Enrollment: Total enrollment 2,862. Undergraduate 2,091. Graduate 771 (full-time 58%). Undergraduate transfer-in students 301.

Characteristics of Student Body: *Ethnic/racial makeup:* Black non-Hispanic: 2%; American Indian or Alaska Native: 5%; Asian or Pacific Islander:1%; Hispanic: 2%; White non-Hispanic: 87%; unknown 2%; nonresident alien 2%. *Age distribution:* number under 18: 4; 18–19: 581; 20–21: 324; 22–24: 169; 25–29: 169; 30–34: 125; 35–39: 96; 40–49: 128; 50–64: 42; 65 and over: 1.

International Students: 58 nonresident aliens enrolled fall 2008. Students from Europe, Asia, Central and South America, Africa, Canada. Programs available to aid students whose native language is not English: social, cultural. No financial aid specifically designated for international students.

Student Life: On-campus residence halls house 45% of student body. *Intercollegiate athletics:* male: baseball, basketball, soccer, track, football, wrestling, cross-country; female: basketball, soccer, track, volleyball, softball, cross-country. *Special regulations:* Residence hall visitation from 11am to 10pm Sun.–Thurs., 11am to 1am Fri. and Sat. *Special services:* Learning Resources Center, medical services, campus transportation system. *Student publications: Kaleidoscope*, a yearbook; *Incense,* an annual literary magazine. *Surrounding community:* Bismarck population 45,000. Minneapolis-St. Paul, 450 miles from campus, is nearest metropolitan area. Served by airport 3.5 miles from campus.

Publications: *Summit* published bimonthly.

Library Collections: 78,500 volumes. Online catalog. Current serial subscriptions: paper 565; microform 2; 6,430 via electronic access. 5.416 audio/videotapes; 923 DVD discs; 1,527 CD-ROMs. Computer work stations available. Students have access to the Internet at no charge.

Most important special holdings include collections on education, nursing, and business.

Buildings and Grounds: Campus area 108 acres. Campus DVD available.

Chief Executive Officer: Sr. Thomas Welder, O.S.B., President.

Address admission inquiries to Dave Heringer, Vice President for Enrollment Management.

University of North Dakota

P.O. Box 8193
University Station
Grand Forks, North Dakota 58202-7106
Tel: (701) 777-4358 **E-mail:** admissions@und.nodak.edu
Fax: (701) 777-2494 **Internet:** www.und.nodak.edu

Institution Description: University of North Dakota is a state institution. *Enrollment:* 12,748. *Degrees awarded:* Baccalaureate, first-professional (law, medicine), master's, doctorate. Specialist certificates in education also awarded.

Academic offerings subject to approval by statewide coordinating bodies. Budget subject to approval by state governing boards.

Accreditation: *Regional:* NCA. *Professional*: art, athletic training, business, chemistry, clinical lab scientist, clinical psychology, computer science, counseling psychology, cytotechnology, dietetics, engineering, industrial technology, law, medicine, music, nurse anesthesia education, nursing, nursing education, occupational therapy, physical therapy, physician assisting, social work, speech-language pathology, surgeon assisting, teacher education, theatre

History: Established and chartered as University of North Dakota 1883; offered first instruction at postsecondary level 1884; awarded first degree (baccalaureate) 1889. *See* Louis G. Geiger, *University of the Northern Plains* (Grand Forks: University of North Dakota Press, 1958) and Robert P. Wilkens, ed., *A Century on the Northern Plains* (Grand Forks: University of North Dakota Press, 1983) for further information.

Institutional Structure: *Governing board:* North Dakota State Board of Higher Education. Extrainstitutional representation: 1 student (voting) and 1 faculty representative (nonvoting). *Composition of institution:* Administrators 82. Vice presidents of academic affairs and provost, finance and operations; health affairs, research, student and outreach services. Full-time instructional faculty 668. Academic governance body, University Senate, meets an average of 8 times per year.

Calendar: Semesters. academic year Aug. to May. Freshmen admitted Aug., Jan., June. Degrees conferred May, Aug., Dec. Formal commencements May, Aug. Summer session of 5 terms from May to Aug. (4 weeks, 6 weeks, 6 weeks, 8 weeks, 12 weeks).

Characteristics of Freshmen: 3,783 applicants (1,730 female, 2,053 male). 70% of applicants admitted, 70% of admitted students enrolled full-time.

84% (1,558 students) submitted ACT scores. *25th percentile*: ACT Composite 21, ACT English 26, ACT Math 26. *75th percentile*: ACT Composite 26, ACT English 26, ACT Math 25.

49% of entering freshmen expected to graduate within 5 years. 52% of freshmen from North Dakota. Freshmen from 49 states and 68 foreign countries.

Admission: Rolling admissions plan. No application deadlines. *Requirements:* 4 units English, 3 mathematics, 3 lab science, 3 social studies. *Entrance tests:* College Board SAT or ACT composite. For foreign students TOEFL. *For transfer students:* 2.0 minimum GPA; maximum transfer credit limited only by residence requirement.

College credit and advanced placement for postsecondary-level work completed in secondary school.

Tutoring available. Developmental courses offered during regular academic year; credit given.

Degree Requirements: *For all baccalaureate degrees:* 125 credit hours. *For all undergraduate degrees:* Minimum 2.0 GPA; 30 hours in residence; general education requirements.

Fulfillment of some degree requirements and exemption from some beginning courses possible by passing departmental examinations, College Board CLEP, AP. *Grading system:* A–F; withdraw (carries time limit); satisfactory-unsatisfactory; incomplete.

Distinctive Educational Programs: Flexible meeting places and schedules; evening classes. Special facilities for using telecommunications in classrooms. Interdisciplinary integrated studies program. Other programs include peace studies, Indian studies. Space Studies, fully-accredited distance MBA program, corporate engineering degree program, entrepreneurship major, MD/Ph.D. program, distance RN program, distance MSW program. Certificate programs in public policy, public administration, health administration, and nursing administration. Student exchange opportunities include Quebec, Canada and the Republic of China in certain programs. Study abroad through International Student Exchange Program in 39 countries.

ROTC: Air Force, Army.

Degrees Conferred: 1,836 *baccalaureate*; 471 *master's*; 110 *doctorate*; 117 *first-professional*. Bachelor's degrees awarded in top five disciplines: transportation and materials moving 376; business, management, marketing, and related support services 281; health professions and related clinical sciences 2111; education 139; engineering 132. Master's degrees awarded in top five disciplines: education 135; public administration and social services 45; business/marketing 43; transportation and materials moving 35. Doctorates awarded: biological/life sciences 3; education 14; engineering 1; English 3; health professions 74; history 1; physical sciences 2; psychology 10. First-professional degrees awarded: law 60; medicine 57.

Fees and Other Expenses: *Full-time tuition per academic year 2008–09:* undergraduate $6,513, nonresident $15,325; contact the university for current graduate and first-professional tuition. *Required fees:* $1,006. *Room and board per academic year:* $6,000. *Books and supplies:* $800. *Other expenses:* $3,120.

Financial Aid: Aid from institutionally generated funds is provided on the basis of academic merit, financial need, athletic ability, other criteria.

Financial aid to full-time, first-time undergraduate students: 82% received some form of aid. Average amount of aid received: federal grants $3,760; Pell grants $2,625; other federal aid $1,270; state/local grants $1,329; institutional grants $1,622.

Departments and Teaching Staff: *Total instructional faculty:* 825 (full-time 668, part-time 157). 705 of faculty hold the doctorate, first-professional, or other terminal degree. Student/faculty ratio: 18:1.

Enrollment: Total enrollment 12,748. Undergraduate 10,129. Graduate 2,619 (full-time 55%). Undergraduate transfer-in students 759.

Characteristics of Student Body: *Ethnic/racial makeup:* Black non-Hispanic: 1%; American Indian or Alaska Native: 3%; Asian or Pacific Islander: 1%; Hispanic: 1%; White non-Hispanic: 87%; unknown 2%; nonresident alien 4%. *Age distribution:* number under 18: 16; 18–19: 2,806; 20–21: 3,525; 22–24: 2,614; 25–29: 764; 30–34: 239; 35–39: 128; 40–49: 134; 50–64: 67; 65 and over: 1.

International Students: 508 nonresident aliens enrolled fall 2008. Students from Europe, Asia, Central and South America, Africa, Canada. Programs available to aid students whose native language is not English: social, cultural. English as a Second Language Program. Financial aid specifically designated for international students: scholarships available annually.

Student Life: On-campus residence halls house 36% of student body. 7% of student body housed in family housing and single student apartments. 11% of females and 16% of mails join Greek organizations. *Intercollegiate athletics:* male: baseball, basketball, cross-country, football, golf, gymnastics, hockey, swimming, track, wrestling; female: badminton, basketball, cross-country, field hockey, golf, gymnastics, softball, swimming, track, volleyball. *Special regulations:* Registered cars with permits allowed; fee charged. Dormitory visitation hours set by residents in individual halls. *Special services:* Learning Resources Center, medical services. *Student publications, radio, television: The Dakota Student*, a biweekly newspaper; *North Dakota Engineer II*, a magazine published 2 times per semester; *Native American Directions,* a Native American newspaper published several times per semester; *Rhadamanthus*, a quarterly law school magazine. Two public radio stations. UND public access tv channel (ResLife Cinema, broadcasting movies and announcements to campus). *Surrounding community:* Grand Forks area population 60,000. Winnipeg (Canada), 150 miles from campus, is nearest metropolitan area. Served by mass transit bus system; airport 6 miles from campus; passenger rail service 3 miles from campus.

Publications: *Academy of Science* (annually), *Journal of Teaching and Learning* (annually), *North Dakota Quarterly, Prairie Naturalist* (quarterly).

Library Collections: 1,507,940 volumes including bound books, serial backfiles, electronic documents, and government documents not in separate collections. Online catalog. 1,652,000 microforms; 18,000 audiovisual materials; 41,500 periodicals including via electronic access. Computer work stations available. Students have access to the Internet at no charge.

Most important special holdings include Orin G. Libby Manuscript collections (1,250 manuscript collection); Fred G. Aandahl collection of books on the Great Plains; University archives.

Buildings and Grounds: Campus area 570 acres.

Chief Executive Officer: Dr. Charles Kupchella, President.

Undergraduates address admission inquiries to Kenton Pauls, Director of Enrollment Services; graduate inquiries to school of interest.

College of Arts and Sciences

Degree Programs Offered: *Baccalaureate* in advertising, American studies, anthropology, biological and physical science, biology, broadcasting, chemistry, communication disorders, computer science, criminal justice studies, earth science, economics, English, French, geography, geology, German, history, humanities, Indian studies, journalism, Latin, languages, mathematics, natural science, peace studies, philosophy, physics, political science, psychology, public relations, religious studies, Russian and Soviet studies, social science, sociology, Spanish, speech, theatre arts, visual arts. *Master's* in forensic science.

Degree Requirements: Generally, 33 credit hours in a single major field with a GPA of 2.2 in those courses by graduation. Proficiency in a foreign language is required in some areas. School of Communications requires students to f pass on English Proficiency Test and have a 2.5 overall GPA. Criminal Justice requires a 2.7 GPA.

Departments and Teaching Staff: *Total instructional faculty:* 243.

Distinctive Educational Programs: Interdepartmental programs in aeronautical studies, American studies, Russian studies.

College of Business and Public Administration

Degree Programs Offered: *Baccalaureate* in accountancy, airport management, aviation administration, banking and finance, economics, industrial technology, information systems, management, marketing, occupational safety and environmental health, managerial finance and corporate accounting, public administration.

Admission: At least 2.5 overall GPA.

Degree Requirements: At least 50 credit hours in business courses with a minimum GPA of 2.5 in those courses. At least 50 credits of non-business courses.

School of Engineering and Mines

Degree Programs Offered: *Baccalaureate* in chemical engineering, civil engineering, electrical engineering, engineering management, environmental geology and technology, geological engineering, mechanical engineering.

UNIVERSITY OF NORTH DAKOTA—*cont'd*

Admission: At least 24 credit hours with a minimum GPA of 2.0. A minimum grade of C in the following courses: general chemistry, English composition, calculus, physics. An additional science course and 4 engineering courses prescribed by the department. *For environmental geology and technology:* general university requirements.

College of Nursing

Degree Programs Offered: *Baccalaureate.*

Admission: Formal application required. At least 24 semester hours including chemistry, biochemistry, anatomy, psychology, sociology, and English composition. At least a "C" grade in the specified courses. Must have 2.5 overall GPA for nursing and 2.60 for dietetics.

Degree Requirements: At least 129 semester hours with a minimum GPA of 2.3.

College of Education and Human Development

Degree Programs Offered: *Baccalaureate* in recreation and leisure services, rehabilitation and human services, social work, business education, early childhood education, elementary education, middle level education, vocational marketing education, science education, social studies education, and physical education; combination courses; teacher preparatory courses and degrees are also offered in cooperation with other university departments in communications, English, French, German, Spanish, industrial technology, biology, chemistry, fisheries and wildlife biology, geology, geography, mathematics, physics, and visual arts.

Admission: Combination of the general university requirements, completion of all major requirements, meeting the departments minimum GPA requirements and for education majors, completion of student teaching requirements.

School of Law

Degree Programs Offered: *First-professional.*

Admission: Must be candidate for or have received a bachelor's degree from an accredited college or university and must have taken the Law School Admission Test.

Distinctive Educational Programs: American Indian Law.

School of Medicine and Health Sciences

Degree Programs Offered: *Baccalaureate* in athletic training, cytotechnology, clinical laboratory science, occupational therapy, physical therapy; *master's* in occupational therapy; physician assistant studies; *doctorate* in physical therapy; *first-professional.*

Admission: M.D. requires 4 years of college including the following courses: chemistry (16 credit hours), biology (8 cr. hrs.), physics (9 credit hours), psychology/sociology (3 credit hours), language arts (6 credit hours), algebra (3 credit hours). Formal admission policy for all programs. All undergraduate programs are very competitive and require specific coursework prior to program admission.

Graduate School

Degree Programs Offered: *Master's* in anatomy, biochemistry, biology, business administration, chemical engineering, chemistry, child study and education, civil engineering, communication, education - general studies, educational administration, educational research/evaluation, electrical engineering, elementary education, English, geography, geology, physical education, physical therapy, history, industrial technology, linguistics, mathematics, mechanical engineering, medical technology, microbiology, music, nursing, pharmacology, physics, physiology, political science, psychology, public administration, reading education, secondary education, social work, sociology, space studies, speech pathology, special education, theater arts, visual arts; *doctorate* in anatomy, biochemistry, biology, chemistry, counseling psychology, educational leadership, English, energy engineering, geology, history, microbiology, physics, physiology, psychology, and teacher education; *master's* and *doctorate* in counseling. A *specialist degree* is available in educational administration.

Admission: Must hold a bachelor's degree and submit a formal application.

Degree Requirements: Vary widely by degree, option, and program of study.

John D. Odegard School of Aerospace Sciences

Degree Programs Offered: *Baccalaureate* in aeronautics, atmospheric sciences, computer science.

Admission: 24 credit hours with at least a 2.5 GPA.

Degree Requirements: 2.5 GPA in all courses.

Valley City State University

101 College Street S.W.
Valley City, North Dakota 58072-4195
Tel: (701) 845-7297 **E-mail:** enrollment.services@vcsu.edu
Fax: (701) 845-7299 **Internet:** www.vcsu.edu

Institution Description: Valley City State University is a state institution. *Enrollment:* 1,019. *Degrees awarded:* Baccalaureate. Certificates also awarded.

Accreditation: *Regional:* NCA. *Professional*: teacher education

History: Established as State Normal School 1890; authorized to award the baccalaureate degree 1921; renamed Valley City State College 1963; adopted present name 1987.

Institutional Structure: *Governing board:* North Dakota State Board of Higher Education. Extrainstitutional representation: 7 trustees appointed by governor of North Dakota; institutional representation: 1 student. *Composition of institution:* Academic affairs headed by vice president for academic affairs. Management/business/finances directed by vice president for business affairs. Full-time instructional faculty 55.

Calendar: Semesters. Academic year Aug. to May. Summer session of 5 weeks.

Characteristics of Freshmen: 266 applicants (109 female, 156 male). 89% of applicants accepted. 68% of accepted applicants enrolled full-time.

8% (13 students) submitted SAT scores; 78% (124 students) submitted ACT scores. *25th percentile*: SAT Math 450; ACT Composite 18, ACT English 16, ACT math 17. *75th percentile*: SAT Math 510; ACT Composite 23. ACT English 22, ACT Math 23.

31% of entering freshmen expected to graduate within 5 years. 72% of freshmen from North Dakota. Freshmen from 21 states and 9 foreign countries.

Admission: Early acceptance available. *Requirements:* General college preparatory program. GED accepted. *Entrance tests:* ACT or SAT. *For transfer students:* Must be eligible to return to last institution attended; official transcript.

College credit for extrainstitutional learning (life experience) on basis of portfolio examination.

Degree Requirements: General education requirements; GPA 2.0. *For all baccalaureate degrees:* 128 semester hours.

Fulfillment of some degree requirements and exemption from some beginning courses possible by passing departmental examinations, College Board CLEP. *Grading system:* A–F; satisfactory-unsatisfactory; withdraw; incomplete; audit.

Distinctive Educational Programs: Internships. Continuing education programs. Project 65. Foreign Language Placement Policy. Study abroad at LaPaz (Mexico), Oaxaca (Mexico), and Brandon (Canada).

Degrees Conferred: 156 *baccalaureate*; 18 *master's*. Bachelor's degrees awarded in top five disciplines: education 120; business, management, marketing, and related support services 59; psychology 13; computer and information sciences services 8; visual and performing arts 5. Master's degrees awarded: education 18.

Fees and Other Expenses: *Full-time tuition per academic year 2008–09:* resident $6,055, nonresident $13,467. *Required fees:* $1,554. *Room and board per academic year:* $5,400. *Books and supplies:* $800. *Other expenses:* $3,000.

Financial Aid: Aid from institutionally generated funds is provided on the basis of academic merit, financial need, athletic ability, other criteria.

Financial aid to full-time, first-time undergraduate students: 100% received some form of aid. Average amount of aid received: federal grants $3,790; Pell grants $2,516; other federal grants 41,387; state/local grants $747; institutional grants $2,258.

Departments and Teaching Staff: *Total instructional faculty:* 91 (full-time 45, part-time 46). 48% of faculty hold the doctorate, first-professional, or other terminal degree:. Student/faculty ratio: 18:1.

Enrollment: Total enrollment 1,019. Undergraduate 900. Graduate 119 (full-time 47%). Undergraduate transfer-in students 58.

Characteristics of Student Body: *Ethnic/racial makeup:* Black non-Hispanic: 3%; American Indian or Alaska Native: 2%; Asian or Pacific Islander: 1%; Hispanic: 1%; White non-Hispanic: 84%; unknown 3%; nonresident alien 5%. *Age distribution:* number under 18: 13; 18–19: 347; 20–21: 267; 22–24: 193; 25–29: 60; 30–34: 37; 35–39: 33; 40–49: 76; 50–64: 33.

International Students: 58 nonresident aliens enrolled fall 2008. Students from Europe, Central and South America, Africa, Canada. No programs available to aid students whose native language is not English. No financial aid specifically designated for international students.

Student Life: On-campus single and family housing available. *Intercollegiate athletics:* male: baseball, basketball, cross-country, football, track and field; female: basketball, cross-country, softball, track and field, volleyball. *Special*

services: medical services, counseling. *Surrounding community:* Valley City, population 8,000, is 50 miles west of Fargo.

Library Collections: 98,000 volumes including bound books, serial backfiles, electronic documents, and government documents not in separate collections. Online catalog. 30,000 microforms, 8,000 audiovisual materials; 13,000 periodicals including via electronic access. Computer work stations available. Students have access to the Internet at no charge.

Most important special holdings include Larry Woiwode Manuscript Collection; North Dakota Collection; Federal Documents Collection.

Buildings and Grounds: Campus area 55 acres.

Chief Executive Officer: Dr. Ellen E. Chaffee, President.

Address admission inquiries to Dan Klein, Director of Enrollment Services.

Ohio

Air Force Institute of Technology

2950 Hobson Way
Wright-Patterson Air Force Base, Ohio 45433-7765
Tel: (937) 255-6231 **E-mail:** counselors@afit.af.mil
Fax: (937) 255-2791 **Internet:** www.afit.af.mil

Institution Description: Air Force Institute of Technology is a federal institution for primarily for graduate study. There are two graduate schools: the Graduate School of Engineering and the Graduate School of Logistics and Acquisition Management; two professional continuing education schools: the Civil Engineer and Services School and the School of Systems and Logistics. There is also a Civilian Institution Program. The majority of students are military members. *Enrollment:* 890. *Degrees awarded:* Master's, doctorate.

Accreditation: *Regional:* NCA. *Professional*: engineering

History: Established as Air School of Application 1919; changed name to Air Service Engineering School 1920, Air Corps Engineering School 1926; school closed 1942; reopened 1944; changed name to Army Air Forces Engineering School; offered first instruction at postsecondary level 1946; awarded first degree (master's) 1956; adopted present name 1962.

Institutional Structure: *Governing board:* Air Force Institute of Technology Subcommittee of the Air University Board of Visitors. 9 members. 1 ex officio. 8 voting. *Composition of institution:* Administrators 10. Academic affairs headed by director, plans and operations. Management/business/finances directed by director, resource management. Full-time instructional faculty 136. Academic governance body, Faculty Senate, meets an average of 1 time per year.

Calendar: Quarters. Academic year Oct. to June. New students admitted Aug., June. Degrees conferred and formal commencement June, Sept., Dec. Mar.

Admission: Apply as early as 1 year, but not later than 6 months, prior to enrollment. *Requirements:* Applicant must be either a commissioned officer of U.S. armed services not currently in permanent change of station, technical training, or professional military education assignment; a federal agency civilian with grade equivalent to that of an officer; or a foreign defense personnel. Some degree programs require math prerequisites. Some engineering degree programs require an ABET accredited engineering bachelor's degree. *Entrance tests:* School of Engineering—GRE, 3.0 overall GPA. School of Logistics and Acquisition Management—GRE or GMAT, 3.0 overall GPA.

Degree Requirements: *For all master's degrees:* 63–68 credit hours, core requirements, thesis, 3.0 GPA. *Grading system:* A–F; withdraw (deadline after which pass-fail is appended to withdraw); incomplete.

Distinctive Educational Programs: Dayton Area Graduate Studies Institute (DAGSI). Consortium of AFIT, Wright State University, and University of Dayton engineering degree programs. Call the Admissions Directorate for specific details.

Degrees Conferred: 371 *master's;* 26 *doctorate.*

Fees and Other Expenses: Fees paid by federal government for full-time resident students. Most of the students are military officers who attend on Air Force quotas at no additional cost to the individual. Part-time students may be required to pay their own way.

Departments and Teaching Staff: *Total instructional faculty:* 136.

Enrollment: Total enrollment 773.

Characteristics of Student Body: *Ethnic/racial makeup:* Black non-Hispanic: 4%; White non-Hispanic: 8%; unknown: 91%.

International Students: No financial aid specifically designated for international students.

Student Life: Students can request to live on base in military housing or can live off base. There is a military medical center on base. *Surrounding community:* Dayton population 185,000. Columbus, 50 miles from campus, is nearest metropolitan area.

Library Collections: 1.2 million volumes. Current periodical subscriptions: paper 910; microform 15; 15,000 via electronic access. Students have access to online information retrieval services and the Internet.

Most important special collections include AFIT Theses, RAND Research Reports; NASA Reports/IEEE Reports.

Buildings and Grounds: Campus area 2 square blocks.

Chief Executive Officer: Colonel Captain Kenneth Ginader, Commandant.

Address admission inquiries to Admissions Office.

Antioch University

150 East South College Street
Yellow Springs, Ohio 45387-1635
Tel: (937) 767-6494 **E-mail:** admissions@antioch.edu
Fax: (937) 767-6475 **Internet:** www.antioch.edu

Institution Description: Antioch University is a private, independent, nonprofit institution. *Enrollment:* 3,464. *Degrees awarded:* Baccalaureate, master's, doctorate.

Accreditation: *Regional:* NCA.

History: Established and incorporated as Antioch College 1852; offered first instruction at postsecondary level 1853; awarded first degree (baccalaureate) 1857; established campuses in various locations in 1960s and 1970s; became Antioch University 1978; current campuses in addition to Antioch College are Antioch New England Graduate School in Keene, (NH) (established 1964); Antioch Southern California in Los Angeles (established 1972) and in Santa Barbara (established 1977); Antioch Seattle (WA) (established 1975); the George Meany Center for Labor Studies in Silver Spring (MD), and the McGregor School of Antioch University in Yellow Springs (OH).

Institutional Structure: *Governing board:* Board of Trustees consisting of 30 members, including 2 ex officio (university president and alumni board president). *Composition of institution:* University-wide academic affairs directed by university vice president and university policy council, with representatives from each campus. University-wide management/business/finances directed by vice president for finance. Each campus administered by a provost. Full-time instructional faculty 161.

Calendar: Quarters (Antioch College, Southern California, Seattle, School for Adult and Experiential Learning); semesters (Antioch New England Graduate School).

Distinctive Educational Programs: Each degree program includes an experiential component, such as cooperative education, field experience, internships. Self-designed and interdisciplinary majors encouraged. Weekend and evening classes in the adult programs. Study abroad through Antioch College's Antioch Education Abroad program in Europe, Asia, and South America.

Degrees Conferred: 344 *baccalaureate:* law 1, letters 7, physical sciences 5, psychology 5, public affairs and services 4, social sciences 8, interdisciplinary studies/liberal arts/general studies 183; 590 *master's:* agriculture and natural resources 13, business and management 28, education 79, psychology 331, public affairs and services 22, interdisciplinary studies 117; 11 *doctorate:* psychology 11.

Fees and Other Expenses: Tuition varies by campus.

Financial Aid: Aid from institutionally generated funds is provided on the basis of financial need.

Financial assistance is available in the form of Pell Grants, College Work-Study, Veterans Administration Benefits, National Direct Student Loans, Supplemental Education Opportunity Grants (SEOG), Higher Education Assistance Loans (HEAL), Stafford Loans, other federal aid programs.

Departments and Teaching Staff: *Total instructional faculty:* 642. *Total tenured faculty:* 33.

Enrollment: Total enrollment 1,116.

International Students: No programs available to aid students whose native language is not English. No financial aid specifically designated for international students.

Chief Executive Officer: Dr. James H. Craiglow, Chancellor.

Address admission inquiries to Mark Thorp, Dean of Admissions.

Antioch University - Antioch College

795 Livermore Street
Yellow Springs, Ohio 45387-1607
Tel: (937) 767-7331 **E-mail:** admissions@antioch-college.edu
Fax: (937) 769-1089 **Internet:** www.antioch-college.edu

Institution Description: Antioch College is a campus of Antioch University. *Enrollment:* 300. *Degrees awarded:* Baccalaureate.

Member of Southwestern Ohio Council for Higher Education; Great Lakes Colleges Association.

Accreditation: *Regional:* NCA.

Calendar: Quarters. New students admitted Sept., Jan. Degrees conferred at formal commencement in June.

Characteristics of Freshmen: 1,282 applicants. 57.2% of applicants accepted. 16.8 of accepted applicants enrolled.

Mid-50% range SAT scores 480–600 verbal, 450–580 mathematical. Mid-50% range ACT composite scores 21–27.

19% of freshmen from Ohio. Freshmen from 35 states.

Admission: For fall acceptance, deadline is Feb. 1 with decisions mailed by Apr. 1. For early decision, deadline is Nov. 15 with decisions mailed by Dec. 15. *Requirements:* Graduation from accredited secondary school or equivalent. Recommend college preparatory curriculum including foreign language and at least 3 years of mathematics, 4 of English. *Entrance tests:* College Board SAT recommended. *For transfer students:* 80 credit hours maximum transfer.

Degree Requirements: 160 credit hours and 6 cooperative education terms (4 for transfer students); 6 hours physical education; general education requirements; cross-cultural experience. Credit for College Board CLEP, AP. *Grading system:* narrative evaluations.

Distinctive Educational Programs: Cooperative education—alternating terms of work and study—required for all students. Five-year or four-year degree completion option. 3-2 dual degree program in engineering in cooperation with Washington University (MO). Interdisciplinary majors in African/African American studies, cross-cultural studies/anthropology, international relations and peace studies, communications, educational studies, environmental science, and women's studies. Self-designed majors possible. Study abroad through Great Lakes Colleges Association and Antioch Education Abroad programs. AEA programs: Buddhist studies program in Bodh Gaya, India; comparative women's studies in Europe; European academic term; German term or year abroad at Eberhard-Karls-University in Tubingen. Students may participate in Brazilia ecosystems program offered by Antioch New England Graduate School. Cross-registration with member institutions of the Southwestern Ohio Council for Higher Education.

Degrees Conferred: 95 *baccalaureate*. Bachelor's degrees awarded in top five disciplines: area, ethnic, and cultural studies 38; multidisciplinary studies 27; liberal arts and sciences, general studies, and humanities 11; natural resources and conservation 11; visual and performing arts 8.

Fees and Other Expenses: *Full-time tuition per academic year:* contact the university for current information.

Financial Aid: Aid from institutionally generated funds is awarded on the basis of financial need.

Financial aid to full-time, first-time undergraduate students: 100% of students received some form of financial aid. Average amount of aid received: federal grants $4,689; state/local grants $7,000; institutional grants 417,821; loans $2,852.

Departments and Teaching Staff: *Total instructional faculty:* 54. 75% of faculty hold the doctorate, first-professional, or other terminal degree.

Enrollment: Total enrollment 300. Undergraduate

Characteristics of Student Body: *Ethnic/racial makeup:* Black non-Hispanic: 3%; American Indian or Alaska Native: 1%; Asian or Pacific Islander: 2%; Hispanic: 1%; White non-Hispanic: 48%; unknown: 46%.

International Students: No programs available to aid students whose native language is not English. No financial aid specifically designated for international students.

Student Life: On-campus residence halls for both sexes house 90% of student body. Housing available for married students. *Special regulations:* Cars permitted without restriction. *Special services:* Medical services. *Student publications, radio: Record*, a weekly newspaper; radio station WYSO-FM. *Surrounding community:* Yellow Springs population 4,000. Dayton, 20 miles from campus, is nearest metropolitan area. Served by airport 26 miles from campus.

Library Collections: 300,000 volumes. 48,000 microforms; 6,350 audiovisual materials; 10,920 current serial subscriptions including electronic access. Online catalog. Students have access to the Internet and online information retrieval services.

Special holdings include the Arthur E. Morgan Papers; Horace Mann Papers.

Buildings and Grounds: Campus area 100 acres; 1,000 acres of nature preserve Glen Helen adjacent to campus. Campus DVD available.

Chief Executive Officer: Dr. Steven W. Laury, President.

Address admission inquiries to Jocelyn Robinson, Director of Admissions.

Antioch University - McGregor

800 Livermore Street
Yellow Springs, Ohio 45387
Tel: (937) 769-1818 **E-mail:** admissions@mcgregor.edu
Fax: (937) 767-1804 **Internet:** www.mcgregor.edu

Institution Description: Antioch University McGregor offers baccalaureate programs in management, human development, humanities, human services administration; master's programs in administration and individualized majors. *Enrollment:* 630.

Accreditation: *Regional:* NCA.

Calendar: Quarters. Students admitted July, Sept., Jan., Mar. Degrees conferred at formal commencement in July.

Admission: Rolling admissions. *Requirements:* For baccalaureate degree, minimum of 1 year of postsecondary study at accredited institution; for master's degree, baccalaureate from an accredited institution.

Degree Requirements: *For baccalaureate degree:* 180 credit hours. *For master's degree:* 64 credit hours for management, 60 for individualized programs. *Grading system:* Narrative evaluations.

Distinctive Educational Programs: Undergraduate program designed for working adults with previous education, offered on weekend college format with classes on Saturdays; credit may be granted for prior experiential learning. Master's in management offered on weekend college format. Individualized master's is external program requiring two residential seminars for orientation and thesis; students design their majors.

Degrees Conferred: 46 *baccalaureate:* business/marketing 14; liberal arts 17; mathematics 22; psychology 10; parks administration and social services 6. 240 *master's:* business/marketing 92; education 101.

Fees and Other Expenses: *Full-time tuition:* contact the school for current fees and expenses.

Financial Aid: Aid from institutionally generated funds is awarded on the basis of financial need.

Departments and Teaching Staff: *Total instructional faculty:* 63 (full-time 24, part-time 39).

Enrollment: Total enrollment 630. Undergraduate 160 (76% female, 24% male). Graduate 470 (full-time 68%). Undergraduate transfer-in students 37.

Characteristics of Student Body: *Ethnic/racial makeup:* Black non-Hispanic: 24%; American Indian or Alaska Native: 3%; Asian or Pacific Islander 1%; Hispanic: 1%; White non-Hispanic: 61%; unknown 11%. unknown: 7. *Age distribution:* number under 20–21: 2; 22–24: 8; 25–29: 26; 30–34: 17; 35–39: 23; 40–49: 47; 50–64: 34; 65 and over: 1.

Library Collections: 325,000 volumes. 4,000 recordings. 10 computer work stations. Students have access to the Internet at no charge.

Most important special holdings include Papers of Horace Mann and Arthur Morgan; Antiochiana.

Chief Executive Officer: Dr. Barbara Gillman-Danley, Chancellor.

Address admission inquiries to Enrollment Services.

Art Academy of Cincinnati

1212 Jackson Street
Cincinnati, Ohio 45202
Tel: (513) 562-6262 **E-mail:** admissions@artacady.edu
Fax: (513) 562-8778 **Internet:** www.artacady.edu

Institution Description: The Art Academy of Cincinnati is a nonprofit museum school, privately owned and operated. *Enrollment:* 167. *Degrees awarded:* Associate, baccalaureate, master's.

Accreditation: *Regional:* NCA. *Professional*: art, interior design

History: Opened as the McMicken School of Art and Design 1869; became the first department of McMicken University which was renamed the University of Cincinnati 1873; became separate institution upon the incorporation of the Cincinnati Museum Association 1881; new building dedicated 1887.

Institutional Structure: *Governing board:* Board of Directors. *Composition of institution:* Director, department heads. Full-time instructional faculty 17.

Calendar: Semesters. Academic year Sept. to May.

Characteristics of Freshmen: 541 applicants (359 female, 182 male). 21% of applicants accepted. 42% of accepted applicants enrolled full-time.

ART ACADEMY OF CINCINNATI—*cont'd*

41% (20 students) submitted SAT scores; 59% (24students) submitted ACT scores. *25th percentile*: SAT Critical Reading 420, SAT Math 420; ACT Composite 18. *75th percentile*: SAT Critical Reading 600, SAT Math 520; ACT Composite 24.

68% of freshmen from Ohio. Freshmen from 6 states and 5 foreign countries.

Admission: For Jan. enrollment, students are advised to submit their applications before Dec. 15. For Aug. enrollment, students are encouraged to apply by June 30. For priority consideration and financial aid assistance, a complete application should be made before Mar. 1. *Requirements:* Transcripts from high school and colleges previously attended; portfolio consisting of 15–20 pieces of artwork; personal interview (may be waived if applicant is more than 150 miles away). *Entrance tests:* College Board SAT or ACT.

Degree Requirements: *For baccalaureate degrees:* 84 semester credits of studio work; acceptance of a thesis in the major field; 33 semester credits in liberal arts; 15 semester credits in art history (total 129 credits).

Distinctive Educational Programs: All seniors are required as part of the coursework in their major discipline to write a substantive statement illustrated with slides or photographs describing their personal concerns in that discipline.

Degrees Conferred: 30 *baccalaureate:* visual and performing arts 30; 6 *master's:* visual and performing arts 6.

Fees and Other Expenses: Contact the academy for current tuition, fees, and housing costs.

Financial Aid: Aid from institutionally generated funds is provided on the basis of academic merit, financial need, artistic merit.

Financial aid to full-time, first-time undergraduate students: 100% of students received some form of financial aid. Average amount of aid received: federal grants $4,297; Pell grants $3,463; other federal grants $3,463; institutional grants $2,385; loans $2,500.

Departments and Teaching Staff: *Total instructional faculty:* 52. Student/faculty ratio: 12:1. Degrees held by full-time faculty: baccalaureate 6%, master's 86%, doctorate 6%.

Enrollment: Total enrollment 218. Undergraduate 166 (63% female, 37% male). Graduate 1 (part-time). Transfer-in students 16.

Characteristics of Student Body: *Ethnic/racial makeup:* Black non-Hispanic: 4%; Asian or Pacific Islander: 1%; Hispanic: 1%; White non-Hispanic: 875; unknown 5%; nonresident alien 1%.

International Students: 2 nonresident aliens enrolled fall 2008. No programs to aid students whose native language is not English. No financial aid specifically designated for international students.

Student Life: No on-campus housing. Most students live in off-campus apartments in surrounding residential neighborhoods. A referral service is available to students through the Admissions Office. New students are contacted by the Admissions Office in July to aid in finding apartments. *Special services:* Health Services (fee charged), tutoring.

Library Collections: 67,000 volumes. 150 current periodical subscriptions. Students have access to the Internet at no charge.

Buildings and Grounds: Campus moved from Eden Park and Mt. Adams in July 2005 and doubled the area occupied previously. Several blocks from the main building is a 6,500 square foot sculpture studio. consists of 2 buildings, one located in Eden Park, the other in nearby Mt. Adams, within 7 minutes walking distance. Eden Park is a 184-acre city park between 2 residential communities, Mt. Adams and Walnut Hills.

Chief Executive Officer: Gregory Allgire Smith, President.

Address admission inquiries to Mary Jane Zumalde, Director of Admissions.

Ashland University

401 College Avenue
Ashland, Ohio 44805
Tel: (419) 289-5052 **E-mail:** auadmsn@ashland.edu
Fax: (419) 289-5999 **Internet:** www.ashland.edu

Institution Description: Ashland University is a private, midsize, liberal arts teaching university. It has an historical relationship with the Brethren Church. *Enrollment:* 6,200. *Degrees awarded:* Associate, baccalaureate, master's, doctorate. Ashland Theological Seminary offers first-professional (master of divinity), master's and doctorate degrees.

Accreditation: *Regional:* NCA. *Professional*: music, nursing, social work, teacher education, theology

History: Established and chartered as Ashland University 1878; offered first instruction at postsecondary level 1879; awarded first degree (baccalaureate) 1882. *See* E. Glenn Mason and Clara Worst Miller, *History of Ashland College* (Ashland, Ohio: Brethren Publishing Company, 1953) for further information.

Institutional Structure: *Governing board:* Ashland University Board of Trustees consisting of 40 members, including 20 church members, 16 members-at-large, 3 alumni. Academic affairs headed by provost. Management/business/finances directed by vice president for business affairs. Full-time instructional faculty 270. Academic governance body: Provost, Deans' Council, Faculty Senate.

Calendar: Semesters. Academic year Aug. to May. Freshmen admitted each semester. Degrees conferred May, Dec. Formal commencement May. Summer session of two 5-week sessions, two six-week sessions, and one 12-week session.

Characteristics of Freshmen: 2,815 applicants (1515 female, 1,300 male). 52% of applicants admitted. 25% of admitted students enrolled full-time.

24% (142 students) submitted SAT scores; 91% (534 students) submitted ACT scores. *25th percentile*: SAT Critical Reading 460, SAT Math 460, SAT Writing 440; ACT Composite 19, ACT English 19, ACT Math 19. *75th percentile*: SAT Critical Reading 560, SAT Math 580; SAT Writing 530; ACT Composite 25, ACT English 25, ACT math 25.

52% of entering freshmen expected to graduate within 5 years. 94% of freshmen from Ohio. Freshmen from 29 states and 14 foreign countries.

Admission: Rolling admissions plan. For fall acceptance, apply as early as Sept. 1 of previous year, but not later than Aug. 10 of year of enrollment. Early acceptance available. *Requirements:* Either graduation from accredited secondary school with 4 units English, 3 unites each of mathematics, science, social studies; or GED. Minimum GPA 2.0. *Entrance tests:* College Board SAT or ACT composite. *For transfer students:* 2.5 minimum GPA; 96 hours maximum transfer credit; from 2-year accredited institution 64 hours.

College credit and advanced placement for postsecondary-level work completed in secondary school.

Tutoring available. Developmental courses offered in summer session and regular academic year; credit given.

Degree Requirements: *For all associate degrees:* 64 credit hours; 2.0 GPA. *For all baccalaureate degrees:* 128 credit hours; 2.0 GPA; 2.25 in major. *For all undergraduate degrees:* Last semester in residence; 2 hours physical education; distribution requirements.

Fulfillment of some degree requirements and exemption from some beginning courses possible by passing departmental examinations, College Board CLEP or APP. *Grading system:* A–F; satisfactory-unsatisfactory; withdraw (may carry penalty; deadline after which pass-fail is appended to withdraw).

Distinctive Educational Programs: *For undergraduates:* Work-experience programs. Dual-degree programs in engineering with University of Akron, University of Toledo. Interdepartmental or interdisciplinary programs in American studies, criminal justice, international studies, public affairs, Renaissance studies. Facilities and programs for independent research, including honors programs, individual majors, tutorials. Preprofessional programs in dentistry, engineering, law, medical technology, medicine, pharmacy, theology, veterinary medicine. Study abroad in 23 countries as member of the College Consortium for International Studies. Junior year at Art Institute of Pittsburgh (PA). U.N. semester in cooperation with Drew University (NJ); Washington (DC) semester in cooperation with American University. Cooperative dietetics program with University of Akron. Off-campus centers include: Columbus, Elyria, Massillon, Lima, Mount Vernon, and Medina. Cross-registration with other colleges in Northwest Ohio Consortium. Associate programs offered at Ohio State Reformatory.

ROTC: Air Force offered in cooperation with Akron University (main campus).

Degrees Conferred: 9 *associate*; 564 *baccalaureate*; 1,001 *master's*; 26 *doctorate*; 43 *first-professional*. Bachelor's degrees awarded in top five disciplines: education 207; business, management, marketing, and related support services 106; health professions and related clinical sciences 34; communication, journalism, and related programs 22; security and protective services 19.

Fees and Other Expenses: *Full-time tuition per academic year 2008–09:* undergraduate $24,342; graduate varies by program. *Books and supplies:* $900. *Room and board per academic year:* $8,876. *Other expenses:* $2,595.

Financial Aid: The university offers a direct lending program. Aid from institutionally generated funds is provided on the basis of academic merit, financial need, athletic ability, other criteria.

Financial aid to full-time, first-time undergraduate students: 99% received some form of financial aid. Average amount of aid received: federal grants $4,010; Pell grants $2,868; other federal aid $1,437; state/local grants $1,450; institutional grants $1,450; loans $16,811.

Departments and Teaching Staff: *Total instructional faculty:* 200. Student/faculty ratio: 17:1. Degrees held by full-time faculty: doctorate 75%, master's 19%, professional 6%. 81% hold terminal degrees.

Enrollment: Total enrollment 6,459. Undergraduate 2,654 (52% female, 48% male). Graduate 3,546 (full-time 41%). Undergraduate transfer-in students 143.

Characteristics of Student Body: *Ethnic/racial makeup (undergraduate):* Black non-Hispanic: 10%; Asian or Pacific Islander: 1%; Hispanic: 3%; White non-Hispanic: 81%. unknown: 4%; nonresident alien 2%.

International Students: 124 nonresident aliens enrolled fall 2008. Students from Europe, Asia, Latin America, Africa, Canada, Australia. Programs available to aid students whose native language is not English: social, cultural. English as a Second Language Program. No financial aid specifically designated for international students.

Student Life: On-campus residence halls, fraternity houses, and sorority suites. Residence halls include for males, females, and co-ed. *Intercollegiate athletics:* NCAA Division II, 19 sports. Male sports include baseball, basketball, cross-country, football, golf, indoor track, outdoor track, soccer, swimming, tennis and wrestling. Female sports include basketball, cross-country, golf, indoor soccer, track, outdoor track, softball, swimming, tennis and volleyball. *Special regulations:* Quiet hours from 9pm to 11am daily, 12 midnight to 11am Fri. and Sat. *Special services:* Health and wellness center, counseling services, University Church, computerized library services. *Student publications, radio, television: The Collegian*, a weekly newspaper; *Masques*, an annual literary magazine; *Pine Whispers*, a yearbook. Radio station WRDL-FM broadcasts 100 hours per week. TV station WRDL-TV2 broadcasts 15 hours per week, plus home sporting events. *Surrounding community:* Ashland population 20,000. Cleveland, 60 miles from campus, is nearest major city with international airport.

Library Collections: 270,200 volumes. 48,000 government documents; 250,000 microforms; 9,000 audiovisual materials; 700 serial subscriptions. Online catalog. Students have access to online information retrieval services and the Internet.

Most important special collections include John M. Ashbrook papers (former Congressman); Harold F. Andrews Collection of Rare and Special Books; Lulu Wood Library of Children's Literature.

Buildings and Grounds: Campus area 150 acres.

Chief Executive Officer: Dr. Frederick Finks, President.

Address admission inquiries to Thomas Mansperger, Director of Admissions.

Athenaeum of Ohio

6616 Beechmont Avenue
Cincinnati, Ohio 45230-2091
Tel: (513) 231-2223 **E-mail:** admissions@athenaeum.edu
Fax: (513) 231-3254 **Internet:** www.athenaeum.edu

Institution Description: The Athenaeum of Ohio, a private institution affiliated with the Archdiocese of Cleveland, Roman Catholic Church, comprises Saint Gregory's Seminary, a college of liberal arts, and Mount Saint Mary's Seminary of the West, a school of theology. *Enrollment:* 283. *Degrees awarded:* First-professional (master of divinity) through Mount Saint Mary's Seminary of the West, master's through both schools.

Member of Greater Cincinnati Consortium of Colleges and Universities, Consortium of Higher Educational Religious Studies.

Accreditation: *Regional:* NCA. *National:* ATS. *Professional*: theology

History: Established and incorporated 1929; offered first instruction at postsecondary level 1831; awarded first degree (baccalaureate) 1929.

Institutional Structure: *Governing board:* Board of Trustees of Athenaeum of Ohio. Representation: 22 trustees, including 2 administrators, 2 students, 3 ex officio. All voting. *Composition of institution:* Administrators 7. Academic affairs headed by president. Management/business/finances directed by treasurer. Full-time instructional faculty 16. Academic governance body, Academic Council, meets an average of 4 times per year.

Calendar: Quarters. Academic year Sept. to June. Entering students admitted Aug., Jan., Mar. Degrees conferred and formal commencement June.

Admission: *Requirements:* For first-professional degree, baccalaureate in liberal arts with 18 hours philosophy; with other baccalaureate degree, 30 hours humanities. For master of arts in theology, baccalaureate in arts; 21 hours philosophy; core preparation in Biblical theology, and the Church and Revelation; 9 hours in a foreign language (with B average) or a reading knowledge of the language; standardized admission test. For master of arts in biblical studies, baccalaureate in arts with 9 hours in a foreign language (with B average); with other baccalaureate degree, 15 hours humanities.

Advanced placement for work completed at other institutions.

Degree Requirements: *For all first-professional degrees:* 174 quarter hours; 2.0 GPA; field education. *For all master's degrees:* 45–50 quarter hours; 3.0 GPA; independent study project. *For all degrees:* Core curriculum; exit competency examinations-comprehensives in individual fields of study. *Grading system:* A–F; withdraw (deadline after which pass-fail is appended to withdraw); incomplete.

Distinctive Educational Programs: Evening classes. Facilities for independent research, including honors programs, individual majors, tutorials.

Degrees Conferred: 24 *baccalaureate:* religious studies; 16 *master's:* theology; 4 *first-professional:* master of divinity.

Fees and Other Expenses: *Full-time tuition per academic year 2008–09:* contact the institution for current undergraduate and graduate graduate tuition, fees, and other costs.

Departments and Teaching Staff: *Total instructional faculty:* 26. Degrees held by full-time faculty: 50% hold terminal degrees.

Enrollment: Total enrollment 253. Undergraduate 134 (20% female, 80% male). Graduate 119 (full-time 80%).

Characteristics of Student Body: *Ethnic/racial makeup:* Black non-Hispanic: 1%; Hispanic 2%; Asian/Pacific Islander 1%; White non-Hispanic: 95%.

International Students: 36 nonresident aliens enrolled fall 2008. No financial aid specifically designated for international students.

Student Life: On-campus residence halls house 100% of student body. *Special regulations:* Registered cars permitted without restrictions. *Special services:* Learning Resources Center. *Surrounding community:* Cincinnati. Served by mass transit bus system; airport and passenger rail service each 10 miles from campus.

Buildings and Grounds: Campus area 90 acres.

Chief Executive Officer: Rev. Edward P. Smith, President and Rector.

Address admission inquiries to Michael E. Sweeney, Registrar.

Baldwin-Wallace College

275 Eastland Road
Berea, Ohio 44017-2088
Tel: (440) 826-2900 **E-mail:** admission@bw.edu
Fax: (440) 826-3830 **Internet:** www.bw.edu

Institution Description: Baldwin-Wallace College is a private college affiliated with the United Methodist Church. *Enrollment:* 4,374. *Degrees awarded:* Baccalaureate, master's. Certificates also awarded.

Accreditation: *Regional:* NCA. *Professional*: music, teacher education

History: Established as Baldwin Institute 1845; offered first instruction at postsecondary level 1846; awarded first degree (baccalaureate) 1850; changed name to Baldwin University 1855; German department became separate institution, German Wallace College, 1863; colleges merged and present name adopted 1913.

Institutional Structure: *Governing board:* Board of Trustees. Extrainstitutional representation: 40 Trustees, 1 Honorary Trustee; 11 Emeriti Trustees; 2 church officials; institutional representation: 2 administrators; 22 alumni. 3 ex officio. 43 voting. *Composition of institution:* Administrators 41. Academic affairs headed by vice president for academic affairs. Management/business/finances directed by vice president for finance. Full-time instructional faculty 200. Academic governance body, Baldwin-Wallace College Faculty, meets an average of 3–5 times per year.

Calendar: Semester. Academic year Aug. to May. Freshmen admitted Aug., Jan., Mar., June, July. Degrees conferred June, Aug., Nov., March. Formal commencement June. Summer session of 2 terms from June to August.

Characteristics of Freshmen: 3,321 applicants (1,843 female, 1,478 male). 67% of applicants admitted. 33% of admitted students enrolled full-time.

55% (410 students) submitted SAT scores; 82% (611 students) submitted ACT scores. *25th percentile*: SAT Critical Reading 500, SAT Math 490; ACT Composite 21, ACT English 20, ACT Math 20. *75th percentile*: SAT Critical Reading 610, SAT Math 600; ACT Composite 26, ACT English 26, ACT Math 26.

68% of entering freshmen expected to graduate within 5 years. 88% of freshmen from Ohio. Freshmen from 36 states and 15 foreign countries.

Admission: Rolling admissions plan. Apply as early as 1 year prior to opening of term for which admission sought, but not later than 3 weeks prior to enrollment. Early acceptance available. *Requirements:* Either graduation from accredited secondary school with academic program or GED with additional college course work (4 units English, 2 in a foreign language, 3 social studies, and 2 additional units). Additional requirements for Conservatory of Music. *Entrance tests:* College Board SAT or ACT composite. *For transfer students:* 2.0 minimum GPA; 92 maximum transfer credit; from 2-year accredited institution 62 hours.

College credit and advanced placement for postsecondary-level work completed in secondary school and for extrainstitutional learning (life experience) on basis of portfolio assessment. Tutoring available.

Degree Requirements: 124 credit hours; 2.0 GPA; last 32 credit hours in residence; exit competency examinations in some departments; 3 physical education courses; distribution requirements.

Fulfillment of some degree requirements and exemption from some beginning courses possible by passing departmental examinations, College Board CLEP,

BALDWIN-WALLACE COLLEGE—*cont'd*

AP. *Grading system:* A–F (plus/minus); satisfactory-unsatisfactory; withdraw (deadline after which pass-fail is appended to withdraw); incomplete.

Distinctive Educational Programs: *For undergraduates:* Off-campus internships through Field Experience program. Dual-degree programs in sociology and biology with Case Western Reserve University; in engineering with Case Western Reserve University, Columbia University (NY), and Washington University (MO); in forestry with Duke University (NC). Cooperative programs in medical technology with area hospitals. Interdepartmental/interdisciplinary programs in criminal justice, international studies, musical theatre, sports, dance, and arts management. Learning and writing laboratory. Study abroad through Baldwin-Wallace programs, including Seminar in Europe, Seminar in Middle East, Seminar in Caribbean, India exchange; affiliated with Edgehill College, Olrmskirk Lancashire England. Study in Germany in cooperation with Junior Year in Heidelberg program; in Salzburg (Austria) in cooperation with Cultural Studies Academy. Other foreign study through Association of Colleges and Universities for International-Intercultural Studies, and by individual arrangement. Off-campus study in U.S. includes Washington (DC) Semester in cooperation with American University, United National Semester in cooperation with Drew University (NJ). Baldwin-Wallace sponsors Upward Bound program for disadvantaged high school students. *For graduate students:* Off-campus centers (at Cleveland and Lorrain, each less than 30 miles away from main institution). *Available to all students:* Evening and weekend classes.

ROTC: Air Force in cooperation with Kent State University.

Degrees Conferred: 850 *baccalaureate*; 311 *master's*. Bachelor's degrees awarded in top five disciplines: business, management, marketing, and related support services 266; education 150; social sciences and history 63; visual and performing arts 53; English language and literature 40. 311 *master's*: business/marketing; education.

Fees and Other Expenses: *Full-time tuition per academic year 2008–09:* $23,524 undergraduate; contact the college for current graduate tuition and fees. *Room and board per academic year:* $7,728. *Books and supplies:* $1,000. *Other expenses:* $2,100.

Financial Aid: Aid from institutionally generated funds is provided on the basis of academic merit, financial need.

Financial aid to full-time, first-time undergraduate students: 99% received some form of financial aid. Average amount of aid received: federal grants $4,250; Pell grants $2,919; other federal aid $1,382; state/local $1,386; institutional grants $1,410; loans $10,803.

Departments and Teaching Staff: *Total instructional faculty:* 360. 73% of faculty hold the doctorate, first-professional, or other terminal degree.

Enrollment: Total enrollment 4,374. Undergraduate 3,673 (female 37%; male 43%). Graduate 702 (full-time 50%). Undergraduate transfer-in students 244.

Characteristics of Student Body: *Ethnic/racial makeup:* Black non-Hispanic: 3%; Asian or Pacific Islander: 1%; Hispanic: 7%; White non-Hispanic: 78%; unknown: 10%; nonresident alien 1%. *Age distribution:* number under 18: 51; 18–19: 1,237; 20–21: 1,320; 22–24: 434; 25–29: 188; 30–34: 118; 35–39: 127; 40–49: 196; 50–64: 196; unknown 8.

International Students: 44 nonresident aliens enrolled fall 2008. Programs available to aid students whose native language is not English: social. English as a Second Language Program. Some financial aid specifically designated for international students: 30 scholarships awarded annually.

Student Life: On-campus residence halls house 63% of student body. Residence halls for males, females, coed and freshman center, special interests. *Intercollegiate athletics:* male: baseball, basketball, cross-country, football, golf, soccer, tennis, track and field, swimming and diving, wrestling; female: basketball, cross-country, softball (fast pitch), soccer, tennis, track and field, swimming and diving, volleyball. *Student activities:* nearly 100 student organizations including Student Government, choral groups, dance, drama, jazz band, music ensembles, musical theater, opera, symphony orchestra, fraternities, sororities, Young Democrats, Young Republicans, Hillel, Newman Club, Protestant religious clubs, community service organizations, Fellowship of Christian Athletes, Black Student Alliance, International Students Association. *Special regulations:* Cars permitted except for freshman year. *Student services:* Learning Resources Center, Freshman Experience, Writing Lab, medical services, counseling services, aptitude testing, career counseling, freshman orientation, employment service (for undergraduates), on-campus day care, placement service for graduates, special advisor for adult students, services/facilities for handicapped. *Student publications, radio: The Exponent*, a weekly newspaper; *The Grindstone*, a yearbook; *The Mill*, a quarterly literary magazine. Radio station WBWC broadcasts 84 hours per week. *Surrounding community:* Berea population 19,000. Cleveland, 14 miles from campus, is nearest metropolitan area. Served by mass transit system; airport 5 miles from campus; passenger rail service 14 miles from campus.

Library Collections: 200,000 volumes. Online catalog. Current serial subscriptions: paper 600; via electronic access 20,000. 10,000 recordings. 2,500 compact discs. Computer work stations available. Students have access to the Internet and online information retrieval services.

Most important special collections include Riemenschneider Bach Institute Collection (original Bach works); Ferne Patterson Jones Collection of Scores and Recordings; United Methodist Historical Collection.

Buildings and Grounds: Campus area 56 acres.

Chief Executive Officer: Dr. Richard W. Dunst, President.

Address admission inquiries to Susan Dileno, Vice President for Enrollment Management.

Bluffton University

1 University Avenue
Bluffton, Ohio 45817-2104

Tel: (419) 358-3000 **E-mail:** admissions@bluffton.edu
Fax: (419) 358-3323 **Internet:** www.bluffton.edu

Institution Description: Bluffton University is a private institution affiliated with the Mennonite Church USA. *Enrollment:* 1,149. *Degrees awarded:* Baccalaureate, master's. Certificates also awarded.

Accreditation: *Regional:* NCA. *Professional*: dietetics, music, social work

History: Established and chartered as Central Mennonite College 1899; offered first instruction at postsecondary level 1900; adopted present name 1914; awarded first degree (baccalaureate) 1915; attained university status 2002. *See* Von Hardesty, *A Narrative of Bluffton College* (Bluffton, Ohio: Bluffton College, 1974) for further information.

Institutional Structure: *Governing board:* Board of Trustees. Extrainstitutional representation: 24 trustees; 3 alumni. All voting. *Composition of institution:* Administrators 6. Academic affairs headed by dean of academic affairs. Management/business/finances directed by vice president of fiscal affairs. Full-time instructional faculty 46. Academic governance body, the faculty, meets an average of 9 times per year.

Calendar: Semesters. Academic year Aug. to May. Freshmen admitted Aug., Jan. Degrees conferred Dec., May, Aug. Formal commencement May. Summer session flexible: 2 extended sessions or 3 intensive sessions from June to Aug.

Characteristics of Freshmen: 77% of applicants admitted. 34% of admitted students enrolled full-time.

23% of applicants submitted SAT scores; 89% ACT scores. *25th percentile*: SAT Critical Reading 480, SAT Math 490; ACT Composite 20. *75th percentile*: SAT Critical Reading 600, SAT Math 610; ACT Composite 25.

55% of entering freshmen expected to graduate within 5 years. 68% of freshmen from Ohio.

Admission: Rolling admissions plan. For fall acceptance, apply as early as July of previous year, but not later than July of year of enrollment. Early acceptance available. *Requirements:* Graduation from accredited secondary school or GED. College preparatory program strongly recommended. *Entrance tests:* College Board SAT ACT composite. *For transfer students:* 2.0 GPA; 92 semester hours maximum transfer credit.

College credit and advanced placement for postsecondary-level work completed in secondary school.

Tutoring available. Developmental courses offered during regular academic year; credit given.

Degree Requirements: 128 semester hours; 30 semester hours in residence; comprehensives in field of study; 2.0 GPA; 2.0 GPA in major field; completion of general education program.

Fulfillment of some degree requirements possible by passing departmental examinations, College Board CLEP or APP. *Grading system:* A–E; CR-NC (credit-no credit); I (incomplete); withdraw (deadline after which pass-fail is appended to withdraw).

Distinctive Educational Programs: Core curriculum general education program. Cross-cultural experiences offerer during May Module. Semester program in Northern Ireland. Accelerated degree completion program in organizational management offered in Bluffton, Piqua, and Archbold. Master's degrees offered in education, organizational management. Criminal Justice program with restorative justice emphasis. Member of Council of Christian Colleges and Universities.

Degrees Conferred: 253 *baccalaureate*; 43 *master's*. Bachelor's degrees awarded in top five disciplines: business/marketing 74; education 63; parks and recreation 28; mathematics 14; family and consumer sciences 10. Master's degrees awarded: business/marketing 34; education 9.

Fees and Other Expenses: *Full-time tuition per academic year 2008–09:* $22,920. *Room and board per academic year:* $7,596. *Required fees:* $400.

Financial Aid: Aid from institutionally generated funds is provided on the basis of academic merit, financial need.

Financial aid to full-time, first-time undergraduate students:

Departments and Teaching Staff: *Total instructional faculty:* 114 (full-time 68, part-time 46). 74% of faculty hold the doctorate, first-professional, or other terminal degree. Student/faculty ratio: 13.1:1.

Enrollment: Total enrollment 1,149. Undergraduate 1,032 (545 female, 48% male). Graduate 107 (full-time 79%). Undergraduate transfer-in students 87.

Characteristics of Student Body: *Ethnic/racial makeup:* Black non-Hispanic: 4%; Hispanic: 2%; White non-Hispanic: 88%; unknown: 4%; nonresident alien 2%.

International Students: 24 nonresident aliens enrolled fall 2008. Programs available to aid students whose native language is not English: social, cultural, financial.

Student Life: On-campus residence halls house 80% of student body. Residence halls for males constitute 49% of such space, for females 51%. *Intercollegiate athletics:* male: baseball, basketball, football, soccer, tennis, track; female: basketball, softball, tennis, track, volleyball, soccer. *Special regulations:* Cars permitted with campus registration. Residence visitation for all halls Fri. from 4pm to midnight, Sat. 11am to midnight, Sun. 11am to 11pm, Tue. and Thurs. 4pm to 11pm. *Special services:* Study Skills Center, medical services. *Student publications:* Ista, a yearbook; *Shalith,* an annual literary magazine; *Witmarsum,* a weekly newspaper. *Surrounding community:* Bluffton population 4,000. Columbus, 110 miles from campus, is nearest metropolitan area. Served by airport 65 miles from campus; passenger rail service 16 miles from campus.

Library Collections: 168,888 volumes including bound books, serial backfiles, electronic documents, and government documents not in separate collections. Online catalog. Current serial subscriptions: 203 paper, 5,153 via electronic access. Students have access to the Internet at no charge.

Most important special collections include Mennonite Historical ' Library (15,000 volumes and church archives); Robert Frost Collection (first editions, autographed editions).

Buildings and Grounds: Campus area 60 acres.

Chief Executive Officer: Dr. James M. Harder, President.

Address admission inquiries to Chris Jebsen, Director of Admissions.

Bowling Green State University

Bowling Green, Ohio 43403

Tel: (419) 372-2531 **E-mail:** admissions@bgnet.bgsu.edu

Fax: (419) 372-7878 **Internet:** www.bgsu.edu

Institution Description: Bowling Green State University is a coeducational institution with an associate degree-granting campus, Firelands College, in Huron. *Enrollment:* 17,874. *Degrees awarded:* Baccalaureate, master's, doctorate. Post-master's certificate also awarded.

Accreditation: *Regional:* NCA. *Professional*: art, accounting, athletic training, business, chemistry, dietetics, environmental health, health information technician, journalism, music, nursing, physical therapy, psychology internship, recreation and leisure services, rehabilitation counseling, respiratory therapy technology, social work, teacher education, theatre

History: Chartered as Bowling Green State Normal College 1910; offered first instruction at postsecondary level 1914; awarded first degree (baccalaureate) 1917; changed name to Bowling Green State College 1929; adopted present name 1935. *See* James Robert Overman, *The History of Bowling Green State University* (Bowling Green: Bowling Green University Press, 1967) for further information.

Institutional Structure: *Governing board:* Board of Trustees. Representation: 11trustees. All voting. *Composition of institution:* Administrators 592. Academic affairs headed by provost and vice vice president for academic affairs. Finance headed by senior vice president for finance. Full-time instructional faculty 885.

Calendar: Semesters. Academic year Aug. to May. Freshmen admitted Aug., Jan., June. Degrees conferred and formal commencement May, Aug., Dec. Summer session from May to Aug.

Characteristics of Freshmen: 11,111 applicants (6,341 female, 4,770 male). 87% of applicants admitted. 32% of admitted students enrolled full-time.

8% (200 students) submitted SAT scores; 93% (2,869 students) submitted ACT scores. *25th percentile*: SAT Critical Reading 450, SAT Math 450; ACT Composite 19, ACT English 18, ACT Math 18. *75th percentile*: SAT Critical Reading 570, SAT Math 570; ACT Composite 24, ACT English 24, ACT Math 24.

54% of entering freshmen expected to graduate within 5 years. 90% of freshmen from Ohio. Freshmen from 48 states and 81 foreign countries.

Admission: Rolling admissions plan. For fall acceptance, apply as early as Aug. 1 of previous year. *Requirements:* Graduation from accredited secondary school or GED. Recommend 4 units in English, 3 college preparatory mathematics, 3 science, 3 social studies, 2 foreign language, 1 performing arts; minimum 2.5 GPA. *Entrance tests:* College Board SAT or ACT composite. For foreign students TOEFL. *For transfer students:* 2.5 GPA.

Degree Requirements: *For all baccalaureate degrees:* 122 semester hours; *For all undergraduate degrees:* 2.0 GPA; 30 hours in residence; demonstrated proficiency in writing.

Fulfillment of some degree requirements possible by passing departmental examinations, College Board CLEP. *Grading system:* A–F; pass-fail; withdraw (deadline after which pass-fail is appended to withdraw).

Distinctive Educational Programs: Work-experience programs. Flexible meeting places and schedules, including off-campus centers (at various area secondary schools). Accelerated degree programs. Special facilities for using telecommunications in the classroom. Interdepartmental studies in Afro-American studies, American studies, Asian studies, Latin American studies, liberal studies, women's studies. Facilities and programs for independent research, including honors programs, individual majors, tutorials. Study abroad in Austria, France, Germany, Japan, Korea, Spain. *Other distinctive programs:* Continuing education. Center for Environmental Research and Services. Center for Study of Popular Culture. Drosophila Stock Center for Genetic Research. Philosophy Documentation Center. Center for Environment Programs. Management Center. First-year learning programs/communities.

ROTC: Army, Air Force.

Degrees Conferred: 3,310 *baccalaureate*; 974 *master's*; 86 *doctorates*. Bachelor's degrees awarded in top five disciplines: education 784, business.marketing 456l visual and performing arts 285; health professions and related clinical sciences 208; English 206. Master's degrees awarded in top five professions: education 467; business/marketing 160; visual and performing arts 71; health professions 35; foreign languages and literature 33. Doctorates awarded: area and ethnic studies 5; biological/life sciences 5; communications/journalism 14; English 5; health professions 2; mathematics 6; philosophy and religious studies 3; physical sciences 12; psychology 17; social sciences 5; visual and performing arts 91.

Fees and Other Expenses: *Full-time tuition per academic year 2008–09:* $9,060 resident undergraduate, $16,368 nonresident; contact the university for current gtraduate tuition and fees. *Room and board per academic year:* $7,220. *Books and supplies:* $1,174. *Other expenses:* $3,182.

Financial Aid: Aid from institutionally generated funds is provided on the basis of academic merit, financial need, other criteria.

Financial aid to full-time, first-time undergraduate students: 87% received some form of aid. Average amount of aid received: federal grants $4,684; Pell grants $2,851; other federal aid $1,063; state/local aid $2,023; loans $5,738.

Departments and Teaching Staff: *Total instructional faculty:* 1,032 (full-time 875, part-time 157). Student/faculty ratio: 19:1. Degrees held by full-time faculty: 80% hold terminal degrees.

Enrollment: Total enrollment 17,874. Undergraduate 14,862 (female 54%, male 46%). Graduate 3,012 (full-time 50%). Undergraduate transfer-in students 587.

Characteristics of Student Body: *Ethnic/racial makeup:* Black non-Hispanic: 10%; American Indian or Alaska Native: 1%; Asian or Pacific Islander: 1%; Hispanic: 3%; White non-Hispanic: 81%; unknown: 3%; nonresident alien 2%. *Age distribution:* number under 18: 301; 18–19: 6,217; 20–21: 5,978; 22–24: 2,605; 25–29: 523; 30–34: 182; 35–39: 90; 40–49: 145; 50–64: 44. 27% of student body attend summer sessions.

International Students: 659 nonresident aliens enrolled fall 2008. Programs available to aid students whose native language is not English: social. Scholarships specifically designated for undergraduate and graduate international students.

Student Life: On-campus residence halls house 45% of student body. 8% of males join fraternities; 11% of females join sororities. *Intercollegiate athletics:* male: baseball, basketball, football, golf, hockey, soccer, swimming, tennis, track and cross-country, wrestling; female: basketball, golf, gymnastics, softball, swimming, tennis, track and cross-country, volleyball. *Special regulations:* Registered cars permitted without restrictions. *Special services:* Medical services. *Student publications, radio, television: BG News*, a daily newspaper; *Key*, a yearbook; *BG News*, a daily newspaper. Radio station WBGU-FM broadcasts 63 hours per week. TV station WBGU broadcasts 117 hours per week. *Surrounding community:* Bowling Green population 30,000. Detroit (MI), 80 miles from campus, is nearest metropolitan area. Served by airport and passenger rail service each 23 miles from campus.

Library Collections: 2,468,800 volumes. 389,000 government documents; 2,119,000 microforms; 657,300 audiovisual materials; 5,400 current periodical subscriptions. Online catalog. Students have access to the Internet and online information retrieval services.

Buildings and Grounds: Campus area 2 square miles. Campus DVD available.

Chief Executive Officer: Dr. Sidney A. Ribeau, President.

Undergraduates address admission inquiries to Gary Swegan, Director of Admissions; graduate inquiries to Terry Lawrence, Director of Graduate Admission.

Capital University

1 College and Main
Columbus, Ohio 43209
Tel: (614) 236-6011 **E-mail:** admissions@capital.edu
Fax: (614) 236-6490 **Internet:** www.capital.edu

Institution Description: Capital University is a private, independent institution affiliated with The Evangelical Lutheran Church in America. *Enrollment:* 3,632. *Degrees awarded:* Baccalaureate, first-professional (law), master's.

Accreditation: *Regional:* NCA. *Professional*: chemistry, law, music, nursing, social work, teacher education

History: Established, chartered, and offered first instruction at postsecondary level 1850; awarded first degree (baccalaureate) 1854; added conservatory of music 1926, school of nursing 1950, law school 1969, graduate school of administration 1971. *See* David B. Owns, *These Hundred Years* (Columbus: Wartburg Press, 1950) for further information.

Institutional Structure: *Governing board:* Board of Trustees. 30 voting and 8 ex officio members. *Composition of institution:* Academic affairs: academic support staff and deans of College of Arts and Sciences, Conservatory of Music, School of Nursing, School of Management, Law School report to provost. Vice president of resource management directs facilities, business, and financial affairs. Full-time instructional faculty 228. Academic governance body, the faculty, meets twice yearly while the undergraduate faculty and the college/school faculties normally meet monthly during the academic year.

Calendar: Semesters. Academic year Aug. to May. Freshmen admitted Aug., Jan., May, June. Degrees conferred May, Aug., Dec. Formal commencement Dec., May. Summer session of 2 terms from May to July. Adult degree program is on a trimester calendar academic year beginning the last of Aug. and ending the first of Aug.

Characteristics of Freshmen: 3,441 applicants (2,133 female, 1,308 male). 77% of applicants accepted. 24% of applicants admitted and enrolled full-time.

34% (219 students) submitted SAT scores; 93% (596 students) submitted ACT scores. *25th percentile*: SAT Critical Reading 470, SAT Math 470; ACT Composite 21, ACT English 19, ACT Math 19. *75th percentile*: SAT Critical Reading 590, SAT Math 590l ACT Composite 26, ACT English 26, ACT Math 25.

57% of entering freshmen expected to graduate within 5 years. 96% of freshmen from Ohio. Freshmen from 13 states and 2 foreign countries.

Admission: Rolling admissions plan. For fall acceptance, apply as early as beginning of senior year but not later than July of year of enrollment with a priority deadline of April 1. Early admission available. *Requirements:* Graduation from accredited secondary school with a minimum of 16 academic units including 4 English, 3 mathematics, 3 natural science, 3 social studies, 2 foreign language, 1 fine arts. GED accepted. *Entrance tests:* College Board SAT or ACT. *For transfer students:* 2.25 minimum GPA; maximum transfer credit limited only by residence requirement.

College credit and advanced placement for postsecondary-level work completed in secondary school. College credit for extrainstitutional learning (life experience) on basis of portfolio and faculty assessments.

Degree Requirements: 2.0 GPA; 30 of last 36 semester hours in residence; completion of 12 course University core.

Fulfillment of some degree requirements and exemption from some beginning courses possible by passing departmental examinations, College Board CLEP, AP (score of 4) or submission of portfolio. *Grading system:* A–F; pass/fail; incomplete.

Distinctive Educational Programs: *For undergraduates:* Externships/internships. Flexible meeting places and schedules. Facilities and programs for independent research, including honors programs, individual majors, tutorials. Capital University sponsors two programs abroad: the Kodaly Institute in Hungary for music students and the Jamaica service learning (internships) program in conjunction with the University of the West Indies and CCIS. Capital is affiliated with four study abroad programs: CCIS, AIFS, Central College, Iowa, and Schiller International University, representing 25 different countries. Information on additional programs and countries is also available. *For graduate students:* Evening and weekend classes. *Available to all students:* Work-experience programs. Evening classes.

ROTC: Army. Air Force offered in cooperation program with The Ohio State University.

Degrees Conferred: 570 *baccalaureate*; 100 *master's*; 181 *first-professional.* Bachelor's degrees awarded in top five disciplines: education 95; business/marketing 89; health professions and related clinical sciences 87; social sciences 64; interdisciplinary studies 53. Master's degrees awarded: business/marketing 87; education 17; health professions 14; law/legal studies 10. First-professional degrees awarded: law 202.

Fees and Other Expenses: *Full-time tuition per academic year 2008–09:* undergraduate $27,680; contact the university for current graduate and professional tuition and fees. *Room and board per academic year:* $9,630.

Financial Aid: Aid from institutionally generated funds is provided on the basis of academic merit, financial need, other criteria.

Financial aid to full-time, first-time undergraduate students: 100% received some form of financial aid. Average amount of aid received: federal grants $4,751; Pell grants $2,803; other federal aid $2,287; state/local grants $1,289; institutional grants $12,078.

Departments and Teaching Staff: *Total instructional faculty:* 419 (full-time 228, part-time 191). *Total tenured faculty:* 106. Student/faculty ratio: 10:1. Degrees held by full-time faculty: master's 20%, doctorates 80%

Enrollment: *Total enrollment:* 3,632. Undergraduate 2,675 (female 38%, male 62%). Graduate 957 (full-time 58%). Undergraduate transfer-in students 151.

Characteristics of Student Body: *Ethnic/racial makeup:* Black non-Hispanic: 10%; American Indian or Alaska Native: 1%; Hispanic: 2%; White non-Hispanic: 81%; unknown: 4%; nonresident alien 1%. 117.*Age distribution:* number under 18: 19; 18–19: 1,116; 20–21: 790; 22–24: 258; 25–29: 150; 30–34: 103; 35–39: 107; 40–49: 178; 50–64: 101; 65 and over: 2.

International Students: 37 nonresident aliens enrolled fall 2008. Students from Europe, Asia, Central and South America, Africa, Middle East. Programs available to aid students whose native language is not English: social cultural. English as a Second Language Program. Financial aid specifically designated for international students: scholarships available annually to qualifying students.

Student Life: On-campus residence halls house 70% of student body. Residence halls for males constitute 40% of such space, for females 60%. *Intercollegiate athletics:* male: baseball, basketball, cross-country, golf, football, soccer, tennis, track; female: basketball, cross-country, golf, soccer, softball, tennis, track, volleyball. *Special regulations:* Registered cars permitted with restrictions. Residence hall visitation from noon to midnight weekdays, noon to 2am weekends. *Special services:* Learning Resources Center, medical services, bus service between main campus and law school. *Student publications: The Capitalian*, a yearbook; *The Chimes*, a weekly newspaper; *The Dionysia*, a literary arts magazine; *Law Review*, a quarterly periodical. *Surrounding community:* Columbus metropolitan area population over 1 million. Served by mass transit bus system; airport 7 miles from campus.

Library Collections: 196,000 volumes including bound books, serial backfiles, electronic documents, and government documents not in separate collections. Online catalog. Current serial subscriptions: 655 paper, 148,000 microform; 6,500 via electronic access. 16,080 audiovisual materials. Computer work stations available. Students have access to the Internet at no charge.

Most important special holdings include Lois Lenski Collection (complete collection of books, manuscripts, medals); Columbus and Ohio Government Documents Collection; music CD-ROM collection.

Buildings and Grounds: Campus area 48 acres. Campus DVD available.

Chief Executive Officer: Dr. Denvy R. Bauman, President.

Undergraduates address admission inquiries to Kim Ebbrecht, Director of Admissions; graduate inquiries to Adult Degree Program Center; MBA Program; Law School.

College of Arts and Sciences

Degree Programs Offered: *Baccalaureate* in art, art therapy, biology, chemistry, education, English, health and fitness management, health and physical education, history, humanities, international studies, mathematics and computer science, modern languages, philosophy, political science, psychology, public administration, public relations, religion, social work, sociology, speech and communication arts, sports medicine.

Admission: *See* main entry above.

Degree Requirements: *For baccalaureate in arts and sciences:* 124 credit hours; 30 of last 36 hours must be completed at Capital. Completion of university core curriculum.

Distinctive Educational Programs: Dual-degree program in engineering and occupational therapy with Washington University (MO) and in engineering with Case Western. Cooperative graduate program in education with University of Dayton. Interdisciplinary programs by individual arrangement. (Adult Degree Program offers credit for life and work experience, prior learning.)

Conservatory of Music

Degree Programs Offered: *Baccalaureate* in composition, instrumental performance, jazz studies, keyboard pedagogy, music education, music media, music merchandising, music industry, organ performance, piano performance, vocal performance, music technology. *Master's* of music in music education.

Admission: In addition to general requirements, audition in one major performing area.

Degree Requirements: *See* general requirements above. *For baccalaureate in music:* 127–137 credit hours. Additional requirements vary with program.

College of Nursing

Degree Programs Offered: *Baccalaureate, master's.*

Admission: For baccalaureate: ACT/SAT, high school transcript, recommendations. Interview may be requested. *For transfer students:* 2.25 GPA.

Degree Requirements: For baccalaureate: 134 credit hours. One summer session required for traditional students. RN's may earn credit by challenge exam.

Capital University Law School

Degree Programs Offered: *First-professional:* LL.M., master of taxation.

Admission: *First-professional:* baccalaureate from accredited college or university, LSAT; *LL.M.:* J.D. or LL.B. from accredited law school (if foreign student from non-English speaking country, also TOEFL); *master of taxation:* baccalaureate from accredited college, 24 hours in accounting, and GMAT, GRE or LSAT.

Degree Requirements: *First-professional:* 86 semester credit hours, 2.0 GPA, 30 hours in residence; *LL.M. and master of taxation:* 26 semester credit hours in residence, 2.75 GPA.

Graduate School of Management

Degree Programs Offered: *Baccalaureate* in business administration and economics.

Admission: For master's degree: baccalaureate from accredited college or university; 2 years work experience.

Degree Requirements: For master's degree: 40 credit hours; 3.0 GPA.

Adult Degree Program

Degree Programs Offered: *Baccalaureate* through College of Arts and Sciences, School of Nursing, School of Management.

Case Western Reserve University

10900 Euclid Avenue
Cleveland, Ohio 44106-7001
Tel: (216) 368-2000 **E-mail:** admission@case.edu
Fax: (216) 368-5111 **Internet:** www.case.edu

Institution Description: Case Western Reserve University is a private, independent, nonprofit institution. *Enrollment:* 9,814. *Degrees awarded:* Baccalaureate, master's, first-professional (dentistry, medicine, law, nursing), doctorate.

Accreditation: *Regional:* NCA. *Professional*: business, chemistry, dentistry, dietetics, engineering, law, medicine, music, nurse anesthesia education, nursing, nursing-midwifery, clinical psychology, social work, speech-language pathology

History: Created by federation of Case Institute of Technology and Western Reserve University in 1967. Case established as Case School of Applied Science 1880; offered first instruction at postsecondary level 1881; awarded first degree (baccalaureate) 1885; changed name to Case Institute of Technology 1947. Western Reserve established in Hudson as Western Reserve College and offered first instruction at postsecondary level 1826; awarded first degree (baccalaureate) 1830; moved to Cleveland and changed name to Adelbert College of Reserve University 1882; incorporated as Western Reserve University 1884; became coeducational 1888. *See* C.H. Cramer, *Case Western Reserve: A History of the University 1826–1976* (Boston: Little, Brown and Company, 1976) for further information.

Institutional Structure: *Governing board:* Case Western Reserve Board of Trustees. Representation: 38 trustees. All voting. *Composition of institution:* Administrators 28. Academic affairs headed by president. Management/business/finances directed by chief financial officer. Full-time instructional faculty 2,521. Academic governance body, Faculty Senate, meets an average of 7 times per year.

Calendar: Semesters. Academic year Aug. to May. Freshmen admitted Aug., Jan., June. Degrees conferred May, Aug., Jan. Formal commencement May. Summer session June to July.

Characteristics of Freshmen: 7,351 applicants (3,176 female, 4,173 male). 73% of applicants admitted. 19% of applicants admitted and enrolled full-time.

86% (869 students) submitted SAT scores; 61% (621 students) submitted ACT scores. *25th percentile*: SAT Critical Reading 600, SAT Math 600; ACT Composite 26, ACT English 26, ACT Math 26. *75th percentile*: SAT Critical Reading 700, SAT Math 730; ACT Composite 31, ACT English 32, ACT Math 33.

76% of freshmen expected to graduate within 5 years. 52% of freshmen from Ohio. Freshmen from 49 states and 27 foreign countries.

Admission: Apply by Jan. 15 for Regular Decision, Nov. 1 for Early Action, December 1 Pre-Professional Scholars Program. *Requirements:* Either graduation from accredited secondary school with 16 units which must include 4 English, 3 mathematics, 1 laboratory science; or GED. Recommend 2 units in a foreign language for liberal arts program. Additional requirements for some programs. *Entrance tests:* College Board SAT or ACT with writing section; *For transfer students:* Transfer credit evaluated on individual basis.

College credit and/or placement possible through College Board Advanced Placement exams, International Baccalaureate, and departmental proficiency exams; determination is made by appropriate department.

Tutoring available. Noncredit developmental courses offered during regular academic year.

Degree Requirements: *Undergraduate:* Minimum 120 credit hours (requirement varies with program); 2.0 GPA; 2 years in residence; 2 semesters physical education; core requirements.

Fulfillment of some degree requirements and exemption from some beginning courses possible by passing departmental examinations, College Board AP. *Grading system:* A–F; pass-fail; withdraw.

Distinctive Educational Programs: Weekend and evening classes. Accelerated degree programs. Special facilities for using telecommunications in the classroom. Interdisciplinary programs. Individual majors. Dual majors; B.A./B.S. degree programs; binary (3-2) engineering degrees with more than 50 liberal arts colleges; Washington Semester; Cooperative Education program for majors in engineering, science, management, and accountancy; Pre-Professional Scholars Program available in dental medicine, law, medicine, and social work. Five-year BS/Master of Accountancy. BS in Mathematics/MS in Management Science. Joint MBA programs with schools of medicine, nursing, law, and social work. Bilateral undergraduate exchange programs with universities in Austria, France, Germany, Singapore, Spain, Turkey, United Kingdom. Domestic exchange program with Fisk University.

ROTC: Air Force available through the Kent State University; Army available through John Carroll University.

Degrees Conferred: 793 *baccalaureate*; 951 *master's*; 718 *doctorate*. Bachelor's degrees awarded in top five disciplines: engineering 279; social sciences 92; business, management, marketing, and related support services 86; biological/life sciences 83. psychology 74. Master's degrees awarded: business/marketing 392; health professions 142; public administration and social services 131; engineering 110; biological/life sciences 55. Doctorates awarded: engineering 68; health professions 47; biological/life sciences 42; business/marketing 23; physical sciences 20. First-professional degrees awarded: dentistry 71; law 237; medicine 30.

Fees and Other Expenses: *Full-time tuition per academic year 2008–09:* $35,204. Tuition varies for graduate and professional programs. *Other fees:* $678. *Room and board per academic year:* $10,450. *Books and supplies:* $1,100. *Other expenses:* $1,300.

Financial Aid: The university offers a direct lending program. Aid from institutionally generated funds is provided on the basis of academic merit, financial need, other criteria.

Financial aid to full-time, first-time undergraduate students:

Departments and Teaching Staff: *Total instructional faculty:* 863. Student/faculty ratio: 10:1. Degrees held by full-time faculty: 85% hold terminal degrees.

Enrollment: Total enrollment 9,814. Undergraduate 4,356 (female 43%, male 37%). Graduate 5,458 (full-time 78%). Undergraduate transfer-in students 66.

Characteristics of Student Body: *Ethnic/racial makeup:* Black non-Hispanic: 6%; Asian or Pacific Islander: 17%; Hispanic: 2%; White non-Hispanic: 57%; unknown: 15%; nonresident alien 4%. *Age distribution:* number under 18: 43; 18–19: 1,732; 20–21: 1,587; 22–24: 595; 25–29: 50; 30–34: 21; 35–39: 17; 40–49: 16; 50–64: 12; 65 and over: 7.

International Students: 1,076 nonresident aliens enrolled fall 2008. Students from Europe, Asia, Central and south America, Africa, Canada, Australia, New Zealand, Middle East, Caribbean. Programs available to aid students whose native language is not English: social, cultural. English as a Second Language Program. No financial aid specifically designated for international students.

Student Life: On-campus residence halls. 33% of males belong to fraternities; 23% of females belong to sororities. *Intercollegiate athletics:* male: baseball, basketball, cross-country, football, soccer, swimming, tennis, track, wrestling; female: basketball, cross-country, soccer, softball, swimming, tennis, track, volleyball. *Special regulations:* Cars with parking permits allowed in designated areas only. *Special services:* Medical services, shuttle bus to and from surrounding area and to public transportation. *Student publications, radio: Observer*, a weekly newspaper. Radio station WRUW-FM broadcasts 168 hours per week. *Surrounding community:* Cleveland population 480,000; metropolitan

CASE WESTERN RESERVE UNIVERSITY—*cont'd*

area 3 million. Served by mass transit bus and rail system; airport 20 miles from campus; passenger rail service 10 miles from campus.

Publications: *Observer*, a weekly newspaper; *Case Reserve Review*, a literary journal; *Case, the Magazine of the Case Western Reserve University*; *Engineering and Science Review; Law Review; Nonprofit Management and Leadership* (Mandel Center for Nonprofit Organizations); *Journal of International Law* (School of Law); *Canada-U.S. Law Journal; Health Matrix* (Law-Medicine Center).

Library Collections: 2,496,000 volumes including bound books, serial backfiles, electronic documents, and government documents not in separate collections. Online catalog. Total serials: 18,422. Audio,video, computer files: 51,929. Computer work stations available. Students have access to the Internet at no charge.

Most important special holdings include Bohn Collection of public policy and urban development; Sherer Collection of German literature and philosophy; collection of Victorian illustrated literature.

Buildings and Grounds: Campus area 150 acres. Campus DVD available.

Chief Executive Officer: Dr. Barbara R. Snyder, President.

Undergraduates address admission inquiries to Elizabeth Woyczynski, Director of Admissions; graduate and professional school inquiries to school or program of interest.

College of Arts and Sciences

Degree Programs Offered: *Baccalaureate, master's, doctorate.*

Distinctive Educational Programs: Pre-Professional Scholars Programs grants freshmen conditional admission to CWRU's professional schools of dentistry, law, management, medicine, nursing, and social work. Joint program in art education with Cleveland Institute of Art; in music education with Cleveland Institute of Music. Undergraduate Scholars Program allows students to design their own majors. Washington Semester and Junior Year Abroad programs. Accelerated programs: 5-year Dual Degree (bachelor's/M.B.A.) Program in Management; 6-year Dental Program (bachelor's/D.D.S.). Integrated degree programs combine studies for the bachelor's degree and an advance degree and allow qualified students to begin graduate study in their senior year. Senior Year in Professional Studies allows undergraduates who are admitted during their junior year to CWRU's schools of dentistry, medicine, or nursing to substitute the first year of professional school for the final undergraduate year. Senior Year *in absentia* privilege allows undergraduates admitted at the end of the junior year to a medical or dental school other than CWRU to substitute the first year of professional school for the final undergraduate year.

Case School of Engineering

Degree Programs Offered: *Baccalaureate, master's, doctorate.*

Admission: Varies with program.

Distinctive Educational Programs: Pre-Professional Scholars Programs grants freshmen conditional admission to CWRU's professional schools of dentistry, law, management, medicine, nursing, and social work. Integrated B.S./M.S. program combines studies for the bachelor's degree and an advanced degree by allowing qualified students to begin graduate study in their senior year. Binary (3–2) program in engineering, astronomy, and biochemistry with more than 50 liberal arts colleges. Minority Engineering Industrial Opportunity Program.

Weatherhead School of Management

Degree Programs Offered: *Baccalaureate, master's, doctorate. Master's* in accountancy, business administration, management science, operations research, and organization development and analysis; *doctorate* in management, operations research, and organizational behavior.

Distinctive Educational Programs: Five-year B.S./M.B.A. Program. Joint M.B.A./master of International Management with the American Graduate School of International Management (Thunderbird) in Glendale, Arizona. International M.B.S. program in cooperation with the International Management Center in Budapest, Hungary. Executive Doctor of Management t(E.D.M.) degree program, designed exclusively for practicing executives. Certificate programs in health systems management, public policy (in addition to certificates in management information systems, nonprofit management, and operations research).

School of Dentistry

Degree Programs Offered: *Master's, first-professional.*

Admission: *For M.S. in dentistry:* DDS or equivalent required. *For first-professional:* 60 semester hours which must include 12 chemistry (6 organic chemistry), 6 biology, 6 physics, 6 English; or equivalent. Dental Admissions Test.

Degree Requirements: 165 credit hours, 36 hours in residence.

School of Law

Degree Programs Offered: *First-professional, master's, doctorate.*

Admission: *For first-professional:* Graduation from accredited college or university, or completion of all work for undergraduate degree; LSAT.

Degree Requirements: *See* general requirements. *For first-professional:* 88 credit hours, 2.0 GPA, 27 hours in residence.

Distinctive Educational Programs: J.D./M.B.A. with Weatherhead School of Management; J.D./M.A. in Legal History; J.D./M.S. in Social Administration with Mandel School of Applied Social Sciences; J.D./M.N.O. with schools of Management and Applied Social Sciences; J.D./M.B. with School of Medicine; J.D./M.A. in Bioethics.

Frances Payne Bolton School of Nursing

Degree Programs Offered: *Bachelor's, master's, first-professional, doctorate.*

Admission: Admission requirements vary with degree and program.

Degree Requirements: Degree requirements vary with program.

Distinctive Educational Programs: *Joint programs:* M.S.N./M.B.A. with Weatherhead School of Management; M.S.N./M.A. in Medical Anthropology, M.S.N./M.A. in Bioethics.

Mandel School of Applied Social Sciences

Degree Programs Offered: *Master's, doctorate.*

Admission: *For master's program:* Bachelor's degree; evidence of capacity to succeed in graduate social work education, through undergraduate record and/or test scores; sufficient number of courses in social and behavioral sciences.

Distinctive Educational Programs: *Joint programs:* M.S.S.A./J.D. with School of Law; M.S.S.A./M.N.O. (Master of Nonprofit Organizations); M.S.S.A./Ph.D. in Social Welfare; joint M.S.S.A./M.B.A..

School of Medicine

Degree Programs Offered: *First-professional, doctorate.*

Admission: Graduation from accredited college or university with coursework in chemistry (general and organic), biology or zoology, physics, English; MCAT; AMCAS.

Cedarville University

251 North Main Street
Cedarville, Ohio 45314

Tel: (937) 766-2211 **E-mail:** admissions@cedarville.edu
Fax: (937) 766-2760 **Internet:** www.cedarville.edu

Institution Description: Cedarville University is a private institution affiliated with the Baptist Church. *Enrollment:* 3,066. *Degrees awarded:* Associate, baccalaureate, master's.

Accreditation: *Regional:* NCA. *Professional*: engineering, nursing

History: Chartered 1887; offered first instruction at postsecondary level 1894; awarded first degree (baccalaureate) 1898.

Institutional Structure: *Governing board:* Board of Trustees. Representation: 30 trustees. *Composition of institution:* Academic affairs headed by academic vice president. Management/business/finances directed by vice president for business. Full-time instructional faculty 208.

Calendar: Semesters. Academic year Sept.to June. Summer session of 2 terms.

Characteristics of Freshmen: 1,926 applicants (1,723 female, 1,267 male). 76% of applicants admitted. 34% of admitted students enrolled full-time.

56% (432 students) submitted SAT scores; 72% (555 tudents) submitted ACT scores. *25th percentile*: SAT Critical Reading 540, SAT Math 520; ACT Composite 23. *75th percentile*: SAT Critical Reading 650, SAT Math 640; ACT Composite 28.

81% of entering freshmen expected to graduate within 5 years. 36% of freshmen from Ohio. Freshmen from 49 states and 15 foreign countries.

Admission: Rolling admissions plan. Early acceptance available. *Requirements:* Graduation from accredited secondary school with 16 units which must include 4 English, 3 mathematics, 3 social studies, 3 natural sciences, 3 of a single foreign language. *Entrance tests:* College Board SAT or ACT composite.

Developmental courses offered.

Degree Requirements: 128 semester hours; 2.0 GPA; 1 year in residence; general education requirements; language requirement; demonstrated proficiency in English; senior capstone course.

Fulfillment of some degree requirements and exemption from some beginning courses possible by passing College Board CLEP, AP. *Grading system:* A–F; credit-no credit; withdraw (deadline after which pass-fail is appended to withdraw).

Distinctive Educational Programs: Internships. Study abroad in Australia, China, Egypt, England, Ireland, Russia, Spain, Uganda.

ROTC: Army in cooperation with Central State University; Air Force in cooperation with Wright State University.

Degrees Conferred: 617 *baccalaureate*; 6 *master's*. Bachelor's degrees awarded in top five disciplines: education 117; business, management, marketing, and related support services 74; health professions and related clinical sciences 67; theology 65; visual and performing arts. Master's degrees awarded: education 6.

Fees and Other Expenses: *Full-time tuition per academic year 2008–09:* $20,992. *Books and supplies:* $900. *Room and board per academic year:* $5,010. *Other expenses:* $1,200.

Financial Aid: Aid from institutionally generated funds is provided on the basis of academic merit, financial need, athletic ability, other criteria. Institution has a Program Participation Agreement with the U.S. Department of Education for eligible students to receive Pell Grants and, depending upon the agreement, other federal aid.

Financial aid to full-time, first-time undergraduate students: 90% received federal grants averaging $2,908; 41% state/local grants averaging $1,171; 75% institutional grants averaging $3,140; 57% received loans averaging $1,500.

Departments and Teaching Staff: *Total instructional faculty:* 262 (full-time 208, part-time 54). Student/faculty ratio: 14:1. Degrees held by full-time faculty: baccalaureate 1%, master's 42%, doctorate 57%. 63% hold terminal degrees.

Enrollment: Total enrollment 3,066. Undergraduate 2,985 (54% female, 46% male). Graduate 81 (part-time 100%). Undergraduate transfer-in students 84.

Characteristics of Student Body: *Ethnic/racial makeup:* Black non-Hispanic: 2%; Asian or Pacific Islander: 1%; Hispanic: 2%; White non-Hispanic: 93%; nonresident alien 1%.

International Students: 31 nonresident aliens enrolled fall 2008. Students from Europe, Asia, Central and South America, Africa, Canada. No programs available to aid students whose native language is not English. No financial aid specifically designated for international students.

Student Life: *Intercollegiate athletics:* male: baseball, basketball, cross-country, golf, soccer, tennis, track and field; female: basketball, cross-country, softball, tennis, track and field, volleyball. *Special regulations:* Freshmen not permitted to have cars during first quarter; registered cars permitted for most other students. *Special services:* Medical services. *Student publications: Cedars*, a newspaper, *The Miracle*, a yearbook; *Surrounding community:* Cedarville population approximately 3,000. Dayton, 20 miles from campus, is nearest metropolitan area.

Publications: *The Cedarville Torch*, published quarterly.

Library Collections: 213,500 volumes including bound books, serial backfiles, electronic documents, and government documents not in separate collections. Online catalog. Current serial subscriptions: 964 paper, 21,396 microform, 6,400 via electronic access. 15,868 audiovisual materials. Computer work stations available. Students have access to the Internet at no charge.

Most important special collections include English Bible Collection, Limited Edition Book Club Collection, Michael Dewine Congressional papers; Elmer W. Engstrom Papers (engineering).

Buildings and Grounds: Campus area 400 acres. Campus DVD available.

Chief Executive Officer: Dr. William E. Brown, President.

Address admission inquiries to Roscoe F. Smith, Director of Admissions.

Central State University

1400 Brush Row Road
Wilberforce, Ohio 45384-1004

Tel: (937) 376-6011 **E-mail:** admissions@centralstate.edu
Fax: (937) 376-6138 **Internet:** www.centralstate.edu

Institution Description: Central State University is a state institution. *Enrollment:* 1,766. *Degrees awarded:* Baccalaureate, master's.

Academic offerings subject to approval by statewide coordinating bodies. Budget subject to approval by state governing boards.

Accreditation: *Regional:* NCA. *Professional*: engineering, music

History: Chartered as Combined Normal and Industrial Department of Wilberforce University 1887; offered first instruction at postsecondary level 1888; awarded first degree 1892; became 4-year institution and changed name to College of Education and Industrial Arts 1941; changed name to Central State College 1951; adopted present name 1965.

Institutional Structure: *Governing board:* Board of Trustees. Representation: 9 trustees (appointed by governor of Ohio). All voting. *Composition of institution:* Administrators 57. Academic affairs headed by vice president for academic affairs. Management/business/finances directed by vice president for administration and finance. Full-time instructional faculty 77. Academic governance body, University Senate, meets an average of 10 times per year.

Calendar: Quarters. Academic year Sept. to June. Freshmen admitted Sept., Jan., Mar., June. Formal commencement June. Summer session from June to Aug.

Characteristics of Freshmen: 39% of applicants accepted. 17% of accepted applicants enrolled.

Mean ACT Composite class score 16.

19% of entering freshmen expected to graduate within 5 years. 74% of freshmen from Ohio. Freshmen from 10 states and 1 foreign country.

Admission: Rolling admissions plan. For fall acceptance, apply no later than June 15 of year of enrollment. Early acceptance available. *Requirements:* Either graduation from accredited secondary school or GED. *Entrance tests:* ACT Composite. *For transfer students:* 2.0 minimum GPA, maximum transfer credit limited only by residence requirements.

College credit and advanced placement for postsecondary-level work completed in secondary school. Tutoring available.

Degree Requirements: *For all baccalaureate degrees:* 186 quarter hours; at least 36 of the final 45 quarter hours in residence; 1 quarter hour physical activities; core curriculum; minimum cumulative and major GPA is required: 2.0 (B.S.), 2.2 (B.A.), 2.5 (B.S.Ed.). *For all master's degrees:* 48 quarter hours; professional cognate studies curriculum; 3.2. GPA.

Fulfillment of some degree requirements and exemption from some beginning courses possible by passing College Board CLEP, AP. *Grading system:* A–F; withdraw (carries time limit).

Distinctive Educational Programs: Cooperative education. Flexible meeting places and schedules, including off-campus centers (at Dayton, less than 30 miles away from main institution) and evening classes. Dual-degree program in engineering with Wright State University. Facilities and programs for independent research, including honors programs, independent study. *Other distinctive programs:* Credit and noncredit continuing education.

ROTC: Army.

Degrees Conferred: 166 *baccalaureate*; business, management, marketing, and related support services; communication, journalism, and related programs 17; social sciences 12; psychology 8; computer and information sciences 8. Master's degrees awarded: 5.

Fees and Other Expenses: *Full-time tuition per academic year 2008–09:* contact the university for current information regarding tuition, fees, and housing costs.

Financial Aid: Aid from institutionally generated funds is provided on the basis of academic merit, athletic ability, financial need, other criteria. Institution has a Program Participation Agreement with the U.S. Department of Education for eligible students to receive Pell Grants and, depending upon the agreement, other federal aid.

Financial aid to full-time, first-time undergraduate students: 93% received some form of financial aid. Average amount of aid received: federal grants $2,699; state/local grants $1,306; institutional grants $2,771; loans $5,429.

Departments and Teaching Staff: *Total instructional faculty:* 90.7 FTE. Student/faculty ratio: 12:1. Degrees held by full-time faculty: doctorate 67%, master's 33%.

Enrollment: *Total enrollment:* 1,766.

Characteristics of Student Body: *Ethnic/racial makeup:* Black non-Hispanic: 90%; Hispanic: .1%; White non-Hispanic: 2%; unknown 6%.

International Students: 17 nonresident aliens enrolled fall 2008. No programs available to aid students whose native language is not English. No financial aid specifically designated for international students.

Student Life: On-campus residence halls house 54% of student body. *Intercollegiate athletics:* male: basketball, golf, track and field; female: basketball, golf, track and field, volleyball. *Special regulations:* Cars permitted. *Special services:* Health services. *Student publications, radio:* A weekly newspaper; a yearbook. Radio station WCSU-FM. *Surrounding community:* Cincinnati, 50 miles from campus, is nearest metropolitan area. Served by Dayton International airport.

Library Collections: 180,000 volumes including bound books, serial backfiles, electronic documents, and government documents not in separate collections. Online catalog. Access to 26,300 periodicals (paper, microform, elec-

CENTRAL STATE UNIVERSITY—*cont'd*

tronic). Computer work stations available. Students have access to the Internet at no charge.

Buildings and Grounds: Campus area 60 acres.

Chief Executive Officer: Dr. John W. Garland, President.

Address admission inquiries to Cleveland James, Director of Admissions.

Chancellor University

112 Prospect Avenue
Cleveland, Ohio 44115-1096
Tel: (216) 696-9000 **E-mail:** admissions@chancellor.edu
Fax: (216) 696-6430 **Internet:** www.dnmyers.edu

Institution Description: Cdhancellor University, formerly named David N. Myers University, is a private, independent, nonprofit college. *Enrollment:* 942. *Degrees awarded:* Associate, baccalaureate.

Accreditation: *Regional:* NCA.

History: Established as Folsom's Mercantile College and offered first instruction at postsecondary level 1848; awarded first degree 1850; changed name to Spencerian College 1877; merged with Dyke School of Commerce and changed name to Dyke and Spencerian College 1942; name shortened to Dyke College 1959; incorporated 1965; renamed David N. Myers College 1995; achieved university status 2002; adopted present name 2007.

Institutional Structure: *Governing board:* Board of Trustees. Representation: 24 trustees, including 7 alumni. All voting. *Composition of institution:* Administrators 23 (director-level positions and up). Professional non-instructional staff 17. Academic affairs headed by provost/dean of instruction. Management/business/finances directed by controller/treasurer. Full-time instructional faculty 117. Academic governance body, Standing Committee on Academic Affairs, meets an average of 10 times per year. *Faculty representation:* Faculty served by collective bargaining agent affiliated with AFT.

Calendar: Semesters. Academic year Sept. to June. Freshmen admitted Sept., Jan., Apr. Degrees conferred and formal commencement June. Summer session from late Apr. to Aug.

Characteristics of Freshmen: The majority of the university's new students are older students and transfer students primarily from community colleges. 95% of applicants accepted. 60% of accepted applicants enrolled.

59% of entering freshmen expected to graduate within 5 years. 100% of freshmen from Ohio.

Admission: Rolling admissions plan. For fall acceptance, apply as early as Oct. 1 of previous year, but not later than Sept. 13 of year of enrollment. Early acceptance available. *Requirements:* Either graduation from accredited secondary school or GED. Minimum GPA 2.0. Lowest acceptable secondary school class standing 20th percentile. *Entrance tests:* ACT composite preferred; College Board SAT accepted. Institutional or other standardized tests may be substituted or required for admissions and placement purposes. For foreign students TOEFL. *For transfer students:* 2.0 minimum GPA; from 4-year accredited institution 92 semester hours maximum transfer credit; from 2-year institution 63 hours.

College credit and advanced placement for extrainstitutional learning (life experience) on basis of portfolio and faculty assessments, personal interviews, letters of recommendation.

Tutoring available. Developmental courses offered in summer session and regular academic year; credit given.

Degree Requirements: *For all associate degrees:* 63 semester hours. *For all baccalaureate degrees:* 126 semester hours; 2 terms in residence. *For all degrees:* 2.0 GPA; general education requirements.

Fulfillment of some degree requirements and exemption from some beginning courses possible by passing departmental examinations and College Board CLEP. *Grading system:* A–F; withdraw (carries time limit).

Distinctive Educational Programs: External degree program in nearly all bachelor's degree majors, with credit for prior learning experience. Work-experience (cooperative education) program for students majoring in accounting, management and business administration, marketing, paralegal education, and secretarial sciences/word processing. Academic Centers in Brecksville, Elyria, and Wickliffe offer accelerated degree, paralegal education, and real estate programs. On-site corporate training and educational programs are available.

Degrees Conferred: 22 *associate*; 137 *baccalaureate*; 34 *master's*. Bachelor's degrees awarded in top five disciplines: business, management, marketing, and related support services 148; security and protective services 31; legal studies 13; computer and information sciences 12; social studies 10.

Fees and Other Expenses: *Full-time tuition per academic year 2008–09:* $10,910. *Books and supplies:* $1,000. *Room and board per academic year:* $7,200. *Other expenses:* $1,000.

Financial Aid: Aid from institutionally generated funds is provided on the basis of academic merit, financial need. Institution has a Program Participation Agreement with the U.S. Department of Education for eligible students to receive Pell Grants and, depending upon the agreement, other federal aid.

89% of undergraduate students received some form of financial aid. Average amount of aid received: federal grants $8,297; state/local grants $3,506; institutional grants $3,053; loans $4,943.

Departments and Teaching Staff: *Total instructional faculty:* 150. Degrees held by full-time faculty: doctorate 5%, master's 75%, baccalaureate 1%, professional 19%. 24% hold terminal degrees.

Enrollment: Total enrollment 422. Undergraduate 352 (female 70%; male 30%).

Characteristics of Student Body: *Ethnic/racial makeup:* Black non-Hispanic: 47%; Hispanic: 3%; White non-Hispanic: 26%; unknown: 23%.

International Students: No programs available to aid students whose native language is not English. No financial aid specifically designated for international students.

Student Life: *Special regulations:* Cars permitted with no restrictions. *Special services:* Learning Resources Center, health service, personal and career counseling. *Student publication: The Voice*, a monthly newspaper. *Surrounding community:* Cleveland population 574,000. Served by mass transit system; airport 16 miles from campus; passenger rail service one block from campus.

Publications: Sources of information about David N. Myers College include *The Diplomat* and *The Sundial*, quarterly publications sent to alumni and community leaders.

Library Collections: 19,300 volumes. 140 serial subscriptions; 490 audiovisual materials. 620 microforms.

Most important special holdings include samples of writing and calligraphy of Spencerian College founder Platt R. Spencer and his students; paralegal education collection; business reference collection.

Buildings and Grounds: Campus area 1 square block.

Chief Executive Officer: Arnold G. Tew, President.

Address admission inquiries to Director of Admissions.

Cincinnati College of Mortuary Science

645 West North Bend Road
Cincinnati, Ohio 45224-1462
Tel: (513) 761-2020 **E-mail:** admissions@ccms.edu
Fax: (513) 761-3333 **Internet:** www.ccms.edu

Institution Description: The Cincinnati College of Mortuary Science is an independent, private, nonprofit college. *Enrollment:* 134. *Degrees awarded:* Associate, baccalaureate.

Accreditation: *Regional:* NCA. *Professional*: mortuary science

History: The oldest college of mortuary science in continuous existence, CCMS was established in 1882 as the Clarke School of Embalming. CCMS was reorganized in 1970 as the Cincinnati Foundation for Mortuary Education, d.b.s. the Cincinnati College of Mortuary Science.

Institutional Structure: Governing board: Board of Trustees for the Cincinnati Foundation for Mortuary Education. 15 trustees, of whom at lest 3 must be public members. The president of CCMS is an ex officio member of the Board. CCMS has 2 full-time administrators, 7 full-time faculty, 4 full-time staff, and 8 part-time faculty.

Calendar: Quarters (12-month year). Entrance dates in Oct. and Apr. of each year.

Characteristics of Freshmen: 95% of students are college-transfer students who have enough general education credits to enroll in the associate or bachelor's degree programs. 5% of students are high school graduates entering the associate degree program directly. 75% male, 25% female. Students typically enroll from 15 states and 2 foreign countries. Fall class enrollment is generally 60–70 students; spring enrollments is 35–40. Average age of students is 23.

Admission: Applicants notified on a rolling basis. Prepayment of first quarter's tuition two weeks before classes begin; thereafter, $25 late charge. No enrollment after first week of class. High school applicants to associate degree program need 15 units (2 biology, 3 English, 1 mathematics, 2 social science, plus electives). College transfer students to associate or bachelor's degree programs must satisfy two sets of requirements: (1) academic and (2) state licensing requirements. CCMS seeks a 2.0 on a 4.0 scale and certain prerequisites in course distribution. State licensing requirements vary widely; student should contact CCMS or appropriate state licensing board.

Degree Requirements: Full 18-month associate degree for high school graduates requires 99 quarter credit hours. Associate degree for college transfer students requires 75 quarter credit hours minimum. Bachelor's degree for transfer students requires 90 quarter credit hours minimum (plus transfer of appropriate general education from another college or university). Fulfillment of some requirements by CLEP or by proficiency testing.

Distinctive Educational Programs: CCMS is the only private college of mortuary science in the United States regionally accredited at the bachelor's degree level. Ohio is the only state to require a bachelor's degree for licensure. The college works with other colleges and universities and offers continuing education options for funeral service and allied health fields.

Degrees Conferred: 35 *associate:* mortuary science; 87 *baccalaureate:* mortuary science.

Fees and Other Expenses: *Full-time tuition per academic year 2008–09:* $17,550. *Books and supplies:* $1,600. *Required fees:* $250. *Room and board per academic year:* Off-campus $7,260. *Other expenses:* $4,260.

Financial Aid: Approximately 70% of students receive some financial aid. CCMS has a limited number of scholarships available. Financial assistance is available in the form of Pell Grants, College Work-Study, Veterans Administration Benefits, National Direct Student Loans, Supplemental Education Opportunity Grants (SEOG), Stafford Loans, other federal aid programs.

Departments and Teaching Staff: *Total instructional faculty:* 7. *Degrees held by full-time faculty:* Baccalaureate 14%, master's 86%. 86% hold terminal degrees.

Enrollment: Total enrollment 131.

Characteristics of Student Body: *Ethnic/racial makeup:* Black non-Hispanic: 7%; White non-Hispanic: 91%; Hispanic 1%; unknown 1%.

International Students: 2 international students are enrolled each year.

Student Life: Most students commute. *Student publications:* yearbook.

Publications: *Mortuary Law*, the standard national textbook for the subject.

Library Collections: 6,500-volume specialized collection on death and dying.

Chief Executive Officer: Dan L. Flory, President.

Address inquiries to Director of Admission.

Cleveland Institute of Art

11141 East Boulevard
Cleveland, Ohio 44106
Tel: (216) 421-7400 **E-mail:** admiss@gate.cia.edu
Fax: (216) 754-3634 **Internet:** www.cia.edu

Institution Description: Cleveland Institute of Art is a private, independent, nonprofit institution. *Enrollment:* 503. >*Degrees awarded:* Baccalaureate.

Member of the consortium Union of Independent Colleges of Art.

Accreditation: *Regional:* NCA. *Professional*: art

History: Established and chartered as Cleveland School of Art and offered first instruction at postsecondary level 1882; adopted present name 1949.

Institutional Structure: *Governing board:* Board of Directors. Representation: 42 trustees, including 5 alumni; 9 honorary trustees. 42 voting. *Composition of institution:* Administrators 19. Academic affairs headed by vice president of academic affairs. Management/business/finances directed by vice president of business affairs. Full-time instructional faculty 37. Academic governance body, Environment Chair Committee, meets an average of 9 times per year.

Calendar: Semesters. Academic year Aug. to May. Freshmen admitted Sept., Jan., June. Degrees conferred and formal commencement May. Summer session of 1 term from mid-June to mid-July.

Characteristics of Freshmen: 422 applicants (female 250, male 172). 87% of applicants accepted. 28% of accepted applicants enrolled full-time.

21 of applicants submitted SAT scores; 70 ACT scores. *25th percentile*: SAT Critical Reading 470, SAT Math 410; ACT Composite 26. *75th percentile*: SAT Critical Reading 560, SAT Math 5540; ACT Composite 25.

52% of entering freshmen expected to graduate within 5 years. 66% of freshmen from Ohio. Freshmen from 16 states and 3 foreign countries.

Admission: Rolling admissions plan. For fall acceptance, apply as early as Oct. 1 of previous year, but not later than Aug. 1. Early acceptance available. *Requirements:* Either graduation from accredited secondary school or GED. Recommend 4 units English, 2 art, 2 mathematics, 2 science, 2 social studies. Portfolio with 12 pieces of recent work exemplifying painting, drawing, and design skills required. Minimum 2.0 GPA. *For transfer students:* 2.0 minimum GPA; from 4-year accredited institution 51 hours maximum transfer credit; from 2-year accredited institution 24 hours. Studio transfer credit through portfolio evaluation.

College credit and advanced placement for postsecondary-level work completed in secondary school. College credit for extrainstitutional learning on basis of portfolio; faculty assessments.

Tutoring available. Developmental courses offered during regular academic year; credit given.

Degree Requirements: 150–153 credit hours; 2.0 GPA; last 2 semesters in residence; one-person show and defense of art work in school gallery.

Fulfillment of some degree requirements and exemption from some beginning courses possible by passing departmental examinations, College Board CLEP. *Grading system:* A–F; pass-fail; withdraw (carries time limit).

Distinctive Educational Programs: Cooperative baccalaureate program in medical illustration with Case Western Reserve University School of Medicine. Preprofessional program in art education leading to baccalaureate and master's degrees from Case Western University. Facilities and programs for independent research, including individual majors, tutorials. Institutionally sponsored semester abroad programs in England, Germany, Italy, Spain. Cross-registration and exchange programs also available through consortium.

Degrees Conferred: 74 *baccalaureate:* visual and performing arts.

Fees and Other Expenses: *Tuition per academic year 2008–09:* $31,010. *Books and supplies:* $1,910. *Room and board per academic year:* $9,148. *Other expenses:* 43,340.

Financial Aid: Aid from institutionally generated funds is provided on the basis of academic merit and financial need. Institution has a Program Participation Agreement with the U.S. Department of Education for eligible students to receive Pell Grants and, depending upon the agreement, other federal

Financial aid to full-time, first-time undergraduate students: 26% received federal grants averaging $3,142; 73% state/local grants averaging $1,665; 92% institutional grants averaging $6,094; 70% received loans averaging $3,887.

Departments and Teaching Staff: *Total instructional faculty:* 101 (full-time 47, part-time 54). 94% of faculty hold the doctorate, first-professional, or other terminal degree. Student/faculty ratio: 9:1.

Enrollment: Total enrollment 503 (undergraduate).

Characteristics of Student Body: *Ethnic/racial makeup:* Black non-Hispanic: 4%; Asian or Pacific Islander: 5%; Hispanic: 3%; White non-Hispanic: 82%; unknown: 1%; nonresident alien 3%.

International Students: 15 nonresident aliens enrolled fall 2008. No programs available to aid students whose native language is not English. No financial aid specifically designated for international students.

Student Life: On-campus residence hall. All unmarried first-year students who do not live with parents or guardians within Cuyahoga Country and who are under 20 years of age are required to live in residence hall. 20% of student body live off-campus in coeducational residence halls at adjoining Case Western Reserve University. *Special regulations:* Parking available to all students for semester fee. *Special services:* Learning Resources Center, medical services, shuttle bus to and from institutions in the University Circle area. *Surrounding community:* Cleveland population 575,000. Served by mass transit bus system; airport 23 miles from campus; passenger rail service 4 miles from campus.

Library Collections: 45,000 volumes including bound books, serial backfiles, electronic documents, and government documents not in separate collections. Card catalog. 3,000 recordings; 500 compact discs; 50 CD-ROMs. Computer work stations available. Students have access to the Internet at no charge.

Most important special holdings include a collection of artists' books, institute archives.

Buildings and Grounds: Campus area 485 acres.

Chief Executive Officer: 'Dr. David L. Deming, President.

Address admission inquiries to Catherine Redhead, Director of Admissions.

Cleveland Institute of Music

11021 East Boulevard
Cleveland, Ohio 44106-1776
Tel: (216) 791-5000 **E-mail:** admissions@cwru.edu
Fax: (216) 791-1530 **Internet:** www.cwru.edu

Institution Description: Cleveland Institute of Music is a part of Case Western Reserve University. *Enrollment:* 462. *Degrees awarded:* Baccalaureate, master's, doctorate. Diplomas also awarded.

Accreditation: *Regional:* NCA. *Professional*: music

History: Established and offered first instruction at postsecondary level 1920; awarded first degree (baccalaureate) 1925; incorporated 1927.

Institutional Structure: *Governing board:* Board of Trustees. Representation: 58 trustees. 4 ex officio. All voting. *Composition of institution:* Administrators 15. Academic affairs directed by vice president of academic affairs and dean. Business and financial affairs directed by vice president. Full-time instructional faculty 31. Academic governance body meets monthly.

Calendar: Semesters. Academic year Aug. to May. Freshmen admitted Aug., Jan., June. Degrees conferred and formal commencement May. Summer session.

Characteristics of Freshmen: 483 applicants (248 female, 257 male). 34% of applicants admitted. 26% of admitted students enrolled full-time.

SAT scores 640 critical reading, 590 mathematical.

Admission: Rolling admissions plan. Dec. 15 application deadline. *Requirements:* Either graduation from accredited secondary school or GED. *Entrance tests:* ACT or SAT; audition; examinations in music theory and general musical

CLEVELAND INSTITUTE OF MUSIC—*cont'd*

knowledge. *For transfer students:* 2.0 minimum GPA; maximum transfer credit limited only by residence requirement.

College credit and advanced placement for postsecondary-level work completed in secondary school.

Tutoring available. Noncredit remedial courses offered during regular academic year.

Degree Requirements: 125-140 semester hours; 4 semesters in residence; general education requirements; junior and senior recitals.

Fulfillment of some degree requirements and exemption from some beginning courses possible by passing institutional examination. *Grading system:* A–F; withdraw (carries time limit).

Distinctive Educational Programs: Cooperative music education and academic program with Case Western Reserve University. Cross-registration with Case Western Reserve University. *Other distinctive programs:* Continuing education, including programs for adults and secondary school students.

Degrees Conferred: 40 *baccalaureate:* visual and performing arts; 74 *master's.*

Fees and Other Expenses: *Full time tuition per academic year 2008–09:* $33,250. *Books and supplies:* $1,050. *Room and board per academic year:* $10,830. *Other expenses:* $3,104.

Financial Aid: Aid from institutionally generated funds is provided on the basis of financial need and musical ability. Institutional funding available. Institution has a Program Participation Agreement with the U.S. Department of Education for eligible students to receive Pell Grants and, depending upon the agreement, other federal aid.

Financial aid to full-time, first-time undergraduate students: 96% received some form of financial aid. Average amount of aid received: institutional grants $11,544; loans $3,599.

Departments and Teaching Staff: *Total instructional faculty:* 112.

Enrollment: Total enrollment 402. Undergraduate 218 (female 52%, male 48%). Graduate 244 (full-time 86%).

Characteristics of Student Body: *Ethnic/racial makeup (undergraduate):* Black non-Hispanic: 3%; American Indian or Alaska Native: 1%; Asian or Pacific Islander: 12%; Hispanic: 3%; White non-Hispanic: 66%. *Age distribution:* 17–21: 54%; 22–24: 27%; 25–29: 15%; 30–34: 2.7%; 35–39: 1%; 40–49: 3%.

International Students: 31 undergraduate nonresident aliens enrolled fall 2008. Students from Europe, Asia, Latin America, Canada, Australia, New Zealand. Programs available to aid students whose native language is not English: English as a Second Language Program. variable number of scholarships and loans available to qualifying international students.

Student Life: Residence hall and board facilities available through Case Western Reserve University. *Special services:* Medical services available through Case Western Reserve University. *Surrounding community:* Cleveland population 575,000. Served by mass transit bus system; airport 15 miles from campus; passenger rail service 1 mile from campus.

Library Collections: 52,500 volumes. 21,000 audiovisual materials; 115 current periodical subscriptions. Online catalog. Students have access to online information retrieval services and the Internet.

Most important special collections include Clara Bickford Collection of autographs of musical luminaries.

Buildings and Grounds: Campus area 2 acres.

Chief Executive Officer: David P. Cerone, President.

Address admission inquiries to William Fay, Director of Admissions.

Cleveland State University

1983 East 24th Street
Cleveland, Ohio 44115
Tel: (216) 687-2000 **E-mail:** admissions@csuohio.edu
Fax: (316) 687-0366 **Internet:** www.csuohio.edu

Institution Description: Cleveland State University is a state institution. *Enrollment:* 15,139. *Degrees awarded:* Baccalaureate, first-professional (law), master's, doctorate. Specialist certificates also given.

Accreditation: *Regional:* NCA. *Professional*: accounting, business, chemistry, engineering, law, music, nursing, occupational therapy, physical therapy, social work, speech-language pathology, teacher education

History: Established as Fenn College and offered first instruction at postsecondary level 1923; awarded first degree (baccalaureate) 1927; chartered and incorporated 1964; added graduate programs and adopted present name 1965; merged with Cleveland-Marshall School of Law 1969.

Institutional Structure: *Governing board:* Board of Trustees. Representation: 9 trustees. All voting. 2 student representatives; 2 faculty (nonvoting). Academic affairs headed by provost and vice president for academic affairs. Management/business/finances directed by vice president for finance and resource planning. Student life/athletics/admissions directed by vice president for administration and student affairs. Alumni and development headed by the vice president for development. Personnel/affirmative action/institutional research directed by vice president and executive assistant to the president. Full-time instructional faculty 524. Academic governance body, Faculty Council, meets an average of 8 times per year.

Calendar: Semesters. Academic year Aug. to June. Freshmen admitted Aug., Jan., Mar., June. Degrees conferred June, Sept., Dec., Mar. Formal commencements June, Sept.

Characteristics of Freshmen: 3,559 applicants (2,121 female, 1,438 male). 82% of applicants accepted. 56% of accepted applicants enrolled full-time.

27% (390 students) submitted SAT scores; 56% (209 students) submitted ACT scores. *25th percentile*: SAT Critical Reading 410, SAT Math 410; ACT Composite 17. *75th percentile*: SAT Critical Reading 540, SAT Math 570; ACT Composite 23.

30% of entering freshmen expected to graduate within 5 years. 96% of freshmen from Ohio. Freshmen from 20 states and 80 foreign countries.

Admission: Rolling admissions plan. For fall acceptance, apply as early as 10 months, but not later than 1 month, prior to enrollment. Early acceptance available. NOTE: new requirements begin with fall 2008. *Requirements:* For freshmen, Ohio residents: graduation from an accredited high school or GED results at 50th percentile. 13 units of state-specified core curriculum in high school (4 units English; 3 units each of mathematics, social science, and natural science; 2 foreign language; 1 unit of visual/performing arts strongly recommended). For freshmen, non-Ohio residents: graduation from an accredited high school in the top half of class with ACT/SAT results at the 50th percentile. For transfers: minimum 2.0 GPA. selective admission in College of Business, Education, and Engineering and in the departments of nursing, occupational therapy, and physical therapy. *Entrance tests:* College Board SAT or ACT composite. For foreign students TOEFL. *For transfer students:* from 4-year accredited institution maximum transfer credit limited only by residence requirement.

College credit and advanced placement for postsecondary-level work completed in secondary school and for extrainstitutional learning. Developmental/remedial courses offered in summer session and regular academic year; credit given.

Degree Requirements: 120–128 semester hours; 2.0 GPA; last 30 hours in residence; 36 hours of upper division course work; 24 credit hours or ½ of the major department courses and 16 credit hours or ½ of the minor department courses; distribution requirements.

Fulfillment of some degree requirements and exemption from some beginning courses possible by passing departmental examinations and College Board CLEP. *Grading system:* A–F; pass-fail.

Distinctive Educational Programs: Work-experience programs. Weekend and evening classes. Interdisciplinary program in urban studies. Facilities for independent research, including honors programs, individual majors, tutorials. Study abroad in England (business); France, Spain, Germany (modern languages). *Other distinctive programs:* Continuing education program.

ROTC: Army offered in cooperation with John Carroll University.

Degrees Conferred: 1,695 *baccalaureate*; 1,373 *master's*; 43 *doctorate*. Bachelor's degrees awarded in top five disciplines: business, management, marketing, and related support services 348; social sciences 247; education 202; psychology 128; health professions and related clinical sciences 122. Master's degrees awarded in top five disciplines: education 497; business/marketing 357; public administration and social services 166; engineering 120; health professions 76. Doctorates awarded: biological/life sciences 6; business/marketing 3; education 9; engineering 7; physical sciences 4; social sciences 3. First-professional degrees awarded: law 220.

Fees and Other Expenses: *Full-time tuition per academic year 2008–09:* $7,970 resident, $10,774 nonresident; contact the university for current graduate and first-professional tuition and fees. *Room and board per academic year:* $8,700. *Books and supplies:* $800. *Other expenses:* $4,300.

Financial Aid: Aid from institutionally generated funds is provided on the basis of academic merit, financial need, athletic ability, other criteria. Institution has a Program Participation Agreement with the U.S. Department of Education for eligible students to receive Pell Grants and, depending upon the agreement, other federal aid.

Departments and Teaching Staff: *Total instructional faculty:* 963 (full-time 524, part-time 439). Student/faculty ratio: 28:1. Degrees held by full-time faculty: master's 13%, doctorate 80%, professional 7%.

Enrollment: Total enrollment 15,139. Undergraduate 9,541 (female 56%, male 44%). Graduate 5,598 (full-time 36%). Undergraduate transfer-in students 1,305.

Characteristics of Student Body: *Ethnic/racial makeup:* Black non-Hispanic: 21%; Asian or Pacific Islander: 3%; Hispanic: 35; White non-Hispanic: 62%; unknown: 7%; nonresident alien 2%. *Age distribution:* number under 18:

313; 18–19: 1,491; 20–21: 1,808; 22–24: 2,278; 25–29: 1,567; 30–34: 816; 35–39: 490; 40–49: 652; 50–64: 244; 65 and over: 816.

International Students: 523 nonresident aliens enrolled fall 2008. Students from Europe, Asia, Central and South America, Africa, Canada, Australia, New Zealand, Middle East. Programs available to aid students whose native language is not English: social, cultural. English as a Second Language Program. No financial aid specifically designated for international students.

Student Life: On-campus residence halls house 3.2% of student body. 1.5% of males join fraternities. 25% of students participate in student governance and student organizations. *Intercollegiate athletics:* male: baseball, basketball, fencing, golf, soccer, swimming, tennis, track, cross-country, wrestling; female: basketball, fencing, softball, swimming, tennis, track, cross-country, volleyball. *Student publications, radio: Cauldron*, a biweekly newspaper; *The Gavel*, an irregularly published law student publication; *Vindicator*, semi-monthly student newspaper with special interest in presenting the news as it affects Black people; *Whiskey Island Magazine*, a literary magazine. WCSB, a university-owned FM station operated by CSU students. *Surrounding community:* Cleveland population 550,000. Served by mass transit bus and rail systems; airport 15 miles from campus; passenger rail service 2 miles from campus.

Library Collections: 1,215,500 volumes including bound books, serial backfiles, electronic documents, and government documents not in separate collections. Online catalog. Current serial subscriptions: 1,870 paper, 44 microform, 1,131 via electronic access. 27,767 audiovisual materials; 894 DVD discs; 1,110 CD-ROMs. Computer work stations available. Students have access to the Internet at no charge.

Most important special collections include Cleveland Press Library, Cleveland Union Terminal Archive, Contemporary Poetry Collection.

Buildings and Grounds: Campus area 80 acres. Campus DVD available.

Chief Executive Officer: Dr. Michael Schwartz, President.

Address admission inquiries to Jill Oakley-Jeppe, Associate Director of Admissions; graduate inquiries to Dr. William Bailey, Director of Graduate Admissions.

College of Arts and Sciences

Degree Programs Offered: *Baccalaureate* in anthropology, art, biology, chemistry, classical and medieval studies; communication, dramatic arts, economics, English, French, geology, German, history, linguistics, mathematics, music, nursing, occupational therapy, philosophy, physical therapy, physics, political science, psychology, religious studies, social science, social service, sociology, Spanish, speech and hearing; *master's* in applied communication theory and methodology, biology, chemistry, economics, English, history, mathematics, music, philosophy, physics, psychology, sociology, speech pathology and audiology; *doctorate* in biology, chemistry.

Admission: In addition to general requirements, 2 units in a foreign language, 3 mathematics, 3 social studies, 1 science; for science majors, 3 mathematics, 3 science (including 1 lab course).

James J. Nance College of Business Administration

Degree Programs Offered: *Baccalaureate* in accounting, business economics, business education, computer and information science, finance, management and labor, marketing, quantitative business analysis; *master's* in accountancy and financial information systems, business administration, computer and information science, labor relations and human resources.

Admission: In addition to general requirements, 2 units mathematics (beginning and intermediate algebra), 2 social studies, 3 units from among foreign language, mathematics, natural science, social studies. Graduate requirements vary.

College of Education

Degree Programs Offered: *Baccalaureate* in early childhood education, elementary education, physical education, special education, *master's* in community health; counselor education; curriculum and instruction; educational administration; postsecondary education supervision; sports management, exercise, or recreation. Specialist certificates in education also given.

Fenn College of Engineering

Degree Programs Offered: *Baccalaureate* in chemical engineering, civil engineering, electrical engineering, industrial engineering, mechanical engineering, technology; *master's* in chemical engineering, civil engineering, electrical engineering, industrial engineering, mechanical engineering; *doctorate* in engineering.

Admission: In addition to general requirements, 3 units in mathematics (algebra, geometry, trigonometry), 2 laboratory science (including chemistry or physics). Minimum 2.5 GPA. Lowest acceptable secondary school class standing upper two-fifths. Minimum of SAT combined score 950 or ACT composite score 22 required.

College of Urban Affairs

Degree Programs Offered: *Baccalaureate, master's, doctorate* in urban studies; *master's* in public administration.

Admission: 2 years or 90 credit hours of college work.

Cleveland-Marshall College of Law

Degree Programs Offered: *First-professional:* juris doctor degree; *master's* in laws; joint degree program (juris doctor/MBA).

Admission: Baccalaureate from accredited college or university; LSAT.

College of Mount St. Joseph

5701 Delhi Road
Cincinnati, Ohio 45233-1670
Tel: (513) 244-4200 **E-mail:** admissions@mail.msj.edu
Fax: (513) 244-4629 **Internet:** www.msj.edu

Institution Description: College of Mount St. Joseph is a private, coeducational institution, sponsored by the Sisters of Charity of Cincinnati, Roman Catholic Church. *Enrollment:* 2,133. *Degrees awarded:* Associate, baccalaureate, master's, doctorate.

Member of Greater Cincinnati Consortium of Colleges and Universities (GCCCU); Association of Catholic Colleges and Universities (ACCU).

Accreditation: *Regional:* NCA. *Professional*: chemistry, clinical lab scientist, law, music, nursing, physical therapy, respiratory therapy, social work

History: Established as Mount St. Vincent Academy 1853; incorporated 1854; changed name to Mount St. Joseph Academy and first instruction at postsecondary level 1906; became 4-year college and adopted present name 1920; awarded first degree (baccalaureate) 1924.

Institutional Structure: *Governing board:* Board of Trustees of the College of Mount St. Joseph. Representation: 27 trustees, including 8 religious, 19 lay persons, president of the college (ex officio). All voting. *Composition of institution:* president, chief academic officer/dean of faculty; chief financial officer; chief information officer; dean of students; vice president for institutional advancement. Full-time instructional faculty 117. Academic governance body, the faculty meets an average of 5 times per year.

Calendar: Semesters. Academic year Aug. to May. Freshmen admitted Aug., Jan., May. Degrees conferred and formal commencement May.

Characteristics of Freshmen: 1,264 applicants (613 female, 651 male). 71% applicants admitted. 35% of applicants admitted and enrolled full-time.

48% (156 students) submitted SAT scores; 82% (264 students) submitted ACT scores. *25th percentile*: SAT Critical Reading 430, SAT Math 430; ACT Composite 19, ACT English 17, ACT math 18. *75th percentile*: SAT Critical Reading 540, SAT Math 540; ACT Composite 23, ACT English 23, ACT math 24.

67% of entering freshmen expected to graduate within 5 years. 86% of freshmen from Ohio. Freshmen from 25 states and 6 foreign countries.

Admission: Rolling admissions plan. For fall acceptance, apply as early as senior year of secondary school, but not later than Aug. 15 of year of enrollment. Early acceptance available. *Requirements:* Either graduation from accredited secondary school with 13-credit core (4 units English, 2 mathematics, 2 social studies, 2 science, 1 fine arts, 2 foreign language); or GED. Minimum GPA 2.25; top 60% of class, ACT or SAT score above 40th percentile. *For transfer students:* same as above and college GPA greater than 2.0.

College credit and advanced placement for postsecondary-level work completed in secondary school. College credit for extrainstitutional learning on basis of portfolio and faculty assessments; personal interview.

Tutoring available. Developmental courses offered during regular academic year; credit given.

Degree Requirements: *For all associate degrees:* 64 credit hours; 1 physical activity course. *For all baccalaureate degrees:* 128 credit hours/ *For all undergraduate degrees:* 2.0 GPA; final 30 semester hours in residence; distribution requirements; demonstrated proficiency in mathematics, reading, and writing.

Fulfillment of some degree requirements and exemption from some beginning courses possible by passing College Board CLEP. *Grading system:* A–F; pass-fail; pass; withdraw (deadline after which pass-fail is appended to withdraw); incomplete (carries time limit).

Distinctive Educational Programs: Associate degree programs; 41 baccalaureate degree programs. Entry level master's degree program in physical therapy; graduate programs in education and religious studies; cooperative education available in all majors; tuition-free credit for service learning; universal computing requirement for all new full-time students beginning in 2000; first

COLLEGE OF MOUNT ST. JOSEPH—*cont'd*

college in the U.S. to offer an ABA-approved certificate program in paralegal studies and paralegal studies for nurses online. Project EXCEL assists students with learning disabilities succeed. Service Learning participation provides tuition-free credit. Honors program. English as a Second Language assists international students.

ROTC: Army offered in cooperation with Xavier University; Air Force in cooperation with University of Cincinnati.

Degrees Conferred: 9 *associate;* 392 *baccalaureate:* biological/life sciences 4; business/marketing 81; communications/communication technologies 19; computer and information sciences 2; education 48; health professions and related sciences 59; interdisciplinary studies 9; law/legal studies 7; liberal arts/general studies 15; mathematics 2; philosophy/religion/theology 4; physical sciences 2; protective services/public administration 9; psychology 12; social sciences and history 15; visual and performing arts 165. 101 *master's:* business/marketing 10; education 54; health professions and related clinical sciences 37; philosophy/religion 2.

Fees and Other Expenses: *Full-time tuition per academic year 2008–09:* $22,000 undergraduate; graduate study tuition charged per credit hour. *Required fees:* $390. *Room and board per academic year:* $9,000. *Books and supplies:* $800. *Other expenses:* $1,800.

Financial Aid: Aid from institutionally generated funds is provided on the basis of academic merit, financial need, other criteria.

Financial aid to full-time, first-time undergraduate students: 100% received some form of financial aid. Average amount of]aid received: federal grants $2,843; state/local grants $1,472; institutional grants $8,066; loans $8,932.

Departments and Teaching Staff: *Total instructional faculty:* 225. Total faculty with doctorate, first-professional, or other terminal degree 89. Student/faculty ratio: 11:1.

Enrollment: Total enrollment 2,133. Undergraduate 1,831 (female 65%, male 35%). Graduate 302 (full-time 43%). Undergraduate transfer-in students 195.

Characteristics of Student Body: *Ethnic/racial makeup:* Black non-Hispanic: 9%; Hispanic: 1%; White non-Hispanic: 84%; unknown: 5%. *Age distribution:* number under 18: 5; 18–19: 20–21: 493; 22–24: 450; 25–29: 173; 30–34: 113; 35–39: 96; 40–49: 172; 50–64: 77; 65 and over: 9.

International Students: No programs available to aid students whose native language is not English. Financial aid specifically designated for international students: 2 scholarships available annually.

Student Life: Emphasis on leadership development and Service Learning through student activities curriculum; over 40 student clubs and organizations. Division III athletics for males and females and member of the Heartland Collegiate Athletic Conference (HCAC); male: baseball, basketball, football, tennis, wrestling; female basketball, cross-country, soccer, softball, tennis, volleyball. On-campus fitness center, running track, gym, multipurpose room, lighted tennis courts. Seton Center features single, double, and apartment style choices; campus facilities include Computer Learning Center, Scholar's Center, Harrington Student Center. Online registration available.

Library Collections: 98,000 volumes including bound books, serial backfiles, electronic documents, and government documents not in separate collections. Online catalog. Current serial subscriptions: 425 paper, 148 microform, 9,000 electronic. 1,791 recordings; 500 compact discs. Computer work stations available. Students have access to the Internet at no charge.

Most important special collection is the Catholic Document Collection.

Buildings and Grounds: Campus area 75 acres.

Chief Executive Officer: Sr. Francis Marie Thrailkill, O.S.U., President.

Address admission inquiries to Peggy Minnich, Director of Admissions; graduate inquires to Marilyn Hoskins, Assistant Director of Admission for Graduate Recruitment.

College of Wooster

1189 Beall Avenue
Wooster, Ohio 44691

Tel: (330) 263-2000 **E-mail:** admissions@wooster.edu
Fax: (330) 263-2621 **Internet:** www.wooster.edu

Institution Description: The College of Wooster is a private, independent, nonprofit college affiliated with the United Presbyterian Church (U.S.A.) *Enrollment:* 1,884. *Degrees awarded:* Baccalaureate.

Member of the consortium Great Lakes College Association.

Accreditation: *Regional:* NCA. *Professional*: music

History: Established and chartered as University of Wooster 1866; offered first instruction at postsecondary level 1870; awarded first degree (baccalaureate) 1871; adopted present name 1914. *See* Lucy Lillian Notestein, *Wooster of the Middle West* (Kent, Ohio: Kent State University Press, 1971) for further information.

Institutional Structure: *Governing board:* The Board of Trustees of The College of Wooster. Representation: 39 trustees, including 6 alumni. 1 ex officio. All voting. *Composition of institution:* Administrators 10. 3 vice presidents: vice president for academic affairs, vice president for finance and business, vice president for development. Full-time instructional faculty 142. Academic governance body, the faculty, meets an average of 8 times per year.

Calendar: Semesters. Academic year Aug. to May. Freshmen admitted Aug., Jan. Degrees conferred May, Oct. Formal commencement May. Summer session May through July.

Characteristics of Freshmen: 3,944 applicants (2,021 female, 1,923 male). 70% applicants accepted. 19% of accepted applicants enrolled full-time.

89% (542 students) submitted SAT scores; 61% (301 students) submitted ACT scores. *25th percentile*: SAT Critical Reading 540, SAT Math 560; ACT Composite 23, ACT English 22, ACT Math 22. *75th percentile*: SAT Critical Reading 670, SAT Math 650, SAT Writing 650; ACT Composite 29, ACT English 26, ACT Math 27.

65% of entering freshmen expected to graduate within 5 years. 52% of freshmen from Ohio. Freshmen from 44 states and 36 foreign countries.

Admission: Rolling admissions plan. For fall acceptance, apply by Mar. 1; students notified of acceptance by Apr. 1; national candidates reply May 1. Early decision available. *Requirements:* Either graduation from accredited secondary school with 16 academic units which must include 4 English, 2 foreign language, 3 mathematics, 3 natural science, 2 science, 2 social studies (1 elective from those listed); or GED. Additional requirements for music program. Minimum 2.7 GPA (exceptions possible). *Entrance tests:* College Board SAT or ACT composite. *For transfer students:* 2.5 minimum GPA; 60 semester hours maximum transfer credit.

College credit and advanced placement for postsecondary-level work completed in secondary school.

Tutoring available. Developmental courses offered in summer session and regular academic year; credit given.

Degree Requirements: 32 courses; 2.0 GPA; 2 years, including final one, in residence; independent study thesis; distribution requirements.

Fulfillment of some degree requirements possible by passing College Board AP or institutional placement examinations. *Grading system:* A–NC.

Distinctive Educational Programs: Dual-degree programs in engineering with Case Western Reserve University, University of Michigan and Washington University (MO); in nursing and social work with Case Western Reserve University. Cooperative programs in business administration with the Amos Tuck Graduate School of Business at Dartmouth College; in economics, mathematics, and physics with the University of Michigan (Ann Arbor); in social science with the School of Applied Social Sciences at Case Western Reserve University. Special facilities for telecommunications in the classroom. Interdepartmental and interdisciplinary programs in Black studies, chemical physics, cultural area studies, general literature, international relations, urban studies, women's studies. Facilities and programs for independent research, including individual majors, tutorials. Institutionally sponsored study in Greece, India, and elsewhere. Study abroad through programs offered by other institutions and associations in Africa, Austria, China, Colombia, England, France, Germany, Greece, India, Japan, Mexico, Scotland, Spain, Russia, Yugoslavia. Domestic off-campus study, including Oak Ridge (TN) science semester, Newberry Library semester in Chicago (IL), United Nations Semester through Drew University (NJ). Internships in political science in Washington (DC); in theatre at the Cleveland (OH) Playhouse, Actors Theatre of Louisville (KY), and at the Great Lakes Shakespeare Festival. Other internships and practicums in the arts, business, chemical research, psychology, sociology, urban studies. *Other distinctive programs:* Junior and Senior Independent Study required of all students, one-on-one with faculty mentor. Required Freshman Seminar with theme tied to Forum series of lectures, performances and discussions that are campus-wide. Interdisciplinary, sophomore-level seminars that research apprenticeships. Leadership and Liberal Learning Program composed of seminar, acquaintanceship with national leaders and national symposium. Jenny Fund, portion of Wooster endowment managed by students. A company of twenty actors, technicians and theatre management personnel, The Stage Right Rep Co., performs four productions in rotating repertory and offers intensive experience in all phases of theatre each summer. The Ohio Light Opera, founded and produced by The College of Wooster, is the only company to have in its repertoire all of Gilbert and Sullivan's operettas. Wooster students and alumni are represented among the 100 actors, musicians, and technicians who make up the company, national auditions are held each winter for the eight-week season.

Degrees Conferred: 398 *baccalaureate*. Bachelor's degrees awarded in top five disciplines: biological/life sciences 33; English language and literature 34; physical sciences 41; social science and history 121; visual and performing arts 27.

Fees and Other Expenses: *Full-time tuition per academic year 2008–09:* $33,770. *Books and supplies:* $900. *Room and board per academic year:* $8,850. *Other expenses:* $600.

Financial Aid: Aid from institutionally generated funds is provided on the basis of academic merit, financial need.

Financial aid to full-time, first-time undergraduate students: 97% received some form of financial aid. Average amount of aid received: federal grants $4,096; state/local grants 1,074; institutional grants $15,391; other $5,995.

Departments and Teaching Staff: *Total instructional faculty:* 184. 90% of faculty hold the doctorate, first-professional, or other terminal degree: Student/faculty ratio: 12:1.

Enrollment: Total enrollment 1,884 (undergraduate). Transfer-in students 17.

Characteristics of Student Body: *Ethnic/racial makeup:* Black non-Hispanic: 4%; Asian or Pacific Islander: 2%; Hispanic: 2%; White non-Hispanic: 73%; unknown: 11%; nonresident alien 5%.

International Students: 94 nonresident aliens enrolled fall 2008. Programs available to aid students whose native language is not English: social and cultural. Financial aid specifically designated for international students: scholarships available annually.

Student Life: On-campus residence halls house 95% of student body. Residence halls for males constitute 29.9% of such space, for females 29.6%, for both sexes 40.5%. Variety of housing options, including small group housing, theme housing, program houses with academic interests. 300 students involved with social service agencies in Wooster city area. *Intercollegiate athletics:* male: baseball, basketball, cross country, football, lacrosse, golf, soccer, swimming, tennis, indoor and outdoor track; female: basketball, cross-country, field hockey, lacrosse, softball, swimming, tennis, indoor and outdoor track, soccer, volleyball. *Special regulations:* Cars permitted for all but freshmen; approval required for those receiving financial aid. *Special services:* medical services, including full-time resident physician. *Student publications, radio:* yearbook; weekly newspaper; biannual literary magazine. Radio station WCWS. *Surrounding community:* Wooster population 25,000. Akron, Canton, and Cleveland are nearest metropolitan areas.

Library Collections: 940,000 volumes. 290,000 government documents; 155,000 microforms; 8,000 audiovisual materials; 1,300 current periodical subscriptions. Online catalog. Students have access to online information retrieval services and the Internet.

Most important special collections include Notestein Collection of 17th-Century British History and Literature; Gregg D. Wolfe Memorial Library of the Theatre; McGregor Collection of Early American (especially 18th century materials).

Buildings and Grounds: Campus area 320 acres. Campus DVD available.

Chief Executive Officer: Dr. R. Stanton Hales, President.

Address admission inquiries to Carol Wheatley, Director of Admissions.

Columbus College of Art and Design

107 North Ninth Street
Columbus, Ohio 43215
Tel: (614) 222-9101 **E-mail:** admissions@ccad.edu
Fax: (614) 222-4040 **Internet:** www.ccad.edu

Institution Description: The Columbus College of Art and Design is a private, independent, nonprofit college. *Enrollment:* 1,558. *Degrees awarded:* Baccalaureate.

Accreditation: *Regional:* NCA. *Professional*: art

History: Established as The Columbus School of Art of The Columbus Gallery of Fine Art, chartered, and offered first instruction at postsecondary level 1879; adopted present name 1959; awarded first degree (baccalaureate) 1969. *See* Rachel N. Stockwell, *The Columbus College of Art and Design: First Hundred Years 1979–1979* (Columbus: privately published, 1979) for further information.

Institutional Structure: *Governing board:* Board of Trustees of the Columbus College of Art and Design. Extrainstitutional representation: 17 trustees; institutional representation: 1 administrator. 1 ex officio. 17 voting. *Composition of institution:* Administrators 83. Academic affairs headed by vice president. Management/business/finances directed by business officer. Full-time instructional faculty 77. Academic governance body, Division Council, meets an average of 25 times per year.

Calendar: Semesters. Academic year Aug. to July. Freshmen admitted Aug., Jan. Degrees conferred May, July, Dec. Formal commencement May. Summer session of 2 terms from May to July.

Characteristics of Freshmen: 76% of applicants accepted. 70% of accepted applicants enrolled.

Applicant test scores: *25th percentile*: SAT Critical Reading 440, SAT Math 410; ACT Composite 18, ACT English 19, ACT Math 16. *75th percentile*: SAT Critical Reading 570, SAT Math 550; ACT Composite 23, ACT English 24, ACT Math 22.

54% of entering freshmen expected to graduate within 5 years. 76% of freshmen from Ohio. Freshmen from 22 states and 7 foreign countries.

Admission: Rolling admissions plan. For fall acceptance, apply as early as Sept. of senior year of secondary school, but not later than Aug. 15 of year of enrollment. *Requirements:* Either graduation from accredited secondary school with 16 units; or GED. Portfolio. Minimum 2.0 GPA. *Entrance tests:* College Board SAT or ACT composite. For foreign students TOEFL. *For transfer students:* 2.0 minimum GPA; 60 hours maximum transfer credit; portfolio.

Tutoring available. Developmental courses offered during regular academic year; credit given.

Degree Requirements: 120 semester hours for BFA degree; 54 credit hours in residence; core curriculum; sophomore English examination; portfolio. *Grading system:* A–F; withdraw (deadline after which pass-fail is appended to withdraw).

Distinctive Educational Programs: Evening classes. Saturday morning art program for ages 6–18; noncredit special programs; Mobility Program; New York Studio Program.

Degrees Conferred: 265 *baccalaureate:* visual and performing arts.

Fees and Other Expenses: *Full-time tuition per academic year 2008–09:* $23,280. *Room and board per academic year:* $6,750. *Books and supplies:* $3,000. *Other fees:* $1,300.

Financial Aid: Aid from institutionally generated funds is provided on the basis of academic merit, financial need.

Financial aid to full-time, first-time undergraduate students: 97% of students received some form of financial aid.

Departments and Teaching Staff: *Total instructional faculty:* 170 (full-time 77, part-time 935). 77% of faculty hold the doctorate, first-professional, or other terminal degree. Student/faculty ratio: 15:1.

Enrollment: Total enrollment 1,558 (undergraduate). Transfer-in students 69.

Characteristics of Student Body: *Ethnic/racial makeup:* Black non-Hispanic: 7%; Asian or Pacific Islander: 3%; Hispanic: 45; White non-Hispanic: 76%; unknown: 4%; nonresident alien 4%. *Age distribution:* number under 18: 7; 18–19: 420; 20 21: 515; 22–24: 230; 25–29: 74; 30–34: 16; 35–39: 9; 40–49: 10; 50–64: 3.

International Students: 64 nonresident aliens enrolled fall 2008. Students from Europe, Asia, Central and South America, Middle East, India, Russia. No programs available to aid students whose native language is not English. No financial aid specifically designated for international students.

Student Life: On-campus residence halls house 21% of student body. Residence halls for both sexes constitute 100% of such space. *Special regulations:* Cars permitted without restrictions. Residence hall visitation from 11am to midnight. *Student publication:* An annual literary magazine. *Surrounding community:* Columbus metropolitan population 1.3 million. Served by mass transit bus system; airport 7 miles from campus.

Library Collections: 51,000 volumes including bound books, serial backfiles, electronic documents, and government documents not in separate collections. Online catalog. Current serial subscriptions: 275 paper; 18,574 microform. Computer work stations available. Students have access to the Internet at no charge.

Most important special collections include Frank L. and Eva L. Packard Memorial Collection (architectural books); International Studio Art/Grove's Dictionary of Art; Columbus Art School Archives.

Buildings and Grounds: Campus area 3 acres.

Chief Executive Officer: Dr. Dennison W.Griffith, President.

Address admission inquiries to Tom Green, Director of Admissions.

Defiance College

701 North Clinton Street
Defiance, Ohio 43512
Tel: (419) 784-4010 **E-mail:** admission@defiance.edu
Fax: (419) 784-0426 **Internet:** www.defiance.edu

Institution Description: Defiance College is a private college affiliated with the United Church of Christ. *Enrollment:* 1,001. *Degrees awarded:* Associate, baccalaureate, master's.

Member of Northwest Ohio Consortium.

Accreditation: *Regional:* NCA. *Professional*: athletic training, business, social work

History: Established and chartered 1850; offered first instruction at postsecondary level 1886; awarded first degree (baccalaureate) 1888; merged with Biblical Institute, Standfordville (NY) 1916; merged with Schauffler College, Cleveland 1967.

DEFIANCE COLLEGE—*cont'd*

Institutional Structure: *Governing board:* Board of Trustees. Extrainstitutional representation: 35 trustees; institutional representation: 2 full-time instructional faculty members; 2 students. 35 voting. *Composition of institution:* Administrators 21. Academic affairs headed by vice president for academic affairs. Management/business/finances directed by controller. Full-time instructional faculty 43. Academic governance body, the faculty, meets an average of 8 times per year.

Calendar: Semesters (two 16-week). Academic year Aug. to May. Freshmen admitted Aug., Jan., June. Degrees conferred and formal commencement May. Summer session of 3 terms from May to Aug.

Characteristics of Freshmen: 76% of applicants accepted. 28% of accepted applicants enrolled.

17% (38 students) submitted SAT scores; 99 % (228 students) submitted ACT scores. *25th percentile*: SAT Critical Reading 410, SAT Math $430; ACT Composite 18, ACT English 16, ACT Math 17. *75th percentile*: SAT Critical Reading 560, SAT Math 560; ACT Composite 23, ACT English 23, ACT Math 23.

51% of entering freshmen expected to graduate within 5 years. 76% of freshmen from Ohio. Freshmen from 9 states.

Admission: Rolling admissions plan. *Requirements:* Either graduation from accredited secondary school or GED. Lowest recommended secondary school class standing 60th percentile. *Entrance tests:* College Board SAT or ACT composite. For foreign students TOEFL. *For transfer students:* 2.0 minimum GPA; from 4-year accredited institution 90 semester hours maximum transfer credit; from 2-year accredited institution 60 semester hours; correspondence/extension students 15 hours.

College credit and advanced placement for postsecondary-level work completed in secondary school.

Degree Requirements: *For all associate degrees:* 60 semester hours; 30 hours in residence. *For all baccalaureate degrees:* 120 semester hours; last 30 hours or 45 of last 60 hours in residence; for all master's degrees: 33 semester hours. . *For all undergraduate degrees:* 2.0 GPA; general education requirements. *For all graduate degree:* 3.0 GPA.

Fulfillment of some degree requirements possible by passing College Board CLEP. *Grading system:* A–F; pass-fail; withdraw (carries time limit).

Distinctive Educational Programs: Work-experience programs, including field experience, internships, and cooperative education. Evening and Saturday classes. Programs for independent and directed study, individualized majors, tutorials. Design for Leadership for church lay workers and Weekend College Program.

ROTC: Army offered in cooperation with University of Toledo.

Degrees Conferred: 7 *associate;* 179 *baccalaureate*; 36 *master's*. Bachelor[s degrees awarded in top five disciplines: business/marketing 42; education 34; security and protective services 19; parks and recreation 17; visual and performing arts 16. Master's degrees awarded: business/marketing 10; education 19.

Fees and Other Expenses: *Full-time tuition per academic year 2008–09:* $21,830 undergraduate; graduate study charged per credit hour. *Required fees:* $240. *Room and board per academic year:* $7,150. *Books and supplies:* $1,350. *Other expenseds:* $2,000.

Financial Aid: Aid from institutionally generated funds is provided on the basis of academic merit, financial need. Institution has a Program Participation Agreement with the U.S. Department of Education for eligible students to receive Pell Grants and, depending upon the agreement, other federal aid.

Departments and Teaching Staff: *Total instructional faculty:* 103 (full-time 43, part-time 60). Student/faculty ratio: 14:1. Degrees held by full-time faculty: baccalaureate 100%, master's 100%, doctorate 70%.

Enrollment: Total enrollment 1,001. Undergraduate 892 (female 53%, male 47%). Graduate 109 (full-time 6%). Undergraduate transfer-in students 6%.

Characteristics of Student Body: *Ethnic/racial makeup:* Black non-Hispanic: 49; American Indian or Alaska Native: 3; Asian or Pacific Islander: 2; Hispanic: 37; White non-Hispanic: 816. *Age distribution:* number under 18: 20; 18–19: 309; 20–21: 297; 22–24: 111; 25–29: 49; 30–34: 40; 35–39: 48; 40–49: 32; 50–64: 23.

International Students: 1 nonresident alien enrolled fall 2008. No programs available to aid students whose native language is not English. No financial aid specifically designated for international students.

Student Life: On-campus residence halls house 62% of student body. Residence halls for males constitute 55% of such space, for females 45%. 13% of males join and 6% live in fraternity housing; 16% of females join and 3% live in sorority housing. *Intercollegiate athletics:* male: baseball, basketball, cross-country, football, golf, soccer, tennis, track; female: basketball, cross-country, golf, soccer, softball, tennis, track, volleyball. *Special regulations:* Cars must be registered. Quiet hours. Residence hall visitation from noon to midnight Sun.–Thurs., noon to 2am Fri. and Sat. *Special services:* Learning Resources Center, medical services. *Student publications: The Defender*, a biweekly newspaper; *Oraculum*, a yearbook. *Surrounding community:* Defiance population 17,000. Toledo, 50 miles from campus, is nearest metropolitan area.

Library Collections: 125,000 volumes. 25,000 microforms; 700 audiovisual materials; 321 current periodical subscriptions. Online catalog. Students have access to online information retrieval services and the Internet.

Most important special holdings include Eisenhower Collection; Indian Wars Collection; Afro-American Collection.

Buildings and Grounds: Campus area 148 acres.

Chief Executive Officer: Dr. Gerald E. Wood, President.

Address admission inquiries to Brad Harsha, Director of Admissions.

Denison University

100 West College Street
Granville, Ohio 43023-1372
Tel: (740) 587-0810 **E-mail:** admissions@denison.edu
Fax: (740) 587-6443 **Internet:** www.denison.edu

Institution Description: Denison University is a private, independent, nonprofit institution. *Enrollment:* 2,200. *Degrees awarded:* Baccalaureate.

Member of Great Lakes College Association (GLCA).

Accreditation: *Regional:* NCA. *Professional*: chemistry, health information administration

History: Established as Granville Literary and Theological Institution 1831; chartered 1832; offered first instruction at postsecondary level 1833; awarded first degree (baccalaureate) 1840; changed name to Granville College 1845; adopted present name 1856; merged with Shepardson College and admitted women 1897. *See* G. Wallace Chessman, *Denison: The Story of an Ohio College* (Granville, Ohio: Denison, 1957) for further information.

Institutional Structure: *Governing board:* Board of Trustees. Extrainstitutional representation: 34 trustees, 20 life trustees, 34 voting. *Composition of institution:* Administrators 113. Academic affairs headed by provost. Management/business/finance directed by vice president for finance and management. Full-time instructional faculty 192. Academic governance conducted by General Faculty, which meets every month during academic year, and by various governing councils.

Calendar: Semesters. Academic year Sept. to May. Optional off-campus Internship Program. Freshmen admitted Sept., Jan. Degrees conferred May, Dec. Formal commencement May. No summer session.

Characteristics of Freshmen: 29% of applicants accepted. 30% of accepted applicants enrolled.

63% (359 students) submitted SAT scores; 29% (167 students) submitted ACT scores. *25th percentile*: SAT Critical Reading 390, SAT I Math 680; ACT Composite 30. *75th percentile*: SAT Critical Reading 580, SAT Math 590; ACT Composite 26.

87% of entering freshmen expected to graduate within 5 years. 39% of freshmen from Ohio. Freshmen from 35 states and 9 foreign countries.

Admission: For fall acceptance, apply as early as Sept. 1 of previous year, but not later than Feb. 1 of year of enrollment. Students are notified of acceptance April. Apply by Jan. 1 for early decision and scholarship consideration. Early acceptance available. *Requirements:* Recommend 4 English, 3 in a foreign language, 4 mathematics, 4 science, 2 social studies, 1 history, 1 academic elective; or GED. Personal interview strongly recommended. Additional requirements for some degrees. *Entrance tests:* College Board SAT or ACT composite; achievements recommended. *For transfer students:* 2.7 minimum GPA.

College credit and advanced placement for postsecondary-level work completed in secondary school. Tutoring available.

Degree Requirements: *For all undergraduate degrees:* 127 credit hours; 2.0 GPA; 6 terms in residence; distribution requirements; comprehensives in individual fields of study in some departments.

Fulfillment of some degree requirements and exemption from some beginning courses possible by passing departmental examinations, or College Board AP (score of 4). *Grading system:* A–F; pass; satisfactory-unsatisfactory; incomplete (carries time limit).

Distinctive Educational Programs: Dual-degree programs in engineering with Case Western Reserve University, Washington University (MO); in occupational therapy with Washington University (MO); in forestry with Duke University (NC); in medical technology with University of Rochester (NY). Four year Honors Program. Service-learning program. Freshman Studies Program with courses in writing, arts, humanities, sciences and social sciences. Interdepartmental/interdisciplinary programs in Black studies, classical studies, environmental studies, international studies, organizational studies, philosophy, politics and economics, women's studies. Many interdepartmental courses available. Facilities for independent research, including individualized majors, Honors projects, senior research projects, independent study, directed study, numerous summer research opportunities. Numerous off-campus internship opportunities and several faculty-led travel seminars available during May term. Semester or academic year of off-campus study through approved programs such as GLCA opportunities in Africa, Europe, Japan, Scotland, China and Hong Kong, Russia, India and several locations in the U.S. (Newberry Library, New York Arts, Oak Ridge National Lab, Philadelphia Center); study through the Institute of European Studies/Institute of Asian Studies; programs through Arcadia College's Center for Education Abroad, Butler University's Institute for Study Abroad and Inter-Study in Australia, Great Britain, Greece, Ireland and South Africa; selected individual programs in Africa, the Caribbean, Europe, Great Britain, and Latin America; study at historically Black institutions.

Degrees Conferred: 541 *baccalaureate*. Bachelor's degrees awarded in top five disciplines: social sciences 131; English 60; biological/life sciences 55; communications/journalism 54; visual and performing arts 50.

Fees and Other Expenses: *Full-time tuition per academic year 2008–09:* $35,300. *Other fees:* $1,200. *Room and board per academic year:* $8,830. *Books and supplies:* $650.

Financial Aid: The university offers a direct lending program. Aid from institutionally generated funds is provided on the basis of academic merit, financial need. 96% of students received some form of financial aid,

Departments and Teaching Staff: *Total instructional faculty:* 208. 98% of faculty hold the doctorate, first-professional, or other terminal degree. Student/faculty ratio: 11:1.

Enrollment: Total enrollment 2,200 (undergraduate).

Characteristics of Student Body: *Ethnic/racial makeup:* Black non-Hispanic: 55; American Indian or Alaska Native: 2%; Hispanic: 3%; White non-Hispanic: 81%.

International Students: 110 undergraduate nonresident aliens enrolled fall 2008. Students from Europe, Asia, Latin America, Africa, Canada. Programs available to aid students whose native language is not English: social. No financial aid specifically designated for international students.

Student Life: On-campus residence halls house 99% of student body. Residence halls for males constitute 5% of such space, for females 6%, for both sexes 89%. 32f% of males join fraternities. 43% of female students join sororities. Fraternity and sorority systems are both nonresidential. *Intercollegiate athletics:* male: baseball, basketball, cross-country, diving, football, golf, indoor and outdoor track and field, lacrosse, soccer, swimming, tennis; female: basketball, cross-country, diving, field hockey, indoor and outdoor track and field, lacrosse, soccer, softball, swimming, tennis, volleyball. *Special regulations:* Cars permitted in designated areas for all students. *Special services:* Learning Resources Center, medical services. *Student publications, radio: The Adytum*, a yearbook; *Bull Sheet*, a daily national news and campus activities sheet; *The Denisonian*, a weekly newspaper; *Denison Journal Religion*, published annually; *Exile Magazine*, an annual literary magazine; *Episteme: A Journal of Undergraduate Philosophy*, published annually; *MoYo, Mind of Your Own*, a magazine of Denison community opinion dedicated to the discussion of controversial campus topics (each issue focuses on a single topic). Radio Station WDUB broadcasts 130 hours per week. *Surrounding community:* Granville population 4,500. Columbus, 30 miles from campus, is nearest metropolitan area. Served by airport 25 miles from campus.

Library Collections: 460,000 volumes including bound books, serial backfiles, electronic documents, and government documents not in separate collections. Online catalog. Current serial subscriptions: 1,145 paper, 118,463 microform, electronic access to over 40,000. 23,877 recordings. Computer work stations available. Students have fee-based access to online information retrieval services and at no charge to the Internet.

Most important special collections include Denisoniana, G.K. Gilbert Collection; music scores; Kirtley F. Mather papers.

Buildings and Grounds: Campus area 1,200 acres.

Chief Executive Officer: Dr. Dale T. Knobel, President. Address admission inquiries to Perry Robinson, Director of Admissions.

Franciscan University of Steubenville

1235 University Boulevard
Steubenville, Ohio 43952-1763
Tel: (740) 283-3771 **E-mail:** admissions@franuniv.edu
Fax: (740) 284-5456 **Internet:** www.franuniv.edu

Institution Description: Franciscan University of Steubenville (formerly University of Steubenville) is a private, independent, nonprofit college affiliated with the Third Order Regular of St. Francis, Roman Catholic Church. *Enrollment:* 2,449. *Degrees awarded:* Associate, baccalaureate, master's.

Accreditation: *Regional:* NCA. *Professional*: nursing

History: Established as The College of Steubenville and offered first instruction at postsecondary level 1946; incorporated 1948; awarded first degree (baccalaureate) 1950; became University of Steubenville and added master's degree program 1980.

Institutional Structure: *Governing board:* Board of Trustees. Extrainstitutional representation: 21 trustees, including 5 alumni; institutional representation: president of college. 2 ex officio. All voting. *Composition of institution:* Administrators 11. Academic affairs headed by dean of faculty. Management/business/finances directed by executive vice president. Full-time instructional faculty 96. Academic governance body, the faculty, meets an average of 12 times per year.

Calendar: Semesters. Academic year Aug. to May. Freshmen admitted Aug., Jan., June, July. Degrees conferred and formal commencement May. Summer session of 2 terms from June to Aug.

Characteristics of Freshmen: 1,328 applicants (852 female, 498 male). 72% of applicants accepted. 41% of accepted applicants enrolled full-time.

72% (865 students) submitted SAT scores; 54% (574 students) submitted ACT scores. *25th percentile*: SAT Critical Reading 540, SAT Math 520; ACT Composite 22, ACT English 21, ACT Math 21. *75th percentile*: SAT Critical Reading 660, SAT Math 640; ACT Composite 29, ACT English 20, ACT Math 27.

57% of entering freshmen expected to graduate within 5 years. 22% of freshmen from Ohio. Freshmen from 34 states and 28 foreign countries.

Admission: Rolling admissions plan. Apply as early as junior year of secondary school, but not later than Aug. 1. Apply by end of junior year for early decision; need not limit application to Steubenville. Early acceptance available. *Requirements:* Graduation from accredited secondary school with a minimum of 10 units in 4 of the following areas: English, foreign language, mathematics, natural science, social studies. GED also accepted. Additional requirements for some programs. 5 additional units recommended. Minimum GPA 2.0. Lowest acceptable secondary school class standing approximately 50th percentile. *Entrance tests:* College Board SAT or ACT composite. *For transfer students:* 2.0 minimum GPA; 94 hours maximum transfer credit.

College credit and advanced placement for postsecondary-level work completed in secondary school. College credit for extrainstitutional learning (life experience) on basis of faculty assessment.

Tutoring available.

Degree Requirements: *For all associate degrees:* 60 credit hours; last 15 hours in residence. *For all baccalaureate degrees:* 124 credit hours, last 30 hours in residence. *For all undergraduate degrees:* 2.0 GPA, distribution requirements.

Fulfillment of some degree requirements and exemption from some beginning courses possible by passing departmental examinations, College Board CLEP or APP. *Grading system:* A–F; pass; withdraw (carries time limit); CE (credit by examination); incomplete.

Distinctive Educational Programs: Franciscan University operates a campus in Gaming, Austria, where all students from the Steubenville campus spend 1 semester studying humanities courses while traveling throughout Europe.

Degrees Conferred: 43 *associate*; 425 *baccalaureate*; 116 *master's*. Bachelor's degrees awarded in top five disciplines: theology 86; business, management, marketing, and related support services 48; health professions and related clinical sciences 48; education 36; English language/literature 30.

Fees and Other Expenses: *Full-time tuition per academic year 2008–09:* $19,100 undergraduate; graduate study charged per credit hour. *Room and board per academic year:* $6,600. *Books and supplies:* $800. *Other expenses:* $2,700.

Financial Aid: Aid from institutionally generated funds is provided on the basis of academic merit, financial need, other criteria. Institution has a Program Participation Agreement with the U.S. Department of Education for eligible students to receive Pell Grants and, depending upon the agreement, other federal aid.

Financial aid to full-time, first-time undergraduate students: 93% received some form of financial aid. Average amount of aid received: federal grants $3,054; state/local grants $1,325; institutional grants $5,962; loans $5,262.

Departments and Teaching Staff: *Total instructional faculty:* 137. Student/faculty ratio: 16:1. Degrees held by full-time faculty: baccalaureate 100%, master's 100%, doctorate 60%. 62% hold terminal degrees.

Enrollment: Total enrollment 2,449. Undergraduate 2,049 (female 60%, male 40%). Graduate 400 (full-time 43%). Undergraduate transfer-in students 161.

Characteristics of Student Body: *Ethnic/racial makeup:* Black non-Hispanic: 1%; American Indian or Alaska Native: 1%; Asian or Pacific Islander: 2%; Hispanic: 55; White non-Hispanic: 84%; unknown: 7%; nonresident alien 1%.

International Students: 25 nonresident aliens enrolled fall 2008. Students from Europe, Asia, Latin America, Africa, Canada, Australia. Programs available to aid students whose native language is not English: social, cultural. English as a Second Language Program. Financial aid available for international students: variable number of scholarships available annually.

Student Life: Residence halls house 46% of student body. *Special regulations:* Freshmen not permitted cars on campus. Residence hall lounge visitation from 7am to 1am Sun. through Thurs.; 7am to 2am Fri. and Sat. All other common areas: 12pm 1am Sun. through Thurs., 12pm to 2am Fri. and Sat. *Special*

FRANCISCAN UNIVERSITY OF STEUBENVILLE—*cont'd*

services: medical services. *Student publications: The Troubadour*, a student weekly newspaper; *The Franciscan*, the student yearbook, *Soundings*, an annual journal of student writings; *Life Matters*, a publication produced by Human Life Concerns. *Surrounding community:* Steubenville population 26,500. Pittsburgh (PA), 41 miles from campus, is nearest metropolitan area. Served by airport 41 miles from campus.

Library Collections: 232,000 volumes. 251,000 units; 3,700 audiovisual materials; 5,870 periodical subscriptions. Online catalog. Students have access to online information retrieval services and the Internet.

Most important special collections include Theology, Franciscan Book Collection; philosophy.

Buildings and Grounds: Campus area 125 acres. Campus DVD available.

Chief Executive Officer: Reverend Terrence Henry, T.O.R., President.

Address undergraduate admission inquiries to Margaret Weber, Director of Admissions.

Franklin University

201 South Grant Avenue
Columbus, Ohio 43215-5399
Tel: (614) 341-6300 **E-mail:** admissions@franklin.edu
Fax: (614) 224-8027 **Internet:** www.franklin.edu

Institution Description: Franklin University is a private, independent, nonprofit institution. *Enrollment:* 7,416. *Degrees awarded:* Associate, baccalaureate, master's. .

Accreditation: *Regional:* NCA. *Professional*: engineering technology, nursing

History: Established as School of Commerce of the Columbus YMCA and offered first instruction at postsecondary level 1902; awarded first degree (baccalaureate) 1923; adopted present name 1933; incorporated as an independent, private, nonprofit institution 1964.

Institutional Structure: *Governing board:* Board of Trustees. Extrainstitutional representation: 25 trustees; institutional representation: president of the university. 1 ex officio. 25 voting. *Composition of institution:* Administrators 15. Academic affairs headed by vice president of academic affairs. Management/business/finances directed by vice president, vice president, business and finance. Full-time instructional faculty 51. Academic governance body, Faculty Assembly, meets an average of 6 times per year.

Calendar: Trimesters. Academic year Sept. to Apr. Freshmen admitted Sept., Jan., Apr. Degrees conferred and formal commencement Apr. Summer session of 1 term from late Apr. to early Aug.

Characteristics of Freshmen: 95% of applicants accepted. 68% of accepted applicants enrolled.

98% of freshmen from Ohio. Freshmen from 13 states and 8 foreign countries.

Admission: Rolling admissions plan. For fall acceptance, apply no later than first week of trimester. Early acceptance available. *Requirements:* Open admissions for secondary school graduates; GED accepted. For science and engineering technology programs, recommend 2 units in algebra, 2 science (including physics), 3 English. *Entrance tests:* Institutional placement tests in English, mathematics, reading. For foreign students TOEFL or other English proficiency examination. *For transfer students:* from 4-year accredited institution 90 hours maximum transfer credit; from 2-year accredited institution 60 hours. Transfer credit also accepted for correspondence / extension students.

College credit for USAFI/DANTES and for extrainstitutional learning.

Tutoring available. Developmental courses offered in summer session and regular academic year; credit given in College of Business and Public Administration.

Degree Requirements: *For all associate degrees:* 60 credit hours. *For all baccalaureate degrees:* 120 credit hours. *For all degrees:* 2.0 GPA; 30 credits in residence; general education requirements.

Fulfillment of some degree requirements and exemption from some beginning courses possible by passing institutional examination, College Board CLEP, other standardized tests. *Grading system:* A–F; pass-fail; withdraw; (deadline after which pass-fail is appended to withdraw).

Distinctive Educational Programs: Flexible meeting places and schedules, including off-campus centers and weekend and evening classes. Accelerated degree programs. Cooperative diploma program in nursing education with Mt. Carmel School of Nursing. Special facilities for using telecommunications in the classroom. Individual studies program. Semester-at-Sea Program. *Other distinctive programs:* Prematriculation program in basic skills and mathematics. Opportunities for nontraditional students to enroll at Franklin while completing secondary school requirements.

ROTC: Army.

Degrees Conferred: 63 *associate*; 1,235 *baccalaureate*; 532 *master's*. Bachelor's degrees awarded in top five disciplines: business, management, marketing, and related support services 905; computer and information sciences 95; communication, journalism, and related programs 50; health professions and related clinical sciences 36; multidisciplinary studies 24.

Fees and Other Expenses: *Full-time tuition per academic year 2008–09:* contact the university for current information.

Financial Aid: Aid from institutionally generated funds is provided on the basis of academic merit, athletic ability, financial need, other criteria. Institution has a Program Participation Agreement with the U.S. Department of Education for eligible students to receive Pell Grants and, depending upon the agreement, other federal aid.

Financial aid to full-time, first-time undergraduate students: 73% received some form of financial aid. Average amount of aid received: federal grants $3,554; state/local grants $2,363; loans $5,704.

Departments and Teaching Staff: *Total instructional faculty:* 51.

Enrollment: Total enrollment 7,416.

Characteristics of Student Body: *Ethnic/racial makeup:* Black non-Hispanic: 21%; American Indian or Alaska Native: 1%; Asian or Pacific Islander: 2%; Hispanic: 35; White non-Hispanic: 86%; unknown: 4%.

International Students: 199 nonresident aliens enrolled fall 2008. No programs available to aid students whose native language is not English. No financial aid specifically designated for international students.

Student Life: No on-campus housing. *Special regulations:* Cars permitted without restrictions. *Student publications: The Almanac*, a student newspaper. *Surrounding community:* Columbus population 565,000. Served by mass transit bus system, airport 12 miles from campus.

Library Collections: 16,000 volumes. 8,000 microforms; 200 current periodicals. Online catalog. Students have access to online information retrieval services and the Internet.

Buildings and Grounds: Campus area 11 acres.

Chief Executive Officer: Dr. Paul J. Otte, President.

Address admission inquiries to Malinda Maloney, Director of New Student Admissions.

Hebrew Union College - Jewish Institute of Religion

3101 Clifton Avenue
Cincinnati, Ohio 45220
Tel: (513) 221-1875 **E-mail:** kkantee@huc.edu
Fax: (513) 221-0321 **Internet:** www.huc.edu

Institution Description: Hebrew Union College - Jewish Institute of Religion is a private institution affiliated with the Union for Reform Judaism. It has branch campuses in Los Angeles, New York, and Jerusalem. *Enrollment:* 292. *Degrees awarded:* First-professional (master of arts in Hebrew letters), master's, doctorate.

Member of Dayton-Miami Valley Consortium and Greater Cincinnati Consortium of Colleges and Universities.

Accreditation: *Regional:* NCA.

History: Established and chartered as Hebrew Union College, and offered first instruction at postsecondary level 1875; first rabbinic ordination 1883; merged with Jewish Institute of Religion (founded in New York 1922) and adopted present name 1950; Los Angeles branch opened 1954; Jerusalem campus opened 1963. *See* Michael Meyer, *Hebrew Union College-Jewish Institute of Religion at 100 Years*, ed. Samuel Karff (Cincinnati: Hebrew Union College Press, 1976) for further information.

Institutional Structure: *Governing board:* Board of Governors. Extrainstitutional representation: 42 members; institutional representation: 4 administrators; 10 alumni. 4 ex officio. All voting. *Composition of institution:* Administrators 11. Academic affairs headed by dean. Management/business/finances directed by executive vice president. Full-time instructional faculty 30. Academic governance body, Faculty Senate, meets an average of 10 times per year.

Calendar: Semesters. Academic year Sept. to May. Entering students admitted Sept. Jan. Degrees conferred and formal commencement May. No summer session.

Admission: Rolling admissions plan. *Requirements:* Baccalaureate from accredited college or university; personal interview, including psychological testing for Rabbinic School. *Entrance tests:* GRE.

Degree Requirements: *For first-professional degree:* 129 semester hours; GPA of pass or C, dependent on system chosen by student; entire program in residence, with first year spent in Jerusalem for intensive study in Hebrew; 3 rabbinic skills practicums; thesis; sermon delivery requirement; demonstrated proficiency in speech; 2 additional years of study for ordination as rabbi. *For all* *master's degrees:* 45 hours; 3.0 GPA; 1 year in residence; language requirement in Hebrew; thesis; distribution requirements. *For Ph.D. degree:* Mastery of well-defined area of study; 72 hours coursework; Hebrew, French, German; candidacy examinations; doctoral dissertation. *Grading system:* A–F.

Distinctive Educational Programs: Work-experience programs, including field, experience, in-service rabbinical training. Special facilities for using telecommunications in the classroom. Facilities and programs for independent research, including individual majors, tutorials. Hebrew Union College is affiliated with the University of Cincinnati, the Greater Cincinnati Consortium of Colleges and Universities, the University of Southern California, San Francisco State University, Washington University in St. Louis, New York University and the Skirball Department of Judaic Hebrew and Judaic Studies, the University of Pittsburgh, and the Hebrew University in Jerusalem. These associations provide variously for cross-registration privileges, the use of libraries and other facilities, joint course offerings and cooperative degrees.

Students of the New York School also have an opportunity to enroll in selected courses at General Theological Seminary and the Jewish Theological Seminary. Special inter-seminary workshops are also offered to all students with General Theological Seminary, Union Theological Seminary, St. Joseph's Catholic Seminary, St. Vladimir's Orthodox Seminary and the Jewish Theological Seminary of America. All first-year rabbinic students attend HUC-JIR in Jerusalem. Jerusalem School houses Nelson Glueck School of Biblical Archaeology.

Degrees Conferred: 8 *first-professional:* rabbinical; 8 *master's;* theology; 4 *doctorate;* theology.

Fees and Other Expenses: *Full-time tuition per academic year 2008–09:* contact the college for current tuition and other fees.

Financial Aid: Aid from institutionally generated funds is provided on the basis of financial need.

Departments and Teaching Staff: *Total instructional faculty:* 26. Student/faculty ratio: 5:1. Degrees held by full-time faculty: doctorate 100%.

Enrollment: Total enrollment 292.

International Students: 10 nonresident aliens enrolled fall 2008. No programs available to aid students whose native language is not English. No financial aid specifically designated for international students.

Student Life: On-campus residence halls house 10% of student body. Residence hall and eating facility constitute 100% of the space. *Special services:* Small membership charge for gym and indoor pool facility usage. *Student organizations:* Graduate Student Association; Graduate and Rabbinic Organization of Women; child-day care co-op. *Student publications: Kolbo,* a quarterly literary magazine. *Surrounding community:* Cincinnati population 1,750,000. Served by mass transit bus system; airport 20 miles from campus.

Publications: *Hebrew Union College Annual; American Jewish Archives Journal; HUC Press* (several and varied scholarly works).

Library Collections: 445,083 volumes. Online catalog. 2,200 current paper, microform, and electronic serial subscriptions. Computer work stations available.

Most important special collections include incunabula and sixteenth century Hebrew books; Hebrew manuscript collection; Solomon B. Freehof Responsa Collection.

Buildings and Grounds: Campus area 20 acres.

Chief Executive Officer: Rabbi David Ellenson, President.

Rabbinic students address admission inquiries to Kenneth Newton, Director, Rabbinical School Admissions.

Heidelberg College

310 East Market Street
Tiffin, Ohio 44883-2462

Tel: (419) 448-2000 **E-mail:** adminfo@heidelberg.edu
Fax: (419) 448-2124 **Internet:** www.heidelberg.edu

Institution Description: Heidelberg College is a private college affiliated with the United Church of Christ. *Enrollment:* 1,546. *Degrees awarded:* Baccalaureate, master's.

Member of East Central Colleges.

Accreditation: *Regional:* NCA. *Professional*: athletic training, music

History: Established and offered first instruction at postsecondary level 1850; chartered as Heidelberg College 1851; awarded first degree (baccalaureate) 1854; changed name to Heidelberg University 1890; readopted present name 1926. *See* E.I.F. Williams, *Heidelberg: Democratic Christian College* (Menasha, WI: The George Banta Publishing Co., 1952) for further information.

Institutional Structure: *Governing board:* Board of Trustees. Extrainstitutional representation: 35 trustees; institutional representation: 1 administrator; 9 alumni. All voting. *Composition of institution:* Administrators 46. Academic affairs headed by vice president for academic affairs and dean of the college, and associate dean. Financial affairs directed by vice president for administration. Full-time instructional faculty 55. Academic governance body, the faculty, meets an average of 9 times per year.

Calendar: Semesters. Academic year Aug. to May. Freshmen admitted Aug., Jan., May. Degrees conferred and formal commencement May. Summer session of 2 terms from May to July.

Characteristics of Freshmen: 70% of applicants admitted. 21% of admitted students enrolled full-time.

16% (72 students) submitted SAT scores; 92% (202 students) submitted ACT scores. *25th percentile*: SAT Critical Reading 440, SAT Math 430; ACT Composite 19, ACT English 17, ACT Math 18. *75th percentile*: SAT Critical Reading 580, SAT math 580; ACT Composite 24, ACT English 24, ACT Math 24.

58% of entering freshmen expected to graduate within 5 years. 90% of freshmen from Ohio. Freshmen from 13 states and 4 foreign countries.

Admission: Rolling admissions plan. For fall acceptance, apply as early as summer of previous year, but not later than July 31 of year of enrollment. Early acceptance available. *Requirements:* Either graduation from accredited secondary school normally in a college preparatory program; or GED. Audition required for music program. *Entrance tests:* College Board SAT or ACT composite. *For transfer students:* From 4-year accredited institution maximum transfer credit limited only by residence requirement; from 2-year accredited institution 60 semester hours; correspondence/extension students 9 hours; good standing at institution previously attended.

College credit and advanced placement for postsecondary-level work completed in secondary school and for USAFI-DANTES. College credit for extrainstitutional learning on basis of faculty assessment; portfolio assessment by Consortium Committee.

Tutoring available.

Degree Requirements: 120 credit hours; 2.0 GPA; last 2 terms in residence; 2 semester hours physical education activities; distribution requirements. Additional requirements for some music programs.

Fulfillment of some degree requirements and exemption from some beginning courses possible by passing College Board CLEP, AP, other standardized tests. *Grading system:* A–F; pass-fail; withdraw (carries time limit).

Distinctive Educational Programs: For adult (nontraditional) students: an on-campus Weekend College (classes on alternate weekends); an on-campus Nontraditional Studies Program through which adults may supplement weekend or daytime schedules with individual-arrangement courses as appropriate; and an off-campus Accelerated Degree-completion Program (evening classes in Maumee, Ohio). Dual-degree programs in engineering and in nursing with Case Western Reserve University, in environmental studies with Duke University (NC). Cooperative baccalaureate programs in medical technology and in nursing with area hospitals. Facilities and programs for independent research, including honors work, and for exceptional students, a comprehensive four-year thematically-driven, service inspired Honors Program. Institutionally sponsored junior year or semester at Heidelberg University, Germany. Study abroad in Africa, Europe, the Far East, and Latin America in cooperation with other universities. Biogeography field trips to the Caribbean during vacations. Summer field work in ecology of unusual habitats at various locations. Water quality internships and study programs at the Heidelberg Water Quality laboratory. Washington (DC) semester at American University. Environmental studies at 4 college-owned nature preserves. American Junior Year at Heidelberg University (Heidelberg, Germany).

Degrees Conferred: 246 *baccalaureate*; 60 *master's*. Bachelor's degrees awarded in top five disciplines: business/marketing 65; education 53; social sciences 21; psychology 20; biological/life sciences 17. Master's degrees awarded: business/marketing 13; education 41; psychology 6.

Fees and Other Expenses: *Full-time tuition per academic year 2008–09:* \$19,922 undergraduate; graduate study charged per semester hour (varies by program). *Books and supplies:* \$1,250. *Room and board per academic year:* \$8,138. *Other expenses:* \$1,000.

Financial Aid: Aid from institutionally generated funds is provided on the basis of academic merit, financial need, other criteria.Institution has a Program Participation Agreement with the U.S. Department of Education for eligible students to receive Pell Grants and, depending upon the agreement, other federal aid.

Financial aid to full-time, first-time undergraduate students: 34% received federal grants averaging \$3,368; 92% state/local grants averaging \$1,615; 46% institutional grants averaging \$6,067; 81% received loans averaging \$5,091.

Departments and Teaching Staff: *Total instructional faculty:* 159 (full-time 55, part-time 104). Student/faculty ratio: 14:1. Degrees held by full-time faculty: master's 25%, doctorate 73.5%, professional 1.5%. 50% hold terminal degrees.

Enrollment: Total enrollment 1,546. Undergraduate 1,398 (female 48%; male 52%).

Characteristics of Student Body: *Ethnic/racial makeup:* Black non-Hispanic: 7%; Hispanic 2%; White non-Hispanic: 81%; unknown: 6%; nonresident alien 3%. *Age distribution:* number under 18: 83; 18–19: 474; 20–21: 449; 22–24: 171; 25–29: 25; 30–34: 33; 35–39: 84; 40–49: 38; 50–64: 13.

HEIDELBERG COLLEGE—*cont'd*

International Students: 45 nonresident aliens enrolled fall 2008. Students from Europe, Africa. Programs available to aid students whose native language is not English: English as a Second Language Program. No financial aid specifically designated for international students.

Student Life: On-campus residence halls house 90% of student body. *Intercollegiate athletics:* male: baseball, basketball, cross-country, football, golf, soccer, tennis, track, wrestling; female: basketball, cross-country, soccer, softball, tennis, track, volleyball. *Special regulations:* Registered cars permitted. Residence hall visitation noon to midnight weekdays, noon to 2am weekends. *Special services:* Learning Center, medical services. *Student publications, radio, television: Aurora*, a yearbook; *Kilikilik*, a bimonthly newspaper; *Morpheus*, an annual literary magazine. Radio station WHEI broadcasts 84 hours per week, WHEI-TV telecasts an evening news program. Numerous honorary organizations in departments plus Omicron Delta Kappa, Alpha Lambda Delta, nine local societies and fraternities. *Governing Bodies:* College Program Board, College Council and Interresidence Hall Council. *Surrounding community:* Tiffin population 19,000. Cleveland, Columbus, Detroit, each 90 miles from campus, are nearest metropolitan areas. Served by airport 2 miles from campus.

Library Collections: 260,000 volumes. 120,000 government documents; 109,000 microforms; 8,500 audiovisual materials. Current periodical subscriptions: paper 460; via electronic access 5,000. 740 audio/videotapes; 32 DVD discs; 185 CD-ROMs. Online catalog. Computer work stations available. Students have access to online information retrieval services and the Internet.

Most important special holdings include Besse Collection of English and American letters (published letters); music recordings.

Buildings and Grounds: Campus area 110 acres.

Chief Executive Officer: Dr. Dominic Dottavio, President.

Address undergraduate admission inquiries to Lindsay Sooy, Director of Admissions.

Hiram College

113 Hilldale Hall
P.O. Box 67
Hiram, Ohio 44234-0067

Tel: (330) 569-3211 **E-mail:** admission@hiram.edu
Fax: (330) 569-5290 **Internet:** www.hiram.edu

Institution Description: Hiram College is a private, independent, nonprofit college affiliated with the Christian Church (Disciples of Christ). *Enrollment:* 1,360. *Degrees awarded:* Baccalaureate, master's.

Member of East Central College Consortium.

Accreditation: *Regional:* NCA. *Professional*: music, teacher education

History: Established as The Western Reserve Eclectic Institute, chartered and offered first instruction at postsecondary level 1850; adopted present name 1867; awarded first degree (baccalaureate) 1869. *See* Mary Bosworth Treudley, *Prelude to the Future* (New York, N.Y.: Association Press, 1950) for further information.

Institutional Structure: *Governing board:* Board of Trustees. Extrainstitutional representation: 34 trustees (6 are alumni); 16 honorary (non-voting trustees). Institutional representation: president of the college; 6 alumni. 19 ex officio. 34 voting. *Composition of institution:* Academic affairs headed by vice president and dean of the college. Management/business/finances directed by vice president for business affairs. Full-time instructional faculty 74. Academic governance body, the faculty, meets an average of 10 times per year.

Calendar: Semesters. Academic year Aug. to May. Freshmen admitted Aug. Degrees conferred and formal commencement May. Summer session of 1 term from May to Aug.

Characteristics of Freshmen: 1,513 applicants (675 female, 838 male). 75% of applicants admitted. 29% of applicants admitted and enrolled full-time.

50% (112 students) submitted SAT scores; 73% (163 students) submitted ACT scores. *25th percentile*: SAT Critical Reading 490, SAT Math 490; ACT Composite 20, ACT English 18, ACT Math 19. *75th percentile*: SAT Critical Reading 620, SAT Math 600; ACT Composite 25, ACT English 25, ACT Math 26.

57% of entering freshmen expected to graduate within 5 years. 96% of freshmen from Ohio. Freshmen from 23 states and 10 foreign countries.

Admission: Rolling admissions plan. For fall acceptance, apply as early as summer following junior year of secondary school, but not later than April 15 of year of enrollment. Students are notified of acceptance beginning Oct. 15. Early acceptance available. *Requirements:* Either graduation from accredited secondary school with 14 to 16 units which must include 4 English, 2 to 3 foreign language, 3 mathematics, 3 science, 2 to 3 social studies. Recommendation from secondary school counselor. *Entrance tests:* College Board SAT or ACT composite. *For transfer students:* 2.5 minimum GPA; 60 semester hours maximum transfer credit.

Tutoring available. Developmental/remedial courses offered during regular academic year; institutional credit given.

Degree Requirements: 120 semester hours; Freshman Colloquium, First Year Seminar; interdisciplinary requirement, distribution requirement, major.

Fulfillment of some degree requirements and exemption from some beginning courses possible by passing institutional examinations, College Board CLEP. *Grading system:* A–F; pass-fail; withdraw (deadline after which pass-fail is appended to withdraw); incomplete (carries time limit).

Distinctive Educational Programs: Modified semester system: each semester consists of a 12-week term (3 courses) and a 3-week intensive term (1 course). Dual-degree programs in engineering with Case Western Reserve University and Washington University (MO); in operations research and nursing with Case Western Reserve. Facilities for independent research including honors programs, individualized majors. Institutional sponsored study abroad (1 term) in Australia, Costa Rica, El Salvador, England, Germany, Guatemala, Ireland, Japan, Mexico, Russia, Spain, Turkey, Zimbabwe; also European study tours. Cooperative program with John Cabot University in Rome, Italy. Summer programs and academic year abroad available. Exchange programs with Bosphorus University (turkey) and Kansai University of Foreign Studies (Japan). Off-campus study in the U.S. including Washington Semester in cooperation with American University (DC); Gulf Coast Research Laboratory (MS); Shoals Marine Laboratory (ME). Hiram College (Biology) Field Station and Northwoods Field Station in Upper Peninsula of Michigan. *Other distinctive programs:* Weekend College for working adults.

Degrees Conferred: 232 *baccalaureate:* area and ethnic studies 1; biological/life sciences 17; business/marketing 79; communications/communication technologies 13; computer and information sciences 10; education 24; English 8; foreign languages and literature 1; health professions and related sciences 10; liberal arts/general studies 3; mathematics 1 natural resources/environmental science 5; philosophy/religion/theology 6; physical sciences 6; psychology 14; social sciences and history 45; trade and industry 12; visual and performing arts 1.

Fees and Other Expenses: *Full-time tuition per academic year 2008–09:* $25,610 undergraduate; graduate study charged per credit hour (contact the college for current rate). *Required fees:* $670. *Room and board per academic year:* $8,380. *Books and supplies:* $700. *Other expenses:* $2,295.

Financial Aid: Aid from institutionally generated funds is provided on the basis of academic merit, financial need.

Financial aid to full-time, first-time undergraduate students: 99% received some form of financial aid. Average amount of aid received: federal grants $4,596; state/local grants $1,892; institutional grants $13,561; loans $5,621.

Departments and Teaching Staff: *Total instructional faculty:* 119 (full-time 74, part-time 45). 96% of faculty hold the doctorate, first-professional, or other terminal degree. Student/faculty ratio: 11:1.

Enrollment: Total enrollment 1,260. Undergradaute 1,355 (female 54%, male 46%). Graduate 25 (full-time 4%). Undergraduate transfer-in students 82.

Characteristics of Student Body: *Ethnic/racial makeup:* Black non-Hispanic: 11%; American Indian or Alaska Native: 1%; Asian or Pacific Islander: 1%; Hispanic: 2%; White non-Hispanic: 86%; unknown 15%; nonresident alien 5%. *Age distribution:* number under 18: 2; 18–19: 245; 20–21: 372; 22–24: 196; 25–29: 56; 30–34: 46; 35–39: 34; 40–49: 106; 50–64: 24; 65 and over: 1.

International Students: 70 nonresident aliens enrolled fall 2008. Students from Europe, Asia, Central and South America, Africa. Programs available to aid students whose native language is not English: social, cultural, financial. English as a Second Language Program. Financial aid specifically designated for international students: scholarships available annually for undergraduate international students.

Student Life: On campus residence halls house 90% of student body. Residence halls for males constitute 35% of such space, for females 45%, for both sexes 20%. *Intercollegiate athletics:* male: baseball, basketball, football, soccer, tennis, track, swimming; female: basketball, soccer, softball, swimming, tennis, track, volleyball. *Special services:* Medical services; campus bus service to nearby cities, university library, and airport; Hiram Inn guest housing. *Student publications, radio: Advance*, a biweekly newspaper. Radio station WHRM broadcasts 35 hours per week. *Surrounding community:* Hiram population 1,330. Cleveland (OH), 45 miles from campus, is nearest metropolitan area. Served by airport 50 miles from campus.

Library Collections: 484,000 volumes. Current serial subscriptions: 920. 220,000 government documents; 5,000 compact discs. 8,100 audiovisual materials. Online catalog. Students have access to online information retrieval services and the Internet.

Most important special collections include President James A. Garfield Collection; Maurice Fox Historic Map Collection; Vachel Lindsay Collection; Disciples of Christ Collection.

Buildings and Grounds: Campus area 130 acres. Campus DVD available.

Chief Executive Officer: Dr. Thomas V. Chema, President.

Address admission inquiries to James F. Barrett, Executive Director of Admission.

John Carroll University

20700 North Park Boulevard
University Heights, Ohio 44118
Tel: (216) 397-1886 **E-mail:** admission@jcu.edu
Fax: (216) 397-4256 **Internet:** www.jcu.edu

Institution Description: John Carroll University is a private institution affiliated with the Society of Jesus, Roman Catholic Church. *Enrollment:* 3,826. *Degrees awarded:* Baccalaureate, master's. Certificates also awarded.

Accreditation: *Regional:* NCA. *Professional*: business, teacher education

History: Established as St. Ignatius College and offered first instruction at postsecondary level 1886; incorporated and awarded first degree (baccalaureate) 1890; changed name to Cleveland University, then adopted present name 1923.

Institutional Structure: *Governing board:* John Carroll University Board of Trustees. Representation: 36 directors (25% of whom must be Jesuits), including president of the college, president of the alumni association and 8 additional alumni; 38 voting. *Composition of institution:* Administrators 25. Academic affairs headed by academic vice president. Management/business/finances directed by vice president for business. Full-time instructional faculty 206. Academic governance body, Faculty Forum, meets an average of 6 times per year.

Calendar: Semesters. Academic year Aug. to May. Freshmen admitted Aug., Jan., June, July. Degrees conferred Jan., May, Aug. Formal commencement May. Summer session of 3 terms from May to Aug.

Characteristics of Freshmen: 3,481 applicants (female 1,687, male 1,794). 82% of applicants admitted. 22% of applicants admitted and enrolled.

43% (303 students) submitted SAT scores; 58% (426 students) submitted ACT scores. *25th percentile*: SAT Critical Reading 520, SAT Math 520; ACT Composite 21. *75th percentile*: SAT Critical Reading 600, SAT Math 630; ACT Composite 25.

75% of entering freshmen expected to graduate within 5 years. 75% freshmen from Ohio. Freshmen from 35 states and 22 foreign countries.

Admission: Rolling admissions plan. For fall acceptance, apply as early as Sept. 1 of previous year, but not later than Feb. 1 of year of enrollment. Early acceptance available. *Requirements:* Either graduation from accredited secondary school with 4 units English, 2 college preparatory mathematics. 1 laboratory science, 1 social studies; or GED. 7 additional units, including a classical or modern language, recommended. For business students, additional units in mathematics (including algebra) recommended. *Entrance tests:* College Board SAT or ACT composite. For foreign students TOEFL. *For transfer students:* 2.0 minimum GPA; from 4-year accredited institution 98 hours maximum transfer credit; from 2-year accredited institution 64 semester hours or 96 quarter hours.

College credit and advanced placement for postsecondary-level work completed in secondary school.

Tutoring available. Developmental courses offered in summer session and regular academic year; credit given for some courses.

Degree Requirements: 128 credit hours; 2.0 GPA; final 30 hours in residence; liberal arts core program; exit competency examinations-comprehensives in individual fields of study.

Fulfillment of some degree requirements and exemption from some beginning courses possible by passing College Board CLEP, AP, IB. *Grading system:* A–F; some + / -, some pass-fail; withdraw (carries time limit, deadline after which pass-fail is appended to withdraw).

Distinctive Educational Programs: Work-experience programs, including cooperative education. Dual-degree programs in engineering with Case Western Reserve University, University of Detroit Mercy (MI). Interdisciplinary programs, including business, economics-mathematics, environmental studies, aging studies, Catholic studies, biochemistry and molecular biology, political communication, international economics and modern language, neuroscience, perspectives on sex and gender, sociology and Spanish, urban studies. Facilities for independent research, including honors programs, tutorials. Study abroad in China, Italy, Japan. *Other distinctive programs:* Noncredit continuing education courses, workshops, and programs, including program for returning female students. Credit and noncredit courses, seminars, and lectures on American values, interreligious studies, and by CEO's of major Ohio corporations through privately endowed program.

ROTC: Army in cooperation with Cleveland State University.

Degrees Conferred: 677 *baccalaureate*; 239 *master's*. Bachelor's degrees awarded in top five disciplines: business/marketing 231; communications/journalism 97; social sciences 84; education 82; psychology 45. Master's degrees awarded in top five disciplines: education 55; business/marketing 52; psychology 34; philosophy and religious studies 10; English 8.

Fees and Other Expenses: *Full-time tuition per academic year 2008–09:* $28,090. *Required fees:* $290. *Room and board per academic year:* $7,934. *Books and supplies:* $1,200. *Other expenses:* $1,800.

Financial Aid: Aid from institutionally generated funds is provided on the basis of academic merit, financial need.

Financial aid to full-time, first-time undergraduate students: 99% of students received some form of financial aid.

Departments and Teaching Staff: *Total instructional faculty:* 365 (full-time 206, part-time 159). Total faculty with doctorate, first-professional, or other terminal degree: 276. Degrees held by full-time faculty: baccalaureate 2%, master's 9.8%, doctorate 90%. 90% hold terminal degrees.

Enrollment: Total enrollment 3,826. Undergraduate 3,117 (female 51%, male 49%). Graduate 709 (ful-time 32%). Undergraduate transfer-in students 114.

Characteristics of Student Body: *Ethnic/racial makeup:* Black non-Hispanic: 6%; Asian or Pacific Islander: 2%; Hispanic: 3%; White non-Hispanic: 79%. *Age distribution:* number under 18: 4; 18–19: 1,261; 20–21: 1,483; 22–24: 473; 25–29: 52; 30–34: 19; 35–39: 11; 40–49: 20; 50–64: 18; 65 and over: 5.

International Students: 33 nonresident aliens enrolled fall 2008. Students from Europe, Asia, Central and South America, Africa, Canada. No programs available to aid students whose native language is not English. No financial aid specifically designated for international students.

Student Life: On-campus residence halls house 60% of student body in single-sex or co-ed residences. *Intercollegiate athletics:* male: baseball, basketball, cross-country, football, golf, soccer, swimming, tennis, track, wrestling; female: basketball, golf, swimming, volleyball, soccer, softball, tennis, track, cross-country. *Special regulations:* Freshmen and sophomore resident students not allowed cars on campus. Quiet hours. Limited residence hall visitation. *Special services:* Learning Resources Center, medical services. *Student publications, radio: The Carroll News*, a weekly student newspaper; *The Carillon*, a yearbook; *The Carroll Quarterly*, a literary publication. Radio station WJCU broadcasts 164 hours per week. *Surrounding community:* University Heights population 15,500. Shaker Heights, 3 miles from campus, is nearest metropolitan area. Served by mass transit bus, trolley, and subway systems; airport 18 miles from campus; passenger rail service 10 miles from campus.

Library Collections: 741,000 volumes including bound books, serial backfiles, electronic documents, and government documents not in separate collections. Online catalog. Current serial subscriptions: 1,305 paper. 10 microform; 23,312 via electronic access. 7,840 recordings. Students have access to the Internet at no charge.

Most important holdings include G.K. Chesterton Collection (editions and manuscripts of the eminent Catholic writer).

Buildings and Grounds: Campus area 60 acres. Campus DVD available.

Chief Executive Officer: Rev. Robert L. Nichoff, S.J., President.

Address admission inquiries to Thomas P. Fanning, Director of Admissions.

Boler School of Business

Degree Programs Offered: *Baccalaureate, master's* in accounting, economics, finance, management, marketing, business logistics. Certificates also given.

Admission: 45 semester hours with minimum average grade of C.

Degree Requirements: *For all baccalaureate degrees:* 128 credit hours; 2.0 GPA; last 30 hours in residence; core business curriculum; comprehensive examinations in business and economics. *For master's degree:* 36 credit hours; 30 hours in residence; B. Average.

Distinctive Educational Programs: Certificate program in business administration.

Kent State University

Kent, Ohio 44242
Tel: (330) 672-3000 **E-mail:** kentadm@kent.edu
Fax: (330) 672-2499 **Internet:** www.kent.edu

Institution Description: Kent State University is a public institution with regional campuses at Ashtabula, East Liverpool, Genauga, Salem, Stark, Trumbull, and Tuscarawas. *Enrollment:* 22,944. *Degrees awarded:* Associate, baccalaureate, master's, doctorate.

Academic offerings subject to approval by statewide coordinating bodies.

Accreditation: *Regional:* NCA. *Professional*: architecture, art, aviation, business, dietetics, engineering, interior design, journalism, librarianship, music, nursing, occupational therapy, physical therapy, psychology internship, rehabilitation counseling, speech-language pathology

History: Established and chartered as Kent State Normal School, and offered first instruction at postsecondary level 1910; awarded first degree (baccalaureate) and changed name to Kent State Normal College 1915; changed name to Kent State College 1929; adopted present name 1935. *See* Phillip R. Shriver, *The*

KENT STATE UNIVERSITY—*cont'd*

Years of Youth (Kent: Kent State University Press, 1960) and William H. Hildebrand, Dean H. Keller, Anita D. Herington, eds., *A Book of Memories: Kent State University 1910–1992* (Kent: Kent State University Press, 1993) for further information.

Institutional Structure: *Governing board:* Kent State University Board of Trustees. Representation: 9 trustees. All voting. 2 student trustees (nonvoting). *Composition of institution:* Executive officers 8. Academic affairs headed by provost. Management/business/finances directed by vice president for administration. Full-time instructional faculty 856. Academic governance body, Faculty Senate, meets regularly. *Faculty representation:* Faculty served by collective bargaining unit affiliated with AAUP.

Calendar: Semesters. Academic year Aug. to Aug. Freshmen admitted Aug., Jan., June, July. Degrees conferred May, Aug., Dec. Formal commencements May, Dec. Summer session of 3 terms from June to Aug.

Characteristics of Freshmen: 12,364 applicants (female 7,843, male 4,821). 86% of applicants admitted. 38% of applicants admitted and enrolled full-time.

5% (185 students) submitted SAT scores; 83% (3,056 students) submitted ACT scores. *25th percentile*: SAT Critical Reading 450, SAT Math 450; ACT Composite 19, ACT English 18, ACT Math 18. *75th percentile*: SAT Critical Reading 570, SAT Math 570; ACT Composite 24, ACT English 24, ACT Math 24.

41% of entering freshmen expected to graduate within 5 years. 87% of freshmen from Ohio. Freshmen from 31 states and 19 foreign countries.

Admission: Rolling admissions plan. For fall acceptance, apply no later than March 15. Early acceptance available. *Requirements:* Recommended GPA 2.5; 16 units of college preparatory curriculum completed and ACT composite score of 21 or better or combined SAT score of 980 or better. Additional requirements for some programs. *Entrance tests:* College Board SAT or ACT composite, *For transfer students:* 2.0 minimum GPA in all previous nonremedial college work; from 4-year and 2-year accredited institutions maximum transfer credit limited only by residence requirement; correspondence/extension students 12 hours.

Advanced placement for postsecondary-level work completed in secondary school. For extrainstitutional learning, college credit and advanced placement on basis of portfolio assessment.

Tutoring available. Developmental courses offered in summer session and regular academic year; credit given.

Degree Requirements: 121 credit hours; 2.0 GPA; last 32 hours in residence. Additional requirements for some programs. Fulfillment of some degree requirements and exemption from some beginning courses possible by passing College Board CLEP, AP, other standardized tests. *Grading system:* A–F; pass-fail; withdraw (carries time limit); satisfactory-unsatisfactory; incomplete; in progress.

Distinctive Educational Programs: Honors College. Center for International and Comparative Programs: Kent in Florence (art history, political science, language, graphic arts); Geneva Semester (international business, economics, political science, French); Spring Semester in Mexico (anthropology, Spanish, sociology, history). Florence Architecture Program; Florence Music Program; Lyman L. Lemnitzer Center for NATO and European Union Studies; Center for Applied Conflict Management; Center for the Study of World Musics; Blossom Festival School (art, music, theatre).

ROTC: Army, Air Force.

Degrees Conferred: 3,841 *Baccalaureate*; 1,198 *master's*; 177 *master's*. Bachelor's degrees awarded in top five disciplines: business/marketing 775; education 466; health professions and related clinical sciences 348; visual and performing arts 266; psychology 221. Master's degrees awarded in top five disciplines: education 413; library science 262; business/marketing 171; psychology 75; health professions 68. Doctorates awarded: biological/life sciences 8; business/marketing 3; communications/journalism 6; computer and information sciences 6; education 42; English 2; health professions and related sciences 4; history 2; physical sciences 17; psychology 15; social sciences 10; visual and performing arts 6.

Fees and Other Expenses: *Full-time tuition per academic year 2008–09:* undergraduate resident $8,430, nonresident $15,862; contact the university for current graduate tuition/fees that may vary by program. *Room and board per academic year:* $7,500. *Books and supplies:* $1,200. *Other expenses:* $4,270.

Financial Aid: Aid from institutionally generated funds is provided on the basis of academic merit, financial need, athletic ability.

Financial aid to full-time, first-time undergraduate students: 87% of students received some form of financial aid.

Departments and Teaching Staff: *Total instructional faculty:* 1,512 (full=-time 856, part-time 656). Total faculty with doctorate, first-professional, or other terminal degree: 664. Student/faculty ratio: 20:1. Degrees held by full-time faculty: 77% hold terminal degrees.

Enrollment: Total enrollment 22,944. Undergraduate 18,156 (female 59%, male 41%). Graduate 4,792. Undergraduate transfer-in students 870.

Characteristics of Student Body: *Ethnic/racial makeup:* Black non-Hispanic: 9%; Asian or Pacific Islander: 2%; Hispanic: 2%; White non-Hispanic: 82%; unknown 4%; nonresident alien 2%. *Age distribution:* number under 18 191; 18–19: 6,483; 20–21: 6,009; 22–24: 3,773; 25–29: 1,233; 30–34: 493; 35–39: 278; 40–49: 439; 50–64: 154; 65 and over: 4.

International Students: 458 nonresident aliens enrolled fall 2008. Students from Europe, Asia, Central and South America, Africa, Canada, Australia. Programs available to aid students whose native language is not English: English as a Second Language Program. No financial aid specifically designated for international students.

Student Life: On-campus residence halls house 28% of student body. Residence halls for males constitute 26% of such space, for females 36%, for both sexes 38%. 3% of males join and 1% live in fraternity housing; 3% of females join and 2% live in sorority housing. 12% of married students request institutional housing; 10% are so housed. *Intercollegiate athletics:* male: baseball, basketball, football, golf, indoor/outdoor track, wrestling; females: basketball, cross-country, field hockey, gymnastics, softball, indoor/outdoor track, volleyball. *Special regulations:* Cars permitted in designated areas only. Quiet hours. Residence hall visitation from 10am to midnight; 24-hour visitation for upper division and graduate students. *Special services:* Learning Resources Center, medical services, bus service for campus and surrounding communities. *Student publications, radio: Chestnut Burr*, a yearbook; *Daily Kent Stater* a newspaper published 4 times per week; *Infinite Dreams*, a biannual science fiction magazine; *Jabberwocky*, a monthly newsletter; *New Kent Quarterly*, a literary magazine; *Spectrum*, a weekly newspaper. Radio station WKSU broadcasts 168 hours per week; associated with National Public Radio. *Surrounding community:* Kent population 26,500. Cleveland, 35 miles from campus, is nearest metropolitan area. Served by a campus-community bus system; airport 20 miles from campus; passenger rail service 30 miles from campus.

Publications: *Civil War History* (quarterly) first published in 1954; *Extrapolation* (quarterly) first published 1958; publication assumed by Kent State 1979; *Mid-Continental Journal of Archeology* (biannually) first published 1976. University press published 22 titles in 1996.

Library Collections: 3,989,000 volumes including bound books, serial backfiles, electronic documents, and government documents not in separate collections. Online catalog. Current serial subscriptions: 13,273 paper; 1,306,967 microform; 41,260 via electronic access. 15,737 recordings. Students have access to the Internet at no charge.

Most important special holdings include Robert L. Baumgartner, Jr., Memorial Collection of Contemporary Poetry; B. George Ulizio Collection of English and American Literature; Kent State University May 4th Archives.

Buildings and Grounds: Campus area 812 acres. Campus DVD available.

Chief Executive Officer: Dr. Lester A. Lefton, President.

Undergraduates address admission inquiries to Nancy Dellovachia, Director of Admissions; graduate inquiries to Dr. John L. West, Dean for Research and Graduate Studies.

College of Arts and Sciences

Degree Programs Offered: *Baccalaureate* in various fields; *master's, doctorate* in various fields.

Distinctive Educational Programs: Interdisciplinary programs in African studies, Asian studies, British studies, comparative literature, German studies, Hellenic studies, Jewish studies, Lithuanian studies, religious studies, Romanian studies, Russian studies, women's studies.

College of Business Administration

Degree Programs Offered: *Baccalaureate, master's, doctorate.*
Distinctive Educational Programs: External degree program.

College of Education

Degree Programs Offered: *Baccalaureate, master's, doctorate.* Specialist certificates also given.

College of Fine and Professional Arts

Degree Programs Offered: *Baccalaureate* in various fields; *master's, doctorate* in various fields.

Distinctive Educational Programs: Summer study program in art, drama, music with university faculty and professional artists.

School of Nursing

Degree Programs Offered: *Baccalaureate* in various fields; *master's* in various fields.

Kenyon College

Gambier, Ohio 43022-9623
Tel: (740) 427-5000 **E-mail:** admissions@kenyon.edu
Fax: (740) 427-5770 **Internet:** www.kenyon.edu

Institution Description: Kenyon College is a private, independent, nonprofit college affiliated with the Protestant Episcopal Church. *Enrollment:* 1,644. *Degrees awarded:* Baccalaureate.

Member of Great Lakes Colleges Association (GLCA).

Accreditation: *Regional:* NCA.

History: Established and chartered as the Theological Seminary of the Protestant Episcopal Church in the Diocese of Ohio and offered first instruction at postsecondary level 1824; the first degree (baccalaureate) awarded 1829; present name adopted 1872; women admitted 1969. *See* George Franklin Smythe, *Kenyon College: Its First Century* (New Haven, CT: Yale University Press, 1924) for further information.

Institutional Structure: *Governing board:* Board of Trustees of Kenyon College. Extrainstitutional representation: 23 trustees, 8 trustees emeriti; 1 honorary trustee, 2 church officials; institutional representation: *Composition of institution:* Administrators 197. Academic affairs headed by provost. Management/business/finances directed by vice president for finance. Full-time instructional faculty 153. Academic governance body, the Faculty of Kenyon College, meets an average of 9 times per year.

Calendar: Semesters. Academic year Aug. to May. Freshmen admitted Sept. Degrees conferred May, Jan. Formal commencement May. No summer session.

Characteristics of Freshmen: 4,510 applicants (female 2,581, male 1,929). 33% of applicants admitted. 32% of applicants admitted and enrolled full-time.

83% (280 students) submitted SAT scores; 35% (160 students) submitted ACT scores. *25th percentile*: SAT Critical Reading 620, SAT Math 610; ACT Composite 27, ACT English 28, ACT Math 26. *75th percentile*: SAT Critical Reading 730, SAT Math 7001 ACT Composite 32, ACT English 24, ACT Math 31. 22 National Merit Scholars.

87% of entering freshmen expected to graduate within 5 years. 20% of freshmen from Ohio. Freshmen from 18 states and 10 foreign countries.

Admission: For fall acceptance, apply as early as Sept. 1 of previous year, but not later than Feb. 1. Students are notified of acceptance Apr. Two early decision programs: Option 1 - apply by Nov, 15 for Dec. 15 notification; Option 2 - apply by Nov. 15 for Feb. 1 notification; must limit application to Kenyon. Early acceptance available. *Requirements:* Either graduation from accredited secondary school with a minimum of 15 academic units which must include 4 English, 3 foreign language, 3 mathematics, 3 laboratory science, 1 social studies, 2 academic electives; or GED. 1 additional unit mathematics recommended. *Entrance tests:* College Board SAT or ACT composite. *For transfer students:* 64 hours maximum transfer credit.

College credit and advanced placement for postsecondary level work completed in secondary school.

Degree Requirements: 16 unit hours; 2.0 GPA; 2 years including final year in residence; senior exercise; distribution requirements.

Fulfillment of some degree requirements possible by passing College Board APP. *Grading system:* A–F; pass-fail; withdraw (deadline after which pass-fail is appended to withdraw).

Distinctive Educational Programs: Dual-degree programs in engineering with Case Western Reserve University, Rensselaer Polytechnic Institute (NY), Washington University (MO). Five-year double-degree program. Special facilities for using telecommunications in the classroom. Interdisciplinary programs, including student-planned synoptic major and Integrated Program in Humane Studies. Facilities and programs for independent research, including honors programs, individual majors, tutorials. Study abroad in England through Kenyon program at University of Exeter. Other off-campus study abroad available through GLCA in varying locations including Africa, Austria, British Isles, Colombia, Costa Rica, Denmark, France, Greece, Hong Kong, India, Italy, Japan, Spain, Yugoslavia. Also available through study abroad programs administered by the Institute of European Studies, the Associated Colleges of the Midwest, and programs sponsored by GLCA include the Philadelphia (PA) Urban Semester, Newberry Library Humanities Program in Chicago (IL), and the Oak Ridge (TN) National Laboratory Science Semester.

Degrees Conferred: 429 *baccalaureate*. Bachelor's degrees awarded in top five disciplines: social sciences 86; education 80; interdisciplinary studies 49; visual and performing arts 38; biological/life sciences 35.

Fees and Other Expenses: *Full-time tuition per academic year 2008–09:* $40,240. *Required fees:* $1,060. *Room and board per academic year:* $6,590. *Books and supplies* $1,300. *Other expenses:* $1,130.

Financial Aid: Aid from institutionally generated funds is provided on the basis of academic merit, financial need.

Financial aid to full-time, first-time undergraduate students: 67% received some form of financial aid.

Departments and Teaching Staff: *Total instructional faculty:* 182 (full-time153, part-time 29). Total faculty with doctorate, first-professional, or other terminal degree: 157. Student/faculty ratio: 10:1. Degrees held by full-time faculty: doctorate 88%, master's 71%, baccalaureate 100%. 96% hold terminal degrees.

Enrollment: Total enrollment 1,644 (undergraduate). Transfer-in student 6.

Characteristics of Student Body: *Ethnic/racial makeup:* Black non-Hispanic: 4%; American Indian or Alaska Native: 1%; Asian or Pacific Islander: 5%; Hispanic: 3%; White non-Hispanic: 81%; unknown: 2%; nonresident alien 4%. *Age distribution:* number under 18: 3; 18–19: 670; 20–21: 694; 22–24: 192; 25–29: 2.

International Students: 64 nonresident aliens enrolled fall 2008. Students from Europe, Asia, Central and South America, Africa, Canada. Programs available to aid students whose native language is not English: social, cultural. No financial aid specifically designated for international students.

Student Life: All students live in on-campus residence halls and apartments. Single-sex and coed living options are available. *Intercollegiate athletics:* male: baseball, basketball, cross-country, football, golf, lacrosse, soccer, swimming, tennis, track; female: basketball, cross-country, field hockey, lacrosse, swimming, tennis, track, volleyball. *Special regulations:* Cars permitted if registered with college and parked in specified lots. *Special services:* Medical services, van service between campus and Mount Vernon, van service between campus and Columbus on designated Saturdays, career development center, counseling center. *Student publications, radio, television: Docemus*, nonfiction journal; *Forewords*, annual magazine featuring art and literary works by freshmen; *The Kenyon Journal*, forum on cultural and political issues; *The Kenyon Collegian*, a weekly newspaper; *The Kenyon Observer*, monthly journal of news and opinion; *HIKA*, an undergraduate literary publication; *Kenyon Visuals*, a magazine featuring student visual art work; *The Messenger*, a magazine with focus on world and campus issues; *Reveille*, college yearbook published annually; *Worldly Wisdom*, a weekly review of world news. Radio station WKCO is the alternative educational and entertainment medium of greater Gambier. KCTV produces a weekly, half-hour news program with a focus on Kenyon news and issues. *Surrounding community:* Gambier population 2,500. Columbus, 55 miles from Gambier, is nearest metropolitan area.

Publications: *Kenyon Review* (quarterly) first published 1939, *Psychological Record* (quarterly) first published 1937.

Library Collections: 430,500 volumes. Online catalog. 1,796 current serial subscriptions plus electronic access to 6,778. 173,800 recordings; 2,700 compact discs, 1,731 CD-ROMS. Computer work stations available. Students have access to the Internet and online information retrieval services.

Most important special holdings include the papers of poet James Wright (Kenyon '52); first and variant editions of the works of William Butler Yeats; books on and works from fine printing presses and typeface designers.

Buildings and Grounds: Campus area 800 acres.

Chief Executive Officer: Dr. S. Georgia Nugent, President.

Address admission inquiries to Jennifer Britz, Dean of Admissions.

Lake Erie College

391 West Washington Street
Painesville, Ohio 44077
Tel: (440) 375-7000 **E-mail:** admissions@lec.edu
Fax: (440) 375-7005 **Internet:** www.lec.edu

Institution Description: Lake Erie College is a private, independent, nonprofit, coeducational college for residential and non-residential students, the latter of whom are mostly adults attending part-time. *Enrollment:* 1,051. *Degrees awarded:* Baccalaureate, master's.

Accreditation: *Regional:* NCA. *Professional*: business, law

History: Established as Lake Erie Seminary and chartered in 1856; offered first instruction at postsecondary level 1898; adopted present name 1908; awarded first degree (baccalaureate) 1910; became coeducational 1985.

Institutional Structure: *Governing board:* Board of Trustees. Extrainstitutional representation: 35 trustees, including 3 alumni; institutional representation: president of the college. 1 ex officio. 34 voting. *Composition of institution:* Administrators 5. Academic affairs headed by dean of the college. Management/business/finances directed by business manager. Full-time instructional faculty 59. Academic governance body, Lake Erie College Faculty, meets an average of 10 times per year.

Calendar: Semesters. Academic year Aug. to May. Degrees awarded Aug., Dec., May. Formal commencement and degrees conferred May.

Characteristics of Freshmen: 987 applicants (female 513, male 474). 36% of applicants admitted. 24% of applicants admitted and enrolled full-time.

LAKE ERIE COLLEGE—*cont'd*

38% (50 students) submitted SAT scores; 76% (100 students) submitted ACT scores. *25th percentile*: SAT Critical Reading 510, SAT Math 500; ACT Composite 18, ACT English 165, ACT Math 17. *75th percentile*: SAT Critical Reading 510, SAT Math 510; ACT Composite 23, ACT English 22, ACT Math 23.

40% of entering freshmen expected to graduate within 5 years. 65% of freshmen from Ohio. Freshmen from 23 states and 1 foreign country.

Admission: Rolling admissions plan. Students may apply any time after the completion of junior year in high school; no admission deadline as candidates are evaluated as they apply. Notification of a decision on admission is usually sent approximately two weeks after the file is complete. *Requirements:* College preparatory program of 7 academic units in English, the sciences, social sciences, and mathematics. Foreign language background is recommended but not required; GED acceptable. Standardized test scores required. An interview with an admissions counselor is recommended. Minimum GPA 2.0, but prefer cumulative GPA 2.5 or higher. *For transfer students:* 2.0 minimum GPA; 96 semester hours maximum transfer credit.

College credit and advanced placement for postsecondary-level work completed in secondary school. College credit for extrainstitutional learning on basis of portfolio and faculty assessments; personal interview.

Degree Requirements: 128 semester hours; 2.0 GPA or better; last 32 hours in residence; general education requirements; completion of requirements for a major field of study.

Fulfillment of some degree requirements possible by passing College Board APP. *Grading system:* A–F; pass-fail; withdraw (deadline after which pass-fail is appended to withdraw).

Distinctive Educational Programs: *For undergraduates:* Work-experience programs. Baccalaureates in equine studies (two majors: facility management and teacher/trainer). Several concentrations available within the equine studies department. Facilities and programs for independent research, including individual majors, tutorials, and alternative plan of study combining independent, classroom, on- and off-campus study. Study abroad at Lake Erie College centers. Internships in community, elsewhere in U.S., and abroad. Evening classes. Management seminars for community members.

Degrees Conferred: 152 *baccalaureate*; 56 *master's*. Bachelor's degrees awarded in top five disciplines: education 48; business/marketing 30; biological/life sciences 16; agriculture 13; interdisciplinary studies 13. Master's degrees awarded: business/marketing 32; education 24.

Fees and Other Expenses: *Full-time tuition per academic year 2008–09:* $25,220 undergraduate; graduate tuition charged per credit hour (contact the college for current rate). *Required fees:* $954. *Room and board per academic year:* $7,850. *Books and supplies:* $900. *Other expenses:* $3,902.

Financial Aid: Aid from institutionally generated funds is provided on the basis of academic merit, financial need.

Financial aid to full-time, first-time undergraduate students: 100% of student body received some form of financial aid.

Departments and Teaching Staff: Total faculty with doctorate, first-professional, or other terminal degree: 39. Student/faculty ratio: 11:1. Degrees held by full-time faculty: master's 20%, doctorate 77%, professional 3%. 80% hold terminal degrees.

Enrollment: Total enrollment 1,051. Undergraduate 854 (female 56%, male 44%). Graduate 217 (full-time 16%). Undergraduate transfer-in students 60.

Characteristics of Student Body: *Ethnic/racial makeup:* Black non-Hispanic: 8%; Hispanic: 1%; White non-Hispanic: 77%, unknown: 13%; nonresident alien 1%. *Age distribution:* number under 18: 21; 18–19: 206; 20–21: 138; 22–24: 146; 25–29: 56; 30–34: 22; 35–39: 19; 40–49: 45; 50–64: 10.

International Students: 11 nonresident aliens enrolled fall 2008. Students form Europe, Canada. No programs available to aid students whose native language is not English. No financial aid specifically designated for international students.

Student Life: On-campus residence halls house 50% of the full-time student body. 50% of residence halls are for females; 25% males; 25% co-ed. *Intercollegiate athletics:* male: baseball, basketball, cross-country, golf, soccer; female: softball, basketball, cross-country, soccer, volleyball. *Special regulations:* Registered cars permitted without restrictions. *Special services:* Learning Resources Center. *Student publications: The Tower*, a monthly newspaper; *Tiber*, a yearbook. *Surrounding community:* Painesville population approximately 15,000. Cleveland, 30 miles from campus, is nearest metropolitan area. Served by airport 42 miles from campus.

Library Collections: 81,121 volumes. Current periodical subscriptions: paper 259; 8,054 via electronic access. 767 recordings; 161 DVD discs; 6 CD-ROMs. Computer work stations avaialble. Students have access to the Internet and online information retrieval services.

Most important special collection: Thomas Harvey Collection (library of the 19th-century American grammarian).

Buildings and Grounds: Campus area 57 acres.

Chief Executive Officer: Dr. Michael T. Victor, President.

Address admission inquiries to Eric Felver, Director of Admissions.

Laura and Alvin Siegal College of Judaic Studies

26500 Shaker Boulevard
Beachwood, Ohio 44122
Tel: (216) 464-4050 **E-mail:** admissions@siegalcollege.edu
Fax: (216) 464-5827 **Internet:** www.siegalcollege.edu

Institution Description: Laura and Alvin Siegal College of Judaic Studies, formerly known as Cleveland College of Jewish Studies, is an independent, coeducational institution. *Enrollment:* 135. *Degrees awarded:* Baccalaureate, master's.

Accreditation: *Regional:* NCA.

History: Founded 1963.

Calendar: Semesters. Academic year July to June.

Characteristics of Freshmen: Average secondary school rank of freshmen to 10%. 75% of applicants accepted. 75% of accepted applicants enrolled

10% of entering freshmen expected to graduate within 5 years. 100% of freshmen from Ohio.

Admission: Rolling admissions. *Requirements:* Personal statement; high school transcript; two letters of recommendation.

Degree Requirements: *For all baccalaureate degrees:* 120 semester hours; 3 years of Hebrew or proven proficiency.

Degrees Conferred: 1 *baccalaureate:* theology; 14 *master's:* theology.

Fees and Other Expenses: *Full-time tuition per academic year 2008–09:* contacat the college for current information. No on-campus housing.

Financial Aid: Aid from institutionally generated funds is provided on the basis of academic merit, athletic ability, criteria. Institution has a Program Participation Agreement with the U.S. Department of Education for eligible students to receive Pell Grants and, depending upon the agreement, other federal aid.

Departments and Teaching Staff: *Total instructional faculty:* 31 (11 full-time, 30 part-time). Total faculty with doctorate, first-professional, or other terminal degree: 15. Student/faculty ratio: 10:1.Degrees held by full-time faculty: doctorate 80%, master's 100%, baccalaureate 100%

Enrollment: Total enrollment: 135.

Characteristics of Student Body: *Ethnic/racial makeup:* number of White non-Hispanic 1, unknown 134.

International Students: No programs available to aid students whose native language is not English. No financial aid specifically designated for international students.

Library Collections: 35,000 volumes including bound books, serial backfiles, electronic documents, and govern documents not in separate collections. Online and card catalogs. Current serial subscriptions: paper, microform, electronic. Computer work stations available. Students have access to the Internet at no charge.

Buildings and Grounds: Campus area 2 acres.

Chief Executive Officer: Dr. David S. Ariel, President.

Address admission inquiries to Ruth Kronick, Director of Student Services.

Lourdes College

6832 Convent Boulevard
Sylvania, Ohio 43560
Tel: (419) 885-3211 **E-mail:** lcadmits@lourdes.edu
Fax: (419) 882-3987 **Internet:** www.lourdes.edu

Institution Description: Lourdes College is a liberal arts college founded and conducted by the Sisters of St. Francis. *Enrollment:* 2,062. *Degrees awarded:* Associate, baccalaureate.

Accreditation: *Regional:* NCA. *Professional:* nursing, social work

History: Founded 1958; Life-long Learning Center established 1978.

Calendar: Semesters. Academic year Aug. to May. Freshmen admitted May, Aug., Jan. Degrees conferred and formal commencement May.

Characteristics of Freshmen: 84% of applicants admitted. 40% of applicants admitted and enrolled.

4 (5 students) submitted SAT scores; 77% (96 students) submitted ACT scores. *25th percentile*: SAT Critical Reading 280, SAT Math 280; ACT Composite 17, ACT English 16,ACT Math 16. *75th percentile*: SAT Critical Reading 560, SAT Math 600; ACT Composite 21, ACT English 21, ACT Math 20.

25% of entering freshmen expected to graduate within 5 years. 90% of freshmen from Ohio. Freshmen from 2 states and 1 foreign country.

Admission: Rolling admissions plan. *Requirements:* Graduation from secondary school or GED. Regular admission granted to students with a minimum high school GPA of 2.0 and a minimum ACT score of 19 or SAT 900 and to transfer students who have earned a minimum of 12 semester hours with a minimum 2.0 GPA average. Special admission may be granted at the discretion of the Director of Admissions for students who do not meet the minimum requirements.

Degree Requirements: Completion of prescribed curriculum.

Distinctive Educational Programs: The Bachelor of Individualized Studies option allows students to create a baccalaureate degree tailored to their personal and career goals.

ROTC: Air Force in cooperation with Bowling Green State University; Army in cooperation with University of Toledo.

Degrees Conferred: 33 *associate*; 247 *baccalaureate*: 33 *master's*. Bachelor's degrees awarded in top five disciplines: business/marketing 51; health professions and related clinical sciences 44; interdisciplinary studies 28; education 24; psychology 14. Master's degrees awarded: business/marketing 16; education 7.

Fees and Other Expenses: *Full-time tuition per academic year 2008–09:* $11,784 undergraduate; graduate study charged per credit hour. *Required fees:* $1,300. *Books and supplies:* $1,008. *Other expenses:* $4,978.

Financial Aid: Aid from institutionally generated funds is provided on the basis of academic merit, financial need.

Departments and Teaching Staff: *Total instructional faculty:* 178. Total faculty with doctorate, first-professional, or other terminal degree: 49. Student/faculty ratio: 12:1.

Enrollment: *Total enrollment:* 2,066. Undergraduate 1,840 (female 81%, male 19%). Graduate 226 (full-time 84%). Undergraduate transfer-in student 305.

Characteristics of Student Body: *Ethnic/racial makeup:* Black non-Hispanic: 15%; Asian or Pacific Islander: 1%; Hispanic: 4%; White non-Hispanic: 74%; unknown: 6%. *Age distribution:* number under 18: 8; 18–19: 90; 20–21: 112; 22–24: 234; 25–29: 250; 30–34: 139; 35–39: 137; 40–49: 202; 50–64: 74; 65 and over: 2.

International Students: 3 nonresident aliens enrolled fall 2008. No programs available to aid students whose native language is not English. No financial aid designated for international students.

Library Collections: 59,500 volumes. Current serial subscriptions: 206. 2,611 recordings. Computer work stations available. Students have access to online information retrieval services and the Internet.

Most important special holdings include Franciscan books.

Buildings and Grounds: Campus area 90 acres.

Chief Executive Officer: Dr. Robert Helmer, President.

Address admission inquiries to Amy Morgen, Director of Admissions.

Malone College

515 25th Street, N.W.
Canton, Ohio 44709-3897

Tel: (330) 471-8100 **E-mail:** admissions@malone.malone.edu
Fax: (330) 471-8478 **Internet:** www.malone.edu

Institution Description: Malone College is a private Christian college for affiliated with the Evangelical Friends Church-Eastern Region. *Enrollment:* 2,296. *Degrees awarded:* Baccalaureate, master's.

Member of Christian College Consortium and the Council for Christian Colleges and Universities.

Accreditation: *Regional:* NCA. *Professional*: business, nursing, social work

History: Established and incorporated as Christian Workers Training School and offered first instruction at postsecondary level 1892; first diploma awarded 1895; changed name to Friends Bible Institute and Training School 1899, Cleveland Bible Institute 1911, Cleveland Bible College 1937; adopted present name and offered first instruction at 4-year college level 1957; awarded first degree (baccalaureate) 1961, (master's) 1992. *See* Byron L. Osborne, *The Malone Story* (Newton, KS: United Printing, Inc., 1970) for further information.

Institutional Structure: *Governing board:* Board of Trustees. Extrainstitutional representation: 17 church representatives, 16 trustees; institutional representation: 1 administrator, 1 alumnus, 3 ex officio. 33 voting. *Composition of institution:* Administrators 6. Academic affairs headed by provost. Management/business/finances directed by executive vice president for finance-administration. Full-time instructional faculty 101. Academic governance body, Deans Council, meets 8 times per year. Faculty Senate meets 25 times per year.

Calendar: Semesters. Academic year Aug. to May. Freshmen admitted on a rolling basis. Degrees conferred and formal commencement May and Aug. Summer sessions from May to Aug.

Characteristics of Freshmen: 1,070 applicants (658 female, 412 male). 81% of applicants admitted. 40% of admitted applicants enrolled full-time.

26% (78 students) submitted SAT scores; 66% (298 students) submitted ACT scores. *25th percentile*: SAT Critical Reading 460, SAT Math 460; ACT Composite 20, ACT English 20, ACT Math 18. *75th percentile*: SAT Critical Reading 590, SAT Math 580; ACT Composite 25, ACT English 25, ACT Math 24.

58% of entering freshmen expected to graduate within 5 years. 85% of freshmen from Ohio. Freshmen from 15 states and 5 foreign countries.

Admission: Rolling admissions plan. *Requirements:* Graduation from accredited secondary school or GED. Core classes recommended. Specific recommendations for some programs. Minimum 2.5 GPA. *Entrance tests:* ACT preferred; SAT accepted. *For transfer students:* 2.0 minimum GPA, complete 30 semester hours at Malone.

Advanced placement classes accepted for college credit. Malone participates in Post-Secondary Enrollment. Free tutoring available.

Degree Requirements: *For most baccalaureate degrees:* 2.0 overall GPA; 2.25 GPA in major (exceptions: nursing 2.25 overall and in major, teacher education 2.75 overall and in major). *For all baccalaureate degrees:* 124 credit hours, 30 hours of which must be in residence. College Assessment of Academic Proficiency (CAAP) required for sophomores.

Academic credit by examination available through CLEP, AP and departmental examinations. *Grading system:* A–F; withdraw (carries time limit); incomplete; credit/no-credit; L (satisfactory progress for long-term course assignment).

Distinctive Educational Programs: American Studies Program, Washington (DC). Institute for Family Studies, Colorado Springs (CO). Los Angeles Film Studies Center, Los Angeles (CA). AuSable Institute for Environmental Studies, Mancelona (MI). Christian College Consortium Visitor Program. Cooperative Education. Credit for Prior Learning. Free Enterprise Program with Greater Canton Chamber of Commerce. International Study Opportunities in Australia, China, Costa Rica, Ecuador, Egypt, Guatemala, Kenya, Mexico, Russia, Spain, Uganda.

Degrees Conferred: 477 *baccalaureate:* biological sciences 6; business and management 251; communications 31; computer and information sciences 7; education 91; English 2; foreign languages 2; health professions 49; liberal arts 17; mathematics 5; parks and recreation 5; philosophy/religion 28; physical sciences 5; protective services 5; psychology 16; social sciences 7; visual and performing arts 7. Master's degrees awarded: 87.

Fees and Other Expenses: *Full-time tuition per academic year 2008–09:* contact the college for current information.

Financial Aid: Aid from institutionally generated funds is provided on the basis of academic merit, financial need, athletic ability, other criteria.

Financial aid to full-time, first-time undergraduate students: 100% received some form of financial aid. Average amount of aid received: federal grants $3,078; state/local grants $1,388; institutional grants $6,213; loans $5,237.

Departments and Teaching Staff: *Total instructional faculty:* 195 (full-time 104, part-time 91). Total faculty with doctorate, first-professional, or other terminal degree: 80. Student/faculty ratio: 14.1:1. Degrees held by full-time faculty: 58% hold terminal degrees.

Enrollment: Total enrollment 2,296.

Characteristics of Student Body: *Ethnic/racial makeup:* number of Black non-Hispanic: 111; American Indian or Alaska Native: 1; Asian or Pacific Islander: 10; Hispanic: 13; White non-Hispanic: 1,774; unknown: 11. *Age distribution:* number under 18: 40; 18–19: 664; 20–21: 555; 22–24: 181; 25–29: 96; 30–34: 94; 35–39: 100; 40–49: 145; 50–64: 48; unknown 13.

International Students: 20 nonresident aliens enrolled fall 2008. Students from Europe, Asia, Central and South America, Africa. No programs available to aid students whose native language is not English. Financial aid specifically designated for international students: variable number of scholarships available annually.

Student Life: On-campus residence halls house 49% of undergraduate student body. Residence halls for males constitute 36% of such space, for females 64%. *Intercollegiate athletics:* male: baseball, basketball, cross-country, football, golf, soccer, tennis, track; female: basketball, cross-country, golf, soccer, softball, tennis, track, volleyball. *Special regulations:* Biweekly chapel attendance; cars permitted without restrictions. *Special services:* Writing Assistance Center, computer labs, career services, medical and counseling services. *Student publications: Aviso*, a weekly newspaper; *Philos*, the yearbook; *From the Catacombs,* a creative works magazine, *Surrounding community:* Canton population 85,000; Stark County population 376,000. Akron, 20 miles from campus; Cleveland, 60 miles from campus. Served by airport 10 miles from campus.

Library Collections: 176,000 volumes including bound books, serial backfiles, electronic documents, and government documents not in separate collections. Online catalog. Current serial subscriptions: 1,172 paper, 287 microform; 6,740 via electronic access. 2,846 recordings; 2,703 compact discs; 408 CD-ROMs. Computer work stations available. Students have access to the Internet at no charge.

MALONE COLLEGE—*cont'd*

Most important holdings include Evangelical Friends Church-Eastern Regional Archives; Quaker (Friends) Collection; Abraham and Richard Shackelton Letters.

Buildings and Grounds: Campus area 78 acres. Campus DVD available.

Chief Executive Officer: Dr. Ronald G. Johnson, President.

Undergraduates address admission inquiries to John Russell, Director of Admissions; graduate inquiries to Jeff Bartolet, Graduate School Recruiter.

Marietta College

215 Fifth Street
Marietta, Ohio 45750
Tel: (800) 331-7896 **E-mail:** admit@marietta.edu
Fax: (740) 376-8888 **Internet:** www.marietta.edu

Institution Description: Marietta College is a private, independent, nonprofit college. *Enrollment:* 1,606. *Degrees awarded:* Baccalaureate, master's. Certificates also awarded.

Member of East Central College Consortium.

Accreditation: *Regional:* NCA. *Professional*: athletic training, chemistry, engineering, physician assisting, surgeon assisting, teacher education

History: Established 1797; incorporated and first instruction at postsecondary level 1835; awarded first degree (baccalaureate) 1838.

Institutional Structure: *Governing board:* Representation: 22 trustees, including president of the college; 18 trustees emeriti; 41 life associate members. 1 ex officio. *Composition of institution:* Administrators 21. Academic affairs headed by dean of the college. Management/business/finances directed by vice president for administration and finance. Full-time instructional faculty 96.

Calendar: Semesters. Academic year Aug. to May. Formal commencement May.

Characteristics of Freshmen: 2,440 applicants (female 1,144, male 1,296). 77% of applicants accepted. 20% of accepted applicants enrolled full-time.

41 (157 students) submitted SAT scores; 79% (304 students) submitted ACT scores. *25th percentile*: SAT Critical Reading 490, SAT Math 490; ACT Composite 20, ACT English 20, ACT Math 19. *75th percentile*: SAT Critical Reading 600, SAT Math 590; ACT Composite 26, ACT English 26, ACT Math 26.

54% of freshmen expected to graduate within 5 years. 61% of freshmen from Ohio. Freshmen from 22 states and 3 foreign countries.

Admission: Apply by April 15. Recommend college preparatory program. *Entrance tests:* College Board SAT or ACT composite. For foreign students TOEFL. *For transfer students:* 2.5 minimum GPA.

College credit and advanced placement for postsecondary-level work completed in secondary school.

Degree Requirements: 120 credit hours; 2.0 GPA; 36 semesters hours in residence. English composition; distribution requirements; demonstrated proficiency in speech.

Fulfillment of some degree requirements and exemption from some beginning courses possible by passing departmental examinations, College Board CLEP, AP, other standardized tests. *Grading system:* A–F; withdraw (carries time limit).

Distinctive Educational Programs: Internships. Dual-degree programs in engineering with Case Western Reserve University, Columbia University (NY), and University of Pennsylvania; in natural resources at the University of Michigan and Duke University (NC); and in nursing at Case Western Reserve University. Interdisciplinary majors. Facilities and programs for independent research, including honors programs, individual majors. Junior year abroad in Austria, China, England, France, Spain, Wales through Central College (IA) or through the Institute of European Studies. Summer study at the University of Dijon. Other study abroad by individual arrangement. Washington (DC) semester through American University or through Washington Center for Learning Alternatives.

Degrees Conferred: 306 *baccalaureate*; 46 *master's*. Bachelor's degrees awarded in top five disciplines: business/marketing 63; communications/journalism 43; visual and performing arts 24; health professions and related clinical sciences 22; education 17. Master's degrees awarded: education 17; health professions and related clinical sciences 24; liberal arts/general studies 3; psychology 2.

Fees and Other Expenses: *Full-time tuition per academic year 2008–09:* \$26,080. *Required fees:* \$615. *Room and board per academic year:* \$7,764. *Books and supplies:* \$712. *Other expenses:* \$1,228.

Financial Aid: The college offers a direct lending program. Aid from institutionally generated funds is provided on the basis of academic merit, financial need. Institution has a Program Participation Agreement with the U.S. Department of Education for eligible students to receive Pell Grants and, depending upon the agreement, other federal aid.

Financial aid to full-time, first-time undergraduate students: 94% of students received some form of financial aid.

Departments and Teaching Staff: *Total instructional faculty:* 145 (full-time 96, part-time 19). Total faculty with doctorate, first-professional, or other terminal degree: 93. Student/faculty ratio: 12:1. Degrees held by full-time faculty: baccalaureate 1%, master's 20%, doctorate 68%, professional 6%. 74% hold terminal degrees.

Enrollment: Total enrollment 1,606 (undergraduate). Graduate 117. Undergraduate transfer-in students 54.

Characteristics of Student Body: *Ethnic/racial makeup:* Black non-Hispanic: 4%; Asian or Pacific Islander: 1%; Hispanic: 2%; White non-Hispanic: 76%; unknown: 9%; nonresident alien 8%. *Age distribution:* number under 18: 20; 18–19: 621; 20–21: 543; 22–24: 1181 25–29: 16; 30–34: 8; 35–39: 5; 40–=64: 1.

International Students: 124 nonresident aliens enrolled fall 2008. Students from Asia, Central and South America, Africa, Canada, Middle East. Programs available to aid students whose native language is not English: social, cultural. English as a Second Language Program. No Financial aid specifically designated for international students: scholarships available to qualifying undergraduate international students.

Student Life: *Intercollegiate athletics:* male: baseball, basketball, crew, football, soccer, tennis, track and field; female: basketball, crew, field hockey, softball, tennis, track and field, volleyball. *Special regulations:* Cars must be registered and have decals; fee charged. *Special services:* medical services. *Student publications, radio, television: The Marcolian*, a weekly newspaper; *The Marietta*, a yearbook; *Confluence*, a literary magazine. Radio stations WCMO and WMRT; television station WCMO. *Surrounding community:* Marietta population 15,000. Columbus, 114 miles from campus, is nearest metropolitan area. Served by mass transit bus system; airport 5 miles from campus.

Library Collections: 280,500 volumes. Online catalog. 136,400 microforms; 8,040 audiovisual materials; 6,230 periodicals including via electronic access. Students have access to online information retrieval services and the Internet.

Most important holdings include the Cutler Collection (correspondence and papers of Ephraim and William Parker Cutler); Rufus Putnam Papers; manuscripts and documents of the Ohio Company of Associates; the letters and documents of Samuel Prescott Hildreth.

Buildings and Grounds: Campus area 60 acres. Campus DVD available.

Chief Executive Officer: Dr. Jean Scott, President.

Address admission inquiries to Jason Turley, Director of Admission.

Medical College of Ohio at Toledo

3000 Arlington Avenue
P.O. Box 10008
Toledo, Ohio 43614-5805
Tel: (419) 383-4172 **E-mail:** admissions@mco.edu
Fax: (419) 383-6100 **Internet:** www.mco.edu

Institution Description: Medical College of Ohio at Toledo is a state-supported academic health science center. *Enrollment:* 1,086. *Degrees awarded:* First-professional (medicine), master's, doctorate.

Academic offerings subject to approval by statewide coordinating bodies. Budget subject to approval by state governing boards.

Accreditation: *Regional:* NCA. *Professional*: medicine, nursing, physical therapy, public health

History: Established as Medical College of Ohio 1964; adopted present name 1967; offered first instruction at postsecondary level 1969; awarded first professional degree 1972; first doctorate 1975.

Institutional Structure: *Governing board:* Board of Trustees. Extrainstitutional representation: 9 trustees. All voting. *Composition of institution:* Administrators 73. Academic affairs headed by executive vice president for provost/dean of the School of Medicine; other executive staff include vice presidents for administration, finance, institutional advancement. Full-time instructional faculty 342. Academic governance body, faculty senate, meets an average of 11 times per year.

Calendar: Semesters. Academic year Aug. to May. Entering students admitted Sept., Jan., June. Degrees conferred and formal commencement June.

Admission: College participates in American College Applications Service Program (AMCAS). For fall acceptance, apply as early as June 15, but not later than Dec. 1 of previous year. Students are notified of acceptance Oct. Apply by Aug. 1 for early decision; must limit application to Medical College of Ohio. *Requirements:* Baccalaureate degree with 1 year each in biology, English, mathematics, physics; 2 years in chemistry, including organic; additional units in biology. *Entrance tests:* MCAT. *For transfer students:* Successful completion of 2 years in accredited school; passing score on part 1 of National Boards. *Graduate School:* Baccalaureate degree; 3.0 GPA; application form with three letters of recommendation; Graduate Record Examination scores; TOEFL where required.

Tutoring available. Noncredit remedial courses offered in summer session.

Degree Requirements: *School of Medicine:* successful completion of medical curriculum, including clinical clerkships with oral and written examinations. *Graduate School:* Successful completion of 40–90 credit hours (depending upon program); maintenance of 3.0 GPA or better; successful defense of a thesis or dissertation (depending upon program). *Grading system:* School of Medicine: Honors, high pass, pass, fail; Graduate School: A–F.

Distinctive Educational Programs: M.D./Ph.D. and M.D./M.S. degree programs. Facilities and programs for independent research, including individual concentrations, independent study. *Other distinctive programs:* Baccalaureate completion program available for registered nurses. Continuing education.

Degrees Conferred: 84 *master's:* health professions; 18 *doctorate:* health professions; 128 *first-professional:* medicine.

Fees and Other Expenses: *Tuition per academic year:* contact the college for current graduate/professional tuition and fees.

Financial Aid: Aid from institutionally generated funds is provided on the basis of academic merit, financial need. Institution has a Program Participation Agreement with the U.S. Department of Education for eligible students to receive Pell Grants and, depending upon the agreement, other federal aid.

Departments and Teaching Staff: *Total instructional faculty:* 390. Degrees held by full-time faculty: doctorate 49%, master's 38%, baccalaureate 2%, professional 49%. 87% hold terminal degrees.

Enrollment: Total enrollment 1,086.

Characteristics of Student Body: *Ethnic/racial makeup:* Black non-Hispanic: 2.2%; American Indian or Alaska Native: .6%; Asian or Pacific Islander: 10.7%; Hispanic: 1.6%; White non-Hispanic: 75.8%; unknown: 3.6%.

International Students: 61 nonresident aliens enrolled fall 2008. Students from Asia, Latin America. No programs available to aid students whose native language is not English. No financial aid specifically designated for international students.

Student Life: No on-campus housing. *Special regulations:* Cars with decals permitted in designated areas; fee charged. *Special services:* medical services. *Student publications: Student Affairs Bulletin,* a quarterly publication; *Ideopath,* a biweekly publication. *Surrounding community:* Toledo population 335,000. Served by mass transit bus system; airport 15 miles from campus; passenger rail service 5 miles from campus.

Library Collections: 115,000 volumes. 1,435 serial subscriptions. 120 computer work stations. Students have access to online information retrieval services and the Internet.

Most important special collections include History of Medicine; Medical Rare Books; Institutional Authors.

Buildings and Grounds: Campus area 498 acres.

Chief Executive Officer: Dr. Lloyd A. Jacobs, President.

Address admission inquiries to Dr. Mary Ann Myers, Associate Director of Admissions.

Methodist Theological School in Ohio

3081 Columbus Pike
P.O. Box 8004
Delaware, Ohio 43015-8004
Tel: (740) 363-1146 **E-mail:** admit@mtso.edu
Fax: (740) 362-3127 **Internet:** www.mtso.edu

Institution Description: Methodist Theological School in Ohio is a private institution affiliated with the United Methodist Church. *Enrollment:* 222. *Degrees awarded:* First-professional (master of divinity), master's.

Member of the consortium The Columbus Cluster of Theological Schools.

Accreditation: *Regional:* NCA. *National:* ATS. *Professional*: theology

History: Established and chartered 1956; incorporated and offered first instruction at postsecondary 1960; awarded degree (first-professional) 1963.

Institutional Structure: *Governing board:* Board of Trustees. Representation: 48 trustees, including 8 alumni, 2 faculty, 1 ex officio. All voting. *Composition of institution:* Administrators 20. Academic affairs headed by dean. Management/business/finances directed by vice president for finance and administration. Full-time instructional faculty 16. Academic governance body, the faculty, meets an average of 9 times per year.

Calendar: Semesters (4-1-4). Academic year Aug. to May. Entering students admitted Sept., Dec., Mar. Degrees conferred and formal commencement May.

Admission: Rolling admissions plan. *Requirements:* Baccalaureate from accredited college or university. Recommend preseminary curriculum with 6 semesters English; 4 in Latin, Greek, Hebrew, German, or French; 6 social science (including 1 psychology); 3 history; 3 philosophy; 3 religion; course work in natural science (physics preferred). Minimum GPA 2.5. *For transfer students:* Individual evaluation.

Degree Requirements: *For first-professional degree:* 85 semester hours. *For master's degree:* 58 semester hours. *For both degrees:* 2.25 GPA; required curriculum; field education. *Grading system:* A–F; pass-fail; withdraw (carries time limit).

Distinctive Educational Programs: Degree in alcoholism and drug abuse ministry. Degree in Liturgical Arts. Specialization for the Master of Divinity include: Rural, Urban, Youth, Christian Education, and Alcohol and Drug Abuse. Interdisciplinary programs.

Degrees Conferred: 17 *master's:* theology; 32 *first-professional:* master of divinity.

Fees and Other Expenses: *Full-time tuition per academic year 2008–09:* contact the seminary for current information.

Financial Aid: Aid from institutionally generated funds is provided on the basis of academic merit, financial need.

Departments and Teaching Staff: *Total instructional faculty:* 38. *Total tenured faculty:* 9. Student/faculty ratio: 9:1. Degrees held by full-time faculty: baccalaureate 100%, doctorate 81%, master's 44%, professional 75%. 81% hold terminal degrees.

Enrollment: Total enrollment 222. First-professional 222.

Student Life: On-campus residence halls house 50% of student body. Housing available for married students with or without children; singles; and commuters. *Special regulations:* Cars permitted without restrictions. *Student publications:* A weekly newsletter. *Surrounding community:* Delaware population 23,500. Columbus, 15 miles from campus, is nearest metropolitan area.

Publications: *1996 Journal of Theology,* a joint publication of United Theological Seminary, Dayton, Ohio and Methodist Theological School in Ohio, Delaware, Ohio.

Library Collections: 138,000 volumes including bound books, serial backfiles, electronic documents, and government documents not in separate collections. Online catalog. Current serial subscriptions: 378. 2,867 recordings; 600 CD-ROMs. Computer work stations available. Students have access to the Internet at no charge.

Most important special collections include Methodist History and Theology; Historic Hymnals; Philip Gatch Papers.

Buildings and Grounds: Campus area 70 acres.

Chief Executive Officer: Rev. Joy Rundell, President.

Address admission inquiries to Rev. Mary Kay Freshour, Director of Admissions.

Miami University

East High Street
Oxford, Ohio 45056
Tel: (513) 529-1809 **E-mail:** admission@muohio.edu
Fax: (513) 529-3841 **Internet:** www.muohio.edu

Institution Description: Miami University is a state institution with branch campuses at Hamilton and Middletown. *Enrollment:* 17,191. *Degrees awarded:* Associate, baccalaureate, master's, doctorate. Specialist certificates also awarded.

Academic offerings subject to approval by statewide coordinating bodies. Member of Dayton-Miami Valley Consortium, Greater Cincinnati Consortium of Colleges and Universities.

Accreditation: *Regional:* NCA. *Professional*: accounting, architecture, art, athletic training, business, chemistry, dietetics, engineering, interior design, manufacturing technology, music, nursing, school psychology, social work, speech-language pathology, teacher education, theatre

History: Established and chartered 1809; offered first instruction at postsecondary level 1824; awarded first degree (baccalaureate) 1826. *See* Walter Havinghurst, *Miami Years* (New York: Putnam, 1969) for further information.

Institutional Structure: *Governing board:* Board of Trustees consisting of 9 voting members and 2 nonvoting members. Trustees are appointed by the Governor for a term of 9 years. *Composition of institution:* Administrators 202. Academic affairs headed by provost. Management/business/finances directed by vice president for finance, business services, and treasurer. Full-time instructional faculty 842. Academic governance body, University Senate, meets regularly.

Calendar: Semesters. Academic year Aug. to May. Freshmen admitted Aug., Jan., May, June, July. Degrees conferred and formal commencements May, Aug., Dec. Summer session from May to Aug.

Characteristics of Freshmen: 15,468 applicants (8,173 female, 6,836 male). 80% of applicants admitted. 30% of applicants admitted and enrolled full-time.

68% (2,480 students) submitted SAT scores; 78% (2,807 students) submitted ACT scores. *25th percentile*: SAT Critical Reading 540, SAT Math 570; ACT

MIAMI UNIVERSITY—*cont'd*

Composite 24, ACT English 23, ACT Math 24. *75th percentile*: SAT Critical Reading 640, SAT Math 660; ACT Composite 29, ACT English 28, ACT Math 27.

81% of entering freshmen expected to graduate within 5 years. 70% of freshmen from Ohio. Freshmen from 49 states and 39 foreign countries.

Admission: Rolling admissions plan. For fall acceptance, apply as early as July 1 of previous year, but not later than Jan. 31 of year of enrollment. *Requirements:* Recommended high school program to include 4 units English, 3 units mathematics (including Algebra II), 3 units social studies (including 1 unit history), 3 units of college preparatory natural science (including both a physical and a biological science), 2 units of foreign language (both in same language), 1 unit fine arts (including art, drama, or music, either appreciation or performance); or GED. *Entrance tests:* College Board SAT or ACT composite. For foreign students TOEFL. *For transfer students:* Required to have earned a high school diploma and have a 2.0 minimum GPA on college courses; from 4-year accredited institution 96 credit hours maximum transfer credit; from 2-year accredited institution 64 hours.

College credit and advanced placement for postsecondary-level work completed in secondary school. College credit for extrainstitutional learning.

Tutoring available. Developmental-remedial courses offered during regular academic year; credit given.

Degree Requirements: *For all associate degrees:* 64 credit hours. *For all baccalaureate degrees:* 128 credit hours. *For all undergraduate degrees:* 2.0 GPA; 2 semesters, and 32 hours, in residence; general education requirements.

Fulfillment of some degree requirements and exemption from some beginning courses possible by passing College Board CLEP, AP. *Grading system:* A–F plus/minus; pass; withdraw (deadline after which pass-fail is appended to withdraw); incomplete; credit-no credit; satisfactory progress-unsatisfactory progress (for independent and honors courses).

Distinctive Educational Programs: Weekend and evening classes. Special facilities for using telecommunications in the classroom. Facilities and programs for independent research, including honors programs, individual majors, tutorials. Study abroad in France, Italy, Japan, Luxembourg, and by individual arrangement. Miami University European Center, Grand Duchy of Luxembourg.

ROTC: Air Force, Navy. Army offered in cooperation with Xavier University.

Degrees Conferred: 281 *associate;* 3,632 *baccalaureate*; 468 *master's*; 50 *doctorate* . Bachelor's degrees awarded in top five disciplines: business/marketing 1,365; social sciences and history 445; education 442; English 275; parks and recreation 132.

Fees and Other Expenses: *Full-time tuition and fees per academic year 2008–09:* $11,443 resident, $25,327 nonresident; contact the university for current graduate tuition and fees. *Room and board per academic year:* $8,998. *Books and supplies:* $1,195. *Other expenses:* $5,098.

Financial Aid: The university offers a direct lending program. Aid from institutionally generated funds is provided on the basis of academic merit, financial need, athletic ability, other criteria.

Financial aid to full-time, first-time undergraduate students: 83% received some form of financial aid.

Departments and Teaching Staff: *Total instructional faculty:* 1,159 (full-time 849, part-time 310). Total faculty with doctorate, first-professional, or other terminal degree: 871. Student/faculty ratio: 17:1. Degrees held by full-time faculty: doctorate 80%, master's 18%, baccalaureate 1%, professional 1%. 81% hold terminal degrees.

Enrollment: Total enrollment 17,191. Undergraduate 14,785 (female 54%, male 46%). Graduate 2,406 (full-time 43%). Undergraduate transfer-in students 273.

Characteristics of Student Body: *Ethnic/racial makeup:* Black non-Hispanic: 4%; American Indian or Alaska Native: 1%; Asian or Pacific Islander: 3%; Hispanic: 2%; White non-Hispanic: 85%; unknown: 4%; nonresident alien 2%. *Age distribution:* number under 18: 195; 18–19: 6,362; 20–21: 6,680; 22–24: 1,436; 25–29: 183; 30–34: 58; 35–39: 40; 40–49: 59; 50–64: 7; 65 and over: 1.

International Students: 342 nonresident aliens enrolled fall 2008. No programs available to aid students whose native language is not English. No financial aid specifically designated for international students.

Student Life: On-campus residence halls house 46% of student body. Coed and single-sex housing available. Housing designated for freshmen only. International student housing is available. Housing available for married students. 24% of undergraduate males are members of 27 national fraternities; 27% of the undergraduate females are members of 21 national sororities. *Intercollegiate athletics:* male: baseball, basketball, cross-country, football, golf, ice hockey, soccer, swimming and diving, tennis, track and field, wrestling; female: basketball, cross-country, field hockey, volleyball, basketball, precision skating, swimming and diving, soccer, tennis, softball, track and field. *Special regulations:* University permission is required to bring a car to school. Residence hall visitation from noon to midnight Mon.–Thurs. and noon Fri. through midnight Sun. *Special services:* Office of Learning Assistance, Office of Disability Resources, Student Health Center, Scholastic Enhancement Program, Emerging Leaders Program, Minority Professional Leadership Program, Scholar Leader Program, Peer Education. *Student publications: Inklings*the undergraduate literary magazine; *Miami Student*, the twice-weekly newspaper; *Recensio*, a yearbook; *Miami Forum*, the issues-oriented paper. *Surrounding community:* Oxford population 18,000. Cincinnati, 30 miles from campus, is nearest metropolitan area.

Publications: *Journal on Excellence in College Teaching; Lifestyles: Family and Economic Issues; Miami University Report* (weekly university newspaper), *Miamian* (quarterly alumni magazine); *Ohio Reading Teacher; The Old Northwest; Oxford Magazine.*

Library Collections: 2,374,000 volumes including bound books, serial backfiles, electronic documents, and government documents not in separate collections. Online catalog. Current serial subscriptions: 13,700 including electronic access. 3,031,247 recordings; 2,218 CD-ROMs. Computer work stations. available. Students have access to the Internet at no charge.

Most important special holdings include collections of Early Children's Literature (16th to 20th centuries); school books of the 19th century; Jefferson Davis Papers.

Buildings and Grounds: Campus area 1,973 acres.

Chief Executive Officer: Dr. Donald Hodge, President.

Address admission inquiries to Laurie Koehler, Director of Admissions; graduate inquiries to Dean of Graduate School.

College of Arts and Science

Degree Programs Offered: *Associate, baccalaureate* in American studies, anthropology, biochemistry, botany, chemistry, classical humanities, clinical laboratory science, diplomacy and foreign affairs, economics, engineering physics, English—literature, English—professional writing, English-technical and scientific communication, French, geography, geology, German, Greek, history, history of art and architecture, international studies, Latin, linguistics, mass communication, medical technology, mathematics and statistics, microbiology, philosophy, physics, political science, psychology, public administration, religion, Russian, sociology, Spanish, speech communication, speech pathology and audiology, statistics, theater, zoology; *master's, doctorate* in various fields.

Distinctive Educational Programs: Interdisciplinary programs in American studies, black world studies, international studies, urban and regional planning. Facilities for research, including computing facilities, environmental science center, herbarium, instrumentation laboratory, psychological clinic, speech and hearing clinic, wildlife preserve. Dual-degree program in biological science and forestry with Duke University (NC). Cooperative doctoral program in physics with Ohio State University. Cooperative baccalaureate in medical technology with approved hospital programs. Dual-degree program in engineering with Case Western Reserve University and Columbia University (NY).

School of Engineering Applied Science

Degree Programs Offered: *Associate* in chemical technology, computer science, electrical engineering technology, mechanical engineering technology, nursing; *baccalaureate* in engineering technology, engineering management, manufacturing engineering, nursing, paper science and engineering, systems analysis; *master's* in paper science and engineering, systems analysis.

Distinctive Educational Programs: Summer internships in pulp and paper science. Facilities include computers, Fourdrinier paper machine, manufacturing numerical controls laboratory.

Richard T. Farmer School of Business Administration

Degree Programs Offered: *Associate* in accounting technology, business management technology, computer-based management technology, finance-banking technology, marketing management technology, real estate technology; *baccalaureate* in accounting, business economics, decision sciences, finance, general business, management/human resource; management/operations, management/organizational behavior, management/purchasing and procurement, management information systems, marketing, personnel management, production and operation management, purchasing management; *master's* in accounting, decision science, economics, finance, management, management information systems, marketing, organizational behavior, production decision sciences.

Distinctive Educational Programs: Interdisciplinary programs in arts-management, international business. Research facilities include computers, Institute of Business and Educational Services, motion and time study laboratory. Cooperative doctorate in economics with Ohio State University.

School of Education and Allied Professions

Degree Programs Offered: *Associate* in general education; *baccalaureate* in biological science, chemistry, communications, consumer service, dietetics, earth science, elementary education, English, food management, French, German, health education, home economics education, housing and interior design, individual and family studies, Latin, mathematics, physical education, physics, retailing, Russian, science, social studies, Spanish, special education, speech, speech pathology and audiology; *master's* in curriculum and supervision, educational administration, educational media, education psychology, elementary education, health education, home economics education, physical education, reading education, secondary education, special education, speech pathology and audiology, child and family studies, food service management, college student personnel services, school psychology, textiles and clothing; *doctorate* in educational administration. Specialist certificates also awarded.

Distinctive Educational Programs: Interdisciplinary program in individual and family studies. Facilities for research, including home management laboratory. McGuffey Laboratory School, nursery school. Cooperative doctorate in guidance and counseling with Ohio State University. Cooperative doctorate in education with Indiana University.

School of Fine Arts

Degree Programs Offered: *Associate* in general studies; *baccalaureate* in architecture, art, art education, interior design, music education, music performance, music theory and composition, theatre, urban and regional planning; *master's* in art, art education, architecture, music composition, music education, music education supervision, music performance, music theory, musicology.

Distinctive Educational Programs: Interdisciplinary program in arts-management. Research facilities, including art museum, electronic music laboratory, visiting professional architect's critique program.

School of Interdisciplinary Studies

Degree Programs Offered: *Associate* in general studies; *baccalaureate* in interdisciplinary studies.

Distinctive Educational Programs: Individual majors. Self-designed senior project.

Mount Union College

1972 Clark Avenue
Alliance, Ohio 44601
Tel: (330) 821-5321 **E-mail:** admission@muc.edu
Fax: (330) 823-35097 **Internet:** www.muc.edu

Institution Description: Mount Union College is a private, independent, nonprofit college affiliated with The United Methodist Church. *Enrollment:* 2,204. *Degrees awarded:* Baccalaureate.

Member of East Central College Consortium.

Accreditation: *Regional:* NCA. *Professional*: athletic training, music, teacher education

History: Established as A Select School 1846; changed name to Mount Union Seminary 1849; chartered and incorporated under present name, offered first instruction at postsecondary level, and awarded first degree (baccalaureate) 1858; merged with Scio College (established 1857). *See* N. Yost Osborne, *A Select School* (Columbus, Ohio: Mount Union College, 1967) and Dr. John Saffell, *Wake the Echoes* for further information.

Institutional Structure: *Governing board:* Board of Trustees. Extrainstitutional representation: 54 trustees, including 6 elected by the Eastern Ohio Conference of the United Methodist Church, 3 elected by the West Ohio Conference, 1 elected by the West Pennsylvania Conference; 3 honorary trustees; institutional representation: 1 administrator; 13 alumni. 6 ex officio. 33 voting. *Composition of institution:* Administrators 40. Academic affairs headed by dean of the college. Management/business/finances directed by the vice president for business affairs. Full-time instructional faculty 124. Academic governance body, the faculty, meets an average of 10 times per year.

Calendar: Semesters. Academic year Aug. to May. Freshmen admitted Sept., Jan., Mar., June. Degrees conferred and formal commencement June, Dec. Summer session of 3 terms May to Aug.

Characteristics of Freshmen: 2,326 applicants (female 1,038, male 1,288). 79% of applicants accepted. 31% of accepted applicants enrolled full-time. *25th percentile:* ACT Composite 19. *75th perdentile:* ACT Composite 25.

66% of entering freshmen expected to graduate within 5 years. 89% of freshmen from Ohio. Freshmen from 26 states and 15 foreign countries.

Admission: Rolling admissions plan. For fall acceptance, apply as early as Oct. 1 of previous year, but not later than Aug. 30. Early acceptance available. *Requirements:* Either graduation from accredited secondary school with minimum recommended 18 units including 4 English, 2 foreign language, 3 laboratory science, 3 mathematics, 3 social studies; or GED; minimum 2.0 GPA. *Entrance tests:* College Board SAT or ACT score results, an essay, official high school transcript (or GED), and proficiency results if required by their state. *For transfer students:* 2.0 minimum GPA; maximum transfer credit limited only by residence requirement.

College credit and advanced placement for postsecondary-level work completed in secondary school and for extrainstitutional learning (life experience) on basis of portfolio assessment.

Degree Requirements: 120 semester hours; 2.0 GPA overall and major/minor; final 30 semester hours in residence; 2 semester hours physical education; required courses in English, speech, religion; distribution requirements; completed major and minor; senior culminating experience.

Fulfillment of some degree requirements and exemption from some beginning courses possible by achieving certain grades in College Board AP or CLEP. *Grading system:* A–F; pass-fail; withdraw (carries time limit); satisfactory/unsatisfactory.

Distinctive Educational Programs: Cooperative education; internships. Evening classes. Dual-degree programs in engineering with University of Pennsylvania, and other schools. Cooperative programs in medical technology with area hospitals; may be individually arranged. Pre-law concentration. Ecological sciences emphases. Special facilities for using telecommunications in the classroom. Interdisciplinary program in American studies; self-defined interdisciplinary major also available. Facilities and programs for independent research, including honors programs, individual majors, independent study. Extensive study abroad possibilities in Japan, Mexico, France, Spain, England, China, and others. Off-campus study in U.S. at Merrill-Palmer Institute in Detroit (MI) and Cooperative Urban Studies Center in Cleveland (OH). Summers or semesters at other accredited colleges or universities. Cross-registration with other schools in consortium. Nontraditional Study Program for mature students.

ROTC: Air Force and Army in cooperation with Kent State University.

Degrees Conferred: 446 *baccalaureate*. Bachelor's degrees awarded in top five disciplines: education 104; business, management, marketing, and related support services 86; social sciences 42; parks and recreation 41; history 27.

Fees and Other Expenses: *Full-time tuition per academic year 2008–09:* $23,120. *Room and board per academic year:* $7,050. *Books and supplies:*$600. *Required fees:* $250. *Other expenses:* $1,500.

Financial Aid: Aid from institutionally generated funds is provided on the basis of academic merit, financial need, other (ministerial). Financial assistance is available in the form of Pell Grants, College Work-Study, Veterans Administration Benefits, National Direct Student Loans, Supplemental Education Opportunity Grants (SEOG), Stafford Loans, other federal aid programs.

Percentage of undergraduate first-time full-time students receiving various forms of financial aid: federal scholarships and grants 83% (average $14,736); state/local scholarships and grants 89% (average $1,170); institutional fellowships 94% (average $6,427); loans 78% (average $3,103).

Departments and Teaching Staff: *Total instructional faculty:* 226. Student/faculty ratio: 13:1. Degrees held by full-time faculty: 116 hold terminal degrees.

Enrollment: Total enrollment 2,204 (undergraduate). Transfer-in students 57.

Characteristics of Student Body: *Ethnic/racial makeup:* Black non-Hispanic; 4%; Asian or Pacific Islander: 1%; Hispanic 1%; White non-Hispanic: 86%; unknown: 3%; nonresident alien 3%.

International Students: 66 nonresident aliens enrolled fall 2008. Students from Europe, Asia, Central and South America, Australia, Middle East. Programs available to aid students whose native language is not English: English as a Second Language Program. No financial aid specifically designated for international students.

Student Life: On-campus residence halls house 65% of student body. *Intercollegiate athletics:* male: baseball, basketball, cross-country, football, golf, indoor track, soccer, swimming, tennis, track; female: basketball, cross-country, indoor track, soccer, softball, swimming, tennis, track, volleyball. *Special regulations:* Cars permitted without restrictions. Residence hall visitation Fri. and Sat. from noon to 2am; Sun. noon to 11pm; Tue. 6pm to 11pm. Open visitation is available in suite-style halls on weekends. *Special services:* medical services. *Student publications, radio: Calliope*, an annual literary magazine; *Dynamo*, a weekly newspaper; *Unonian*, a yearbook. Radio station WRMU broadcasts 126 hours per week. *Surrounding community:* Alliance population 25,000. Cleveland, 65 miles from campus, is nearest metropolitan area. Served by airport 15 miles from campus.

Library Collections: 229,601 volumes. 408,000 government documents; 52,400 microforms; 752 current periodical subscriptions. Online catalog. Students have access to online information retrieval services and the Internet.

Most important holdings include Southern Classical Collection; Samuel Austin Bible Collection.

Buildings and Grounds: Campus area 122 acres. Campus DVD available.

MOUNT UNION COLLEGE—*cont'd*

Chief Executive Officer: Dr. Richard F. Geise, President.

Address admission inquiries to Director of Enrollment Services.

Mount Vernon Nazarene University

800 Martinsburg Road
Mount Vernon, Ohio 43050-5000
Tel: (740) 392-6868 **E-mail:** admissions@mvnc.edu
Fax: (740) 397-7609 **Internet:** www.nvnc.edu

Institution Description: Mount Vernon Nazarene University is a private liberal arts institution affiliated with the Church of the Nazarene. *Enrollment:* 2,558. *Degrees awarded:* Associate, baccalaureate, master's.

Accreditation: *Regional:* NCA.

History: Established and incorporated 1966; offered first instruction at postsecondary level 1968; awarded first associate degree 1970, first baccalaureate degree 1976, first graduate degree 1994.

Institutional Structure: *Governing board:* Board of Trustees. Representation: 44 trustees. All voting. *Composition of institution:* Administrators 10. Academic affairs headed by vice president for academic affairs. Management/business/finances directed by vice president for finance and management. Full-time instructional faculty 112. Academic governance body, Academic Council, meets an average of 12 times per year.

Calendar: Semesters (4-1-4 plan). Academic year Sept. to May. Freshmen admitted Sept. Jan., Feb., June. Degrees conferred and formal commencement May, Dec. Summer sessions June to July.

Characteristics of Freshmen: 813 applicants (female 518, male 297). 81% of applicants admitted. 54% of applicants admitted and enrolled full-time.

18% (6398 students) submitted SAT scores; 90% (330 students) submitted ACT scores. *25th percentile*: SAT Critical Reading 490, SAT Math 460; ACT Composite 19, ACT English 19, ACT Math 18. *75th percentile*: SAT Critical Reading 580, SAT Math 680; ACT Composite 25, ACT English 26, ACT Math 25.

39% of entering freshmen expected to graduate within 5 years. 92% of freshmen from Ohio. Freshmen from 27 states and 7 foreign countries.

Admission: Rolling admissions plan. For fall acceptance, apply no later than May 15. *Requirements:* Either graduation from accredited secondary school with 21 recommended units which must include 4 English, 3 mathematics, 3 social studies, 3 science; or GED. 2 units of foreign language and 1 unit of health and physical education. *Entrance tests:* ACT Composite. For foreign students TOEFL or other standardized test of English. *For transfer students:* 2.0 minimum GPA; from 4-year accredited institution 94 hours maximum transfer credit; from 2-year accredited 64 hours; correspondence/extension students 15 hours.

College credit and advanced placement for postsecondary-level work completed in secondary school. Tutoring available. Developmental/remedial courses offered during regular academic year; nondegree credit given.

Degree Requirements: *For all associate degrees:* 64 credit hours. *For all baccalaureate degrees:* 124 credit hours. *For all degrees:* 2.0 GPA; 30 hours in residence; 2 hours physical education; general education core requirements.

Fulfillment of some degree requirements and exemption from some beginning courses possible by passing College Board CLEP, AP. *Grading system:* A–F; withdraw (carries time limit).

Distinctive Educational Programs: New Bachelor of Science in Nursing program began fall 2008. Some evening classes in business. Preprofessional programs in engineering, law, medical technology, medicine, nursing, pharmacy. Facilities and programs for independent research, including independent study, directed study, internships. Council of Christian Colleges and Universities Programs. January interim travel courses.

Degrees Conferred: 10 *associate;* 545 *baccalaureate:*; 255 *master's.* Bachelor's degrees awarded in top five disciplines: business/marketing 300; education 59; philosophy and religious studies 23; education 59; visual and performing arts 6. Master's degrees awarded in various disciplines.

Fees and Other Expenses: *Full-time tuition per academic year 2008–09:* $19,330; contact the university for current graduate tuition that varies by programs. *Required fees:* $520. *Room and board per academic year:* $5,550. *Books and supplies:* $1,000. *Other expenses:* $2,795.

Financial Aid: Aid from institutionally generated funds is provided on the basis of academic merit, financial need, athletic ability, other criteria.

Financial aid to full-time, first-time undergraduate students: 100% of students received some form of financial aid.

Departments and Teaching Staff: *Total instructional faculty:* 244 (full-time 112 part-time 152). Total faculty with doctorate, first-professional, or other terminal degree: 101. Student/faculty ratio: 16:1. Degrees held by full-time faculty: doctorate 60%, master's 40%. 72% hold terminal degrees. *Faculty development:* 3 faculty members awarded sabbaticals 2008–09.

Enrollment: Total enrollment 2,558. Undergraduate 2,090 (female 60%, male 40%). Graduate 468 (full-time 59%). Undergraduate transfer-in students 201.

Characteristics of Student Body: *Ethnic/racial makeup:* Black non-Hispanic: 5%; Asian or Pacific Islander: 1%; Hispanic: 1%; White non-Hispanic: 90%; unknown: 2%; nonresident alien 1%. *Age distribution:* number under 18: 93; 18–19: 595; 20–21: 505; 22–24: 137; 25–29: 24; 30–34: 8; 35–39: 2; 40–49: 5.

International Students: 26 nonresident aliens enrolled fall 2008. Students from Asia, Central and South America, Canada. Programs available to aid students whose native language is not English: social, cultural, financial. Financial aid specifically designated for undergraduate international students: 9 scholarships available annually; 9 totaling $48,000 awarded 2008–09.

Student Life: On-campus residence halls house 78% of student body. Residence halls for males constitute 47% of such space, for females 53%. *Intercollegiate athletics:* male: baseball, basketball, soccer, tennis; female: basketball, fast pitch softball, soccer, volleyball. *Special regulations:* Cars permitted without restrictions. Dress must be in keeping with Christian modesty. *Special services:* Learning Resources Center, Instructional Resources Center, health ser vices. *Student publications: The Lakeholm Viewer,* a newspaper; *Enerazan,* a yearbook. *Surrounding community:* Mount Vernon population 15,800. Columbus, 45 miles from campus, is nearest metropolitan area.

Library Collections: 108,000 volumes including bound books, serial backfiles, electronic documents, and government documents not in separate collections. Library is member of OhioLink with access to 24 million volumes. Online catalog. Current serial subscriptions: paper 411; microform 2; via electronic access 6,900. 1,710 audio/videotapes; 86 DVD discs; 446 CD-ROMs. Students have access to the Internet and online information retrieval services.

Most important special collections include Church of the Nazarene Archives; Holiness and Christianity; Education and Business.

Buildings and Grounds: Campus area 335 acres. Campus DVD available.

Chief Executive Officer: Dr. E. LeBron Fairbanks, President.

Address undergraduate admission inquiries to Tim Endes, Director of Admissions; graduate inquires for Education: Jay Mahan, Director of Admissions.

Muskingum College

163 Stomont Street
New Concord, Ohio 43762
Tel: (740) 826-8211 **E-mail:** adminfo@muskingum.edu
Fax: (740) 826-8404 **Internet:** www.muskingum.edu

Institution Description: Muskingum College is a private college affiliated with The Presbyterian Church (U.S.A.). *Enrollment:* 2,135. *Degrees awarded:* Baccalaureate, master's.

Member of the East Central College Consortium.

Accreditation: *Regional:* NCA. *Professional*: chemistry, music

History: Established, chartered, and offered first instruction at postsecondary level 1837; awarded first degree (baccalaureate) 1839. *See* William L. Fisk, *History of Muskingum College* (New Concord: Muskingum College, 1978) for further information.

Institutional Structure: *Governing board:* Board of Trustees. *Representation:* 37 trustees, including president of the college, 1 full-time instructional faculty member, 1 student. 3 ex officio. All voting. *Composition of institution:* Administrators 53. Academic affairs headed by dean of the college. Management/business/finances directed by treasurer. Full-time instructional faculty 94. Academic governance body, the faculty, meets an average of 8 times per year.

Calendar: Academic year Aug. to May. Freshmen admitted Aug., Jan. Degrees conferred and formal commencement May. Summer session May to July.

Characteristics of Freshmen: 2,051 applicants (947 female, 1,104 male). 70% applicants admitted. 30% of applicants admitted and enrolled full-time.

28% (108 students) submitted SAT scores; 88% (410 students) submitted ACT scores. *25th percentile*: SAT Critical Reading 460, SAT Math 460; ACT Composite 19, ACT English 19, ACT Math 18. *75th percentile*: SAT Critical Reading 580, SAT Math 590; ACT Composite 24, ACT English 24, ACT Math 25.

59% of entering freshmen expected to graduate within 5 years. 87% of freshmen from Ohio. Freshmen from 28 states and 14 foreign countries.

Admission: Rolling admissions plan. Apply as early as 1 year prior to enrollment. Early acceptance available. *Requirements:* Either graduation from accredited secondary school with 15 units; or GED. Recommend 4 units in English, 2 in a foreign language, 3 college preparatory mathematics, 2 laboratory science, 3 social studies. *Entrance tests:* College Board SAT or ACT composite. For foreign students minimum TOEFL score 400. *For transfer students:* 2.0 minimum

GPA; from 4-year accredited institution 90 hours maximum transfer credit; from 2-year accredited institution 62 hours.

College credit and advanced placement for postsecondary-level work completed in secondary school and for extrainstitutional learning (life experience) on basis of portfolio assessment.

Tutoring available. Noncredit developmental courses offered during regular academic year.

Degree Requirements: 124 credit hours; 2.0 GPA; 2 semesters in residence; 3 semester hours physical education; distribution requirements.

Fulfillment of some degree requirements and exemption from some beginning courses possible by passing departmental examinations, College Board CLEP, AP (score of 3). *Grading system:* A–F; satisfactory-unsatisfactory; withdraw (time limit).

Distinctive Educational Programs: Work-experience programs, including field experience, internships. Flexible meeting places and schedules. Dual-degree program in nursing with Case Western Reserve University. Cooperative baccalaureate in medical technology with southwest General Hospital. Interdisciplinary programs in American studies, humanities, public and international affairs. Facilities and programs for independent research, including individual majors, tutorials, independent study. One-for-one student exchange study abroad program with 13 international institutions. Off-campus study in the U.S., including Washington (DC) semester at American University; United Nations semester through Drew University (NJ). English Support Program. Plus Program. *Other distinctive programs:* Binary engineering program with Case Institute of Technology of Case Western Reserve University; interdisciplinary program in international business; Center for the Advancement of Learning and PLUS program for learning disabled college students.

Degrees Conferred: 299 *baccalaureate*; 110 *master's*. Bachelor's degrees awarded in top five disciplines: business/marketing 51; education 50; social sciences 37; biological/life sciences 32; psychology 22. Master's degrees awarded: education 110.

Fees and Other Expenses: *Full-time tuition per academic year 2008–09:* undergraduate $18,960; graduate study charged per credit hour (contact the college for current rate). *Room and board per academic year:* $7,350. *Books and supplies:* $1,000. *Other expenses:* $1,505.

Financial Aid: Aid from institutionally generated funds is provided on the basis of academic merit, financial need.

Financial aid to full-time, first-time undergraduate students: 100% received some form of financial aid. Average amount of aid received: federal grants $3,385; state/local grants $1,829; institutional grants $7,937; loans $4,999.

Departments and Teaching Staff: Total faculty with doctorate, first-professional, or other terminal degree: 98. Student/faculty ratio: 15:1. Degrees held by full-time faculty: baccalaureate 100%, master's 92%, doctorate 72%. 92% hold terminal degrees.

Enrollment: Total enrollment 2,135. Undergraduate 1,689 (female 52%, male 48%). Graduate 446 (full-time 28%). Undergraduate transfer-in students 70.

Characteristics of Student Body: *Ethnic/racial makeup:* Black non-Hispanic: 5%; Asian or Pacific Islander: 1%; Hispanic: 1%; White non-Hispanic: 86%; unknown: 6%; nonresident alien 1%. *Age distribution:* number under 18: 1; 18–19: 604; 20–21: 617; 22–24: 284; 25–29: 26; 30–34: 14; 35–39: 5; 40–49: 9; 50–64: 3; 65 and over: 1.

International Students: 21 nonresident aliens enrolled fall 2008. Students from Europe, Asia, Central and South America, Africa. Programs available to aid students whose native language is not English: social, cultural, financial. Financial aid specifically designated for international students; scholarships available annually to qualifying students.

Student Life: On-campus residence halls house 705 of student body. 7% of student body live on campus in college-owned houses. 50% of males join and 20% live in fraternity housing; 50% of females join and 12% live in sorority housing. *Intercollegiate athletics:* male: baseball, basketball, cross-country, football, golf, soccer, tennis, track, wrestling; female: basketball, cross-country, soccer, softball, tennis, track, volleyball. *Special regulations:* Cars permitted. Quiet hours. Residence halls establish visitation hours. *Special services:* Student health service. *Student publications, radio, television: The Black and Magenta*, a weekly newspaper; *The First Circle*, a literary arts magazine; *Muscoljuan*, a yearbook. Radio station WMCO broadcasts 119 hours per week. TV station WMCO broadcasts 10 hours per week. *Surrounding community:* Columbus, 70 miles from campus, is nearest metropolitan area. Served by airport 70 miles from campus; bus service in Cambridge, 7 miles east.

Library Collections: 203,000 volumes. Current serial subscriptions: paper 5,655, microform 17,000; via electronic access 5,000. Computer work stations avaialble. Students have access to online information retrieval services and the Internet.

Most important special collections are Ohio History; Papers of Muskingum College Presidents; British History.

Buildings and Grounds: Campus area 215 acres.

Chief Executive Officer: Dr. Anne C. Steele, President.

Address undergraduate admission inquiries to Beth Dalonzo, Director of Admissions; graduate inquiries to Ruthann Fagan, Dean of Graduate and Continuing Studies.

Northeastern Ohio Universities College of Medicine and Pharmacy

4209 State Route 44
P.O. Box 95
Rootstown, Ohio 44272-0095
Tel: (330) 325-2511 **E-mail:** admission@neoucom.edu
Fax: (33G) 325-7943 **Internet:** www.neoucom.edu

Institution Description: Northeastern Ohio Universities College of Medicine is a public state university partnered with the University of Akron, Kent State University, and Youngstown State University. *Enrollment:* 602. *Degree awarded:* first-professional (doctor of medicine).

Budget subject to approval by state coordinating bodies.

Accreditation: *Professional*: medicine

History: Established 1973.

Institutional Structure: *Governing board:* Board of Trustees. Extrainstitutional representation: 9 trustees; Academic Council of 34 members. *Composition of institution:* Administrators 8, president/dean, senior vice president and executive associate dean for academic affairs; vice president for administration and finance; vice president for institutional advancement for public relations and development; associate dean for clinical affairs; associate dean for research and sponsored programs. Full-time instructional faculty 48, 1,8=954 clinical physicians teach in the college's 18 associated hospitals.

Calendar: The innovative 6-year curriculum leading to the combined BS/MD degree accepts recent high school graduates not previously enrolled in a college program; it provides a total of 24 quarters of academic experience which can be taken in a minimum of 6 years but which may be extended.

Characteristics of Freshmen: Average secondary school rank 95th percentile. Mean ACT composite score 30.

18% of applicants accepted. 401% of accepted applicants enrolled.

90% of freshmen from Ohio. Students from 7 states.

Admission: The college has 3 admission access points. Students are accepted for the combined BS/MD program directly from high school. Applications for the program are due Dec. 15 of the year preceding admission. Students are accepted by one of the 3 consortium universities (University of Akron, Kent State University, Youngstown State University) for the first 2 years of premedical study. After satisfactory performance, they are promoted to the medical phase of the program, which lasts 4 years. The second admission point follows a premedical curriculum at an accredited college or university. Students applying for the four-year M.D. degree program make application through the American Medical College Application Service, Suite 301, 1776 Massachusetts Avenue, NW, Washington, DC 20036. The third admission point occurs after a student has enrolled in another medical school and wishes to transfer to NEOUCOM. Applications for advanced standing (transfer) admission can be obtained through NEOUCOM. Further information on the competitive admissions procedures should be obtained through NEOUCOM admissions office.

Degree Requirements: Students in the combined BS/MD degree program must satisfy all requirements for their BS degrees through the University of Akron, Kent State University, or Youngstown State University. M.D. requirements through NEOUCOM include achieving at least a satisfactory grade in all required courses; demonstrating appropriate human qualities; completing B.S. degree requirements; passing steps 1 and 2 of the U.S. Medical Licensing Examination; being in full-time attendance at NEOUCOM for at least 2 consecutive years including the junior medical year.

Distinctive Educational Programs: NEOUCOM offers the only six-year combined BS/MD program in Ohio. There is also a Center for Studies of Clinical Performance.

Degrees Conferred: 101 *first-professional:* medicine.

Fees and Other Expenses: *Full-time tuition per academic year 2008–09:* conact the institution for current information regarding tuition, fees, and other costs.

Financial Aid: Aid from institutionally generated funds is provided on the basis of financial need.

Institutional funding for graduate students: 39 federal and state-funded grants totaling $653,842; 378 federal and state-funded loans totaling $13,123,510; 202 other fellowships and grants totaling $477,298.

Departments and Teaching Staff:

Total instructional faculty: 46. Degrees held by full-time faculty: doctorate 100%.

Enrollment: Total enrollment 602. First-professional 602.

NORTHEASTERN OHIO UNIVERSITIES COLLEGE OF MEDICINE AND PHARMACY—*cont'd*

Characteristics of Student Body: *Ethnic/racial makeup:* Black non-Hispanic: 4%; Asian or Pacific Islander: 27%; Hispanic: 2%; White non-Hispanic: 61%; unknown: 5%.

International Students: No programs available to aid students whose native language is not English. No financial aid specifically designated for international students.

Publications: Viewbook, catalog, minority brochure, NEOUCOM Newsletter, Dean's Update.

Library Collections: 126,000 volumes. 256 paper serial subscriptions; 3,493 via electronic access. 876 audio/videotapes; 25 DVD discs; 220 CD-ROMs. Computer work stations available. Students have access to online information retrieval services and the Internet.

Most important special collections include Ron. G. Randolph Library of the Human Ecology Research Foundation; Medical Education Development Corporation Manuscripts Collection; Albany Medical College Inaugural Theses.

Buildings and Grounds: Campus area 54 acres.

Chief Executive Officer: Dr. Lois Margaret Nora, M.D., J.D., President and Dean.

Address admission inquiries to Polly Moss, Assistant Dean, Student Affairs and Admissions.

Notre Dame College of Ohio

4545 College Road
Cleveland, Ohio 44121-4293
Tel: (216) 381-1680 **E-mail:** admissions@ndc.edu
Fax: (216) 381-3802 **Internet:** www.ndc.edu

Institution Description: Notre Dame College of Ohio is a private college affiliated with the Sisters of Notre Dame, Roman Catholic Church. *Enrollment:* 1,637. Men are admitted through cross-registration with area colleges. *Degrees awarded:* Associate, baccalaureate, master's.

Member of the Northeast Ohio Council on Higher Education.

Accreditation: *Regional:* NCA.

History: Established as Notre Dame College and offered first instruction postsecondary level 1922; chartered 1923; awarded first degree (baccalaureate) 1926; registered trade name Notre Dame College of Ohio 1965.

Institutional Structure: *Governing board:* Board of Trustees. Representation: 7 members, all Sisters of Notre Dame, including provincial superior of congregation of sisters and president of the college. 2 ex officio. All voting. *Composition of institution:* Administrators 27. Academic affairs headed by dean of academic affairs. Management/business/finances directed by comptroller. Full-time instructional faculty 26. Academic governance body, Academic Council, meets an average of 28 times per year.

Calendar: Semesters. Academic year Aug. to May. Freshmen admitted Aug., Jan. Degrees conferred and formal commencement May. Summer session from June to July.

Characteristics of Freshmen: 1,950 applicants (female 1,950, male 699). 52% of applicants admitted. 30% of admitted students enrolled full-time.

35% (79 students) submitted SAT scores; 76% (171 students) submitted ACT scores. *25th percentile*: SAT Critical Reading 425, SAT Math 430; ACT Composite 18, ACT English 16, ACT Math 17. *75th percentile*: SAT Critical Reading 530, SAT Math 530; ACT Composite 21, ACT English 21, ACT Math 21.

34% of entering freshmen expected to graduate within 5 years. 95% of freshmen from Ohio. Freshmen from 8 states and 8 foreign countries.

Admission: Rolling admissions plan. For fall acceptance, apply as early as June 15 of previous year. Early acceptance available. *Requirements:* Either graduation from accredited secondary school with 15 academic units which must include 4 English, 2 in same foreign language, 3 mathematics, 2 social studies, 2 laboratory science, 2 electives; or GED. Additional requirements for some programs. Minimum 2.56 GPA. *Entrance tests:* College Board SAT or ACT composite. *For transfer students:* 2.0 minimum GPA; 96 semester hours maximum transfer credit; from 2-year accredited institution 64 semester hours.

Advanced placement for postsecondary-level work completed in secondary school. College credit and advanced placement for extrainstitutional learning on basis of portfolio and faculty assessment, personal interviews.

Tutoring available. Noncredit developmental courses offered during regular academic year.

Degree Requirements: *For all associate degrees:* 64 credit hours; 2.0 GPA by graduation; 1 semester in residence. *For all baccalaureate degrees:* 128 credit hours; 2.0 GPA by end of sophomore year; 2 semesters in residence; 2 courses physical education. *For all degrees:* exit competency examination and/or comprehensives in some fields of study; distribution requirements.

Fulfillment of some degree requirements and exemption from some beginning courses possible by passing College Board CLEP, AP. *Grading system:* A–F; pass-fail; withdraw (carries deadline) incomplete (carries deadline).

Distinctive Educational Programs: Cooperative education. Weekend and evening classes. Dual-degree programs in engineering with Case Western Reserve University. Cooperative baccalaureate in medical technology with area hospitals. Interdisciplinary studies include programs on international business, human resources development, nutrition services, marketing, chemistry, management. Summer tours and courses abroad as arranged by college; year abroad through programs offered by Notre Dame or other approved institutions. Cross-registration with other colleges in consortium. Continuing education through The Weekend College. Associate and baccalaureate degree programs in Basic Catechetics and Lay Leadership in Ministry through Center for Pastoral Ministry.

Degrees Conferred: 8 *associate;* 97 *baccalaureate*; 97 *master's*; 26 *doctorate*. Bachelor's degrees awarded in top five disciplines: business, management, marketing, and related support services 31; education 19; psychology 3; legal studies 3; communication, journalism, and related programs 3.

Fees and Other Expenses: *Full-time tuition per academic year 2008–09:* $22,096 undergraduate; contact the college for current graduate tuition and fees. *Books and supplies:* $1,785. *Room and board per academic year:* $7,732. *Other expenses:* $1,541.

Financial Aid: Aid from institutionally generated funds is provided on the basis of financial need, other criteria. Institution has a Program Participation Agreement with the U.S. Department of Education for eligible students to receive Pell Grants and, depending upon the agreement, other federal aid.

Financial aid to full-time, first-time undergraduate students: 100% received some form of financial aid. Average amount of aid received: federal grants $3,209; state/local grants $1,869; institutional grants $9,779; loans $5,268.

Departments and Teaching Staff: *Total instructional faculty:* 79. Student/faculty ratio: 11:1. Degrees held by full-time faculty: doctorate 91%, master's 50%.

Enrollment: Total enrollment 1,637. Undergraduate 1,452 (female 66%, male 34%). Graduate 185 (part-time 100%). Undergraduate transfer-in students 189.

Characteristics of Student Body: *Ethnic/racial makeup:* Black non-Hispanic: 19%; Asian or Pacific Islander 1%; Hispanic: 2%; White non-Hispanic: 58%; unknown 17%; nonresident alien 1%.

International Students: 16 nonresident aliens enrolled fall 2008. No programs available to aid students whose native language is not English. No financial aid specifically designated for international students.

Student Life: On-campus residence halls house 17% of student body. *Intercollegiate athletics:* Basketball, volleyball. *Special regulations:* Cars permitted without restrictions. *Special services:* Learning Resources Center, medical services. *Student publications: Notre Dame News*, published monthly; *Pivot*, a yearbook and literary publication. *Surrounding community:* Cleveland population 506,000. Served by mass transit system; airport 25 miles from campus; passenger rail service 14 miles from campus.

Library Collections: 89,500 volumes. 14,500 microforms; 1,800 audiovisual materials; 300 current periodical subscriptions. Students have access to online information retrieval services and the Internet.

Most important special holdings include collections on theology, education, and philosophy.

Buildings and Grounds: Campus area 53 acres.

Chief Executive Officer: Dr. Andrew P. Roth, President.

Address admission inquiries to David A. Armstrong, Dean of Admissions.

Oberlin College

70 North Professor Street
Oberlin, Ohio 44074
Tel: (440) 775-8411 **E-mail:** admissions@oberlin.edu
Fax: (440) 775-6905 **Internet:** www.oberlin.edu

Institution Description: Oberlin College is a private, independent, nonprofit college and conservatory of music. *Enrollment:* 2,841. *Degrees awarded:* Baccalaureate, performance diploma, master's, artist diploma.

Member of consortium Great Lakes Colleges Association.

Accreditation: *Regional:* NCA. *Professional*: music

History: Established as Oberlin Collegiate Institute 1833; chartered and offered first instruction at postsecondary level 1834; awarded first degree (baccalaureate) 1837; adopted present name 1850. *See* Robert S. Fletcher, *A History of Oberlin College from Its Foundation Through the Civil War* (Oberlin: Oberlin College, 1943) for further information.

Institutional Structure: *Governing board:* Board of Trustees of Oberlin College. Extrainstitutional representation: 27 trustees, including 6 alumni, 3 class trustees; institutional representation: president of the college, ex officio. All voting. *Composition of institution:* Administrators 219. Academic affairs headed by deans of the college of arts and sciences and conservatory of music. Full-time instructional faculty 288. Academic governance body, General Faculty, meets an average of 10 times per year.

Calendar: Semesters (4-1-4 plan). Academic year Sept. to May. Freshmen admitted Sept., Feb. Degrees conferred May, Dec. Formal commencement May. No summer session.

Characteristics of Freshmen: 6,686 applicants (3,848 female, 2,838 male). 34% of applicants admitted. 37% of admitted students enrolled full-time.

89% (640 students) submitted SAT scores; 31% (222 students) submitted ACT scores. *25th percentile*: SAT Critical Reading 650, SAT Math 620; ACT Composite 27. *75th percentile*: SAT Critical Reading 750, SAT Math 710; ACT Composite 31.

82% of entering freshmen expected to graduate within 5 years. 9% of freshmen from Ohio. Freshmen from 45 states and 30 foreign countries.

Admission: For fall acceptance, apply as early as Sept. 15 of previous year, but not later than Feb. 15. Students are notified of acceptance Apr. Apply by Feb. 1 for early decision; must withdraw other applications if accepted at Oberlin. Early acceptance available. *Requirements:* No specific requirements. Recommend 15 academic units, including 4 in English (with an emphasis on writing), 4 in mathematics, and 3 each in one foreign language, natural science, and social studies, including history. Minimum recommended GPA 3.0. *Entrance tests:* College Board SAT or ACT composite. For foreign students TOEFL. *For transfer students:* 56 hours maximum transfer credit.

College credit and advanced placement for postsecondary-level work completed in secondary school.

Tutoring available. Developmental courses offered during regular academic year; credit given.

Degree Requirements: *For undergraduate degrees:* In order to graduate, all arts and sciences students must complete the requirements for a major, earn 3 winter term credits, demonstrate quantitative and writing proficiency, and complete 112 credit hours. No more than half of these credits can be from a single department or program, and no more than three-quarters can be from any one division. In addition, students are required to complete 9 credit hours in each of Oberlin's three divisions (arts and humanities, social and behavioral sciences, and natural sciences and humanities). Finally, each student must take 9 credit hours in courses that deal with cultural diversity.

Fulfillment of some degree requirements and exemption from some beginning courses possible by passing departmental examinations, College Board, AP. *Grading system:* A–C; no entry; pass.

Distinctive Educational Programs: *For undergraduates:* 3/2 engineering programs with Case Western Reserve University, the University of Pennsylvania, and Washington University (MO). 5-year double-degree program leading to a baccalaureate in arts plus a baccalaureate in music awarded by the college's conservatory of music. Interdisciplinary programs in archaeological studies, Black studies, comparative literature, East Asian studies, environmental studies, Judaic and Near Eastern studies, Latin American studies, law and society, neuroscience and biopsychology, women's studies. Facilities for independent research, including honors programs, individual majors, tutorials, senior scholar's program. Institutionally sponsored study abroad in London, France, China, Vienna, Ireland, Austria, and Germany; at the college's archaeological excavation in Tell el-Hesi, Israel, during summer; in Mexico during winter term. Also foreign study in Japan through the Associated Kyoto Program; in Leningrad through the Council on International Educational Exchange; in Rome through the Intercollegiate Center for Classical Studies. Study abroad programs through the consortium in the Dominican Republic, East and West Africa, Hong Kong, India, Japan, Scotland, Yugoslavia. Study abroad may also be individually arranged. Off-campus study in the U.S. includes institutionally sponsored summer archaeological field studies and geological field work in the Appalachian and Rocky Mountains. Also through the consortium, New York City arts program, Newberry Library (IL) humanities program; Oak Ridge (TN) science semester, Philadelphia urban semester. Off-campus study also available by individual arrangement. Exchange programs with Fisk University (TN) and Gallaudet. Winter term provides opportunity for group or individual study on- or off-campus. *Available to all students:* Experimental College offers student-taught special interest courses, some for credit. Allen Memorial Art Building houses materials dating from antiquity to the present, including collections of 17th-century Dutch paintings, 19th- and 20th-century European and American paintings, 1,500 Japanese woodcuts, contemporary painting and sculpture. *Other distinctive programs:* Oberlin's Business Initiatives Program secures private-sector internships in which students are expected to solve problems, accomplish specific goals, and use their analytical skills. Most of these internships take place during the summer and fall into one of three categories: general business internships in such areas as economic forecasting, sales management, and industrial relations; scientific internships requiring the same kind of intellectual and theoretical rigor as academic fellowships; and communications internships, such as newspaper reporting, advertising copy writing, public relations work, and television news broadcasting.

Degrees Conferred: 685 *baccalaureate*; 6 *master's*. Bachelor's degrees awarded in top five disciplines: business, management, marketing, and related support services 192; social sciences 106; English language/literature 80; biomedical/biological sciences 54; area and ethnic studies 52.

Fees and Other Expenses: *Full-time tuition per academic year 2008–09:* contact the college for current information.

Financial Aid: Aid from institutionally generated funds is provided on the basis of financial need. Institution has a Program Participation Agreement with the U.S. Department of Education for eligible students to receive Pell Grants and, depending upon the agreement, other federal aid.

Financial aid to full-time, first-time undergraduate students: 56% received some form of financial aid. Average amount of aid received: federal grants $3,952; state/local grants $1,811; institutional grants $19,720; loans $3,964.

Departments and Teaching Staff: *Total instructional faculty:* 258. Student/faculty ratio: 10:1. Degrees held by full-time faculty: baccalaureate 100%, master's 100%, doctorate 94%. 92% hold terminal degrees.

Enrollment: Total enrollment 2,841.

Characteristics of Student Body: *Ethnic/racial makeup:* Black non-Hispanic: 5%; American Indian or Alaska Native: 1%; Asian or Pacific Islander: 8%; Hispanic: 5%; White non-Hispanic: 76%.

International Students: 170 nonresident aliens enrolled fall 2008. Students from Europe, Asia, Central and South America, Africa, Canada, Australia, New Zealand. No programs available to aid students whose native language is not English. Financial aid specifically designated for international students: scholarships available annually to qualifying students.

Student Life: On-campus residence halls house 75% of student body. Residence halls for males constitute 2% of such space, for females 3%, for both sexes 95%. 8% of student body housed in cooperative facilities. *Intercollegiate athletics:* male: baseball, basketball, cross-country, football, lacrosse, soccer, swimming, tennis, indoor and outdoor track; female: basketball, cross-country, field hockey, lacrosse, soccer, swimming, tennis, indoor and outdoor track, volleyball. *Special regulations:* In general, freshmen are not permitted to have cars, but they may obtain permission for a car for critical medical reasons. Sophomores, juniors, and seniors must register vehicles with security department. Students may park but not operate vehicles on campus. Quiet hours set by residence hall. *Special services:* career development and placement office; student support services center offering tutoring, workshops, counseling, and other services; medical services; security escorts provide transportation when necessary. *Student publications, radio: Nommo*, a Black student newspaper; *Hi-O-Hi*, the yearbook; *The Oberlin Review*, a weekly student newspaper; *Perspective*, a newsmagazine; *Plum Creek Review*, a literary magazine; *Rain*, a Black literary magazine. WOBC-FM, a student-run radio station. *Surrounding community:* Oberlin population 8,000. Cleveland, 35 miles from campus, is nearest metropolitan area. Airport 25 miles from campus; commercial limousine service between airport and campus available; passenger rail service 8 miles from campus.

Publications: *Field* (biannually) first published in 1969.

Library Collections: 1,353,000 volumes. 21,000 serial subscriptions including electronic access. 87,000 audiovisual materials. Online catalog. Students have access to online information retrieval services and the Internet.

Most important holdings include antislavery collection (1,435 titles, including 80 volumes of bound pamphlets); Violin Society of America/Goodkind Collection on the history and construction of the violin; Frederick B. Artz Collection on the history of the book.

Buildings and Grounds: Campus area 440 acres.

Chief Executive Officer: Dr. Nancy S. Dye, President.

Address admission inquiries to College Admissions.

The Oberlin Conservatory of Music

Degree Programs Offered: *Baccalaureate* in performance, composition, music education, music history, historical performance, electronic and computer music, and jazz studies; *master of music* in performance on historical instruments; 3 combined undergraduate and graduate programs leading to a master of music in conducting or opera theater, master of music education, or master of music in teaching. Performance and artist diplomas in certain departments.

Admission: *See* general requirements. In addition to general requirements, audition required for all but prospective composition majors. Graduate requirements vary.

Degree Requirements: *For baccalaureate degree:* 124 credit hours; 4 semesters in residence. *For baccalaureate in performance:* Recital requirements. Graduate requirements vary.

OBERLIN COLLEGE—*cont'd*

Distinctive Educational Programs: Music theory and accompanying may be pursued as part of a double major. Ethnomusicology is offered as a minor. 5-year double degree program leads to baccalaureate in music plus baccalaureate of arts from College of Arts and Sciences. Extensive series of summer institutes includes programs for high school- and college-student musicians, as well as professional musicians. Among these is the Baroque Performance Institute.

Ohio Christian University

1476 Lancaster PIke
P.O. Box 458
Circleville, Ohio 43113-0458
Tel: (740) 474-8896 **E-mail:** enroll@ohiochristian.edu
Fax: (740) 477-7755 **Internet:** www.ohiochristian.edu

Institution Description: Ohio Christian University, formerly named Circleville Bible College, is an institution of higher learning of the Churches of Christ in Christian Union. *Enrollment:* 730. *Degrees awarded:* Associate, baccalaureate.

Accreditation: *Regional:* NCA. *National:* ABHE.

History: Established 1948.

Calendar: Semesters. Academic year Aug. to May.

Characteristics of Freshmen: 311 applicants (fenale 112, male 199). 90% of applicants admitted. 29% of applicants admitted and enrolled full-time.

91% (48 students) submitted ACT scores. *25th percentile*: ACT Composite 16, ACT English 18, ACT Math 15. *75th percentile*: ACT Composite 22, ACT English 24, ACT Math 21.

87% of freshmen from Ohio. Freshmen from 4 states.

Admission: *Requirements:* Graduation from secondary school in upper half. *Entrance tests:* College Board SAT or ACT.

Degree Requirements: Completion of prescribed curriculum; chapel attendance required.

Degrees Conferred: 5 *associate;* 104 *baccalaureate:* theology and religious studies.

Fees and Other Expenses: *Full-time tuition per academic year 2008–09:* $14,060. *Required fees:* $1,090. *Room and board per academic year:* $5,990. *Books and supplies:* $1,900. *Other expenses:* $6,000.

Financial Aid: Aid from institutionally generated funds is provided on the basis of academic merit, financial need. Institution has a Program Participation Agreement with the U.S. Department of Education for eligible students to receive Pell Grants and, depending upon the agreement, other federal aid.

Departments and Teaching Staff: *Total instructional faculty:* 38 (full-time 15, part-time 23). Student/faculty ratio: 13:1. Degrees held by full-time faculty: master's 100%, doctorate 20%.

Enrollment: Total enrollment 730 (undergradaute). Transfer-in students 139.

Characteristics of Student Body: *Ethnic/racial makeup:* Black non-Hispanic: 23%; American Indian or Alaska Native: 1%; Asian or Pacific Islander: 1%; Hispanic: 2%; White non-Hispanic: 71%; nonresident alien 1%. *Age distribution:* number under 18: 8; 18–19: 66; 20–21: 80; 22–24: 70; 25–29: 48; 30–34: 27; 35–39: 46; 40–49: 63; 50–64: 23.

International Students: 7 nonresident aliens enrolled fall 2008. Students from Europe, Asia, Africa. No programs for students whose native language is not English. No financial aid specifically designated for international students.

Library Collections: 51,000 volumes including bound books, serial backfiles, electronic documents, and government documents not in separate collections. Online catalog. Current serial subscriptions: 255 paper, 950 via electronic access. Computer work stations avaialble. Students have access to the Internet and online information retrieval services.

Most important special collections include Wesleyan-Holiness Theology; Stout Bible Collection.

Buildings and Grounds: *New buildings:* Campus Ministry Center completed 2007.

Chief Executive Officer: Dr. Mark A. Smith, President.

Address admission inquiries to Dr. Michael Egenreider, Director of Enrollment Services.

Ohio College of Podiatric Medicine

10515 Carnegie Avenue
Cleveland, Ohio 44106
Tel: (216) 231-3300 **E-mail:** admissions@ocpm.edu
Fax: (216) 231-0453 **Internet:** www.ocpm.edu

Institution Description: The Ohio College of Podiatric Medicine is a private college offering a four-year course of study leading to the Doctor of Podiatric Medicine degree. *Enrollment:* 386. *Degrees awarded:* First-professional.

Accreditation: *Regional:* NCA. *Professional*: podiatry

History: Established 1916.

Calendar: Semesters. Academic year Aug. to May.

Admission: *Requirements:* 90 semester or 135 quarter hours of undergraduate studies at an accredited college or university; coursework should include biology, chemistry, organic chemistry, and physics. *Entrance tests:* MCAT.

Degree Requirements: Completion of prescribed curriculum.

Degrees Conferred: 77 *first-professional:* podiatric medicine.

Fees and Other Expenses: *Full-time tuition per academic year 2008–09:* contact the college for current information.

Financial Aid: Aid from institutionally generated funds is provided on the basis of academic merit, financial need. *Graduate aid:* 143 students received $803,218 in federal and state-funded fellowships/grants; 861 received $9,950,595 in federal and state-funded loans; 167 received $267,584 for college-assigned jobs.

Departments and Teaching Staff: *Total instructional faculty:* 26. Degrees held by full-time faculty: master's 1%, doctorate 99%. 99% hold terminal degrees.

Enrollment: Total enrollment 386 (First-professional).

International Students: 20 nonresident aliens enrolled fall 2008. No programs available to aid students whose native language is not English. No financial aid specifically designated for international students.

Student Life: Several service fraternities, clubs, sports, IFC. *Student publications: Footprints; Occopodian*, a yearbook.

Library Collections: 16,000 volumes. 75 current periodical subscriptions; access to 300 other titles via electronic access. 558 recordings. 18 DVD discs. Computer work stations available. Students have access to online information retrieval services and the Internet.

Most important special collections include podiatric medicine collection.

Buildings and Grounds: *New buildings:* Carnegie Surgery Center.

Chief Executive Officer: Dr. Thomas Meilillo, President.

Address admission inquiries to Lois Lott, Dean of Student Affairs.

Ohio Dominican University

1216 Sunbury Road
Columbus, Ohio 43219
Tel: (614) 253-2741 **E-mail:** admissions@ohiodominican.edu
Fax: (614) 252-0776 **Internet:** www.ohiodominican.edu

Institution Description: Ohio Dominican University is a private institution affiliated with the Dominican Sisters of Saint Mary of the Springs, Roman Catholic Church. *Enrollment:* 3,117. *Degrees awarded:* Associate, baccalaureate, master's. Certificates also awarded.

Accreditation: *Regional:* NCA.

History: Established as College of Saint Mary of the Springs, chartered, and offered first instruction at postsecondary level 1911; awarded first degree (baccalaureate) 1927; became Ohio Dominican College 1968; achieved university status 2002.

Institutional Structure: *Governing board:* Board of Trustees. Representation: 36 trustees, including 14 alumni and university president. 4 ex officio. All voting. *Composition of institution:* Administrators 30. Academic affairs headed by vice president for academic affairs. Management/business/finances directed by vice president for university resources. Full-time instructional faculty 70. Academic governance body, Faculty Assembly, meets an average of 4 times per year.

Calendar: Semesters. Academic year Aug. to May. Freshmen admitted Sept., Jan., June. Degrees conferred May, Dec., Aug. Formal commencement May, Dec. Summer session from June to Aug.

Characteristics of Freshmen: 73% of applicants admitted. 25% of applicants admitted and enrolled.

90% (319 students) submitted ACT scores. *25th percentile*: ACT Composite 18. *75th percentile*: ACT Composite 25.

49% of entering freshmen expected to graduate within 5 years. 92% of freshmen from Ohio. Freshmen from 27 states.

Admission: Rolling admissions plan. For fall acceptance, apply as early as 1 year prior to enrollment, but not later than 1 week before registration. Early acceptance available. *Requirements:* Either graduation from accredited secondary school with college preparatory program or GED. 16 units including 4 English, 3 foreign language, 3 mathematics, 3 social studies, 3 science. Minimum 2.0 GPA. *Entrance tests:* College Board SAT or ACT composite. *For transfer students:* 2.0 minimum GPA; from 4-year accredited institution maximum transfer credit limited only by residence requirements; from 2-year accredited institution 68 hours maximum.

College credit and advanced placement for postsecondary-level work completed in secondary school. College credit for extrainstitutional learning.

Tutoring available. Developmental courses offered in summer session and regular academic year; credit given.

Degree Requirements: *For all associate degrees:* 62 semester hours; 24 hours in residence, including 12 in major or closely related field. *For all baccalaureate degrees:* 124 semester hours; 32 of last 60 hours in residence including 12 in major; exit competency examinations/comprehensives in some fields of study. *For all undergraduate degrees:* 2.0 GPA; 1 hour physical education; distribution requirements.

Fulfillment of some degree requirements and exemption from some beginning courses possible by passing College Board CLEP or APP. *Grading system:* A–F; pass; withdraw (carries time limit); incomplete.

Distinctive Educational Programs: Evening and weekend classes. Preprofessional program in engineering. Special facilities for using telecommunications in the classroom. Interdepartmental/interdisciplinary programs in general studies, liberal studies, social sciences. Facilities and programs for independent research, including honors programs, individual majors, tutorials. Study abroad by individual arrangement. Servicemembers Opportunity College. Weekend College.

ROTC: Army offered in cooperation with Capital University.

Degrees Conferred: 77 *associate;* 451 *baccalaureate*; 254 *master's*. Bachelor's degrees awarded in top five disciplines: business/marketing 144; education 92; social sciences 27; liberal arts/general studies 21; communications/communication technologies 13. Master's degrees awarded: business/marketing 132; education 9; liberal arts/general studies; philosophy/religious studics 3; other'110.

Fees and Other Expenses: *Full-time tuition per academic year 2008–09:* $23,140; contact the university for current graduate tuition/fees. *Required fees:* $70. *Room and board per academic year:* $7,590. *Books and supplies:* $1,000. *Other expenses* $2,100.

Financial Aid: Aid from institutionally generated funds is provided on the basis of academic merit, financial need, other criteria. Financial assistance is available in the form of Pell Grants, College Work-Study, Veterans Administration Benefits, National Direct Student Loans, Supplemental Education Opportunity Grants (SEOG), Stafford Loans, other federal aid programs.

Financial aid to full-time, first-time undergraduate students: 100% received some form of financial aid.

Departments and Teaching Staff: *Total instructional faculty:* 217 (full-time 70, part-time 147). Total faculty with doctorate, first-professional, or other terminal degree: 116. Student/faculty ratio: 14:1. Degrees held by full-time faculty: doctorate 71%, master's 26%, professional 3%. 75% hold terminal degrees.

Enrollment: Total enrollment 2,854. Undergraduate 2,430 (female 61%; male 39%). Graduate 687 (full-time 80%). Undergraduate transfer-in students 106.

Characteristics of Student Body: *Ethnic/racial makeup:* Black non-Hispanic: 22%; Asian or Pacific Islander: 1%; Hispanic: 2%; White non-Hispanic: 73%; unknown: 1%; nonresident alien 1%. *Age distribution:* number under 18: 171; 18–19: 609; 20–21: 470; 22–24: 277; 25–29: 325; 30–34: 220; 35–39: 173; 40–49: 208; 50–64: 64; 65 and over: 1. 38% of student body attend summer sessions.

International Students: 31 nonresident aliens enrolled fall 2008. Students from Europe, Asia, Central and South Latin America, Africa, Canada, Australia. Programs available to aid students whose native language is not English: social, cultural. English as a Second Language courses. No financial aid specifically designated for international students.

Student Life: On-campus residence halls house 25% of student body. Residence halls for for both sexes 100f%. *Intercollegiate athletics:* male: baseball, basketball, football, golf, soccer; female: basketball, golf, soccer, softball, volleyball. *Special regulations:* Cars permitted without restrictions. *Special services:* Academic Resource Center, medical services. *Student publications, radio: Gesture*, a literary magazine published 3 times a year; *The Tower*, a quarterly newspaper. Radio station WODR broadcasts regularly. *Surrounding community:* Columbus population 565,000. Served by mass transit bus system; airport 2 miles from campus.

Library Collections: 114,739 volumes. Online and card catalog. Current serial subscriptions: paper 511; microform 10,030, via electronic access 6,950. 3,470 recordings; 559 DVD discs; 208 CD-ROMs. Students have access to online information retrieval services and the Internet.

Most important special holdings include Monsignor Wolz Collection (Biblical studies and archaeology); Anne O'Hare McCormick papers (personal correspondence and articles); Columbus Catholic Diocese Newspaper (1875 to present).

Buildings and Grounds: Campus area 80 acres.

Chief Executive Officer: Dr. Jack P. Calarreo, President.

Address admission inquiries to Nicole Evans, Director of Admissions.

Ohio Northern University

525 South Main Street
Ada, Ohio 45810
Tel: (419) 772-2000 **E-mail:** admissions@onu.edu
Fax: (419) 772-1932 **Internet:** www.onu.edu

Institution Description: Ohio Northern University is a private institution affiliated with the United Methodist Church. *Enrollment:* 3,721. *Degrees awarded:* Baccalaureate, first-professional (law, pharmacy). Member of Ohio College Association.

Accreditation: *Regional:* NCA. *Professional*: athletic training, business, chemistry, engineering, law, music, nursing, pharmacy, teacher education

History: Established as Northwestern Ohio Normal School and offered first instruction at postsecondary level 1871; awarded first degree (baccalaureate) 1874; chartered and changed name to Ohio Normal University 1885; adopted present name 1903.

Institutional Structure: *Governing board:* The Board of Trustees of Ohio Northern University. Extrainstitutional representation: 40 trustees, bishop of West Ohio Conference, 12 life trustees; institutional representation: president of the university, 2 full-time instructional faculty members, 2 students; president of the alumni association 40 voting. *Composition of institution:* Academic affairs headed by vice president for academic affairs. Management/business/finances directed by vice president for financial affairs. Advancement, publications, alumni, planned giving headed by a vice president. Student affairs, housing, placement, counseling, and multicultural affairs headed by a vice president. Full-time instructional faculty 229. University Council; 4 standing faculty committees (budget and appropriations, personnel, academic affairs, student activities); 5 operational committees (grievance, promotion and tenure appeal, athletics, international affairs, cultural affairs). Committees and Council meet weekly or biweekly. Faculty meets 9 times per year.

Calendar: Quarters. Academic year Sept. to May. Law: semesters. Academic year Aug. to May. Freshmen admitted Sept., Dec., Mar., May. Degrees conferred Dec., May and formal commencement May. Summer sessions from June to Aug.

Characteristics of Freshmen: 3,294 applicants (female 1,656, male 1,642). 87% of applicants admitted. 27% of applicants admitted and enrolled full time.

48% (566 students) submitted SAT scores; 90% (687 students) submitted ACT scores. *25th percentile*: SAT Critical Reading 520, SAT Math 540; ACT Composite 23, ACT English 21, ACT Math 24. *75th percentile*: SAT Critical Reading 630, SAT Math 650, ACT Composite 28, ACT English 29, ACT Math 29. 11 National Merit Scholars.

84% of entering freshmen expected to graduate within 5 years. 86% of freshmen from Ohio. Freshmen from 42 states and 18 foreign countries.

Admission: Rolling admissions plan (except in pharmacy). Maximum consideration for academic scholarships is made for students accepted prior to Dec. 1 of their senior year. *Requirements:* Either graduation from accredited secondary school with 16 units (12 from academic areas), or GED. Minimum 2.5 GPA and class rank of 50% or higher. *Entrance tests:* standards vary by college entrance test scores, high school GPA, rank and curriculum are all taken into consideration. *For transfer students:* 2.0 minimum GPA; from 4- and 2-year accredited institution maximum transfer credit limited only by residence requirement.

College credit for postsecondary-level work completed in secondary school (subject to review). Tutoring available.

Degree Requirements: *For undergraduate degrees:* 2.0 GPA; last 45 quarter hours in residence; 3 hours physical education for all but engineering and pharmacy students; 1 religion course; 2 writing courses, 1 in engineering.

Fulfillment of some degree requirements possible by passing College Board CLEP, AP, other standardized tests. *Grading system:* A–F; pass-fail; withdraw (carries time limit).

Distinctive Educational Programs: Facilities and programs for independent research. Interdepartmental and interdisciplinary programs. Faculty-directed consulting work at the Small Business Institute. Cross-college programs. Honors Program. co-op program in U.S. and abroad for computer science, engineering, mathematics and technology students; internship/externship opportunities in

OHIO NORTHERN UNIVERSITY—*cont'd*

most departments/colleges. Washington Center and Washington Semester programs. Study abroad programs in Costa Rica, Cuba, England, Finland, France, Germany, Japan, Korea, Mexico, Netherlands, Spain, Wales.

ROTC: Army and Air Force in cooperation with Bowling Green State University.

Degrees Conferred: 448 *baccalaureate:*; 8 *master's*; 277 *first-professional.* Bachelor's degrees awarded in top five disciplines: engineering 88; business/marketing 79; education 47; biological/life sciences 44; communications/journalism 24. Master's degrees awarded: education 4. First-professional degrees awarded: pharmacy 116; law 111.

Fees and Other Expenses: *Full-time tuition academic year 2008–09:* undergraduate $30,765; contact the university for current graduate (law) tuition. *Required fees:* $210. *Room and board per academic year:* $7,890. *Books and supplies:* $1,500. *Other expenses:* $1,920.

Financial Aid: Aid from institutionally generated funds is provided on the basis of academic merit, financial need. 99% of first-time, first-year undergraduate students received some form of financial aid.

Departments and Teaching Staff: *Total instructional faculty:* 317 (full-time 229, part-time 88). Total faculty with doctorate, first-professional, or other terminal degree: 201. Student/faculty ratio: 14:1. Degrees held by full-time faculty: baccalaureate 1%, master's 24%, doctorate 75%. 79% hold terminal degrees.

Enrollment: Total enrollment 3,721. Undergraduate 2,745 (female 47%, male 53%). Graduate 976 (full-time 97%). Undergraduate transfer-in students 81.

Characteristics of Student Body: *Ethnic/racial makeup:* Black non-Hispanic: 4%; Asian or Pacific Islander: 2%; Hispanic: 2%; White non-Hispanic: 90%; nonresident alien 2%. *Age distribution:* number under 18: 62; 18–19: 1,318; 20–21: 906; 22–24 249 v25–29: 22; 30–34: 12; 35–39: 12; 40–49: 20; 50–64: 19; 65 and over: 1.

International Students: 74 nonresident aliens enrolled fall 2008. Students from Europe, Asia, Africa, Middle East. Programs available to aid students whose native language is not English: social, cultural. Financial aid specifically designated for international students,

Student Life: On-campus residence halls house 61% of student body. Residence halls for males constitute 32% of such space, for females 34%. Some students live in institutionally owned housing. 17% of males join and 7% live in fraternity housing; 20% of females join and 9% live in sorority housing. *Intercollegiate athletics:* male: baseball, basketball, cross-country, football, golf, soccer, swimming, tennis, track, wrestling and intramural sports; female: basketball, golf, softball, soccer, swimming, tennis, track, cross-country, volleyball and intramural sports. *Special regulations:* Registered cars permitted without restrictions. Quiet hours: Sun.–Thurs. 8pm to 10am and Fri.–Sat. 1am to 10am. Residence hall visitation from 10am to 11pm Sun.–Thurs.; 10am to 1am Fri.–Sat. *Special services:* Medical services. *Student publications, radio: The Northern Review*, a weekly newspaper; *The Northern Yearbook; The Polaris*, a quarterly literary magazine; *Delirium*, a student-produced web magazine. Radio Station WONB broadcasts 24 hours a day year-round and is on the Internet. *Surrounding community:* Ada population 5,000. Toledo, 75 miles from campus, is nearest metropolitan area. Served by airport 75 miles from campus; passenger rail service 40 miles from campus.

Publications: *Ampule* (semiannually), *Engineering Newsletter* (semiannually), *Foreign Exchange Newsletter* (semiannually), *Law Review* (9 quarterly publications), *Alumni Directory* (every ten years), *The Endowment Book* (annually), *Speakers Directory* (annually), *Shakespeare and the Classroom*, (semiannually), *The Writ*, (annually.).

Library Collections: 268,000 volumes including bound books, serial backfiles, electronic documents, and government documents not in separate collections. Online catalog. Current serial subscriptions: 830 paper, 5,500 via electronic access. 5,684 recordings; 1,053 DVD discs; 1,352 CD-ROMs. Computer work stations available. Students have access to the Internet at no charge.

Most important special holdings include ONU Archives; Anthony J. Calebrezze Judicial Archives; William McCullough Papers (Ohio Congressional Representative).

Buildings and Grounds: Campus area 285 acres. Campus DVD available.

Chief Executive Officer: Dr. Kendall L. Baker, President.

Undergraduates address admission inquiries to Karen P. Concdeni, Dean of Enrollment Management; Pettit College of Law: Office Admissions, Pettit College of Law.

Getty College of Arts and Sciences

Degree Programs Offered: *Baccalaureate* in art, athletic training, biochemistry, biology, chemistry, communication arts, criminal justice, elementary education, environmental studies, French, health, health education, history, technology, international studies, mathematics, music, music education, music performance, philosophy, religion, physical education, physics, political science, psychology, religion, sociology, Spanish, sport management.

Admission: In addition to general requirements, 4 units in English, 2 mathematics, 6 from among foreign language, history, natural science, or social studies. Secondary school rank in upper half of class. Recommend secondary school language study.

Degree Requirements: 182 quarter hours including general requirements and completion of an approved major.

Distinctive Educational Programs: Dual-degree programs in arts-engineering; arts-pharmacy; arts-business; interdisciplinary majors. Opportunities for study-abroad in all majors as well as exchange programs.

College of Business Administration

Degree Programs Offered: *Baccalaureate* in accounting, international business and economics, and management.

Admission: *See* general requirements. In addition to general requirements, 4 units English, 3 mathematics (including algebra and geometry), 6 from among foreign language, history, natural science, or social studies. Recommend secondary school language study.

Degree Requirements: 182 quarter hours including general requirements.

Distinctive Educational Programs: Small Business Institute allows students to do faculty-directed consulting work. Internship program provides student on-the-job experiences. International Business Program provides both study and work abroad opportunities for student as well as Summer Business tours. Dual-degree program in business-arts, business-engineering, and business-pharmacy. The college houses a Center of Cuban Business Studies to serve the needs of businesses, government agencies, researchers, faculty, students, and others interested din Cuban commercial affairs.

Thomas Jefferson Smull College of Engineering

Degree Programs Offered: *Baccalaureate* in civil, computer, electrical, and mechanical engineering, computer science.

Admission: In addition to general requirements, 4 units in English, 4 mathematics (2 algebra, 1 geometry, 1/2 trigonometry), 2 science (physics and preferably chemistry), 6 units history, social studies, language or natural science. Recommend secondary school foreign language study. ACT Composite of at least 20 with no individual score less than 20.

Degree Requirements: 192 quarter hours including general requirements; 2.0 GPA in engineering courses and a 2.0 GPA overall.

Distinctive Educational Programs: Dual-degree program for computer science majors with the College of Business; Engineer in Residence program; Project for Industry Ready Engineers; Engineering Research and Assistance Center.

Rudolph H. Raabe College of Pharmacy

Degree Programs Offered: *First-professional, doctor* of pharmacy.

Admission: In addition to general requirements, 4 units in English; 4 mathematics (algebra I and II; plane geometry; trigonometry or precalculus or calculus); 4 science (biology chemistry, and physics); 6 units in history, social studies, languages or natural sciences.

Degree Requirements: 224 quarter hours.

Distinctive Educational Programs: Drug Information Service provides course in drug information retrieval and serves the northwest Ohio medical, pharmaceutical, and nursing professions, providing answers on drug-related questions. Instructional Resources Center provides continuing education for area pharmacists and specialized study for students, including audio and visual programs, journals. There is a Nontraditional Doctor of Pharmacy program designed for Bachelor's trained pharmacists. Double-degree program in arts-pharmacy, business-pharmacy.

Claude W. Pettit College of Law

Degree Programs Offered: *First-professional.*

Admission: Baccalaureate from accredited college or university, LSAT, registration with LSDAS.

Degree Requirements: 87 semester hours, 2.0 GPA, 6 semesters in residence.

The Ohio State University

1900 North Oval Mall
Columbus, Ohio 43210
Tel: (614) 292-1311 **E-mail:** askbuckeye@osu.edu
Fax: (614) 292-3658 **Internet:** www.osu.edu

Institution Description: The Ohio State University is a state institution and land-grant college with regional campuses at Lima, Mansfield, Marion, and Newark, and a 2-year institution, Agricultural Technical Institute, at Wooster. *Enrollment:* 53,715. *Degrees awarded:* Associate, baccalaureate, first-professional, (dentistry, law, medicine, optometry, pharmacy, veterinary medicine), master's, doctorate. Specialist certificates also awarded.

Academic offerings subject to approval by statewide coordinating bodies. Member of Committee on Institutional Cooperation, Inter-university Consortium for Social and Political Research, Midwest Universities Consortium for International Activities, The Ohio College Association.

Accreditation: *Regional:* NCA. *Professional*: architecture, art, business, chemistry, dental hygiene, dentistry, engineering, health services administration, journalism, landscape architecture, law, medical illustration, medical record administration, medicine, music, nurse anesthesia education, nursing, occupational therapy, pharmacy, physical therapy, planning, psychology internship, respiratory therapy, psychology internship, social work, speech-language pathology, teacher education, veterinary medicine

History: Established and chartered as Ohio Agricultural and Mechanical College 1870; offered first instruction at postsecondary level 1873; awarded first degree (baccalaureate) and adopted present name 1878. *See* James E. Pollard, *History of Ohio State University* (Columbus: Ohio State University Press, 1952) for further information.

Institutional Structure: *Governing board:* Board of Trustees. Representation: 9 voting trustees, 2 non-voting student trustees. *Composition of institution:* president's planning cabinet has 12 members. Academic affairs headed by executive vice president and provost. Management/business directed by vice president for business and administration; infrastructure directed by senior vice president for business and finance. Full-time instructional faculty 3,012. Academic governance body, University Senate, meets an average of 9 times per year.

Calendar: Quarters. Academic year Sept. to June. Freshmen admitted June, Sept., Jan., Mar. Degrees conferred and formal commencements Aug., Dec., Mar., June. Summer session of 2 terms from June to Sept. College of Law: Semesters. Academic year Aug. to May. Degrees conferred and formal commencements Dec., June.

Characteristics of Freshmen: 20,932 applicants (10,214 female, 10,718 male). 65% of applicants accepted. 33% of accepted applicants enrolled full-time.

62% (3,193 students) submitted SAT scores; 88% (5,507 students) submitted ACT scores. *25th percentile*: SAT Critical Reading 430, SAT Math 560; ACT Composite 24, ACT English 23, ACT Math 24. *75th percentile*: SAT Critical Reading 640, SAT Math 670; ACT Composite 29, ACT English 29, ACT Math 29.

66% of entering freshmen expected to graduate within 5 years. 87% of freshmen from Ohio. Freshmen from 50 states and 82 foreign countries.

Admission: For freshmen: competitive admission for summer, autumn and winter quarters (Columbus campus only). Application deadline Feb. 15 for autumn quarter admission, notified of acceptance by March 31. There is an Early Entrance Plan where highly qualified students may matriculate at Ohio State before graduating from high school (The Ohio State Academy), but they must reapply for official admittance to Freshman class. There is no early decision plan. *Requirements:* For new first quarter freshmen, competitive admissions for both in-state and out-of-state residents. 3 units math (4 recommended); 2 social sciences (3 recommended); 2 science (3-4 recommended, 2 must be lab); 2 foreign language (3 recommended); 1 music/arts and 1 additional unit from above. GED accepted. *Entrance tests:* SAT, ACT, College Board scores used as positive indicators and for merit-based financial aid, placement, and counseling. *Foreign students:* TOEFL. *Transfer students:* Both secondary school and college transcripts required for transfer applicants with fewer than 45 credit hours; 2.0 minimum college GPA. Minimum of 45 quarter hours must be earned at The Ohio State University.

College credit and advanced placement for postsecondary-level work determined by Advanced Placement tests, CLEP-subject examinations, CLEP-general examination, university/department evaluations and the PEP (ACT) exam for nursing RN option. Credit granted for extrainstitutional learning as determined by department.

Tutoring available. Developmental and remedial courses offered in summer session and regular academic year.

Degree Requirements: *For all associate degrees:* 90–100 quarter hours; distribution requirements. *For all baccalaureate degrees:* minimum of 190 quarter hours required by all colleges; requirements vary by college of enrollment; general education requirements; demonstrated proficiency in written English. *For all undergraduate degrees:* 2.0 GPA; 45 hours in residence; additional requirements for some programs.

Fulfillment of some degree requirements and exemption from some beginning courses possible by passing College Board CLEP, APP. *Grading system:* A–E; pass-fail; withdraw (carries time limit).

Distinctive Educational Programs: Touch-tone registration and pay-by-mail system. Weekend and evening classes. Streamlined registration process for adult and nontraditional students. College reentry workshops. Innovative summer programming, such as Summer Writing Series and Institute for the Advancement of the Arts in Education. State-of-the-art computer equipment, facilities, and instruction. Study abroad in various countries including Canada, China, England, France, Germany, Japan, Mexico, Russia, Spain; study travel in various locations including Costa Rica, Egypt, Greece, India, and Italy. *Other distinctive programs:* Continuing professional education. Academic and scientific conferences.

ROTC: Air Force, Army, Navy.

Degrees Conferred: 342 *associate*; 8,721 *baccalaureate*; 2,576 *master's*; 721 *doctorate;*; 885 *first-professional*. Bachelor's degrees awarded in top five disciplines: business/marketing 1,333; social sciences 1,190; engineering 769; health professions and related clinical sciences 557; communications/journalism 564. Master's degrees awarded in top five disciplines: education 735; business/marketing 436; health professions 346; engineering 248; public administration and social services 202. Doctorates awarded in top five disciplines: engineering 118; education 111; physical sciences 3; biological/life sciences 59; health professions 44. First-professional degrees awarded: dentistry 99; optometry 62; pharmacy 131; veterinary medicine 133; law 258; medicine 202.

Fees and Other Expenses: *Full-time tuition per academic year 2008–09:* undergraduate resident $8,619, out-of-state $21,918. Professional and graduate school tuition/fees vary; contact the school of interest for current information. *Required fees:* $261. *Room and board per academic year:* $8,689. *Books and supplies:* $1,383. *Other expenses:* $4,140.

Financial Aid: Aid from institutionally generated funds is provided on the basis of academic merit, financial need, athletic ability, other criteria.

Financial aid to full-time, first-time undergraduate students: 95% of students received some form of financial aid. Average amount of aid received: federal grants $3,872; Pell grants $3,644; other federal aid $910; state/local grants $2,736; institutional grants $5,265.

Departments and Teaching Staff: *Total instructional faculty:* 4,031 (full-time 3,012, part-time 1,019). Total faculty with doctorate, first-professional, or other terminal degree: 2,982. Student/faculty ratio: 13,2:1.

Enrollment: Total enrollment 53,715. Undergraduate 40,212 (full-time 91%; female 46%, male 53%). Graduate 13,503 (full-time 67%). Undergraduate transfer-in students 2,005.

Characteristics of Student Body: *Ethnic/racial makeup:* Black non-Hispanic 7%; African Indian or Alaska Native: 5%; Hispanic Hispanic: 3%; White non-Hispanic: 79%; unknown 2%; nonresident alien 3%. *Age distribution:* 17–21: 424; 22–24: 12,182; 25–29: 14,526; 30–34: 706; 35–39: 386; 40–49: 371; 50–59: 178; 65 and over 6

International Students: 3,638 undergraduate nonresident aliens enrolled fall 2008. Students from Europe, Central and South America, Africa, Canada, Australia, New Zealand, Middle East. Programs available to aid students whose native language is not English: social, cultural. English as a Second Language Program. Financial aid specifically designated for international students.

Student Life: On-campus residence halls house 24% of undergraduate student body. Housing available for married and handicapped students. *Intercollegiate athletics:* male: football, wrestling, baseball; female: crew, fencing, field hockey, synchronized swimming, softball; both sexes: basketball, ice hockey, lacrosse, pistol/rifle, volleyball, golf, cross-country, tennis, track, gymnastics, swimming; *Special regulations:* Cars with decals permitted in designated areas. Quiet hours and dormitory visitation hours vary according to residence hall. *Special services:* Learning Resources Center, medical services. Services/programs available for women, Hispanic, Black, commuter, minority, and handicapped students. *Surrounding community:* Greater Columbus population 1,460,000. Served by mass transit bus system; airport 6 miles from campus.

Publications: Publications include *Lantern* a daily newspaper, *On Campus, Quest, Frontiers, Arts Advocate, Synergy, Alumni Magazine, Dimensions, Makio Yearbook* and various departmental publications and academic journals.

Library Collections: 5,891,000 volumes. Online catalog. Current serial subscriptions: paper 12,975; microform 242; via electronic access 11,894. 51,500 audio/videotapes; 16,954 CD-ROMs. Computer work stations avaialble for staff and public. Students have access to information retrieval services and the Internet.

Most important special holdings include Charvat Collection of American fiction; Cartoon Graphic Arts and Photographic Arts Research Library; Hilandar Research Library.

THE OHIO STATE UNIVERSITY—*cont'd*

Buildings and Grounds: Campus area 6,491 acres. Campus DVD available.

Chief Executive Officer: Dr. Karen A. Holbrook, President.

Address undergraduate admission inquiries to Director of Undergraduate Admissions; graduate inquiries to Director of Graduate, International, and Professional Admissions.

Colleges of the Arts and Sciences

Degree Programs Offered: *Baccalaureate* in actuarial science, African-American and African Studies, ancient history and classics, anthropology, Arabic, art, art education, astronomy, aviation, biochemistry, biology, ceramic art, chemistry, Chinese, classics, communication, comparative studies, computer and information science, criminology and criminal justice, dance, economics, English, entomology, French, general fine arts, geography, geological sciences, German, Hebrew, history, history of art, interdisciplinary honors contract, interior design, international studies, Islamic studies, Italian, Japanese, jazz studies, Jewish studies, journalism, linguistics, mapping and land information science, mathematical sciences, mathematics, medieval and renaissance studies, microbiology, modern Greek, molecular genetics, music, music education, music history, music theory and composition, orchestral instrument, personalized study program, philosophy, Portuguese, physics, physiological optics, piano, plant biology, political science, product design, psychology, religious studies, Russian, sculpture, sociology, Spanish, speech and hearing science, theatre, visual communication design, voice, women's studies, zoology.

Distinctive Educational Programs: Accelerated degree program leading to baccalaureate and master's in cooperation with Graduate School; leading to baccalaureate and first-professional in cooperation with Colleges of Dentistry, Medicine, Optometry, Veterinary Medicine; leading to two baccalaureate degrees in cooperation with the colleges of Business, Education, and Nursing. Joint baccalaureate and certificate in dental hygiene in cooperation with College of Dentistry. Minor programs in cooperation with the colleges of Business, Engineering, and Home Economics; and the schools of Architecture and Natural Resources. *College of the Arts, School of Music:* Center for Experimental Activities in the Arts. Computer Graphics Center. Dance Notation Bureau. Theater Research Institute. Wexner Center for the Visual Arts. Logan Elm Press featuring 19th-century printing press. Saturday school in art education and dance providing practical experience and community service. Cooperative baccalaureate program in recording engineering with College of Engineering. Interdepartmental program in music theater and opera with College of Arts. *College of Biological Sciences:* Biotechnology Center. Field Laboratory at Lake Erie. Research facilities for study of electron microscopy, nuclear magnetic resonance, mass spectrometry. *College of Humanities:* Interdisciplinary programs in East Asian studies, folklore, international studies, language-agriculture-business, medieval and Renaissance studies, women's studies. Annual symposia in the humanities. *College of Mathematical and Physical Sciences:* Interdisciplinary program in biostatistics. Domestic study at Utah Geological Field Camp. Lowell Observatory, Flagstaff, Arizona. Chemical Instrumentation Center. Van de Graaff Linear Accelerator. *College of Social and Behavioral Sciences:* Laboratories for behavioral sciences, polimetrics, cartography, climatology.

College of Food, Agricultural and Environmental Sciences

Degree Programs Offered: *Baccalaureate* in agribusiness and applied economics, agricultural and construction systems management, agricultural communication, agricultural education, animal sciences, crop science, food business management, landscape agriculture, plant health management, turfgrass science, food science and nutrition; *School of Natural Resources: Baccalaureate* in environmental communication, education and interpretation, environmental science, fisheries management, forestry, parks/recreation/tourism administration, soil science, sustainable resource management, urban forestry, wildlife management.

Distinctive Educational Programs: Accelerated degree program leading to baccalaureate and master's in agriculture in cooperation with Graduate School; leading to baccalaureate and first-professional in cooperation with Colleges of Dentistry, Medicine, Optometry, Veterinary Medicine. *School of Natural Resources:* Accelerated degree program leading to baccalaureate and master's in cooperation with Graduate School. Cooperative educational program (optional).

Fisher College of Business

Degree Programs Offered: *Baccalaureate* in accounting, economics, finance, human resources, information systems, international business administration, marketing, operations management, real estate and urban analysis, risk management and insurance, transportation and logistics, special major; *master of business administration*

Distinctive Educational Programs: Two-year full-time MBA program or part-time MBA programs taught in the evenings and weekends.

College of Dentistry

Degree Programs Offered: *First-professional.* Certificates also awarded.

Admission: 90 quarter hours from accredited college or university with 2 quarters English composition and literature, 3 each biology or zoology (with laboratory) and general chemistry (including quantitative analysis), 2 each organic chemistry and physics (both with laboratory); DAT; personal interview. 20 hours observation in private general practice dental office. Letters of recommendation. Credentials must be assembled by AADSAS.

Degree Requirements: 272–277 credit hours; 2.0 GPA.

Distinctive Educational Programs: Joint D.D.S.-Ph.D. program in cooperation with Graduate School. Continuing professional education.

College of Education

Degree Programs Offered: *Baccalaureate* in exercise science education, sports and leisure studies, technical education and training, technology education.

Distinctive Educational Programs: Teacher education in the College of Education is at the graduate level. Undergraduate students who seek teaching credentials should first complete an undergraduate degree and then apply to the Master of Education degree program. Cooperative baccalaureate in the arts in education with College of the Arts. Joint baccalaureate in education-certificate in dental hygiene with College of Dentistry.

College of Engineering

Degree Programs Offered: College of Engineering includes the School of Architecture. *Baccalaureate* in aeronautical and astronautical engineering, aviation, ceramic engineering, chemical engineering, civil engineering, computer science and engineering, electrical and computer engineering, engineering physics, food/agriculture/biological engineering, geomatics engineering, industrial and systems engineering, materials and science engineering, mechanical engineering, metallurgical engineering, welding engineering. *School of Architecture: Baccalaureate* in architecture, landscape architecture.

Distinctive Educational Programs: The College of Engineering offers combined bachelor's/master's degree in various disciplines. The college also maintains research centers, research laboratories, and specialized labs.

College of Human Ecology

Degree Programs Offered: *Baccalaureate* in family resource management, human development and family science, human nutrition and food management, hospitality management (hotel administration, restaurant management), textiles and clothing (apparel studies, fashion merchandising, textiles).

Distinctive Educational Programs: Accelerated degree program leading to baccalaureate and master's in cooperation with Graduate School. The Sophie Rogers Family Studies Laboratory provides experience with infants through four-year olds and in family dynamics. The Honors Program provides special academic experiences and programs. Annual study tours abroad provide opportunities for international experiences. The Historic Costume and Textile Collection contribute to research and instruction programs.

College of Law

Degree Programs Offered: *First-professional.* Certificate of study in Environmental Law, Certificate in International Trade and Development and Alternate Dispute Resolution.

Admission: Competitive. Baccalaureate from accredited college or University; LSAT required. Requires LSDAS report. Affirmative action admissions program.

Degree Requirements: 88 semester hours, including the completion of 11 required courses; 6 semesters in residence; maintenance of a 2.0 GPA. Successful completion of seminar, writing course, legal professions course and an Horizons course designated by faculty.

Distinctive Educational Programs: Clinical courses are offered in 8 areas. Interdisciplinary opportunities available through the Center for Law, Policy, and Social Science.

College of Medicine

Degree Programs Offered: College of Medicine includes School of Allied Medical Professions. *College of Medicine:* First-professional. *School of Allied Medical Professions: Baccalaureate* in circulation technology, health information and management, medical communications, medical dietetics, medical illustration, medical record administration, medical technology, occupational therapy, physical therapy, radiologic technology, respiratory technology.

Admission: *For first-professional students:* Baccalaureate from accredited college or university with 1 year each biology (including vertebrate structure), general chemistry (including quantitative analysis), organic chemistry, physics (all with laboratory); MCAT; personal interviews; AMCAS; letters of recommendation.

Degree Requirements: *For first-professional degree:* 288 credit hours; 35 months in residence.

Distinctive Educational Programs: Joint M.D.-Ph.D. degree program in cooperation with Graduate School. Medical research opportunities which may be funded by Samuel Roessler Foundation.

College of Nursing

Degree Programs Offered: *Baccalaureate, master's, doctorate.*

Admission: Baccalaureate program: 45 quarter credit hours from an accredited college or university with 5 hours human anatomy, 5 hours biology, 10 hours chemistry, 5 hours English, 5 hours psychology, 5 hours sociology, 10 hours of other coursework. Minimum 2.5 GPA (3.0 GPA recommended).

Degree Requirements: Baccalaureate program: 196 quarter credit hours; 2.0 GPA.

Distinctive Educational Programs: Ph.D. Program in Nursing prepares scholars to conduct research that develops the discipline of nursing and adds to the body of knowledge for the practice of professional nursing. The curriculum for the Master of Science degree is an integrated program with strong theoretical and clinical components and designed to allow students the flexibility to plan a course of study which best reflects their individual interests and needs. Graduate Entry Program admits students with a bachelor's degree in an area other than nursing and prepares them to meet RN licensure requirements and MS degree requirements in an accelerated manner.

College of Optometry

Degree Programs Offered: *First-professional.*

Admission: Baccalaureate from accredited college or university with 5 quarter hours English; 10 in a foreign language; 15 each general chemistry, organic chemistry, physics, mathematics (including calculus); 10 each humanities, social sciences; 10 each biology, zoology, psychology, 5 biochemistry. Mean GPA 3.43. Personal interview; writing sample. OAT. For students without baccalaureate, 101 quarter hours in program outlined above; applicants with GPA of 3.0 or higher will be given first consideration.

Degree Requirements: 235 credit hours; 2.0 GPA. Complete NBEO examination.

Distinctive Educational Programs: Joint O.D.-M.S., Ph.D. degree program in cooperation with Graduate School.

College of Pharmacy

Degree Programs Offered: *Bachelor of Science in Pharmacy; first-professional* in pharmacy; *Doctor of Pharmacy.*

Admission: Bachelor of Science in Pharmacy: 90 quarter hours from accredited college or university with 24 chemistry, 15 mathematics, 5 biology, 5 English, 15 humanities/social sciences, 5 microbiology, 15 physics. Minimum 2.0 GPA. ACT/SAT/PCAT. Doctor of Pharmacy: baccalaureate from accredited College of Pharmacy; minimum 3.0 GPA.

Degree Requirements: Bachelor of science in pharmacy: 190 quarter hours; prescribed curriculum; 2.0 GPA. Doctor of pharmacy: 194 quarter hours; prescribed curriculum; 2.0 GPA.

College of Social Work

Degree Programs Offered: *Baccalaureate.*

Admission: Selective and limited. Completion of 91 quarter credits; 2.0 GPA.

Distinctive Educational Programs: Combined master's program in social work and public administration in cooperation with Graduate School and School of Public Policy and Management. Graduate level interdisciplinary specialization in aging and specialization in school social work offered.

College of Veterinary Medicine

Degree Programs Offered: *First-professional:* doctor of veterinary medicine.

Admission: 96-101 quarter hours from accredited college or university with 5 English, 15 general chemistry, 6 organic chemistry, 5 biochemistry, 10 biology, 5 genetics, 5–12 microbiology, 5 mathematics, 10 general physics, 20 humanities and social sciences, 10 electives at student's discretion; minimum 3.0 GPA; personal interview; choice of Veterinary Aptitude Test, Graduate Record Exam (general only), or Medical College Admission Test; one-page autobiography; work experience outline; 2 recommendations; personal interview.

Degree Requirements: 233 credit hours; 2.0 GPA; core curriculum.

Distinctive Educational Programs: Joint D.V.M.-Ph.D. degree program in cooperation with Graduate School. Joint first-professional-baccalaureate degree program in cooperation with College of Agriculture. Interdisciplinary program in microscopic anatomy. Research facilities including Electron Microscopic Laboratory and Microscopic Anatomy Laboratory.

Graduate School

Degree Programs Offered: *Master's* in African-American and African Studies; allied medical professions; architecture; art; arts policy and administration; Black studies; business administration; comparative studies; dance; dentistry; health services management and policy; industrial, interior, and visual communication design; journalism; landscape architecture; liberal studies; medical science; Near Eastern languages and cultures; physical therapy; Slavic and East European studies; women's studies; *doctorate* in biostatistics; neuroscience; nutrition; soil science; vocational education (comprehensive); *master's, doctorate* in accounting and management information systems; aeronautical and astronautical engineering; agricultural education; agricultural engineering; agricultural, environmental, and developmental economics; anatomy; animal science; anthropology; art education; astronomy; atmospheric sciences; biochemistry; biophysics; biomedical engineering; business administration; chemical engineering; chemical physics; chemistry; city and regional planning, civil engineering; classics; communication; computer and information science; dairy science; East Asian languages and literatures; economics; education; electrical engineering; engineering mechanics; English; entomology; environmental science; evolution, ecology, and organismal biology; family resource management; food science and nutrition; French and Italian; geodetic science and surveying; geography; geological sciences; health, physical education, and recreation; history; history of art; horticulture and crop science; human nutrition and food management, human development and family science, human microbiology; industrial and systems engineering; labor and human resources, linguistics; mathematics; mechanical engineering; medical biochemistry; molecular, cellular, and developmental biology; molecular virology, immunology, and medical genetics; molecular genetics; music; natural resources; nuclear engineering; nursing; pathology; pharmacology; pharmacy; philosophy; physics; physiological optics; physiology and cell biology; plant biology; plant pathology; political science; poultry science; psychology; public policy and management; public health; Slavic and East European languages and literatures; social work; sociology; Spanish and Portuguese; speech and hearing science; statistics; textiles and clothing; theater; veterinary bioscience; veterinary clinical sciences; veterinary preventive medicine; welding engineering; *doctorate* in neuroscience, nutrition, soil science.

Departments and Teaching Staff: Faculty members are drawn from other colleges within the university.

Distinctive Educational Programs: Joint master's degree programs in cooperation with various departments. Interdisciplinary research units, including Advanced Computing Center for Art and Design; Atmospheric Sciences Program; Biomedical Engineering Center; Campus Chemical Instrumentation Center; Center for Biotechnology; Center for Comparative Studies in the Humanities; Comprehensive Cancer Center; Computer Graphics Research Group; Electroscience Laboratory; Center for Human Resources Research; Center for International Studies; Center for International Trade Assistance and Research; Center for Lake Erie Area Research; Center for Mapping; Center for Medieval and Renaissance Studies; Mershon Center for Research and Education in National Security and Public Policy; National Regulatory Research Institute; Neurosciences Research Laboratory; Nisonger Center for Mental Retardation; Ohio Rehabilitation Center; Center for Real Estate Education and Research; Tuberculosis Treatment Service and Center; Water Resources Center; Center for Women's Studies; National Center for Research in Vocational Education. Off-campus domestic study in cooperation with Universities of Chicago, Illinois, Iowa, Michigan, Minnesota, and Wisconsin; Indiana, Michigan State, Northwestern, and Purdue Universities.

The Ohio State University at Lima

Lima, Ohio 45804

Tel: (419) 221-1641 **E-mail:** admissions@lima.ohio-state.edu
Fax: (419) 995-8483 **Internet:** www.lima.ohio-state.edu

Institution Description: *Enrollment:* 1,409. *Degrees awarded:* Associate, baccalaureate, master's.

Academic offerings subject to approval by statewide coordinating bodies.

Accreditation: *Regional:* NCA.

THE OHIO STATE UNIVERSITY AT LIMA—*cont'd*

Admission: *See* The Ohio State University.

Degree Requirements: *See* The Ohio State University.

Degrees Conferred: Degrees are awarded from the Columbus campus.

Fees and Other Expenses: *Full-time tuition per academic year 2008–09:* in-state resident $5,664, out-of-state $18,903. *Off-campus room and board:* $7,500. *Books and supplies:* $1,383. *Other expenses:* $5,040.

Financial Aid: Aid from institutionally generated funds is provided on the basis of academic merit, financial need, other criteria. Institution has a Program Participation Agreement with the U.S. Department of Education for eligible students to receive Pell Grants and, depending upon the agreement, other federal aid.

93% of full-time, first-time undergradaute students received some form of financial aid.

Departments and Teaching Staff: *Total instructional faculty:* 56.

Enrollment: Total enrollment 1,409. Undergraduate 1,351 (88% full-time; female 51%, male 49%). Gradaute 58 (full-time 38%). Undergraduate transfer-in students 55.

Characteristics of Student Body: *Ethnic/racial makeup:* Black non-Hispanic: 2.3%; American Indian or Alaska Native: .2%; Asian or Pacific Islander: .8%; Hispanic: 1.3%; White non-Hispanic: 94%; unknown: 1.45.

International Students: No programs to aid students whose native language is not English. No financial aid specifically designated for international students.

Student Life: 79,000 volumes. 9,000 audiovisual materials. 520 periodical subscriptions.

Buildings and Grounds: Campus area 565 acres.

Chief Executive Officer: Dr. John R. Snyder, President.

Address admission inquiries to Beth A. Keehn, Director of Admissions.

The Ohio State University at Mansfield

1680 University Drive
Mansfield, Ohio 44906-1599
Tel: (419) 755-4226 **E-mail:** admissions@mansfield.ohio-state.edu
Fax: (419) 755-4211 **Internet:** www.mansfield.ohio-state.edu

Institution Description: *Enrollment:* 1,545. *Degrees awarded:* Associate, baccalaureate, master's.

Academic offerings subject to approval by statewide coordinating bodies.

Accreditation: *Regional:* NCA.

Calendar: Quarters. Academic year Sept. 25 to June 12.

Admission: *See* The Ohio State University.

Degree Requirements: *See* The Ohio State University.

Distinctive Educational Programs: Bachelor of Science in Education, a pre-education degree with liberal arts content. Post-degree program: Master's of Education with certification for liberal arts graduates wishing to prepare as elementary school teachers.

Degrees Conferred: Degrees are awarded from the Columbus campus.

Fees and Other Expenses: *Full-time tuition per academic year 2008–09:* in-state resident $5,664, out-of-state $18,903. *Room and board per academic year:* $4,579. *Books and supplies:* $1,383. *Other expenses:* $4,140.

Financial Aid: Aid from institutionally generated funds is provided on the basis of academic merit, financial need. Institution has a Program Participation Agreement with the U.S. Department of Education for eligible students to receive Pell Grants and, depending upon the agreement, other federal aid.

Financial aid to full-time, first-time undergraduate students: 35% received federal grants averaging $2,664; 27% state/local grants averaging $1,229; 38% institutional grants averaging $1,749; 47% received loans averaging $3,124.

Departments and Teaching Staff: *Total instructional faculty:* 62. Degrees held by full-time faculty: master's 10.5%, doctorate 89.5%.

Enrollment: Total enrollment 1,545. Undergraduate 1,476 (full-time 72%; female 59%, male 41%). Graduate 69 (full-time 43%). Undergraduate transfer-in students 35.

Characteristics of Student Body: *Ethnic/racial makeup:* Black non-Hispanic: 4.7%; American Indian or Alaska Native: .3%; Asian or Pacific Islander: 1.6%; Hispanic: 1.1%; White non-Hispanic: 90.1%; unknown: 2.2%.

Publications: *Interspeak*, internal weekly; *Connections*, external quarterly.

Library Collections: 59,000 volumes. 17,500 microforms; 2,200 audiovisual materials; 410 current periodical subscriptions. Students have access to online information retrieval services and the Internet.

Most important special holdings include Louis Bromfield papers.

Buildings and Grounds: Campus area 600 acres.

Chief Executive Officer: Dr. Evelyn B. Freeman, Dean. Address admission inquiries to Henry Thomas, Coordinator of Admissions.

The Ohio State University at Marion

1465 Mt. Vernon Avenue
Marion, Ohio 43302-5695
Tel: (740) 389-3766 **E-mail:** admissions@marion.ohio-state.edu
Fax: (740) 292-5817 **Internet:** www.marion.ohio-state.edu

Institution Description: *Enrollment:* 1,673. *Degrees awarded:* Associate, baccalaureate, master's.

Academic offerings subject to approval by statewide coordinating bodies.

Accreditation: *Regional:* NCA.

Calendar: Quarters. Academic year Sept. to June.

Characteristics of Freshmen: 96% of applicants accepted. 88% of accepted applicants enrolled.

Mean SAT scores 428.2; mean ACT scores 19.8.

50% of entering freshmen expected to graduate within 5 years. 100% of freshmen from Ohio.

Admission: *See* The Ohio State University.

Degree Requirements: *See* The Ohio State University.

Degrees Conferred: All degrees are awarded through the Columbus campus.

Fees and Other Expenses: *Full-time tuition per academic year 2008–09:* in-state resident $5,664, out-of-state $18,903. *Books and supplies:* $1,383. *Off-campus room and board per academic year:* $8,000. *Other expenses:* $5,040.

Financial Aid: Aid from institutionally generated funds is provided on the basis of academic merit, athletic ability, financial need, other criteria. Institution has a Program Participation Agreement with the U.S. Department of Education for eligible students to receive Pell Grants and, depending upon the agreement, other federal aid.

Financial aid to full-time, first-time undergraduate students: 30% received federal grants averaging $2,848; 23% state/local grants averaging $1,135; 37% institutional grants averaging $1,790; 38% received loans averaging $3,037.

Departments and Teaching Staff: *Total instructional faculty:* 54. Degrees held by full-time faculty: doctorate 95%. 95% hold terminal degrees.

Enrollment: Total enrollment 1,673. Undergraduate 1,594 (full-time 85%; female 54%, male 46%). Graduate 79 (full-time 62%). Undergraduate transfer-in students 61.

Characteristics of Student Body: *Ethnic/racial makeup:* Black non-Hispanic: 2.8%; American Indian or Alaska Native: .25; Asian or Pacific Islander: 1.7%; Hispanic: 1.9%; White non-Hispanic: 91.3%; unknown: 1.9%.

International Students: Programs available to aid students whose native language is not English: English as a Second Language Program offered through Columbus campus. No financial aid specifically designated for international students.

Chief Executive Officer: Dr. Gregory S. Rose, President.

Address admission inquiries to Mathieu Moreau, Coordinator of Admissions.

The Ohio State University at Newark

1179 University Drive
Newark, Ohio 43055-1797
Tel: (740) 366-9333 **E-mail:** admissions@newark.ohio-state.edu
Fax: (740) 366-9460 **Internet:** www.newark.ohio-state.edu

Institution Description: *Enrollment:* 2,472. *Degrees awarded:* Associate, baccalaureate, master's.

Accreditation: *Regional:* NCA.

Calendar: Quarters. Academic year June to June.

Admission: *See* The Ohio State University.

Degree Requirements: *See* The Ohio State University.

Degrees Conferred: All degrees are awarded from the Columbus campus.

Financial Aid: Aid from institutionally generated funds is provided on the basis of academic merit, financial need, other criteria. Institution has a Program Participation Agreement with the U.S. Department of Education for eligible students to receive Pell Grants and, depending upon the agreement, other federal aid.

Financial aid to full-time, first-time undergraduate students: 29% received federal grants averaging $2,614; 20% state/local grants averaging $1,213; 25% institutional grants averaging $1,379; 47% received loans averaging $3,176.

Departments and Teaching Staff: *Total instructional faculty:* 29.

Enrollment: Total enrollment 2,472. Undergraduate 2,364 (full-time 88%; female 52%, male 48%). Graduate 108 (full-time 40%). Undergraduate transfer-in students 88.

Characteristics of Student Body: *Ethnic/racial makeup:* Black non-Hispanic: 5.3%;American Indian or Alaska Native: .8%; Asian or Pacific Islander: 2.3%; Hispanic: 1.2%; White non-Hispanic: 88.8%; unknown: 1.5%.

International Students: No financial aid specifically designate for international students.

Library Collections: 50,000 volumes. 18,000 microforms; 3,500 audiovisual materials; 430 current periodical subscriptions. Students have access to online information retrieval services and the Internet.

Buildings and Grounds: Urban campus. Campus DVD available.

Chief Executive Officer: Dr. William L. MacDonald, Dean.

Address admission inquiries to Ann Donahue, Coordinator of Admissions.

Ohio University

Athens, Ohio 45701-2979

Tel: (740) 593-4100 **E-mail:** admissions@ohiou.edu
Fax: (740) 593-0560 **Internet:** www.ohiou.edu

Institution Description: Ohio University is a state institution with separately accredited associate degree-granting regional campuses in Chillecothe, Ironton, Lancaster, St. Clairsville, and Zanesville. *Enrollment:* 21,369. *Degrees awarded:* Associate, baccalaureate, first-professional (osteopathic medicine), master's, doctorate.

Accreditation: *Regional:* NCA. *Professional*: athletic training, business, chemistry, dance, dietetics, engineering, interior design, health services administration, industrial technology, journalism, music, nursing, osteopathy, physical therapy, psychology internship, social work, speech-language pathology, teacher education

History: Established and chartered 1804; offered first instruction at postsecondary level 1808; awarded first degree (baccalaureate) 1815. *See* Thomas N. Hoover, *History of Ohio University* (Athens: Ohio University Press, 1954) for further information.

Institutional Structure: *Governing board:* Ohio University Board of Trustees. Representation: 9 trustees, including 5 alumni. All voting (2 nonvoting students). *Composition of institution:* Administrators 985. Academic affairs headed by provost. Management/business/finances directed by vice president for operations. Full-time instructional faculty 869. Academic governance body, Faculty Senate, meets an average of 12 times per year.

Calendar: Quarters. Academic year Sept. to June. Freshmen admitted Sept., Jan., Mar., June, July. Degrees conferred June, Aug., Nov., Mar. Formal commencement June. Summer session of 2 terms from June to Aug.

Characteristics of Freshmen: 14,046 applicants (7,605 female, 6,441 male). 85% of applicants admitted. 38% of applicants admitted and enrolled full-time.

54% (2,221 students) submitted SAT scores; 88% (3,590 students) submitted ACT scores. *25th percentile*: SAT Critical Reading 490, SAT Math 490; ACT Composite 21, ACT English 20, ACT Math 20. *75th percentile*: SAT Critical Reading 600, SAT Math 600; ACT Composite 26, ACT English 26, ACT Math 26. 11 National Merit Scholars.

69% of entering freshmen expected to graduate within 5 years. 91% of freshmen from Ohio. Freshmen from 35 states and 109 countries.

Admission: Rolling admissions plan. For fall acceptance, apply as early as Sept. of previous year, but not later than Feb. 1 of year of enrollment. Early acceptance available. *Requirements:* Admissions is based upon high school performance (class rank, GPA, curriculum), aptitude test scores (ACT and/or SAT), recommendation of high school, and special ability, talent, or achievement. Admissions to the university does not guarantee admission to a specific program of study. Limited and/or selective admissions policies are in effect for programs of study in athletic training, engineering, all programs in the College of Business, College of Communication, Honors Tutorial College, and the College of Fine Arts. For foreign students TOEFL. *For transfer students:* 2.0 minimum GPA.

College credit and advanced placement for postsecondary-level work completed in secondary school. For extrainstitutional learning on basis of portfolio assessment; faculty assessment; personal interview.

Tutoring available. Developmental courses offered in summer session and regular academic year; credit given.

Degree Requirements: *For all associate degrees:* 90 credit hours; 2 terms in residence. *For all baccalaureate degrees:* 192 credit hours; 3 terms in residence; general education requirements. *For all undergraduate degrees:* 2.0 GPA.

Fulfillment of some degree requirements and exemption from some beginning courses possible by passing College Board CLEP, AP. *Grading system:* A–F; pass-fail; withdraw (carries time limit).

Distinctive Educational Programs: Work-experience programs. Evening classes. Special facilities for using telecommunications in the classroom. Interdepartmental programs in African studies, economics education, international affairs, Latin American studies, mass communications, Southeast Asia studies, visual communication. Facilities and programs for independent research, including honors programs, individual majors, tutorials, independent study. Study abroad worldwide.

ROTC: Army, Air Force.

Degrees Conferred: 52 *associate*; 4,025 *baccalaureate*; 956 *master's*; 147 *doctorate*. Bachelor's degrees awarded in top five disciplines: communications/journalism 677; business, management, marketing, and related support services 505; education 470; social sciences 364; liberal arts/general studies 304. Master;s degrees awarded in top five disciplines: education 218; social sciences 117; business/marketing 90; engineering 78; parks and recreation 52. Doctorates awarded: communications/journalism 18; education 19; engineering 16; health professions and related clinical sciences 17; history 4; interdisciplinary studies 4; mathematics 1; physical sciences 15; psychology 7; visual and performing arts 7. First-professional degrees awarded: osteopathic medicine 106.

Fees and Other Expenses: *Full-time tuition per academic year 2008–09:* undergraduate resident $8,907, nonresident $17,871; contact the university for current graduate/first-professional tuition that vary by program. *Room and board per academic year:* $8,946. *Books and supplies* $873. *Other expenses:* $3,651.

Financial Aid: The university offers a direct loan program. Aid from institutionally generated funds is provided on the basis of academic merit, financial need.

Financial aid to full-time, first-time undergraduate students: 75% of students received some form of financial aid. Average amount of aid received: federal grants $4,065; Pell grants $2,870; other federal aid $1,463; institutional grants $2,006; loans $4,421.

Departments and Teaching Staff: *Total instructional faculty:* 1,188 (full-time 869, part-time 319). Total faculty with doctorate, first-professional, or other terminal degree: 966. Student/faculty ratio: 19:1. Degrees held by full-time faculty: baccalaureate 1%, master's 12%, doctorate 82%, professional 5%.

Enrollment: Total enrollment 21,369. Undergraduate 17,571 (full-time 72%; female 50%, male 50%). Graduate 3,798 (full-time 77%). Undergraduate transfer-in students 559.

Characteristics of Student Body: *Ethnic/racial makeup (undergraduate):* Black non-Hispanic: 5%; Asian or Pacific Islander: 1%; Hispanic: 2%; White non-Hispanic: 89%; nonresident alien 2%. *Age distribution:* undergraduate number under 18: 15; 18–19: 6,197; 20–21: 6,509; 22–24: 2,806; 25–29: 288; 30–34: 749; 35–39: 292; 40–49: 41; 50–64: 7; 65 and over: 1.

International Students: 1,066 nonresident aliens enrolled fall 2008. Students from Europe, Asia, Central and South America, Africa, Canada, Australia, Middle East. Programs available to aid students whose native language is not English: social, cultural. English as a Second Language Program. No financial aid specifically designated for international students.

Student Life: On-campus residence halls house 42% of student body. 12% of males join fraternities, 16% of females join sororities. *Intercollegiate athletics:* male: baseball, basketball, cross-country, football, golf, soccer, swimming and diving, track, wrestling; female: basketball, cross-country, field hockey, golf, softball, swimming and diving, track, volleyball. *Special regulations:* Students may not bring cars to campus during their first two years. Curfews, quiet hours, and residence hall visitation vary according to residence hall. *Special services:* Learning Resources Center, medical services. *Student publications, radio: The Post*, a daily newspaper; yearbook. Radio station ACRN, WOUB-AM/FM. *Surrounding community:* Athens population 21,700. Columbus, 75 miles from campus, is nearest metropolitan area. Served by limited transit bus system; noncommercial airport 10 miles from campus.

Publications: *Milton Quarterly, Ohio Review* (quarterly) first published 1959. University press publishes an average of 44 titles per year.

Library Collections: 2,731,000 books, serials, and government documents; 27,606 periodicals and newspapers. Computer work stations available. Students have access to the Internet and online information retrieval services.

Most important special holdings include private library of Edmund Blunden; manuscripts collections of E.W. Scripps, Cornelius Ryan, Sammy Kaye; fine printing and artists' books; Morgan Collection on the History of Chemistry.

Buildings and Grounds: Campus area 1,678 acres.

Chief Executive Officer: Dr. Roderick J. McDavis, President.

Undergraduates address admission inquiries to T. David Garcia, Director of Admissions; graduate inquiries to Office of Graduate Student Services; first-professional inquiries to College of Osteopathic Medicine.

Ohio Wesleyan University

61 South Sandusky Street
Delaware, Ohio 43015-2370
Tel: (740) 368-2000 **E-mail:** admit@owu.edu
Fax: (740) 368-3314 **Internet:** www.owu.edu

Institution Description: Ohio Wesleyan University is a private institution affiliated with the United Methodist Church. *Enrollment:* 1,959. *Degrees awarded:* Baccalaureate.

Member of the consortium Great Lakes Colleges Association.

Accreditation: *Regional:* NCA. *Professional*: music, teacher education

History: Established and chartered 1842; offered first instruction at postsecondary level 1844; awarded first degree (baccalaureate) 1846; merged with Ohio Wesleyan Female College 1877. *See* Henry Clyde Hubbart, *Ohio Wesleyan University's First One Hundred Years* (Hammond, IN: W.B. Conkey Co., 1944) and Bernard Clyde Hubbert's "Noted Achievements: The History of Ohio Wesleyan University from 1942 to 1992" for further information.

Institutional Structure: *Governing board:* Board of Trustees. Representation: 67 trustees including 59 alumni and the university president. 3 ex officio. 40 voting. *Composition of institution:* Administrators 101. Academic affairs headed by provost. Management/business/finances directed by vice president for business affairs. Public relations/alumni relations/development headed by vice president for university relations. Full-time instructional faculty 134. Academic governance body meets an average of 5 times per year.

Calendar: Semesters. Academic year Aug. to May. Freshmen admitted Aug., Jan. Degrees conferred upon completion of degree requirements. Formal commencement May. Summer session from May to June.

Characteristics of Freshmen: 4,244 applicants (2,145 female, 2,099 male). 63% of applicants admitted. 59% of admitted students enrolled full-time.

76% (131 students) submitted SAT scores; 59% (337 students) submitted ACT scores. *25th percentile*: SAT Critical Reading 530, SAT Math 535; ACT Composite 29, ACT English 29, ACT Math 23. *75th percentile*: SAT Critical Reading 650, SAT math 660; Composite 28, ACT English 30, ACT Math 28.

68% of entering freshmen expected to graduate within 5 years. 59% of freshmen from Ohio. Freshmen from 43 states and 42 foreign countries.

Admission: For fall acceptance, apply as early as preceding Sept. 15, but not later than Mar. 1 for priority consideration (Dec. 1 for early decision, Dec. 15 for early action). Students are notified of admission decisions on a rolling basis beginning Jan. 15 (early decision/early action notification by Dec. 31). Applications received after Mar. 1 are considered as space is available; For second semester admission, apply by Dec. 1. *Requirements:* Graduation from accredited secondary school or GED. College preparatory program is recommended, including 4 units English, 3 mathematics, 3 natural sciences, 3 social sciences, 2 foreign language, 1 arts. Standardized test scores (College Board SAT or ACT composite) are required, but are secondary to classroom performance. *For transfer students:* must include transcripts of college work and a Dean of Students report. Graduation requires a minimum of 2 years at Ohio Wesleyan.

Degree Requirements: 34 course units; 2.0 GPA; 2 years (16 units) in residence; competency requirements in English (all degrees) and a foreign language (B.A. only); distribution requirements in natural sciences, social sciences, humanities-literature, and the arts; completion of an academic major.

Fulfillment of some degree requirements and exemption from some beginning courses possible by passing AP or institutional examinations. *Grading system:* A–F; withdraw passing; withdraw failing; S (credit, no grade); incomplete; P (in progress, for courses requiring more than 1 semester to complete).

Distinctive Educational Programs: The National Colloquium, through weekly guest lectures, seminar sessions and a spring symposium, promotes a year-long examination of an issue of central public importance and concern. The Woltemade Center for Economics and Business develops programs in economics, management, accounting, and international business. Honors program. Student-designed majors. Dual-degree programs in engineering with California Institute of Technology, Case Western Reserve University, Georgia Institute of Technology, Rensselaer Polytechnic Institute, Washington University in St. Louis (MO), and Polytechnic Institute of New York. Preprofessional programs in art therapy, dentistry, law, medical technology, medicine, music therapy, occupational therapy, optometry, pharmacy, physical therapy, public administration, theology, veterinary medicine. Interdisciplinary studies in Black world, chemistry-commerce, international business, ancient, medieval, Renaissance and urban affairs (programs may be individually arranged). Apprenticeships and career internships for upperclass students. Off-campus study includes programs in Segovia (Spain) and Paris (France), as well as overseas programs through GLCA consortium in Africa, China, Yugoslavia, India, Latin America, Japan, and Scotland; European term in comparative urban studies; additional foreign study options available. Off-campus programs in the United States include consortium programs in New York (fine arts), Philadelphia (urban studies), Chicago (Newberry Library humanities program) and Oak Ridge, Tennessee (engineering, mathematics, sciences). Additional programs in Washington, D.C. (political science and government).

Degrees Conferred: 380 *baccalaureate*. Bachelor's degrees awarded in top five disciplines: social sciences 91; business, management, marketing, and related support services 56; psychology 51; biological/life sciences 41; visual and performing arts 29. *Honorary degrees awarded 2005–06:* Doctor Human Letters 1, Doctor of Laws 1, Doctor of Humanities 1.

Fees and Other Expenses: *Full-time tuition per academic year 2008–09:* $33,700. *Books and supplies:* $1,000. *Required fees:* $420. *Room and board per academic year:* $8,370. *Other expenses:* $1,050.

Financial Aid: The university offers a direct lending program. Aid from institutionally generated funds is provided on the basis of academic merit, financial need, other criteria. Institution has a Program Participation Agreement with the U.S. Department of Education for eligible students to receive Pell Grants and, depending upon the agreement, other federal aid.

Financial aid to full-time, first-time undergraduate students: 20% received federal grants averaging $5,633; 51% state/local grants averaging $1,495; 97% institutional grants averaging $15,935; 67% received loans averaging $4,411.

Departments and Teaching Staff: *Total instructional faculty:* 182. Student/faculty ratio: 13:1. Degrees held by full-time faculty: doctorate 99%, master's 1%.

Enrollment: Total enrollment 1,959. Full-time 1,935 (female 989, male 946); part-time 24 (female 19, male 6). Transfer-un students: 29.

Characteristics of Student Body: *Ethnic/racial makeup:* Black non-Hispanic: 4.2%; American Indian or Alaska Native: .1%, Asian or Pacific Islander: 1.6%; Hispanic: 1.4%; White non-Hispanic: 81.6%; unknown: 1.7%.

International Students: 158 nonresident aliens enrolled fall 2008. Students from Europe, Asia, Latin America, Africa, Canada, Middle East. No programs available to aid students whose native language is not English. Financial aid specifically designated for international students: scholarships available annually; to qualifying students.

Student Life: On-campus residence halls house, small living units, and university-owned fraternity houses. Together these house 84% of the student body. 12% of student body live in university-owned fraternity housing. *Intercollegiate athletics:* male: baseball, basketball, cross-country, football, golf, lacrosse, soccer, swimming, tennis, indoor/outdoor track; female: basketball, cross-country, field hockey, lacrosse, soccer, softball, swimming, tennis, indoor/outdoor track, volleyball; both sexes: sailing. *Special regulations:* Cars permitted except for freshmen and sophomores. Quiet hours from 11pm to 7am weekdays. *Special services:* Writing Resource Center, counseling, advising and placement center, medical services, van service to Columbus as needed and to and from airport at school recess. *Student publications, radio/tv: In the Know*, an annual student handbook; *Owl*, a semiannual literary magazine; *ONYX*, a bisemester newsletter by Students United for Black Awareness. Radio station WSLN and the university's cablevision access TV channel broadcast to the community. *Surrounding community:* Delaware population 28,000. Columbus, 20 miles from campus, is nearest metropolitan area. Served by airport 30 miles from campus.

Library Collections: 462,000 volumes including bound books, serial backfiles, electronic documents, and government documents not in separate collections. 116,000 microforms. 3,4100 audiovisual materials. Online catalog. Current serial subscriptions: 8,125 including via electronic access. Computer work stations available. Students have access to the Internet at no charge.

Most important special collections include Leland Schubert Collection of Popular Fiction First Editions; Walt Whitman Collection; Robert Jaccand Collection on American Presidential Elections.

Buildings and Grounds: Campus area 200 acres.

Chief Executive Officer: Dr. Mark W. Huddleston, President.

Address admission inquiries to Carol Del Propost, Vice president for Admissions.

Otterbein College

College and Grove Streets
Westerville, Ohio 43081
Tel: (614) 890-3000 **E-mail:** admissions@otterbein.edu
Fax: (614) 823-1200 **Internet:** www.otterbein.edu

Institution Description: Otterbein College is a private, independent, nonprofit college affiliated with the United Methodist Church. *Enrollment:* 3,131. *Degrees awarded:* Associate, baccalaureate.

Accreditation: *Regional:* NCA. *Professional*: music, nursing, teacher education

History: Established as Otterbein University 1847; incorporated 1849; offered first instruction at postsecondary level 1853; awarded first degree (baccalaureate) 1857; adopted present name 1917. *See* Harold Hancock, *History of*

Otterbein College (Kansas City, KS: American Yearbook Publishing Co., 1971) for further information.

Institutional Structure: *Governing board:* Otterbein College Board of Trustees. Extrainstitutional representation: 11 trustees, 8 members of the United Methodist Church; institutional representation: 3 full-time instructional faculty members; 3 students; 4 alumni. 4 ex officio. 33 voting. *Composition of institution:* Administrators 8. Academic affairs headed by vice president of academic affairs. Management/business/finances directed by vice president of business affairs. Full-time instructional faculty 97. Academic governance body, College Senate, meets and average of 6 times per year.

Calendar: Quarters. Academic year Sept. to June. Freshmen admitted Sept., Jan., Mar., June. Degrees conferred June, Sept. Formal commencement June. Summer session of 1 term June to Aug.

Characteristics of Freshmen: 3,381 applicants (2,700 female, 1,281 male). 76% of applicants admitted. 31% of admitted students enrolled full-time.

40% (266 students) submitted SAT scores; 90% (502 students) submitted ACT scores. *25th percentile*: SAT Critical Reading 460, SAT Math 470, SAT Writing 460; ACT Composite 20, ACT English 20, ACT Math 19. *75th percentile*: SAT Critical Reading 650, SAT Math 590, SAT Writing 580; ACT Composite 26, ACT English 26, ACT Math 25.

70% of entering freshmen expected to graduate within 5 years. 86% of freshmen from Ohio. Freshmen from 23 states and 15 foreign countries.

Admission: Rolling admissions plan. For fall acceptance, apply as early as June 1 of junior year in secondary school, but not later than Aug. 15 of year of enrollment. Early acceptance available. *Requirements:* Either graduation from accredited secondary school with 16 academic units or GED. Additional units recommended for nursing program. Minimum GPA 2.0. *Entrance tests:* College Board SAT or ACT Composite. *For transfer students:* From 4-year accredited institution 90 quarter hours maximum transfer credit; from 2-year accredited institution 90 quarter hours; correspondence/extension students 10 hours. Good standing at institution previously attended.

College credit and advanced placement for postsecondary-level work completed in secondary school. College credit for extrainstitutional learning. Tutoring available. Developmental courses offered during regular academic year; credit given.

Degree Requirements: *For all associate degrees:* 90 credit hours; 2 terms in residence; 5 courses in integration studies. *For all baccalaureate degrees:* 180 credit hours; 4 terms in residence; 10 courses in integrative studies. *For all undergraduate degrees:* 2.0 GPA; 3 hours physical education.

Fulfillment of some degree requirements and exemption from some beginning courses possible by passing departmental examinations, ACT-PEP, College Board CLEP or AP. *Grading system:* A–F; withdraw (may carry penalty).

Distinctive Educational Programs: Cooperative education programs; internships. Flexible meeting places and schedule, including weekend and evening classes. Special facilities for using telecommunications in the classroom. Integrative studies. Interdisciplinary programs in computer science, equine science and stable management; also interpretive naturalist program. Dual-degree program in forestry with Duke University (NC). Cooperative baccalaureate degree programs in medical technology with Miami Valley Hospital and in nuclear medicine, radiology education, radiology management, radiology technology with Riverside Methodist Hospital. Study abroad programs at University of Dijon (France) and Segovia (Spain); through Institute of International Education at University of Bonn (Germany), through University of Colorado's Semester at Sea. Other off-campus study includes autumn term at McCurdy Schools (NM) for selected elementary and secondary education students; Washington (DC) semester in cooperation with American University, and Philadelphia semester.

ROTC: Air Force offered in cooperation with Ohio State University in Columbus.

Degrees Conferred: 594 *baccalaureate*; 93 *master's*. Bachelor's degrees awarded in top five disciplines: business, management, marketing, and related support services 96; communication, journalism, and related programs 64; education 56; visual and performing arts 53; health professions and related clinical sciences 45. Master's degrees awarded in various disciplines 93.

Fees and Other Expenses: *Full-time tuition per academic year 2008–09:* $26,319. *Room and board per academic year:* $7,461. *Books and supplies:* $1,017. *Other expenses:* $2,112.

Financial Aid: Aid from institutionally generated funds is provided on the basis of academic merit, financial need, other criteria. Institution has a Program Participation Agreement with the U.S. Department of Education for eligible students to receive Pell Grants and, depending upon the agreement, other federal aid.

Financial aid to full-time, first-time undergraduate students: 97% received some form of financial aid. Average amount of aid received: federal grants $3,614; state/local grants $1,334; institutional grants $9,983; loans $3,350.

Departments and Teaching Staff: *Total instructional faculty:* 124. Student/faculty ratio: 16:1. Degrees held by full-time faculty: master's 35%, doctorate 59%.

Enrollment: *Total enrollment:* 3,184. Undergraduate 2,754 (full-time 84%; female 63%, male 37%). Graduate 377 (full-time 21%). Undergraduate transfer-in students 144.

Characteristics of Student Body: *Ethnic/racial makeup:* Black non-Hispanic: 6%; Asian or Pacific Islander: 1%; Hispanic: 2%; White non-Hispanic: 89%; unknown: 3%.

International Students: 55 nonresident aliens enrolled fall 2008. Programs available to aid students whose native language is not English: social. English as a Second Language Program. No financial aid specifically designated for international students.

Student Life: On-campus residence halls house 49% of student body. Residence halls for males constitute 47% of such space, for females 51%. 52% of males join and 9% live in fraternity housing; 55% of females join and 5.6% live in sorority housing. *Intercollegiate athletics:* male: baseball, basketball, football, golf, tennis, track, soccer, cross-country; female: basketball, soccer, softball, cross-country, tennis, track, volleyball. *Special regulations:* Cars with decals permitted; fee charged. Quiet hours set by residents in each residence hall. Visitation 9am to midnight Sun.-Thurs; 9am to 2am Fri. and Sat. *Special services:* Learning Resources Center, Career Development Center, medical services, personal counseling. *Student publications, radio, television: Tan and Cardinal*, a weekly newspaper; *Quiz and Quill*, a quarterly; *Sibyl*, a yearbook. Radio station WOBN broadcasts 100 hours per week. Television station WOCC broadcasts 75 hours per week. *Surrounding community:* Westerville population 28,000. Columbus, 1.5 miles from campus, is nearest metropolitan area. Served by mass transit bus system; airport 12 miles from campus.

Publications: *Otterbein Miscellany* (annually) first published 1965; *Towers* Magazine.

Library Collections: 300,000 volumes. 55,705 government documents; 236,000 microforms; 8,200 recordings/tapes; 1,015 current periodical subscriptions. Online catalog. Students have access to online information retrieval services and the Internet.

Most important special collections include United Brethren Church Historical Records; Otterbein College Historical Records; The Benjamin Hanby Collection.

Buildings and Grounds: Campus area 70 acres.

Chief Executive Officer: Dr. C. Brent DeVore, President.

Address admission inquiries to Catherine M. Johnson, Director of Admissions.

Pontifical College Josephinum

7625 North High Street
Columbus, Ohio 43235

Tel: (614) 885-5585 **E-mail:** admissions@pcj.edu
Fax: (614) 885-2307 **Internet:** www.pcj.edu

Institution Description: The Pontifical College Josephinum is an independent, nonprofit college affiliated with the Roman Catholic Church and primarily for seminarians. *Enrollment:* 184. *Degrees awarded:* Baccalaureate, first-professional (divinity), master's.

Academic Member of the consortium, The Columbus Cluster of Theological Schools.

Accreditation: *Regional:* NCA. *National:* ATS. *Professional*: theology

History: Established in 1888; first instruction at postsecondary level 1892; incorporated 1894; awarded first degree (baccalaureate) 1896.

Institutional Structure: *Governing board:* Board of Trustees. Extrainstitutional representation: 20 trustees, including 3 alumni; institutional representation: 3 administrators, 2 full-time instructional faculty members; 2 students. 3 ex officio. All voting. *Composition of institution:* Administrators 19. Academic affairs headed by dean of studies-academic dean. Management/business/finances directed by president/rector. Full-time instructional faculty 25. Academic governance body, the faculty, meets an average of 10 times per year.

Calendar: Semesters. Academic year Aug. to May. Freshmen admitted Sept., Jan. Degrees conferred and formal commencement May. No summer session.

Characteristics of Freshmen: 92% of applicants accepted. 97% of accepted applicants enrolled.

31% (4 students) submitted SAT scores; 74% (14 students) submitted ACT scores. *25th percentile*: SAT Critical Reading 540. SAT Math 550; ACT Composite 20, ACT English 21, ACT 19. *75th percentile*: SAT Critical Reading 580, SAT Math 590; ACT Composite 24, ACT English 29, ACT Math 24.

100% of freshmen expected to graduate within 5 years. 45% of freshmen from Ohio. Freshmen from 9 states and 3 foreign countries.

PONTIFICAL COLLEGE JOSEPHINUM—*cont'd*

Admission: Rolling admissions plan. For fall acceptance, apply as early as 1 year prior to enrollment, but not later than the week of registration. *Requirements:* Either graduation from accredited secondary school or preparatory seminary or GED. Minimum 2.0 GPA. *For transfer students:* 2.0 minimum GPA; from 4-year accredited institution 104 hours maximum transfer credit; from 2-year accredited institution 60 hours.

College credit and advanced placement for postsecondary-level work completed in secondary school.

Tutoring available. Remedial courses offered during regular academic year; credit given.

Degree Requirements: 132 semester hours; 2.0 GPA; 2 semester in residence; undergraduate Assessment Program Area Tests and GRE; 2 semester physical education; general education requirements. *Graduate:* 57 semester hours. *First-professional:* 129,5 semester hours; baccalaureate in sacred theology 99 semester hours.

Fulfillment of some degree requirements possible by passing College Board CLEP. *Grading system:* A–F; pass-fail, withdraw.

Distinctive Educational Programs: Field experience. Special facilities for using telecommunications in the classroom. Individual majors. Cross-registration through consortium.

Degrees Conferred: 17 *baccalaureate:* English 2; philosophy and religious studies 15; 4 *master's:* theology; 9 *first-professional:* master of divinity.

Fees and Other Expenses: *Full-time tuition per academic year 2008–09:* undergraduate $15,597; contact the college for current graduate tuition. *Required fees:* $660. *Room and board per academic year:* $7,798. *Books and supplies:* $650. *Other expenses:* $3,900.

Financial Aid: Aid from institutionally generated funds is provided on the basis of financial need.

Financial aid to full-time, first-time undergraduate students: 26% of students received some form of financial aid.

Departments and Teaching Staff: *Total instructional faculty:* 53. Degrees held by full-time faculty: doctorate 54%, master's 38%, baccalaureate 5%, professional 1%.

Enrollment: Total enrollment 184. Undergraduate 115.

Characteristics of Student Body: *Ethnic/racial makeup:* Asian or Pacific Islander: 3%; Hispanic: 9%; White non-Hispanic: 77%; nonresident alien 9%. *Age distribution:* number under 20–21: 21; 22–24: 32; 25–29: 26; 30–34: 5; 35–39: 3; 40–49: 1.

International Students: 15 nonresident aliens enrolled fall 2008. Programs available to aid students whose native language is not English: social, cultural. English as a Second Language Program. No financial aid specifically designated for international students.

Student Life: On-campus residence halls house 95% of student body. Residence halls for males constitute 100% of such space. *Intercollegiate athletics:* male: basketball. *Special regulations:* Cars permitted for all but freshmen; registration required. Moderate and appropriate dress as befits a seminarian. Curfews. Quiet hours. Students are to be in their rooms during quiet hours. Guests are not permitted in rooms. *Special services:* Learning Resources Center, medical services. *Surrounding community:* Columbus population 565,000. Served by mass transit bus system; airport 20 miles from campus.

Library Collections: 130, 000 volumes. 1,000 microforms; 2,592 audiovisual materials; 520 current periodical subscriptions. 120 recordings; 12 CD-ROMs. 8 computer work stations. Students have access to online information retrieval services and the Internet.

Major special collections in Catholic theology and philosophy.

Buildings and Grounds: Campus area 100 acres.

Chief Executive Officer: Rev. Msgr. Paul J. Langefield, S.T.S., President/Rector.

Address admission inquiries to Dr. Perry Cahall, Director of Admissions.

Saint Mary Seminary and Graduate School of Theology

Center for Pastoral Leadership
28700 Euclid Avenue
Wickliffe, Ohio 44092-2585
Tel: (440) 943-7600 **E-mail:** admissions@stmarysem.edu
Fax: (440) 943-7577 **Internet:** /www.stmarysem.edu

Institution Description: The seminary was formerly known as St. Mary Seminary. It has served the diocese of Cleveland for 160 years. *Enrollment:* 130. *Degrees offered:* Master's, doctorate, first-professional.

Accreditation: *Regional:* NCA. *National:* ATS. *Professional*: theology

Calendar: Semesters. Academic year from Aug. to May.

Degree Requirements: Completion of prescribed curriculum.

Degrees Conferred: 13 *masters:* theology; 6 *first-professional:* master of divinity; 1 *doctorate:* theology.

Fees and Other Expenses: *Full-time tuition per academic year 2008–09:* $315 per credit hour.

Departments and Teaching Staff: *Total instructional faculty:* 24. Student/faculty ratio: 10:1. Degrees held by full-time faculty: doctorate 90%, master's 100%, professional 60%. 90% hold terminal degrees.

Enrollment: Total enrollment 130. First-professional

Characteristics of Student Body: *Ethnic/racial makeup:* number of Black non-Hispanic: 1; Asian or Pacific Islander: 1; White non-Hispanic: 108. *Age distribution:* number 22–24: 10; 25–29: 12; 30–34: 5; 35–39: 27; 40–49: 29; 50–64: 2; 65 and over: 8.

International Students: 3 nonresident aliens enrolled fall 2008. No programs available to aid students whose native language is not English. Some financial aid specifically designated for international students.

Library Collections: 74,000 volumes including bound books, serial backfiles, electronic documents, and government documents not in separate collections. Online catalog. Current serial subscriptions: 325. 1,179 audio/videotapes. Computer work stations available. Students have access to the Internet at no charge.

Most important special collection is the Horstmann Collection.

Chief Executive Officer: Rev. Thomas W. Tifft, President. Address admissions inquiries to Paulette Bsin, Registrar.

Shawnee State University

940 Second Street
Portsmouth, Ohio 45662-4303
Tel: (740) 351-3169 **E-mail:** to_ssu@shawnee.edu
Fax: (740) 351-3111 **Internet:** www.shawnee.edu

Institution Description: Shawnee State University, formerly Shawnee State Community College, is a 4-year state university. *Enrollment:* 3,976. *Degrees awarded:* Associate, baccalaureate, master's.

Accreditation: *Regional:* NCA.

History: Created as Shawnee State General and Technical College by a merger of the Ohio University Regional Campus and Scioto Technical College 1975; changed name to Shawnee State Community College 1978; adopted present name 1986.

Institutional Structure: *Governing board:* Shawnee State University Board of Trustees. Officers include president, provost, vice president for business affairs, vice president and general counsel; vice president for student affairs.

Calendar: Quarters. Academic year Sept. to June.

Characteristics of Freshmen: 100% of applicants accepted. 17% of applicants admitted and enrolled.

82% (369 students) submitted ACT scores. *25th percentile*: ACT Composite 17, ACT English 16, ACT Math 16. *75th percentile*: ACT Composite 23, ACT English 23, ACT Math 22.

19% of entering freshmen expected to graduate within 5 years. 95% of freshmen from Ohio. Freshmen from 7 states and 7 foreign countries.

Admission: Open enrollment. Applicants must provide high school or GED transcript. ACT or SAT scores required of applicants under age 21. Admission of health science applicants is selective with limited enrollments.

Degree Requirements: Minimum 180 quarter hours including a 50-hour core curriculum required of all baccalaureate candidates. 90 quarter hour minimum required for the associate degree.

Degrees Conferred: 270 *baccalaureate*; 1 *master's.* Bachelor's degrees awarded in top five disciplines: business/marketing 69; social sciences 65; education 58; visual and performing arts 27; health professions and related clinical sciences 23. Master's degrees awarded: health professional 1.

Fees and Other Expenses: *Full-time tuition per academic year 2008–09:* resident $5,832, nonresident $10,176. *Required fees:* $630. *Room and board per academic year:* $7,670. *Books and supplies:* $1,440. *Other expenses:* $6,938.

Financial Aid: Aid from institutionally generated funds is provided on the basis of academic merit, financial need, athletic ability. Institution has a Program Participation Agreement with the U.S. Department of Education for eligible students to receive Pell Grants and, depending upon the agreement, other federal aid.

92% of first-time, full-time undergarduate students received some form of aid.

Departments and Teaching Staff: *Total instructional faculty:* 304 (full-time 143, part-time 161). Total faculty with doctorate, first-professional, or other terminal degree: 72. Student/faculty ratio: 17:1. Degrees held by full-time faculty: doctorate 41%, master's 43%, baccalaureate 10%, professional 3%. 55% hold terminal degrees.

Enrollment: Total enrollment 3,976. Undergraduate3,935 (full-time 82%; female 59%, male 41%). Graduate 41 (full-time 100%). Undergraduate transfer-in students 130.

Characteristics of Student Body: *Ethnic/racial makeup:* Black non-Hispanic: 3%; American Indian or Alaska Native: 1%; White non-Hispanic: 87%; unknown: 8%; nonresident alien 1%. *Age distribution:* number under 18: 129; 18–19: 1,235; 20–21: 918; 22–24: 558; 25–29: 357; 30–34: 233; 35–39: 158; 40–49: 196; 50–64: 62; 65 and over: 11; unknown: 2.

International Students: 40 nonresident aliens enrolled fall 2008. Students from Europe, Asia, Central and South America, Africa. Programs available to aid students whose native language is not English: English as a Second Language Program. No financial aid specifically designated for international students.

Student Life: On- and off-campus housing available. Sports activities include male and female basketball and cross-country; male baseball, golf, soccer; female softball, tennis, volleyball. Various student activities available.

Library Collections: 188,000 volumes. 31,000 microform; 480 audiovisual materials. Current periodical subscriptions: 18,700 including via electronic access. Computer work stations available. Students have access to the Internet and online information retrieval services.

Most important special collections include Vern Riffe Memorabilia Collection; Jesse Stuart Collection; Shawnee State University Archives.

Buildings and Grounds: 25-acre campus. Campus DVD available.

Chief Executive Officer: Dr. Rita Rice Morris, President.

Address admission inquiries to Robert Trusz, Director of Admissions.

Tiffin University

155 Miami Street
Tiffin, Ohio 44883
Tel: (419) 447-6442 **E-mail:** admiss@tiffin.edu
Fax: (419) 443-5006 **Internet:** www.tiffin.edu

Institution Description: Tiffin University is a private, independent, nonprofit institution. *Enrollment:* 2,674. *Degrees awarded:* Associate, baccalaureate, master's.

Accreditation: *Regional:* NCA. *Professional*: business

History: Established 1888; awarded first degree (baccalaureate) 1924; moved to present campus 1956.

Institutional Structure: *Governing board:* Board of Trustees. Extrainstitutional representation: 18 trustees; institutional representation: 1 ex officio, 1 full-time instructional faculty member. 18 voting. *Composition of institution:* Administrators 22. Academic affairs headed by academic dean. Full-time instructional faculty 49. Academic governance body, curriculum committee meets an average of 5 times per year.

Calendar: Semesters. Academic year Aug. to May. Freshmen admitted Sept., Jan. Degrees conferred and formal commencement May. Summer sessions (6 weeks) begin May and July.

Characteristics of Freshmen: 2,212 applicants (1,039 female, 1,173 male). 74% of applicants admitted. 35% of applicants admitted and enrolled full-time.

14% (44 students) submitted SAT scores; 86% (263 students) submitted ACT scores. *25th percentile*: SAT Critical Reading 430, SAT Math 450; ACT Composite 18, ACT English 18, ACT Math 17. *75th percentile*: SAT Critical Reading 560, SAT Math 540; ACT Composite 23, ACT English 24, ACT Math 22.

20% of entering freshmen expected to graduate within 5 years. 85% of freshmen from Ohio. Freshmen from 9 states and 3 foreign countries.

Admission: Rolling admissions plan. For fall acceptance, apply during senior year of secondary school, but not later than 2 days after classes begin. Early acceptance available. *Requirements:* secondary school units recommended with 4 English, 3 mathematics, 3 science, 3 social studies. Students with a 3.0 GPA or higher in college preparatory classes and ACT score of 20 or higher or SAT 890 or higher will receive priority in the admission process. *Transfer students:* four-year transfer students must complete 25% and two-year students 50% of course-work at Tiffin University.

College credit and advanced placement for postsecondary-level work completed in secondary school. College credit for extrainstitutional learning.

Tutoring available. Developmental courses offered in summer session and regular academic year; credit given.

Degree Requirements: *For all associate degrees:* 61 semester hours. *For bachelor of arts, business administration or criminal justice:* 121 semester hours. *For all baccalaureate degrees:* 2.0 minimum GPA. *Master's degree:* business administration requires 36 semester hours, criminal justice 30 semester hours; 3.0 GPA.

Fulfillment of some degree requirements and exemption from some beginning courses possible by passing departmental examinations and College Board CLEP. *Grading system:* A–F; withdraw (carries time limit), deadline after which pass-fail is appended to withdrawal, (automatic failure for withdrawal without notification).

Internship hours are required for some degrees. Students are also required to participate in 26 clock hours (2 units of co-curricular activity in order to graduate).

Distinctive Educational Programs: Accelerated degree program, independent study, evening classes, and internships. Arts Administration major; Forensic Psychology; Sports Management. Study abroad at Regents College, London, England.

Degrees Conferred: 3 *associate;* 271 *baccalaureate*; 196 *master's*. Bachelor's degrees awarded in top five disciplines: business and management 143; protective services/public administration 28; parks and recreation 12; psychology 8. computer and information sciences 6. Master's degrees awarded: various disciplines 196.

Fees and Other Expenses: *Full-time tuition per academic year 2008–09:* $17,220 undergraduate; graduate study charged per credit hour (contact the university for current rate). *Room and board per academic year:* $7,580. *Books and supplies:* $1,500. *Other expenses:* $1,500.

Financial Aid: The university offers a direct lending program. Aid from institutionally generated funds is provided on the basis of academic merit, financial need, athletic ability, other criteria.

Financial aid to full-time, first-time undergraduate students: 96% received some form of financial aid. Average amount of aid received: federal grants $2,097; state/local grants $1,462; institutional grants $1,556; loans $5,633.

Departments and Teaching Staff: *Total instructional faculty:* 117 (full-time 50, part-time 67). Total faculty with doctorate, first-professional, or other terminal degree: 64. Student/faculty ratio: 18:1. Degrees held by full-time faculty: master's 38%, doctorate 64%, professional 7%.

Enrollment: Total enrollment 2,674. Undergraduate 1,810 (full-time 87%; female 55%, male 45%). Graduate 864 (full-time 32%). Undergraduate transfer-in students 211.

Characteristics of Student Body: *Ethnic/racial makeup:* Black non-Hispanic: 16%; Asian or Pacific Islander: 1%; Hispanic: 3%; White non-Hispanic: 64%, unknown 11%; nonresident alien 5%. *Age distribution:* number under 18: 3; 18–19: 138; 20–21: 193; 22–24: 121; 25–29: 34; 30–34: 22; 35–39. 23, 40–49: 16; 50–64: 5; 65 and over: 3.

International Students: 134 nonresident aliens enrolled fall 2008. Students from Europe, Asia, Central and South America, Africa, Canada. Programs available to aid students whose native language is not English: social, cultural. Some financial aid specifically designated for undergraduate international students.

Student Life: All first- and second-year students are required to live on campus unless their permanent residence is within a 45-mile commuting distance. On-campus residence halls available in 6 residence halls, 10 campus houses, and an apartment buildings. *Intercollegiate athletics:* male: baseball, basketball, cross-country, football, golf, soccer, tennis, track and field; female: basketball, cross-country, golf, soccer, softball, tennis, track and field, volleyball. Club sports offered in bowling, cheerleading, dance, incline hockey, volleyball. Academic clubs, Greek life, student government, university bands, vocal music groups, Work Student Association. *Special regulations:* Cars permitted without restrictions. *Special services:* Medical services. *Student publications: The Dragonsayer*, quarterly student newspaper; *Dragon Droppings*, a weekly student newspaper. *Surrounding community:* Tiffin population 18,500. Toledo, 60 miles from campus, is nearest metropolitan area.

Library Collections: 52,500 volumes including bound books, serial back-files, electronic documents, and government documents not in separate collections. Online catalog. Current serial subscriptions: 255 paper, 190 microform, 1.690 via electronic access. Computer work stations available. Students have access to the Internet at no charge.

Most important special collections include National Criminal Justice Reference Service Document Collection; University Archives.

Buildings and Grounds: *New buildings:* Hertzer Technology Center; Hayes Center for the Arts. Campus DVD available.

Chief Executive Officer: Dr. Paul Marion, President.

Address undergraduate admission inquiries to Cam Cruickshank, Vice President of Enrollment Management.

Trinity Lutheran Seminary

2199 East Main Street
Columbus, Ohio 43209-2334
Tel: (614) 235-4136 **E-mail:** info@trinitylutheran.edu
Fax: (614) 238-0263 **Internet:** www.trinitylutheran.edu

Institution Description: Trinity Lutheran Seminary is a private institution affiliated with the Evangelical Lutheran Church in America and The American

TRINITY LUTHERAN SEMINARY—*cont'd*

Lutheran Church. *Enrollment:* 146. *Degrees awarded:* First-professional (master of divinity), master's.

Accreditation: *Regional:* NCA. *National:* ATS. *Professional*: theology

History: Established as Evangelical Lutheran Seminary in Canton, Ohio, chartered, and offered first instruction at postsecondary level 1830; moved to Columbus in 1832 and became theological school of Capital University 1850; awarded first degree (first-professional) in 1928; became independent 1959; merged with Hamma School of Theology (established 1845) and adopted present name 1978.

Institutional Structure: *Governing board:* Board of Directors. Extrainstitutional representation: 28 directors, including 15 laypersons. All voting. *Composition of institution:* Administrators 19. Academic affairs headed by academic dean. Management/business/finance directed by Vice President of Business and Finance. Full-time instructional faculty 17. Academic governance body, the faculty, meets an average of 10 times per year.

Calendar: Quarters. Academic year Sept. to May. New students admitted Sept., Jan., July. Degrees conferred and formal commencement May. Summer session June.

Admission: *Requirements:* Baccalaureate from an accredited college or university. Broad liberal arts background preferred. Recommend 2.5 minimum GPA. *For transfer students:* Must be in good standing at institution previously attended. Maximum transfer credit limited only by residence requirement.

Degree Requirements: *For first-professional degree:* 128 quarter hours; 2 years field experience in ministry; 1 clinical term; 1 year internship; demonstrated competence in Greek; yearly comprehensive evaluations. *For all master's degrees:* 84–128 quarter hours. *For Div. degrees:* Final year in residence; core and distribution requirements. Additional requirements for some majors.

Exemption from some beginning courses possible by passing departmental examinations. *Grading system:* pass-marginal-fail.

Distinctive Educational Programs: Summer clinical pastoral education program. Independent study. Study abroad on archaeological sites in Israel through American Schools of Oriental Research. Cross-registration with Methodist Theological School in Ohio and Pontifical College Josephinum. Students may enroll for interprofessional courses at Ohio State University. *Other distinctive programs:* Continuing professional education.

Degrees Conferred: 47 *first-professional:* master of divinity.

Fees and Other Expenses: *Tuition per academic year 2008–09:* contact the seminary for current information regarding tuition, fees. housing, and other costs. Students who are members of congregations of the Evangelical Lutheran Church in America receive reduced rates.

Financial Aid: Aid from institutionally generated funds is provided on the basis of academic merit and financial need. Institution has a Program Participation Agreement with the U.S. Department of Education for eligible students to receive Pell Grants and, depending upon the agreement, other federal aid.

Departments and Teaching Staff: *Total instructional faculty:* 25.

Enrollment: Total enrollment 146. First-professional 146.

Characteristics of Student Body: *Ethnic/racial makeup:* Black non-Hispanic: 9%; Hispanic: 1%; Asian or Pacific Islander 2%; White non-Hispanic: 85%; nonresident alien 35.

International Students: 3 nonresident aliens enrolled fall 2008. No programs available to aid students whose native language is not English. No financial aid specifically designated for international students.

Student Life: On-campus residence halls house 15% of student body. 50% of married students request institutional housing; 42% are so housed. *Special regulations:* Cars permitted without restrictions. *Special services:* medical services. *Surrounding community:* Columbus metropolitan population over 1 million. Served by mass transit bus system; airport 4 miles from campus.

Library Collections: 150,000 volumes. 3,236 microforms; 4,980 audiovisual materials; 625 current periodical subscriptions.

Buildings and Grounds: Campus area 1½ square blocks.

Chief Executive Officer: Dr. Mark R. Ramseth, President.

Address admission inquiries to Rev. Sheri Ayers, Director of Admissions.

Union Institute

440 East McMillan Street
Cincinnati, Ohio 45206-1925
Tel: (513) 861-6400 **E-mail:** admissions@tui.edu
Fax: (513) 861-0779 **Internet:** www.tui.edu

Institution Description: The Union Institute is a private, independent, nonprofit university authorized by the Ohio Board of Regents to grant degrees. The Union Institute's College of Undergraduate Studies operates 5 learning centers located in Cincinnati, Ohio; Miami, Florida; and Sacramento, Los Angeles, and San Diego, California. The college also has a distance learning program, the Center for Distant Learning. The Graduate College's doctoral programs are administered from the University's headquarters in Cincinnati, Ohio. *Enrollment:* 2,051. *Degrees awarded:* Baccalaureate, master's, doctorate.

Accreditation: *Regional:* NCA.

History: Established 1964; incorporated 1969; awarded first degree (doctoral) 1971.

Institutional Structure: *Governing board:* Board of Trustees. *Composition of institution:* President, vice president for institutional advancement, vice president for finance and administration, vice president for academic affairs; vice president for social responsibility. Deans for each of the Graduate College's two schools, and for each undergraduate learning centers; directors for administrative departments. Full-time instructional faculty 88. Adjunct faculty varies by term.

Calendar: Semesters. Academic year July through June. Undergraduate students enter July, Nov., Mar; graduate students enter monthly. Degrees conferred individually as earned. Formal commencement held annually.

Characteristics of Freshmen: 45 applicants (30 female, 15 male). 89% of applicants admitted. 79% of applicants admitted and enrolled full-time. 90% of undergraduate learners enter with some previous college. First-time freshman are the exception, rather than the rule.

Admission: Rolling admissions plan. *Requirements:* For the undergraduate program, admissions decisions are based on evidence of ability to benefit, including graduation from an accredited secondary school or GED. Graduate College applicants must hold an earned master's degree from an accredited institution. *For transfer students:* requirements are the same for applicants who had previously attended other postsecondary institutions. A maximum of 96 semester credits may be accepted in transfer toward the baccalaureate degree; transfer credits are not accepted toward the doctorate.

Tutoring available.

Degree Requirements: *For baccalaureate degree:* 128 semester credits; senior thesis. *For doctoral degree:* minimum full-time enrollment of two calendar years (24 months), 35 day residence, internship, dissertation. Graduate program is not credit hour based.

Fulfillment of some degree requirements and exemption from some beginning courses possible by passing College Board CLEP, AP. *Grading system:* Results of student learning contracts are individually evaluated.

Distinctive Educational Programs: All degree programs are individually designed to meet the needs and goals of the student. Both degree programs are designed as educational alternatives for adults who require more options and flexibility than usually available in residentially-based universities. Each Union Institute degree program is individually designed to meet needs and goals of the adult learner. They offer flexible scheduling, alternative delivery systems, limited residency requirements, and independent study/tutorial-based learning.

Degrees Conferred: 444 *baccalaureate*; 246 *master's*; 55 *doctorate*. Bachelor's degrees awarded in top five disciplines: liberal arts and sciences, general studies, and humanities 108; security and protective services 74; education 65; business, management, marketing, and related support services 28; public administration 20.

Fees and Other Expenses: *Full-time tuition per academic year 2008–09:* contact the school for current information regarding tuition, fees, housing, and other costs.

Financial Aid: Aid from institutionally generated funds is provided on the basis of academic merit, financial need.

Financial aid to full-time, first-time undergraduate students: 79% received some form of financial aid. 54% received federal grants; 46% received state/local grants; 32% received institutional grants; 79% received loans.

Departments and Teaching Staff: *Total instructional faculty:* 88 (full-time 51, part-time 37). Degrees held by full-time faculty: doctorate 95% hold earned doctorate; 100% hold earned master's.

Enrollment: Total enrollment 2,051.

Characteristics of Student Body: *Ethnic/racial makeup:* Black non-Hispanic: 19%; Asian or Pacific Islander: 1%; Hispanic: 11%; White non-Hispanic: 44%; unknown: 14%.

International Students: No programs available to aid students whose native language is not English. No financial aid specifically designated for international students.

Student Life: The Union Institute's educational programs are designed for adults who continue to live and work while earning their degrees.

Library Collections: 45,000 volumes. 150 current periodical subscriptions. Library houses doctoral dissertations of Union Institute graduates.

Chief Executive Officer: Dr. Roger H. Bublett, President.

Address admission inquiries to Dr. Neal Meier, Director of Enrollment Management.

United Theological Seminary

1810 Harvard Boulevard
Dayton, Ohio 45406
Tel: (937) 278-5817 **E-mail:** admissions@united.edu
Fax: (937) 278-1218 **Internet:** www.united.edu

Institution Description: United Theological Seminary is a private institution affiliated with the United Methodist Church. *Enrollment:* 228. *Degrees awarded:* First-professional (master of divinity), master's, doctorate.

Member of the Southern Ohio Council for Higher Education.

Accreditation: *Regional:* NCA. *National:* ATS. *Professional*: theology

History: Established as Union Biblical Seminary and offered first instruction at postsecondary level 1871; chartered 1873; awarded first degree (first-professional) 1874; changed name to Bonebrake Theological Seminary 1909; adopted present name 1954.

Institutional Structure: *Governing board:* Board of Trustees. Extrainstitutional representation: 35 trustees; institutional representation: 1 full-time instructional faculty member, 1 student, 3 ex officio. All voting. *Composition of institution:* Administrators 5. Academic affairs headed by vice president for academic affairs. Management/business/finances directed by vice president for administration/treasurer. Financial development directed by vice president for institutional development. Full-time instructional faculty 15. Academic governance body, the faculty, meets an average of 12 times per year.

Calendar: Semesters. Academic year Aug. to June. Degrees conferred and formal commencement May, Dec.

Admission: Rolling admissions plan. For fall acceptance, apply no later than registration period (foreign students no later than Dec. 31). *Requirements:* Baccalaureate or equivalent from accredited college or university. Recommend Biblical study and coursework in English, languages, history, philosophy, religion, and social sciences. *Entrance tests:* For foreign students minimum TOEFL score 550. *For transfer students:* From institutions accredited by Association of Theological Schools, maximum transfer credit limited only by residence requirement.

Degree Requirements: *For first professional degree:* 90 semester hours; first and second year comprehensive evaluation and preparation of senior plan. *For master's degree:* 60 semester hours. *For both degrees:* 120 semester hours; final year in residence; field education. *Grading system:* Honors-satisfactory-minimum competence-no credit; withdraw; incomplete; written evaluation by faculty and field supervisors.

Distinctive Educational Programs: Work-experience programs, including internships and clinical pastoral education. Off-campus learning centers at more than 30 area social service agencies and 100 area parishes. Evening classes. Joint master of divinity-master's degree. Cross-registration through consortia. Special facilities for using telecommunications and computers. Judaic studies in cooperation with University of Dayton and Wright State University. Tutorials. Specialized training for rural ministries, urban ministries, outdoor ministry; telecommunications. Women's center sponsors study groups, workshops, retreats for women. *Other distinctive programs:* Continuing education for laypersons and clergy; Diaconal Ministry, Environmental Ministry, Youth Ministry.

Degrees Conferred: 7 *master's,* 54 *doctorate:* theology; 17 *first-professional* theology.

Fees and Other Expenses: *Full-time tuition per academic year 2008–09:* contact the seminary for current information.

Financial Aid: Aid from institutionally generated funds is provided on the basis of academic merit, financial need.

Departments and Teaching Staff: *Total instructional faculty:* 36. Degrees held by full-time faculty: baccalaureate 100%, master's 100%, doctorate 88%, professional 83%.

Enrollment: Total enrollment 228.

International Students: 5 nonresident aliens enrolled fall 2008. Students from Europe, Asia, Africa, Canada. No programs available to aid students whose native language is not English. Some financial aid specifically designated for international students.

Student Life: On-campus 25% of student body lives in institutionally controlled apartments. Housing available for married students. *Special regulations:* Cars permitted without restrictions. *Special services:* Learning Resources Center. *Surrounding community:* Dayton metropolitan area population 800,000. Served by mass transit bus system; airport 10 miles from campus.

Publications: *Journal of Theology* published annually in June. An annual report; *Keeping In Touch,* published twice a year; *Telescope Messenger,* published twice a year; quarterly newsletters to major donors.

Library Collections: 105,000 volumes. 8,218 microforms; 6,503 audiovisual materials; 14,432 current periodical subscriptions. Access to online information retrieval systems.

Most important special collections include Evangelical United Brethren Collection; Union Biblical Seminary Collection; Edmund S. Lorenz Hymnal Collection.

Buildings and Grounds: Campus area 35 acres.

Chief Executive Officer: Dr. G. Edwin Zeiders, President.

Address admission inquiries to Betty J. Statler, Director of Admissions.

University of Akron

302 Buchtel Common
Akron, Ohio 44325
Tel: (330) 972-7111 **E-mail:** admission@uakron.edu
Fax: (330) 972-6168 **Internet:** www.akron.edu

Institution Description: The University of Akron, the fourth-largest state-assisted university in Ohio, is a comprehensive university with 9 degree-granting colleges and a 2-year Community and Technical College. Its branch campus, Wayne College, is located in Orrville, Ohio. *Enrollment:* 24,119. *Degrees awarded:* Associate, baccalaureate, master's, first-professional (law). Certificates also given. The university offers a 6-year bachelor's of science and doctor of medicine degree through the Northeastern Ohio Universities College of Medicine (NEOUCOM), a consortium of The University of Akron, Kent State University, and Youngstown State University.

Accreditation: *Regional:* NCA.*Professional*: art, business, chemistry, dance, dietetics, counseling, engineering, engineering technology, interior design, law, medical assisting, music, nursing, psychology, public administration, respiratory therapy, speech-language pathology, teacher education, social work

History: Established by the Universalist Church of Ohio as the nonsectarian Buchtel College and chartered 1870; offered first instruction at postsecondary level 1871; awarded first degree (baccalaureate) 1874; became public institution and changed name to the Municipal University of Akron 1914; adopted present name 1926; became state-affiliated 1963; became state university 1967. *See* George Knepper, *New Lamps for Old* (Akron: The University of Akron, 1970) and *Summit's Glory* (Akron, The University of Akron Press, 1990) for further information.

Institutional Structure: *Governing board:* Board of Trustees. Representation: 11 members, 9 voting. *Composition of institution:* Administrators 496. Student affairs headed by senior vice president and provost. Legal services, finance and administration, capital planning and facilities management, public affairs and development, and information technologies headed by vice presidents. Full-time instructional faculty 729. Academic governance body, Faculty Senate, meets an average of 8 times per year.

Calendar: Semesters. Academic year Aug. to May. Degrees conferred and formal commencement Dec., May, Aug. Summer session May to Aug.

Characteristics of Freshmen: 79% of applicants admitted. 43% of applicants admitted and enrolled.

71% (256 students) submitted SAT scores; 93% (3,429 students) submitted ACT scores. *25th percentile*: SAT Critical Reading 440, SAT Math 460; ACT Composite 18, ACT English 16, ACT Math 17. *75th percentile*: SAT Critical Reading 560, SAT Math 590; ACT Composite 23, ACT English 23, ACT Math 24.

28% of entering freshmen expected to graduate within 5 years. 97% of freshmen from Ohio. Freshmen from 23 states and 11 foreign countries.

Admission: Rolling admissions plan. *Requirements:* Either graduation from accredited secondary school or GED. Minimum 2.0 GPA. *Entrance tests:* College Board SAT or ACT composite.

Advanced placement for postsecondary-level work completed in secondary school.

Tutoring available. Noncredit developmental courses offered in summer session and regular academic year.

Degree Requirements: *For all associate degrees:* 64 credit hours; the last 16 credit hours in residence, unless excused in writing by dean of college. *For all baccalaureate degrees:* 128–140 credit hours; the last 32 credit hours in residence, unless excused in writing by dean of college; physical education requirements for students under 25 years of age; general education requirements.

Fulfillment of some degree requirements and exemption from some beginning courses possible by passing departmental examinations, College Board CLEP. *Grading system:* A–F; credit-noncredit; withdraw (carries time limit).

Distinctive Educational Programs: Flexible meeting places and schedules, including weekend and evening classes. Accelerated degree programs. University Honors Program. Special facilities for using telecommunications in the classroom. Interdisciplinary and interdepartmental programs in Pan-American studies, aging services, emergency medical services, alcohol services aide, applied politics, cartographic specialization, child care worker, commercial photography, computer physics, computer science, computer software for business, criminal justice technology, criminal justice/security emphasis, drafting and computer drafting technology, environmental health, environmental studies, fire

UNIVERSITY OF AKRON—*cont'd*

protection technology, gerontology, hospitality management, interior design, Latin American studies, paralegal studies, library studies, linguistic studies, manual communication, office administration, peace studies, planning with an emphasis on city or regional resource studies, professional communication, programming skills enrichment, real estate, small business management, Soviet area studies, supervision and management, surgeon's assistant, surgical technologist, teaching English as a second language, volunteer program management, and women's studies. Facilities and programs for independent research, including honors programs, individual majors. Study abroad in Denmark, France, Germany, Ghana, Japan, Mexico, Netherlands, People's Republic of China, Peru, Puerto Rico, Rumania, Russia, South Korea, United Kingdom.

ROTC: Air Force offered in crosstown agreement with Ashland University and Malone College.

Degrees Conferred: 365 *associate;* 2,219 *baccalaureate*; 954 *master's*; 110 *doctorate*; 152 *first-professional*. Bachelor's degrees awarded in top five disciplines: business/marketing 465; education 404; health professions 300; communications/journalism 188;engineering 179. Master's degrees awarded in top five disciplines: education 297; business/marketing 133; health professions 114; public administration and social services 67; social sciences 41. Doctorates awarded: education 15; engineering 34; health professions 8; physical sciences 43; psychology 12; social sciences 7. First-professional degrees awarded: law 152.

Fees and Other Expenses: *Full-time tuition per academic year 2006=07:* undergraduate resident $8,612, nonresident $17,861; contact the university for current graduate and first-professional tuition that vary with program. *Room and board per academic year:* $8,311. *Books and supplies:* $900. *Other expenses:* $2,520.

Financial Aid: Aid from institutionally generated funds is provided on the basis of academic merit, financial need, athletic ability.

Financial aid to full-time, first-time undergraduate students: 87% of students received some form of financial aid. Average amount of aid received: federal grants $3,673; Pell grants $2,820; other federal aid $1,225; state/local grants $1,068; institutional grants $4,495.

Departments and Teaching Staff: *Total instructional faculty:* 1,590 (full-time 729, part-time 861). Student/faculty ratio: 18:1. *Degrees held by full-time faculty:* Doctorate 84,5%, master's 14.33%, baccalaureate 1.2%. 84.5% hold terminal degrees.

Enrollment: Total enrollment 24,119. Undergraduate 19,817 (full-time 77%; female 50%, male 50%). Graduate 4,306 (full-time 49%). Undergraduate transfer-in students 890.

Characteristics of Student Body: *Ethnic/racial makeup:* Black non-Hispanic: 13%; Asian or Pacific Islander: 2%; Hispanic: 1%; White non-Hispanic: 78%; unknown 4%; nonresident alien 1%. *Age distribution:* number under 18: 394; 18–19: 5,290; 20–21: 4,666; 22–24: 4,055; 25–29: 2,275; 30–34: 988; 35–39: 766; 40–49: 849; 50–64: 337; 65 and over: 52. 41% of student body attend summer sessions.

International Students: 771 nonresident aliens enrolled fall 2008. Students from Europe, Asia, Central and South America, Africa, Canada, Australia, Middle East. Programs to aid students whose native language is not English: social, cultural. English as a Second Language. Financial aid specifically designated for international students.

Student Life: On-campus affiliated housing and residence halls house 15% of undergraduates. 2% of males join fraternities; 2% of females join sororities. *Intercollegiate athletics:* male: baseball, basketball, cross-country, football, golf, indoor and outdoor track, riflery, soccer; female: basketball, cross-country, indoor and outdoor track, riflery, soccer, softball, swimming/diving, tennis, volleyball. *Special services:* Division of Student Affairs provides a wide range of resources, programs, and professional consulting; student financial aid and employment; career planning and placement; counseling and testing; student health services; residence hall program board, ecumenical campus ministry; Pan African Center for Community Studies. *Student organizations:* More than 200 student organizations, including 22 fraternities and sororities. *Student publications, radio, television: Akron Review*, a biannual literary journal; *ARETE*, a biannual law journal; *Buchtelite*, a biweekly newspaper; *Tel-Buch*, a yearbook; Radio station WZIP-FM has 96,000 listeners each week. *Surrounding community:* The university is located in the midst of Akron, population 212,000. Served by mass transit bus system and two major airports. The university is 13 miles from Akron-Canton Regional Airport and 40 miles from Cleveland Hopkins International Airport.

Publications: The University of Akron Press publishes scholarly books and poetry with special interests in environmental studies and regional history. They publish a series on International History, Ohio History and Culture, Technology and the Environment, and the Akron Series in Poetry with the Akron Poetry Prize Competition. The press also distributes publications of Principa Press.

Library Collections: 1,260,000 volumes including bound books, serial backfiles, electronic documents, and government documents not in separate collections. Online catalog. 14,800 periodicals including via electronic access. 1,683,000 microforms; 48,500 audiovisual units. Students have access to the Internet and online information retrieval services.

Most important special holdings include Herman Muehlstein Rare Book Collection; Paul L. Flory Personal Library (founder of modern polymer chemistry); Sylvia Smith Archives (new music); B-26 Marauder Collection; Archives of the History of American Psychology.

Buildings and Grounds: Main campus area of 218 acres with 151 acres at Wayne College branch. Campus DVD available.

Chief Executive Officer: Dr. Luis M. Proenza, President. Address undergraduate admission inquiries to Diane Raybuck, Director of Admissions; graduate inquiries to Dr. George R. Newkome, Dean of Graduate School; first-professional inquiries to Lauri S. File, Assistant Dean of Law Admissions and Financial Aid.

Buchtel College of Arts and Sciences

Degree Programs Offered: *Baccalaureate* in biology, botany, classical studies, ecology/evolution, microbiology, animal physiology and zoology, chemistry, computer science, economics (labor economics), English, geography (geography/cartography, planning), geology (engineering geology, geophysics), history, humanities, interdisciplinary studies, mathematics (applied mathematics), modern languages (French, Spanish), natural sciences (combined B.S./M.D.), philosophy, physics, political science (criminal justice, American politics, international politics; law, courts and politics), psychology, social sciences, social sciences-PPE Track, sociology (criminology/law enforcement), statistics (statistical computer science, actuarial science); *master's, doctorate* awarded through the Graduate School.

Distinctive Educational Programs: Center for Conflict Management Center for Environmental Studies. Center for Peace Studies. Institute for Health and Social Policy. Center for Statistical Consulting. English Language Institute. Institute for Lifespan Development and Gerontology. Center for Policy Studies, Ray C. Bliss Institute of Applied Politics. 5-year cooperative work-experience program in chemistry, mathematics, applied mat hematics, or computer science. Joint baccalaureate program in geography/travel and tourism, political science/criminal justice, sociology/law, and sociology/corrections with the Community and Technical College. Joint graduate programs: baccalaureate and doctor of medicine (B.S./M.D.) with Northeastern Ohio Universities College of Medicine; master's joint J.D. and public administration program with the School of Law (J.D./M.P.A.), Ph.D. in sociology with Kent State University; Ph.D in urban studies and public affairs with Cleveland State University.

College of Business Administration

Degree Programs Offered: *Baccalaureate* in accounting, industrial accounting, business administration, finance, international business, management (industrial management/production, personnel, quality management, information systems, materials), marketing (marketing management, sales management; international, marketing communications, physical distribution, retail management), entrepreneurship; *master's* awarded through the Graduate School.

Distinctive Educational Programs: Center for Organizational Development. Joint master's/first professional programs in legal and administrative studies (J.D./M.B.A.) and in legal and taxation studies (J.D./M.Tax.) with the School of Law. William and Rita Fitzgerald Institute for Entrepreneurial Studies. Institute for Global Business; Fisher Institute for Professional Selling.

Summit College

Degree Programs Offered: *Associate* arts, business management technology (accounting), community services technology (addiction, gerontology, social service), computer information services- networking, criminal justice technology (security administration), computer information, drafting and computer drafting technology, early childhood development, electronic engineering technology, fire protection technology, hospitality management (culinary arts, hotel/lodging management, hotel marketing and sales, restaurant management), individualized study, paralegal studies, manufacturing engineering technology (computer-aided manufacturing, industrial supervision), marketing and sales technology (advertising, fashion, retailing, sales), mechanical technology, medical assisting technology, office administration (administrative assistant, international, medical), radiologic technology, respiratory care, surgical technology, surveying and construction engineering technology, *baccalaureate* in automated manufacturing engineering technology, construction engineering technology, surveying engineering technology, emergency management, electronic engineering technology, mechanical engineering technology.

Distinctive Educational Programs: Center for Emergency Management/ Homeland Security, Training Center for Fire and Hazardous Materials; Training Center for Criminal Justice and Law Enforcement, CISCO Academy, Workfoce Development and Continuing Education, and Tech/Prep Programs.

College of Education

Degree Programs Offered: *Baccalaureate* in bilingual multicultural education, early childhood, elementary education (dual certification, kindergarten, prekindergarten), sports and exercise science, certification in dance, physical education, secondary education (all fields), special education (developmentally handicapped, multihandicapped, orthopedically handicapped, severe behavior handicapped, specific learning disabled), technical education; *master's, doctorate* awarded through the Graduate School.

Distinctive Educational Programs: Center for Economic Education. Center for the Study for Urban and Higher Education. Center for the Study of Urban Education. Graduate program offers 7 educational administrative specialist certificates and certificates in school psychology, elementary, and secondary school principal. Joint doctorate program in counseling psychology with Buchtel College of Arts and Sciences.

College of Engineering

Degree Programs Offered: *Baccalaureate* in biomedical engineering, chemical engineering, civil engineering, computer engineering, engineering, electrical engineering, mechanical engineering, mechanical polymer engineering; *master's, doctorate* awarded through the Graduate School.

Distinctive Educational Programs: Institute for Biomedical Engineering Research. Process Research Center. 5-year cooperative work-experience program. Joint program in construction technology with Community and Technical College. Joint master's and doctorate with Northeastern Ohio Universities College of Medicine.

College of Fine and Applied Arts

Degree Programs Offered: *Baccalaureate* in art (art education, studio art, history of art), fine arts (art education, ceramics, crafts, drawing, graphic design, metalsmithing, painting, photography, printmaking, sculpture), business and organizational communication (broadcasting, business and organizational communications, interpersonal and public communication, corporate video), clothing/textiles and interiors (business, interior design, theatre costume), speech-language pathology (clinical or non-clinical), communication/rhetoric, dance, dietetics, family and consumer sciences, family and child development, food science, home economics education, clothing/textiles and interiors, mass media-communication, music (accompanying, history and literature, jazz studies, music education, performance, theory-composition), social work, theatre (theatre arts, acting, design/technology, musical theatre); *master's, doctorate* awarded through the Graduate School.

Distinctive Educational Programs: Audiology and Speech Center. Center for Family Studies. Electronic music laboratory. Speech and Hearing Center. Deaf interpreters' training program. Work-experience and senior honors program in home economics and family ecology. Interdisciplinary program in child care worker, community services technology, computer programming technology, criminal justice technology, fashion, restaurant management, retailing, and social service with Community and Technical College.

College of Nursing

Degree Programs Offered: *Baccalaureate* in basic, registered nurse, LPN/ BSN; *master's* awarded through the Graduate School.

Distinctive Educational Programs: Center for Nursing.

School of Law

Degree Programs Offered: *Juris Doctor.*

Admission: Baccalaureate from accredited college or university; LSAT; LSDAS.

Distinctive Educational Programs: Center for Taxation Studies. *See* Buchtel College of Arts and Sciences and College of Business Administration.

Graduate School

Degree Programs Offered: *Master's* in accounting, entrepreneurship, applied mathematics, biology, business administration (accounting, finance, management, marketing, international business), chemical engineering, civil engineering, communication, counseling, electrical engineering, engineering (general, biomedical, polymer), mechanical engineering, chemistry, economics, educational administration, educational foundations, elementary education, elementary school principal, secondary school principal, English, geography, geology, history, management, mathematics, music (composition, music education, music history and literature, accompanying, winds/strings/percussion, voice, keyboard, theory), nursing, physical education and health education, physics, public administration, school psychology, secondary education, Spanish, social work, special education, sociology, statistics, taxation, theatre arts, urban planning, urban studies; *doctorate* in audiology, chemistry, counseling psychology, education (school administration, higher education administration), elementary education, guidance and counseling, engineering, history, integrated bioscience, psychology, secondary education, sociology, urban studies.

Departments and Teaching Staff: Faculty members drawn from colleges within the University.

Distinctive Educational Programs: *See* Buchtel College of Arts and Sciences, College of Business Administration, College of Education, College of Engineering, College of Fine and Applied Arts, College of Nursing, College of Polymer Science and Polymer Engineering. Interdisciplinary and Certificate Programs: applied politics, composition, divorce mediation, gerontology, higher education, home-based intervention therapy, mid-career program in urban studies, public policy, Soviet area studies, teaching English as a second language.

College of Polymer Science and Polymer Engineering

Degree Programs Offered: *Master's, doctorate* awarded through the Graduate School.

Distinctive Educational Programs: Photonics Center, Nanotechnology Center, Institute of Polymer Engineering. Institute of Polymer Science. Molding Development Center.

University College

Degree Programs Offered: Basic undergraduate program of general education and prerequisite courses for advancement to the degree-granting colleges.

Distinctive Educational Programs: Learning Communities - discipline specific, University Honors Program, Living-Learning (residential), and Emerging Leaders LC, Service Learning, Transfer Services.

Wayne College

Degree Programs Offered: *Associate* in technical studies, arts/science, social services technology, business management technology, office administration; *certificate* in administrative secretary, data management, gerontological social services, medical transcription, personal computer repair, word processing.

Degree Requirements: Associate degree must complete a minimum of 64 credit hours with a minimum GPA of 2.0; actual required credits for a specific associate degree may be greater.

Distinctive Educational Programs: Offers first 2 years of general baccalaureate education for transfer to the main campus of The University of Akron or to any other college or university.

University of Cincinnati

2624 Clifton Avenue
Cincinnati, Ohio 45221
Tel: (513) 556-6000 **E-mail:** admissions@uc.edu
Fax: (513) 556-1105 **Internet:** www.uc.edu

Institution Description: University of Cincinnati is a state institution. *Enrollment:* 29,617. *Degrees awarded:* Associate, baccalaureate, first-professional (law, medicine), master's, doctorate. Certificates also awarded.

Member of Greater Cincinnati Consortium of Colleges and Universities.

Accreditation: *Regional:* NCA. *Professional*: architecture, art, business, chemistry, cytotechnology, dietetics, engineering, engineering technology, health services administration, interior design, law, medicine, music, nuclear medicine technology, nursing, pharmacy, physical therapy, planning, psychology internship, radiography, social work, speech-language pathology, teacher education

History: Established and incorporated as Cincinnati College and Medical College of Ohio and first instruction at postsecondary level 1819; awarded first degree (baccalaureate) 1823; adopted present name 1870. Created the nation's first program of cooperative education 1906. *See Grace and Hand, The University of Cincinnati* (Montgomery, AL, Community Communications, Inc., 1995) for further information.

Institutional Structure: *Governing board:* Board of Trustees. Extrainstitutional representation: 9 trustees; institutional representation: 2 full-time instructional faculty members, 2 undergraduate students, 1 graduate student, 2 alumni. 9 voting. *Composition of institution:* Academic affairs headed by two senior vice presidents. Access and outreach programs directed by vice president and pro-

UNIVERSITY OF CINCINNATI—*cont'd*

vost. Research and advanced studies directed by vice president. Student affairs and services directed by vice president. Finance/budget directed by treasurer. Administrative services, computing and telecommunications, physical plant, auxiliary enterprises directed by vice president for administrative services. Human resources and human relations directed by vice president. Public affairs directed by vice president. Medical Center directed by one senior vice president and provost. Hospital and clinics directed by vice president. Academic governance body, Faculty Senate, meets monthly. All-University Faculty meet twice annually. *Faculty representation:* Faculty served by collective bargaining agent affiliated with AAUP.

Calendar: Quarters, except College of Law which is on semesters. Academic year Sept. to June. Freshmen admitted Sept., Jan., Mar., June. Degrees conferred quarterly. Summer quarter and summer terms of various lengths from June to Aug.

Characteristics of Freshmen: 11,876 applicants (female 6,117, male 5,759). 75% of applicants accepted. 40% of accepted applicants enrolled full-time.

62% (1,899 students) submitted SAT scores; 85% (2,603 students) submitted ACT scores. *25th percentile*: SAT Critical Reading 480, SAT Math 500; ACT Composite 20, ACT English 19, ACT Math 19. *75th percentile*: SAT Critical Reading 610, SAT Math 630; ACT Composite 26, ACT English 26, ACT Math 27.

42% of entering freshmen expected to graduate within 5 years. 90% of freshmen from Ohio. Freshmen from 50 states and 116 foreign countries.

Admission: Rolling admissions plan. For fall acceptance, apply as early as Oct. 1 of senior year of secondary school, but not later than Dec. 15 for assured consideration in baccalaureate programs. *Requirements for baccalaureate programs:* Graduation from accredited secondary school with 4 years English, 3 mathematics, 2 science, 2 foreign language, 2 social studies, 1 fine arts plus 2 additional from the above. Architecture, computer science, engineering, information systems, interior design, and quantitative analysis require 4 years mathematics. Architecture, engineering and interior design require physics. Engineering also requires chemistry. Audition for College-Conservatory of Music. GED accepted for College of Evening and Continuing Education. Lowest acceptable secondary school class standing 50th percentile; for music, business, engineering, and nursing programs 66th percentile or higher for more competitive programs. *Entrance tests:* College Board SAT or ACT composite. Additional tests for some programs. *For transfer students:* From 4-year accredited institution 2.0 minimum GPA. More competitive programs such as architecture, business, design and engineering might have higher GPA requirements. *From 2-year accredited institution:* 2.5 GPA; maximum transfer credit limited only by residence requirements. *Requirements for associate programs:* Open enrollment for most programs in University College, Raymond Walters College and Clermont College. Graduation from accredited secondary school or GED accepted. Special programs will have additional requirements.

College credit and advanced placement for postsecondary-level work completed in secondary school.

Tutoring available. Developmental courses offered in summer session and regular academic year; credit given.

Degree Requirements: *For all associate degrees:* 90–115 quarter hours. *For all baccalaureate degrees:* 186–247 quarter hours. *For all undergraduate degrees:* 2.0 GPA; 1 year in residence. Professional practice (co-op) required for College of Engineering programs and some programs in College of Design, Architecture, Art and Planning. *See* individual colleges for additional degree requirements. Fulfillment of some degree requirements and exemption from some beginning courses possible by passing College Board CLEP, AP. *Grading system:* A–F; 4.0 system.

Distinctive Educational Programs: Work-experience programs. Weekend and evening classes. Interdisciplinary programs in music-liberal arts, education-liberal arts, applied science. Facilities and programs for independent research, including honors programs, individual majors, tutorials. Study abroad in France, Germany, Latin America, Spain. International engineering. Innovative undergraduate business curriculum, one-year MBA program. Combined degree program: College of Engineering and College of Medicine. Distance learning. *Other distinctive programs:* Continuing education.

ROTC: Army, Air Force.

Degrees Conferred: 174 *associate;* 3,546 *baccalaureate*; 2,056 *master's*; 408 *doctorate*; 278 *first-professional*. Bachelor's degrees awarded in top five disciplines: business, management, marketing, and related support services 608; engineering 353; visual and performing arts 330; health professions and related clinical sciences 241; English language/literature 235. Master's degrees awarded in top five disciplines: business/marketing 295; engineering 222; security and protective services 174; health professions 157; visual and performing arts 154. Doctorates awarded in top five disciplines: health professions 126; engineering 56; biological/life sciences 10; visual and performing arts 5; physical sciences 16. First-professional degrees awarded: pharmacy 76; law 122; medicine 153.

Fees and Other Expenses: *Full-time tuition per academic year 2008–09:* undergraduate resident $9,399, nonresident $23,922; contact the university for current graduate/professional schools tuition that vary by program. *Room and board per academic year:* $9,240. *Required fees:* $1,503. *Books and supplies:* $1,275. *Other expenses:* $5,970.

Financial Aid: Aid from institutionally generated funds is provided on the basis of academic merit, financial need, athletic ability, other criteria.

Financial aid to full-time, first-time undergraduate students: 84% received some form of aid. Average amount of aid received: federal grants $4,031; Pell grants $2,956; other federal aid $1,270; state/local grants $1,949; institutional grants $5,082.

Departments and Teaching Staff: *Total instructional faculty:* 1,263 (full-time 1,224, part-time 3942). Total faculty with doctorate, first-professional, or other terminal degree: 834. Student/faculty ratio: 14:1.

Enrollment: Total enrollment 29,617. Undergraduate 20,914 (full-time 83%; female 51%, male 49%). Graduate 8,703 (full-time 59%). Undergraduate transfer-in students 1,026.

Characteristics of Student Body: *Ethnic/racial makeup:* Black non-Hispanic: 11%; Asian or Pacific Islander: 3%; Hispanic: 2%; White non-Hispanic: 77%; unknown 8%; nonresident alien 1%.

International Students: 2,961 nonresident aliens enrolled fall 2008. Students from Europe, Asia, Central and South America, Africa, Canada, Australia, Middle East. Programs available to aid students whose native language is not English: English as a Second Language Program. No financial aid specifically designated for international students.

Student Life: On-campus residence halls house 10% of full-time main campus student body. *Intercollegiate athletics:* male: baseball, basketball, cross-country, football, golf, soccer, swimming, track; female: basketball, cross-country, golf, soccer, swimming, tennis, volleyball. *Special regulations:* Cars permitted without restrictions. Quiet hours on some residence hall floors. *Special services:* Veterans services, disabled student services, ethnic student services, female programs and services, African-American Cultural and Research Center, Learning Resources Center, medical services, intercampus shuttle bus. *Student publications:* student newspaper published four times a week. *Student activities:* Over 250 student groups, including 31 national fraternities and sororities. A full range of student leadership development opportunities are offered, highlighted by an activities transcript program. International Liaison Services available. *Surrounding community:* Cincinnati metropolitan area population 1,865,000. Served by mass transit bus system; airport 16 miles from campus; passenger rail service 5 miles from campus.

Publications: *Cincinnati Law Review* (quarterly) first published 1932; *Human rights Quarterly, Cincinnati Poetry Review, Horizons, UC Currents*, and various departmental publications and academic journals.

Library Collections: 2,120,000 volumes. 400,000 government documents; 3,010,000 microforms; 50,000 audiovisual materials; 19,431 current periodicals. Online catalog. Students have access to online information retrieval services and the Internet.

Most important special holdings include Modern Greek Collection; collection of 18th century English literature, travel and exploration; George Elliston Collection of 20th century English language poetry.

Buildings and Grounds: Campus area 424 acres (two main campuses and three geographically separate access campuses).

Chief Executive Officer: Dr. Nancy L. Zimpher, President.

Undergraduates address admission inquiries to Director of Admissions; others to individual colleges.

McMicken College of Arts and Sciences

Degree Programs Offered: *Baccalaureate* in African-American studies, anthropology, Asian studies, biochemistry, biology, chemistry, classical civilization, classics, communication arts, communication sciences and disorders, comparative literature, computer science, cultural geography, economics, English literature, French, French studies, general studies, geology, German, German studies, history, international affairs, Judaic studies, Latin American studies, linguistics, mathematical sciences, medical technology, music, nuclear medicine technology, philosophy, physical geography, physics, political science, pre-personnel and industrial relations, psychology, sociology, Spanish, Spanish studies; *master's, doctorate* in various fields. Certificates also awarded.

Distinctive Educational Programs: Washington, D.C., semester. Internships. 3 study abroad programs.

College of Applied Science

Degree Programs Offered: *Associate* in architectural technology, electrical engineering technology, fire science technology, manufacturing engineering technology, mechanical engineering technology; *baccalaureate* in architectural engineering technology, construction management, electrical engineering technology, fire and safety engineering technology, mechanical engineering technology. Certificates also given.

Degree Requirements: Residency requirement 45 credit hours. Professional practice (co-op) required for all full-time students for the associate degree and some programs for the baccalaureate degree.

Distinctive Educational Programs: Cooperative education.

College of Business

Degree Programs Offered: *Baccalaureate* in accounting, finance, industrial management, information systems, management, marketing, operations management, quantitative analysis, real estate; *master's* in finance, information systems, management, marketing, operations management, quantitative analysis, real estate; *doctorate* in accounting, finance, information systems, management, marketing, operations management, quantitative analysis.

Distinctive Educational Programs: Cooperative education.

School of Social Work

Degree Programs Offered: *Baccalaureate* and *master's* in social work.

Admission: Baccalaureate students are admitted to the program at the beginning of their junior year and complete the work in 2 academic years.

Degree Requirements: *Baccalaureate:* 2.50 GPA, 90 hours while in School of Social Work, 180 hours overall. *Master's:* 3.00 GPA, ⅔ grades of B or above, 90 quarter hours in approved course of study. Must complete the program within 4 academic years.

College of Design, Architecture, Art, and Planning

Degree Programs Offered: *Baccalaureate* in architecture, art education, art history, fashion design, fine arts, graphic design, health services/administration, industrial design, interior design, urban planning, urban studies; *master's* in architecture, art education, art history, community planning, design, fine arts, health planning.

Distinctive Educational Programs: Cooperative education.

College of Education, Criminal Justice, and Human Sciences

Degree Programs Offered: *Baccalaureate* in criminal justice, early childhood education; elementary education, health promotion and education, nutrition and dietetics, secondary education; *master's* in counseling, criminal justice, curriculum and instruction, early childhood, educational administration, educational foundations, elementary education, health promotion and education, literacy, nutrition, rehabilitation counselor training, school psychology, secondary education, special education; *doctorate* in counseling, curriculum and instruction, criminal justice, educational administration, educational foundations, elementary education, literacy, school psychology, secondary education, special education.

College of Engineering

Degree Programs Offered: *Baccalaureate* in materials engineering; *baccalaureate, master's, doctorate* in aerospace engineering, chemical engineering, civil engineering, computer engineering, electrical engineering, engineering mechanics, industrial engineering, mechanical engineering, nuclear engineering; *master's, doctorate* in computing sciences, environmental engineering, environmental science, health physics, materials science, metallurgical engineering, solid state electronics.

Distinctive Educational Programs: Cooperative education. International engineering.

College-Conservatory of Music

Degree Programs Offered: *Baccalaureate* in dance, drama, electronic media, music, musical theater, theater production; *master's* in arts administration, directing, drama, music, music education, theater production, voice; *doctorate* in music, music education.

College of Law

Degree Programs Offered: *First-professional.*

Admission: Baccalaureate; LSAT; LSDAS.

Degree Requirements: 88 credit hours; 2.0 honor points; 36 months in residence.

College of Nursing and Health

Degree Programs Offered: *Baccalaureate, master's, doctorate.*

Admission: GRE required for master's program.

College of Pharmacy

Degree Programs Offered: *Baccalaureate, master's* in pharmaceutical sciences; *doctorate* in pharmaceutical sciences, pharmacy.

Admission: *Baccalaureate:* College-level coursework, including 9 quarter hours English, 13 organic chemistry with laboratory, 15 general chemistry with laboratory, 15 physics with laboratory, 15 biology with laboratory, 9 calculus and 3 statistics. 2.0 GPA on prepharmacy courses.

Degree Requirements: *For baccalaureate:* 245 credit hours; 2.0 GPA.

College of Medicine

Degree Programs Offered: *First-professional:* (graduate program); *master's* in blood transfusion medicine, radiology/radiological sciences; *doctorate* in anatomy and cell biology, interdisciplinary studies programs in biomedical science (M.D./Ph.D.) and neuroscience, pharmacology and cell biophysics; *master's, doctorate* in developmental biology, environmental health, molecular genetics, biochemistry and microbiology, pathology and laboratory medicine, physiology and biophysics; *doctorate* in surgery.

Admission: *For first-professional degree:* 90 semester hours from an accredited 4-year, degree granting institution, baccalaureate degree preferred, but not required; completion of MCAT. All undergraduate majors are considered. Although there are no specific required courses for admission, students should have the knowledge usually obtained in one year courses in biology, chemistry, organic chemistry, physics, and mathematics. In addition, effective oral and written communication skills are important. Applicants are also expected to have a basic understanding of the social, cultural, and behavioral factors which influence individuals, families and communities. *For graduate programs:* Varies with department.

Degree Requirements: *For first-professional degree:* 4 years in residence. *For graduate programs:* (Master's) completion of 45–90 credit hours, 1 year residence, plus departmental requirements; (doctorate) completion of at least 135 credit hours, 1 year residence, plus departmental requirements. Requirements vary with department.

College of Allied Health Sciences

Degree Programs Offered: *Associate* ,in physical therapy assisting; *baccalaureate* in dietetics, nutrition, medical technology, nuclear medical technology, physical therapy, communication sciences and disorders; *master's* in nutrition, speech language pathology or audiology; *doctorate* in speech pathology or audiology.

Raymond Walters College

Degree Programs Offered: *Associate* in business management technology, accounting technology, computer programming technology, computer support technology, office administration technology, office technology, industrial laboratory technology, nursing, registered nursing technology, dental hygiene, emergency services technology, nuclear medicine technology, radiologic technology, radiation therapy technology, veterinary technology, library/instructional media technology, commercial art, technical studies, automotive technology, manufacturing engineering technology, liberal arts, pre-law, pre-medicine, pre-dentistry, pre-pharmacy, pre-dietetic, pre-medical technology, pre-chemistry, pre-biology, pre-elementary education, pre-secondary education, pre-economics, pre-business administration, pre-social work, pre-computer science, general studies, pre-engineering, pre-design and art, pre-music, pre-urban professions, women's studies, crisis counseling; *professional certificate* in accountancy, business, international business, commercial art, computer programming, industrial lab technology-bio chemical, industrial lab technology-environmental control/protection, industrial lab technology-general, industrial management, library/instructional media technology, radiation therapy, real estate, sales/marketing.

Clermont College

Degree Programs Offered: *Associate* in office automation, business management technology, accounting option, records information management, computer information systems, administrative support, business and office administration, legal assisting, electrical engineering technology, social services technology, criminal justice technology, educational mobility for registered nurses, general studies, pre-elementary education, pre-social work, pre-law, pre-urban professions, liberal arts, pre-secondary education, pre-business administration, pre-pharmacy; *one-year programs* in pre-design and art, pre-nursing, pre-computer science, pre-dentistry, pre-med, pre-med technology, pre-optom-

UNIVERSITY OF CINCINNATI—*cont'd*

etry, pre-veterinary, pre-engineering; *certificate programs* in computer operations, business management, office services management, office automation, real estate, accounting, gerontology, hospitality management, marketing/sales, mental retardation.

University of Dayton

300 College Park Avenue
Dayton, Ohio 45322
Tel: (937) 229-4000 **E-mail:** admission@udayton.edu
Fax: (937) 229-4729 **Internet:** www.udayton.edu

Institution Description: The University of Dayton is a private institution affiliated with the Society of Mary, Roman Catholic Church. *Enrollment:* 10,290. *Degrees awarded:* Baccalaureate, first-professional (law), master's, doctorate.

Member of Consortium for Higher Education Religion Studies; Dayton-Miami Valley Consortium.

Accreditation: *Regional:* NCA. *Professional*: business, dietetics, engineering, engineering technology, law, music, teacher education

History: Established as St. Mary's School for Boys 1850; awarded first degree (baccalaureate) 1891; incorporated, offered first instruction at postsecondary level, and adopted present name 1920; became coeducational 1935. *See* Br. Edward H. Knust, *Hallowed Memories* (Dayton: privately published, 1950) for further information.

Institutional Structure: *Governing board:* University of Dayton Board of Trustees. Representation: 33 trustees, including 11 Marianists, 1 ex officio. All voting. *Composition of institution:* Academic affairs headed by senior vice president for administration. Full-time instructional faculty: 458. Academic governance body, Academic Senate, meets regularly.

Calendar: Semesters. Academic year Aug. to May. Freshmen admitted Aug., Jan., May, June. Degrees conferred and formal commencements Apr., Dec. Summer session of 1 term from May to June.

Characteristics of Freshmen: 11,610 applicants (femal 4,801, male 5,809). 74% of applicants admitted. 23% of applicants admitted and enrolled full-time.

42% (735 students) submitted SAT scores; 65% (1,142 students) submitted ACT scores. *25th percentile*: SAT Critical Reading 510 SAT Math 530; ACT Composite 23, ACT English 22, ACT Math 22. *75th percentile*: SAT Critical Reading 620, SAT Math 650; ACT Composite 28, ACT English 27, ACT Math 28.

76% of entering freshmen expected to graduate within 5 years. 66% of freshmen from Ohio. Freshmen from 46 states and 33 foreign countries.

Admission: Modified rolling admissions plan. Students are notified of acceptance beginning Nov. *Requirements:* Either graduation from accredited secondary school with 15–18 units from among English, foreign language, mathematics, laboratory science, social studies; or GED. *Entrance tests:* College Board SAT or ACT composite. For foreign students TOEFL or other demonstrated proficiency in English. *For transfer students:* 2.0 minimum GPA; maximum transfer credit limited only by residence requirement.

College credit and advanced placement for postsecondary-level work completed in secondary school.

Tutoring available. Noncredit developmental courses offered during regular academic year.

Degree Requirements: *For all baccalaureate degrees:* 120 credit hours; 2 terms in residence; general curriculum requirements. *For all undergraduate degrees:* 2.0 GPA; additional requirements for some programs.

Fulfillment of some degree requirements and exemption from some beginning courses possible by passing departmental examinations, College Board CLEP, other standardized tests. *Grading system:* A–F; pass-fail; withdraw (carries time limit).

Distinctive Educational Programs: Work-experience programs. The University of Dayton maintains off-campus centers for graduate study in education and allied professions (Lima and Columbus). Weekend and evening classes. Accelerated degree programs. Facilities and programs for independent research, including honors programs, individual majors, tutorials. Study abroad in varying locations.

ROTC: Air Force, Army. Air Force offered in cooperation with Wright State University.

Degrees Conferred: 1,584 *baccalaureate*; 735 *master's* ; 146 *doctorate*; 163 *first-professional*. Bachelor's degrees awarded in top five disciplines: business, management, marketing, and related support 339; education 187; communications/journalism 179; engineering 160; social sciences 78. Master's degrees awarded in top five disciplines: education 392; engineering 106; psychology 75; public administration and social services 23. Doctorates awarded: education 4; engineering 14; p physical sciences 4. First-professional degrees awarded: law 163.

Fees and Other Expenses: *Full-time tuition per academic year 2008–09:* undergraduate $27,330; graduate varies (contact the university for current rate). *Room and board per academic year:* $7,480. *Books and supplies:* $800. *Other expenses:* $2,100.

Financial Aid: Aid from institutionally generated funds is provided on the basis of academic merit, financial need, athletic ability, other criteria.

Financial aid to full-time, first-time undergraduate students: 99% received some form of aid. Average amount of aid received: federal grants $4,736; Pell grans $2,363; other federal aid $1,638; state/local grants $1,658; institutional grants $10,769.

Departments and Teaching Staff: *Total instructional faculty:* 914 (full-time 458, part-time 456). Student/faculty ratio: 14:1. 92% hold terminal degrees.

Enrollment: Total enrollment 10,290. Undergraduate 7,731 (full-time 92%; female 50%, male 50%). Graduate 189 (full-time 50%). Undergraduate transfer-in students 144.

Characteristics of Student Body: *Ethnic/racial makeup:* Black non-Hispanic: 3%; Asian or Pacific Islander: 1%; Hispanic: 2%; White non-Hispanic: 85%; unknown: 6%; nonresident alien 2%. *Age distribution:* number under 18: 53; 18–19: 3,064; 20–21: 2,943; 22–24: 787; 25–29: 96; 30–34: 50; 35–39: 37; 40–49: 81; 50–64: 42; 65 and over: 5.

International Students: 204 nonresident aliens enrolled fall 2008. Students from Europe, Asia, Central and South America, Africa, Canada. Programs available to aid students whose native language is not English: social, cultural. English as a Second Language Program. Financial aid specifically designated for qualifying international students.

Student Life: 80% of full-time undergraduates reside in university-owned housing (13% in apartments, 29% in houses, 46% in residence halls, 11% in suites). *Intercollegiate athletics:* male: football, soccer, golf, cross-country, wrestling, basketball baseball, tennis; female: volleyball, tennis, soccer, cross-country, basketball, softball. *Special regulations:* Limited parking available on basis of need. *Special services:* Medical services. *Student publications, radio: Daytonian*, a yearbook; *Flyer News*, a biweekly newspaper; *Orpheus*, a quarterly literary magazine. Radio station Flyer Radio broadcasts 168 hours per week. Flyer TV is the on-campus television station. *Surrounding community:* Dayton metropolitan area population 848,153. 000. Served by mass transit bus system, airport 20 miles from campus.

Library Collections: 1,3342,558 volumes including bound books, serial backfiles, electronic documents, and government documents not in separate collections. Online catalog. Current serial subscriptions: 2,252 paper, 6,180 via electronic access. 121 computer work stations. Students have access to the Internet at no charge.

Most important special holdings include Marian Library; Whalen Papers; Jacobs Collection.

Buildings and Grounds: Campus area 245 acres.

Chief Executive Officer: Dr. Daniel J. Currant, President.

Address admission inquiries to Robert F. Durkle, Director of Admission; graduate school inquiries to Dr. Gordon A. Sargent, Vice President for Graduate Studies and Research; School of Law inquiries to Janet L. Hein, Director of Admissions and Financial Aid, School of Law.

The University of Findlay

1000 North Main Street
Findlay, Ohio 45840
Tel: (419) 422-8313 **E-mail:** admissions@findlay.edu
Fax: (419) 424-4898 **Internet:** /www.findlay.edu

Institution Description: The University of Findlay, formerly Findlay College, is a private institution affiliated with the Churches of God, General Conference. *Enrollment:* 5,761. *Degrees awarded:* Associate, baccalaureate, master's.

Member of Northwest Ohio Consortium; Small College Consortium.

Accreditation: *Regional:* NCA. *Professional*: teacher education

History: Established and chartered 1882; offered first instruction at postsecondary level 1886; awarded first degree (baccalaureate) 1888.

Institutional Structure: *Governing board:* Board of Trustees. Extrainstitutional representation: 43 trustees; institutional representation: college president. 1 ex officio. 43 voting. *Composition of institution:* vice president for academic affairs and dean of the faculty, vice president for student affairs, vice president for business affairs, dean of academic support service, dean of liberal arts, dean of sciences, dean of business, dean of education. Full-time instructional faculty 169. Academic governance body, Faculty Senate, meets an average of 9 times per year.

Calendar: Semesters. Academic year Aug. to May. Freshmen admitted Aug., Jan, June. Degrees conferred and formal commencements May and Dec. Summer session of 3 terms.

Characteristics of Freshmen: 78% of applicants accepted. 23% of accepted applicants enrolled.

26% (217 students) submitted SAT scores; 74% (631 students) submitted ACT scores. *25th percentile*: SAT Critical Reading 430, SAT Math 470, SAT Writing 460; ACT Composite 20, ACT English 19, ACT Math 19. *75th percentile*: SAT Critical Reading 560, SAT Math 580, SAT Writing 590; ACT Composite 25, ACT English 25, ACT Math 25.

55% of entering freshmen expected to graduate within 5 years. 75% of freshmen from Ohio. Freshmen from 36 states and 30 foreign countries.

Admission: Rolling admissions plan. For fall acceptance, apply as early as Sept. of previous year, but not later than July. Early acceptance available. *Requirements:* Either graduation from accredited secondary school with college preparatory course of study or GED. 16 secondary school units, which include 4 English, 2 mathematics, 2 natural science, 2 social studies recommended. Minimum GPA 2.0. Lowest acceptable secondary school class standing approximately 40th percentile. *Entrance tests:* College Board SAT or ACT composite. *For transfer students:* 2.0 minimum GPA or associate degree; 94 hours maximum transfer credit; from 2-year accredited institution 62 hours.

College credit and advanced placement for postsecondary-level work completed in secondary school and for extrainstitutional learning (life experience) on basis of portfolio and faculty assessment.

Tutoring available. Developmental courses offered during regular academic year.

Degree Requirements: *For all associate degrees:* 62 credit hours; 1 term in residence; 2 credit hours wellness. *For all baccalaureate degrees:* 124 credit hours; 30 credit hours in residence; 2 credit hours wellness; freshman seminar. *For all undergraduate degrees:* 2.0 GPA; exit competency examinations (writing, reading, information retrieval); distribution requirements.

Fulfillment of some degree requirements and exemption from some beginning courses possible by passing department examinations, College Board CLEP, or APP. *Grading system:* A–F; withdraw (carries time limit); satisfactory-unsatisfactory; incomplete; extended course.

Distinctive Educational Programs: Environmental and hazardous materials management, pre-veterinary medicine, nuclear medicine technology, equestrian studies, bilingual multicultural and business education, occupational therapy, intergenerational studies, physical therapy, physicians's assistant. Japanese. Dual-degree programs in preveterinary medicine and pre-engineering. Freshman Seminar program. Mazza School Extension program affiliated with Mazza Centennial Collection of original art from children's books. Weekend College. Intensive English Language Institute for international students. Degree programs at Lima and Allen Correctional Institutions. Study abroad programs through the College Consortium for International Studies (26 countries); exchange with Interamerican University in Puerto Rico.

Degrees Conferred: 68 *associate;* 540 *baccalaureate*; 524 *master's.*

Fees and Other Expenses: *Full-time tuition per academic year 2008–09:* undergraduate $24,670; graduate fees vary by program (contact the university for current information). *Room and board per academic year:* $8,306. *Required fees:* $1,060. *Books and supplies:* $950. *Other expenses:* $990.

Financial Aid: Aid from institutionally generated funds is provided on the basis of academic merit, financial need, athletic ability.

Financial aid to full-time, first-time undergraduate students: 99% received some form of aid. Average amount of aid received: federal grants $3,174; Pell grants $2,674; other federal aid $500; state/local grants $1,480; institutional grants $12,860.

Departments and Teaching Staff: *Total instructional faculty:* 299 (full-time 169, part-time 130). Total tenured faculty: 69. Student/faculty ratio: 18:1. Degrees held by full-time faculty: doctorate 52%, master's 100%. 58% hold terminal degrees.

Enrollment: Total enrollment 5,761. Undergraduate 4,210 (full-timed 65%, female 63%, male 37%). Graduate 1,551 (full-time 27%). Undergraduate transfer-in students 197.

Characteristics of Student Body: *Ethnic/racial makeup:* Black non-Hispanic: 2%; Asian or Pacific Islander: 1%; Hispanic: 1%; White non-Hispanic: 54%; unknown 38%; nonresident alien 5%.

International Students: 288 nonresident aliens enrolled fall 2008. Students from Europe, Asia, Central and South America, Africa, Canada, Middle East. Programs available to aid students whose native language is not English: social, cultural. English as a Second Language Program. No financial aid specifically designated for international students.

Student Life: On-campus residence halls house, fraternities/sororities, and special interest residences house 40% of the full-time undergraduate student body. Housing for males constitute 40% of such space, for females 60%. 8% of males join and 3% live in fraternity housing; 4% of females join and 1% live in sorotity housing. *Intercollegiate athletics:* male: baseball, basketball, cross-country, football, golf, soccer, swimming, tennis, track, wrestling; female: basketball, cross-country, golf, soccer, softball, swimming, tennis, track, volleyball. *Special regulations:* No alcohol permitted on campus. Cars must be registered. Residence hall visitation from 11am to midnight Sun.–Thurs., 11am to 2am Fri. and Sat. *Special services:* health services, counseling, career placement, tutoring, disability services. *Student publications, radio: The Pulse,* , a newspaper. Radio station WLFC. *Surrounding community:* Findlay population 36,000. Detroit, 100 miles from campus, is nearest metropolitan area.

Publications: *Findlay,* magazine for alumni and friends; *MainLine,* newsletter for alumni and parents of students; *Advancing,* newsletter for alumni; *Curtain Call,* for theatre enthusiasts; *Mazza Collection Newsletter* for supporters of UF's art from children's picture book collection; *It's Your Business* newsletter for UF business affiliates; *Horse Tales* newsletter for alumni of equestrian and preveterinary medicine programs; *Varsity F Newsletter* for alumni athletes.

Library Collections: 135,000 volumes; 81,726 government documents; 176,314 microforms; 11,967 audiovisual materials; 958 current periodical subscriptions. Students have access to online information retrieval services and the Internet.

Most important special collections include Jackson Betts Collection (Congressional Papers, 1951–73); Tennyson Guyer Collection (Congressional Papers 1973–81); History of University of Findlay Archives.

Buildings and Grounds: Main campus area 25 acres.

Chief Executive Officer: Dr. DeBow Freed, President. Address admission inquiries to Robin Hopkins, Director of Admissions.

University of Toledo

2801 West Bancroft Street
Toledo, Ohio 43606-3390
Tel: (419) 530-4636 **E-mail:** admissions@utoledo.edu
Fax: (419) 530-4504 **Internet:** www.utoledo.edu

Institution Description: The University of Toledo is a state institution. *Enrollment:* 22,336. *Degrees awarded.* Associate, baccalaureate, first-professional (law, pharmacy), master's, doctorate. Specialist certificates also awarded.

Academic offerings subject to approval by statewide coordinating bodies.

Accreditation: *Regional:* NCA. *Professional*: business, engineering, engineering technology, law, music, nursing, pharmacy, teacher education

History: Established and chartered as Toledo University of Arts and Trades 1872; offered first instruction at postsecondary level 1875; changed name to Toledo University 1884; awarded first degree (baccalaureate) 1910; changed name to University of the City of Toledo 1921; adopted present name 1940; became state institution 1967. *See* Frank Hickerson, *Tower Builders* (Toledo: University of Toledo, 1972) for further information.

Institutional Structure: *Governing board:* Board of Trustees. Representation: 9 trustees. All voting. *Composition of institution:* Administrators 28. Academic affairs headed by vice president for academic affairs. Management/business/finances directed by vice president for business affairs. Full-time instructional faculty 176. Academic governance body, Faculty Senate, meets an average of 12 times per year.

Calendar: Semesters. Academic year Sept. to June. Degrees conferred and formal commencement June and Dec. Summer sessions from June to Aug.

Characteristics of Freshmen: 90% of applicants accepted. 54% of accepted applicants enrolled.

22% of freshmen from Ohio. Freshmen from 45 states and 100 foreign countries.

Admission: Rolling admissions plan. For fall acceptance, apply as early as Sept. of senior year of secondary school, but not later than 2 weeks prior to registration. Students are notified of acceptance beginning Nov. 10. Early acceptance available. *Requirements:* Graduation from accredited secondary school or GED. Additional requirements for some programs. For out-of-state students minimum 2.0 GPA. *Entrance tests:* ACT composite or SAT required for out-of-state applicants; recommended for in-state. For foreign students TOEFL. *For transfer students:* 2.0 minimum GPA; 141 quarter hours maximum transfer credit.

College credit and advanced placement for postsecondary-level work completed in secondary school and for extrainstitutional learning on basis of faculty assessment.

Tutoring available. Developmental courses offered in summer session and regular academic year; credit given.

Degree Requirements: *For all associate degrees:* 90 credit hours. *For all baccalaureate degrees:* 186 credit hours. *For all undergraduate degrees:* 2.0 GPA; last 45 hours in residence; general education requirements.

Fulfillment of some degree requirements and exemption from some beginning courses possible by passing departmental examinations, College Board CLEP, AP. *Grading system:* A–F; pass-fail; withdraw; incomplete (carries time limit).

UNIVERSITY OF TOLEDO—*cont'd*

Distinctive Educational Programs: Weekend and evening classes. Interdepartmental programs in Black studies, business and economics. Facilities and programs for independent research, including honors programs, individual majors. Study abroad in Costa Rica, England, France, Germany, Ireland, Japan, Mexico, Malaysia, Singapore, Scotland, Spain. *Other distinctive programs:* Continuing education through University College.

ROTC: Army.

Degrees Conferred: 118 *associate*; 2,480 *baccalaureate*; 834 *master's*; 332 *doctorate*; 116 *first-professional*: law. Bachelor's degrees awarded in top five disciplines: engineering 333; business, management, marketing, and related support services 328; health professions and related clinical sciences education 288; education 226; communication, journalism, and related programs 113. Master's and doctorates awarded in various disciplines.

Fees and Other Expenses: *Full-time tuition per academic year 2008–09:* resident undergraduate $7,927, nonresident $16,738. *Books and supplies:* $750. *Room and board per academic year:* $9,0'19. *Books and supplies:* $750. *Other expenses:* $3,327. Contact the university for current graduate and law school tuition and fees.

Financial Aid: Aid from institutionally generated funds is provided on the basis of academic merit, financial need, athletic ability, other criteria. Institution has a Program Participation Agreement with the U.S. Department of Education for eligible students to receive Pell Grants and, depending upon the agreement, other federal aid.

Financial aid to full-time, first-time undergraduate students: 91% received some form of financial aid. Average amount of aid received: federal grants $2,679; state/local grants $1,463; institutional grants $3,056; loans $5,562.

Departments and Teaching Staff: *Total instructional faculty:* 1,154. Student/faculty ratio: 17:1. Degrees held by full-time faculty: baccalaureate 3%, master's 17%, doctorate 74%. 80% hold terminal degrees.

Enrollment: Total enrollment 22,336. Undergraduate 17,591 (full-time 81%; female 50%, male 50%). Graduate 4,745 (full-time 66%). Undergraduate transfer-in students 1,150.

Characteristics of Student Body: *Ethnic/racial makeup:* Black non-Hispanic: 14%; Asian or Pacific Islander: 2%; Hispanic: 3%; White non-Hispanic: 73%; unknown: 5%; nonresident alien 3%.

International Students: 670 nonresident aliens enrolled fall 2008. Students from Europe, Asia, Central and South America, Africa, Canada, Australia, New Zealand. Programs available to aid students whose native language is not English: social, cultural, financial. English as a Second Language Program.

Student Life: On-campus residence halls house 9% of student body. Residence halls for males constitute 31% of such space, for females 8%, for both sexes 61%. 3% of males join and 1% live in fraternity housing. *Intercollegiate athletics:* male: baseball, basketball, cross-country, football, golf, soccer, swimming, tennis, track, volleyball, wrestling; female: basketball, field hockey, tennis, volleyball. *Special regulations:* Cars with permits allowed in designated areas only. *Special services:* Learning Resources Center, medical services, bus and shuttle services. *Student publications, radio: The Collegian*, a newspaper published twice weekly; an annual student directory; a yearbook. Radio station WERC broadcasts 119 hours per week; alternative radio station WXUT campus phone and address directory. *Surrounding community:* Toledo metropolitan area population 795,000. Served by mass transit bus system; airport 12 miles from campus; passenger rail service 6 miles from campus.

Library Collections: 2,161,000 volumes. 712,000 government documents; 1,615,000 microforms; 8,000 periodical subscriptions. 7,800 audiovisual materials. Online catalog. Students have access to online information retrieval services and the Internet.

Most important special holdings include Ezra Pound Collection; Libbey-Owens-Ford Archives; Kohler Papers, 1914–78; William U. McDonald/Eudora Welty Scholarship and criticism collection.

Buildings and Grounds: Campus area 454 acres.

Chief Executive Officer: Dr. Lloyd A. Jacobs, President.

Address admission inquiries to Lorinda L. Bishop, Registrar.

College of Arts and Sciences

Distinctive Educational Programs: Interdepartmental programs in American studies, Asian studies, comparative literature, European studies, general studies, international studies, Latin American studies, urban studies.

College of Business Administration

Degree Programs Offered: *Baccalaureate* in accounting, computer systems and production management, finance, management, marketing; *master's* in accounting, business administration.

College of Education

Degree Programs Offered: *Baccalaureate* in public affairs and community services, speech; *baccalaureate, master's* in art education, educational media, elementary and early childhood education, health, music education, physical education, physical therapy, recreation and leisure education, secondary education, special education, vocational education; *master's* in administration and supervision, guidance and counseling, higher education; *doctorate* in administration and supervision, educational technology, elementary and early childhood education, guidance and counseling, health, higher education, physical education, secondary education, special education. Specialist certificates in curriculum and instruction, educational administration, guidance and counseling also given.

College of Engineering

Degree Programs Offered: *Baccalaureate* in computer science and engineering, engineering technology; *baccalaureate, master's* in chemical engineering, civil engineering, electrical engineering, industrial engineering, mechanical engineering; *master's* in engineering science; *doctorate* in chemical and biological transport; engineering mechanics; materials, electronics, and energy; systems theory and engineering.

College of Law

Degree Programs Offered: *First-professional.*

Admission: Baccalaureate from accredited college or university; LSAT.

Degree Requirements: 126 credit hours; 2.0 GPA; 9 months in residence.

College of Pharmacy

Degree Programs Offered: *Baccalaureate, master's, first-professional.*

Admission: *For first-professional degree:* 90 quarter hours of college work with units in general chemistry, biology, mathematics, physics, organic chemistry, pharmacology.

Degree Requirements: *See* general requirements. *For first-professional degree:* 249 quarter hours; 2.0 GPA.

Community and Technical College

Degree Programs Offered: *Associate* in agricultural technology, chemical engineering technology, civil engineering technology, climate control technology, correctional technology, data center management, data processing technology, drafting and design technology, electronic engineering technology, environmental health technology, food preparation, human growth, industrial engineering technology, industrial hygiene and safety, information services technology, law enforcement technology, legal assisting, legal secretarial, marketing and sales, mechanical engineering technology, medical assisting technology, mental health technology, natural science, nursing, real estate, retail management, respiratory therapy therapist, social child management, social gerontology, social services technology, traffic management technology, water quality control. Certificates also awarded.

Urbana University

579 College Way
Urbana, Ohio 43078
Tel: (937) 494-1360 **E-mail:** pbrown@urbana.edu
Fax: (937) 484-1322 **Internet:** www.urbana.edu

Institution Description: Urbana University is a private institution affiliated with the Swedenborgian Church. *Enrollment:* 1,354. *Degrees awarded:* Associate, baccalaureate.

Member of Dayton-Miami Valley Consortium.

Accreditation: *Regional:* NCA.

History: Established and chartered as Urbana University 1850; offered first instruction at postsecondary level 1851; awarded first degree (baccalaureate) 1857; became a 2-year institution and changed name to Urbana College Junior College 1920; became a Urbana College and a 4-year institution 1967; adopted present name 1984. *See* Frank Higgins, *The Will to Survive, Urbana College 1850–1975* (Urbana, OH: Urbana College, 1977) for further information.

Institutional Structure: *Governing board:* Urbana University Board of Trustees. Representation: 20 trustees, including 5 alumni, president of the college, president of general convention of Swedenborgian Church. 2 ex officio. 20 voting. *Composition of institution:* Administrators 30. Academic affairs headed by dean of the college. Management/business/finances directed by executive vice president for finance. Full-time instructional faculty 55. Academic governance body, Faculty of Urbana University, meets an average of 12 times per year.

Calendar: Quarters. Academic year early Jan. to late Nov. Freshmen admitted Sept., Jan., Mar., June. Degrees conferred and formal commencement June. Summer sessions from June to Aug.

Characteristics of Freshmen: 959 applicants (416 female, 543 male). 58% of applicants admitted. 62.5% of admitted applicants enrolled full-time. Mean ACT composite score 15.

Admission: Rolling admissions plan. For fall acceptance, apply as early as Nov. 1 of previous year, but not later than Sept. 1 of year of enrollment. Early acceptance available. *Requirements:* Either graduation from accredited secondary school or GED. Recommend 16 units from among English, history, mathematics, science, social studies. Minimum 2.0 GPA. Lowest acceptable secondary school class standing 50th percentile. *Entrance tests:* ACT composite. *For transfer students:* 2.0 minimum GPA; from 4-year accredited institution 145 quarter hours maximum transfer credit; from 2-year accredited institution 115 quarter hours; correspondence/extension students 45 hours.

College credit for extrainstitutional learning on basis of faculty assessment.

Tutoring available. Remedial courses offered in summer session and regular academic year; credit given.

Degree Requirements: 190 or more credit hours; minimum 2.0 QPA; successful demonstration of competency in mathematics, reading comprehension, speech, and writing; fulfillment of the requirements of a major program; core curriculum courses.

Fulfillment of some degree requirements and exemption from some beginning courses possible by passing College Board CLEP. *Grading system:* A–F; pass-fail; withdraw (carries time limit).

Distinctive Educational Programs: Flexible meeting places and schedules, including off-campus centers (at Bliss College and Miami-Jacobs, each 50 miles away from main institution; and at various other centers throughout the state). Weekend and evening classes. Interdisciplinary studies program. Individual majors.

Degrees Conferred: 59 *associate;* 208 *baccalaureate:* business, management, marketing, and related support services 95; communications/communication technologies 18; computer and information sciences 1, education 70; English 3; law/legal studies 15; parks and recreation 19; psychology 3; social sciences and history 1. *Master's*: education 33.

Fees and Other Expenses: *Full-time tuition per academic year 2008–09:* $19,416. *Books and supplies:* $1,000. *Room and board per academic year:* $7,860. *Other expenses:* $1,000.

Financial Aid: Aid from institutionally generated funds is provided on the basis of academic merit, financial need, athletic ability, other criteria.

Financial aid to full-time, first-time undergraduate students: 91% received some form of financial aid. Average amount of aid received: federal grants $2,167; state/local grants $1,982; institutional grants $6,743; loans $4,792.

Departments and Teaching Staff: *Total instructional faculty:* 120. Student/faculty ratio: 17:1. Degrees held by full-time faculty: doctorate 50%, master's 100%, professional 2%. 50% hold terminal degrees.

Enrollment: Total enrollment 1,354. Undergraduate 1,220 (full-time 88%; female 52%, male 48%). Graduate 134 (full-time 20%). Undergraduate transfer-in students 249.

Characteristics of Student Body: *Ethnic/racial makeup:* Black non-Hispanic: 19%; Hispanic: 1%; White non-Hispanic: 74%; unknown 4%; nonresident alien 1%.

International Students: 14 nonresident aliens enrolled fall 2008. Programs available to aid students whose native language is not English: social. English as a Second Language Program. No financial aid specifically designated for international students.

Student Life: On-campus residence halls house 26% of student body. Residence halls for both sexes constitute 100% of such space. *Intercollegiate athletics:* male: baseball, basketball, wrestling; female: baseball, basketball, volleyball. *Special regulations:* Cars with decals permitted in designated areas. Quiet hours. Residence hall visitation from 11am to midnight. *Special services:* Medical services. *Student publications: Lancer*, a newspaper; *Oakleaf*, a yearbook. *Surrounding community:* Urbana population 11,000. Columbus, 50 miles from campus, is nearest metropolitan area.

Library Collections: 75,000 volumes. Online catalog. 8,200 microforms; 2,100 audiovisual materials; 955 current periodical subscriptions. Students have access to online information retrieval services and the Internet.

Most important special collections include Curriculum Collection (1,924 titles); Swedenborg Collection (2,036 titles); Sheet Music Collection (1,747 titles).

Buildings and Grounds: Campus area 128 acres.

Chief Executive Officer: Dr. Robert L. Head, President.

Address admission inquiries to Melissa Tolle, Director of Admissions.

Ursuline College

2550 Lander Road
Pepper Pike, Ohio 44124
Tel: (440) 442-4200 **E-mail:** admissions@ursuline.edu
Fax: (440) 489-2235 **Internet:** www.ursuline.edu

Institution Description: Ursuline College is a private, nonprofit college primarily for women affiliated with the Roman Catholic Church. *Enrollment:* 1,632. *Degrees awarded:* Baccalaureate, master's. Certificates also awarded.

Accreditation: *Regional:* NCA.

History: Established and chartered as Ursuline College for Women, and offered first instruction at postsecondary level 1872; adopted present name and accepted males as degree candidates 1969.

Institutional Structure: *Governing board:* Board of Trustees of Ursuline College. Representation: 23 trustees. All voting. *Composition of institution:* Academic affairs headed by vice president for academic affairs. Management/business/finances directed by vice president for financial administration. Student affairs directed by vice president for student affairs. Full-time instructional faculty 72. Academic governance body, Academic Senate, meets an average of 8 times per year.

Calendar: Semesters. Academic year Aug. to May. Students admitted Aug., Jan., June. Degrees conferred Dec., May. Formal commencement May. Summer session.

Characteristics of Freshmen: 324 applicants (female 309, male 15). 91% of applicants admitted. 41,7% of admitted students enrolled full-time.

38% (48 students) submitted SAT scores; 62% (38 students) submitted ACT scores. *25th percentile*: SAT Critical Reading 430, SAT Math 420; ACT Composite 18, ACT English 17, ACT Math 17. *75th percentile*: SAT Critical Reading 550, SAT Math 510; ACT Composite 22, ACT English 23, ACT Math 24.

47% of entering freshmen expected to graduate within 5 years. 99% of freshmen from Ohio.

Admission: Rolling admissions plan. For fall acceptance, apply as early as end of junior year in secondary school, but not later than April. Apply by beginning of senior year for early decision; need not limit application to Ursuline College. Early acceptance available. *Requirements:* Graduation from accredited secondary school with 4 units in English, 2 history, 2 mathematics including algebra, 1 laboratory science. For liberal arts students, 2 units in a foreign language. For nursing students 2 units laboratory science including chemistry. GED accepted. 4 academic electives recommended. *Entrance tests:* College Board SAT or ACT composite. *For transfer students:* 2.0 minimum GPA; 96 hours maximum transfer credit (50 hours for nursing program).

College credit and advanced placement for postsecondary-level work completed in secondary school. College credit for extrainstitutional learning (life experience) on basis of departmental examinations.

Tutoring available. Developmental courses offered during regular academic year.

Degree Requirements: *For all baccalaureate degrees:* 128–132 hours. *For all undergraduate degrees:* 2.0 GPA; 43 semester hour in residence; general education requirements. Additional residence requirements for nursing program.

Fulfillment of some degree requirements and exemption from some beginning courses possible by passing departmental examinations or College Board CLEP, APP, or Achievement Tests. *Grading system:* A–F; pass-fail; pass; withdraw (deadline after which pass-fail is appended to withdraw).

Distinctive Educational Programs: Work-experience programs. Flexible meeting places and schedules, including off-campus centers, weekend and evening classes. Interdisciplinary programs in art therapy, behavioral sciences, biology-chemistry. Certificate programs in early childhood education; elementary education; secondary education; women in management; and, in cooperation with other local colleges, special education. Study abroad in England and France; may be individually arranged. Cross-registration with cluster colleges: Baldwin-Wallace College, Case Western Reserve University, Cuyahoga Community College, Cleveland State University, David M. Myers University, Notre Dame College.

Degrees Conferred: 215 *baccalaureate*; 791 *master's*. Bachelor's degrees awarded in top five disciplines: health professions and related clinical sciences 96; business, management, marketing, and related support services 53; education 34; visual and performing arts 12; history 10. Master's degrees awarded: business/marketing 10; education 44; health professions 28; liberal arts/general studies 3; philosophy and religious studies 4.

Fees and Other Expenses: *Full-time tuition per academic year:* $19,840 undergraduate; $12,690 graduate. *Room and board per academic year:* $6,684. *Required fees:* $330.

Financial Aid: Aid from institutionally generated funds is provided on the basis of academic merit, financial need, other criteria. Institution has a Program Participation Agreement with the U.S. Department of Education for eligible stu-

URSULINE COLLEGE—*cont'd*

dents to receive Pell Grants and, depending upon the agreement, other federal aid.

Financial aid to full-time, first-time undergraduate students: 48% received federal grants averaging $3,400; 99% state/local grants averaging $2,445; 90% institutional grants averaging $7,097; 91% received loans averaging $3,767.

Departments and Teaching Staff: *Total instructional faculty:* 213 (full-time 72, part-time 141). Student/faculty ratio: 9:1. Degrees held by full-time faculty: doctorate 52%, master's 43%, baccalaureate 5%. 52% hold terminal degrees.

Enrollment: Total enrollment 1,639. Undergraduate

Characteristics of Student Body: *Ethnic/racial makeup:* Black non-Hispanic: 306; American Indian or Alaska Native: 5; Asian or Pacific Islander: 14; Hispanic: 22; White non-Hispanic: 810; unknown 15. *Age distribution:* number under 18: 9; 18–19: 2220: 22–24: 2251 25–29: 140; 39–34: 106; 35–39: 93; 40–49: 132; 50–64: 58; 65 and over: 3. 51% of students attend summer sessions.

International Students: 9 undergraduate nonresident aliens enrolled fall 12006. No programs available to aid students whose native language is not English. No financial aid specifically designated for international students.

Student Life: On-campus residence halls house 15% of student body. Co-ed residence hall available. Female-only residence hall available. *Special regulations:* Cars permitted without restrictions. Residence hall visitation Sun.–Thurs. 9am to midnight; visitation Fri.–Sat. 9am to 2am; student room Sun.–Thur. noon to midnight, Fri.–Sat. noon to 2am. *Special services:* Learning Resources Center, medical services, shuttle bus to cluster colleges. *Student publications: Inscape*, an annual literary magazine. *Surrounding community:* Pepper Pike population 6,500. Cleveland, 15 miles from campus, is nearest metropolitan area. Served by mass transit system.

Library Collections: 131,000 volumes. 4,900 microforms; 7,800 audiovisual materials; 335 current periodical subscriptions. Online catalog. Students have access to the Internet and online information retrieval services.

Most important special collections include Ralph M. Besse River Collection; Sister Kenan Dulzer Collection of Religious Studies.

Buildings and Grounds: Campus area 115 acres.

Chief Executive Officer: Sr. Diana Stano, O.S.U., Ph.D., President.

Address admission inquiries to Sarah Sundermeier, Director of Admissions; address graduate inquiries to Shandra O'Dell, Graduate Studies Administrative Assistant.

Walsh University

2020 East Maple, N.W.
North Canton, Ohio 44720

Tel: (330) 499-7090 **E-mail:** admissions@alex.walsh.edu
Fax: (330) 490-7165 **Internet:** www.walsh.edu

Institution Description: Walsh University is a private institution affiliated with the Roman Catholic Church. *Enrollment:* 2,738. *Degrees awarded:* Associate, baccalaureate, master's.

Accreditation: *Regional:* NCA.

History: Established and chartered 1958; offered first instruction at postsecondary level 1960; awarded first degree (baccalaureate) 1964.

Institutional Structure: *Governing board:* Walsh University Board of Trustees. Representation: 36 trustees, president of the university, 3 administrators. 4 ex officio. 26 voting. *Composition of institution:* Administrators: 6 vice presidents. Academic affairs headed by vice president for academic affairs/dean of the university. Management/business/finances directed by vice president for finance and business. Full-time instructional faculty 92. Academic governance body, Academic Assembly, meets an average of 8 times per year.

Calendar: Semesters. Academic year Aug. to Apr. Freshmen admitted Sept., Jan., June, July. Degrees conferred and formal commencement May. Summer session of 3 terms from June to Aug.

Characteristics of Freshmen: 1,493 applicants (863 female, 123 male). 81% of applicants admitted. 43% of applicants admitted and enrolled full-time.

23% (110 students) submitted SAT scores; 97% (460 students) submitted ACT scores. *25th percentile*: SAT Critical Reading 450, SAT Math 470; ACT Composite 19, ACT English 18, ACT math 18. *75th percentile*: SAT Critical Reading 560, SAT math 580; ACT Composite 24, ACT English 24, ACT Math 24.

56% of entering freshmen expected to graduate within 6 years.

Admission: Rolling admissions plan. For fall acceptance, apply as early as Oct. of previous year, but not later than Aug. 15 of year of enrollment. *Requirements:* Either graduation from accredited secondary school or GED. Recommend 4 units English, 2 foreign language, 3 mathematics, 3 social studies, 3 laboratory science. Minimum 2.3 GPA. Lowest acceptable secondary school class standing 25th percentile. *Entrance tests:* ACT or SAT. For foreign students TOEFL. *For transfer students:* 2.0 minimum GPA; from 2-year and 4-year accredited institutions 96 semester hours maximum transfer credit.

College credit and advanced placement for postsecondary-level work completed in secondary school. College credit for extrainstitutional learning on basis of portfolio and faculty assessment; personal interviews.

Tutoring and Structured Semester available. Developmental/remedial courses offered in summer session and regular academic year; credit given.

Degree Requirements: *For all associate degrees:* 60 semester hours; last 30 hours in residence. *For all baccalaureate degrees:* 130 semester hours; last 32 hours in residence; 2 hours physical education; freshman seminar. *For all master's degrees:* 36–48 semester hours. *For all degrees:* 2.0 GPA; core curriculum and distribution requirements.

Fulfillment of some degree requirements and exemption from some beginning courses possible by passing departmental examinations, College Board CLEP, AP. *Grading system:* A–F; withdraw (carries time limit).

Distinctive Educational Programs: Weekend and evening classes. Facilities and programs for independent research, including honors programs, individual majors, tutorials. Accelerated degree program for adult learners with all evening and weekend classes.

Degrees Conferred: 4 *associate;* 366 *baccalaureate*; 123 *master's*; 5 *doctorate*. Bachelor's degrees awarded in top five disciplines: business/marketing 95; education 53; health professions and related clinical sciences 27; communications/journalism 22; social sciences 16. Master's degrees awarded: biological/life sciences 22; business/marketing 19; education 31; health professions 9; theology 1. Master's degrees awarded in various disciplines 123. Doctorates awarded: physical therapy 5.

Fees and Other Expenses: *Full-time tuition per academic year 2008–09:* $20,050 undergraduate; contact the school for current graduate tuition. *Required fees:* $570. *Room and board per academic year:* $7,760. *Books and supplies:* $966. *Other expenses:* $1,776.

Financial Aid: The university offers a direct lending program. Aid from institutionally generated funds is provided on the basis of academic merit, financial need.

Financial aid to full-time, first-time undergraduate students: 100% received some form of financial aid.

Departments and Teaching Staff:

Total instructional faculty: 217 (full-time 92, part-time 125). Total faculty with doctorate, first-professional, or other terminal degree: 89. Student/faculty ratio: 14:1. Degrees held by full-time faculty: master's 37%, doctorate 63%. 63% hold terminal degrees.

Enrollment: Total enrollment 2,738. Undergraduate 2,291 (full-time 81%; female 65%, male 35%). Graduate 447 (full-time 31%). Undergraduate transfer-in students 113.

Characteristics of Student Body: *Ethnic/racial makeup:* Black non-Hispanic: 5%; American Indian or Alaska Native: 1%; Hispanic: 1%; White non-Hispanic: 81%; unknown 12%; nonresident elien 1%. *Age distribution:* number under 18: 119, 18–19: 802, 20–21: 533; 22–24: 233; 25–29: 123; 30–34: 98; 35–39: 69; 40–49: 125; 50–64: 42; 65 and over: 1. 30.8% of students attend summer sessions.

International Students: 27 nonresident aliens enrolled fall 2008. Students from Europe, Central and South America, Africa, Canada. Programs available to aid students whose native language is not English: social, cultural, financial. English as a Second Language Program. Financial aid designated for qualifying international students.

Student Life: On-campus residence halls house 50% of student body. Approval of Dean of Residence Life in order to live off-campus. *Intercollegiate athletics:* male: baseball, basketball, cross-country, football, golf, soccer, tennis, track; female: basketball, cross-country, golf, softball, synchronized swimming, track, tennis, volleyball. *Special regulations:* Cars permitted without restriction. Residence halls: quiet hours available; coeducational housing or single-sex housing available (by floors only). *Special services:* Medical services. *Student publications: Spectator*, a biweekly newspaper; *Memory Book*, an annual literary magazine. *Surrounding community:* Canton population 100,000. Cleveland, 50 miles from campus, is nearest metropolitan area. Served by airport 5 miles from campus; passenger rail service 8 miles from campus.

Library Collections: 142,500 volumes. 8,700 microforms; 2,600 audiovisual materials; 31,620 periodicals including via electronic access. Computer work stations available. Students have access to the Internet at no charge.

Most important special collections include counseling, nursing, and education collections.

Buildings and Grounds: Campus area 108 acres.

Chief Executive Officer: Dr. Richard Jussseaume, President.

Address admission inquiries to Brett Freshove, Director of Enrollment Management.

Wilberforce University

1055 North Bickett Road
Wilberforce, Ohio 45384-1001
Tel: (937) 376-2911 **E-mail:** admissions@wilberforce.edu
Fax: (937) 376-4752 **Internet:** www.wilberforce.edu

Institution Description: Wilberforce University is a private institution affiliated with the African Methodist Episcopal Church. *Enrollment:* 785. *Degrees awarded:* Baccalaureate.

Member of Dayton-Miami Valley Consortium.

Accreditation: *Regional:* NCA.

History: Founded by the Methodist Episcopal Church as Ohio African University 1843; established as Wilberforce University of the Methodist Episcopal Church, chartered, incorporated, and offered first instruction at postsecondary level 1856; awarded first degree (baccalaureate) 1857; changed affiliation to the African Methodist Episcopal Church and changed name to Wilberforce University 1863. *See* Frederick McGinnis, *A History and an Interpretation of Wilberforce University* (Blanchester, Ohio: Brown Publishing Company, 1941) for further information.

Institutional Structure: *Governing board:* Wilberforce University Board of Trustees. Extrainstitutional representation: 26 trustees, including 14 alumni; institutional representation: president of the college, 1 full-time instructional faculty member, 1 student. 1 ex officio. 27 voting. *Composition of institution:* Administrators 52. Academic affairs headed by vice president and academic dean. Management/business/finances directed by vice president for administrative and financial affairs. Full-time instructional faculty 52. Academic governance body, the faculty, meets an average of 9 times per year.

Calendar: Semesters. Academic year Aug. to Aug. Freshmen admitted Aug., Jan., Apr. Degrees conferred and formal commencement Apr., July.

Characteristics of Freshmen: 2,717 applicants (1,630 female, 1,057 male). 50% of applicants admitted. 13% of admitted students enrolled full-time.

19% (37 students) submitted SAT scores; 55% (105 students) submitted ACT scores. *25th percentile:* SAT Critical Reading 340, SAT Math 310; ACT Composite 14, ACT English 12, ACT Math 14. *75th percentile*: SAT Critical Reading 430, SAT Math 420; ACT Composite 18, ACT English 18, ACT Math 17.

85% of entering freshmen expected to graduate within 5 years. 36% of freshmen from Ohio. Freshmen from 32 states and 2 foreign countries.

Admission: Rolling admissions plan. For fall acceptance, apply as early as junior year of secondary school. Apply by June 1 for early decision; need not limit application to Wilberforce. *Requirements:* Either graduation from accredited secondary school with 12 units which normally include 4 English, 3 mathematics, 3 science, 2 social studies; or GED. 3-4 additional electives recommended. Minimum GPA 2.0. Lowest acceptable school class rank in top two-thirds. *Entrance tests:* ACT composite recommended. For foreign students TOEFL. *For transfer students:* 2.0 minimum GPA; from 4-year accredited institution 90 hours maximum transfer credit; from 2-year accredited institution 60 hours.

College credit and advanced placement for postsecondary-level work completed in secondary school.

Tutoring available. Developmental courses offered during regular academic year; credit given.

Degree Requirements: 122 credit hours; 2.0 GPA; 30 of last 36 hours in residence; successful completion of 2 cooperative education placements; 2 credits health/physical education; demonstrated proficiency in English.

Fulfillment of some degree requirements and exemption from some beginning courses possible by passing departmental examinations, College Board CLEP, AP. *Grading system:* A–F; withdraw (carries time limit).

Distinctive Educational Programs: Cooperative education. Dual-degree program in engineering and computer science in conjunction with University of Dayton. Credential for Leadership for Management and Business (CLIMB) program offers evening courses for adults desiring a management degree (must be at least 25 years of age, have 2 years of college and 2 years of work experience). Interdepartmental programs in economics and political science, and humanities and theology. Facilities and programs for independent research. Cross-registration through consortium of colleges.

ROTC: Air Force in conjunction with Wright State University; Army in conjunction with Central State University.

Degrees Conferred: 172 *baccalaureate*; 3 *master's*. Bachelor's degrees awarded in top five disciplines: business, management, marketing, and related support services 157; computer and information sciences 45; communication, journalism, and related programs 22; health professions and related clinical sciences 21; social sciences 8. Master's degrees awarded: health professions 3.

Fees and Other Expenses: *Full-time tuition per academic year 2008–09:* $11,560. *Room and board per academic year:* $5,320. *Books and supplies:* $1,000. *Other expenses:* $3,600.

Financial Aid: Aid from institutionally generated funds is provided on the basis of academic merit, financial need.

Financial aid to full-time, first-time undergraduate students: 96% received some form of financial aid. Average amount of aid received: federal grants $5,370; state/local grants $3,001; institutional grants $4,506; loans $8,202.

Departments and Teaching Staff: *Total instructional faculty:* 63. Student/faculty ratio: 12:1. Degrees held by full-time faculty: doctorate 31%, master's 69%.

Enrollment: Total enrollment 785. Undergraduate 778 (full-time 98%; female 51%, male 43%). Graduate 7 (full-time 100%). Undergraduate transfer-in students 15.

Characteristics of Student Body: *Ethnic/racial makeup:* Black non-Hispanic: 92%; American Indian or Alaska Native: 1%; Hispanic: 1%; White non-Hispanic: 4%; unknown: 2%.

International Students: 79 nonresident aliens enrolled fall 2008. No programs available to aid students whose native language is not English. No financial aid specifically designated for international students.

Student Life: On-campus residence halls house 90% of student body. Residence halls for males constitute 40% of such space, for females 44%, for both sexes 16%. 8% of student body live in married student apartments; 6% in honor residence halls. *Intramural sports:* basketball, softball, soccer, tennis, volleyball. *Special regulations:* Registered cars permitted without restrictions. *Special services:* Learning Resources Center, medical services. *Student publications: The Mirror*, a bimonthly newspaper. *Surrounding community:* Wilberforce population 2,600. Dayton, 22 miles from campus, is nearest metropolitan area. Served by airport 30 miles from campus; passenger rail service 22 miles from campus.

Library Collections: 110,000 volumes. 42,000 microforms; 15,000 audiovisual materials; 400 serial subscriptions. Students have access to online information retrieval services and the Internet.

Most important special holdings include African Methodist Episcopal Church records; history of Wilberforce University.

Buildings and Grounds: Campus area 165 acres.

Chief Executive Officer: Rev. Dr. Floyd H. Flake, President.

Address admission inquiries to Director of Admissions.

Wilmington College

251 Ludovic Street
Wilmington, Ohio 45177
Tel: (937) 382-6661 **E-mail:** admissions@wilmington.edu
Fax: (937) 382-8542 **Internet:** www.wilmington.edu

Institution Description: Wilmington College is a private college affiliated with the Wilmington Yearly Meeting of the Society of Friends, with branch campuses in Sharonville, Cincinnati, and at Lebanon and Warren Correctional Institutes. *Enrollment:* 1,542. *Degrees awarded:* Baccalaureate, master's.

Member of Greater Cincinnati Consortium of Colleges and Universities; Southwest Council for Higher Education.

Accreditation: *Regional:* NCA.

History: Established 1870; offered first instruction at postsecondary level 1871; chartered and awarded first degree (baccalaureate) 1875.

Institutional Structure: *Governing board:* Wilmington College Board of Trustees. Extrainstitutional representation: 24 trustees; institutional representation: faculty and student observers. 24 voting. *Composition of institution:* Administrators 51. Academic affairs headed by vice president for academic affairs. Management/Business/Finance directed by vice president for finance and administration. Full-time instructional faculty 71. Academic government meets an average of 24 times per year.

Calendar: Semesters. Academic year Aug. to Aug. Summer session offered.

Characteristics of Freshmen: 2,205 applicants (1,224 female, 981 male). 95% of applicants accepted. 25% of accepted applicants enrolled full-time.

15% (62 students) submitted SAT scores; 86% (858 students) submitted ACT scores. *25th percentile*: SAT Critical Reading 430, SAT Math 430; ACT Composite 18, ACT English 17, ACT Math 18. *75th percentile*: SAT Critical Reading 550, SAT Math 550; ACT Composite 23. ACT English 23, ACT Math 23.

94% of freshmen from Ohio. Freshmen from 12 states and 16 foreign countries.

Admission: Rolling admissions plan. For fall acceptance, apply as early as Sept. 1 of previous year, but not later than Aug. 1 of year of enrollment. Early acceptance available. *Requirements:* Either graduation from accredited secondary school with 16 units including 4 units English, minimum 2 units each of mathematics, social studies, laboratory sciences, and foreign languages (optional) or GED. Lowest acceptable secondary school class standing in upper four-fifths. *Entrance tests:* College Board SAT or ACT composite. *For transfer students:* Encouraged to apply. Must meet College requirements for good academic standing; from 4-year and 2-year accredited institutions, maximum trans-

WILMINGTON COLLEGE—*cont'd*

fer credit limited only by residence requirement; correspondence/extension students 45 hours; vocational/technical students 18 hours; good standing at institution previously attended.

College credit and advanced placement for postsecondary-level work completed in secondary school. College credit for extrainstitutional learning on basis of faculty assessment.

Tutoring available.

Degree Requirements: *For all baccalaureate degrees:* 124 semester hours. *For all degrees:* 2.0 GPA; 30 hours in residence; distribution requirements.

Fulfillment of some degree requirements and exemption from some beginning courses possible by passing departmental examinations, College Board CLEP, AP. *Grading system:* A–F; Pass-Fail.

Distinctive Educational Programs: Work-experience programs, including internships and labs. Flexible meeting places including off-campus centers and evening classes. Special facilities for using telecommunications in the classroom. Interdepartmental programs in communications, criminal justice, peace studies, nationally accredited program in athletic training, new minor in equine studies. Facilities and programs for independent research, including individual majors, tutorials, independent study. Midwest Consortium for Study Abroad (Vienna, Austria); Council on International Educational Exchange, Universite Bretagne, Rennes, Brittany; Cemanahuac Educational Community (Curenavaca, Morelas, Mexico).

Degrees Conferred: 248 *baccalaureate:* agriculture 35, athletic training 7, biological and life sciences 18, communications 120, computer and information science 1, criminal justice 10, education 48, fine and applied arts 5, liberal arts 1, mathematics 2, physical sciences 2, psychology 4, social sciences and history 10, social work 7, sports management 8. Master's degrees awarded: education 5.

Fees and Other Expenses: *Full-time tuition per academic year 2008–09:* $23,372. *Books and supplies:* $1,250. *Room and board per academic year:* $8,010. *Other expenses:* $1,200.

Financial Aid: Aid from institutionally generated funds is provided on the basis of academic merit, financial need.

Financial aid to full-time, first-time undergraduate students: 99% received some form of financial aid. Average amount of aid received: federal grants $3,922; Pell grants $2,829; other federal aid $1,003; state/local grants $1,729; institutional grants $9,822.

Departments and Teaching Staff: *Total instructional faculty:* 129 (full-time 70, part-time 59). Total faculty with doctorate, first-professional, or other terminal degree: 50. Student/faculty ratio: 12:1. Degrees held by full-time faculty: master's 40%, doctorate 60%. 72% hold terminal degrees.

Enrollment: Total enrollment 1,542. Undergraduate 1,496 (full-time 80%; female 54%, male 46%).

Characteristics of Student Body: *Ethnic/racial makeup:* Black non-Hispanic: 10%; Hispanic: 1%; White non-Hispanic: 69%; unknown: 19%; nonresident alien 1%. *Age distribution:* 17–21: 54%; 22–24: 10%; 25–29: 9 %; 30–34: 6%; 35–39: 7%; 40–49: 11%; 50–59: 1%; 60–up: 1%; unknown 1%.

International Students: 15 nonresident aliens enrolled fall 2008. Students from Europe, Asia, Africa, New Zealand. Programs available to aid students whose native language is not English: social, cultural. Financial aid specifically designated for international students: 15 scholarships made available annually for undergraduate international students.

Student Life: On-campus residence halls house 70% of the main campus day students. Single-sex and coeducational halls are available. Approximately 20% of day students are involved in fraternities/sororities. *Intercollegiate athletics:* Member of NCAA Division III, Ohio Athletic Conference. Male: football, soccer, cross-country, basketball, golf, wrestling, baseball, track and field, swimming, tennis; female: indoor track, volleyball, basketball, softball, tennis, track and field, soccer, swimming, cross-country. *Special regulations:* All students permitted to have cars but must pay a fee to park on campus. *Special services:* Professionally staffed Academic Resource Center; world-famous Peace Resources Center; 7 farms used as commercial operations; teaching laboratories. *Student publications: Wilmingtonian*, a yearbook; *The Witness*, a student newspaper; *Woodhouse*, an annual literary magazine. *Surrounding community:* Wilmington population 12,000. Dayton (OH), 34 miles from campus, is nearest metropolitan area. Served by airport 50 miles from campus.

Library Collections: 110,000 volumes including bound books, serial backfiles, electronic documents, and government documents not in separate collections. Online catalog. 42,000 microforms; 1,400 audiovisual materials; 400 Current serial subscriptions. Computer work stations available. Students have access to the Internet at no charge.

Most important special collections include the college archives and Quaker Collection (Quaker history, philosophy and practice).

Buildings and Grounds: Campus area 63.5 acres.

Chief Executive Officer: Dr. Daniel A. DiBiasio, President.

Address admission inquiries to Tina Garland, Director of Admissions.

Winebrenner Theological Seminary

950 North Main Street
Findlay, Ohio 45840
Tel: (419) 434-4200 **E-mail:** admissions@winebrenner.edu
Fax: (419) 434-4267 **Internet:** www.winebrenner.edu

Institution Description: Winebrenner Theological Seminary is a private institution offering graduate training in theology. *Enrollment:* 99.

Accreditation: *Regional:* NCA. *National:* ATS. *Professional*: theology

History: Winebrenner was established in 1942 and is associated with the Churches of God, General Conference.

Institutional Structure: Trimesters. Academic year Aug. to July.

Admission: *Requirements:* Admission to the seminary is by approval of its Admissions Committee upon receipt of application, application fee, statement of faith/call, transcripts, and appropriate recommendation forms.

Degree Requirements: Completion of the prescribed curriculum.

Degrees Conferred: 5 *master's:* theology; 12 *first-professional:* master of divinity; 4 *doctorate*: theology and religious vocations.

Fees and Other Expenses: *Full-time tuition per academic year 2008–09:* contact the seminary for current information regarding tuition, fees, housing, and other costs.

Financial Aid: Aid from institutionally generated funds is provided on the basis of financial need.

Departments and Teaching Staff: *Total instructional faculty:* 19 (full-time 8, part-time 11). Total faculty with doctorate, first-professional, or other terminal degree: 14. Student/faculty ratio: 8:1. Degrees held by full-time faculty: doctorate 100%.

Enrollment: Total enrollment 99. First-professional 99.

Library Collections: 50,000 volumes. 400 microform titles; 110 current periodical subscriptions. Computer work stations available. Students have access to online information retrieval services and the Internet.

Most important special holdings include Churches of God, General Conference Rare Book Collection; Rosenbery Family Collection.

Chief Executive Officer: Dr. David E. Draper, President.

Address admissions inquiries to Chris Williams, Admissions Counselor.

Wittenberg University

Ward Street at North Wittenberg Avenue
P.O. Box 720
Springfield, Ohio 45501-0720
Tel: (800) 677-7558 **E-mail:** admission@wittenberg.edu
Fax: (937) 327-6379 **Internet:** www.wittenberg.edu

Institution Description: Wittenberg University is a private, independent, nonprofit institution affiliated with the Evangelical Lutheran Church in America. *Enrollment:* 1,976. *Degrees awarded:* Baccalaureate, master's.

Member of the consortium International Education Association of Ohio Colleges and Universities.

Accreditation: *Regional:* NCA. *Professional*: chemistry, music, teacher education

History: Established 1842; chartered and offered first instruction at postsecondary level 1845; awarded first degree (baccalaureate) 1851; adopted present name 1959. *See* William A. Kinnison, *Wittenberg: A Concise History* (Springfield: Wittenberg University, 1976) for further information.

Institutional Structure: *Governing board:* The Board of Directors of Wittenberg University. Extrainstitutional representation: 37 directors; institutional representation: president of the college; 24 alumni. All voting. *Composition of institution:* Administrators 113. Academic affairs headed by provost. Management/business/finances directed by vice president for business and finance. Full-time instructional faculty 148. Academic governance body, Wittenberg University Faculty, meets an average of 9 times per year.

Calendar: Semesters. Academic year Aug. to May. Freshmen admitted Aug., Jan., May., June. Degrees conferred and formal commencement June. Summer sessions from June to July.

Characteristics of Freshmen: 2,890 applicants (1,419 female, 1,471 male). 73% of applicants admitted. 26% of applicants admitted and enrolled full-time.

33% (193 students) submitted SAT scores; 65% (377 students) submitted ACT scores. *25th percentile*: SAT Critical Reading 520, SAT Math 530; ACT Composite 22, ACT English 21, ACT Math 20. *75th percentile*: SAT Critical Reading 650, SAT Math 640, ACT Composite 27, ACT English 28, ACT Math 24.

70% of entering freshmen expected to graduate within 5 years. 76% of freshmen from Ohio. Freshmen from 40 states and 17 foreign countries.

Admission: Rolling admissions plan. Early acceptance available. *Requirements:* Graduation from accredited secondary school. Required 4 units English, 3 foreign language, 3 mathematics, 3 science, 3 social studies. *Entrance tests:* College Board SAT or ACT composite. For foreign students 550 minimum TOEFL. *For transfer students:* 2.0 minimum GPA; 28 courses maximum transfer.

College credit and advanced placement for postsecondary-level work completed in secondary school.

Degree Requirements: 130 semester hours; 2.0 GPA overall and in major(s), minor(s); last 8 courses in residence; 3 courses in physical education or dance; general education requirements including foreign language competency; community service; exit competency exams in writing and math basic skills; comprehensives in individual fields of study.

Fulfillment of some degree requirements and exemption from some beginning courses possible by passing departmental examinations, College Board Achievement Test, AP. *Grading system:* A–F; credit-no credit; withdraw (carries time limit).

Distinctive Educational Programs: Work-experience programs. Evening classes. Accelerated degree programs, including a program which enables a Wittenberg student to enter a graduate program after 3 years of undergraduate study. Dual-degree programs in engineering with Case Western Reserve University, Columbia University (NY), Georgia Institute of Technology, Washington University (MO); in forestry and environmental studies with Duke University (NC); in nursing with Case Western Reserve University; and in occupational therapy with Washington University (MO). Preprofessional programs in dentistry, medicine, veterinary medicine. Interdisciplinary programs in American studies, East Asian studies, Russian Area studies, and minor programs in urban studies, global studies and women's studies. Facilities and programs for independent research, including honors programs, interdepartmental majors. Study abroad in England, Germany, Japan, Switzerland, People's Republic of China, Russia, and other countries through the Institute of European Studies, Institute of Asian Studies, International Student Exchange Program, and Council on International Student Exchange. Off-campus study in the U.S. includes spring term at Duke University (NC) Marine Station; Urban Internship Term in Philadelphia (PA). *Other distinctive programs:* School of Community Education offers credit courses toward a baccalaureate; baccalaureate completion program for registered nurses; liberal studies major for the non-traditional student. Summer study programs include Global Issues and World Churches in Geneva Switzerland; Biology/geology field study programs in San Salvador (Bahamas).

ROTC: Army and Air Force in cooperation with Central State University and Wright State University.

Degrees Conferred: 456 *baccalaureate:* area and ethnic studies 19; biological/life sciences 44; business/marketing 74; communications/communication technologies 27; computer and information sciences 4; education 54; English 44; foreign languages and literature 16; liberal arts/general studies 6; mathematics 11; philosophy/religion/theology 6; physical sciences 17; psychology 44; social sciences and history 70; visual and performing arts 21. *Master's*: education 2.

Fees and Other Expenses: *Full-time tuition per academic year 2008–09:* $33,236. *Required fees:* $156. *Room and board per academic year:* $8,314. *Books and supplies:* $1,000. *Other expenses:* $2,000.

Financial Aid: Aid from institutionally generated funds is provided on the basis of academic merit, financial need, leadership, community service.

Financial aid to full-time, first-time undergraduate students: 100% received some form of financial aid. Average amount of aid received: federal grants $4,043; state/local grants $2,039; institutional grants $14,249; loans $5,996.

Departments and Teaching Staff: *Total instructional faculty:* 202 (full-time 148, part-time 54). Total faculty with doctorate, first-professional, or other terminal degree: 155. Student/faculty ratio: 13:1. Degrees held by full-time faculty: master's 8%, doctorates 92%.

Enrollment: Total enrollment 1,976. Undergradaute 1,967 (full-time 94%; female 56%, male 44%). Graduate 4 (full-time 100%).

Characteristics of Student Body: *Ethnic/racial makeup:* Black non-Hispanic: 4%; Asian or Pacific Islander: 1%; Hispanic: 1%; White non-Hispanic: 76%; unknown: 15%. *Age distribution:* number under 18: 83; 18–19: 990; 20–21: 850; 22–24: 129; 25–29: 42; 30–34: 16; 35–39: 13; 40–49: 34; 50–64: 14; 65 and over: 4; unknown: 2. 20% of student body attend summer sessions.

International Students: 40 nonresident aliens enrolled fall 2008. Students from Europe, Asia, Latin America, Africa. Programs available to aid students whose native language is not English: social, cultural, financial. English as a Second Language Program. Financial aid specifically designated for undergraduate international students: variable number of scholarships available annually.

Student Life: On-campus residence halls house 56% of student body. Residence halls for males constitute 34% of such space, for females 36%, for both sexes, 30%. 30% of males join and 16% live in fraternity housing; 50% of females join and 18% live in sorotity housing. *Intercollegiate athletics:* male: basketball, golf, football, soccer, swimming, tennis, track, lacrosse; female: baseball, basketball, field hockey, lacrosse, softball, swimming, tennis, track, volleyball. *Special regulations:* Quiet hours. Residence hall visitation from 10am to 12:30pm Sun.–Thurs., 10am to 2:30am Fri. and Sat. *Special services:* Medical services. *Student publications, radio: History Journal*, an annual publication; *Torch*, a weekly newspaper; *Witt Revue*, an annual literary journal. Radio station WUSO broadcasts 168 hours per week. *Surrounding community:* Springfield population 70,000. Dayton, 25 miles from campus, is nearest metropolitan area. Served by mass transit bus system; airport 28 miles from campus.

Library Collections: 418,000 volumes. 87,500 microforms; 22,900 audiovisual materials; 6,620 current periodical subscriptions. Online catalog. OhioLink member. Students have access to online information retrieval services and the Internet.

Most important holdings include Luther-Reformation (writings, original letters, out-of-print books about Luther); Cyril Dos Passos Collection on lepidoptera (including journals and specimens); paintings and writings of Walter Tittle, local artist; art work of Robert Kipness.

Buildings and Grounds: Campus area 70 acres. Campus DVD available.

Chief Executive Officer: Dr. Mark H. Erickson, President.

Address admission inquiries to Bradley Pochard, Director of Admissions.

Wright State University

3640 Colonel Glenn Highway
Dayton, Ohio 45435
Tel: (937) 775-3333 **E-mail:** admissions@wright.edu
Fax: (937) 775-5795 **Internet:** www.wright.edu

Institution Description: Wright State University is a state institution with an associate degree-granting branch campus, Lake Campus, at Grand Lake St. Marys. *Enrollment:* 16,672. *Degrees awarded:* Baccalaureate, first-professional (medicine, psychology), master's, doctorate.

Member of Dayton-Miami Valley Consortium.

Accreditation: *Regional:* NCA. *Professional*: business, chemistry, engineering, music, nursing, social work

History: Established as branch of Ohio State University and Miami University of Ohio 1964; changed name to Wright State Campus of Miami and Ohio State Universities 1965; chartered as independent institution, granted full independent university status and adopted present name 1967; established School of Medicine 1973; established School of Professional Psychology 1979.

Institutional Structure: *Governing board:* Board of Trustees (state-appointed). Representation: 9 trustees, 2 student trustees. All voting. *Composition of institution:* Academic affairs headed by vice president for academic affairs. Management/business/finances directed by vice president of business and finance. Academic governance body, Academic Council, meets approximately 10 times per year.

Calendar: Quarters. Academic year Sept. to Aug. Freshmen admitted Sept., Jan., Mar., June, July. Degrees conferred June, Aug., Dec. Mar. Formal commencements Dec., June. Summer session of 3 terms from June to Aug.

Characteristics of Freshmen: 80% of applicants admitted. 51% of applicants admitted and enrolled.

35% (799 students) submitted SAT scores; 92% (2,125 students) submitted ACT scores. *25th percentile*: SAT Critical Reading 420, SAT Math 430; ACT Composite 18. *75th percentile*: SAT Critical Reading 570, SAT Math 560; ACT Composite 21.

35% of entering freshmen expected to graduate within 5 years. 97% of freshmen from Ohio.

Admission: Rolling admissions plan. Early acceptance available. *Requirements:* Either graduation from accredited secondary school or GED. Open admissions for in-state residents. *Entrance tests:* ACT Composite or SAT. For foreign students TOEFL score 500.

College credit for extrainstitutional learning.

Tutoring available. Noncredit remedial courses offered during regular academic year.

Degree Requirements: 183 quarter hours; 2.0 GPA; 45 hours in residence; general education requirements. Additional requirements for some programs.

Fulfillment of some degree requirements and exemption from some beginning courses possible by passing College Board CLEP. *Grading system:* A–F; pass-fail.

Distinctive Educational Programs: Work-experience programs. Flexible meeting places and schedules, including off-campus centers, weekend and evening classes. Special facilities for using telecommunications in the classroom. Facilities and programs for independent research, including honors programs, individual majors, tutorials.

ROTC: Army, Air Force.

Degrees Conferred: 2,287 *baccalaureate:*; 1,199 *master's*; 55 *doctorate*; 91 *first-professional*. Bachelor's degrees awarded in top five disciplines: business/marketing 549; education 297; health professions and related clinical sciences

WRIGHT STATE UNIVERSITY—*cont'd*

243; social sciences 191; engineering 133. Master's degrees awarded in top five disciplines: education 468; business/marketing 468; engineering 191; health professions 63; psychology 50. Doctorates awarded: engineering 13; interdisciplinary studies 6; psychology 24. First-professional degrees awarded: medicine 91.

Fees and Other Expenses: *Full-time tuition per academic year 2008–09:* undergraduate resident $7,018 nonresident $13,744; contact the university for current graduate and first-professional tuition that vary by program. *Books and supplies:* $1,764. *Room and board per academic year:* $7,335.

Financial Aid: Aid from institutionally generated funds is provided on the basis of academic merit, financial need, athletic ability, other criteria.

Departments and Teaching Staff: *Total instructional faculty:* 756 (full-time 722, part-time 34). Student/faculty ratio: 20:1.

Enrollment: Total enrollment 16,672. Undergraduate 12,772 (full-time 85%; female 55%, male 45%). Graduate 3,900 (full-time 60%). Undergraduate transfer-in students 941.

Characteristics of Student Body: *Ethnic/racial makeup:* Black non-Hispanic: 14%; Asian or Pacific Islander: 3%; Hispanic: 2%; White non-Hispanic: 74%; unknown: 6%; nonresident alien 1%. *Age distribution:* number under 18: 1951 18–19: 3,741; 20–21: 47; 22–24: 278; 25–29: 1,049; 30–34: 417; 35–39: 267; 40–49: 326; 50–64: 133; 65 and over: 37.

International Students: 590 nonresident aliens enrolled fall 2008. Students from Europe, Asia, Central and South America, Africa, Canada, Australia, Middle East. Programs available to aid students whose native language is not English: social, cultural. English as a Second Language Program. No financial aid specifically designated for international students.

Student Life: On-campus residence halls house 18% of student body. Residence halls for males and females constitute 100% of such space. *Intercollegiate athletics:* male: baseball, basketball, cross-country, golf, soccer, swimming, tennis, volleyball, wrestling; female: basketball, soccer, softball, swimming, tennis, volleyball. *Special services:* Learning Resources Center, medical services, shuttle bus to and from parking areas. *Student publications, radio, television: The Daily Guardian*, a newspaper. Radio station WWSU broadcasts 119 hours per week. Wright State broadcasts twice a week on TV station WPTD. *Surrounding community:* Dayton 205,000. Served by mass transit system; Dayton International Airport 15 miles from campus.

Library Collections: 2,170,200 volumes including books, serial backfiles, electronic documents, and government documents not in separate collection. Online catalog. Computer work stations available. students have access to online information retrieval services and the Internet.

Most important special holdings include papers of Orville and Wilbur Wright; manuscripts, books, periodicals on early aviation history; McFarland Collection (aerospace medicine/human factor engineering); local history collection.

Buildings and Grounds: Campus area 628 acres.

Chief Executive Officer: Dr. Kim Goldenberg, President.

Address admission inquiries to Cathy Davis, Director of Admissions.

College of Liberal Arts

Degree Programs Offered: *Baccalaureate* in anthropology, art and art history, classical humanities, communication, mass communication, organizational communication, dance, economics, English, French, geography, German, Greek, history, international studies, Latin, motion pictures, music, music education, philosophy, political science, religion, selected studies, social and industrial communication, social work, sociology, Spanish, theater arts, urban administration, urban studies; *B.F.A.* in art and theater; *master's* in English, humanities, history, and music.

Distinctive Educational Programs: Interdisciplinary program in urban studies.

College of Business and Administration

Degree Programs Offered: *Baccalaureate* in accountancy, business economics, finance, financial services, human resource management, management, management information systems, operations management, marketing; *master's of business administration* with concentrations in finance, financial administration, health care management, international business, logistics management, management, management science, marketing, project management; *master of science* in social and applied economics, logistics management.

College of Education and Human Services

Degree Programs Offered: *Baccalaureate* in art education, biological science education, business education, chemistry education, computer science education, earth science education, economics education, English education, general science education, geography education, health education, history education, language education, mathematics education, physical education, physics education, political science education, psychology/sociology education, music education, speech/communication education, science education, social studies education, vocational business education. The *bachelor of science* degree is also offered in rehabilitation. *Master's* offered in educational administration, school counseling, school social work, art therapy, rehabilitation counseling, substance abuse, mental health counseling, classroom teaching, and business and industry counseling. The educational specialist degree in educational leadership.

Distinctive Educational Programs: Cooperative doctoral programs with Bowling Green State University in Educational Leadership. National resource center on Arts for the Handicapped and a Center for Arts for the Disabled and Handicapped. A Center for Professional Services.

College of Nursing and Health

Degree Programs Offered: *Baccalaureate, master's.*

College of Engineering and Computer Science

Degree Programs Offered: *Bachelor of science* in biomedical engineering, computer science, computer engineering, electrical engineering, engineering physics, human factors engineering, materials engineering, mechanical engineering. *Master of science* in computer science, computer engineering, systems engineering (biomedical, electrical, human factors, materials, mechanical). *Ph.D.* in computer science and engineering.

Distinctive Educational Programs: Cooperative education. Interdisciplinary programs in biomedical engineering, systems engineering and human factors engineering; 2 interdisciplinary doctoral programs, 1 in biomedical sciences in cooperation with the School of Medicine and the other in computer science and computer engineering in cooperation with the College of Science and Mathematics.

School of Medicine

Degree Programs Offered: *First-professional.*

Admission: 90 semester hours or 135 quarter hours from approved college or university, 2 years chemistry (including organic chemistry), 1 year each biology, physics, mathematics, English; MCAT.

Degree Requirements: 304 credit hours, 2.0 GPA.

Distinctive Educational Programs: Biomedical Sciences Ph.D. Program in collaboration with College of Science and Mathematics.

School of Professional Psychology

Degree Programs Offered: *Doctorate.*

College of Science and Mathematics

Degree Programs Offered: *Baccalaureate, master's, doctorate.*

Distinctive Educational Programs: Cooperative education. Interdisciplinary programs in environmental health and human factors psychology; 2 interdisciplinary doctoral programs, 1 in biomedical sciences in cooperation with the School of Medicine and the other in computer science and computer engineering in cooperation with the College of Engineering and Computer Science. Research opportunities available through the School of Medicine and the College of Engineering and Computer Science.

Xavier University

3800 Victory Parkway
Cincinnati, Ohio 45207

Tel: (513) 745-3301 **E-mail:** xuadmit@xu.edu
Fax: (513) 745-4319 **Internet:** www.xu.edu

Institution Description: Xavier University is a private institution affiliated with the Society of Jesus, Roman Catholic Church. *Enrollment:* 6,884. *Degrees awarded:* Associate, baccalaureate, master's, doctorate.

Member of the Greater Cincinnati Consortium of Colleges and Universities.

Accreditation: *Regional:* NCA. *Professional*: business, chemistry, clinical psychology, health services administration, nursing, occupational therapy, radiography, social work

History: Established as the Athenaeum, for seminarians and lay males, 1831; offered first instruction at postsecondary level and changed name to St. Xavier College 1840; chartered 1842; awarded first degree (baccalaureate) 1843; adopted present name 1930. *See* Roger Fortino, *To See Great Wonders: A History of Xavier University, 1831–2006*, University of Scranton Press, 2006.

Institutional Structure: *Governing board:* Board of Trustees. Extrainstitutional representation: 42 trustees including alumni and community members; institutional representation: president of the university, rector of Jesuit community. *Composition of institution:* Administrators 94. Academic affairs headed by vice president and provost. Management/business/finances directed by vice president, business-finance. Full-time instructional faculty 299.

Calendar: Semesters. Academic year Aug. to May. Freshmen admitted Aug., Jan., June, July. Degrees conferred Aug., Dec., May. Formal commencement May. Summer session of 2 terms from May to Aug. plus several special sessions for teachers.

Characteristics of Freshmen: 8,151 applicants (female 3,350, male 3,801). 72% of applicants admitted. 15% of applicants admitted and enrolled full-time.

75% (610 students) submitted SAT scores; 87% (675 students) submitted ACT scores. *25th percentile*: SAT Critical Reading 530, SAT Math 540; ACT Composite 23, ACT English 22, ACT Math 23. *75th percentile*: SAT Critical Reading 640, SAT Math 620; ACT Composite 29, ACT English 28, ACT Math 29. 78% of entering freshmen expected to graduate within 5 years.

60% of freshmen from Ohio. Freshmen from 42 states and 38 foreign countries.

Admission: Rolling admissions plan. For fall acceptance, apply as early as fall of senior year of secondary school, but not later than beginning of term. Early acceptance available. Admissions may close prior to the start of the fall semester. *Requirements:* Either graduation from accredited secondary school with 21 units which normally include 4 English, 2 foreign language, 3 mathematics, 3 science, 3 social studies, 1 health/physical education; 5 or more electives; or GED. *Entrance tests:* College Board SAT or ACT composite. For foreign students TOEFL or other standardized test of English proficiency. *For transfer students:* 2. 0 minimum GPA; maximum transfer credit limited only by residence requirement.

College credit and advanced placement for postsecondary-level work completed in secondary school.

Tutoring available. Remedial courses offered in summer session and regular academic year; credit given.

Degree Requirements: *For all associate degrees:* 60 semester hours. *For all baccalaureate degrees:* minimum 120 semester hours. *For all undergraduate degrees:* 2.0 GPA; 30 hours in residence; core curriculum and distribution requirements. *Grading system:* A–F; withdraw (carries time limit).

Distinctive Educational Programs: Internships. Co-op Program in Business. Flexible schedules. Evening and weekend classes. Cooperative baccalaureate in medical technology with approved hospitals. Degrees in Montessori education. Special facilities for using telecommunications in the classroom. Facilities for independent research, including honors programs, individual majors, tutorials. Full-year (on scholarship) in Paris, France. Summer programs in Spain, Austria, France. Exchange agreements with Sophia University (Japan); Sogang University (South Korea); Javeriana University (Columbia) Katholische Universitat (Germany); University of Valencia (Spain).

ROTC: Air Force in cooperation with University of Cincinnati.

Degrees Conferred: 18 *associate;* 927 *baccalaureate*; 792 *master's*; 20 *doctorate.* Bachelor's degrees awarded in top five disciplines: business, management, marketing, and related support services 203; liberal arts and sciences, general studies, and humanities 138; communication, journalism, and related programs 68; education 63; health professions and related clinical sciences 49. Master's degrees awarded in top five disciplines: education 396; business/marketing 306; health professions and related clinical sciences 69; parks and recreation 44; psychology 28. Doctorates awarded: psychology 17.

Fees and Other Expenses: *Full-time tuition per academic year 2008–09:* undergraduate $26,860; graduate varies by program (contact the university for current rate). *Books and supplies:* $1,000. *Other expenses:* $2,000.

Financial Aid: Aid from institutionally generated funds is provided on the basis of academic merit, financial need, athletic ability, other criteria.

98% of students received some form of financial aid.

Departments and Teaching Staff: *Total instructional faculty:* 600 (full-time 299, part-time 301). Total faculty with doctorate, first-professional, or other terminal degree 318. Student/faculty ratio: 13:1. Degrees held by full-time faculty: baccalaureate 1%, master's 21%, doctorate 78%. 80% hold terminal degrees.

Enrollment: Total enrollment 6,666. Undergraduate 3,923 (full-time 87%; female 56%, male 44%). Graduate 2,661 (full-time 30%). Undergraduate transfer-in students 91.

Characteristics of Student Body: *Ethnic/racial makeup:* Black non-Hispanic: 11%; Asian or Pacific Islander: 2%; Hispanic: 3%; White non-Hispanic: 78%; unknown: 2%; nonresident alien 3%. *Age distribution:* number under 18: 46; 18–19: 1,4391; 20–21: 1,517; 22–24: 362; 25–29: 182; 30–34: 1151 35–39: 90; 40–49: 309; 50–64: 40; 65 and over: 10.

International Students: 204 nonresident aliens enrolled fall 2008. Students from Europe, Asia, Central and South America, Africa, Canada, Australia, Middle East. Programs available to aid students whose native language is not English: English as a Second Language Program. Financial aid specifically designated for international students.

Student Life: 90% of freshman and 46% of undergraduates reside in university housing. 100% co-ed residence halls, apartments, and houses. *Intercollegiate athletics:* male: baseball, basketball, cross-country, golf, soccer, swimming, tennis; female: basketball, cross-country, rifle, soccer, swimming, tennis, volleyball. *Special regulations:* Registered cars permitted in designated areas only; fee charged. Quiet hours. Residence hall visitation from noon to midnight Sun.-Thus., noon to 2am Fri. and Sat. *Special services:* First-year orientation, health and counseling services, intramural athletics, over 100 student clubs and organizations, offices of international students, commuters, and multicultural students. *Student publications, Athenaeum*, a biannual literary magazine; *Musketeer*, a yearbook; *Xavier Newswire*, a weekly newspaper. *Surrounding community:* Cincinnati metropolitan population 2 million. Served by mass transit bus system; airport 15 miles from campus; passenger rail service 4 miles from campus.

Library Collections: 366,500 volumes. 751,000 microforms; 9,925 audiovisual matrials; 47,800 periodicals including via electronic access. Online catalog. Computer work stations available. Students have access to online information retrieval services.

Most important special collections include manuscripts and complete works of Fr. Francis Finn, S.J.; Jesuit materials; incunabula.

Buildings and Grounds: Campus area 125 acres. Campus DVD available.

Chief Executive Officer: Dr. Michael J. Graham, President.

Address admission inquiries to Maureen Mthis, Director of Admissions.

Youngstown State University

One University Plaza
Youngstown, Ohio 44555-3101

Tel: (330) 742-3000 **E-mail:** enroll@ysu.edu
Fax: (330) 742-3674 **Internet:** www.ysu.edu

Institution Description: Youngstown State University is a state institution. *Enrollment:* 13,704. *Degrees awarded.* Associate, baccalaureate, master's, doc torate.

Academic offerings subject to approval by statewide coordinating bodies.

Accreditation: *Regional:* NCA. *Professional*: art, business, chemistry, clinical lab scientist, counseling, dental hygiene, dietetics, EMT-paramedic, engineering, medical laboratory technology, music, nurse anesthesia education, nursing, physical therapy, respiratory therapy, social work, teacher education, theatre

History: Established as School of Law of the Youngstown Association School and offered first instruction at postsecondary level 1908; changed name to Youngstown Institute of Technology 1921, Youngstown College 1928; incorporated 1944; changed name to The Youngstown University 1955; adopted present name 1967.

Institutional Structure: *Governing board:* University Board of Trustees. Representation: 9 trustees. All voting. *Composition of institution:* Administrators 24. Academic affairs headed by provost. Management/business/finances directed by executive vice president. Full-time instructional faculty 427. Academic governance body, Academic Senate, meets an average of 9 times per year. *Faculty representation:* Faculty served by collective bargaining agent, Youngstown State University chapter of Ohio Education Association, affiliated with NEA.

Calendar: Semesters. Academic year Aug. to May. Freshmen admitted Aug., Jan., June. Degrees conferred and formal commencement June, Aug., Mar. Summer session from June to Aug.

Characteristics of Freshmen: 99.5% of applicants accepted. 57% of accepted applicants enrolled.

8.7% (161 students) submitted SAT scores; 91.3% (694 students) submitted ACT scores. *25th percentile*: SAT Critical Reading 410, SAT Math 390; ACT Composite 17. *75th percentile*: SAT Critical Reading 540, SAT Math 540; ACT Composite 23.

30% of entering freshmen expected to graduate within 5 years. 91% of freshmen from Ohio. Freshmen from 39 states and 58 foreign countries.

Admission: Rolling admissions plan. For fall acceptance, apply no later than Aug. 15 of year of enrollment. Early acceptance available. *Requirements:* Ohio residents and residents of Mercer and Lawrence Counties in Pennsylvania must have graduated from high school or passed the GED. Nonresidents must have graduated from high school with a state approved diploma and be ranked in the upper two-thirds of their high school class; or have an ACT composite score of 17 or higher; or have a combined SAT score of 820 or higher. *Entrance tests:* College Board SAT or ACT composite with results sent directly to the Undergraduate and Recruitment Office. *For transfer students:* 2.0 minimum GPA; from 4-year accredited institution no maximum hours transfer credit; from 2-

YOUNGSTOWN STATE UNIVERSITY—*cont'd*

year institution all work completed for associate degree; correspondence/extension students evaluated individually.

College credit and advanced placement for postsecondary-level work completed in secondary school. College credit for extrainstitutional learning.

Tutoring available.

Degree Requirements: *For all associate degrees:* 64 credit hours; last 20 hours in residence. *For all baccalaureate degrees:* 124 credit hours; last 30 hours in residence; distribution requirements; demonstrated proficiency in English. *For all undergraduate degrees:* 2.0 GPA.

Fulfillment of some degree requirements and exemption from some beginning courses possible by passing departmental examinations, College Board CLEP, AP, other standardized test. *Grading system:* A–F; pass-fail; credit-no credit; withdraw (carries time limit).

Distinctive Educational Programs: Flexible meeting places and schedules, including off-campus centers (at varying locations in metropolitan area), weekend and evening classes. Combined baccalaureate and first-professional program in medicine through consortium. Special facilities for using telecommunications in the classroom. Interdisciplinary programs in American studies, Black studies, labor studies, urban studies. Facilities and programs for independent research, including honors programs, individual majors, tutorials.

ROTC: Army.

Degrees Conferred: 226 *associate*; 1,478 *baccalaureate*; 308 *master's*; 2 *doctorate*. Bachelor's degrees awarded in top five disciplines: education 314; business, management, marketing, and related support services 246; engineering 140; protective services/public administration 122; health professions and related clinical sciences 110. Master's degrees awarded: various disciplines 308. Doctorates awarded: education 2.

Fees and Other Expenses: *Full-time tuition per academic year 2008–09:* undergraduate resident $6,721, out-of-state $9,414; contact the university for current resident/nonresident graduate tuition and fees. *Room and board per academic year:* $7,090. *Books and supplies:* $1,140. *Other expenses:* $4,296.

Financial Aid: Aid from institutionally generated funds is provided on the basis of academic merit, financial need, athletic ability, other criteria.

Financial aid to full-time, first-time undergraduate students: 89% received some form of financial aid. Average amount of aid received: federal grants $3,499; Pell grants $3,104; other federal aid $833; state/local grants $1,602; institutional grants $3,623.

Departments and Teaching Staff: *Total instructional faculty:* 989. Degrees held by full-time faculty: doctorate 75.8%, master's 22.7%, professional 1%. 80.2% hold terminal degrees.

Enrollment: Total enrollment 13,704. Undergraduate 12,405 (full-time 79%; female 54%, male 46%). Graduate 1,299. Undergraduate transfer-in students 535.

Characteristics of Student Body: *Ethnic/racial makeup:* Black non-Hispanic: 15%; Asian or Pacific Islander: 1%; Hispanic: 2%; White non-Hispanic: 72%; unknown: 9%; nonresident alien 1%. *Age distribution:* number under 18: 132, 18–19: 3,077, 20–21: 2,904, 22–24: 2,397, 25–29: 2,397, 30–34: 729, 35–39: 453, 40–49: 580; 50–64: 219; 65 and over: 6.

International Students: 137 nonresident aliens enrolled fall 2008. Students from Europe, Asia, Latin America, Africa, Canada, Middle East. Programs available to aid students whose native language is not English: social and cultural. English as a Second Language Program. No financial aid specifically designated for international students.

Student Life: On-campus residence halls house 10 of student body. Residence halls and apartments for both males and females constitute 100% of such space. 1.3% of males join and live in fraternity housing; 9% of females join and live in sorority housing. *Intercollegiate athletics:* male: baseball, football, basketball, cross-country, golf, tennis, indoor track and field, outdoor track and field; female: basketball, cross-country, softball, tennis, golf, indoor track and field, outdoor track and field, soccer, swimming, volleyball. *Special regulations:* Registered cars permitted without restrictions. *Special services:* Learning resources centers including writing, math, reading and study skills; first-year student services; individual and group tutoring; Supplemental Instruction; counseling and testing; services for students with disabilities; career services; health services; minority student services; international services. *Student publications, radio: Jambar*, a biweekly newspaper; *Penguin Review*, an annual literary magazine; *The Neon*, an annual yearbook. Radio station WYSU broadcasts 24 hours a day. *Surrounding community:* Youngstown population 90,000. Pittsburgh (PA), 60 miles from campus, is nearest metropolitan area. Served by mass transit bus system.

Library Collections: 923,000 volumes. 217,435 government documents (separate collection); 847,199 microforms; 14,944 audiovisual materials; 9,700 periodical subscriptions (including electronic access). 20,216 recordings. Online catalog. Computer work stations available. Students have access to the Internet and online information retrieval services.

Most important special collections include Pacific Northwest Railroad Service Collection; Early Collection of Americana; Bliss Music Collection; Nursing Collection.

Buildings and Grounds: Campus area 160 acres.

Chief Executive Officer: Dr. David C. Sweet, President.

Address undergraduate admission inquiries to Susan R. Davis, Director of Undergraduate Admissions; graduate inquiries to Dr. Peter J. Kasvinsky, Dean, School of Graduate Studies.

Oklahoma

Bacone College

2299 Old Bacone Road
Muskogee, Oklahoma 74403-1597
Tel: (918) 683-4581 **E-mail:** admissions@bacone.edu
Fax: (918) 781-7416 **Internet:** www.bacone.edu

Institution Description: Bacone College is an independent institution related to the American Baptist Churches, U.S.A. The college maintains its commitment to serve Native Americans within a culturally diverse community. *Enrollment:* 958. *Degrees awarded:* Associate, baccalaureate.

Accreditation: *Regional:* NCA. *Professional*: nursing, radiography, teacher education

History: Established 1880; named Bacone Indian University 1n 1910. became Bacone College in 1938.

Institutional Structure: *Governing board:* Board of Trustees. Extrainstitutional representation: 25 trustees.

Calendar: Semesters. Academic year Aug. to May.

Admission: Rolling admissions plan. For fall acceptance, apply as early as Sept. of previous year, but not later than Aug. of year of enrollment. Early acceptance available. *Requirements:* Either graduation from accredited secondary school or GED. Recommend 4 units English, 2 lab science, 3 mathematics, 2 history, 1 citizenship skills, 3 additional units (electives). *Entrance tests:* ACT or SAT I.

Tutoring available. Developmental/remedial courses offered during regular academic year; no credit given.

Degree Requirements: *For all associate degrees:* 60 credit hours. *For all baccalaureate degrees:* 120 credit hours. *For all degrees:* 2.0 GPA;

Fulfillment of some degree requirements and exemption from some beginning courses possible by passing departmental examinations, College Board CLEP, DANTES, ACT PEP, AP. *Grading system:* A=F; withdraw (carries time limit and penalty).

Degrees Conferred: 75 *associate*: 58 *baccalaureate*. Bachelor's degrees awarded in top disciplines: business, management, marketing, and related support services 22; health professions and related clinical sciences 3.

Fees and Other Expenses: *Full-time tuition per academic year 2008–09:* $10,478. Various miscellaneous fees apply. *Room and board per academic year:* $7,000. *Books and supplies:* $2,000. *Other expenses:* $1,700.

Financial Aid: Aid from institutionally generated funds is provided on the basis of academic merit, financial need. Institution has a Program Participation Agreement with the U.S. Department of Education for eligible students to receive Pell Grants and, depending upon the agreement, other federal aid.

Financial aid to full-time, first-time undergraduate students: 86% received some form of financial aid. Average amount of aid received: federal grants $2,595; Pell grants $3,152; other federal aid $660; institutional grants $2,431.

Departments and Teaching Staff: *Total instructional faculty:* 84 (full-time 25, part-time 59). Total faculty with doctorate, first-professional, or other terminal degree: 18. Number of degrees held by full-time faculty: doctorate 18, master's 51, baccalaureate 15.

Enrollment: Total enrollment 958 (undergraduate). Transfer-in students 151.

Characteristics of Student Body: *Ethnic/racial makeup:* Black non-Hispanic: 245; American Indian or Alaska Native: 31%; Asian or Pacific Islander: 1%; Hispanic: 6%; White non-Hispanic: 24%; unknown 2%. *Age distribution:* number of 18–19: 154; 20–21: 182; 22–24: 146; 25–29: 81; 30–34: 45; 35–39: 10; 40–49: 62; 50–64: 26. 38% of student body attend summer sessions.

International Students: Programs available to aid students whose native language is not English: social. No financial aid specifically designated for international students.

Student Life: On-campus residence halls available. Freshmen and sophomores shall be residential students. Students receiving athletic scholarships and students receiving 50% scholarships are required to live in campus housing. Activities sponsored by Student Life and Associate Students of Bacone College. *Intercollegiate athletics:* male: baseball, basketball, cross-country, golf, tennis, track and field; female: basketball, cross-country, soccer, softball, tennis, track and field, volleyball. *Special services:* Learning Resources Center, medical services. Office of American Native Concerns. The college is located in Muskogee, historically known as the "Indian Capital of the World."

Library Collections: 4,000 bound periodical volumes; 7,000 volumes in Native American Collection; 1,000,000 online full-text documents; laptop computers and desktop computers available for student use.

Most important special collection is the Native American Collection.

Chief Executive Officer: Dr. Robert J. Duncan, Jr. President.

Address admission inquiries to Dr. James Stoutermire, Director of Admissions and Enrollment Management.

Cameron University

2800 West Gore Boulevard
Lawton, Oklahoma 73505-8377
Tel: (580) 581-2230 **E-mail:** admissions@cameron.edu
Fax: (580) 581-5514 **Internet:** www.cameron.edu

Institution Description: Cameron University is a state institution. *Enrollment:* 5,449. *Degrees awarded:* Associate, baccalaureate, master's.

Academic offerings subject to approval by statewide coordinating bodies Budget subject to approval by state governing boards.

Accreditation: *Regional:* NCA. *Professional*: music, nursing

History: Established as Cameron State School of Agriculture 1908; changed name to Cameron Agriculture College and offered first instruction at postsecondary level 1927; awarded first degree (associate) 1929; changed name to Cameron State Agricultural College 1970, Cameron College 1971; adopted present name 1974.

Institutional Structure: *Governing board:* Board of Regents for the Oklahoma State University and the Agricultural and Mechanical Colleges. Representation: 7 members (appointed by governor of Oklahoma). *Composition of institution:* Administrators 109. Academic affairs headed by vice president of academic affairs. Management/business/finances directed by vice president for business and finance. Full-time instructional faculty 155. Academic governance body, Faculty Council, meets an average of 10 times per year.

Calendar: Semesters. Academic year Aug. July. Freshmen admitted Aug., Jan., June. Degrees conferred and formal commencement May. Summer session of 1 term from June to July.

Characteristics of Freshmen: 99% of applicants admitted. 65% of applicants admitted and enrolled.

69% (584 students) submitted ACT scores. *25th percentile*: ACT Composite 17, ACT English 16, ACT Math 16. *75th percentile*: ACT Composite 22, ACT English 21, ACT Math 23.

28% of entering freshmen expected to graduate within 5 years. 79% of freshmen from Oklahoma. Freshmen from 49 states and 14 foreign countries.

Admission: Rolling admissions plan. For fall acceptance, apply as early as Jan., but not later than Aug. 15. Early acceptance available. *Requirements:* Graduation from accredited secondary school or GED. Minimum GPA 2.0. *Entrance tests:* ACT Composite 20. For foreign students TOEFL. *For transfer students:* 2.0 minimum GPA; from 4-year accredited institution 98 hours maximum transfer credit; from 2-year accredited institution 32 hours.

College credit and advanced placement for postsecondary-level work completed in secondary school. College credit for extrainstitutional learning.

Tutoring available. Remedial courses offered in summer session and regular academic year; credit given.

Degree Requirements: *For all associate degrees:* 64 credit hours; 15 semester hours in residence. *For all baccalaureate degrees:* 128 credit hours; 30 semester hours in residence. *For all undergraduate degrees:* 2.0 GPA; 4 semester hours physical education; distribution requirements.

Fulfillment of some degree requirements and exemption from some beginning courses possible by passing departmental examinations, College Board CLEP, AP. *Grading system:* A–F; withdraw (carries time limit).

Distinctive Educational Programs: *For undergraduates:* Evening classes. Cooperative baccalaureate. *Other distinctive programs:* Servicemembers

CAMERON UNIVERSITY—*cont'd*

Opportunity College. Allied Health with Western Oklahoma State College, University of Oklahoma, and Great Plains Technology Center. Online programs in general education and the MBA. Special programs designed for military personnel.

ROTC: Army.

Degrees Conferred: 191 *associate;* 527 *baccalaureate*; 102 *master's*. Bachelor's degrees awarded in top five disciplines: business/marketing 129; interdisciplinary studies 82; education 75; security and protective services 71; computer and information sciences 39. Master's degrees awarded: business/marketing 27; education 59; psychology 14.

Fees and Other Expenses: *Full-time tuition per academic year 2008–09:* $4,020 in-state resident, out-of-state $9,742. *Room and board per academic year:* $7,215. *Required fees:* $1,080. *Books and supplies:* $1,280. *Other expenses:* $2,642. Contact the university for current graduate tuition and any other applicable fees.

Financial Aid: Aid from institutionally generated funds provided on the basis of academic merit, financial need, athletic ability, other criteria.

Financial aid to full-time, first-time undergraduate students: 84% of students received some form of aid. Average amount of aid received: federal grants $3,436; Pell grants $3,147; other federal aid $733; state/local grants $1,942; institutional grants $2,627.

Departments and Teaching Staff: *Total instructional faculty:* 313 (full-time 155, part-time 158). Total faculty with doctorate, first-professional, or other terminal degree: 138. Student/faculty ratio: 20:1.

Enrollment: Total enrollment 5,449. Undergraduate 5,068 (full-time 84%; female 60%, male 40%). Graduate 381 (full-time 34%). Undergraduate transfer-in students 161.

Characteristics of Student Body: *Ethnic/racial makeup:* Black non-Hispanic: 15%; American Indian or Alaska Native: 8%; Asian or Pacific Islander: 3%; Hispanic: 8%; White non-Hispanic: 55%; unknown 5%; nonresident alien 5%. *Age distribution:* number under 18 128; 20–21: 1,036; 22–24: 907; 25–29: 846; 30–34: 502; 35–39: 153; 40–49: 466; 50–64: 128, 65 and over: 17.

International Students: 275 nonresident aliens enrolled fall 2008. Students from Europe, Asia, Latin America, Africa, Canada, Australia, Middle East. Programs available to aid students whose native language is not English: English as a Second Language Program. No financial aid specifically designated for international students.

Student Life: On-campus residence halls house 1% of student body. Residence halls for males and females. *Intercollegiate athletics:* male: baseball, basketball, football, golf, tennis; female: basketball, softball, tennis. *Special regulations:* Registered cars with decals permitted. Curfew and quiet hours. Dormitory visitation allowed. *Special services:* Learning Resources Center, medical services. *Student publications: Cameron Collegian*, a weekly newspaper; *Wichita*, a yearbook. *Surrounding community:* Lawton population 110,000. Oklahoma City, 100 miles from campus, is nearest metropolitan area. Served by airport 5 miles from campus.

Library Collections: 346,000 volumes including bound books, serial backfiles, electronic documents, and government documents not in separate collections. Online catalog. 46,000 microforms; 7,000 audiovisual materials; 17,220 periodicals including via electronic access. Computer work stations available. Students have access to the Internet at no charge.

Most important holdings include collections on Western History, Native American History.

Buildings and Grounds: Campus area 390 acres.

Chief Executive Officer: Dr. Cynthia S. Ross, President.

Address undergraduate admission inquiries to Zoe DuRant, Director of Admissions; graduate inquiries to Dr. David Carl, Graduate School Admissions.

East Central University

1100 East 14th Street
Ada, Oklahoma 74820
Tel: (580) 332-8000 **E-mail:** admissions@ecok.edu
Fax: (580) 819-5432 **Internet:** www.ecok.edu

Institution Description: East Central University is a state institution. *Enrollment:* 4,361. *Degrees awarded:* Baccalaureate, master's.

Accreditation: *Regional:* NCA. *Professional*: business, medical record administration, music, nursing, social work, rehabilitation counseling, teacher education

History: Established as East Central State Normal School and offered first instruction at postsecondary level 1909; changed name to East Central State Teachers College and awarded first degree (baccalaureate) 1920; changed name to East Central State College 1939; changed name to East Central Oklahoma State University 1974; became East Central University 1985.

Institutional Structure: *Governing board:* Board of Regents for Oklahoma Colleges. Representation:8 regents (appointed by governor of Oklahoma), state superintendent of public instruction. 1 ex officio. All voting. *Composition of institution:* Administrators 15. Academic affairs headed by vice president for academic affairs. Management/business/finances directed by vice president for fiscal affairs. Full-time instructional faculty 191.

Calendar: Semesters. Academic year Aug. to May. Degrees conferred May, July. Formal commencement May. Summer session June to July.

Characteristics of Freshmen: 792 applicants (421 female, 421 male). 96% of applicants accepted. 73% of accepted applicants enrolled full-time.

60% (615 students) submitted ACT scores; *25th percentile*: ACT Composite 18, ACT English 17, ACT Math 18. *75th percentile*: ACT Composite 23, ACT English 23, ACT Math 22.

97% of freshmen from Oklahoma. Freshmen from 21 states and 22 foreign countries.

Admission: Rolling admissions plan. *Requirements:* Graduation from secondary school; 2.7 GPA or upper ⅔ of class; ACT score of 20. *Entrance tests:* College Board SAT or ACT composite. For foreign students TOEFL.

Degree Requirements: 124 semester hours; 2.00 GPA; 30 hours in residence. *Grading system:* A–F.

Distinctive Educational Programs: *For undergraduates:* Honors program.

Degrees Conferred: 701 *baccalaureate; 262 master's.*

Fees and Other Expenses: *Tuition per academic year 2008–09:* $3,578 undergraduate resident, $8,674 nonresident. Contact the university for current graduate resident/nonresident tuition/fees. *Room and board per academic year:* $4,204. *Books and supplies:* 900.

Financial Aid: Aid from institutionally generated funds is provided on the basis of academic merit, financial need, athletic ability, other criteria. Institution has a Program Participation Agreement with the U.S. Department of Education for eligible students to receive Pell Grants and, depending upon the agreement, other federal aid.

Financial aid to full-time, first-time undergraduate students: 59% received some form of financial aid. Average amount of aid received: federal grants $1,969; state/local grants $1,014; institutional grants $936; loans $2,180.

Departments and Teaching Staff: *Total instructional faculty:* 203 FTE. Student/faculty ratio: 19:1. Degrees held by full-time faculty: doctorate 70%, master's 30%. 70% hold terminal degrees.

Enrollment: Total enrollment 4,361. Undergradaute 3,536 (full-time 82%; female 59%, male 41%). Graduate 825 (full-time 27%). Undergraduate transfer-in students 377.

Characteristics of Student Body: *Ethnic/racial makeup:* Black non-Hispanic: 4%; American Indian or Alaska Native: 21%; Asian or Pacific Islander: 9%; Hispanic: 3%; White non-Hispanic: 65%; unknown: 4%; nonresident alien 3%.

International Students: 132 nonresident aliens enrolled fall 2008. Students from Europe, Asia, Central and South America, Africa, Canada, Australia. No programs to aid students whose native language is not English. No financial aid specifically designated for international students.

Student Life: On-campus residence halls available. *Special regulations:* All single undergraduate students under 21 years of age must live in college residence halls unless they live with their parents. *Special services:* Placement services, health services. *Student publications: East Central University Journal*, a weekly newspaper; *Originals*, a magazine published annually; *The Pesagi*, a yearbook. *Surrounding community:* Ada is a commercial, industrial, service, and medical center for a substantial metropolitan and rural area located 100 miles southeast of Oklahoma City.

Library Collections: 215,000 volumes. 1,200 serial subscriptions. Computer work stations available campus-wide. Students have access to online information retrieval services and the Internet.

Special collections include Gutenburg Bible facsimile; Nuremberg Trial Transcripts; Oklahoma regional materials.

Buildings and Grounds: Campus area 140 acres.

Chief Executive Officer: Dr. Robert S. Raffes, President.

Address admission inquiries to Pamela Armstrong, Director of Admissions.

Langston University

102 Page Hall
Langston, Oklahoma 73050
Tel: (405) 466-2231 **E-mail:** admissions@lunet.edu
Fax: (405) 466-3381 **Internet:** www.lunet.edu

Institution Description: Langston University is a state institution and land-grant college. *Enrollment:* 2,754. *Degrees awarded:* Associate, baccalaureate, master's, doctorate.

Academic offerings subject to approval by statewide coordinating bodies. Budget subject to approval by state governing boards. Member of International Studies Consortium.

Accreditation: *Regional:* NCA. *Professional*: teacher education

History: Established as Colored Agricultural and Normal University, chartered, and offered first instruction at postsecondary level 1897; awarded first degree (baccalaureate) 1901; adopted present name 1941. *See* Zella J. Black Patterson, *Langston University: A History* (Norman, OK: University of Oklahoma Press, 1979) for further information.

Institutional Structure: *Governing board:* Board of Regents for the Oklahoma State University and the Agricultural and Mechanical Colleges. Representation:8 members (appointed by governor of Oklahoma); president of State Board of Agriculture. 1 ex officio. All voting. *Composition of institution:* Administrators 14. Academic affairs headed by vice president of academic affairs. Management/business/finances directed by vice president for fiscal and administrative affairs. Full-time instructional faculty 115. Academic governance body, Academic Policies Committee, meets an average of 12 times per year.

Calendar: Semesters. Academic year Aug. to May. Freshmen admitted Aug., Jan., May. Degrees conferred and formal commencement May, July. Summer session from May to July.

Characteristics of Freshmen: Freshmen from 20 states and 5 foreign countries.

Admission: Rolling admissions plan. Early acceptance available. *Requirements:* Either graduation from accredited secondary school or GED. *Entrance tests:* ACT Composite. For foreign students TOEFL. *For transfer students:* Out-of-state students 2.0 minimum GPA; 2.0 minimum GPA; from 4-year accredited institution maximum transfer credit limited only by residence requirement; from 2-year accredited institution 64 hours.

College credit and advanced placement for postsecondary-level work completed in secondary school.

Tutoring available. Noncredit developmental courses offered in summer session and regular academic year.

Degree Requirements: *For all associate degrees:* 64 credit hours. *For all baccalaureate degrees:* 124 credit hours. *For all degrees:* 2.0 GPA; 36 weeks and last 30 hours in residence; 4 semesters physical education; distribution requirements.

Fulfillment of some degree requirements and exemption from some beginning courses possible by passing departmental examinations. *Grading system:* A=F; pass; withdraw (carries time limit).

Distinctive Educational Programs: Work-experience programs, including cooperative education, internships. Flexible meeting places and schedules including off-campus centers (at Oklahoma City, 45 miles away from main institution; at Tulsa, 90 miles away) and evening classes. Cooperative baccalaureate program in medical technology with approved hospitals. Special facilities for using telecommunications in the classroom. Interdepartmental program in Black studies. Preprofessional programs in dentistry, medicine, veterinary science.

Degrees Conferred: 14 *associate*; 320 *baccalaureate*; 41 *master's*; 7 *doctorate*. Bachelor's degrees awarded in top five disciplines: business, management, marketing, and related support services 86; health professions and related clinical sciences 57; psychology 45; education 41; liberal arts/general studies 31. Master's degrees awarded: education 25; health professions 16. Doctorates awarded: health professions 7.

Fees and Other Expenses: *Full-time tuition per academic year 2008–09:* $3,827 resident, $9,407 nonresident; contact the university for current graduate tuition and any other applicable fees. *Room and board per academic year:* $7,625. *Books and supplies:* $1,287. *Other expenses:* #2,221.

Financial Aid: Aid from institutionally generated funds is provided on the basis of academic merit, athletic ability. Institution has a Program Participation Agreement with the U.S. Department of Education for eligible students to receive Pell Grants and, depending upon the agreement, other federal aid.

Financial aid to full-time, first-time undergraduate students: 88% received some form of aid. Average amount of aid received: federal grants $3,424; Pell grants $3,153; other federal aid $1,697; state/local grants $851; institutional grants $3,491.

Departments and Teaching Staff: *Total instructional faculty:* 162. Degrees held by full-time faculty: doctorate 75%, master's 25%. 75% hold terminal degrees.

Enrollment: Total enrollment 2,734. Undergraduate 2,479 (full-time 845; female 59%, male 41%). Graduate 255 (full-time 69%). Undergraduate transfer-in students 252.

Characteristics of Student Body: *Ethnic/racial makeup:* Black non-Hispanic: 83%; American Indian or Alaska Native: 2%; Asian or Pacific Islander 1%; Hispanic: 1%; White non-Hispanic: 11%; nonresident alien 1%. *Age distribution:* number under 18: 5; 18–19: 728; 20–21: 606; 22–24: 571; 101; 25–29: 257; 30–34: 101; 35–39: 44; 40–49: 66; 50–64: 20.

International Students: 27 nonresident aliens enrolled fall 2008. No programs available to aid students whose native language is not English. No financial aid specifically designated for international students.

Student Life: On-campus residence halls house 50% of student body. Residence halls for males constitute 60% of such space, for females 40%. 10% of student body live off campus in institutionally controlled apartments. 5% of married students request institutional housing. 2% are so housed. *Intercollegiate athletics:* male: baseball, basketball, football, track; female: basketball, track. *Special regulations:* Cars permitted without restrictions. Quiet hours. Residence hall visitation from 6pm to 11pm. *Special services:* Learning Resources Center, medical services, campus transportation system. *Student publications, radio: Gazette*, a weekly newspaper. *Lion*, a yearbook. Radio station KALU broadcasts 64 hours per week. *Surrounding community:* Langston. Dallas (TX), 250 miles from campus, is nearest metropolitan area.

Library Collections: 155,000 volumes. 10,000 government documents; 3,275 microforms; 900 audiovisual materials; 665 current periodical subscriptions.

Chief Executive Officer: Dr. JoAnn W. Haysbert, President.

Address admission inquiries to Gayle Robertson, Director Admissions.

Mid-America Christian University

3500 S.W. 119th Street
Oklahoma City, Oklahoma 73170
Tel: (405) 691-3800 **E-mail:** admissions@macu.edu
Fax: (405) 692-3165 **Internet:** www.macu.edu

Institution Description: Mid-America Christian University, formerly named Mid-America Bible College, is a private college affiliated with the Church of God. *Enrollment:* 771. *Degrees awarded:* Associate, baccalaureate.

Accreditation: *Regional:* NCA.

History: Established as South Texas Bible Institute, chartered, incorporated, and offered first instruction at postsecondary level 1953; became 4-year institution and changed name to Gulf-Coast Bible College 1955; awarded first degree (baccalaureate) 1957; changed name to Mid-America Bible College and moved to Oklahoma City 1985.

Institutional Structure: *Governing board:* Board of Trustees. Extrainstitutional representation: 25 trustees; institutional representation: president of the college. 1 ex officio. All voting. *Composition of institution:* Administrators 7. Academic affairs headed by academic dean. Management/business/finances directed by business manager. Full-time instructional faculty 17. Academic governance body, the faculty, meets an average of 9 times per year.

Calendar: Semesters. Academic year Aug. to June. Freshmen admitted Aug., Jan. Degrees conferred and formal commencement May. Summer session of 4 terms from May to July.

Characteristics of Freshmen: 98% of applicants accepted. 85% of accepted applicants enrolled.

28% of freshmen expected to graduate within 5 years. 63% of freshmen from Oklahoma. Freshmen from 30 states and 7 foreign countries.

Admission: Rolling admissions plan. For fall acceptance, apply as early as senior year of secondary school, but not later than Sept. 1 of year of enrollment. *Requirements:* Either graduation from accredited secondary school or GED. Recommend 4 units English, 2 foreign language or mathematics and/or science, 2½ social studies, 2 mathematics, 2 science, ½ academic electives. *Entrance tests:* SAT or ACT composite. For foreign students TOEFL. *For transfer students:* 2.0 minimum GPA; from 4-year accredited institution 90 hours maximum transfer credit; from 2-year accredited institution 64 hours; correspondence/extension students 18 hours.

College credit and advanced placement for postsecondary-level work completed in secondary school and for extrainstitutional learning.

Developmental courses offered during regular academic year; credit given.

Degree Requirements: *For all associate degrees:* 64 credit hours; 4 semesters of Christian service. *For all baccalaureate degrees:* 124 credit hours (teacher education 135 hours with a 2.5 cumulative GPA in the major); 6 semesters of Christian service; exit competency examination in writing. *For all degrees:* 2.0 GPA; 2 terms in residence; chapel attendance 2 times weekly; 2 hours physical education; core requirements.

Fulfillment of some degree requirements and exemption from some beginning courses possible by passing departmental examinations, College Board CLEP, AP. *Grading system:* A–F; pass-fail.

Distinctive Educational Programs: Internships, in-service training, field experience. Individualized courses for qualified seniors. *Other distinctive programs:* Continuing education for clergymen and church leaders. Teacher Education Program accredited by the state of Oklahoma. Leadership Education for Adult Development. Accelerated degree completion program earn a B.S. in management and ethics. Online Internet course offered; pilot program offered at a special price.

MID-AMERICA CHRISTIAN UNIVERSITY—*cont'd*

Degrees Conferred: 1 *associate;* 158. Bachelor's degrees awarded in top disciplines: business, management, marketing, and related support services 61; computer and information sciences 3; education 11; liberal arts/general studies 3; philosophy/religion/theology 26; protective services/public administration 34.

Fees and Other Expenses: *Full-time tuition per academic year 2008–09:* contact the university for current information regarding tuition, fees, housing, and other costs.

Financial Aid: Aid from institutionally generated funds is provided on the basis of academic merit, financial need. Institution has a Program Participation Agreement with the U.S. Department of Education for eligible students to receive Pell Grants and, depending upon the agreement, other federal aid.

Financial aid to full-time, first-time undergraduate students: 100% received some form of financial aid. Average amount of aid received: federal grants $2,568; state/local grants $2,918; institutional grants $3,142; loans $5,252.

Departments and Teaching Staff: *Total instructional faculty:* 27.64 FTE. Degrees held by full-time faculty: doctorate 47%, master's 94%. 47% hold terminal degrees.

Enrollment: Total enrollment 771.

Characteristics of Student Body: *Ethnic/racial makeup:* number of Black non-Hispanic: 66; American Indian or Alaska Native: 45; Hispanic: 24; White non-Hispanic: 551; unknown: 10.

International Students: No programs available to aid students whose native language is not English. No financial aid specifically designated for international students.

Student Life: On-campus residence halls house 42% of student body. *Intramural athletics:* flag football, volleyball, softball, sand volleyball. *Special regulations:* Dress code prescribes a modest appearance. Curfews from Mon.–Thurs. and Sat. midnight to 6am; Fri. and Sun. 1am to 6am. *Special services:* Learning Resources Center, medical services. *Student publications: Clarion*, a yearbook; *Messenger*, a monthly newspaper.

Library Collections: 50,000 volumes including bound books, serial backfiles, electronic documents, and government documents not in separate collections. 47,575 electronic titles. Online and card catalogs. Current serial subscriptions: 250 paper, 7 electronic databases. 1,520 recordings; 15 compact discs. 10 computer work stations. Students have access to the Internet at no charge.

Most important special holdings include Charles Ewing Brown Collection (books and periodicals); Kenneth E. Jones Collection (books); Curriculum Collection (books and periodicals); Faculty Theses.

Chief Executive Officer: Rev. John D. Fozaro, President.

Address admission inquiries to Haley Hope, Director of Admissions.

Northeastern State University

600 North Grand
Tahlequah, Oklahoma 74464-2399
Tel: (918) 456-5511 **E-mail:** nsuinfo@nsuok.edu
Fax: (918) 458-2342 **Internet:** www.nsuok.edu

Institution Description: Northeastern State University (Northeastern State College until 1975) is a state institution. *Enrollment:* 8,771. *Degrees awarded:* Baccalaureate, master's, first-professional, doctorate.

Academic offerings subject to approval by statewide coordinating bodies. Budget subject to approval by state governing boards.

Accreditation: *Regional:* NCA. *Professional*: business, dietetics, nursing, optometry, social work, speech-language pathology, teacher education

History: Established as Cherokee Female Seminary 1846; chartered as Northeastern State Normal School, became coeducational, and offered first instruction at postsecondary level 1909; changed name to Northeastern State Teacher's College and became 4-year institution 1919; awarded first degree (baccalaureate) 1921; changed name to Northeastern State College 1939; adopted present name 1975.

Institutional Structure: *Governing board:* Oklahoma State Regents for Higher Education. Representation: 8 regents (appointed by governor of Oklahoma), state superintendent of public instruction. 1 ex officio. All voting. *Composition of institution:* Administrators 15. Academic affairs headed by president. Management/business/finances directed by director of business affairs. Full-time instructional faculty 306. Academic governance body, Curriculum and Education Policies Committee, meets an average of 12 times per year.

Calendar: Semesters. Academic year Aug. to May. Freshmen admitted Aug., Jan., June, July. Degrees conferred and formal commencement May. Summer sessions from June to July.

Characteristics of Freshmen: 2,544 applicants (1,399 female, 1,005 male). 70% of applicants admitted. 61% of applicants admitted and enrolled full-time.

92% (1,034 students) submitted ACT scores. *25th percentile*: ACT Composite 18, ACT English 17, ACT Math 16. *75th percentile*: ACT Composite 23, ACT English 23, ACT Math 24.

94% of freshmen from Oklahoma. Freshmen from 9 states and 18 foreign countries.

Admission: Rolling admissions plan. For fall acceptance, apply as early as June after junior year of secondary school, but not later than 1 week after the end of registration. Early acceptance available. *Requirements:* Graduation from accredited secondary school. In-state residents must have 2.7 GPA and be ranked in upper one-half of secondary school class or have ACT score among upper three-fourths of secondary school seniors. Out-of-state students must have 2.7 GPA, or be ranked in upper half of secondary school class, or have ACT score among upper half of secondary school seniors. GED accepted. *Entrance tests:* ACT composite. For foreign students TOEFL. *For transfer students:* 2.0 minimum GPA, depending on credit hours transferred; from 4-year accredited institution maximum transfer credit limited only by residence requirement; from 2-year accredited institution 64 credit hours; correspondence / extension students 31 hours.

College credit for extrainstitutional learning. Tutoring available. Developmental courses: no credit; offered in summer session and regular academic year.

Degree Requirements: 120 credit hours; 2.0 GPA; 30 hours in residence; general education requirements.

Fulfillment of some degree requirements and exemption from some beginning courses possible by passing departmental examinations, College Board CLEP. *Grading system:* A=F; withdraw (deadline after which pass-fail is appended to withdraw).

Distinctive Educational Programs: Flexible meeting places and schedules, including weekend and evening classes. Special facilities for using telecommunications in the classroom. Interdisciplinary program in Indian studies. College of Optometry on main campus.

ROTC: Army.

Degrees Conferred: 1,525 *baccalaureate;* 261 *master's;* 27 *first-professional:* optometry. Bachelor's degrees awarded in top five disciplines: education 907; business/marketing; security and protective services 104; psychology 64; public administration and social services 60. Master's degrees awarded: area and ethnic studies 1; business/marketing 17; communications/journalism 10; education 138; engineering technologies 3; English 9; health professions 13; library science 12; parks and recreation 6; psychology 21; security and protective services 10. First-professional degrees awarded: optometry 27.

Fees and Other Expenses: *Full-time tuition per academic year 2008–09:* undergraduate resident $4,155, nonresident $10,245; contact the university for current graduate and first-professional tuition and any other applicable fees. *Room and board per academic year:* $4,872. *Books and supplies:* $1,000. *Other expenses:* $2,504.

Financial Aid: Aid from institutionally generated funds is provided on the basis of academic merit, athletic ability, financial need, other criteria.

Financial aid to full-time, first-time undergraduate students: 92% of students received some form of aid. Average amount of aid received: federal grants $3,548; Pell grants $3,047; other federal aid $581; state/local grants $2,855; institutional grants $2,213.

Departments and Teaching Staff: *Total instructional faculty:* 459 (full-time 306, part-time 153). Student/faculty ratio: 23:1.

Enrollment: Total enrollment 8,771. Undergraduate 7,613 (full-time 73%; female 61%, male 39%). Graduate 1,098 (full-time 35%). Undergraduate transfer-in students 925.

Characteristics of Student Body: *Ethnic/racial makeup:* Black non-Hispanic: 5%; American Indian or Alaska Native: 30%; Asian or Pacific Islander: 1%; Hispanic: 2%; White non-Hispanic: 58%; nonresident alien 3%. *Age distribution:* number under 18: 89; 18–19: 1,542; 20–21: 1,958; 22–24: 1,961; 25–29: 1,173; 30–34: 681; 35–39: 425; 40–49: 482; 50–64: 178; 65 and over: 10.

International Students: 263 nonresident aliens enrolled fall 2008. Students from Europe, Asia, Central and South America, Africa, Canada, Australia, Middle East, No programs available to aid students whose native language is not English. No financial aid specifically designated for international students.

Student Life: On-campus residence halls house 16% of student body. *Intercollegiate athletics:* male: baseball, basketball, football, golf, soccer; female: basketball, softball, tennis. *Special regulations:* Cars permitted without restrictions. Quiet hours. Residence hall visitation 6am to midnight Wed., Fri., Sat.; 1pm to 8pm Sun. *Special services:* Learning Resources Center, medical services. *Student publications: The Northeastern*, a weekly newspaper. *Surrounding community:* Tahlequah population 16,000. Tulsa, 72 miles from campus, is nearest metropolitan area.

Library Collections: 466,256 volumes. 178,668 microforms; 4,942 audiovisual materials; 5,337 current periodicals. Students have access to online information retrieval services and the Internet.

Most important special collections Indian Territory Documents and Resources (5 tribes); Indian Territory Genealogical Society Library.

Buildings and Grounds: Campus area 200 acres.

Chief Executive Officer: Dr. Larry Williams, President.

Address admission inquiries to Admissions and Records.

College of Arts and Sciences

Degree Programs Offered: *Baccalaureate* in art, English, foreign languages, journalism, mathematics, music, natural sciences, physical sciences, social sciences, speech-drama, vision sciences; *first-professional* in optometry; *master's* in criminal justice. Certificates also awarded.

Admission: *For first-professional:* 66 semester hours of preprofessional courses, 2.7 GPA, OCAT.

Degree Requirements: *For first-professional:* 147 credit hours, 48 semester hours in residence, 2.0 GPA, baccalaureate degree from 4 year professional optometry curriculum.

Distinctive Educational Programs: Cooperative baccalaureate in medical technology with affiliated hospitals. Preprofessional programs in allied health fields, dentistry, dietetics, engineering, medicine, nursing, optometry, pharmacy, veterinary medicine. Internships for qualified secondary school students. Animal care facility. Aquatic laboratory. Christian School Study Greenhouses. Mobile environment laboratory. Nature school and sanctuary. State Academy of Science Library. State Ornithological Society Library. Sycamore Springs underground laboratory.

College of Behavioral Sciences

Degree Programs Offered: *Baccalaureate* in bilingual teacher education, early childhood education, health and physical education, junior college education, health and physical education, junior college education, learning disabilities, library media, mental retardation, speech and hearing therapy, speech pathology and audiology; *master's* in counseling, junior college teaching, school administration, secondary education, special education; *baccalaureate, master's* in elementary education, psychology, reading. Certificates also given.

Distinctive Educational Programs: Interdisciplinary programs in elementary education, junior college teaching; secondary education.

College of Business and Industry

Degree Programs Offered: *Baccalaureate* in accounting, business education, economics, finance, home economics, industrial arts, management, marketing, office administration; *master's* in tribal management; *baccalaureate, master's* in business administration, industrial technology. Certificates also awarded.

Northwestern Oklahoma State University

709 Oklahoma Boulevard
Alva, Oklahoma 73717-2799
Tel: (580) 327-1700 **E-mail:** recruit@nwosu.edu
Fax: (580) 327-1881 **Internet:** www.nwosu.edu

Institution Description: Northwestern Oklahoma State University (Northwestern State College until 1974) is a state institution. *Enrollment:* 2,074. *Degrees awarded:* Baccalaureate, master's.

Academic offerings subject to approval by statewide coordinating bodies. Budget offerings subject to approval by statewide coordinating bodies.

Accreditation: *Regional:* NCA. *Professional*: nursing, teacher education

History: Established as Northwestern Territorial Normal School, chartered, and offered first instruction at postsecondary level 1897; changed name to Northwestern State Normal School 1907; became 4-year institution and changed name to Northwestern State Teacher's College 1919; awarded first degree (baccalaureate) 1921; changed name to Northwestern State College 1939; adopted present name 1974; branch campuses created at Enid and Woodward 1996.

Institutional Structure: *Governing board:* Board of Regents of Oklahoma Colleges. Extrainstitutional representation: 9 regents, including state superintendent of public instruction. 1 ex officio. All voting. *Composition of institution:* Administrators 3. Academic affairs headed by executive vice president. Management/business/finances directed by vice president for administration. Full-time instructional faculty 85. Academic governance body, Faculty Senate, meets an average of 6 times per year.

Calendar: Semesters. Academic year Aug. to May. Freshmen admitted Aug., Jan., May. Degrees conferred and formal commencement May. Summer session from June to July.

Characteristics of Freshmen: 590 applicants (female 299, male 391). 100% of applicants admitted. 64% of applicants admitted and enrolled full-time.

9% (19 students) submitted SAT scores; 92% (217 students) submitted ACT scores. *25th percentile*: ACT Composite 17. *75th percentile*: ACT Composite 22.

35% entering freshmen expected to graduate within 5 years. 80% of freshmen from Oklahoma. Freshmen from 31 states and 21 foreign countries.

Admission: Rolling admissions plan. Apply by end of registration for semester in which admission is sought. Early acceptance available. *Requirements:* Graduation from accredited secondary school with 4 units of English, 2 laboratory sciences, 3 mathematics, 2 history; 2.0 GPA and in upper 50% of graduating class, or ACT composite score of 20. *Entrance tests:* in-state residents ACT composite, out-of-state students SAT accepted. *For transfer students:* 2.0 minimum GPA depending on the amount of transfer credit; from 4-year accredited institution 94 hours maximum transfer credit; from 2-year accredited institution 64 hours.

College credit and advanced placement for postsecondary-level work completed in secondary school. College credit for USAFI/DANTES and for extrainstitutional learning.

Tutoring available. Developmental courses offered in summer session and regular academic year; institutional credit given; not applicable toward degree.

Degree Requirements: 124 credit hours; 2.0 GPA; 30 semester hours in residence; general education requirements; demonstrated proficiency in English.

Fulfillment of some degree requirements and exemption from some beginning courses possible by passing departmental examinations, College Board CLEP subject examinations. *Grading system:* A=F; pass-fail; withdraw.

Distinctive Educational Programs: Evening classes. Accelerated degree programs. Preprofessional programs in agriculture, animal sciences and industry, business administration, dentistry, engineering, industrial technology, law enforcement, medicine, nursing, optometry, osteopathic medicine, pharmacy, physicians associate, wildlife ecology. Facilities and programs for independent research, including honors program, individual majors, tutorials.

Degrees Conferred: 320 *baccalaureate*; 62 *master's*. Bachelor's degrees awarded in top five disciplines: business/marketing 70; education 67; health professions 57; psychology 36; agriculture 29. Master's degrees awarded: education 42; personal and military services; psychology 20.

Fees and Other Expenses: *Full-time tuition per academic year 2006–07:* undergraduate resident $4,247, nonresident $10,478; contact the university for current graduate tuition and other applicable fees. *Room and board per academic year:* $3,580. *Books and supplies:* $1,200. *Other expenses:* $2,700.

Financial Aid: Aid from institutionally generated funds is provided on the basis of academic merit, financial need, athletic ability, participation. Financial aid to full-time, first-time undergraduate students: 95% received some form of aid. Average amount of aid received: federal grants $3,404; Pell grants $3,054; other federal aid $773; state/local grants $2,715; institutional grants $2,176.

Departments and Teaching Staff: *Total instructional faculty:* 156 (full-time 85, part-time71). Student/faculty ratio: 17:1. Degrees held by full-time faculty: doctorate 54%, baccalaureate 2%, professional 44%.

Enrollment: Total enrollment 2,074. Undergraduate 1,836 (full-time 78%; female 57%, male 43%). Graduate 238 (full-time 29%). Undergraduate transfer-in students 258.

Characteristics of Student Body: *Ethnic/racial makeup:* Black non-Hispanic: 5%; American Indian or Alaska Native: 5%; Hispanic 4%; White non-Hispanic: 84%; nonresident alien 1%. *Age distribution:* number under 18: 17; 18–19: 390; 20–21: 493; 22–24: 510; 25–29: 202; 30–34: 100; 35–39: 73; 40–49: 106; 50–64: 31.

International Students: 21 nonresident aliens enrolled fall 2008. No programs available to aid students whose native language is not English. No financial aid specifically designated for international students.

Student Life: On-campus residence halls house 20% of student body. Residence halls for males constitute 55% of such space, for females 45%. *Intercollegiate athletics:* male: baseball, basketball, football, golf, track; female: basketball, golf, softball, track. *Special regulations:* Registered cars permitted without restrictions. *Special services:* Learning Resources Center, medical services. *Student publications: Northwestern News*, a weekly student newspaper. *Surrounding community:* Alva population 5,500. Oklahoma City, 150 miles from campus, is nearest metropolitan area. Served by airport 2 miles from campus.

Library Collections: 127,500 volumes. Online catalog. Current periodical subscriptions: 556 paper; 4 microform; 3,587 via electronic access. 786 recordings. 209 compact discs. Computer work stations available. Students have access to online information retrieval systems and the Internet.

Most important special holdings include collections on education, psychology, and social science.

Buildings and Grounds: Campus area 360 acres with 29 buildings.

Chief Executive Officer: Dr. Janet Cunningham, President.

Address undergraduate admission inquiries to Matt Adair, Director of Recruitment; graduate inquires to Dr. Rodney Murrow, Director of Graduate Studies.

Oklahoma Baptist University

500 West University
Shawnee, Oklahoma 74801
Tel: (405) 275-2850 **E-mail:** admissions@okbu.edu
Fax: (405) 878-2046 **Internet:** www.okbu.edu

Institution Description: Oklahoma Baptist University is a private institution affiliated with the Oklahoma Baptist General Convention. *Enrollment:* 1,769. *Degrees awarded:* Associate, baccalaureate.

Accreditation: *Regional:* NCA. *Professional*: business, music, nursing, teacher education

History: Established as Oklahoma Baptist College 1906; chartered 1910; offered first instruction at postsecondary level and awarded first degree (baccalaureate) 1911; adopted present name 1921. *See* James Newton Owens, *Annals of O.B.U.* (Shawnee: The Bison Press, 1956) for further information.

Institutional Structure: *Governing board:* Board of Trustees. Extrainstitutional representation: 32 trustees. All voting. *Composition of institution:* Administrators 17. Academic affairs headed by vice president for academic affairs. Management/business/finances directed by vice president for business affairs. Full-time instructional faculty 102. Academic governance body, the faculty, meets an average of 7 times per year.

Calendar: Semesters. Academic year Aug. to May. Freshmen admitted Aug., Jan., Feb., June. Degrees conferred May, Aug., Dec. Formal commencement May, Dec. Summer session of 2 terms during June and July.

Characteristics of Freshmen: 3,207 applicants (2,098 fenale, 1,109 male). 63% of applicants admitted. 19% of applicants admitted and enrolled full-time.

19% (69 students) submitted SAT scores; 89% (320 students) submitted ACT scores. *25th percentile*: SAT Critical Reading 490, SAT Math 490, SAT Writing 490; ACT Composite 19, ACT English 20, ACT Math 18. *75th percentile*: SAT Critical Reading 620, SAT Math 590, SAT Writing 620; ACT Composite 27, ACT English 28, ACT Math 26.

53% of entering freshmen expected to graduate within 5 years. 48% of freshmen from Oklahoma. Freshmen from 24 states and 8 foreign countries.

Admission: Rolling admissions plan. For fall acceptance, apply as early as Sept. of previous year, but not later than week of enrollment. Early acceptance available. *Requirements:* Either graduation from accredited secondary school or GED. Minimum 2.0 GPA. Lowest acceptable secondary school class standing 50th percentile. *Entrance tests:* ACT Composite preferred; College Board SAT accepted. *For transfer students:* 2.0 minimum GPA; from 4-year accredited institution maximum transfer credit limited only by residence requirement; from 2-year accredited institution 64 hours; correspondence/extension students 36 hours.

College credit and advanced placement for postsecondary-level work completed in secondary school. College credit for extrainstitutional learning on basis of portfolio assessment.

Tutoring available. Developmental courses offered in summer session, regular academic year, and Jan. interim; credit given.

Degree Requirements: 128 credit hours; 2.0 GPA; 40 of last 60 hours in residence; weekly chapel attendance; 3 physical education courses (2 activity, 1 classroom); distribution requirements; demonstrated proficiency in written English.

Fulfillment of some degree requirements and exemption from some beginning courses possible by passing departmental examinations, ACT PEP, College Board CLEP, AP. *Grading system:* A=F; pass-fail; withdraw (carries time limit); incomplete (carries time limit).

Distinctive Educational Programs: Cooperative education. Flexible meeting places and schedules, including off-campus center (at Oklahoma City, 45 miles away from main institution) and evening classes. Special facilities for using telecommunications in the classroom. Interdisciplinary programs available in most areas of study. Facilities for independent research, including honors programs, individual majors, tutorials. Institutionally sponsored study abroad in Europe and Japan. Continuing education; degree-granting evening college; televised courses available through Oklahoma Televised Instruction System. Study abroad exchange programs with Seinan-Gakuin University, Fukuoka, Japan; with universities in China and Hungary; special courses meeting in Asia, Europe, South America.

Degrees Conferred: 257 *baccalaureate*. Bachelor's degrees awarded in top five disciplines: philosophy/religion/theology 80; education 53; health professions and related clinical sciences 34; psychology 30; visual and performing arts 25.

Fees and Other Expenses: *Full-time tuition per academic year 2008–09:* $16,728. *Room and board per academic year:* $5.200. *Books and supplies:* $950. *Other expenses:* $1,500.

Financial Aid: Aid from institutionally generated funds is provided on the basis of academic merit, financial need, other criteria.

Financial aid to full-time, first-time undergraduate students: 91% received some form of financial aid. Average amount of aid received: federal grants $2,549; state/local grants $2,717; institutional grants $6,256; loans $8,733.

Departments and Teaching Staff: *Total full-time instructional faculty:* 152 (111 full-time, 41 part-time). Total faculty with doctorate, first-professional, or other terminal degree: 80. Student/faculty ratio: 14:1. Degrees held by full-time faculty: doctorate 54%, master's 44%, professional 2%. 56% hold terminal degrees.

Enrollment: Total enrollment 1,769. Undergraduate 1,719 (full-time 85%; female 57%, male 43%). Graduate 50 (full-time 50%). Undergraduate transfer-in students 146.

Characteristics of Student Body: *Ethnic/racial makeup:* Black non-Hispanic: 6%; American Indian or Alaska Native: 7%; Asian or Pacific Islander: 1%; Hispanic: 3%; White non-Hispanic: 75%; unknown: 35; nonresident alien 6%. *Age distribution:* number under 18: 18; 18–19: 687; 20–21: 562; 22–24: 207; 25–29: 37; 30–34: 37; 35–39: 22; 40–49: 48; 50–64: 51; 65 and over: 15.

International Students: 70 nonresident aliens enrolled fall 2008. Students from Europe, Asia, Central and South America, Africa, Canada. Programs available to aid students whose native language is not English: social, cultural. English as a Second Language Program. No financial aid specifically designated for international students.

Student Life: On-campus residence halls house 75% of student body. Residence halls for males constitute 42% of such space, for females 58%. *Intercollegiate athletics:* male: baseball, basketball, soccer, tennis, track; female: basketball, soccer, softball, volleyball. *Special regulations:* Cars permitted without restrictions. Curfews for first-semester freshmen begin 11pm Sun.–Thurs., 1am Fri. and Sat. *Special services:* Learning Resources Center. *Student publications: The Bison*, a weekly newspaper; *Yahnseh*, a yearbook. *Surrounding community:* Shawnee population 26,500. Oklahoma City, 35 miles from campus, is nearest metropolitan area.

Publications: Sources of information about Oklahoma Baptist include *Bison Hill-topics*, a quarterly publication sent to financial supporters and church leaders.

Library Collections: 330,000 volumes. Online catalog. 40,700 government documents; 1,500 audiovisual materials; 247 current periodical subscriptions. Students have access to online information retrieval services and the Internet.

Most important special holdings include School of Christian Service Collection; Oklahoma Baptist Historical Collection; Western Civilization and Literature Collection.

Buildings and Grounds: Campus area 126 acres.

Chief Executive Officer: Dr. Mark A. Brister, President.

Address admission inquiries to Bruce Perkins, Director of Admissions.

Oklahoma Christian University

2501 East Memorial
Oklahoma City, Oklahoma 73136-1100
Tel: (405) 425-5200 **E-mail:** info@oc.edu
Fax: (405) 425-5208 **Internet:** www.oc.edu

Institution Description: Oklahoma Christian University is a private, independent, nonprofit college affiliated with the Churches of Christ. *Enrollment:* 2,060. *Degrees awarded:* Baccalaureate, master's.

Accreditation: *Regional:* NCA. *Professional*: engineering, teacher education

History: Incorporated 1949; established as Central Christian College and offered first instruction at postsecondary level 1950; awarded first degree (associate) 1951; became Oklahoma Christian College 1959; adopted present name 1990. *See* W. O. Beeman *Oklahoma Christian College: Dream to Reality*, (Delight, AK: Gospel Light Publishing Co., 1970) for further information.

Institutional Structure: *Governing board:* Board of Trustees. Representation: 28 trustees. All voting. *Composition of institution:* Administrators 10. Academic affairs headed by academic vice president. Management/business/finances directed by business manager. Full-time instructional faculty 92. Academic governance body, Divisional Council, meets an average of 12 times per year.

Calendar: Semesters. Academic year Aug. to Apr. Freshmen admitted Sept., Jan., May, June. Degrees conferred and formal commencement Apr., Dec. Summer session of 2 terms from May to Aug.

Characteristics of Freshmen: 90% of applicants accepted. 35% of accepted applicants enrolled.

30% (157 students) submitted SAT scores; 70% (366 students) submitted ACT scores. *25th percentile*: SAT Critical Reading 660, SAT Math 670; ACT Composite 20, ACT English 20, ACT Math 18. *75th percentile*: SAT Critical Reading 740, SAT Math 720; ACT Composite 26, ACT English 27, ACT Math 26.

47% entering freshmen expected to graduate within 5 years. 36% of freshmen from Oklahoma. Freshmen from 49 states and 34 foreign countries.

Admission: Rolling admissions plan. For fall acceptance, apply as early as junior year of secondary school, but not later than 2 weeks after beginning of term. Early acceptance available. *Requirements:* Either graduation from accredited secondary school or GED. *Entrance tests:* ACT or SAT. *For transfer students:* 2.0 minimum GPA; from 4-year accredited institution 96 hours maximum transfer credit; from 2-year accredited institution 65 hours; correspondence / extension students 60 hours.

College credit and advanced placement for postsecondary-level work completed in secondary school. College credit for extrainstitutional learning.

Tutoring available. Developmental courses offered during regular academic year; credit given.

Degree Requirements: 126 credit hours; 2.0 GPA (2.5 for teacher education); 30 semester hours in residence; daily chapel attendance; 1 hour physical education; general education requirements, including courses in religion; demonstrated proficiency in writing.

Fulfillment of some degree requirements and exemption from some beginning courses possible by passing departmental examinations, College Board CLEP, APP, IB. *Grading system:* A–F; pass; withdraw (deadline after which pass-fail is appended to withdrawal); incomplete (carries time limit).

Distinctive Educational Programs: Work-experience programs. Special facilities for using telecommunications in the classroom. Independent study. Institutionally sponsored study abroad in Europe and Japan.

ROTC: Army in cooperation with University of Central Oklahoma.

Degrees Conferred: 246 *baccalaureate*; 5 *master's*. Bachelor's degrees awarded in top five disciplines: business/marketing 45; engineering 30; education 27; liberal arts/general studies 23; biological/life sciences 18. Master's degrees awarded: business/marketing 117; theology and religious studies 5.

Fees and Other Expenses: *Full-time tuition per academic year 2008–09:* contact the university for current information regarding tuition, fees, housing, and other applicable costs.

Financial Aid: Aid from institutionally generated funds is provided on the basis of academic merit, financial need, athletic ability. Institution has a Program Participation Agreement with the U.S. Department of Education for eligible students to receive Pell Grants and, depending upon the agreement, other federal aid.

Departments and Teaching Staff: *Total instructional faculty:* 183. Student/faculty ratio: 15:1. Degrees held by full-time faculty: doctorate 67%, master's 33%. 67% hold terminal degrees.

Enrollment: Total enrollment 2,060.

Characteristics of Student Body: *Ethnic/racial makeup:* number of Black non-Hispanic: 115; American Indian or Alaska Native: 40; Asian or Pacific Islander: 27; Hispanic: 55; White non-Hispanic: 1,564; unknown: 84. *Age distribution:* number under 18: 18; 18–19: 711; 20–21: 7801 22–24: 805; 25–29: 125; 30–34: 44; 35–39: 37; 40–49: 41; 50–64: 16; 65 and over: 3.

International Students: Programs available to aid students whose native language is not English: financial. English as a Second Language Program.

Student Life: On-campus residence halls house 70% of student body. Residence halls for males constitute 45% of such space, for females 55%. 30% of student body housed on campus in apartments. 66% of married students request institutional housing and are so housed. 96% of students live on campus. *Intercollegiate athletics:* male: baseball, basketball, cross-country, golf, tennis, track; female: basketball, cross-country, tennis, track. *Special regulations:* Cars permitted without restrictions. Curfews begin 11:15pm Sun.–Thurs., 12:30am Fri., midnight Sat. *Special services:* Learning Resources Center, medical services. *Student publications, radio: Talon*, a weekly newspaper. Radio station KOCC. *Surrounding community:* Oklahoma City population 405,000. Airport 25 miles from campus.

Library Collections: 128,000 volumes including bound books, serial backfiles, electronic documents, and government documents not in separate collections. Online catalog. Current serial subscriptions: 291 paper; 577 microform, 6,978 electronic. 1,912 audio/videotapes; 369 DVDs; 1,038 CD-ROMs. Computer work stations available. Students have access to the Internet at no charge.

Most important special holdings include Oklahoma Publishing Company (clipping files of the Daily Oklahoman 1907–1981); Oklahoma City Symphony Orchestra Master Tapes 1948–1984; Living Legends Library (oral history tapes of Oklahoma).

Buildings and Grounds: Campus area 200 acres.

Chief Executive Officer: Dr. Michael E. O'Neal, President.

Address admission inquiries to Risa Forrester, Director of Admissions.

Oklahoma City University

2501 North Blackwelder
Oklahoma City, Oklahoma 73106
Tel: (405) 208-5000 **E-mail:** admissions@okcu.edu
Fax: (405) 208-6047 **Internet:** www.okcu.edu

Institution Description: Oklahoma City University is a private institution affiliated with the United Methodist Church. *Enrollment:* 3,884. *Degrees awarded:* Baccalaureate, first-professional (law), master's.

Accreditation: *Regional:* NCA. *Professional*: business, law, music, nursing

History: Chartered as Epworth University and offered first instruction at postsecondary level 1907; changed name to Methodist University of Oklahoma 1911, Oklahoma City College 1919; adopted present name 1924.

Institutional Structure: *Governing board:* Board of Trustees. Extrainstitutional representation: 43 trustees, including Bishop's Cabinet members. 8 ex officio. All voting. *Composition of institution:* Administrators 6. Academic affairs headed by vice president for academic affairs. Management directed by provost. Business and finance directed by chief financial officer. Full-time instructional faculty: 156.

Calendar: Semesters. Academic year Aug. to May. Degrees conferred and formal commencement May, Dec. Summer session.

Characteristics of Freshmen: 1,085 applcants (713 female, 352 male). 79% of applicants admitted. 43% of applicants admitted and enrolled full-time.

36% (126 students) submitted SAT scores; 79% (265 students) submitted ACT scores. *25th percentile*: SAT Critical Reading 550, SAT Math 520; ACT Composite 22, ACT English 22, ACT Math 19. *75th percentile*: SAT Critical Reading 640, SAT Math 640; ACT Composite 27, ACT English 28, ACT Math 26.

52% of entering freshmen expected to graduate within 5 years. 55% of freshmen from Oklahoma. Freshmen from 33 states and 22 foreign countries.

Admission: Early acceptance available. *Requirements:* Graduation from secondary school. Require 4 units English, 2 in a foreign language, 2 algebra, 3 science with laboratory, 1 geometry, 1 state history and civics, 1 U.S. history, 1 world history. *Entrance tests:* College Board SAT or ACT composite. *For transfer students:* From 2-year accredited institution 68 hours maximum transfer credit; from 4-year accredited institution 94 hours maximum transfer credit; correspondence/extension students 9 hours.

College credit and advanced placement for postsecondary-level work completed in secondary school.

Degree Requirements: *For all baccalaureate degrees:* 124 credit hours; 30 hours including last 15 (last 6 in major) in residence.

Fulfillment of some degree requirements and exemption from some beginning courses possible by passing College Board CLEP, AP, other standardized test. Fulfillment of degree requirements also possible by passing departmental examinations. *Grading system:* A–F; withdraw (carries time limit).

Distinctive Educational Programs: Evening classes. Study abroad in Australia, Asia, Europe, Latin America. Washington semester program with American University (DC). United Nations semester with Drew University (NJ).

ROTC: Air Force in cooperation with University of Oklahoma; Air Force in cooperation with University of Central Oklahoma.

Degrees Conferred: 467 *baccalaureate*; 386 *master's*; 170 *first-professional*. Bachelor's degrees awarded in top five disciplines: liberal arts/general studies 185; visual and performing arts 101; health professions and related clinical sciences 67; business/marketing 35; social sciences 23. Master's degrees awarded: business/marketing 352; computer and information sciences 51; liberal arts/general studies 19; philosophy and religious studies 2; social sciences 11; visual and performing arts 14. First-professional degrees awarded: law 170.

Fees and Other Expenses: *Full-time tuition per academic year 2008–09:* undergraduate $23,400; contact the univesity for current graduate and law school tuition and other applicable fees. *Room and bard per academic year:* $9,200. *Books and supplies:* $1,500. *Other expenses:* $2,700.

Financial Aid: Aid from institutionally generated funds is provided on the basis of academic merit, financial need, athletic ability, art/music talent.

Financial aid to full-time, first-time undergraduate students: 93% received some form of aid. Average amount of aid received: federal grants $3,360; Pell grants $2,851; other federal aid $1,459; state/local grants $3,024; institutional grants $13,765.

Departments and Teaching Staff: *Total instructional faculty:* 298 (full-time 156, part-time 142). Total faculty with doctorate, first-professional, or other terminal degree: 210. Student/faculty ratio: 12:1. Degrees held by full-time faculty: doctorate 40%, master's 19%, baccalaureate 2%, professional 19%. 79% hold terminal degrees.

Enrollment: Total enrollment 3,884. Undergraduate 2,276 (full-time 83%; female 61%, male 39%). Graduate 1,608 (full-time 77%).

OKLAHOMA CITY UNIVERSITY—*cont'd*

Characteristics of Student Body: *Ethnic/racial makeup:* Black non-Hispanic: 9%; American Indian or Alaska Native: 4%; Asian or Pacific Islander: 4%; Hispanic 9%; White non-Hispanic: 56%; unknown 1%; nonresident alien 22%. *Age distribution:* number under 18: 14; 18–19: 622; 20–21: 645; 22–24: 364; 25–29: 169; 30–34: 761 35–39: 49; 40–49: 75; 50–64: 29; 65 and over: 3, 39% of student body attend summer sessions.

International Students: 980 nonresident aliens enrolled fall 2008. Students from Europe, Asia, Central and South America, Africa, Canada, Australia. Middle East. Programs available to aid students whose native language is not English: social, cultural. English as a Second Language Program. Financial aid specifically designated for international students.

Student Life: On-campus housing available. *Intercollegiate athletics:* male: baseball, basketball, crew, golf, soccer, wrestling; female: basketball, crew, soccer, softball, tennis, volleyball. *Student publications: The Campus*, a newspaper; *The Keshena*, a yearbook. *Surrounding community:* Oklahoma City. Served by airport; rail, and major interstate highways.

Library Collections: 161,000 volumes. 250,000 government documents; 649,000 microforms; 10,115 audiovisual materials; Current periodical subscriptions: paper 765; via electronic access 14,880. 1,584 audio/videotapes; 37 CD-ROMs. Computer work stations available. Online catalog. Students have fee-based access to online information retrieval services and the Internet.

Most important special collections include University and United Methodist Conference of Oklahoma Archives; Foundation Center Collection; Depository of U.S. Government Documents.

Buildings and Grounds: Campus area 75 acres.

Chief Executive Officer: Dr. Thomas J. McDaniel, President.

Undergraduates address admission inquiries to Dean of Admissions and Enrollment Management; Law School inquiries to Dean for Law School Admissions; graduate inquiries to Director of Graduate Admissions.

Oklahoma Panhandle State University

325 Eagle Avenue
Goodwell, Oklahoma 73939-0430
Tel: (580) 349-2611 **E-mail:** admissions@opsu.edu
Fax: (580) 349-2302 **Internet:** www.opsu.edu

Institution Description: Oklahoma Panhandle State University (Oklahoma Panhandle State College until 1974) is a state institution offering an agricultural, technical, and liberal arts curriculum. *Enrollment:* 1,223. *Degrees awarded:* Associate, baccalaureate. Certificates also awarded.

Academic offerings subject to approval by statewide coordinating bodies. Budget subject to approval by state governing boards.

Accreditation: *Regional:* NCA. *Professional*: teacher education

History: Established and chartered as Pan-Handle Agricultural Institute, a secondary school, 1909; became 2-year institution, offered first instruction at postsecondary level, and changed name to Panhandle Agricultural and Mechanical College 1921; became 4-year institution and awarded first degree (baccalaureate) 1926; changed name to Oklahoma Panhandle State College of Agriculture and Applied Science 1967; adopted present official name, Oklahoma Panhandle State University of Agriculture and Applied Science, 1974. *See* Kathryn A. Sexton, *The Heritage of the Panhandle - The History of Panhandle State University* (Norman, OK: Oklahoma University Press, 1979) for further information.

Institutional Structure: *Governing board:* Board of Regents for the Oklahoma State University and the Agricultural and Mechanical Colleges. Representation: 8 regents (appointed by governor of Oklahoma), president of State Board of Agriculture. 1 ex officio. All voting. *Composition of institution:* Administrators 7. Academic affairs headed by dean of academics and administration. Management/business/finances directed by business manager. Full-time instructional faculty 52. Academic governance body, Academic Council, meets an average of 9 times per year.

Calendar: Semesters. Academic year Aug. to May. Freshmen admitted Aug., Jan. Degrees conferred May, Dec. Formal commencement May. Summer session of 2 terms from May to Aug.

Characteristics of Freshmen: 616 applicants (female 277, amle 339). 100% of applicants admitted. 50% of admitted students enrolled full-time.

20% of applicants submitted SAT scores; 73% submitted ACT scores. *25th percentile*: SAT Critical Reading 350, SAT Math 380, ACT Composite 16, ACT English 14, ACT Math 16. *75th percentile*: SAT Critical Reading 470, SAT Math 530; ACT Composite 23, ACT English 21, ACT Math 21.

33% of entering freshmen expected to graduate within 5 years. 64% of freshmen from Oklahoma. Freshmen from 12 states and 5 foreign countries.

Admission: Rolling admissions.

College credit and advanced placement for postsecondary-level work completed in secondary school. For extrainstitutional learning on basis of faculty assessment.

Developmental/remedial courses offered during regular academic year.

Degree Requirements: *Degree requirements:* 124 minimum semester hours; 2.0 GPA; 30 hours, including last 15 hours, in residence; 2 credit hours of physical education courses; general education requirements.

Fulfillment of some degree requirements and exemption from some beginning courses possible by passing College Board CLEP, ACT composite. *Grading system:* A–F; pass-fail; withdraw; incomplete.

Distinctive Educational Programs: *For undergraduates:* 2,160-acre university farm includes range unit. Credit transfer agreement between Panhandle Graduate Center and Oklahoma State University. Continuing education for public school teachers and other adults. Agronomy experiment station. Rodeo arena.

Degrees Conferred: 183 *baccalaureate*. Bachelor's degrees awarded in top five disciplines: agriculture 43; education biological/life sciences 23; business, management, marketing, and related support services 15; education 14; psychology 12.

Fees and Other Expenses: *Full-time tuition per academic year 2008–09:* resident $4,244, nonresident $8,844. >*Required fees:* $1,157. *Room and board per academic year:* $3,420. *Books and supplies:* $240. *Other expenses:* $1,400.

Financial Aid: Aid from institutionally generated funds is provided on the basis of academic merit, financial need, athletic ability. Institution has a Program Participation Agreement with the U.S. Department of Education for eligible students to receive Pell Grants and, depending upon the agreement, other federal aid.

Financial aid to full-time, first-time undergraduate students: 94% received some form of financial aid. Average amount of aid received: federal grants $1,006; state/local grants $2,599; institutional grants $5,896; loans $9,818.

Departments and Teaching Staff: *Total instructional faculty:* 81. Degrees held by full-time faculty: doctorate 49%, master's 47%, baccalaureate 4%. 49% hold terminal degrees.

Enrollment: Total enrollment 1,223. Undergraduate 1,223 (full-time 80%, female 51%, male 49%).

Characteristics of Student Body: *Ethnic/racial makeup:* Black non-Hispanic: 9%; American Indian or Alaska Native: 3%; Hispanic: 13%; White non-Hispanic: 70%; unknown: 2%; nonresident alien 4%. 67. *Age distribution:* number under 18: 27; 18–19: 331; 20–21: 298; 22–24: 222; 25–29: 89; 30–34: 52; 35–39: 47; 40–49: 44; 50–64: 22; 65 and over: 10.

International Students: 23 nonresident aliens enrolled fall 2008. Students from Europe, Asia, Central America, Africa, Canada, Australia. Programs available to aid students whose native language is not English: cultural. No financial aid specifically designated for international students.

Student Life: On-campus residence halls. 10% of married students request institutional housing and are so housed. 53% of students live on campus. *Intercollegiate athletics:* male: baseball, basketball, football, track; female: basketball, track, volleyball. *Special regulations:* Cars permitted without restrictions. *Special services:* Learning Resources Center, medical services. *Student publications, radio: Collegian*, a bimonthly newspaper. Radio station KPSU-FM broadcasts 70 hours per week. *Surrounding community:* Goodwell population 1,500. Oklahoma City, 275 miles from campus, is nearest metropolitan area. Served by airport 50 miles from campus.

Library Collections: 124,500 volumes. Current serial subscriptions: paper 203, microform 40; 5,000 via electronic access. 3,022 audio/videotapes; 241 DVD discs; 250 CD-ROMs. Online catalog. Computer work stations available. Students have access to online information retrieval services and the Internet.

Most important holdings include curriculum collection; Howsley Poetry Collection (first editions of critical works, commentaries, and biographies, particularly on Shakespeare and Chaucer); children's literature collection.

Buildings and Grounds: Campus area 90 acres.

Chief Executive Officer: Dr. David A. Bryant, President.

Address admission inquiries Bobby Jenkins, Director of Admissions.

Oklahoma State University

107 Whitehurst Hall
Stillwater, Oklahoma 74078-0004
Tel: (405) 744-5000 **E-mail:** admit@okstate.edu
Fax: (405) 744-5285 **Internet:** www.okstate.edu

Institution Description: Oklahoma State University is a state institution with five campuses in Stillwater, Tulsa, Oklahoma City, and Oknulgee. Two colleges are now centers: Center for Health Sciences (osteopathic medicine) and Center for Veterinary Sciences. *Enrollment:* 23,461. *Degrees awarded:* Associate, baccalaureate, first-professional (doctor of veterinary medicine), master's, doctorate.

Academic offerings subject to approval by statewide coordinating bodies. Budget subject to approval by state governing boards.

Accreditation: *Regional:* NCA. *Professional*: architecture, business, chemistry, dietetics, engineering, engineering technology, forestry, journalism, music, osteopathy, psychology internship, rehabilitation counseling, speech-language pathology, teacher education, veterinary medicine

History: Established as Oklahoma Agricultural and Mechanical College 1890; offered first instruction at postsecondary level 1891; awarded first degree (baccalaureate) 1896; adopted present official name 1957. *See* Philip Reed Rulon, *Oklahoma State University—Since 1890* (Stillwater: Oklahoma State University Press, 1975) for further information.

Institutional Structure: *Governing board:* Board of Regents for the Oklahoma State University and the Agricultural and Mechanical Colleges. Representation: 8 regents (appointed by the governor of Oklahoma), president of the state board of agriculture. 1 ex officio. All voting. *Composition of institution:* Administrators 116. Academic affairs headed by provost and vice president for academic affairs. Management/business/finances directed by vice president for business and finance. Full-time instructional faculty 1,059. Academic governance body, Faculty council, meets an average of 12 times per year.

Calendar: Semesters. Academic year Aug. to May. Freshmen admitted Aug., Jan., June. Degrees conferred May, July, Dec. Formal commencement May. Summer session June to July.

Characteristics of Freshmen: 6,730 applicants. 87% of applicants accepted. 54% of accepted applicants enrolled full-time.

26% (839 students) submitted SAT scores; 92% (2,982 students) submitted ACT scores. *25th percentile*: SAT Critical Reading 490, SAT Math 510; ACT Composite 22, ACT English 21, ACT Math 20. *75th percentile*: SAT Critical Reading 810, SAT Math 640; ACT Composite 27, ACT English 28, ACT Math 26.

43% of entering freshmen expected to graduate within 5 years. 85% of freshmen from Oklahoma. Freshmen from 39 states and 43 foreign countries.

Admission: Rolling admissions plan. For fall acceptance, apply as early as 1 year prior to enrollment, but not later than first week of classes. Early acceptance available. *Requirements:* Graduate from accredited secondary school. Student must rank in top one-third of secondary school class and earn minimum GPA of 3.0 or have ACT composite score of 22 or SAT of 1030. Some exceptions through Affirmative Action Program. *Entrance tests:* ACT composite. For foreign students TOEFL. *For transfer students:* 2.0 minimum GPA.

College credit and advanced placement for postsecondary-level work completed in secondary school. College credit for extrainstitutional learning.

Tutoring available. Noncredit developmental courses offered in summer session and regular academic year.

Degree Requirements: *For all associate degrees:* 60 credit hours; 1 semester in residence. *For all baccalaureate degrees:* 120–128 hours; 2 semesters in residence. *For all undergraduate degrees:* Generally 2.0 GPA; general education requirements. For College of Arts and Sciences, exit competency examination in English and mathematics.

Fulfillment of some degree requirements and exemption from some beginning courses possible by passing departmental examinations, College Board CLEP Subject Examinations. *Grading system:* A–F; pass-fail; withdraw (carries time limit).

Distinctive Educational Programs: Internships. Flexible meeting places and schedules, including off-campus centers (at Tinker Air Force Base, 70 miles away from main institution; Ponca City 40 miles away; and other locations throughout the state) and evening classes. Cooperative baccalaureate in medical technology with approved hospitals. Interdepartmental programs in biosystems engineering, environmental sciences, cell and molecular biology, telecommunications management, hospitality administration, biological sciences, computer connection, general studies, global studies, humanities, natural sciences, physical sciences, social sciences. Preprofessional programs in pre-med, pre-dental, pre-law, pre-veterinary science, pre-osteopathic medicine. Facilities and programs for independent research, including honors programs, individual majors. Study abroad in Peoples Republic of China (Chinese language and culture); France, Germany, Russia (liberal arts and foreign language), Kyoto, Japan, and other locations. *Other distinctive programs:* Continuing education on a year-round basis.

ROTC: Army, Air Force.

Degrees Conferred: 3,698 *baccalaureate*; 904 *master's*; 177 *doctorate*. 68 *first-professional*. Bachelor's degrees awarded in tip five disciplines: business, management, marketing, and related support services 998; education 307; agriculture/agriculture operations and related sciences 286; engineering 272; family and consumer sciences/humans sciences 264. *First-professional:* veterinary medicine 68.

Fees and Other Expenses: *Full-time tuition per academic year 2008–09:* contact the university for current information regarding tuition, fees, housing, and other applicable fees for undergraduate, graduate, and first-professional enrollment.

Financial Aid: Aid from institutionally generated funds is p basis of academic merit, financial need, athletic ability, other cri

Financial aid to full-time, first-time undergraduate students: 86% rece some form of financial aid. Average amount of aid received: federal grants $3,040; state/local grants $3,056; institutional grants $3,124; loans $3,650.

Departments and Teaching Staff: *Total instructional faculty:* 923 (full-time 893, part-time 291). Total faculty with doctorate, first-professional, or other terminal degree: 788. Student/faculty ratio: 20:1. Degrees held by full-time faculty: baccalaureate 2.5%, master's 11.2%, doctorate 79.2%, professional 4.6%. 91.1% hold terminal degrees.

Enrollment: Total enrollment 23,461.

Characteristics of Student Body: *Ethnic/racial makeup:* number of Black non-Hispanic: 714; American Indian or Alaska Native: 1,655; Asian or Pacific Islander: 286; Hispanic: 377; White non-Hispanic: 14,845.

International Students: 756 undergraduate nonresident aliens enrolled fall 2008. Programs available to aid students whose native language is not English: social, cultural. English as a Second Language Program (fee charged). Financial aid specifically designated for international students.

Student Life: On-campus residence halls house 16% of student body. 12% of males join and 8% live in fraternity housing; 18.5% of females join and 5% live in sorority housing. Housing available for married students. *Intercollegiate athletics:* male: baseball, basketball, football, golf, tennis, track and cross-country; female: basketball, golf, softball, tennis, track and cross-country. *Special regulations:* Cars permitted on limited basis. Quiet hours. Residence hall visitation from noon to midnight Sun.–Thurs., weekend hours until 2:00am. *Special services:* Learning Resources Center, medical services. *Student publications, radio:* Daily newspaper. Radio station KOSU broadcasts 126 hours per week. *Surrounding community:* Stillwater population 42,000. Oklahoma City and Tulsa, each 65 miles from campus, are nearest metropolitan areas. Served by airport 2 miles from campus.

Publications: *Cimarron Review* (quarterly) first published 1967. *Publisher:* Oklahoma State University Press.

Library Collections: 2,624,000 volumes; 4,458,000 microform units; 404,200 audiovisual materials. Online catalog. 30,000 periodicals including via electronic access. Computer work stations available. Laptops available for checkout. Students have access to the Internet at no charge.

Most important special holdings include Angie Debois Papers; Senator/Governor Henry Bellman Papers; Paul Miller Papers; Women's Archives; Streater Flynn History of Railroads and Memorabilia.

Buildings and Grounds: Campus area 938 acres. *New buildings:* Rodeo Arena completed 2002; ConocoPhillips OSU Alumni Center 2005.

Chief Executive Officer: Dr. David J. Schmidly, President.

Undergraduates address admission inquiries to Karen Lucas, Director of Admissions; first-professional inquiries to Director Manager, Veterinary Medicine Student Services; graduate inquiries to Director of Graduate Student Services.

Oklahoma Wesleyan University

2201 Silver Lake Road
Bartlesville, Oklahoma 74006

Tel: (918) 335-6200 **E-mail:** admissions@bwc.edu
Fax: (918) 335-6229 **Internet:** www.bwc.edu

Institution Description: Oklahoma Wesleyan University, formerly named Bartlesville Wesleyan College is a private college affiliated with the Wesleyan Church. *Enrollment:* 1,021. *Degrees awarded:* Associate, baccalaureate.

Accreditation: *Regional:* NCA. *Professional*: nursing, teacher education

History: Established as Central Pilgrim College through merger of Colorado Springs Bible College (established 1910), Pilgrim Bible College (established 1917), Holiness Evangelical Institute (established 1923), chartered, incorporated, and offered first instruction at postsecondary level 1959; awarded first degree (associate) 1961; named Bartlesville Wesleyan College 1968; merged with Miltonvale Wesleyan College (established 1909) and began 4-year curriculum 1972; adopted present name 2000.

Institutional Structure: *Governing board:* Board of Trustees. Extrainstitutional representation: 24 trustees, including 1 church official; institutional representation: president of the college, 1 alumnus, 3 ex officio. 24 voting. *Composition of institution:* Administrators 5. Academic affairs headed by academic dean. Management/business/finances directed by controller. Full-time instructional faculty 24. Academic governance body, the faculty, meets an average of 16 times per year.

Calendar: Semesters. Academic year Aug. to July. Freshmen admitted Aug., Jan., May, June. Degrees conferred May, Aug., Dec. Formal commencement May, Dec. Summer session of 2 terms from May to July.

OKLAHOMA WESLEYAN UNIVERSITY—*cont'd*

Characteristics of Freshmen: 73% of applicants admitted. 37% of applicants admitted and enrolled.

15% (17 students) submitted SAT scores; 85% (94 students) submitted ACT scores. *25th percentile*: SAT Critical Reading 450, SAT Math 440; ACT Composite 18, ACT English 18, ACT Math 16. *75th percentile*: SAT Critical Reading 610, SAT Math 540; ACT Composite 24, ACT English 24, ACT Math 24.

42% of entering freshmen expected to graduate within 5 years. 42% of freshmen from Oklahoma. Freshmen from 20 states and 1 foreign country.

Admission: Rolling admissions plan. For fall acceptance, apply as early as Sept. of previous year, but not later than Aug. of year of enrollment. Early acceptance available. *Requirements:* Either graduation from accredited secondary school or GED. *Entrance tests:* ACT composite. *For transfer students:* 2.0 minimum GPA; from 4-year accredited institution 100 hours maximum transfer credit; from 2-year accredited institution 65 hours.

College credit and advanced placement for postsecondary-level work completed in secondary school. College credit for extrainstitutional learning.

Tutoring available. Developmental/remedial courses offered during regular academic year; no credit given.

Degree Requirements: *For all associate degrees:* 64 credit hours; 2 semesters physical education. *For all baccalaureate degrees:* 126 credit hours; 24 semester hours in residence. *For all degrees:* 2.0 GPA; 2 semesters in residence; chapel attendance 3 times per week; general education requirements; 9 semester hours biblical literature/philosophy.

Fulfillment of some degree requirements and exemption from some beginning courses possible by passing departmental examinations, College Board CLEP, DANTES, ACT PEP, AP. *Grading system:* A=F; withdraw (carries time limit and penalty).

Distinctive Educational Programs: Evening classes.

Degrees Conferred: 29 *associate;* 218 *baccalaureate*. Bachelor's degrees awarded in top disciplines: biological/life sciences 4; business/marketing 4; communications/communication technologies 1; computer and information sciences 2; education 9; English 1; health professions and related sciences 1; mathematics 1; parks and recreation 3; philosophy/religion/theology 7; psychology 1; social sciences and history 2; visual and performing arts 2. Master's degrees awarded: various disciplines 39.

Fees and Other Expenses: *Full-time tuition per academic year 2008–09:* $15,565. *Room and board per academic year:* $6,050. *Books and supplies:* $900. *Other expenses:* $3,300.

Financial Aid: Aid from institutionally generated funds is provided on the basis of academic merit, financial need, athletic ability.

Financial aid to full-time, first-time undergraduate students: 100% received some form of financial aid. Average amount of aid received: federal grants $3,509; Pell grants $2,723; other federal aid $1,568; state/local grants $2,783; institutional grants $7,513.

Departments and Teaching Staff: *Total instructional faculty:* 33 (full-time 24, part-time 9). 50% of faculty hold the withdoctorate, first-professional, or other terminal degree. Student/faculty ratio: 10:1.

Enrollment: Total enrollment 1,021. Undergradaute 952 (full-time 59%; female 61%, male 39%). Transfer-in students 168.

Characteristics of Student Body: *Ethnic/racial makeup:* Black non-Hispanic: 6%; American Indian or Alaska Native: 11%; Asian or Pacific Islander: 1%; Hispanic: 2%; White non-Hispanic: 75%; unknown 3%; nonresident alien 1%. *Age distribution:* number under 18: 21; 18–19: 148; 20–21: 148; 22–24: 111; 25–29: 61; 30–34: 75; 35–39: 77; 40–49: 153; 50–64: 58. 60% of student body attend summer sessions.

International Students: 10 nonresident aliens enrolled fall 2008. Students from Asia, Central and South America, Africa, Canada. Programs available to aid students whose native language is not English: English as a Second Language Program. All international students receive a $1,500 scholarship.

Student Life: On-campus residence halls house 37% of student body. Residence halls for males constitute 45% of such space, for females 55%. Chapel attendance required 2 times per week. *Intercollegiate athletics:* male: baseball, basketball, cross-country, golf, tennis, track and field; female: basketball, cross-country, soccer, softball, tennis, track and field, volleyball. *Special regulations:* Insured cars permitted in designated areas. Curfews. *Special services:* Learning Resources Center, medical services. *Student publications: Reflections*, a yearbook; *Eagle*, a monthly newspaper. *Surrounding community:* Bartlesville population 35,000. Tulsa, 40 miles from campus, is nearest metropolitan area. Served by airport 40 miles from campus.

Library Collections: 120,000 volumes including bound books, serial backfiles, electronic documents, and government documents not in separate collections. Online catalog. Current serial subscriptions: 145 paper, 38 microform. 1,046 recordings; 27 CD-ROMs. Computer work stations available. Students have access to the Internet at no charge.

Most important special collection is the Wesleyan Holiness Collection.

Buildings and Grounds: Campus area 37 acres.

Chief Executive Officer: Dr. Everett G. Piper, President.

Address admission inquiries to Audrey Kelleher, Associate Vice President for Enrollment.

Oral Roberts University

7777 South Lewis Avenue
Tulsa, Oklahoma 74171

Tel: (918) 495-6161 **E-mail:** admission@oru.edu
Fax: (918) 495-6222 **Internet:** www.oru.edu

Institution Description: Oral Roberts University is a private, independent, nonprofit institution. *Enrollment:* 3,244. *Degrees awarded:* Baccalaureate, first-professional (medicine, theology); master's, doctorate.

Accreditation: *Regional:* NCA. *Professional*: engineering, music, nursing, social work, theology

History: Chartered and incorporated 1963; offered first instruction at postsecondary level 1965; awarded first degree (baccalaureate) 1968.

Institutional Structure: *Governing board:* Board of Regents. Extrainstitutional representation: 40 regents; institutional representation: 1 administrator. 1 ex officio. All voting. *Composition of institution:* Administrators 22. Academic affairs headed by vice president for academic affairs. Management/business/finances directed by executive vice president for financial affairs.

Calendar: Semesters. Academic year Aug. to May.

Characteristics of Freshmen: 1,363 applicants (765 female, 598 male). 84% of applicants admitted. 72% of admitted students enrolled full-time.

53% (318 students) submitted SAT scores; 78% (465 students) submitted ACT scores. *25th percentile*: SAT I Verbal 490; SAT I Math 460; ACT Composite 20, ACT English 20, ACT Math 17. *75th percentile*: SAT I Verbal 600, SAT I Math 580; ACT Composite 26, ACT English 27, ACT Math 25.

30% of freshmen from Oklahoma.

Admission: Rolling admissions plan. For fall acceptance, apply as early as summer following junior year of secondary school. Early acceptance available. *Requirements:* Either graduation from accredited secondary school with 16 units which must include 4 English, 2 in a foreign language, 2 mathematics, 2 science (1 in laboratory science), 2 social studies; or GED. Additional units foreign language, laboratory science, and mathematics recommended. *Entrance tests:* College Board SAT or ACT composite. For foreign students TOEFL. *For transfer students:* 2.5 minimum GPA; from 2-year accredited institution 64 semester hours maximum transfer credit.

College credit and advanced placement for postsecondary-level work completed in secondary school.

Degree Requirements: 128 semester hours; 2.0 GPA; last 30 hours in residence; twice weekly chapel attendance; 4 credits in physical education courses; senior paper or project; general education requirements. *Grading system:* A–F; pass-no pass (option for juniors and seniors).

Degrees Conferred: 532 *baccalaureate*; 91 *master's*; 38 *doctorate*; 39 *first-professional*. Bachelor's degrees awarded in top five disciplines: business, management, marketing, and related support services 132; theology 125; communication, journalism, and related programs 79; education 48; psychology 37.

Fees and Other Expenses: *Full-time tuition per academic year 2008–09:* contact the the university for current tuition, fees, housing, and other applicable costs.

Financial Aid: Institution has a Program Participation Agreement with the U.S. Department of Education for eligible students to receive Pell Grants and, depending upon the agreement, other federal aid.

Financial aid to full-time, first-time undergraduate students: 98% received some form of financial aid. Average amount of aid received: federal grants $1,006; state/local grants $2,599; institutional grants $5,896; loans $9,818.

Departments and Teaching Staff: *Total instructional faculty:* 185. Student/faculty ratio: 17:1. Degrees held by full-time faculty: doctorate 51%, master's 46%, baccalaureate 2%, professional 1%. 51% hold terminal degrees.

Enrollment: Total enrollment 3,244.

Characteristics of Student Body: *Ethnic/racial makeup:* Black non-Hispanic: 16%; American Indian or Alaska Native: 2%; Asian or Pacific Islander: 2%; Hispanic: 6%; White non-Hispanic: 63%.

International Students: 140 undergraduate nonresident aliens enrolled fall 2008. Students from Europe, Asia, Latin America, Africa, Canada, Australia. Programs available to aid students whose native language is not English: social, cultural. Financial aid specifically designated for international students: variable number of scholarships available annually.

Student Life: On-campus residence halls house. *Special regulations:* Registered cars permitted; fee charged. Dress code. *Surrounding community:* Tulsa is a major metropolitan area of northeastern Oklahoma.

Library Collections: 750,000 volumes including bound books, serial backfiles, electronic documents, and government documents not in separate collections. Online catalog. Current serial subscriptions: 450 paper, 185 microform, 5,250 electronic. 14,536 recordings; 333 compact discs; 1,306 CD-ROMs. Computer work stations available. Students have access to the Internet at no charge.

Major special collection is Holy Spirit Research Center Library; Elmar Camillo Dos Santos Collection; William Sanford LaSor Collection.

Buildings and Grounds: Campus area 500 acres.

Chief Executive Officer: Dr. Richard L. Roberts, President.

Address undergraduate inquiries to Chris Belcher, Director of Admissions.

Rogers State University

1701 Will Rogers Boulevard
Claremore, Oklahoma 74017-3262
Tel: (918) 343-7777 **E-mail:** info@rsu.edu
Fax: (918) 343-7595 **Internet:** www.rsu.edu

Institution Description: Rogers State University in northeastern Oklahoma governed by the University of Oklahoma Board of Regents. *Degrees awarded:* Associate, baccalaureate. *Enrollment:* 3,913.

Accreditation: *Regional:* NCA. *Professional*: nursing

History: Rogers State University was founded in 1909 as the Eastern University Preparatory School and became the Oklahoma Military Academy in 1919. In 1982 the academy became Claremore Junior College. The institution was renamed Rogers State College. In 1996 Rogers University was created by merger of Rogers State College and the University Center at Tulsa. These two entities were separated in 1998 to become a branch of Oklahoma State University in Tulsa and Rogers State University, a new regional university.

Institutional Structure: Governing Board. *Representation:* 9 members appointed by the governor. *Composition of institution:* administrators 912. Academic affairs headed by vice president of academic affairs. Business finances directed by vice president. Full time instructional faculty 92.

Calendar: Semesters. Academic year Aug. to May. Summer session June to July.

Characteristics of Freshmen: 84% of applicants admitted. 63% of applicants admitted and enrolled.

90% (708 students) submitted ACT scores. *25th percentile*: ACT Composite 17, ACT English 16, ACT Math 16. *75th percentile*: ACT Composite 22, ACT English 23, ACT Math 21.

15% of entering freshmen expected to graduate within five years. 98% of freshmen from Oklahoma. Freshmen from 9 states.

Admission: *Requirements:* Either graduation from accredited secondary school; ACT or SAT; top 50% of graduating class. High school curricular requirements are 4 units English, 3 mathematics, 3 history and citizenship skills (including 1 unit of American history and 1/2 unit of government), 2 units lab science, 3 additional units of subjects previously listed or selected from computer science or foreign language. *Foreign students:* score of 500 or higher on TOEFL and meet same admission requirements as other students.

For more detailed information, see www.rsu.edu.

Degree Requirements: 120 semester hours with a committed retention/graduation GPA of 2.,0 in a all coursework attempted. A minimum of 60 hours must be taken at a baccalaureate degree-granting institution; at least 30 credit hours taken in residence. *For all associate degrees:* 60 credit hours; 2.0 GPA; at least 15 of final 30 hours taken in residence. *grading system:* A–F; pass-fail; withdraw.

ROTC: Air Force in cooperation with Oklahoma State University - Tulsa.

Degrees Conferred: 159 *baccalaureate*: biological/life sciences 10; business/marketing 65; engineering and engineering technologies 27; liberal arts/general studies 16; security and protective services 6; social sciences 38.

Fees and Other Expenses: *Full-time tuition per academic year 2008–09:* resident $4,217, nonresident $9,734. *Room and board per academic year:* $8,322. *Books and supplies:* $1,200. *Other expenses:* $8,045.

Financial Aid: Institution has a Program Participation Agreement with the U.S. Department of Education for eligible students to receive Pell Grants and, depending upon the agreement, other federal aid.

Financial aid to full-time, first-time undergraduate students: 85% received some form of aid. Average amount of aid received: federal grants $3,051; Pell grants $3,1010; other federal aid $1,163; state/local grants $2,115; institutional grants $2,189.

Departments and Teaching Staff: *Total instructional faculty:* 204 (full-time 92, part-time 112). Total faculty with doctorate, first-professional, or other terminal degree: 73. Student/faculty ratio: 21.7:1.

Enrollment: Total enrollment 3,913. Undergraduate 3,913 (full-time 60%; female 82%, male 38%).

Characteristics of Student Body: *Ethnic/racial makeup:* Black non-Hispanic: 2%; American Indian or Alaska Native: 13%; Asian or Pacific Islander: 1%; Hispanic: 3%; White non-Hispanic: 63%; unknown 17%; nonresident alien 1%. *Age distribution:* number under 18: 272; 18–19: 908; 20–21: 685; 22–24: 579; 25–29: 526; 30–34: 347; 35–39: 254; 40–49: 284; 50–64: 88; 65 and over: 4. 23% of student body attend summer sessions.

International Students: 4 nonresident aliens enrolled fall 2008. Student from Europe, Asia, Africa, Canada. No programs available to aid students whose native language is not English. No financial aid specifically designated for international students.

Student Life: On-campus apartments and food service available. Over 25 clubs and organizations for student participation. Intramural sports include basketball, football, soccer, volleyball. Club sports include baseball, rodeo club, rugby. *Special services:* Student health center. *Surrounding community:* Claremore population 17,000; located 25 miles from Tulsa.

Library Collections: 72,000 volumes including bound books, serial backfiles, electronic documents, and government documents not in separate collections. Online catalog. Current serial subscriptions: 422 paper; 100 microform; 1,601 via electronic access. 5,415 audio/videotapes; 315 DVD discs; 25 CD-ROMs. Computer work stations available. Students have access to the the Internet at no charge.

Most important special collections include War of the Rebellion; official records of the Union; Confederal history and Confederal military history.

Chief Executive Officer: Dr. Joe Wiley, President.

Address undergraduate inquiries to Lindsay Fields, Director of Enrollment Management.

St. Gregory's University

1900 West MacArthur
Shawnee, Oklahoma 74804
Tel: (405) 878-5100 **E-mail:** admissions@stgregorys.edu
Fax: (405) 878-5198 **Internet:** www.stgregorys.edu

Institution Description: St. Gregory's University is a private institution in the Roman Catholic and Benedictine traditions. *Enrollment:* 745. *Degrees awarded:* Associate, baccalaureate, master's.

Accreditation: *Regional*: NCA.

History: Established in Konowa, Oklahoma in 1875 as Sacred Heart College; became the Catholic University of Oklahoma in Shawneee in 1916; principally a boarding high school with a small junior college through 1965; high school closed and was a residential junior college through 1996 when the school adopted its present name and began offering bachelor's degrees.

Institutional Structure: A membership corporation with certain reserved powers plus a lay board of directors; president with 5 vice presidents. for financial affairs.

Calendar: Semesters. Academic year Aug. to May. 5-week summer session. Formal commencement May, Dec.

Characteristics of Freshmen: 366 applicants (female 230, male 136). 97% of applicants admitted. 27% of applicants admitted and enrolled full-time.

15% (30 students) submitted SAT scores; 94% (199 students) submitted ACT scores. *25th percentile*: SAT Critical Reading 450, SAT Math 450; ACT Composite 16. *75th percentile*: SAT Critical Reading 500, SAT Math 490; ACT Composite 22.

Freshmen from 13 states and 16 foreign countries.

Admission: Students are admitted when all paperwork is complete. *Requirements:* Either graduation from accredited secondary school; ACT 21, 2.75 GPA, or top 50% of graduating class.

Degree Requirements: 2.0 GPA; 2.5 GPA and no grades lower than a C in area of concentration; 40 hours upper division courses; writing portfolio at end of the Composition class; Life portfolio at end of sophomore year; senior portfolio in degree area. Last 30 hours must be completed in residence.

Distinctive Educational Programs: All students participate in four (4) semesters Tradition and Conversation (Great Books) seminars. Partners in Learning program provides special support for students with particular learning differences. Conservation Biology prepares students for the practical work of studying and protecting the environment. Performing arts (theater and dance).

Degrees Conferred: 91 *baccalaureate*: biological/life sciences 2; business/marketing 43; communications/journalism 3; education 5; English 1; health professions and related clinical sciences 4; interdisciplinary studies 1; liberal arts/general studies 9; natural resources/environmental science 1; parks and recreation 4; psychology 4; security and protective services 1; social sciences 10; visual and performing arts 3.

Fees and Other Expenses: *Full-time tuition per academic year 2008–09:* $15,560. *Room and board per academic year:* $6,288. *Required fees:* $850. *Books and supplies:* $900. *Other expenses:* $4,914.

ST. GREGORY'S UNIVERSITY—*cont'd*

Financial Aid: Institution has a Program Participation Agreement with the U.S. Department of Education for eligible students to receive Pell Grants and, depending upon the agreement, other federal aid.

Financial aid to full-time, first-time undergraduate students: 95% received some form of financial aid.

Departments and Teaching Staff: *Total instructional faculty:* 46 (full-time 27 / part-time 19). 51% of faculty hold the doctorate, first-professional, or other terminal degree. Student/faculty ratio: 25:1.

Enrollment: Total enrollment 745. Undergradaute 702 (full-time 42%; female 635, male 37%). Graduate 244 (full-time 2%). Undergraduate transfer-in students 127.

Characteristics of Student Body: *Ethnic/racial makeup:* Black non-Hispanic: 6%; Asian or Pacific Islander: 1%; Hispanic: 8%; White non-Hispanic: 72%; nonresident alien 4%. *Age distribution:* number 18–19: 53; 20–21: 93; 22–24: 137; 25–295–295–29: 114; 30–34: 93; 35–39: 70; 40–49: 115; 50–64: 48; 65 and over: 1.

International Students: 60 nonresident aliens enrolled fall 2008. Students from Europe, Asia, Central and South America, Africa, Canada, Australia, Middle East. No programs available to aid students whose native language is not English. Financial aid specifically designated for international students.

Student Life: On-campus residence halls house 70% of students. Musical performance groups; dance team. Buckley Outreach Team provides retreats and workshops for Catholic youth throughout Oklahoma and Arkansas. Campus Ministry. Non-residential sororities and fraternities. *Varsity athletics:* male and female basketball, cross-country, golf, soccer, track and field; male baseball; female fast-pitch softball, volleyball. Many intramural sports. *Student publications: The Chant,* student-produced newspaper published 4 times per semester; *The Gregforia*, yearbook is produced in DVD format.

Library Collections: 86,000 volumes including bound books, serial backfiles, electronic documents, and government documents not in separate collections. Online catalog. Current serial subscriptions in paper, microform, and electronic formats. 232 VHS tapes; 182 audiotapes. Computer work stations available. Students have access to the Internet at no charge.

Major special collection include the Oklahoma Collection; Fr. Gregory Gerrer Collection; Native American Collection.

Chief Executive Officer: Fr. Lawrence Stasyzen, Chancellor/President.

Address undergraduate inquiries to William Hallbach, Director of Admissions.

Southeastern Oklahoma State University

Fifth and University
Durant, Oklahoma 74701-0609
Tel: (580) 745-2000 **E-mail:** admissions@sosu.edu
Fax: (580) 745-7502 **Internet:** www.sosu.edu

Institution Description: Southeastern Oklahoma State University (formerly Southeastern State College) is a state institution. *Enrollment:* 3,866. *Degrees awarded:* Baccalaureate, master's.

Academic offerings subject to approval by statewide coordinating bodies. Budget subject to approval by state governing boards.

Accreditation: *Regional:* NCA. *Professional*: music, teacher education

History: Established as Southeastern Normal School, chartered, and offered first instruction at postsecondary level 1909; changed name to Southeastern State College 1939; adopted present name 1974.

Institutional Structure: *Governing board:* Board of Regents of Oklahoma Colleges. Representation: 9 regents (8 appointed by governor of Oklahoma with senatorial approval), including state superintendent of public instruction. 1 ex officio. All voting. *Composition of institution:* Administrators 10. Chief academic officer is the vice president for academic affairs. Management/business/finances directed by vice president for business services. Full-time instructional faculty 141. Academic governance body, Academic Council, meets an average of 6 times per year.

Calendar: Semesters. Academic year Aug. to May. Freshmen admitted Aug., Jan., May. Degrees conferred and formal commencements May, Dec. Summer session of 1 term from June to July.

Characteristics of Freshmen: 1,416 applicants (female 472, male 944). 81% of applicants accepted. 82% of accepted applicants enrolled full-time.

13% (67 students) submitted SAT scores; 86% (530 students) submitted ACT scores. *25th percentile*: ACT Composite 18, ACT 17, English ACT Math 16. *75th percentile*: ACT Composite 23, ACT English 23, ACT Math 22.

17% of entering freshmen expected to graduate within 5 years. 77% of freshmen from Oklahoma. Freshmen from 39 states and 26 foreign countries.

Admission: Rolling admissions plan. For fall acceptance, apply as early as one year prior to, but not later than Aug. 15 of year of enrollment. Early acceptance available. *Requirements:* Graduation from accredited secondary school; minimum GPA 2.7. Age 21 and over GED accepted. Lowest acceptable secondary school class standing 45th percentile for in-state residents. *Entrance tests:* ACT composite with score for in-state residents in upper 50th percentile of secondary school seniors. *For transfer students:* 2.0 minimum GPA; from 4-year accredited institution 94 hours maximum transfer credit; from 2-year accredited institution 64 hours; correspondence/extension students 31 hours.

Advanced placement for postsecondary-level work completed in secondary school. College credit for extrainstitutional learning on basis of portfolio and faculty assessments;personal interviews.

Tutoring available. Developmental courses offered in summer session and regular academic year.

Degree Requirements: 124 credit hours; 2.0 GPA; 30 hours in residence; 40 hours upper division work; distribution requirements. For elementary education degree, exit competency examinations in writing and mathematics.

Fulfillment of some degree requirements and exemption from some beginning courses possible by passing departmental examinations and College Board CLEP Subject Examinations, AP. *Grading system:* A–F; pass, withdraw; incomplete (carries time limit).

Distinctive Educational Programs: *For undergraduates:* Work-experience programs. Accelerated degree programs. Honors programs, tutorials. *Available to all students:* Flexible meeting places and schedules, including off-campus centers (Ardmore, McAlister, Tinker Air Force Base, Oklahoma City, Idalee). Evening classes. Interdisciplinary programs in biomedical science, aviation. Facilities and programs for independent research. Four-year program in aviation. *Other distinctive programs:* Community development, Oklahoma Small Business Development Center; Small Business Institute.

Degrees Conferred: 616 *baccalaureate*; 106 *master's*. Bachelor's degrees awarded in top five disciplines: education 147; business/marketing 79; engineering technologies 60; liberal arts/general studies 50; communications/journalism 39. Master's degrees awarded: business/marketing 16; education 37; engineering 32; psychology 11.

Fees and Other Expenses: *Full-time tuition per academic year 2008–09:* $4,316 resident; $10,687 nonresident; contact the institution for current graduate tuition/fees. *Required fees:* $677. *Room and board per academic year:* $5,626. *Books and supplies:* $1,000. *Other expenses:* $2,881.

Financial Aid: Aid from institutionally generated funds is provided on the basis of academic merit, financial need, athletic ability.

Financial aid to full-time, first-time undergraduate students: 93% received some form of aid. Average amount of aid received: federal grans $3,148; Pell grants $2,778; other federal aid $794; state/local grants $794; institutional grants $1,435.

Departments and Teaching Staff: *Total instructional faculty:* 229 (full-time 141, part-time 88). 67% of faculty hold the doctorate, first-professional, or other terminal degree. Student/faculty ratio: 19:1.

Enrollment: Total enrollment 3,866. Undergraduate 3,434 (full-time 79%; female 55%, male 45%). Graduate 436 (full-time 27%). Undergraduate transfer-in students 584.

Characteristics of Student Body: *Ethnic/racial makeup:* Black non-Hispanic: 5%; Indian or Alaska Native: 31%; Asian or Pacific Islander: 1% Hispanic: 3%; White non-Hispanic: 59%; nonresident alien 1%

International Students: 39 undergraduate nonresident aliens enrolled fall 2008. Students from Europe, Asia, Central and South America, Africa, Middle East. Programs available to aid students whose native language is not English: social. No financial aid specifically designated for international students.

Student Life: On-campus residence halls house 15% of student body. Residence halls for males constitute 30% of such space, for females 10%, for both sexes 60%. 5% of males join fraternities; 5% of females join sororities. *Intercollegiate athletics:* male: baseball, basketball, football, golf, tennis, female: basketball, cross-country, softball, tennis. *Special regulations:* Cars permitted. *Special services:* Medical services. *Student publications, radio: The Southeastern* a weekly newspaper. Radio station KSSU broadcasts 24 hours 7 days per week. *Surrounding community:* Durant population 13,500. Dallas (TX), 90 miles from campus, is nearest metropolitan area.

Library Collections: 306,000 volumes including bound books, serial backfiles, electronic documents, and government documents not in separate collections. Online catalog. 591,000 microforms; 9,300 audiovisual materials; 840 vurrent serial subscriptions: Computer work stations available. Students have access to the Internet at no charge.

Most important special collections include Oklahoma publications; curriculum materials; government documents.

Buildings and Grounds: Campus area 200 acres.

Chief Executive Officer: Dr. Glen D. Johnson, President. Address admission inquiries to Kristie Luke, Director of Admissions.

Southern Nazarene University

6729 NW 39th Expressway
Bethany, Oklahoma 73008
Tel: (405) 491-6324 **E-mail:** admiss@snu.edu
Fax: (405) 491-6320 **Internet:** www.snu.edu

Institution Description: Southern Nazarene University is a private institution affiliated with the Church of the Nazarene. *Enrollment:* 2,069. *Degrees awarded:* Associate, baccalaureate, master's. Member of Council of Christian College and Universities.

Accreditation: *Regional:* NCA. *Professional*: athletic training, music, nursing, teacher education

History: Established as Peniel University in Peniel (TX) and offered first instruction at postsecondary level 1899; awarded first degree (baccalaureate) 1905; chartered 1909; moved to present location, merged with Oklahoma Holiness College, and changed name to Bethany-Peniel College 1920; merged with Central Nazarene University (Tex.) 1929, Arkansas Holiness College 1931, Bresee College (KS) 1940; known as Bethany Nazarene College through March 1986; adopted present name 1986. *See* Roy H. Cantrell, *The History of Bethany Nazarene College* (Doctoral diss., Southwestern Baptist Theological Seminary, 1955) for further information.

Institutional Structure: *Governing board:* Board of Trustees of Southern Nazarene University. Extrainstitutional representation: 55 trustees including 2 alumni representatives, president of the university. All voting. *Composition of institution:* president and 6 administrators. Instructional areas divided into 6 undergraduate schools and three undergraduate division, and one school of graduate studies. Academic affairs headed by vice president for academic affairs. Management/business/finances directed by vice president for financial affairs. Full-time instructional faculty 88. Academic governance body, the faculty, meets an average of 10 times per year.

Calendar: Semesters. Academic year Aug. to May. Freshmen admitted on continuing basis. Degrees conferred May, Aug., Jan. Formal commencements May, Jan. Summer session of 2 terms from May to June.

Characteristics of Freshmen: 100% of applicants admitted. 50% of applicants admitted and enrolled.

18% (62 students) submitted SAT scores; 83% (237 students) submitted ACT scores. *25th percentile*: ACT Composite 19. *75th percentile*: ACT Composite 25.

45% of entering freshmen expected to graduate within 5 years. 43% of freshmen from Oklahoma. Freshmen from 28 states and 2 foreign countries.

Admission: Rolling admissions plan. For fall acceptance, apply no later than 2 weeks prior to beginning of semester. Early acceptance available. *Requirements:* Either graduation from accredited secondary school or GED. Language requirements for foreign students. Minimum 2.5 GPA on a 4.0 scale. Secondary school class rank in one-half. *Entrance tests:* ACT composite required to enroll; SAT accepted for admissions purposes. *For transfer students:* From 4-year accredited institution 94 hours maximum transfer credit; from 2-year accredited institution 62 hours; correspondence/extension students 30 hours.

College credit for College Board CLEP and AP exams and for extrainstitutional learning on basis of faculty assessment.

Tutoring available. Developmental/remedial courses offered during regular academic year; credit given.

Degree Requirements: 124 credit hours; 2.0 GPA; 30 hours in residence; chapel attendance 2 times weekly; 2 hours physical education; general education distribution requirements.

Fulfillment of some degree requirements and exemption from some beginning courses possible by passing College Board CLEP, some courses credit by examination. *Grading system:* A–F; pass/fail; credit/no credit; withdraw-withdraw failing.

Distinctive Educational Programs: Management of Human Resources major or Family Studies and Gerontology major for adults over 24 with available credit for life-learning experience. *For undergraduates:* Interdepartmental program in mass communication/journalism, international studies, or human relations. Preprofessional curricula. *Available to all students:* Evening classes. Special facilities for using telecommunications in the classroom. Study abroad programs in Costa Rica and England.

ROTC: Army offered in cooperation with University of Central Oklahoma. Air Force offered in cooperation with University of Oklahoma.

Degrees Conferred: 3 *associate*; 538 *baccalaureate*; 214 *master's*. Bachelor's degrees awarded in top five disciplines: business/marketing 266; health professions and related clinical sciences 32; psychology 36; education 34; computer and information sciences 28. Master's degrees awarded: business/marketing 78; education 23; health professions 14; psychology 49; theology and religious vocations 5; other disciplines 53.

Fees and Other Expenses: *Full-time tuition per academic year 2008–09:* $16,824 undergraduate; contact the university for current graduate tuition. *Required fees:* $624. *Room and board per academic year:* $5,987. *Books and supplies:* $1,000. *Other expenses:* $3,600.

Financial Aid: Aid from institutionally generated funds is provided on the basis of academic merit, financial need, athletic ability.

Financial aid to full-time, first-time undergraduate students: 90% of students received some form of aid.

Departments and Teaching Staff: *Total instructional faculty:* 140. Student/faculty ratio: 18:1. Degrees held by full-time faculty: doctorate 53%, master's 41%, baccalaureate 2%, professional 4%. 53% hold terminal degrees.

Enrollment: Total enrollment 2,069. Undergraduate 2,069 (full-itme 96%; female 53%, male 47%). Graduate 441 (full-time 98%).

Characteristics of Student Body: *Ethnic/racial makeup:* Black non-Hispanic: 12%; American Indian or Alaska Native: 6%; Asian or Pacific Islander: 3%; Hispanic: 6%; White non-Hispanic: 71%; nonresident alien 2%.

International Students: 42 undergraduate nonresident aliens enrolled fall 2008. Programs available to students whose native language is not English: social. English as a Second Language Program. Financial aid specifically designated for international students.

Student Life: On-campus residence halls house 675% of traditional student body. Residence halls for males constitute 41% of such space, for females 47%. 12% of students live in campus apartments. *Intercollegiate athletics:* male: baseball, basketball, cross-country, football, golf, soccer, tennis, track and field; female: basketball, cross country, golf, soccer, softball, tennis, track and field, volleyball. *Intramural athletics:* coed: softball; male: basketball, cross-country, golf, female: volleyball, aerobics. *Special regulations:* Cars permitted without restrictions. Curfews for freshmen only begin midnight Sun.–Thurs. 1am Fri. and Sat. Study hours are set by residential life staff. Residence hall visitation is allowed in parlors at all times and in entire residence halls during monthly open houses. *Special services:* Learning Resources Center, health care services, counseling services. *Student organizations:* 29 active campus organizations. *Student publications: The Arrow*, a yearbook; *Reveille Echo*, a weekly newspaper. *Surrounding community:* Bethany population 20,000. Oklahoma city is adjoining metropolitan area. Served by mass transit bus systems; airport 15 miles from campus.

Publications: *Southern Lights* is a quarterly alumni publication.

Library Collections: 113,000 volumes. 220,000 microforms; 3,500 audiovisual materials; 670 current periodical subscriptions. Computer work stations available. Online catalog. Students have access to online information retrieval services and the Internet.

Special collections include R.T. Williams Holiness Collection; Hymnological Collection; Bible Collection.

Buildings and Grounds: Campus area 40 acres.

Chief Executive Officer: Dr. Loren Gresham, President.

Address admission inquiries to Warren Rogers, Director of Admissions.

Southwestern Christian University

7300 Northwest 39th Expressway
P.O. Box 340
Bethany, Oklahoma 73008-0340
Tel: (405) 789-7661 **E-mail:** admissions@swcu
Fax: (405) 475-0078 **Internet:** www.swcu.edu

Institution Description: Southwestern Christian University, formerly named Southwestern College of Christian Ministries, is a private institution affiliated with the Pentecostal Holiness Church. *Enrollment:* 291. *Degrees awarded:* Associate, baccalaureate, master's.

Accreditation: *Regional:* NCA.

History: Established as Oklahoma City Southwestern College 1946; name changed to Southwestern College of Christian Ministries; adopted present name 2001.

Institutional Structure: *Governing board:* Southwestern Board of Regents. Extrainstitutional representation: 28 members; institutional representation: 1 administrator, 1 ex officio. All voting. *Composition of institution:* Administrators 6. Academic affairs headed by academic dean. Management/business/finances directed by controller. Full-time instructional faculty 7.

Calendar: Semesters. Academic year Aug. to May. Formal commencement May. Miniterms in January and May.

Characteristics of Freshmen: 70 applicants (22 female, 48 male). 74% of applicants accepted. 60% of accepted applicants enrolled.

11% (8 students) submitted SAT scores; 80% (37 students) submitted ACT scores. *25th percentile*: SAT Critical Reading 340, SAT Math 370, SAT Writing 410; ACT Composite 16, ACT English 15, ACT Math 16. *75th percentile*: SAT Critical Reading 470, SAT Math 635, SAT Writing 490; ACT Composite 23, ACT English 22, ACT Math 20.

SOUTHWESTERN CHRISTIAN UNIVERSITY—*cont'd*

60% of entering freshmen expected to graduate within 5 years. 80% of freshmen from Oklahoma. Freshmen from 6 states and 1 foreign country.

Admission: Rolling admissions plan. *Requirements:* Graduation from accredited secondary school or GED. *Entrance tests:* ACT Composite.

Degree Requirements: *For associate degree:* 66 credit hours; 2.0 GPA; 30 hours in residence; 2 times weekly chapel attendance; general education; Bible core. *For baccalaureate degrees:* 137 credit hours; 2.0 GPA; 30 hours in residence; 2 times weekly chapel attendance; general education; Bible-theology core requirements.

Degrees Conferred: 3 *associate;* 37 *baccalaureate:* theology; 22 *master's:* theology; 7 *doctorate:* theology.

Fees and Other Expenses: *Full-time tuition per academic year 2008–09:* $9,800. *Room and board per academic year:* $4,600. *Books and supplies:* $1,000. *Other expenses:* $4,000.

Financial Aid: Aid from institutionally generated funds is provided on the basis of academic merit, financial need. Institution has a Program Participation Agreement with the U.S. Department of Education for eligible students to receive Pell Grants and, depending upon the agreement, other federal aid.

Financial aid to full-time, first-time undergraduate students: 100% received some form of financial aid. Average amount of aid received: federal grants $3,432; state/local grants $2,364; institutional grants $1,635; loans $3,646.

Departments and Teaching Staff: *Total instructional faculty:* 23 (full-time 8, part-time 15). Total faculty with doctorate, first-professional, or other terminal degree: 10. *Student/faculty ratio:* 14:1. Degrees held by full-time faculty: doctorate 20%, master's 60%, professional 20%.

Enrollment: Total enrollment 291. Undergraduate 208 (full-time 93%; female 50%, male 50%). Graduate 83 (full-time 75%). Undergraduate transfer-in students 49.

Characteristics of Student Body: *Ethnic/racial makeup:* Black non-Hispanic: 21%; American Indian or Alaska Native: 3%; Asian or Pacific Islander: 7%; Hispanic: 4%; White non-Hispanic: 61%; nonresident alien 3%.. *Age distribution:* number 18–19: 49; 20–21: 39; 22–24: 34; 25–29: 10; 30–34: 8; 35–39: 6; 40–49: 12; 50–64: 6.

International Students: 9 nonresident aliens enrolled fall 2008. No programs to aid students whose native language is not English. No financial aid specifically designated for international students.

Library Collections: 32,000 volumes including bound books, serial backfiles, electronic documents, and government documents not in separate collections. Card catalog. Current serial subscriptions: 52 paper. 600 recordings; 40 CD-ROMs. Computer work stations available. Students have access to the Internet at no charge.

Special holdings include Noel Books Collection; Pentecostal Resource Center.

Buildings and Grounds: Campus area 20 acres.

Chief Executive Officer: Dr. Robert R. Ely, President.

Address admission inquiries to Joan Perdue, Registrar.

Southwestern Oklahoma State University

100 Campus Drive
Weatherford, Oklahoma 73096-3098
Tel: (580) 772-6611 **E-mail:** admissions@swosu.edu
Fax: (580) 774-3795 **Internet:** www.swosu.edu

Institution Description: Southwestern Oklahoma State University is a state institution. *Enrollment:* 3,866. *Degrees awarded:* Baccalaureate, first-professional (pharmacy), master's.

Accreditation: *Regional:* NCA. *Professional*: business, chemistry, health information administration, music, nursing, pharmacy, teacher education

History: Established as Southwestern Normal School 1901; offered first instruction at postsecondary level 1903; changed name to Southwestern State Teacher's College 1920; awarded first degree (baccalaureate) 1921; changed name to Southwestern State College of Diversified Occupations 1939, to Southwestern Institute of Technology 1941, to Southwestern State College 1949; adopted present name 1974; Sayre Junior College (now called Southwestern Oklahoma State University at Sayre) became a branch campus.

Institutional Structure: *Governing board:* Board of Regents of Oklahoma Colleges. Representation: 9 regents (appointed by governor of Oklahoma). state superintendent of public instruction. 1 ex officio. All voting. *Composition of institution:* Administrators 29. Academic affairs headed by vice president for academic affairs. Management/business/finances directed by executive vice president for business affairs. Full-time instructional faculty 198.

Calendar: Semesters. Academic year Aug. to May.

Characteristics of Freshmen: 926 applicants (female 472, male 444). 89% of applicants admitted. 72% of admitted students enrolled full-time.

94% (804 students) submitted ACT scores. *25th percentile*: ACT Composite 18, ACT English 17, ACT Math 17. *75th percentile*: ACT Composite 24, ACT English 24, ACT Math 24.

31% of entering freshmen expected to graduate within 5 years. 93% of freshmen from Oklahoma. Freshmen from 10 states and 19 foreign countries.

Admission: Rolling admissions plan. *Requirements:* Either graduation from accredited secondary school or GED. *Entrance tests:* ACT composite. For foreign students TOEFL.

Degree Requirements: *For baccalaureate degrees:* 124 credit hours; 2.0 GPA; 30 semester hours in residence; general education requirements. *Grading system:* A–F.

Degrees Conferred: 616 *baccalaureate*; 106 *master's*; 78 *first-professional.* Bachelor's degrees awarded in top five disciplines: education 147; business, management, marketing, and related support services 122; health professions and related clinical sciences 71; visual and performing arts 49; biomedical/biological sciences 29.

Fees and Other Expenses: *Full-time tuition per academic year 2008–09:* undergraduate resident $4,316, nonresident $10,887; contact the university for current graduate tuition/fees *Room and board per academic year:* $5,626. *Books and supplies:* $1,000. *Other expenses:* $2,881.

Financial Aid: Aid from institutionally generated funds is provided on the basis of academic merit, financial need, athletic ability. Institution has a Program Participation Agreement with the U.S. Department of Education for eligible students to receive Pell Grants and, depending upon the agreement, other federal aid.

Financial aid to full-time, first-time undergraduate students: 93% received some form of financial aid. Average amount of aid received: federal grants $2,677; state/local grants $2,403; institutional grants $2,338; loans $3,484.

Departments and Teaching Staff: *Total instructional faculty:* 198. Student/faculty ratio: 19:1. Degrees held by full-time faculty: doctorate 62%, master's 31%, baccalaureate 1%. 69% hold terminal degrees.

Enrollment: Total enrollment 3,866. Undergraduate 3,434 (full-time 79%; female 55%; amle 45%). Graduate 432 (full-time 23%). Undergraduate transfer-in students 584.

Characteristics of Student Body: *Ethnic/racial makeup:* Black non-Hispanic: 5.2%; American Indian or Alaska Native: 7.2%; Asian or Pacific Islander: 3.8%; Hispanic: 4.3%; White non-Hispanic: 81.1%.

International Students: 39 nonresident aliens enrolled fall 2008. Students from Europe, Asia, Central and South America, Africa, Canada. No programs available to aid students whose native language is not English. No financial aid specifically designated for international students.

Library Collections: 207,000 volumes. 40,000 government documents; 1,100,000 microforms; 7,500 audiovisual materials; 1,550 serial subscriptions. Online catalog. Students have access to online information retrieval services and the Internet.

Most important holdings in the areas of pharmacy and education.

Buildings and Grounds: *New buildings:* General Thomas P. Stafford Center; School of Business; Conference Center. Campus DVD available.

Chief Executive Officer: Dr. John W. Hays, President.

Undergraduates address admission inquiries to Robert J. Klaassen, Registrar.

University of Central Oklahoma

100 North University Drive
Edmond, Oklahoma 73034-0170
Tel: (405) 974-2000 **E-mail:** admituco@ucok.edu
Fax: (405) 341-4964 **Internet:** www.ucok.edu

Institution Description: The University of Central Oklahoma is a state institution. *Enrollment:* 15,724. *Degrees awarded:* Baccalaureate, master's. Certificates also awarded.

Accreditation: *Regional:* NCA. *Professional*: business, funeral service education, nursing, teacher education

History: Established as The Normal School of the Territory of Oklahoma and chartered 1890; offered first instruction at postsecondary level 1891; changed name to Central State Normal School 1907, Central State Teachers College 1919; awarded first degree (baccalaureate) 1921; changed name to Central State College 1939; changed name to Central State University 1971; adopted present name 1991.

Institutional Structure: *Governing board:* Board of Regents of Oklahoma Colleges. Representation: 8 regents (appointed by governor of Oklahoma), state superintendent of public instruction. 1 ex officio. All voting. *Composition of institution:* Administrators 31. Academic affairs headed by vice president for academic affairs. Management/business/finances directed by vice president for administration. Full-time instructional faculty 401. Academic governance body, Faculty Senate, meets an minimum of 9 times per year.

Calendar: Semesters. Academic year Aug. to May. Freshmen admitted Aug., Jan., June. Degrees conferred May, July, Dec. Formal commencement May, July. Summer session of from June to July.

Characteristics of Freshmen: 4,614 applicants (2,582 female, 2,032 male). 89% of applicants accepted. 67% of accepted applicants enrolled full-tme.

1,945 students submitted ACT scores. *25th percentile*: ACT Composite 19, ACT English 18, ACT Math 17. *75th percentile*: ACT Composite 24, SAT Math 25, ACT Math 23.

24% of entering freshmen expected to graduate within 5 years. 88% of freshmen from Oklahoma. Freshmen from 24 states and 51 foreign countries.

Admission: Rolling admissions plan. For fall acceptance, apply as early as Apr. 21, but not later than Aug. 24. Early acceptance available. *Requirements:* Either graduation from accredited secondary school or GED. Minimum GPA 2.7. Lowest acceptable secondary school class standing: in-state residents 50th percentile, out-of-state students 50th percentile. *Entrance tests:* College Board SAT or ACT Composite. *For transfer students:* 2.0 minimum GPA; from 4-year accredited institution 94 hours maximum transfer credit; from 2-year accredited institution 64 hours; correspondence/extension students 62 hours.

College credit and advanced placement for postsecondary-level work completed in secondary school and for extrainstitutional learning.

Tutoring available. Developmental/remedial courses offered in summer session; credit given.

Degree Requirements: 124 credit hours; 30 semester hours minimum residence requirement including at least 15 of the final 30 applied toward the degree; 2.25 GPA minimum; 2 hours physical education; general education requirements. *Grading system:* A=F; pass-fail; withdrawal (carries time limit).

Distinctive Educational Programs: Evening classes. Special facilities for using telecommunications in the classroom. Interdisciplinary programs in general studies, international studies. Preprofessional programs in dentistry, dietetics, engineering, funeral services, medicine, optometry, pharmacy, veterinary medicine. Facilities and programs for independent research, including honors programs, individual majors, tutorials.

Degrees Conferred: 2,184 *baccalaureate*; 406 *master's*. Bachelor's degrees awarded in top five disciplines: business, management, marketing, and related support services 527; education 283; communication, journalism, and related programs 158; visual and performing arts 128; social sciences and history 103. Master's degrees awarded: various disciplines 406.

Fees and Other Expenses: *Full-time tuition per academic year 2008=09:* undergraduate resident $4,223, nonresident $10,652; contact the university for current graduate resident/nonresident tuition and fees. *Books and supplies:* $1,000. *Room and board per academic year:* $7,488. *Other expenses:* $3,800.

Financial Aid: Aid from institutionally generated funds is provided on the basis of academic merit, financial need, athletic ability. Institution has a Program Participation Agreement with the U.S. Department of Education for eligible students to receive Pell Grants and, depending upon the agreement, other federal aid.

Financial aid to full-time, first-time undergraduate students: 71% received some form of financial aid. Average amount of aid received: federal grants $3,504; Pell grants $2,916; other federal aid $801; state/local grants $2,595; institutional grants $819.

Departments and Teaching Staff: *Total instructional faculty:* 802 (full-time 407, part-time 395). 70% of faculty hold the doctorate, first-professional, or other terminal degree. Student/faculty ratio: 23:1.

Enrollment: Total enrollment 15,724. Undergraduate 14,156 (full-time 88%; female 58%, male 42%). Graduate 1,568 (full-time 34%). Undergraduate transfer-in students 1,564.

Characteristics of Student Body: *Ethnic/racial makeup:* Black non-Hispanic: 9%; American Indian or Alaska Native: 5%; Asian or Pacific Islander: 4%; Hispanic: 4%; White non-Hispanic: 60%; unknown: 13%; nonresident alien 6%. *Age distribution:* number under 18: 124; 18–19: 5,387; 20–21: 3,589; 22–24: 3,368; 25–29: 1,834; 30–34: 757; 35–39: 363; 40–49: 537; 50–64: 166; 65 and over: 10.

International Students: 907 nonresident aliens enrolled fall 2008. Students from Europe, Asia, Central and South America, Africa, Canada. Programs available to aid students whose native language is not English: social, cultural. English as a Second Language Program. No financial aid specifically designated for international students.

Student Life: On-campus residence halls house 9% of student body. Residence halls for males constitute 46% of such space, for females 54%. 1.1% of student body live in married student apartments. 2% of males join and 1% live in fraternity housing; 2% of females join and 1% live in sorority housing. *Intercollegiate athletics:* male: baseball, basketball, football, golf, tennis, track, wrestling; female: basketball, softball, tennis, track, volleyball. *Special regulations:* Registered cars with required decals ($40 per year) permitted. Quiet hours. Residence hall visitation from 1pm to 11pm Sun.–Thurs., 1pm to 1am Fri. and Sat. *Special services:* Medical services. *Student publications, radio: Bronze Book*, a yearbook; *Vista*, a biweekly newspaper. Radio station KCSC broadcasts classical music 24 hours a day. Member of National Public Radio and American Public Radio. *Surrounding community:* Edmond population 70,000. Oklahoma City, 8 miles south of campus, is nearest metropolitan area. Served by airport 25 miles from campus.

Library Collections: 439,000 volumes including bound books, serial backfiles, electronic documents, and government documents not in separate collections. Online catalog. Current serial subscriptions: 5,350 including electronic access and paper, 966,565 microform units. 14,975 recordings. Computer work stations available campus-wide. Students have access to the Internet at no charge.

Most important special holdings include Oklahoma Collection; Lloyd Rader Papers; Oklahoma Townsite Cases; Oklahoma Collection.

Buildings and Grounds: Campus area 200 acres.

Chief Executive Officer: Dr. W. Roger Webb, President.

address admission inquiries to Linda Lofton, Director of Admissions; graduate inquiries to Dean, Graduate College.

University of Oklahoma

660 Parrington Oval
Norman, Oklahoma 73109
Tel: (405) 325-0311 **E-mail:** admrec@ou.edu
Fax: (405) 325-7605 **Internet:** www.ou.edu

Institution Description: The University of Oklahoma is a major, comprehensive research university serving the educational, cultural and economic needs of the state, region, and nation. The University has 19 colleges offering 147 areas for undergraduate study; 152 areas for master's degrees; doctoral programs in 81 fields; and a professional degree law. *Enrollment:* 26,140. *Degrees awarded:* Baccalaureate, first-professional (law), master's, doctorate. Graduate certificates also awarded.

Academic offerings subject to approval by statewide coordinating bodies. Budget subject to approval by state governing boards.

Accreditation: *Regional:* NCA. *Professional*: accounting, architecture, aviation, business, computer science, construction education, counseling psychology, dentistry, engineering, health services administration, interior design, journalism, landscape architecture, law, librarianship, music, nuclear medicine technology, nursing, pharmacy, planning, social work, speech-language pathology, teacher education

History: Established 1890; chartered 1891; offered first instruction at postsecondary level 1892; awarded first degree (baccalaureate) 1896. *See* Carolyn G. Hart and Charles F. Long, *The Sooner Story, 1890–1980* (Norman: University of Oklahoma Foundation, Inc., 1980) for further information.

Institutional Structure: *Governing board:* Board of Regents of The University of Oklahoma. Representation: 7 regents appointed by governor. All voting. *Composition of institution:* Academic affairs headed by provost. Management/business/finances directed by vice president for administrative affairs. Full-time instructional faculty 1,246. Academic governance body, Faculty Senate, meets an average of 20 times per year.

Calendar: Semesters. Academic year Aug. to May. Freshmen admitted Aug., Jan., June. Degrees conferred May, July, Dec. Formal commencement May. Summer session from June to Aug.

Characteristics of Freshmen: 10,863 applicants (5,960 female, 4,883 male). 73% of applicants admitted. 48% of applicants admitted and enrolled full-time.

45% (1,013 students) submitted SAT scores; 86% (3,091 students) submitted ACT scores. *25th percentile*: ACT Composite 23. *75th percentile*: ACT Composite 28.

48% of entering freshmen expected to graduate within 5 years. 72% of freshmen from Oklahoma. Freshmen from 50 states and 76 foreign countries.

Admission: Rolling admissions plan with application deadlines for undergraduates and international students. For fall acceptance, apply as early as August of previous year. Early acceptance available and encouraged. *Requirements:* Graduation from secondary school or GED or home schooled. A 3.0 unweighted GPA on a 4.0 scale and rank in the top 30% of graduating class or ACT composite score of 24 or SAT combined verbal and math score of 1090 or a 3.0 GPA on the best 15 core curricular units. Curricular units include: 4 English, 3 college preparatory mathematics, 2 history, 2 lab science, 1 citizenship, 3 additional units from subject areas mentioned previously or computer science or foreign language. Recommend 2 units coursework in music, art, drama, or speech; 1 additional unit of lab science and 1 additional unit in mathematics. *For transfer students:* minimum 2.0 GPA required as well as high school curricular requirements; students with less than 24 semester hours of college-level work must also meet direct from high school performance requirements; maximum transfer credit from a 4-year accredited institution is 90 semester hours; from a 2-year accredited institution, 60 semester hours.

UNIVERSITY OF OKLAHOMA—*cont'd*

College credit for extrainstitutional learning on basis of advanced standing examinations and PONSI recommendations; advanced placement on the basis of university assessment.

Tutoring available. Developmental/remedial courses offered in summer session and regular academic year; nondegree credit given.

Degree Requirements: *For undergraduate degrees:* 124 semester hours; 2.0 GPA; last 30 hours in residence; 6 hours English composition; 6 hours American history and government; general education requirements.

Fulfillment of some degree requirements and exemption from some beginning courses possible by passing departmental examinations, College Board CLEP, other standardized tests. *Grading system:* A–F; pass-fail; withdraw (carries time limit).

Distinctive Educational Programs: Weekend and evening classes. External degree programs in liberal studies and advanced programs offered through Oklahoma Center for Continuing Education. Special facilities for using telecommunications in the classroom. Facilities and programs for independent research, including honors programs, individual majors, tutorials. Study abroad in Austria, Bulgaria, Denmark, Ireland, Italy, The Netherlands, Russia, Nigeria, Ghana, Korea, Costa Rica, Thailand, Canada, France, England, Scotland, Sweden, Mexico, Venezuela, Japan,China, Taiwan, Bolivia, Brazil, Germany, Spain, India, Argentina, Ecuador, Panama.

ROTC: Air Force, Army, Navy, Marine Corps, Air Force in cooperation with Oklahoma Christian University of Arts and Sciences, Oklahoma Baptist University, Oklahoma City University, University of Central Oklahoma, Southern Nazarene University, Rose State College, St. Gregory's University, and Oklahoma City Community College.

Degrees Conferred: 3,877 *baccalaureate*; 1,476 *master's*; 337 *doctorate*; 466 *first-professional*. Bachelors' degrees awarded in top five disciplines: business/marketing 685; communication/journalism 459; social sciences 451; health professions and related clinical sciences 430; liberal arts/general studies 281. Master's degrees awarded in top five disciplines: business/marketing 563; health professions 317; public administration and social services 157; engineering 133; education 125. Doctorates awarded in top five disciplines: education 35; engineering 23; biological/life sciences 22; physical sciences 22; social sciences 14. First-professional degrees awarded: dentistry 50; pharmacy 114; law 167; medicine 135.

Fees and Other Expenses: *Full-time tuition per academic year 2008–09:* undergraduate resident $7,425, nonresident $17,404; contact the university for current graduate/first-professional tuition and applicable fees. Different colleges charge computer course fees ranging from $5 to $25 per credit hour. *Room and board per academic year:* $7,316. *Books and supplies:* $958. *Other expenses:* $4,591.

Financial Aid: Aid from institutionally generated funds is provided on the basis of academic merit, financial need, athletic ability, other criteria.

Financial aid to full-time, first-time undergraduate students: 78% received some form of aid. Average amount of aid received: federal grants $4,186; Pell grants $3,575; other federal aid $2,470; state/local grants $3,568; institutional grants $3,966.

Departments and Teaching Staff: *Total instructional faculty:* 1,719 (full-time 1,346, part-time 373). 88% of faculty hold the doctorate, first-professional, or other terminal degree.

Enrollment: Total enrollment 26,140. Undergraduate 19,450 (full-time 88%; female 50%, male 50%). Graduate 6,690 (full-time 65%). Undergraduate transfer-in student 1,682.

Characteristics of Student Body: *Ethnic/racial makeup:* Black non-Hispanic: 6%; American Indian or Alaska Native: 7%; Asian or Pacific Islander: 5%; Hispanic: 4%; White non-Hispanic: 75%; *Age distribution:* number under 18: 160; 18–19: 8,453; 20–21: 7,261; 22–24: 4,996; 25–29: 1,297; 30–34: 481; 35–39: 201; 40–49: 211; 50–64: 52; 65 and over: 9.

International Students: 592 nonresident aliens enrolled fall 2008. Students from Europe, Asia, Central and South America, Africa, Canada, Australia, New Zealand. Programs available to aid students whose native language is not English: social, cultural, financial. English as a Second Language. Some financial aid specifically designated for international students.

Student Life: On-campus residence halls and university apartments house 21% of student body. 18% of males belong to fraternities; 24% of females belong to sororities. *Intercollegiate athletics:* male: baseball, basketball, cross-country, football, golf, gymnastics, soccer, tennis, track, wrestling; female: basketball, cross-country, golf, gymnastics, soccer, softball, track, tennis, volleyball. *Special regulations:* Restricted parking during day. Quiet hours. Residence hall visitation hours for freshmen from 7am to midnight Sun.–Thurs., 7am to 2am Fri. and Sat. 24-hour visitation for upperclassmen. *Special services:* Learning Resources Center, medical services, trolley and bus services. *Student publications, radio: Oklahoma Daily*, a newspaper; *Windmill*, a biannual literary publication. Radio station KGOU-FM broadcasts 133 hours per week. *Surrounding community:* Norman population 90,000. Oklahoma City, 18 miles from campus, is nearest metropolitan area. Served by airport 20 miles from campus.

Library Collections: 5 million volumes including bound books, serial backfiles, electronic documents, and government documents not in separate collections. Online catalog. Current serial subscriptions: 13,732 paper; 793 microform; 34,623 via electronic access. 12,805 audio/videotapes; 5,055 DVD discs/DC-ROMs. Computer work stations available. Students have access to the Internet at no charge.

Most important special holdings include Degolyer History of Science Collection; Western History Collections; Bass Business History Collection.

Buildings and Grounds: Campus area 5.3 square miles.

Chief Executive Officer: Dr. David L. Boren, President.

Undergraduates address admission inquiries to Office of Prospective Student Services; graduate inquiries to Graduate College; Law inquiries to College of Law.

College of Allied Health

Degree Programs Offered: *Baccalaureate* in communication sciences and disorders, nuclear medicine, nutritional sciences, radiation sciences, radiation therapy, radiography, and sonography. *First-professional*in audiology, occupational therapy, and physical therapy. *Master's* in allied health science, nutritional sciences, rehabilitation sciences and speech pathology. *Doctorate* in allied health sciences, audiology, and speech pathology.

College of Architecture

Degree Programs Offered: *Baccalaureate* in architecture, construction administration, environmental design, interior design; *master's* in architecture, landscape architecture, construction science (with an M.B.A. joint degree option) and regional and city planning.

Distinctive Educational Programs: Work-experience programs. Study abroad in England. Research and experimental design opportunities for students and faculty members.

College of Arts and Sciences

Degree Programs Offered: *Baccalaureate* in African and African-American studies, anthropology, arts and sciences planned program, astronomy, astrophysics, biochemistry, botany, broadcasting and electronic media, chemistry, classics, communication, economics, English, ethics and religion, film and video studies, French, geography, German, health and sport sciences, history, international and area studies, journalism, laboratory technology, studies, law enforcement administration, letters, linguistics, mathematics, microbiology, Native American studies, philosophy, physics, political science, professional writing, psychology, public affairs and administration, public relations, Russian, social work, sociology, Spanish, women's studies, zoology; *master's, doctorate* through Graduate College.

Distinctive Educational Programs: Interdisciplinary programs in African and African-American studies, international and area studies with emphases in East Asian, European, Latin American, and Russian and East European studies, urban studies, women's studies; interdepartmental program in Native American studies. Joint doctoral program in ecology with Oklahoma State University. Field courses in petroleum geophysics conducted at Oklahoma Geology camp located in Canon City (CO). Professional programs in ecology conducted at Biological Station, Lake Texhoma. Summer Washington (D.C.) internship. Language programs offered by Summer Institute of Linguistics in cooperation with Wycliffe Bible Translators.

Michael F. Price College of Business

Degree Programs Offered: *Baccalaureate* in accounting, economics, energy management, finance, international business, management, management information systems, marketing, real estate; *master's* in various fields; various dual degrees with MBA and other master's programs at the university.

Distinctive Educational Programs: Joint M.B.A.-J.D. program with College of Law, joint bachelor and master of accountancy, energy management program, integrated business core for undergraduates. Business Communication Center, Center for Economic and Management Research, JCPenney Leadership Center, Amoco Business Information Resource Center, Center for MIS Studies, Oklahoma Institute for Enterprise and Family Business, and the Student Investment Fund.

College of Dentistry

Degree Programs Offered: *Baccalaureate* in dental hygiene; *first-professional*: doctor of dental surgery; *master's* in orthodontics and periodontics.

College of Earth and Energy

Degree Programs Offered: *Baccalaureate* in geology; geological engineering; geophysics and petroleum engineering; *master's* in geological engineering, geology, geophysics, natural gas engineering and management, petroleum engineering; *doctorate* in geological engineering, geology, geophysics, petroleum engineering.

College of Education

Degree Programs Offered: *Baccalaureate* in early childhood education, elementary education, foreign language education, health and physical education, journalism education, language arts education, mathematics education, music education, professional studies, science education, social studies, special education; *master's, doctorate* in various fields.

College of Engineering

Degree Programs Offered: *Baccalaureate* in aerospace engineering, chemical engineering, civil engineering, computer engineering, computer science, electrical engineering, engineering, engineering physics, environmental engineering, environmental science, geological engineering, industrial engineering, mechanical engineering, petroleum engineering; *master's, doctorate* in various fields.

Admission: 24 hours of college-level courses with 2.0 GPA for Oklahoma residents and students who enter direct from high school. 3.0 in 24 or more credit hours for nonresident transfer students. Computer science 2.80 GPA; electrical engineering 2.80 for full admission.

Degree Requirements: 121–139 hours. 2.0 cumulative GPA at OU; 2.0 retention GPA and transfer work; 2.0 retention GPA in all major work; 2.0 retention GPA in all curriculum work.

Distinctive Educational Programs: Freshmen Engineering Club; Student Mentors Program, Multidisciplinary Professional Development Core Courses, Engineering Entrepreneurship Minor, Multicultural Engineering Program, Dual US/European Degree Programs.

Gaylord College of Journalism and Mass Communication

Degree Programs Offered: *Baccalaureate* in journalism advertising, broadcasting and electronic media, journalism, professional writing, public relations; *master's* in journalism and mass communication, professional writing.

College of Liberal Studies

Degree Programs Offered: *Baccalaureate* in liberal studies; *master's* in liberal studies.

Admission: 2.0 minimum GPA.

Degree Requirements: 126 credit hours (30 from College of Liberal Studies); 2.0 GPA.

Distinctive Educational Programs: Liberal Studies Electronic Delivery.

Weitzenhoffer Family College of Fine Arts

Degree Programs Offered: *Baccalaureate* in art history, ballet pedagogy; ballet performance, ceramics, film making, metal design, modern dance pedagogy, modern dance performance, music composition, music education (vocal and instrumental), music theatre (drama or music emphasis), organ, painting, photography, piano, piano pedagogy, printmaking, sculpture, theatre, video, visual communications, voice, and wind/percussion/string instruments.

Admission: All dance, music and theatre majors must audition to gain full admission into the program; art majors must pass a portfolio review. *Sophomore:* art 2.50 GPA, dance 2.24, dram 2.25; *Junior, Senior:* art 2.50 GPA, dance 2.50, drama 2.50, music 2.50. drama 2.25, music 2.50.

Distinctive Educational Programs: Charles M. Russell Center for Study of the Art of the American West; state-of-the-art recording studio/electronic music laboratory; MIDI labs.

College of Atmospheric and Geosciences

Degree Programs Offered: *Baccalaureate* in geography, geology, environmental geology, petroleum geology, geophysics, geosciences, meteorology; *master's* and *doctorate* in various fields.

Distinctive Educational Programs: Master's program in professional meteorology.

College of Law

Degree Programs Offered: *First-professional*: combined J.D.-M.B.A.

Admission: Baccalaureate from accredited college or university; LSAT.

Degree Requirements: 90 credit hours, 4.0 GPA on a 12-point scale.

College of Nursing

Degree Programs Offered: *Baccalaureate* in nursing, nursing MSN.*Master's* in nursing, family nurse practitioner, pediatric nurse practitioner, clinical nurse specialist,m nurse administration/management, nurse education.

College of Pharmacy

Degree Programs Offered: *First-professional, master's, doctorate:* in pharmaceutical sciences.

College of Public Health

Degree Programs Offered: *Master's, doctorate* in various disciplines in the field of public health.

College of Continuing Education

Degree Programs Offered: *Baccalaureate* in aviation with emphasis in aviation management or professional pilot; professional studies.

University of Oklahoma Health Sciences Center

1000 Stanton L. Young Boulevard
Oklahoma City, Oklahoma 73126-0901

Tel: (405) 271-4000 **E-mail:** admissions@ouhsc.edu
Fax: (405) 271-3032 **Internet:** www.ouhsc.edu

Institution Description: The University of Oklahoma Health Sciences Center offers upper division baccalaureate, professional, and graduate study. *Enrollment:* 3,790. *Degrees awarded:* Baccalaureate, first professional (dentistry, medicine, pharmacy), master's, doctorate.

Accreditation: *Regional:* NCA. *Professional*: audiology, dental hygiene, dentistry, dietetics, medicine, nuclear medicine technology, nursing, occupational therapy, oral and maxillofacial surgery, orthodontic and dentofacial orthopedics, periodontics, pharmacy, physical therapy, physician assisting, psychology internship, public health, radiation therapy, radiography, surgeon assisting, speech-language pathology

Institutional Structure: *Composition of institution:* Academic affairs headed by and management/business/finances directed by provost. Full-time instructional faculty 320.

Calendar: Semesters. Academic year Aug. to May. Degrees conferred May, Aug., Dec. Formal commencement May. Summer session from June to July (8 weeks).

Admission: Rolling admissions plan. For fall acceptance, apply as early as Oct. 1 of previous year, but not later than Mar. 1 of year of enrollment. *Requirements:* 60-64 credits from accredited college or university. Minimum GPA 2.0.

Degree Requirements: *For undergraduate degrees:* 124 semester hours; 2.0 GPA; 4 terms in residence. *Grading system:* A–F.

Degrees Conferred: 430 *baccalaureate:* health professions and related sciences 333 *master's:* various disciplines; 25 *doctorate:* health professions; 299 *first-professional:* dentistry, medicine.

Fees and Other Expenses: *Full-time tuition per academic year 2008–09:* contact the university for current tuition and fees.

Financial Aid: Aid from institutionally generated funds is provided on the basis of academic merit, financial need, other criteria. Financial assistance is available in the form of Pell Grants, College Work-Study, Veterans Administration Benefits, National Direct Student Loans, Supplemental Education Opportunity Grants (SEOG), Stafford Loans, other federal aid programs.

Departments and Teaching Staff: *Total full-time instructional faculty:* 320.

Enrollment: Total enrollment 3,790.

Characteristics of Student Body: *Ethnic/racial makeup:* Black non-Hispanic: 3.6.%; American Indian or Native Alaskan: 8.8%; Asian or Pacific Islander: 3.1%; Hispanic: 3.6%; White non-Hispanic: 77.8%.

International Students: 20 undergraduate nonresident aliens enrolled fall 2008. No programs available to aid students whose native language is not English. No financial aid specifically designated for international students.

Student Life: No on-campus housing. *Special regulations:* Cars with decals permitted. *Special services:* Medical services, bus service. *Surrounding community:* Oklahoma City metropolitan area population over 1 million. Served by mass transit bus system; airport 10 miles from campus.

UNIVERSITY OF OKLAHOMA HEALTH SCIENCES CENTER—*cont'd*

Library Collections: 210,000 volumes. 650 microforms; 2,515 audiovisual materials; 2,563 current periodical subscriptions. Students have access to online information retrieval services and the Internet.

Most important holdings include collections on history of medicine, Indian health.

Buildings and Grounds: Campus area 86 acres.

Chief Executive Officer: Dr. Joseph J. Ferretti, President.

Address admission inquiries to Heath Burge, Director of Admissions.

College of Allied Health

Degree Programs Offered: *Baccalaureate* in clinical dietetics, communication disorders, cytotechnology, medical technology, nuclear medicine technology, occupational therapy, physical therapy, radiography, radiation therapy, ultrasound technology; *master's* in audiology, nutritional sciences, physical therapy, speech pathology, education of deaf; *doctorate* in audiology, speech pathology.

Admission: 2.50 minimum GPA. 60–64 semester hours of prerequisite coursework from accredited college or university which must include 6 hours English, 3 U.S. history, 3 U.S. government, 4 zoology plus 1 lab, 3 intro. psychology, 3 understanding art forms. Each program has additional requirements.

Distinctive Educational Programs: Practical clinical training. Practicums through Speech and Hearing Center. Energized Laboratories in nuclear medicine, radiation therapy, radiography, ultrasound.

College of Nursing

Degree Programs Offered: *Baccalaureate; master's* offered through Graduate College.

College of Dentistry

Degree Programs Offered: *Baccalaureate* in dental hygiene; *first-professional.*

Admission: 60 semester hours from accredited college or university with 6 hours English, 8 biological science (with laboratory), 8 each inorganic and organic chemistry (with laboratory), 8 physics (with laboratory); 2.0 GPA. Priority given to in-state residents.

Degree Requirements: 212 credit hours; 2.0 GPA; first-professional four-year curriculum.

College of Medicine

Degree Programs Offered: *First-professional.*

Admission: Baccalaureate from accredited liberal arts college or 90 semester hours with 3 semesters English; 2 general chemistry; 2 organic chemistry, both aromatic and aliphatic series; 3 from among sociology, psychology, anthropology, philosophy, humanities, or foreign language; 1 vertebrate zoology (with laboratory); 1 from among genetics, comparative anatomy, embryology, histology, or cell biology; MSCAT.

Degree Requirements: 1st year 941 clock hours; 2nd year 959 clock hours; 3rd year 48 weeks; 4th year 35 weeks. 2.0 GPA; last 2 years in residence.

College of Pharmacy

Degree Programs Offered: *First-professional, master's, doctorate.*

Admission: 60 semester hours prepharmacy coursework from accredited college or university which must include 6 hours English, 19 chemistry, 9 mathematics, 6 social science, 4 physics, 4 zoology, 3 economics or accounting.

Degree Requirements: 160 credit hours; 2.0 GPA; 6 semesters in residence.

Graduate College

Degree Programs Offered: *Master's* in anatomical sciences, biochemistry and molecular biology, biological psychology, biostatistics and epidemiology, clinical dietetics, communication disorders, health administration and policy, health promotion policy, microbiology and immunology, nursing, occupational and environmental health, orthodontics, periodontics, pharmaceutical sciences, pharmacology, physical therapy, physiology and biophysics, prosthodontics and radiological sciences; *doctorate* in anatomical sciences, biochemistry and molecular biology, biological psychology, biostatistics and epidemiology, communication disorders, health administration and policy, health promotion policy, microbiology and immunology, occupational and environmental health, pathology, pharmaceutical sciences, pharmacology, physiology and biophysics, and radiological sciences.

Departments and Teaching Staff: Faculty members are drawn from other colleges within the Health Sciences Center.

Distinctive Educational Programs: Gerontology center. Animal resources and facilities. Oklahoma Center for Alcohol and Drug Related Studies. John W. Keys Speech and Hearing Center. Drug analysis laboratory. Traveling scholar program.

College of Public Health

Degree Programs Offered: *Master's, doctorate* in biostatistics and epidemiology, occupational and environmental health, health administration and policy, and health promotion sciences.

Admission: Baccalaureate or equivalent; 3.0 GPA.

Degree Requirements: 36–51 credit hours; 3.0 GPA.

College of Medicine - Tulsa

Degree Programs Offered: *First-professionalf.*

Admission: College of Medicine - Tulsa offers 3rd and 4th year study only. One-fourth of the class may transfer to Tulsa for the clinical training.

Degree Requirements: 3,320 clock hours; 2.0 GPA; 24 months in residence.

Physician Associate Program

Degree Programs Offered: *Baccalaureate* in College of Medicine as Physician Associate.

Admission: 60 semester hours of prerequisite coursework from accredited college or university with minimum GPA of 2.0. Rolling admissions plan. For fall acceptance, apply as early as Oct. 1 of previous year, but not later than April 1 of year of enrollment.

Degree Requirements: 1st year: 1456 didactic clock hours; 2nd year: 2080 clinical clock hours. 2.0 GPA.

University of Science and Arts of Oklahoma

1127 West Alabama Avenue
Chickasha, Oklahoma 73018-5322
Tel: (405) 224-3140 **E-mail:** registrar@usao.edu
Fax: (405) 574-1220 **Internet:** www.usao.edu

Institution Description: University of Science and Arts of Oklahoma (Oklahoma College of Liberal Arts until 1974) is a state institution. *Enrollment:* 1,174. *Degrees awarded:* Baccalaureate.

Academic offerings subject to approval by statewide coordinating bodies. Budget subject to approval by state governing boards.

Accreditation: *Regional:* NCA. *Professional*: audiology, music, teacher education

History: Established as Industrial Institute and College for Girls 1908; offered first instruction at postsecondary level 1909; awarded first degree (baccalaureate) 1915; changed name to Oklahoma College for Women 1916; became coeducational and changed name to Oklahoma College of Liberal Arts 1965; adopted present name 1974.

Institutional Structure: *Governing board:* Board of Regents. Representation: 7 regents. All voting. *Composition of institution:* Academic affairs headed by vice president for academic affairs. Management/business/finances directed by vice president for fiscal affairs. Full-time instructional faculty 53. Academic governance body, Academic Council, meets an average of 18 times per year.

Calendar: Trimesters. Academic year Aug. to Apr. Freshmen admitted Aug., Jan, May. Degrees conferred Apr., Dec., Aug. Formal commencement Dec., Apr. Summer session from June to Aug.

Characteristics of Freshmen: 392 applicants (female 261, male 131). 93% of applicants admitted. 61% of applicants admitted and enrolled full-time.

45% (230 students) submitted ACT scores. *25th percentile*: ACT Composite 18, ACT English 17, ACT Math 17. *75th percentile*: ACT Composite 24, ACT English 22, ACT Math 25.

26% of entering freshmen expected to graduate within 5 years. 92% of freshmen from Oklahoma. Freshmen from 22states and 13 foreign countries.

Admission: Rolling admissions plan. Early acceptance available. *Requirements:* Either graduation from accredited secondary school or GED; ACT 22 or high school GPA 2.0 and upper 50%. *Entrance tests:* ACT Composite. *For foreign students:* TOEFL. *For transfer students:* 2.0 minimum GPA; from 4-year accredited institution 94 semester hours maximum transfer credit; from 2-year accredited institution and for correspondence / extension students 62 hours.

College credit and advanced placement for postsecondary-level work completed in secondary school. College credit for extrainstitutional learning.

Tutoring available. Noncredit Developmental courses offered in summer session and regular academic year.

Degree Requirements: 124 semester hours; 2.0 GPA; 30 hours in residence; exit competency examination in writing; 1 physical activity course; general education requirements.

Fulfillment of some degree requirements and exemption from some beginning courses possible by passing departmental examinations, College Board CLEP, AP. *Grading system:* A–F; limited pass-fail; withdraw deadline (after which pass-fail is appended to withdraw).

Distinctive Educational Programs: Flexible meeting places and schedules, including off-campus centers (at Anadarko, less than 30 miles away from main institution; Carnegie, 40 miles away) and evening classes. Accelerated degree programs. Professional programs in dentistry, medicine, nursing, pharmacy, veterinary medicine. Interdisciplinary programs in human ecology, Indian studies, issues for man. Facilities and programs for independent research, including honors programs, individual majors, tutorials, independent study. *Other distinctive programs:* Continuing education. Educational training for deaf educators and educators of the deaf.

Degrees Conferred: 217 *baccalaureate*. Bachelor's degrees awarded in top five disciplines: business, management, marketing, and related support services 31; visual and performing arts 30; education 22; psychology 17; communications/journalism 14.

Fees and Other Expenses: *Full-time tuition per academic year 2008–09:* $3,552 resident, $8,448 nonresident; contact the university graduate program expenses. *Required fees:* $864. *Room and board per academic year:* $4,860. *Books and supplies:* $800. *Other expenses:* $3,806.

Financial Aid: Aid from institutionally generated funds is provided on the basis of academic merit, financial need, athletic ability, other criteria.

Financial aid to full-time, first-time undergraduate students: 94% received some form of aid. Average amount of aid received: federal grants $2,481; Pell grants $2,720; other federal aid $1,084; state/local grants $2,661; institutional grants $3,238.

Departments and Teaching Staff: *Total instructional faculty:* 89 (full-time 53, part-time 36). Student/faculty ratio: 18:1. Degrees held by full-time instructional faculty: doctorate 65%, master's 31%, professional 45. 75% hold terminal degrees.

Enrollment: Total enrollment 1,174. Undergradaute 1,174 (full-time 80%; female 64%, male 36%). Transfer-in students 110.

Characteristics of Student Body: *Ethnic/racial makeup:* Black non-Hispanic: 3%; American Indian or Alaska Native: 1%; Asian or Pacific Islander: 20%; Hispanic: 5%; White non-Hispanic: 66%; nonresident alien 5%. *Age distribution:* number under 18: 12; 18–19: 348; 20–21: 354; 22–24: 263; 25–29: 129; 30–34: 78; 35–39: 42; 40–49: 77; 50–64: 56; 65 and over: 133.

International Students: 10 nonresident aliens enrolled fall 2008. No programs available to aid students whose native language is not English. No financial aid specifically designated for international students.

Student Life: On-campus residence halls house 33% of student body. Residence halls for males constitute 50% of such space, for females 50%. *Intercollegiate athletics:* male: baseball, basketball, soccer; female: basketball, soccer, softball. *Special regulations:* Cars permitted without restrictions. Quiet hours. *Special services:* Learning Resources Center, medical services. *Student publications: Trend*, a biweekly student newspaper. *Surrounding community:* Chickasha population 16,000. Oklahoma City, 35 miles from campus, is nearest metropolitan area.

Library Collections: 69,000 volumes. 154,000 microforms; 4,200 audiovisual materials; 140 current periodical subscriptions. (10,122 via electronic access). Online catalog. Computer work stations available. Students have access to online information retrieval services and the Internet.

Most important holdings include speech and hearing studies materials; Native American collection; music.

Buildings and Grounds: Campus area 75 acres. Campus DVD available.

Chief Executive Officer: Dr. John H. Feaver, President.

Address admission inquiries to Kellee Johnson, Director of Admissions.

University of Tulsa

600 South College Avenue
Tulsa, Oklahoma 74104-3189

Tel: (918) 631-2000 **E-mail:** admission@utulsa.edu
Fax: (918) 631-2622 **Internet:** www.utulsa.edu

Institution Description: The University of Tulsa is a private, independent, nonprofit institution. *Enrollment:* 4,192. *Degrees awarded:* Baccalaureate, first-professional (law), master's, doctorate.

Accreditation: *Regional:* NCA. *Professional*: athletic training, business, chemistry, computer science, engineering, law, music, nursing, speech-language pathology, teacher education

History: Established in Muskogee, Indian Territory, as Henry Kendall College and offered first instruction at postsecondary level 1894; awarded first degree (baccalaureate) 1898; moved to Tulsa 1907; adopted present name 1920; chartered 1920.

Institutional Structure: *Governing board:* Board of Trustees of The University of Tulsa. Extrainstitutional representation: 40 trustees; 14 honorary members; institutional representation: president of the university. 40 voting. *Composition of institution:* Administrators 36. Academic affairs headed by provost and vice president for academic affairs. Management/business/finances directed by vice president for business and finance. Student affairs headed by vice president for enrollment and student services. Full-time instructional faculty 311. Academic governance body, University Senate and its councils, meets an average of 9 times a year.

Calendar: Semesters. Academic year Aug. to May. Degrees conferred May, Aug., Dec. Formal commencement May. Summer session of 2 terms from May to Aug.

Characteristics of Freshmen: 4,712 applicants (female 2,550, male 2,162). 46% of applicants admitted. 32% of applicants admitted and enrolled full-time.

51% (337 students) submitted SAT scores; 80% (505 students) submitted ACT scores. *25th percentile*: SAT Critical Reading 530, SAT Math 540; ACT Composite 23, ACT English 23, ACT Math 22. *75th percentile*: SAT Critical Reading 690, SAT Math 690; ACT Composite 30, ACT English 32, ACT Math 29. 66 National Merit Scholars.

60% of entering freshmen expected to graduate within 5 years. 55% of freshmen from Oklahoma. Freshmen from 44 states and 47 foreign countries.

Admission: Rolling admissions plan. Apply as early as 1 year prior to enrollment, but not later than first week of class. Early acceptance available. *Requirements:* Either graduation from accredited secondary school or GED. *Entrance tests:* College Board SAT or ACT composite. For foreign students TOEFL. *For transfer students:* 2.5 recommended GPA from 4-year accredited institution; maximum transfer credit limited only by residence requirement; from 2-year accredited institution 62 hours.

College credit and advanced placement for postsecondary-level work completed in secondary school. Tutoring available.

Degree Requirements: *For undergraduate degrees:* 124-137 credit hours, depending on major; 2.0 GPA; last 45 hours in residence; general education requirements.

Fulfillment of some degree requirements and exemption from some beginning courses possible by passing departmental examinations, AP, International Baccalaureate. *Grading system:* A–F; pass-fail; withdraw.

Distinctive Educational Programs: The Tulsa Curriculum, a university-wide humanities-based curriculum featuring core requirements in writing, computer literacy, and either a foreign language (B.A., B.F.A., B.Mus., B.M.E.) or mathematics (B.S.) and general curriculum requirements in the following areas: artistic imagination, social inquiry, cultural interpretation, scientific investigation, contemporary experience, and methods of inquiry. Interdisciplinary programs/self-design areas (e.g., religion, classics). dual major programs (e.g., law and society, international studies). Five-year joint bachelor's degree/M.B.A. to prepare undergraduates in the College of Arts and Sciences and College of Engineering and Applied Sciences for graduate study in business; fulfills some first-year M.B.A. requirements at The University of Tulsa and other institutions. Entrepreneurial studies in the College of Business Administration. Joint program leading to a bachelor of arts degree and a juris doctorate degree after six years. *Other distinctive programs:* The University of Tulsa participates in the following study abroad programs: Institute of European Studies/Institute of Asian Studies, American Institute of Foreign Study, Council on International Educational Exchange, and Regents College, London, England. Locations include Durham and London, England; Freiburg, Germany; Madrid, Spain; Nantes and Paris, France; Vienna, Austria; Moscow, Russia; Tokyo, Japan; Singapore; Adelaide, Australia; Salamanca, Spain; Grenoble, France; Salzburg, Austria. In addition, the University has developed cooperative programs with the University of Malaga, Spain, and the University of Costa Rica, San Jose. The university is developing academic exchange programs in Russia, Union, Romania, and Hungary. The College of Law has a program with The University of Komenius, Bratislava, Slovakia. Customized program options; Honors Program; Tulsa Undergraduate Research Challenge; Cyber Corps Program; Program in International Business and Language; internship opportunities.

ROTC: Air Force in cooperation with Oklahoma State University.

Degrees Conferred: 561 *baccalaureate*; 203 *master's*; 20 *doctorate*. Bachelor's degrees awarded in top five disciplines: business, management, marketing, and related support services 131; engineering 70; biological/life sciences 42; visual and performing arts 38; health professions and related clinical sciences 33. Master's degrees awarded in top five disciplines: business/marketing 71; engineering 45; computer and information sciences 27; psychology 12; physical sciences 8. Doctorates awarded: engineering 9; English 6; psychology 5. First-professional degrees awarded: law 212.

UNIVERSITY OF TULSA—*cont'd*

Fees and Other Expenses: *Full-time tuition per academic year 2008–09:* undergraduate $24,365; contact the university for current graduate and first-professional tuition and other applicable fees. *Room and board per academic year:* $7,876. *Books and supplies:* $1,200. *Other expenses:* $4,089.

Financial Aid: Aid from institutionally generated funds is provided on the basis of academic merit, financial need, athletic ability.

Financial aid to full-time, first-time undergraduate students: 91% received some form of aid. Average amount of aid received: federal grants $4,707; Pell grants $2,871; other federal aid $1,592; state/local grants $4,892; institutional grants $12,435.

Departments and Teaching Staff: *Total instructional faculty:* 376 (full-time 312, part-time 64). 96% of faculty hold the doctorate, first-professional, or other terminal degree. Student/faculty ratio: 8:1.

Enrollment: Total enrollment 4,192. Undergraduate 3,049 (full-time 94%, female 48%, male 52%). Graduate 1,143 (full-time 72%). Undergraduate transfer-in students 148.

Characteristics of Student Body: *Ethnic/racial makeup:* Black non-Hispanic: 6%; American Indian or Alaska Native: 3%; Asian or Pacific Islander: 45; Hispanic: 4%; White non-Hispanic: 63%; unknown: 7%; nonresident alien 12%. *Age distribution:* number under 18: 42; 18–19: 1,136; 20–21: 1,057; 22–24: 411; 25–29: 120; 30–34: 43; 35–39: 21; 40–49: 32; 50–64: 18; 65 and over: 1.

International Students: 459 nonresident aliens enrolled fall 2008. Students from Europe, Asia, Central and South America, Africa, Canada, Australia, New Zealand, Middle East. Programs available to aid students whose native language is not English: social, cultural. English as a Second Language Program. No financial aid specifically designated for international students.

Student Life: 64% of undergraduate students live on campus in residence halls, university-owned apartments, and fraternity and sorority houses. Co-ed residence halls constitute 61%of such space; for males 21% of such space; for females 18%. 21% of males belong to fraternities; 23% of females belong to sororities. *Intercollegiate athletics:* male: basketball, football, golf, soccer, tennis, track; female: basketball, golf, tennis, track, volleyball, soccer, softball, rowing. *Special regulations:* Students must register cars and obtain parking permits. *Special services:* health-medical services, handicapped services, career and personal development services, international student services, communicative disorders services. *Student publications, radio: Collegian*, a student weekly newspaper; *Kendallabrum*, a yearbook. *Surrounding community:* Tulsa metropolitan area population approximately 700,000. Served by mass transit bus system; international airport 5 miles from campus.

Publications: *James Joyce Quarterly, Lithic Technology, Nimrod: International Journal, Petroleum Abstracts, Russian Studies in History, Tulsa Law Journal, Tulsa Studies in Women's Literature.*

Library Collections: 1,200,000 volumes including bound books, serial backfiles, electronic documents, and government documents not in separate collections. Online catalog. 3.4 million microforms; 19,000 audiovisual materials; 28,000 periodicals including via electronic access. Computer work stations available campus-wide. Students have access to the Internet at no charge.

Most important special holdings include Anglo-Irish and American Literature, especially British women writers; John W. Shleppey Collection of Native American Materials; Alice Robertson Archives; V.S. Naipaul Archives; James Joyce Collection; literature related to the petroleum industry.

Buildings and Grounds: Campus area 200 acres.

Chief Executive Officer: Dr. Steadman Upham, President.

Undergraduates address admission inquiries to John C. Corso, Dean of Admission; law school inquiries to Robert A. Butkin, Dean of the College of Law; graduate inquiries to Dr. Janet A. Haggerty, Dean of Research and Graduate Studies.

Henry Kendall College of Arts and Sciences

Degree Programs Offered: *Baccalaureate* in anthropology, art, arts management, communications, economics, deaf education, education, English, film studies, foreign languages and comparative literature, history, international studies, law and society, music, musical theatre, philosophy, political science, psychology, religion, sociology, speech-language pathology, theater; *master's* in anthropology, art, education, education and related fields, English language and literature, history, music, clinical psychology, industrial/organizational psychology, speech/language pathology; English language and literature, history, industrial/organizational psychology; *doctorate* in English language and literature, clinical psychology, industrial/organizational psychology.

Admission: *See* general requirements for undergraduate admission. *For graduate students:* Baccalaureate degree from accredited college or university. GPA of at least 3.0 on a 4.0 scale in undergraduate major, although some programs require a GPA of over 3.0. Satisfaction of course prerequisites for specific program. *Entrance tests:* GRE General Tests; GRE Subject Tests may be required at discretion of some programs.

Degree Requirements: *See* general requirements for undergraduate degree. *For master's:* (minimum only) 30 semester hours (60 hours for M.F.A.). Many programs require thesis and comprehensive examination. *For doctorate:* (minimum only) 90 semester hours (60 beyond master's degree); at least 2 consecutive semesters in residence at university as full-time student. Qualifying examination. Dissertation.

College of Business Administration

Degree Programs Offered: *Baccalaureate* in accounting, athletic training, business administration, economics, exercise and sports science, finance, international business and language, management, management information systems, marketing; nursing; *master's* in accounting and information systems, business administration, engineering and technology management (with College of Engineering and Natural Sciences). business administration, taxation; *J.D./M. of Taxation* (with College of Law) in taxation; *J.D./M.B.A.* (with College of Law) in business administration;

Admission: *See* general requirements for undergraduate admission. *For Graduate School:* Baccalaureate degree from accredited college or university. GPA of at least 3.0 on a 4.0 scale in undergraduate major, although some programs require GPA of over 3.0. Satisfaction of course prerequisites for specific program. *Entrance test:* GMAT.

Degree Requirements: *See* general requirements for undergraduate degree. *For master's:* (minimum only) 30 semester hours.

College of Engineering and Natural Sciences

Degree Programs Offered: *Baccalaureate* in applied mathematics, biochemistry, biological sciences, biology, chemical engineering, chemistry, computer information systems, computational science, computer science, earth science, electrical engineering, engineering physics, geosciences, mathematics, mechanical engineering, petroleum engineering, petrophysics; *master's* in applied mathematics, biological science, chemical engineering, chemistry, computer science, electrical engineering, engineering and technology management (with College of Business Administration), engineering management, environmental science, geosciences, mechanical engineering, petroleum engineering; *doctorate* in biological science, chemical engineering, computer science, geosciences, mechanical engineering, petroleum engineering.

Admission: *See* general requirements for undergraduate admission. *For graduates:* Baccalaureate degree from accredited college or university. GPA of at least 3.0 on a 4.0 scale in undergraduate major, although some programs require a GPA of over 3.0. Satisfaction of course prerequisites for specific program. *Entrance tests:* GRE General Tests; GRE Subject Tests may be required at discretion of some programs.

Degree Requirements: *See* general requirements for undergraduate degree. *For master's:* (minimum only) 33 semester hours. Thesis and non-thesis options. Comprehensive examination. *For doctorate:* (minimum only) 90 semester hours above baccalaureate. Computer language and/or foreign language. Qualifying examination. Dissertation.

College of Law

Degree Programs Offered: *First-professional*: J.D./M. (with the College of Arts and Sciences) in English language and literature, history, industrial/organizational psychology; *J.D./M.S.* (with College of Engineering and Natural Sciences) in biological sciences, geology. *J.D./M. of Taxation* (with the College of Business Administration) in taxation; *J.D./M.B.A.* (with the College of Business Administration) in business administration.

Admission: Baccalaureate degree from accredited college or university. GPA in light of careful evaluation of transcript. LSAT (60th percentile or higher).

Degree Requirements: 88 credit hours. 2.0 GPA.

Oregon

Art Institute of Portland

2000 SW Fifth Avenue
Portland, Oregon 97201
Tel: (503) 228-6528 **E-mail:** aipdadm@aii.edu
Fax: (503) 227-1945 **Internet:** www.aii.edu

Institution Description: The Art Institute of Portland is a private college affiliated with the Art Institutes International that is headquartered in Pittsburgh (PA). independent, nonsectarian institution. *Enrollment:* 1,621. *Degrees awarded:* Associate, baccalaureate.

Accreditation: *Regional:* NWCCU.

History: Founded 1963 as Bassist School for Fashion Careers. Formerly named Bassist College; present name adopted in1998; awarded first associate degree 1978 and first baccalaureate 1989.

Institutional Structure: *Governing board:* Extrainstitutional representation: 5 directors; institutional representation: administrators. All voting. *Composition of institution:* Administrators 7. Academic affairs headed by vice president/director or academic affairs. Full-time instructional faculty 27. Academic governance body, the faculty, meets an average of 8 times per year.

Calendar: Quarters. Academic year Oct. to June.

Characteristics of Freshmen: Average secondary school rank of freshmen males 83rd percentile, females 89th percentile. 59% of applicants accepted. 57% of accepted applicants enrolled.

50% of entering freshmen expected to graduate within 5 years. 75% of freshmen from Oregon. Freshmen from 6 states and 3 foreign countries.

Admission: Rolling admissions plan. For fall acceptance, apply as early as end of junior year of secondary school. *Requirements:* Either graduation from secondary school or GED. Essay and interview required. Portfolio, test scores accepted, placement scores required. *For transfer students:* credits must be at appropriate level, at least a grade of C.

Degree Requirements: *For all associate degrees:* 105 quarter hour credits; 45 credits in residence. *For all baccalaureate degrees:* 180 quarter hour credits; 45 credits in residence. *Grading system:* A–F.

Distinctive Educational Programs: Each academic program offers internships in the subject of study; 2-week traveling seminar to international destination.

Degrees Conferred: 160 *baccalaureate*: visual and performing arts.

Fees and Other Expenses: *Full-time tuition per academic year 2008–09:* contact the institute for current information regarding tuition, fees, housing, and other applicable costs.

Financial Aid: Aid from institutionally generated funds is provided on the basis of academic merit, financial need, other criteria.

Departments and Teaching Staff: *Total instructional faculty:* 104 (full-time 27, part-time 77). Student/faculty ratio: 16:1. Degrees held by full-time faculty: doctorate 20%, master's 70%, baccalaureate 10%. 20% hold terminal degrees.

Enrollment: Total enrollment 1,621 (undergraduate)

Characteristics of Student Body: *Ethnic/racial makeup:* number of Black non-Hispanic: 37; American Indian or Alaska Native: 57; Asian or Pacific Islander: 103; Hispanic: 92; White non-Hispanic: 1,068; unknown: 269. *Age distribution:* number under 18: 7;18–19: 288; 20–21: 310; 22–24: 349; 25–29: 315; 30–34: 116; 35–39: 38; 40–49: 29; 50–64: 14; 65 and over: 4. 88% of student body attend summer quarter.

International Students: 15 nonresident aliens enrolled fall 2008. Students from Asia, Canada. No programs available to aid students whose native language is not English. No financial aid specifically designated for international students.

Student Life: Portland population 545,000. Served by airport 8 miles from campus.

Library Collections: 26,078 volumes. Online catalog. 1,000 audiovisual materials; 200 current periodical subscriptions. Students have access to the Internet and online information retrieval services.

Most important special holdings include collections on historic costumes, furniture and interior decor, and retail management.

Chief Executive Officer: Dr. Steven Goldman, President.
Address admission inquiries to Kelly Alston, Director of Admissions.

Concordia University

2811 NE Holman Street
Portland, Oregon 97211-6099
Tel: (503) 288-9371 **E-mail:** admissions@cu-portland.edu
Fax: (503) 280-8661 **Internet:** www.cu-portland.edu

Institution Description: Concordia University, named Concordia College until 1996, is a private college affiliated with The Lutheran Church-Missouri Synod. *Enrollment:* 1,709. *Degrees awarded:* Baccalaureate, master's.

Accreditation: *Regional:* NWCCU. *Professional*; business, teacher education

History: Established as Evangelical Lutheran Concordia College 1905; chartered and incorporated under present name 1941; offered first instruction at postsecondary level 1950; awarded first degree (associate) 1952; became accredited junior college 1962; became 4-year institution 1977; achieved university status 1996.

Institutional Structure: *Governing board:* Board of Regents. Representation: 9 regents, 1 ex officio. All voting. *Composition of institution:* Administrators 5 including president, vice president for academics, vice president for student services, vice president for finance, vice president for development. Full-time instructional faculty 48. Academic governance body, Educational Policies Committee, meets an average of 35 times per year.

Calendar: Quarters. Academic year Sept. to June. Freshmen admitted Sept., Jan., Mar. Degrees conferred as earned. Formal commencement June, Dec. Summer session June to Sept.

Characteristics of Freshmen: 867 applicants (644 female, 223 male). 65% of applicants accepted. 33% of applicants accepted and enrolled full-time.

86% (157 students) submitted SAT scores; 31% (56 students) submitted ACT scores. *25th percentile*: SAT Critical Reading 450, SAT Math 450; ACT Composite 18, ACT English 16A, ACT Math 18. *75th percentile*: SAT Critical Reading 560, SAT Math 560; ACT Composite 25, ACT English 24, ACT Math 23. 75% of freshmen from Oregon. Freshmen from 14 states and 19 foreign countries.

Admission: Rolling admissions plan. For fall acceptance, apply no later than Sept. 1. *Requirements:* Either graduation from accredited secondary school or GED. Recommend 4 units English, 2 foreign language, 3 mathematics, 3 science, 1 health-physical education, 1 music-art, typing. Minimum GPA 2.50. *Entrance tests:* College Board SAT, ACT composite, or Washington Pre-college Test (WPCT). *For transfer students:* 2.0 minimum GPA; 140 credit hours maximum transfer credit.

College credit and advanced placement for postsecondary-level work completed in secondary school.

Tutoring available. Remedial courses offered during regular academic year; nondegree credit given.

Degree Requirements: *For all associate degrees:* 93 hours. *For all baccalaureate degrees:* 185 hours. *For all degrees:* 1 year in residence; general education requirements. Additional requirements for some programs.

Fulfillment of some degree requirements and exemption from some beginning courses possible by passing College Board CLEP, AP. *Grading system:* A–F; withdraw.

Distinctive Educational Programs: Evening classes. Accelerated degree program. Internships.

Degrees Conferred: 251 *baccalaureate*; 238 *master's*. Bachelor's degrees awarded in top five disciplines: business/marketing 76; education 58; health professions and related clinical sciences 16; psychology 14; biological/life sciences 13. Master's degrees awarded: various disciplines 238.

Fees and Other Expenses: *Full-time tuition per academic year 2008–09:* $22,010. *Room and board per academic year:* $6,480. *Required fees:* $200. *Books and supplies:* $800. *Other expenses:* $2,250.

Financial Aid: Aid from institutionally generated funds is provided on the basis of academic merit, financial need, athletic ability, other criteria.

CONCORDIA UNIVERSITY—*cont'd*

Financial aid to full-time, first-time undergraduate students: 99% received some form of financial aid. Average amount of aid received: federal grants $4,265; Pell grants $3,371; other federal aid $1,790; state/local grants $3,319; institutional grants $11,092.

Departments and Teaching Staff: *Total instructional faculty:* 138 (full-time 38, part-time 110). Student/faculty ratio: 20:1. Degrees held by full-time faculty: doctorate 46%, master's 44%, baccalaureate 10%. 50% hold terminal degrees.

Enrollment: Total enrollment 1,709. Undergraduate 1,085 (full-time 83%; female 65%; male 35%). Graduate 644 (full-time 68%). Undergraduate transfer-in students 143.

Characteristics of Student Body: *Ethnic/racial makeup:* Black non-Hispanic: 75; American Indian or Alaska Native: 1%; Asian or Pacific Islander: 5%; Hispanic: 5%; White non-Hispanic: 68%; unknown: 13%; nonresident alien 1%. *Age distribution:* number under 18: 18; 18–19: 202; 20–21: 217; 22–24: 144; 25–29: 82; 30–34: 55; 35–39: 41; 40–49: 70; 50–64: 21; 65 and over: 1.

International Students: 17 nonresident aliens enrolled fall 2008. Students from Europe, Asia, Canada. No programs available to aid students whose native language is not English. No financial aid specifically designated for international students.

Student Life: On-campus residence halls house 45% of student body. Housing available for married students. *Intercollegiate athletics:* male: baseball, basketball, soccer; female: basketball, volleyball. *Special regulations:* Residence hall visitation from noon to midnight Sun.–Thurs., noon to 2am Fri.-Sat. *Special services:* Learning Resources Center, medical services. *Student publications: The Concordian*, published every other week; *Mihi Lux*, a yearbook. *Surrounding community:* Portland. Served by mass transit light rail train and bus system. Airport and passenger rail service 5 miles from campus.

Library Collections: 70,000 volumes. Current periodical subscriptions: 424. 37,000 microforms. 3,000 audiovisual materials. Online catalog. Computer work stations available. Students have access to online information retrieval services and the Internet.

Most important special holdings include Lutheran Studies; Shakespeare.

Buildings and Grounds: Campus area 13 acres.

Chief Executive Officer: Dr. Charles E. Schlimpert, President.

Address admission inquiries to Robert Swan, Dean of Admissions.

Corban College

5000 Deer Park Drive, SE
Salem, Oregon 97301
Tel: (503) 581-8600 **E-mail:** admissions@wbc.edu
Fax: (503) 585-4316 **Internet:** www.wbc.edu

Institution Description: Corban College, formerly known as Western Baptist College, is a private independent college. *Enrollment:* 1,031. *Degrees awarded:* Associate, baccalaureate, master's.

Accreditation: *Regional:* NWCCU. *Professional*: teacher education

History: Established as Western Baptist Bible and Theological Seminary and offered first instruction at postsecondary level 1936; awarded first degree (baccalaureate) 1954; changed name to Western Baptist Bible College 1969; became Western Baptist College 1978; adopted present name 2006.

Institutional Structure: *Governing board:* Board of Trustees of Western Baptist College. Extrainstitutional representation: 25 trustees (including some alumni); institutional representation: 1 administrator. 1 ex officio. 21 voting. *Composition of institution:* Administrators 8. Academic affairs headed by academic dean. Management/business/finances directed by business manager. Full-time instructional faculty 30. Academic governance body, Academic Affairs Committee, meets an average of 30 times per year.

Calendar: Semesters. Academic year Sept. to May. Freshmen admitted Aug., Jan. Degrees conferred and formal commencement May.

Characteristics of Freshmen: 498 applicants (333 female, 165 male). 79% of applicants accepted. 47% of accepted applicants enrolled full-time.

89% (170 students) submitted SAT scores; 25% (48 students) submitted ACT scores. *25th percentile*: SAT Critical Reading 490, SAT Math 480; ACT Composite 20, ACT English 20, ACT Math 18. *75th percentile*: SAT Critical Reading 600, SAT Math 600; ACT Composite 24, ACT English 26, ACT Math 24.

45% of entering freshmen expected to graduate within 5 years. 70% of freshmen from Oregon. Freshmen from 30 states and 5 foreign countries.

Admission: Rolling admissions plan. For fall acceptance, apply by Aug. 15. *Requirements:* Either graduation from accredited secondary school or GED. Applicant must show evidence of being born again and living consistent Christian life as indicated by his or her personal testimony and pastor's recommendation. Minimum 2.5 GPA. *Entrance tests:* College Board SAT. *For transfer students:* 2.0 minimum GPA; 70 hours maximum transfer credit.

Degree Requirements: *For all undergraduate degrees:* 2.0 GPA; 30 semester hours in *For all baccalaureate degrees:* 128 semester hours; 2 units physical education. *For all associate degrees:* 64 semester hours; 2 units physical education.

Fulfillment of some baccalaureate degree requirements possible by passing College Board CLEP, AP. *Grading system:* A–F; pass-fail; withdraw (carries penalty and time limit); incomplete (work must be completed by end of following semester); time extended for completion of work.

Distinctive Educational Programs: Latin American, Middle East, and Russian Study Programs in conjunction with Council for Christian Colleges and Universities.

Degrees Conferred: 4 *associate*; 152 *baccalaureate:*; 6 *master's*. Bachelor's degrees awarded: business and management 49, education 38, liberal arts/general studies 5, mathematics 3, philosophy/religious studies 33, personal and miscellaneous services 6, psychology 48. Master's degrees awarded: education 6.

Fees and Other Expenses: *Full-time tuition per academic year 2008–09:* $22,520. *Books and supplies:* $900. *Room and board per academic year:* $8,068. *Other expenses:* $3,202.

Financial Aid: The college offers a direct lending program. Aid from institutionally generated funds is provided on the basis of academic merit, financial need, athletic ability, other criteria. Institution has a Program Participation Agreement with the U.S. Department of Education for eligible students to receive Pell Grants and, depending upon the agreement, other federal aid.

Financial aid to full-time, first-time undergraduate students: 78% received some form of financial aid. Average amount of aid received: federal grants $1,522; state/local grants $2,617; institutional grants $6,981; loans $7,206.

Departments and Teaching Staff: *Total instructional faculty:* 53. Student/faculty ratio: 17:1. Degrees held by full-time faculty: doctorate 37%, master's 63%. 37% hold terminal degrees.

Enrollment: Total enrollment 1,031. Undergraduate 926 (full-time 81%; female 62%, male 38%). Graduate 105 (full-time 27%). Undergraduate transfer-in students 40.

Characteristics of Student Body: *Ethnic/racial makeup:* Black non-Hispanic: 1%; American Indian or Native Alaskan: 1%; Asian or Pacific Islander: 3%; Hispanic: 1%; White non-Hispanic: 87%.

International Students: No programs available to aid students whose native language is not English. No financial aid specifically designated for international students.

Student Life: On-campus residence halls house 49% of student body. Residence halls for males constitute 42% of such space, for females 58%. *Intercollegiate athletics:* male: baseball, basketball, soccer; female: basketball, soccer. volleyball. *Special regulations:* Cars permitted with campus registration. *Special services:* Learning Resources Center, medical services. *Surrounding community:* Salem population 115,000. Portland, 50 miles from campus, is nearest metropolitan area. Served by airport 3 miles from campus; passenger rail service 5 miles from campus.

Library Collections: 82,000 volumes including bound books, serial backfiles, electronic documents, and government documents not in separate collections. Online catalog/ Current serial subscriptions: 550. 41,000 microforms; 4,500 audiovisual materials. Computer work stations available. Students have access to online information retrieval services and the Internet.

Most important special collections include Bible and Theology; Missions; Northwest Fellowship of Regular Baptist Churches (papers); Museum of Middle Eastern Archeology.

Buildings and Grounds: Campus area 108 acres.

Chief Executive Officer: Dr. Reno Hoff, President.

Address admission inquiries to Marty Ziesermer, Dean of Admissions.

Eastern Oregon University

One University Boulevard
La Grande, Oregon 97850-2807
Tel: (541) 962-3393 **E-mail:** admissions@eou.edu
Fax: (541) 962-3418 **Internet:** www.eou.edu

Institution Description: Eastern Oregon University (Eastern Oregon State College until 1977) is a state institution. *Enrollment:* 3,666. *Degrees awarded:* Baccalaureate, master's.

Academic offerings subject to approval by statewide coordinating bodies. Budget subject to approval by state governing boards. Member of the consortia Council for Advancement of Experiential Learning, National Student Exchange, Pacific Northwest International/Intercultural Education Consortium, and Western Interstate Commission for Higher Education.

Accreditation: *Regional:* NWCCU. *Professional*: teacher education

History: Established as Eastern Oregon Normal School and offered first instruction at postsecondary level 1929; changed name to Eastern Oregon College of Education 1939; awarded first degree (baccalaureate) 1941; changed name to Eastern Oregon College 1956; changed name to Eastern Oregon State College 1972; adopted present name 1974.

Institutional Structure: *Governing board:* Oregon University System: 9 members, 2 students. All voting. *Composition of institution:* Administrators 18. Academic affairs headed by provost and vice president. Management/business/ finances directed by vice president for administration and finance. Full-time instructional faculty 87. Academic governance body, Eastern Oregon University Assembly, meets an average of 9 times per year.

Calendar: Quarters. Academic year Sept. to June. Freshmen admitted Sept., Jan., Mar., June, July. Degrees conferred June, Sept., Dec., Mar. Formal commencement June. Summer session of 2 terms from June to Sept.

Characteristics of Freshmen: 725 applicants (female 388, male 357). 44% of applicants accepted. 38% of accepted applicants enrolled full-time.

70% (252 students) submitted SAT scores; 25% (71 students) submitted ACT scores. *25th percentile*: SAT Critical Reading 430, SAT Math 450; ACT Composite 18, ACT English 18, ACT Math 18. *75th percentile*: SAT Critical Reading 550, SAT Math 550; ACT Composite 24, ACT English 23, ACT Math 23.

30% of freshmen expected to graduate within 5 years. 70% of freshmen from Oregon. Freshmen from 42 states and 26 foreign countries.

Admission: Rolling admissions plan. Early acceptance available. *Requirements:* Minimum high school 3.0 GPA in 14 core subject areas for entering freshmen for both in-state and out-of-state students. *Entrance tests:* SAT, ACT, or WPCT. For foreign students TOEFL. *For transfer students:* 2.0 minimum GPA; from 4-year accredited institution transfer credit limited only by residence requirement; from 2-year accredited institution 104 quarter hours; correspondence/extension students 25 quarter hours.

College credit and advanced placement for postsecondary-level work completed in secondary school and for extrainstitutional learning on basis of portfolio and faculty assessments; personal interviews.

Tutoring available. Developmental courses offered during regular academic year; credit given.

Degree Requirements: *For all associate degrees:* 93 quarter hours. *For all baccalaureate degrees:* 180 quarter hours; minimum 45 hours in residence; general education requirements; *For all undergraduate degrees:* 2.0 GPA.

Fulfillment of some degree requirements and exemption from some beginning courses possible by passing departmental examinations, College Board CLEP, AP. *Grading system:* A–F; satisfactory-unsatisfactory; withdraw; incomplete (carries time limit).

Distinctive Educational Programs: Cooperative baccalaureate programs with Oregon State University in agriculture, business management, crop science, rangeland resources, natural resources and environmental economic policy and management. Nursing degree offered through Oregon Health Sciences University. Distance education program.

Degrees Conferred: 625 *baccalaureate*; 76 *master's*. Bachelor's degrees awarded in top five disciplines: liberal arts and sciences, general studies, and humanities 149; business, management, marketing, and related support services 115; interdisciplinary studies 75; social sciences 30; visual and performing arts 26. Master's degrees awarded: education 76.

Fees and Other Expenses: *Full-time tuition (defined as 12 credits) and fees per academic year 2008–09:* $6,225 resident/nonresident undergraduate; contact the university for current graduate tuition/fees. *Room and board per academic year:* $9,020. *Required fees:* $1,332. *Books and supplies:* $1,152. *Other expenses:* $2,217.

Financial Aid: Aid from institutionally generated funds is provided on the basis of academic merit, financial need.

Financial aid to full-time, first-time undergraduate students: 89% received some form of aid. Average amount of aid received: federal grants $2,925; Pell grants $2,713; other federal aid $662; state/local grants $1,481; institutional grants $2,541.

Departments and Teaching Staff: *Total instructional faculty:* 115 (full-time 102, part-time 13). Student/faculty ration: 28:1. Degrees held by full-time faculty: doctorate 84.6%, master's 15.4%. 96% hold terminal degrees.

Enrollment: Total enrollment 3,666. Undergraduate 3,127 (full-time 54%; female 52%, male 38%). Graduate 539 (full-time 24%). Undergraduate transfer-in students 529.

Characteristics of Student Body: *Ethnic/racial makeup:* Black non-Hispanic: 2%; American Indian or Alaska Native: 2%; Asian or Pacific Islander: 45; Hispanic: 2%; White non-Hispanic: 77%;' unknown: 11%; nonresident alien 1%.

International Students: 37 nonresident aliens enrolled. Students from Europe, Asia, Central and south America, Africa. No programs available to aid students whose native language is not English. No financial aid specifically designated for international students.

Student Life: On-campus residence halls house 25% of student body. Residence halls for males constitute 35% of such space, for females 34%, for both sexes 31%. 3% of student body live on campus in married student housing. *Intercollegiate athletics:* basketball, cross-country, football, soccer, softball, track; volleyball. *Special regulations:* Cars with parking permit allowed (fee charged). Quiet hours and visitation hours vary according to residence hall. *Special services:* Learning Resources Center, medical services. *Student publications, radio: The Voice*, prints bimonthly; *Oregon East*, a student literary magazine. Radio station KEOL broadcasts regularly. *Surrounding community:* La Grande population 12,000. Portland, 260 miles from campus, is nearest metropolitan area. Served by airport 50 miles from campus.

Library Collections: 601,000 volumes. 168,000 government documents; 114,000 microforms; 13,000 audiovisual materials; 1,000 current periodical subscriptions. Students have access to online information retrieval services and the Internet.

Most important special collections include Oregon and local history; Native American Literature Collection; Pacific Northwest Literary Collection.

Buildings and Grounds: Campus area 120 acres.

Chief Executive Officer: Dr. Khosrow Fatemi, President.

Address admission inquiries to Jamie Contreras, Director of Admissions.

Eugene Bible College

2155 Bailey Hill Road
Eugene, Oregon 97405-1194
Tel: (541) 485-1780 **E-mail:** admissions@ebc.edu
Fax: (541) 343-5801 **Internet:** www.ebc.edu

Institution Description: Eugene Bible College is a private institution of the Pacific Coast Division of the Open Bible Standard Churches. *Enrollment:* 129. *Degrees awarded:* Baccalaureate.

Accreditation: *National:* ABHE.

Calendar: Semesters. Academic year Sept. to June.

Characteristics of Freshmen: 90% of applicants admitted. 74% of applicants admitted and enrolled.

Mean SAT scores males 390 critical reading, 401 mathematical.

46% of entering freshmen expected to graduate within 5 years. 56% of freshmen from Oregon. Freshmen from 15 states and 2 foreign countries.

Admission: *Requirements:* Graduation from secondary school; non-high school graduates may be considered. *Entrance tests:* College Board SAT or ACT.

Degree Requirements: Completion of prescribed curriculum.

Degrees Conferred: 51 *baccalaureate:* education 1; interdisciplinary studies 5; social sciences 5; theology and religious vocations 40.

Fees and Other Expenses: *Full-time tuition per academic year 2008–09:* $10,355. *Required fees:* $705. *Room and board per academic year:* $5,400. *Books and supplies:* $900. *Other expenses:* $1,800.

Financial Aid: Aid from institutionally generated funds is provided on the basis of academic merit, financial need.

Financial aid for first-time, full-time undergraduate students: 73% received some form of aid.

Departments and Teaching Staff: *Total instructional faculty:* 22 (full-time 9, part-time 13).

Enrollment: Total enrollment 184 (undergraduate). Transfer-in students

Characteristics of Student Body: *Ethnic/racial makeup:* Black non-Hispanic: 1%; American Indian or Alaska Native: 3%; Hispanic: 2%; White non-Hispanic: 93%; nonresident alien 1%. *Age distribution:* number under 18: 4; 18–19: 31; 20–21: 49; 22–24: 51; 25–29: 18; 30–34: 4; 35–39: 6; 40–49: 10; 50–64: 8; 65 and over: 3. 3% of student body attend summer sessions.

International Students: 2 nonresident aliens enrolled fall 2009. No programs available to aid students whose native language is not English. Financial aid designated for international students.

Library Collections: 35,000 volumes. 50 compact discs. Computer work stations available. Current serial subscriptions: paper 251; via electronic access 17,000. Students have access to the Internet at no charge.

Chief Executive Officer: Dr. David L. Cole, President.

Address admission inquiries to Trent Combs, Director of Admissions.

George Fox University

414 North Meridian Street
Newberg, Oregon 97132-2697
Tel: (503) 538-8383 **E-mail:** admissions@georgefox.edu
Fax: (503) 538-7234 **Internet:** www.georgefox.edu

Institution Description: George Fox University was formed by a merger of George Fox College and Western Evangelical Seminary in 1996. The university is a private, nonprofit institution affiliated with the Northwest Yearly Meeting of

GEORGE FOX UNIVERSITY—*cont'd*

Friends Church. *Enrollment:* 3,383. *Degrees awarded:* Baccalaureate, master's, doctorate.

Academic offerings subject to approval by statewide coordinating bodies. Member of the Christian College Consortium and the Coalition of Christian Colleges and Universities.

Accreditation: *Regional:* NWCCU. *Professional*: athletic training, engineering, music, psychology internship, social work, teacher education, theology

History: Established as Pacific College in 1891; chartered 1893; awarded first degree (baccalaureate) 1892; became George Fox College 1949; merged with Western Evangelical Seminary and adopted present name 1996.

Institutional Structure: *Governing board:* George Fox University Board of Trustees. Extrainstitutional representation: 37 trustees, superintendent of Northwest Yearly Meeting of Friends; institutional representation: president of the university; 6 alumni. 2 ex officio. 43 voting. *Composition of institution:* Administrators 5. Academic affairs headed by provost. Management/business/finances directed by vice president for financial affairs. Full-time instructional faculty 158. Academic governance body, the faculty, meets an average of 15 times per year.

Calendar: Semesters. Academic year Aug. to May. Freshmen admitted Sept., Jan. Degrees conferred May, Dec. 3-week May term.

Characteristics of Freshmen: 1,212 applicants (741 femlae, 471 male). 83% of applicants admitted. 41% of admitted students enrolled full-time.

89% (371 students) submitted SAT scores; 25% (106 students) submitted ACT scores. *25th percentile*: SAT Critical Reading 480, SAT Math 480; ACT Composite 20, ACT English 19, ACT Math 19. *75th percentile*: SAT Critical Reading 610, SAT Math 610; ACT Composite 26, ACT English 26, ACT Math 26.

63% of entering freshmen expected to graduate within 5 years. 68% of freshmen from Oregon. Freshmen from 27 states and 10 foreign countries,

Admission: Rolling admissions plan. Early acceptance available and early action available. For fall acceptance, Feb. 1 is the priority date. *Requirements:* Either graduation from accredited secondary school with 16 units or GED. Recommend 4 units English, 2 in a foreign language, 2 mathematics, 3 science, 2 social studies,, 2 history. *Entrance tests:* College Board SAT or ACT composite. *For transfer students:* 2.6 minimum GPA; from 2-year accredited institution 64 hours.

Degree Requirements: 126 semester hours; 2.0 GPA; 30 hours in residence; chapel attendance 2 days weekly; completion of general education requirements.

Fulfillment of some degree requirements and exemption from some beginning courses possible by passing departmental examinations, College Board CLEP, AP (score of 3). *Grading system:* A–F; pass-fail; withdraw (carries time limit); incomplete (carries time limit).

Distinctive Educational Programs: Work-experience programs. Evening classes. Interdisciplinary programs in liberal arts, music-religion, physical education-religion, home economics and business or social services, science-business. Facilities and programs for independent study and research, including honors program and individualized majors. Independent study for teacher in service. Programmed instruction. All students are provided a computer. Institutionally sponsored career and cultural off-campus study through Field Education program. Additional off-campus study available through consortium and in Washington (DC) through American Studies Program and in Costa Rica. Junior year 3-week study abroad program.

Degrees Conferred: 513 *baccalaureate*; 410 *master's*; 54 *doctorate*. Bachelor's degrees awarded in top five disciplines: business, management, marketing, and related support services 197; interdisciplinary studies 56; biological/biomedical sciences; visual and performing arts 33; theology and religious vocations 22. Master's degrees awarded: business/marketing 98; education 217; health professions 14; psychology 59; theology and religious vocations 16. Doctorates awarded: theology 29, psychology 15.

Fees and Other Expenses: *Full-time tuition per academic year 2008=09:* $25,190. Graduate tuition depends on program; contact the university for further information. *Room and board per academic year:* $8,000. *Books and supplies:* $700. *Required fees:* $320. *Other expenses:* $1,300.

Financial Aid: The university offers a direct lending program. Aid from institutionally generated funds is provided on the basis of academic merit, financial need.

87% of first-time, first-year undergraduates received some form of financial aid. Average amount of aid received: federal grants $4,049; Pell grants $2,771, other federal aid $1,373; state/local grants $3,488; institutional grants $10,478.

Departments and Teaching Staff: *Total instructional faculty:* 324 (full-time 158, part-time 166). Student/faculty ratio: 12:1. Degrees held by full-time faculty: doctorate 69%, master's 29%, baccalaureate 2%. 69% hold terminal degrees. *Faculty development:* 9 faculty members awarded sabbaticals 2008–09.

Enrollment: Total enrollment 3,383. Undergraduate 1,980 (full-time 80%; female 61%, male 39%). Graduate 1,403 (full-time 27%). Undergraduate transfer-in students 161.

Characteristics of Student Body: *Ethnic/racial makeup:* Black non-Hispanic: 2%; American Indian or Alaska Native: 2%; Asian or Pacific Islander: 5%; Hispanic: 4%; White non-Hispanic: 74%; unknown: 8%; nonresident alien 4%. *Age distribution:* number under 18: 26; 18–19: 735; 20–21: 641; 22–24: 169; 25–29: 68; 30–34: 521 35–39: 411 40–49: 801 50–64: 371 65 and over: 1. 38% of student body attend summer sessions.

International Students: 136 nonresident aliens enrolled fall 2008. Student from Europe, Asia, South America, Africa, Canada. Programs available to aid students whose native language is not English: social, cultural. English as a Second Language Program. Financial aid specifically designated for international students.

Student Life: On-campus residence halls/apartments/houses for 70% of student body. *Intercollegiate athletics:* male: baseball, basketball, cross-country, soccer, tennis, track; female: basketball, cross-country, golf, soccer, softball, track, volleyball. *Special regulations:* Registered cars permitted without restriction. Quiet hours from 10pm to 9am/ *Special services:* Learning Resources Center, medical and counseling services. *Student publications, radio: The Crescent*, a weekly newspaper. Radio station KFOX broadcasts 20 hours a week. *Surrounding community:* Newberg population 20,465. Portland, 20 miles from campus, is nearest metropolitan area.

Library Collections: 208,500 volumes. Current serial subscriptions: paper 990; via electronic access 3,357. 5,992 audio/videotapes; 363 DVD discs. Computer work stations available. Online catalog. Students have access to the Internet and fee-based access to the online information retrieval services.

Most important special collections include Quaker Collection; Hoover Collection; Peace Collection.

Buildings and Grounds: Campus area 85 acres.

Chief Executive Officer: Dr. H. David Brandt, President.

Address admission inquiries to Ryan Dougherty, Director of Admissions.

Lewis and Clark College

0615 SW Palatine Hill Road
Portland, Oregon 97219-7899
Tel: (503) 768-7040 **E-mail:** admissions@lclark.edu
Fax: (503) 768-7055 **Internet:** www.lclark.edu

Institution Description: Lewis and Clark College is a private, independent, nonprofit institution. *Enrollment:* 3,565. *Degrees awarded:* Baccalaureate, first-professional (law), master's.

Accreditation: *Regional:* NWCCU. *Professional*: law, music, teacher education

History: Established as Albany College, incorporated, and offered first instruction at postsecondary level 1867; awarded first degree 1873; present name adopted 1942; Northwestern College of Law merged with Lewis and Clark College 1965. *See* Martha Frances Montague, *Lewis and Clark College 1867–1967* (Portland, Ore.: Binfords and Mort, Publishers, 1968) for further information.

Institutional Structure: *Governing board:* Board of Trustees. Extrainstitutional representation: 33 trustees (including president and heads of the two alumni associations). *Composition of institution:* Administrators 175. Academic affairs headed by vice president for academic affairs and dean of the college. Management/business/finances directed by vice president for business and finance. Full-time instructional faculty of 129.

Calendar: Semesters. Academic year Aug. to May. Freshmen admitted Sept., Jan., Mar. Degrees conferred and formal commencements June, Aug. Summer session of 2 terms from June to Aug.

Characteristics of Freshmen: 5,551 applicants (3,353 female, 2,198 male). 58% of applicants accepted. 17% of accepted applicants enrolled full-time.

70% (301 students) submitted SAT scores; 31% (157 students) submitted ACT scores. *25th percentile*: SAT Critical Reading 620, SAT Math 590, SAT Writing 590; ACT Composite 26, ACT English 25, ACT Math 26/ *75th percentile*: SAT Critical Reading 700, SAT Math 680. SAT Writing 680; ACT Composite 30, ACT English 31, ACT Math 22.

60% of entering freshmen expected to graduate within 5 years. 20% of freshmen from Oregon. Freshmen from 46 states and 40 foreign countries.

Admission: Admission is selective. Early Decision application is due Nov. 15; notification Dec. 15; must withdraw applications from other institutions if admitted to Lewis and Clark. Early Action due date Dec. 15, notified Jan. 15. Regular Decision due date Feb. 1., notified April 1. Students applying Early Action and Regular have until May 1 to respond to the offer of admission. *Requirements:* The Admissions Committee views the selection of courses in high school as evidence of an applicant's serious preparation for college. Recommended preparation: 4 years of English, 3–4 years mathematics, 3 years social studies/history, 2 years laboratory science, 3 years foreign language, 1 year fine arts. GED accepted. *Entrance tests:* SAT or ACT required unless the student is applying through the Portfolio Path to admission. *For transfer students:* Transfer applicants are evaluated on the same selective basis as freshmen.

College credit may be granted for AP and I.B. tests.

Degree Requirements: 128 semester hours. Academic residency 60 semester credits including 28 of the final 32 at Lewis & Clark. General education requirements: core. international studies, scientific and quantitative reasoning; creative arts, foreign language, physical education.

Credit granted for AP scores of 4 or 5 and higher level IB exams. *Grading system:* A–F; pass-fail; withdraw (carries time limit).

Distinctive Educational Programs: *For undergraduates:* Dual-degree programs in engineering with Washington University (MO), University of Washington and Oregon Graduate Institute. (Students may earn 2 baccalaureate degrees or a baccalaureate and a master's). Tutorials. *Available to all students:* Work-experience programs. Free University: sponsored by students and open to all in college community. Flexible meeting places and schedules, including off-campus centers, weekend and evening classes. Interdepartmental/interdisciplinary majors, including international affairs, environmental studies. Preprofessional programs in dentistry, medicine. Facilities and programs for independent research, including honors programs, individual majors. overseas study in countries throughout the world with college-sponsored groups. Academic year in Munich in cooperation with Reed College, Willamette University, and the University of Munich. Off-campus programs of 1 semester in New York, Arizona, Hawaii, Alaska, Washington (DC), and other locations in North and Central America. *Other distinctive programs:* Small nuclear reactor owned jointly with Reed College and located on Reed campus allows students to work with radioactive isotopes.

Degrees Conferred: 464 *baccalaureate*; 246 *master's*; 238 *first-professional*. Bachelor's degrees awarded: various disciplines 464. Master's degrees awarded: various disciplines 246. First-professional degrees awarded: law 238.

Fees and Other Expenses: *Full-time tuition per academic year 2008–09:* undergraduate $33,726; graduate and law scholl tuition charged per semester hour (contact the university for current rates). *Books and supplies:* $1,050. *Room and board per academic year:* $8,820. *Other expenses:* $1,960.

Financial Aid: Aid from institutionally generated funds is provided on the basis of academic merit, financial need.

Financial aid to full-time, first-time undergraduate students: 80% received some form of financial aid. Average amount of aid received: federal grants $3,997; Pell grants $2,958; other federal aid $1,236; institutional grants $16,039.

Departments and Teaching Staff: *Total instructional faculty:* 188. 94% of faculty hold the doctorate, first-professional, or other terminal degree. Student/faculty ratio: 15:1.

Enrollment: Total enrollment 3,365. Undergraduate 1,999 (full-time 99%; female 61%, male 39%). Graduate 1,566 (full-time 58%). Undergraduate transfer-in students 45.

Characteristics of Student Body: *Ethnic/racial makeup:* Black non-Hispanic: 2%; American Indian or Alaska Native: 1%; Asian or Pacific Islander: 6%; Hispanic: 2%; White non-Hispanic: 58%; unknown: 21%; nonresident alien 8%.

International Students: 288 nonresident aliens enrolled fall 2008. Programs available to aid students whose native language is not English: social, cultural. English as a Second Language Program. No financial aid specifically designated for international students.

Student Life: On-campus residence halls house 50% of the undergraduate population. First-year students required to live in campus housing. Housing options include male only (4%), female only (15%), and co-ed (81%). *Intercollegiate athletics:* male: baseball, basketball, cross-country, football, golf, soccer, swimming, tennis, track and field; female: basketball, cross-country, soccer, softball, swimming, tennis, track and field, volleyball. *Special regulations:* Cars permitted for all but first-year students. *Special services:* Health Center, Counseling Center, Writing Center, Math Skills Center, Student Support Services. *Student publications, radio: Pioneer Log*, a weekly newspaper; a yearbook, literary review, radio station KLC. *Surrounding community:* Portland population 550,000. Served by mass transit bus system; airport 16 miles from campus; passenger rail service 8 miles from campus.

Library Collections: 501,500 volumes. 54,300 government documents; 711,000 microforms; 15,000 audiovisual materials; 7,000 current periodicals including electronic access. Online catalog. Students have access to online information retrieval services and the Internet.

Most important special holdings include the Lewis and Clark Collection; Lincoln Collection; William Stafford Collection.

Buildings and Grounds: Campus area 137 acres.

Chief Executive Officer: Dr. Thomas Hochstettler, President.

Address admission inquiries to Mike Sexton, Dean of Admissions.

Northwestern School of Law of Lewis and Clark

Degree Programs Offered: *First-professional* in law; *Master of Law* in environmental and natural resources law (LL.M.).

Admission: Baccalaureate from accredited college or university; LSAT.

Degree Requirements: 86 credit hours; 1.7 GPA on .5 to 4.3 scale; 6 semesters in residence if day student, 8 if evening student; prescribed first-year program; constitutional law, seminar, and writing requirements. Students are also required to take a professionalism course (either Law 132, Legal Profession course; Law 700, Legal Clinic; or a year-long Professionalism seminar — "Senior Counsel Program" by appointment).

Distinctive Educational Programs: Legal clinic. Access to Westlaw and LEXIS computer systems for information retrieval. Work-study at National Resources Law Institute.

Graduate School of Professional Studies

Degree Programs Offered: *Master's* in counseling psychology, educational administration, special education (deaf education, teacher education).

Admission: Each program requires applicants to take the Miller Analogies Test, the Graduate Record Examination, the National Teachers Examination, and/or the California Basic Educational Skills Test (CBEST).

Degree Requirements: Requirements vary according to degree program.

Linfield College

900 S.E. Baker Street
McMinnville, Oregon 97128-8894
Tel: (503) 883-2200 **E-mail:** admission@linfield.edu
Fax: (503) 883-2472 **Internet:** www.linfield.edu

Institution Description: Linfield College is an independent, coeducational, nonprofit college affiliated with the American Baptist Church. *Enrollment:* 1,720. *Degrees awarded:* Baccalaureate, master's.

Accreditation: *Regional:* NWCCU. *Professional*: athletic training, music, nursing, teacher education

History: Established as Oregon City College 1849; relocated and changed name to Baptist College at McMinnville 1854; offered first instruction at postsecondary level 1865; awarded first degree (baccalaureate) 1884; changed name to McMinnville College 1890; adopted present name 1922. Established the Division of Continuing Education for working adults 1975; opened the Linfield-Good Samaritan School of Nursing on the Portland campus in 1982.

Institutional Structure: *Governing board:* Board of Trustees. Extrainstitutional representation: 26 trustees at large, 19 from nominations from American Baptist organizations. Institutional representation: president, 1 faculty member, 1 student, 3 alumni. All voting. *Composition of institution:* Administrators 140. Academic affairs headed by vice president for academic affairs. Management/business/finances directed by vice president for finance and administration. Regular instructional faculty 142. Academic governance body, the Faculty Assembly and its executive council meet throughout the year.

Calendar: Semesters (4-1-4 plan). Academic year Sept. to May. Freshmen admitted Sept., Feb. Degrees conferred and formal commencement May, Dec. Summer session from June to Aug.

Characteristics of Freshmen: 2,066 applicants (female 1,054, male 1,012). 78% of applicants admitted. 29% of admitted applicants enrolled full-time.

86^ (187 students) submitted SAT scores; 16% (70 students) submitted ACT scores. *25th percentile*: SAT Critical Reading 510, SAT Math 520; ACT Composite 23. *75th percentile*: SAT Critical Reading 610, SAT Math 620; Composite 27.

Admission: Priority deadline for fall acceptance, Feb. 15 (apply as early as Sept. 1 of previous year); notification beginning Apr. 1. Deadline for early action acceptance, Nov. 15 of previous year; notification begins Jan. 1. Priority deadline for spring acceptance, Dec. 1; notification begins Dec. 15. *Requirements:* Recommend 4 secondary school units of English, 2–4 foreign language, 3–4 social sciences, 4 mathematics, 3–4 natural sciences. GED accepted. *Entrance tests:* College Board SAT or ACT. International students evidence of current level of English proficiency, usually the TOEFL (ESL programs available for those who do not yet meet the proficiency requirements). *McMinville Campus Transfer Admission:* Priority deadline for all acceptance Apr. 15; notification begins May 15. Priority deadline for spring acceptance Dec. 1; notification begins Dec. 15. Requirements: 2.0 minimum GPA. of 85 semester hours transfer credit from 4-year accredited institution; from 2-year accredited institution 72 semester hours. *Portland Campus Transfer Admission School of Nursing*: Deadline Feb. 15; notification begins Apr. 15. Requirements: nursing prerequisite courses must be completed with a grade of C or better; cumulative GPA of 2.25 in all courses that will transfer into the major. *Division of Continuing Education*: Rolling admission.

LINFIELD COLLEGE—*cont'd*

College credit and advanced placement for postsecondary-level work completed in secondary school and for extrainstitutional learning on basis of portfolio and faculty assessments.

Tutoring available.

Degree Requirements: 125 credit hours; 2.0 GPA; mathematics proficiency; inquiry seminar and general education requirement, BA (2 semesters foreign language); BS (2 semesters science, math, or social sciences); paracurricular courses, major field. Fulfillment of some degree requirements and exemption from some beginning courses possible by passing College Board CLEP, AP. *Grading system:* A–F; pass-fail; withdraw (carries penalty and time limit); M (mastery); CE (credit by examination); incomplete (carries time limit).

Distinctive Educational Programs: *For undergraduates:* Work-experience programs. Dual-degree programs in engineering with Oregon State University, University of Southern California, Washington State University. Cooperative baccalaureate program in medical technology with University of Oregon Health Sciences Center or other approved institutions. Interdisciplinary programs in biochemistry, biomathematics, biophysics, communications, environmental studies, general science, natural sciences, religious studies, sociology and anthropology, systems analysis. Preprofessional programs in allied health fields. Facilities for independent research, including honors programs, individual majors. Institutionally sponsored study abroad in France, Japan, Austria, England, Korea, China. Off-campus study at Malheur Environmental Field Station (cosponsored by Linfield and other Oregon colleges). College-owned cabin provides facilities for educational and recreational activities and wilderness training. Pre-kindergarten Laboratory School. Cross-registration with any other independent colleges in Oregon. Women's Center. Linfield Research Institute encourages and supports research by the faculty and provides research training for students, primarily in physical sciences and psychology. *Available to all students:* Weekend and evening classes. Facilities and programs for independent research including tutorials, independent study. *Other distinctive programs:* Off-campus baccalaureate-completion program in liberal arts for adult learners, offered at varying locations and through televised courses. Noncredit continuing education program. High school seniors may enroll in 1 course per semester.

ROTC: Air Force offered in cooperation with University of Portland.

Degrees Conferred: 619 *baccalaureate:* business/marketing 175; health professions and related clinical sciences 125; social sciences 31; parks and recreation 36; education 33.

Fees and Other Expenses: *Full-time tuition per academic year 2008–09:* $27,414. *Other fees:* $244. *Room and board per academic year:* $7,770. *Other expenses:* $1,300.

Financial Aid: Aid from institutionally generated funds is provided on the basis of academic merit, financial need.

Financial aid to full-time, first-time undergraduate students: 96% received some form of aid. Average amount of aid received: federal grants $4,980; Pell grants $2,952; other federal aid $2,369; state/local grants $3,092; institutional grants $11,401.

Departments and Teaching Staff: *Total instructional faculty:* 274 (132 full-time, 142 part-time). *Student/faculty ratio:* 13:1. Degrees held by full-time faculty: baccalaureate 100%, master's 100%, doctorate 62. 62% hold terminal degrees.

Enrollment: Total enrollment 1,729. Undergraduate 1,729 (full-time 98%; female 56%, male 44%). Transfer-in students 52.

Characteristics of Student Body: *Ethnic/racial makeup:* Black non-Hispanic: 1%; American Indian or Alaska Native: 2%; Asian or Pacific Islander: 8%; Hispanic: 5%; White non-Hispanic: 70%; unknown: 9%; nonresident alien 5%. *Age distribution:* number under 18: 22; 18–19: 863; 20–21: 800; 22–24: 244; 25–29: 170; 30–34: 139; 35–39: 127; 40–49: 178; 50–64: 176. 23% of student body attend summer sessions.

International Students: 85 nonresident aliens enrolled fall 2008. Students from Europe, Asia, Central and South America, Africa, Canada, Micronesia. Programs available to aid students whose native language is not English: social, cultural. English as a Second Language Program. Financial aid specifically designated for international students: variable scholarships available annually for undergraduate students/

Student Life: On-campus residence halls and apartments house 76% of student body. Housing for males constitutes 26% of such space, for females 34%. 25% of students join fraternities or sororities. *Intercollegiate athletics:* male: baseball, basketball, cross-country, football, golf, soccer, swimming, tennis, track and field; female: basketball, cross-country, golf, lacrosse, soccer, swimming, tennis, track,and field, volleyball. *Special regulations:* Cars permitted without restrictions. Quiet hours vary according to residence hall; visitation from 10am to midnight Sun.–Thurs., 10am to 2am Fri. and Sat. (hours may vary in some residence halls). *Special services:* Transportation to and from airport at beginning of semesters. *Student publications, radio: Linfield Review,* a weekly newspaper; *Oakleaves,* a yearbook; *Comas,* a literary magazine. KSLC 90.3 radio; Wildcat Productions; video productions. *Surrounding community:* McMinnville population 30,000. Portland, 35 miles from campus, is nearest metropolitan area. Served by airport 50 miles from campus; passenger rail service 25 miles from campus.

Library Collections: 180,000 volumes including bound books, serial backfiles, electronic documents, and government documents not in separate collections. Online catalog. 1,052 recordings; 1,826 compact discs; 256 CD-ROMs. Computer work stations available. Students have access to the Internet at no charge.

Most important special holdings include collections on Pacific Northwest history; Baptist history (PNW).

Buildings and Grounds: Campus area 193 acres.

Chief Executive Officer: Dr. Thomas L. Hellif, President.

Address admission inquiries to Lisa Knodle-Bragiel, Director of Admissions.

Marylhurst University

17600 Pacific Highway
P.O. Box 261
Marylhurst, Oregon 97036-0261

Tel: (503) 636-8141 **E-mail:** admissions@marylhurst.edu
Fax: (503) 636-9526 **Internet:** www.marylhurst.edu

Institution Description: Marylhurst University is a private, independent, nonprofit college offering traditional liberal arts programs and has a nontraditional curriculum primarily for adult students. *Enrollment:* 1,802. *Degrees awarded:* Baccalaureate, master's.

Accreditation: *Regional:* NWCCU. *Professional*: music

History: Established as Saint Mary's Academy 1859; incorporated 1886; offered first instruction at postsecondary level 1893; awarded first degree (baccalaureate) 1898; changed name to Marylhurst College 1930; became a nontraditional coeducational college 1974; achieved university stat 1998.

Institutional Structure: *Governing board:* Board of Trustees. Extrainstitutional representation: not less than 12 or more than 35 trustees, plus president (voting ex officio member). One-third plus one of the Board must be Sisters of the Holy Names. *Composition of institution:* President, vice president for academic affairs, vice president for finance and facilities, vice president for institutional advancement; vice president for human resources. Chairperson for each academic department. Total instructional faculty 225. Academic governance body, Academic Administrators Council, meets an average of 24 times per year.

Calendar: Quarters. Academic year Sept. to Aug. Freshmen admitted Sept., Jan., Mar. Degrees conferred and formal commencements June, Dec. Summer session June to Aug.

Admission: Rolling admissions plan. *Requirements:* Graduation from accredited secondary school or GED. Open admissions policy. *For transfer students:* maximum transfer credit limited only by residence requirement.

College credit and advanced placement for postsecondary-level work completed in secondary school. College credit for extrainstitutional learning.

Tutoring available. Developmental courses offered in summer session and regular academic year; credit given (departmental restrictions may limit application of experiential and/or transfer credit and acceptance into a major).

Degree Requirements: 180 quarter hours; 3.0 GPA; 45 hours in residence; distribution requirements; LIFE Seminar. Graduate programs have varying requirements.

Fulfillment of some degree requirements and exemption from some beginning courses possible by passing College Board CLEP, other standardized tests. *Grading system:* A–F; pass-fail; pass; withdraw (deadline after which pass-fail is appended to withdraw).

Distinctive Educational Programs: Bachelor's of Music Therapy; graduate degrees in art therapy, business administration, interdisciplinary studies, applied theology.

Degrees Conferred: 141 *baccalaureate*; 123 *master's*; 1 *doctorate*. Bachelor's degrees awarded in top five disciplines: business and management 45, communications 28, liberal arts 18, visual and performing arts 21, multi/interdisciplinary studies 28. Master's degrees awarded: various disciplines 142.

Fees and Other Expenses: *Tuition per academic year 2008–09:* $18,200 undergraduate; contact the university for current graduate tuition/fees. *Room and board per academic year:* $8,550. *Books and supplies:* $1,440. *Other expenses:* $3,360.

Financial Aid: Aid from institutionally generated funds is provided on the basis of financial need.

Financial aid to full-time, first-time undergraduate students: 57% received some form of aid.

Departments and Teaching Staff: *Instructors* 23, *part-time faculty* 200. *Total instructional faculty:* 223. Degrees held by full-time faculty: doctorate 50%, master's 50%.

Enrollment: Total enrollment 1,802. Undergraduate 946 (full-time 25%; female 69%, male 31%). Graduate 858 (full-time 19%). Undergraduate transfer-in students 199.

Characteristics of Student Body: *Ethnic/racial makeup:* Black non-Hispanic: 3%; Asian or Pacific Islander: 2%; Hispanic: 2%; White non-Hispanic: 56%; unknown: 53%; nonresident alien 5%.

International Students: 90 nonresident aliens enrolled fall 2008. Programs available to aid students whose native language is not English: social, cultural. English as a Second Language Program. No financial aid specifically designated for international students.

Student Life: Limited on-campus housing. *Special regulations:* Cars permitted without restrictions. *Surrounding community:* Nearby Portland population 550,,000. Served by mass transit system, airport 24 miles from campus, passenger rail service 10 miles from campus.

Publications: *The Mirror* and *Chalk Talk*, monthly publications for students, faculty, and alumni.

Library Collections: 89,500 volumes. 4,520 microforms; 400 current periodical subscriptions. Online catalog.

Most important special holdings include collections on Western and contemplative thought; art therapy; sacred music.

Buildings and Grounds: Campus area 60 acres.

Chief Executive Officer: Dr. Marty Wilgenbusch, President.

Address admission inquiries to Katie Abbot, Assistant Director of Admissions.

Multnomah University

8435 N.E. Glisan Street
Portland, Oregon 97220-5814
Tel: (503) 255-0332 **E-mail:** admiss@multnomah.edu
Fax: (503) 254-1268 **Internet:** www.multnomah.edu

Institution Description: Multnomah University, formerly named Multnomah Bible College and Biblical Seminary, is a private, independent, nonprofit institution. *Enrollment:* 840. *Degrees awarded:* Baccalaureate, master's. Graduate certificates also awarded.

Accreditation: *Regional:* NWCCU. *National:* ABHE, ATS. *Professional*: theology

History: Established 1936; first diplomas awarded 1939.

Institutional Structure: *Governing board:* Board of Trustees. Extrainstitutional representation: 21 trustees; institutional representation: 4 administrators. All voting. *Composition of institution:* Administrators 19. Academic affairs headed by vice president-academic dean. Management/business/finances directed by vice president-finance. Full-time instructional faculty 31. Academic governance body, the college faculty, meets an average of 15 times per year.

Calendar: Semesters. Academic year Aug. to May. Freshmen admitted Aug., Jan., June. Degrees conferred Dec., May; formal commencement May. Summer session of 4 weeks.

Characteristics of Freshmen: 159 applicants (female 81, male 78). 84% of applicants accepted. 56% of accepted applicants enrolled full-time.

78.8% (63 students) submitted SAT scores; 32.5% (26 students) submitted ACT scores. *25th percentile*: SAT Critical Reading 510, SAT Math 470; ACT Composite 18. *75th percentile*: SAT Critical Reading 630, SAT Math 580; ACT Composite 27.

337 of entering freshmen expected to graduate within 5 years. 43% of freshmen from Oregon. Freshmen from 22 states and 7 foreign countries.

Admission: Rolling admissions plan. For fall acceptance, apply as early as end of junior year of secondary school but not later than July 15 prior to beginning of term. *Requirements:* Graduation from secondary school; GED accepted. Upper-half of secondary school class standing recommended. *Entrance tests:* College Board SAT. *For transfer students:* 2.0 minimum GPA.

Degree Requirements: Bachelor of Science degrees: 128 hours (56 hours bible curriculum, 40–45 hours of general education, and 33 in second major); Bachelor of Arts degrees: 129 semester hours. *For all degrees:* GPA 2.0. Graduate Certificate: 32 semester hours; Master of Arts in Biblical Studies: 62 semester hours, 3.0 GPA; Master of Arts in Pastoral Studies: 64 semester hours, 2.5 GPA; Master of Divinity: 90–95 hours, 2.5 GPA.

Distinctive Educational Programs: Emphasis on undergraduate Bible and theology comprises first major. Second major or minor available in biblical languages, journalism, public address, educational ministries, intercultural studies, music ministry, pastoral ministry, women's ministry, youth ministry, historical studies.

Degrees Conferred: 113 *baccalaureate:* theology/Bible/religious studies; 58 *master's:* theology/Bible/religious studies.

Fees and Other Expenses: *Full-time tuition per academic year 2008–09:* undergraduate $14,100. *Room and board per academic year:* $5,840. *Books and suppies:* $1,000. *Other expenses:* $2,800.

Financial Aid: Aid from institutionally generated funds is provided on the basis of academic merit, financial need, other criteria.

Financial aid to full-time, first-time undergraduate students: 79% of students received some form of financial aid.

Departments and Teaching Staff: *Total instructional faculty:* 62 (full-time 31, part-time 31). Student/faculty ratio: 19:1. Degrees held by full-time faculty: doctorate 61%, master's 29%, baccalaureate 10%. 60% hold terminal degrees.

Enrollment: Total enrollment 840. Undergraduate 502 (full-time 88%; female 45%, male 55%). Graduate 258 (full-time 60%). Undergraduate transfer-in students 97.

Characteristics of Student Body: *Ethnic/racial makeup:* Black non-Hispanic: 1%; American Indian or Alaska Native: 1%; Asian or Pacific Islander: 3%; Hispanic: 2%; White non-Hispanic: 87%; unknown 5%; nonresident alien 1%. *Age distribution:* number under 18: 6L 18–19: 119; 20–21: 64; 22–24: 161; 25–29: 87; 30–34: 23; 35–39: 9; 40–49: 20; 50–64: 10.

International Students: 8 nonresident aliens enrolled fall 2008. No programs available to aid students whose native language is not English. No financial aid specifically designated for international students.

Student Life: On-campus residence halls house over 50% of student body. *Intercollegiate athletics:* male: soccer, basketball, tennis; female: basketball, volleyball. *Student publications: The Voice*, a biweekly newspaper; *The Ambassador*, a yearbook. *Surrounding community:* Portland population 479,000. Easy access to suburban and downtown by mass transit bus and train system.

Library Collections: 169,000 volumes. Current serial subscriptions: paper 373; microform 4,420; via electronic access 8,000. 1,203 audio/videotapes; 188 DVD discs; 271 CD-ROMs. Online catalog. Computer work stations available. Students have access to the Internet and online information retrieval services.

Buildings and Grounds: Campus area 17 acres.

Chief Executive Officer: Dr. Daniel R. Lockwood, President. Address admission inquiries to Amy Stephens, Director of Admissions.

Northwest Christian University

828 East Eleventh Avenue
Eugene, Oregon 97401-3745
Tel: (541) 343-1641 **E-mail:** admissions@nwcc.edu
Fax: (541) 343-9159 **Internet:** www.nwcc.edu

Institution Description: Northwest Christian University is a private institution affiliated with the Christian Church/Disciples of Christ and Christian Churches (Churches of Christ). *Enrollment:* 534. *Degrees awarded:* Associate, baccalaureate, master's. Certificates also awarded.

Accreditation: *Regional:* NWCCU.

History: Established as Eugene Divinity School, incorporated and offered first instruction at postsecondary level 1895; awarded first degree (baccalaureate) 1896; changed name to Eugene Bible University 1908, adopted present name 2007.

Institutional Structure: *Governing board:* Board of Trustees. Representation: 32 trustees, including president of the college. All voting. *Composition of institution:* Academic affairs headed by vice president for academic affairs. Finances directed by vice president for finances/chief financial officer. Full-time instructional faculty 21.

Calendar: Semesters. Sept. to June. Freshmen admitted Sept., Jan., Mar. Degrees conferred and formal commencement May. No summer session.

Characteristics of Freshmen: 935 applicants (female 656, male 278). 61% of applicants admitted. 28% of applicants admitted and enrolled full-time.

94% (62 students) submitted SAT scores; 12% (6 students) submitted ACT scores. *25th percentile*: SAT Critical Reading 440, SAT Math 470; ACT Composite 21, ACT English 19, ACT Math 21. *75th percentile*: SAT Critical Reading 540, SAT Math 560; ACT Composite 23, ACT English 22, ACT Math 26.

29% of freshmen expected to graduate within five years. 92% of freshmen from Oregon. Freshmen from 8 states.

Admission: Rolling admissions. *Requirements:* Either graduation from accredited secondary school or GED. Minimum GPA 2.0. *Entrance tests:* College Board SAT or ACT composite.

College credit and advanced placement for postsecondary-level work completed in secondary.

Degree Requirements: *For associate degree:* 60 credit hours. *For all baccalaureate degrees:* 124 credit hours; 2.0 GPA; 30 of last 60 hours in residence; weekly chapel attendance. *For master's degree:* minimum of 36 credit hours.

Fulfillment of some degree requirements and exemption from some beginning courses possible by passing departmental examinations, College Board CLEP,

NORTHWEST CHRISTIAN UNIVERSITY—*cont'd*

AP. *Grading system:* A–F; pass-fail; withdraw (deadline after which pass-fail is appended to withdraw).

Distinctive Educational Programs: Internships. Evening classes. Special facilities for using telecommunications in the classroom. Study abroad in Israel. American Studies, Washington, DC; Latin American Studies Program, San Jose, Costa Rica; L.A. Film Studies Center, Los Angeles CA; Middle East Studies, Cairo, Egypt; Russian Studies, Novgored/St. Petersburg, Russia; Institute of the Holy Lands, Jerusalem.

Degrees Conferred: 8 *associate;* 118 *baccalaureate*; 17 *master's.* Bachelor's degrees awarded in top five disciplines: business/marketing 42; education 24; philosophy/religion 8; psychology 4; visual and performing arts 4. Master's degrees awarded: business/marketing 9; education 8; other disciplines 23.

Fees and Other Expenses: *Full-time tuition per academic year 2008–09:* $21,900 undergraduate; contact the college for current graduate tuition/fees. *Room and board per academic year:* $6,200. *Other expenses:* $2,340.

Financial Aid: Aid from institutionally generated funds is provided on the basis of academic merit, financial need, other criteria.

Financial aid to full-time, first-time undergraduate students: 90% received some form of aid. Average amount of aid received: federal grants $1,511; state/local grants $2,004; institutional grants $4,119; loans $2,351.

Departments and Teaching Staff: *Total instructional faculty:* 80 (full-time 21, part-time 59). 505 of faculty hold the doctorate, first-professional, or other terminal degree. Student/faculty ratio: 9:1. Degrees held by full-time faculty: doctorate 50%, master's 50%. 50% hold terminal degrees.

Enrollment: Total enrollment 534. Undergraduate 437 (full-time 71%; female 59%, male 41%). Graduate 97. Undergraduate transfer-in students 75.

Characteristics of Student Body: *Ethnic/racial makeup:* Black non-Hispanic: 3%; American Indian or Alaska Native: 2%; Asian or Pacific Islander: 2%; Hispanic: 4%; White non-Hispanic: 70%; unknown: 2%.

International Students: 1 nonresident alien from Asia enrolled fall 2008. No programs available to aid students whose native language is not English. No financial aid specifically designated for international students.

Student Life: On-campus housing available. *Surrounding community:* Eugene population 150,000.

Library Collections: 61,000 volumes. 12,400 audiovisual materials; 282 current periodical subscriptions. Online catalog. Access to online information retrieval systems.

Most important special collections include rare book and Bible collections; Disciples of Christ historical collections; Northwest collection.

Buildings and Grounds: Campus area 8 acres.

Chief Executive Officer: Dr.David W. Wilson, President.

Address admission inquiries to Jennifer Samples, Director of Admissions.

Oregon Health and Science University

3181 SW Sam Jackson Park Road
Portland, Oregon 97201-3098
Tel: (503) 494-7800 **E-mail:** admissions@ohsu.edu
Fax: (503) 494-4629 **Internet:** www.ohsu.edu

Institution Description: Oregon Health and Science University (formerly University of Oregon Health Sciences Center) is a state institution. *Enrollment:* 2,424. *Degrees awarded:* Associate, baccalaureate, first-professional (dentistry, medicine), master's, doctorate.

Academic offerings subject to approval by statewide coordinating bodies. Budget subject to approval by state governing boards.

Accreditation: *Regional:* NWCCU. *Professional*: cytotechnology, dental hygiene, dentistry, medicine, radiation therapy technology

History: Established as University of Oregon Health Sciences Center by merger of Oregon Dental School and University of Oregon Medical School 1974; awarded first degree 1975; adopted present name 1981.

Institutional Structure: *Governing board:* Oregon State Board of Higher Education. Representation: 9 board members, 2 students. All voting. *Composition of institution:* Administrators 9. Academic affairs headed by vice president for academic affairs. Management/business/finances directed by vice president for finance and administration. Academic governance body, Faculty Senate, meets an average of 10 times per year.

Calendar: Quarters.

Admission: For fall acceptance, apply as early as Sept. 1 of previous year, but not later than Feb. 1 for medical technology students; Feb. 15 for nursing and dental hygiene students. *Requirements:* Minimum 2.5 GPA. *For transfer students:* Requirements vary depending on program.

Degree Requirements: 186 credit hours (including prior college work); 2.0 GPA; 45 semester hours of final 60 hours in residence; prescribed curriculum for each program. *Grading system:* A–F; pass-fail.

Distinctive Educational Programs: Interdisciplinary programs in biomedical sciences. Individual majors.

Degrees Conferred: 209 *baccalaureate*; 204 *master's*; 52 *doctorate*; 162 *first-professional.* Bachelor's. master's, doctorate degrees awarded: health professions and related clinical sciences. First-professional degrees awarded in dentistry, medicine,

Fees and Other Expenses: *Full-time tuition per academic year:* contact the university for current information regarding tuition/fees which vary among departments and professional schools.

Financial Aid: Aid from institutionally generated funds is provided on the basis of financial need. Institution has a Program Participation Agreement with the U.S. Department of Education for eligible students to receive Pell Grants and, depending upon the agreement, other federal aid.

Enrollment: Total enrollment 2,424. Undergraduate 804 (full-time 74%; female 85%, male 15%). Graduate 1,820 (full-time 75%). Undergraduate transfer-in students 296.

Characteristics of Student Body: *Ethnic/racial makeup:* Black non-Hispanic: 1%; American Indian or Alaska Native: 2%; Asian or Pacific Islander: 3%; Hispanic: 5%; White non-Hispanic: 81%; unknown 7%; nonresident alien 1%.

International Students: 24 undergraduate nonresident aliens enrolled fall 2008. No programs available to aid students whose native language is not English.

Student Life: On-campus residence hall houses 1% of student body. *Special regulations:* Only those vehicles registered in parking program permitted. *Special services:* Learning Resources Center, medical service, campus transportation system. *Surrounding community:* Portland. Served by mass transit bus system; airport 10 miles from campus; passenger rail service 4 miles from campus.

Library Collections: 205,000 volumes. 2,110 current serial subscriptions. Online catalog. Students have access to online information retrieval services and the Internet.

Most important special holdings include History of Medicine Collection; History of Dentistry Collection; dental and medical audiovisual materials.

Buildings and Grounds: Campus area 116 acres.

Chief Executive Officer: Dr. Peter O. Kohler, President.

Address admission inquiries to Director of Admissions.

School of Dentistry

Degree Programs Offered: *Baccalaureate* in dental hygiene; *first-professional: master's* in anatomy, biochemistry, dental materials science, endontology, microbiology, orthodontics, pedodontics, pharmacology, physiology. Specialty certificates in endontology, orthodontics, pedodontics, periodontology also given.

Admission: *For first-professional:* 90 quarter hours of undergraduate work, including 1 year general chemistry with laboratory, 1 biology or zoology with laboratory, 8 quarter hours organic chemistry, 1 year general physics with laboratory, undergraduate school English composition course.

Degree Requirements: *For first-professional:* Prescribed curriculum. 2.0 GPA, 36 months in residence.

School of Medicine

Degree Programs Offered: *Baccalaureate* in medical technology; *first-professional; master's, doctorate* in basic sciences. Certificates also given.

Admission: *For first-professional:* 3 years of college required, 4 years recommended: 24 quarter hours chemistry (including organic), 9 biology, 12 physics, 12 college mathematics, 6 general psychology. MCAT. Preference given to residents of Oregon and neighboring western states.

Degree Requirements: *For first-professional:* 216 credit hours, 18 months in residence.

Distinctive Educational Programs: Continuing education for physicians.

School of Nursing

Degree Programs Offered: *Baccalaureate, master's.*

Admission: *For baccalaureate:* 30 semester hours from college or university, including 1 year chemistry with laboratory, 1 course human nutrition, 1 course algebra. Registered nurses with 1 year work experience are eligible for admission. 2.5 minimum GPA; from 2-year accredited institution 108 hours maximum transfer credit.

Degree Requirements: *For baccalaureate:* Liberal arts requirement.

Distinctive Educational Programs: Continuing education program for nurses.

Oregon Institute of Technology

3201 Campus Drive
Klamath Falls, Oregon 97601-8801
Tel: (541) 885-1161 **E-mail:** admissions@oit.edu
Fax: (541) 885-1865 **Internet:** www.oit.edu

Institution Description: Oregon Institute of Technology (Oregon Technical Institute until 1973) is a state institution. *Enrollment:* 3,515. *Degrees awarded:* Baccalaureate, master's.

Academic offerings subject to approval by statewide coordinating bodies. Budget subject to approval by state governing boards.

Accreditation: *Regional:* NWCCU. *Professional*: dental hygiene, engineering technology, nursing

History: Established and chartered as Oregon Vocational School 1946; offered first instruction at postsecondary level 1947; changed name to Oregon Technical Institute, and awarded first degree (associate) 1948; adopted present name 1973. *See* W.D. Purvine, *Oregon Tech's First 30 Years, 1946–76* (Klamath Falls: Oregon Institute of Technology, 1978) for further information.

Institutional Structure: *Governing board:* Oregon State Board of Higher Education. Representation: 11 board members, 1 student. All voting. *Composition of institution:* Administrators 33. Academic affairs headed by provost. Management/business/finances directed by dean of administration. full-time instructional faculty 107. Academic governance body, Faculty Senate, meets an average of 10 times per year.

Calendar: Quarters. Academic year Sept. to June. Degrees conferred and formal commencement June. Summer session June to Aug.

Characteristics of Freshmen: 630 applicants (female 389, male 304). 86% of applicants accepted. 43% of accepted applicants enrolled full-time.

84% (222 students) submitted SAT scores. *25th percentile*: SAT Critical Reading 450, SAT Math 480. *75th percentile*: SAT Critical Reading 586; SAT Math 610.

85% of freshmen from Oregon. Freshmen from 34 states and 16 foreign countries.

Admission: Rolling admissions plan. For fall acceptance, apply as early as Oct. 15 of previous year, but not later than Aug. 1 of year of enrollment. *Requirements:* Either graduation from accredited secondary school (subject requirements) or GED. Minimum GPA 2.50. *Entrance tests:* College Board SAT or ACT composite. For foreign students minimum TOEFL score 520. *For transfer students:* from 4-year accredited institution 2.0 GPA, unlimited transfer credit; from 2-year accredited institution 2.25 minimum GPA, 108 hours; correspondence/extension students 2.0 minimum GPA, 30 hours.

College credit and advanced placement for postsecondary-level work completed in secondary school. College credit for extrainstitutional learning.

Tutoring available. Noncredit developmental courses offered in summer session and regular academic year.

Degree Requirements: *For all associate degrees:* 99–104 quarter hours; 50 hours in residence. *For all baccalaureate degrees:* 198–208 hours; 90 hours in residence; distribution requirements. *For all degrees:* 2.0 GPA; 2 physical education courses; course in personal health.

Fulfillment of some degree requirements and exemption from some beginning courses possible by passing departmental examinations, College Board CLEP, AP. *Grading system:* A–F; withdraw (carries time limit).

Distinctive Educational Programs: Upper division technical courses at the Portland Center; baccalaureate programs at that site in cooperation with Portland State University. Baccalaureate degrees in specialized technologies, such as laser electro-optics and medical imaging (radiologic). Cooperative education with hospitals and industry. Facilities and programs for independent research, including geo-heat. Heavy computer emphasis with completely networked campus. Evening Associate of Arts degree program. Study abroad programs in Australia, Japan.

Degrees Conferred: 81 *associate*; 434 *baccalaureate*; 4 *master's*. Bachelor's degrees awarded in top five disciplines: engineering technologies 147; health professions and related clinical sciences 198; business, management, marketing, and related support services 50; psychology 45; English language/literature 18. Master's degrees awarded: engineering 4.

Fees and Other Expenses: *Full-time tuition per academic year 2008–09:* undergraduate resident $6,297, nonresident $16,692; contact the institute for graduate tuition/fees. *Room and board per academic year:* $7,598. *Books and supplies:* $1,000. *Other expenses:* $2,400.

Financial Aid: Aid from institutionally generated funds is provided on the basis of academic merit, financial need, athletic ability, other criteria.

Financial aid to full-time, first-time undergraduate students: 87% received some form of financial aid. Average amount of aid received: federal grants $3,682; Pell grants $3,170; other federal aid $893; state/local grants $2,853; institutional grants $2,320.

Departments and Teaching Staff: *Total instructional faculty:* 152. Student/faculty ratio: 14:1. Degrees held by full-time faculty: baccalaureate 4%, master's 38%, doctorate 25%. 26% hold terminal degrees.

Enrollment: Total enrollment 3,515. Undergraduate 3,492 (full-time 55%; female 48%, male 52%). Graduate 21 (full-time 29%). Undergraduate transfer-in students 425.

Characteristics of Student Body: *Ethnic/racial makeup:* Black non-Hispanic: 1%; American Indian or Alaska Native: 2%; Asian or Pacific Islander: 6%; Hispanic: 4%; White non-Hispanic: 77%; unknown: 9%; nonresident alien 1%.

International Students: 35 nonresident aliens enrolled fall 2008. Students from Europe, Asia, Canada, Australia. Programs available to aid students whose native language is not English: social, cultural. English as a Second Language Program. Financial aid specifically designated for international students: scholarships awarded annually to qualifying students.

Student Life: On-campus residence halls house 18% of student body. Residence halls for both sexes constitute 100% of such space. *Intercollegiate athletics:* male: basketball, cross-country, track and field; female: softball, cross-country, track and field, volleyball. *Special regulations:* Registered cars permitted without restrictions. *Special services:* Learning Resources Center, medical services, services for students with disabilities. *Student publications, radio: The Edge*, a monthly newspaper; Radio station KTEC. *Surrounding community:* Klamath Falls population 35,000. Portland, 280 miles from campus, is nearest major city. Served by mass transit bus system; airport 7 miles from campus; passenger rail service 3 miles from campus.

Publications: Geo-Heat Utilization Center publishes a quarterly bulletin; *Journal of the Shaw Historical Library*, an annual, began publication in 1986.

Library Collections: 146,000 volumes including bound books, serial backfiles, electronic documents, and government documents not in separate collections. Online catalog. Current serial subscriptions: 1,815 (paper, microform, electronic). 1,693 recordings. Computer work stations available campus-wide. Students have access to the Internet at no charge.

Most important special holdings include Shaw Historical Library (Western U.S. history).

Buildings and Grounds: Campus area 170 acres.

Chief Executive Officer: Dr. Martha Anne Dow, President.

Address admission inquiries to Palmer Muntz, Director of Admissions.

Oregon State University

Corvallis, Oregon 97331-4501
Tel: (541) 737-0123 **E-mail:** osuadmit@orst.edu
Fax: (541) 737-2400 **Internet:** www.osu.orst.edu

Institution Description: Oregon State University is a state institution and land-grant college. *Enrollment:* 20,305. *Degrees awarded:* Baccalaureate, first-professional (pharmacy, veterinary medicine), master's, doctorate. Certificates also awarded.

Academic offerings subject to approval by statewide coordinating bodies. Budget subject to approval by state governing boards. Member of the consortia National Student Exchange, Western Interstate Commission for Higher Education (WICHE).

Accreditation: *Regional:* NWCCU. *Professional*: accounting, business, construction education, counseling, engineering, engineering technology, forestry, journalism, music, pharmacy, teacher education

History: Established 1850; incorporated as Corvallis College 1858; offered first instruction at postsecondary level 1865; changed name to Oregon State Agricultural College 1868; awarded first degree (baccalaureate) 1870; changed name to Oregon State College 1920; adopted present name 1961.

Institutional Structure: *Governing board:* Oregon State Board of Higher Education. Representation: 9 directors, 2 students. All voting. *Composition of institution:* Administrators 34. Five vice presidents: academic affairs; finance and administration; university relations; student affairs; research, graduate studies, and international affairs. Academic governance body, Faculty Senate, meets an average of 9 times per year.

Calendar: Quarters. Academic year Sept. to June. Freshmen admitted Sept., Jan., Mar., June. Degrees conferred and formal commencement June. Summer session from June to Sept.

Characteristics of Freshmen: 8,149 applicants (3,990 female, 4,159 male). 88% of applicants accepted. 45% of accepted applicants enrolled full-time.

93% (2,717 students) submitted SAT scores; 16% (471 students) submitted ACT scores. *25th percentile*: SAT Critical Reading 470, SAT Math 470; ACT Composite 20, ACT English 18, ACT Math 17. *75th percentile*: SAT Critical Reading 590, SAT Math 610; ACT Composite 26, ACT English 25, ACT Math 26.

78% of entering freshmen expected to graduate within 5 years. 85% of freshmen from Oregon. Freshmen from 49 states and 90 foreign countries.

OREGON STATE UNIVERSITY—*cont'd*

Admission: Rolling admissions plan. For fall acceptance, apply as early as Oct. 15 of previous year, but not later than 30 days prior to beginning of term. *Requirements:* Either graduation from accredited secondary school or GED. *Entrance tests:* College Board SAT or ACT composite, with minimum score of 30 on SAT Test of Standard Written English or 12 on ACT English. For foreign students TOEFL. *For transfer students:* 2.0 minimum GPA; from 4-year accredited institution hours maximum transfer credit limited only by residence requirement; from 2-year accredited institution 108 quarter hours; correspondence/extension students 60 hours.

College credit and advanced placement for postsecondary-level work completed in secondary school.

Tutoring available. Developmental/remedial courses offered during regular academic year; credit given.

Degree Requirements: 192–240 credit hours; 2.0 GPA; 45 of last 60 hours in residence; 3 credit hours physical education; general education requirements.

Fulfillment of some degree requirements and exemption from some beginning courses possible by passing departmental examinations, College Board CLEP, AP. *Grading system:* A–F; satisfactory-unsatisfactory; pass-no credit; withdraw.

Distinctive Educational Programs: Cooperative education. Evening classes. Access to various professional programs outside of the state through WICHE student exchange program. Cross-registration with state system institutions. Special facilities for using telecommunications in the classroom. Interdepartmental program in gerontology; master's program in interdisciplinary studies. Courses in community studies; marine and maritime technology; Northwest studies; science, technology, and values through Humanities Development Program. Facilities for independent research, including honors programs, individual majors, tutorials. Study abroad in Australia, England, France, Germany, Japan, Mexico, New Zealand. *Other distinctive programs:* Noncredit courses for the community through Experimental College. Credit and noncredit continuing education.

ROTC: Army, Navy, Air Force.

Degrees Conferred: 3,267 *baccalaureate*; 874 *master's*; 173 *doctorate*; 118 *first-professional*. Bachelor's degrees awarded in top five disciplines: business, management, marketing, and related support services 471; engineering 474; family and consumer science 284; natural and environmental science 200; biomedical/biological sciences 199. Master's degrees awarded: various disciplines 874. Doctorates awarded: various disciplines 113; first-professional degrees awarded: pharmacy 74; veterinary medicine 44.

Fees and Other Expenses: *Full-time tuition per academic year:* $6,187 undergraduate resident, $18,823 nonresident; contact the university for graduate/professional school tuition and fees. *Books and supplies:* $1,527. *Room and board per academic year:* $6,208. *Other expenses:* $2,403.

Financial Aid: Aid from institutionally generated funds is provided on the basis of academic merit, athletic ability, financial need, other criteria.

Financial aid to full-time, first-time undergraduate students: 74% received some form of financial aid. Average amount of aid received: federal grants $3,704; Pell grants $2,964; other federal aid $1,496; state/local grants $1,968; institutional grants $3,627.

Departments and Teaching Staff: *Total instructional faculty:* 1,554. Student/faculty ratio: 12:1. Degrees held by full-time faculty: 85% hold terminal degrees.

Enrollment: Total enrollment 20,305. Undergraduate 16,673 (full-time 84%; female 47%, male 53%). Graduate 3,632. Undergraduate transfer-in students 1,221.

Characteristics of Student Body: *Ethnic/racial makeup:* Black non-Hispanic: 2%; American Indian or Alaska Native: 1%; Asian or Pacific Islander: 9%; Hispanic: 5%; White non-Hispanic: 71%; unknown: 10%; nonresident alien 2%.

International Students: 406 nonresident aliens enrolled fall 2008. Programs available to aid students whose native language is not English: social, cultural. English Language Institute. Financial aid specifically designated for international students: undergraduate and graduate scholarships available to qualifying students.

Student Life: On-campus residence halls house 23% of student body. Residence halls for males constitute 16% of such space, for females 23%, for both sexes 62%. Housing available for married students. *Intercollegiate athletics:* male: baseball, basketball, crew, football, golf, track, wrestling; female: basketball, crew, golf, gymnastics, softball, swimming, tennis, track, volleyball. *Special regulations:* Cars with parking permits allowed; central campus closed to student cars from 7:00am to 5:00pm Mon-Fri. Residence hall visitation hours set by residents. *Special services:* Learning Resources Center, medical services. *Student publications, radio, television: The Beaver*, a yearbook; *Fusser's Guide*, an annual telephone directory; *The Oregon State Daily Barometer*, a newspaper; *Prism*, a biannual literary magazine. Radio station KBVR-FM broadcasts 120 hours per week. TV station KBVR broadcasts 12 hours per week. *Surrounding community:* Corvallis, population 40,000. Portland, 80 miles from campus, is nearest metropolitan area. Served by mass transit bus system; airport 41 miles from campus; passenger rail service 11 miles from campus.

Library Collections: 1,404,000 volumes. 14,800 current serial subscriptions in paper, microform, electronic. Online catalog. Students have access to online information retrieval services and the Internet.

Most important holdings include collected papers of Linus Pauling; McDonald Collection; History of Science.

Buildings and Grounds: Campus area 400 acres.

Chief Executive Officer: Dr. Edward J. Ray, President.

Address admission inquiries to Michele L. Sandlin, Director of Admissions.

College of Liberal Arts

Degree Programs Offered: *Baccalaureate* in American studies, anthropology, art, economics, English, fine arts, foreign languages and literature, history, liberal studies, music, philosophy, political science, psychology, religious studies, sociology, speech communication, technical journalism. Certificates in human services, Latin American affairs, women's studies also given.

Distinctive Educational Programs: Interdisciplinary programs in American studies, human services, Latin American affairs, liberal studies, women's studies.

College of Agriculture

Degree Programs Offered: *Baccalaureate* in agricultural engineering technology, general agriculture; *baccalaureate, masters, doctorate* in agricultural and resource economics, animal science, crop science, fisheries and wildlife, food science and technology, horticulture, poultry science, rangeland resources, soil science.

Distinctive Educational Programs: Cooperative baccalaureate in agricultural technology with College of Engineering. Student exchange and work programs in New Zealand. Oregon Agricultural Experiment Station. Extension Service programs in forestry, agriculture, and other fields. Extension Methods program to train students in designing informal educational programs.

College of Business

Degree Programs Offered: *Baccalaureate* in administrative office management, business administration, health care administration, hotel and restaurant management, office management; *master's* in business administration, management science.

Distinctive Educational Programs: Cooperative baccalaureate in health care administration with Colleges of Home Economics, and Health and Physical Education; in hotel and restaurant management with College of Home Economics.

College of Education

Degree Programs Offered: *Baccalaureate* in elementary education, secondary education, vocational-technical education; *master's* in adult education, elementary education, reading; *master's, doctorate* in college student services administration, counseling, guidance and counseling, secondary education, vocational-technical education.

Distinctive Educational Programs: Cooperative master's program in counseling with Western Oregon State College. Cooperative doctorate in community college education with Portland State University and University of Oregon.

College of Engineering

Degree Programs Offered: *Baccalaureate* in architectural engineering, chemical engineering, civil engineering, construction engineering management, industrial engineering, mechanical engineering, metallurgical engineering, mining engineering, nuclear engineering; *master's* in engineering, materials science, ocean engineering; *doctorate* in engineering.

Distinctive Educational Programs: Cooperative education. Double-degree program in civil and forest engineering with College of Forestry. Cooperative baccalaureate programs in geological engineering, metallurgical engineering, mining engineering with University of Idaho. Cooperative manufacturing engineering degree with area industries. Off-campus, cooperative master's degree with area industries. Off-campus, cooperative master's degree with Tektronix, Inc. Ocean engineering and nuclear reactor research facilities.

College of Forestry

Degree Programs Offered: *Baccalaureate* in forest engineering, forest management, forest products, resource recreation management; *master's, doctorate* in forest engineering, forest management, forest products, forest science.

Distinctive Educational Programs: Forest Engineering Institute operated with U.S. Forest Service to train Forest Service Employees. *See* College of Engineering.

College of Health and Physical Education

Degree Programs Offered: *Baccalaureate* in health, physical education.
Distinctive Educational Programs: Preprofessional program in therapy. *See* College of Business.

College of Home Economics

Degree Programs Offered: *Baccalaureate* in home economics; *master's* in apparel, interiors, and merchandising; family life; family resource management; foods and nutrition; home economics education; institution management; *doctorate* in foods, nutrition, child development, family relations, family resource management.
Distinctive Educational Programs: Training opportunities with Crippled Children's Division of the University of Oregon Health Sciences Center. *See* College of Business.

College of Science

Degree Programs Offered: *Baccalaureate* in atmospheric sciences, biochemistry and biophysics, biology, botany and plant pathology, chemistry, computer science, entomology, general science, geography, geology, mathematical sciences, mathematics, medical technology, microbiology, physics, zoology; *master's, doctorate* in genetics, statistics, and various other fields.

College of Pharmacy

Degree Programs Offered: *Baccalaureate* in pharmacy; *master's* in hospital pharmacy; *master's, doctorate* in pharmaceutical chemistry, pharmacognosy, pharmacology, pharmacy administration.

College of Veterinary Medicine

Degree Programs Offered: *First-professional, master's.*
Admission: 112 quarter hours from accredited college or university with 68 hours physical and biological sciences; courses in written communications, arts, humanities, social sciences; work experience with a veterinarian; GRE.
Degree Requirements: 210 quarter hours; 2.0 GPA; passing grade in all prescribed veterinary courses; must have earned baccalaureate degree; comprehensive examination.

College of Oceanography

Degree Programs Offered: *Master's* in marine resource management; *master's, doctorate* in biological oceanography, chemical oceanography, geological oceanography, geophysics, physical oceanography.
Distinctive Educational Programs: Interdisciplinary program in marine science management. Oceanographic research vessel at Mark O. Hatfield Marine Science Center in Newport.

Pacific Northwest College of Art

1219 NW Johnson Avenue
Portland, Oregon 97209-3023
Tel: (503) 226-4391 **E-mail:** admissions@pnca.edu
Fax: (503) 226-3587 **Internet:** www.pnca.edu

Institution Description: Pacific Northwest College of Art (Museum Art School until 1981) is a private, independent, nonprofit institution. *Enrollment:* 507. *Degrees awarded:* Baccalaureate.

Accreditation: *Regional:* NWCCU. *Professional*: art

History: Established as Museum Art School 1909; offered first instruction at postsecondary level 1950; awarded first degree (baccalaureate) 1969; adopted present name 1981.

Institutional Structure: *Governing board:* Board of Governors. Representation: 25 members. All voting. *Composition of institution:* Administrators 4. Academic affairs headed by director. Management/business/finances directed by chief accountant. Full-time instructional faculty 17. Academic governance body, Faculty Council, meets an average of 9 times per year.

Calendar: Semesters. Academic ear Sept. to May. Freshmen admitted Aug. Degrees conferred and formal commencement May. Special workshops available from June to July.

Admission: Rolling admissions plan. *Requirements:* Either graduation from accredited secondary school or GED. Drawing test. Written essay recommended. *For transfer students:* 2.0 minimum GPA, maximum transfer credit limited only by residence requirement.

Advanced placement for postsecondary-level work completed in secondary school and for extrainstitutional learning on basis of faculty assessment.

Degree Requirements: 120 semester credits; 2.0 GPA; 4 semesters in residence; humanities requirements; completion of thesis project. *Grading system:* A–F; withdraw.

Distinctive Educational Programs: Work-experience programs, including internships, cooperative education. Evening classes. Individual majors. Study abroad by individual arrangement.

Degrees Conferred: 96 *baccalaureate:* visual and performing arts.

Fees and Other Expenses: *Full-time tuition per academic year 2008–09:* $22,006. *Books and supplies:* $1,710. *Room and board per academic year:* $7,550. *Other expenses* $1,797.

Financial Aid: Aid from institutionally generated funds is provided on the basis of academic merit, financial need.

Financial aid to full-time, first-time undergraduate students: 97% received some form of financial aid.

Departments and Teaching Staff: *Total instructional faculty:* 49. Student/faculty ratio: 10:1. Degrees held by full-time faculty: master's 99%, doctorate 1%.

Enrollment: Total enrollment 507. Undergraduate 477 (full-time 92%, female 65%, male 35%). Graduate 30 (full-time 100%). Undergraduate transfer-in students 103.

Characteristics of Student Body: *Ethnic/racial makeup:* Black non-Hispanic: 2%; American Indian or Alaska Native: 1%; Asian or Pacific Islander: 6%; Hispanic: 6%; White non-Hispanic: 80%; unknown 2%; nonresident alien 1%. *Age distribution:* 18=19: 34; 20–21: 57; 22–24: 88; 25–29: 93; 30–34: 23; 35–39: 6; 40–49: 6; 50–64: 2.

International Students: No programs available to aid students whose language is not English. Some financial aid specifically designated for international students.

Library Collections: 15,000 volumes. Online catalog. 460 audiovisual materials; 115 current periodical subscriptions. Students have access to the Internet.

Most important special holdings include student thesis papers dating back to 1966; Zine Library.

Buildings and Grounds: Campus area 3 square blocks.

Chief Executive Officer: Dr. Thomas Manley, President.

Address admission inquiries to Chris Sweet, Director of Admissions.

Pacific University

2043 College Way
Forest Grove, Oregon 97116
Tel: (877) 722-8648 **E-mail:** admissions@pacificu.edu
Fax: (562) 353-6157 **Internet:** www.pacificu.edu

Institution Description: Pacific University is a private, independent, nonprofit institution related to the United Church of Christ. *Enrollment:* 3,167. *Degrees awarded:* Baccalaureate, first-professional (optometry), master's, doctorate.

Member of the consortia Malheur Field Station and Oregon Independent College Association.

Accreditation: *Regional:* NWCCU. *Professional*: music, occupational therapy, optometry, physician assisting, physical therapy, psychology internship

History: Established as Tualation Academy and chartered 1849; offered first instruction at postsecondary level 1853; adopted present name 1854; awarded first degree (baccalaureate) 1863; joined with North Pacific College of Optometry (founded 1921) 1945.

Institutional Structure: *Governing board:* Pacific University Board of Trustees. Representation: 34 trustees, including president of the university, 2 full-time instructional faculty members, 2 students. All voting. *Composition of institution:* Administrators 50. Academic affairs headed by provost/vice president for academic affairs. Management/business/finances directed by vice president for finance and administration. Alumni relations directed by vice president of university relations. Admissions, financial aid, and registrar's office directed by vice president for enrollment management. Full-time instructional faculty 87. Academic governance through various all-campus committees that meet throughout the year; ultimately the University Council, chaired by vice president for academic affairs.

Calendar: Semesters. Academic year Sept. to May. Freshmen enrolled Sept., Jan. Degrees conferred May, Aug., Dec. Formal commencement May. Summer session of 3 terms from June to Aug.

Characteristics of Freshmen: 1,516 applicants (977 female, 539 male). 84% of applicants admitted. 34% of applicants admitted and enrolled full-time.

PACIFIC UNIVERSITY—*cont'd*

87% (313 students) submitted SAT scores; 27% (97 students) submitted ACT scores. *25th percentile*: SAT Critical Reading 480, SAT Math 510; ACT Composite 20, ACT English 20, ACT Math 21. *75th percentile*: SAT Critical Reading 590, SAT 610; ACT Composite 26, ACT English 26, ACT Math 26.

50% of entering freshmen expected to graduate within 5 years. 50% of freshmen from Oregon. Freshmen from 31 states and 8 foreign countries.

Admission: Rolling admissions plan. For fall acceptance, apply as early as Nov. 1 of senior year of secondary school, but not later than Aug. 15 of year of enrollment. *Requirements:* College preparatory program; GED accepted. Lowest secondary school class standing 50th percentile. *Entrance tests:* College Board SAT or ACT. *For transfer students:* Transfer credit accepted.

College credit and advanced placement for postsecondary-level work completed in secondary school. College credit for extrainstitutional learning. Tutoring available.

Degree Requirements: 124 semester hours; 30 of last 40 hours in residence; general education and distribution requirements, including writing requirement.

Fulfillment of some degree requirements possible by passing departmental examinations, College Board CLEP, AP (score of 3). Exemption from some beginning courses possible by passing College Board AP. *Grading system:* A–F; pass-fail; withdraw (carries time limit).

Distinctive Educational Programs: Experiential Year options include career internships, independent off-campus research projects, study abroad. Evening classes. Dual-degree programs in electronic science with Oregon Graduate Center; in engineering with Washington State University, Washington University (MO). Special facilities for using telecommunications in the classroom. Other interdisciplinary programs in environmental sciences, humanities, integrated sciences. Off-campus study in U.S. at Malheur Field Station through consortium. Study abroad in Austria, China, Costa Rica, Ecuador, England, France, Germany, India, Ireland, Japan, The Netherlands, Northern Ireland, Spain, Switzerland, Vietnam.

ROTC: Air Force in cooperation with Portland State University; Army in cooperation with University of Portland.

Degrees Conferred: 236 *baccalaureate*; 340 *master's*; 65 *doctorate*; 88 *first-professional*. Bachelor's degrees awarded in top five disciplines: business, management, marketing, and related support services 57; biological/life sciences 43; education 24; parks and recreation 25; communication, journalism, and related programs 22. Master's degrees awarded: various disciplines 340. Doctorates awarded: various disciplines 65. First-professional degrees awrded: optometry 88.

Fees and Other Expenses: *Full-time tuition per academic year* $28,270; contact the university for current graduate/first-professional tuition/fees. *Books and supplies:* $950. *Room and board per academic year:* $7,482. *Other expenses:* $1,500.

Financial Aid: Aid from institutionally generated funds is provided on the basis of academic merit, financial need, other criteria.

Financial aid to full-time, first-time undergraduate students: 98% received some form of financial aid. Average amount of aid received: federal grants $4,141; Pell grants $2,929; other federal aid $1,327; state/local grants $5,392; institutional grants $12,465.

Departments and Teaching Staff: *Total instructional faculty:* 278. 78% of faculty hold the doctorate, first-professional, or other terminal degree. Student/faculty ratio: 12:1.

Enrollment: Total enrollment 3,167. Undergraduate 1,481 (full-time 95%; female 64%, male 36%). Graduate 1,686 (full-time 84%) Graduate 1,686 (full time 84%). Undergraduate transfer-in students 140.

Characteristics of Student Body: *Ethnic/racial makeup:* Black non-Hispanic: 1%; American Indian or Alaska Native: 1%; Asian or Pacific Islander: 23%; Hispanic: 5%; White non-Hispanic: 60%; unknown: 9%; nonresident alien 1%. *Age distribution:* number under 18: 19; 18–19: 522; 20–21: 473; 22–24: 124; 25–29: 44; 30–34: 21; 35–39: 9; 40–49: 17; 50–64: 3.

International Students: Programs available to aid students whose native language is not English: social, cultural. English as a Second Language Program. No financial aid specifically designated for international students.

Student Life: Freshmen and sophomores not living at home must reside on campus. On-campus residence halls house 60% of student body. Residence halls for males constitute 30% of such space, for both sexes 70%. *Intercollegiate athletics:* male: baseball, basketball, cross-country, golf, soccer, tennis, track and field, wrestling; female: basketball, cross-country, golf, soccer, softball, swimming/diving, tennis, track and field, volleyball. *Special regulations:* Cars permitted without restrictions. *Special services:* Learning Resources Center, medical services. *Student publications, radio: Heart of Oak*, a yearbook; *Index*, a biweekly newspaper; *Pacific Review*, a biannual literary magazine; optometry yearbook. Radio station KPUR. *Surrounding community:* Forest Grove population 18,500. Portland, 25 miles from campus, is nearest metropolitan area. Served by airport 40 miles from campus; light rail service 5 miles from campus.

Library Collections: 152,000 volumes. 85,000 government documents; 77,000 microforms; 3,710 audiovisual materials; 945 current periodical subscriptions. 1,758 recordings. 3,424 compact discs. Online catalog. Computer work stations available. Students have access to online information retrieval services and the Internet.

Most important special holdings include collections on allied health, English literature, historical optometry, Pacificana.

Buildings and Grounds: Campus area 55 acres.

Chief Executive Officer: Dr. Phillip D.Creighton, President.

Address admission inquiries to Beth Woodward, Director of Admissions.

College of Optometry

Degree Programs Offered: *First-professional.*

Admission: 52 semester hours with minimum grade of C, completion of pre-optometry course requirements, OCAT.

Degree Requirements: Baccalaureate degree, 135 credit hours (including 133 in optometry core requirements), 2.0 GPA, 4 years in residence.

Portland State University

724 SW Harrison
P.O. Box 751
Portland, Oregon 97207
Tel: (503) 725-3000 **E-mail:** admissions@pdx.edu
Fax: (503) 725-5525 **Internet:** www.pdx.edu

Institution Description: Portland State University is a state institution. *Enrollment:* 26,382. *Degrees awarded:* Baccalaureate, master's, doctorate. Certificates also awarded.

Academic offerings subject to approval by statewide coordinating bodies. Budget subject to approval by state governing boards.

Accreditation: *Regional:* NWCCU. *Professional*: business, chemistry, engineering, music, planning, public administration, social work, speech-language pathology, teacher education

History: Established and chartered as Vanport Extension Center, and offered first instruction at postsecondary level 1946; changed name to Portland State Extension Center 1952; chartered as Portland State College and awarded first degree (baccalaureate) 1955; adopted present name 1969. *See* John Elrot Allen, ed., *Portland State University: The First 25 Years, 1955–1980* (Portland: Portland State University, 1980) for further information.

Institutional Structure: *Governing board:* Oregon State Board of Higher Education. Representation: 9 board members, 2 students. All voting. *Composition of institution:* Administrators 80. Academic affairs headed by provost. Management/business/finances directed by vice president for finance and administration. Vice president for university relations oversees alumni, government relations, communications. Full-time instructional faculty 729. Academic governance body, Faculty Senate, meets an average of 9 times per year. *Faculty representation:* Full-time faculty served by collective bargaining agent affiliated with AAUP, part-time by collective bargaining agent affiliated with AFT.

Calendar: Quarters. Academic year Sept. to June. Freshmen admitted Sept., Jan., Mar., June. Summer session of 1 term beginning June offering courses lasting from one to 10 weeks with the majority being 8-week courses.

Characteristics of Freshmen: 4,262 applicants (2,351 female, 1,911 male). 80% of applicants admitted. 49% of admitted applicants enrolled full-time. 78% (1,161 students) submitted SAT scores; 15% (228 students) submitted ACT scores. *25th percentile*: SAT Math 460; ACT Composite 18, ACT English, ACT Math 19. *75th percentile*: SAT Math 600; ACT Composite 25, ACT English 24, ACT math 25.

31% of freshmen expected to graduate within 5 20 years. 87% of freshmen from Oregon. Freshmen from 47 states and 98 foreign countries.

Admission: Rolling admissions plan. Early acceptance available. *Requirements:* Either graduation from secondary school or GED. Minimum high school GPA for residents and nonresidents 3.0 (alternative to GPA requirement: either 1000 SAT or 21 ACT). High school subject requirements: 4 units English, 3 mathematics, 2 science, 3 social studies, 2 foreign language. *Entrance tests:* College Board SAT or ACT composite. For foreign students TOEFL. *For transfer students:* 2.0 minimum GPA for residents, 2.25 GPA for nonresidents; from 4-year accredited institution maximum transfer credit limited only by residence requirement; credit; from 2-year accredited institution 108 hours; correspondence/extension students 60 hours.

College credit and advanced placement for postsecondary-level work completed in secondary school. Tutoring available. Developmental courses offered during regular academic year; credit given.

Degree Requirements: Minimum 180 credits (greater in some programs); 72 upper-division. University Studies program; Freshman Inquiry, Sophomore Inquiry, Upper-Division Cluster, and Senior Capstone Experience. For the Bachelor of Arts degree: 2 years of foreign language or equivalent proficiency; for the Bachelor of Music degree: completion of program of music and applied music as prescribed the Department of Music; for the Bachelor of Science degree: completion of 36 units from the science academic distribution area or 36 units from the social science academic distribution area.

Fulfillment of some degree requirements and exemption from some beginning courses possible by passing College Board CLEP, APP. *Grading system:* A–F; pass-fail; withdraw.

Distinctive Educational Programs: School of Extended Studies. Evening and weekend classes. Special facilities for using telecommunications in the classroom. Interdisciplinary programs in Black studies, child and family studies, international business, Central European studies, Latin American studies, Middle East studies, women's studies. Environmental studies undergraduate program and environmental sciences and resources doctoral program. Master's in international management. Pre-professional programs in agriculture, chiropractic, naturapathic medicine, occupational therapy, optometry, physical therapy, physician assistant, veterinary medicine, cytotechnology, dental hygiene, dentistry, medicine, osteopathy, podiatry, forestry, law, medical technology, nuclear medicine technology, nursing, pharmacy. Dual enrollment for high school students. Honors program. Teacher preparatory program. Study abroad programs in Argentina, Australia, Belgium, Brazil, Chile, China, Costa Rica, Czech Republic, Denmark, Dominican Republic, Ecuador, England, France, Germany, Greece, Hungary, Indonesia, Italy, Japan, South Korea, Mexico, The Netherlands, Poland, Russia, Spain, Taiwan, Thailand, Tunisia, Vietnam.

ROTC: Army. Air Force in cooperation with University of Portland.

Degrees Conferred: 3,289 *baccalaureate*; 1,508 *master's*; 41 *doctorate*. Bachelor's degrees awarded in top five disciplines: business, management, marketing, and related support services 824; social sciences 648; physical sciences 282; psychology 233; liberal arts/general studies 217. Master's degrees awarded in top five disciplines: education 552; public administration and social services 241; business/marketing 156; engineering technologies 124; social sciences 76. Doctorates awarded: computer and information sciences 1; education 8; engineering technologies 3; interdisciplinary studies 9; mathematics 1; natural resources and environmental sciences 7; public administration and social services 4; social sciences 8.

Fees and Other Expenses: *Full-time tuition per academic year 2008–09:* undergraduate resident $6,147, nonresident $18,857; contact the university for current graduate tuition. *Room and board per academic year:* $9,486. *Books and supplies:* $1,000. *Other expenses:* $2,889.

Financial Aid: Aid from institutionally generated funds is provided on the basis of academic merit, financial need, athletic ability.

Financial aid to full-time, first-time undergraduate students: 86% received some form of financial aid. Average amount of aid received: federal grants $3,680; Pell grants $3,069; other federal aid $994; state/local grants $1,815; institutional grants $3,851.

Departments and Teaching Staff: *Total instructional faculty:* 1,260 (full-time 739, part-time 521). 90% of faculty hold the doctorate, first-professional, or other terminal degree. Student/faculty ratio: 18:1.

Enrollment: Total enrollment 26,382. Undergraduate 20,330 (full-time 63%, female 53%, male 47%). Graduate 6,052 (full-time 41%). Undergraduate transfer-in students 2,906.

Characteristics of Student Body: *Ethnic/racial makeup:* Black non-Hispanic: 3%; American Indian or Alaska Native: 1%; Asian or Pacific Islander: 10%; Hispanic: 5%; White non-Hispanic: 65%; unknown: 11%; nonresident alien 5%. *Age distribution:* number under 18: 613; 18–19: 1,632; 20–21: 3,331; 22–24: 4,220; 25–29: 3,651; 30–34: 1,558; 35–39: 335; 40–49: 780; 50–64: 352; 65 and over: 8.

International Students: 1,432 nonresident aliens enrolled fall 2008. Programs available to aid students whose native language is not English: social, cultural. English as a Second Language Program. No financial aid specifically designated for international students.

Student Life: PSU offers on- and off-campus housing through College Housing Northwest (CHNW), a nonprofit housing corporation. 11% of student body lives in CHNW housing. *Intercollegiate athletics:* male: baseball, basketball, cross-country, football, golf, indoor/outdoor track, wrestling; female: basketball, cross-country, soccer, softball, tennis, indoor/outdoor track, volleyball. *Special services:* Disabilities Services for Students, Academic Support Program, mentor program for returning women students, student athlete academic advising, counseling and testing, medical services, career information/placement service, on-campus daycare, international student services, legal services, veterans' services, ethnic student services, student parent services, and mentors for new students. *Student publications: The Vanguard*, the daily university newspaper; and *The Portland State University Review*, a campus literary magazine. *Surrounding community:* Portland population 503,000. Served by mass transit bus system, mass transit light rail system 10 blocks from campus, airport 12 miles from campus, passenger rail service 2 miles from campus. PSU is 80 miles from the coast and 55 miles from Mt. Hood.

Library Collections: 1,710,000 volumes. 10,038 serials; 2,373,000 microforms. 87,000 audiovisual materials. Computer work stations available. Students have access to online information retrieval services and the Internet.

Most important special holdings include Middle East Studies Collection.

Buildings and Grounds: Campus area 49 acres.

Chief Executive Officer: Daniel O. Bernstine, President. Address admission inquiries to Samuel Collie, Director of Admissions.

Reed College

3203 SE Woodstock Boulevard
Portland, Oregon 97202-8199
Tel: (503) 771-1112 **E-mail:** admission@reed.edu
Fax: (503) 777-7769 **Internet:** www.reed.edu

Institution Description: Reed College is a private, independent, nonprofit college. *Enrollment:* 1,471. *Degrees awarded:* Baccalaureate, master's.

Accreditation: *Regional:* NWCCU. *Professional*: chemistry

History: Incorporated 1908; established 1909; offered first instruction at postsecondary level 1911; first degrees (baccalaureate, master's) awarded 1915.

Institutional Structure: *Governing board:* Board of Trustees of the Reed Institute. Representation: 34 trustees, including 22 alumni, president of the college (ex officio). 34 voting members. *Composition of institution:* AAministrators 71. Academic affairs headed by dean of the faculty. Management/business/finances directed by vice president and treasurer. Full-time instructional faculty 119. Academic governance body, the Faculty of Reed College, meets an average of 10 times per year.

Calendar: Semesters. Academic year Aug. to May. Freshmen admitted Aug., Jan. Degrees conferred and formal commencement May. No summer session.

Characteristics of Freshmen: 3,485 applicants (female 1,982, male 1,503). 32% of applicants admitted. 29% of applicants admitted and enrolled full-time.

94% (355 students) submitted SAT scores; 33 (126 students) submitted ACT scores. *25th percentile*: SAT Critical Reading 660, SAT Math 610; ACT Composite 28, ACT English 28, ACT Math 26. *75th percentile*: SAT Critical Reading 750, SAT Math 710; ACT Composite 32, ACT English 34, ACT Math 31. 6 National Merit Scholars.

72% entering freshmen expected to graduate within 5 years. 72 of freshmen from Oregon. Freshmen from 49 states and 85 foreign countries.

Admission: For fall acceptance, closing date Jan. 15; applicants notified on or about Apr. 1. Two early decision plans: fall option (deadline Nov. 15, notification Dec. 15), and winter option (deadline Jan. 2, notification Feb. 1). Deferred and early admission available. *Requirements:* Graduation from accredited secondary school with the following units recommended: 4 units English, 3 nits foreign language, 4 units mathematics, 3 science, and 3-4 social studies; or GED. *Entrance tests:* College Board SAT required, 3 Achievement tests, and TOEFL For foreign students. *For transfer students:* 3.0 minimum GPA; 2-year residency requirements.

Advanced placement possible for postsecondary-level work completed in secondary school. College credit and advanced placement possible for extrainstitutional learning.

Tutoring available.

Degree Requirements: *For undergraduate degrees:* 120 semester hours; 2 years in residence; 3 semesters physical education; distribution requirements; senior thesis; exit competency examinations (junior qualifying examinations, senior oral examination).

Fulfillment of some degree requirements and exemption from some beginning courses possible by passing College Board CLEP, AP. *Grading system:* A–F; credit-no credit; withdraw (carries time limit); incomplete (deadline after which no credit is given).

Distinctive Educational Programs: Computer Science program by arrangement with the University of Washington; Computer Science and Engineering Master of Science from OGI School of Science and Engineering; Engineering Program with California Institute of Technology, Columbia University School of Engineering, and the Rensselaer Polytechnic Institute; Forestry-Environmental Sciences with Duke University; Preprofessional program in medicine and veterinary medicine; Visual Arts Program. Interdisciplinary/interdepartmental majors in American studies; chemistry-physics; classics-religion; dance-theatre; history-literature; international studies; literature-philosophy; literature-theatre; mathematics-economics; mathematics-physics; mathematics-sociology; philosophy-mathematics; philosophy-religion; other interdisciplinary majors may be individually arranged. Institutionally sponsored study abroad in China, Costa Rica, Ecuador, Egypt, England, France, Germany, Hungary, Ireland, Israel, Italy, Morocco, Russia, South Africa, Spain. Exchange programs through Howard University.

Degrees Conferred: 299 *baccalaureate*; 5 *master's*. Bachelor's degrees awarded in top five disciplines: social sciences 47; English 39; biological/life

REED COLLEGE—*cont'd*

sciences 35; foreign languages and literature 27; physical sciences 26. Master's degrees awarded: liberal arts and sciences 5.

Fees and Other Expenses: *Full-time tuition per academic year 2008–09:* $38,190. *Room and board per academic year:* $9,920. *Required fees:* $230. *Books and supplies:* $950. *Other expenses:* $900.

Financial Aid: Aid from institutionally generated funds is awarded on the basis of financial need.

Financial aid to full-time, first-time undergraduate students: 52% of students received some form of aid.

Departments and Teaching Staff: *Total instructional faculty:* 132 (full-time 119, part-time 13). 835 of faculty hold the doctorate, first-professional, or other terminal degree. Student/faculty ratio: 10:1.

Enrollment: Total enrollment 1,471. Undergraduate 1,442 (full-time 97%; female 58%, male 44%). Graduate 29 (full-time 100%). Undergraduate transfer-in students 27.

Characteristics of Student Body: *Ethnic/racial makeup:* Black non-Hispanic: 3%; American Indian or Alaska Native: 1%; Asian or Pacific Islander: 7%; Hispanic: 3%; White non-Hispanic: 56%; unknown: 18%; nonresident alien 6%. *Age distribution:* number under 18: 18; 18–19: 5@5; 20–21: 606; 22–24: 231; 25–29: 15; 30–34: 6; 40–49: 1; 50–64: 2.

International Students: 122 nonresident aliens enrolled fall 2008. Students from Europe, Asia, Central and South America, Africa, Canada. No programs available to aid students whose native language is not English. Financial aid specifically designated for international students: 40 scholarships available annually for qualifying undergraduate and graduate international students.

Student Life: On-campus housing accommodates 60% of the student body and is comprised of residence halls (41%) and apartments (10%). Residence halls for males constitute 16% of such space, for females 12%, for both sexes 72%. *Special regulations:* Cars permitted without restrictions. *Special services:* Medical services. *Student publications, radio: Quest*, a weekly newspaper; *Exile*, a literary magazine; *Griffin*, a yearbook; *Praxis*, a journal of practical criticism; and *Rude Girl Press*, a feminist forum. Radio station KRRC broadcasts 12 hours a day, 7 days a week. *Surrounding community:* Portland population 529,000. Served by mass transit bus and light rail system; airport 12 miles from campus; passenger rail service 8 miles from campus.

Library Collections: 565,000 volumes. Online catalog. 274,000 government documents; 146,179 microforms; 14,543 audiovisual materials. Paper, microform, electronic access to 10,232 periodicals. Computer work stations available. Students have access to online information retrieval services and the Internet.

Most important special holdings include Simeon Garnet Reed Papers (including letters and business records of 19th-century transportation and mining magnate whose monies financed the founding of The Reed Institute); Thomas Lamb Eliot Papers (includes manuscripts, correspondence, journals, notebooks, sermons, and miscellaneous personal papers of 19th-20th century Unitarian minister, educator and civic leader instrumental in founding Reed); Lloyd Reynolds Collection (more than 300 volumes of books, letters, miscellaneous papers on the history of printing, book manufacture, calligraphy).

Buildings and Grounds: Campus area 110 acres.

Chief Executive Officer: Dr. Colin S. Diver, President.

Undergraduates address admission inquiries to Paul Marthers, Dean of Admissions; graduate inquiries to Brian Henley, Director of Admissions.

Southern Oregon University

1250 Siskiyou Boulevard
Ashland, Oregon 97520
Tel: (541) 552-7672 **E-mail:** admissions@sou.edu
Fax: (541) 552-6614 **Internet:** www.sou.edu

Institution Description: Southern Oregon University, formerly named Southern Oregon State College, is a state institution. *Enrollment:* 5,079. *Degrees awarded:* Baccalaureate, master's.

Academic offerings subject to approval by statewide coordinating bodies. Budget subject to approval by state governing boards. Member of the consortium Western Interstate Commission for Higher Education.

Accreditation: *Regional:* NWCCU. *Professional*: chemistry, music, nursing, teacher education

History: Established as Southern Oregon Normal School, chartered, and offered first instruction at postsecondary level 1926; changed name to Southern Oregon College of Education 1939; awarded first degree (baccalaureate) 1942; changed name to Southern Oregon College 1956; became Southern Oregon State College 1975; adopted present name 1997.

Institutional Structure: *Governing board:* Oregon University System. Representation: 9 board members, 2 students. All voting. *Composition of institution:* Administrators 54. Academic affairs headed by provost. Management/business/finances directed by vice president for administration and finance. Full-time instructional faculty 224. Academic governance body, Faculty Senate, meets an average of 15 times per year. *Faculty representation:* Faculty served by collective bargaining agent, Associated Professors of Southern Oregon University, affiliated with the Oregon Educational Association.

Calendar: Quarters. Academic year Sept. to June. Freshmen admitted Sept., Jan., May, June. Degrees conferred June, Aug., Dec., Mar. Formal commencement June. Summer sessions, including pre-session, regular session, and post-session from June to Aug.

Characteristics of Freshmen: 1,887 applicants (1,163 female, 784 male). 80% of applicants accepted. 41% of accepted applicants enrolled.

Mean SAT class scores

90% (684 students) submitted SAT scores; 17% (127 students) submitted ACT scores. *25th percentile*: SAT Critical Reading 460, SAT Math 460; ACT Composite 20, ACT English 19, ACT Math 18. *75th percentile*: SAT Critical Reading 580, SAT Math 580; ACT Composite 25, ACT English 25, ACT Math 24.

37% of entering freshmen expected to graduate within 5 years. 71% of freshmen from Oregon. Freshmen from 43 states and 40 foreign countries.

Admission: For fall acceptance, apply as early as Sept. 1 of previous year, but not later than day of registration. Early acceptance available. *Requirements:* high school diploma from a standard or accredited high school with a 2.75 cumulative GPA *or* a total score on the SAT of 1010 or ACT 21 and satisfactory completion of 14 units of college preparatory work in the areas of English, mathematics, science, social studies, and other approved courses. *For transfer students:* 2.25 minimum GPA; from 4-year accredited institution maximum transfer credit limited only by residence requirement; from 2-year accredited institution 108 quarter hours; correspondence/extension students 60 hours. If fewer than 36 term hours, freshmen admission requirements must be met.

College credit and advanced placement for postsecondary-level work completed in secondary school. College credit and advanced placement on basis of portfolio assessment.

Degree Requirements: *For all baccalaureate degrees:* 180 credit hours. *For all undergraduate degrees:* 2.0 GPA; 45 of last 60 hours in residence; general education requirements; demonstrated proficiency in written and oral communication. *For bachelor of arts:* 2 years of college study, or the equivalent, of a foreign language.

Fulfillment of some degree requirements and exemption from some beginning courses possible by passing departmental examinations, College Board CLEP, AP. *Grading system:* A–F; pass-fail; withdraw.

Distinctive Educational Programs: *For undergraduates:* Interdisciplinary program in business-chemistry. Preprofessional programs in agriculture, chiropractic, dentistry, engineering, engineering technology, physical therapy, podiatry, veterinary medicine. Preprofessional programs in dental hygiene and medical technology leading to degree awarded by University of Oregon, applied optics and optometry leading to degree awarded by Pacific University, pharmacy leading to degree awarded by Oregon State University. College participates in National Aeronautics and Space Administration (NASA) Cooperative Education Program. Honors programs. Tutorials. Study abroad in Australia, Austria, China, Denmark, Ecuador, England, France, Germany, Greece, Italy, Japan, Korea, Mexico, Norway, Thailand. Program of support services for educationally or economically disadvantaged students from other cultures. *For graduate students:* Interdisciplinary studies major. Nondegree teacher preparation program. *Available to all students:* Evening courses. Special facilities for using telecommunications in the classroom. Individual majors. *Other distinctive programs:* Off-campus credit and noncredit continuing education program.

Degrees Conferred: 663 *baccalaureate*; 260 *master's*. Bachelor's degrees awarded in top five disciplines: business, management, marketing, and related support services 148; social sciences 84; communication, journalism, and related programs 81; visual and performing arts 78; psychology 68. Master's degrees awarded: various disciplines 260.

Fees and Other Expenses: *Full-time tuition per academic year 2008–09:* undergraduate resident $5,661, nonresident $18,669. *Room and board per academic year:* $8,418. *Books and supplies:* $1,350. *Other expenses:* $3,750.

Financial Aid: Aid from institutionally generated funds is provided on the basis of academic merit, financial need, athletic ability, other criteria.

Financial aid to full-time, first-time undergraduate students: 88% received some form of financial aid. Average amount of aid received: federal grants $3,801; Pell grants $2,896; other federal aid $1,118; state/local grants $1,553; institutional grants $2,680.

Departments and Teaching Staff: *Total instructional faculty:* 272. Student/faculty ratio: 18:1. Degrees held by full-time faculty: doctorate 90%, master's 10%. 91% hold terminal degrees.

Enrollment: Total enrollment 5,079. Undergraduate 4,459 (full-time 74%; female 58%, male 42%). Graduate 620 (full-time 34%). Undergraduate transfer-in students 480.

Characteristics of Student Body: *Ethnic/racial makeup:* Black non-Hispanic: 2%; American Indian or Alaska Native: 2%; Asian or Pacific Islander: 4%; Hispanic: 5%; White non-Hispanic: 77%; unknown: 8%; nonresident alien 2%.

International Students: 102 undergraduate nonresident aliens enrolled fall 2008. Students from Europe, Asia, Central and South America, Africa, Canada. Programs available to aid students whose native language is not English: social and cultural. English as a Second Language Program. Financial aid specifically designated for international students: scholarships available annually to undergraduate international students.

Student Life: On-campus residence halls house 25% of student body. Residence halls are co-ed. Some students live off campus in college-controlled facilities. Housing available for married students and those with children. *Intercollegiate athletics:* male: basketball, cross-country, football, track, wrestling; female: basketball, cross-country, softball, tennis, track, volleyball. *Special regulations:* Cars with permits allowed; fee charged. *Special services:* Medical services. *Student publications, radio: The Raider*, a yearbook; *Siskiyou*, a weekly newspaper. Radio station KSOR broadcasts 138 hours per week. *Surrounding community:* Ashland population 18,000. Portland, 300 miles from campus, is nearest metropolitan area. Served by mass transit bus system; airport 20 miles from campus.

Library Collections: 330,000 volumes including bound books, serial backfiles, electronic documents, and government documents not in separate collections. Online catalog. Current serial subscriptions: 2,000 paper, microform, and electronic. 370 recordings. Computer work stations available. Students have access to the Internet at no charge.

Most important special collections include Margery Bailey Renaissance Collection (5,000 volumes with emphasis on Shakespeare); Southwest Oregon Local History Collection; Geological Survey Map Collection; Children's Curriculum and Textbook Collection.

Buildings and Grounds: Campus area 160 acres.

Chief Executive Officer: Dr. Elizabeth Zinser, President.

Address admission inquiries to Mark Bottorf, Director of Admissions.

University of Oregon

1226 University of Oregon
Eugene, Oregon 97403-1226
Tel: (541) 346-3201 **E-mail:** uoadmit@uoregon.edu
Fax: (541) 346-5815 **Internet:** www.uoregon.edu

Institution Description: University of Oregon is a state institution. *Enrollment:* 21,452. *Degrees awarded:* Baccalaureate, first-professional (law), master's, doctorate.

Academic offerings subject to approval by statewide coordinating bodies. Budget subject to approval by state governing boards. Member of the consortium Malheur Environmental Field Station.

Accreditation: *Regional:* NWCCU. *Professional*: architecture, athletic training, business, chemistry, dietetics, interior design, journalism, landscape architecture, law, music, psychology internship, planning, recreation and leisure services, speech-language pathology, teacher education

History: Chartered 1872; established and offered first instruction at postsecondary level 1876; awarded first degree (baccalaureate) 1878; offered first graduate degree programs 1896. *See* Henry David Sheldon, *The History of the University of Oregon* (Portland: Binford-Mort, 1940) for further information.

Institutional Structure: *Governing board:* Oregon State Board of Higher Education. Representation: 9 board members, 2 students. All voting. *Composition of institution:* Administrators 28. Academic affairs headed by vice president for academic affairs and provost. Management/business/finances directed by vice president for administration and finance. Full-time instructional faculty 737. Academic governance body, University Assembly, meets an average of 10 times per year.

Calendar: Quarters (semesters for law school). Academic year Sept. to June. Freshmen admitted Sept., Jan., Mar., June. Degrees conferred Dec., Mar., June, Aug. Formal commencements June, Aug. Summer session June to Sept.

Characteristics of Freshmen: 11,287 applicants (female 6,004, male 5,283). 88% of applicants admitted. 35% of applicants admitted and enrolled full-time.

94% (2,975 students) submitted SAT scores. *25th percentile*: SAT Critical Reading 458, SAT Math 500. *75th percentile*: SAT Critical Reading 606, SAT Math 611. 44 National Merit Scholars.

62% of freshmen expected to graduate within 5 years. 68^ of freshmen from Oregon. Freshmen from 43 states and 26 foreign countries.

Admission: Rolling admissions plan. For fall acceptance, apply by Nov. 1 for early notification (Dec. 15). Jan 16 postmark deadline for freshman admissions, general university scholarships, and Clark Honors College Admissions. *Requirements:* Either graduation from accredited secondary school or GED. Recommend 4 units English, 3 social studies, 3 mathematics, 2 science, 2 foreign language, 2 electives. Minimum 3.0 GPA; score of 30 on Test of Standard Written English or 15 on ACT English. *Entrance tests:* College Board SAT or ACT composite. *For transfer students:* 2.25 minimum GPA for in-state residents, 2.50 for nonresidents.

College credit and advanced placement for postsecondary-level work completed in secondary school and for extrainstitutional learning.

Tutoring available. Developmental and remedial courses offered in summer session and regular academic year; credit given.

Degree Requirements: 186 credit hours (220 for architecture); passing grade on 85% of all work completed at University of Oregon; 45 credits in residence; general education requirements.

Fulfillment of some degree requirements and exemption from some beginning courses possible by passing College Board CLEP, AP. *Grading system:* A–F; pass-fail.

Distinctive Educational Programs: Freshman Interest Groups; Society of College Scholars Freshman Seminary; Residential Academy; James Warsaw Sports Marketing Center; Lundquist Center for Entrepreneurship; Students in Resource Assistance for Rural Environments; Green Chemistry Laboratory; Alice C. tyler Instrumentation Center; Future Music Oregon. Off-campus centers (at UO Portland Center, 110 miles from main campus; Cascades Campus in Bend, 117 miles away; Oregon Institute of Marine Biology in Charleston, 130 miles away; Pine Mountain Observatory, 155 miles away). Freshman seminars. Accelerated degree programs. Special facilities for using telecommunications in the classroom. Honors programs. Individual majors. Tutorials. Study abroad in Australia, China (Beijing), Czech Republic, Denmark, Ecuador, England, Finland, France, Germany, Hungary,Indonesia, Israel, Italy, Japan, Korea, Mexico, The Netherlands, Norway, Poland, Russia, Scotland, Spain, Sweden, Thailand, Vietnam. *Other distinctive programs:* Continuing education; Jordan Schnitzer Museum of Art; Museum of Natural and Cultural History.

ROTC: Army.

Degrees Conferred: 3,836 *baccalaureate*; 856 *master's*; 151 *doctorate*; 182 *first-professional*. Bachelor's degrees awarded in top five disciplines: social sciences and history 862; business, management, marketing, and related support services 411; communication, journalism, and related programs 369; visual and performing arts 289; foreign languages and literature 250. Master's degrees awarded: various disciplines 856. Doctorates awarded: various disciplines 151. First-professional degrees awarded: law 182.

Fees and Other Expenses: *Full-time tuition per academic year 2008–09:* undergraduate resident $6,435, nonresident $19,992. contact the university for current graduate and law school tuition. *Room and board per academic year:* $8,211. *Books and supplies:* $1,050. *Other expenses:* $2,412.

Financial Aid: The university offers a direct lending program. Aid from institutionally generated funds is provided on the basis of academic merit, financial need, athletic ability, other criteria.

Financial aid to full-time, first-time undergraduate students: 61% received some form of aid. Average amount of aid received: federal grants $3,708; Pell grants $2,920; other federal aid $1,081; state/local grants $1,658; institutional grants $2,501.

Departments and Teaching Staff: *Total instructional faculty:* 1,129. 85% of faculty hold the doctorate, first-professional, or other terminal degree. Student/faculty ratio: 18:1.

Enrollment: Total enrollment 21,452. Undergraduate 17,619 (full-time 92%; female 51%, male 49%). Graduate 3,833 (full-time 71%). Undergraduate transfer-in students 1,158.

Characteristics of Student Body: *Ethnic/racial makeup:* Black non-Hispanic: 2%; American Indian or Alaska Native: 2%; Asian or Pacific Islander: 1%; Hispanic: 4%; White non-Hispanic: 75%; unknown: 7%; nonresident alien 5%. *Age distribution:* number under 18: 134; 18–19 5,376; 20–21: 5,877; 22–24: 3,064; 25–29: 1,073; 30–34: 357; 35–39: 165; 40–49: 207; 50–64: 89; 65 and over: 6. 42% of student body attend summer sessions.

International Students: 1,207 nonresident aliens enrolled fall 2008. Students from Europe, Asia, Central and South America, Africa, Canada, Australia, New Zealand, Middle East. Programs available to aid students whose native language is not English: social, cultural. English as a Second Language Program. Some financial aid specifically designated for international students.

Student Life: On-campus residence halls house 3,200 single students. There are halls for graduate and undergraduate males, females, special interest groups and co-ed by floor; 5 cooperative houses. *Intercollegiate athletics:* male: basketball, football, golf, tennis, track, cross-country, wrestling; female: basketball, golf, soccer, softball, tennis, track, cross-country, volleyball. *Special regulations:* Cars with parking permits allowed; fee charged. *Special services:* Learning Resources Center, medical services, counseling services. *Student publications, radio: Oregon Daily Emerald*, a newspaper; *Oregon Law Review*, a quarterly publication. Radio station KWVA broadcasts music and news on 88.1 and online. Classical station KWAX offers an all-music format. *Surrounding community:* Eugene population 148,000. Portland (OR) 110 miles from campus,

UNIVERSITY OF OREGON—*cont'd*

is nearest metropolitan area. Served by mass transit bus system; airport 10 miles from campus; passenger rail service 2 miles from campus.

Publications: *Comparative Literature* (quarterly) first published in 1949; *Northwest Review* (3 times annually) first published 1957; *Oregon Quarterly, Oregon Law Review, Inquiry.* 787 2,787,476 volumes including bound books, serial backfiles, electronic documents, and government documents not in separate collections. Online catalog.Current serial subscriptions: 12,385 paper, 1,934,675 microform, 695 electronic. 55,47,990 recordings; 18,164 compact discs. 2,082 CD-ROMs. 305 public computer work stations. Students have access to the Internet at no charge.

Most important special holdings include Research Collection of Conservative and Libertarian Studies; papers of authors and illustrators of children's literature; Burgess Collection of medieval manuscripts and incunabula; American Far East Missionaries' papers supported by an extensive Orientalia Collection; Oregon Collection.

Buildings and Grounds: Campus area 205 acres. Campus DVD available.

Chief Executive Officer: Dr. Dave Frohnmayer, President.

Address admission inquiries to Brian Henley, Direcotr of Admissions.

College of Arts and Sciences

Degree Programs Offered: *Baccalaureate, master's, doctorate* in various fields.

Distinctive Educational Programs: Robert Donald Clark Honors College and numerous interdisciplinary and special programs such as American studies, Asian studies, Australian studies, Canadian studies, classical archaeology, cognitive science, comparative literature, environmental studies, folklore and ethnic studies, humanities, international studies, general science, Latin American studies, medieval studies, neuroscience, Russian and East European studies, statistics, women's studies. Various preparatory programs for a variety of professional and technical careers are also offered.

School of Architecture and Allied Arts

Degree Programs Offered: *Baccalaureate* in architecture, art education/fine and applied arts, arts management, art history, fine arts, interior architecture, landscape architecture; *master's* in architecture, art education, art history, fine arts, historic preservation, landscape, urban planning; *doctorate* in art education, art history.

Distinctive Educational Programs: 2-year program leading to M.S. in historic preservation. Center for Environmental Research.

College of Education

Degree Programs Offered: *Baccalaureate* in communication disorders, educational psychology, educational studies; special education, teacher education; *master's, doctorate* in various fields. Certificates also offered.

Distinctive Educational Programs: Measurement, evaluation and research; school psychology; general educational psychology; speech pathology-audiology; severely handicapped learner endorsement programs; special education in mild disabilities; rehabilitation; early childhood education; elementary and secondary teacher education.

School of Law

Degree Programs Offered: *First-professional;* concurrent *J.D./M.B.A.* with College of Business Administration.

Distinctive Educational Programs: Special programs in ocean law and environmental and natural resources law.

School of Music

Degree Programs Offered: *Baccalaureate, master's, doctorate:* jazz studies, music, music composition, music education, music performance, music theory, music history.

Charles H. Lundquist College of Business

Degree Programs Offered: *Baccalaureate, master's, doctorate.*

Distinctive Educational Programs: Forest industries management, industrial relations, international business, J.D./M.B.A. (in cooperation with the School of Law).

School of Journalism and Communication

Degree Programs Offered: *Baccalaureate, master's* in journalism; *doctorate* in communication and society.

University of Portland

5000 North Willamette Boulevard
Portland, Oregon 97203-5798
Tel: (503) 943-7911 **E-mail:** admissions@uoport.edu
Fax: (503) 283-7399 **Internet:** www.uoport.edu

Institution Description: University of Portland is a private, independent, nonprofit institution affiliated with the Roman Catholic Church. *Enrollment:* 3,661. *Degrees awarded:* Baccalaureate, master's. Certificates also awarded.

Accreditation: *Regional:* NWCCU. *Professional*: business, engineering, nursing, teacher education

History: Established as Columbia University 1901; chartered 1909; offered first instruction at postsecondary level 1923; awarded first degree (baccalaureate) 1929; adopted present name 1935. *See* James Covert, *Point of Pride: The University of Portland Story* (Portland: University of Portland Press, 1976) for further information.

Institutional Structure: *Governing board:* Board of Regents. Extrainstitutional representation: 40 regents, 9 emeriti. *Composition of institution:* Administrators 36. Academic affairs headed by academic vice president; management/business/finances directed by executive and financial vice president; student services/residence life/computing headed by vice president for student services; alumni/development/public relations directed by vice president for university relations. Full-time instructional faculty 138. Academic governance body, Academic Senate, meets an average of 8 times per year.

Calendar: Semesters. Academic year Aug. to May. Freshmen admitted Sept., Jan., June. Degrees conferred May, Aug. Formal commencement May, Aug. Summer session May to August.

Characteristics of Freshmen: 6,156 applicants (female 3,885, male 2,271). 92% of applicants accepted. 36% of accepted applicants enrolled full-time.

Mean SAT scores 561 critical reading, 585 mathematical.

58% of entering freshmen expected to graduate within 5 years. 48% of freshmen from Oregon. Freshmen from 41 states and 38 foreign countries.

Admission: Rolling admissions plan. For fall acceptance, apply as early as Sept. 1 of previous year, but not later than Aug. 1 of year of enrollment. Early decision available. *Requirements:* Graduation from accredited secondary school with academic units which normally include 4 English, 1 history, 2 laboratory science, 2 mathematics, 2 foreign language, 1 social studies; or GED. Minimum GPA 2.6. *Entrance tests:* College Board SAT I or ACT. For foreign students TOEFL. *For transfer students:* 2.3 minimum GPA; 90 semester hours maximum transfer credit.

College credit and advanced placement for postsecondary-level work completed in secondary school. Tutoring available.

Degree Requirements: *For all undergraduate degrees:* A minimum of 120 credit hours; 2.0 GPA; 30 hours in residence; general education requirements; comprehensives in individual fields of study.

Fulfillment of some degree requirements and exemption from some beginning courses possible by passing departmental examinations, College Board CLEP, AP. *Grading system:* A–F; pass; withdraw (carries time limit); incomplete (carries time limit).

Distinctive Educational Programs: Honors program. Freshman Seminar Program. Integrated Writing Program. BSN-MS program for RNs. Research-based B.S. in biology. Study abroad in Salzburg, Austria; Oviedo, Spain; London, England; Watford, England; Tokyo, Japan.

ROTC: Air Force, Army.

Degrees Conferred: 702 *baccalaureate*; 214 *master's.* Bachelor's degrees awarded in top five disciplines: business, management, marketing, and related support services 106; health professions and related clinical sciences 98; biomedical/biological sciences 65; engineering 58; education 46. Master's degrees awarded: various disciplines 214.

Fees and Other Expenses: *Full-time tuition per academic year 2008–09:* undergraduate $36,450; graduate charged per semester hour (contact the university for current rate). *Books and supplies;* $1,000. *Room and board per academic year:* $8,756. *Required fees:* $390. *Other expenses:* $1,800.

Financial Aid: Aid from institutionally generated funds is provided on the basis of academic merit, financial need, athletic ability, other criteria.

Financial aid to full-time, first-time undergraduate students: 95% received some form of aid. Average amount of aid received: federal grants $4,469, Pell grants $2,921; other federal aid $1,673; state/local grants $3,251; institutional grants $12,047.

Departments and Teaching Staff: *Total instructional faculty:* 309. Student/faculty ratio: 14:1. Degrees held by full-time faculty: master's 6%, doctorate 92%, professional 1%. 95% hold terminal degrees.

Enrollment: Total enrollment 3,661. Undergraduate 3,041. Graduate 620 (full-time 26%). Graduate 620 (full-time 26%). Undergraduate transfer-in students: 110.

Characteristics of Student Body: *Ethnic/racial makeup:* Black non-Hispanic: 1%; American Indian or Alaska Native: 1%; Asian or Pacific Islander: 10%; Hispanic: 5%; White non-Hispanic: 71%; unknown: 10%; nonresident alien 2%.

International Students: 74 nonresident aliens enrolled fall 2008. Students from Europe, Asia, Central and South America, Africa, Canada, Australia, New Zealand. Programs available to aid students whose native language is not English: social, cultural. English as a Second Language Program. Financial aid specifically designated for international students: scholarships available annually for undergraduate students.

Student Life: On-campus residence halls house over 50% of full-time undergraduates and 85% of freshmen. Females-only residence halls constitute 34% of available housing space; males-only halls constitute 23% of space; co-ed halls constitute 43% of space. *Intercollegiate athletics:* male: baseball, basketball, cross-country, golf, soccer, tennis, track; female: basketball, cross-country, soccer, tennis, track, volleyball. *Special regulations:* Cars permitted in designated areas; fee charged. Residence hall visitation from 10am to midnight Sun. through Thurs. and from 10am to 2am Fri. and Sat. *Special services:* University Center for Health, personal and career counseling, minority advisor, adult programs, campus ministry, volunteer service programs. *Student publications, radio: Beacon*, a weekly newspaper; *Log*, a yearbook. Radio station KDUP broadcasts 80 hours per week. *Surrounding community:* Portland metropolitan area population 1,500,000. Served by mass transit bus and light rail system; airport 10 miles from campus; passenger rail service 5 miles from campus.

Publications: *University of Portland Review; University of Portland Writers; Portland Magazine* (quarterly)

Library Collections: 380,000 volumes. 8,200 government documents; 540,000 microforms, 13,000 audiovisual materials, 1,580 current periodical subscriptions. Students have access to online information retrieval services and the Internet. Most important special holdings include collections on Catholic theology, American history, and Spanish literature.

Buildings and Grounds: Campus area 92 acres.

Chief Executive Officer: Rev. E. William Beauchamp, O.S.C., President.

Address admission inquiries to Director of Admissions.

College of Arts and Sciences

Degree Programs Offered: *Baccalaureate* in biology, chemistry, communications, computer applications management, computer science, criminal justice, drama, engineering chemistry, English, environmental science, environmental studies, history, interdisciplinary studies, journalism, life science, mathematics, music, organizational communication, philosophy, physics, political science, psychology, science communications, social work, sociology, Spanish, theater management, theology; *master's* in communications, drama, music, theology.

Distinctive Educational Programs: Individual majors. Interdisciplinary program in peace studies and individually designed fields. Cooperative baccalaureate in medical technology with approved hospitals.

School of Business Administration

Degree Programs Offered: *Baccalaureate* in accounting, marketing, international business, finance, management; *master's* in business administration.

School of Education

Degree Programs Offered: *Baccalaureate* in elementary education, music education, secondary education; *master's* in college student personnel administration, elementary education, general curriculum, music education, secondary education. Certificates in religious education.

Admission: 1010 or better score on the College Board tests for clear admission; 920–1010 may be admitted after review and may be required to take additional coursework.

Degree Requirements: Successful completion of all course work with a cumulative GPA of 2.50 and 2.67 in all education courses (applies to both elementary education and secondary education). Secondary education: develop a major in one or more of 15 areas with a GPA of at least 2.67.

School of Engineering

Degree Programs Offered: *Baccalaureate* in civil, electrical, engineering management, mechanical engineering, and engineering science; *master's* in civil, electrical, mechanical engineering.

Distinctive Educational Programs: Interdisciplinary programs in computer science and engineering science. Cooperative master's and doctoral programs in materials science with Oregon Graduate Center.

School of Nursing

Degree Programs Offered: *Baccalaureate, master's* in community health nursing, adult nurse practitioner.

Admission: Although students are admitted as freshmen or transfer students into the School of Nursing, acceptance into the upper division nursing major is dependent upon: (1) maintenance of at lest 2.5 GPA; (2) a cumulative GPA of 2.5 or above must be earned in the sciences with a minimum grade of C in each science course. Pass/no pass are not allowed; (3) completion of all prerequisite coursework; (4) all entering freshmen will demonstrate proficiency in General Chemistry or enrolled in CHM 101; (5) all entering freshmen whose recentered score is less than 530 on the SAT or its equivalent, must take ENG 107.

Warner Pacific College

2219 SE 68th Avenue
Portland, Oregon 97215
Tel: (503) 517-1000 **E-mail:** admiss@warnerpacific.edu
Fax: (503) 517-1352 **Internet:** www.warnerpacific.edu

Institution Description: Warner Pacific College is a private college affiliated with the Church of God. *Enrollment:* 973. *Degrees awarded:* Associate, baccalaureate, master's.

Member of Teacher Education Consortium.

Accreditation: *Regional:* NWCCU.

History: Established, chartered, incorporated as Pacific Bible College, and offered first instruction at postsecondary level 1937; awarded first degree (baccalaureate) 1941; adopted present name 1959.

Institutional Structure: *Governing board:* Board of Trustees. Extrainstitutional representation: 30 trustees; institutional representation: president of the college. 1 ex officio. 30 voting. *Composition of institution:* Academic affairs headed by academic dean. Management/business/finances directed by vice president for finance. Full-time instructional faculty 30. Academic governance body, Center Directors Council, meets an average of 10 times per year.

Calendar: Semesters. Academic year Aug. to May. Freshmen admitted on a rolling basis. Degrees conferred and formal commencement Dec., May. Summer semester of 3 sessions May to July.

Characteristics of Freshmen: 388 applicants (260 female, 128 male). 55% of applicants accepted. 22% of accepted applicants enrolled full-time.

41% (56 students) submitted SAT scores; 13% (18students) submitted ACT scores. *25th percentile*: SAT Critical Reading 450, SAT Math 490, SAT Writing 430; ACT Composite 19, ACT English 12, ACT Math 17. *75th percentile*: SAT Critical Reading 580, SAT Math 580, SAT Writing 550; ACT Composite 25, ACT English 23, ACT Math 25.

19% of freshmen expected to graduate within 5 years. 80% of freshmen from Oregon. Freshmen from 18 states and 6 foreign countries.

Admission: Rolling admissions plan. For fall acceptance, apply no later than Sept. 15. *Requirements:* Either graduation from accredited secondary school or GED. Recommend 4 units in English, 2 mathematics, 3 social studies, 2 laboratory science, 1 health and physical education. Minimum 2.5 GPA. *Entrance tests:* College Board SAT preferred; ACT composite accepted. For foreign students TOEFL. *For transfer students:* 2.0 minimum GPA; from 4-year accredited institution maximum transfer credit limited only by residence requirement; from 2-year accredited institution 72 hours; correspondence/extension students 30 hours.

College credit and advanced placement for postsecondary-level work completed in secondary school. College credit for extrainstitutional learning on basis of portfolio and faculty assessments; personal interviews.

Tutoring available. Developmental courses offered in summer session and regular academic year; credit given.

Degree Requirements: *For all baccalaureate degrees:* 124 credit hours; 30 hours in residence; 2 semester hours in physical education. *For all undergraduate degrees:* 2.0 GPA; chapel attendance; 42 credit hours minimum general education requirements.

Fulfillment of some degree requirements and beginning courses possible by passing departmental examinations, College Board CLEP, AP, other standardized tests. *Grading system:* A–F; pass-fail; withdraw (deadline after which pass-fail is appended to withdraw).

WARNER PACIFIC COLLEGE—*cont'd*

Distinctive Educational Programs: Field work. Evening classes. Accelerated degree programs. Interdisciplinary programs in American studies, liberal studies. Preprofessional programs in dentistry, nursing, optometry, pharmacy, physical therapy, pre-med. Facilities and programs for independent research, including individualized majors, tutorials. Degree completion program (evening) for working adults toward degrees in business administration and human development. *Other distinctive programs:* Credit and noncredit continuing education through consortium. Off-campus programs in Washington DC, Los Angeles Film Center. Various study abroad programs.

ROTC: Army, Air Force in cooperation with University of Portland.

Degrees Conferred: 19 *associate*; 190 *baccalaureate*; 14*master's*. Bachelor's degrees awarded in top five disciplines: family and consumer sciences 63; business, management, marketing, and related support services; philosophy/religion 8; public administration 6; English language/literature 4. Master's degrees awarded: business/management 190.

Fees and Other Expenses: *Full-time tuition per academic year 2008–09:* undergraduate $20,480; graduate study charged per credit (contact the college for current rate). *Room and board per academic year:* $6,328. *Books and supples:* $1,200. *Other expenses:* $3,556.

Financial Aid: Aid from institutionally generated funds is provided on the basis of academic merit, financial need, athletic ability, other criteria.

Financial aid to full-time, first-time undergraduate students: 98% received some form of financial aid. Average amount of aid received: federal grants $3,316; state/local grants $2,333; institutional grants $8,385; loans $9,735.

Departments and Teaching Staff: *Total instructional faculty:* 40. Student/faculty ratio: 14:1. Degrees held by full-time faculty: doctorate 50%, master's 100%. 50% hold terminal degrees.

Enrollment: Total enrollment 973. Undergraduate 874 (full-time 97%; female 62%, male 38%). Graduate 99 (full-time 93%).

Characteristics of Student Body: *Ethnic/racial makeup:* Black non-Hispanic: 7%; Asian or Pacific Islander: 3%; Hispanic: 5%; White non-Hispanic: 72%; unknown: 13%.

International Students: 6 undergraduate nonresident aliens enrolled fall 2008. Programs available to aid students whose native language is not English: social. No financial aid specifically designated for international students.

Student Life: On-campus residence halls house 60% of student body. Housing available for married students. Intramural club sports. *Special regulations:* Registered cars permitted; fee charged. Modest dress is favored. Quiet hours. *Special services:* Medical services. *Student publications: Knight Line*, a student newspaper; *Beacon*, a yearbook; *Excalibur*, electronic discussion web page.*Surrounding community:* Portland. Served by airport 10 miles from campus.

Library Collections: 53,000 volumes. 1,100 audiovisual materials; 125 microform titles; 400 current periodical subscriptions. Online catalog. Computer work stations available. Students have access to the Internet at no charge.

Most important holdings include Church of God archives; Wesley Collection; Liberation Theology Collection.

Buildings and Grounds: Campus area 14 acres.

Chief Executive Officer: Dr. Jay A. Barber, Jr., President.

Address admission inquiries to Dr. Jack P. Powell, Director of Enrollment Management.

Western Oregon University

345 North Monmouth Avenue
Monmouth, Oregon 97361-1934
Tel: (503) 838-8000 **E-mail:** admissions@wou.edu
Fax: (503) 838-8067 **Internet:** www.wou.edu

Institution Description: Western Oregon University, formerly named Western Oregon State College, is a comprehensive regional state institution that includes a School of Education and a School of Liberal Arts and Sciences. The college is part of the Oregon State University System. *Enrollment:* 4,885. *Degrees awarded:* Associate, baccalaureate, master's.

Accreditation: *Regional:* NWCCU. *Professional*: music, teacher education

History: Established as Monmouth University and offered first instruction at postsecondary level 1856; changed name to Oregon State Normal School 1881; closed 1909; reopened as Oregon Normal School 1910; changed name to Oregon College of Education 1939; became Western Oregon State College 1981; attained university status and adopted present name 1997.

Institutional Structure: *Governing board:* Oregon State University System. Representation: 9 board members, 2 students. All voting. Academic affairs headed by provost. Management/business/finances directed by dean of administration. Full-time instructional faculty 182. Academic governance body, Faculty Senate, meets an average of 9 times per year. *Faculty representation:* Faculty service by collective bargaining agent affiliated with AFT.

Calendar: Quarters. Academic year Sept. to June. Students admitted Sept., Jan., Mar., June. Degrees conferred and formal commencement June. Six-week summer session.

Characteristics of Freshmen: 1,888 applicants (female 1,129, male 759). 92% of applicants accepted. 49% of accepted applicants enrolled.

87% (764 students) submitted SAT scores; 15% (131 students) submitted ACT scores. *25th percentile*: SAT Critical Reading 390, SAT Math 430m SAT Writing 380; ACT Composite 17, ACT English 15, ACT Math 16. *75th percentile*: SAT Critical Reading 530, SAT Math 550, SAT Writing 490; ACT Composite 23, ACT English 23, ACT Math 24.

91% of freshmen from Oregon. Freshmen from 22states and 19 foreign countries.

Admission: Rolling admissions plan. *Requirements:* Graduation from accredited secondary school with minimum 2.5 GPA or GED; and 14 units of college preparatory work: 4 units English, 3 mathematics, 2 science, 2 social studies, 1 history, 2 foreign language. *For transfer students:* 2.0 minimum GPA from accredited institution. Those with 24 or more hours will be evaluated only on their college work. International students must have a minimum TOEFL score of 500.

Advanced placement for postsecondary-level work completed in secondary school.

Tutoring available. Developmental/remedial courses offered during regular academic year.

Degree Requirements: *For all associate degrees:* 93 quarter hours; 24 hours in residence. *For all baccalaureate degrees:* 192 hours; 45 hours in residence; 5 credit hours of physical education courses; core requirements. *For all undergraduate degrees:* 2.0 GPA.

Fulfillment of some degree requirements and exemption from some beginning courses possible by passing College Board CLEP, AP. *Grading system:* A–F; pass-fail; withdraw (carries time limit); incomplete.

Distinctive Educational Programs: Flexible meeting places and schedules, including off-campus centers (at locations less than 30 miles away from main institution) and evening classes. Accelerated degree programs. Special facilities for using telecommunications in the classroom. Interdisciplinary programs in humanities, natural science, social science, and liberal arts. Preprofessional programs in dentistry, medicine, nursing, optometry, pharmacy, physical therapy, veterinary medicine. Institutionally sponsored study abroad in England, France, Germany, Japan, Mexico. *Other distinctive programs:* Regional Resource Center of Deafness. Summer reading clinic for children and adults. Educational Evaluation Center for children with learning disabilities.

ROTC: Army. Air Force in cooperation with Oregon State University.

Degrees Conferred: 1 *associate*; 805 *baccalaureate*; 207 *master's*. Bachelor's degrees awarded in top five disciplines: education 218; business, management, marketing, and related support services 96; multidisciplinary studies 87; security and protective services 77; social sciences 74.

Fees and Other Expenses: *Full-time tuition per academic year 2008–09:* resident $4,818, nonresident $14,823. *Room and board per academic year:* $7,630. *Books and supplies:* $1,125.

Financial Aid: Aid from institutionally generated funds is provided on the basis of academic merit, financial need, other considerations.

Financial aid to full-time, first-time undergraduate students: 85% received some form of financial aid. Average amount of aid received: federal grants $3,568; state/local grants $1,464; institutional grants $1,463; loans $3,891.

Departments and Teaching Staff: *Total instructional faculty:* 279 (full-time 131, part-time 148). Degrees held by full-time faculty: doctorate 86%.

Enrollment: Total enrollment 4,885.

Characteristics of Student Body: *Ethnic/racial makeup:* Black non-Hispanic: 1.3%; American Indian or Native Alaskan: 1.6%; Asian or Pacific Islander: 3%; Hispanic: 4.6%; White non-Hispanic: 83.2%; unknown: 3.8%.

International Students: 84 nonresident aliens enrolled fall 2008. Students from Europe, Asia, Central and South America, Africa, Canada. Programs available for students whose native language is not English: social, cultural. English as a Second Language. Financial aid designated for international students: scholarships available annually to qualifying students.

Student Life: On-campus residence halls house 30% of student body. Residence halls for males and females constitute 100% of such space. *Intercollegiate athletics:* male: baseball, basketball, cross-country, football, tennis, track; female: basketball, cross-country, soccer, softball, track, volleyball. *Student publication:* weekly newspaper. *Surrounding community:* Monmouth population 7,000. Salem, the state capital, is 15 miles from campus.

Library Collections: 181,000 volumes. Government depository library; 1,775 current periodicals. Online catalog. Students have access to online information retrieval services and the Internet.

Buildings and Grounds: Campus area 157 acres.

Chief Executive Officer: Dr. John P. Minahan, President.

Address admission inquiries to Robert Kvidt, Director of Admissions.

Western Seminary

5511 SE Hawthorne Boulevard

Portland, Oregon 97215

Tel: (503) 517-1800 **E-mail:** admiss@westernseminary.edu
Fax: (503) 517-1801 **Internet:** www.westernseminary.edu

Institution Description: Western Seminary, formerly Western Conservative Baptist Seminary, is a private institution affiliated with the Conservative Baptist Association of America. Branch campuses are located in Sacramento and San Jose CA. *Enrollment:* 748. *Degrees awarded:* First-professional (master of divinity), master's, doctorate. Certificates and diplomas also are awarded.

Member of the consortium Institute of Theological Studies.

Accreditation: *Regional:* NWCCU. *Professional*: theology

History: Established as Western Baptist Theological Seminary, chartered, and offered first instruction at postsecondary level 1927; awarded first degree (first-professional) 1928; adopted present name 1968.

Institutional Structure: *Governing board:* Western Seminary Board of Trustees. Representation: 14 trustees, including 8 alumni. All voting. *Composition of institution:* President's Council is composed of the president, provost, director of advancement, academic dean, director of enrollment. controller, director of distance education. Full-time instructional 24. Academic governance body, the faculty, meets monthly.

Calendar: Semesters. Academic year Sept. to Aug.

Admission: Rolling admissions plan. For fall acceptance, apply as early as one year prior to enrollment, but not later than Aug. 15. *Requirements:* Baccalaureate from accredited college or university. Additional requirements for some programs. *For transfer students:* 3.0 minimum GPA; from accredited seminary minimum 3.0 GPA.

Degree Requirements: *For all first-professional degrees:* 90 semester hours; *For all master's degrees:* 60–71 semester hours; thesis or final project. *For doctoral degrees:* 37 hours (D.Miss.), 30 hours (D.Min.) *For all degrees:* 2.0–3.0 GPA; 30 semester hours in residence; core requirements; demonstrated proficiency in English and Biblical literature. Additional requirements for some programs. *Grading system:* A–F; satisfactory-unsatisfactory.

Distinctive Educational Programs: Study abroad in Israel through the Jerusalem University College.

Degrees Conferred: 144 *master's:* theology; 5 *doctorate:* theology; 25 *first-professional:* master of divinity.

Fees and Other Expenses: *Full-time tuition per academic year 2008–09:* contact the seminary for current information regarding tuition, fees, housing, and other costs.

Financial Aid: Aid from institutionally generated funds is provided on the basis of academic merit, financial need.

Departments and Teaching Staff: *Total instructional faculty:* 116 (full-time 28, part-time 96). Degrees held by full-time faculty: 88% hold terminal degrees.

Enrollment: Total enrollment 748.

International Students: 22 nonresident aliens enrolled fall 2008. Programs available to aid students whose native language is not English: social, cultural. No financial aid specifically designated for international students.

Student Life: No on-campus housing. *Special services:* Learning Resources Center. *Surrounding community:* Portland area population 1.8 million. Served by mass transit bus system; airport 5 miles from campus; passenger rail service 6 miles from campus.

Library Collections: 91,000 volumes including bound books, serial backfiles, electronic documents, and government documents not in separate collections. Online and card catalogs. Current serial subscriptions: 751 paper, 370 microform. 5,300 recordings; 14 CD-ROMs. Computer work stations available. Students have access to the Internet at no charge.

Most important special collections include Northwest Baptist History; Conservative Baptist Movement.

Buildings and Grounds: Main campus (Portland) area 5 acres.

Chief Executive Officer: Dr. Bert Downs, President. Address admission inquiries to Dave Brady, Associate Director of Enrollment.

Western States Chiropractic College

2900 NE 132nd Avenue

Portland, Oregon 97230

Tel: (503) 256-3180 **E-mail:** admissions@wschiro.edu
Fax: (503) 251-5723 **Internet:** www.wschiro.edu

Institution Description: Western States Chiropractic College is a private, independent, nonprofit institution offering a four-year program leading to the first-professional degree, Doctor of Chiropractic. A bachelor of science degree is also offered in human biology. *Enrollment:* 449. *Degrees awarded:* First-professional.

Accreditation: *Regional:* NASC. *Professional*: chiropractic education

History: Originated in 1904 with the founding of Pacific Chiropractic College; reorganized as a nonprofit institution and adopted present name 1932; four-year program of study implemented in 1932.

Institutional Structure: *Governing board:* Extrainstitutional representation: 15 trustees, all voting; institutional representation: 3 administrators, 1 Alumni Association member, 1 student (nonvoting). Management/business/office/finances directed by chief fiscal officer. Full-time instructional faculty 37. Academic governance body, the Academic Council, meets weekly.

Calendar: Quarters. Academic year Sept. to June. New class admitted fall and winter terms. Degrees conferred Mar., June, Sept., Dec. Summer session of 1 term from July. to Sept.

Admission: Rolling admissions plan. Fall and winter entry. Apply during year prior to entry. *Requirements:* Full-year sequence for each of the sciences; 24 semester hours (36 quarter hours) of social sciences and humanities, to include 6 semester hours (9 quarter hours) in English/communication and 3 semester (4.5 quarter) credits in psychology. All prerequisite courses must be those leading to a four-year degree. To make suitable response to the typical applicant, a returning adult learner, all applicants with the prerequisites are given full consideration. *Entrance tests:* None required.

Tutoring available.

Degree Requirements: 376 credit hours (4,512 clock hours); 2.0 GPA; two academic years residence; senior year includes 720 hour internship in public outpatient clinic. Students must pass clinical competency examination. *Grading system:* A–F; pass-fail.

Distinctive Educational Programs: Weekend and evening elective courses. Facilities and programs for independent research. Full library services with Medline search capability. Instructional Media Center; x-ray pathology reading library for independent study. Extensive postgraduate and continuing education program.

Degrees Conferred: 14 *baccalaureate:* human biology; 124 *first-professional:* chiropractic.

Fees and Other Expenses: *Tuition and fees per academic year 2008–09:* $7,343 undergraduate; contact the college for current chiropractic tuition and fees. No on-campus housing.

Financial Aid: Aid from institutionally generated funds is provided on the basis of academic merit, other criteria. Institution has a Program Participation Agreement with the U.S. Department of Education for eligible students to receive Pell Grants and, depending upon the agreement, other federal aid.

Departments and Teaching Staff: *Total instructional faculty:* 41. Degrees held by full-time faculty: doctorate 14%, master's 11%, professional 75%. 92% hold terminal degrees.

Enrollment: Total enrollment 449.

Characteristics of Student Body: *Ethnic/racial makeup:* number of Black non-Hispanic: 2; American Indian or Native Alaskan: 3; Asian or Pacific Islander: 18; Hispanic: 4; White non-Hispanic: 272. *Age distribution:* 17–24: 40%; 25–29: 27%; 30–34: 18%; 35–39: 10%; 40–up: 5%.

International Students: Students from Europe, Asia, Canada. No programs available to aid students whose native language is not English. No financial aid specifically designated for international students.

Student Life: No on-campus housing. Intramural sports activities and clubs available. *Student publications: The Axis*, a student newspaper published 6 times a year. *Surrounding community:* Portland population 503,000. Airport 4 miles from campus. Community served by mass area transit.

Publications: *Visions*, an alumni and college news magazine published quarterly.

Library Collections: 18,000 volumes. 3,000 microforms; 2,100 audiovisual materials; 410 current periodical subscriptions. Students have access to online information retrieval services and the Internet.

Most important special holdings include historical chiropractic and alternative healing collection.

WESTERN STATES CHIROPRACTIC COLLEGE—*cont'd*

Chief Executive Officer: Dr. Joseph Brimhall, President. Address admission inquiries to Dr. Leo Smith, Director of Enrollment Services.

Willamette University

900 State Street
Salem, Oregon 97301
Tel: (503) 370-6303 **E-mail:** admissions@willamette.edu
Fax: (503) 375-5363 **Internet:** www.willamette.edu

Institution Description: Willamette University is a private institution affiliated with the United Methodist Church. *Enrollment:* 2,721. *Degrees awarded:* Baccalaureate, first-professional (law), master's.

Accreditation: *Regional:* NWCCU. *Professional*: law, music

History: Established as Oregon Institute 1842; chartered as Wallamet University and offered first instruction at postsecondary level 1853; awarded first degree (baccalaureate) 1859; adopted present name 1904.

Institutional Structure: *Governing board:* Board of Trustees. Representation: 703 trustees. All voting. *Composition of institution:* Administrators 43. Academic affairs headed by vice president for academic affairs. Management/business/finances directed by vice president for financial affairs. Full-time instructional faculty 137. Academic governance body, the faculty, meets an average of 9 times per year.

Calendar: Semesters. Academic year Sept. to May. Freshmen admitted Sept., Jan. Degrees conferred May, Dec. Formal commencement May.

Characteristics of Freshmen: 4,023 applicants (2,301 female, 1,722 male). 76% of applicants accepted. 22% of accepted applicants enrolled full-time.

58% (433 students) submitted SAT scores; 42% (199 students) submitted ACT scores. *25th percentile*: SAT Critical Reading 580, SAT Math 580; ACT Composite 24, ACT English 24, ACT Math 23. *75th percentile*: SAT Critical Reading 690, SAT Math 670; ACT Composite 30, ACT English 30, ACT Math 28.

78% of entering freshmen expected to graduate within 5 years. 40% of freshmen from Oregon. Freshmen from 41 states and 18 foreign countries.

Admission: For fall acceptance, apply as early as Nov. 1 of previous year, but not later than Feb. 1 of year of enrollment. Students are notified of acceptance Apr. 1. Apply by Nov. 1 for early decision; need not limit application to Willamette. Early acceptance available. *Requirements:* Either graduation from accredited secondary school GED. *Entrance tests:* College Board SAT or ACT composite. For foreign students TOEFL. *For transfer students:* minimum 2.5 GPA; from 4-year accredited institution 60 semester hours maximum transfer credit; correspondence/extension students 8 semester hours.

College credit and advanced placement for postsecondary-level work completed in secondary school.

Degree Requirements: 124 semester hours; 2.0 GPA; 60 hours in residence, including senior year; general education requirements; comprehensives in individual fields of study.

Fulfillment of some degree requirements and exemption from some beginning courses possible by passing departmental examinations, College Board AP. *Grading system:* A–F; pass-fail; pass; withdraw (carries time limit).

Distinctive Educational Programs: Internships. Dual-degree programs in engineering with Columbia University (NY), University of Southern California, Washington University (MO); in forestry with Duke University (NC). Double-degree program in public and business administration with Atkinson School of Administration. Interdisciplinary programs in international studies, environmental science. Facilities and programs for independent research. Institutionally sponsored study abroad in Australia, Ecuador, England, China, France, Germany, Japan, Mexico, Spain, Ukraine.

Degrees Conferred: 451 *baccalaureate*; 158 *master's*. Bachelor's degrees awarded in top five disciplines: social sciences 107; English language 49; biomedical/biological sciences 38; visual and performing arts 84; Master's degrees awarded: various disciplines 158. psychology 32. *First-professional:* law 110.

Fees and Other Expenses: *Full-time tuition per academic year 2008–09:* undergraduate $33,960; contact the university for current tuition and fees for graduate/professional programs. *Books and supplies:* $900. *Room and board per academic year:* $7,950. *Other expenses:* $1,100.

Financial Aid: Aid from institutionally generated funds is provided on the basis of academic merit, financial need.

Financial aid to full-time, first-time undergraduate students: 95% received some form of financial aid. Average amount of aid received: federal grants $5,962; Pell grants $2,899; other federal aid $3,299; state/local grants $4,464; institutional grants $14,898.

Departments and Teaching Staff: *Total instructional faculty:* 237. Student/faculty ratio: 9:1. Degrees held by full-time faculty: 93% hold terminal degrees.

Enrollment: Total enrollment 2,721. Undergraduate 1,865 (full-time 95%; female 57%, male 43%). Graduate 856 (fullt9me 75%). Undergraduate transfer-in students 48.

Characteristics of Student Body: *Ethnic/racial makeup:* Black non-Hispanic: 2%; American Indian or Alaska Native: 1%; Asian or Pacific Islander: 7%; Hispanic: 4%; White non-Hispanic: 56%; unknown: 23%; nonresident alien 6%.

International Students: 117 undergraduate nonresident aliens enrolled fall 2008. Students from Europe, Asia, Central and South America, Africa, Canada. Programs available to aid students whose native language is not English: social and cultural. Financial aid specifically designated for undergraduate international students: scholarships available to qualifying students.

Student Life: On-campus housing (including fraternities and sororities) for 80% of student body. 33% of males live in fraternity housing; 23% of females in sorority housing. *Intercollegiate athletics:* male: baseball, basketball, crew, cross-country, golf, football, soccer, swimming, tennis, track, volleyball; female: basketball, crew, cross-country, field hockey, soccer, softball, swimming, tennis, track, volleyball. *Special regulations:* Cars permitted without restrictions. *Special services:* Learning Resources Center, medical services. *Student publications:* weekly newspaper, yearbook, and literary magazine. *Surrounding community:* Salem population 110,000. Portland, 50 miles from campus, is nearest metropolitan area. Served by mass transit bus system; airport 1.5 miles from campus; passenger rail service less than 1 mile from campus.

Library Collections: 373,000 volumes. 3,341,000 microforms; 10,500 audiovisual materials; 1,625 current periodicals (including electronic access). Online catalog. Students have access to online information retrieval services and the Internet.

Buildings and Grounds: Campus area 70 acres.

Chief Executive Officer: Dr. M. Lee Pelton, President.

Undergraduates address admission inquiries to Robin Brown, Vice President for Enrollment; first-professional students to Dean of Admissions, School of Law; graduate inquiries to Graduate School of Management, Director of Admissions.

School of Law

Degree Programs Offered: *First-professional.*

Admission: Baccalaureate from accredited institution, LSAT, LSDAS.

Degree Requirements: 88 credit hours; minimum grade average of 70 on a scale of 90; 4 terms in residence.

George H. Atkinson Graduate School of Management

Degree Programs Offered: *Master's, doctorate.*

Pennsylvania

Albright College

13th and Bern Streets
Reading, Pennsylvania 19612-5234
Tel: (610) 921-2381 **E-mail:** admissions@albright.edu
Fax: (610) 921-7530 **Internet:** www.albright.edu

Institution Description: Albright College is a private college affiliated with the United Methodist Church. *Enrollment:* 2,305. *Degrees awarded:* Baccalaureate, master's.

Accreditation: *Regional:* MSA/CHE. *Professional*: chemistry

History: Established as Union Seminary, chartered, and offered first instruction at postsecondary level 1856; awarded first degree (baccalaureate) 1859; changed name to Central Pennsylvania College 1887; consolidated with Albright Collegiate Institute (founded 1895 and adopted present name 1902); merged with Schuylkill Seminary (founded 1881) and changed name to Albright College of the Evangelical Church 1928; readopted present name 1972. *See* Eugene Barth and Wilbur Gingrich, *A History of Albright College* (Reading, Pa.: Albright College, 1956) for further information.

Institutional Structure: *Governing board:* Board of Trustees. Extrainstitutional representation: 45 trustees; institutional representation (non-voting advisory members): 5 administrators, 2 full-time instructional faculty members, 2 students. *Composition of institution:* Administrators 62. Academic affairs headed by vice president-academic affairs and academic dean. Management/business/finances directed by vice president-finance. Full-time instructional faculty 111. Academic governance body, the faculty, meets an average of 9 times per year.

Calendar: Semesters with January interim session (4-1-4 plan). Academic year Aug. to May. Freshmen admitted Sept., Feb. Degrees conferred and formal commencement May. Summer session of 3 terms from June to Aug.

Characteristics of Freshmen: 4,561 applicants (2,492 female, 2,069 male). 55% of applicants accepted. 20% of accepted applicants enrolled.

92% (423 students) submitted SAT scores. *25th percentile*: SAT Critical Reading 460. SAT Math 460. *75th percentile*: SAT Critical Reading 550, SAT Math 560.

71% of entering freshmen expected to graduate within 5 years. 62% of freshmen from Pennsylvania. Freshmen from 24 states and 21 foreign countries.

Admission: Rolling admissions plan. For fall acceptance, apply as early as Sept. 1, but no later than March 15. Apply by Dec. 15 for early decision; need not limit applications to Albright, but must withdraw other applications if accepted. Early acceptance available. Admissions interview strongly encouraged. *Requirements:* 15 secondary school units which must include 4 English, 2 foreign language, 2 history and social studies, 2 college preparatory mathematics, 2 science, 3 additional college preparatory courses. For some science programs, 4 mathematics (including trigonometry) recommended. *Entrance tests:* College Board SAT or ACT composite; College Board Achievement Tests (English composition, foreign language, mathematics). For foreign students TOEFL. *For transfer students:* 2.5 GPA; 16 course units (equivalent to 60 credit hours) maximum transfer credit.

Tutoring available.

Degree Requirements: 32 course units; 2.0 GPA (cumulative and in major); 6 physical education units; completion of Cultural Experience Program (attendance at 16 cultural events); general education requirements, including competency in a foreign language.

Fulfillment of some degree requirements and exemption from some introductory courses possible by passing standardized tests (CLEP, AP, College Board, Achievement Tests) and departmental examinations. *Grading system:* A–F; plus/minus; quality/non-quality; withdraw (deadline after which pass-fail is appended to withdraw).

Distinctive Educational Programs: Dual-degree programs in forestry and environmental studies with Duke University (NC); in natural resource management with the University of Michigan; in engineering with Pennsylvania State University and University of Pennsylvania. Interdisciplinary programs in American civilization, biochemistry, child and family studies, environmental science, government service, psychobiology. Preprofessional programs in elementary and secondary education, Christian education, dentistry, dietetics, law, medical technology, medicine, theology, veterinary medicine. Alpha Program for students undecided about their major field. Honors Program. Combined majors. Evening program for adult students. Facilities and programs for independent study and research, including individual majors. Individually arranged study abroad through accredited organizations and other colleges and universities. Study abroad January Interim courses in Australia, Bahamas, Panama, Italy, Israel, Thailand, Greece, Turkey, England, Ireland, China, France. Off-campus study for human ecology students at Philadelphia College of Textiles and Science and Fashion Institute of Technology (NY). Washington (DC) internship programs through the Washington Center and in cooperation with American University.

Degrees Conferred: 491 *baccalaureate*; 4 *master's*. Bachelor's degrees awarded in top five disciplines: business/marketing 140; social sciences 68; visual and performing arts 46; computer and information sciences 30; history 27. Master's degrees awarded: education 4.

Fees and Other Expenses: *Full-time tuition per academic year 2008–09:* \$30,570. *Required fees:* \$800. *Room and board per academic year:* \$8,670. *Books and supplies:* \$1,000. *Other expenses:* \$1,500.

Financial Aid: Aid from institutionally generated funds is provided on the basis of academic merit, financial need, other considerations.

Financial aid to full-time, first-time undergraduate students: federal grants \$4,874; Pell grants \$2,643; other federal aid \$2,732; state/local grants \$3,770; institutional grants \$13,060.

Departments and Teaching Staff: *Total instructional faculty:* 156 (full-time 111, part-time 46). Total faculty with doctorate, first-professional, or other terminal degree: 101. Student/faculty ratio: 13:1. Degrees held by full-time faculty: master's 17%, doctorate 83%. 92% hold terminal degrees.

Enrollment: Total enrollment 2,305. Undergraduate 2,245. Graduate 80 (full-time 100%). Undergraduate transfer-in students 92.

Characteristics of Student Body: *Ethnic/racial makeup:* Black non-Hispanic: 10%; Asian or Pacific Islander: 2%; Hispanic: 5%; White non-Hispanic: 73%; unknown: 5%; nonresident alien 6%. *Age distribution:* number under 18: 24; 18–19: 783; 20–21: 677; 22–24: 167; 25–29: 101; 30–34: 101; 35–39: 95; 40–49: 115; 50–64: 34. 30% of student body attend summer sessions.

International Students: 93 nonresident aliens enrolled fall 2008. Students from Europe, Asia, Central and South America, Africa. Programs available to aid students whose native language is not English: English as a Second Language Program. No financial aid specifically designated for international students.

Student Life: On-campus residence halls house 78% of student body. 1 residence hall for males (capacity 120) and 1 for females (capacity 120). 25% of males join fraternities; 27% of females join sororities. *Intercollegiate athletics:* male: cross-country, football, soccer, basketball, track and field, wrestling, tennis, golf, baseball, swimming; female: field hockey, cross-country, basketball, badminton, volleyball, tennis, track and field, softball, swimming. *Special regulations:* Cars permitted after freshman year. Individual residence halls set visitation hours. *Special services:* Counseling center, medical services. *Student publications, radio: The Agon*, a literary magazine; *Albrightian*, the student newspaper; *The Cue*, the yearbook. Radio station WXAC broadcasts 82 hours per week. *Surrounding community:* Reading population 80,000. Philadelphia, 60 miles from campus, is nearest metropolitan area. Served by mass transit and inter-city bus systems; airport 4 miles from campus.

Library Collections: 240,000 volumes. Online catalog. Current periodical subscriptions: paper 628; microform 49; via electronic access 13,449. 5,750 recordings. Students have access to online information retrieval services and the Internet.

Most important special holdings include J. Bennett Nolan Collection of local history; Martha Dick Collection of fine and limited editions; Byron Vazakas Manuscripts; Holocaust Resource Collection; Albrightiana.

Buildings and Grounds: Campus area 118 acres.

Chief Executive Officer: Dr. Lex O. McMillan, President.

Address admission inquiries to Gregory E. Eichhorn, Vice President for Enrollment Management.

Allegheny College

520 North Main Street
Meadville, Pennsylvania 16335-3902
Tel: (814) 332-3100 **E-mail:** admiss@alleg.edu
Fax: (814) 337-0431 **Internet:** www.alleg.edu

Institution Description: Allegheny College is a private, independent, nonprofit college affiliated with the United Methodist Church. *Enrollment:* 2,125. *Degrees awarded:* Baccalaureate.

Accreditation: *Regional:* MSA/CHE.

History: Established 1815; offered first instruction at postsecondary level 1816; chartered 1817; awarded first degree (baccalaureate) 1821; admitted women 1870. *See* Jonathan Helmreich, *Through All the Years, A History of Allegheny College* (Meadville, Pa., Allegheny College, 2005) for further information.

Institutional Structure: *Governing board:* Board of Trustees. Extrainstitutional representation: 24–50 trustees, currently include 32 alumni among 39 total; institutional representation: president of the college. *Composition of institution:* Administrators 115. Academic affairs headed by Dean of the College. Management/business/finances directed by Vice President for Finance and Planning. Full-time instructional faculty 137. Academic governance body, the faculty, meets 9 times per year.

Calendar: Semesters. Academic year Sept. to May. Freshmen admitted Sept., Jan. Degrees conferred Sept., Jan., May. Formal commencement May.

Characteristics of Freshmen: 4,243 applicants (female 2,300, male 1,943). 63% of applicants accepted. 25% of accepted applicants enrolled.

Mean SAT scores 598 Critical Reading, 598 Mathematical. Mean ACT Composite scores 24.7.

73% of entering freshmen expected to graduate within 5 years. 64% of freshmen from Pennsylvania. 63% of freshmen from Pennsylvania. Freshmen from 40 states and 33 foreign countries.

Admission: Apply by Feb. 15 for regular admission; early decision application due Nov. 15. Early acceptance available. *Requirements:* strong college preparatory program that includes 4 major academic subjects per year for 3 years. *Entrance tests:* College Board SAT or ACT composite. For foreign students TOEFL. *For transfer students:* 2.0 minimum GPA; 64 semester credit hours maximum transfer credit.

College credit and advanced placement for postsecondary-level work completed in secondary school.

Tutoring available. Developmental courses offered during academic year; credit given.

Degree Requirements: 131 semester credit hours; 2.0 GPA (all course work and in major); 67 semester credit hours in residence; senior research project in major field; two freshman seminars (fall and spring), a sophomore seminar, and a series of 3 one-credit academic planning units.

Fulfillment of some degree requirements and exemption from some beginning courses possible by passing College Board CLEP, AP, other standardized tests. *Grading system:* A–F; credit/no credit; incomplete; withdraw (deadline after which pass-fail is appended to withdraw).

Distinctive Educational Programs: *For all undergraduates:* Internships. Required Liberal Studies Program. Accelerated degree programs. Dual-degree programs in engineering (Case Western Reserve, Columbia, Duke, Pittsburgh, Washington U.), environmental management and forestry (Duke), nursing (Rochester, Case Western Reserve, Thomas Jefferson); minors in Latin American and Caribbean studies, Black studies, Critical Languages (tutorial) Program in Arabic, Chinese, Japanese, etc. Interdisciplinary majors in international studies, neuroscience, women's studies. Facilities and programs for independent research, including individual majors, tutorials, on- and off-campus independent study. College-sponsored study abroad programs in France, Germany, Spain, England, Ecuador, Costa Rica, Japan, South Africa, Australia, Niger, Russia; consortia opportunities in more than 20 additional countries in Asia, Africa, Europe, South America; others individually arranged.

ROTC: Army.

Degrees Conferred: 434 *baccalaureate*. Bachelor's degrees awarded in top five disciplines: social sciences 99; biological/biomedical sciences 56; psychology 48; multidisciplinary English 44; physical sciences 31.

Fees and Other Expenses: *Full-time tuition per academic year 2008–09:* $32,000. *Books and supplies* $900. *Required fees:* $300. *Room and board per academic year:* $8,000. *Other expenses.* $1,600.

Financial Aid: Aid from institutionally generated funds is provided on the basis of academic merit, financial need.

Financial aid to full-time, first-time undergraduate students: 20% received federal grants averaging $3,434; 49% state/local grants averaging $3,551; 96% institutional grants averaging $12,022; 72% received loans averaging $7,967.

Departments and Teaching Staff: *Total instructional faculty:* 167. Student/faculty ratio: 14:1. Degrees held by full-time faculty: 93% hold terminal degrees.

Enrollment: Total enrollment 2,125 (undergraduate).

Characteristics of Student Body: *Ethnic/racial makeup:* Black non-Hispanic: 3%; Asian or Pacific Islander 3%; Hispanic: 3%; White non-Hispanic: 90%; nonresident alien 2%.

International Students: 25 nonresident aliens enrolled fall 2008. Students from Europe, Asia, Central and South America, Africa, Canada, Australia, Middle East. Programs available to aid students whose native language is not English: social, cultural, financial. English as a Second Language Program. Financial aid specifically designated for international students: scholarships available annually for qualifying students.

Student Life: On-campus houses and residence halls accommodate 78% of student body: male 4%, female 11%, co-ed 64%. 19% in college apartments. 18% of males join and 8% live in fraternities. 76% of students live on campus. *Intercollegiate athletics:* male: baseball, basketball, cross-country, football, golf, soccer, swimming, tennis, track; female: basketball, cross-country, golf, lacrosse, soccer, softball, swimming, tennis, track, volleyball. *Special regulations:* Cars permitted for all students. Quiet hours and visitation policy determined by particular living group. Students required to live on camps through junior year. Honor code. *Special services:* Learning Resources Center, career planning and placement, personal counseling, medical services. *Student publications, radio: Allegheny Review*, the only national undergraduate literary journal; *The Campus*, a weekly newspaper; *Kaldron*, a yearbook; *Golem* poetry and short fiction; Radio station WARC-FM broadcasts 133 hours per week; ACTV television station. *Surrounding community:* Meadville population 14,500. Cleveland (OH), 80 miles from campus, is nearest metropolitan area.

Library Collections: 922,500 volumes including bound books, serial backfiles, electronic documents, and government documents not in separate collections. Online catalog. 491,300 microforms; 8,400 audiovisual materials; 18,000 periodicals including via electronic access. Ccomputer work stations available. Students have access to the Internet at no charge.

Most important special holdings include the original library of the College (3,900 volumes from colonial Massachusetts given to the college c. 1815); the papers of alumna Ida M. Tarbell, 19th century biographer and muckraker; archives of the Western Pennsylvania Conference, United Methodist Church.

Buildings and Grounds: Campus area 542 acres.

Chief Executive Officer: Dr. Richard J. Cook, President.

Address admission inquiries to Jennifer Winge, Director of Admissions.

Alvernia College

400 St. Bernardine Street
Reading, Pennsylvania 19607
Tel: (610) 796-8820 **E-mail:** admissions@alvernia.edu
Fax: (610) 796-8336 **Internet:** www.alvernia.edu

Institution Description: Alvernia College is a private college conducted by the Benardine Sisters of the Third Order of St. Francis, Roman Catholic Church. *Enrollment:* 2,809. *Degrees awarded:* Associate, baccalaureate, master's.

Accreditation: *Regional:* MSA/CHE. *Professional*: athletic training, nursing, occupational therapy, social work, teacher education

History: Established and offered first instruction at postsecondary level 1958; chartered and incorporated 1960; awarded first degree (baccalaureate) 1961; became coeducational 1971; continuing education/evening division program established 1985; master's degree program established 1999; doctoral program established 2006.

Institutional Structure: *Governing board:* Board of Trustees. All voting. *Composition of institution:* President, President's Cabinet. Four Vice Presidents for Academics, Student Affairs, Finance/Administration, College Relations/Development. Full-time instructional staff 83. Academic governance body, Administrative Council, meets on an average of 12 times per year. Faculty Council meets on an average of 9 times per year.

Calendar: Semesters. Academic year Aug. to May. Freshmen admitted Aug., Jan., June. Degrees conferred and formal commencement May, Dec. Summer sessions May to Aug.

Characteristics of Freshmen: 1,575 applicants (990 female, 585 male). 73% of applicants accepted. 30% of accepted applicants enrolled.

Mean SAT scores 465 Critical Reading, 452 Math.

55% of entering freshmen expected to graduate within 5 years. 53% of freshmen from Pennsylvania. Freshmen from 13 states and 14 foreign countries.

Admission: Rolling admissions plan. Early acceptance available. *Requirements:* Either graduation from accredited secondary school with 16 units or GED; 4 units of English, 2 modern language, 2 mathematics, 2 science, 2 social studies. Minimum 2.0 GPA. *Entrance tests:* College Board SAT or ACT composite. *For transfer students:* 2.0 minimum GPA; from 4-year accredited institution 90 hours maximum transfer credit; from 2-year accredited institution 60 hours.

Advanced placement for postsecondary-level work completed in secondary school.

Degree Requirements: *For all associate degrees:* at least 60 credit hours. *For all baccalaureate degrees:* at least 123 credit hours. *For all undergraduate degrees:* 2.0 GPA; 45 hours in residence; *For all master's degrees:* 2.0 GPA; 27 hours in residence.

Fulfillment of some degree requirements and exemption from some beginning courses possible by passing departmental examinations, College Board CLEP, AP. *Grading system:* A–F; pass; withdraw (carries time limit).

Distinctive Educational Programs: Weekend and evening classes. Alternative modular calendar features evening classes in six 8-week terms per year, enabling graduation accelerated basis. Integrated basic science. Internships. Nursing competency portfolio enables diploma nurses accelerated completion of a BSN degree. Degree-granting weekend program and certificate program in substance abuse/addiction.

ROTC: Offered in cooperation with Lehigh University.

Degrees Conferred: 17 *associate*; 451 *baccalaureate*; 175 *master's*. Bachelor's degrees awarded in top five disciplines: health professions and related clinical sciences 95; business, management, marketing, and related support services 74; security and protective services 69; psychology education 34; computer and information sciences 16. Master's degrees awarded: business/marketing 75; education 73; health professions 12; liberal arts 14; psychology 1.

Fees and Other Expenses: *Full-time tuition and fees per academic year 2008–09:* $23,200 undergraduate; graduate study charged per credit hour (contact the college for current rate). *Books and supplies:* $1,500. *Other expenses:* $2,202.

Financial Aid: Aid from institutionally generated funds is provided on the basis of academic merit, financial need. Institution has a Program Participation Agreement with the U.S. Department of Education for eligible students to receive Pell Grants and, depending upon the agreement, other federal aid.

Departments and Teaching Staff: *Total instructional faculty:* 273. Student/faculty ratio: 13:1. Degrees held by full-time faculty: master's 46%, doctorate 54%. 40% hold terminal degrees.

Enrollment: Total enrollment 2,809. Undergraduate 2,024 (full-time 78%; female 69%, male 31%). Graduate 785 (full-time 20%). Undergraduate transfer-in students 102.

Characteristics of Student Body: *Ethnic and racial makeup:* Black non-Hispanic 10%; Asian or Pacific Islander 1%; Hispanic 6%; White non-Hispanic 80%; unknown 2%; nonresident alien 1%.

International Students: 28 nonresident aliens enrolled 2006. No programs available to aid students whose native language is not English. No financial aid specifically designated for international students.

Student Life: On-campus townhouses and residence halls provide housing for 30% of males and females enrolled. *Intercollegiate athletics:* male: basketball, baseball; female: field hockey, basketball, volleyball, softball. *Special regulations:* Cars permitted without restrictions. *Special services:* Student Government Association sponsors numerous social, educational, and service events throughout the year. *Student publications:* Newspaper, yearbook, and literary publication. *Surrounding community:* Philadelphia, 50 miles from campus, is nearest metropolitan area. Served by air, bus and nearby rail transportation.

Publications: Alumni newsletter; all-constituent magazine with president's annual reports inserted in fall issue; recruitment publications for traditional and non-traditional students; college catalog; publications for special events.

Library Collections: 88,000 volumes. 1,985 microforms; 24,701 audiovisual materials; 386 current periodical subscriptions. Online catalog. Computer work available. Students have access to online information retrieval service sand the Internet.

Most important special holdings include 1,561 books in Polish language.

Buildings and Grounds: Campus area 80 acres.

Chief Executive Officer: Dr. Thomas F. Flynn, President.

Address admission inquiries to Catherine Emery, Dean of Admissions.

The American College

270 Bryn Mawr Avenue
Bryn Mawr, Pennsylvania 19010-2196
Tel: (610) 526-1000 **E-mail:** admissions@amercoll.edu
Fax: (610) 526-1486 **Internet:** www.amercoll.edu

Institution Description: The American College offers professional certification and graduate degree distance education to men and women in the insurance and financial services industry. *Designations:* Chartered Life Underwriter and Chartered Financial Consultant, Registered Health Underwriter, Registered Employee Benefits Consultant. *Enrollment:* 17,752 (distance learning of which 540 are enrolled in master's program). *Degrees awarded:* Master's.

Accreditation: *Regional:* MSA/CHE.

History: Established, chartered, and incorporated as The American College of Life Underwriters 1927; offered first instruction at postsecondary level and awarded first master's degrees in 1977. Adopted present name 1978. *See* Mildred Stone, *A Calling and Its College* (Richard D. Irwin, Inc., Homewood, Ill., 1963) for more information.

Institutional Structure: *Governing board:* Board of Trustees. Extrainstitutional representation: 39 trustees, 4 ex officio. Institutional representation: president of the college. All voting. *Composition of institution:* Administrators 20. Academic affairs directed by vice president and treasurer. 35 full- and part-time faculty. Academic governance body, the faculty, meets an average of 4 times per year.

Calendar: All courses available as distance education for independent self study. Standardized national examinations scheduled by student. Formal conferment of degrees Oct.

Admission: Rolling admissions plan. *Requirements for graduate program:* Baccalaureate from accredited institution or demonstrated academic ability. *For transfer students:* 9 hours maximum transfer credit from an accredited institution.

Degree Requirements: 40 credit hours; 2 one-week on-campus residency sessions; prescribed curriculum; competency examinations. *Grading system:* pass-fail.

Distinctive Educational Programs: External degree programs. Independent study. Special lectures, conferences, and seminars scheduled throughout year.

Degrees Conferred: 61 *master's*: business, management, marketing, and related support services.

Fees and Other Expenses: *Tuition and fees per academic year 2008–09:* contact the college for current tuition and fees.

Enrollment: Total enrollment: 540.

Characteristics of Student Body: *Ethnic/racial makeup:* Black non-Hispanic: 2%; American Indian or Alaska Native: 1%; Asian or Pacific Islander: 1%; Hispanic: 1%; White non-Hispanic: 50%, unknown: 45%.

International Students: No programs available to aid students whose native language is not English. No financial aid specifically designated for international students.

Student Life: Graduate degree candidates spend 2 one-week residencies on campus. All other courses are by self-study. *Special regulations:* Cars permitted without restrictions. *Surrounding community:* Located in suburban area; Philadelphia, 10 miles from campus, is nearest metropolitan area. Served by mass transit bus and train system; airport 20 miles from campus.

Library Collections: 12,000 books, 600 periodicals.

Buildings and Grounds: Campus area 40 acres, 7 buildings.

Chief Executive Officer: Dr. Laurence Barton, President.

Address admission inquiries to Shirley P. Steinman, Registrar and Certification Officer.

Arcadia University

450 South Easton Road
Glenside, Pennsylvania 19038-3295
Tel: (215) 572-2900 **E-mail:** admiss@beaver.edu
Fax: (215) 572-4049 **Internet:** www.beaver.edu

Institution Description: Arcadia University, formerly named Beaver College, is a coeducational, private college which maintains a historic relationship with the United Presbyterian Church (U.S.A.) *Enrollment:* 3,868. *Degrees awarded:* Baccalaureate, master's, doctorate. Specialist certificates also awarded.

Accreditation: *Regional:* MSA/CHE. *Professional:* art, chemistry, counseling psychology, physician assisting, physical therapy

History: Established and chartered as Beaver Female Seminary 1853; incorporated 1857; changed name to Beaver College and Musical Institute and offered first instruction at postsecondary level 1872; awarded first degree (baccalaureate) c. 1875; adopted present name 1907; relocated to present site 1929; became coeducational 1972; graduate program commenced 1973; assumed current name 2001.

Institutional Structure: *Governing board:* Board of Trustees of Arcadia University. Extrainstitutional representation: 33 trustees (including 6 alumni), 8 emeriti trustees, 2 life trustees, 1 honorary trustee; institutional representation: president of the college; president of the Women's Board; president of the Alumni Association. 3 ex officio 26 voting. *Composition of institution:* Administrators 38. Academic affairs headed by vice president for academic affairs and dean. Management/business/finances directed by vice president for finance and treasurer. Student affairs directed by vice president for student affairs and dean

ARCADIA UNIVERSITY—*cont'd*

of students. Full-time instructional faculty 111. Academic governance body, the faculty, meets an average of 8 times per year.

Calendar: Semesters. Academic year Sept. to May. Freshmen and transfer admitted Sept., Jan. Degrees conferred and formal commencement May.

Characteristics of Freshmen: 4,706 applicants (3,416 female, 1,266 male). 79 of applicants accepted. 24% of accepted applicants enrolled.

87% (506 students) submitted SAT scores; 91% (59 students) submitted ACT scores. *25th percentile*: SAT Critical Reading 599, SAT Math 480; ACT Composite 21, ACT English 20, ACT Math 19. *75th percentile*: SAT Critical Reading 620, SAT Math 590; ACT Composite 26, ACT English 27, ACT Math 25.

63% of entering freshmen expected to graduate within 5 years. 68% of freshmen from Pennsylvania. Freshmen from 24 states and 12 foreign countries.

Admission: Rolling admissions plan. Apply by Oct. 15 for early decision. Early acceptance available. *Requirements:* Either 16 secondary school units which must include 4 English, 2 in a foreign language, 3 college preparatory mathematics, 3 history and social studies, 2 laboratory sciences, 3 electives; or GED. *Entrance tests:* SAT or ACT composite. *For foreign students:* TOEFL. *For transfer students:* 2.5 GPA recommended; from 4-year accredited institution 90 semester hours maximum transfer credit; from 2-year accredited institution 75 semester hours transfer credit.

College credit and advanced placement for postsecondary-level work completed in secondary school. Tutoring available.

Degree Requirements: *For all baccalaureate degrees:* 120–128 credit hours; general education core and distribution requirements. *For all undergraduate degrees:* 2.0 GPA; last 2 terms in residence.

Fulfillment of some degree requirements and exemption from some beginning courses possible by passing departmental examinations, College Board APP, CLEP subject or CLEP general examinations. *Grading system:* A–F; pass/fail (limited); withdraw (deadline after which pass/fail is appended to withdraw); incomplete (carries time limit).

Distinctive Educational Programs: *For undergraduates:* Work-experience programs, including cooperative education, internships. Dual-degree programs in engineering with Columbia University; accelerated doctorate in association with Pennsylvania College of Optometry. Dual degree programs in physical therapy and special education. Interdisciplinary honors seminars; majors in interdisciplinary science and psychobiology; interdepartmental courses; science illustration. Preprofessional programs in law, dentistry, physician assistant studies, physical therapy, medicine, nursing, theology, veterinary medicine. Doctoral program in physical therapy. Honors programs, individual majors, tutorials. Foreign study through Beaver College Center for Education Abroad in Vienna, Austria; Cork, Dublin, and Galway, Ireland; British programs at Aberdeen, Bangor, Bristol, Edinburgh, Lancaster, London, Nottingham, Norwich, Southampton, and York; in France, Italy, Spain, and Germany through programs offered by other institutions; may be individually arranged. Off-campus study in U.S. in Washington (DC) in cooperation with American University. *For graduate students:* Full-time entry level master's programs in genetic counseling, physician's assistant studies, physical therapy. Interdepartmental/interdisciplinary master's program in humanities. Facilities and programs for independent research. *Available to all students:* Evening and weekend classes. Facilities and programs for independent research.

Degrees Conferred: 445 *baccalaureate*; 429 *master's*; 56 *doctorate*. Bachelor's degrees awarded in top five disciplines: business, management, marketing, and related support services 62; education 61; visual and performing arts 47; biological/life sciences 35. Master's degrees awarded in top five disciplines: education 283; health professions 66; security and protective services 20; library science 14; interdisciplinary studies 17. Doctorates awarded: various disciplines 56.

Fees and Other Expenses: *Full-time tuition per academic year 2008–09:* undergraduate $29,700; contact the university for current graduate tuition and other applicable fees. *Required fees:* $340 (undergraduate). *Room and board per academic year:* $16,500. *Books and supplies:* $1,000. *Other expenses:* $1,500.

Financial Aid: Aid from institutionally generated funds is provided on the basis of academic merit, financial need, cocurricular activities, leadership activities.

99% of first-time, full-time undergraduate students received some form of financial aid. Average amount of aid received: federal grants $3,549; Pell grants $2,679; other federal aid $975; state/local aid $3,731; institutional aid $12,900.

Departments and Teaching Staff: *Total instructional faculty:* 393. Total faculty with doctorate, first-professional, or other terminal degree: 174. Degrees held by full-time faculty: doctorate 76%, master's 24%. 91% hold terminal degrees.

Enrollment: Total enrollment 3,868. Undergraduate 2,203 (full-time 90%; female 73%, male 27%). Graduate 1,665 (full-time 35%). Undergraduate transfer-in students 154.

Characteristics of Student Body: *Ethnic/racial makeup:* Black non-Hispanic: 7%; Asian or Pacific Islander: 3%; Hispanic: 4%; White non-Hispanic: 69%; unknown: 15%; nonresident alien 2%. *Age distribution:* number under 18: 9; 18–19: 772; 20–21: 648; 22–24: 234; 25–29: 105; 30–34: 36; 35–39: 37; 40–49: 62; 50–64: 20; 65 and over: 1.

International Students: 78 nonresident aliens enrolled fall 2008. Students from Europe, Asia, Central and south America, Africa, Canada. No programs available to aid students whose native language is not English. Financial aid designated for international students: variable number of scholarships available annually.

Student Life: On-campus residence halls house 67% of undergraduate students in daytime programs. Residence halls for females 12%, for both sexes 94%. *Intercollegiate athletics:* male: baseball, basketball, cross-country, golf, soccer, swimming, tennis; fenakeL basketball, cross-country, field hockey, lacrosse, softball, soccer, swimming, tennis, volleyball. *Special regulations:* Freshmen not permitted cars. *Special services:* medical services, Career Resource Center, academic tutoring, personal counseling. *Student publications: The Tower*, a biweekly newspaper; *The Log*, a yearbook; *To Be Continued*, biannual newsletter for continuing education students. More than 30 student organizations; weeknight and weekend options for student social activities. *Surrounding community:* Glenside, 15,000 population. Philadelphia, 12 miles from campus, is nearest metropolitan area. Served by mass transit bus system; airport 18 miles from campus; passenger rail service one mile from campus.

Publications: Sources of information about Beaver College include *Beaver College Profile, Beaver College Update*.

Library Collections: 150,000 volumes including bound books, serial backfiles, electronic documents, and government documents not in separate collections. Online catalog. 50,000 microforms; 3,300 audiovisual materials; 8,000 periodicals. Computer work stations available. Students have access to the Internet at no charge.

Most important special collections include late 19th and early 20th century juvenile literature; Spruance prints.

Buildings and Grounds: Campus area 55 acres.

Chief Executive Officer: Dr. Jerry Greiner, President.

Address admission inquiries to Enrollment Management Office.

Baptist Bible College and Seminary

538 Venard Road
Clarks Summit, Pennsylvania 18411
Tel: (570) 586-2400 **E-mail:** admissions@bbc.edu
Fax: (570) 586-1753 **Internet:** www.bbc.edu

Institution Description: Baptist Bible College and Seminary is a private, independent, nonprofit college, approved by the General Association of Regular Baptist Churches. *Enrollment:* 910. *Degrees awarded:* Associate, baccalaureate. Certificates and diplomas also awarded. Baptist Bible Seminary awards first-professional (master of divinity), master of ministry, and master of theology degrees.

Accreditation: *Regional:* MSA/CHE. *National:* ABHE.

History: Established, chartered as Baptist Bible Seminary at Johnson City (NY) and offered first instruction at postsecondary level 1932; added 4th year courses 1947; awarded first degree (baccalaureate) 1955; moved to present location 1968; adopted present name 1970; added graduate seminary 1972.

Institutional Structure: *Governing board:* Board of Trustees. Representation: 25 trustees, including 12 alumni, all voting. *Composition of institution:* President and 6 vice-presidents, one over each of the following: academic affairs, seminary, student development, business and finance, development, alumni services, summer ministries. Full-time instructional faculty 44.

Calendar: Semesters. Academic year Aug. to May. Freshmen admitted Aug., Jan., May. Degrees conferred and formal commencement May. Summer session of two terms from May to June.

Characteristics of Freshmen: 350 applicants (223 femlae, 127 male). 70% of applicants admitted. 43% of admitted applicants enrolled full-time. Mean SAT scores 528 Critical Reading, 484 Math. 37% of freshmen from Pennsylvania. Freshmen students from 24 states.

Admission: Rolling admissions plan. For fall acceptance, apply as early as Sept. of previous year, but not later than Aug. 15 of year of enrollment. Early acceptance available. *Requirements:* Either graduation from approved secondary school or GED. *Entrance tests:* College Board SAT preferred; ACT composite accepted. *For transfer students:* 2.0 minimum GPA; 60 semester hours maximum transfer credit; correspondence/extension student credit evaluated individually.

College credit for postsecondary-level work completed in secondary school. Developmental courses offered during regular academic year; credit given.

Degree Requirements: *For all associate degrees:* 60–66 credit hours. *For all baccalaureate degrees:* 124–162 hours; exit competency examinations in bible and doctrine. *For all undergraduate degrees:* 2.0 GPA; 30 credits in residence; daily chapel attendance; physical education courses; distribution requirements; participation in Christian Service Program. *Grading system:* A–F; withdraw (deadline after which pass-fail is appended to withdraw); AU (audit); S-U (satisfactory-unsatisfactory); I (incomplete).

Distinctive Educational Programs: Evening classes. Continuing education degrees and flexible in-service training for clergy through the graduate seminary program. Summer study in Israel through Institute of Holy Land Studies. Junior year in Ecuador. Seminary extension site in South Africa.

Degrees Conferred: 8 *associate*; 102 *baccalaureate*; 35 *master's*; 7 *doctorate*. Bachelor's degrees awarded in top four disciplines: theology 59; education 33; business/marketing 4; communication, journalism, and related programs 4. Master's degrees awarded: education 13; theology 22. Doctorate's awarded: theology 7.

Fees and Other Expenses: *Full-time tuition per academic year 2008–09:* undergraduate $15,840; contact the college for current graduate/first-professional tuition/fees. *Books and supplies:* $600. *Room and board per academic year:* $5,900. *Other expenses:* $1,225.

Financial Aid: Aid from institutionally generated funds is provided on the basis of academic merit, financial need, other criteria.

Financial aid to full-time, first-time undergraduate students: 99% received some form of financial aid.

Departments and Teaching Staff: *Total instructional faculty:* 44. Degrees held by full-time faculty: doctorate 33%, master's 67%. 33% hold terminal degrees.

Enrollment: Total enrollment 910. Undergraduate 550 (full-time 99%; female 61%, male 39%). Graduate 360 (full-time 44%). Undergraduate transfer-in students 69.

Characteristics of Student Body: *Ethnic/racial makeup:* Black non-Hispanic: 1%; American Indian or Alaska Native: 1%; Hispanic: 1%; White non-Hispanic: 94%; unknown: 2%; nonresident alien 1%.

International Students: 20 nonresident aliens enrolled fall 2008. No programs available to aid students whose native language is not English. No financial aid specifically designated for international students.

Student Life: On-campus residence halls house 80% of student body. *Intercollegiate athletics:* male: basketball, soccer, cross-country, track, wrestling; female: basketball, volleyball, cheerleading, cross-country, soccer, track. *Special services:* Learning Resources Center, medical services, campus security. *Student activities:* Musical groups, recitals, artist series, choral concerts, drama productions, socials, student government, various interest groups, chapel, intramural program, special productions. *Student publications: Contact*, a quarterly newspaper; *The Tower*, a yearbook; *The Bulletin*, a triennial paper. *Surrounding community:* Wilkes-Barre population 50,000. Philadelphia, 140 miles from campus, is nearest major metropolitan area. Served by mass transit bus system; airport 20 miles from campus.

Library Collections: 102,832 volumes. Current serial subscriptions: paper 393; microform 4,350; via electronic access 10,777. 6,754 audio/videotapes. Students have access to online information retrieval services and the Internet.

Buildings and Grounds: Campus area 120 acres.

Chief Executive Officer: Dr. James E. Jeffery, President.

Address undergraduate admission inquiries to Beth Alt, Admissions Assistant. graduate inquiries to Director of Recruitment and Admissions for the Seminary.

Bloomsburg University of Pennsylvania

400 East Second Street
Bloomsburg, Pennsylvania 17815
Tel: (570) 389-4000 **E-mail:** buadmiss@bloomu.edu
Fax: (570) 389-3700 **Internet:** www.bloomu.edu

Institution Description: Bloomsburg University of Pennsylvania is one of 14 state-owned universities that compose the Pennsylvania State System of Higher Education. a state institution. *Enrollment:* 8,855. *Degrees awarded:* Associate, baccalaureate, master's, doctorate.

Academic offerings subject to approval by statewide coordinating bodies. Budget subject to approval by state governing boards.

Accreditation: *Regional:* MSA/CHE. *Professional*: audiology, business, chemistry, nursing, social work, speech-language pathology, teacher education

History: Established as Bloomsburg Academy and offered first instruction at postsecondary level 1839; chartered and changed name to Bloomsburg Literary Institute 1856; changed name to Bloomsburg Literary Institute and State Normal School 1869; to Bloomsburg State Normal School 1916, to Bloomsburg State Teachers College 1927; awarded first degree (baccalaureate) 1929; became Bloomsburg State College 1960; adopted present name 1983.

Institutional Structure: *Governing board:* Board of Governors of the State System of Higher Education; Bloomsburg Universities' Council of Trustees. Extrainstitutional representation: 15 directors. All voting. *Composition of institution:* Administrators 31. Academic affairs headed by provost and vice president for academic affairs. Management/business/finances directed by vice president for general administration. Full-time instructional faculty 363. Academic governance body, Council of Academic Deans, meets an average of 26 times per year. *Faculty representation:* Faculty served by collective bargaining agent, Association of Pennsylvania State Colleges and Universities, affiliated with AAUP and AFT.

Calendar: Semesters. Academic year Aug. to May. Freshmen admitted Aug., Jan., June. Degrees conferred and formal commencements May, Dec. Summer session from May to Aug.

Characteristics of Freshmen: 9,868 applicants (3,965 female, 3,903 male). 60% of applicants accepted. 18% of accepted applicants enrolled.

Mean SAT class scores 510 Critical Reading, 505 Math.

60% of entering freshmen expected to graduate within 5 years. 90% of freshmen from Pennsylvania. Freshmen from 18 states and 28 foreign countries.

Admission: Rolling admissions plan. Early acceptance available. *Requirements:* Either graduation from accredited secondary school with 16 units which must include 4 English, 2 language, 3 mathematics, 4 social studies, 3 science, 2 science labs; or GED. 2 additional units recommended. Minimum 2.0 GPA. Lowest acceptable secondary school class standing 40th percentile. *Entrance tests:* College Board SAT. For foreign students TOEFL. *For transfer students:* 2.0 minimum GPA; from 4-year accredited institution hours 90 maximum transfer credit; from 2-year accredited institution 60 hours; correspondence/extension students 15 hours.

College credit and advanced placement for postsecondary-level work completed in secondary school and for extrainstitutional learning on basis of portfolio assessment.

Tutoring available. Noncredit developmental courses offered in summer session and regular academic year.

Degree Requirements: *For all associate degrees:* 64 credit hours; 15 credits in residence; 3 semester hours physical education. *For all baccalaureate degrees:* 120 credit hours; 32 of last 64 credits in residence; 3 semester hours physical education. *For all undergraduate degrees:* 2.0 GPA; general education and distribution requirements.

Fulfillment of some degree requirements and exemption from some beginning courses possible by passing departmental examinations, College Board CLEP, AP. *Grading system:* A–F; pass-fail; withdraw (deadline after which pass-fail is appended to withdraw).

Distinctive Educational Programs: Work-experience programs, including cooperative education, internships. Flexible meeting places and schedules, including off-campus centers; evening and weekend classes. A 3-2 cooperative dual-degree program in engineering with Pennsylvania State University or Wilkes University. Cooperative baccalaureate in medical technology with approved schools of medical technology. Interdisciplinary programs in computer and information sciences. Facilities and programs for independent research, including tutorials, independent study. Study abroad by individual arrangement and in cooperation with other institutions; student teaching abroad; locations in Scotland, England, Ireland, France, Germany, Italy, Austria, Mexico, Ecuador, Brazil, and Japan.

ROTC: Air Force, Army. Air Force available in cooperation with Wilkes University; Army with Bucknell University.

Degrees Conferred: 1,545 *baccalaureate*; 335 *master's*; 10 *doctorate*. Bachelor's degrees awarded in top five disciplines: business, management, marketing, and related support services 328; education 237; health professions and related clinical sciences 141; social sciences 125; psychology 73. Master's degrees awarded: various disciplines 335. Doctorates awarded: health professions 10.

Fees and Other Expenses: *Full-time tuition per academic year 2008–09:* undergraduate resident $6,648, nonresident $14,978; contact the university for current graduate tuition and applicable fees. *Required fees:* $1,374. *Books and supplies:* $1,200. *Room and board per academic year:* $8,292. *Other expenses:* $4,060.

Financial Aid: Aid from institutionally generated funds is provided on the basis of academic merit, financial need, athletic ability, other criteria.

Financial aid to full-time, first-time undergraduate students: 74% received some form of financial aid. Average amount of aid received: federal grants $3,820; Pell grants $2,894; other federal aid $1,019; state/local grants $3,195; institutional grants $2,492.

Departments and Teaching Staff: *Total instructional faculty:* 314. Student/faculty ratio: 21:1. Degrees held by full-time faculty: 75% hold terminal degrees.

Enrollment: Total enrollment 8,844. Undergraduate 8,081 (full-time 93%; female 58%, male 42%). Graduate 714 (full-time 42%). Undergraduate transfer-in students 418.

BLOOMSBURG UNIVERSITY OF PENNSYLVANIA—*cont'd*

Characteristics of Student Body: *Ethnic/racial makeup:* Black non-Hispanic: 7%; Asian or Pacific Islander: 1%; Hispanic: 3%; White non-Hispanic: 79%; unknown 9%; nonresident alien 1%.

International Students: 88 nonresident aliens enrolled fall 2008. *Programs available to aid students whose native language is not English:* English as a Second Language Program. Some financial aid available for qualifying international student.

Student Life: On-campus residence halls house 46% of student body. Residence halls are co-ed. 20% of males join and 5% live in fraternities; 20% of females join and 3% live in sororities. *Intercollegiate athletics:* male: baseball, basketball, cross-country, football, soccer, swimming, tennis, track, wrestling; female: basketball, cross-country, field hockey, lacrosse, soccer, softball, swimming, tennis, track. *Special regulations:* Cars permitted in restricted lots for for a semester fee. *Special services:* Learning Resources Center, Counseling Center, medical services, Career Development Center, Campus Child Center, campus transportation. *Student publications, radio: Campus Voice*, a weekly newspaper; *The Pilot*, student handbook; *Obiter*, annual yearbook; *Bloomsburg Literary Journal*; Radio station WBU-FM broadcasts 70 hours per week; BUTV. *Surrounding community:* Bloomsburg population 12,000. Harrisburg, 85 miles from campus, is nearest metropolitan area. Served by airport 40 miles from campus.

Library Collections: 473,000 volumes including bound books, serial backfiles, electronic documents, and government documents not in separate collections. Online catalog. Current serial subscriptions: 1,747 paper and microform, 74 electronic. Computer work stations available campus-wide. Students have access to the Internet (charges included in mandatory fees).

Most important special holdings include an art exhibition catalog collection; books on covered bridges; literacy movement led by Frank C. Laubach; radical labor publications; collection of all Caldecott and Newberry Awards winners.

Buildings and Grounds: Campus area 192 acres.

Chief Executive Officer: Dr. Jessica S. Kozloff, President.

Undergraduates address admission inquiries to Christopher J. Keller, Director of Admissions; graduate inquiries to Dr. Patrick J. Schloss, Assistant Vice President and Dean, Graduate Studies.

Bryn Athyn College of the New Church

2895 College Drive
Bryn Athyn, Pennsylvania 19009-0717
Tel: (215) 938-2543 **E-mail:** admissions@brynathyn.edu
Fax: (215) 938-2658 **Internet:** www.newchurch.edu/college

Institution Description: Bryn Athyn College of the New Church is a private institution affiliated with the General Church of the New Jerusalem. *Enrollment:* 164. *Degrees awarded:* Associate, baccalaureate, first-professional (master of divinity).

Accreditation: *Regional:* MSA/CHE.

History: Established and offered first instruction at postsecondary level 1876; chartered 1877; awarded first degree (baccalaureate) 1879.

Institutional Structure: *Governing board:* Board of Directors. Representation: 20 trustees, including the chancellor of the college; 1 administrator, 2 ex officio. 18 voting. *Composition of institution:* Administrators 6. Academic affairs headed by dean of the college. Management/business/finances directed by treasurer. Full-time instructional faculty 24. Academic governance body, the faculty, meets an average of 14 times per year.

Calendar: Three 12-week terms. Academic year early Aug. to May. Students accepted on a rolling basis for all terms. Formal commencement May. No summer session.

Characteristics of Freshmen: 58 applicants (22 female, male 36). 93% of applicants accepted. 68% of accepted applicants enrolled.

83% (34 students) submitted SAT scores; 2% (1 student) submitted ACT scores. *25th percentile*: SAT Critical Reading 430, SAT math 480, SAT Writing 425. *75th percentile*: SAT Critical Reading 570, SAT Math 580, SAT Writing 560.

20% of entering freshmen expected to graduate within 5 years. 65% of freshmen from Pennsylvania. Students from 13 states and 10 foreign countries.

Admission: Rolling admissions plan. For fall acceptance, the priority deadline Feb. 1; however applications accepted as late as July 1. *Requirements:* Either graduation from accredited secondary school with 15 units or GED. Minimum GPA 2.3. *Entrance tests:* College board SAT or ACT Composite. *For transfer students:* 2.2 minimum GPA; 68 hours maximum transfer credit.

Advanced placement for postsecondary-level work completed in secondary school and for extrainstitutional learning.

Tutoring available.

Degree Requirements: Core Program 47 credits comprised of Skills and Disciplinary Perspectives. Associate degree: 13 tracks, 62 credits, cumulative GPA at least 2.0, 3 terms at the college. Baccalaureate degree: 6 majors, 124 credits, 2 years in residence. *Grading system:* A–F; pass-fail; withdraw (deadline after which pass-fail is appended to withdraw); incomplete.

Distinctive Educational Programs: Evening classes. Accelerated degree programs. Teacher Intern Program leading to master's degree in education awarded by Lehigh University. Special facilities for using telecommunications in the classroom. Interdisciplinary major.

Degrees Conferred: 15 *baccalaureate*; 4 *master's*; 3 *first-professional*. Bachelor's degrees awarded : biological/life sciences 2; education 1; English 2; history 2; interdisciplinary studies 6; philosophy and religious studies 2. Master's degrees awarded: religious studies 4. First-professional degrees awarded: master of divinity 3.

Fees and Other Expenses: *Full-time tuition per academic year 2008–09:* \$10,620. *Room and board per academic year:* \$5,474.

Financial Aid: Aid from institutionally generated funds is provided on the basis of financial need.

Financial aid to full-time, first-time undergraduate students: 62% received received some form of financial aid.

Departments and Teaching Staff: *Total instructional faculty:* 49.

Enrollment: Total enrollment 155.

Characteristics of Student Body: *Ethnic/racial makeup:* Black non-Hispanic: 1%; Asian or Pacific islander 1%; White non-Hispanic: 68%; unknown: 6%; nonresident alien 21%.

International Students: 25 nonresident aliens enrolled fall 2008. Programs available to aid students whose native language is not English: Financial.

Student Life: On-campus residence halls house 57% of student body. *Intercollegiate athletics:* male: hockey, lacrosse, soccer; women only: lacrosse, volleyball. *Special regulations:* Cars permitted for all but first-term freshmen. Curfews. Quiet hours. *Publications: Bacon Bits*. *Special services:* Medical services. *Surrounding community:* Bryn Athyn population 950. Philadelphia, 17 miles from campus, is nearest metropolitan area. Served by mass transit railroad system; airport 25 miles from campus; passenger rail service 2 miles from campus.

Library Collections: 119,000 volumes. 1,500 microforms; 3,800 audiovisual materials; 360 current periodical subscriptions. Students have access to online information retrieval services and the Internet.

Most important special holdings include Swedenborgiana Library (collection of books about life and times of scientist and theologian Emmanuel Swedenborg); archives, including manuscripts and primary source material about the General Church of the New Jerusalem; New Church Collateral Literature Collection (copies of journals, magazines, addresses, and sermons).

Buildings and Grounds: Campus area 120 acres.

Chief Executive Officer: Rt. Rev. Brian W. Keith, President.

Address admission inquiries to Director of Admissions.

Academy of the New Church Theological School

Degree Programs Offered: *First-professional.*

Admission: Baccalaureate from accredited college or university with courses in education, Greek, Hebrew, Latin, religion, philosophy.

Degree Requirements: 9 months in residence; annual faculty assessment.

Bryn Mawr College

101 North Merion Avenue
Bryn Mawr, Pennsylvania 19010-2899
Tel: (610) 526-5000 **E-mail:** admissions@brynmawr.edu
Fax: (610) 526-7471 **Internet:** www.brynmawr.edu

Institution Description: Bryn Mawr College is a private, independent, nonprofit college. *Enrollment:* 1,799 (admits women students at the undergraduate level and men and women at the graduate level). *Degrees awarded:* Baccalaureate, master's, doctorate.

Accreditation: *Regional:* MSA/CHE. *Professional*: chemistry, social work

History: Established and chartered 1880; offered first instruction at postsecondary level 1885; awarded first degrees (baccalaureate and doctorate) 1888. *See* Lynde Meigs, *What Makes a College? A History of Bryn Mawr* (New York: Macmillan Publishing Company, Inc., 1956) for further information.

Institutional Structure: *Governing board:* Board of Trustees of Bryn Mawr College. Representation: 32 voting members (6 nominated by the Alumnae Association). 2 ex officio. 5 special representatives, the chairman of the board of Haverford College, 21 trustees emeriti. *Composition of institution:* Administrators 189. Academic affairs headed by provost. Management/business/finances directed by treasurer. Full-time instructional faculty 146. Academic governance body, the general faculty, meets an average of 4 times per year.

Calendar: Semesters. Academic year Aug. to May. Freshmen admitted Sept., Jan. Degrees conferred May, Dec. Formal commencement May. Summer session of 2 terms from June to Aug.

Characteristics of Freshmen: 2,150 applicants (female 2,150). 44% of applicants accepted. 38% accepted applicants enrolled.

93% (331 students) submitted SAT scores; 34% (121 students) submitted ACT scores. *25th percentile*: SAT Critical Reading 630, SAT Math 590, SAT Writing 630; ACT Composite 27, ACT English 27, ACT Math 25/ *75th percentile*: SAT Critical Reading 740, SAT Math 680, SAT Writing 720; ACT Composite 31, ACT English 33, ACT Math 29.

79% of entering freshmen expected to graduate within 5 years. 18% of freshmen from Pennsylvania. Freshmen from 48 states and 43 foreign countries.

Admission: For fall acceptance, apply as early as Aug., of previous year, but not later than Jan. 15 of year of enrollment. Students are notified of acceptance Apr. Apply by Nov. 15 and by Jan. 1 for early decision; need not limit application to Bryn Mawr. Early acceptance available. *Requirements:* 16 secondary school units which must include 4 in English, 3 units in a foreign language, 3 mathematics, some work in a laboratory science recommended. *Entrance tests:* College Board SAT, 3 Achievement tests (1 in English composition). *For transfer students:* 3.0 minimum GPA; 64 semester hours maximum transfer credit.

College credit and advanced placement for postsecondary-level work completed in secondary school.

Tutoring available.

Degree Requirements: 128 semester hours; minimum 2.0 GPA in half of all courses; 6 semesters in residence; 2 years physical education courses; foreign language, quantitative mathematics, and English requirement; distribution requirements; comprehensives in some fields of study; departmental senior conference in most fields.

Fulfillment of some degree requirements and exemption from some beginning courses possible by passing departmental examinations, College Board AP, Achievement tests. *Grading system:* 0–4.0; pass-fail.

Distinctive Educational Programs: Dual-degree programs in engineering with University of Pennsylvania; in city and regional programming with University of Pennsylvania. Prefreshman summer program. Interdisciplinary programs in classical languages, classical studies, growth and structure of cities, Hispanic studies, feminist and gender studies, East Asian studies, African studies, peace studies, Romance languages. Facilities and programs for independent research, individual majors, tutorials. Archaeological projects in Turkey, Greece, and Italy. Study abroad in Intercollegiate Center for Classical Studies and the American Academy in Rome, and the American School of Classical Studies in Athens; summer study in France, Italy, Spain, Russia, all sponsored by Bryn Mawr. Post-baccalaureate premedical program for students holding B.A. International economic relations program offers courses in international economics and language with summer work. Extensive cross-registration with Haverford College; students may also register for courses at Swarthmore College and University of Pennsylvania. Qualified students who have the approval of their major departments and their dean may apply for permission to study in a foreign country for a semester or a year. The college has approved approximately 50 programs in colleges and universities in other countries.

Degrees Conferred: 311 *baccalaureate*; 128 *master's*; 18 *doctorate*. Bachelor's degrees awarded in top five disciplines: social sciences 431 biological/life sciences 32; foreign languages 32; English language/literature 31; physical science 21.

Fees and Other Expenses: *Full-time tuition per academic year 2008–09:* undergraduate $36,540; contact the college for current graduate tuition/fees. *Books and supplies:* $1,000. *Room and board per academic year:* $11,520. *Other expenses:* $1,000.

Financial Aid: Aid from institutionally generated funds is provided on the basis of financial need.

Financial aid to full-time, first-time undergraduate students: 62% received some form of financial aid. Average amount of aid received: federal grants $4,221; state/local grants $2,134; institutional grants $21,496; loans $3,500.

Departments and Teaching Staff: *Full-time instructional faculty:* 146. Student/faculty ratio: 9.62:1. Degrees held by full-time faculty: 100% hold terminal degrees.

Enrollment: Total enrollment 1,799. Undergraduate 1,287.

Characteristics of Student Body: *Ethnic/racial makeup:* Black non-Hispanic: 6%; Asian or Pacific Islander: 12%; Hispanic: 3%; White non-Hispanic: 48%.

International Students: 83 nonresident aliens enrolled fall 2008. Students from Europe, Asia, Central and South America, Africa, Canada. Programs available to aid students whose native language is not English: social, cultural, financial. Financial aid specifically designated for international students: scholarships available annually.

Student Life: On-campus residence halls house 97% of student body. Residence halls for females constitute 86% of such space, for both sexes 14%. 5% of student body housed in college-operated cooperative facilities. (Some figures include Haverford College students who live on Bryn Mawr campus through the residence hall exchange program). *Intercollegiate athletics:* female: basketball, badminton, cross-country, field hockey, lacrosse, soccer, swimming, diving, tennis, volleyball. *Special regulations:* Cars are not permitted for resident freshmen. Residence hall quiet hours determined by residence hall residents. *Special services:* Medical services; bus service between Bryn Mawr, Haverford, and Swarthmore Colleges; shuttle service to outlying campus buildings. *Student publications: Musomania, Red Tree, Color,* annual and biannual magazines; *The Howl,* biannual humor magazine, *The Bryn Mawr-Haverford Bi-College News,* weekly newspaper; *The College News,* bimonthly newspaper. *Surrounding community:* Lower Merion Township, located in metropolitan Philadelphia area. Served by commuter rail lines and mass transit bus system; airport located 20 miles from campus; passenger rail less than 1 mile from campus.

Publications: *Bryn Mawr College Monographs* (annual) published 1901–1916; *Reprint Series* (annual) published 1901–1923; *Bryn Mawr Notes and Monographs* (annual) published 1921–27 and 1940; *Bryn Mawr Classical Review* (quarterly) published since 1990; various specialized collections volumes published occasionally.

Library Collections: 1,725,200 volumes including bound books, serial backfiles, electronic documents, and government documents not in separate collections. Online catalog. Current serial subscriptions: 1,860 paper, 61 microform, 66 electronic. 4,000 audiovisual materials. Computer work stations available. Students have access to the Internet at no charge.

Most important special collections include the Goodhart Gordon Collection of Incunables; Seymour Adelman Collection of British and American Literature; Bryn Mawr College Archives; Spanish American books; the works of Marianne Moore.

Buildings and Grounds: Campus area 135 acres.

Chief Executive Officer: Dr. Nancy J. Vickers, President.

Undergraduates address admission inquiries to Jennifer Rickard, Director of Admissions; graduate inquiries to James Wright, Dean of the Graduate School of Arts and Sciences or Nancy Kirby, Dean of the Graduate School of Social Work and Social Research.

Bucknell University

Lewisburg, Pennsylvania 17837

Tel: (570) 577-2000 **E-mail:** admissions@bucknell.edu
Fax: (570) 577-3760 **Internet:** www.bucknell.edu

Institution Description: Bucknell University is a private, independent, nonprofit institution. *Enrollment:* 3,759. *Degrees awarded:* Baccalaureate, master's.

Accreditation: *Regional:* MSA/CHE. *Professional*: chemistry, computer science, engineering, music

History: Established as University at Lewisburg, chartered and offered first instruction at postsecondary level 1846; awarded first degree (baccalaureate) 1851; adopted present name 1886. *See* J. Orin Oliphant, *The Rise of Bucknell University* (New York: Appleton-Century-Crofts, 1965) for further information.

Institutional Structure: *Governing board:* Board of Trustees limited to 50 members (currently 4 non-alumni and 35 alumni), plus president of the university, ex officio; 3 nonvoting representatives of faculty, students, and parents. *Composition of institution:* Academic affairs headed by vice president; student services headed by vice president for student services and athletics; business/finance directed by vice president for finance and administration; alumni/parent/volunteer relations, public relations and publications, development activities headed by vice president for university relations. Full-time instructional faculty 301. Academic governance body, the Faculty, meets monthly.

Calendar: Semesters. Academic year Aug. to May. Freshmen admitted Sept., Feb. June. Degrees conferred May or June, Aug., Jan. Formal commencement May, Dec., June. Summer session from June to July.

Characteristics of Freshmen: 8,029 applicants (3,855 female, 4,169 male). 33% of applicants accepted. 31% of accepted applicants enrolled.

90% (831 students) submitted SAT scores; 19% (179 students) submitted ACT scores. *25th percentile*: SAT Critical Reading 600, SAT 630; ACT Composite 27. *75th percentile*: SAT Critical Reading 680, SAT Math 710; ACT Composite 30.

89% of entering freshmen expected to graduate within 5 years. 21% of freshmen from Pennsylvania. Freshmen from 47 states and 43 foreign countries.

Admission: For fall acceptance, apply by Nov. 15 for early decision, but not later than 1 year of enrollment. Apply by Dec. 1 for early decision; need not limit application to Bucknell. Early acceptance available. *Requirements:* Either graduation from accredited secondary school with 4 units English, 2 foreign language, 4 social studies, 3 mathematics, 2 natural or physical science; or GED. *Entrance tests:* College Board SAT. *For transfer students:* 2.5 minimum GPA; no more than 80 semester hours transferable credits; 48 residency requirement.

College credit and advanced placement for postsecondary-level work completed in secondary school.

BUCKNELL UNIVERSITY—*cont'd*

Degree Requirements: 32 courses; 2.0 GPA; 2 semesters of junior and senior year, including final semester, in residence; distribution requirements. For engineering degree, 34 courses.

Fulfillment of some degree requirements and exemption from some beginning courses possible by passing departmental examinations, College Board CLEP, AP. *Grading system:* A, A–, B+, B, B–, C+, C, C–, D, F.

Distinctive Educational Programs: *For undergraduates:* Interdisciplinary programs in international relations, legal studies, peace studies, Latin American studies, Japanese studies, East Asian studies, Caribbean studies, women's studies, environmental studies, animal behavior, cell biology and biochemistry, neuropsychology and comparative Western humanities. All students in the College of Arts and Sciences complete a Freshman Seminar and a senior Capstone Course. All engineering students enroll in "Exploring Engineering" and complete a Senior Design Project. Residential colleges are available to first-year students, with theme halls in six areas: arts, humanities, environment, international, social justice, and technology and society. Facilities and programs for independent research, including honors programs, individual majors, tutorials. Five-year engineering B.S./B.A. program, and B.S./M.S. programs in several disciplines. Off-campus study opportunities available to students in all majors in Asia, Africa, Latin America, Europe, Australia, and New Zealand; in the United States at Woods Hole Laboratories and internships in Washington, D.C. The Institute for Leadership in Technology and Management is a two-summer program combining interdisciplinary study on-campus with off-campus internships. Financial aid is portable. *Available to all students:* Special facilities for using telecommunications in the classroom. Study abroad in England, France, Barbados, Japan, Sweden, and other countries through the institute of European and Asian Studies.

ROTC: Army.

Degrees Conferred: 896 *baccalaureate*; 34 *master's*. Bachelor's degrees awarded in top five disciplines: social sciences 240; business/marketing 148; biological/life sciences 78; psychology 70; foreign languages and literature 65. Master's degrees awarded: biological/life sciences 4; education 10; engineering 11; English 4; physical sciences 2; psychology 3.

Fees and Other Expenses: *Full-time tuition per academic year 2008–09:* undergraduate $39,652; contact the university for current graduate tuition. *Other fees:* $196. *Room and board per academic year:* $8,728. *Books and supplies:* $870. *Other expenses:* $1,000.

Financial Aid: Aid from institutionally generated funds is provided on the basis of financial need.

Financial aid to full-time, first-time undergraduate students: need-based scholarships/grants totaling $29,139,245, self-help $13,211,700; awards non-need-based scholarships/grants totaling $202,000, parent loans $5,517,734, tuition waivers $2,200,000, athletic awards $110,000. *Graduate aid:* 83 students received fellowships and grants totaling$1,074,920; 51 students held teaching/research assistantships totaling $470,000 (ranging from $4,125 to $8,250).

Departments and Teaching Staff: *Total instructional faculty:* 321 (full-time 301, part-time 20). Total faculty with doctorate, first-professional, or other terminal degree: 288. Student/faculty ratio: 12:1.

Enrollment: Total enrollment 3,759. Undergraduate 3,624 (full-time 99%; female 53%, male 47%). Graduate 135 (full-time 56%). Undergraduate transfer-in students 4.

Characteristics of Student Body: *Ethnic/racial makeup:* number of Black non-Hispanic: 102; American Indian or Alaska Native: 20; Asian or Pacific Islander: 261; Hispanic: 128; White non-Hispanic: 2,819; unknown: 120. *Age distribution:* number under 18: 59, 18–19: 1,675; 20–21: 1,526; 22–24: 119; 25–29: 13; 30–34: 2; 35–39: 4; 40–49: 5; 50–64: 4. 8% of student body attend summer sessions.

International Students: 113 nonresident aliens enrolled fall 2008. Students from Europe, Asia, Central and South America, Africa, Canada. Programs available to aid students whose native language is not English: social, cultural. Financial aid specifically designated for international students: scholarships available annually to qualifying students.

Student Life: Four-year residency requirement, but non-freshmen may apply for permission to live off-campus. 73% of non-freshmen live in residence halls, 9% in fraternity houses, 14% off-campus, and 4% participate in off-campus study programs. 72% of non-freshmen females live in residence halls, 22% live off-campus, and 6% participate in off-campus study programs. Fraternity/sorority rush occurs in the sophomore year; 51% of eligible males belong to fraternities; 57% of the eligible females belong to sororities. *Intercollegiate athletics:* male: baseball, basketball, crew, cross-country, football, golf, indoor track, lacrosse, soccer, swimming, tennis, track, water polo, wrestling; female: basketball, crew, cross-country, field hockey, golf, indoor track, lacrosse, soccer, softball, swimming, tennis, track, volleyball, water polo. *Special regulations:* Registered cars permitted for all except freshmen (semester registration fee). *Special services:* medical services, psychological services. *Student publications, radio:* *Bucknellian*, weekly newspaper; *The Bucknell Engineer*, a magazine published 3 times per year; *Tristram*, a biannual literary magazine. Radio station WVBU broadcasts 126 hours per week. *Surrounding community:* Lewisburg population 18,700. Harrisburg, 75 miles south, provides air service and nearest passenger rail service. Nearest airport is 30 miles from campus in Williamsport.

Publications: *Bucknell Review* (biannually) first published in 1941; *Bucknell World* (alumni tabloid) published 6 times per year. University Press publishes approximately 15 titles annually.

Library Collections: 849,000 volumes including bound books, serial backfiles, electronic documents, and government documents not in separate collections. Online catalog. Current serial subscriptions: 5,279 paper; 63 microform; 10,078 via electronic access. 243 recordings; 4,778 compact discs; 1,893 CD-ROMs. Computer work stations available. Students have access to the Internet at no charge.

Most important special collections include Irish Authors (especially William Butler Yeats, Oliver St. John Gogarty; D.H. Lawrence; George Bernard Shaw); Fine Press Editions.

Buildings and Grounds: Campus area 393 acres.

Chief Executive Officer: Dr. Brian C, Mitchell, President.

Undergraduates address admission inquiries Kurt Thisde, Director of Admissions; graduate inquiries to Dr. M. Lois Huffines, Director of Graduate Studies.

Cabrini College

610 King of Prussia Road
Radnor, Pennsylvania 19087-3698
Tel: (610) 902-8100 **E-mail:** admit@cabrini.edu
Fax: (610) 902-8309 **Internet:** www.cabrini.edu

Institution Description: Cabrini College is a private institution affiliated with the Roman Catholic Church. *Enrollment:* 3,580. *Degrees awarded:* Baccalaureate, master's.

Accreditation: *Regional:* MSA/CHE.

History: Chartered as institution for women 1957; awarded first degree (baccalaureate) 1961; became coeducational 1970.

Institutional Structure: *Governing board:* Board of Trustees. Representation: 26 trustees, 3 emeriti, president of the college. 2 ex officio. *Composition of institution:* Academic affairs headed by vice president. Management/business/finances directed by vice president for finance and administration. Full-time instructional faculty 61.

Calendar: Semesters. Academic year Sept. to May. Freshmen admitted Sept. Formal commencement May. Summer sessions May to Aug. 12-week session May to Aug.

Characteristics of Freshmen: 4,631 applicants (3,072 female, 1,559 male). 94% (524 students) submitted SAT scores; 9% (49 students) submitted ACT scores. *25th percentile*: SAT Critical Reading 440, SAT Math 440 ACT Composite 16. *75th percentile*: SAT Critical Reading 530, SAT Math 520; ACT Composite 21.

57% of freshmen from Pennsylvania. Freshmen from 27 states and 1 foreign country.

Admission: Rolling admissions plan. Early acceptance available. *Requirements:* Graduation from accredited secondary school with 4 units English, 2 foreign language, 2 mathematics, 2 social studies, 1 science. *Entrance tests:* College Board SAT or ACT composite. *For transfer students:* 2.2 minimum GPA; from 4-year and 2-year accredited institutions 78 hours maximum transfer credit.

College credit for extrainstitutional learning on basis of portfolio assessment. Developmental courses offered.

Degree Requirements: 123 credit hours; 2.0 GPA; 45 credits in residence; 45–60 credit core curriculum requirements.

Fulfillment of some degree requirements possible by passing College Board CLEP, AP. *Grading system:* A–F; pass; withdraw; incomplete.

Distinctive Educational Programs: Cooperative education. Organizational Management Program and Professional Communications, accelerated degree completion programs. Student exchange program with Eastern College, Valley Forge College, Rosemont College. Cooperative baccalaureate in medical technology and laboratory sciences with affiliated hospitals. Interdepartmental-interdisciplinary programs in American studies, women's studies. Facilities and programs for independent research, including honors programs, individual major. Preprofessional programs in nursing, pharmacy, physical therapy, occupational therapy. Master of Education program. *Other distinctive programs:* Sports science and graphic design; CLEP/Dante's Assessment of Prior Learning Program (credit for life experience).

ROTC: Army in cooperation with Valley Forge Military Academy.

Degrees Conferred: 316 *baccalaureate*; 185 *master's*. Bachelor's degrees awarded in top five disciplines: business, management, marketing, and related support services 91; education 74; communication, journalism, and related programs 49; social sciences 18; psychology 17. Master's degrees awarded: various disciplines 185.

Fees and Other Expenses: *Full-time tuition per academic year 2008–09:* $30,010. *Required fees:* $800. *Room and board per academic year:* $10,890. *Books and supplies:* $1,050. *Other expenses:* $2,845.

Financial Aid: Aid from institutionally generated funds is provided on the basis of academic merit, financial need.

Financial aid to full-time, first-time undergraduate students: 97% received some form of aid. Average amount of aid received: federal grants $4,991; Pell grants $3,225; other federal aid $1,937; state/local grants $3,866; institutional grants $11,883.

Departments and Teaching Staff: *Total instructional faculty:* 224. Total faculty with doctorate, first-professional, or other terminal degree: 86. Student/faculty ratio: 16:1. Degrees held by full-time faculty: master's 100%, doctorate 54%. 79% hold terminal degrees.

Enrollment: Total enrollment 3,580. Undergraduate 1,836 (full-time 92%; female 66%, male 34%). Graduate 1,744. Undergraduate transfer-in students 94.

Characteristics of Student Body: *Ethnic/racial makeup:* Black non-Hispanic: 7%; Asian or Pacific Islander: 2%; Hispanic: 2%; White non-Hispanic: 82%; unknown: 6%.

International Students: 4 nonresident aliens enrolled fall 2008 Students from Europe, Asia, Latin America, Africa, Canada. Programs available to aid students whose native language is not English: social, cultural. Some financial aid specifically designated for qualifying international students.

Student Life: On-campus residence halls and houses available. *Intercollegiate athletics:* male: basketball, cross-country, golf, lacrosse, soccer, tennis, track; female: basketball, field hockey, lacrosse, soccer, softball, tennis, track, volleyball. *Special services:* Medical services; shuttle bus to public transportation. *Student publications, radio, television: Cryptic*, a literary magazine; *Loquitur*, a newspaper; *Woodcrest*, a yearbook; AM and FM radio stations, TV studio. *Surrounding community:* Radnor township population 35,000. Philadelphia is nearest metropolitan area. Served by mass transit bus and rail systems, airport, passenger rail service.

Library Collections: 229,000 volumes. 33,000 microforms; 8,500 audiovisual materials; 240 current periodical subscriptions. Students have access to online information retrieval services and the Internet.

Most important special collection is the Franklin D. Roosevelt Collection.

Buildings and Grounds: Campus area 112 acres.

Chief Executive Officer: Dr. Antoinette Iadarola, President.

Address admission inquiries to Mark Osborn, Director of Admissions.

California University of Pennsylvania

250 University Avenue
California, Pennsylvania 15419-1394
Tel: (724) 938-4404 **E-mail:** inquiry@cup.edu
Fax: (724) 938-4564 **Internet:** www.cup.edu

Institution Description: California University of Pennsylvania is a state institution. *Enrollment:* 7,720. *Degrees awarded:* Associate, baccalaureate, master's.

Academic offerings subject to approval by statewide coordinating bodies. Budget subject to approval by state governing boards.

Accreditation: *Regional:* MSA/CHE. *Professional*: nurse anesthesia education, social work, teacher education

History: Established as California Academy 1852; chartered and offered first instruction at postsecondary level 1865; awarded first degree (baccalaureate) 1930; became California State College 1959; renamed California University of Pennsylvania 1983. *See* Dr. Regis J. Serinko, *California State College: The People's College in the Monongahela Valley* (Dubuque: Kendall/Hunt Publishing Co., 1975) for further information.

Institutional Structure: *Governing board:* Council of Trustees of California University. Extrainstitutional representation: 10 trustees; institutional representation: 1 student. All voting. *Composition of institution:* Administrators 31. Academic affairs headed by provost for academic affairs. Management/business/finances directed by vice president of administrative affairs. Full-time instructional faculty 286. Academic governance body, Executive Committee of the Faculty Union, meets an average of 15 times per year. *Faculty representation:* Faculty served by collective bargaining agents affiliated with Association of Pennsylvania State College and University Faculty.

Calendar: Semesters. Academic year Sept. to May. Freshmen admitted Sept., Jan., June. Degrees conferred May, Dec. Formal commencement May. Summer session from June to Aug.

Characteristics of Freshmen: 78% of applicants accepted. 47% of accepted applicants enrolled.

93% (936 students) submitted SAT scores; 13% (131 students) submitted ACT scores. *25th percentile*: SAT Critical Reading 450, SAT Math 450; ACT Composite 17. *75th percentile*: SAT Critical Reading 530, SAT Math 530; ACT Composite 21.

36% of entering freshmen expected to graduate within 5 years. 95% of freshmen from Pennsylvania. Freshmen from 35 states and 20 foreign countries.

Admission: Rolling admissions plan. For fall acceptance, apply as early as Sept. 1 of previous year, but not later than Aug. 1. Apply by Dec. 1 for early decision. Early acceptance available. *Requirements:* Either graduation from accredited secondary school 16 units or GED. Additional requirements for some programs. Minimum 2.0 GPA. Lowest acceptable secondary school class standing 40th percentile. *Entrance tests:* Recommend College Board SAT. For foreign students TOEFL. *For transfer students:* 2.0 minimum GPA; maximum transfer credit 75 hours.

College credit and advanced placement for postsecondary-level work completed in secondary school; credit on basis of personal interviews.

Tutoring available. Credit developmental courses offered in summer session and regular academic year.

Degree Requirements: *For all associate degrees:* 64 credit hours. *For all baccalaureate degrees:* 128 credit hours. *For all undergraduate degrees:* 2.0 GPA; 2 terms in residence; distribution requirements.

Fulfillment of some degree requirements and exemption from some beginning courses possible by passing departmental examinations, College Board CLEP, AP. *Grading system:* A–F; pass-fail; withdraw (deadline after which pass-fail is appended to withdraw).

Distinctive Educational Programs: Internships. Flexible meeting places and schedules; weekend and evening classes. Accelerated degree programs; dual-degree programs in engineering with Pennsylvania State University and University of Pittsburgh. Study abroad in various countries in cooperation with other colleges. *Other distinctive programs:* Continuing education. Teacher Enhancement Centers; joint programs with hospitals; internship with business and industry.

Degrees Conferred: 37 *associate*; 1,130 *baccalaureate*; 546 *master's*. Bachelor's degrees awarded in top five disciplines: education 336; business, management, marketing, and related support services 104; social sciences 60; security and protective services 56; computer and information sciences.

Fees and Other Expenses: *Full-time tuition per academic year 2008–09:* contact the university for current information regarding tuition, fees, housing, and other applicable costs.

Financial Aid: Aid from institutionally generated funds is provided on the basis of academic merit, financial need, athletic ability. Institution has a Program Participation Agreement with the U.S. Department of Education for eligible students to receive Pell Grants and, depending upon the agreement, other federal aid.

Financial aid to full-time, first-time undergraduate students: 83% received some form of financial aid. Average amount of aid received: federal grants $2,878; state/local grants $2,697; institutional grants $2,494; loans $4,734.

Departments and Teaching Staff: *Total instructional faculty:* 319. Degrees held by full-time faculty: doctorate 64%, master's 35%, baccalaureate 1%. 72% hold terminal degrees.

Enrollment: Total enrollment 7,720.

International Students: 63 nonresident aliens enrolled fall 2008. Students from Europe, Asia, Central and south America, Africa, Canada, Australia. Programs available to aid students whose native language is not English: social and cultural. No financial aid specifically designated for international students.

Student Life: On-campus residence halls house 40% of student body. Residence halls for males constitute 55% of such space, for females 45%. 7% of males join and 2% live in fraternity housing; 12% of females join and 2% live in sorority housing. *Intercollegiate athletics:* male: baseball, basketball, cross-country, fencing, golf, tennis, track; female: basketball, cross-country, fencing, softball, tennis, track, volleyball. *Special regulations:* Cars permitted without restrictions. Quiet hours. Limited residence hall visitation. *Special services:* Learning Resources Center, medical services. *Student publications, radio:* Annual literary magazine, weekly newspaper, yearbook. Radio station WVCS broadcasts 168 hours per week. *Surrounding community:* California population 6,000. Pittsburgh, 45 miles from campus, is nearest metropolitan area. Served by mass transit bus system, airport 60 miles from campus.

Library Collections: 1,850,000 volumes including bound books, serial backfiles, electronic documents, and government documents not in separate collections. Online catalog. Current serial subscriptions: 1,022 paper, 4,578 electronic. Students have access to the Internet at no charge.

Most important special holdings include industrial arts collection; government document collection; English literature collection.

Buildings and Grounds: Campus area 88 acres. Campus DVD available.

Chief Executive Officer: Dr. Angelo Armenti, Jr., President.

Address admission inquiries to William Edmonds, Director of Admissions.

Carlow University

3333 Fifth Avenue
Pittsburgh, Pennsylvania 15213-3165
Tel: (412) 578-6000 **E-mail:** admissions@carlow.edu
Fax: (412) 578-6019 **Internet:** www.carlow.edu

Institution Description: Carlow University is a private institution affiliated with the Pittsburgh Sisters of Mercy, Roman Catholic Church. *Enrollment:* 2,128. *Degrees awarded:* Baccalaureate, master's. Certifications also awarded.

Member of Pittsburgh Council for Higher Education.

Accreditation: *Regional:* MSA/CHE. *Professional*: nursing, social work

History: Established as Mount Mercy College; incorporated, and offered first instruction at postsecondary level 1929; awarded first degree (baccalaureate) 1933; adopted present name 1969; admitted men early 1970s. *See: A Community of Learners*, available in the college library and published in the late 1970s for further information.

Institutional Structure: *Governing board:* Board of Trustees. Representation: 27 trustees, including president of the college. 2 ex officio. All voting. *Composition of institution:* Administrators 4. Academic affairs headed by vice president for academic affairs. Management/business/finances directed by vice president for the chief financial officer and the chief operating officer. Full-time instructional faculty 72. Academic governance body, The Faculty Assembly, meets an average of 10 times per year.

Calendar: Semesters. Academic year Aug. to May. Freshmen admitted Sept., Jan., May. Degrees conferred May, Aug., Dec. Formal commencement May. Summer session of 1 term from May to Aug.

Characteristics of Freshmen: 1,053 applicants (female 979, male 64). 60% of applicants accepted. 38% of accepted applicants enrolled.

83% (219 students) submitted SAT scores; 28% (73students) submitted ACT scores. *25th percentile*: SAT Critical Reading 450, SAT Math 440; ACT Composite 19, ACT English 19, ACT Math 17. *75th percentile*: SAT Critical Reading 560, SAT Math 540; ACT Composite 25, ACT English 26, ACT Math 24.

61% of entering freshmen expected to graduate within 5 years. 97% of freshmen from Pennsylvania. Freshmen from 15 states and 6 foreign countries.

Admission: Rolling admissions plan. For fall acceptance, apply as early as Sept. 1 of previous year. *Requirements:* Either graduation from accredited secondary school with 18 units which must include 4 English, 3 mathematics, 3 natural science, 4 arts/humanities, 4 academic electives; or GED. Nursing applicants must have completed as a minimum: 4 units English, 3 social studies, 2 math (1 must be algebra), 2 units of lab science. *Entrance tests:* College Board SAT preferred. For foreign students TOEFL. *For transfer students:* 2.0 minimum GPA.

Advanced placement for students who have successfully completed college-level courses in secondary school and have submitted the results of the College Board Advanced Placement tests with appropriate scores.

Tutoring available. Noncredit developmental/remedial courses offered.

Degree Requirements: 120 credit hours; nursing majors must have 135 credits. 2.0 GPA; 32 credits normal residency requirement; core curriculum required; comprehensive evaluation or departmental equivalent to demonstrate competence in major field.

Fulfillment of some degree requirements and exemption from some courses possible by passing College Board AP. Courses may be challenged by examination for credit or exemption. *Grading system:* A+–F-; pass-fail; credit/no credit.

Distinctive Educational Programs: Work-experience programs. Flexible meeting places and schedules, including 5 off-campus sites in Beaver, Cranberry, Greensburg, and at Carlow Hill College and Blue Cross of Western Pennsylvania. Weekend and evening classes. Interdisciplinary program in women's studies. Facilities and programs for independent research, including individual majors, tutorials. Certificate in Perfusion Technology 18 months after biology degree is awarded. 3/2 programs with Carnegie Mellon University in chemistry/chemical engineering and mathematics/engineering. 3/2 program with Duquesne University in biology/environmental engineering. Study abroad individually arranged through an accredited American college or university. Cross-registration through the consortium. *Other distinctive programs:* Degree programs available through weekend classes and also through an accelerated program of evening classes.

ROTC: Army, Navy, Air Force offered in cooperation with University of Pittsburgh, Duquesne University, and Carnegie Mellon University.

Degrees Conferred: 341 *baccalaureate*; 208 *master's*. Bachelor's degrees awarded in top five disciplines: health professions and related clinical sciences 75; education 50; business, management, marketing, and related support services 44; psychology 30; computer and information sciences 20. Master's degrees awarded: various disciplines 208.

Fees and Other Expenses: *Full-time tuition per academic year 2008–09:* $20,684; contact the university for current graduate tuition/fees. *Room and board per academic year:* $8,146. *Books and supplies* $700. *Other expenses:* $2,000.

Financial Aid: Aid from institutionally generated funds is provided on the basis of academic merit, financial need, athletic ability.

Financial aid to full-time, first-time undergraduate students: 94% received some form of financial aid. Average amount of aid received: federal grants $4,223; Pell grants $2,927; other federal aid $1,381; state/local grants $3,989; institutional grants $7,750.

Departments and Teaching Staff: *Total instructional faculty:* 108 FTE. Student/faculty ratio: 13:1. Degrees held by full-time faculty: master's 28%, doctorate 72%. 51% of full-time faculty hold terminal degrees.

Enrollment: Total enrollment 2,128. Undergraduate 1,575 (full-time 75%; female 94%, male 6%). Graduate 613 (full-time 29%). Undergraduate transfer-in students 191.

Characteristics of Student Body: *Ethnic/racial makeup:* Black non-Hispanic: 17%; American Indian or Alaska Native: 1%; Asian or Pacific Islander: 1%; Hispanic: 1%; White non-Hispanic: 67%; unknown: 13%.

International Students: Programs available to aid students whose native language is not English: social, cultural. Intensive English program upon demand. Financial aid specifically designated for international students: variable number of scholarships available annually.

Student Life: On-campus residence halls house 33% of day student body. Residence halls are females only. *Intercollegiate athletics:* female: softball, basketball, crew, cross-country, tennis, volleyball. *Special regulations:* Cars permitted for commuters. *Special services:* Career Service, Campus Ministry, Health and Wellness Center, Learning Center. 31 organizations available for student participation. *Surrounding community:* Pittsburgh population 450,000. Served by mass transit bus system; airport 20 miles from campus; passenger rail service 5 miles from campus.

Library Collections: 129,000 volumes including bound books, serial backfiles, electronic documents, and government documents not in separate collections. Online catalog. Current serial subscriptions: 429 paper. 1,681 recordings; 17 CD-ROMs. Computer work stations available. Students have access to the Internet at no charge.

Most important special holdings include Black Studies Collection; Career Resource Collection; Peace Studies Collection.

Buildings and Grounds: Campus area 13 acres.

Chief Executive Officer: Dr. Grace Ann Geibel, RSM, President.

Address admission inquiries to Christine Devine, Director of Admissions.

Carnegie Mellon University

5000 Forbes Avenue
Pittsburgh, Pennsylvania 15213-3890
Tel: (412) 268-2000 **E-mail:** admissions@cmu.edu
Fax: (412) 268-7838 **Internet:** www.cmu.edu

Institution Description: Carnegie Mellon University is a private, independent, nonprofit institution. *Enrollment:* 10,875. *Degrees awarded:* Baccalaureate, master's, doctorate.

Member of the consortium Pittsburgh Council on Higher Education.

Accreditation: *Regional:* MSA/CHE. *Professional*: architecture, art, business, chemistry, engineering, music, planning, public administration

History: Established as Carnegie Technical School 1900; offered first instruction at postsecondary level 1905; incorporated as Carnegie Institute of Technology and awarded first degree (baccalaureate) 1912; merged with Mellon Institute and adopted present name 1967. *See* Arthur W. Tarbell, *The Story of Carnegie Tech (1900–1935)* (Pittsburgh: Carnegie Institute Press, 1937) for further information.

Institutional Structure: *Governing board:* Board of Trustees. Extrainstitutional representation: 68 trustees (including 35 alumni). 6 ex officio, 21 trustees emeriti; institutional representation: President of the university. Full board meets 3 times a year. *Composition of institution:* Administrators 1,924. Top administration: president, provost, senior vice president for academic affairs, vice presidents for business affairs, university planning, research, education, development, enrollment, for university relations, legal affairs. Full-time instructional faculty 1,042.

Calendar: Semesters. Academic year Aug. to May. Freshmen admitted Aug. Degrees conferred May, Aug., Dec. Formal commencement May. Summer session of 2 terms.

Characteristics of Freshmen: 22,023 applicants (8,133 female, 12,890 male). 34% of applicants accepted. 22% of accepted applicants enrolled.

87% (1,248 students) submitted SAT scores; 16% (228 students) submitted ACT scores. *25th percentile*: SAT Critical Reading 620; SAT Math 690, SAT Writing 610; ACT Composite 28, ACT English 27, ACT Math 27. *75th percen-*

tile: SAT Critical Reading 710, SAT Math 780, SAT Writing 700; ACT Composite 32, ACT English 333, ACT Math 33.

76% of entering freshmen expected to graduate within 5 years. 22% of freshmen from Pennsylvania. Freshmen from 50 states and 103 foreign countries.

Admission: For fall acceptance, apply as early as Oct. 1 of previous year, but not later than Jan. 1 of year of enrollment (Dec. 15 for College of Fine Arts); Students are notified of acceptance by Apr. 15. Apply by Nov. 15 for early decision (Nov. 1 for College of Fine Arts); need not limit applications to Carnegie Mellon. Early acceptance available. Application deadline for transfer students Mar. 15. *Requirements:* Either graduation from accredited secondary school with 4 units in English, 4 mathematics, 3 science, 3 laboratory, 1 social studies, 2 foreign language; or GED. For music and drama programs, audition; for art, design and some drama programs, portfolio. *Entrance tests:* College Board SAT or ACT. For foreign students TOEFL. *For transfer students:* transfer credit varies.

College credit and advanced placement for postsecondary-level work completed in secondary school. Tutoring available.

Degree Requirements: Defined by the college or department in which a student majors. Minimum requirements include: 360-486 units; 2.0 GPA; 90 units in residence.

Fulfillment of some degree requirements possible by passing College Board AP. *Grading system:* A–F; pass-fail; withdraw (carries penalty).

Distinctive Educational Programs: Common university core curriculum for general education in undergraduate colleges. Double major and major/minor combinations available within and across colleges. A series of Professional Concentrations in the Humanities and Social Sciences; Writing (creative, technical, and professional) programs in English; Applied History and European Studies (double major) in History; Pre-Law Advisement and Health Professions Program; Computer Science Tracks in Chemistry, Applied Math, and Physics. Joint bachelors-masters degree with Heinz School or Graduate School of Industrial Administration. Interdisciplinary degree programs include: Engineering/Engineering and Public Policy; Engineering/Biomedical Engineering (all levels); Master's: Advanced Building (Architecture/Urban and Public Affairs/Civil Engineering), Colloids, Polymers and Surfaces (Chemical Engineering/Chemistry); Ph.D.: Architecture/Urban and Public Affairs; Public Policy Analysis (Urban and Public Affairs/Social and Decision Sciences); Social and Decision Sciences/Applied History; Decision Making (Social and Decision Sciences/Statistics); Industrial Administration and Public Management and Policy (GSIA/Heinz School). Dual-degree programs include: MSIA in Industrial Administration and Juris Doctor (with University of Pittsburgh Law School); MS in Public Management and Juris Doctor (with University of Pittsburgh Law School); MS in Public Management and Master of Divinity (with Pittsburgh Theological Seminary); Ph.D. in Computational Linguistics (with University of Pittsburgh). Facilities and programs for individual research, including honors programs and individual majors. Work-experience programs. Washington (DC) semester. Study abroad in Switzerland. Summer abroad programs in Germany and France.

ROTC: Army, Air Force, and Navy.

Degrees Conferred: 1,295 *baccalaureate*; 1,621 *master's*; 258 *doctorate*. Bachelor's degrees awarded in top five disciplines: engineering 313; computer and information sciences 22; visual and performing arts 162; business/marketing 142; biological/life sciences 66.

Fees and Other Expenses: *Full-time tuition per academic year 2008–09:* $39,564 undergraduate; contact the university for current graduate tuition/fees. *Books and supplies:* $990. *Room and board per academic year:* $10,050. *Other expenses:* $1,356.

Financial Aid: Aid from institutionally generated funds is provided on the basis of academic merit, financial need.

Financial aid to full-time, first-time undergraduate students: 68% received some form of financial aid. Average amount of aid received: federal grants $5,916; state/local grants $2,880; institutional grants $16,891; loans $5,759.

Departments and Teaching Staff: *Total instructional faculty*: 856. Student/faculty ratio: 10:1. Degrees held by full-time faculty: 98% hold terminal degrees.

Enrollment: Total enrollment 10,875. Undergraduate 5,809 (full-time 97%; female 40%, male 60%).

Characteristics of Student Body: *Ethnic/racial makeup:* Black non-Hispanic: 5%; Asian or Pacific Islander: 24%; 5%; White non-Hispanic: 41%; unknown: 13%; nonresident alien 12%.

International Students: 719 undergraduate nonresident aliens enrolled fall 2008. Students from Europe, Asia, Latin America, Africa, Canada, Australia, New Zealand. Programs available to aid students whose native language is not English: English as a Second Language Program. No financial aid specifically designated for international students.

Student Life: On-campus residence halls house 60% of undergraduate student body. Residence halls for males constitute 19% of such space, for females only 10%, for both sexes 71%. 11% of undergraduates reside in other institutionally controlled living space. 11% of undergraduates are members of fraternities or sororities, and of these 64% live in fraternity or sorority housing. *Intercollegiate athletics:* male: basketball, cross-country, football, golf, soccer, swimming, tennis, track; female: basketball, cross-country, soccer, swimming, tennis, track, volleyball. 12 club sports for males and females. 40 intramural sports engaging 4,000 students yearly. *Special regulations:* Registered cars permitted in designated areas only; fee charged. Quiet hours. *Special services:* Learning Resources Center, medical services, transportation to and from outlying dormitories and off-campus housing. *Student publications, radio: Oakland Review*, an annual literary magazine; *Tartan*, a weekly newspaper. Radio station WRCT broadcasts 168 hours per week. *Surrounding community:* Pittsburgh population 450,000. Served by mass transit bus, subway, train systems; airport 20 miles from campus; passenger rail service 4 miles from campus.

Library Collections: 937,000 volumes including bound books, serial backfiles, electronic documents, and government documents not in separate collections. Online catalog. Current serial subscriptions: 3,209 paper, 1,805 electronic. 24,305 recordings. Computer work stations available campus-wide. Students have access to the Internet at no charge.

Buildings and Grounds: Campus area 103 acres.

Chief Executive Officer: Dr. Jared L. Cohon, President.

Address admission inquiries to Michael Steidel, Director of Admissions.

Cedar Crest College

100 College Drive
Allentown, Pennsylvania 18104-6196
Tel: (610) 606-4666 **E-mail:** cccadmis@cedarcrest.edu
Fax: (610) 606-4648 **Internet:** www.cedarcrest.edu

Institution Description: Cedar Crest College is a private, independent, nonprofit women's college affiliated with the United Church of Christ. *Enrollment:* 1,872. Men are admitted through the exchange program of the consortium Lehigh Valley Association of Independent Colleges, Inc. (LVAIC) and to continuing education programs. *Degrees awarded:* Baccalaureate. Certificates also awarded.

Accreditation: *Regional:* MSA/CHE. *Professional*: Nuclear medicine technology, nursing, social work, teacher education

History: Established as Allentown Female College and offered first instruction at postsecondary level 1867; chartered 1868; changed name to Allentown College for Women 1893; adopted present name 1913; awarded first degree (baccalaureate) 1918. *See* H.M.J. Klein, *Cedar Crest College 1867–1947* (Allentown: Privately printed, 1948) for further information.

Institutional Structure: *Governing board:* Cedar Crest College Board of Trustees. Extrainstitutional representation: 19 trustees, 6 life trustees; institutional representation: 1 full-time instructional faculty member, 1 student, 15 alumnae. 1 ex officio. 21 voting. *Composition of institution:* Administrators 73. Academic affairs headed by Provost. Management/business/finances directed by vice president for enrollment management and executive vice president. Full-time instructional faculty 86. Academic governance body, the faculty, meets an average of 9 times per year.

Calendar: Semesters. Academic year Aug. to May. Freshmen admitted Aug., Jan. Degrees conferred and formal commencement May, Aug. Summer session of multiple terms from May to Aug.

Characteristics of Freshmen: 1,725 applicants (female 1,718, male 7). 63% of applicants accepted. 16% of accepted applicants enrolled.

97% (247 students) submitted SAT scores; 16% (40 students) submitted ACT scores. *25th percentile*: SAT Critical Reading 4480, SAT Math 470; ACT Composite 20, ACT English 18, ACT Math 19. *75th percentile*: SAT Critical Reading 580, SAT Math 580; ACT Composite 26, ACT English 26, ACT Math 26.

57% of entering freshmen expected to graduate within 5 years. 83% of freshmen from Pennsylvania. Freshmen from 30 states and 38 foreign countries.

Admission: Rolling admissions plan. For fall acceptance, apply as early as Sept. 1 of previous year, but not later than July 1 of year of enrollment. Early acceptance available. *Requirements:* Either graduation from accredited secondary school with 16 units which normally include 4 English, 2 foreign language, 3 mathematics, 3 social studies, 1 laboratory science; or GED. *Entrance tests:* College Board SAT or ACT composite. *For transfer students:* 2.0 minimum GPA; from 4-year accredited institution 90 semester hours maximum transfer credit; from 2-year accredited institution 60 semester hours.

Advanced placement for postsecondary-level work completed in secondary school. College credit for extrainstitutional learning on basis of portfolio and faculty assessments. Tutoring available. Noncredit developmental courses offered during regular academic year.

Degree Requirements: 120 semester hours; 2.0 GPA; 2 terms in residence; distribution requirements. Fulfillment of some degree requirements and exemption from some beginning courses possible by passing departmental examinations, College Board CLEP, AP. *Grading system:* A–F; pass-fail; withdraw (deadline after which pass-fail is appended to withdraw).

Distinctive Educational Programs: Freshman year program with writing taught in a computer network environment. analytical Thinking, the Construc-

CEDAR CREST COLLEGE—*cont'd*

tion of Knowledge, and Scientific Literacy aimed at preparing students for continuing scholarship, research and creativity, and success in the information age. A two-track Honors Program, one-track emphasizing interdisciplinary courses and senior thesis or creative project, the other emphasizing undergraduate research in the discipline and senior thesis or creative project. Study abroad opportunities coordinated through established JYA Programs. Extended (freshman through senior year) undergraduate research in biological sciences. Extensive undergraduate research and independent study opportunities. A self-designed major option. Academic Advising and Academic Support Programs to support student success. Extensive internship experience. Programs in support of Pre-Med, Pre-Dental, Pre-Veterinarian, and Pre-Law preparation. Dual degree programs in engineering with Georgia Tech or Washington University (MO). Cross registration through LVAIC consortium. The college offers a traditional two-term schedule plus evening, weekend, and summer sessions.

ROTC: Army and Air Force in cooperation with Lehigh University.

Degrees Conferred: 327 *baccalaureate*; 28 *master's*. Bachelor's degrees awarded in top five disciplines: health professions and related clinical sciences 01; psychology 38; biological/life sciences 34; visual and performing arts 29; business/marketing 28. Master's degrees awarded: education 28.

Fees and Other Expenses: *Full-time tuition per academic year 2008–09:* $26,968 undergraduate; contact the college for current graduate tuition and applicable fees. *Room and board per academic year:* $9,000. *Books and supplies:* $1,500. *Other expenses:* $1,500.

Financial Aid: Aid from institutionally generated funds is provided on the basis of academic merit, financial need.

Financial aid to full-time, first-time undergraduate students: 95% of students received some form of aid. Average amount of aid received: federal grants $3,654; Pell grants $2,843; other federal aid $888; state/local grants $3,805; institutional grants $11,905.

Departments and Teaching Staff: *Total instructional faculty* 188 (full-time 87, part-time 101). Total faculty with doctorate, first-professional, or other terminal degree: 72. Student/faculty ratio: 11:1. Degrees held by full-time faculty: master's 24%, doctorate 76%. 76% hold terminal degrees.

Enrollment: Total enrollment 1,872. Undergraduate 1.701 (full-time 56%; female 94%, male 6%). Graduate 171 (full-time 20%). Undergraduate transfer-in students 181.

Characteristics of Student Body: *Ethnic/racial makeup:* Black non-Hispanic: 45; American Indian or Alaska Native: 1%; Asian or Pacific Islander: 2%; Hispanic: 4%; White non-Hispanic: 79%; unknown: 4%; nonresident alien 1%. *Age distribution:* 18–19: 180; 20–21: 266; 22–24: 356; 25–29: 267; 30–34: 152; 35–39: 164; 40–49: 227; 50–64: 99; 65 and over: 1.

International Students: 19 nonresident aliens enrolled fall 2008. Programs available to aid students whose native language is not English: social, cultural, financial. English as a Second Language Program. No financial aid specifically designated for international students.

Student Life: On-campus residence halls house 602% of traditional student body. Residence halls for females constitute 100% of such space. *Intercollegiate athletics:* basketball, cross-country, field hockey, lacrosse, softball, tennis, volleyball. *Special regulations:* Cars permitted without restrictions. Quiet hours. Residence hall visitation from noon to 11pm Sun.–Thurs., 24-hour visitation Fri. and Sat. *Special services:* Academic Resource Center, Career Planning Office and Library, Internships, Health and Counseling Services, over 50 campus organizations and clubs. *Student publications: Crestiad*, a bimonthly newspaper; *Espejo*, a yearbook. *Surrounding community:* Allentown population 104,000. Philadelphia, 60 miles from campus, is nearest metropolitan area. Served by mass transit bus system; airport 5 miles from campus.

Library Collections: 141,000 volumes. Current periodical subscriptions: paper 476, microform 20, 1,765 via electronic access. 2,671 audio/videotapes; 344 DVD discs; 98 CD-ROMs. Students have access to online information retrieval services. Computer work stations available.

Most important special holdings include Women's Studies, 20th Century American Poetry, social work.

Buildings and Grounds: Campus area 70 acres.

Chief Executive Officer: Dr. Carol Pullham, President.

Address admission inquiries to Judith Neyart, Executive Vice President for Enrollment Management.

Chatham University

Woodland Road
Pittsburgh, Pennsylvania 15232
Tel: (412) 365-1290 **E-mail:** admissions@chatham.edu
Fax: (412) 365-1609 **Internet:** www.chatham.edu

Institution Description: Chatham University is a private, independent, nonprofit institution for women. *Enrollment:* 2,184. *Degrees awarded:* Baccalaureate, master's, doctorate.

Member of the consortium Pittsburgh Council on Higher Education.

Accreditation: *Regional:* MSA/CHE. *Professional*: chemistry, physical therapy, social work, teacher education

History: Established as Pennsylvania Female College 1869; chartered and offered first instruction at postsecondary level 1870; awarded first degree (baccalaureate) 1873; changed name to Pennsylvania College for Women 1890; became Chatham College 1955; achieved university status 2005. .

Institutional Structure: *Governing board:* Board of Trustees. Extrainstitutional representation: 34 trustees; institutional representation: president of the college 12alumnae. 2 ex officio. All voting. *Composition of institution:* Administrators 6. Academic affairs headed by dean of the faculty. Management/business/finances directed by vice president and treasurer. Full-time instructional faculty 71. Academic governance body, the faculty, meets monthly.

Calendar: Semesters. Academic year Aug. to May. Freshmen admitted Aug., Feb. Degrees conferred and formal commencement May. Summer session.

Characteristics of Freshmen: 638 applicants (female 638). 71% of applicants admitted. 39% of applicants admitted and enrolled.

93% (85 students) submitted SAT scores; 23% (21 students) submitted ACT scores. *25th percentile*: SAT Critical Reading 510, SAT Math 470; ACT Composite 22, ACT English 21, ACT Math 20. *75th percentile*: SAT Critical Reading 620, SAT Math 580; ACT Composite 27, ACT English 29, ACT Math 27.

51% of entering freshmen expected to graduate within 5 years. 79% of freshmen from Pennsylvania. Freshmen from 32 states and 12 foreign countries.

Admission: Rolling admissions plan. For fall acceptance, apply as early as Sept. 15 of previous year, but not later than Aug. 1 of year of enrollment. Early acceptance available. *Requirements:* Graduation from accredited secondary school or GED. Recommended: 4 units English, 3 college preparatory mathematics, 2 laboratory sciences; 2 foreign language; history, social sciences. *For transfer students:* 2.0 minimum GPA; 73.5 hours maximum transfer credit.

College credit and advanced placement for postsecondary-level work completed in secondary school and for extrainstitutional learning (life experience) on basis of portfolio and faculty assessments.

Tutoring available. Remedial courses offered during regular academic year; no credit given.

Degree Requirements: *For undergraduate degrees:* 120 credits; last 20 credits in residence.

Fulfillment of some degree requirements and exemption from some beginning courses possible by passing College Board CLEP, AP. *Grading system:* A–F; pass-fail; withdraw.

Distinctive Educational Programs: Accelerated 3-2 bachelor's/master's and bachelor's/doctorate in 10 fields; accelerated 4-1 in 5 files with Carnegie Mellon University; new programs in distance learning (5 fields). Study-travel through Chatham-sponsored programs; study through programs offered by other institutions. Washington (DC) semester at American University. Cross-registration through consortium. *Other distinctive programs:* Gateway Program offers degree and nondegree study for adult women returning to school. Workshops and noncredit courses promoted for women in the community. Secondary school students may enroll in college courses for credit.

ROTC: Army, Air Force in cooperation with University of Pittsburgh; Navy in cooperation with Carnegie Mellon University.

Degrees Conferred: 124 *baccalaureate*; 258 *master's*; 74 *doctorate*. Bachelor's degrees awarded in top five disciplines: psychology 22; English language/literature 16; biological/life sciences 14; social business, management, marketing, and related support services 11; sciences and history 10.

Fees and Other Expenses: *Full-time tuition per academic year 2008–09:* $27,176; contact the university for graduate tuition and fees. *Required fees:* $216. *Room and board per academic year:* $8,286. *Books and supplies:* $860. *Other expenses:* $2,862.

Financial Aid: Aid from institutionally generated funds is provided on the basis of academic merit, financial need, other criteria.

Financial aid to full-time, first-time undergraduate students: 100% received some form of financial aid. Average amount of aid received: federal grants $2,775; state/local grants $3,276; institutional grants $10,034; loans $9,636.

Departments and Teaching Staff: *Total instructional faculty:* 94. Student/faculty ratio: 12:1. Degrees held by full-time faculty: doctorate 71%, master's 24%, baccalaureate 4%. 97% hold terminal degrees.

Enrollment: Total enrollment 2,184. Undergraduate 1,056 (full-time 66%; female 93%, male 7%). Graduate 1,128 (full-time 56%). Undergraduate transfer-in students 74.

Characteristics of Student Body: *Ethnic/racial makeup:* Black non-Hispanic: 8%; Asian or Pacific Islander: 1%; Hispanic: 1%; White non-Hispanic: 58%; unknown: 25%; nonresident alien 6%.

International Students: 88 nonresident aliens enrolled fall 2008. Students from Europe, Asia, Africa, Middle East. Programs available to aid students whose native language is not English: social, cultural. English as a Second Language Program. Financial aid specifically designated for international students: variable number of scholarships available annually to qualifying students.

Student Life: On-campus residence halls house 79% of student body. *Intercollegiate athletics:* females: basketball, field hockey, soccer, softball, tennis, volleyball. *Special regulations:* Cars permitted for upper division students only. Quiet hours. Residence hall visitation hours set by residents in individual halls. *Special services:* Medical services, minibus service for students cross-registered at other institutions. *Student publications: The Cornerstone*, a yearbook; *First Edition*, a bimonthly newspaper; *The Minor Bird*, an annual literary magazine; *Communique*, monthly campus newspaper. *Surrounding community:* Pittsburgh population 450,000. Served by mass transit bus system, airport 25 miles from campus, passenger rail service 5 miles from campus.

Library Collections: 100,000 volumes. 8,500 microforms; 600 current periodical subscriptions. Students have access to online information retrieval services and the Internet.

Most important special holdings include Snowdon Collection dealing with Mayan civilization and culture; Wendall Wray Collection of African-American Books; curriculum collection.

Buildings and Grounds: Campus area 50 acres.

Chief Executive Officer: Dr. Esther L. Barazzone, President.

Address undergraduate admission inquiries to Donald Williams, Vice President for Enrollment.

Chestnut Hill College

9601 Germantown Avenue
Philadelphia, Pennsylvania 19118-2693

Tel: (215) 248-7000 **E-mail:** admissions@chc.edu
Fax: (215) 248-7056 **Internet:** www.chc.edu

Institution Description: Chestnut Hill College is a private women's college affiliated with the Sisters of Saint Joseph, Roman Catholic Church. *Enrollment:* 2,085. Men are admitted as accelerated and graduate students. *Degrees awarded:* Associate, baccalaureate, master's, doctorate.

Accreditation: *Regional:* MSA/CHE. *Professional*: chemistry

History: Chartered in 1871; became Mt. St. Joseph Collegiate Institute 1905; became Mt. St. Joseph College for Women 1924; became Chestnut Hill College 1938; women's College 1924 to 2003; became coeducational 2003. *See* John Lukacs, *A Sketch of the History of Chestnut Hill College 1924–1974* (n.p., 1975) for further information and *Chestnut Hill College 1924–1999: Tradition and Risk,* (n.p., 1999).

Institutional Structure: *Governing board:* The Board of Directors. Extrainstitutional representation: 21 directors; institutional representation: president of the college. 6 ex officio. All voting. *Composition of institution:* Administrators 6. Academic affairs headed by vice president for academic affairs. Management/business/finances directed by vice president for financial affairs. Full-time instructional faculty 79. Academic governance body, Faculty Senate, meets an average of 6 times per year.

Calendar: Academic year Sept. to late Aug. Freshmen admitted Sept., Jan. Degrees conferred and formal commencement May.

Characteristics of Freshmen: 1,614 applicants (1,062 female, 552 male). 74% of applicants accepted. 19% of accepted applicants enrolled.

98% (211 students) submitted SAT scores; 11% (22 students) submitted ACT scores. *25th percentile*: SAT Critical Reading 450, SAT Math 420; ACT Composite 18. *75th percentile*: SAT Critical Reading 560, SAT Math 520; ACT Composite 24.

50% of entering freshmen expected to graduate within 5 years. 80% of freshmen from Pennsylvania. Freshmen from 22 states and 4 foreign countries.

Admission: Rolling admissions plan. For fall acceptance, apply as early as 1 year, but not later than 1 month, prior to enrollment. Early acceptance available. *Requirements:* Either graduation from accredited secondary school or GED. Recommend full 4-year academic program of 4 units English, 3 math, 3 science, 4 social sciences/history and 2 foreign language. *Entrance tests:* For full-time students, College Board SAT or ACT composite. *For transfer students:* 2.0 minimum GPA; maximum transfer credits limited only by residence requirement.

College credit and advanced placement for postsecondary-level work completed in secondary school. Tutoring available.

Degree Requirements: *For all associate degrees:* 60–62 credit hours; 30 hours in residence. *For all baccalaureate degrees:* 124 credit hours; 45 hours in residence; 2 semesters physical activity; swimming test; senior seminar in major field. *For all undergraduate degrees:* 2.0 GPA; core curriculum; freshman seminar.

Fulfillment of some degree requirements and exemption from some beginning courses possible by passing departmental examinations, College Board CLEP, AP. *Grading system:* A–F; pass-fail; withdraw (deadline after which pass-fail is appended to withdraw); incomplete (carries time limit).

Distinctive Educational Programs: Student and faculty exchange program with the 12 other members of the Sisters of St. Joseph College Consortium located throughout the U.S. Complementary career preparation programs in mass media communications, international studies. Interdisciplinary Honors Program open to students in any major with a qualifying GPA. *Other distinctive programs:* Interdisciplinary Scholars Program (4-year honors program); departmental honors program (research focus). Baccalaureate degree in international business. Study abroad can be arranged for most foreign countries.

ROTC: Army available through Temple University.

Degrees Conferred: 235 *baccalaureate*; 128 *master's*; 15 *doctorate*. Bachelor's degrees awarded in top five disciplines: business/marketing 46; public administration and social services 31; psychology 22; education 17; security and protective services 15. Master's degrees awarded: education 52; psychology 75; theology 1. Doctorates awarded: psychology 15.

Fees and Other Expenses: *Full-time tuition per academic year 2008–09:* $26,000 undergraduate; contact the college for current graduate tuition and applicable fees. *Room and board per academic year:* $8,550. *Books and supplies:* $1,000. *Other expenses:* $2,100.

Financial Aid: Aid from institutionally generated funds is provided on the basis of academic merit, financial need. Institution has a Program Participation Agreement with the U.S. Department of Education for eligible students to receive Pell Grants and, depending upon the agreement, other federal aid.

99% of first-time, full-time undergraduate students received some form of aid. Average amount of aid received: federal grants $4,041; Pell grants $2,874; other federal aid $1,186; state/local aid $3,517; institutional grants $11,148.

Departments and Teaching Staff: *Total instructional faculty:* 265 (full-time 70, part-time 195). Student/faculty ratio: 10:1. Degrees held by full-time faculty: doctorate 75%, master's 21%, professional 4%. 79% hold terminal degrees.

Enrollment: Total enrollment 2,085. Undergraduate 1,329 (full-time 77%; female 70%, male 30%). Graduate 756 (full-time 28%).

Characteristics of Student Body: *Ethnic/racial makeup:* Black non-Hispanic 37%; Asian or Pacific Islander 2%; Hispanic: 5%; White non-Hispanic: 48%; unknown 6%; nonresident alien 1%. *Age distribution:* number under 18: 551 18–19: 341; 20–21: 233; 22–24: 116; 25–29: 104; 30–34: 79; 35–39: 64; 40–49: 106; 0–64: 54; 65 and over: 2.

International Students: 21 nonresident aliens enrolled fall 2008. Students from Europe, Asia, Africa. Programs available to aid students whose native language is not English: social, cultural. English as a Second Language Program. No financial aid specifically designated for international students.

Student Life: On-campus residence halls house 65% of student body. Residence halls for females constitute 100% of such space. *Intercollegiate athletics:* female: basketball, field hockey, lacrosse, softball, tennis, volleyball. *Special regulations:* Freshman not permitted to have cars on campus except in exceptional circumstances. without restrictions. *Special services:* medical and counseling services, international student advisor. *Student publications: Aurelian*, a yearbook; *Kosmos*, annual foreign-language newspaper; *CHC Voices*, a student newspaper. *Surrounding community:* Philadelphia metropolitan population 5,000,000. Served by mass transit bus and train systems; passenger rail service 1 mile from campus.

Library Collections: 145,000 volumes including bound books, serial backfiles, electronic documents, and government documents not in separate collections. Online catalog. Current serial subscriptions: 586 paper and microform, 10 electronic. Computer work stations available. Students have access to the Internet at no charge.

Most important special collections include Irish Literature Collection; Morton Rare Book Collection (rare first editions).

Buildings and Grounds: Campus area 45 acres.

Chief Executive Officer: Sr. Carol Jean Vale, S.S.J., President.

Address admission inquiries to Jodie King, Director of Admissions.

Cheyney University of Pennsylvania

1837 University Circle
Cheyney, Pennsylvania 19319
Tel: (610) 399-2000 **E-mail:** admissions@cheyney.edu
Fax: (610) 399-2415 **Internet:** www.cheyney.edu

Institution Description: Cheyney University of Pennsylvania is a member of the Pennsylvania State System of Higher Education. *Enrollment:* 1,488. *Degrees awarded:* Baccalaureate, master's. Certification in education.

Academic offerings subject to approval by statewide coordinating bodies. Budget subject to approval by state governing boards. Member of Philadelphia Partnership Program, Cheyney-Lincoln-Temple Cluster, Council on Life-long Educational Opportunities (CLEO), Philadelphia School District University Inservice Teacher Education Consortium.

Accreditation: *Regional:* MSA/CHE. *Professional*: teacher education

History: Established in Philadelphia by Quakers 1837; chartered as the Institute for Colored Youth 1842; moved to Cheyney 1902; name changed to Cheyney Training School for Teachers 1913; purchased by state and name changed to State Normal School 1921; offered first instruction at postsecondary level 1931; awarded first degree (baccalaureate) 1932; changed name to Cheyney State Teachers College 1951; became Cheyney State College 1959; adopted present name 1982. *See* Charline Fay Howard Conyers, *A History of Cheyney State Teachers College 1837–1951* (Ann Arbor, MI: University Microfilms, 1975) for further information.

Institutional Structure: *Governing board:* Board of Governors and Chancellor. Extrainstitutional representation: 19 member Board of Governors. All voting. *Composition of institution:* Administrators 54. Academic affairs headed by vice president of academic affairs. Management/business/finances directed by vice-president for finance and administration. Full-time instructional faculty 91. Academic governance body, Academic Council meets as necessary. *Faculty representation:* Faculty is served by a collective bargaining agent affiliated with AAUP, AFT, and the Association of Pennsylvania State College and University Faculties (APSCUF).

Calendar: Semesters. Winter session, summer sessions. Academic year Sept. to May. Degrees conferred May, Dec. Formal commencement May.

Characteristics of Freshmen: 78% of applicants accepted. 28% of accepted applicants enrolled.

Mean SAT class scores: Critical Reading 389; Math 381.

24% of entering freshmen expected to graduate within 5 years. 82% of freshmen from Pennsylvania. Freshmen from 9 states and 6 foreign countries.

Admission: Rolling admissions plan. For fall acceptance, apply up to June 30. For spring admission apply up to Nov. 1. Apply by Nov. 30 for fall semester early decision. *Requirements:* Either graduation from accredited secondary school or GED. Recommend 4 units English, 3 mathematics, 2 science, 3 social science. *Entrance tests:* For full-time students, College Board SAT or ACT composite. *For transfer students:* 2.0 minimum GPA, maximum transfer credit limited only by residency requirement.

College credit for postsecondary-level work completed in secondary school and for College Board CLEP.

Tutoring available. Remedial courses offered in summer session and regular academic year; credit given.

Degree Requirements: 128 credit hours; 2.0 GPA; final 32 hours in residence; 2 courses physical education; general education requirements. *Grading system:* A–F; withdraw (carries penalty, time limit, and deadline after which pass-fail is appended to withdraw).

Distinctive Educational Programs: *Available to all students:* Work-experience programs. Cluster colleges. Flexible meeting places and schedules, including off-campus Urban Center (located in Philadelphia, approximately 30 miles from main campus) and evening classes. Tutorials. Telecourses. *For undergraduates:*Dual-degree in biology and chemistry. Double majors. Areas of concentration available. Independent Study. Allied Health Careers Opportunity Program with Jefferson University. Cross-registration with West Chester University of Pennsylvania. Compact for Life-long Educational Opportunities (CLEO). Office of Latino Programs offers Latinas Organized for Vitality and Education (LOVE) mentoring program, Latino Early Admissions Program (LEAP), and honors program. *For graduates:* Combined Ed.D. or Ed.S. degree program with Temple University.

ROTC: Army offered in cooperation with Widener University.

Degrees Conferred: 147 *baccalaureate*; 49 *master's*. Bachelor's degrees awarded in top five disciplines: social studies 47; business, management, marketing, and related support services 39; parks and recreation 20; communication, journalism, and related programs 15; psychology 13.

Fees and Other Expenses: *Full-time tuition per academic year:* undergraduate resident $7,089, nonresident $15,219. *Books and supplies:* $1,300. *Room and board per academic year:* $7,156. *Other expenses:* $2,655.

Departments and Teaching Staff: *Total instructional faculty:* 97.31 FTE. Student/faculty ratio: 17:1. Degrees held by full-time faculty: doctorate 55%, master's 43%, baccalaureate 2%. 55% hold terminal degrees.

Enrollment: Total enrollment 1,488. Undergraduate 1,333 (full-time 92%; female 55%; male 45%). Graduate 135 (full-time 31%). Undergraduate transfer-in students 62.

Characteristics of Student Body: *Ethnic/racial makeup:* Black non-Hispanic: 93%; White non-Hispanic: 1%; unknown 5%; nonresident alien 1%.

International Students: 14 nonresident aliens enrolled fall 2008.

Student Life: On-campus residence halls house 67% of student body. Residence halls for males constitute 545% of such space, for females 46%. *Intercollegiate athletics:* male: basketball, cross-country, football, soccer, tennis, track and field, wrestling; female: basketball, cross-country, tennis, track and field, volleyball. Intramural sports available for both men and women. *Special regulations:* Cars permitted. Commuting students must park in designated areas. Residence hall visitation in freshman halls: Sun.–Thurs. 3PM to 11pm, Fri.–Sat. 3pm to midnight; other halls: Sun.–Thurs. 3pm to midnight, Fri.–Sat. 3:00pm to 1am. *Special services:* Learning Resources Center, medical services; campus van service. *Student publications, radio: Beacon*, a yearbook; *Cheyney Record*, a monthly newspaper; *Cheyney's Campus Currents*, published irregularly by the Office of Media Relations. Radio station WCUB broadcasts 30 hours per week; jazz/popular music format. *Surrounding community:* Cheyney (unincorporated) is within the townships of Thornbury, population 1,200 and Westtown, population 9,500. Philadelphia, 24 miles from campus, is nearest metropolitan area. Served by mass transit bus system; airport 15 miles from campus; passenger rail service 1 mile from campus.

Library Collections: 290,000 volumes. 60,500 government documents; 795,000 microforms; 1,450 audiovisual materials; 485 current periodicals. Students have access to the Internet at no charge.

Chief Executive Officer: Dr. Wallace C. Arnold, President.

Address admission inquiries to Jemma Stanley, Director of Admissions.

Clarion University of Pennsylvania

840 Wood Street
Clarion, Pennsylvania 16214
Tel: (814) 226-2000 **E-mail:** admissions@clarion.edu
Fax: (814) 226-2030 **Internet:** www.clarion.edu

Institution Description: Clarion University of Pennsylvania is a state institution with a branch campus (Venango Campus) in Oil City. *Enrollment:* 7,100. *Degrees awarded:* Associate, baccalaureate, master's. Certificates also awarded.

Academic offerings subject to approval by statewide coordinating bodies. Budget subject to approval by state governing boards.

Accreditation: *Regional:* MSA/CHE. *Professional*: librarianship, nursing, teacher education

History: Established and chartered as Carrier Seminary 1867; changed name to Clarion State Normal School 1887; offered first instruction at postsecondary level 1920; awarded first degree (baccalaureate) and changed name to Clarion State Teacher's College 1929; changed name to Clarion State College 1960; university status granted and present name adopted 1983. *See* Samuel A. Farmerie, *Clarion State College: Centennial History* (Clarion: Alumni Association, 1968) for further information.

Institutional Structure: *Governing board:* Board of Trustees. Representation: 9 members, including 1 student appointed by the governor of Pennsylvania. Administrators 33. Academic affairs headed by provost and academic vice president. Academic affairs headed by provost and academic vice president. Management/business/finances directed by vice president for administration. Full-time instructional faculty 375. Academic governance body, Academic Affairs Executive Board, meets an average of 7 times per year. *Faculty representation:* Faculty is served by collective bargaining agent affiliated with AAUP, AFT, and Association of Pennsylvania State College and University Faculties.

Calendar: Semesters. Academic year Aug. to May. Freshmen admitted Aug., Jan., June, July. Degrees conferred May, Aug., Dec. Formal commencements May, Dec. Summer session of 3 terms.

Characteristics of Freshmen: 4,297 applicants (female 2,397, male 1,900). 69% of applicants accepted. 49% accepted applicants enrolled. 89% (1,248 students) submitted SAT scores. *25th percentile*: SAT Critical Reading 420, SAT Math 420; SAT Writing 590. *75th percentile*: SAT Critical Reading 520, SAT Math 530, SAT Writing 510.

60% of entering freshmen expected to graduate within 5 years. 96% of freshmen from Pennsylvania. Students from 45 states and 34 foreign countries.

Admission: Rolling admissions plan. For fall acceptance, apply as early as July 1 of previous year, but not later than 1 month prior to registration. Apply by summer for early decision; need not limit application to Clarion. Early acceptance available. *Requirements:* Graduation from accredited secondary school or

SAT scores at or above the national average. GED accepted. Lowest acceptable secondary school class standing 60th percentile or 40th percentile with SAT scores at or above the national average. Additional requirements for some programs. *Entrance tests:* College Board SAT or ACT composite. For language majors, achievement test. For foreign students, TOEFL or other demonstration of proficiency in English. *For transfer students:* 2.0 GPA; from 4-year accredited institution 98 hours maximum transfer credit; from 2-year accredited institution 64 hours.

College credit for postsecondary-level work completed in secondary school and for extrainstitutional learning.

Tutoring available. Developmental/remedial courses offered in summer session and regular academic year; credit given.

Degree Requirements: *For all associate degrees:* 64 credit hours. *For all baccalaureate degrees:* 128 hours. *For all undergraduate degrees:* 2.0 GPA; 30 hours in residence; 2 hours physical education; general education requirements (nursing and business administration majors excluded).

Fulfillment of some degree requirements and exemption from some beginning courses possible by passing departmental examinations, College Board CLEP, AP. *Grading system:* A–F.

Distinctive Educational Programs: Evening classes. Dual-degree program in engineering with University of Pittsburgh. Cooperative program in medical technology with approved hospitals. Preprofessional programs in dentistry, engineering, medicine, pharmacy. Special facilities for using telecommunications in the classroom. Facilities and programs for independent research, including honors programs, tutorials. Honors/curriculum program. Foreign study in Canada, France, Mexico, Spain, Germany. *Other distinctive programs:* School of Continuing Education offers noncredit courses, credit courses which meet professional needs, and conferences which are developed for specific groups.

ROTC: Army.

Degrees Conferred: 130 *associate*; 822 *baccalaureate*; 268 *>master's*. Bachelor's degrees awarded in top five disciplines: education 251; business, management, marketing, and related support services 97; communication, journalism, and related programs 130; health professions and related clinical sciences 85; social sciences 74. Master's degrees awarded: various disciplines 268.

Fees and Other Expenses: *Full-time tuition per academic year:* $7,102 resident, $12,552 nonresident. *Room and board per academic year:* $6,550. *Books and supplies:* $850. *Other expenses:* $3,000.

Financial Aid: Aid from institutionally generated funds is provided on the basis of academic merit, athletic ability, financial need, other criteria.

Financial aid to full-time, first-time undergraduate students: 87 received some form of financial aid. Average amount of aid received: federal grants $2,873; Pell grants $2,886; state/local grants $3,116 institutional grants $2,374.

Departments and Teaching Staff: *Total instructional faculty:* 375. Degrees held by full-time faculty: doctorates 58%, master's 32%, baccalaureates 2%, professional 8%. 64% hold terminal degrees.

Enrollment: Total enrollment 7,100. Undergraduate 5,975 (full-time 86%; female 61%, male 39%). Graduate 1,125 (full-time 18%). Undergraduate transfer-in students 300.

Characteristics of Student Body: *Ethnic/racial makeup:* Black non-Hispanic: 6%; Asian or Pacific Islander: 1%; Hispanic: 1%; White non-Hispanic: 91%; unknown 1%; nonresident alien 1%.

International Students: 71 nonresidents enrolled fall 2008. Programs available to aid students whose native language is not English: social, cultural.

Student Life: On-campus residence halls house 43% of student body. Residence halls for males constitute 5% of such space, for females 19%, for both sexes 76%. 11% of student body live in a college-supervised, privately owned, off-campus residence hall. 18% of males join and 3% live in fraternity houses. *Intercollegiate athletics:* male: baseball, basketball, gymnastics, softball, swimming, tennis, volleyball; both sexes: cross-country, rifle, track. *Special regulations:* Cars with permits allowed; parking fee. *Special services:* Medical services. *Student publications, radio: Clarion Call*, a biweekly newspaper; *Dare*, an annual creative writing magazine; *The Sequelle*, a yearbook. Radio station WCCB-AM broadcasts 122 hours per week; WCUC-FM, 126 hours. *Surrounding community:* Clarion population 7,000. Pittsburgh, 90 miles from campus, is the nearest metropolitan area.

Library Collections: 443,500 volumes. Current serial subscriptions; 20,200 including electronic access. 1,604,000 microforms; 1,050 audiovisual materials. Other resources (journals on microfilm, government documents and technical reports on microfiche, business information services, juvenile literature collection). Students have access to online information retrieval services and the Internet.

Buildings and Grounds: Campus area 128 acres.

Chief Executive Officer: Dr. Joseph P. Grunaewald, President.

Address admission inquiries to William D. Bailey, Associate Director of Admissions.

Curtis Institute of Music

1726 Locust Street
Philadelphia, Pennsylvania 19103
Tel: (215) 893-5252 **E-mail:** admissions@curtis.edu
Fax: (215) 893-9065 **Internet:** www.curtis.edu

Institution Description: The Curtis Institute of Music is a private institute. *Enrollment:* 162. *Degrees awarded:* Associate, baccalaureate, master's.

Accreditation: *Regional:* MSA/CHE. *Professional*: music

History: Founded 1924.

Calendar: Semesters. Academic year Sept. to May.

Characteristics of Freshmen: 96% of entering freshmen expected to graduate within 5 years. 16% of freshmen from Pennsylvania. Freshmen from 17 states and 11 foreign countries.

Admission: *Requirements:* Graduation from secondary school or equivalent; audition or examination of original compositions.

Degree Requirements: Completion of prescribed curriculum.

Fees and Other Expenses: Students are accepted on a scholarship basis only and pay no tuition. *Required fees:* $2,185. *Books and supplies* $900. *Room and board per academic year* $11,250. *Other expenses:* $4,410.

Financial Aid: Aid from institutionally generated funds is provided on the basis of financial need. Financial assistance is available in the form of Pell Grants, College Work-Study, Veterans Administration Benefits, National Direct Student Loans, Supplemental Education Opportunity Grants (SEOG), Stafford Loans, other federal aid programs.

Departments and Teaching Staff: *Total instructional faculty:* 86 (full-time 1; part-time 85). 100% of faculty hold professional degrees.

Enrollment: Total enrollment 162. Undergraduate 133 (full-time 100%; female 47%, male 53%)

Characteristics of Student Body: *Ethnic/racial makeup:* number of Black non-Hispanic: 5; Asian or Pacific Islander: 13; Hispanic:2; White non-Hispanic: 58.

International Students: 62 nonresident aliens enrolled fall 2008. Students from Europe, Asia, Central and South America, Africa, Canada. Programs available to aid students whose native language is not English: English as a Second Program. No financial specifically designated for international students.

Library Collections: 72,000 volumes. 100 microforms; 15,500 audiovisual materials; 55 current periodical subscriptions. Students have access to online information retrieval services and the Internet.

Most important special holdings include Leopold Stokowski Collection; Charles H. Jarvis Collection; Carlos Salzedo Collection; Anton Torello Collection.

Buildings and Grounds: Roberta Diaz, President. Address admission inquiries to Jude L. Guttone, Admissions Officer.

Delaware Valley College

700 East Butler Avenue
Doylestown, Pennsylvania 18901-2697
Tel: (215) 345-1500 **E-mail:** admissions@devalcol.edu
Fax: (215) 345-5277 **Internet:** devalcol.edu

Institution Description: Delaware Valley College is a private, independent, nonprofit, state-aided college. *Enrollment:* 2,029. *Degrees awarded:* Associate, baccalaureate, master's.

Accreditation: *Regional:* MSA/CHE. *Professional*:

History: Chartered and incorporated as The National Farm School 1896; became 3-year junior college 1945; offered first instruction at postsecondary level and changed name to The National Farm School and Junior College 1946 became 4-year institution and changed name to National Agricultural College 1948; awarded first degree (baccalaureate) 1950; became Delaware Valley College of Science and Agriculture 1960; adopted present name 1989.

Institutional Structure: *Governing board:* Board of Trustees. Representation: 23 trustees, president of the college. *Composition of institution:* Administrators: vice presidents for academic affairs/dean of faculty, student affairs/dean of students, business and finance, institutional development; special assistant to the president, dean of enrollment management, dean of arts and sciences, dean of agriculture and environmental sciences, dean of business and computer services, registrar, controller; directors of admission, financial aid, institutional research, athletics, academic support services, continuing education, career services, public relations, public safety, residence life, grants, alumni affairs. Full-time instructional faculty 79. Academic governance body, Faculty Council.

DELAWARE VALLEY COLLEGE—*cont'd*

Calendar: Semesters. Academic year Aug. to May. Freshmen admitted Sept., Jan. Degrees conferred and formal commencement May. Summer session of 2 terms from May to Aug.

Characteristics of Freshmen: 71% of applicants accepted. 40% of accepted applicants enrolled.

94% (380 students) submitted SAT scores; 6% (23 students) submitted ACT scores. *25th percentile*: SAT Critical Reading 450, SAT Math 460, SAT Writing 435; ACT Composite 21, ACT English 19, ACT Math 17. *75th percentile*: SAT Critical Reading 550, SAT math 560, SAT Writing 540; ACT Composite 25, ACT English 24, ACT Math 25.

63% of entering freshmen expected to graduate within 5 years. 67% freshmen from Pennsylvania. Freshmen from 22 states and 1 foreign country.

Admission: Rolling admissions plan. Apply as early as 1 year, but not later than 1 week, prior to enrollment. Early acceptance available. *Requirements:* Either graduation from accredited secondary school with 3 units English, 2 mathematics (algebra I and II), 2 social studies, 1 biology, 1 chemistry, 6 electives; or GED. *Entrance tests:* College Board SAT or ACT composite. For foreign students TOEFL. *For transfer students:* 2.0 minimum GPA; maximum transfer credit limited only by residence requirement.

College credit and advanced placement for postsecondary-level work completed in secondary school.

Tutoring available. Noncredit developmental courses offered during regular academic year.

Degree Requirements: 128 credit hours; 2.0 GPA; 48 hours in residence; 2 physical education courses; 24 weeks employment in job related to major field; general education requirements.

Fulfillment of some degree requirements and exemption from some beginning courses possible by passing College Board AP, CLEP subject examinations. *Grading system:* A–F; withdraw (deadline after which pass-fail is appended to withdraw).

Distinctive Educational Programs: Cooperative education. Evening classes. Facilities and programs for independent research, including honors programs, tutorials.

Degrees Conferred: 6 *associate*; 319 *baccalaureate*; 13 *master's*. Bachelor's degrees awarded in top five disciplines: agriculture 147; business, management, marketing, and related support services 69; computer and information sciences 25; biomedical/biological sciences 34; security and protective services 17.

Fees and Other Expenses: *Full-time tuition per academic year 2008–09:* $23,300. *Books and supplies:* $850. *Room and board per academic year:* $8,900.

Financial Aid: Aid from institutionally generated funds is provided on the basis of academic merit, financial need.

Financial aid to full-time, first-time undergraduate students: 95% received some form of financial aid. Average amount of aid received: federal grants $2,824; state/local grants $8,418; institutional grants $10,451; loans $2,956.

Departments and Teaching Staff: *Total instructional faculty:* 80. Degrees held by full-time faculty: doctorate 52%, master's 46%, baccalaureate 1%. Student/faculty ratio: 20:1. 53% hold terminal degrees.

Enrollment: Total enrollment 2,029. Undergraduate 1,863. Graduate 166.

International Students: No programs available to aid students whose native language is not English. No financial aid specifically designated for international students.

Student Life: On-campus residence halls house 65% of student body. Residence halls for males constitute 48% of such space, for females 52%. *Intercollegiate athletics:* male: baseball, basketball, cross-country, football, golf, soccer, track, wrestling; female: basketball, cross-country, field hockey, golf, soccer, softball, track, volleyball. *Special regulations:* Cars permitted for all students. Limited dormitory visitation. *Special services:* Learning Resources Center, medical services, campus transportation system. *Student publications: Cornucopia*, a yearbook; *The Gleaner*, a literary magazine; *Ram Pages*, a weekly newspaper. *Surrounding community:* Doylestown population 9,000. Philadelphia, 20 miles from campus, is nearest metropolitan area. Served by mass transit bus system; airport 20 miles from campus; passenger rail service on campus.

Library Collections: 70,000 volumes including bound books, serial backfiles, electronic documents, and government documents not in separate collections. Online catalog. Current serial subscriptions: 730 paper, 163 microform. Computer work stations available. Students have access to the Internet at no charge.

Most important special collections include USDA, state extension, and related pamphlets; Rabbi Joseph Krauskopf personal library (philosophy, Judaic writing); College Archives; student research reports.

Buildings and Grounds: Campus area 800 acres.

Chief Executive Officer: Dr. Thomas C. Leamer, President.
Address admission inquiries to Steven W. Zenko, Director of Admissions.

DeSales University

2755 Station Avenue
Center Valley, Pennsylvania 18034-9568
Tel: (610) 282-1100 **E-mail:** admiss@desales.edu
Fax: (610) 282-2210 **Internet:** www.desales.edu

Institution Description: DeSales University, formerly names Allentown College of St. Francis de Sales is a private, independent, Catholic liberal arts college administered by the Oblates of St. Francis de Sales. *Enrollment:* 3,162. *Degrees awarded:* Baccalaureate, master's. Certificates also awarded.

Member of the consortium Lehigh Valley Association of Independent Colleges (LVAIC).

Accreditation: *Regional:* MSA/CHE. *Professional*: nursing

History: Established and chartered 1964; offered first instruction at postsecondary level 1965; awarded first degree (baccalaureate) 1969; introduced Master of Science in Nursing 1984; Master of Science in Information Systems 1988; Master of Education 1989, Master of Business Administration 1991, Master of Physician Assistant Studies 1997.

Institutional Structure: *Governing board:* Board of Trustees (1/3 religious, 2/3 lay). Administered by president, vice presidents for finance, academic affairs, program development, and development. Deans include enrollment management, students, graduate education, undergraduate education, lifelong learning. Full-time instructional faculty 97. Academic governance body, the faculty, meets an average of 8 times per year.

Calendar: Semesters. Academic year Aug. to May. Freshmen admitted Sept., Jan. Degrees conferred and formal commencement May.

Characteristics of Freshmen: 1,975 applicants (female 1,163, male 812). 75% of applicants accepted. 27% of accepted applicants enrolled.

Mean SAT scores 529 Critical Reading, 520 Math.

65% of entering freshmen expected to graduate within 5 years. 75% of freshmen from Pennsylvania. Freshmen from 11 states and 1 foreign country.

Admission: Rolling admissions plan. Apply as early as 1 year prior to enrollment, but not later than Aug. 1 for the fall and Dec. 1 for spring. Early acceptance available. *Requirements:* Either graduation from accredited secondary school or GED. Recommend 4 units English, 2 in a foreign language, 3 college preparatory mathematics, 2 laboratory science. Additional requirements for some programs. Minimum GPA 2.0. *Entrance tests:* College Board SAT or ACT composite. *For transfer students:* 20 courses maximum transfer credit.

College credit and advanced placement for postsecondary-level work completed in secondary school. College credit for extrainstitutional learning.

Tutoring available. Developmental courses offered in summer session and regular academic year; credit given.

Degree Requirements: 120 credit hours; 2.0 GPA; 2 semesters residence; 3 physical education courses, general education core requirements.

Fulfillment of some degree requirements and exemption from some beginning courses possible by passing departmental examinations, College Board CLEP, APP. *Grading system:* A–F; pass-fail; withdraw and incomplete (both have time limit).

Distinctive Educational Programs: Work-experience and service-learning programs. Flexible accelerated degree program for working adults. Facilities and programs for independent research, including tutorials, independent study. Faculty/student exchange study abroad program in England, through LVAIC study abroad in France, Germany, Spain, and other countries. Cross-registration through LVAIC. Post-baccalaureate certificate programs.

ROTC: Army, Air Force offered in cooperation with Lehigh University.

Degrees Conferred: 420 *baccalaureate*; 242 *master's*. Bachelor's degrees awarded in top five disciplines: business, management, marketing, and related support services 118; visual and performing arts 69; security and protective services 47; education 42; health professions and related clinical sciences 33. Master's degrees awarded: business/marketing 100; computer and information sciences 5; education 30; health professions and related sciences 45; other disciplines 62.

Fees and Other Expenses: *Full-time tuition per academic year 2008–09:* undergraduate $25,500; contact the university for current graduate tuition. *Books and supplies:* $1,500. *Room and board per academic year:* $9,330. *Other expenses:* $3,000.

Financial Aid: Aid from institutionally generated funds is provided on the basis of academic merit, financial need.

Financial aid to full-time, first-time undergraduate students: 95% received some form of aid. Average amount of aid received: federal grants $4,967; Pell grants $4,851; other federal aid $7,246; state/local grants $3,316; insitutional grants $10,071.

Departments and Teaching Staff: *Total instructional faculty:* 172. Student/faculty ratio: 15:1. Degrees held by full-time faculty: baccalaureate 100%, master's 100%, doctorate 57%, professional 8%. 72% hold terminal degrees.

Enrollment: Total enrollment 3,162. Undergraduate 2,389 (full-time 76%; female 60%; male 40%). Graduate 773 (full-time 7%). Undergraduate transfer-in students 62.

Characteristics of Student Body: *Ethnic/racial makeup:* Black non-Hispanic: 2%; Asian or Pacific Islander: 2%; Hispanic: 3%; White non-Hispanic: 63%; unknown: 31%.

International Students: 10 nonresident aliens enrolled fall 2008. Students from Europe, Asia, Africa. No programs available to aid students whose native language is not English. No financial aid specifically designated for international students.

Student Life: 66% of students live on campus in residence halls and townhouses with 50% of resident students are male and 50% female. *Student organizations:* 32 clubs and organizations, 4 media organizations, strong class and student government tradition. *Intercollegiate athletics:* Middle Atlantic Conference, NCAA Division III. Men only: baseball, basketball, cross-country, lacrosse, soccer, golf, tennis; women only: basketball, cross-country, soccer, softball, tennis. *Special regulations:* All students may have cars. Hall visitation from 11am to midnight, Sun.–Thurs., 11am to 2am Fri. and Sat. *Special services:* Learning Center. *Student publications: L'Histoire,* a yearbook; *Minstrel,* a monthly newspaper; *Transitions,* an annual literary magazine. Radio station WACR broadcasts 70 hours per week. *Surrounding community:* Center Valley, located within Allentown-Easton-Bethlehem metropolitan area. Served by airport 13 miles from campus; bus service.

Library Collections: 158,000 volumes including bound books, serial backfiles, electronic documents, and government documents not in separate collections. Online catalog. Current serial subscriptions: 591 paper, 5 microform, 12,000 via electronic access. 2,452 recordings; 424 compact discs; 51 CD-ROMs. Computer work stations available. Students have access to the Internet at no charge.

Most important special holdings include a collections in nursing; Kohl Theatre Collection; Salesian Collection.

Buildings and Grounds: Campus area 375 acres.

Chief Executive Officer: Dr. Bernard F. O'Connor, President.

Address admission inquiries to Mry Birkhead, Director of Admissions.

Dickinson College

College and Luther Streets
Carlisle, Pennsylvania 17013-2896
Tel: (717) 245-1231 **E-mail:** admit@dickinson.edu
Fax: (717) 245-5121 **Internet:** www.dickinson.edu

Institution Description: Dickinson College is a private, independent, nonprofit college. *Enrollment:* 2,388. *Degrees awarded:* Baccalaureate.

Member of Central Pennsylvania Consortium.

Accreditation: *Regional:* MSA/CHE.

History: Established 1773; chartered and offered first instruction at postsecondary level 1783; awarded first degree (baccalaureate) 1787. *See* Charles Coleman Sellers, *Dickinson College: A History* (Middletown, Conn.: Wesleyan University Press, 1973) for further information.

Institutional Structure: *Governing board:* Dickinson College Board of Trustees. Extrainstitutional representation: 32 term trustees, 2 alumni trustees, chairman of board of advisors, 1 life trustee; institutional representation: president of the college. All voting. *Composition of institution:* Administrators 72. Academic affairs headed by dean of the college. Management/business/finances directed by treasurer. Full-time instructional faculty 177. Academic governance body, the faculty, meets an average of 9 times per year.

Calendar: Semesters. Academic year early Sept. to May. Freshmen admitted Sept., Jan. Degrees conferred May, summer, Feb. Formal commencement May. Summer session from July to Aug.

Characteristics of Freshmen: 5,282 applicants (female 3,083, male 2,219). 44% of applicants accepted. 26% of accepted applicants enrolled full-time.

Mean SAT scores 647 Critical Reading, 631 Math.

80% of entering freshmen expected to graduate within 5 years. 26% of freshmen from Pennsylvania. Freshmen from 37 states and 22 foreign countries.

Admission: For fall acceptance, apply as early as Sept. 1 of previous year, but not later than Feb. 1 of year of enrollment. Students are notified of acceptance in Mar. Apply by Nov. 15 for Early Decision I, Jan. 15 for Early Decision II. Early acceptance available. *Requirements:* Either graduation from accredited secondary school with 16 units, including 4 English, 2–3 in a foreign language, 3 mathematics, 3 natural science, 2 social studies, and remaining units in the academic subjects listed above; or GED. *Entrance tests:* College Board SAT or ACT composite. *For transfer students:* 2.0 minimum GPA; maximum transfer credit limited only by residence requirement.

College credit and advanced placement for postsecondary-level work completed in secondary school.

Degree Requirements: 4 half-semester blocks physical education; 2.0 GPA; 16 courses in residence; competency in a foreign language; distribution requirements.

Fulfillment of some degree requirements and exemption from some beginning courses possible by passing College Board AP. *Grading system:* A–F; pass-fail; withdraw (carries penalty; carries deadline, up to final exam period).

Distinctive Educational Programs: Freshmen seminars. Independent study and research. Internships. Departmental honors. Tutorial and self-developed interdisciplinary majors. Interdepartmental/interdisciplinary programs in American studies, comparative civilizations, East Asian studies, environmental studies, financial and business analysis, international business and management, international studies, Italian studies, Judaic studies, Latin American studies, policy and management studies, women's studies and Russian and Soviet area studies. Study abroad through Dickinson College programs in Australia, China, England, France, Germany, Italy, Japan, Russia, and Spain; through programs offered by the Institute of European Studies, the Intercollegiate Center for Classical Studies in Rome, the International Student Exchange Program, and other U.S. colleges and universities; individual arrangement with a foreign university. Off-campus study opportunities in the U.S. include an interdisciplinary marine studies program offered by Dickinson plus the Appalachian Semester at Union College (KY), South Asian studies at the University of Pennsylvania, the Washington (DC) Semester in cooperation with American University. Dual-degree programs in engineering with University of Pennsylvania, Case Western Reserve University (OH), and Rensselaer Polytechnic Institute (NY). Exchange program with other Central Pennsylvania Consortium colleges (Franklin and Marshall, Gettysburg). 3–3 program with Dickinson School of Law. Off-campus study can also be pursued at other U.S. universities and colleges by individual arrangement.

ROTC: Army. Also offered to students from Harrisburg Area Community College, Pennsylvania State University (Capitol College), and Lebanon Valley College.

Degrees Conferred: 528 *baccalaureate.* Bachelor's degrees awarded in top five disciplines: social sciences 146; psychology 52; biological/life sciences 53; business/marketing 50; history 48.

Fees and Other Expenses: *Full-time tuition per academic year 2008–09:* \$38,234. *Fees:* \$334. *Room and board per academic year:* \$9,600. *Books and supplies:* \$1,000. *Other expenses:* \$1,500.

Financial Aid: Aid from institutionally generated funds is provided on the basis of academic merit, financial need.

Financial aid to full-time, first-time undergraduate students: 89% received some form of aid. Average amount of aid received: federal grants \$8,197; Pell grants \$2,929; other federal aid \$5,713; state/local grants \$3,053; institutional grants \$20,897.

Departments and Teaching Staff: *Total instructional faculty:* 208 (full-time 1778, part-time 31). Total faculty with doctorate, first-professional, or other terminal degree: 176. Degrees held by full-time faculty: baccalaureate 2.7%, master's 8.7%, doctorate 88.7%. 96% hold terminal degrees.

Enrollment: Total enrollment 2,388 (undergraduate).

Characteristics of Student Body: *Ethnic/racial makeup:* Black non-Hispanic: 4%; Asian or Pacific Islander: 5%; Hispanic: 5%; White non-Hispanic: 71%; unknown 2%; nonresident alien 65. *Age distribution:* number under 18: 75; 18–19: 1,101; 20–21: 1,032; 22–24: 92; 25–29: 4; 30–34: 1; 35–39: 2; 40–49: 6.

International Students: 144 nonresident aliens enrolled fall 2008. Students from Europe, Asia, Central and South America, Africa, Canada, Australia. Programs available to aid students whose native language is not English: social, cultural. English as a Second Language Program. Financial aid specifically designated for international students: variable number of scholarships available annually to qualifying students.

Student Life: On-campus residence halls and fraternities house 90% of student body. *Intercollegiate athletics:* male: baseball, basketball, cross-country, football, golf, lacrosse, soccer, swimming, tennis, indoor track and field; female: basketball, cross-country, field hockey, golf, lacrosse, soccer, softball, swimming, tennis, indoor track and field, volleyball. *Special regulations:* Registered cars permitted. Quiet hours vary according to residence hall. *Special services:* Medical services. *Student publications, radio: Belles Lettres*, an annual literary magazine; *The Dickinson Viewbook*, a weekly newspaper; *Microcosm*, a yearbook. Radio station WDCV broadcasts 138 hours per week. *Surrounding community:* Carlisle population 20,000. Harrisburg, 20 miles from campus, is nearest metropolitan area. Served by mass transit bus system, airport 20 miles from campus, passenger rail service 20 miles from campus.

Publications: Sources of information about Dickinson include *The Dickinson College Magazine, Dickinson Today.*

DICKINSON COLLEGE—*cont'd*

Library Collections: 655,000 volumes including bound books, serial backfiles, electronic documents, and government documents not in separate collections. Online catalog. Current serial subscriptions: 1,300 paper, 190,922 microform units. 12,833 recordings. Computer work stations available campus-wide. Students have access to the Internet at no charge.

Most important special holdings include a major collection of tapes and documents pertaining to the 1979 Three Mile Island incident and subsequent investigation; materials of Joseph Priestley, the discoverer of oxygen; papers of James Buchanan, a graduate of Dickinson who was 15th President of the United States, and of prominent colonial figureheads who were founders of the College (e.g., Benjamin Rush, John Dickinson); Jacobs Collection (Asian documents and materials).

Buildings and Grounds: Campus area 120 acres.

Chief Executive Officer: Dr. William G. Durden, President.

Address admission inquiries to Christopher Seth Allen, Dean of Admissions.

Dickinson School of Law

150 South College Street
Carlisle, Pennsylvania 17013-2899
Tel: (717) 240-5000 **E-mail:** dsladmit@psu.edu
Fax: (717) 245-1899 **Internet:** www.dsi.psu.edu

Institution Description: The Dickinson School of Law is the law school of Pennsylvania State University, a public land-grant university. *Enrollment:* 628. *Degrees awarded:* First-professional (J.D., LL.M. in Comparative Law).

Accreditation: *National:* ABA. *Professional*: law

History: Established by Judge John Reed in 1834; awarded first degrees 1836; incorporated 1890; merged with Penn State in 2000; operates as a unified enterprise with facilities in both University Park and in Carlisle, Pa.

Institutional Structure: *Governing board:* Board of Trustees of Pennsylvania State University. Administration headed by dean who serves as chief executive officer. Each location has an academic dean for academic affairs.

Calendar: Semesters. Academic year Aug. to May. Entering students admitted Aug. Summer seminars abroad (optional).

Admission: Applicants for admission are encouraged to submit appropriate materials by Feb. 15; admissions decisions are made for enrollment in the fall semester only; no mid-year admissions. *Requirements:* Baccalaureate or equivalent degree; LSAT scores; 2 recommendations, college transcripts (no application will be considered until all required material is received). *Entrance tests:* LSAT. *For foreign students:* Foreign lawyers who have a law degree not founded substantially on an English Common Law curriculum are eligible for admission to the LL.M. in Comparative Law degree program. *For transfer students:* Students enrolled in good standing in a law school that is a member of the Association of American Law Schools and is approved by the American Bar Association are eligible for transfer into the second-year class; transfer applications due on or before May 1.

Degree Requirements: *For Juris Doctor (J.D.) degree:* Minimum 88 semester hours earned during 6 semesters of study in residence. *For LL.M. in Comparative Law degree:* Minimum 24 semester hours earned during 2 semesters in residence; completion of prescribed curriculum.

Distinctive Educational Programs: Law students are referred to as juniors, middlers, or seniors according to their year of study. Limitations are placed upon the total enrollment in each course, and, whenever practical, courses are divided into two sections. Seminar class sizes are limited to 25 students. *Other distinctive programs:* The school maintains fully accredited foreign programs in Florence, Italy (Comparative Law Seminars in June); Vienna, Austria, and Strasbourg, France (Comparative Law Seminars in July). The school also maintains several different programs designed to provide practical experience and foster professional responsibility. Clinical education includes the Family Law and Disability Law clinics on campus, clinics for prison inmates and two state correctional facilities, administrative law clinics and seven state government agencies in Harrisburg, clinics in legal services offices, public defender officers, and state and federal courts as well as art law, sports law, and entertainment law clinics. Dickinson offers training to participants in numerous appellate moot court and mock trial programs. Top-rated student advocates are chosen to represent the law school at regional and national competitions.

Degrees Conferred: *First-professional:* law 200, LL.M. 8.

Fees and Other Expenses: *Full-time tuition per academic year 2008–09:* contact the school for current information regarding tuition, fees, housing, and other applicable costs.

Financial Aid: Aid from institutionally generated funds is provided on the basis of academic merit, financial need, other criteria.

Departments and Teaching Staff: *Total instructional faculty:* 88. Degrees held by full-time faculty: baccalaureate 100%, master's 48%, doctorate 4%, professional 100%. 4% hold terminal degrees.

Enrollment: Total enrollment 620.

Characteristics of Student Body: *Ethnic/racial makeup:* Black non-Hispanic: 6.7%; American Indian or Alaska Native: .2%; Asian or Pacific Islander: 5.8%; Hispanic: 5.8%; White non-Hispanic: 79.8%.

International Students: 11 nonresident aliens enrolled fall 2008. Programs available to aid students whose native language is not English: social. No financial aid specifically designated for international students.

Student Life: Housing for law school students in and around Carlisle is both affordable and available. *Student publications: Dickinson Law Review*, published 4 times a year; *The Dickinson Journal of International Law*, published three times a year. Students also publish a newsletter and a yearbook. *Surrounding community:* Dickinson is close to major East Coast centers. Philadelphia, Pittsburgh, Baltimore, Washington and New York are all within comfortable traveling distance.

Library Collections: 515,935 volumes. 551,000 microforms; 310 audiovisual materials, 1,250 current periodical subscriptions. Students have access to online information retrieval services and the Internet.

Most important special holdings include collections on jurisprudence, intellectual property, and Jewish law. Library is a federal depository for U.S. government documents and for briefs and records of Pennsylvania appellate courts.

Buildings and Grounds: The School of Law is located in a quiet residential neighborhood adjacent to the Dickinson College campus. A new facility is under construction in University Park and scheduled for completion in 2009.

Chief Executive Officer: Paul J. McConaughay, Dean.

Address admission inquiries to Barbara W. Guillaume, Director of Law Admissions Services.

Drexel University

3141 Chestnut Street
Philadelphia, Pennsylvania 19104
Tel: (215) 895-2000 **E-mail:** enroll@.drexel.edu
Fax: (215) 895-5939 **Internet:** www.drexel.edu

Institution Description: Drexel is a private, nonprofit, independent institution. *Enrollment:* 19,860. *Degrees awarded:* Baccalaureate, master's, doctorate, first-professional. Graduate-level certificates also awarded.

Accreditation: *Regional:* MSA/CHE. *Professional*: architecture, business, computer science, dietetics, engineering, interior design, librarianship

History: Established as Drexel Institute of Art, Science, and Industry 1891; offered first instruction at postsecondary level 1892; chartered 1894; awarded first degree (baccalaureate) 1915; changed name to Drexel Institute of Technology 1936; adopted present name 1970; merged with Hahnnemann University and established Drexel University College of Medicine 2002. *See* David McDonald and Edward Martin Hinton, *Drexel Institute of Technology, 1891–1914* (Philadelphia: Haddon Craftsmen, Inc., 1942) for further information.

Institutional Structure: *Governing board:* Board of Trustees. Extrainstitutional representation: 56 trustees; institutional representation: president of the university, vice president and treasurer; 1 alumnus. 1 ex officio. 27 voting. *Composition of institution:* Administrators 314. Academic affairs headed by vice president for academic affairs. Management/business/finances directed by vice president and treasurer. Full-time instructional faculty 853. Academic governance body, University Faculty, meets an average of 5 times per year.

Calendar: Quarters (college of Medicine on semester basis). Academic year Sept. to June. Freshmen admitted Sept., Jan. Degrees conferred and formal commencement June. Summer term June to Aug.

Characteristics of Freshmen: 73% of applicants admitted. 18% of applicants admitted and enrolled.

96% (2,082 students) submitted SAT scores. *25th percentile*: SAT Critical Reading 540, SAT Math 560. *75th percentile*: SAT Critical Reading 640,

52% of entering freshmen are expected to graduate within 5 years. 58% of freshmen from Pennsylvania. Freshmen from 50 states and 100 foreign countries.

Admission: Rolling admissions plan. For fall acceptance, apply as early as Sept. 1 of previous year, but not later than Mar. 1 of year of enrollment. *Requirements:* Either graduation from accredited secondary school or GED with 4 years of mathematics through trigonometry and 2 years of a laboratory science for engineering and science students; 3 years of mathematics through algebra II and 1 year of a laboratory science for business, design arts, humanities and social sciences, information studies. *Entrance tests:* College Board SAT or ACT. 3 Achievements required for engineering and science students. *For transfer students:* 2.5 minimum GPA (on 4.0 scale; engineering students require a 3.0).

Transfer credit available if work done in an accredited college, grade is a C or better, and part of the Drexel curricula.

College credit and advanced placement for postsecondary-level work completed in secondary school. For extrainstitutional learning (life experience), college credit and advanced placement on basis of faculty assessment; for design students, on basis of portfolio assessment.

Tutoring available. Developmental courses offered in summer session and regular academic year; credit given.

Degree Requirements: 180–192 quarter hours; 2.0 GPA; 4 quarters in residence; 3 quarters physical education; general education requirements. *Grading system:* A–F; pass-fail.

Distinctive Educational Programs: In Drexel's mandatory cooperative education program (one of the nation's first, established in 1919), periods of full-time study and full-time paid employment in work related to a student's major are alternated. This program allows students to complete between 6 and 8 months of full-time employment, depending on their major. The program includes some 1,400 employers in 26 states and 6 foreign countries. The University's microcomputer program, initiated in 1983, integrates microcomputers into all undergraduate disciplines. *Other distinctive programs:* Faculty research in areas such as electrical and computer engineering, materials science, physics, sociology, and anthropology reflects the interplay between theory (basic research) and application (contracted projects). Interdisciplinary programs are offered in biomedical engineering and science, and environmental engineering and science.

ROTC: Army; Navy in cooperation with University of Pennsylvania; Air Force with Saint Joseph's University.

Degrees Conferred: 2,314 *baccalaureate*; 1,286 *master's*; 141 *doctorate*. Bachelor's degrees awarded in top five disciplines: business, management, marketing, and related support services 598; engineering 389; computer and information sciences 337; health professions and related clinical sciences 228; visual and performing arts 167. *First-professional*: medicine 238.

Fees and Other Expenses: *Tuition per academic year 2008–09:* $2600 undergraduate; graduate tuition varies by program. *Required fees:* $1,580. *Room and board per academic year:* $12,000. *Books and supplies:* $1,655.

Financial Aid: Aid from institutionally generated funds is provided on the basis of academic merit, financial need, athletic ability.

Financial aid to full-time, first-time undergraduate students: 92% received some form of financial aid. Average amount of aid received: federal grants $2,391; state/local grants $4,330; institutional grants $11,620; loans $14,618.

Departments and Teaching Staff: *Total instruction faculty:* 1,247 (full-time 689, part-time 558). Student/faculty ratio: 10:1. Degrees held by full-time faculty: 97% hold terminal degrees.

Enrollment: *Total enrollment:* 19,860.

Characteristics of Student Body: *Ethnic/racial makeup:* number of Black non-Hispanic: 1,140; American Indian or Alaska Native: 21; Asian or Pacific Islander: 1,384; Hispanic: 295; White non-Hispanic: 7,302; unknown: 739.

International Students: 1,034 nonresident aliens enrolled fall 2008. Programs available to aid students whose native language is not English: social, cultural. English as a Second Language Program. No financial aid specifically designated for international students.

Student Life: On-campus residence halls house approximately 26% of student body. 6% of males join and 6% live in fraternity housing; 6% of females join and some live in sorority housing. *Intercollegiate athletics:* male: basketball, crew, golf, lacrosse, soccer, swimming, tennis, wrestling, female: basketball, crew, field hockey, lacrosse, soccer, softball, swimming, tennis. *Special regulations:* Cars permitted without restrictions. *Special services:* Medical services, campus bus system. *Student publications, radio: Lexerd*, a yearbook; *Maya*, an annual literary magazine; *Triangle*, a weekly newspaper; a biannual technical journal. Radio station WKDU broadcasts 128 hours per week. *Surrounding community:* Philadelphia area population 1,700,000. Served by mass transit bus and subway systems; airport 2.5 miles from campus; passenger rail service .25 miles from campus.

Library Collections: 570,000 volumes. Online catalog. 650,000 microforms; 2,500 audiovisual materials; current serial subscriptions 8,321 paper; 273,500 microform . Students have access to online information retrieval services and the Internet.

Most important special holdings include Drexeliana (materials pertaining to A.J. Drexel and the Drexel family).

Buildings and Grounds: Campus area 37 acres.

Chief Executive Officer: Dr. Constantine N. Papadakis, President.

Address admission inquiries to David Eddy, Director of Admissions.

College of Engineering

Degree Programs Offered: *Baccalaureate* in chemical, civil, electrical engineering, engineering, materials engineering, mechanical engineering and mechanics, computer science; *master's* in engineering management; *master's, doctorate* in biomedical, chemical, civil, electrical, environmental, materials, mechanical engineering; computer science.

College of Business and Administration

Degree Programs Offered: *Baccalaureate, master's, doctorate* in accounting, economics, finance, management, marketing.

Distinctive Educational Programs: Interdisciplinary program in commerce and engineering.

College of Media Arts and Design

Degree Programs Offered: *Baccalaureate* in graphic design; interior design; fashion design; design and merchandising; music industry, printing technology management and architecture; digital media/screenwriting; film and video; hotel, restaurant and institutional management; *master's* in architecture, interior design, fashion design, publication management.

College of Arts and Science

Degree Programs Offered: *Baccalaureate* in history-politics; literature; applied philosophy; science, technology, and the humanities; technical and science communication; corporate communication, film and video production, music; psychology; sociology; psychology-sociology-anthropology (interdisciplinary major); international area studies; biological sciences, chemistry, clinical dietetics, environmental science, mathematics, nutrition and food science, physics, unified science; biological sciences, chemistry, clinical dietetics, environmental science, mathematics, nutrition and food science, physics, unified science; *master's* in arts administration, neuropsychology, and technical and science communication, biological sciences, biomedical science, chemistry, environmental science, mathematics, physics and atmospheric sciences; *doctorate* in biological sciences, biomedical science, chemistry, environmental science, mathematics, physics and atmospheric science.

College of Information Science and Technology

Degree Programs Offered: *Baccalaureate* in information systems; *master's, doctorate* in information systems, library and information science. Graduate certificates.

Goodwin College of Professional Studies

Degree Programs Offered: *Baccalaureate* in architecture, business administration, chemical engineering, chemistry, civil engineering, computer science, construction management, electrical engineering, food service management, general studies, industrial engineering, materials and metallurgical engineering, mathematics, mechanical engineering, physics.

College of Nursing and Health Professions

Degree Programs Offered: *Baccalaureate* in behavioral and addictions counseling, health services administration, nursing, emergency medial sciences. *Master's* in family therapy, creative arts in therapy, emergency and public safety, nursing, physician assistant; *doctorate* in family therapy, rehabilitation sciences, physical therapy, nursing practice.

College of Medicine

Degree Programs Offered: *Master's* biochemistry, microbiology and immunology, molecular cell biology; biology and genetics, molecular biology, neuroscience, pharmacology, physiology, clinical research, research management and development; *M.D* in medicine.

School of Education

Degree Programs Offered: *Bachelor's* and *master's* addiction; *doctorate* in educational leadership and learning technology.

School of Public Health

Degree Programs Offered: *Master's* and *doctorate* in public health.

School of Biomedical Engineering, Science, and Health Systems

Degree Programs Offered: *Bachelor's* and *master's* in biomedical engineering; *master's, doctorate* in biomedical engineering, biomedical sciences.

Duquesne University

600 Forbes Avenue
Pittsburgh, Pennsylvania 15282
Tel: (412) 396-5000 **E-mail:** admissions@duq.edu
Fax: (412) 396-5644 **Internet:** www.duq.edu

Institution Description: Duquesne University, officially known as Duquesne University of the Holy Spirit, is a private institution owned by the Congregation of the Holy Ghost, Roman Catholic Church. *Enrollment:* 10,106. *Degrees awarded:* Baccalaureate, first-professional (law, pharmacy), master's, doctorate.

Member of the consortium Pittsburgh Council on Higher Education.

Accreditation: *Regional:* MSA/CHE. *Professional*: athletic training, business, counseling, English language education, health services administration, law, music, nursing, nursing education, occupational therapy, pharmacy, physical therapy, physician assisting, psychology internship, school psychology, speech-language pathology,teacher education

History: Established as Pittsburgh Catholic College of the Holy Ghost and offered first instruction at postsecondary level 1878; incorporated and awarded first degree (baccalaureate) 1882; changed name to University of the Holy Ghost, to Duquesne University of the Holy Ghost 1911, to Duquesne University 1935; adopted the name Duquesne University of the Holy Ghost 1960; became Duquesne University of the Holy Spirit 2001.

Institutional Structure: *Governing board:* Duquesne University Board of Directors. Extrainstitutional representation: 17. institutional representation: president of the university. 6 ex officio. 23 voting. *Composition of institution:* Administrators 75. Academic affairs headed by provost and vice president for academic affairs. Management/business/finances directed by executive vice president for management and business. Student life is headed by executive vice president for student life. Full-time instructional faculty 429. Academic governance body, Academic Council, meets an average of 17 times per year.

Calendar: Semesters. Academic year Aug. to May. Freshmen admitted Aug., Jan., May. Degrees conferred May, Aug., Dec. Formal commencement May. Summer session of 2 terms from May to Aug.

Characteristics of Freshmen: 5,715 applicants (female 3,400, male 2,235). 76% of applicants admitted. 33% of applicants admitted and enrolled.

95% (1,259 students) submitted SAT scores; 30% (393 students) submitted ACT scores. *25th percentile*: SAT Critical Reading 510, SAT Math 520; ACT Composite 21, ACT English 21, ACT Math 21. *75th percentile*: SAT Critical Reading 600, SAT Math 620; ACT Composite 26, ACT English 27, ACT Math 26.

<66% of entering freshmen expected to graduate within 5 years. 76% of freshmen from Pennsylvania. Freshmen from 26 states and 14 foreign countries.

Admission: For fall acceptance, apply as early as July 1 of previous year, but not later than July 1 of year of enrollment. Apply by Nov. 1 for early decision; need not limit application to Duquesne. Early acceptance available. Early admission is available for mature candidates who have completed less than 4 years of high school. Early action for specific programs deadline Dec. 1. *Requirements:* Either graduation from accredited secondary school with 16 units which normally include 4 in English, 8 from among foreign language, mathematics, social studies, and science; or GED. *Entrance tests:* College board SAT or ACT composite. For foreign students TOEFL recommended. *For transfer students:* 2.5 minimum GPA; transfer credit varies.

College credit and advanced placement for postsecondary-level work completed in secondary school and for extrainstitutional learning on basis of faculty assessment of nursing experience and music theory training.

Tutoring available. Developmental courses offered in summer session and regular academic year; credit given.

Degree Requirements: 120 semester hours; 2.0 GPA; 30 credits in residence; general education requirements.

Fulfillment of some degree requirements and exemption from some beginning courses possible by passing College Board CLEP, AP. *Grading system:* A–F; withdraw (carries time limit).

Distinctive Educational Programs: Work-experience programs, including cooperative education, internships. Weekend and evening classes. Accelerated degree programs. Basic Skill Programs designed to help students improve their basic skills for college work. Special facilities for doing computer assisted projects in all schools. Special facilities for using telecommunications in the classroom. Facilities and programs for independent research, including honors programs, individual majors, tutorials. Cross-registration through consortium. Study abroad in Australia, Argentina, Austria, Belgium, Chile, China, Costa Rica, England, France, Germany, Greece, Hungary, Ireland, Italy, Mexico, Japan, Scotland, Spain.

ROTC: Air Force, Army, Navy. Air Force in cooperation with University of Pittsburgh; Army offered on-campus; Navy offered in cooperation with Carnegie Mellon University.

Degrees Conferred: 1,184 *baccalaureate*; 865 *master's*; 144 *doctorate*; *first-professional:* 270. Bachelor's degrees awarded in top five disciplines: business, management, marketing, and related support services 311; health professions and related clinical sciences 226; education 123; biological/life sciences 122; liberal arts/general studies 82. Master's degrees awarded in top five disciplines: education 275; business/marketing 135; health professions 105; liberal arts/general studies 71; psychology 31. Doctorates awarded: biological/life sciences 2; education 24; English 12; health professions 9; philosophy and religious studies 7; physical sciences 2; psychology 10; theology 4. *First-professional:* law 160; pharmacy 110.

Fees and Other Expenses: *Full-time tuition per academic year 2008–09:* undergraduate $25,475; graduate charged per credit hour; first-professional tuition varies by program. *Required fees:* $1,810. *Board and board per academic year:* $6,858. *Other expenses:* $1,150.

Financial Aid: Aid from institutionally generated funds is provided on the basis of academic merit, financial need, athletic ability, other criteria.

Financial aid to full-time, first-time undergraduate students: need-based scholarships/grants totaling $34,069,318, self-help $34,037,456, parent loans $9,068,169, tuition waivers $2,528,502, athletic awards $1,677,336; non-need-based scholarships/grants totaling $9,458,733, self-help $3,649,741, 1,970,022, parent loans $1,970,022. tuition waivers $1,305,276, athletic awards $1,925,461.

Departments and Teaching Staff: *Total instructional faculty:* 875 (full-time 419, part-time 466). Total faculty with doctorate, first-professional, or other terminal degree: 367. Student/faculty ratio: 15:1. Degrees held by full-time faculty: 96% hold terminal degrees.

Enrollment: Total enrollment 10,106. Undergraduate 5,656 (full-time 95%; female 58%. male 43%). Graduate 4,450 (full-time 76%). Undergraduate transfer-in students 161.

Characteristics of Student Body: *Ethnic/racial makeup:* Black non-Hispanic: 4%; Asian or Pacific Islander: 2%; Hispanic: 1%; White non-Hispanic: 83%; unknown: 8%; nonresident alien 2%. *Age distribution:* number under 18: 41; 18–19: 2,377; 20–21: 1,967; 22–24: 472; 25–29: 110; 30–34: 69; 35–39: 54; 40–49: 77; 50–64: 22.

International Students: 202 nonresident aliens enrolled fall 2008. Students from Europe, Asia, Central and South America, Africa, Canada, Australia, Middle East. Programs available to aid students whose native language is not English: social, cultural. English as a Second Language Program. Financial aid specifically designated for international students: variable number of scholarships available annually for international students.

Student Life: 57% of undergraduates live on campus. *Intercollegiate athletics:* male: baseball, basketball, cross-country, football, golf, soccer, swimming and diving, tennis, wrestling; female: basketball, crew, cross-country, lacrosse, soccer, swimming and diving, tennis, track and field, volleyball. *Special regulations:* Quiet hours. Residence hall visitation from noon to midnight Mon.–Fri., noon to 2am Sat.–Sun. *Special services:* Learning Resources Center, medical services. *Student publications, radio: The Duke*, a weekly newspaper; *The Duquesne Magazine*, a biannual publication; *The Duquesne Yearbook*. Radio station WDUQ broadcasts 24 hours per day. *Surrounding community:* Pittsburgh population 350,363. Served by mass transit bus system; airport 20 miles from campus; passenger rail service 3 miles from campus; downtown Pittsburgh served by subway system.

Library Collections: 724,000 volumes. Online catalog. Current serial subscriptions: paper 1,124; microform 31; via electronic access 8,746. 4,849 compact discs, 1,121 CD-ROMs; 449 DVDs. Computer work stations available. Students have access to online information retrieval services and the Internet.

Most important holdings include Rabbi Hailperin on Medieval Christian and Jewish Religious Thought; Silverman Center Collection of World Literature in Phenomenology; John Cardinal Wright's Collection (his sermons, personal papers, correspondence).

Buildings and Grounds: Campus area 50 acres. Campus DVD available.

Chief Executive Officer: Dr. Charles J. Dougherty, President.

Undergraduates address admission inquiries to Paul-James Cukanna, Director of Admissions; graduate inquiries to Dean of appropriate graduate school.

College of Liberal Arts

Degree Programs Offered: *Baccalaureate* in classical civilization, classical languages, modern languages, liberal arts, international relations, pre-osteopathic medicine, classical Greek, media management and production, art history, multimedia development, integrated marketing communication, corporate communication, rhetoric, public relations and advertising, web design and development. communication studies, computer science, economics, English, history, journalism, classical Latin, mathematics, philosophy, political science, psychology, sociology, Spanish, studio arts, theater arts, theology, world literature; *master's* in communications, computational mathematics, English literature, health care ethics, history, philosophy, social and public policy, theology and pastoral ministry, religious education, liberal studies; multimedia technology. *doctorate* in English literature, health care ethics, philosophy, rhetoric, systematic theology. clinical psychology.

Distinctive Educational Programs: Interdepartmental program in world literature. Interdisciplinary program in education and business. Dual-degree program in engineering with Case Western Reserve University (OH). Programs in pre-law and pre-health. Study abroad programs available. English as a Second Language Program accommodates International Students.

School of Business Administration

Degree Programs Offered: *Bachelor of Science* in Business Administration. Concentrations in accounting, finance, international business, investment management, marketing, sports marketing, supply chain management; *master of science* in information systems management, accountancy, taxation.

Distinctive Educational Programs: Individual majors. Small Business Development Center provides support services for small businesses.

School of Education

Degree Programs Offered: *Baccalaureate* in early childhood education, elementary education, secondary education; *master's* in educational administration, child psychology, school counseling, community counseling services, marriage and family therapy, early childhood education, early childhood/elementary education, educational studies, instructional technology, program planning and evaluation, special education/community mental health, English as a Second Language, elementary education, reading and language arts, special education; *doctorate* in educational and instructional leadership, school psychology, counselor education and supervision, instructional technology, inter disciplinary doctoral program for educational leaders.

Distinctive Educational Programs: Joint undergraduate and graduate degree programs with the College of Liberal Arts and Natural and Environmental Sciences.

School of Music

Degree Programs Offered: *Baccalaureate* in music education, music therapy, music performance, music technology. *master's* in music education, music performance, music technology, theory/composition, sacred music, and an Artist-Diploma program.

School of Nursing

Degree Programs Offered: *Baccalaureate* in nursing (generic, RN/BSN, and 2nd Degree option); *master of science* in nursing (acute care clinical nurse specialist, family nurse practitioner, forensic nursing, psychiatric/mental health clinical nurse specialist) RN-SN-MSN. *doctorate* in nursing.

School of Law

Degree Programs Offered: *First-professional:* Juris Doctorate degree (day and evening divisions, part-time day); Juris Doctorate/Master of Business Administration; Juris Doctorate/Master of Divinity; Juris Doctorate/Bachelor of Arts or Sciences; Juris Doctorate/Bachelor of Science in Business and Administration; Juris Doctorate/Master of Environmental Science and Management.

Admission: Candidates applying for the JD, BA, BS or BSBA must have completed all undergraduate work at Duquesne University. LSAT;registration with LSDAS.

Distinctive Educational Programs: The Law School has a growing list of 3/3 Early Admission Program partners through the Western Pennsylvania region and beyond. These include Carnegie Mellon University College of Humanities and Social Sciences, Gannon University, Juniata College, Seton Hill University, Mercyhurst College, Waynesburg College, Washington and Jefferson College, St. Francis College and Westminster College.

School of Pharmacy

Degree Programs Offered: The School of Pharmacy offers a six-year, entry-level doctor of pharmacy program and a nontraditional doctor of pharmacy program designed for working pharmacy practitioners to obtain a Pharm.D. degree.

Admission: *For entry-level doctor of pharmacy:* the six-year entry-level doctor of pharmacy program is configured into a two-year preprofessional and a four-year professional curricular format. Students are accepted directly into the pharmacy school from high school or as a transfer student into the first year of the professional curriculum. For nontraditional doctor of pharmacy, 3.0 GPA, B.S. in pharmacy from ACPE-accredited school or college of pharmacy and maintenance of current pharmacist licensure and registration.

Degree Requirements: Minimum cumulative and science/math GPA of 2.5 and no grade lower than C in each of the required courses in the preprofessional curriculum; completion of the Pharmacy College Admissions Test with a composite score of 180.

Distinctive Educational Programs: Independent study and research for undergraduate students; B.S. in Pharmacy/MBA and B.S. in Pharmacy/M.S. in Pharmaceutical Sciences combined degree programs.

Graduate School of Pharmaceutical Sciences

Degree Programs Offered: *Master of Science* in pharmaceutics, pharmacy administration, medicinal chemistry, pharmacology/toxicology; *MBA/M.S.* in industrial pharmacy (with School of Business and Administration); *doctorate* in pharmaceutics, medicinal chemistry, pharmacology/toxicology.

Admission: 3.0 GPA with baccalaureate degree in chemistry, biology, pharmacy. Non-English speaking international students must submit TOEFL and TSE (if teaching assistant).

Degree Requirements: *For master of science:* 3.0 GPA and 30 credit hours (including 6 credit hours of thesis research). *For MBA/M.S. in industrial pharmacy:* 3.0 GPA and 83 credit sin core business administration course work and 26 credits of course work in the pharmaceutical sciences are required. *For doctorate:* 3.0 GPA and 60 credit hours (including 12 credit hours of dissertation research).

School of Health Sciences

Degree Programs Offered: Four-year *bachelor of science* degree programs in athletic training (B.S. in athletic training), health management systems. Five-year entry-level *master's* degree programs in occupational therapy (M.O.T.), physician assistant (M.P.A.); speech-language pathology, health management systems and rehabilitation sciences

Admission: Graduation from an approved secondary school in the upper two-fifths of the class; demonstrated exemplary personal conduct in that institution. Applicants who have not completed 4 years of high school must submit a High School Equivalent Diploma issued by their state department of education. Consult the university catalog for further information.

Degree Requirements: Specific number of credits needed for the degree varies among programs. All students must complete pre-professional and professional phases of curriculum, and research project where required.

School of Leadership and Professional Advancement

Degree Programs Offered: *Bachelor of Science in Professional Studies* for students that complete a major in various disciplines (consult the university catalog for specific majors); *masters's* degrees also offered in various majors.

Degree Requirements: Vary by academic program.

Distinctive Educational Programs: Saturday accelerated program; online bachelor's degree completion; professional certificates in account, computer technology, database technology, electronic communications, information technology,leadership; noncredit programs in paralegal and financial planning.

School of Natural and Environmental Sciences

Degree Programs Offered: *Bachelor of Science* degree for students that complete a major in biology, chemistry, physics, biochemistry; environmental chemistry, environmental science, *master of science* degrees in biology, chemistry, environmental science and management, forensic science and law; *doctorate* in biology, chemistry.

East Stroudsburg University

200 Prospect Street
East Stroudsburg, Pennsylvania 18301-2999
Tel: (570) 422-3211 **E-mail:** admissions@esu.edu
Fax: (570) 422-3777 **Internet:** www.esu.edu

Institution Description: East Stroudsburg University is a member of the Pennsylvania State System of Higher Education. *Enrollment:* 7,234. *Degrees awarded:* Associate, baccalaureate, master's.

Academic offerings subject to approval by statewide coordinating bodies. Budget subject to approval by statewide coordinating bodies. Member of Marine Science Consortium and Pennsylvania Consortium for International Education.

Accreditation: *Regional:* MSA/CHE. *Professional*: health information administration, nursing, recreation and leisure services, teacher education

History: Established as East Stroudsburg Normal School 1893; changed name to East Stroudsburg State Normal School 1920; offered first instruction at postsecondary level 1926; changed name to East Stroudsburg State Teachers

EAST STROUDSBURG UNIVERSITY—*cont'd*

College and awarded first degree (baccalaureate) 1927; became East Stroudsburg State College 1960; adopted present name 1982.

Institutional Structure: *Governing board:* Board of State College and University Directors (policymaking body for 13 state colleges and Indiana University of Pennsylvania). Extrainstitutional representation:15 directors. All voting. Board of Trustees of East Stroudsburg State College (Appointed by governor of Pennsylvania with state senatorial approval). Extrainstitutional representation: 8 trustees; institutional representation; 1 student. All voting. *Composition of institution:* Administrators 32. Academic affairs headed by vice president for academic affairs. Management/business/finances directed by dean for administration and finance. Full-time instructional faculty 258. Academic governance body, Curriculum meets an average of 12 times per year. *Faculty representation:* Faculty served by collective bargaining agent, Association of Pennsylvania State Colleges and Universities, affiliated with AAUP and AFT.

Calendar: Semesters. Academic year Sept. to May. Freshmen admitted Sept., Jan., June. Degrees conferred and formal commencement May, Aug., Dec. Summer session from June to Aug.

Characteristics of Freshmen: 5,799 applicants (female 3,104, male 2,515). 21% of applicants accepted. 100% of accepted applicants enrolled.

Mean SAT scores: Critical Reading 444, Math 466.

55% entering freshmen expected to graduate within 5 years. 75% of freshmen from Pennsylvania. Students from 27 states and 18 foreign countries.

Admission: Rolling admissions plan. For fall acceptance, apply as early as Sept. 1 or previous year but not later than June 1 of year of enrollment. Early acceptance available. *Requirements:* Either graduation from accredited secondary school or GED. Lowest acceptable secondary school class standing 25th percentile. *Entrance tests:* College Board SAT. For foreign students TOEFL. *For transfer students:* 2.0 GPA; from 4-year accredited institution maximum transfer credit limited only by residence requirement; from 2-year accredited institution 70 semester hours.

College credit and advanced placement for postsecondary-level work completed in secondary school. College credit for extrainstitutional learning.

Tutoring available. Noncredit developmental courses offered in summer session and regular academic year.

Degree Requirements: 128 semester hours; 2.0 GPA; 1 year in residence; 3 physical activity courses; general education requirements; distribution requirements.

Fulfillment of some degree requirements and exemption from some beginning courses possible by passing departmental examinations, College Board CLEP, AP. *Grading system:* A–F; pass-fail; withdraw (deadline after which pass-fail is appended to withdraw).

Distinctive Educational Programs: *For undergraduates:* Internships. Dual-degree programs in engineering with Pennsylvania State University; in chemistry with Hahnemann Medical College; in chemistry and pharmacy with Temple University; in biology and podiatry with Pennsylvania College of Podiatric Medicine. Cooperative baccalaureate program in medical technology with approved hospital programs; in pharmacy with Temple University. Interdepartmental programs in environmental studies. Facilities and programs for independent research, including tutorials, independent study. *For graduate students:* Weekend classes. Interdepartmental programs in general science. *Available to all students:* Evening classes. Special facilities for using telecommunications in the classroom. Study abroad by individual arrangement. *Other distinctive programs:* Continuing education. Support services for educationally and economically disadvantaged students offered through Educational Opportunity Program.

ROTC: Army in cooperation with Lafayette College; Air Force in cooperation with Lehigh University.

Degrees Conferred: 1,230 *baccalaureate*; 312 *master's*. Bachelor's degrees awarded in top five disciplines: education 210; business, management, marketing, and related support services 123; social sciences 120; parks and recreation 96; health professions and related clinical sciences 78. Master's degrees awarded: various disciplines 312.

Fees and Other Expenses: *Full-time tuition per academic year 2008–09:* $7,090 resident, $18,221 nonresident. *Room and board per academic year:* $6,148. *Books and supplies:* $1,000. *Other expenses:* $2,363.

Financial Aid: Aid from institutionally generated funds is provided on the basis of academic merit, financial need, other criteria.

Financial aid to full-time, first-time undergraduate students: 80% received some form of financial aid. Average amount of aid received: federal grants $3,733; Pell grants $2,966; other federal aid $882; state/local grants $2,951; institutional grants $2,963.

Departments and Teaching Staff: *Total instructional faculty:* 258.

Enrollment: Total enrollment 7,913. Undergraduate

Characteristics of Student Body: *Ethnic/racial makeup:* Black non-Hispanic: 5%; Asian or Pacific Islander: 3%; Hispanic: 5%; White non-Hispanic: 79; unknown 8%.

International Students: No programs available to aid students whose native language is not English. Financial aid specifically designated for international students: scholarships available to qualifying students.

Student Life: On-campus residence halls house 53% of student body. Residence halls for males constitute 29% of such space, for females 44%, for both sexes 27%. 5% of males join and 4% live in fraternity housing. *Intercollegiate athletics:* male: archery, baseball, basketball, football, golf, gymnastics, soccer, swimming, tennis, track, volleyball; female: archery, basketball, gymnastics, field hockey, lacrosse, softball, swimming, tennis, track, volleyball. *Special regulations:* Cars permitted for juniors and seniors only. *Special services:* Learning Resources Center, medical services. *Student publications, radio: Stroud*, a yearbook; *Stroud Courier*, a weekly newspaper. Radio station WESS broadcasts 60 hours per week. *Surrounding community:* East Stroudsburg population 8,000. Allentown-Bethlehem-Easton, 25 miles from campus, is nearest metropolitan area.

Library Collections: 466,000 volumes. 1.4 million microforms; 8,700 audiovisual materials; 18,400 periodicals including via electronic access. Student have access to online information retrieval services and the Internet.

Buildings and Grounds: Campus area 184 acres.

Chief Executive Officer: Dr. Robert J. Dillman, President.

Address admission inquiries to Alan Chesterton, Director of Admission.

Eastern Baptist Theological Seminary

6 Lancaster Avenue
Philadelphia, Pennsylvania 19096-3495
Tel: (610) 896-5000 **E-mail:** admissions@ebts.edu
Fax: (610) 649-3834 **Internet:** www.ebts.edu

Institution Description: Eastern Baptist Theological Seminary is a private institution affiliated with the American Baptist Churches/USA. *Enrollment:* 443. *Degrees awarded:* First-professional (divinity), doctorate.

Member of the consortium Association of Philadelphia Area Theological Seminaries.

Accreditation: *Regional:* MSA/CHE. *Professional*: theology

History: Established and offered first instruction at postsecondary level 1925; awarded first degree (baccalaureate) 1937.

Institutional Structure: *Governing board:* Board of Directors. Extrainstitutional representation: 33 directors, 3 directors emeriti; institutional representation: president of the seminary. 1 ex officio. 36 voting. *Composition of institution:* Administrators 16. Academic affairs headed by vice president and dean. Management/business/finances directed by vice president for business affairs. Full-time instructional faculty 14 men / 2 women.

Calendar: Semesters. Academic year early Sept. to May. Entering students admitted Sept., Feb. Formal commencement May. Summer session June.

Admission: *Requirements:* Baccalaureate or equivalent from accredited college or university. Recommend courses in English, history (including non-Western), philosophy, physical and life sciences, fine arts and music, a modern language, public speaking, religion. Minimum recommended GPA 2.5. Evidence of Christian character and call to Christian service. *Entrance tests:* Miller Analogies Test or GRE Aptitude. For foreign students: test of proficiency in English. *For transfer students:* 2.0 minimum GPA.

Degree Requirements: *For first-professional degree:* 96 credit hours; 4 semesters supervised field education. *For master's degree:* 64 credit hours; 2 semesters supervised field education. *For all degrees:* C average; 32 hours in residence; core curriculum. *Grading system:* A–D, no credit; credit-no credit; withdraw (carries penalty).

Distinctive Educational Programs: Joint M.Div.-M.S.W. with accredited college or university. Interdisciplinary programs include Black perspectives in theology and ministry, Hispanic studies and ministry. Cross-registration through consortium. Continuing education program.

Degrees Conferred: 39 *master's*; 18 *doctorate*: (all theology). 39 *first-professional:* master of divinity.

Fees and Other Expenses: *Tuition per academic year 2008–09:* contact the seminary for current tuition, fees, and expenses.

Financial Aid: Aid from institutionally generated funds is provided on the basis of financial need. Institution has a Program Participation Agreement with the U.S. Department of Education for eligible students to receive Pell Grants and, depending upon the agreement, other federal aid.

Departments and Teaching Staff: *Total instructional faculty:* 16.

Enrollment: Total enrollment 443.

Characteristics of Student Body: *Ethnic/racial makeup:* Black non-Hispanic: 51%; Asian or Pacific Islander: 1.8%, Hispanic: 2.7%; White non-Hispanic: 40.4%.

International Students: 18 nonresident aliens enrolled fall 2008. No programs available to aid students whose native language is not English. Financial aid specifically designated for international students: scholarships available to qualifying students.

Student Life: Residence halls and apartments available for married students. *Special regulations:* Cars permitted without restrictions. *Special services:* Learning Resources Center, medical services. *Surrounding community:* Philadelphia area population 1,725,000. Served by mass transit system; airport 7 miles from campus; passenger rail service 1 block from campus.

Library Collections: 120,000 volumes. Students have access to online information retrieval services and the Internet.

Buildings and Grounds: Campus area 8 acres.

Chief Executive Officer: Rev. Dr. Wallace Charles Smith, President.

Address admission inquiries to Dr. Stephen H. Hutchison, Director of Admissions.

Eastern University

1300 Eagle Road
St. Davids, Pennsylvania 19087-3696
Tel: (610) 341-5800 **E-mail:** ugadm@eastern.edu
Fax: (610) 341-1375 **Internet:** www.eastern.edu

Institution Description: Eastern University is a private college affiliated with the American Baptist Church. *Enrollment:* 4,364. *Degrees awarded:* Baccalaureate, master's.

Accreditation: *Regional:* MSA/CHE. *Professional.* nursing, social work

History: Established as department of Eastern Baptist Theological Seminary 1932; awarded first baccalaureate 1938; chartered as separate 4-year institution 1952; moved to present location 1954; adopted the name Eastern College: A Baptist Institution, 1972 (generally known as Eastern College); achieved university status 2002.

Institutional Structure: *Governing board:* Board of Directors. Extrainstitutional representation: 33 directors, 3 directors emeriti; institutional representation: president of the university. 1 ex officio. All voting. *Composition of institution:* Academic affairs headed by Provost-Chief Academic Officer, Dean of Arts and Sciences, Dean of Graduate Program, Dean of Non-traditional Education, Associate Dean of Continuing Education. Management/business/finance headed by Chief Operating Officer, Director of Finance. Full-time instructional faculty 64. Academic governance body, Faculty Senate, meets an average of 9 times per year.

Calendar: Semesters. Academic year Sept. to May. Freshmen admitted Fall and Spring semesters. Winterim session Jan. Summer session of 2 terms from May to Aug.

Characteristics of Freshmen: 1,550 applicants (female 969, male 561). 62% of applicants accepted. 46% of accepted applicants enrolled.

96% (431 students) submitted SAT scores; 14% (16 students) submitted ACT scores. *25th percentile*: SAT Critical Reading 480, SAT Math 470; ACT Composite 19, ACT English 17, ACT Math 17. *75th percentile*: SAT Critical Reading 550, SAT Math 570; ACT Composite 25, ACT English 25, ACT Math 24.

50% of entering freshmen expected to graduate within 5 years. 60% of freshmen from Pennsylvania. Students from 38 states and 27 foreign countries.

Admission: Rolling admissions plan. For fall acceptance, apply as early as end of junior year of secondary school. Early decision and early acceptance available. *Requirements:* Either graduation from accredited secondary school with 15 academic units which should include humanities, laboratory sciences, mathematics, social studies; or GED. *Entrance tests:* College Board SAT or ACT composite. For foreign students TOEFL. *For transfer students:* 2.0 minimum GPA; transfer credit from nonaccredited institutions considered on individual basis.

College credit for postsecondary-level work completed in secondary school. Tutoring available. Developmental/remedial courses offered in summer session and during regular academic year; credit given.

Degree Requirements: 127 semester credits; 2.0 GPA and grade of C or better in all required courses in major; core curriculum requirements including 9 hours religion; last 32 hours in residence. For some programs, comprehensive exit examinations in individual fields of study. *Grading system:* A–F; pass-fail; pass; withdraw failing; pass-no credit; audit.

Distinctive Educational Programs: Cooperative baccalaureate in medical technology with Bryn Mawr Hospital and other area hospitals. Preprofessional program in nursing. Interdisciplinary programs in American studies, health administration. Latin American studies, school nursing. Study abroad at approved universities in Africa, Asia, England, Europe, Latin America. Cross-registration with Cabrini College and Rosemont College. Baccalaureate completion program for registered nurses. *Other distinctive programs:* Co-op programs in political science, philosophy, and astronomy with Villanova University; in engineering with Widener University. American studies summer program for secondary school teachers.

ROTC: Army at Valley Forge Military Junior College; Air Force at St. Joseph's University.

Degrees Conferred: 83 *associate*; 537 *baccalaureate*; 353 *master's*; 47 *doctorate*. Bachelor's degrees awarded in top five disciplines: business, management, marketing, and related support services 277; theology 53; education 51; psychology 41; health professions and related clinical sciences 33. Master's degrees awarded: various disciplines 353. Doctorates awarded: various disciplines 47.

Fees and Other Expenses: *Full-time tuition per academic year 2008–09:* $22,715 undergraduate; contact the university for current graduate and first-professional tuition and fees. *Books and supplies:* $1,200. *Room and board per academic year:* $8,080. *Other expenses:* $3,600.

Financial Aid: Aid from institutionally generated funds is provided on the basis of academic merit, financial need.

Financial aid to full-time, first-time undergraduate students: 99% received some form of financial aid. Average amount of aid received: federal grants $3.654; Pell grants $3,014; other federal aid $1,219; state/local grants $3,982; institutional grants $9,654.

Departments and Teaching Staff: *Total instructional faculty:* 71. Degrees held by full-time faculty: master's 32%, doctorate 66%, not specified 2%. 38% hold terminal degrees.

Enrollment: Total enrollment 4,364. Undergraduate 2,668 (full-time 90%; female 68%, male 32%). Graduate 1,696 (full-time 52%). Undergraduate transfer-in students 84.

Characteristics of Student Body: *Ethnic/racial makeup:* Black non-Hispanic: 19%; Asian or Pacific Islander: 2%; Hispanic: 9%; White non-Hispanic: 61%; unknown: 6%; nonresident alien 2%.

International Students: 88 nonresident aliens enrolled fall 2008. Programs available to aid students whose native language is not English: social, cultural. English as a Second Language Program.

Student Life: On-campus residence halls available. *Intercollegiate athletics:* male: baseball, basketball, cross-country, soccer, tennis; female: basketball, cross-country, field hockey, lacrosse, soccer, softball, tennis, volleyball. *Special regulations:* Cars permitted without restrictions. *Special services:* Learning Resources Center, medical services. *Student publications, radio: Inklings*, an annual literary magazine; *Log*, a yearbook; *Waltonian*, a biweekly newspaper. Radio station WECR. *Surrounding community:* St. Davids. Philadelphia, 25 miles from campus, is nearest metropolitan area. Served by airport 25 miles from campus, passenger rail service 2 miles from campus.

Library Collections: 131,000 volumes. 76,500 microforms; 13,300 audiovisual materials; 1,100 current periodical subscriptions. Students have access to online information retrieval services and the Internet.

Most important special holdings include Marcus Aurelius Collection of 200 editions; Non-Profit Management Collection.

Buildings and Grounds: Campus area 100 acres.

Chief Executive Officer: Dr. David R. Black, President.

Address admission inquiries to David Urban, Director of Admissions.

Edinboro University of Pennsylvania

219 Medville Street
Edinboro, Pennsylvania 16444
Tel: (814) 732-2000 **E-mail:** admissions@edinboro.edu
Fax: (814) 732-2420 **Internet:** www.edinboro.edu

Institution Description: Edinboro University of Pennsylvania is a state institution. *Enrollment:* 7,671. *Degrees awarded:* Associate, baccalaureate, master's. Certificates also awarded.

Academic offerings subject to approval by statewide coordinating bodies. Budget subject to approval by state governing boards. Member of Coordinated Undergraduate Program in Dietetics, Marine Science Consortium, McKeever Environmental Center, Northwestern Interlibrary Cooperative of Pennsylvania.

Accreditation: *Regional:* MSA/CHE. *Professional*: dietetics, music, nursing, rehabilitation counseling, social work, speech-language pathology, teacher education

History: Established and chartered as Edinboro Academy 1856; changed name to Edinboro Normal School 1857; rechartered as Edinboro State Normal School and offered first instruction at postsecondary level 1861; changed name to Edinboro State Teachers College and awarded first degree (baccalaureate) 1927; incorporated liberal arts curriculum and became Edinboro State College 1960; adopted present name upon achieving university status. *See* Russell E. Vance, Jr., *A Portrait of Edinboro from Private Academy to State College 1856–1976* (Rochester, N.Y.: PSI Publishers, 1977) for further information.

Institutional Structure: *Governing boards:* State System of Higher Education, Council of Trustees of Edinboro University (appointed by governor of Pennsylvania with state senatorial approval). *Composition of institution:* Aca-

EDINBORO UNIVERSITY OF PENNSYLVANIA—*cont'd*

demic affairs headed by provost and vice president for academic affairs. Management/business/finances directed by vice president for finance and administration. Full-time instructional faculty 363. Academic governance body, College Senate, meets an average of 9 times per year. *Faculty representation:* Faculty served by collective bargaining agent, Association of Pennsylvania State Colleges and Universities, affiliated with AAUP and AFT.

Calendar: Semesters. Academic year Aug. to May. Freshmen admitted Sept., Jan., June. Degrees conferred and formal commencement May, Dec. Summer session 2 terms from June to Aug. Three-week winter session.

Characteristics of Freshmen: 3.853 applicants (female 2,245, male 1,588). 74% of applicants accepted. 44% of accepted applicants enrolled full-time.

82% (1,045 students) submitted SAT scores; 17% (220 students) submitted ACT scores. *25th percentile*: SAT Critical Reading 410, SAT 410, ACT Composite 16. *75th percentile*: SAT Critical Reading 530, SAT Math 530, ACT Composite 21.

45% of entering freshmen expected to graduate within 5 years. 87% of freshmen from Pennsylvania. Freshmen from 179 states and 3 foreign countries.

Admission: Rolling admissions plan. For fall acceptance, apply as early as July 1 of previous year, but not later than Sept. of year of enrollment. Early acceptance available. *Requirements:* Either graduation from accredited secondary school or equivalent preparation, including GED. *Entrance tests:* College Board SAT or ACT composite. Requirement may be waived for older students. *For transfer students:* 2.0 minimum GPA; transfer applicants with associate degrees from publicly supported 2-year colleges in Pennsylvania will receive credit for all grades of 1.0 or higher.

College credit and advanced placement for postsecondary-level work completed in secondary school and for extrainstitutional learning on basis of portfolio and faculty assessments.

Tutoring available. Developmental courses offered in summer session and regular academic year; credit given.

Degree Requirements: *For all associate degrees:* 60 credit hours; last semester in residence. *For all baccalaureate degrees:* 128 credit hours; last two semesters in residence; 3 hours physical education. *For all undergraduate degrees:* 2.0 GPA; distribution requirements.

Fulfillment of some degree requirements and exemption from some beginning courses possible by passing departmental examinations, College Board CLEP, APP. *Grading system:* A–F; pass-fail; withdraw (deadline after which pass-fail is appended to withdraw); incomplete (carries time limit).

Distinctive Educational Programs: *For undergraduates:* Dual-degree programs in engineering with Case Western Reserve University (OH), Pennsylvania State University, University of Pittsburgh. Interdisciplinary programs in environmental sciences, environmental studies/geography, forensic chemistry,urban studies. Preprofessional programs in dentistry, medicine, osteopathy, pharmacy, veterinary science. Off-campus study in U.S. includes semester internships in Harrisburg. Cross-registration with 10 area colleges through Region V Cross Registration Program. Study abroad in China, England, Morocco, Pakistan, Scotland. *For graduate students:* Interdisciplinary programs in social sciences. *Available to all students:* Internships. Weekend and evening classes. Accelerated degree programs. Special facilities for using telecommunications in the classroom. Programs for independent research, including individual majors, independent study courses. Cooperative summer program at University of Pittsburgh's Pymatuming Laboratory of Ecology. *Other distinctive programs:* Institute for Research for Community Services sponsors regional conferences, workshops, publications, provides research services.

ROTC: Army offered in cooperation with Gannon University.

Degrees Conferred: 83 *associate*: 1,049 *baccalaureate*; 189 *master's*. Bachelor's degrees awarded in top five disciplines: education 210; visual and performing arts 201; education 156; security and protective services 112; communications/journalism 107; business/marketing 101. Master's degrees awarded biological/life sciences 1; communications/journalism 32; computer and information sciences 3; education 186; health professions 21; psychology 14; public administration 19; social sciences 4; visual and performing arts 5.

Fees and Other Expenses: *Full-time tuition per academic year 2008–09:* undergraduate resident $7,042, nonresident $9,814; contact the university for current graduate tuition. *Other fees:* $1,446. *Room and board per academic year:* %$6,450. *Other expenses:* $2,200.

Financial Aid: Aid from institutionally generated funds is provided on the basis of academic merit, financial need, athletic ability, other criteria.

Financial aid to full-time, first-time undergraduate students: 89% received some form of aid. Average amount of aid received: federal grants $3,295; Pell grants $2,918; other federa ail $994; state/local grants $3,051; institutional grants $2,851.

Departments and Teaching Staff: *Total instructional faculty:* 403 (full-time 363, part-time 40). Total faculty with doctorate, first-professional, or other terminal degree: 36. Student/faculty ratio: 18:1. Degrees held by full-time faculty: 65% hold terminal degrees.

Enrollment: Total enrollment 7,671. Undergraduate 6,155 (full-time 88%; female 51%, male 43%). Graduate 1,516 (full-time 32%). Undergraduate transfer-in students 287.

Characteristics of Student Body: *Ethnic/racial makeup:* Black non-Hispanic: 9%; Asian or Pacific Islander: 1%; Hispanic: 2%; White non-Hispanic: 87%; nonresident alien 1%. *Age distribution:* number under 18: 58; 18–19: 2,010; 20–21: 2,059; 22–24: 1,381; 25–29: 501; 30–34: 252; 35–39: 179; 40–49: 225; 50–64: 63; 65 and over: 7.

International Students: 77 nonresident aliens enrolled fall 2008. Students from Europe, Asia, Central and South America, Africa, Canada. No programs available to aid students whose native language is not English. *Financial aid specifically designated for international students:* scholarships for tuition and incidental fees available annually for qualifying undergraduate students.

Student Life: On-campus residence halls house 24% of the student body. Residence halls for males constitute 40% of such space, for females 59%, for both sexes 1%. Housing available for married students. *Intercollegiate athletics:* male: baseball, basketball, cross-country, football, tennis, track, volleyball, wrestling; female: basketball, softball, tennis, track, volleyball; both sexes: swimming. *Special regulations:* Cars permitted for upper division, graduate students. *Special services:* Learning Resources Center, medical services. Specially equipped vans transport wheelchair students to and from classes, special events. *Student publications, radio: Spectator*, a weekly newspaper; *Tartan*, a yearbook. Radio station WFSE-FM broadcasts 120 hours per week. *Surrounding community:* Edinboro population 6,500. Cleveland (OH), 75 miles from campus, is nearest metropolitan area. Served by mass transit bus system; airport 20 miles from campus; passenger rail service 18 miles from campus.

Publications: Sources of information about Edinboro University include *President's Report, In Touch Newsletter, Edinboro University Fact Book*.

Library Collections: 492,000 volumes including bound books, serial backfiles, electronic documents, and government documents not in separate collections. Online catalog. Current serial subscriptions: 1,523 paper, 1,401,944 microform. Computer work stations available. Students have access to the Internet at no charge.

Most important special holdings include collection of Audubon Prints; papers of Edinboro Presidents Ross and Van Houten; William Alexander Musical Instrument Collection.

Buildings and Grounds: Campus area 585 acres.

Chief Executive Officer: Dr. Frank G. Pogue, President.

Undergraduates address admission inquiries to Melissa Manning, Director of Admissions; graduate inquiries to Dr. R. Scott Baldwin, Dean of Graduate Studies.

Elizabethtown College

One Alpha Drive
Elizabethtown, Pennsylvania 17022-2298
Tel: (717) 361-1000 **E-mail:** admissions@etown.edu
Fax: (717) 361-1148 **Internet:** www.etown.edu

Institution Description: Elizabethtown College is a private college affiliated with the Church of the Brethren. *Enrollment:* 2,311. *Degrees awarded:* Associate, baccalaureate, master's. .

Accreditation: *Regional:* MSA/CHE. *Professional*: chemistry, music, occupational therapy, social work.

History: Established and offered first instruction at postsecondary level 1899; awarded first degree (baccalaureate) 1903. *See* Ralph W. Schlosser, *History of Elizabethtown College* (Elizabethtown, Pa.: Elizabethtown College, 1971) for further information.

Institutional Structure: *Governing board:* Board of Trustees. Extrainstitutional representation: 43 trustees including 9associate trustees, 1 honorary trustee, 27 alumni, 33 voting. *Composition of institution:* Administrators 40. Academic affairs headed by provost. Management/business/finances directed by treasurer. Full-time instructional faculty 125. Faculty-based academic governance body.

Calendar: Semesters. Academic year Aug. to May. Freshmen admitted Sept., Jan. Degrees conferred May, Aug., Dec. Formal commencement May. Summer session of 2 terms from May to July.

Characteristics of Freshmen: 3,370 applicants (female 2,224, male 1,146). 58% of applicants accepted. 25% of accepted applicants enrolled full-time.

98% (527 students) submitted SAT scores. *25th percentile*: SAT Critical Reading 500, SAT Math 500. *75th percentile*: SAT Critical Reading 600, SAT Math 620.

67% of entering freshmen expected to graduate within 5 years. 66% of freshmen from Pennsylvania. Freshmen from 20 states and 26 foreign countries.

Admission: Rolling admissions. For fall acceptance, apply as early as end of junior year of secondary school. Students are notified of acceptance beginning in early December. Early acceptance available. *Requirements:* Either graduation from accredited secondary school with 18 units including 4 English, 3 mathematics, 2 lab sciences, 2 foreign language, 2 social studies, and 5 electives; or GED. Recommended 2.5 GPA. *Entrance tests:* College Board SAT or ACT. *For transfer students:* 2.5 recommended GPA; from 4-year accredited institution maximum transfer credit limited only by residence requirement; 2-year accredited institution 64 hours maximum transfer credit.

College credit and advanced placement for postsecondary-level work completed in secondary school. Tutoring available.

Degree Requirements: *For all baccalaureate degrees:* 125 or more credit hours; 30 of final 60 hours in residence; 3 hours physical education; completion of Liberal Art Core Program. *For all undergraduate degrees:* 2.0 GPA.

Fulfillment of some degree requirements and exemption from some beginning courses possible by passing departmental examinations, College Board AP. *Grading system:* A–F; pass-fail withdraw (deadline after which pass-fail is appended to withdraw); incomplete.

Distinctive Educational Programs: Flexible meeting places and schedule including off-campus center in Harrisburg, less than 30 miles away from main institution, evening classes. Dual-degree programs in engineering with Pennsylvania State University (University Park campus) and in forestry and environmental studies with Duke University (NC). Cooperative baccalaureate program in nursing, medical technology, and other allied health professions with Thomas Jefferson University (Philadelphia). Majors in occupational therapy and music therapy. Facilities for communications and telecommunications. Interdepartmental/interdisciplinary program in international studies; teaching certification programs in general science, social studies, music, early childhood education. Varied business program. Facilities and programs for independent research, including individual majors, independent and directed study. Foreign study through Brethren Colleges Abroad at St. Mary's College in Cheltenham, England; University of Strasbourg, France; University of Barcelona, Spain; Philips-Universitat in Marburg/Lahn, Germany; University of Hokusei Gakuen, Sapporo, Japan; University of Nancy, Nancy, France; University of Azuay, Cuenca, Ecuador; University of LaVerne/Athens Center, Athens, Greece.

Degrees Conferred: 21 *associate*; 516 *baccalaureate*; 18 *master's*. Bachelor's degrees awarded in top five disciplines: business, management, marketing, and related support services 100; health professions and related clinical sciences 77; education 65; communication, journalism, and related programs 41; psychology 23. Master's degrees awarded: health professions 18.

Fees and Other Expenses: *Full-time tuition and fees per academic year 2008–09:* $30,850. *Books and supplies:* $700. *Room and board per academic year:* $7,950. *Other expenses:* $750.

Financial Aid: Aid from institutionally generated funds is provided on the basis of academic merit, financial need, other criteria.

Financial aid to full-time, first-time undergraduate students: 100% received some form of financial aid. Average amount of aid received: federal grants $3,137; state/local grants $3,656; institutional grants $11,599; loans $5,826.

Departments and Teaching Staff: *Total instructional faculty:* 152. Degrees held by full-time faculty: baccalaureate 2%, master's 27%, doctorate 69%, professional 2%. 71% hold terminal degrees.

Enrollment: Total enrollment 2,311. Undergraduate 2,258 (full-time 82%; female 65%, male 35%). Graduate 53 (full-time 79%).

Characteristics of Student Body: *Ethnic/racial makeup:* Black non-Hispanic: 3%; Asian or Pacific Islander: 2%; Hispanic: 3%; White non-Hispanic: 90%; nonresident alien 2%.

International Students: 46 nonresident aliens enrolled fall 2008. Students from Europe, Asia, Latin America, Africa. Programs available to aid students whose native language is not English: English as a Second Language Program. Financial aid specifically designated for international students: variable number of scholarships available annually for qualifying undergraduate students.

Student Life: On-campus residence halls, honor houses and apartments house 90% of student body. Single-gender and co-educational housing available. No fraternities or sororities. *Intercollegiate athletics:* male: baseball, wrestling; female: field hockey, softball, volleyball; both sexes: basketball, soccer, tennis, swimming, cross-country. *Special regulations:* Cars permitted for all students. *Special services:* Learning Center (tutoring provided free of charge for all students) and campus health service. *Student publications, radio: The Etownian*, a weekly newspaper; also a yearbook and a literary magazine; radio station WWEC-FM; cable television station WWEC-TV. *Surrounding community:* Elizabethtown population 20,000. Lancaster and Harrisburg are 18 miles away; Philadelphia and Baltimore are 75 miles from campus. Served by airport 10 miles from campus (Harrisburg). Amtrak rail station is 1 mile from campus.

Library Collections: 200,000 volumes. 157,000 non-print items; 912 current periodical subscriptions. Students have access to online information retrieval services and the Internet.

Most important special collections include Church of the Brethren Archives; private collection on history of Pennsylvania; college archives.

Buildings and Grounds: Campus area 185 acres.

Chief Executive Officer: Dr. Theodore E. Long, President.

Address admission inquiries to Director of Admissions.

Evangelical School of Theology

121 South College Street
Myerstown, Pennsylvania 17067-1299
Tel: (717) 866-5775 **E-mail:** enrollment@evangelical.edu
Fax: (717) 866-4667 **Internet:** www.evangelical.edu

Institution Description: Evangelical School of Theology is a private interdenominational graduate seminary affiliated with the Evangelical Congregational Church. *Enrollment:* 177. *Degrees awarded:* First-professional (master of divinity), master's.

Accreditation: *Regional:* Middle States. *National:* ATS. *Professional*: theology

History: Established 1953; awarded first degree (baccalaureate 1958); changed to master's curriculum 1971.

Institutional Structure: *Governing board:* Board of Trustees (4 members). *Composition of institution:* President, academic dean, business manager, vice president for development. Full-time instructional faculty 6.

Calendar: Semesters with January term. Academic year Sept. to May. Degrees conferred and formal commencement May.

Admission: *Requirements:* For graduate degree, MAT or GRE. For first-professional degree, graduation from accredited college with preseminary curriculum; 2.5/4.0 GPA.

Degree Requirements: *For all first-professional degree:* 96 semester hours. *For master's degree:* 56 hours. *For all degrees:* 2.5 GPA; 32 hours in residence. *Grading system:* A–F; satisfactory-unsatisfactory; withdraw (deadline after which pass-fail is appended to withdraw).

Distinctive Educational Programs: Independent study options. Opportunity for study in Israel; associated with Jerusalem University College.

Degrees Conferred: 15 *master's:* theology; 11 *first-professional:* master of divinity.

Fees and Other Expenses: *Full-time tuition and fees per academic year 2008–09:* contact the seminary for current tuition, fees, and other costs.

Financial Aid: Aid from institutionally generated funds is provided on the basis of academic merit, financial need. Institution has a Program Participation Agreement with the U.S. Department of Education for eligible students to receive Pell Grants and, depending upon the agreement, other federal aid.

Departments and Teaching Staff: *Total instructional faculty:* 20. Degrees held by full-time faculty: doctorates 100%.

Enrollment: Total enrollment 177. Undergraduate

Characteristics of Student Body: *Ethnic/racial makeup:* Black non-Hispanic: 2%; Hispanic: 2%; White non-Hispanic: 95%.

International Students: 1 nonresident alien enrolled fall 2008. No programs available to aid students whose native language is not English. Financial aid specifically designated for international students: scholarships available annually to qualifying students.

Student Life: On-campus housing for single males, single females, and for married students and their families. *Special services:* Personal and career counseling. Daily chapel program. Annual lecture series and other events. *Student publication: The Communique*, a weekly newssheet. *Surrounding community:* Myerstown is 60 miles from Philadelphia.

Publications: *Evangelical Journal*, published twice per year; *The Evangelical Call*, an informational publication published three times per year.

Library Collections: 70,000 volumes including bound books, serial backfiles, electronic documents, and government documents not in separate collections. Online catalog. Current serial subscriptions: 535 paper, 5 electronic. 506 recordings; 9 CD-ROMs. Computer work stations available. Students have access to the Internet at no charge.

Most important special holdings include William F. Heil Papers; Maurer Pietism Collection; Evangelical Congregational Church Archives.

Buildings and Grounds: Campus area 12 acres.

Chief Executive Officer: Rev. Dr. Kirby N. Keller, President.

Address admission inquiries to Director of Enrollment Services.

Franklin and Marshall College

P.O. Box 3003
Lancaster, Pennsylvania 17604-3003
Tel: (717) 291-3911 **E-mail:** admission@fandm.edu
Fax: (717) 291-4389 **Internet:** www.fandm.edu

Institution Description: Franklin and Marshall College is a private, coeducational liberal arts college. *Enrollment:* 2,164. *Degrees awarded:* Baccalaureate.

Accreditation: *Regional:* MSA/CHE.

History: Chartered as Franklin College, offered first instruction at postsecondary level 1787; awarded first degree (baccalaureate) 1791; merged with Marshall College (established 1834) and adopted present name 1853.

Institutional Structure: *Governing board:* Board of Trustees. Extrainstitutional representation: 38 trustees; institutional representation: president of the college. *Composition of institution:* Administrators 138. Academic affairs headed by provost; academic affairs/dean of the college. Management/business/finances directed by the vice president for finance and administration. Student affairs headed by vice president of the college/dean of educational services. Alumni, development, extension relations headed by vice president for advancement. Full-time instructional faculty 175. Academic governance body, Faculty Council.

Calendar: Semesters. Academic year Sept. to May. Freshmen admitted Sept., Feb. Degrees conferred and formal commencement May 17. Summer session of 2 terms.

Characteristics of Freshmen: 5,632 applicants (female 3,007, male 2,625). 36% of applicants admitted. 29% of applicants admitted and enrolled full-time.

73% (380 students) submitted SAT scores. *25th percentile*: SAT Critical Reading 580, SAT Math 600. *75th percentile*: SAT Critical Reading 670, SAT Math 690.

82% of entering freshmen expected to graduate within 5 years. 353% of freshmen from Pennsylvania. Students from 25 states and 19 foreign countries.

Admission: For fall acceptance, apply by Feb. 1. Notification of acceptance by by Apr. 1. Apply by Nov. 15 or Jan. 15 for 2 rounds of early decision. *Requirements:* Graduation from accredited secondary school. Recommend college preparatory program with 4 units English, 3 in a foreign language, 3 mathematics, 3 laboratory science, 3 social studies. *Entrance tests:* College Board SAT or ACT composite and English Achievement. Standardized tests optional if in top 10% of class. *For transfer students:* Maximum transfer credit limited only by residence requirement.

College credit and advanced placement for postsecondary-level work completed in secondary school.

Degree Requirements: *For all baccalaureate degrees:* 32 courses; 16 courses and last semester in residence; demonstrated proficiency in English. *For all degrees:* 2.0 GPA; general education requirements. *Grading system:* A–F; pass-no pass; withdraw (carries time limit).

Distinctive Educational Programs: Interdisciplinary majors in African studies, American studies, biochemistry, biological foundations of behavior (animal behavior or neuroscience), environmental science, environmental studies, scientific and philosophic study of mind, women's studies, minors in Asian studies, Judaic studies, environmental studies, and science technology and society. 3/2 engineering and forestry programs. One in four students participate in off-campus study experiences. General education includes three foundations courses in the area of mind, self, spirit; Community Culture Society; Natural World. Study approved programs in Europe, Asia, Africa, Latin American, Middle East, Australia, New Zealand.

ROTC: Army in cooperation with Millersville University.

Degrees Conferred: 440 *baccalaureate:* area and ethnic studies 11; biological/life sciences 41; business and management 92; English 34; foreign languages 22; interdisciplinary studies 46; liberal arts and sciences, general studies, and humanities 24; mathematics 13; philosophy/religion 16; physical sciences 27; psychology 36; social sciences 130; visual and performing arts 17.

Fees and Other Expenses: *Full-time tuition per academic year 2008=09:* $38,630. *Other fees:* $50. *Room and board per academic year:* $9,870. *Books and supplies:* $650. *Other expenses:* $950.

Financial Aid: Aid from institutionally generated funds is provided on the basis of academic merit, financial need.

Financial aid to full-time, first-time undergraduate students: 57% received some form of financial aid. Average amount of aid received: federal grants 42,642; state/local grants $3,500; institutional grants $6,361; loans $2,655.

Departments and Teaching Staff: *Total instructional faculty:* 207 (full-time 161, part-time 46). Total faculty with doctorate, first-professional, or other terminal degree: 178. Student/faculty ratio: 11:1. Degrees held by full-time faculty: baccalaureate 99.4%, master's 100%, doctorate 91.9%, professional 3.1%. 95% hold terminal degrees.

Enrollment: Total enrollment 2,164. Undergraduate 2,165 (full-time 98%; female 52%, male 48%).

Characteristics of Student Body: *Ethnic/racial makeup:* Black non-Hispanic: 4%; Asian or Pacific Islander: 4%; Hispanic: 4%; White non-Hispanic: 69%; unknown: 10%; nonresident alien 9%.

International Students: 198 nonresident aliens enrolled fall 2008. Students from Europe, Asia, Central and South America, Africa, Canada, Caribbean. No programs available to aid students whose native language is not English. Financial aid specifically designated for international students: scholarships available annually to qualifying students.

Student Life: On-campus residence halls. Juniors and seniors may live off-campus if they choose. *Intercollegiate athletics:* male: baseball, basketball, cross-country, football, golf, lacrosse, soccer, squash, swimming, tennis, track, wrestling; female: basketball, cross-country, field hockey, golf, lacrosse, soccer, softball, squash, swimming, tennis, track, volleyball; both sexes: golf. Club sports include crew and rugby for males and females; male ice hokcy. *Special regulations:* Registered cars permitted on campus. *Student organizations:* Over 110 recognized student clubs and organizations on campus, including academic, educational, honorary societies, literary, musical, political, religious, service and social. *Student media: College Reporter,* a weekly newspaper; *Commentator,* a journal on political and economics affairs; *Conundrum,* a humor brochure; *Encyclopedia Nevonia,* a guide to life at F. & M. and the Lancaster community; *Hullaballo,* a humor magazine; *Kitutiwan,* an annual journal of student papers in anthropology; *Oriflamme,* a yearbook; *Prolog,* an annual literary magazine. Radio station WFNM-AM and FM. Cable television station WFMC. *Student programming: Bens Underground,* a student-managed restaurant/nite club that provides many social and recreational opportunities for students; College Entertainment Committee, a student board that programs concerts, films, lectures, etc. Student Arts Council sponsors Fall and Spring Arts entertainment weekends. *Surrounding community:* Lancaster County population 425,000. Campus is 90 minutes from Baltimore and Philadelphia; midway between Washington D.C. and New York City. Served by rail and regional airport.

Publications: *F&M News,* a tabloid published 6 times a year for alumni, parents, and friends of the college.

Library Collections: 437,000 volumes including bound books, serial backfiles, electronic documents, and government documents not in separate collections. Online catalog. 231,000 microforms; 10,000 audiovisual materials; 3,000 Current serial subscriptions. Computer work stations available. Students have access to the Internet at no charge.

Most important special holdings include German American Imprints; Reynolds Family Paper; Franklin J. Schaffner Film Library.

Buildings and Grounds: Main campus area 71 acres; nearby Baker Memorial campus 54 acres. Campus DVD available.

Chief Executive Officer: Dr. John A. Fry, President.

Address admission inquiries to Dennis Trotler, Director of Admissions.

Gannon University

University Square
Erie, Pennsylvania 16451
Tel: (800) 871-7000 **E-mail:** admissions@.gannon.edu
Fax: (814) 871-5803 **Internet:** /www.gannon.edu

Institution Description: Gannon University is a private institution affiliated with the Diocese of Erie, Roman Catholic Church. *Enrollment:* 4,197. *Degrees awarded:* Associate, baccalaureate, master's, doctorate. Certificates also awarded.

Accreditation: *Regional:* MSA/CHE. *Professional*: dietetics, engineering, medical assisting, nurse anesthesia education, nursing, occupational therapy, physical therapy, physician assisting, respiratory therapy, social work, teacher education

History: Established as Cathedral College, a junior college, 1933; changed name to Gannon School of Arts and Sciences 1941; chartered and changed name to Gannon College 1944; awarded first degree (baccalaureate) 1945; adopted present name 1979; merged with Villa Maria College in 1989.

Institutional Structure: *Governing board:* Gannon University Board of Trustees. Representation: 41 trustees, including 7 trustees emeriti and 5 ex-officio; president of the university, presidents of the faculty senate, student government association, alumni association. 41 voting. *Composition of institution:* Administrators 172/ Academic affairs headed by provost and vice president for academic affairs; other vice presidents include vice president for finance and administration and vice president for university advancement. Full-time instructional faculty 181. Academic governance body, University Senate, meets several times each year.

Calendar: Semesters. Academic year Aug. to May. Freshmen admitted Sept., Jan. Degrees conferred Aug., Dec., May. Formal commencement May. Summer session of 2 terms from June to Aug.

Characteristics of Freshmen: 3,021 applicants (female 1,757, male 1,264). 82% of applicants accepted. 25% of accepted applicants enrolled full-time.

89% (517 students) submitted SAT scores; 33% (192 students) submitted ACT scores. *25th percentile*: SAT Critical Reading 460, SAT Math 460; ACT Composite 19, ACT English 18, ACT Math 18. *75th percentile*: SAT Critical Reading 540, SAT Math 580; ACT Composite 24, ACT English 24, ACT Math 24.

64% of entering freshmen expected to graduate within 5 years. 76% of freshmen from Pennsylvania. Freshmen from 17 states and 3 foreign countries.

Admission: Rolling admissions plan. For fall acceptance, apply as early as Sept. 1 of previous year, but not later than beginning of classes. Early acceptance available. Some programs also have application deadlines: occupational therapy, physician assistant, radiological science Jan. 15; medical scholars program Dec. 15. *Requirements:* Either graduation from accredited secondary school with 16 academic units; or GED. Minimum 2.0 GPA. *Entrance tests:* College Board SAT or ACT composite. *For transfer students:* 2.0 minimum GPA; from 4-year accredited institution 98 hours maximum transfer credit; from 2-year accredited institution 64 hours.

College credit and advanced placement for postsecondary-level work completed in secondary school.

Tutoring available. Noncredit developmental courses offered in summer session and regular academic year.

Degree Requirements: *For all associate degrees:* 64–70 credit hours. *For all baccalaureate degrees:* 128–135 credit hours. *For all undergraduate degrees:* 2.0 GPA; final year in residence; distribution requirements.

Fulfillment of some degree requirements and exemption from some beginning courses possible by passing College Board CLEP, AP. *Grading system:* A–F; pass-fail; withdraw (carries time limit).

Distinctive Educational Programs: *For undergraduates:* Accelerated medical programs in optometry and podiatry; pre-professional programs in medicine, dentistry, osteopathy, physical therapy, pharmacy and veterinary medicine. Honors program. Study abroad by individual arrangement. Cooperative education/internships available in most majors. ABET accredited engineering programs. *Graduate studies:* 22 master's degree programs; full-time physical therapy program; variety of certificates; evening and weekend classes. 3–3 early admissions law program; 2–4 pharmacy program; entrepreneurial science. *For all students:* Day, evening, and weekend classes; main campus, and outreach centers; professional and personal development classes; Open University and Adult Educational Services. Doctoral program in counseling psychology and physical therapy.

ROTC: Army.

Degrees Conferred: 442 *baccalaureate*; 449 *master's*; 30 *doctorate*. Bachelor's degrees awarded in top five disciplines: health professions and related clinical sciences 118; business, management, marketing, and related support services 85; education 47; engineering/engineering biological/life sciences 26; psychology 15. Master's degrees warded in top five disciplines: education 217; health professions 888; business/marketing 30; engineering 24; psychology 15. Doctorates awarded: health professions 30.

Fees and Other Expenses: *Full-time tuition per academic year 2008–09:* $23,332 undergraduate; contact the university for current graduate tuition. *Required fees:* $496. *Room and board per academic year:* $8,710. *Books and supplies:* $1,200. *Other expenses:* $2,558.

Financial Aid: Aid from institutionally generated funds is provided on the basis of academic merit, financial need, athletic ability, other criteria.

Financial aid to full-time, first-time undergraduate students: 100% received some form of aid. Average amount of aid received: federal grants $3,599; Pell grants $3,070; other federal aid $753; state/local grants $3,843; institutional grants $10,217.

Departments and Teaching Staff: *Total instructional faculty:* 312. Total faculty with doctorate, first-professional, or other terminal degree: 150. Student/faculty ratio: 11:1. Degrees held by full-time faculty: baccalaureate 3.6%, master's 40%, doctorate 52%, professional .6%. 85% hold terminal degrees.

Enrollment: Total enrollment 4,197. Undergraduate 2,824 (full-time 83%; female 59%, male 41%). Graduate 1,272 (full-time 38%). Undergraduate transfer-in students 103.

Characteristics of Student Body: *Ethnic/racial makeup:* Black non-Hispanic: 4%; Asian or Pacific Islander: 1%; Hispanic: 2%; White non-Hispanic: 88%; unknown: 4%; nonresident alien 1%. *Age distribution:* number under 18: 186; 18–19: 1,098; 20–21: 846; 22–24: 251; 25–29: 87; 30–34: 66; 35–39: 52; 40–49: 67; 50–64: 18; 65 and over: 4.

International Students: 212 nonresident aliens enrolled fall 2008. Students from Europe, Asia, Central and South America, Africa, Canada, Australia, Middle East. No programs available to aid students whose native language is not English. No financial aid specifically designated for international students.

Student Life: 46% of students live in on-campus housing. On-campus residence halls house 47% of student body. Residence halls for nakes constitute 43% of such space, for females 57%. 5% of students are housed off-campus in university-subsidized apartments. Freshmen must live on campus for first two years unless they are within a 25-mile radius of the campus. There are 5 fraternities and 5 sororities. *Intercollegiate athletics:* male: baseball, basketball, cross-country, football, golf, soccer, swimming, water polo, wrestling; female: basketball, cross-country, golf, lacrosse, soccer, softball, swimming, water polo, volleyball. *Special regulations:* Cars permitted. Quiet hours. Residence hall visitation hours. *Special services:* Learning Resources Center, medical services, counseling and career services, security escort services. *Student publications, media: The Gannon Knight*, a weekly newspaper; *The Phoenix*, an annual literary magazine. *Surrounding community:* Erie metropolitan area population 276,000. Erie is located within a 130 mile radius of Cleveland (OH), Buffalo (NY), and Pittsburgh (PA). Served by mass transit bus system, airport 8 miles from campus, passenger rail service 1 mile from campus.

Library Collections: 270,000 volumes. 834,900 microforms; 3,028 audiovisual materials; 2,073 current serial subscriptions. Students have access to online information retrieval services and the Internet.

Most important special holdings include the Chesterton Collection; the Symmons Collection of Polish History; the Early American Imprints on microcard.

Buildings and Grounds: The university's buildings offer a variety of architectural styles ranging from Victorian mansions to modern sports and recreation complexes.

Chief Executive Officer: Dr. Antoine M. Garibaldi, President.

Address admission inquiries to Director of Admissions.

Geneva College

3200 College Avenue
Beaver Falls, Pennsylvania 15010-3599

Tel: (724) 846-5100 **E-mail:** admissions@geneva.edu
Fax: (724) 847-6776 **Internet:** www.geneva.edu

Institution Description: Geneva College is a private college affiliated with the Reformed Presbyterian Church of North America. *Enrollment:* 1,951. *Degrees awarded:* Associate, baccalaureate, master's.

Accreditation: *Regional:* MSA/CHE. *Professional*: chemistry

History: Established as Geneva Hall and offered first instruction at postsecondary level 1848; incorporated 1850; awarded first degree (baccalaureate) 1852; adopted present name 1873. *See* William M. Glasgow, *The Geneva Book* (Philadelphia: Westbrook, 1908) for further information.

Institutional Structure: *Governing board:* Board of Trustees. Extrainstitutional representation: 33 trustees; 5 alumni. All voting. Administrators *****. Academic affairs headed by vice president for academic affairs. Management/business/finances directed by vice president for business/finance. Full-time instructional faculty 75. Academic governance body, the faculty, meets an average of 10 times per year.

Calendar: Semesters. Academic year Aug. to May. Freshmen admitted Aug., Jan., June. Degrees conferred May, Aug., Jan.

Characteristics of Freshmen: 1,264 applicants (female 623, male 641). 81% of applicants accepted. 38% of accepted applicants enrolled full-time.

89% (262 students) submitted SAT scores; 11% (32 students) submitted ACT scores. *25th percentile*: SAT Critical Reading 490, SAT Math 480; ACT Composite 26, ACT English 23, ACT Math 23. *75th percentile*: SAT Critical Reading 610, SAT Math 590; ACT Composite 25, ACT English 25, ACT Math 25.

73% of freshmen from Pennsylvania. Freshmen from 38 states and 19 foreign countries.

Admission: Rolling admissions plan. For fall acceptance, apply as early as Sept. of previous year, but not later than one week before classes begin. *Requirements:* Either graduation from accredited secondary school with 16 units which normally include 4 English, 2 foreign language, 2 college preparatory mathematics, 1 science, 3 social studies, 4 electives; or GED. Minimum GPA 2.0. Lowest acceptable secondary school class standing 40th percentile. *Entrance tests:* College Board SAT or ACT composite. *For transfer students:* 2.0 minimum GPA; from 4-year accredited institution 96 hours maximum transfer credit; from 2-year accredited institution and for correspondence/extension students 64 hours.

College credit and advanced placement for postsecondary-level work completed in secondary school, College Board AP, and extrainstitutional learning on basis of portfolio; faculty assessment.

Tutoring available. Developmental courses offered during regular academic year; credit given.

Degree Requirements: *For all associate degrees:* 63–67 credit hours; 1 semester physical education. *For all baccalaureate degrees:* 126–137 credit hours; 2 semesters physical education. *For all undergraduate degrees:* 2.0 GPA; 48 hours from Geneva.

GENEVA COLLEGE—*cont'd*

Fulfillment of some degree requirements and exemption from some beginning courses possible by passing departmental examinations, College Board CLEP, AP. *Grading system:* A–F; credit-no credit; withdraw.

Distinctive Educational Programs: Flexible meeting places and schedules, including off-campus center (at Center for Urban Theological Studies in Philadelphia, 300 miles away from main institution), weekend and evening classes. Dual-degree program in nursing in cooperation with Case Western Reserve University, Cleveland, Ohio. Degree programs in life support technology affiliated with The Fairfax Hospital of Falls Church, Virginia and in medical technology with the University Hospitals of Cleveland through Case Western Reserve University. Interdisciplinary/preprofessional programs in allied health, Christian school teaching, communications, and general science. Degree Completion Program offers a bachelor of science in human resources management to nontraditional working students. Program consists of 42 hours offered over 15 months in classes which meet once a week in various locations in surrounding communities. Study abroad various countries in cooperation with the Council of Christian Colleges and Universities. Business aviation degree in cooperation with Beaver County Community College and Beaver County Airport.

Degrees Conferred: 11 *associate*; 424 *baccalaureate*; 141 *master's*. Bachelor's degrees awarded in top five disciplines: business, management, marketing, and related support services 139; education 90; theology 60; Engineering 23; public administration 21. Master's degrees awrded: various disciplines 141.

Fees and Other Expenses: *Full-time tuition/fees per academic year 2008–09:* $20,400. *Room and board per academic year:* $7,450. *Books and supplies:* $900. *Other expenses:* $1,150.

Financial Aid: Aid from institutionally generated funds is provided on the basis of academic merit, financial need, athletic ability.

Financial aid to full-time, first-time undergraduate students: 95% received some form of financial aid. Average amount of aid received: federal grants $3,824; Pell grants $2,515; other federal aid $1,481; state/local grants $3,548; institutional grants $8,625.

Departments and Teaching Staff: *Total instructional faculty:* 148. Student/faculty ratio: 18:1. Degrees held by full-time faculty: master's 100%, doctorate 70%. 70% hold terminal degrees.

Enrollment: Total enrollment 1,951. Undergraduate 1,719 (full-time 91%; female 54%, male 46%). Graduate 232 (full-time 54%). Undergraduate transfer-in students 64.

Characteristics of Student Body: *Ethnic/racial makeup:* Black non-Hispanic: 11%; Asian or Pacific Islander: 1%; Hispanic: 1%; White non-Hispanic: 84%; nonresident alien 1%.

International Students: 20 nonresident aliens enrolled fall 2008. Students from Europe, Asia, Central and South America, Africa, Canada. Programs available to aid students whose native language is not English: social, cultural, financial. English as a Second Language Program.

Student Life: On-campus residence halls house 72% of student body. Residence halls for males 47% of such space, for females 53%. 1% of students live off-campus in college-approved private homes. *Intercollegiate athletics:* male: baseball, basketball, cross-country, football, soccer, tennis, track; female: basketball, cross-country, soccer, softball, tennis, track, volleyball. *Special regulations:* Cars permitted in designated areas only. *Special services:* medical services. *Student publications, radio: The Cabinet*, a weekly newspaper; *Chimes*, an annual literary magazine; *The Genevan*, a yearbook. Radio station WGEV-FM broadcasts 84 hours per week year round (special emphasis given to contemporary Christian and gospel music); WGEV-TV on air 24 hours a day with 2 hours a day student-produced programming. *Surrounding community:* Beaver Falls population 15,000. Pittsburgh, 35 miles from campus, is nearest metropolitan area. Served by mass transit bus system; airport 25 miles from campus; passenger rail service 35 miles from campus.

Library Collections: 167,200 volumes. 12,900 audiovisual materials. 198,000 microform units. 890 serial subscriptions. Students have access to online information retrieval services and the Internet.

Most important holdings include Convenanter Collection (materials on the history of the Reformed Presbyterian Church of North America); library and personal papers of Dr. Clarence Edward Macartney; historical collection on Geneva College; Coleman Political Science Collection of Christian Worldview of Government.

Buildings and Grounds: Campus area 50 acres.

Chief Executive Officer: Dr. Kenneth A. Smith, President.

Undergraduates address admission inquiries to Director of Admissions; graduate inquires to Robin Ware, Graduate Psychology Program or Dr. James Dittmar, Graduate Organizational Leadership Program.

Gettysburg College

300 North Washington Street
Gettysburg, Pennsylvania 17325-1486
Tel: (717) 337-6000 **E-mail:** admiss@gettysburg.edu
Fax: (717) 337-6145 **Internet:** www.gettysburg,edu

Institution Description: Gettysburg College is a private, independent, nonprofit institution affiliated with the Lutheran Church in America. *Enrollment:* 2,480. *Degrees awarded:* Baccalaureate.

Member of Central Pennsylvania Consortium (CPC).

Accreditation: *Regional:* MSA/CHE. *Professional*: chemistry

History: Established as Pennsylvania College at Gettysburg and offered first instruction at postsecondary level 1832; awarded first degree (baccalaureate) 1833; changed name to Gettysburg College 1921. *See* Samuel Gring Hefelbower, *The History of Gettysburg College, 1832–1932* (Gettysburg: Gettysburg College, 1932) for further information.

Institutional Structure: *Governing board:* The Board of Trustees. Extrainstitutional representation: 24 trustees, 8 representatives of Lutheran Church in America, 1 (nonvoting) representative of the Women's General League; institutional representation: president of the college; 6 alumni. 3 ex officio. 39 voting. *Composition of institution:* Administrators 82. Academic affairs headed by provost. Management/business/finances directed by treasurer and business manager. Full-time instructional faculty 108. Academic governance body, the Faculty of Gettysburg College, meets an average of 9 times per year.

Calendar: Semesters. Academic year Aug. to May. Freshmen admitted Sept., Feb. Degrees conferred June, Aug., Dec., Jan. Formal commencement May. No summer session.

Characteristics of Freshmen: 5,794 applicants (female 3,088, male 2,706). 43% of applicants accepted. 32% of accepted applicants enrolled full-time.

94% (655 students) submitted SAT scores; 6% (40 students) submitted ACT scores. *25th percentile*: SAT Critical; Reading 600, SAT Math 610; ACT Composite 27. *75th percentile*: SAT Critical Reading 680, SAT Math 690; ACT Composite 30.

75% of entering freshmen expected to graduate within 5 years. 25% of freshmen from Pennsylvania. Students from 40 states and 35 foreign countries.

Admission: For fall acceptance, apply as early as July 1 of previous year, but not later than Feb. 15. Students are notified of acceptance April. Apply by Nov. 15 for early decision. Early acceptance available. *Requirements:* Graduation from accredited secondary school, preferably with program that includes strong and varied selection of academic courses; or GED. *Entrance tests:* College Board SAT preferred; ACT composite accepted. *For transfer students:* 3.0 minimum GPA; transfer credits accepted through junior year standing.

College credit and advanced placement for postsecondary-level work completed in secondary school.

Degree Requirements: 122.5 credit hours; 2.0 GPA; final year in residence; 4 terms physical education; exit competency examinations-standardized tests in economics, business administration, and sociology.

Fulfillment of some degree requirements and exemption from some beginning courses possible by passing departmental examinations and College Board APP. *Grading system:* A–F; pass-fail; withdraw (carries deadline after which pass-fail is appended to withdraw).

Distinctive Educational Programs: Dual-degree programs in engineering with Rensselaer Polytechnic Institute (NY), Pennsylvania State University, and Washington University (MO); and in forestry with Duke University (NC). Interdepartmental/interdisciplinary programs for some seniors and students with special majors. Facilities for independent research, including honors programs, individualized majors, tutorials. Study abroad program in India during junior year. CPC sponsors The Harrisburg Urban Studies (THUS) program of semester internships in cooperation with Franklin and Marshall, Dickinson Colleges, and Bucknell University. Study abroad through programs in Spain, France, England, Italy, Mexico, Japan, Hungary, Australia, Africa.

Degrees Conferred: 645 *baccalaureate*. Bachelor's degrees awarded in top five disciplines: business, management, marketing, and related support services 133; social sciences 101; history 49; psychology 48; English language/literature 44.

Fees and Other Expenses: *Full-time tuition per academic year 2008–09:* $7,730. *Room and board per academic year:* $9,100. *Books and supplies:* $500. *Other expenses:* $500.

Financial Aid: Aid from institutionally generated funds is provided on the basis of academic merit, financial need.

Financial aid to full-time, first-time undergraduate students: 70% received some form of financial aid. Average amount of aid received: federal grants $1,708; Pell grants $3,087; other federal aid $1,018; state/local grants $2,789; institutional grants $20,601.

Departments and Teaching Staff: *Total instructional faculty:* 184.5 FTE. Degrees held by full-time faculty: doctorate 89.5%, master's 6.8%. 85% hold terminal degrees.

Enrollment: *Total enrollment:* 2,480. Undergraduate 2,480 (full-time 99%; female 53%, male 27%). Transfer-in students 6.

Characteristics of Student Body: *Ethnic/racial makeup:* Black non-Hispanic: 5%; Asian or Pacific Islander 1%; Hispanic 3%; White non-Hispanic: 84%; unknown 5%; nonresident alien 2%.

International Students: 48 nonresident aliens enrolled fall 2008. Students from Europe, Asia, Central and South America, Africa, Canada. Programs available to aid students whose native language is not English: cultural, financial.

Student Life: On-campus residence halls house 66% of student body. Residence halls for males constitute 10% of such space, for females 22%, for both sexes 68%. 70% of males join and 34% live in fraternity housing. *Intercollegiate athletics:* male: baseball, basketball, football, lacrosse, soccer, swimming, tennis, track; female: basketball, hockey, lacrosse, softball, swimming, tennis, track, volleyball. *Special regulations:* Cars permitted without restrictions. Both "open" dorms and restricted visitation options are available. *Special services:* Learning Resources Center, medical services. *Student publications, radio: The Gettysburgian*, a weekly student newspaper; *Mercury*, an annual literary magazine; *The Spectrum*, a yearbook. Radio station WZBT broadcasts 98 hours per week. *Surrounding community:* Gettysburg population 8,000. Baltimore, 60 miles from campus, is nearest metropolitan area. Served by airport 36 miles from campus; passenger rail service 36 miles from campus.

Publications: Sources of information about Gettysburg College include *Gettysburg,* the college magazine. *The Gettysburg Review* is a literary journal founded in 1986 and began publication in 1987.

Library Collections: 485,000 volumes. 36,000 microforms; 24,933 audiovisual materials; 1,416 current periodical subscriptions. Students have access to online information retrieval services and the Internet.

Most important special holdings include Civil War Collection; H.L. Mencken Collection; John H. W. Stuckenberg Collection.

Buildings and Grounds: Campus area 200 acres.

Chief Executive Officer: Dr. Katherine H. Will, President.

Address admission inquiries to Gail Sweezey, Director of Admissions.

Gratz College

7605 Old York Road
Melrose Park, Pennsylvania 19027
Tel: (215) 635-7300 **E-mail:** admissions@gratz.edu
Fax: (215) 635-7320 **Internet:** www.gratz.edu

Institution Description: Gratz College is a private, independent, nondenominational college of Jewish, Hebraic, and related Middle East studies. *Enrollment:* 423. *Degrees awarded:* Baccalaureate, master's, first-professional. Certificates also awarded.

Accreditation: *Regional:* MSA/CHE.

History: Chartered 1849; established 1895; offered first instruction at postsecondary level 1897; awarded first degree (baccalaureate) 1952.

Institutional Structure: *Governing board:* Board of Overseers. 42 regular members (plus voting honorary members), plus president, 1 faculty representative, 1 student representative; president of alumni association as ex officio. *Composition of institution:* Administrators 8 plus part-time administrator/faculty members, including chairman of faculty who is responsible for academic affairs. Management/business/finances directed by financial affairs officer. Academic governance body, the faculty, meets monthly during the academic year. A Faculty Senate represents full-time academic professionals *vis a vis* the Board and Administration.

Calendar: Semesters. Academic year Sept. to May. Freshmen admitted Sept., Feb. Degrees conferred and formal commencement June. Summer session from June to July.

Characteristics of Freshmen: 90% of applicants admitted. 80% of applicants admitted and enrolled.

81% of entering freshmen expected to graduate within 5 years. 80% of freshmen from Pennsylvania.

Admission: Rolling admissions plan. Apply any time up to the second week of classes. *Requirements:* Graduation from accredited secondary school or GED; for Bachelor of Hebrew Literature, proficiency in Hebrew language. *Entrance tests:* College Board SAT and/or institutional examinations *may* be required. For foreign students TOEFL. *For transfer students:* 40-46 semester hours maximum transfer credits accepted in Jewish or Hebrew studies; liberal arts credits generally accepted (40 or 60 as required). *For graduate students:* B.A. from accredited institution required; GRE or MAT *may* be required; letter of recommendation and interview required; maximum of 12 transfer credits accepted.

Degree Requirements: *For all undergraduate degrees:* 120–152 semester hours which must include 40–60 liberal arts credits earned at an accredited college or university; 50% of program in residence; distribution requirements; some required courses. *For graduate degrees:* 30 graduate credits; undergraduate prerequisites *may* be required; comprehensives; thesis optional in some programs. *Grading system:* A–F.

Distinctive Educational Programs: Undergraduate programs in Jewish studies and Hebrew language and literature and Jewish education; joint programs in education with Beaver College and Temple University and a joint program with the College of Liberal Arts of Temple University; graduate programs in Jewish studies, Jewish education, Hebrew literature, and Jewish music; certificate programs in Jewish chaplaincy, Judaica librarianship; Sephardic studies and Jewish communal studies.

Degrees Conferred: 275 *master's*: education 255; philosophy 20.

Fees and Other Expenses: *Full-time tuition per academic year 2008–09:* undergraduate $12,000; contact the college for current graduate tuition and fees. *Books and supplies:* $790; *Off-campus room and board per academic year:* $6,500. *Other expenses:* $3,000.

Financial Aid: Aid from institutionally generated funds is provided on the basis of academic merit, financial need. Institution has a Program Participation Agreement with the U.S. Department of Education for eligible students to receive Pell Grants and, depending upon the agreement, other federal aid.

Departments and Teaching Staff: *Total instructional faculty:* 41 (full-time 9, part-time 32). Total faculty with doctorate, first-professional, or other terminal degree: 17.

Enrollment: Total enrollment 423. Undergraduate 12 (full-time 25%; female 83%, male 17%). Graduate 471 (full-time 2%).

International Students: No programs available to aid students whose native language is not English. No financial aid specifically designated for international students.

Student Life: No on-campus housing available. *Surrounding community:* Philadelphia population 1,650,000. Served by mass transit bus and train systems; airport 25 miles from campus; passenger rail service ¼ mile from campus.

Publications: *90th Anniversary Festschrift;* occasional papers.

Library Collections: 100,000 volumes. 10,000 audiovisual materials; 115 current periodical subscriptions. Access to online information retrieval services.

Most important special collections include Holocaust Oral History Archives; Jewish Education Collection; Schreiber Library of Jewish Music.

Buildings and Grounds: Campus area 28 acres.

Chief Executive Officer: Dr. Jonathan Rosenbaum, President.

Address admission inquiries to Dr. Jill K. Sigman, Director of Admissions.

Grove City College

100 Campus Drive
Grove City, Pennsylvania 16127-2104
Tel: (724) 458-2187 **E-mail:** admissions@gcc.edu
Fax: (724) 458-3828 **Internet:** www.gcc.edu

Institution Description: Grove City College is a private college affiliated with the Presbyterian Church (USA). *Enrollment:* 2,499. *Degrees awarded:* Baccalaureate.

Accreditation: *Regional:* MSA/CHE. *Professional*: engineering

History: Established and offered first instruction at postsecondary level 1876; incorporated 1884; awarded first degree (baccalaureate) 1885. *See* David M. Dayton, *'Mid the Pines* (Grove City: Grove City College Alumni Association, 1971) for further information.

Institutional Structure: *Governing board:* Grove City College Board of Trustees. Extrainstitutional representation: 31 trustees, including 23 alumni; institutional representation: president of the college. 1 ex officio. 34 voting. *Composition of institution:* Administrators 25. Academic affairs headed by Executive Vice President and Dean of the College. Also, Vice President for Student Life and Learning, Management/business/finances directed by vice president for financial affairs. Full-time instructional faculty 131. Academic governance body, Grove City College Faculty, meets an average of 9 times per year plus in numerous committee meetings.

Calendar: Semesters. Academic year Sept. to May. Freshmen admitted Sept., Jan. Degrees conferred and formal commencement May. Intersessions Jan., May. No summer session.

Characteristics of Freshmen: 1,847 applicants (female 966, male 881). 56% of applicants admitted. 60% of applicants admitted and enrolled full-time.

25th percentile: SAT Critical Reading 576, SAT Math 589; ACT Composite 26. *75th percentile*: SAT Critical Reading 691, SAT Math 697; ACT Composite 30. 19 National Merit Scholars.

80% of entering freshmen expected to graduate within 5 years. 44% of freshmen from Pennsylvania. Freshmen from 36 states and 2 foreign countries.

GROVE CITY COLLEGE—*cont'd*

Admission: For fall acceptance, apply as early as 15 months prior to enrollment, but not later than Feb. 1 of year of enrollment. A formal Early Decision program is available for a limited number of well-qualified students who desire to attend Grove City College as their first choice college. Applicants for Early Decision must submit the completed application for admission, supplemental Early Decision form, the secondary school records through the junior year, and results of the SAT or ACT taken as a junior before November 15 of the senior year. Students considering several colleges and seeking Regular Decision must submit the completed application for admission, the current secondary school records, and most recent results of the SAT or ACT before February 1 of the senior year. *Requirements:* Either graduation from accredited secondary school or GED. Recommend 4 units English, 2 foreign language, 3 mathematics, 2 science, 2 social studies, 3 academic electives. *Entrance tests:* College Board SAT or ACT composite. *For transfer students:* 2.0 minimum GPA; from 4-year accredited institution 90 hours maximum transfer credit; from 2-year accredited institution 60 hours.

College credit and advanced placement for postsecondary-level work completed in secondary school. Credits for remedial, developmental, technical, and correspondence courses are not transferable to Grove City College. Tutoring available.

Degree Requirements: 128 credit hours, except 136 credit hours required for engineering majors; 2.0 GPA and 2.0 MQPA; last 2 semesters in residence; 16 chapel attendance required; 2 semester hours physical education; General Education and major curricula required.

Fulfillment of some degree requirements and exemption from some beginning courses possible by passing College Board CLEP, AP, IB. *Grading system:* A–F; withdraw (deadline after which F is appended); incomplete (carries time limit).

Distinctive Educational Programs: Interdepartmental majors available in industrial management, business/computer systems management, international studies/business. Facilities for independent research, including honors programs, individual majors, interactive computer-video. Study abroad may be individually arranged.

Degrees Conferred: 568 *baccalaureate:* biological sciences 57; business and management 146; communications 29; computer and information sciences 29; education 76; engineering 47; English 47; foreign languages 9; mathematics 17; philosophy/religion 21; physical sciences 12; psychology 39; social sciences 47; visual and performing arts 6.

Fees and Other Expenses: *Full-time tuition per academic year 2008–09:* $12,074. *Room and board per academic year:* $6,440. *Books and supplies:* $900. *Other expenses:* $850.

Financial Aid: Aid from institutionally generated funds is provided on the basis of academic merit, financial need, other criteria.

Financial aid to full-time, first-time undergraduate students: 67% receuved sine firn if aid.

Departments and Teaching Staff: *Total instructional faculty:* 189 (full-time 131 part-time 58). Total faculty with doctorate, first-professional, or other terminal degree: 108. Student/faculty ratio: 17:1. Degrees held by full-time faculty: 75% hold terminal degrees.

Enrollment: Total enrollment 2,499. Undergraduate 2,499 (full-time 99%; female 50%, male 50%).

Characteristics of Student Body: *Ethnic/racial makeup:* Black non-Hispanic: 1%; Asian or Pacific Islander: 2%; Hispanic: 1%; White non-Hispanic: 94%; unknown: 1%; nonresident alien 1%.

International Students: 25 nonresident aliens enrolled fall 2008. Students from Europe, Asia, Central America, Africa, Middle East. No programs available to aid students whose native language is not English. Some financial aid specifically designated for international students: 15 scholarships awarded 2008–09 totaling $102,203.

Student Life: On-campus residence halls house 92% of student body. Residence halls for males constitute 90% of such space, for females 93%. *Intercollegiate athletics:* male: baseball, basketball, cross-country, football, golf, lacrosse, rugby, soccer, tennis, swimming, track, water polo; female: basketball, cross-country, golf, lacrosse, softball, track, tennis, soccer, swimming, volleyball. *Special regulations:* Cars permitted for all but freshmen. Quiet hours for freshmen 2pm to 5pm and 7pm to 7am Mon.–Fri. Residence hall visitation from 1pm to 5pm Sat.–Sun., 7pm to 1am Fri. (female's), and 8pm to 2am Sat. (males). *Special services:* medical and counseling services. *Student publications, radio:* *The Collegian*, college newspaper; *The Bridge*, a yearbook; *The Echo*, a literary magazine. Radio station WSAJ-FM broadcasts classical music 24 hours a day. Radio station WGCC, a student radio station broadcasts a limited daily schedule. *Surrounding community:* Grove City population 8,000. Pittsburgh, 60 miles south of campus, is nearest metropolitan area.

Library Collections: 134,000 volumes. 300,000 microforms; 1,600 current periodical subscriptions. Computer work stations available. Students have access to online information retrieval services and the Internet.

Most important special holdings include Locke Papers, Von Mises Papers; American and British Literature and History Book Collections.

Buildings and Grounds: Campus area 150 acres.

Chief Executive Officer: Dr. Richard G. Jewell, President.

Address admission inquiries to Jeff Mincey, Director of Admissions.

Gwynedd-Mercy College

1325 Sumneytown Pike
P.O. Box 901
Gwynedd Valley, Pennsylvania 19437-0901
Tel: (215) 641-7300 **E-mail:** admissions@gmc.edu
Fax: (215) 641-5573 **Internet:** www.gmc.edu

Institution Description: Gwynedd-Mercy College is a private, independent, nonprofit college affiliated with the Sister of Mercy, Roman Catholic Church. *Enrollment:* 2,548. *Degrees awarded:* Associate, baccalaureate, master's.

Accreditation: *Regional:* MSA/CHE. *Professional*: medical record technology, nursing, radiography, respiratory therapy, respiratory therapy technology

History: Established as Gwynedd-Mercy Junior College and offered first instruction at postsecondary level 1948; incorporated 1958; adopted present name 1963; awarded first degree (baccalaureate) 1965.

Institutional Structure: *Governing board:* Board of Directors. Extrainstitutional representation: 22 directors; institutional representation: 1 administrator, 2 ex officio. All voting. *Composition of institution:* Administrators 14. Academic affairs headed by vice president for academic affairs. Management/business/finances directed by vice president for financial affairs. Full-time instructional faculty 75.

Calendar: Semesters. Academic year July to June. . Freshmen admitted Sept., Jan. Degrees conferred May, Aug., Jan.

Characteristics of Freshmen: 1,901 applicants (female 1,271, male 430). 57% of applicants accepted. 27% of accepted applicants enrolled full-time.

89% (246 students) submitted SAT scores. *25th percentile*: SAT Critical Reading 450, SAT Math 460. *75th percentile*: SAT Critical Reading 550, SAT Math 548.

80% of entering freshmen expected to graduate within five years. 93% of freshmen from Pennsylvania. Freshmen from 10 states and 28 foreign countries.

Admission: Rolling admissions plan. *Requirements:* Either graduation from accredited secondary school or GED. *Entrance tests:* College Board SAT or ACT composite.

Degree Requirements: *For all associate degrees:* 65 credit hours. *For all baccalaureate degrees:* 125 credit hours. *For all undergraduate degrees:* 2.0 GPA; 45–50 credits in residence; general education requirements. *Grading system:* A–F. *For graduate degree:* 45 credit hours; 3.0 GPA; maximum 6 credits accepted in transfer.

Distinctive Educational Programs: Center for Creative Studies; Business Outreach; Center for Professional Development.

Degrees Conferred: 227 *associate*; 391 *baccalaureate*; 153 *master's*. Bachelor's degrees awarded: biological/life sciences 5; business/marketing 35; computer and information sciences 13; education 47; English 7; health professions 100; mathematics 1; philosophy/religion 1; psychology 10; social sciences and history 9;. Master's degrees awarded: various disciplines 153.

Fees and Other Expenses: *Full-time tuition per academic year 2008–09:* $22,790.; graduate study charged per credit hour (contact the college for current rate). *Room and board per academic year:* $8,900. *Other fees:* $500. *Books and supplies:* $700. *Other expenses:* $950.

Financial Aid: Aid from institutionally generated funds is provided on the basis of academic merit, financial need, other criteria.

Financial aid to full-time, first-time undergraduate students: 93% received some form of financial aid. Average amount of aid received: federal grants $2,128; Pell grants $2,541; other federal aid $1,201; state/local grants $3,763; institutional grants $8,918.

Departments and Teaching Staff: *Total instructional faculty:* 280 (full-time 80, part-time 200). Total faculty with doctorate, first-professional, or other terminal degree: 178. Student/faculty ratio: 19:1. Degrees held by full-time faculty: doctorate 40%, master's 50%, baccalaureate 10%. 40% hold terminal degrees.

Enrollment: Total enrollment 2,548. Undergraduate 2,018 (full-time 72%; female 73%, male 27%). Graduate 530 (full-time 22%). Undergraduate transfer-in students 177.

Characteristics of Student Body: *Ethnic/racial makeup:* Black non-Hispanic: 17%; American Indian or Alaska Native: 1%; Asian or Pacific Islander: 9%; Hispanic: 2%; White non-Hispanic: 75%; unknown 2%; nonresident alien 1%.

International Students: 25 undergraduate nonresident aliens enrolled fall 2008. Students from Europe, Asia, Central and south America, Africa, Canada, Middle East. Programs available to aid students whose native language is not English: social and cultural. English as a Second Language Program. No financial aid specifically designated for international students.

Student Life: On-campus residence halls house 10% of student body. *Division III intercollegiate sports:* baseball, basketball, field hockey, lacrosse, softball, volleyball, tennis. *Special services:* health service; babysitting service for children of students. *Student publications: Gwynmercian*, a newspaper; *The Seed*, a literary publication. *Surrounding community:* Gwynedd Valley is located 20 miles from center city Philadelphia; jitney service to train connection available; other public transportation limited.

Library Collections: 102,000 volumes including bound books, serial backfiles, electronic documents, and government documents not in separate collections. Online catalog. Current serial subscriptions: 690 paper, 58 microform, 400 electronic. 268 recordings; 208 compact discs. Computer work stations available. Students have access to the Internet at no charge.

Most important special collections include Health (allied health, nursing, medical); Abraham Lincoln Collection; Irish Collection/Book of Kells.

Buildings and Grounds: Campus includes 10 buildings.

Chief Executive Officer: Dr. Kathleen C. Owens, President.

Address admission inquiries to James Abbuhl, Vice President for Enrollment Management.

Haverford College

370 Lancaster Avenue
Haverford, Pennsylvania 19041-1392
Tel: (610) 896-1000 **E-mail:** admitme@haverford.edu
Fax: (610) 896-1538 **Internet:** www.haverford.edu

Institution Description: Haverford College is a private, nonsectarian liberal arts college. *Enrollment:* 1,189. *Degrees awarded:* Baccalaureate.

Accreditation: *Regional:* MSA/CHE. *Professional*: chemistry

History: Established as Haverford School Incorporated, and offered first instruction at postsecondary level 1833; adopted present name 1856; admitted women as transfer students 1978; admitted women as freshmen 1980.

Institutional Structure: *Governing board:* The Board of Managers, Haverford College. Representation: 33 managers, including 12 nominated by Board of Managers, 14 nominated by the Corporation of Haverford College including the President and Secretary of the Corporation, 6 nominated by the Alumni Association, and the president of the college. 2 full-time faculty members and 2 students are representatives to the Board. *Composition of institution:* Administrators 45. Academic affairs headed by provost. Management/business/finances directed by vice president for finance and administration. *Full-time instructional faculty:* 112. Academic governance body, Academic Council, meets an average of 30 times per academic year.

Calendar: Semesters. Academic year Aug. to May. Freshmen admitted Sept. Degrees conferred and formal commencement May. No summer session.

Characteristics of Freshmen: 3,311 applicants (female 1,789, male 1,522). 27% of applicants admitted. 37% of applicants admitted and enrolled full-time.

100% (314 students) submitted SAT scores. *25th percentile*: SAT Critical Reading 640, SAT Math 650. *75th percentile*: SAT Critical Reading 760, SAT Math 740.

94% of entering freshmen expected to graduate within 5 years. 86% of freshmen from Pennsylvania.

Admission: For fall acceptance, apply as early as Sept. 1 of previous year, but not later than Jan. 15 of year of enrollment. Students are notified of acceptance April. Apply by Nov. 15 for early decision. Early acceptance available. *Requirements:* 13 secondary school units which must include 4 English, 3 foreign language, 3 mathematics, 1 laboratory science, 2 history/social studies. Most candidates will have taken advanced or honors courses. *Entrance tests:* College Board SAT and 3 Achievements (including English composition). *For transfer students:* 3.0 minimum GPA.

College credit for performance on Advanced Placement Examinations. Tutoring available.

Degree Requirements: 32 courses required for graduate; at least 2 years in residence. Students must take three courses in each of the three divisions: humanities, natural sciences, social sciences. One of the nine courses must fulfill a quantitative reasoning requirement. Students must also fulfill one year of foreign language at placement level, a one-semester social justice requirement, and one semester of freshman English. Physical education requirement, major requirement, and semester credit requirement. Major requires synthesis and self-evaluation in senior year usually through comprehensive examination or thesis.

Credit granted for AP examinations; exemption from some beginning courses possible by passing departmental placement examinations. *Grading system:* Numerical grading system on scale 0.7–4.0; pass-fail; withdraw (carries time limit).

Distinctive Educational Programs: Close cooperative program (socially and academically) with Bryn Mawr College, and an exchange program with Swarthmore College and the University of Pennsylvania; accelerated degree programs; freshman program; interdepartmental/interdisciplinary programs which may be individually arranged; facilities for independent research, individual majors, and tutorials; study abroad in 33 countries (approved programs of international study); exchange programs with Spelman College and Claremont McKenna College; 3-2 Engineering Program with Cal Tech; Gest Center for the cross-cultural study of religion offers lectures and seminars by visiting authorities on various religious faiths.

Degrees Conferred: 301 *baccalaureate*. Bachelor's degrees awarded in top five disciplines: social sciences 89; biological/life sciences 36; physical sciences 31; English 33; history 29.

Fees and Other Expenses: *Full-time tuition per academic year 2008–09:* $7,525. *Other fees:* $316. *Room and board per academic year:* $11,450. *Books and supplies:* $1,194. *Other expenses:* $1,488.

Financial Aid: Aid from institutionally generated funds is provided on the basis of financial need.

Financial aid to full-time, first-time undergraduate students: 59% received some form of aid.

Departments and Teaching Staff: *Total instructional faculty:* 117 (full-time 110, part-time 17). Total faculty with doctorate, first-professional, or other terminal degree: 111. Student/faculty ratio: 8:1. Degrees held by full-time faculty: master's 3%, doctorate 97%. 97% hold terminal degrees.

Enrollment: Total enrollment 1,189. Undergraduate 1,189 (full-time 100%; female 53%, male 47%).

Characteristics of Student Body: *Ethnic/racial makeup:* Black non-Hispanic: 8%; American Indian or Alaskan Native 10%; Asian or Pacific Islander: 1%; Hispanic: 9%; nonresident alien 3%.

International Students: 43 nonresident aliens enrolled fall 2008. Students from Europe, Asia, Central and South America, Africa, Canada, Australia, Middle East. No programs available to aid students whose native language is not English. No financial aid specifically designated for foreign students.

Student Life: On-campus residence halls house 96% of student body. Single-sex housing is available; students may reside and take meals at Bryn Mawr College through a dorm and meal plan exchange program. *Intercollegiate athletics:* male: baseball, basketball, cricket, cross-country, fencing, lacrosse, soccer, squash, tennis, track; female: basketball, cross-country, fencing, field hockey, lacrosse, soccer, softball, squash, tennis, track, volleyball. *Special regulations:* Cars not permitted for freshmen. *Special services:* Medical services; shuttle bus between Haverford, Bryn Mawr, and Swarthmore. *Student publications, radio:* weekly newspaper; literary review; yearbook. Radio station WHRC broadcasts daily to campus. *Surrounding community:* Philadelphia 10 miles from campus. Served by bus and rail systems; airport 15 miles from campus; passenger rail service adjoining campus.

Publications: *Haverford* (quarterly) first published 1959.

Library Collections: 773,500 volumes including bound books, serial backfiles, electronic documents. 200,000 and government documents. Online catalog. Current serial subscriptions: 2,093 paper, microform, electronic. 10,000 videos, LPs, and CDs; 2,500 photographs. Students have access to the Internet at no charge.

Most important special collections include Quaker Collection (32,000 books; 250,000 manuscripts); Phillips Collection (Elizabethan and Renaissance literature); Roberts Collection (20,000 autographed manuscripts).

Buildings and Grounds: Campus area 216 acres.

Chief Executive Officer: Dr. Thomas R. Tritton, President.

Address admission inquiries to Jess Lord, Director of Admissions.

Holy Family University

9701 Frankford Avenues
Philadelphia, Pennsylvania 19114-2094
Tel: (215) 637-7700 **E-mail:** rnolan@hfc.edu
Fax: (215) 281-1022 **Internet:** www.hfc.edu

Institution Description: Holy Family University is an independent (Roman Catholic) institution sponsored by the Congregation of the Sisters of the Holy Family of Nazareth. *Enrollment:* 3,471. *Degrees awarded:* Associate, baccalaureate, master's degrees; certificates alswo awarded.

Accreditation: *Regional:* MSA/CHE. *Professional*: nursing, radiography

History: Established by Sisters of the Holy Family of Nazareth, chartered, incorporated, and offered first instruction at postsecondary level 1954; awarded first degree (baccalaureate) 1958; achieved university status 2001. *See* Peter W.

HOLY FAMILY UNIVERSITY—*cont'd*

Frey, *Holy Family College, a History of Its Growth and Development* (Philadelphia: Holy Family College, 1959) for further information.

Institutional Structure: *Governing board:* Board of Trustees. Extrainstitutional representation: 24 trustees; institutional and ex officio representation: 1 administrator; 2 trustee emeriti; 24 voting. *Composition of institution:* 6 senior administrators: president, vice president and dean for academic affairs, vice president for student services, vice president for financial affairs and administration, vice president for institutional advancement, vice president for technology. Full-time instructional faculty 75. Senior administrators meet weekly.

Calendar: Semesters. Academic year Aug. to May. Freshmen and transfers admitted Sept., Jan., May, July. Degrees conferred and formal commencement winter and May. Summer session of 2 terms from May to August.

Characteristics of Freshmen: 925 applicants (female 692, male 233). 68% or applicants accepted. 45% of accepted applicants enrolled.

99% (281 students) submitted SAT scores; 1% (2 students) submitted ACT scores. *25th percentile*: SAT Critical Reading 440, SAT Math 420; ACT Composite 19, ACT English 24. ACT Math 16. *75th percentile*: SAT Critical Reading 510, SAT Math 500; ACT Composite 20, ACT English 21, ACT Math 18.

66% of entering freshmen expected to graduate within 5 years. 90% of freshmen from Pennsylvania. Freshmen from 7 states and 18 foreign countries.

Admission: Rolling admissions plan. For fall acceptance, apply as early as June of previous year. Early acceptance available. *Requirements:* Either graduation from accredited secondary school with 4 units English, 2 in a modern foreign language, 2 history, 2 laboratory science, 3 mathematics, 3 electives; or GED. *Entrance tests:* College Board SAT. *For transfer students:* 2.0 minimum GPA; 75 maximum transfer credits.

College credit and advanced placement for postsecondary-level work completed in secondary school.

Degree Requirements: 120 credit hours; 2.0 GPA; 45 credits at Holy Family College; comprehensives in individual fields of study (may be oral as well as written and may include research project).

Fulfillment of some degree requirements and exemption from some beginning courses possible by passing departmental examinations, College Board CLEP or APP. *Grading system:* A–F; pass-fail; withdraw (carries time limit).

Distinctive Educational Programs: Weekend and evening classes. Accelerated degree programs. Interdisciplinary programs in biology, humanities, international business, psychology, social studies. Alternate Admissions Program; Associate of Science in Radiography. Senior core course in ethics. Freshman one-credit orientation. Study abroad during summer or academic year in England and Switzerland individually arranged. Continuing education program. Cooperative education program. Graduate programs in education, nursing, and counseling psychology.

Degrees Conferred: 23 *associate*: 342 *baccalaureate*: 365 *master's*. Bachelor's degrees awarded in top five disciplines: education 131; health professions and related clinical sciences 70; business, management, marketing, and related support services 57; psychology 31; communication, journalism, and related programs 12.

Fees and Other Expenses: *Full-time tuition and fees per academic year 2008–09:* $18,850. Graduate study charged per credit hour; contact the university for current rates. *Off-campus room and board per academic year:* $8,600. *Books and supplies:* $926.

Financial Aid: Aid from institutionally generated funds is provided on the basis of academic merit, financial need, other criteria.

Financial aid to full-time, first-time undergraduate students: 72% received some form of financial aid. Average amount of aid received: federal grants $2,879; state/local grants $3,382; institutional grants $6,720; loans $3,110.

Departments and Teaching Staff: *Total instructional faculty:* 134 FTE. Student/faculty ratio: 10:1. Degrees held by full-time faculty: baccalaureate 1%, master's 30%, doctorate 69%. 69% hold terminal degrees.

Enrollment: Total enrollment 3,971.

Characteristics of Student Body: *Ethnic/racial makeup:* Black non-Hispanic: 7%; Asian or Pacific Islander: 4% Hispanic: 3%; White non-Hispanic: 72%; unknown: 12%.

International Students: 69 nonresident aliens enrolled fall 2008. Students from Europe, Asia, Latin America, Africa. English as a Second Language Program available. No financial aid specifically designated for international students.

Student Life: No on-campus housing. *Intercollegiate athletics:* male: basketball, golf, soccer; female: basketball, cross-country, soccer, softball. *Special regulations:* Cars permitted without restrictions. *Special services:* Learning Resources Center. *Student publications: Familogue*, a yearbook; *Folio*, an annual literary magazine; *Tiger Talk*, a weekly newsletter; *Tri-lite*, a monthly newspaper. *Surrounding community:* Philadelphia metropolitan area population 4,725,000. Served by mass transit bus system; airport 19 miles from campus; passenger rail service less than 1 mile from campus.

Library Collections: 120,000 volumes including bound books, serial backfiles, electronic documents, and government documents not in separate collections. Online catalog. Current serial subscriptions: 850 paper, 43 microform, 7 databases. 1,813 recordings; 142 CD-ROMs. Computer work stations available. Students have access to the Internet at no charge.

Most important special holding include 5,000 volume Curriculum and Children's Literature Collection; Polish Language and Literature Collection.

Buildings and Grounds: Campus area 46 acres.

Chief Executive Officer: Sr. Francesca Onley, CSFN, Ph.D., President.

Undergraduates address admission inquiries to Lauren Campbell, Director of Undergraduate Admissions; graduate inquiries to Dr. Antoinette Schiavo, Dean of Graduate Studies.

Immaculata University

1145 King Road
Immaculata, Pennsylvania 19345
Tel: (610) 647-4400 **E-mail:** admiss@immaculata.edu
Fax: (610) 647-7635 **Internet:** www.immaculata.edu

Institution Description: Immaculata University is a private liberal arts institution for women affiliated with the Roman Catholic Church and conducted by the Sisters, Servants of the Immaculate Heart of Mary. *Enrollment:* 3,862. women. Men are admitted as residential students (began 2005). *Degrees awarded:* Associate, baccalaureate, master's, doctorate.

Accreditation: *Regional:* MSA/CHE. *Professional*: clinical psychology, dietetics, music, nursing

History: Established and chartered as Villa Maria College 1920; offered first instruction at postsecondary level 1921; awarded first degree (baccalaureate) 1925; adopted present name 1928; men admitted as residential students 2005; achieved university status 2001.

Institutional Structure: *Governing board:* Immaculata University Board of Trustees. Extrainstitutional representation: 30 trustees. 3 ex officio. 30 voting. *Composition of institution:* Administrators 10. Academic affairs headed by vice president for academic affairs. Management/business/finances directed by vice president for financial affairs. Full-time instructional faculty 88. Academic governance body, Academic Policy Committee, meets an average of 4 times per year.

Calendar: Semesters. Academic year July to June. Freshmen admitted Sept., Jan. Degrees conferred Jan., May, Aug. Evening Division summer session of 2 terms from May to Aug.

Characteristics of Freshmen: 80% of applicants admitted. 25% of applicants admitted and enrolled.

25th percentile: SAT Critical Reading 420, SAT Math 450. *75th percentile*: SAT Critical Reading 520, SAT Math 550.

52% of entering freshmen expected to graduate within 5 years. 68% of freshmen from Pennsylvania. Freshmen from 9 states and 3 foreign countries.

Admission: Rolling admissions plan. For fall acceptance, apply as early as Sept. of previous year, but not later than June of year of enrollment. Students are notified of acceptance by May. Apply by Dec. 15 for early decision; need not limit application to Immaculata. Early acceptance available. *Requirements:* Either graduation from accredited secondary school with 16 units which must include 4 English, 2 in a foreign language, 2 mathematics, 2 history, 2 science, 4 electives; or GED. Minimum 2.5 GPA. *Entrance tests:* College Board SAT. *For transfer students:* 2.0 minimum GPA; 64 hours maximum transfer credit; from 2-year accredited institution 60 hours.

College credit and advanced placement for postsecondary-level work completed in secondary school. College credit and advanced placement for College Board CLEP.

Tutoring available. Noncredit developmental courses offered during regular academic year.

Degree Requirements: 126 credit hours; 2.0 GPA; 4 contact hours physical education for traditional students.

Fulfillment of some degree requirements and exemption from some beginning courses possible by advanced placement, and by passing CLEP and departmental examinations. *Grading system:* A–F; high pass; pass; withdraw; incomplete.

Distinctive Educational Programs: Internship programs and study abroad. Graduate programs in cultural and linguistics diversity studies, counseling psychology, educational leadership/administration, information technology, international business/foreign language, nutrition education, music therapy, and doctoral degree in clinical psychology educational administration, special education. Interdisciplinary majors available; honors program; independent study; early childhood, elementary, and secondary education certification. *Other distinctive programs:* Certification in music therapy, BSN for RNs, and professional preparation for medical and health professions.

Degrees Conferred: 11 *associate;* 463 *baccalaureate*; 109 *master's* ; 46 *doctorate*. Bachelor's degrees awarded in top five disciplines: health professions and related clinical sciences 185; business/marketing 162; psychology 46; social sciences 19; English 12. Master's degrees awarded business/marketing 9; education 61; health professions 5; psychology 34. Doctorates awarded: education 33; psychology 13.

Fees and Other Expenses: *Full-time tuition per academic year 2008=09* $20,575; contact the university for current information regarding housing and other applicable costs.

Financial Aid: Aid from institutionally generated funds is provided on the basis of academic merit, financial need, talent. Institution has a Program Participation Agreement with the U.S. Department of Education for eligible students to receive Pell Grants and, depending upon the agreement, other federal aid.

Departments and Teaching Staff: *Total instructional faculty:* 397 (full-time 98, part-time 299). Total faculty with doctorate, first-professional, or other terminal degree: 113. Student/faculty ratio: 11:1. Degrees held by full-time faculty: 61% doctorate, 39% master's. 65% hold terminal degrees.

Enrollment: Total enrollment 3,053.

Characteristics of Student Body: *Ethnic/racial makeup:* number of Black non-Hispanic: 203; American Indian or Alaska Native: 3; Asian or Pacific Islander: 35; Hispanic: 45; White non-Hispanic: 2,481; unknown: 48. *Age distribution:* number under 18: 27; 18–19: 218; 20–21: 226; 22–24: 257; 25–29: 346; 30–34: 339; 35–39: 338; 40–49: 734; 50–64: 325; 65 and over: 14.

International Students: 23 nonresident aliens enrolled fall 2008. Students from Europe, Asia, Central and South America, Africa. Programs available to aid students whose native language is not English: social, cultural. English as a Second Language Program. No financial aid specifically designated for international students.

Student Life: Promotes individual and group development, student integration, and student involvement. Many leadership opportunities; services for international students; active campus ministry program. 85% of traditional-age students are residents; residence halls are for women only. *Intercollegiate athletics:* female: basketball, cross-country, field hockey, soccer, tennis, volleyball. *Special services:* health services, career advisement, counseling and testing. *Student publications: Immaculatan*, a student newspaper; *The Laureate*, a literary magazine; *Gleaner*, a yearbook. *Surrounding community:* Philadelphia, 20 miles from campus, is nearest metropolitan area. Served by airport 15 miles from campus; passenger rail service 5 miles from campus. Local bus transportation and college van service is also provided.

Library Collections: 162,000 volumes including bound books, serial backfiles, electronic documents, and government documents not in separate collections. Online catalog. Current serial subscriptions: 768 paper, 1,322 microform, 216 electronic. 620 recordings. Computer work stations available. Students have access to the Internet at no charge.

Buildings and Grounds: Campus area 373 acres.

Chief Executive Officer: Sr. Patricia S. Fadden, President.

Address undergraduate admission inquiries to Michael Walden, Director of Admissions; graduate inquiries to Sandra Rollison, Director of Graduate Admissions.

Indiana University of Pennsylvania

101 South Drive
Indiana, Pennsylvania 15705-1098
Tel: (724) 357-2100 **E-mail:** admission_inquiry@iup.edu
Fax: (724) 357-2498 **Internet:** www.iup.edu

Institution Description: Indiana University of Pennsylvania is a state institution. Branch campuses are located in Punxsutawney and Kittanning. *Enrollment:* 14,310. baccalaureate, master's, doctorate.

Academic offerings subject to approval by the State System of Higher Education. Member of Marine Science Consortium, Pennsylvania Consortium for International Education, National Student Exchange, International Exchange Programs.

Accreditation: *Regional:* MSA/CHE. *Professional*: chemistry, clinical lab scientist, culinary education, dietetics, engineering, music, nursing, psychology internship, respiratory therapy, speech-language pathology, teacher education, theatre

History: Chartered as Indiana Normal School 1871; established 1875; offered first instruction at postsecondary level 1876; became state institution and changed name to Indian State Normal School 1920 awarded first degree (baccalaureate), became 4-year college, and changed name to State Teachers College at Indiana, Pennsylvania 1927; added liberal arts program and changed name to Indiana State College 1960; authorized to grant master's degrees, initiated doctorate program, and adopted present name 1965; Robert E. Cooke Honors College admitted first 100 students in 1996. *See* John Edward Merryman, *The Indiana Story 1875–1975* (Clearfield, Pa.: Kurtz Brothers Printers and Lithographers, 1976) for further information.

Institutional Structure: *Governing board:* Commonwealth of Pennsylvania State System of Higher Education. Extrainstitutional representation: 15 directors. All voting. Board of Trustees of Indiana University of Pennsylvania (appointed by governor of Pennsylvania with state senatorial approval); 10 trustees; institutional representation: 1 student. All voting. *Composition of institution:* Administrators 121. Academic affairs headed by provost and vice president for academic affairs. Other vice presidents: finance, administration, student affairs, institutional advancement. Full-time instructional faculty 734. Academic governance body, University Senate, meets an average of 8 times per year. *Faculty representation:* Faculty served by collective bargaining agent, Association of Pennsylvania State Colleges and Universities, affiliated with AAUP and AFT.

Calendar: Semesters. Academic year Sept. to May. Freshmen admitted Sept., Jan., June, July, Aug. Degrees conferred May, Aug., Dec. Formal commencement May. Summer session June to Aug.

Characteristics of Freshmen: 10,116 applicants (female 5,916, male 4,200). 59% of applicants accepted. 42% of accepted applicants enrolled full-time.

Mean SAT scores class 537 Critical Reading, 523 Math.

85% of entering freshmen expected to graduate within 5 years. 74% of freshmen from Pennsylvania. Freshmen from 208 states and 151 foreign countries.

Admission: Rolling admissions. For fall acceptance, apply as early as summer following junior year of secondary school. Dec. 31 is usual deadline but applications accepted until places filled. Students are notified of acceptance Jan. Apply by Oct. 1 for early decision; need not limit application to Indiana University. Early acceptance available. *Requirements:* Either graduation from accredited secondary school or GED. *Entrance tests:* College Board SAT or ACT composite. For foreign students minimum TOEFL score 500. *For transfer students:* 2.0 minimum GPA; from 4-year accredited institution 94 hours maximum transfer credit; from 2-year accredited institution 60 hours.

College credit and advanced placement for postsecondary-level work completed in secondary school. College credit for extrainstitutional learning.

Developmental and remedial courses offered in summer session and regular academic year; credit given.

Degree Requirements: *For all associate degrees:* 60 credit hours. *For all baccalaureate degrees:* 124 credit hours; last 30 hours in residence; 4 hours physical education; distribution requirements. *For all undergraduate degrees:* 2.0 GPA with some requiring higher QPA.

Fulfillment of some degree requirements and exemption from some beginning courses possible by passing departmental examinations, College Board CLEP, AP, other standardized tests. *Grading system:* A–F; pass-fail; withdraw (carries time limit); incomplete (carries time limit).

Distinctive Educational Programs: *For undergraduates:* Accelerated degree programs. Dual-degree programs in engineering with Drexel University; in forestry and environmental studies with Duke University (NC); in medicine with Jefferson Medical College of Thomas Jefferson University; in podiatry with Pennsylvania College of Podiatric Medicine. Cooperative baccalaureate programs in engineering at University of Pittsburgh; optometry at Pennsylvania College of Optometry; graphic design at the Art Institute of Pittsburgh; metalry at Bowman Technical School; Marine Science Consortium at NASA–Wallops Island (VA); medical technology with approved hospitals; in respiratory therapy with Western Pennsylvania Hospital. Interdepartmental program in environmental health. Honors programs. Institutionally sponsored study abroad in France at University of Nancy; in Spain at University of Valladolid; in Germany at University of Duisberg; Mexico summer program at Jalapa; England at Wroxton-Oxford University; in Austria at Salzburg University; in Hungary at Pecs University; in Japan at Minami-Hokaido; and in Dublin, Ireland at Trinity University. Foreign study tours also available. National Student Exchange facilitates international and domestic exchanges. Robert E. Cook Honors College. Self-instruction in critical languages. *For graduate students:* Interdepartmental program in professional growth. Individual majors. *Available to all students:* Internships. Flexible meeting places and schedules, including off-campus centers, weekend and evening classes. Special facilities for using telecommunications in the classroom. Facilities and programs for independent research, including tutorials. *Other distinctive programs:* University school, for kindergarten through 8th grade, provides laboratory and research opportunities. Continuing education program offers degree and nondegree programs at the main and two branch campuses.

ROTC: Army.

Degrees Conferred: 13 *associate*; 2,099 *baccalaureate*; 720 *master's*; 79 *doctorate*. Bachelor's degrees awarded in top five disciplines: business, management, marketing, and related support services 462; social sciences 342; education communications/journalism 201; education 196; family and consumer sciences 131. Master's degrees awarded in top five disciplines: education 137; business/marketing 123; psychology 67; social sciences 45; English 39. Doctorates awarded: education 23; English 45; psychology 9; public administration 6.

Fees and Other Expenses: *Full-time tuition per academic year 2008–09:* resident undergraduate $6,959, nonresident $15,089; contact the university for

INDIANA UNIVERSITY OF PENNSYLVANIA—*cont'd*

current graduate tuition. *Required fees:* $1,352. *Books and supplies:* $1,100. *Room and board per academic year:* $5,778. *Other expenses:* $3,069.

Financial Aid: Aid from institutionally generated funds is provided on the basis of academic merit, financial need, other criteria.

Financial aid to full-time, first-time undergraduate students: 87% received some form of aid. Average amount of aid received: federal grants $3,846; Pell grants $2,986; other federal aid $1,086; state/local grants $3,094; institutional grants $2,206.

Departments and Teaching Staff: *Total instructional faculty:* 795. Degrees held by full-time faculty: baccalaureate 100%, master's 92%, doctorate 83%. 83% hold terminal degrees.

Enrollment: Total enrollment 14,310. Undergraduate 11,928 (full-time 92%; female 55%, male 45%). Graduate 2,382 (full-time 44%). Undergraduate transfer-in students 574.

Characteristics of Student Body: *Ethnic/racial makeup:* Black non-Hispanic: 11%; Asian or Pacific Islander: 1%; Hispanic: 2%; White non-Hispanic: 77%; unknown 7%; nonresident alien 2%. *Age distribution:* number under 18: 187; 18–19: 4,207; 20–21: 4,395; 22–24: 2,170; 25–29: 464; 30–34: 172; 35–39: 1311 40–49: 177; 50–64: 60; 65 and over: 4.

International Students: 551 nonresident aliens enrolled fall 2008. Programs available to aid students whose native language is not English: English as a Second Language Program. Financial aid specifically designated for international students: scholarships available annually to qualifying students.

Student Life: On-campus residence halls and apartments house 30% of student body. Additional housing is available in privately-owned residence hall, etc. *Intercollegiate athletics:* male: baseball, basketball, cross-country, football, golf, soccer swimming, track, wrestling; female: basketball, cross-country, field hockey, gymnastics, softball, swimming, tennis, track, volleyball; both sexes: rifle, fencing. *Special regulations:* Resident students only permitted to keep cars on campus for medical, academic, or work-related reasons. *Special services:* Medical services, campus transportation system. *Student publications, radio, television: Indiana Penn*, a newspaper published 3 times per week; *IUP Magazine, New Growth*, a literary magazine for creative writing; *Aristeia*, the IUP myth journal; *Oak*, a yearbook. Radio station WIUP-FM broadcasts 98 hours per week; CIUP-TV broadcasts 45 hours per week. *Surrounding community:* Indiana population 29,000. Pittsburgh, 50 miles from campus, is nearest metropolitan area. Served by airport 4 miles from campus.

Publications: *The Criminal Justice Policy Review*, published quarterly; *Hispanic Journal* (biannually) first published 1979; *Studies in the Humanities* (every 9 months) first published 1973.

Library Collections: 905,500 volumes. 21,000 government documents (separate collection). Current periodical subscriptions: paper 1,713; via electronic access 16,497. 26,414 audio/videotapes; 2,263 DVD discs; 16,497 CD-ROMs. Students have access to online information retrieval services and the Internet.

Most important special holdings include Herman Melville collection; papers of the United Mine Workers, Districts 2 and 5; papers of the Rochester and Pittsburgh Coal Company; Pennsylvania History Collection.

Buildings and Grounds: Campus area 342 acres.

Chief Executive Officer: Dr. Anthony Atwater, President.

Undergraduates address admission inquiries to James Begany, Director of Admissions; graduate inquiries to Dean, Graduate School and Research.

Juniata College

1700 Moore Street
Huntingdon, Pennsylvania 16652
Tel: (814) 641-3000 **E-mail:** admissions@juniata.edu
Fax: (814) 641-3355 **Internet:** www.juniata.edu

Institution Description: Juniata College is a private, independent, nonprofit college. *Enrollment:* 1,526. *Degrees awarded:* Baccalaureate.

Accreditation: *Regional:* MSA/CHE. *Professional*: chemistry, social work

History: Established as Huntingdon Normal School 1876; chartered and changed name to Brethren's Normal College 1878; offered first instruction at postsecondary level 1892; adopted present name 1894; accredited as a 4-year institution 1896; awarded first degree (baccalaureate) 1897. *See* Earl C. Kaylor, Jr., *Truth Sets Free: A Centennial History of Juniata College, 1876–1976* (Cranbury, NJ: A.S. Barnes and Co., Inc., 1977) for further information.

Institutional Structure: *Governing board:* Board of Trustees of Juniata College. Extrainstitutional representation: 38 trustees, including 32 alumni, 16 emeriti trustees (including 12 alumni); institutional representation: President of the college (ex officio). 39 voting. *Composition of institution:* Administrators 145. Academic affairs headed by provost and vice president for student development. Management/business/finances directed by vice president for finance and operations. Full-time instructional faculty 104. Academic governance body, The faculty of Juniata College, meets an average of 9 times per year.

Calendar: Semesters. Academic year Aug. to May. Freshmen admitted Aug., Jan. Degrees conferred May, Aug., Dec. Formal commencement May. Summer session from June to Aug.

Characteristics of Freshmen: 2,349 applicants (female 1,218, male 1,031). 69% of applicants admitted. 28% of applicants admitted and enrolled full-time.

95% (326 students) submitted SAT scores. *25th percentile*: SAT Critical Reading 540, SAT Math 550. *75th percentile*: SAT Critical Reading 630, SAT Math 640. 2 National Merit Scholars.

76% of entering freshmen expected to graduate within 5 years. 67% of freshmen from Pennsylvania. Freshmen from 14 states and 10 foreign countries.

Admission: Rolling admissions plan. For fall acceptance, apply by Mar. 15. Students are notified on a rolling basis beginning Fe. 28. . Early decision available; students must apply by Nov. 1. *Requirements:* Either graduation from accredited secondary school with a college preparatory curriculum of 16 units (4 English, 3 math, 3 science of which 2 must be in laboratory science, 2 foreign language, 4 social studies/history); or GED. *Entrance tests:* College Board SAT preferred. ACT accepted. For foreign students TOEFL, minimum score of 550 required. *For transfer students:* 2.5 minimum GPA; from 4-year accredited 90 credit hours maximum transfer credit: from 2-year accredited institution 60 credit hours.

College credit and advanced placement for postsecondary-level work completed in secondary school.

Degree Requirements: 120 credit hours; 2.0 GPA; residency requirement; distribution requirements.

Fulfillment of some degree requirements and exemption from some beginning courses possible by passing departmental examinations, College Board AP. *Grading system:* A–F; withdraw (carries time limit); incomplete (deadline after which A–F is assigned).

Distinctive Educational Programs: Internships available in virtually all disciplines. Dual-degree programs in engineering with Clarkson, Columbia University (NY), Georgia Institute of Technology, Pennsylvania State University (University Park Campus), Washington University (MO); in forestry with Duke University (NC); in podiatry with Pennsylvania College of Podiatric Medicine. Cooperative baccalaureate programs in nursing and allied health technology with Boston University, Washington University, Case Western Reserve University, Columbia University, Johns Hopkins University, Thomas Jefferson University, and in medicine with area hospitals. Special facilities for using telecommunications in the classroom. Interdepartmental/interdisciplinary programs in environmental, international, and peace and conflict studies. Facilities for independent research, including honors programs, individual majors, tutorials. Semester or academic year abroad through Brethren Colleges Abroad in England, France, Japan, Spain, Germany, Ecuador, China and Greece. International exchange programs in France at the University and Polytechnic Federation, in Germany at the Universities of Muenster and Marburg, and the Muenster Polytechnic Institute. Study abroad may be individually arranged. Off-campus study in U.S. includes programs in environmental science at American University and through the Great Lakes College Association's Philadelphia Urban Semester and the College of Wooster's Urban Studies Program. Other off-campus study in U.S. includes programs in political science at the Washington (DC) Center for Learning Alternatives, summer programs in health fields at the Deborah Heart and Lung Center (NJ) and the Armed Forces Institute of Pathology (DC). Environmental studies at institution's Raystown Lake Field Station.

Degrees Conferred: 328 *baccalaureate*. Bachelor's degrees awarded in top five disciplines: biological/life sciences 58; business/marketing 37; education 32; social sciences 24; psychology 23.

Fees and Other Expenses: *Full-time tuition per academic year 2008–09:* $30,280. *Required fees:* $640. *Room and board per academic year:* $8,420. *Books and supplies:* $600. *Other expenses:* $1,250.

Financial Aid: Aid from institutionally generated funds is provided on the basis of academic merit, financial need, other criteria.

Financial aid to full-time, first-time undergraduate students: 100% received some form of aid. Average amount of aid received: federal grants $4,671; Pell grants $2,657; other federal aid 2,039; state/local grants $8,420; institutional grants $14,029.

Departments and Teaching Staff: *Total instructional faculty:* 130 (full-time 99, part-time 31). Total faculty with doctorate, first-professional, or other terminal degree: 101. Student/faculty ratio: 13:1. Degrees held by full-time faculty: baccalaureate 100%, master's 18%, doctorate 81%. 91% hold terminal degrees.

Enrollment: Total enrollment 1,526. Undergraduate 1,526 (full-time 95%; female 56%, male 44%). Transfer-in students 73.

Characteristics of Student Body: *Ethnic/racial makeup:* Black non-Hispanic: 1%; Asian or Pacific Islander: 2%; Hispanic: 1%; White non-Hispanic: 85%; unknown: 2%; nonresident alien 8%.

International Students: 120 nonresident aliens enrolled fall 2008. Students from Europe, Asia, Central and South America, Africa, Middle Easzt. Programs available to aid students whose native language is not English: social, cultural. English as a Second Language Program. No financial aid specifically designated for international students.

Student Life: On-campus residence halls house 80% of student body. Residence halls for males constitute 12% of such space, for both sexes 88%. *Intercollegiate athletics:* male: baseball, basketball, cross-country, football, golf, soccer, track and field, volleyball; female: basketball, cross-country, field hockey, soccer, softball, swimming, tennis, track and field, volleyball. *Special regulations:* Registered cars permitted without restrictions. Residence hall options include international floors, a wellness floor, and a co-ed floor. Visitation varies according residence hall. *Special services:* Learning Resources Center, medical services. *Student publications, radio: Alfarata*, a yearbook; *Juniatian*, a weekly newspaper; *Kvasir*, a triennial literary magazine. Radio station WKVR broadcasts 94 hours per week. *Surrounding community:* Huntingdon borough population 8,000. Pittsburgh, 150 miles from campus, is nearest metropolitan area. Served by airport 30 miles from campus; passenger rail service 2 miles from campus.

Library Collections: 300,000 volumes including bound books, serial backfiles, electronic documents, and government documents not in separate collections. Online catalog. 200 microform units; 1,300 audiovisual units. 60 computer work stations. Students have access to the Internet at no charge. Total budget for books, periodicals, audiovisual materials, microforms 2008–09: $375,000.

Most important special holdings include Abraham H. Cassel Collection; W. Emmert Swigart Collection; Snow Hill Collection.

Buildings and Grounds: Campus area 800 acres.

Chief Executive Officer: Dr. Thomas R. Kepple, Jr., President

Address admission inquires to Dean of Enrollment.

King's College

133 North River Street
Wilkes-Barre, Pennsylvania 18711
Tel: (570) 208-5900 **E-mail:** admssns@kings.edu
Fax: (570) 825-9049 **Internet:** www.kings.edu

Institution Description: King's College is a private, independent, nonprofit college affiliated with the Congregation of Holy Cross, Roman Catholic Church. *Enrollment:* 2,673. *Degrees awarded:* Associate, baccalaureate, master's. Certificates also awarded.

Accreditation: *Regional:* MSA/CHE. *Professional*: athletic training, chemistry, teacher education, physician assisting

History: Established as men's college, chartered, and offered first instruction at postsecondary level 1946; awarded first degree (baccalaureate) 1950; became coeducational 1970.

Institutional Structure: *Governing board:* Board of Directors of King's College. Representation: 40 directors including 20 alumni. *Composition of institution:* Administrators 27. Academic affairs headed by vice president for academic affairs with 2 associate vice presidents and a dean of the William G. McGowan School of Business. Management/business/finances directed by vice president for business affairs. Other vice presidents for development, student affairs, Full-time instructional faculty 116. Academic governance body, Faculty Council, meets an average of 9 times per year.

Calendar: Semesters. Academic year Aug. to May. First-year students admitted Sept., Jan., July. Degrees conferred May, Aug. Formal commencement May. Summer session of 4 terms from May to Aug.

Characteristics of Freshmen: 2,233 applicants (female 1,024, male 1,139). 80% of applicants accepted. 31% of accepted applicants enrolled.

Mean SAT scores 502 Critical Reading, 407 Math.

68% of entering freshmen expected to graduate within 5 years. 75% of freshmen from Pennsylvania. Freshmen from 18 states and 8 foreign countries.

Admission: Rolling admissions plan. For fall acceptance, apply as early as Sept. 1 of previous year, but not later than Aug. 1 of year of enrollment. Early acceptance available. *Requirements:* 16 academic units which must include 4 English, 3 mathematics, 3 social science, 3 natural science, 2 language, 1 history; or GED. Additional requirements for some programs. *Entrance tests:* College Board SAT or ACT Composite recommended for placement. *For transfer students:* 2.0 minimum GPA for liberal arts, 2.5 for business school; 2.75 for physical assistant; 2.85 for education. 60 hours maximum transfer credit.

College credit and advanced placement for postsecondary-level work completed in secondary school. College credit for extra-institutional learning (life experience) on basis of portfolio and faculty assessment. College credit for College Board CLEP subject exams only.

Tutoring available. Developmental/remedial courses offered in summer session and regular academic year; credit given.

Degree Requirements: *For most associate degrees:* 60 credit hours; 30 credits in residence. *For most baccalaureate degrees:* 120 credit hours; 60 credits in residence. *For most undergraduate degrees:* 2.0 GPA.

Fulfillment of some degree requirements possible by passing CLEP and AP tests. *Grading system:* A–F; pass-fail; withdraw (carries time limit).

Distinctive Educational Programs: Work-experience programs. Evening classes. College features a core curriculum stressing the transferable skills of liberal learning (critical thinking, effective writing, computer literacy, effective oral communication, and quantitative reasoning) with the intention that these skills will be utilized and developed throughout the core, the major and one's career. A competency-based course-embedded assessment factor provides for student and faculty learning/teaching assessment at all levels. College provides for 3 to 12 credit internship opportunities in most majors; offers cross-registration with College Misericordia and Wilkes University; a Center for Lifelong Learning provides programs for the non-traditional student in a day and/or evening setting; an Honors program with offerings across the curriculum; Learning Resources Center available; individually arranged study abroad and internships locally, nationally, and abroad; intensive program of career planning across the curriculum; course of preprofessional advisement; 5-year physician assistant master's program.

ROTC: Army and Air Force optional. Air Force offered in cooperation with Wilkes University.

Degrees Conferred: 2 *associate*; 436 *baccalaureate*; 79 *master's*. Bachelor's degrees awarded in top five disciplines: business, management, marketing, and related support services 121; education 57; security and protective services 53; psychology 44; health professions and related clinical sciences 41. Master's degrees awarded: business/marketing 1; education 15; health professions 35' various disciplies 28.

Fees and Other Expenses: *Full-time tuition per academic year 2008–09:* $24,880 undergraduate; graduate study charged per credit hour (contact the college for current rate). *Room and board per academic year:* $9,370. *Books and supplies:* $1,160. *Other expenses:* $1,842.

Financial Aid: Aid from institutionally generated funds is provided on the basis of academic merit, financial need. Institution has a Program Participation Agreement with the U.S. Department of Education for eligible students to receive Pell Grants and, depending upon the agreement, other federal aid.

Departments and Teaching Staff: *Total instructional faculty:* 197 (full-time 116, part-time 81). Total faculty with doctorate, first-professional, or other terminal degree 112. Student/faculty ratio: 16:1. Degrees held by full-time faculty: baccalaureate 2%, master's 25%, doctorate 73%. 85% hold terminal degrees.

Enrollment: Total enrollment 2,673. Undergraduate 2,339 (full-time 85%; female 52%, male 48%). Graduate 334 (full-time 19%). Undergraduate transfer-in students 88.

Characteristics of Student Body: *Ethnic/racial makeup:* Black non-Hispanic: 2%; Asian or Pacific Islander: 1%; Hispanic: 3%; White non-Hispanic: 77%; unknown: 16%. *Age distribution:* number under 18: 28; 18–19: 804; 20–21: 789; 22–24: 167; 25–29: 27; 30–34: 9; 35–39: 7; 40–49: 3; unknown: 2.

International Students: 5 nonresident aliens enrolled fall 2008. Students from Europe, Asia, Africa. Programs available to aid students whose native language is not English: English as a Second Language Program. Financial aid specifically designated for international students.

Student Life: On-campus residence halls house 45% of student body. Residence halls for males constitute 35% of such space, for females 35%, coed apartment buildings 30%. *Intercollegiate athletics:* male: baseball, basketball, football, golf, lacrosse, soccer, tennis, wrestling; female: basketball, lacrosse, field hockey, soccer, softball, tennis, volleyball. *Special regulations:* Cars permitted without restriction. Residence hall visitation from 10am to 12pm Sun.–Thurs., 10am to 2am Fri. and Sat. *Special services:* Learning Resources Center, medical services. *Student publications, radio: The Crown*, a weekly newspaper; *Regis*, yearbook; *The Scope*, an annual literary magazine. Radio station WRKC broadcasts 24 hours per day during school session, and 133 hours per week during vacations. Programs include public affairs and radio home visitor for the blind. *Surrounding community:* Wilkes-Barre population 50,000. Philadelphia, 2 hours from campus, is nearest metropolitan area. Served by airport 6 miles from campus.

Library Collections: 176,500 volumes including bound books, serial backfiles, electronic documents, and government documents not in separate collections. Online catalog. Current serial subscriptions: 490 paper, 563,298 microform, 15,184 via electronic access. 2,163 audio/videotapes; 463 DVD discs; 169 CD-ROMs. 45 computer work stations. Students have access to the Internet at no charge.

Most important special collections include Daniel J. Flood Collection.

Buildings and Grounds: Campus area 13 acres.

Chief Executive Officer: Rev. Thomas J. O'Hara, C.S.C., Ph.D., President.

KING'S COLLEGE—*cont'd*

Address admission inquiries to Michelle Lawrence-Schmude, Director of Admissions; graduate inquiries to Dr. Elizabeth S. Lott, Director of Graduate Programs.

Kutztown University of Pennsylvania

15200 Kutztown Road
Kutztown, Pennsylvania 19530-0730
Tel: (610) 683-4000 **E-mail:** admissions@kutztown.edu
Fax: (610) 683-4010 **Internet:** www.kutztown.edu

Institution Description: Kutztown University is a state institution. *Enrollment:* 10,393. *Degrees awarded:* Baccalaureate, master's.

Accreditation: *Regional:* MSA/CHE. *Professional*: art, interior design, music, nursing, social work, teacher education

History: Chartered as Keystone Normal School 1866; changed name to Kutztown State Teachers College and offered first instruction at postsecondary level 1926; awarded first degree (baccalaureate) 1928; renamed Kutztown State College 1960; adopted present name 1983.

Institutional Structure: *Governing board:* Council of Trustees. Representation: 12 trustees. *Composition of institution:* Administrators 18. Academic affairs headed by provost and vice president for academic affairs. Student affairs headed by vice president for student affairs. University advancement headed by vice president for advancement. Management/business/finances directed by vice president for administration. Full-time instructional faculty 451.

Calendar: Semesters. Academic year Aug. to May. Formal commencements May, Dec. Summer sessions; January term.

Characteristics of Freshmen: 9,456 applicants (female 5,548, male 3,908). 61% of applicants accepted. 31% of accepted applicants enrolled full-time.

Mean SAT class scores 496 Critical Reading, 489 Math.

48% of entering freshmen expected to graduate within 5 years. 90% of freshmen from Pennsylvania. Freshmen from 20 states and 64 foreign countries.

Admission: *Requirements:* Graduation from accredited secondary school or equivalent. Additional requirements for some programs. College Board SAT or ACT composite. *For transfer students:* 2.0 minimum GPA.

Degree Requirements: 128 credit hours; 2.0 GPA in major and overall; 16 of last 32 credits in residence; one-half of total number of credits in major must be taken in residence (may not be applicable to ally majors); 10-year rule: courses in major previously taken may not be used if student has not been in attendance for a period of ten years; general education requirements.

Fulfillment of some degree requirements and exemption from some beginning courses possible by passing departmental examinations, College Board CLEP, AP. *Grading system:* A–F; pass-fail; withdraw (deadline after which pass-fail is appended to withdraw).

Distinctive Educational Programs: Study abroad programs in Belize, Costa Rica, Denmark, England, Hungary, Italy, Kenya, The Netherlands, Russia.

Degrees Conferred: 1,652 *baccalaureate*; 256 *master's*. Bachelor's degrees awarded in top five disciplines: education 278; business, management, marketing, and related support services 242; psychology 133; English 128; security and protective services 112. Master's degrees awarded: various disciplines 256.

Fees and Other Expenses: *Full-time tuition per academic year 2008–09:* undergraduate resident $7,126, nonresident $15,258; contact the university for current graduate tuition/fees. *Required fees:* $1,581. *Room and board (off-campus) per academic year:* $7,330. *Books and supplies:* $1,100. *Other expenses:* $2,800.

Financial Aid: Aid from institutionally generated funds is provided on the basis of academic merit, financial need, athletic ability, other criteria.

Financial aid to full-time, first-time undergraduate students: 81% received some form of aid. Average amount of aid received: federal grants $3,419; Pell grants $3,003; other federal aid $768; state/local grants $3,184; institutional grants $2,374.

Departments and Teaching Staff: *Total instructional faculty:* 501 (full-time 451, part-time 50). Student/faculty ratio: 20:1. Degrees held by full-time faculty: doctorate 64%, master's 36%. 72% hold terminal degrees.

Enrollment: Total enrollment 10,343. Undergraduate 9,404 (full-time 90%; female 58%, male 42%). Graduate 989 (full-time 31%). Undergraduate transfer-in students 742.

Characteristics of Student Body: *Ethnic/racial makeup:* Black non-Hispanic: 6%; Asian or Pacific Islander: 1%; Hispanic: 45; White non-Hispanic: 86%; unknown 1%; nonresident alien 1%. *Age distribution:* number under 18: 98; 18–19: 3,530l 20–21: 3,296; 22–24: 1,646; 25–29: 730; 30–34: 279; 35–39: 210; 40–49: 384; 50–64: 113; 65 and over: 7.

International Students: 103 undergraduate nonresident aliens enrolled fall 2008. Students from Europe, Asia, Latin America, Africa, Canada, Australia, New Zealand, Middle East. Programs available to aid students whose native language is not English: social, cultural. No financial aid specifically designated for international students.

Student Life: On-campus housing available. *Intercollegiate athletics:* baseball, basketball, cross-country, field hockey, football, golf, soccer, softball, swimming, tennis, track and field, volleyball, wrestling. *Special services:* Career and psychological counseling. *Student radio, television:* Campus radio and TV station. *Publications:* campus newspaper. *Surrounding community:* Kutztown population 4,000.

Library Collections: 538,000 volumes including bound books, serial backfiles, electronic documents, and government documents not in separate collections. Online catalog. Current serial subscriptions: 1,937 paper, 20 electronic providing access to 2,780 full text journals. 2,141 recordings; 690 compact discs; 190 CD-ROMs. Computer work stations available. Students have access to the Internet at no charge.

Most important special holdings include Map Collection (including Braille, topographic and raised relief); Russian Culture Collection; Curriculum Collection.

Chief Executive Officer: Dr. F. James Cavallos, President.

Undergraduates address admission inquiries to Dr. William J. Stahler, Director of Admissions; graduate inquiries to Dean, Graduate Studies and Extended Learning.

La Roche College

9000 Babcock Boulevard
Pittsburgh, Pennsylvania 15237-5898
Tel: (412) 367-9300 **E-mail:** admsns@laroche.edu
Fax: (412) 536-1199 **Internet:** www.laroche.edu

Institution Description: La Roche College is a private, nonprofit college founded by the Sisters of Divine Providence, Roman Catholic Church. *Enrollment:* 1,425. *Degrees awarded:* Associate, baccalaureate, master's.

Academic offerings subject to approval by statewide coordinating bodies. Member of Pittsburgh Council on Higher Education.

Accreditation: *Regional:* MSA/CHE. *Professional*: business, interior design, nurse anesthesia education, nursing

History: Established, chartered, offered first instruction at postsecondary level 1963; awarded first degree (baccalaureate) 1965; added graduate program 1981.

Institutional Structure: *Governing board:* Board of Trustees. Representation: 30 trustees; including 1 administrator, 1 alumna. 4 ex officio. 22 voting. *Composition of institution:* Administrators 25. Academic affairs headed by academic dean. Management/business/finances directed by treasurer. Full-time instructional faculty 64. Academic governance body, Academic Senate, meets an average of 20 times per year.

Calendar: Semesters. Academic year Aug. to May. Freshmen admitted Sept., Jan., May. Degrees conferred May, Aug., Dec. Formal commencement May. Summer session from May to Aug.

Characteristics of Freshmen: 1,114 applicants (female 683, male 431). 57% of applicants accepted. 36% of accepted applicants enrolled.

25% (220 students) submitted SAT scores; 11% (28 students) submitted ACT scores. *25th percentile*: SAT Critical Reading 410, SAT Math 420; ACT Composite 15, ACT English 16, ACT Math 16. *75th percentile*: SAT Critical Reading 540, SAT Math 520; ACT Composite 21, ACT English 21, ACT Math 22.

45% of entering freshmen expected to graduate within 5 years. 84% of freshmen from Pennsylvania. Freshmen from 15 states and 45 foreign countries.

Admission: Rolling admissions plan. For fall acceptance, apply as early as end of junior year in secondary school, but not later than first week of classes. Early acceptance available. *Requirements:* Either graduation from accredited secondary school or GED. Special veterans acceptance policy. 14-16 academic units recommended. Minimum GPA 2.0. Lowest acceptable secondary school class standing 20th percentile. *Entrance tests:* College Board SAT or ACT composite recommended. *For transfer students:* 2.0 minimum GPA; 90 semester hours maximum transfer credit; from 2-year accredited institution 66 hours; correspondence / extension students 15 hours.

College credit and advanced placement for postsecondary-level work completed in secondary school for extrainstitutional learning on basis of portfolio and faculty assessment.

Tutoring available. Developmental courses offered in summer session and regular academic year; credit given.

Degree Requirements: 120 credit hours; 2.0 GPA; 2 terms in residence; major requirements.

Fulfillment of some degree requirements and exemption from some beginning courses possible by passing College Board CLEP or APP, other standardized tests, or departmental examinations. *Grading system:* A–F; pass-fail; withdraw (deadline after which pass-fail is appended to withdraw); incomplete.

Distinctive Educational Programs: For undergraduates: Work-experience programs. Facilities and programs for independent research, including honors programs, tutorials. Study abroad by individual arrangement. Cross-registration through Pittsburgh Council on Higher Education with other colleges in consortia. Weekend College for undergraduate students: interdisciplinary program in psychology and business. *Available to all students:* Evening classes.

ROTC: Army offered cooperation with Duquesne University; Air Force with University of Pittsburgh (main campus).

Degrees Conferred: 22 *associate*; 236 *baccalaureate*; 71 *master's*. Bachelor's degrees awarded in top five disciplines: business, management, marketing, and related support services 98; communication, journalism, and related programs 80; education 47; visual and performing arts 38; psychology 29. Master's degrees awarded: various disciplines 71.

Fees and Other Expenses: *Full-time tuition and fees per academic year 2008–09:* $20,330. *Room and board per academic year:* $8,340. *Books and supplies:* $1,000. *Other expenses:* $1,350.

Financial Aid: Aid from institutionally generated funds is provided on the basis of academic merit, financial need.

Financial aid to full-time, first-time undergraduate students: 98% received some form of financial aid. Average amount of aid received: federal grants $2,531, state/local grants $3,924, institutional grants $7,800, loans $3,977.

Departments and Teaching Staff: *Total instructional faculty:* 84. Degrees held by faculty: doctorate 49%, master's 51%. 49% hold terminal degrees.

Enrollment: Total enrollment 1,425. Undergraduate 1,293 (full-tikme 83%; female 65%, male 35%). Graduate 132 (full-time 42%). Undergraduate transfer-in students 117.

Characteristics of Student Body: *Ethnic and racial makeup:* Black non-Hispanic: 5%; Asian or Pacific Islander: 1%; Hispanic 1%; White non-Hispanic: 71%; unknown: 10%; nonresident alien 11%.

International Students: 136 nonresident aliens enrolled fall 2008. Students from Europe, Asia, Africa, Canada. Programs available to aid students whose native language is not English: social, cultural. English as a Second Language Program. No financial aid specifically designated for international students.

Student Life: On-campus residence halls and apartment-style suites. Residence halls for both sexes constitute 100% of such space. *Intercollegiate athletics:* male: baseball, basketball, soccer, cross-country, golf; female: soccer, tennis, basketball, volleyball, cross-country, softball. *Special regulations:* Cars permitted without restrictions. *Special services:* Learning Resources Center. *Student publications: Courier*, a newspaper; *Campus Commuter*, a newsletter; *The Rock*, a yearbook; *La Roche College Magazine*. *Surrounding community:* Pittsburgh metropolitan area population 3 million. Served by mass transit system; airport 20 miles from campus; passenger rail service 9 miles from campus.

Library Collections: 116,500 volumes. 35,000 microforms; 12,080 audiovisual materials; 7,900 current periodical subscriptions including electronic access. Students have access to online information retrieval services and the Internet.

Most important special collections include government documents; Louder Collection (health sciences); education books.

Buildings and Grounds: Campus area 100 acres.

Chief Executive Officer: Sr. Candace Introcasso, President.

Address admission inquiries to Thomas Hasset, Director of Enrollment Management.

La Salle University

1900 West Olney Avenue
Philadelphia, Pennsylvania 19141-1199
Tel: (215) 951-1000 **E-mail:** admiss@lasalle.edu
Fax: (215) 951-1086 **Internet:** www.lasalle.edu

Institution Description: La Salle University is a private institution conducted by the Roman Catholic Brothers of the Christian Schools. *Enrollment:* 6,176. *Degrees awarded:* Associate, baccalaureate, master's.

Accreditation: *Regional:* MSA/CHE. *Professional*: business, chemistry, nursing, social work

History: Established and chartered 1863; offered first instruction at postsecondary level 1869; awarded first degree (baccalaureate) 1871; became La Salle University 1984. *See* Thomas J. Donaghy, *Conceived in Crisis* (Philadelphia: La Salle College, 1966) for further information.

Institutional Structure: *Governing board:* Board of Trustees of La Salle University. Extrainstitutional representation: 40 members with no fewer than 10 members of the Brothers of the Christian Schools; 4 alumni. 1 ex officio; institutional representation: president of the University. *Composition of institution:* Administrators 80. Academic affairs headed by provost. Management/business/finances directed by vice president for business affairs. Full-time instructional faculty 233. Academic governance body, the University Council, meets an average of 9 times per year.

Calendar: Semesters. Academic year Sept. to May. Freshmen admitted Sept., Jan. Degrees conferred and formal commencement May. Summer session of 5 terms from May to Aug.

Characteristics of Freshmen: 5,962 applicants (female 3,561, male 2,401). 68% of applicants admitted. 22% of applicants admitted and enrolled.

94% (788 students) submitted SAT scores. *25th percentile*: SAT Critical Reading 480, SAT Math 480. *75th percentile*: SAT Critical Reading 580, SAT Math 580.

83% of entering freshmen expected to graduate within 5 years. 49% of freshmen from Pennsylvania. Freshmen from 26 states and 4 foreign countries.

Admission: Rolling admissions plan. For fall acceptance, apply as early as 1 year prior to opening of term, but not later than May 1. Early acceptance available. *Requirements:* Either graduation from accredited secondary school with 16 units which must include 4 English, 2 foreign language, 2 mathematics, 1 history, 1 natural science; or GED. Minimum 2.0 GPA. Lowest acceptable secondary school class standing 60th percentile. *Entrance tests:* College Board SAT. *For transfer students:* 2.5 minimum GPA; 70 hours maximum transfer credit.

College credit and advanced placement for postsecondary-level work completed in secondary school and for extrainstitutional learning.

Tutoring available. Noncredit remedial courses offered in summer session and regular academic year.

Degree Requirements: *For all associate degrees:* 60 credit hours. *For all baccalaureate degrees:* 120 credit hours. *For all undergraduate degrees:* 2.0 GPA; 3 terms in residence.

Fulfillment of some degree requirements and exemption from some beginning courses possible by passing College Board CLEP or APP. *Grading system:* A–F; pass-fail; withdraw (carries time limit); incomplete.

Distinctive Educational Programs: *For undergraduates:* Cooperative education programs. Flexible meeting places and schedules, including off-campus centers, weekend and evening classes. Interdepartmental/interdisciplinary programs in urban studies, international studies, women's studies. Facilities for independent research, including honors programs, individualized majors. Study abroad in Switzerland and Spain.

ROTC: Air Force in cooperation with St. Joseph's University; Army in cooperation with Drexel University.

Degrees Conferred: 40 *associate*; 890 *baccalaureate*; 506 *master's*; 18 *doctorate*. Bachelor's degrees awarded in top five disciplines: health professions and related clinical sciences 218; business, management, marketing, and related support services 211; communication, journalism, and related programs 97; education 56; computer and information sciences 42. Master's degrees awarded: area and ethnic studies 4; business/marketing 215; communications/journalism 34; computer and information sciences 35; education 60; health professions 74; history 1; interdisciplinary studies 8; psychology 78; theology 11. Doctorates awarded: psychology 11. Doctorates awarded: pasychology 18.

Fees and Other Expenses: *Full-time tuition per academic year 2008–09:* $31,200. *Required fees:* $200. *Room and board per academic year:* $9,760. *Books and supplies:* $619. *Other expenses:* $1,000.

Financial Aid: Aid from institutionally generated funds is provided on the basis of academic merit, financial need, athletic ability, other criteria.

Financial aid to full-time, first-time undergraduate students: 96% received some form of aid. Average amount of aid received: federal grants $4,652; Pell grants $2,960; other federal aid $1,794; state/local grants $3,700; institutional grants $13,789.

Departments and Teaching Staff: *Total instructional faculty:* 371 (full-time 233, part-time 138). Total faculty with doctorate, first-professional, or other terminal degree: 168. Student/faculty ratio: 17:1. Degrees held by full-time faculty: master's 14%, doctorate 85%, professional 1%. 85% hold terminal degrees.

Enrollment: Total enrollment 6,176. Undergraduate 4,270 (full-time 75%; female 64%, male 36%). Graduate 1,906 (full-time 19%). Undergraduate transfer-in students 260.

Characteristics of Student Body: *Ethnic/racial makeup:* Black non-Hispanic: 17%; Asian or Pacific Islander: 4%; Hispanic: 8%; White non-Hispanic: 59%; unknown: 11%; nonresident alien 1%. *Age distribution:* number under 18: 29; 18–19: 222; 20–21: 1,945; 22–24: 627; 25–29: 198; 30–34: 203; 35–39: 176; 40–49: 259; 50–64: 152; 65 and over: 3.

International Students: 62 nonresident aliens enrolled fall 2008. Students from Europe, Asia, Latin America, Africa, Canada. Programs available to students whose native language is not English: social, cultural. English as a Second Language Program. No financial aid specifically designated for international students.

Student Life: On-campus residence halls house 58% of student body. Residence halls for both sexes constitute 100% of such space. Other institutional residence arrangements, apartments and special interest houses, accommodate 10% of student body. 10.5% of males join fraternities; some males reside there. 9% of

LA SALLE UNIVERSITY—*cont'd*

females join sororities. *Intercollegiate athletics:* male: baseball, basketball, crew, cross-country, golf, soccer, swimming and diving, tennis, track, wrestling; female: basketball, crew, cross-country, field hockey, golf, soccer, softball, swimming and diving, tennis, track, volleyball. *Special regulations:* Registered cars permitted on campus. Residence hall visitation from noon to midnight Mon.–Thurs. and noon to 2am Fri. and Sat. *Special services:* Critical Reading Skills Center, medical services. *Student publications, radio: Collegian*, a weekly newspaper; *Grimoire*, an annual literary magazine; *Explorer*, a student yearbook. Radio station WEXP broadcasts 72 hours per week. *Surrounding community:* Philadelphia metropolitan area population 4,800,000. Served by mass transit systems; airport 14 miles from campus; passenger rail service 1 mile from campus.

Publications: Sources of information about La Salle include *La Salle Bulletin, La Salle Option, La Salle View Book.*

Library Collections: 580,000 volumes. 334,000 microforms; 8,850 audiovisual materials; 1,750 current periodical subscriptions. Online catalog. 5,000 audiovisual materials. Students have access to online information retrieval services and the Internet.

Most important special holdings include Vietnam War Literature; Graham Greene Collection; Japanese Tea Ceremony.

Buildings and Grounds: Campus area 86 acres.

Chief Executive Officer: Brother Michael J. McGinniss, F.S.C., President.

Undergraduates address admission inquiries to Robert Voss, Dean of Admission and Financial Aid; graduate inquiries to Paul Reilly, Director, Graduate Enrollment.

Lafayette College

High Street

Easton, Pennsylvania 18042

Tel: (610) 330-5000 **E-mail:** admissions@lafayette.edu

Fax: (610) 330-5127 **Internet:** www.lafayette.edu

Institution Description: Lafayette College is an independent, nonprofit college affiliated with the United Presbyterian Church (U.S.A.). *Enrollment:* 2,382. *Degrees awarded:* Baccalaureate.

Member of Lehigh Valley Association of Independent Colleges.

Accreditation: *Regional:* MSA/CHE. *Professional*: chemistry, engineering

History: Established, chartered, and incorporated as a men's college 1826; offered first instruction at postsecondary level 1832; awarded first degree (baccalaureate) 1836; admitted women 1970. *See* Albert W. Gendebien, *The Biography of a College III* (Easton, PA: Lafayette College, 1986) for further information.

Institutional Structure: *Governing board:* Lafayette College Board of Trustees. Extrainstitutional representation: up to 35 trustees including the college president, all voting. *Composition of institution:* Administrators 88. Academic affairs headed by provost and dean of the faculty. Finances directed by vice president for business affairs. Full-time instructional faculty 195. Academic governance body, Faculty of Lafayette College, meets an average of 9 times per year.

Calendar: Semesters. Academic year Aug. to May. Freshmen admitted Aug., Jan., June. Degrees conferred and formal commencement May or June. Summer session of 2 terms from June to July.

Characteristics of Freshmen: 6,357 applicants (female 2,793, male 3,564). 37% of applicants accepted. 25% of accepted applicants enrolled full-time.

98% (620 students) submitted SAT scores; 15% (92 students) submitted ACT scores. *25th percentile*: SAT Critical Reading 580, SAT Math 520, SAT Writing 580; ACT Composite 24. *75th percentile*: SAT Critical Reading 670, SAT Math 710, SAT Writing 620; ACT Composite 29.

91% of entering freshmen expected to graduate within 5 years. 27% of freshmen from Pennsylvania. Freshmen from 30 states and 40 foreign countries.

Admission: For fall acceptance, apply as early as Sept. 1 of previous year, but not later than Feb. 1 of year of enrollment. Students are notified of acceptance Mar.-Apr. Deadlines for early decision applications are Nov. 1 and Jan. 1. Early acceptance available. *Requirements:* Either graduation from accredited secondary school with 16 units which must include 4 English, 2 in a foreign language, 3 mathematics, 2 laboratory science; or GED. Average GPA between 3.55 and 4.00. *Entrance tests:* College Board SAT optional. 3 Achievements. *For transfer students:* 60 hours maximum transfer credit.

College credit and advanced placement for postsecondary-level work completed in secondary school, International Baccalaureate, or college APP. Tutoring available.

Degree Requirements: 120–132 credit hours; 2.5 GPA; at least 2 years including senior year in residence.

Fulfillment of some degree requirements and exemption from some beginning courses possible by passing International Baccalaureate or College Board APP. *Grading system:* A–F; pass-fail; withdraw.

Distinctive Educational Programs: Work-experience programs. Evening courses. Marquis Scholars Program. Interdepartmental/interdisciplinary programs, including majors in American civilization and international affairs. Technology Clinic; study abroad programs (locations vary annually). Cross-registration through consortium. Facilities for independent research, including honors programs, individual majors, and tutorials.

ROTC: Army offered in cooperation with Lehigh University.

Degrees Conferred: 659 *baccalaureate:* area studies 8, biological sciences 36, computer and information sciences 8, engineering 105, fine and applied arts 18, foreign languages 9, letters 50, mathematics 21, physical sciences 18, psychology 64, social sciences 189, interdisciplinary studies 4, philosophy 3.

Fees and Other Expenses: *Tuition and fees per academic year 2008–09:* $38,090. *Room and board per academic year:* $11,245. *Books and supplies:* $850. *Other expenses:* 1,000.

Financial Aid: Aid from institutionally generated funds is provided on the basis of financial need, academic merit. Institution has a Program Participation Agreement with the U.S. Department of Education for eligible students to receive Pell Grants and, depending upon the agreement, other federal aid.

Financial aid to full-time, first-time undergraduate students: 66% received some form of financial aid. Average amount of aid received: federal grants $5,127; Pell grans $2,877; other federal aid $2,340; state/local grants $3,166; institutional grants $23,477.

Departments and Teaching Staff: *Total instructional faculty:* 183. Student/faculty ratio: 11:1. Degrees held by full-time faculty: doctorate 100%

Enrollment: Total enrollment 2,382. Undergraduate 2,382 (full-time 95%; female 46%, male 54%). Transfer-in students 9.

Characteristics of Student Body: *Ethnic/racial makeup:* Black non-Hispanic: 5%; Asian or Pacific Islander: 4%; Hispanic: 55; White non-Hispanic: 71%; unknown 9%; nonresident alien 7%.

International Students: 143 nonresident aliens enrolled fall 2008. *Programs available to aid students whose native language is not English:* Social and cultural. English as a Second Language Program. No financial aid specifically designated for international students.

Student Life: On-campus residence halls house 90% of student body. College-owned housing provides residences for 95% mof males and 98% of females 14% of the males live in college-owned fraternity houses leased by alumni corporations. 16% of femlaes women live in sorority houses. *Intercollegiate athletics:* male: baseball, basketball, cross-country, football, lacrosse, soccer, swimming and diving, tennis, track and field; female: basketball, cross-country, field hockey, lacrosse, softball, swimming and diving, tennis, track and field, volleyball; co-ed: fencing, golf. *Special regulations:* Cars permitted for upper division students, lower division by permission. *Special services:* Learning Resources Center, medical services, counseling services, special interest residential houses. *Student publications, radio: Lafayette*, a weekly student newspaper; *Aya*, a black student publication; *Marquis*, a semiannual literary magazine; *Melange*, a yearbook. Radio station WJRH. *Surrounding community:* Easton, population 26,500, is located in the Lehigh Valley with a total population of over 1 million. Philadelphia, 60 miles to the southeast, and New York City, 70 miles to the east, are the nearest metropolitan areas. Served by mass transit bus system, Allentown-Bethlehem-Easton Airport is 10 miles from campus.

Publications: *The Journal of Interdisciplinary History*, an academic journal; *Shakespeare Bulletin*, a journal of performance criticism and scholarship.

Library Collections: 510,000 volumes. 120,000 microforms; 6,000 audiovisual materials; 2,000 current periodical subscriptions. Students have access to online information retrieval services and the Internet.

Most important special holdings include collections on the Marquis de Lafayette; William A. Simon Collection; Stephen Crane Collection; 3 collections on angling.

Buildings and Grounds: Campus area 110 acres plus 70 acres at Metzgar Fields.

Chief Executive Officer: Dr. Arthur J. Rothkopf, President.

Address admission inquiries to Carol Rowlands, Director of Admissions.

Lancaster Bible College

901 Eden Road
P.O. Box 83403
Lancaster, Pennsylvania 17601
Tel: (717) 569-7071 **E-mail:** admissions@lbc.edu
Fax: (717) 560-8213 **Internet:** www.lbc.edu

Institution Description: Lancaster Bible College is a private, independent, nonprofit college. *Enrollment:* 931. *Degrees awarded:* Associate, baccalaureate, master's.

Accreditation: *Regional:* MSA/CHE. *National:* ABHE.

History: Established as Lancaster School of the Bible and offered first instruction at postsecondary level 1933; incorporated 1939; awarded first degree (baccalaureate) and adopted present name 1973; awarded first associate degree 1982; awarded first master's degree 1998.

Institutional Structure: *Governing board:* Board of Trustees. Representation: 19 trustees, president of the college. All voting. *Composition of institution:* Administrators 8. Academic affairs headed by vice president of academic affairs. Finances directed by director of finance. Full-time instructional faculty 48. Faculty meets an average of 12 times per year.

Calendar: Semesters. Academic year Aug. to May. Freshmen admitted Aug., Jan., May, June. Degrees conferred and formal commencement Jan., May. Summer session of 3 terms from May to June and Aug.

Characteristics of Freshmen: 433 applicants (female 237, male 196). 63% of applicants accepted. 65% of accepted applicants enrolled.

78% (186 students) submitted SAT scores; 24$ (57 students) submitted ACT scores. *25th percentile*: SAT Critical Reading 480, SAT Math 460; ACT composite 17. *75th percentile*: SAT Critical Reading 580, SAT Math 570; ACT Composite 23.

54% of entering freshmen expected to graduate within five years. 83% of freshmen from Pennsylvania. Freshmen from 17 states and 1 foreign country.

Admission: Rolling admissions plan. For fall acceptance, apply as early as 1 year in advance of enrollment, but not later than Aug. 15 of year of enrollment. Early acceptance available. *Requirements:* Graduation from secondary school or GED. 500-word autobiographical sketch, including satisfactory evidence of Christian conversion. Minimum GPA 2.0. *Entrance tests:* ACT composite or SAT. *For transfer students:* 2.0 minimum GPA; from 4-year accredited institution 90 hours maximum transfer credit; from 2-year accredited institution 60 hours.

College credit and advanced placement for postsecondary-level work completed in secondary school. College credit for extrainstitutional learning on basis of faculty assessment.

Tutoring available. Developmental courses offered during regular academic year.

Degree Requirements: *For associate degree:* 61 credit hours; 15 of last 30 credits in residence. *For all baccalaureate degrees:* minimum 120 credit hours; 2.0 GPA; 30 of last 60 credits in residence; general education requirements.

Fulfillment of some degree requirements and exemption from some beginning courses possible by passing departmental examinations, College Board CLEP, AP. *Grading system:* A–F; pass-fail; withdraw (deadline after which pass-fail is appended to withdraw).

Distinctive Educational Programs: Evening classes. Facilities for independent research. Summer study abroad programs offered occasionally. Third year study abroad at Jerusalem University College available. One- and two-year courses available.

Degrees Conferred: 160 *baccalaureate*: theology 144; education 16/ Master's degrees awarded: theology 24; education 1.

Fees and Other Expenses: *Full-time tuition per academic year 2008–09:* undergraduate $15,290; graduate study charged per credit hour (contact the college for current rate). *Books and supplies:* $1,000. *Required fees:* $600. *Room and board per academic year:* $6,540. *Other expenses:* $2,500.

Financial Aid: Aid from institutionally generated funds is provided on the basis of academic merit, financial need. Institution has a Program Participation Agreement with the U.S. Department of Education for eligible students to receive Pell Grants and, depending upon the agreement, other federal aid.

Departments and Teaching Staff: *Total instructional faculty:* 91. Student/faculty ratio: 17:1. Degrees held by full-time faculty: doctorates 62%, master's 100%, baccalaureates 100. 62% hold terminal degrees.

Enrollment: Total enrollment 931. Undergraduate 779 (full-time 72%; female 49%, male 51%). Graduate 152 (full-time 3%). Undergraduate transfer-in students 85.

Characteristics of Student Body: *Ethnic/racial makeup:* Black non-Hispanic: 4%; Asian or Pacific Islander: 1%; Hispanic: 2%; White non-Hispanic: 88%; unknown 4%.

International Students: 10 nonresident aliens enrolled fall 2008. Students from Asia, Latin America, Africa, Canada. No programs available to aid students whose native language is not English. Financial aid specifically designated for international students: 10 scholarships available annually to qualifying students.

Student Life: On-campus residence halls house 62% of student body. Residence halls for males constitute 38% of such space, for females 62%. Housing available for married students. *Intercollegiate athletics:* male: baseball, basketball, soccer, tennis; female: basketball, softball, volleyball. *Special regulations:* Cars permitted without restriction. Curfews Sunday through Thursday 12pm, Fri. and Sat. 1am. Quiet hours from 2pm to 4 pm, 7pm to 9pm, 10pm to 8am. *Special services:* Learning Resources Center, medical services. *Student publications: Envoy* student newspaper; *Ichthus*, a yearbook. *Surrounding community:* Lancaster County population 425,000. Philadelphia, 65 miles from campus, is nearest metropolitan area. Served by airport 2 miles from campus; passenger rail service 1.5 miles from campus.

Library Collections: 150,000 volumes. 2,504 recordings; 512 current periodical subscriptions. Computer work stations available. Students have access to online information retrieval services and the Internet.

Most important special collections include the Lancaster Bible College Collection; Curriculum Resource Center; Dr. Lloyd M. Perry Collection.

Buildings and Grounds: Campus area 36 acres.

Chief Executive Officer: Dr. Peter W. Teaque, President.

Address admission inquiries to Joanne Roper, Director of Admissions.

Lebanon Valley College

101 North College Avenue
Annville, Pennsylvania 17003-1400
Tel: (717) 867-6181 **E-mail:** admiss@lvc.edu
Fax: (717) 867-6026 **Internet:** www.lvc.edu

Institution Description: Lebanon Valley College is a private college affiliated with the United Methodist Church. *Enrollment:* 1,965. *Degrees awarded:* Associate, baccalaureate, master', doctorate.

Accreditation: *Regional:* MSA/CHE. *Professional*: chemistry, music

History: Established and offered first instruction at postsecondary level 1866; chartered 1867; awarded first degree (baccalaureate) 1870. *See* Paul A. W. Wallace, *Lebanon Valley College: A Centennial History* (Annville, Pa.; Lebanon Valley College, 1966) for further information.

Institutional Structure: *Governing board:* The Board of Trustees of Lebanon Valley College. Extrainstitutional representation: 30 trustees, 2 student trustees, 19 trustees emeriti, 3 honorary trustees, 32 voting. *Composition of institution:* Administrators 100. Academic affairs headed by vice president and dean of faculty. Management/business/finances directed by vice president and controller. Full-time instructional faculty 100. Academic governance body, The Faculty of Lebanon Valley College, meets an average of 15 times per year.

Calendar: Semesters. Academic year Sept. to May. Freshmen admitted Sept., Jan., June. Degrees conferred May, Aug., Jan. Formal commencement May. Summer session of 2 terms from June to Aug.

Characteristics of Freshmen: 1,885 applicants (female 945, male 940). 73% of applicants admitted. 29% of applicants admitted and enrolled.

99% (443 students) submitted SAT scores; 10% (44 students) submitted ACT scores. *25th percentile*: SAT Critical Reading 490, SAT Math 500, SAT Writing 420; ACT Composite 21, ACT English 20, ACT Math 20. *75th percentile*: SAT Critical Reading 600, SAT Math 620, Critical Writing 580; ACT Composite 25, ACT English 26, ACT Math 25.

67% of entering freshmen are expected to graduate within 5 years. 75% of freshmen from Pennsylvania. Freshmen from 20 states and 5 foreign countries.

Admission: Rolling admissions plan. For fall acceptance, apply as early as Sept. of previous year. Early acceptance available. *Requirements:* Either graduation from accredited secondary school with 16 units which must include 4 English, 3 mathematics, 2 science, 1 social studies; or GED. *Entrance tests:* College Board SAT or ACT composite. *For transfer students:* 2.0 minimum GPA; 90 hours maximum transfer credit; from 2-year accredited institution 60 hours.

College credit and advanced placement for postsecondary-level work completed in secondary school and for College Board CLEP. For extrainstitutional learning, college credit on basis of interview and faculty assessment.

Tutoring available.

Degree Requirements: 120 credit hours; 2.0 GPA; 2.0 GPA in major; 30 of last 36 credit hours in residence; 2 units physical education; 6 credits in writing skills; distribution requirements.

Fulfillment of some degree requirements and exemption from some beginning courses possible by passing College Board CLEP or APP. *Grading system:* A–F; high pass/pass-fail; withdraw (carries time limit); incomplete.

LEBANON VALLEY COLLEGE—*cont'd*

Distinctive Educational Programs: Flexible meeting places and schedules (including off-campus location in Lancaster); weekend and evening classes. Accelerated degree programs. Dual-degree programs in engineering with Case Western Reserve and Widener University; in forestry with Duke University. Preprofessional programs in the allied health fields. Facilities for independent research, including individualized majors, tutorials. Study abroad programs in Australia, England, France, Germany, Greece, Italy, The Netherlands, New Zealand, Spain. Urban semester programs in Philadelphia and Washington (DC).

ROTC: Army offered jointly with Millersville University.

Degrees Conferred: 1 *associate*; 398 *baccalaureate*; 22 *master's* ; 8 *doctorate*. Bachelor's degrees awarded in top five disciplines: education 83; business, management, marketing, and related support services 82; psychology 47; social sciences and history 37. visual and performing arts 28.

Fees and Other Expenses: *Full-time tuition per academic year 2008–09:* undergraduate $29,550; contact the college for current graduate tuition/fees. *Other fees:* $650. *Room and board per academic year:* $7,760. *Books and supplies:* $1,000. *Other expenses:* $1,500.

Financial Aid: Aid from institutionally generated funds is provided on the basis of academic merit, financial need.

Financial aid to full-time, first-time undergraduate students: 99% received some form of financial aid. Average amount of aid received: federal grants $3,795; Pell grants $2,627; other federal aid $1,327; state/local grants $3,855; institutional grants $12,206.

Departments and Teaching Staff: *Total instructional faculty:* 66. *Degrees held by full-time faculty:* Doctorate 49%, master's 51%. 49% hold terminal degrees.

Enrollment: Total enrollment 1,965. Undergraduate 1,747 (full-time 92%; female 55%, male 45%). Graduate 218 (full-time 21%). Undergraduate transfer-in students 66.

Characteristics of Student Body: *Ethnic and racial makeup:* Black non-Hispanic: 2%; Asian or Pacific Islander: 2%; Hispanic 3%; White non-Hispanic: 89%; unknown: 4%.

International Students: No programs available to aid students whose native language is not English. No financial aid specifically designated for international students.

Student Life: On-campus residence halls house 75% of the full-time student body. with 58% of the space co-ed residence halls, 12% female's, 7% male's. 1% of housing for disabled students. 10% of men join and 12% of women join fraternities and sororities. *Intercollegiate athletics:* male: baseball, basketball, cross-country, football, golf, ice hockey, soccer, track, swimming, wrestling; female: basketball, cross-country, field hockey, soccer, softball, swimming, volleyball, track. *Special regulations:* Cars permitted without restrictions. Males may visit female's rooms and females, male's rooms from noon to midnight daily and by vote of individual residence halls from Friday noon to Sunday midnight. *Special services:* Learning Resources Center, medical services, writing center, tutorial center. *Student publications, radio: La Vie Collegienne,* a weekly student newspaper; *Quittapahilla*, a yearbook. Radio station WLVC broadcasts 168 hours per week. *Surrounding community:* Annville township population 4,500. Harrisburg, 17 miles from campus, is nearest metropolitan area. Served by mass transit system; airport 20 miles from campus; passenger rail service 20 miles from campus.

Publications: Sources of information about Lebanon Valley College include *The Valley*, the alumni magazine published twice annually; *The Courier*, a biweekly newsletter.

Library Collections: 187,000 volumes including bound books, serial backfiles, electronic documents, and government documents not in separate collections. Online catalog. Current serial subscriptions: 820 paper, 251 microform, 11,137 via electronic access. 5,258 recordings. Computer work stations. available. Students have access to the Internet at no charge.

Most important special holdings include Paul A.W. Wallace Family Papers; Heilman Collection of Early Pennsylvania Imprints; C.B. Montgomery Memorial Collection on Pennsylvania German History and Customs.

Buildings and Grounds: Campus area 340 acres.

Chief Executive Officer: Dr. Stephen C. MacDonald, President.

Undergraduates address admission inquiries to Susan Sarisky, Director of Admissions and Financial Aid; graduate inquiries to Elaine D. Feather, Director of Graduate Studies and Continuing Education.

Lehigh University

27 Memorial Drive West
Bethlehem, Pennsylvania 18015-5094
Tel: (610) 758-3100 **E-mail:** admissions@lehigh.edu
Fax: (610) 758-4361 **Internet:** www.lehigh.edu

Institution Description: Lehigh University is a private, independent, nonprofit institution. *Enrollment:* 994,641. *Degrees awarded:* Associate, baccalaureate, master's, doctorate.

Accreditation: *Regional:* MSA/CHE. *Professional*: accounting, business, chemistry, computer science, engineering, teacher education, theatre

History: Established 1865; chartered and offered first instruction at postsecondary level 1866; awarded first degree (baccalaureate) 1869; added graduate school 1936.

Institutional Structure: *Governing board:* Lehigh University Board of Trustees. Extrainstitutional representation: 36 trustees; institutional representation: 8 administrators, 3 full-time instructional faculty members, 2 students. 19 ex officio. 36 voting. *Composition of institution:* Administrators 60. Academic affairs headed by provost. Full-time instructional faculty 391. Academic governance body, the faculty, meets an average of 6 times per year.

Calendar: Semesters. Academic year Aug. to May. Freshmen admitted Aug., Jan. Degrees conferred June, Jan. Formal commencements June, Jan. Summer session of 2 terms from June to Aug.

Characteristics of Freshmen: 12,941 applicants (female 5,520, male 7,421). 285 of applicants accepted. 33% of accepted applicants enrolled.

Mean SAT scores: Critical Reading 606, Math 643.

82% of entering freshmen expected to graduate within 5 years. 26% of freshmen from Pennsylvania. Freshmen from 46 states and 45 foreign countries.

Admission: For fall acceptance, apply as early as Oct. 1 of previous year, but not later than Jan. 1 of year of enrollment. Students are notified of acceptance by Apr. 1. Apply by Nov. 15 for early decision; need not limit application to Lehigh. Early acceptance available. *Requirements:* Graduation from secondary school with 4 units English, 2 foreign language, 3 mathematics, 2 lab science, 2 social studies, 3 electives. For engineering and science programs, 1 chemistry. *Entrance tests:* College Board SAT required. *For transfer students:* 3.0 minimum GPA, 90 semester hours maximum transfer credit.

College credit and advanced placement for postsecondary-level work completed in secondary school. Tutoring available.

Degree Requirements: *For undergraduate degrees:* 120 semester hours; 2.0 GPA; 90 hours or last 30 hours in residence; English requirement; distribution requirements.

Fulfillment of some degree requirements and exemption from some beginning courses possible by passing College Board APP; exemption also possible by passing institutional examinations. *Grading system:* A–F; pass-fail; withdraw (may carry penalty, carries time limit).

Distinctive Educational Programs: Work experience programs. Accelerated degree programs. Joint B.A.-M.D. program with Medical College of Pennsylvania; joint B.A.-D.D.S. program with University of Pennsylvania. Interdisciplinary programs include Afro-American studies, American studies, arts-engineering, biochemistry, earth and environmental science, environmental science, fundamental science, geophysics, Latin American studies, natural science, Russian studies, urban studies. Honors program. Study abroad programs in Australia, Austria, Belgium, China, Costa Rica, Denmark, Ecuador, England, France, Germany, Greece, Ireland, Israel, Italy, Japan, Kenya, Korea, Mexico, Russia, Scotland, Senegal, Spain, Sweden, Taiwan.

ROTC: Army.

Degrees Conferred: 1,092 *baccalaureate*; 526 *master's*; 98 *doctorate*. Bachelor's degrees awarded in top five disciplines: business, management, marketing, and related support services 311; engineering 290; social sciences and history 121; computer and information sciences and support services; psychology 67. Master's degrees awarded: various disciplines 526. Doctorates awarded: various disciplines 98.

Fees and Other Expenses: *Full-time tuition per academic year 2008–09:* $37,550. *Required fees:* $240. Contact the university for current graduate tuition/fees. *Books and supplies:* $1,000. *Room and board per academic year:* $9,770. *Other expenses* $1,220.

Financial Aid: Aid from institutionally generated funds is provided on the basis of academic merit, financial need, athletic ability.

Financial aid to full-time, first-time undergraduate students: 60% received some form of aid. Average amount of aid received: federal grants $3,498; Pell grants $2,883; other federal aid $882; state/local grants $3,257; institutional grants $2,1526.

Departments and Teaching Staff: *Total instructional faculty:* 597 (full-time 432, part-time 165). Total faculty with doctorate, first-professional, or other terminal degree: 428. Student/faculty ratio: '10:1. Degrees held by full-time faculty: 99% hold terminal degrees.

Enrollment: Total enrollment 6,994. Undergraduate 4,876 (full-time 99%; female 42%, male 58%). Graduate 2,118 (full-time 45%).

Characteristics of Student Body: *Ethnic/racial makeup:* Black non-Hispanic: 3%; Asian or Pacific Islander: 6%; Hispanic: 5%; White non-Hispanic: 74%; unknown: 9%; nonresident alien 35.

International Students: 210 nonresident aliens enrolled fall 2008. Students from Europe, Asia, Latin American, Africa, Canada, Australia. Programs available to aid students whose native language is not English: social, cultural. English as a Second Language Program. Financial aid specifically designated for international students: scholarships available annually to qualifying students.

Student Life: On-campus residence halls house 45% of student body. Residence halls for males constitute 20% of such space, for females 20%, for both sexes 60%. 41% of males join and 35% live in fraternity housing; 44% of females join and 20% live in sorority housing. Housing available for married students. 69% of students live on campus. *Intercollegiate athletics:* male: baseball, basketball, football, golf, lacrosse, soccer, swimming, tennis, track, wrestling; female: basketball, field hockey, lacrosse, soccer, softball, swimming, tennis, volleyball; male and female: crew, cross-country, track. *Special regulations:* Cars permitted for all but freshmen. *Special services:* Learning Resources Center, medical services, bus service for athletic playing fields. *Student publications: Brown and White*, a biweekly newspaper. *Surrounding community:* Bethlehem population 70,000. Philadelphia, 55 miles from campus, is nearest metropolitan area. Served by airport 3 miles from campus; bus service less than 1 mile from campus.

Publications: *Lehigh University Research Review* first published 1970; *Lehigh Research Perspective* published annually.

Library Collections: 1,400,000 volumes including bound books, serial backfiles, electronic documents, and government documents not in separate collections. Online catalog. Current serial subscriptions: 5,473 paper, microform, and electronic. 3,915 audiovisual materials. Compute work stations avaialble campus-wide. Students have access to the Internet at no charge.

Most important special holdings include Birds of America by John J. Audubon; first and early editions of Charles Darwin; *De re Metallica* by Agricola (yr. 1556).

Buildings and Grounds: Campus area 1,600 acres.

Chief Executive Officer: Dr. Gregory C. Farrington, President.

Address admission inquiries Jason B. Honsel, Associate Director, Admissions.

Lincoln University

1570 Baltimore Pike
Lincoln University, Pennsylvania 19352-0999
Tel: (610) 932-8300 **E-mail:** admiss@lincoln.edu
Fax: (610) 932-2089 **Internet:** www.lincoln.edu

Institution Description: Lincoln University is a state-related, private, independent, nonprofit institution. *Enrollment:* 2,524. *Degrees awarded:* Baccalaureate, master's.

Accreditation: *Regional:* MSA/CHE. *Professional*: chemistry, physical therapy, teacher education

History: Established and chartered as Ashmun Institute and offered first instruction at postsecondary level 1854; changed name to Lincoln University 1866; offered first degree (baccalaureate) 1859; adopted present formal name as Lincoln University of the Commonwealth System of Higher Education 1972. *See* Horace Mann Bond, *Education for Freedom* (Princeton: Princeton University Press, 1976) for further information.

Institutional Structure: *Governing board:* Lincoln Board of Trustees. Extrainstitutional representation: 35 trustees, including the Secretary of Education, Governor, 6 alumni; institutional representation: president of the college. All voting. *Composition of institution:* Administrators 149. Academic affairs headed by the Vice President for Academic Affairs. Management/business/finances directed by Vice President for Fiscal Affairs. Instructional faculty 86. Academic governance body, the Faculty. *Faculty representation:* Faculty served by collective bargaining agent, AAUP.

Calendar: Semesters. Academic year Aug. to Apr. Freshmen admitted Aug., Jan., May. Degrees conferred Dec., May. Formal commencement May. Summer session of 1 semester from mid-May to July.

Characteristics of Freshmen: 5,893 applicants (female 3,687, male 2,226). 35% of applicants accepted. 30% of accepted applicants enrolled.

95% (630 students) submitted SAT scores; 4 (27 students) submitted ACT scores. *25th percentile*: SAT Critical Reading 360, SAT Math 350; ACT Composite 15, ACT English 13, ACT 15. *75th percentile*: SAT Critical Reading 450, SAT Math 450; ACT Composite 18, ACT English 19, ACT Math 18.

30% of entering freshmen expected to graduate within 5 years. 38% of freshmen from Pennsylvania. 43% of freshmen from Pennsylvania. Freshmen from 26 states and 23 foreign countries.

Admission: Rolling admissions plan. For fall acceptance, apply as early as Jan. but no later than Aug. 1 of year of enrollment. Apply by Dec. 1 for spring enrollment. Early acceptance is available. *Requirements:* Either graduation from an accredited secondary school with 21 units or GED. Minimum 2.0 GPA. *Entrance tests:* College Board SAT. TOEFL for foreign students.

Degree Requirements: *For all baccalaureate degrees:* 120–128 semester hours; 2 terms in residence. *For all undergraduate degrees:* 2.0 GPA; 2 physical education courses; exit competency exam in English proficiency.

Fulfillment of some degree requirements and exemption from some beginning courses possible by passing College Board AP and CLEP. *Grading system:* A–F; pass-fail; withdraw; incomplete (carries time limit).

Distinctive Educational Programs: *For undergraduates:* Cooperative education and internships. Dual-degree programs in engineering with Drexel University, Lafayette College, Pennsylvania State University, New Jersey Institute of Technology, City College of New York, University of Delaware. Interdisciplinary program in public affairs. Facilities and programs for independent research, including honors programs and tutorials. Institutionally sponsored language study abroad programs in Japan. *For graduate students:* Weekend classes.

ROTC: Available in conjunction with the University of Delaware.

Degrees Conferred: 227 *baccalaureate*; 194 *master's*. Bachelor's degrees awarded in top five disciplines: business, management, marketing, and related support services 50; biological/life science 21; education 20; security and protective services 18; computer and information sciences 13.

Fees and Other Expenses: *Full-time tuition per academic year 2008–09:* resident undergraduate $8,075, nonresident $12,882; contact the university for current graduate tuition/fees. *Books and supplies:* $1,380. *Room and board per academic year:* $7,850. *TOther expenses:* $2,118.

Financial Aid: Aid from institutionally generated funds is provided on the basis of academic merit, financial need.

Financial aid to full-time, first-time undergraduate students: 96% received some form of financial aid. Average amount of aid received: federal grants $3,979; Pell grants $3,243; other federal aid: $1,289; state/local grants $3,587; institutional grants $4,899.

Departments and Teaching Staff: *Total instructional faculty:* 66. *Degrees held by full-time faculty:* Doctorate 49%, master's 51%. 49% hold terminal degrees.

Enrollment: Total enrollment 2,524. Undergraduate 1,973 (full-time 97%; female 60%, male 40%). Graduate 551 (full-time 68%). Undergraduate transfer-in students 55.

Characteristics of Student Body: *Ethnic and racial makeup:* Black non-Hispanic: 1%; Asian or Pacific Islander 1%; Hispanic 1%; White non-Hispanic 94%; unknown 3%; nonresident alien 2%.

International Students: 50 nonresident aliens enrolled fall 2008. Students from Europe, Asia, Latin America, Africa, Canada. No programs available to aid students whose native language is not English. No financial aid specifically designated for international students.

Student Life: On-campus residence halls house 95% of student body. Residence halls for males constitute 49% of such space, for females 51%. *Intercollegiate athletics:* baseball, track, volleyball, soccer. *Special regulations:* Cars permitted for all but freshmen. *Special services:* Learning Resources Center, medical services, van available. *Student publications, radio: The Lincolnian.* Radio station WLIU broadcasts 50 hours per week. *Surrounding community:* Lower Oxford Township population 4,000. Philadelphia, 45 miles from campus, is nearest metropolitan area. Airport 40 miles from campus. Passenger rail service 30 miles from campus.

Library Collections: 189,500 volumes including bound books, serial backfiles, electronic documents, and government documents not in separate collections. Online catalog. 212,000 microforms; 2,700 audiovisual materials; cCurrent serial subscriptions: 540 paper, 183 microform. Computer work stations available. Students have access to the Internet at no charge.

Most important special holdings include the African American Collection; Personal Library of Langston Hughes; University Archives including Lincolniana and Rare Books.

Buildings and Grounds: Campus area 422 acres and an Urban Center in Philadelphia for most of the graduate programs.

Chief Executive Officer: Dr. Ivory V. Nelson, President.

Address admission inquiries to Michael Taylor, Director of Admissions.

Lock Haven University of Pennsylvania

401 North Fairview Street
Lock Haven, Pennsylvania 17745-2390
Tel: (570) 893-2027 **E-mail:** admissions@lhup.edu
Fax: (570) 893-2432 **Internet:** www.lhup.edu

Institution Description: Lock Haven University of Pennsylvania is an institution of the Pennsylvania State System of Higher Education. *Enrollment:* 5,266. *Degrees awarded:* Associate, baccalaureate, master's.

Academic offerings and budget subject to approval by State System of Higher Education.

Accreditation: *Regional:* MSA/CHE. *Professional*: athletic training, nursing, social work, teacher education

History: Established and chartered as Central State Normal School 1870; offered first instruction at postsecondary level 1877; changed name to State Teachers College at Lock Haven and awarded first degree (baccalaureate) 1927; name changed to Lock Haven State College 1960; School of Arts and Sciences started 1962; changed name to Lock Haven University 1983; master's degree first offered 1987; Clearfield campus established 1989. *See* Harold C. Wisor, *A History of Teacher Education at Lock Haven State College, 1970–1960* (Diss., Pennsylvania State University, 1966) for further information.

Institutional Structure: *Governing board:* Board of Governors for State System of Higher Education. Extrainstitutional representation: 20 directors. All voting. Council of Trustees of Lock Haven University (joint appointment). 11 trustees. Institutional representation: 1 student. *Composition of institution:* Executive administrators 22. . Academic affairs headed by vice president for academic affairs and provost; administration, finance, and technology by vice president for administration, finance, and technology; student affairs by vice president for study affairs; university relations by vice president for university relations. Full-time instructional faculty 236. 86 women. Academic governance body, University Curriculum Committee, meets an average of 18 times per year. *Faculty representation:* Faculty served by collective bargaining agent, Association of Pennsylvania State Colleges and Universities Faculties (APSCUF).

Calendar: Semesters. Academic year Aug. to May. Freshmen admitted June, Aug., Jan. Degrees conferred May, Aug., and Dec. Formal commencement May, Dec. Summer session of 2 terms from June to July.

Characteristics of Freshmen: 4,776 applicants (female 2,691, male 2,079). 74% of applicants accepted. 35% of accepted applicants enrolled full-time.

95% (1,042 students) submitted SAT scores; 87% (84 students) submitted ACT scores. *25th percentile*: SAT Critical Reading 420, SAT Math 420; ACT Composite 17. *75th percentile*: SAT Critical Reading 510, SAT Math 520; ACT Composite 22.

49% of entering freshmen expected to graduate within 5 years. 90% of freshmen from Pennsylvania. Freshmen from 34 states and 39 foreign countries.

Admission: Rolling admissions plan. For fall acceptance, apply as early as Aug. 1 of previous year, but not later than June 1 of year of enrollment. Early acceptance available. *Requirements:* Either graduation from approved secondary school with college preparatory program or GED. Additional requirements for some programs. *Entrance tests:* College Board SAT or ACT composite. For foreign students minimum TOEFL score of 213 is acceptable. *For transfer students:* 2.0 minimum GPA; 90 hours maximum transfer credit. *Graduate admission:* Baccalaureate degree from accredited school; maximum credits that may be accepted in transfer varies by program.

College credit and advanced placement for postsecondary-level work completed in secondary school. College credit for extrainstitutional learning on basis of portfolio assessment.

Tutoring available. Developmental courses offered in summer session and regular academic year; credit given.

Degree Requirements: 128 credit hours; 2.0 GPA; 2 terms in residence; 3 hours wellness courses; general education courses. For arts and science students, 9 hours liberal arts seminars (B.A.); demonstrated proficiency in a foreign language (B.A.). For master's degree: 30 credit hours; 2.7 GPA. For associate degree in nursing: 67 credit hours; 2.5 GPA.

Fulfillment of some degree requirements and exemption from some beginning courses possible by passing institutional examinations, College Board CLEP, AP. *Grading system:* A–F; pass-fail; credit- no credit; withdraw (carries time limit).

Distinctive Educational Programs: Dual-degree program in engineering with Pennsylvania State University (University Park). Honors Program. Facilities for using telecommunications in the classroom. Interdisciplinary programs in general studies, international education, management science. Preprofessional program in physical therapy. Individual majors. Study abroad in Australia, Austria, Belgium, China, Costa Rica, Croatia, Ukraine, England, France, Italy, Russia, Scotland, Spain, Italy, Japan, Mexico, Poland, Taiwan. NATA recognized athletic training program. *Other distinctive programs:* International studies, health science (athletic training sports medicine certification). Preprofessional programs include prelaw, prevet, premed, predental, prepharmacy, and prephysical therapy; master's program in health science (physician assistant in rural primary health care).

ROTC: Army offered in cooperation with Pennsylvania State University.

Degrees Conferred: 76 *associate;* 837 *baccalaureate*; 83 *master's*. Bachelor's degrees awrded: area studies 8; biological/life sciences 34; business and management 56; communications 24; computer and information sciences 8; education 165; fine and applied arts 2; foreign languages 4; health professions 170; liberal arts 11; library science 1; mathematics 1; physical sciences 20; psychology 41; social sciences and history 56; visual and performing arts 6. Master's degrees awarded: various disciplines 83.

Fees and Other Expenses: *Full-time tuition per academic year 2008–09:* undergraduate resident $6,917, nonresident $13,047; contact the university for graduate tuition/fees. *Room and board per academic year:* $6,160. *Books and supplies:* $1,100. *Other expenses:* $2,322.

Financial Aid: Aid from institutionally generated funds is provided on the basis of academic merit, financial need, athletic ability. Institution has a Program Participation Agreement with the U.S. Department of Education for eligible students to receive Pell Grants and, depending upon the agreement, other federal aid.

Financial aid to full-time, first-time undergraduate students: need-based scholarships/grants totaling $10,651,104; self-help $24,864,200; non-need-based scholarships/grants totaling $949,482 parent loans $3,654,081, tuition waivers $744,316, athletic awards $614,007.

Departments and Teaching Staff: *Total instructional faculty:* 256 (full-time 236, part-time 20). Total faculty with doctorate, first-professional, or other terminal degree: 159. Student/faculty ratio: 18:1. Degrees held by full-time faculty: doctorate 54%, master's 43%, baccalaureate 3%. 58% hold terminal degrees.

Enrollment: Total enrollment 5,266. Undergraduate 4,988 (full-time 92%; female 57%, male 43%). Graduate 278 (full-time 44%). Undergraduate transfer-in students 230.

Characteristics of Student Body: *Ethnic/racial makeup:* Black non-Hispanic: 7%; Asian or Pacific Islander: 1%; Hispanic: 2%; White non-Hispanic: 87%; unknown: 1%; nonresident alien 2%.

International Students: 106 nonresident aliens enrolled fall 2008. Students from Europe, Asia, Latin America, Africa, Canada. Programs available to aid students whose native language is not English: social, cultural, financial. English as a Second Language Program.

Student Life: On-campus residence halls house 43% of student body. Residence halls for females constitute 10%; both sexes 33%. Each hall has its own governing structure. *Intercollegiate athletics:* male: baseball, basketball, cross-country, football, soccer, track, wrestling; female: basketball, cross-country, swimming, track, lacrosse, softball, field hockey, volleyball. *Special regulations:* cars permitted for students who have earned 48 hours credit. *Special services:* Learning Resources Center, medical services, computer laboratories. *Student publications: Crucible*, an annual literary magazine; *Eagle Eye*, a weekly newspaper. *Surrounding community:* Lock Haven population 10,000. Pittsburgh, 170 miles from campus, is nearest metropolitan area. Served by airport 35 miles from campus.

Library Collections: 430,000 volumes including bound books, serial backfiles, electronic documents, and government documents not in separate collections. Online catalog. 644,000 microforms; 10,000 audiovisual materials; 20,500 periodicals including via electronic access. Computer work stations available. Students have access to the Internet at no charge.

Most important special collection: Eden Phillpotts Collection (100 first editions and some letters of the British writer and contemporaries of Thomas Hardy).

Buildings and Grounds: Campus area 156 acres. Campus DVD available.

Chief Executive Officer: Dr. Keith I. Miller, President.

Address inquiries to Stephen Lee, Director of Admissions.

Lutheran Theological Seminary at Gettysburg

61 Seminary Ridge
Gettysburg, Pennsylvania 17325-1795
Tel: (717) 334-6286 **E-mail:** info@ltsg.edu
Fax: (717) 334-3469 **Internet:** www.ltsg.edu

Institution Description: Lutheran Theological Seminary at Gettysburg is a private institution affiliated with the Evangelical Lutheran Church in America. *Enrollment:* 211. *Degrees awarded:* First-professional (master of divinity), master's.

Member of Washington Theological Consortium.

Accreditation: *Regional:* MSA/CHE. *National:* ATS. *Professional*: theology

History: Established and offered first instruction at postsecondary level 1826; incorporated 1827; awarded first degree (first-professional) 1828; admitted women 1945; oldest Lutheran theological seminary in the United States. *See* Abdel Ross Wentz, *History of the Gettysburg Theological Seminary* (Philadelphia: United Lutheran Publication House, 1966) for further information.

Institutional Structure: *Governing board:* Board of Directors. Representation: 26 directors (including 2 bishops). 26 voting members; 9 ex officio. *Composition of institution:* Administrative staff 6 men / 8 women. Academic affairs headed by dean. Management/business/finances directed by vice president for finance and administration. Full-time instructional faculty 14. Academic governance body, the faculty, meets an average of 12 times per year.

Calendar: Semesters. Academic year Sept. to May. Entering students admitted Sept., Jan., Feb. Degrees conferred and formal commencement May. Summer intensive courses offered May-July.

Admission: Rolling admissions plan. For fall acceptance, apply as early as 1 year prior to enrollment, but not later than Apr. *Requirements:* Baccalaureate from an accredited college or university. Minimum 2.7 GPA. *For transfer students:* maximum transfer credit limited only by residence requirements. Seminarians must give evidence of good standing at seminary previously attended.

Degree Requirements: *For first-professional degrees:* 90.5 credit hours; 1-year internship; clinical pastoral education program; 1 other field education experience; multicultural concerns programs; 1 course through consortium; demonstrated proficiency in reading Greek. *For master's degrees:* 25.5–61 credit hours. *For all degrees:* Final year in residence; distribution requirements.

Fulfillment of some degree requirements possible by passing divisional examinations. *Grading system:* Pass-fail (with descriptive reports) or letter grades; withdraw (deadline after which pass-fail is appended to withdraw).

Distinctive Educational Programs: Work-experience programs, including internships, field education. Opportunity for academic concentration in Town and County Ministry. Opportunity for study through the Lutheran Center for Theology and Public Life in Washington DC, 77 miles from main institution. Evening classes. Interdisciplinary program in multicultural concerns. Facilities for independent research, including honors programs, tutorials, independent study. *Other distinctive programs:* Cooperative master's program in sacred theology. The Institute for Luther Studies. Continuing education for church leaders and laity. Study abroad in Munich, Germany.

Degrees Conferred: 8 *master's:* theology7, religion 1; 37 *first-professional:* master of divinity.

Fees and Other Expenses: *Full-time tuition per academic year 2008–09:* contact the seminary for current tuition, fees, and other costs.

Financial Aid: Aid from institutionally generated funds is provided on the basis of academic merit, financial need.

Departments and Teaching Staff: *Total instructional faculty:* 26 (full-time 11, part-time 15; women 5, men 21; members of minority groups 3). Total faculty with doctorate, first-professional, or other terminal degree: 26. Student/faculty ratio: 13:1.

Enrollment: Total enrollment 211.

Characteristics of Student Body: *Ethnic/racial makeup:* Black non-Hispanic: 5%; Asian or Pacific Islander: 1%; Hispanic: 8%; White non-Hispanic: 92%.

International Students: 5 nonresident aliens enrolled fall 2008. Students from Europe, Africa. No programs available to aid students whose native language is not English. Some scholarships available for international students.

Student Life: On-campus housing fro 60% of student body. Residence halls constitute 25% of such space. *Special regulations:* Cars permitted without restrictions. *Special services:* Learning Resources Center, technology connections, cable TV, handicapped accessibility. YWCA with swimming pool, gym, and fitness center on campus. *Student publications: The Daily Redactor*, a daily news bulletin. *Surrounding community:* Gettysburg population 8,000. Harrisburg, 37 miles from campus, is nearest metropolitan area served by airport 38 miles from campus; passenger rail service 38 miles from campus.

Publications: Sources of information about Lutheran Theological Seminary at Gettysburg include the *Seminary News*, quarterly newsletter distributed to alumni and church leaders; *Seminary & Ridge Review*, a semiannual journal; *Alumninews*, a monthly electronic newsbrief for alumni and friends of the seminary; *Vocations* a monthly electronic newsletter distributed to prospective students. pastors.

Library Collections: 179,000 volumes including bound books, serial backfiles, electronic documents, and government documents not in separate collections. Online and card catalogs. Current serial subscriptions: 509 paper. 588 recordings; 20 compact discs; 38 CD-ROMs. Computer work stations available. Students have access to the Internet at no charge.

Most important special collections include the S.S. Schmucker papers, a collection of 150 letters and sermons from the 19th-century pastor and founder of Gettysburg College and the Lutheran Theological Seminary at Gettysburg; theological periodicals; Lutheran Historical Society Collection.

Buildings and Grounds: Campus area 52 acres.

Chief Executive Officer: Dr. Michael Cooper-White, President.

Address admission inquiries to Nancy E. Gable, Associate Dean for Church Vocations and Deaconal Ministry.

Lutheran Theological Seminary at Philadelphia

7301 Germantown Avenue
Philadelphia, Pennsylvania 19119
Tel: (215) 248-4616 **E-mail:** ltsadmis@ltsp.edu
Fax: (215) 248-4577 **Internet:** www.ltsp.edu

Institution Description: The Lutheran Theological Seminary at Philadelphia is a private institution affiliated with 21 synods of the Evangelical Lutheran Church in America. *Enrollment:* 423. *Degrees awarded:* First-professional (master of divinity, master of arts in religion), master of sacred theology, doctor of ministry, doctor of theology.

Accreditation: *Regional:* MSA/CHE. *National:* ATS. *Professional*: theology

History: Established and offered first instruction at postsecondary level 1864; awarded first degree (first-professional) 1865; incorporated 1893. *See* Theodore G. Tappert, *History of the Lutheran Theological Seminary at Philadelphia: 1864-1964* (Philadelphia: The Lutheran Theological Seminary 1964) for further information.

Institutional Structure: *Governing board:* Board of Trustees with 22 members; both lay and clergy, including the president of the seminary. 15 members elected by synods, four by national church's Division for Ministry, 2 bishops elected by peers of supporting synods. *Composition of institution:* president, dean of academic affairs, director of seminary advancement, chief financial officer. Full-time instructional faculty 18. Academic governance body, The Faculty, meets an average of 12 times per year.

Calendar: Semesters. Academic year Aug. to June. Entering students admitted Aug., Sept., Jan., Feb., June. Degrees conferred and formal commencement May. Graduate school summer term (3 sessions in June).

Admission: Rolling admissions plan. For fall acceptance, apply as early as 1 year prior to enrollment, but not later than July 1 of year of enrollment. Th.D. applicants apply by June 15. *Requirements:* Baccalaureate degree from accredited college or university; approval from candidate's home synod or other church denominational body. Liberal arts program recommended. *For transfer students:* Good standing at institution previously attended; maximum transfer credit limited only by residence requirement.

Degree Requirements: *For first-professional degrees:* 30 course units; internship; 2.0 GPA; final year in residence, core curriculum, field education. *For master's degrees:* 20 course units; final year in residence, core curriculum, field education; summer study program; 2.0 GPA. *For S.T.M.:* 8 courses plus thesis or 10 courses plus comprehensive evaluative examination; 3.0 GPA. *For D.Min.:* 8 courses, 2 colloquia, project; 3.0 GPA. For ThD.: 12 courses.

Fulfillment of some degree requirements and exemption from some beginning courses possible by passing institutional examinations. *Grading system:* A–F; pass-fail used in field education supplemented by descriptive evaluations; incomplete (subject to time limitation imposed by faculty in each case).

Distinctive Educational Programs: *For first-professional students:* Accelerated degree programs. *For first-professional and master's students:* Internships and field experience. Evening and weekend classes. Facilities and programs for independent research, including individual majors, tutorials, independent study. Cross-registration with Eastern Baptist Theological Seminary, St. Charles Borromeo Seminary, Westminster Theological Seminary. Interseminary seminars with area institutions. *Other distinctive programs:* Degree-granting Urban Theological Institute. One-year program for Lutheran seminarians studying at other denominational seminaries. Noncredit continuing education program primarily for in-service pastors. Globalization study-trips/tours: one country annually May-June.

Degrees Conferred: 13 *master's:* religion/theology; 8 *doctorate:* religion/theology; 33 *first-professional* master of divinity.

Fees and Other Expenses: *Full-time tuition per academic year 2008–09:* contact the seminary for current information regarding tuition, fees, housing, and other applicable costs.

Financial Aid: Aid from institutionally generated funds is provided on the basis of academic merit and financial need.

Departments and Teaching Staff: *Total instructional faculty:* 40. Degrees held by full-time faculty: doctorate 89%, master's 100%, first-professional 100%.

Enrollment: Total enrollment 423.

International Students: 14 nonresident aliens from enrolled fall 2008. Students from Europe, Asia, Latin America, Africa, Middle East. No programs

LUTHERAN THEOLOGICAL SEMINARY AT PHILADELPHIA—*cont'd*

available to aid students whose native language is not English. Some financial aid specifically designated for international students.

Student Life: Full-time students eligible for on-campus housing. 60% live on campus—34% in dormitory, 26% in apartments. *Special regulations:* Cars permitted with registration fee. *Student publications: The Seminarian*, a periodic newspaper. *Surrounding community:* Philadelphia metropolitan area population 4,725,000. Served by mass transit bus, train, and streetcar systems; airport 15 miles from campus; passenger rail service 3 blocks from campus.

Publications: *Academy Accents*, a periodical newsletter on preaching; *Parish Practice Notebook*, a periodic newsletter for parish pastors.

Library Collections: 197,634 volumes including bound books, serial backfiles, electronic documents, and government documents not in separate collections. Online catalog. Current serial subscriptions in paper, microform, electronic. 5,326 recordings; 584 compact discs; 15 CD-ROMs. Computer work stations available. Students have access to the Internet at no charge.

Most important special collections include the Lutheran Archives Center at Philadelphia; Reformation imprints; Continental Europe Kirchenerdnungen.

Buildings and Grounds: Campus area 14 acres. *New buildings:* Brossmen Learning Center completed 2005.

Chief Executive Officer: Rev. Philip D. Krey, President.

Address admission inquiries to Rev. Richard H. Summy, Director of Admissions.

Lycoming College

700 College Place

Williamsport, Pennsylvania 17701-5192

Tel: (570) 321-4000 **E-mail:** admissions@lycoming.edu

Fax: (570) 321-4337 **Internet:** www.lycoming.edu

Institution Description: Lycoming College is a private, independent, liberal arts college affiliated with the United Methodist Church. *Enrollment:* 1,328. *Degrees awarded:* Baccalaureate.

Accreditation: *Regional:* MSA/CHE.

History: Established as the Williamsport Academy and chartered 1812; changed name to Williamsport Dickinson Seminary 1848; offered first instruction at postsecondary level and changed name to Williamsport Dickinson Seminary and Junior College 1929; adopted present name 1947; awarded first degree (baccalaureate) 1949.

Institutional Structure: *Governing board:* Board of Trustees. Representation: 35 trustees (including 27 alumni), 9 emeritus members. 35 voting. *Composition of institution:* Administrators 6. Academic affairs headed by academic dean. Management/business/finances directed by vice president/treasurer of the college. Full-time instructional faculty 85. Academic governance body, the faculty, meets an average of 8 times per year, represented by a Faculty Executive Council.

Calendar: Semesters. Academic year Aug. to Apr. Freshmen admitted Aug., Jan., May, June. Degrees conferred May, Jan., Sept. Formal commencement May. Summer session of 1 term from June to July.

Characteristics of Freshmen: 1,601 applicants (female 827, male 774). 89% of applicants admitted. 31% of applicants admitted and enrolled full-time.

98% of applicants submitted SAT scores; 8% ACT scores. *25th percentile*: SAT Verbal 500, SAT Math 490. *75th percentile*: SAT Verbal 610, SAT Math 600.

63% of entering freshmen expected to graduate within 5 years. 79% of freshmen from Pennsylvania. Freshmen from 24 states.

Admission: Rolling admissions plan. For fall acceptance, apply as early as Sept. 1 of previous year, but not later than July 1 of year of enrollment. Early acceptance available. *Requirements:* Either graduation from accredited secondary school or GED with college preparatory program including units in English, foreign language, mathematics, natural science, social studies. *Entrance tests:* College Board SAT or ACT composite. *For transfer students:* 2.00 minimum GPA; 96 hours maximum transfer credit.

College credit for postsecondary-level work completed in secondary school.

Degree Requirements: 128 credit hours; 2.00 GPA; final year in residence; 2 semesters physical education; distribution requirements; Writing Across the Curriculum Program; completion of a major program with minimum GPA of 2.00 in those courses.

Fulfillment of some degree requirements and exemption from some beginning courses possible by passing College Board CLEP, AP, DANTES, ACT PEP, and the International Baccalaureate. *Grading system:* A–F; pass-fail; withdraw.

Distinctive Educational Programs: 34 traditional and interdisciplinary majors. Unique programs: creative writing, astronomy, archaeology, actuarial mathematics, American studies. Accelerate programs in optometry and podiatry. Cooperative programs in engineering (Pennsylvania State University and Washington University, MO); forestry and environmental studies (Duke University, NC); and medical technology (accredited hospitals). Pre-professional programs in dentistry, medicine, law, and theology. Off-campus study includes programs in England at Westminster College (Oxford), Regent's College (London), and Anglia Polytechnic University (Cambridge); Lancaster University (England); Universite de Grenoble (France); Washington (DC) semester at American University, United Nations semester at Drew University (NJ), and Philadelphia Urban semester. Special May-term study/travel in archeology, art, business and economics, foreign language, psychology, religion, marine biology, history. Scholar's program, independent study, and internships available.

ROTC: Army offered in cooperation with Bucknell University.

Degrees Conferred: 331 *baccalaureate.* Bachelor's degrees awarded in top five disciplines: soical sciences 56; psychology 2; business/marketing 46; biological/life sciences 35; visual and performing arts 29.

Fees and Other Expenses: *Full-time tuition per academic year 2008–09:* $28,764. *Other fees:* $485. *Room and board per academic year:* $7,672. *Books and supplies:* $800. *Other expenses:* $2,851.

Financial Aid: Aid from institutionally generated funds is provided on the basis of academic merit, financial need.

Financial aid to full-time, first-time undergraduate students: 98% received some form of aid. Average amount of aid received: federl grants $4,271; Pell grants $2,834; other federal aid $1,460; state/local grants $3,720; institutional grants $12,459.

Departments and Teaching Staff: *Total instructional faculty:* 132 (full-time 92, part-time 40). Total faculty with doctorate, first-professional, or other terminal degree: 79. Student/faculty ratio: 15:1. Degrees held by full-time faculty: baccalaureate 1%, master's 19%, doctorate 72%. 81% hold terminal degrees.

Enrollment: Total enrollment 1,328. Undergraduate 1,328 (full-time 99%; female 55%, male 45%). Transfer-in students 35.

Characteristics of Student Body: *Ethnic/racial makeup:* Black non-Hispanic: 3%; Asian or Pacific Islander: 1%; Hispanic: 2%; White non-Hispanic: 935; nonresident alien 1%. *Age distribution:* number under 18: 11; 18–19: 609; 20–21: 629; 22–24: 126; 25–29: 12; 30–34: 1; 35–39: 4; 40–49: 50–54: 2. 18.3% of students attend summer sessions.

International Students: 13 nonresident aliens enrolled fall 2008. Sstudents from Europe, Asia, Latin America, Africa, Canada. No programs available to aid students whose native language is not English. No financial aid specifically designated for international students.

Student Life: On-campus residence halls house 85% of student body in traditional, suite, and apartment-style housing. There are 19 male and female intercollegiate athletic tams including female softball, soccer, volleyball, cross-country, basketball, track and field, lacrosse, tennis, and swimming; and male football, soccer, cross-country, basketball, track and field, lacrosse, golf, tennis, and swimming. *Student life:* 71 active student organizations including communications and publications organizations, student government, Greek organizations, music and performing arts, nationality and ethnic organizations, residence halls' special interest groups, sports and recreational related organizations, and radio and television stations. *Surrounding area:* Williamsport, population 35,000.Harrisburg is 90 miles south of the college. Philadelphia, Pittsburgh, Washington (DC), and Baltimore (MD) are within a 200 mile radius. Williamsport is served by a mass transit bus system and airport.

Publications: *The Tributary*, an annual literary magazine; *The Lycourier*, published biweekly; *Alumni Magazine*, published 4 times per year; *Brilliant Corners*, published twice per year.

Library Collections: 186,000 volumes including bound books, serial backfiles, electronic documents, and government documents not in separate collections. Online catalog. Current serial subscriptions: 717 paper, 485 via electronic access. Computer work stations available. Students have access to the Internet at no charge.

Most important special holdings include the archives of the Central Pennsylvania Conference, United Methodist Church; business information sources; nursing.

Buildings and Grounds: Campus area 32 acres.

Chief Executive Officer: Dr. James E. Douthat, President.

Address admission inquiries to James D. Spencer, Dean of Admissions and Financial Aid.

Mansfield University of Pennsylvania

5 Academy Street
Mansfield, Pennsylvania 16933
Tel: (717) 662-4000 **E-mail:** admissions@mnsfld.edu
Fax: (717) 662-4121 **Internet:** www.mnsfld.edu

Institution Description: Mansfield University is a state institution. *Enrollment:* 3,422. *Degrees awarded:* Associate, baccalaureate, master's.

Accreditation: *Regional:* MSA/CHE. *Professional*: music, nursing, teacher education

History: Established as Mansfield Classical Seminary 1854; offered first instruction postsecondary level 1857; changed name to State Normal School at Mansfield 1862, to Mansfield State Normal School 1920, to Mansfield State Teachers College 1927; awarded first degree (baccalaureate) 1930; became Mansfield State College 1960; became Mansfield University 1983.

Institutional Structure: *Governing board:* Board of Trustees. Representation: 9 trustees. *Composition of institution:* Administrators 18. Academic affairs headed by vice president for academic affairs. Management/business/finances directed by directed by dean of finance and planning. Full-time instructional faculty 156.

Calendar: Semesters. Academic year Aug. to May.

Characteristics of Freshmen: 3,367 applicants (female 2,117, male 1,250). 70% of applicants accepted. 29% of accepted applicants admitted full-time. 91% (651 students) submitted SAT scores; 10% (70 students) submitted ACT scores.

Admission: Rolling admissions plan. For fall acceptance, apply as early as July 1 following junior year of secondary school, but not later than Apr. 1 of year of enrollment. Apply by Sept. of year prior to enrollment for early decision. *Requirements:* Graduation from accredited secondary school or equivalent preparation as determined by Credentials Evaluation Division of Pennsylvania Department of Education. Recommend 3 units English, 2 foreign language, 2 algebra or geometry, 2 laboratory science, 2 social studies, 5 electives. Lowest acceptable secondary school class standing 40th percentile. Open admissions for associate degree graduates from Luzerne County Community College. *Entrance tests:* College Board SAT (minimum combined score of 920) or ACT composite (minimum score 19). *For transfer students:* 2.0 minimum GPA; from 4-year accredited institution hours maximum transfer credit limited only by residence requirement; credit; from 2-year accredited institution 67 semester hours.

College credit and advanced placement for postsecondary-level work completed in secondary school and for extrainstitutional learning.

Degree Requirements: *For all associate degrees:* 64 semester hours; 15 hours in residence. *For all baccalaureate degrees:* 128 semester hours; 32 hours in residence. *For all undergraduate degrees:* 2.0 GPA; three 1-credit physical education courses; general education requirements.

Fulfillment of some degree requirements and exemption from some beginning courses possible by passing institutional examinations, College Board CLEP, AP. *Grading system:* A–F; pass-fail; withdraw passing; withdraw-failing; satisfactory-unsatisfactory; credit by exam; audit.

Distinctive Educational Programs: Accelerated degree programs. Interdisciplinary programs. Honors programs. Continuing education. Study abroad exchange program with Volgravrad University.

Degrees Conferred: 29 *associate*; 508 *baccalaureate*: 152 *master's*. Bachelor's degrees awarded in top five disciplines: education 108; business, management, marketing, and related support services 77; security and protective services 57; visual and performing arts 53; English language/literature 42. Master's degrees awarded: various disciplines 152.

Fees and Other Expenses: *Full-time tuition per academic year 2008–09:* \$7,359 undergraduate resident, \$15,488 nonresident. *Books and supplies:* \$1,200. *Room and board per academic year:* \$6,672. *Other expenses:* \$2,100.

Financial Aid: Aid from institutionally generated funds is provided on the basis of academic merit, financial need, athletic ability, other criteria.

Financial aid to full-time, first-time undergraduate students: 94% of received some form of financial aid. Average amount of aid received: federal grants \$1,217; Pell grants \$1,693; other federal aid \$419; state/local grants \$1,652; institutional grants \$1,234.

Departments and Teaching Staff: *Total instructional faculty:* 157. Degrees held by full-time faculty: doctorate 68%, master's 23%, professional 7%.

Enrollment: Total enrollment 3,422. Undergraduate 2,944 (full-time 91%; female 62%, male 38%). Graduate 478 (full-time 14%). Undergraduate transfer-in students 210.

Characteristics of Student Body: *Ethnic/racial makeup:* Black non-Hispanic: 6%; American Indian or Alaska Native: 1%; Asian or Pacific Islander: 1%; Hispanic: 2%; White non-Hispanic: 82%; unknown: 8%; nonresident alien 1%.

International Students: 34 nonresident aliens enrolled fall 2008. Programs available to aid students whose native language is not English: social, cultural. Some financial aid specifically designated for international students.

Student Life: On-campus housing available. *Intercollegiate athletics:* male: baseball, basketball, cross-country, football, golf, tennis, track, wrestling; female: basketball, field hockey, swimming, tennis, track, volleyball; both sexes: bowling. *Special regulations:* Registered cars permitted in designated areas only. *Special services:* Medical services. *Student publications: Carontawan*, a yearbook; *The Flashlight*, a newspaper. *Surrounding community:* Mansfield population 3,500.

Library Collections: 246,200 volumes. 212,000 government documents; 818,000 microforms; 27,000 audiovisual materials; 3,000 current periodical subscriptions. Online catalog. Students have access to online information retrieval services and theInternet.

Most important special holdings include collections on music, education, psychology.

Buildings and Grounds: Campus area 175 acres.

Chief Executive Officer: Dr. John R. Halstead, President.

Undergraduates address admission inquiries to Brain D. Barden, Director of Admissions; graduate inquiries to Director of Graduate School.

Marywood University

2300 Adams Avenue
Scranton, Pennsylvania 18509-1598
Tel: (570) 348-6211 **E-mail:** ugadm@marywood.edu
Fax: (570) 961-4763 **Internet:** www.marywood.edu

Institution Description: Marywood University, formerly named Marywood College, is a private, independent, nonprofit institution, conducted by the Congregation of the Sisters, Servants of the Immaculate Heart of Mary Corporation, Scranton, Pennsylvania, Roman Catholic Church. *Enrollment:* 3,378. *Degrees awarded:* Associate, baccalaureate, master's, doctorate. Certificates also awarded.

Accreditation: *Regional:* MSA/CHE. *Professional*: art, business, counseling, dietetics, music, nursing, physician assisting, social work, speech-language pathology, surgeon assisting, teacher education

History: Established and offered first instruction at postsecondary level 1915; incorporated 1917; awarded first degree (baccalaureate) 1919; initiated graduate program in arts and sciences 1922; Graduate School of Arts and Sciences founded 1969; School of Social Work founded 1969; initiated doctoral program in human development 1996.

Institutional Structure: *Governing board:* Marywood College Board of Trustees. Representation: 24 trustees and 2 ex officio members. All voting. *Composition of institution:* Administrators 41. Academic affairs headed by vice president for academic affairs. Management/business/finances directed by vice president for business affairs and treasurer. Full-time instructional faculty 140. Besides the formal administrative structure, the college is governed by a system of committees made up of faculty, administrators, professional personnel, and students.

Calendar: Semesters. Academic year Sept. to May. Freshmen admitted Sept., Jan., June. Degrees conferred and formal commencement May. Summer session of 2 terms from May to Aug.

Characteristics of Freshmen: 1,774 applicants (1,282 female, 492 male). 78% of applicants accepted. 34% of accepted applicants enrolled full-time.

Average secondary school rank of freshmen top 33%. Mean SAT class scores 526 Critical Reading, 514 Math.

57% of entering freshmen expected to graduate within 5 years. 74% of freshmen from Pennsylvania. Freshmen from 20 states and 21 foreign countries.

Admission: Rolling admissions plan. Common application accepted. For fall acceptance, apply as early as Sept. of previous year. Apply by Nov. 1 for early decision; need not limit application to Marywood University. Early acceptance available. *Requirements:* Either graduation from accredited secondary school with 16 units which must include 4 English, 3 social studies, 2 college preparatory mathematics, 1 laboratory science; or GED. Additional requirements for some programs. Minimum GPA 3.0. *Entrance tests:* College Board SAT or ACT composite. For foreign students TOEFL. *For transfer students:* 2.5 minimum GPA; maximum transfer credit limited only by residence requirement.

College credit and advanced placement for postsecondary-level work completed in secondary school. For extrainstitutional learning, college credit on basis of portfolio and faculty assessments.

Tutoring available. Developmental courses offered in summer session and regular academic year; credit given.

Degree Requirements: 126 credit hours; 2.0 GPA (2.5 in major); 60 credits in residence; 2 credits physical education; distribution requirements; demonstrated competency in reading, speech, writing.

MARYWOOD UNIVERSITY—*cont'd*

Fulfillment of some degree requirements and exemption from some beginning courses possible by passing College Board CLEP, APP. *Grading system:* A-F, deadline after which pass-fail is appended to withdraw; incomplete (carries time limit).

Distinctive Educational Programs: *For undergraduates:* Accelerated degree program. Cooperative baccalaureate programs in dietetics, medical technology, nursing with affiliated hospitals. Interdisciplinary programs in fashion merchandising, interior design, international business, music therapy, recreational studies. Preprofessional program in law. Facilities and programs for independent research, including honors programs, individual majors, tutorials. Study abroad in France and Spain; other countries by individual arrangement. *For graduate students:* Flexible meeting places and schedules, including off-campus center (at Allentown, 110 miles away from main institution), weekend classes. *Available to all students:* Work-experience programs, including cooperative education, internships. Evening classes. Special facilities for using telecommunications in the classroom. Off-campus degree program. Independent study. Suraci Gallery for art exhibitions by students and professionals.

Degrees Conferred: 355 *baccalaureate*; 363 *master's*; 14 *doctorate*. Bachelor's degrees awarded in top five disciplines: health professions and related clinical sciences 56; education 54; visual and performing arts 50; psychology 26; business, management, marketing, and related support services 24. Master's degrees awarded: various disciplines 363. Doctorates awarded: education 14.

Fees and Other Expenses: *Full-time tuition per academic year 2008–09:* undergraduate $25,390; graduate courses charged per credit (contact the university for current information). *Books and supplies:* $900. *Required fees:* $920. *Room and board per academic year:* $11,000. *Other expenses:* $1,300.

Financial Aid: Aid from institutionally generated funds is provided on the basis of academic merit, financial need, other criteria. Institution has a Program Participation Agreement with the U.S. Department of Education for eligible students to receive Pell Grants and, depending upon the agreement, other federal aid.

Financial aid to full-time, first-time undergraduate students: 99% received some form of aid. Average amount of aid received: federal grants $4,244; Pell grants $2,936; other federal aid $1,363; state/local grants $3,795; institutional grants $12,072.

Departments and Teaching Staff: *Total instructional faculty:* 313 (full-time 140, part-time 173). Student/faculty ratio: 12:1. Degrees held by full-time faculty: 90% hold terminal degrees.

Enrollment: Total enrollment 3,378. Undergraduate 2,071 (full-time 93%; female 70%, male $30%). Graduate 1,307 (full-time 43%). Undergraduate transfer-in students 190.

Characteristics of Student Body: *Ethnic/racial makeup:* Black non-Hispanic: 1%; Asian or Pacific Islander: 2%; Hispanic: 3%; White non-Hispanic: 83%; unknown: 9%; nonresident alien 2%.

International Students: 68 nonresident aliens enrolled fall 2008. Students from Europe, Asia, Latin America, Africa, Australia. No programs available to aid students whose native language is not English. No financial aid specifically designated for international students.

Student Life: Apartments, houses, and traditional residence halls house 25% of the student body. Coed and single sex housing available. *Intercollegiate athletics:* NCAA III female basketball, volleyball, tennis, softball, field hockey; pre-NCAA male basketball, soccer, baseball, tennis. *Regulations for residents:* No curfews; opposite sex visiting on Saturdays only; anyone may have a car on campus. *Activities:* Over 50 clubs and organizations and over 15 national honor societies. *Student media: Tourmaline,* a yearbook; *Wood Word,* a newspaper; *Bayleaf,* a literary magazine; *ARS,* arts annual; *Intercom*, a monthly in-house newsletter. Radio station WSMW. *Surrounding community:* Residential neighborhood. Scranton population 80,000. Active performing arts groups, quality ski slopes and sports stadium within city limits, public transportation directly to and from campus. Nearest metropolis is Philadelphia, 127 miles (2½ hours by car); nearest airport is 12 miles from campus. Computer and word processing facilities available to all students at no cost; all residences computer-wired and networked by modem to Library VAX system.

Publications: Sources of information about Marywood University include *Marywood Impressions; Annual Report* distributed to all constituencies (alumni, donors, friends of the college, local and regional businesses, state representatives and senators).

Library Collections: 223,000 volumes including bound books, serial backfiles, electronic documents, and government documents not in separate collections. Online catalog. 378,000 microforms; 21,000 audiovidual materials; 15,000 periodicals including via electronic access. Computer work stations available campus-wide. Students have access to the Internet at no charge.

Most important special holdings include college archives; Graduate School Professional Contributions; Justine Ward Record Collection.

Buildings and Grounds: Campus area 185 acres. Campus DVD available.

Chief Executive Officer: Sr. Mary Reap, I.H.M., President.

Undergraduates address admission inquiries to Robert W. Reese, Director of Admissions; graduate inquiries to Dean, Graduate School of Arts and Sciences and Dean, Graduate School of Social Work.

Mercyhurst College

501 East 38th Street
Erie, Pennsylvania 16546
Tel: (814) 824-2000 **E-mail:** admissions@mercyhurst.edu
Fax: (814) 824-2071 **Internet:** www.mercyhurst.edu

Institution Description: Mercyhurst College is a private college affiliated with the Roman Catholic Church. *Enrollment:* 4,326. *Degrees awarded:* Associate, baccalaureate, master's.

Accreditation: *Regional:* MSA/CHE. *Professional*: athletic training, dietetics, music, physical therapy, social work

History: Established and offered first instruction at postsecondary level 1926; chartered 1928 awarded first degree (baccalaureate) 1929; added master's program 1978. *See* Sr. M. Eustace Taylor, *The History of Mercyhurst College* (Erie: Privately published, 1976) for further information.

Institutional Structure: *Governing board:* Board of Trustees. Extrainstitutional representation: 36 trustees; institutional representation: 1 administrator, 2 full-time instructional faculty members, 1 student, president of President's Associate Board; 1 alumnus. 8 ex officio. 27 voting. *Composition of institution:* Administrators 134. Academic affairs headed by vice president of academic affairs and dean of the college. Management/business/finances directed by vice president of administration and finance. Full-time instructional faculty 88. Academic governance body, College Senate, meets an average of 9 times per year.

Calendar: Trimesters. Academic year early Sept. to May. Freshmen admitted Sept., Jan., Mar., June, July. Degrees conferred Sept., Nov., Feb., Aug. Formal commencement May. Summer session of 1 term from June to Aug.

Characteristics of Freshmen: 78% of applicants admitted. 34% of applicants admitted and enrolled.

72% (520 students) submitted SAT scores; 43% (314 students) submitted ACT scores. *25th percentile*: SAT Critical Reading 490, SAT Math 500; ACT Composite 19. *75th percentile*: SAT Critical Reading SAT Math 590; ACT Composite 25.

46% of entering freshmen expected to graduate within 5 years. 30% of freshmen from Pennsylvania. Freshmen from 30 states and 11 foreign countries.

Admission: Rolling admissions plan. For fall acceptance, apply as early as completion of junior year of secondary school, but not later than 2 weeks prior to beginning of term. Early acceptance available. *Requirements:* Either graduation from accredited secondary school or GED. Recommend college preparatory program with 16 units. Minimum 2.2 GPA. *Entrance tests:* College Board SAT or ACT composite. For foreign students TOEFL. *For transfer students:* 2.0 minimum GPA; 75 credit hours maximum transfer credit.

College credit and advanced placement for postsecondary-level work completed in secondary school. For extrainstitutional learning on basis of faculty assessment, college credit and advanced placement on basis of departmental examinations.

Tutoring available. Developmental courses offered in summer session and regular academic year; credit given.

Degree Requirements: *For all associate degrees:* 60 credit hours. *For all baccalaureate degrees:* 120 hours. *For all undergraduate degrees:* 2.0 GPA; 45 credits in residence; distribution requirements.

Fulfillment of some degree requirements and exemption from some beginning courses possible by passing departmental examinations, College Board CLEP, AP. *Grading system:* A–F; pass-fail; withdraw (carries time limit).

Distinctive Educational Programs: *For undergraduates:* Work-experience programs, including cooperative education, internships. McAuley Division offers one-year Educational Foundation Program and one-year certificate Career Programs at three off-campus centers (at North East, 20 miles from main campus; at Cory, 30 miles from main campus; and in Erie). Accelerated degree programs. Cooperative baccalaureate programs in dietetics with Edinboro State University and Gannon University. Facilities and programs for independent research, including honors programs, individual majors. *Available to all students:* Weekend and evening classes. Dual-degree program in nursing with Villa Maria College. *Other distinctive programs:* Evening-Weekend College offers degrees, certificates, enrichment courses. Summer program available in Switzerland at Schiller University.

ROTC: Army in cooperation with Gannon University.

Degrees Conferred: 194 *associate;* 590 *baccalaureate*; 85 *master's*. Bachelor's degrees awarded in top five disciplines: business, management, marketing, and related support services 101; education 74; social sciences and history 50; visual and performing arts 36; home economics and vocational home economics 32.

Fees and Other Expenses: *Full-time tuition per academic year 2008–09:* undergraduate $23,286; contact the college for current graduate tuition/fees. *Books and supplies:* $1,000. *Room and board per academic year:* $8,196. *Other expenses:* $1,600.

Financial Aid: Aid from institutionally generated funds is provided on the basis of academic merit, financial need, athletic ability.

Financial aid to full-time, first-time undergraduate students: 97% received some form of aid. Average amount of aid received: federal grants $1,511; state/local grants $2,004; institutional grants $4,119; loans $2,351.

Departments and Teaching Staff: *Total instructional faculty:* 237 (full-time 159, part-time 78). 52% of faculty hold the doctorate, first-professional, or other terminal degree. Student/faculty ratio: 19:1.

Enrollment: Total enrollment 4,326. Undergraduate 4,013 (full-time 87%; female 60%, male 40%). Graduate 313 (full-time 55%). Undergraduate transfer-in students 180.

Characteristics of Student Body: *Ethnic/racial makeup:* Black non-Hispanic: 6%; Asian or Pacific Islander: 1%; Hispanic: 2%; White non-Hispanic: 77%; unknown: 10%; nonresident alien 4%. *Age distribution:* number under 18: 48; 18–19: 1,448; 20–21: 1,263; 22–24: 433; 25–29: 18; 30–34: 138; 35–39: 114; 40–49: 154; 50–64: 39; 65 and over: 2.

International Students: 172 nonresident aliens enrolled fall 2008. Students from Europe, Asia, Latin America, Africa, Canada, Australia. No programs available to aid students whose native language is not English. Financial aid specifically designated for international students: variable number of scholarships available annually for undergraduate students.

Student Life: On-campus housing includes 4 dormitories, 13 apartment buildings and 16 townhouses. 65% of full-time student body live in campus housing. *Intercollegiate athletics:* male: baseball, basketball, crew, football, hockey, soccer, tennis; female: basketball, crew, soccer, softball, tennis, volleyball; both sexes: cross-country, golf. *Special regulations:* Cars permitted without restrictions. Quiet hours. Dormitory visitation from 1pm to midnight. *Special services:* Learning Resources Center, medical services. *Student publications, radio: Merciad*, weekly newspaper; annual literary magazine; yearbook. Radio station WMCE broadcasts 126 hours per week. *Surrounding community:* Erie population 120,000. Buffalo (NY), 89 miles from campus, is nearest metropolitan area. Served by mass transit bus system; airport 10 miles from campus; passenger rail service 3 miles from campus.

Library Collections: 180,000 volumes. 51,000 microforms; 4,400 audiovisual materials; 850 current periodical subscriptions. Online catalog. Students have access to online information retrieval services and the Internet.

Most important special holdings include collection on Northwest Pennsylvania History; Sisters of Mercy archives; women's organizations archives; La Follette Papers.

Buildings and Grounds: Campus area 150 acres. Campus DVD available.

Chief Executive Officer: Dr. Michael J. McQuillen, President.

Address undergraduate admission inquiries to J.P. Cooney, Director of Undergraduate Admissions; graduate inquiries to Emily Crawford, Director of Admissions.

Messiah College

One College Avenue
Grantham, Pennsylvania 17027
Tel: (717) 766-2511 **E-mail:** admiss@messiah.edu
Fax: (717) 691-6025 **Internet:** www.messiah.edu

Institution Description: Messiah College is a Christian college of the liberal and applied arts and sciences. The college is committed to an embracing evangelical spirit rooted in the Anabaptist, Pietist, and Wesleyan traditions of the Christian Church. *Enrollment:* 2,802. *Degrees awarded:* Baccalaureate.

Member of Council for Christian Colleges and Universities.

Accreditation: *Regional:* MSA/CHE. *Professional*: athletic training, dietetics, engineering, music, nursing, social work

History: Chartered as Messiah Bible School and Missionary Training Home 1909; became junior college and offered first instruction at postsecondary level 1920; changed name to Messiah Bible College 1924; awarded first degree and adopted present name 1951; merged with Upland College in California 1965.

Institutional Structure: *Governing board:* Board of Trustees. *Composition of institution:* Administrators 144. Senior administrators include the president, provost, vice president for administration and finance, vice president for advancement, and vice president for planning. Full-time faculty: 173.

Calendar: Semesters. Academic year Aug. to May. Freshmen admitted Aug., Jan., May. Degrees conferred and formal commencement May. Summer session from May through June.

Characteristics of Freshmen: 2,829 applicants (1,763 female, 1,050 male). 71% of applicants admitted. 36% of applicants admitted and enrolled.

92% (679 students) submitted SAT scores; 16% (115 students) submitted ACT scores. *25th percentile*: SAT Critical Reading 520, SAT Math 520; ACT Composite 22. *75th percentile*: SAT Critical Reading 640, SAT Math 640; ACT Composite 28.

71% of freshmen expected to graduate within 5 years. 54% of freshmen from Pennsylvania. Freshmen from 30 states and 7 foreign countries.

Admission: Messiah requires the SAT or ACT exam. Applicants must have graduated from an accredited high school or the equivalent. Usually prep courses include 4 units English, 3 or 4 mathematics, 3 natural science, 3 social studies, 3 foreign languages, 4 academic electives. Applications accepted online via the Internet.

Degree Requirements: 123 semester hours; 2.0 GPA; 30 semester hours in residence.

Fulfillment of some degree requirements and exemption from some beginning courses possible by passing institutional examination, College Board CLEP, AP. *Grading system:* A–F with +/-; pass-fail.

Distinctive Educational Programs: Philadelphia campus, in cooperation with Temple University, offers study to students. Honors program; study abroad programs; other off-campus programs.

Degrees Conferred: 617 *baccalaureate*. Bachelor's degrees awarded in top five disciplines: education 123; business, management, marketing, and related support services 79; health professions and related clinical sciences 50; social sciences and history 48; psychology 45.

Fees and Other Expenses: *Full-time tuition per academic year 2008–09:* $25,670. *Other fees:* $690. *Room and board per academic year:* $7,610. *Other expenses:* $1,830.

Financial Aid: Aid from institutionally generated funds is provided on the basis of academic merit, financial need, other criteria.

Financial aid to full-time, first-time undergraduate students: 99% received some form of aid. Average amount of aid received: federal grants $3,841; Pell grants $2,492; other federal aid $1,406; state/local grants $$3,359; institutional grants $9,917.

Departments and Teaching Staff: *Total instructional faculty:* 310 (full-time 170, part-time 140). 77% of faculty hold the doctorate, first-professional, or other terminal degree. Student/faculty ratio: 13:1.

Enrollment: Total enrollment 2,802. Undergraduate 2,802 (full-time 98%; female 63%, male 37%). Transfer-in students 82.

Characteristics of Student Body: *Ethnic/racial makeup:* Black non-Hispanic: 2%; Asian or Pacific Islander: 2%; Hispanic: 1%; White non-Hispanic: 85%; nonresident alien 3%.

International Students: 84 nonresident aliens enrolled fall 2008. Students from Europe, Asia, Latin America, Africa, Canada. No programs available to aid students whose native language is not English. Financial aid specifically designated for international students: scholarships available annually to qualifying students.

Student Life: On-campus residence halls house 86% of full-time students in a variety of traditional and apartment-style buildings. Very active student activities program including a strong community service/outreach emphasis. Student association charters more than 48 register organizations in addition to active music, theater, and rec-sports programs. *Intercollegiate athletics:* male: baseball, basketball, cross-country, golf, lacrosse (club), soccer, tennis, track and field, volleyball (club), wrestling; female: basketball, cross-country, field hockey, soccer, softball, tennis, track and field, and volleyball. *Special regulations:* Cars permitted except for freshmen living within 150 miles of campus; required chapel attendance; lifestyle statement applies to students and employees. *Student media:* WVMM campus radio; *Swinging Bridge,* student newspaper; *Clarion,* yearbook; *Community News,* weekly news sheet. *Surrounding community:* Grantham, a rural suburb 10 miles south of Harrisburg (state capitol). Near the intersection of 3 major intestates. Easy access to Baltimore, Washington, Philadelphia. Harrisburg International Airport 20 miles from campus; train and bus depots 12 miles from campus. Several malls within 10 minutes of campus.

Library Collections: 298,000 volumes including bound books, serial backfiles, electronic documents, and government documents not in separate collections. Online catalog. 120,000 microforms; 21,000 audiovisual materials; 1,,212 serial subscriptions, 4,761 via electronic access. Computer work stations available. Students have access to the Internet at no charge.

Most important holdings include Brethren in Christ and College Archives; W. Jim Neidhartt Collection (science and religion); artists' books.

Buildings and Grounds: Campus area 485acres. Campus DVD available.

Chief Executive Officer: Dr. Kim S. Phipps. President.

Address admission inquiries to Johm Chopka, Dean for Enrollment Management.

Millersville University of Pennsylvania

P.O. Box 1002
Millersville, Pennsylvania 17551-0302
Tel: (717) 872-3024 **E-mail:** admissions@millersville.edu
Fax: (717) 871-2147 **Internet:** www.millersville.edu

Institution Description: Millersville University of Pennsylvania (formerly Millersville State College) is a state institution. *Enrollment:* 8,320. *Degrees awarded:* Associate, baccalaureate, master's. Certificates and specialist certificates also awarded.

Academic offerings subject to approval by statewide coordinating bodies.Budget subject to approval by state governing boards. Member of Marine Science Consortium.

Accreditation: *Regional:* MSA/CHE. *Professional*: business, chemistry, computer science, music, nursing, occupational health and safety, psychology internship, respiratory therapy, social work, teacher education

History: Established as Lancaster Country Normal Institute, chartered, and offered first instruction at postsecondary level 1855; became first state normal school 1859; changed name to Millersville State Teachers' College 1927; awarded first degree (baccalaureate) 1928; changed name to Millersville State College 1959; adopted present name 1982. *See* Lee Graver, *History of the First Pennsylvania State Normal School* (Millersville: Millersville State Teachers' College, 1959) for further information.

Institutional Structure: *Governing board:* Board of Governors of the State System of Higher Education. Extrainstitutional representation: 16 governors. All voting. Council of Trustees of Millersville University (appointed by governor of Pennsylvania with Senate approval). 10 trustees; institutional representation: 1 student trustee. All voting. *Composition of institution:* Full-time instructional faculty 312. Academic governance body, Faculty Senate, meets an average of 20 times per year. *Faculty representation:* faculty served by collective bargaining agent, Association of State College and University Faculty/Millersville University.

Calendar: Semesters. Academic year Aug. to May. Freshmen admitted Aug., Jan., June. Degrees conferred and formal commencements May, Aug., Dec. Summer session of 2 terms from June to Aug.

Characteristics of Freshmen: 6,689 applicants (3,986 female, 2,701 male). 55% of applicants admitted. 36% of applicants admitted and enrolled.

99% (1,353 students) submitted SAT scores. *25th percentile*: SAT Critical Reading 490, SAT Math 480. *75th percentile*: SAT Critical Reading 570, SAT Math 480.

64% of entering freshmen expected to graduate within 5 years. 96% of freshmen from Pennsylvania. Freshmen from 17 states and 48 foreign countries.

Admission: Rolling admissions plan. Priority deadline Jan. 1. Early acceptance available. Alternative admission programs available for applicants who are beyond traditional college-going age or who are educationally or economically deprived. *Requirements:* Either graduation from approved secondary school or GED. *Entrance tests:* College Board SAT or ACT composite. *For transfer students:* 2.0 minimum GPA; from 4-year accredited institution 90 hours maximum transfer credit; from 2-year accredited institution 60 hours.

College credit and advanced placement for postsecondary-level work completed in secondary school.

Tutoring available. Developmental courses offered in summer session and regular academic year; credit given.

Degree Requirements: *For all associate degrees:* 60–64 credit hours. *For all baccalaureate degrees:* 120–134 credit hours; demonstrated competency in English composition and speech; 3 hours health and physical education. *For all undergraduate degrees:* general education requirements; 2.0 GPA; 30 credit hours and half of coursework in major field in residence.

Fulfillment of some degree requirements and exemption from some beginning courses possible by passing institutional examination, College Board CLEP, APP. *Grading system:* A–F; pass-fail; withdraw; incomplete (carries time limit).

Distinctive Educational Programs: Dual-degree programs in engineering with Pennsylvania State University, University of Pennsylvania. Exchange program with Franklin and Marshall College. Honors programs. Special programs for disadvantaged students. Internships. Cooperative education program. Independent study. Evening programs for graduate students. Summer workshops for teachers. Summer school; student and faculty exchanges; developmental courses. Study abroad programs in Chile, England, France, Germany, Japan, Scotland, and Spain. Adult continuous education. Exchange agreement with Lancaster Theological Seminary and Franklin and Marshall College; The Harrisburg Internship Semester (THIS).

ROTC: Air Force, Army.

Degrees Conferred: 4 *associate*; 1,426 *baccalaureate*; 235 *master's*. Bachelor's degrees awarded in top five disciplines: education 218; social sciences and history 168; business, management, marketing, and related support services 155; communication, journalism, and related programs 119; psychology 106. Master's degrees awarded: various disciplines 235.

Fees and Other Expenses: *Full-time tuition per academic year 2008–09:* undergraduate resident $8,155, nonresident $14,996; contact the university for current graduate tuition. *Room and board per academic year:* $7,308. *Books and supplies:* $1,000. *Other expenses:* $1,687.

Financial Aid: Aid from institutionally generated funds is provided on the basis of academic merit, financial need, athletic ability, other criteria.

Financial aid to full-time, first-time undergraduate students: 83% of students received some form of aid. Average amount of aid received: federal grants $3,383; Pell grants $2,737; other federal aid $855; state/local grants $3,080; institutional grants $2,500.

Departments and Teaching Staff: *Total instructional faculty:* 457 (full-time 326, part-time 131). 81% of faculty hold the doctorate, professional, or other terminal degree. Student/faculty ratio: 18:1.

Enrollment: Total enrollment 8,320. Undergraduate 7,217 (full-time 91%; female 56%, male 44%). Graduate 1,103 (full-time 23%). Undergraduate transfer-in students 494.

Characteristics of Student Body: *Ethnic/racial makeup:* Black non-Hispanic: 7%; Asian or Pacific Islander: 2%; Hispanic: 4%; White non-Hispanic: 78%; unknown: 9%; nonresident alien 1%. *Age distribution:* number under 18: 126; 18–19: 1,532; 20–21: 2,527; 22–24: 1,163; 25–29: 294; 30–34: 129; 35–39: 29; 40–49: 97; 50–64: 32; 65 and over: 2.

International Students: 83 nonresident aliens enrolled fall 2008. Students from Europe, Asia, Africa, Canada, Australia. No programs available to aid students whose native language is not English. No financial aid specifically designated international students.

Student Life: On-campus residence halls house 35% of student body. *Intercollegiate athletics:* male: baseball, football, golf, wrestling; female: cheerleading, field hockey, lacrosse, softball, swimming, volleyball; both sexes: basketball, cross-country, soccer, tennis, track and field. *Special regulations:* Cars with decals permitted for juniors and seniors. *Special services:* Counseling center, health center, career services. *Student publications, radio: George Street Carnival*, a literary magazine; *The Snapper*, a weekly newspaper; *Touchstone*, the university yearbook. Radio station WIXQ broadcasts 105 hours per week. *Surrounding community:* Millersville population 7,700. Philadelphia, 70 miles from campus, is nearest metropolitan area. Served by mass transit bus system; airport 20 miles from campus; passenger rail service 5 miles from campus.

Library Collections: 516,000 volumes. Online catalog. 552,000 microforms; 14,000 audiovisual materials; 10,000 periodicals including via electronic access.

Most important special collections include Pennsylvania German Collection; Wickersham Collection of 19th-Century Pedagogy and Textbooks; Pre-1865 Pennsylvania Imprints; Carl Van Vechten Memorial Collection of Afro-American Arts and Letters; Leo Aschor Center for the Study of Operetta Music.

Buildings and Grounds: Campus area 220 acres.

Chief Executive Officer: Dr. Francis McNairy, President.

Undergraduates address admission inquiries to Dr. Douglas Zander, Director of Admissions; graduate inquiries to Dr. Victor S. DeSantis, Dean of Graduate Studies.

Misericordia University

301 Lake Street
Dallas, Pennsylvania 18612-1098
Tel: (570) 674-6400 **E-mail:** admiss@miseri.edu
Fax: (570) 675-2441 **Internet:** www.miseri.edu

Institution Description: Misericordia University, formerly named College Misericordia, is a private, independent, nonprofit institution affiliated with the Religious Sisters of Mercy, Roman Catholic Church. *Enrollment:* 2,501. *Degrees awarded:* baccalaureate, master's, doctorate.

Accreditation: *Regional:* MSA/CHE. *Professional*: nursing, occupational therapy, physical therapy, social work

History: Established and chartered 1924; awarded first degree (baccalaureate) 1927; added master's degree program 1979; added doctoral program 2005; adopted present name 2007.

Institutional Structure: *Governing board:* College Misericordia Board of Trustees. Extrainstitutional representation: 34 trustees; institutional representation: president of the college; 8 alumni. 3 ex officio. 26 voting. *Composition of institution:* Administrators 29. Academic affairs headed by vice president for academic affairs. Management/business/finances directed by vice president of finance and administration. Full-time instructional faculty 98. Academic governance body, College Senate, meets an average of 10 times per year.

Calendar: Semesters. Academic year Aug. to May. Freshmen admitted Aug., Jan., June, July. Degrees conferred May, Aug., Dec. Formal commencement May. Summer session from May to Aug.

Characteristics of Freshmen: 1,430 applicants (958 female, 474 male). 71% of applicants accepted. 17% of accepted applicants enrolled full-time. 90% (342 students) submitted SAT scores; 5% (17 students) submitted ACT scores.

Mean SAT scores 500 Critical Reading, 510 Math.

71% of entering freshmen expected to graduate within 5 years. 79% of freshmen from Pennsylvania. Students from 20 states and 2 foreign countries.

Admission: Rolling admissions plan. For fall acceptance, apply as early as Sept. 1 of year prior to enrollment, but not later than 4 weeks before start of term. *Requirements:* Either graduation from accredited secondary school or GED. 16 academic units recommended. *Entrance tests:* College Board SAT or ACT composite. *See* specific programs for additional requirements. *For transfer students:* 2.0 minimum GPA; 90 hours maximum transfer credit; from 2-year institution 60 hours.

College credit for postsecondary-level work completed in secondary school. Tutoring available. Developmental courses offered in summer session and regular academic year; credit given.

Degree Requirements: *For all baccalaureate degrees:* 120 credit hours; 30 credits in residence; distribution requirements. *For all undergraduate degrees:* 2.0 GPA. Additional requirements for some programs.

Fulfillment of some degree requirements possible by passing College Board CLEP or AP. *Grading system:* A–F; withdraw.

Distinctive Educational Programs: *For undergraduates:* Accelerated degree programs. Cooperative baccalaureate program in medical technology with area hospitals. Interdisciplinary programs. Facilities and programs for independent research, including honors programs, tutorials. Cross-registration for juniors and seniors with Wilkes University. Expressway Program with Luzerne County Community College and Northampton Community College. Continuing education programs, including Weekend College. *Available to all students:* Evening classes. Individually-designed majors, independent study, directed study. Five-year freshman entry master's in physical therapy, occupational therapy, and speech and language pathology. Alternative Learners' Program for students with disabilities.

ROTC: Air Force offered in cooperation with Wilkes University; Army in cooperation with Kings College.

Degrees Conferred: 188 *baccalaureate*; 104 *master's*; *doctorate*: 36. Bachelor's degrees awarded in top five disciplines: health professions and related clinical sciences 50; business/marketing 64; education 50; visual and performing arts 33; public administration and social services 27. Master's degrees awarded: business/marketing 22; education 3; health professions 69. Doctorates awarded: health professions 36.

Fees and Other Expenses: *Full-time tuition per academic year 2008–09:* undergraduate $23,150; graduate study charged per credit hour (contact the university for current rate). *Room and board per academic year:* $9,850. *Books and supplies:* $800. *Other expenses:* $1,000.

Financial Aid: Aid from institutionally generated funds is provided on the basis of academic merit, financial need.

Financial aid to full-time, first-time undergraduate students: 99% received some form of aid. Average amount of aid received: federal grants $3,741; Pell grants $2,934; other federal aid $857; state/local grants $3,904; institutional grants $8,781.

Departments and Teaching Staff: *Total instructional faculty:* 256. Student/faculty ratio: 12:1. Degrees held by full-time faculty: doctorate 56%, master's 44%.

Enrollment: Total enrollment 2,501. Undergraduate 3,183 (full-time 72%; female 71%, male 29%). Graduate 318 (full-time 100%). Undergraduate transfer-in students 130.

Characteristics of Student Body: *Ethnic/racial makeup:* Black non-Hispanic: 1%; Asian or Pacific Islander: 1%; Hispanic: 1%; White non-Hispanic: 96%; unknown: 1%. *Age distribution:* number under 18: 18; 18–19: 567; 20–21: 558; 22–24: 195; 25–29: 53; 30–34: 12; 35–39: 14; 40–49: 10.

International Students: 2 nonresident aliens enrolled fall 2008. No programs available to aid students whose native language is not English. No financial aid specifically designated for international students.

Student Life: On-campus residence halls house 53% of student body. *Intercollegiate athletics:* male: baseball, basketball, cross-country, golf, lacrosse, soccer, swimming, track and field; female: basketball, cheerleading, cross-country, field hockey, lacrosse soccer, softball, swimming, tennis, track and field, volleyball. *Special services:* Learning Resource Center provides counseling, tutorial, advising, and placement services. On-campus public transportation provides service to shopping malls, ski resorts, campgrounds and other community activities and facilities. *Student publications: Instress*, an annual literary magazine; *The Highlander*, a monthly newspaper. *Surrounding community:* Dallas population 7,000. Wilkes-Barre 10 minutes away. Philadelphia and New York City 2 hours from campus.

Library Collections: 83,000 volumes. Online catalog. 3,600 microforms; 8,200 audiovisual materials; 575 current periodical subscriptions. 5,542 recordings. Students have access to online information retrieval services and the Internet.

Most important special holdings include all ANA–NLN publications currently in print; selected award-winning children's literature.

Buildings and Grounds: Campus area 120 acres in suburban community.

Chief Executive Officer: Dr. Michael A. MacDowell, President.

Address admission inquiries to Glenn Bozinski, Director of Admissions.

Moore College of Art and Design

The Parkway at 20th Street
Philadelphia, Pennsylvania 19103
Tel: (215) 568-4515 **E-mail:** admiss@moore.edu
Fax: (215) 568-3547 **Internet:** www.moore.edu

Institution Description: Moore College of Art and Design is a private, independent, nonprofit college for women. *Enrollment:* 556. *Degrees awarded:* Baccalaureate.

Accreditation: *Regional:* MSA/CHE. *Professional*: art, interior design

History: Established as Philadelphia School of Design for Women 1848; chartered and offered first instruction at postsecondary level 1853; incorporated and changed name to Moore Institute of Art, Science and Industry 1932; awarded first degree (baccalaureate) 1934; adopted name of Moore College of Art in 1963; adopted present name 1988.

Institutional Structure: *Governing board:* Board of Trustees composed of 8 lifetime members and Board of Managers (policy-making body). Representation: 21 managers, including 8 trustees. All voting. *Composition of institution:* Administrators 7. Academic affairs headed by Academic Deans. Management/business/finances headed by Director of Finance and Administration. Full-time instructional faculty 34. Academic governance body, Faculty Union, meets an average of 2 times per year. *Faculty representation:* Faculty served by collective bargaining agent, Moore Federation of Teachers, affiliated with AFT.

Calendar: Semesters. Academic year Aug. to May. Freshmen admitted Aug. and Jan. Degrees conferred and formal commencement May.

Characteristics of Freshmen: 549 applicants (549 female). 59% of applicants accepted. 34% of accepted applicants enrolled full-time.

59% of entering freshmen expected to graduate within 5 years. 61% of freshmen from Pennsylvania. Freshmen from 29 states and 7 foreign countries.

Admission: Rolling admissions plan. Early acceptance available. *Requirements:* Either graduation from accredited secondary school or GED. Portfolio of art work including 6 drawings from observation plus 6 more pieces of the student's choice. Minimum GPA 2.0; minimum combined SAT score of 830 or ACT composite of 17. A slide portfolio is required for all transfer students. Minimum TOEFL score of 500 required for students who have English as a second language. Most students apply by May 1.

Degree Requirements: 125.5-135.5 credit hours depending upon degree pursued; 2.0 GPA; 2 terms in residence; core curriculum; portfolio. *Grading system:* A–F; withdraw (carries time limit).

Distinctive Educational Programs: Cooperative education. Evening classes. Interdisciplinary programs. Individual majors. Certificate programs in desktop publishing, decorative arts and art education, fifth year competitive program allows students to study outside of their major for 1 year without incurring tuition cost. *Other distinctive programs:* Continuing education. Young People's Art Workshop for community children.

Degrees Conferred: 86 *baccalaureate:* visual and performing arts 86.

Fees and Other Expenses: *Full-time tuition per academic year 2008–09:* $27,718. *Required fees:* $795. *Room and board per academic year:* $10,501. *Books and supplies:* $2,000. *Other expenses:* $3,500.

Financial Aid: Aid from institutionally generated funds is provided on the basis of financial need, artistic merit, other criteria.

Financial aid to full-time, first-time undergraduate students: 98% of students receiveed some form of aid. Average amount of aid received: federal grants $2,428; Pell grants $3,252; other federal aid $1,000; state/local grants $4,125; institutional grants $8,500.

Departments and Teaching Staff: *Total instructional faculty:* 112 (full-time 32, part-time 80). Total faculty with doctorate, first-professional, or other terminal degree: 48. Student/faculty ratio: 9:1. Degrees held by full-time faculty: baccalaureate 18.2%, master's 69.7%, doctorate 12.1%.

Enrollment: Total enrollment 546. Undergraduate 524; graduate 32.

Characteristics of Student Body: *Ethnic/racial makeup:* Black non-Hispanic: 12%; Asian or Pacific Islander: 2%; Hispanic: 6%; White non-Hispanic: 74%; unknown 1%; nonresident alien 2%. *Age distribution:* number under 18–19: 138; 20–21: 184; 22–24: 111; 25–29: 40; 30–34: 13; 35–39: 1; 40–49: 10; 50–64: 4.

International Students: 12 nonresident aliens enrolled fall 2008. Students from Europe, Asia, Latin America, Africa. No programs available to aid students

MOORE COLLEGE OF ART AND DESIGN—*cont'd*

whose native language is not English. No financial aid specifically designated for international students.

Student Life: On-campus housing available. On-site personal counseling and nurse practitioner's office as well as contract with local family medicine practice; strong leadership development program for Student Government, Student Mentors and Residence Life Staff; faculty supervised yearbook, school newspaper; Fitness Center; extensive recreational, educational, cultural programming for residents and commuters which takes advantage of the many opportunities in the city of Philadelphia; two highly regarded art galleries—The Galleries at Moore—with exhibitions throughout the year; PECO Distinguished Artist Series brings visiting artists to campus.

Library Collections: 40,000 volumes. 125,000 audiovisual materials. 130 current periodical subscriptions. Students have access to online information retrieval services and the Internet.

Most important holdings include archival material documenting early history of college and art education for women; Sartain Family Papers, 1795–1944; Folio collection of costumes, textile design and ornament.

Chief Executive Officer: Dr. Henry C. Fernandez, President.

Address admission inquiries to Wendy Pyle Elliot, Director of Admissions.

Moravian College and Theological Seminary

1200 Main Street
Bethlehem, Pennsylvania 18018-6650
Tel: (610) 861-1300 **E-mail:** admissions@moravian.edu
Fax: (610) 861-3956 **Internet:** www.moravian.edu

Institution Description: Moravian College is a private, independent, nonprofit institution affiliated with the Moravian Church in America. The Church Street campus, located in an historic area developed in the 1700s by Moravian settlers, houses music and art facilities and some dormitories. All other facilities are on the Main Street campus, .8 of a mile to the north. *Enrollment:* 2,040. *Degrees awarded:* Baccalaureate. Moravian Theological Seminary offers first-professional (master of divinity), master's, and doctoral degrees.

Accreditation: *Regional:* MSA/CHE. *National:* ATS. *Professional*: theology

History: Formed 1954 by merger of Moravian Seminary for Women (founded 1742) and The School for Men at Nazareth (founded 1746, offered first-professional degree as Moravian Theological Seminary 1807, offered first baccalaureate as Moravian College and Theological Seminary 1846). The coeducational institution awarded its first baccalaureate 1954. *See* John R. Weinlick, *Moravian College: Challenge and Response* (Bethlehem, Pa.: Alumni Association of Moravian College, 1977) for further information.

Institutional Structure: *Governing board:* Moravian College Board of Trustees. Elected by the trustees: 27 (including 2 faculty and 2 students). 6 ex officio. All voting. *Composition of institution:* Administrators 88. Academic affairs headed by vice president for academic affairs and dean of the college. Management/business/finances directed by vice president for administration. Full-time instructional faculty 114. Academic governance body, the faculty, meets an average of 9 times per year.

Calendar: Semesters. Academic year Aug. to May. Freshmen admitted Aug., Jan., Feb., June. Degrees conferred and formal commencement May. Summer session from June to Aug.

Characteristics of Freshmen: 2,098 applicants (1,185 female, 913 male). 70% of applicants accepted. 26% of accepted applicants enrolled.

87% (326 students) submitted SAT scores; 10% (38 students) submitted ACT scores. *25th percentile*: SAT Critical Reading 510, SAT Math 510, SAT Writing 500; ACT Composite 19. *75th percentile*: SAT Critical Reading 600, SAT Math 610, SAT Writing 590; ACT Composite 21.

79% of entering freshmen expected to graduate within 5 years. 49% of freshmen from Pennsylvania. Freshmen from 22 states and 5 foreign countries.

Admission: Rolling admissions plan. For fall acceptance, apply as early as Sept. 1 of previous year, but not later than Mar. 1 of year of enrollment. Apply by Jan. 15 for early decision; need not limit application to Moravian. Early acceptance available. *Requirements:* Graduation from accredited secondary school with 4 units English, 2 in a foreign language, 3 mathematics, 2 laboratory science, 2 social studies; or GED. 3-5 additional units recommended. Minimum GPA 3.0. Preferred secondary school class standing in top two fifths. *Entrance tests:* College Board SAT, essay. *For transfer students:* 2.5 minimum GPA; 90 hours maximum transfer credit; from 2-year accredited institution 2.75 minimum GPA, 64 hours maximum transfer credit.

Advanced placement for postsecondary-level work completed in secondary school.

Degree Requirements: 124 credit hours; 1.8 GPA; 2 terms in residence; 4 terms physical education; 2 January terms; distribution requirements; 2.0 GPA in major field.

Fulfillment of some degree requirements and exemption from some beginning courses possible by passing College Board CLEP or APP. *Grading system:* A–F; pass-fail (no credit); withdraw (carries time limit); incomplete (carries time limit).

Distinctive Educational Programs: Work-experience programs. Evening classes. Dual-degree programs in natural resource management in cooperation with Duke University (NC), engineering with Lafayette College and the University of Pennsylvania, and nursing with Columbia University (NY). Interdepartmental/interdisciplinary programs. Facilities for independent research, including individualized majors and honors programs. Study abroad during January Term and through programs offered by LVAIC members and other colleges (summer programs in Spain, France, Germany). January Term program in Europe, Near East, Africa, and Caribbean. Programs may also be individually arranged. Add-Venture program allows students to design their own academic programs. Washington (DC) Semester in cooperation with American University. Cross-registration through LVAIC with Allentown, Cedar Crest, Lafayette, and Muhlenberg Colleges and Lehigh University.

ROTC: Army, Air Force offered in cooperation with Lehigh University.

Degrees Conferred: 383 *baccalaureate*; 26 *master's*; 13 *first-professional*. Bachelor's degrees awarded in top five disciplines: social sciences 80; business, management, marketing, and related support services 69; psychology 65; visual and performing arts 42; English language/literature 26. Master's degrees awarded: various disciplines 26. First-professional degrees awarded: theology 13.

Fees and Other Expenses: *Full-time tuition per academic year 2008–09:* $30,062. *Books and supplies* $900. *Room and board per academic year:* $8,312. *Other expenses:* $$1,824. Contact the college for current seminary costs.

Financial Aid: Aid from institutionally generated funds is provided on the basis of academic merit, financial need.

Financial aid to full-time, first-time undergraduate students: 93% received some form of financial aid. Average amount of aid received: federal grants $4,341; Pell grants $2,786; other federal aid $1,598; state/local grants $5,809; institutional grants $12,741.

Departments and Teaching Staff: *Total instructional faculty:* 147. Student/faculty ratio: 13:1. Degrees held by full-time faculty: doctorate 81%.

Enrollment: Total enrollment 2,040. Undergraduate 1,816 (full-time 87%; female 60%, male 40%). Gradaute 224 (full-time 15%). Undergraduate transfer-in students 78.

Characteristics of Student Body: *Ethnic/racial makeup:* Black non-Hispanic: 2%; Asian or Pacific Islander: 2%; Hispanic: 4%; White non-Hispanic: 89%; unknown: 2%; nonresident alien 1%.

International Students: 20 nonresident aliens enrolled fall 2008. Students from Europe, Asia, Latin America, Africa, Canada. Programs available to aid students whose native language is not English: social, cultural. Financial aid specifically designated for international students: scholarships available annually to qualifying students.

Student Life: 65% of students reside in college housing, of which 63% is allocated for men and 68% for women. 13% of students live in college apartments. 20% of males join and 6% live in fraternity housing. 23% of females join and 4% live in sorority housing. 11% of students live off-campus in privately owned housing. *Intercollegiate athletics:* male: baseball, basketball, cross-country, football, golf, soccer, tennis, track and field, wrestling; female: softball, basketball, cross-country, field hockey, tennis, track and field, volleyball. *Special regulations:* Cars permitted without restrictions. Quiet hours midnight to 10am. Residence hall visitation 10am to midnight Sun.–Thurs., until 2am Fri. and Sat. *Special services:* Medical services, college-operated transport between campuses. *Student publications, radio: Benigna*, a yearbook; *Comenian*, a weekly newspaper; *The Manuscript*, an annual literary journal. Radio station WRMC broadcasts approximately 45 hours per week. *Surrounding community:* Bethlehem population 70,000. Philadelphia, 60 miles from campus, is nearest metropolitan area. Served by mass transit bus system; airport 2 miles from campus.

Publications: Sources of information about Moravian College include *Moravian*, alumni quarterly.

Library Collections: 263,000 volumes. 11,000 microforms; 5,400 audiovisual materials; 15,500 periodicals including via electronic access. Online catalog. Students have access to online information retrieval services.

Most important special holdings include History of the Moravian Church Collection; map collection (20,273 maps); Moravian Theological Seminary Collection; Adler Collection (4,500 records contained in the Music Department); Edward S. Curtis Collection on the North American Indian; notable small presses.

Buildings and Grounds: Campus area 70 acres.

Chief Executive Officer: Dr. Ervin J. Rokke, President.

Address admission inquiries to James P. Mackin, Director of Admissions.

Moravian Theological Seminary

Degree Programs Offered: *First-professional* in divinity; *master's* in Christian education in cooperation with Presbyterian School of Christian Education (VA), pastoral counseling in cooperation with Pastoral Institute of the Lehigh Valley, theological studies; *doctorate* in cooperation with Drew University School of Theology (NJ).

Admission: Baccalaureate degree from accredited college or university.

Degree Requirements: 30 credits in residence.

Mount Aloysius College

7373 Admiral Perry Highway
Cresson, Pennsylvania 16830-1999
Tel: (814) 886-4131 **E-mail:** admissions@mtaloy.edu
Fax: (814) 886-6441 **Internet:** www.mtalogy.edu

Institution Description: Mount Aloyisius College is a private Catholic College sponsored by the Sisters of Mercy. *Enrollment:* 1,644. *Degrees awarded:* Associate, baccalaureate, master's.

Accreditation: *Regional:* MSA/CHE. *Professional*: nursing, occupational therapy, physical therapy

History: Opened in 1853 as the Mount Aloyisius Academy and 1939 became Mount Aloyisius Junior College; became a senor college in 1995; first offered master's degrees 2002.

Institutional Structure: *Governing board:* Board of Trustees.

Calendar: Semesters. Academic year Aug. to Apr.

Characteristics of Freshmen: 1,158 applicants (844 female, 314 male). 74% of applicants accepted. 35% of accepted applicants enrolled full-time.

70% (236 students) submitted SAT scores; 30% (102 students) submitted ACT scores. *25th percentile*: SAT Critical Reading 410, SAT Math 400, SAT Writing 400; ACT Composite 17. *75th percentile*: SAT Critical Reading 510, SAT Math 510, SAT Writing 490; ACT Composite 20.

Admission: Rolling admissions. Health and nursing have January deadline. *Requirements:* Either graduation from accredited secondary school with 16 units which must include 4 English, 2 in a foreign language, 3 mathematics, 2 laboratory science; or GED. *Entrance tests:* College Board SAT or ACT.

College credit and advanced placement for postsecondary-level work completed in secondary school.

Degree Requirements: 2.0 GPA; for associate degrees 60 credits of which 20 must be earned in residence; bachelor's degree 120 credits of which 30 must earned in residence; C or better in all major courses. *Grading system:* A-F, pass-fail.

Distinctive Educational Programs: Pre-Law; Nursing; Radiography/Medical Imaging; Criminology.

Degrees Conferred: 189 *associate*; 158 *baccalaureate*. Bachelor's degrees awarded in business/marketing 15; computer and information sciences; education 15; English 2; foreign language 5; health professions and related clinical sciences 20; interdisciplinary studies 4; liberal arts 3; public administration 15; psychology 15; social sciences and history 2; other disciplines 62.

Fees and Other Expenses: *Tuition and fees per academic year 2008–09:* $16,580 undergraduate; contact the college for current graduate tuition. *Books and supplies:* $1,600. *Room and board per academic year:* $6,950. *Other expenses* $3,000.

Financial Aid: Aid from institutionally generated funds is provided on the basis of financial need, academic merit. Institution has a Program Participation Agreement with the U.S. Department of Education for eligible students to receive Pell Grants and, depending upon the agreement, other federal aid.

Financial aid to full-time, first-time undergraduate students: 99% received some form of financial aid.

Departments and Teaching Staff: *Total instructional faculty:* 160 (full-time 60, part-time 100). Total faculty with doctorate, first-professional, or other terminal degree: 26. Student/faculty ratio: 14:1.

Enrollment: Total enrollment 1,644. Undergraduate 1,594 (full-time 72%; female 72%, male 28%). Graduate 50 (full-time 88%). Undergraduate transfer-in students 134.

Characteristics of Student Body: *Ethnic/racial makeup:* Black non-Hispanic: 3%; Hispanic 1%; White non-Hispanic: 81%; unknown: 14%; nonresident alien 1%. *Age distribution:* number 18–19: 329; 20–21: 262; 22–24: 21; 25–29: 221; 30–34: 112; 35–39: 120; 40–49: 168; 50–64: 35; 65 and over: 1.

International Students: 16 nonresident aliens enrolled fall 2008. No programs to aid students whose native language is not English. No financial aid specifically designated for international students.

Student Life: Over 100 activities. 11 NCAA division 3 athletic programs. 4 residence halls. Choir, theatre, newspaper. Honors Program.

Library Collections: 84,500 volumes. 5,000 microforms; 2,450 audiovisual materials; 275 Current serial subscriptions. Online catalog. Students have access to online information retrieval services and the Internet.

Most important special holdings include Ecumenical Studies College; College Archives; law reference materials.

Buildings and Grounds: Campus area 165 acres.

Chief Executive Officer: Dr. Mary Ann Dillon, A.S.M., President.

Address admission inquiries to Frank Crouse, Director of Enrollment Management.

Muhlenberg College

2400 Chew Street
Allentown, Pennsylvania 18104
Tel: (484) 664-3100 **E-mail:** admissions@muhlenberg.edu
Fax: (484) 664-3234 **Internet:** www.muhlenberg.edu

Institution Description: Muhlenberg College is a private, independent, nonprofit college related to the Evangelical Lutheran Church in America, Southeastern Pennsylvania, Slovak Zion, and Northeastern Pennsylvania Synods. *Enrollment:* 2,446. *Degrees awarded:* Associate (through Wescoe School), baccalaureate, master's.

Member of the Lehigh Valley Association of Independent Colleges consortium.

Accreditation: *Regional:* MSA/CHE.

History: Established as Allentown Seminary 1848; chartered as Allentown Collegiate Institute and Military Academy and offered first instruction at postsecondary level 1864; adopted present name 1867; awarded first degree (baccalaureate) 1868. *See* James E. Swain, *A History of Muhlenberg College: 1848–1967* (New York: Appleton-Century-Crofts, 1967) for further information.

Institutional Structure: *Governing board:* Board of Directors. Representation: 40 elected trustees; 3 bishops of Lutheran Church Synods and President of the College, ex officio. All voting. *Composition of institution:* Administrators 160 (includes provost, dean of the college for academic life, dean of students, dean of admissions, vice president for finance and treasurer, vice president of development and alumni relations, vice president of public relations, vice president for human resources). Full-time instructional faculty 114. Academic governance body, the faculty, meets an average of 8 times per year.

Calendar: Semesters. Academic year Aug. to May. Freshmen admitted Aug. Transfer students admitted Aug., Jan. Degrees conferred Jan., May, Oct. Formal commencement May. Summer session of terms from May to Aug.

Characteristics of Freshmen: 1,158 applicants (844 female, 514 male). 74% of applicants accepted. 35% of accepted applicants enrolled full-time.

Average secondary school rank of men top 16%, women top 12%, class top 14%. Mean SAT class scores 591 Critical Reading, 596 Math.

81% of entering freshmen expected to graduate within 5 years. 24% of freshmen from Pennsylvania. Freshmen from 23 states and 1 foreign country.

Admission: Common Application accepted. For fall acceptance, apply as early as Sept. 1 of previous year, but not later than Feb. 15. Students are notified of acceptance beginning Mar. 15. Apply by Jan. 15 for early decision. *Requirements:* Either graduation from accredited secondary school with 16 Carnegie units which must include 4 English, 2–3 in a foreign language, 2–3 mathematics, 2 history, 2 science; or GED. Additional requirements for some programs. *Entrance tests:* All candidates are required to submit the results of the SAT I or ACT, or have an interview and submit a graded paper with teacher's grade and comments. *For transfer students:* maximum transfer credit limited by residence requirement; interview required.

College credit and advanced placement for postsecondary-level work completed in secondary school.

Degree Requirements: 34 course units; 2.0 GPA (2.0 in major field); 17 course units in residence and certification in a major; fulfillment of physical education requirement; general academic requirements.

Candidates with Advanced Placement (AP) scores of 4 or 5 are offered automatic credit; scores of 3 are offered placement. *Grading system:* A+–F; pass-fail; audit; withdraw (carries time limit); incomplete (carries time limit).

Distinctive Educational Programs: Internships. Accelerated degree program. Combined plan programs in engineering with Columbia University (NY), Washington University (MO); in forestry or environmental studies with Duke University (NC); in nursing with the Columbia University School of Nursing; in dentistry with the University of Pennsylvania School of Dental Medicine. Cooperative programs through the Lehigh Valley Association of Independent Colleges. First-year seminars. College-sponsored London Theatre Studies program for theatre majors. Dana Associates and Muhlenberg Scholar programs. Interdisciplinary majors in American Studies, history/government, international studies, Natural Science, Russian area studies, philosophy/political thought,

MUHLENBERG COLLEGE—*cont'd*

political economy, human resources administration. Facilities and programs for independent research, including honors programs, individual majors, independent study, other interdisciplinary concentrations. Study abroad programs in Australia, Denmark, England, France, Israel, Italy, The Netherlands, Republic of South Africa, Scotland, Spain. *Other distinctive programs:* Tuition-free audit program for senior citizens.

ROTC: Army offered in cooperation with Lehigh University.

Degrees Conferred: 189 *associate*; 329 *baccalaureate*. Bachelor's degrees awarded: business/marketing 118; social sciences 96; visual and performing arts 79; psychology 71; communications/journalism 57. Master's degrees awarded: education 16.

Fees and Other Expenses: *Full-time tuition per academic year 2008–09:* $30,980. *Other fees:* $225. *Books and supplies:* $800. *Room and board per academic year:* $7,525.

Financial Aid: Aid from institutionally generated funds is provided on the basis of academic merit, financial need, other criteria.

Financial aid to full-time, first-time undergraduate students: 93% received some form of financial aid. Average amount of aid received: federal grants $3,882; Pell grants $2,828; other federal aid $1,450; state/local grants $3,667; institutional grants $3,936.

Departments and Teaching Staff: *Total instructional faculty:* 267. Degrees held by full-time faculty: master's 24%, doctorate 75%, baccalaureate 1%. 88% hold terminal degrees. Student/faculty ratio: 12:1.

Enrollment: Total enrollment 2,500. Undergraduate 2,450 (full-time 92%; female 72%, male 28%). Graduate 50 (full-time 68%). Undergraduate transfer-in students 134.

Characteristics of Student Body: *Ethnic/racial makeup:* Black non-Hispanic: 3%; Hispanic: 1%; White non-Hispanic: 81%; unknown: 14%; nonresident alien 1%. *Age distribution:* number under 18: 22; 18–19: 1,001; 20–21: 1,029; 22–24: 203; 25–29: 49; 30–34: 43; 35–39: 30; 40–49: 62; 50–64: 22; 65 and over: 1.

International Students: 5 nonresident aliens enrolled fall 2008. Students from Europe, Latin America, Asia, Africa, Canada. Programs available to aid students whose native language is not English: social, cultural, financial.

Student Life: Housing for students consists of 8 traditional residence halls (1 for women exclusively), 11 small houses, 14-apartment MacGregor Village Complex, 4 small apartment complexes, an international house, 3 sororities, 5 fraternities, and a number of Muhlenberg Independent Living Experiment (MILE) houses in the adjacent neighborhood. Approximately 92% of full-time students reside on campus. *Intercollegiate athletics:* male: football, soccer, cross-country, basketball, wrestling, baseball, track, golf, and tennis; female: field hockey, volleyball, cross-country, basketball, softball, lacrosse, track, tennis and soccer. Club sports for males: ice hockey; females: rugby; coed: Tae Kwo Do, equestrian, fencing. *Special services:* Counseling and Development Program, medical services, academic support services. *Student publications, radio: Ciarla,* a yearbook; *Arcade*, a literary magazine; *Weekly*, a student newspaper. Radio station WMUH. *Special interest organizations:* Academic department clubs, Christian fellowship, choirs, bands, international affairs. *Surrounding community:* Allentown (PA), on the edge of the picturesque Pennsylvania Dutch country. 55 miles north of Philadelphia, 90 miles west of New York City.

Publications: Sources of information about the college include *Muhlenberg*, a quarterly magazine distributed to corporate and community leaders and alumni.

Library Collections: 225,000 volumes including bound books, serial backfiles, electronic documents, and government documents not in separate collections. Online catalog. 137,000 microforms; 15,400 audiovisual materials; 19,000 periodicals including via electronic access. Computer work stations available. Students have access to the Internet at no charge.

Most important special holdings include Muhlenberg Family Collection; Pennsylvania German Collection; Abram Samuels American Sheet Music Collection; Edward Curtis Photographs of American Indians.

Buildings and Grounds: Campus area 75 acres.

Chief Executive Officer: Dr. Peyton R. Helm, President.

Address admission inquiries to Christopher Hoover-=Hoving, Director of Admissions.

Neumann College

One Neumann Drive
Aston, Pennsylvania 19104-1298
Tel: (610) 459-0905 **E-mail:** neumann@neumann.edu
Fax: (610) 459-1370 **Internet:** www.neumann.edu

Institution Description: Neumann College (Our Lady of Angels College until 1980) is a private college affiliated with the Roman Catholic Church. *Enrollment:* 3,037. *Degrees awarded:* Associate, baccalaureate, master's.

Accreditation: *Regional:* MSA/CHE. *Professional*: clinical lab scientist, nursing, physical therapy

History: Established as Our Lady of Angels College, chartered, and offered first instruction at postsecondary level 1965; awarded first degree (baccalaureate) 1967; adopted present name and became coeducational 1980.

Institutional Structure: *Governing board:* Board of Trustees. Extrainstitutional representation: 18 trustees; institutional representation: president of the college; 1 alumnae. *Composition of institution:* Administrators 10. Academic affairs headed by vice president for academic affairs. Management/business/finances directed by vice president for finance and administration. Full-time instructional faculty 85. Academic governance body, Faculty Council, meets monthly Aug.–Apr.

Calendar: Semesters. Academic year Aug. to May. Freshmen admitted Aug., Jan., May. Degrees conferred and formal commencement May. Summer session from May to Aug.

Characteristics of Freshmen: 2,333 applicants (1,514 female, 819 male). 95% of applicants accepted. 24% of accepted applicants enrolled full-time.

99% (537 students) submitted SAT scores. *25th percentile:* SAT Critical Reading 410, SAT Math 400. *75th percentile:* SAT Critical Reading 490, SAT Math 500. >r<55% of entering freshmen expected to graduate within 5 years. 64% of freshmen from Pennsylvania. Freshmen from 6 states and 5 foreign countries.

Admission: Rolling admissions plan. For fall acceptance, apply as early as July of previous year, but not later than Aug. of year of enrollment. Early acceptance available. *Requirements:* Either graduation from accredited secondary school with 16 units which normally include 4 English, 2 in a foreign language, 2 mathematics, 2 history, social studies, 2 science, 4 academic electives; or GED. Minimum GPA 2.0. Lowest acceptable secondary school class standing 50th percentile. *Entrance tests:* College Board SAT or ACT composite. For foreign students TOEFL. *For transfer students:* 2.0 minimum GPA; from 4-year accredited institution 90 semester hours; from 2-year accredited institution 60 hours. College credit and advanced placement for postsecondary-level work completed in secondary school. For extrainstitutional learning, college credit and advanced placement on basis of portfolio and faculty assessment.

Tutoring available. Developmental, remedial courses offered in summer session and regular academic year; credit given.

Degree Requirements: 120–130 semester hours; 2.0 GPA overall and in major field; 30 hours in residence; distribution requirements.

Fulfillment of some degree requirements and exemption from some beginning courses possible by passing College Board CLEP, AP. *Grading system:* A–F; pass-fail; withdraw (deadline after which pass-fail is appended to withdraw).

Distinctive Educational Programs: Weekend and evening classes. Multidisciplinary major in liberal studies; interdisciplinary studies courses also available. Independent study. Study abroad by individual arrangement. Baccalaureate completion program for registered nurses. Child development Center provides student laboratory experience and community service in preschool instruction. *Other distinctive programs:* Individualized, degree-granting continuing education designed primarily as an evening program for adults. Deferred Opportunity Education program provides counseling and other support services for adult women wishing to return to the classroom. Online courses available. Associate degree program available online.

ROTC: Army through cross-enrollment with Widener University.

Degrees Conferred: 27 *associate*; 407 *baccalaureate*; 196 *master's*; 33 *doctorate*. Bachelor's degrees offered in top five disciplines: liberal arts/general studies 116; social sciences 65; education 59; health professions and related clinical sciences 58; business/marketing 50. Master's degreees awarded: various disciplines 196. Doctorates awarded: health professsions 33.

Fees and Other Expenses: *Full-time tuition per academic year 2008–09:* $20,402 undergraduate; contact the college for current graduate tuition. *Required fees:* $640. *Room and board per academic year:* $9,258. *Books and supplies:* $1,500. *Other expenses:* $2,300.

Financial Aid: Aid from institutionally generated funds is provided on the basis of academic merit, financial need. Institution has a Program Participation Agreement with the U.S. Department of Education for eligible students to receive Pell Grants and, depending upon the agreement, other federal aid.

Financial aid to full-time, first-time undergraduate students: 95% received some form of aid. Average amount of aid received: federal grants $3,110; Pell grants $3,164; other federal aid $350; state/local grants $3,000; institutional grants $9,000.

Departments and Teaching Staff: *Total instructional faculty:* 263. Student/faculty ratio: 14:1. Degrees held by full-time faculty: doctorate 59%, master's 37%. 63% hold terminal degrees.

Enrollment: Total enrollment 3,037. Undergraduate 2,484 (full-time 82%; female 66%, male 34%). Graduate 553 (full-time 22%). Undergraduate transfer-in students 74.

Characteristics of Student Body: *Ethnic/racial makeup:* Black non-Hispanic: 14%; Asian or Pacific Islander: 1%; Hispanic: 2%; White non-Hispanic: 61%; unknown: 19%; nonresident alien 2%. *Age distribution:* number under 18: 83; 18–19: 757; 20–21: 562; 22–24: 263; 25–29: 132; 30–34: 79; 35–39: 90; 40–49: 162; 50–64: 67; 65 and over: 2.

International Students: 60 nonresident aliens enrolled fall 2008. No programs available to aid students whose native language is not English. No financial aid specifically designated for international students.

Student Life: Campus residence offered 1997. *Intercollegiate athletics:* male: baseball, basketball, cross-country, golf, ice hockey, lacrosse, soccer, tennis; female: basketball, cross-country, field hockey, lacrosse, soccer, softball, tennis, volleyball. *Special services:* Learning Assistance Center, Career Development Office, experiential educational programs, Child Development Center (pre-school and daycare), computer laboratories, counseling services, health services, Student Activities Center, Student Leadership Program. *Student organizations:* Neumann Business Association, Black Student Union, Gold Key Society, Professional Education Society, Psychology Club, Student Nurses Association, Student Alumni Association, Theater Ensemble, Community Chorus. *Student publications, The Campus Press*, student newspaper; *The Looking Glass*, student magazine. *Surrounding community:* Aston population 14,500. Philadelphia, 19 miles from campus, is nearest metropolitan area. Served by mass transit bus system; airport 18 miles from campus; passenger rail service 5 miles from campus.

Publications: *Accent*, the Neumann College alumni magazine.

Library Collections: 90,000 volumes. 100,000 microforms; 36,500 audiovisual materials; 700 current periodical subscriptions. Computer work stations available. Students have access to the Internet and online information retrieval services.

Most important holdings include Sister Clare Immaculate McDonnel Franciscan Resource Room; Betty Neumann Archives (papers of internationally-known nurse theoretician); extensive holdings in nursing.

Buildings and Grounds: Campus area 50 acres.

Chief Executive Officer: Dr. Rosalie M. Mirenda, President.

Address admission inquiries to Christian Riyo, Director of Admissions.

The Pennsylvania State University - Harrisburg Capital College

777 West Harrisburg Pike
Middletown, Pennsylvania 17057-4898
Tel: (717) 948-6000 **E-mail:** admissions@hbg.psu.edu
Fax: (717) 948-6008 **Internet:** www.hbg.psu.edu

Institution Description: The Pennsylvania State University - Harrisburg Capital College provides upper division baccalaureate and graduate study only. *Enrollment:* 3,936. *Degrees awarded:* Baccalaureate, master's, doctorate.

Accreditation: *Regional:* MSA/CHE. *Professional*: engineering technology, public administration.

History: Established, chartered, and offered first instruction at postsecondary level 1966; awarded first degree (baccalaureate) 1968; adopted present name 1986.

Institutional Structure: *Composition of institution:* Administrators 20. Academic affairs headed by provost and dean. Management/business/finances directed by financial officer. Full-time instructional faculty 138. Academic governance body, Faculty Senate, meets an average of 10 times per year.

Calendar: Semesters. Academic year Aug. to May. Entering students admitted Aug., Jan. Summer courses available.

Admission: Modified rolling admissions plan. For fall acceptance, apply as early as Sept. of previous year. *Requirements:* For undergraduate admission - either 60 academic credits or associate degree; completion of appropriate College Board CLEP Tests; or diploma from accredited school of nursing; minimum GPA 2.0; GPA requirements vary by program. Maximum transfer credits vary by program. TOEFL required for foreign students.

Degree Requirements: *For all baccalaureate degrees:* 2.0 GPA (higher for some programs); 36 of last 60 semester hours in residence; specific requirements vary by program.

ROTC: Army offered in cooperation with Dickinson College.

Degrees Conferred: 4 *associate*; 598 *baccalaureate*; 498 *master's*; 8 *doctorate*. Bachelor's degrees awarded in top five disciplines: business, management, marketing, and related support services 159; engineering 97; education 73; communication, journalism, and related programs 42; security and protective services 38.

Fees and Other Expenses: *Full-time tuition and fees per academic year 2008–09:* resident $12,222, nonresident $18,370; contact the university for current graduate tuition/fees. *Books and supplies:* $1,264. *Room and board per academic year:* $8,262. *Other expenses:* $3,510.

Financial Aid: Aid from institutionally generated funds is provided on the basis of academic merit, financial need.

Financial aid to full-time, first-time undergraduate students: 81% received some form of financial aid. Average amount of aid relieved: federal grants $4,085; Pell grants $2,946; other federal aid $1,869; state/local grants $1,437; institutional grants $5,153.

Departments and Teaching Staff: *Total instructional faculty:* 138. Degrees held by full-time faculty: doctorate 84%, master's 16%.

Enrollment: Total enrollment 3,936. Undergraduate 2,259. Graduate 1,677.

Characteristics of Student Body: *Ethnic/racial makeup (undergraduate):* Black non-Hispanic: 8%; Asian or Pacific Islander: 7%; Hispanic: 4%; White 79%; nonresident alien 2%.

International Students: 44 nonresident aliens enrolled fall 2008. Programs available to aid students whose native language is not English: English as a Second Language Program. No financial aid specifically designated for international students.

Student Life: Student housing available; housing also available for married students. *Special regulations:* Cars permitted without restrictions. *Special services:* Medical services. *Student publications:* Student newspaper, student literary magazine. *Surrounding community:* Middletown, population 10,500, is located in Harrisburg metropolitan area.

Library Collections: 250,000 volumes. 813,500 microforms; 2,000 audiovisual materials; 2,500 serial subscriptions. Students have access to online information retrieval services and the Internet.

Buildings and Grounds: Campus area 218 acres.

Chief Executive Officer: Dr. Marilyn L. Hanes, Provost and Dean.

Address admission inquiries to Dr. Thomas Streveler, Director of Admissions.

The Pennsylvania State University - University Park Campus

201 Old Main
University Park, Pennsylvania 16804-3000
Tel: (814) 865-4700 **E-mail:** admissions@psu.edu
Fax: (814) 863-7590 **Internet:** www.psu.edu

Institution Description: *Enrollment:* 44,406. *Degrees awarded:* Associate, baccalaureate, master's, doctorate.

Accreditation: *Regional:* MSA/CHE. *Professional*: architecture, business, chemistry, dietetics, engineering, engineering technology, forestry, health information administration, journalism, landscape architecture, medicine, music, nursing, physician assisting, psychology internship, rehabilitation counseling, social work, speech-language pathology, teacher education

History: Established 1855; offered first instruction at postsecondary level 1859; awarded first degree (baccalaureate) 1861; designated as Pennsylvania's land-grant college 1863; changed name to Pennsylvania State College 1874; added doctoral program 1924; adopted present name 1953. *See* W. F. Dunaway, *The Pennsylvania State College History* (Lancaster, PA: Lancaster Press, 1946) for further information.

Institutional Structure: *Governing board:* Board of Trustees. *Composition of institution:* Administrators 205. Academic affairs headed by provost. Management/business/finances directed by senior vice president for finance and operations. Full-time instructional faculty 2,218. . Academic governance body, University Faculty Senate, meets an average of 10 times per year.

Calendar: Semesters. Academic year Aug. to May.

Characteristics of Freshmen: 39,551 applicants (18,937 female, 20,613 male). 51% of applicants accepted. 32% of accepted applicants enrolled.

47% (5,274 students) submitted SAT scores; 12% (773 students) submitted ACT scores. *25th percentile*: SAT Critical Reading 530, SAT Math 570; ACT Composite 23, ACT English 22, ACT Math 23. *75th percentile*: SAT Critical Reading 630, SAT Math 670; ACT Composite 28, ACT English 29, ACT Math 29.

79% of entering freshmen expected to graduate within 5 years. 75% of freshmen from Pennsylvania. Freshmen from 50 states.

THE PENNSYLVANIA STATE UNIVERSITY - UNIVERSITY PARK CAMPUS—*cont'd*

Admission: Rolling admissions plan. For fall acceptance, apply as early as Sept. of previous year. Students notified of acceptance beginning Nov. *Requirements:* Graduation from accredited secondary school with 15 units which must include 4 in English, 3 in science, 3 in math; 2 units of foreign language required for some programs; or GED. *Entrance tests:* College Board SAT or ACT. *For transfer students:* 2.0 minimum GPA; transfer credit varies.

College credit and advanced placement for postsecondary-level work completed in secondary school.

Degree Requirements: *For all associate degrees:* 60–72 semester hours; 18 of last 30 hours in residence. *For all baccalaureate degrees:* 130–178 semester hours; 36 of the last 60 hours in residence; 3 hours physical education. *For all undergraduate degrees:* 2.0 GPA (higher for some programs); general education requirements (common to all degree programs and compose about one-third of the coursework). All students mus complete a writing across the curriculum course.

Students admitted after Spring 2005 must complete 3 credits in United States Cultures and 3 credits in International Cultures to satisfy the diversity component requirement.

Fulfillment of some degree requirements and exemption from some beginning courses possible by passing departmental examinations, College Board CLEP, AP. *Grading system:* A–F; withdraw (deadline after which pass-fail is appended to withdraw).

Distinctive Educational Programs: Developmental courses offered in summer session and regular academic year; credit given. Work-experience programs, internships. Dual-degree programs in liberal arts-engineering and liberal arts-earth and mineral sciences with 22 institutions. Special facilities for using telecommunications in the classroom. Interdisciplinary programs in acoustics; bioengineering; African and African American Studies; ecology; environmental pollution control; genetics; marine sciences; philosophy; physiology; regional planning; science, technology, and society; solid state science. Preprofessional programs in law and medicine. Facilities and programs for independent research, including honors programs, individual majors. Study abroad programs offered throughout Europe, the Middle East, the Far East, South America, Africa, and Australia. Continuing education program.

ROTC: Air Force, Army, Navy.

Degrees Conferred: 102 *associate;* 9,442 *baccalaureate*; 1,267 *master's*; 643 *doctorate*. Bachelor's degrees awarded in top five disciplines: business, management, marketing, and related support services 1,874; engineering/engineering technologies 1,172; communication, journalism, and related programs 854; education 600; social sciences and history 514. Master's degrees awarded: various disciplines 643. Doctorates awardced: various disciplines 643.

Fees and Other Expenses: *Full-time tuition per academic year 2008–09:* undergraduate resident $13,706, nonresident $24,940; contact the university for current graduate tuition and any other applicable fees. *Books and supplies:* $1,264. *Room and board per academic year:* $8,262. *Other expenses:* $3,510.

Financial Aid: Aid from institutionally generated funds is provided on the basis of academic merit, financial need, athletic ability. Institution has a Program Participation Agreement with the U.S. Department of Education for eligible students to receive Pell Grants and, depending upon the agreement, other federal aid.

Financial aid to full-time, first-time undergraduate students: 73% received some form of financial aid. Average amount of aid received: federal grants $4,734; Pell grants $2,858; other federal aid $2,748; state/local grants $3,624; institutional grants $5,788.

Departments and Teaching Staff: *Total instructional faculty:* 2,543. Total faculty with doctorate, first-professional, or other terminal degree: 1,803. Student/faculty ratio: 17:1. Degrees held by full-time faculty: baccalaureate 1%, master's 11%, doctorate 88%.

Enrollment: Total enrollment 44,406. Undergraduate 39,988 (full-time 97%; female 45%, male 55%). Graduate 6,418 (full-time 85%). Undergraduate transfer-in students 369.

Characteristics of Student Body: *Ethnic/racial makeup:* Black non-Hispanic: 4%; Asian or Pacific Islander: 6%; Hispanic: 4%; White non-Hispanic: 83%; nonresident alien 3%.

International Students: 1,332 nonresident aliens enrolled fall 2008. Programs available to aid students whose native language is not English: English as a Second Language. No financial aid specifically designated for international students.

Student Life: 37% of undergraduates live in university housing. Some males join and live in off-campus fraternity housing. some women join and live in sorority accommodations in residence halls. Housing available for married students. *Intercollegiate athletics:* male: baseball, basketball, cross-country and track, football, golf, gymnastics, lacrosse, soccer, swimming, tennis, volleyball, wrestling; female: basketball, cross-country and track, fencing, field hockey, golf, gymnastics, lacrosse, soccer, softball, swimming, tennis, volleyball. *Special regulations:* Registered cars allowed; freshmen under age 21 not permitted to possess or operate cars on campus. *Special services:* Medical services, campus bus service. *Student publications, radio: Daily Collegian*, a newspaper; *LaVie*, a student yearbook. Radio station WDFM broadcasts 168 hours per week. *Surrounding community:* State College population 41,000. Harrisburg, 100 miles from campus, is nearest metropolitan area.

Library Collections: 5,604,000 volumes. 2,150,000 microforms; 68,000 audiovisual materials; 22,880 serial subscriptions. Online catalog. Students have access to online information retrieval services and the Internet.

Most important special holdings include Penn State Collection; Joseph Priestly Collection; John O'Hara Collection.

Buildings and Grounds: Campus area 5,162 acres.

Chief Executive Officer: Dr. Graham B. Spanier, President.

Undergraduates address admission inquiries to Randall Deike, Associate Vice Provost for Enrollment Management; graduate inquiries to Cynthia Nicosia, Director of Graduate Enrollment Services.

The Pennsylvania State University - Milton S. Hershey Medical Center

500 University Drive
Hershey, Pennsylvania 17033
Tel: (717) 531-8521 **E-mail:** admissions@hmc.psu.edu
Fax: (717) 531-6225 **Internet:** www.hmc.psu.edu

Institution Description: *Enrollment:* 791. *Degrees awarded:* First-professional (medicine), master's, doctorate. Associate degree in physician's assistant and certificates also awarded.

Accreditation: *Regional:* MSA/CHE. *Professional*: clinical pastoral education, medicine, physician assisting

History: Established and chartered 1964; offered first instruction at postsecondary level 1967; awarded first degree (first-professional) 1971.

Institutional Structure: *Composition of institution:* Administrators 93. Academic affairs headed by provost. Management/business/finances directed by deputy controller. Full-time instructional faculty 255 men / 48 women. Academic governance body, Faculty Senate, meets an average of 10 times per year.

Calendar: Semesters. Academic year Aug. to May. Entering students admitted Aug., Jan.

Admission: Modified rolling admissions plan. For August acceptance, apply as early as Sept. of previous year. *Requirements:* first-professional students need a baccalaureate degree from accredited college or university; MCAT. Graduate students must have a baccalaureate degree from accredited college or university; GRE for some programs; specific entrance requirements vary by program.

Degree Requirements: *For first-professional degree:* satisfactory completion of prescribed curriculum; entire third year and at least 1 term of the fourth year in residence. *Grading system:* A–F; withdraw (deadline after which pass-fail is appended to withdraw).

Distinctive Educational Programs: Cooperative affiliations with numerous area clinical facilities. Special facilities for using telecommunications in the classroom. Independent study. *Other distinctive programs:* Continuing medical education for practicing physicians and other health personnel.

Degrees Conferred: 11 *master's:* biological sciences; 20 *doctorate:* biological sciences; 123 *first-professional:* medicine.

Fees and Other Expenses: *Full-time tuition per academic year:* contact the school for current tuition, fees, and expenses. No on-campus housing.

Financial Aid: Aid from institutionally generated funds is provided on the basis of academic merit, financial need.

Departments and Teaching Staff: *Total instructional faculty:* 345. Degrees held by full-time faculty: doctorate 91%, master's 5%, baccalaureate 4%.

Enrollment: Total enrollment 791.

Characteristics of Student Body: *Ethnic/racial makeup:* Black non-Hispanic: 6%; American Indian or Alaska Native: 1%; Asian or Pacific Islander: 11%; Hispanic: 2%; White non-Hispanic: 70%.

International Students: 79 nonresident aliens enrolled fall 2008. No programs available to aid students whose native language is not English. No financial aid specifically designated for international students.

Student Life: No on-campus housing. *Special regulations:* Cars permitted without restrictions. *Special services:* Medical services. *Surrounding community:* Hershey, population 7,500, is located in the Harrisburg metropolitan area.

Library Collections: 115,000 volumes. 581 audiovisual materials; 1,682 current periodical subscriptions. Students have access to online information retrieval services and the Internet.

Buildings and Grounds: Campus area 194 acres.

Chief Executive Officer: Dr. Darrell G. Kirch, Vice President and Dean.

Address admission inquiries to Director of Admissions.

Philadelphia Biblical University

200 Manor Avenue
Langhorne, Pennsylvania 19047
Tel: (215) 752-5800 **E-mail:** admissions@pbu.edu
Fax: (215) 702-4341 **Internet:** www.pbu.edu

Institution Description: Philadelphia Biblical University, is a private, independent, nonprofit university. *Enrollment:* 1,335. *Degrees awarded:* Associate, baccalaureate, master.

Accreditation: *Regional:* MSA/CHE. *National:* ABHE. *Professional*: music, social work, teacher education

History: Formed by merger of Bible Institute of Pennsylvania (established as National Bible Institute of Philadelphia, 1913) and Philadelphia School of the Bible (established 1914) 1951; became 4-year college and became Philadelphia College of Bible in 1958; awarded first degree (baccalaureate) 1959; adopted present name 2000.

Institutional Structure: *Governing board:* Board of Trustees. Representation: 36 trustees including president of the college, 8 alumni, 2 trustees emeriti. *Composition of institution:* Administrators: 8. Academic affairs headed by senior vice president for academic affairs. Management/business/finances directed by senior vice president for administration. Full-time instructional faculty 54. Academic governance body, the faculty, meets an average of 15 times per year.

Calendar: Semesters. Academic year Aug. to May. Freshmen admitted Aug., Jan., May, June. Degrees conferred May, Aug., Dec. Formal commencement May. Summer session from May to July.

Characteristics of Freshmen: 324 applicants (197 female, 127 male). 75% of applicants accepted. 62% of accepted applicants enrolled.

Mean SAT scores: Critical Reading 548, SAT Math 526. Mean ACT Composite score 22.8.

52% of entering freshmen expected to graduate within 5 years. 48% of freshmen from Pennsylvania. Freshmen from 19 states and 5 foreign countries.

Admission: Rolling admissions plan. For fall acceptance, apply as early as Sept. of previous year, but not later than Aug. of year of enrollment. Early acceptance available. *Requirements:* Either graduation from accredited secondary school or GED. Home schooled students will be evaluated on an individual basis. Recommend 4 units English, 2 in a foreign language, 3 social studies, 2 science, 1 mathematics. *Entrance tests:* SAT or ACT composite. *For transfer students:* 2.0 minimum GPA; from accredited institution 68 hours maximum transfer credit; correspondence/extension students 12 credit limit.

College credit and advanced placement for postsecondary-level work completed in secondary school. For extrainstitutional learning (life learning) college credit on basis of USAFI program.

Degree Requirements: Associate: minimum of 60 credit hours and 2.0 GPA; baccalaureate: minimum 126 credit hours; 2.0 GPA; 60 hours in residence; master's: minimum of 30 credit hours; 2.5 GPA.

Fulfillment of some degree requirements and exemption from some beginning courses possible by passing College Board CLEP, APP. *Grading system:* A–F; satisfactory-unsatisfactory; withdraw (carries penalty if failing); incomplete (carries time limit).

Distinctive Educational Programs: Internships. Evening classes. Dual degree programs in business, music, social work, and teacher education. Four-year cooperative programs with B.S. in Bible and A.A. in either accounting, computer application development, PC and end user support, networking technology, or office administration and technology. Bible with Camping Ministries emphasis spending freshman and senior years at campus in Wisconsin; 20-month accelerated degree completion for working adults; Israel program with one semester in Jerusalem.

ROTC: Air Force in cooperation with St. Joseph's University.

Degrees Conferred: 15 *associate;* 276 *baccalaureate:* business 25; education 38; philosophy/religion/theology 190; public administration and social services 14; visual and performing arts 16. Master's degrees awarded: theology and religious vocations 82.

Fees and Other Expenses: *Full-time tuition per academic year 2008–09:* contact the institution for current rates.

Financial Aid: Aid from institutionally generated funds provided on the basis of academic merit, financial need, other criteria.

Financial aid to full-time, first-time undergraduate students:

Departments and Teaching Staff: *Total instructional faculty:* 128 (full-time 54, part-time 74). 54% of faculty hold the doctorate, first-professional, or other terminal degree. Student/faculty ratio: 12:1.

Enrollment: Total enrollment 1,335. Undergraduate 1,023 (full-time 93%; female 35%, male 45%). Graduate 312 (full-time 14%). Undergraduate transfer-in students 92.

Characteristics of Student Body: *Ethnic/racial makeup:* Black non-Hispanic: 13%; Asian or Pacific Islander: 4%; Hispanic: 3%; White non-Hispanic: 77%; unknown: 2%; nonreident alien 2%. *Age distribution:* number under 18: 23; 18–19: 312; 20–21: 306; 22–24: 160; 25–29: 32; 30–34: 28; 35–39: 34; 40–49: 56; 50–64: 47; 65 and over: 4.

International Students: 26 nonresident aliens enrolled fall 2008. Students from Europe, Asia, Latin America, Africa, Canada. No programs available to aid students whose native language is not English. Financial aid specifically designated for graduate international students: 3 scholarships awarded annually.

Student Life: On-campus residence halls house 60% of undergraduates. *Intercollegiate athletics:* male: baseball, basketball, golf, soccer, tennis, volleyball; female: basketball, field hockey, soccer, softball, tennis, volleyball. *Special regulations:* Registered cars permitted in designated areas. Midnight curfew for main campus dormitory students. *Special services:* medical services. *Student publications: Milestone*, a yearbook; *Scroll*, a newspaper. *Surrounding community:* Langhorne population 820. Philadelphia, 25 miles from campus, is nearest metropolitan area. Served by mass transit rail system; passenger rail service .5 mile from campus.

Publications: *Alumni Newsletter* published 2 times per year.

Library Collections: 167,000 volumes including bound books, serial backfiles, electronic documents, and government documents not in separate collections. Online catalog. Current serial subscriptions: 803 paper. 8,978 via electronic access. 5,112 recordings; 454 compact discs; 62 CD-ROMs. Computer work stations available. Students have access to the Internet at no charge.

Most important special collections include Early English and American Hymnals; books on the conservative-evangelical tradition in Christianity (18,000 items); teacher education; music.

Buildings and Grounds: Campus area 114 acres. Campus DVD available.

Chief Executive Officer: Dr. W. Sherrill Babb, President.

Address admission inquiries to Lisa Yoder, Director, Undergraduate Admissions; graduate inquiries to Susan Bosch, Director, Graduate Admissions.

Philadelphia College of Osteopathic Medicine

4150 City Avenue
Philadelphia, Pennsylvania 19131
Tel: (215) 871-6700 **E-mail:** admissions@pcom.edu
Fax: (215) 871-6719 **Internet:** www.pcom.edu

Institution Description: The Philadelphia College of Osteopathic Medicine is the result of a merger of the Osteopathic Hospital of Philadelphia and the Osteopathic Foundation of Philadelphia. *Enrollment:* 1,605. *Degrees awarded:* First-professional, master's, doctorate.

Accreditation: *Regional:* MSA/CHE. *Professional*: medical record technology, osteopathy

History: Founded 1899.

Institutional Structure: The campus is student and learning focused. The buildings and lecture halls have been expanded and renovated with cutting-edge technology.

Calendar: Trimesters. Academic year Aug. to May.

Admission: *Requirements:* For undergraduate study—graduation from accredited secondary school; for first-professional study—baccalaureate degree from an accredited college or university; completion of 6 semester hours of English, 8 biology, 8 inorganic chemistry, 8 organic chemistry, 8 physics. *Entrance tests:* MCAT.

Degree Requirements: Completion of prescribed curriculum.

Distinctive Educational Programs: Doctor of Osteopathic Medicine (D.O.); Master of Science in Biomedical Science (M.S>); Doctor of Psychology (Psy.D.); Master of Science in Clinical Health Psychology (M.S.); Master of Science in Physician Assistant Studies (M.S.); MS and PsyD in School Psychology.

Degrees Conferred: 135 *master's:* biomedical sciences 30; health professions 55; psychology 50; 281 *doctorate:* biomedical sciences 3; health professions 238; 40 psychology. 413 *first-professional:* osteopathic medicine 238; other graduate 175.

Fees and Other Expenses: *Full-time tuition per academic year:* contact the college for current tuition, fees, and expenses.

Financial Aid: Aid from institutionally generated funds is provided on the basis of academic merit, financial need. Institution has a Program Participation Agreement with the U.S. Department of Education for eligible students to receive Pell Grants and, depending upon the agreement, other federal aid.

Departments and Teaching Staff: *Total instructional faculty:* 1,081 (full-time 88, part-time 65). Total faculty with doctorate, first-professional, or other terminal degree: 936.

PHILADELPHIA COLLEGE OF OSTEOPATHIC MEDICINE—*cont'd*

Enrollment: Total enrollment 1,605. First-professional 1,605.

Characteristics of Student Body: *Ethnic/racial makeup:* number of Black non-Hispanic: 169; American Indian or Alaska Native: 4; Asian or Pacific Islander: 136; Hispanic: 40; White non-Hispanic: 1,214; unknown: 40.

International Students: 2 nonresident aliens enrolled fall 2008.

Chief Executive Officer: Dr. Matthew Schure, President.

Address admission inquiries to Carol A. Fox, Assistant Vice President for Enrollment Management.

Philadelphia University

School House Lane and Henry Avenue
Philadelphia, Pennsylvania 19144
Tel: (215) 951-2803 **E-mail:** admissions@philau.edu
Fax: (215) 951-2907 **Internet:** www.philau.edu

Institution Description: Philadelphia University, formerly known as Philadelphia College of Textiles and Science, is a private, independent, nonprofit university. *Enrollment:* 3,360. *Degrees awarded:* Associate, baccalaureate, master's.

Accreditation: *Regional:* MSA/CHE. *Professional*: architecture, chemistry, engineering, interior design, occupational therapy, physician assisting

History: Founded by Philadelphia Manufacturers Association and incorporated as Philadelphia Textile School of the Pennsylvania Museum of Art 1884; name changed to Philadelphia Textile Institute of the Philadelphia Museum of Art 1941; first instruction at postsecondary level 1942; awarded first degree (baccalaureate) 1946; incorporated as independent institution 1949; became Philadelphia College of Textiles and Science 1960; achieved university status in 1999 and adopted its present name.

Institutional Structure: *Governing board:* Board of Trustees. Extrainstitutional representation: 28 trustees; institutional representation: 1 administrator. 29 voting. *Composition of institution:* Administrators 75. Academic affairs headed by vice president for academic affairs. Business/finances directed by vice president for finance. Full-time instructional faculty 104. Academic governance body meets an average of 6 times per year.

Calendar: Semesters. Academic year Aug. to Apr. Freshmen admitted Aug., May, July. Degrees conferred May, Aug., Dec. Formal commencement May. Summer sessions May to Aug.

Characteristics of Freshmen: 1,695 applicants (2,864 female, 1,231 male). 68% of applicants admitted. 25% of applicants admitted and enrolled.

99% of applicants submitted SAT score. *25th percentile*: SAT Critical Reading 480, SAT Math 490. *75th percentile*: SAT Critical Reading 560, SAT Math 590.

52% of entering freshmen expected to graduate within 5 years. 53% of freshmen from Pennsylvania. Freshmen from 28 states and 16 foreign countries.

Admission: Rolling admissions plan. For fall acceptance, apply as early Aug. 1 of previous year, but not later than June 1 of year of enrollment. Early acceptance available. *Requirements:* Graduation from accredited secondary school with 4 units English, 3 college preparatory mathematics (4 years for science and engineering majors), 2 history and social studies, 2 laboratory science; or GED; or state equivalency examination. 7 additional units recommended. *Entrance tests:* College Board SAT or ACT composite. *For transfer students:* 2.5 minimum GPA; 60 hours maximum transfer credit.

College credit for postsecondary-level work completed in secondary school. College credit for extrainstitutional learning on basis of faculty assessment.

Tutoring available. Noncredit developmental courses offered in summer session and regular academic year.

Degree Requirements: *For all associate degrees:* 60 credit hours; 2 terms in residence. *For all baccalaureate degrees:* 120 credit hours; 4 terms in residence; 2 physical education courses. *For all undergraduate degrees:* 2.0 GPA.

Fulfillment of some degree requirements possible by passing College Board CLEP. *Grading system:* A–F; pass-fail, withdraw (carries time limit).

Distinctive Educational Programs: *For undergraduates:* Co-op programs. Weekend classes. Study abroad. *Available to all students:* Evening classes. Facilities and programs for independent research.

Degrees Conferred: 11 *associate;* 561 *baccalaureate*; 224 *master's*. Bachelor's degrees awarded: architecture 89; biological and life sciences 11; business 183, communication, journalism, and related programs 14, computer and information sciences 25l education 20; engineering 10; health professions and related clinical sciences 26, interdisciplinary studies 1; physical sciences 3; psychology 14; visual and performing arts 116. Master's degrees awarded: various disciplines 224.

Fees and Other Expenses: *Full-time tuition per academic year 2008–09:* $26,800; contact the university for current graduate tuition and other applicable fees. *Required fees:* $70. *Books and supplies:* $1,600. *Room and board per academic year:* $8,914. *Other expenses:* $3,040.

Financial Aid: Aid from institutionally generated funds is provided on the basis of academic merit, financial need, athletic ability.

Financial aid to full-time, first-time undergraduate students: 99% received some form of financial aid. Average amount of aid received: federal grants $4,318; Pell grants $2,888; other federal aid $1,430 state/local grants $3,650; institutional grants $10,298.

Departments and Teaching Staff: *Total instructional faculty:* 428 (full-time 104, part-time 524). Total faculty with doctorate, first-professional, or other terminal degree: 76. Student/faculty ratio: 12:1. Degrees held by full-time faculty: doctorate 85%.

Enrollment: Total enrollment 3,360. Undergraduate 2,782. Gradaute 578 (full-time 48%). Undergraduate transfer-in students 98.

Characteristics of Student Body: *Ethnic/racial makeup:* Black non-Hispanic: 10%; Asian or Pacific Islander: 3%; Hispanic: 3%; White non-Hispanic: 73%; unknown: 8%; nonresident alien 25. *Age distribution:* number under 18: 55; 18–19: 1,090; 20–21: 855; 22–24: 287; 25–29: 56; 30–34: 8; 35–39: 7; 40–49: 3; 50–64: 2; 65 and over: 1.

International Students: 78 nonresident aliens enrolled fall 2008. Programs available to aid students whose native language is not English: social, cultural. English as a Second Language Financial aid specifically designated for undergraduate students: variable number of scholarships available annually.

Student Life: On-campus residence halls house 54% of student body. *Intercollegiate athletics:* male: baseball, basketball, golf, soccer, tennis; female: basketball, lacrosse, softball, soccer, field hockey, tennis. *Special regulations:* Registered cars permitted in designated areas. *Special services:* Learning Resources Center, medical services, van transportation between main campus and residence areas. *Student publications, radio: The Text*, a bimonthly newspaper. Radio station WTEX broadcasts 70 hours per week. *Surrounding community:* Philadelphia metropolitan area. Served by mass transit and rail systems; airport 10 miles from campus; passenger rail service .5 mile from campus.

Library Collections: 110,000 volumes. 125,000 microforms; 51,000 audiovisual materials; 1,000 current periodical subscriptions. Computer work stations avaialble. Students have access to online information retrieval services and the Internet.

Most important special holdings: Textile Industry Historical Collection (5,000 volumes); Itodes Dyestuff Collection; Textile Trade and Ephemera Collection.

Buildings and Grounds: Campus area 100 acres.

Chief Executive Officer: Dr. James P. Gallagher, President.

Address admission inquiries to Christine Greb, Director of Admissions; graduate inquiries to William Firman, Director of Graduate Admissions.

Pittsburgh Theological Seminary

616 North Highland Avenue
Pittsburgh, Pennsylvania 15206
Tel: (412) 362-5610 **E-mail:** admissions@pts.edu
Fax: (412) 363-3260 **Internet:** www.pts.edu

Institution Description: Pittsburgh Theological Seminary is a private institution affiliated with the Presbyterian Church (U.S.A.). *Enrollment:* 318. *Degrees awarded:* First-professional (master of divinity), master's (master of arts and master of sacred theology), doctorate (doctor of ministry).

Accreditation: *Regional:* MSA/CHE. *National*: ATS. *Professional*: theology

History: Established as service seminary 1794; changed name to Xenia Theological Seminary 1858; merged with Pittsburgh Seminary (established 1825), changed name to Pittsburgh-Xenia Seminary, and affiliated with Newburgh Seminary (established 1805) 1930; merged with Western Theological Seminary (established 1825) 1958; incorporated as Pittsburgh Theological Seminary 1959.

Institutional Structure: *Governing board:* Board of Directors. Representation: 32 directors. *Composition of institution:* Administrators 17. Academic affairs headed by dean of the faculty. Management/business/finances directed by business manager. Full-time instructional faculty 22.

Calendar: Quarters. Academic year Sept. to May. Formal commencement May. No summer session.

Admission: For fall acceptance, apply as early as one year prior to but not later than June 30 of year of enrollment. Application for second or third term should be made at least six weeks before the beginning of the term desired. *Requirements:* Baccalaureate from accredited college or university.

Degree Requirements: *For first-professional degree:* 111 credit hours. *For master of arts degree:* 72 credit hours; thesis. *for master of sacred theology degree:* 36 credit hours; thesis. *For all degrees:* 2.0 GPA; 1 year in residency. *Grading system:* A–F; withdraw (with faculty approval).

Distinctive Educational Programs: Work-experience programs. Cooperative M.Div.-master's program in social work with University of Pittsburgh and the J.D. with Duquesne University. Facilities and programs for independent research, including majors, tutorials. Continuing education program. Metro-Urban Institute. Center for Business, Religion, and Public Life.

Degrees Conferred: 12 *master's:* theology; 21 *doctorate:* theology; 39 *first-professional:* master of divinity.

Fees and Other Expenses: *Full-time tuition per academic year 2008–09:* contact the seminary for current information.

Financial Aid: Aid from institutionally generated funds is provided on the basis of financial need.

Departments and Teaching Staff: *Total instructional faculty:* 22. Student/faculty ratio: 16:1. Degrees held by full-time faculty: doctorate 100%. 100% hold terminal degrees.

Enrollment: Total enrollment 318. First-professional 318.

International Students: 12 nonresident aliens enrolled fall 2008. Students from Europe, Asia, Latin America, Africa. Financial aid specifically designated for international students.

Student Life: On-campus residence halls and other institutionally controlled living space available for single and married students. *Surrounding community:* Pittsburgh population 369,900. Served by mass transit bus system; airport 20 miles from campus; passenger rail service 5 miles from campus.

Library Collections: 382,000 volumes including bound books, serial backfiles, electronic documents, and government documents not in separate collections. Online catalog. Current serial subscriptions: 896 paper; 82,842 microform units. 9,883 audiovisual materials. Computer work stations available. Students have access to the Internet at no charge.

Most important special collections include John M. Mason Memorial Collection (classical theological works); James Warrington Collection of Hymnology (several thousand hymn and song books); Anderson Room (rare book collection); Pittsburgh Theological Seminary Archives and related historical collection.

Buildings and Grounds: Campus area 13 acres.

Chief Executive Officer: Dr. William J. Carl, III, President.

Address admission inquiries to Sherry Sparks, Director of Admissions.

Point Park University

201 Wood Street
Pittsburgh, Pennsylvania 15222
Tel: (412) 391-4100 **E-mail:** enroll@ppc.edu
Fax: (412) 391-1980 **Internet:** www.ppc.edu

Institution Description: Point Park University is a private, independent, nonprofit institution. *Enrollment:* 3,784. *Degrees awarded:* Associate, baccalaureate, master's.

Member of the consortia Pittsburgh Council on Higher Education (PCHE), Pennsylvania Association of Colleges and Universities, Commission for Independent Colleges and Universities.

Accreditation: *Regional:* MSA/CHE. *Professional*: business, dance, engineering technology

History: Established and chartered as Point Park Junior College and offered first instruction at postsecondary level 1960; awarded first degree (associate) 1961; became Point Park College 1966; adopted present name 2003.

Institutional Structure: *Governing board:* Board of Trustees of Point Park University. Extrainstitutional representation: 34 trustees (including 5 alumni), 12 honorary trustees; institutional representation: president of the university, president of faculty assembly, president of the Alumni Association. 34 voting. *Composition of institution:* Administrators 104. Academic affairs headed by vice president and academic dean. Management/business/finances directed by treasurer. Full-time instructional faculty 100. Academic governance body, Faculty Assembly, meets monthly during academic year.

Calendar: Semesters. Academic year Aug. to May. Freshmen admitted Jan., May, June, Aug. Degrees conferred and formal commencement Apr. Summer session of 3 terms from May to Aug.

Characteristics of Freshmen: 2,936 applicants. (2,055 female, 881 male). 78% of applicants accepted. 37% of accepted applicants enrolled full-time.

Mean SAT class scores: Critical Reading 515; Math 491; Writing 509; Mean ACT Composite 22.

45% of entering freshmen expected to graduate within 5 years. 83% of freshmen from Pennsylvania. Freshmen from 32 states and 36 foreign countries.

Admission: Rolling admissions plan. For fall acceptance, apply as early as 1 year prior to entrance, but not later than 1 month prior to entrance. Early acceptance available. *Recommendations:* 4 English, 4 math, 4 science, 2 foreign language, 4 social studies, 4 history, e electives. *Entrance tests:* College Board SAT or ACT composite. *For transfer students:* 2.0 minimum GPA; maximum transfer credit limited only by residence requirement.

College credit for postsecondary-level work completed in secondary school. For extrainstitutional learning, college credit on basis of portfolio and faculty assessments; personal interview.

Tutoring available. Noncredit developmental courses offered in summer session and regular academic year.

Degree Requirements: *For all associate degrees:* 60–77 credits; 21 credits in residence. *For all baccalaureate degrees:* 120–135 credits; 30 credits in residence. *For all degrees:* 2.0 QPA.

Fulfillment of some degree requirements and exemption from some beginning courses possible by passing College Board CLEP, APP, or departmental examinations. *Grading system:* A–F; pass-fail; withdraw (carries time limit); incomplete.

Distinctive Educational Programs: More than 50 majors and concentrations are available in the baccalaureate level. Preprofessional preparation in law, medicine, dentistry, and other health-related professions. Several associate degree programs are offered, as well as an honors program and opportunities to study abroad. The college offers capstone programs in applied arts, criminal justice, funeral service, general studies, health services, human resources management, international studies, legal studies, management services and systems process control engineering technology. Other Capstone programs in hotel/restaurant management; fashion merchandising; planning; management for service industries. Special facilities for using telecommunications in the classroom. Honors programs, individualized majors. Cross-registration through Pittsburgh Council on Higher Education (PCHE). Internships and practica are also available.

ROTC: Air Force in cooperation with University of Pittsburgh; Army with Duquesne University.

Degrees Conferred: 4 *associate*; 610 *baccalaureate*; 216 *master's*. Bachelor's degrees awarded in top five disciplines: business, management, marketing, and related support services 130; visual and performing arts 119; security and protective services 77; education 61; communication/journalism 60.

Fees and Other Expenses: *Full-time tuition per academic year 2008–09:* undergraduate $20,570. *Books and supplies:* $1,000. *Room and board per academic year:* $8,940. *Other expenses:* $4,590.

Financial Aid: Aid from institutionally generated funds is provided on the basis of academic merit, financial need, athletic ability. Institution has a Program Participation Agreement with the U.S. Department of Education for eligible students to receive Pell Grants and, depending upon the agreement, other federal aid.

Financial aid to full-time, first-time undergraduate students: 98% received some form of aid. Average amount of aid received: federal grants $3,532; Pell grants $2,784; other federal aid $1,250; state/local grants $3,731; institutional grants $5,461.

Departments and Teaching Staff: *Total instructional faculty:* 431 (full-time 100, part-time 331). 54% of faculty hold the doctorate, first-professional, or other terminal degree. Student/faculty ratio: 14:1.

Enrollment: Total enrollment 3,784. Undergraduate 3,259 (full-time 71%; female 60%, male 40%). Graduate 525 (full-time 42%). Undergraduate transfer-in students 488.

Characteristics of Student Body: *Ethnic/racial makeup:* Black non-Hispanic: 20%; Asian or Pacific Islander: 1%; Hispanic: 2%; White non-Hispanic: 76%; unknown 1%; nonresident alien 1%. *Age distribution:* number under 18: 38; 18–19: 696; 20–21: 600; 22–24: 407; 25–29: 385; 30–34: 224; 35–39: 144; 40–49: 175; 50–64: 48.

International Students: 38 nonresident aliens enrolled fall 2008. Programs available to aid students whose native language is not English: social, cultural. English as a Second Language Program. Financial aid specifically designated for international students: variable number of scholarships available annually.

Student Life: On-campus residence halls available. 68% of first-time first-year freshmen live in on-campus residence halls; 22% of undergraduates live in on-campus residence halls. *Intercollegiate athletics:* male: baseball, basketball, cross-country, soccer; female: basketball, cross-country, softball, volleyball. *Special regulations:* Quiet hours from 8pm to 1pm Sun.–Thurs., 1am to 8am Fri. and Sat. Residence hall visitation from 4pm to 1am Mon.–Fri., 8am to midnight Sat. and Sun. Overnight guests allowed Fri. and Sat. with fee. *Special services:* medical services, college vehicle service. *Student publications, radio, television: The Globe*, a weekly newspaper; *The Pioneer*, a laboratory monthly newspaper; *The Parktonian,* a yearbook. Radio station WPPJ broadcasts 90 hours per week. TV station WPPC includes an in-house cable system. *Surrounding community:* Pittsburgh population 375,000. Served by mass transit bus systems; airport 17 miles from campus; passenger rail service ½ mile from campus.

Library Collections: 125,000 volumes. 29,590 microforms; 2,278 audiovisual materials; 274 current periodical subscriptions. Computer work stations available. Online catalog. Students have access to online information retrieval services and the Internet.

POINT PARK UNIVERSITY—*cont'd*

Most important special collections include Journalism and Communications; International Business Management; play/script collection.

Buildings and Grounds: The Point Park College campus includes 2 city blocks in downtown Pittsburgh and Point Park College Playhouse in Oakland. Campus DVD available.

Chief Executive Officer: Dr. Paul Henningan, President.

Address admission inquiries to Joell Minford, Director of Admissions; graduate inquiries to Kathy Ballias, Director, Adult and Professional Studies.

Robert Morris University

6001 University Boulevard
Moon Township, Pennsylvania 15108-1189
Tel: (412) 262-8200 **E-mail:** admissions@rmu.edu
Fax: (412) 262-8619 **Internet:** www.rmu.edu

Institution Description: Robert Morris University is a private, independent, nonprofit institution. *Enrollment:* 4,815. *Degrees awarded:* Associate, baccalaureate, master's, doctorate. Certificates also awarded.

Member of Pittsburgh Council on Higher Education.

Accreditation: *Regional:* MSA/CHE. *Professional*: accounting, business

History: Established as Pittsburgh School of Accountancy and offered first instruction at postsecondary level 1921; changed name to Robert Morris School 1935; chartered as Robert Morris Junior College 1962; awarded first degree (associate) 1964; became Robert Morris College 1969; added graduate program 1972; achieved university status 2001.

Institutional Structure: *Governing board:* The Trustees of Robert Morris University. Extrainstitutional representation: 31 trustees, including 6 alumni. All voting. *Composition of institution:* Administrators 32. Academic affairs headed by vice president for academic affairs. Management/business/finances directed by directed by vice president for financial affairs. Full-time instructional faculty 166. Academic governance body, The Dean's Council, meets an average of 26 times per year. *Faculty representation:* Faculty served by collective bargaining agent, AFT Local 3412.

Calendar: Semesters. Academic year Aug. to May. Freshmen admitted Sept., Jan., May. Degrees conferred May, Aug., Dec. Formal commencement May. Summer session of 3 terms from May to Aug.

Characteristics of Freshmen: 3,611 applicants (1,797 female, 1,814 male). 75% of applicants accepted. 24% of accepted applicants enrolled full-time.

91% (595 students) submitted SAT scores; 8% (50 students) submitted ACT scores. *25th percentile*: SAT Critical Reading 430, SAT Math 440; ACT Composite 18, ACT English 16, ACT Math 17. *75th percentile*: SAT Critical Reading 530, SAT Math 560; ACT Composite 22, ACT English 21, ACT Math 22.

56% of entering freshmen expected to graduate within 5 years. 87% of freshmen from Pennsylvania. Freshmen from 37 states and 15 foreign countries.

Admission: Rolling admissions plan. For fall acceptance, apply as early as 1 year prior to enrollment, but not later than Aug. 1 of year of enrollment. Early acceptance available. *Requirements:* Either graduation from accredited secondary school with 16 academic units; or GED. Minimum GPA 2.0. *Entrance tests:* College Board SAT or ACT composite recommended. For foreign students TOEFL. *For transfer students:* 2.0 minimum GPA; from 4-year accredited institution 90 hours maximum transfer credit; from 2-year accredited institution 69 hours; correspondence/extension students evaluated individually.

College credit and advanced placement for postsecondary-level work completed in secondary school and for College Board CLEP.

Tutoring available. Developmental courses offered in summer session and regular academic year; credit given.

Degree Requirements: *For all baccalaureate degrees:* 126 credit hours (varies with program). *For all undergraduate degrees:* 2.0 GPA; 30 credits in residence.

Fulfillment of some degree requirements and exemption from some beginning courses possible by passing departmental examinations, College Board CLEP, AP, other standardized tests. *Grading system:* A–F; pass-fail; pass; withdraw (deadline after which pass-fail is appended to withdraw); incomplete (carries time limit).

Distinctive Educational Programs: Evening classes. Honors courses. Cooperative education. Cross-registration through the consortia.

ROTC: Air Force in cooperation with University of Pittsburgh.

Degrees Conferred: 70 *associate;* 835 *baccalaureate*; 403 *master's*; 15 *doctorate*. Bachelor's degrees awarded in top five disciplines: business/marketing 451; communications/journalism 64; computer and information sciences 45; parks and recreation 33; education 29. Master's degrees awarded in top five disciplines: business/markeitng 140; education 71; computer and information sciences 41; engineering 22; interdisciplinary studies 17. Doctorates awarded: computer and information sciences 9, education 6.

Fees and Other Expenses: *Full-time tuition per academic year 2008–09:* $19,740 undergraduate; contact the university for current graduate tuition and other applicable fees. *Required fees:* $200. *Room and board per academic year:* $9,880. *Books and supplies:* $1,209. *Other expenses:* $2,600.

Financial Aid: Aid from institutionally generated funds is provided on the basis of academic merit, financial need, other criteria.

Financial aid to full-time, first-time undergraduate students: 99% received some form of aid. Average amount of aid received: federal grants $3,394; Pell gants $2,912; other federal aid $710; state/local grants $3,929; institutional grants $6,776.

Departments and Teaching Staff: *Total instructional faculty:* 364 (full-time 166, part-time 198). Total faculty holding the doctorate, first-progessiona, or other terminal degree: 190. Student/faculty ratio: 16:1.

Enrollment: Total enrollment 4,815. Undergraduate 3,783 (full-time 85%; female 45%, male 55%). Graduate 1,059 (full-time 100%). Undergraduate transfer-in students 333.

Characteristics of Student Body: *Ethnic/racial makeup:* Black non-Hispanic: 8%; Asian or Pacific Islander: 1%; Hispanic: 1%; White non-Hispanic: 84%; unknown: 3%; nonresident alien 2%. *Age distribution:* number under 18: 91; 18–19: 1,129; 20–21: 1,174; 22–24: 631=29: 30–34: 364; 35–39: 142; 40–49: 196; 50–64: 43,

International Students: 96 undergraduate nonresident aliens enrolled fall 2008. Programs available to aid students whose native language is not English: International Student Counselor.

Student Life: On-campus residence halls house 29% of student body. *Intercollegiate athletics:* male: only: basketball, cross-country, ice hockey, lacrosse, track (indoor and outdoor), tennis, soccer, golf; female: basketball, field hockey, lacrosse, ice hockey, softball, soccer, volleyball, tennis, cross-country, track (indoor and outdoor); club sports: men's ice hockey, rugby. *Special regulations:* Cars permitted without restrictions. *Special services:* Academic Media Center, medical services. *Student publications, television: The Sentry*, a biweekly newspaper. RMC-TV channel 10 provides educational, informational, sports, and entertainment programs to the campus and cable subscribers in the Moon Township area. *Surrounding community:* Coraopolis and Moon Township population 26,500. Pittsburgh, 17 miles from campus, is nearest metropolitan area. Limited service by Pittsburgh mass transit bus system; airport 2 miles from campus; passenger rail service and bus service 17 miles from campus.

Library Collections: 136,000 volumes. 199,865 government documents; 322,000 microforms; 23,903 audiovisual materials; 912 current periodical subscriptions. Computer work stations available. Students have access to online information retrieval services and the Internet.

Most important special collections include Business Collection (emphasis on management, marketing, taxation); Curriculum Library Collection for training of elementary and secondary school business teachers.

Buildings and Grounds: Campus area 230 acres. Campus DVD available.

Chief Executive Officer: Dr. Gregory S. Dellomo, President.

Address admission inquiries to Kellie Laurenzi, Dean of Admissions. graduate inquires to Barry Bilitski, Assistant Dean of Graduate Enrollment.

Rosemont College

1400 Montgomery Avenue
Rosemont, Pennsylvania 19010-1699
Tel: (610) 527-0200 **E-mail:** admissions@rosemont.edu
Fax: (610) 527-0341 **Internet:** www.rosemont.edu

Institution Description: Rosemont College is a private, independent, liberal arts college in the Catholic tradition. *Enrollment:* 995. *Degrees awarded:* Baccalaureate, master's.

Accreditation: *Regional:* MSA/CHE.

History: Established 1921; chartered and offered first instruction at postsecondary level 1922; awarded first degree (baccalaureate) 1925.

Institutional Structure: *Governing board:* Rosemont College Board of Trustees. Extrainstitutional representation: 21 trustees; institutional representation: president of the college. *Composition of institution:* Administrators 33. Academic affairs headed by academic dean. Management/business/finances directed by business manager. Full-time instructional faculty 31. Academic governance body, General Faculty, meets an average of 8 times per year.

Calendar: Semesters. Academic year Sept. to May. Freshmen admitted Sept. Degrees conferred and formal commencement May. Summer session.

Characteristics of Freshmen: 450 applicants (450 fenale). 58% of applicants accepted. 27% of accepted applicants enrolled full-time.

100% of students submitted SAT scores. *25th percentile*: SAT Critical Reading 470, SAT Math 450, SAT Writing 440. *75th percentile*: SAT Critical Reading 580, SAT Math 550; SAT Writing 580.

72% of entering freshmen expected to graduate within 5 years. 14% of freshmen from Pennsylvania. Freshmen from 18 states and 12 foreign countries.

Admission: Rolling admissions plan. *Requirements:* Either graduation from accredited secondary school with 16 academic units which must include 4 English, 2 in a foreign language, 2 college preparatory mathematics, 2 history, 1 laboratory science; or GED. *Entrance tests:* College Board SAT. 3 Achievements recommended. For foreign students TOEFL. *For transfer students:* 2.0 minimum GPA; 19 units maximum transfer credit.

College credit and advanced placement for postsecondary-level work completed in secondary school. College credit for extrainstitutional learning (life experience) on basis of faculty assessment.

Noncredit developmental courses offered during regular academic year.

Degree Requirements: 120 credits; 2.0 GPA; 4 semesters in residence; 2 semesters physical education courses; general education requirements; exit competency examinations; comprehensives in individual fields of study.

Fulfillment of some degree requirements and exemption from some beginning courses possible by passing College Board AP (score of 3). *Grading system:* A–F; pass-fail; withdraw (carries time limit).

Distinctive Educational Programs: Cooperative education. Evening classes. Accelerated degree programs. Interdisciplinary programs in American studies, humanities, Italian studies, social sciences. Facilities and programs for independent research, including individual majors, independent study. Study abroad in Italy in cooperation with Villanova University; study also available by individual arrangement. Cross-registration with Villanova University, Eastern and Cabrini Colleges. Early assurance program, Allegheny University of Health Sciences MCP, Hahneman School of Medicine.

Degrees Conferred: 131 *baccalaureate*; 152 *master's*. Bachelor's degrees awarded in top five disciplines: business, management, marketing, and related support services 132; social sciences 19; psychology 17; visual and performing arts 12; biological/life sciences 6. Master's degrees awarded: various disciplines 152.

Fees and Other Expenses: *Full-time tuition per academic year 2008–09:* $21,700. *Books and supplies:* $1,000. *Room and board per academic year:* $9,200.

Financial Aid: Aid from institutionally generated funds is provided on the basis of academic merit, financial need.

Financial aid to full-time, first-time undergraduate students: 100% received some form of financial aid. Average amount of aid received: federal grants $4,053; state/local grants $3,555; institutional grants $13,742; loans $5,634.

Departments and Teaching Staff: *Total instructional faculty:* 162. Degrees held by full-time faculty: doctorate 75%, master's 23%, baccalaureate 2%. 80% hold hold terminal degrees.

Enrollment: Total enrollment 995.

Characteristics of Student Body: *Ethnic/racial makeup:* Black non-Hispanic: 33%; American Indian or Alaska Native: 7%; Asian or Pacific Islander: 5%; Hispanic: 7%; White non-Hispanic: 48%. unknown: 4%.

International Students: 12 nonresident aliens enrolled fall 2008. Students from Europe, Asia, Latin America, Africa. Programs available to aid students whose native language is not English: English as a Second Language Program. No financial aid specifically designated for international students.

Student Life: On-campus residence halls house 80% of student body. *Intercollegiate athletics:* baseball, field hockey, softball, tennis, volleyball. Member of NCAA Division III. *Special regulations:* Registered cars permitted in designated areas. Quiet hours. *Special services:* Learning Resources Center, Wellness Center, counseling services, career services, shuttle service between Rosemont, Cabrini, Eastern and Villanova University. *Student publications: Cornelian*, a yearbook; *Rambler*, a monthly newspaper; *Thorn*, a biannual literary portfolio. *Surrounding community:* Rosemont is located 11 miles west of Philadelphia. Served by mass transit bus, trolley, train systems; airport 20 miles from campus; passenger rail service 1 mile from campus.

Library Collections: 160,800 volumes. 25,000 microforms; 3,800 audiovisual materials; 565 current periodical subscriptions. Online catalog. Students have Access to online information retrieval services and the Internet.

Most important holdings include collection on early Pennsylvania history; Rosemont College Archives.

Buildings and Grounds: Campus area 56 acres. Campus DVD available.

Chief Executive Officer: Dr. Ann M. Amore, President.

Address admission inquiries to Rennie H. Andrews, Dean of Admissions.

Saint Charles Borromeo Seminary

100 East Wynnewood Road
Wynnewood, Pennsylvania 19096
Tel: (610) 617-3394 **E-mail:** admissions@scs.edu
Fax: (610) 617-9267 **Internet:** www.scs.sedu

Institution Description: Saint Charles Borromeo Seminary is owned and operated by the Roman Catholic Archdiocese of Philadelphia. Comprising one institution under a common administration, Saint Charles Seminary consists of 3 divisions: College, Theology, Religious Studies. Catholic men who are sincerely desirous of ordination to the Catholic priesthood are eligible for admission to the College and Theology Divisions. The student population in these 2 divisions consists of seminarians from 20 dioceses and 2 religious congregations. The Religious Studies Division serves priests, religious and laity who wish to take undergraduate or graduate courses in Theology, Scripture or related areas. Evening and summer courses are offered by this division. *Enrollment:* 243. *Degrees awarded:* Baccalaureate, master's, first-professional (master of divinity).

Accreditation: *Regional:* MSA. *National*: ATS. *Professional*: theology

History: Saint Charles Borromeo Seminary is located in Wynnewood, Pennsylvania, and is owned and operated by the Roman Catholic Archdiocese of Philadelphia. Saint Charles Seminary was founded in 1832 by the Most Reverend Francis P. Kenrick, third Bishop of Philadelphia. In 1838, under the legal designation of the Philadelphia Theological Seminary of Saint Charles Borromeo, it received from the legislature of the Commonwealth of Pennsylvania a charter of legal incorporation along with the power to grant and confirm degrees. A revised version of this charter was approved May 18, 1987. The Board of Trustees of Saint Charles Seminary currently consists of 17 members with the Archbishop of Philadelphia as President. *See* Rev. Msgr. James F. Connelly, *History of the Theological Seminary of Saint Charles* (Philadelphia: William J. Dornan, Inc., 1979) for further information.

Institutional Structure: *Governing board:* Board of Trustees. Extrainstitutional representation: 161 trustees; institutional representation: 1 administrator (Rector-President). *Composition of institution:* Administrators 20. Academic affairs headed by divisional academic deans (College, Theology, Religious Studies). Business and finances directed by vice president of finance and operations. Full-time instructional faculty 21 men / 3 women. General Administration meets monthly. General faculty meets an average of 4 times per year. Division faculties meet an average of 4 times per year.

Calendar: Semesters. Academic year Sept. to May. Freshmen admitted Sept. Degrees conferred May. Formal commencement May.

Characteristics of Freshmen: 6 applicants (6 male). 100% of applicants accepted. 100% of accepted applicants enrolled. 67% of entering freshmen expected to graduate within 5 years. 76% of freshmen from Pennsylvania. Freshmen from 3 states.

Admission: Students seeking Fall admission to the College or Theology Divisions should apply as early as possible and not later than July 1. Undergraduates may transfer credits. Level of entry depends on academic background. The Academic Dean, College Division, determines which credits can be transferred to meet general education and/or elective requirements. College Board SAT or equivalent required. Level of entry for an applicant who holds a bachelor's degree or above is Pre-Theology (two year program) or First Theology (if person has required background in philosophy and theology). Persons wishing to enroll in the Religious Studies Division may apply prior to the Fall, Spring, or Summer sessions. Division offices will provide additional information upon request.

College credit and advanced placement for postsecondary-level work completed in secondary school.

Degree Requirements: *For all undergraduate degrees:* 125 credit hours; 2.00 GPA; humanities, philosophy, theology requirements. Residency requirement. *Grading system:* A–F; pass/fail. *Master of divinity and master of arts programs in the Theology Division:* specific core and elective requirements during 4 years of full-time study. Field education, internship, residency requirements. *Master of arts programs in the Religious Studies Division:* 30 credit hours; 3.00 GPA; core and area of concentration requirements; comprehensive examinations.

Distinctive Educational Programs: *Religious Studies Division:* Graduate program of Catholic theology for part-time students leading to master of arts degree; certificate and diploma programs in Catholic theology for part-time undergraduate and graduate students.

Degrees Conferred: 10 *baccalaureate:* philosophy/religious studies 28; *master's:* theology; 16 *first-professional:* master of divinity. 1 *honorary degree awarded:* Doctor of Humane Letters.

Fees and Other Expenses: *Full-time tuition per academic year 2008–09:* contact the seminary for current information regarding tuition, fees, housing, and other applicable costs.

SAINT CHARLES BORROMEO SEMINARY—*cont'd*

Financial Aid: Aid from institutionally generated funds is provided on the basis of financial need, other criteria.

Departments and Teaching Staff: *Total instructional faculty:* 27 (full-time 20, part-time 7). 81% of faculty hold the doctorate, first-professional, or other terminal degree. Student/faculty ratio: 7:1.

Enrollment: Total enrollment 243. Undergraduate 125 (full-time 83%; female 23%, male 77%). Gradaute 118 (full-time 58%). Undergraduate transfer-in students 11.

Characteristics of Student Body: *Ethnic/racial makeup:* Black non-Hispanic: 12%; Asian or Pacific Islander: 1%; Hispanic: 1%; White non-Hispanic: 82%;' unknown: 1%; nonresident alien 3%. *Age distribution:* number under 18: 1; 18–19: 16; 20–21: 26; 22–24: 43; 25–29: 7; 30–34: 20; 35–39: 28; 40–49: 45; 50–64: 52; 65 and over: 8.

International Students: 7 nonresident aliens enrolled fall 2008. Students from Latin America, Africa. Programs available to aid students whose native language is not English: English as a Second Language Program. No financial aid specifically designated for international students.

Student Life: On-campus residence halls house 98% of full-time student body. Athletic facilities include indoor swimming pool, outdoor tennis courts, exercise and weight room. *Special services:* Medical services. *See* Student Handbook for student regulations. *Student publications: Gaudeamus,* a yearbook; *The Brook,* alumni newsletter. *Surrounding community:* Saint Charles Seminary is located in Montgomery County on the borderline of Philadelphia. Served by mass transit bus and train system; passenger rail service less than 1 mile from campus; airport 10 miles from campus.

Library Collections: 131,000 volumes including bound books, serial backfiles, electronic documents, and government documents not in separate collections. Card catalog. Current serial subscriptions: 565 paper, 443 microform, 3 electronic. Computer work stations available. Students have access to the Internet at no charge.

Most important holdings include The Ryan Memorial Library Rare Books Collection (15,000 volumes from the late 15th to the 20th century, with emphasis on theology, philosophy, and history); Fine Arts Collection (17th–20th century European and American paintings).

Buildings and Grounds: Campus area 77 acres.

Chief Executive Officer: Rev. Joseph G. Prior, Rector-President.

Address admission inquiries to Rev. Msgr. Michael J. Fitzgerald, Vice Rector.

Saint Francis University

P.O. Box 600
Loretto, Pennsylvania 15940
Tel: (814) 472-3000 **E-mail:** admissions@sfcpa.edu
Fax: (814) 472-3003 **Internet:** www.sfcpa.edu

Institution Description: Saint Francis University is a private institution affiliated with the Third Order Regular of Saint Francis, Roman Catholic Church. *Enrollment:* 2,210. *Degrees awarded:* Associate, baccalaureate, master's.

Accreditation: *Regional:* MSA/CHE. *Professional*: nursing, occupational therapy, physician assisting, physical therapy, social work, teacher education

History: Established as Saint Francis Academy 1847; chartered 1858; offered first instruction at postsecondary level 1911; awarded first degree (baccalaureate) 1914; became Saint Francis College 1910; rechartered 1920; achieved university status 2001. *See: The New Catholic Encyclopedia* (Washington, D.C.: Catholic University of America, 1965), S.V. "Saint Francis College (Loretto, Pa.)" for further information.

Institutional Structure: *Governing board:* Board of Trustees. Extrainstitutional representation: 33 trustees (including 6 religious and Minister Provincial of Third Order Regular of St. Francis); institutional representation: 1 administrator. 24 voting. *Composition of institution:* Administrators 152. Academic affairs headed by vice president for academic affairs. Management/business/finances directed by vice president for finance. Full-time instructional faculty 97. Academic governance body, Faculty Senate, meets an average of 18 times per year.

Calendar: Semesters. Academic year Aug. to May. Freshmen admitted Aug., Jan., May. Degrees conferred May, Aug., Dec. Formal commencement May. Summer session of 2 terms from May to July.

Characteristics of Freshmen: 1,533 applicans (888 female, 645 male). 75% of applicants admitted. 36% of applicants admitted and enrolled full-time.

83% (323 students) submitted SAT scores; 17% (65 students) submitted ACT scores. *25th percentile*: SAT Critical Reading 450, SAT Math 70; ACT Composite 20. *75th percentile*: SAT Critical Reading 560, SAT Math 580; ACT Composite 22.

60% of entering freshmen expected to graduate within 5 years. 69% of freshmen from Pennsylvania. Freshmen from 16 states and 4 foreign countries.

Admission: Rolling admissions plan. For fall acceptance, apply as early as Sept. 1 of senior year. Students are notified of acceptance beginning Oct. 1. *Requirements:* Either graduation from accredited secondary school with 4 units English, 2 mathematics, 2 social studies, 1 science, 7 academic electives; or GED. Additional units required for some programs. *Entrance tests:* College Board SAT or ACT composite. *For transfer students:* 2.0 minimum QPA for all majors except nursing (2.5) and physician assistant (2.75). All transfer students must complete a minimum of 64 credits in residence for a bachelor's degree.

College credit for advanced placement testing and CLEP. 32 credits maximum (CLEP and AP) applied to bachelor's degree. College credit given for postsecondary-level work completed in high school.

Tutoring; Learning Resource Center; extensive career planning and placement services.

Degree Requirements: *For all associate degrees:* credit hours vary by program. *For all baccalaureate degrees:* 128 credit hours. *For all undergraduate degrees:* 2.0 GPA (2.0 in major field); last 30 hours in residence; distribution requirements.

Fulfillment of some degree requirements and exemption from some beginning courses possible by passing College Board CLEP, AP. *Grading system:* A–F; pass-fail; withdraw (carries time limit).

Distinctive Educational Programs: *For undergraduates:* Internships. Flexible meeting places and schedules including off-campus centers. Dual-degree program in engineering with Clarkson University, Pennsylvania State University (University Park), and University of Pittsburgh; in forestry and environmental management with Duke University. Interdisciplinary programs in American studies, international business/modern language. Independent study and tutorials. Study abroad by individual arrangement; French language and culture in Quebec, Spanish language and culture in Mexico. Honors program. Learning Resource Center. Institute for Contemporary Franciscan Life. Center for International Education and Outreach. One-year developmental program for nonmatriculated freshmen. *For graduate students:* Off-campus centers (at Pittsburgh, 80 miles away from main institution; Harrisburg, 140 miles away). *Available to all students:* Evening classes. *Other distinctive programs:* Degree-granting, credit and noncredit continuing education. Associate member of Marine Science Consortium.

Degrees Conferred: 4 *associate*; 328 *baccalaureate*; 226 *master's*; 16 *doctorate*. Bachelor's degrees awarded in top five disciplines: business, management, marketing, and related support services 82; health professions and related clinical sciences 49; education 30; psychology 17; social sciences 9. Master's degrees awarded: business/marketing 52; education 59; health professions 99. Doctorates awarded: health professions and related clinical sciences 17.

Fees and Other Expenses: *Full-time tuition per academic year 2008–09:* $24,840 undergraduate; graduate tuition varies by program. *Room per and board academic year:* $8,422. *Required fees:* $1,050. *Books and supplies:* $1,500. *Other expenses:* $1,500.

Financial Aid: Aid from institutionally generated funds is provided on the basis of academic merit, financial need, athletic ability, other criteria.

Financial aid to full-time, first-time undergraduate students: 96% received some form of aid. Average amount of aid received: federal grants $3,206; Pell grants $2,661; other federal aid $1,048; state/local grants $3,582; institutional grants $12,147.

Departments and Teaching Staff: *Total instructional faculty:* 187 (full-time 97, part-time 90). Total faculty with doctorate, first-professional, or other terminal degree: 87. Student/faculty ratio: 16:1.

Enrollment: Total enrollment 2,210. Undergraduate 1,612 (full-time 92%; female 60%, male 40%). Graduate 598 (full-time 29%). Undergraduate treansfer-in students 53.

Characteristics of Student Body: *Ethnic/racial makeup:* Black non-Hispanic: 5%; Asian or Pacific Islander: 1%; Hispanic: 1%; White non-Hispanic: 86%; unknown: 7%. *Age distribution:* number under 18: 6; 18–19: 553; 20–21: 420; 22–24: 130; 25–29: 34; 30–34: 19; 35–39: 24; 40–49: 27; 50–64: 6; unknown: 113.

International Students: 28 nonresident aliens enrolled fall 2008. Student from Latin America, Africa, Canada. No programs available to aid students whose native language is not English. Financial aid specifically designated for international students: variable number of scholarships awarded.

Student Life: On-campus residence halls house 73% of student body. Residence halls for males constitute 46% of such space, for females 54%. *Intercollegiate athletics:* male: basketball, cross-country, football, golf, indoor and outdoor track, soccer, tennis, volleyball; female: basketball, cross-country, golf, indoor and outdoor track, soccer, softball, tennis, volleyball. *Special regulations:* Residence hall visitation from 10am to midnight Sun.–Thurs. and noon to 2am Fri.–Sat. *Special services:* Medical services, student union vans for transportation to and from off-campus activities. *Student publications: The Bell Tower*, a yearbook; *The Troubadour*, a weekly newspaper; *The Pine Cone*, an annual literary magazine. *Surrounding community:* Loretto population 1,500. Pittsburgh, 80 miles from campus, is nearest metropolitan area. Served by airport and passenger rail service, each 27 miles from campus.

Library Collections: 137,000 volumes including bound books, serial backfiles, electronic documents, and government documents not in separate collections. Online catalog. Current serial subscriptions: 168 paper, 813 microform, 9,233 via electronic access. 218 recordings; 415 CD-ROMs. Computer work stations available. Students have access to the Internet at no charge.

Most important special holdings include Captain Paul Boyton Collection; Saint Francis Collection; Franciscan Archives.

Buildings and Grounds: Campus area 600 acres.

Chief Executive Officer: Rev. Gabriel Zeis, T.O.R., President.

Address admission inquiries to Evan Lipp, Dean of Enrollment Management. graduate inquiries to Jeffrey Scarangella, Coordinator of Graduate/Professional Studies.

Saint Joseph's University

5600 City Avenue
Philadelphia, Pennsylvania 19131
Tel: (610) 660-1000 **E-mail:** admit@sju.edu
Fax: (610) 660-'1246 **Internet:** www.sju.edu

Institution Description: Saint Joseph's University (Saint Joseph's College until 1978) is a private institution conducted by the Society of Jesus, Roman Catholic Church. *Enrollment:* 7,900. *Degrees awarded:* Baccalaureate, master's. Certificates are also awarded. Associate awards through University College.

Accreditation: *Regional:* MSA/CHE. *Professional*: chemistry, teacher education

History: Established under former official name, The Saint Joseph's College in the City of Philadelphia, and offered first instruction at postsecondary level 1851; chartered 1852; awarded first degree (baccalaureate) 1858; adopted present name 1978. *See* David H. Burton and Frank Gerrity, *Saint Joseph's College: A Family Portrait 1851–1976* (Philadelphia: Saint Joseph's College, 1977) for further information.

Institutional Structure: *Governing board:* Board of Trustees. Extrainstitutional representation: 35 members, 34 extrainstitutional, 1 institutional (President of the University, Ex Officio). *Composition of institution:* Administrators 136. Academic affairs headed by provost. Management/business/finances directed by vice president for financial affairs. Full-time instructional faculty 262. Academic governance body, University Council, meets an average of 12 times per year.

Calendar: Semesters. Academic year Aug. to May. Freshmen admitted Sept., Jan., May, July. Degrees conferred May, Sept., Jan. Formal commencement May.

Characteristics of Freshmen: 7,012 applicants (3.831 female, 3.181 male). 86% of applicants accepted. 25% of accepted applicants enrolled full-time.

100% (1,021 students) submitted SAT scores. *25th percentile*: SAT Critical Reading 520, SAT Math 540; ACT Composite 23. *75th percentile*: SAT Critical Reading 610, SAT math, 620; ACT Composite 27.

72% of entering students expected to graduate within 5 years. 51% of freshmen from Pennsylvania. Freshmen from 37 states and 36 foreign countries.

Admission: *Full-time undergraduate:* For fall acceptance, apply in senior year, but not later than March 1. Students are notified of acceptance during the third week of March. For Early Decision apply by Dec. 1 or Jan. 15; students accepted through this program must enroll. Early Acceptance available. *Requirements:* Graduation from accredited secondary school. Recommend 4 units of English, at least 2 units of foreign language, 3 units of mathematics, 2 units of history, 2 units of science. *Entrance tests:* SAT or ACT. For foreign students TOEFL. *For transfer students:* 2.5 minimum GPA. Transfer students must complete 4 regular semesters at the university.

College credit and advanced placement for postsecondary-level work completed in secondary school. Tutoring available.

Degree Requirements: 120 credit hours; 2.0 GPA; 4 terms, including the last 2, in residence; distribution requirements.

Fulfillment of some degree requirements and exemption from some beginning courses possible by passing College Board CLEP, AP. *Grading system:* A–F; pass-no penalty; withdraw (carries time limit); incomplete (carries time limit).

Distinctive Educational Programs: *For undergraduates:* Work-experience programs, including cooperative education, internships. Interdisciplinary programs in American studies, faith-justice studies, Latin American studies, medieval studies, and by individual arrangement. Facilities and programs for independent study, including honors programs, individual majors, tutorials, College Scholar program of self-directed study for seniors. Institutionally sponsored study abroad in England, France, Ireland, Japan, Mexico; study at locations through American Institute for Foreign Study or by individual arrangement. Off-campus study in the U.S. through exchange program with other Jesuit colleges and universities. Washington (DC) internship semester through Washington Center for Learning Alternatives. *Available to all students:* Evening classes. Independent study. *Other distinctive programs:* Academic support services for educationally and economically disadvantaged students.

ROTC: Air Force. Army and Navy in cooperation with area institutions.

Degrees Conferred: 11 *associates*; 1,103 *baccalaureate*; 799 *master's*; 4 *doctorate*.

Fees and Other Expenses: *Full-time tuition per academic year 2008–09:* $32,860. *Books and supplies:* $1,500. *Room and board per academic year:* $11,500. *Other expenses:* $2,500.

Financial Aid: Aid from institutionally generated funds is provided on the basis of academic merit, financial need, athletic ability. Institution has a Program Participation Agreement with the U.S. Department of Education for eligible students to receive Pell Grants and, depending upon the agreement, other federal aid.

Financial aid to full-time, first-time undergraduate students: 94% received some form of financial aid. Average amount of aid received: federal grants $5,179; Pell grants $3,031; other federal aid $2,317; state/local grants $3,583; institutional grants $13,106.

Departments and Teaching Staff: *Total instructional faculty:* 572 (full-time 262, part-time 310). Student/faculty ratio: 15:1. Degrees held by full-time faculty: doctorate 90%, professional 35%. 93% hold terminal degrees.

Enrollment: Total enrollment 7,900. Undergraduate 5,331 (full-time 85%; female 53%, male 47%). Graduate 3,569 (full-time 38%). Undergraduate transfer-in students 194.

Characteristics of Student Body: *Ethnic/racial makeup:* Black non-Hispanic: 8%; Asian or Pacific Islander: 3%; Hispanic: 3%; White non-Hispanic: 81%; unknown: 4%; nonresident alien 2%.

International Students: 158 nonresident undergraduate aliens enrolled fall 2008. Programs available to aid students whose native language is not English: social, cultural. English as a Second Language Program. No financial aid specifically designated for international students.

Student Life: On-campus residence halls, houses, apartments for 54% of student body. *Intercollegiate athletics:* NCAA Division I male: baseball, basketball, golf, soccer, tennis, crew, cross-country, track; female: basketball, field hockey, soccer, softball, tennis, crew, cross-country, *Special regulations:* Cars with decals permitted in designated areas. Quiet hours and visitation hours in residence halls vary by residence. *Special services:* Learning Resource Center, handicap students, multicultural office, van service links campus. *Student publications, radio: Crimson and Gray*, an annual literary magazine; *Greatonian*, a yearbook; *Hawk*, a weekly newspaper. Radio station WSJR broadcasts online. *Surrounding community:* Philadelphia population 1,600,000. Served by mass transit bus and rail systems; airport 12 miles from campus; passenger rail service within walking distance of campus.

Library Collections: 353,000 volumes. 860,000 microforms; 5,200 audiovisual materials; 10,600 periodicals including via electronic access. Online catalog. Computer work stations available. Students have access to online information retrieval services and the Internet.

Most important special holdings include Campbell Library (food marketing); Archives (Saint Joseph's University history; Jesuit history); U.S. Government Documents (selective depository).

Buildings and Grounds: Campus area 60 acres. Campus DVD available.

Chief Executive Officer: Timothy R. Lanron, S.J., President.

Undergraduates address admission inquiries to Office of Undergraduate admissions; graduate inquiries to Office of Graduate Admissions.

University College

Degree Programs Offered: *Associate* in arts and sciences; *baccalaureate* in biological sciences, business and management, education, letters, psychology, public affairs and services, social sciences theology. Certificates also given.

Admission: *See* general requirements. Required units for all students in degree programs 3 English, 2 college preparatory mathematics, 1 history, 1 laboratory science, 5 academic electives (2 in a foreign language preferred). For chemistry students, 1/2 unit trigonometry.

Degree Requirements: *See* general requirements. *For associate in arts and sciences:* 60 credit hours. *For baccalaureate:* 30 hours in residence.

Distinctive Educational Programs: Interdisciplinary programs in liberal arts, social science. Continuing education program.

Saint Vincent College and Seminary

300 Fraser Purchase Road
Latrobe, Pennsylvania 15650-2690
Tel: (724) 539-9761 **E-mail:** admission@stvincent.edu
Fax: (724) 532-5065 **Internet:** www.stvincent.edu

Institution Description: Saint Vincent College is a private, coeducational college conducted by the Benedictine Society of Westmoreland County, Roman Catholic Church. *Enrollment:* 2,021. *Degrees awarded:* Baccalaureate.

Accreditation: *Regional:* MSA/CHE.

History: Established 1846; offered first instruction at postsecondary level 1849; chartered 1870; awarded first degree (baccalaureate) 1871.

Institutional Structure: *Governing board:* Saint Vincent College Board of Directors. Extrainstitutional representation: 46 directors; institutional representation: 4 administrators. 33 voting. *Composition of institution:* Administrators 59. Academic affairs headed by vice president. Business/administration by vice president. Full-time instructional faculty 97. Academic governance body, the faculty, meets an average of 10 times per year.

Calendar: Semesters. Academic year Aug. to May. Freshmen admitted Aug., Jan., June. Degrees conferred May, Dec. Aug. Formal commencement May. Summer session of multiple terms from May to Aug.

Characteristics of Freshmen: 1,843 applicants (812 female, 1,031 male). 65% of applicants accepted. 37% of accepted applicants enrolled full-time.

98% (429 students) submitted SAT scores; 15% (65 students) submitted ACT scores. *25th percentile*: SAT Critical Reading 460, SAT math 480; ACT Composite 20, ACT English 18.5, ACT Math 18. *75th percentile*: SAT Critical Reading 580, SAT Math 580; ACT Composite 26, ACT English 25, ACT Math 24.

20% of freshmen expected to graduate within 5 years. 87% of freshmen from Pennsylvania. Freshmen from 24 states and 16 foreign countries.

Admission: Rolling admissions plan. For fall acceptance, apply as early as end of junior year, but not later than Aug. of year of enrollment. Early acceptance available. *Requirements:* Either graduation from accredited secondary school with 4 units English, 3 mathematics, 1 natural sciences, 3 social studies, and 5 electives; or GED. 2 additional units in science. 3.2 GPA for incoming freshmen. *Entrance tests:* College Board SAT. *For transfer students:* 2.0 minimum GPA; 90 hours maximum transfer credit; from 2-year accredited institution 62 hours.

College credit and advanced placement for postsecondary-level work completed in secondary school. College credit for extrainstitutional learning on basis of portfolio and faculty assessments.

Tutoring available. Developmental courses offered in summer session and regular academic year; credit given.

Degree Requirements: 124 hours; 2.0 GPA; last 24 credits in residence; comprehensives in some majors; general education requirements.

Fulfillment of some degree requirements possible by passing College Board AP or other specified examinations. *Grading system:* A–F; pass-fail; withdraw (carries time limit).

Distinctive Educational Programs: Work-experience programs. Evening classes. Dual-degree program in engineering with Boston University (MA), University of Pittsburgh (PA), Pennsylvania State University, Catholic University of America (DC). Cooperative programs in law, business administration, occupational therapy, physical therapy, physician assistant, and pharmacy with Duquesne University. Accelerated dual-degree program in podiatry with Pennsylvania College of Podiatric Medicine, Ohio College of Podiatric Medicine. Cooperative program with Seton Hill College in Greensburg where students may take courses at either campus. Facilities and programs for independent research, including honors programs and tutorials. Study abroad through Central College of Iowa in Austria, Australia, France, Germany, England, Holland, Wales, Spain, and Mexico. Asian Study Abroad Program in Taiwan at FuJen Catholic University.

ROTC: Air Force offered in cooperation with University of Pittsburgh.

Degrees Conferred: 302 *baccalaureate*. Bachelor's degrees awarded in top five disciplines: business/marketing 66; social sciences 59; psychology 37; mathematics 27; English 20. Master's degrees awarded: various disciplines 50.

Fees and Other Expenses: *Tuition per academic year 2008–09:* $25,735 undergraduate; contact the college/seminary for current graduate/first-professional tuition and applicable fees. *Room and board per academic year:* $8,280. *Books and supplies:* $1,050. *Other expenses:* $1,600.

Financial Aid: Aid from institutionally generated funds is provided on the basis of academic merit, financial need, athletic ability, other criteria. Institution has a Program Participation Agreement with the U.S. Department of Education for eligible students to receive Pell Grants and, depending upon the agreement, other federal aid.

Departments and Teaching Staff: *Total instructional faculty:* 187 (full-time 97, part-time 90). 79% of faculty hold the doctorate, first-professional, or other terminal degree. Student/faculty ratio: 13:1.

Enrollment: Total enrollment 2,021. Undergraduate 1,773 (full-time 94%; female 48%, male 52%). Graduate 248 (full-time 50%). Undergraduate transfer-in students 51.

Characteristics of Student Body: *Ethnic/racial makeup:* Black non-Hispanic: 4%; Asian or Pacific Islander: 1%; Hispanic: 2%; White non-Hispanic: 90%; unknown: 1%. *Age distribution:* number under 18: 15; 18–19: 612; 20–21: 510; 22–24: 166; 25–29: 36; 30–34: 16; 35–39: 17; 40–49: 23; 50–64: 5; 65 and over: 9.

International Students: 20 nonresident aliens enrolled fall 2008. Students from Europe, Asia, Latin America, Africa, Canada, Turkey.

No programs available to aid students whose native language is not English. Financial aid specifically designated for international students: variable number available; .

Student Life: On-campus residence halls house 76% of student body. All campus residence halls coeducational, 24-hour quiet residence hall available. *Intercollegiate athletics:* male: baseball, basketball, football, soccer, cross-country, golf, ice hockey (club), swimming, tennis, lacrosse; female: basketball, cross-country, equestrian (club), golf, lacrosse, soccer, softball, swimming, tennis, volleyball. *Special regulations:* Cars permitted with on-campus parking. Residence hall visitation from 10am to midnight Sun.–Thurs., 10am to 2am Fri. and Sat. *Special services:* Learning Resources Center, medical services. *Student publications, media: The Review,* a monthly campus newspaper. Radio station WSVC broadcasts 30 hours per week. WSVC-TV broadcasts on campus via cable 24 hours a week. *Surrounding community:* Latrobe population 11,000. Pittsburgh, 35 miles from campus, is nearest metropolitan area. Served by airport 1 mile from campus.

Library Collections: 279,000 volumes. 98,800 microforms; 5,500 audiovisual materials; 2,500 current periodical subscriptions. Online catalog. Computer work stations available. Students have access to online information retrieval services and the Internet.

Most important special holdings include Benedictiana Collection; Pennsylvania Collection; Liturgical Collection; first edition of *Canterbury Tales*.

Buildings and Grounds: Campus area 200 acres.

Chief Executive Officer: Dr H. James Towey, President.

Address admission inquiries to David Collins, Assistant Vice President for Admission and Financial Aid.

St. Vincent Seminary

Degree Programs Offered: *First-professional* in divinity; *master's* with concentrations in sacred scripture, systematic theology, monastic studies.

Admission: *For first-professional degree:* Baccalaureate from accredited college with 18 credits in philosophy; 12 credits in Christian theology; 3 letters of recommendation; personal interview. *For M.A. degree:* baccalaureate from accredited college with 24 credits in philosophy and Christian theology (no less than 6 credits in each area); 3 letters of recommendation; personal interview; GRE if requested.

Degree Requirements: *For first-professional degree:* 75 credit hours (9 credits in history, 12 pastoral studies, 14 sacred scripture, 18 theology, 2 in New testament Greek, 20 electives including one seminar); 2.5. 0 GPA. *For master of arts:* 36 credits: 18 in area of concentration, 9 in theology, 6 electives, 3 other with 3 M.A. seminars included in the 36 credits; language requirements depends upon concentration; written and oral comprehensive examinations; GPA of 3.0.

Seton Hill University

One Seton Hill Drive
Greensburg, Pennsylvania 15601
Tel: (724) 834-2200 **E-mail:** admit@setonhill.edu
Fax: (724) 830-1902 **Internet:** www.setonhill.edu

Institution Description: Seton Hill University is a private, independent, nonprofit institution affiliated with the Sisters of Charity, Roman Catholic Church. *Enrollment:* 2,087. *Degrees awarded:* Baccalaureate, master's.

Accreditation: *Regional:* MSA/CHE. *Professional*: business, chemistry, dietetics, music, social work, physician assisting

History: Established and chartered 1883 as a girls' academy; offered first instruction at postsecondary level 1914; chartered as 4-year institution and adopted present name 1918; awarded first degree (baccalaureate) 1919; awarded first master's degree 1997.*See* Sister Mary Electa Boyle, *Mother Seton's Sisters of Charity in Western Pennsylvania* (Greensburg, PA: Sisters of Charity, Seton Hill College, 1946) for further information.

Institutional Structure: *Governing board:* Board of Trustees. Extrainstitutional representation: 36 trustees, including 1 alumna. All voting. *Composition*

of institution: Academic affairs headed by Vice President for Academic Affairs and Dean of the Faculty. Management/business/finances directed by Vice President for Financial Affairs. Full-time instructional faculty 67. Academic governance body, the faculty, meets an average of 8 times a year.

Calendar: Semesters. Academic year Aug. to May. Freshmen admitted Aug., Jan. J Term offered in Jan. M Term offered in May. Degrees conferred and formal commencement May. Summer session of 3 terms from May through Aug.

Characteristics of Freshmen: 1,703 applicants (1,013 female, 890 male). 63% of applicants admitted. 30% of applicants admitted and enrolled full-time.

90% of students submitted SAT scores. *25th percentile*: SAT Critical Reading 450, SAT Math 440. *75th percentile*: SAT Critical Reading 550, SAT Math 560.

54% of entering freshmen expected to graduate within 5 years. 79% of freshmen from Pennsylvania. Freshmen from 14 states and 4 foreign countries.

Admission: Rolling admissions plan. For fall acceptance, apply as early as July 1 of previous year, but not later than Aug. 1 of year of enrollment. Early acceptance available. *Requirements:* Graduation from accredited secondary school with 15 units which must include 4 English, 2 college preparatory mathematics, 2 social studies, 1 laboratory science, 4 electives, and 2 units in a foreign language are recommended. Additional requirements for some programs. *Entrance tests:* College Board SAT or ACT composite. *For transfer students:* 72 credits maximum accepted toward degree.

College credit and advanced placement for postsecondary-level work completed in secondary school and for College Board CLEP.

Tutoring available. Developmental/remedial courses offered during regular academic year. Peer and professional tutors employed by college in each academic department.

Degree Requirements: 120 credit hours; 2.0 GPA; university distribution requirements for most programs; portfolio.

Fulfillment of some degree requirements and exemption from some beginning courses possible by passing College Board CLEP, APP. *Grading system:* A–F; pass-fail; withdraw (carries time limit).

Distinctive Educational Programs: School of Fine Arts for men and women. Work-experience programs. Weekend and evening classes. Dual-degree programs in engineering with Georgia Institute of Technology, Pennsylvania State University (University Park), University of Pittsburgh. Interdepartmental/interdisciplinary programs in American studies, art therapy, family studies, management, medical technology. Facilities for independent research, including honors programs, individual majors, tutorials. Study abroad in England, France, Italy, South America, Germany, and elsewhere; may be individually arranged.

ROTC: Air Force in cooperation with Indiana University of Pennsylvania; Army with University of Pittsburgh.

Degrees Conferred: 264 *baccalaureate;* 127 *master's.*

Fees and Other Expenses: *Full-time tuition per academic year 2008–09:* undergraduate $6,002; contact the university for current graduate tuition and applicable fees. *Room and board per academic year:* $8,170. *Books and supplies:* $1,000. *Other expenses:* $2,500.

Financial Aid: Aid from institutionally generated funds is provided on the basis of academic merit, financial need, athletic ability, other criteria.

Financial aid to full-time, first-time undergraduate students: 96% feceived some form of aid. Average amount of aid received: federal grants $5,201; Pell grants $2,105; other federal aid $1,140; state/local grants $3,652; institutional grants $14,951.

Departments and Teaching Staff: *Total instructional faculty:* 192 (full-time 67, part-time 125). 67% of faculty hold the doctorate, first-professional, or other terminal degree. Student/faculty ratio: 14:1.

Enrollment: Total enrollment 2,087. Undergraduate 1,650. Graduate 437 (full-time 34%). Undergraduate transfer-in students 72.

Characteristics of Student Body: *Ethnic/racial makeup:* Asian or Pacific Islander: 1%; Hispanic: 1%; White non-Hispanic: 83%; unknown: 5%; nonresident alien 2%. *Age distribution:* number 18–21: 800; 22–24: 83; 25–29: 61; 30–39: 53; 40–49: 37; 50–64: 16.

International Students: 42 nonresident aliens enrolled fall 2008. Programs available to aid students whose native language is not English: English as a Second Language Program. Financial aid specifically designated for international students: variable number of scholarships available annually.

Student Life: On-campus residence halls house 69% of student body. *Intercollegiate athletics:* female: basketball, cross-country, equestrian, field hockey, lacrosse, tennis, volleyball; men's baseball, basketball, cross-country, equestrian, football, lacrosse. *Special regulations:* Cars permitted without restrictions. *Special services:* Academic and personal counseling, writing lab, tutorial center, computer lab, Internet available to all dormitories; medical services; van service available. *Student publications:* annual literary magazine; *Setonian,* a student newspaper. *Surrounding community:* Greensburg population 18,000. Pittsburgh, 35 miles from campus, is nearest metropolitan area. Served by airport 9 miles from campus; passenger rail service .5 mile from campus.

Library Collections: 124,000 volumes. 5,654 microforms; 6,700 audiovisual materials; 420 current periodical subscriptions. Students have access to online information retrieval services and the Internet.

Most important special holdings include collections on women's studies, children's literature, Holocaust Collection.

Buildings and Grounds: Campus area 200 acres. Campus DVD available.

Chief Executive Officer: Dr. JoAnne W. Boyle, President.

Address admission inquiries to Shem Bett, Director of Admissions.

Shippensburg University of Pennsylvania

1871 Old Main Drive
Shippensburg, Pennsylvania 17257-2299
Tel: (717) 477-7447 **E-mail:** admiss@ship.edu
Fax: (717) 477-1273 **Internet:** www.ship.edu

Institution Description: Shippensburg University of Pennsylvania is a state institution. *Enrollment:* 7,942. *Degrees awarded:* Baccalaureate, master's.

Academic offerings and budget subject to approval by State System of Higher Education.

Accreditation: *Regional:* MSA/CHE. *Professional*: business, chemistry, counseling, social work, teacher education

History: Established as Cumberland Valley State Normal School 1871; offered first instruction at postsecondary level 1873; chartered and awarded first degree (baccalaureate) 1926; changed name to Shippensburg State Teachers College 1927; became Shippensburg State College 1960; adopted present name 1983. *See* John E. Hubley, *Hilltop Heritage, Shippensburg State's First Hundred Years* (Shippensburg: Shippensburg Press, 1971) for further information.

Institutional Structure: *Governing board:* State System of Higher Education of the Commonwealth of Pennsylvania is guided by a chancellor and a 20-member Board of Governors; all of whom are appointed by the governor of Pennsylvania. Guided by a 11-member board of governors and an 11-member council of trustees that includes 1 student appointed with the advice and consent of the governor and state senatorial approval. Academic affairs headed by vice president. Management/business/finances directed by vice president. Full-time instructional faculty 331. Academic governance body, University Forum and Academic Deans Council, meet regularly throughout the year. *Faculty representation:* Faculty served by collective bargaining agent, Association of Pennsylvania State College and University Faculties (APSCUF).

Calendar: Semesters. Academic year Aug. to May. Freshmen admitted Sept., Jan., June, July, Aug. Degrees conferred and formal commencement May, Dec. Summer session of 3 terms from May to Aug.

Characteristics of Freshmen: 6,164 applicants 3,312 (female, 2,852 male). 75% of applicants admitted. 37% of applicants admitted and enrolled full-time.

100% (1,498 students) submitted SAT scores; 7% (104 students) submitted ACT scores. *25th percentile*: SAT Critical Reading 450, SAT Math 460. *75th percentile*: SAT Critical Reading 550, SAT Math 560.

62% of entering freshmen expected to graduate within 5 years. 95% of freshmen from Pennsylvania. Freshmen from 21 states and 15 foreign countries.

Admission: Rolling admissions plan. *Requirements:* Either graduation from secondary school or GED. Recommend 4 units English, 3 mathematics, 3 social science, 3 laboratory science, 2 foreign language. Additional requirements recommended for some programs. *Entrance tests:* College Board SAT. For foreign students TOEFL. *For transfer students:* 2.0 minimum GPA; A minimum of 45 hors at Shippensburg.

College credit and advanced placement for postsecondary-level work completed in secondary school.

Degree Requirements: 120 credit hours; 2.0 GPA; distribution requirements.

Fulfillment of some degree requirements and exemption from some beginning courses possible by passing departmental examinations, College Board CLEP, APP. *Grading system:* A–F; pass-fail; withdraw; incomplete (carries time limit).

Distinctive Educational Programs: *For undergraduates:* Preprofessional programs in law, medicine, chiropractic, veterinary science, pharmacy, dentistry, optometry, physical therapy, podiatry. 3–2 engineering programs with Pennsylvania State University, University of Maryland. Member of Marine Science Consortium. Off-campus study possible at Wallops Island, Virginia. Member of Pennsylvania Consortium for International Education. Exchange programs with Art Institute of Philadelphia, Art Institute of Pittsburgh, six other design schools, and Wilson College. Visiting student program. Study abroad in Argentina, Australia, Costa Rica, Canada, Denmark, England, France, Germany, Ireland, Mexico, Scotland, New Zealand, The Netherlands, Dominican Republic, Italy.

ROTC: Army.

Degrees Conferred: 1,269 *baccalaureate*; 349 *master's*. Bachelor's degrees awarded in top five disciplines: education 212; security and protective services 109; communications/journalism 104; English 100; psychology 90. Master's degrees awarded in top five disciplines: education 132; business/marketing 37;

SHIPPENSBURG UNIVERSITY OF PENNSYLVANIA—*cont'd*

security and protective services 31; computer and information sciences 16; interdisciplinary studies 16.

Fees and Other Expenses: *Full-time tuition per academic year 2008–09:* undergraduate resident $7,099, nonresident $15,229; contact the university for current graduate tuition and applicable fees. *Other fees:* $1,511. *Room and board per academic year:* $6,252. *Books and supplies:* $1,090.

Financial Aid: Aid from institutionally generated funds is provided on the basis of academic merit, financial need, athletic ability.

Financial aid to full-time, first-time undergraduate students: 82% received some form of aid. Average amount of aid received: federal grants $3,398; Pell grants $2,668; other federal aid $889; state/local grants $2,873; institutional grants $2,853.

Departments and Teaching Staff: *Total instructional faculty:* 378 (full-time 331, part-time 47). Total faculty with doctorate, first-professional, or other terminal degree: 314. Student/faculty ratio: 19:1. Degrees held by full-time faculty: master's 13%, doctorate 87%.

Enrollment: Total enrollment 7,942. Undergraduate 6,733 (full-time 95%, female 53%, male 47%). Graduate 1,209 (full-time 23%). Undergraduate transfer-in students 371.

Characteristics of Student Body: *Ethnic/racial makeup:* Black non-Hispanic: 7%; Asian or Pacific Islander: 2%; Hispanic: 2%; White non-Hispanic: 83%; unknown 7%. *Age distribution:* number under 8: 94; 18–19: 3,627; 20–21: 2,503; 22–24: 819; 25–29: 189; 30–34: 68; 35–39: 41; 40–49: 61; 50–64: 19; 65 and over: 1.

International Students: 27 nonresident aliens enrolled fall 2008. Students from Europe, Asia, Latin America, Africa, Canada. No programs available to aid students whose native language is not English. No financial aid specifically designated for international students.

Student Life: On-campus residence halls house 39% of undergraduate students. *Intercollegiate athletics:* male: baseball, basketball, cross-country, football, golf, swimming, track and field, wrestling; female: basketball, cross-country, field hockey, lacrosse, soccer, softball, swimming, tennis, track and field, volleyball. *Special regulations:* Cars permitted without restrictions. Quiet hours set by residents in individual halls. *Special services:* Learning Assistance Center, writing center. *Student publications, radio: Reflector*, an annual literary magazine; *Slate*, a weekly newspaper. *Surrounding community:* Shippensburg borough population 5,500. Washington (DC), 100 miles from campus, is nearest metropolitan area. Served by airport 50 miles from campus; passenger rail service 40 miles from campus.

Publications: *Proteus*, a journal of ideas. Shippensburg Collegiate Press published several titles per year. Shippensburg University Magazine published quarterly.

Library Collections: 454,000 volumes including bound books, serial backfiles, electronic documents, and government documents not in separate collections. Online catalog. 1.3 million microforms; 72,500 audiovisual materials; Current serial subscriptions: 1,240 paper. Computer work stations avaialble campus-wide. Students have access to the Internet at no charge.

Most important special holdings include collections on education and business; University Archives; Pennsylvania History.

Buildings and Grounds: Campus area 200 acres. Campus DVD available.

Chief Executive Officer: Dr. G.F. Harpster, President.

Undergraduates address admission inquiries to Dr. Thomas Speakman, Director of Enrollment Services graduate inquiries to Dean of Graduate Studies.

Slippery Rock University of Pennsylvania

Slippery Rock, Pennsylvania 16057

Tel: (724) 738-9000 **E-mail:** apply@sru.edu
Fax: (724) 738-2913 **Internet:** www.sru.edu

Institution Description: Slippery Rock University of Pennsylvania is a state institution. *Enrollment:* 8,458. *Degrees awarded:* Baccalaureate, master's, doctorate.

Academic offerings subject to approval by statewide coordinating bodies. Budget subject to approval by state governing boards. Member of Marine Science Consortium, Pennsylvania Consortium for International Education (PCIE), Southwestern Pennsylvania Higher Education Council, Inc.

Accreditation: *Regional:* MSA/CHE. *Professional*: athletic training, business, counseling, music, nursing, occupational therapy, physical therapy, recreation and leisure services, social work, teacher education

History: Established and chartered as Slippery Rock State Normal School 1889; changed name to Slippery Rock State Teachers College 1926; offered first instruction at postsecondary level and awarded first degree (baccalaureate) 1927; became Slippery Rock State College 1960; adopted present name 1983.

Institutional Structure: *Governing board:* Board of Governors of PA State System of Higher Education, Council of Trustees of Slippery Rock University, President. *Composition of institution:* Academic affairs headed by vice president for academic affairs and provost who reports to the president. Vice presidents head divisions of Finance and Administrative Affairs, Student Affairs, and University Advancement. Full-time instructional faculty 366. *Faculty representation:* Faculty represented by collective bargaining agent, Association of Pennsylvania State College and University Faculty, affiliated with AAUP and AFT.

Calendar: Semesters. Academic year Aug. to May. freshmen admitted Aug., Jan., June. Degrees conferred and formal commencements May, Dec.

Characteristics of Freshmen: 4,736 applicants (2,030 female, 2,106 male). 70% of applicants accepted. 45% of accepted applicants enrolled.

94% (1,377 students) submitted SAT scores; 19% (284 students) submitted ACT scores. *25th percentile*: SAT Critical Reading 450, SAT Math 450; ACT Composite 18, ACT English 17, ACT Math 17. *75th percentile*: SAT Critical Reading 540, Sat Math 55o; ACT Composite 23, ACT English 23, ACT Math 24.

45% of freshmen expected to graduate within 5 years. 90% of freshmen from Pennsylvania. Freshmen from 35 states and 48 foreign countries.

Admission: Rolling admissions plan. For fall acceptance, apply after July following junior year in secondary school, but not later than May 1 of the year for which admissions is sought. Early acceptance available. *Requirements:* Graduation from accredited secondary school; GED; or equivalent preparation. *Entrance tests:* College Board SAT or ACT composite. *For transfer students:* 2.5 minimum GPA; from 2-year accredited institution 67 hours maximum transfer credit; from other institutions, transfer credit limited only by residence requirement.

College credit and advanced placement for postsecondary-level work completed in secondary school.

Tutoring available. Developmental courses offered in summer session and regular academic year; credit given.

Degree Requirements: *For undergraduate degrees:* 128 credit hours minimum, 2.0 major plus cumulative QPA (higher in some majors), 36 final hours in residence, 2 hours of physical education, 2 intensive writing courses.

Fulfillment of some degree requirements possible by passing College Board CLEP or APP. *Grading system:* A–F; pass-fail; withdraw (deadline after which pass-fail is appended to withdraw); incomplete.

Distinctive Educational Programs: A revised Liberal Studies program was implemented in 1991; approximately 80 fields of study and 15 teacher certification areas can be pursued in the 8 baccalaureate degrees that are offered. A variety of fields of study including teacher education, accounting, and public administration can be pursued at the master's level. Physical therapy can be pursued at the doctoral level. Continuing education and off-campus educational opportunities are available. Cooperative baccalaureate degree programs in medical technology and engineering can be pursued with neighboring hospitals and other universities. Undergraduate interdisciplinary programs in environmental science, environmental studies, women's studies, and gerontology are available. Extensive study abroad opportunities possible in European and Asian settings. Wide offering of evening classes, special facilities for using telecommunication in the classroom exist. Tutorial assistance is available.

ROTC: Army offered in cooperation with Indiana University of Pennsylvania, Grove City College students have the opportunity of enrolling for ROTC classes at Slippery Rock University.

Degrees Conferred: 1,506 *baccalaureate*; 193 *master's*; 51 *doctorate*. Bachelor's degrees awarded in top five disciplines: education 206; parks and recreation 183; business, management, marketing, and related support services 175; health professions and related clinical sciences 123; communication, journalism, and related programs 83. Master's degrees awarded: various disciplines 193. Doctorates awarded: education 51.

Fees and Other Expenses: *Full-time tuition per academic year 2008–09:* undergraduate resident $6,935, nonresident $9,767; contact the university for graduate tuition/fees. *Room and board per academic year:* $8,270. *Books and supplies:* $1,322. *Other expenses:* $1,678.

Financial Aid: Aid from institutionally generated funds is provided on the basis of academic merit, financial need, athletic ability.

Financial aid to full-time, first-time undergraduate students: 89% received some form of financial aid. Average amount of aid received: federal grants $3,367; Pell grants $2,669; other federal aid $1,010; state/local grants $3,151; institutional grants $2,085.

Departments and Teaching Staff: *Total instructional faculty:* 442. Student/faculty ratio: 18:1. Degrees held by full-time faculty: baccalaureate 1%, master's 30%, doctorate 69%. 73% hold terminal degrees.

Enrollment: Total enrollment 8,458. Undergraduate 7,691 (full-time 93%; female 56%, male 44%). Graduate 767 (full-time 49%). Undergraduate transfer-in students 637.

Characteristics of Student Body: *Ethnic/racial makeup:* Black non-Hispanic: 5%; Asian or Pacific Islander: 1%; Hispanic: 1%; White non-Hispanic: 84%; unknown: 7%; nonresident alien 1%.

International Students: 85 nonresident aliens enrolled fall 2008. Students from Europe, Asia, Latin America, Africa, Canada, New Zealand. Programs available to aid students whose native language is not English: social, cultural, financial. Financial aid specifically designated for international students: tuition waivers available to qualifying students.

Student Life: On-campus residence halls house 38% of student body. Residence halls for males constitute 11% of such space, for females 26%. Co-ed housing accounts for 63% of the residence hall population. Approximately 21% of the student body live in privately owned and operated residence halls and 30% of the student body live off-campus. Married student housing is not available on campus, but abundant housing adjacent to campus is available for married students. *Intercollegiate athletics:* male: baseball, football, wrestling; female: field hockey, softball, volleyball; both sexes: basketball, cross-country, diving, golf, soccer, swimming, tennis, track, water polo. *Special regulations:* All students must have parking permits; parking in designated areas only. No special dress regulations. Residence hall visitation permitted from 10am to midnight weekdays; 24 hours a day on weekends. *Special services:* Learning Resources Center, health services, career services, tutorial center. *Student publications, radio, television: The Rocket*, a student newspaper, *Ginger Hill*, a literary publication; *African American Review,* a newspaper; student directory; yearbook. WRSK and WSRU. Cable Channel 6 university-wide channel available to students and faculty. *Surrounding community:* Slippery Rock population 3,000. Pittsburgh, 50 miles from campus, is nearest metropolitan area.

Library Collections: 503,000 volumes. Online catalog. Current serial subscriptions: 1,300. 1.5 million microforms; 23,000 audiovisual materials. Students have access to the Internet and online information retrieval services.

Most important special holdings include Japan Collection, health sciences collection.

Buildings and Grounds: Campus area 611 acres. Campus DVD available.

Chief Executive Officer: Dr. Robert M. Smith, President.

Undergraduates address admission inquiries to James Barrett, Director of Admissions; graduate inquiries to Dean, Graduate Studies and Research.

Susquehanna University

514 University Avenue

Selinsgrove, Pennsylvania 17870-1025

Tel: (570) 372-0101 **E-mail:** suadmiss@susqu.edu

Fax: (570) 372-2722 **Internet:** www.susqu.edu

Institution Description: Susquehanna University is a private, independent, nonprofit institution affiliated with the Lutheran Church in America. *Enrollment:* 2,137. *Degrees awarded:* Associate, baccalaureate.

Accreditation: *Regional:* MSA/CHE. *Professional*: music, nurse anesthesia education

History: Established, chartered, and incorporated as Missionary Institute of the Evangelical Lutheran Church and offered first instruction at postsecondary level 1858; merged with Susquehanna Female College 1873; adopted present name 1895; awarded first degree (baccalaureate) 1896. *See* William S. Clark and Arthur Herman Wilson, *The Story of Susquehanna University* (Selinsgrove: Susquehanna University Press, 1958) for further information.

Institutional Structure: *Governing board:* The Board of Directors of Susquehanna University. Extrainstitutional representation: 38 directors; institutional representation: president of the university, 2 full-time instructional faculty members, 2 students. All voting. *Composition of institution:* Administrators 41. Academic affairs headed by vice president for academic affairs. Management/business/finances directed by vice president for finance and development. Full-time instructional faculty 122. Academic governance body, the faculty, meets an average of 9 times per year.

Calendar: Semesters. Academic year Sept. to May. Freshmen admitted Sept., Dec., Mar., June. Degrees conferred and formal commencement May, Sept. Summer session from June to Aug.

Characteristics of Freshmen: 2,882 applicants (1,558 female, 1,324 male). 73% of applicants accepted. 29% of accepted applicants enrolled full-time.

86% (458 students) submitted SAT scores. *25th percentile*: SAT Critical Reading 580, SAT Math 510. *75th percentile*: SAT Critical Reading 600, SAT Math 600.

71% of entering freshmen expected to graduate within 5 years. 51% of freshmen from Pennsylvania. Freshmen from 13 states and 5 foreign countries.

Admission: Rolling admissions plan. For fall acceptance, apply as early as Aug. 1 of previous year, but not later than March 15 of year of enrollment. Apply by Dec. 15 for early decision; need not limit application to Susquehanna University. Early acceptance available. *Requirements:* Either graduation from accredited secondary school or GED. Recommend 18 units including 3 English, 2 in a foreign language, 3 mathematics, 3 social studies, 2 laboratory science. Minimum GPA 2.0. Lowest acceptable secondary school class standing 75th percentile. *Entrance tests:* College Board SAT or ACT Composite. *For transfer students:* 2.0 minimum GPA; 60 semester hours maximum transfer credit.

College credit and advanced placement for postsecondary-level work completed in secondary school. and for extrainstitutional learning on basis of portfolio and faculty assessments.

Tutoring available. Developmental courses offered in summer session and regular academic year; credit given.

Degree Requirements: *For all associate degrees:* 17 course units; 3 terms in residence. *For all baccalaureate degrees:* 35 course units; 6 terms in residence; 4 terms physical education. *For all degrees:* 2.0 GPA; distribution requirements.

Fulfillment of some degree requirements and exemption from some beginning courses possible by passing departmental examinations, College Board CLEP. *Grading system:* A–F; pass-fail, withdraw (carries time limit); incomplete (carries time limit).

Distinctive Educational Programs: Internships and practicums. Evening classes. Dual-degree programs in engineering with University of Pennsylvania; in forestry and environmental management with Duke University (NC). Cooperative baccalaureate program in anesthesiology with Geisinger Medical Center. Facilities for independent research, including honors programs, individual majors. Institutionally sponsored study abroad in Japan and at Oxford University in England; through Institute of European Studies in Europe, Latin America. Off-campus study in the U.S. includes Appalachian semester at Union College (KY), United Nations semester at Drew University (NJ); Washington (DC) semester at American University.

ROTC: Army offered in cooperation with Bucknell University.

Degrees Conferred: 7 *associate;* 455 448 *baccalaureate*. Bachelor's degrees awarded in top five disciplines: business, management, marketing, and related support services 137; communication, journalism, and related programs 42; education 40; psychology 34; biological/life sciences 30.

Fees and Other Expenses: *Full-time tuition per academic year 2008–09:* $31,080. *Books and supplies:* $850. *Room and board per academic year:* $8,400. *Other expenses:* $1,070.

Departments and Teaching Staff: *Total instructional faculty:* 122. 96% hold terminal degrees. Student/faculty ratio: 14:1.

Enrollment: Total enrollment: 2,137. Undergraduate 2,137 (full-time 97%; female 54%, male 46%). Transfer-in students 41.

Characteristics of Student Body: *Ethnic/racial makeup:* Black non-Hispanic: 3%; Asian or Pacific Islander: 2%; Hispanic: 2%; White non-Hispanic: 89%; unknown: 3%; nonresident alien 1%.

International Students: 21 nonresident aliens enrolled fall 2008. No programs available to aid students whose native language is not English. No financial aid specifically designated for international students.

Student Life: On-campus residence halls house 69% of student body. Residence halls for males constitute 12% of such space, for females 21%, for both sexes 67%. 9% of student body live on campus in houses for students working as volunteers with community service agency. 25% of males join and 19% live in off-campus fraternity housing. *Intercollegiate athletics:* male: baseball, basketball, cross-country, football, golf, soccer, swimming, tennis, track; female: basketball, field hockey, softball, swimming, tennis, track, volleyball. *Special regulations:* Cars permitted without restrictions. Quiet hours vary according to dormitory. Residence hall visitation from 7am to 10pm Sun.–Thurs., 7am Fri. to 2am Sun. *Special services:* Learning Resources Center, medical services. *Student publications, radio: The Crusader;* a weekly newspaper, *Focus*, an annual literary magazine; *Lanthorn*, a yearbook. Radio station WQSU broadcasts 127 hours per week. *Surrounding community:* Selinsgrove population 5,500. Baltimore (MD), 122 miles from campus, is nearest metropolitan area. Served by airport and passenger rail service, each 50 miles from campus.

Publications: *Susquehanna University Studies* (annual) first published in 1936.

Library Collections: 341,000 volumes. 126,000 microforms; 11,000 audiovisual materials; 16,500 periodicals including via electronic access.

Most important holdings include The Wilt Collection on Music (2,000 volumes of criticism of 19th century American and European music).

Buildings and Grounds: Campus area 200 acres.

Chief Executive Officer: Dr. L. J. Lemons, President.

Address admission inquiries to Chris Markle, Director of Admissions.

Swarthmore College

500 College Avenue
Swarthmore, Pennsylvania 19081
Tel: (610) 328-8300 **E-mail:** admissions@swarthmore.edu
Fax: (610) 328-8580 **Internet:** www.swarthmore.edu

Institution Description: Swarthmore College is a private, independent, nonprofit college. *Enrollment:* 1,498. *Degrees awarded:* Baccalaureate, master's.

Accreditation: *Regional:* MSA/CHE. *Professional*: engineering

History: Established and chartered by the Religious Society of Friends 1864; offered first instruction at postsecondary level 1869; awarded first degree (baccalaureate) 1873. *See* Homer D. Babbidge, Jr., *Swarthmore College in the 19th Century, A Quaker Experience in Education* (Diss., Yale University, 1953) for further information. Nonsectarian, but reflects Quaker traditions.

Institutional Structure: *Governing board:* Swarthmore College Board of Managers. Extrainstitutional representation: 3 trustees; institutional representation: president of the college; 43 alumni. 1 ex officio. *Composition of institution:* Administrators 38. Academic affairs headed by provost. Management/business/finances directed by vice president for finance and planning. Full-time instructional faculty 169. Academic governance body, the faculty, meets an average of 6–8 times per year.

Calendar: Semesters. Academic year Sept. to June. Freshmen admitted Sept. Degrees conferred and formal commencement May. No summer session.

Characteristics of Freshmen: 6,121 applicants (3,667 female, 2,454 male). 16% of applicants admitted. 39% of admitted applicants enrolled full-time. 97% (360 students) submitted SAT scores; 25% (91 students) submitted ACT scores. *25th percentile*: SAT Critical Reading 660, SAT Math 660, SAT Writing 650; ACT Composite 28, ACT English 27, ACT Math 29. *75th percentile*: SAT Critical Reading 770, SAT Math 770, SAT Writing 760; ACT Composite 34, ACT English 34, ACT Math 34.

91% of entering freshmen expected to graduate within 5 years. 13 of freshmen from Pennsylvania. Freshmen from 38 states and 28 foreign countries.

Admission: For fall acceptance, apply no later than Jan. 1. Students are notified of acceptance Apr. 1. Apply by Nov. 15 for fall early decision, by Jan. 1 for early decision; must enroll if accepted. Early acceptance available. *Requirements:* Recommend units in foreign languages; history and social studies; literature, art, and music; the sciences. For engineering students, units in chemistry, mathematics, and physics. *Entrance tests:* College Board SAT or ACT, plus 3 SAT IIs including writing. *For transfer students:* 2 years maximum transfer credit.

College credit and advanced placement for postsecondary-level work completed in secondary school.

Tutoring available. Developmental courses offered during regular academic year.

Degree Requirements: 32 courses; 2.0 GPA; 4 semesters in residence; 2 semesters physical education; swimming requirement; distribution requirements; foreign language or equivalent requirement; exit competency examinations (comprehensives in individual fields of study; external examinations in honors program).

Fulfillment of some degree requirements and exemption from some beginning courses possible by passing departmental examinations. *Grading system:* A–D, no credit; credit-no credit; withdraw (carries time limit).

Distinctive Educational Programs: Honors Program. Accelerated degree programs. Student exchange programs with Middlebury College (VT), Mills and Pomona Colleges (CA), Rice University (TX), Tufts University (MA). Interdisciplinary programs in Asian studies, Black studies, international relations, public policy. *For undergraduates:* Interdepartmental programs in linguistics-psychology, literature, Medieval studies. Facilities and programs for independent research, including honors programs, individual majors, tutorials. Study abroad in Colombia, France, Italy, Spain, West Poland, Germany. Cross-registration with Bryn Mawr and Haverford Colleges and the University of Pennsylvania.

ROTC: Air Force in cooperation with Widener University; Army with University of Pennsylvania; Navy with St. John's University.

Degrees Conferred: 374 *baccalaureate:* area and ethnic studies 3; biological sciences 53; computer and information sciences 6; education 21; engineering 20; English 35; fine and applied arts 12; foreign languages 105; mathematics 8; natural resources/environmental science 2; philosophy and religious studies 28; physical sciences 13; psychology 221 social sciences and history 107; visual and performing arts 13.

Fees and Other Expenses: *Full-time tuition per academic year 2008–09:* $36,470. *Required fees:* $320. *Room and board per academic year:* $11,314. *Books and supplies:* $1,110. *Other expenses:* $1,467.

Financial Aid: Aid from institutionally generated funds is provided on the basis of academic merit, financial need.

Financial aid to full-time, first-time undergraduate students: 48% received some form of aid. Average amount of aid received: federal grants $5,851; Pell grants $3,698; other federal aid $2,315; state/local grants $3,276; institutional grants $1,467.

Departments and Teaching Staff: *Total instructional faculty:* 205 (full-time 169, part-time 36). Total faculty with doctorate, first-professional, or other terminal degree: 189. Student/faculty ratio: 8:1.

Enrollment: Total enrollment 1,498. Undergradaute 1,498 (full-time 99%; female 52%, male 48%). Transfer-in students 16.

Characteristics of Student Body: *Ethnic/racial makeup:* Black non-Hispanic: 9%; American Indian or Alaska Native: 1%; Asian or Pacific Islander: 17%; Hispanic: 11%; White non-Hispanic: 44%; unknown: 11%; nonresident alien 7%. *Age distribution:* number under 18: 34; 18–19: 712; 20–21: 666; 22–24: 63; 25–29: 6; 30–34: 1; 35–39: 0; 40–49: 2; unknown: 2.

International Students: 89 nonresident aliens enrolled fall 2008. Programs available to aid students whose native language is not English: English as a Second Language Program. Financial aid specifically designated for international students: scholarships available annually.

Student Life: On-campus residence halls house 90% of student body. Residence halls for males constitute 15% of such space, for females 11%; for both sexes 74%. *Intercollegiate athletics:* male: baseball, basketball, cross-country, golf, lacrosse, soccer, swimming, tennis, track, wrestling; female: badminton, basketball, field hockey, gymnastics, lacrosse, soccer, softball, swimming, tennis, track, volleyball. All campus social and cultural activities are free to students. *Special regulations:* Cars with decals permitted on campus in designated areas. *Special services:* Medical services, psychological services, campus shuttle van. *Student publications, radio: Halcyon*, a yearbook; a weekly newspaper and daily student paper, *small craft warnings*, a biannual literary magazine. Radio station WSRN broadcasts 140 hours per week. *Surrounding community:* Swarthmore population 6,000. Philadelphia, 11 miles from campus, is nearest metropolitan area. Served by mass transit bus, train systems; airport 11 miles from campus; passenger rail service on campus.

Library Collections: 809,000 including bound books, serial backfiles, electronic documents, and government documents not in separate collections. Online catalog. 71,000 microforms; 24,000 audiovisual materials; 11,000 periodicals including via electronic access. Computer work stations available. Students have access to the Internet at no charge.

Most important special collections include Society of Friends and Peace Collections; W.H. Auden Collection; private press publications.

Buildings and Grounds: Campus area 330 acres.

Chief Executive Officer: Dr. Alfred H. Bloom, President.

Address admission inquiries to James L. Beck III, Dean of Admissions and Financial Aid.

Temple University

1801 North Broad Street
Philadelphia, Pennsylvania 19122
Tel: (215) 204-7200 **E-mail:** tuadm@vm.temple.edu
Fax: (215) 204-5694 **Internet:** www.temple.edu

Institution Description: Temple University is an independent, state-related institution. *Enrollment:* 35,490. *Degrees awarded:* Associate, baccalaureate, first-professional (dentistry, law, medicine, pharmacy podiatry), master's, doctorate.

Accreditation: *Regional:* MSA/CHE. *Professional*: architecture, art, business, dentistry, engineering, engineering technology, health services administration, journalism, law, medical record administration, medicine, music, nursing, occupational therapy, pharmacy, physical therapy, psychology internship, public administration, public health, radiography, recreation and leisure services, social work, speech-language pathology, teacher education

History: Established 1884; chartered as Temple College 1888; offered first instruction at postsecondary level 1891; awarded first degree (baccalaureate) 1892; changed name to Temple University 1907; adopted present name 1965.

Institutional Structure: *Governing board:* Board of Trustees. Extrainstitutional representation: 24 university trustees (elected by the corporation or board); 12 commonwealth trustees (4 appointed by the speaker of the House of Representatives, 4 by the president pro tempore of the Senate and 4 by the governor of the Commonwealth). All voting. institutional representation: *Composition of institution:* Academic affairs headed by provost. Student affairs, management directed by executive vice president for administration. Financial and auxiliary services directed by vice president for financial affairs. Full-time instructional faculty 1,232. Academic governance body, Faculty Senate, meets an average of 9 times per year. *Faculty representation:* Faculty served by collective bargaining agent affiliated with AAUP.

Calendar: Semesters. Academic year Aug. to May. Freshmen admitted Sept., Jan. Degrees conferred May, Aug., Jan. Formal commencement May. Summer session from May to Aug.

Characteristics of Freshmen: 18,670 applicants (10,798 female, 7,872 male). 61% of applicants accepted. 36% of accepted applicants enrolled full-time.

98% (3,902 students) submitted SAT scores; 7% (287 students) submitted ACT scores. *25th percentile*: SAT Critical Reading 490, SAT Math 500, SAT Writing 480; ACT Composite 20. *75th percentile*: SAT Critical Reading 590, SAT Math 600, SAT Writing 580; ACT Composite 25.

45% of entering freshmen expected to graduate within 5 years. 78% of freshmen from Pennsylvania. Freshmen from 47 states and 101 foreign countries.

Admission: Rolling admissions plan. *Requirements:* Either graduation from accredited secondary school with 4 units English, 2 in a foreign language, 2 college preparatory mathematics, 1 history, 1 laboratory science, 3 from among foreign language, mathematics, science, social studies; or GED. Substitutions possible in some programs. *Entrance tests:* College Board SAT or ACT composite. For foreign students TOEFL. *For transfer students:* 2.3 minimum GPA; from 4-year accredited institution maximum transfer credit limited only by residence requirement; from 2-year accredited institution 64 semester hours.

College credit and advanced placement for postsecondary-level work completed in secondary school. College credit for extrainstitutional learning (life experience) on basis of portfolio and faculty assessment. Tutoring available.

Degree Requirements: *For all associate degrees:* 64–71 credit hours. *For all baccalaureate degrees:* 125–144 hours; writing proficiency requirement. *For all undergraduate degrees:* 2.0 GPA; 30 hours in residence.

Fulfillment of some degree requirements and exemption from some beginning courses possible by passing departmental examinations, College Board CLEP, AP. *Grading system:* A–F; pass; withdraw (carries time limit); credit-no credit.

Distinctive Educational Programs: Cooperative education. Core curriculum. Exchange program with University of Puerto Rico - Rio Piedras, University of Hamburg, and Netherlands School of Business. Continuing education program. *Other distinctive programs:* Study abroad through Temple Rome (art, architecture, liberal arts); Temple Japan in Tokyo (liberal arts, business); London (communications, theater, criminal justice); Dublin (literature); summer programs in Paris, Sicily, and other locations.

ROTC: Air Force in cooperation with St. Joseph;s University; Army available on-campus; Navy in cooperation with University of Pennsylvania.

Degrees Conferred: 0 *associate*; 4,979 *baccalaureate*; 1,273 *master's*; 383 *doctorate*; 827 *first-professional*. Bachelor's degrees awarded in top five disciplines: business, management, marketing, and related support services 1,920; engineering/engineering technologies 547; visual and performing arts 435; social sciences and history 266; protective services/public administration 260. Master's degrees awraded: various disciplines 1,273. Doctorates awarded: various disciplines 383. First-professional degrees awarded: dentistry 115; law 323; medicine 194; pharmacy 125; podiatry 65; other health professions 499.

Fees and Other Expenses: *Full-time tuition per academic year 2008–09:* undergraduate resident $11,448, nonresident $20,468; contact the university for current graduate/first-professional tuition/fees that vary by program. *Room and board per academic year:* $8,884. *Books and supplies:* $1,000. *Other expenses:* $3,900.

Financial Aid: Aid from institutionally generated funds is provided on the basis of academic merit, financial need, athletic ability, other criteria.

Financial aid to full-time, first-time undergraduate students: 84% received some form of financial aid. Average amount of aid received: federal grants $3,505; Pell grants $3,059; other federal grants $1,450; state/local grants $3,486; institutional grants $4,758.

Departments and Teaching Staff: *Total instructional faculty:* 3,783. Student/faculty ratio: 17:4. Degrees held by full-time faculty: 87% hold terminal degrees.

Enrollment: Total enrollment: 35,498. Undergraduate 26,195 (full-time 88%, female 54%, male 46%). Graeduate 9,295 (full-time 63%). Undergraduate transfer-in students 2,767.

Characteristics of Student Body: *Ethnic/racial makeup:* Black non-Hispanic: 17%; Asian or Pacific Islander: 10%; Hispanic: 4%; White non-Hispanic: 58%; unknown: 9%; nonresident alien 3%. *Age distribution:* number under 18: 344; 18–19: 7,009; 20–21: 6,979; 22–24: 4,023; 25–29: 1,182; 30–34: 293; 35–39: 133; 40–49: 129; 50–64: 43; 65 and over: 46.

International Students: 1,593 nonresident aliens enrolled fall 2008. Programs available to aid students whose native language is not English: social, cultural. English as a Second Language Program. Financial aid specifically designated for international students available annually.

Student Life: On-campus residence halls house 14% of student body. Housing available for married students. *Intercollegiate athletics:* male: football, soccer, basketball, gymnastics, crew, tennis, baseball, track, golf; female: basketball, softball, field hockey, crew, gymnastics, track and field, soccer, volleyball, fencing, lacrosse, tennis. *Special regulations:* Cars permitted without restrictions. *Special services:* Learning Resources Center, medical services, campus van service. *Student publications, radio: Spice*, a monthly newspaper; *Temple News*, a daily newspaper. Radio station WRTI broadcasts 153 hours per week. *Surrounding community:* Philadelphia population 1,650,000. Served by mass transit bus, subway, and train systems; airport 10 miles from campus; passenger rail service adjacent to main campus.

Library Collections: 6,352,775 volumes including bound books, serial backfiles, electronic documents, and government documents not in separate collections. Online catalog. 3.2 million microforms; 30,000 audiovisual materials; 22,000 periodicals inlcuding vis electronic access. Computer work stations available. Students have access to the Internet at no charge.

Most important special holdings include Urban Archives/photojournalism; Blockson Afro-American History Collection; Contemporary Culture Collection.

Buildings and Grounds: Campus area 376 acres.

Chief Executive Officer: Dr. David Adamany, President.

Undergraduates address admission inquiries to Dr. Timm Rinehart, Director of Admissions; first-professional inquiries to Director of Admissions for respective schools; graduate inquires to Dean of Graduate School.

College of Arts and Sciences

Degree Programs Offered: *Baccalaureate, master's, doctorate* in various fields.

Distinctive Educational Programs: Interdisciplinary programs in American studies, pan-African studies, Puerto Rican studies, urban studies, women's studies. Honors programs. Work-experience and field study programs. Study abroad in China; Dublin, Ireland; Rome, Italy; Japan; Latin America. *Other distinctive programs:* Center for Holocaust Studies, Center for the Study of Remedial Learning, Center for the Study of Federalism, Social Services Data Library, Applied Research Center of Urban Studies.

College of Allied Health Professions

Degree Programs Offered: *Baccalaureate* in health records administration, clinical laboratory sciences, nursing, occupational therapy, physical therapy; *master's* in clinical laboratory sciences, occupational therapy, and physical therapy.

Tyler School of Art

Degree Programs Offered: *Baccalaureate* in fine arts (also available with teaching certification), graphic design; *master's* in fine arts, ceramics/glass, graphic design, metals and jewelry, painting, printmaking, photography, sculpture, fibers and fabric design, art history, education (with a major in art), visual design.

Distinctive Educational Programs: Study abroad in Rome. Internship program. Student mobility program in cooperation with the East Coast Art Schools Consortium.

School of Business and Management

Degree Programs Offered: *Associate, baccalaureate, master's, doctorate.*

Distinctive Educational Programs: Combined M.B.A.-master's in chemistry program. Cooperative education.

School of Communications and Theater

Degree Programs Offered: *Baccalaureate, master's, doctorate.*

Distinctive Educational Programs: Special facilities include television studios, radio station, video display terminals, wire services, darkroom, graphics laboratory, film editing equipment. *Other distinctive programs:* Speech forensics, audiology.

College of Education

Degree Programs Offered: *Baccalaureate, master's, doctorate.* Teacher certification also awarded.

College of Engineering, Computer Sciences and Architecture

Degree Programs Offered: *Associate* in building construction technology; electronics engineering technology; environmental technology; mechanical engineering technology; *baccalaureate* in architecture; biomedical engineering technology; civil engineering; civil engineering and construction technology; electrical engineering technology; electrical engineering; engineering science; engineering technology; environmental engineering technology; mechanical engineering; mechanical engineering technology.

TEMPLE UNIVERSITY—*cont'd*

College of Health, Physical Education, Recreation, and Dance

Degree Programs Offered: *Baccalaureate, master's, doctorate* in dance, health, physical education, recreation and leisure.

Distinctive Educational Programs: Master's program in community health education. Biokinetics laboratory for research in exercise physiology.

Ambler Campus - Department of Horticulture and Landscape Design

Degree Programs Offered: *Associate* in horticulture.

Distinctive Educational Programs: Continuing education programs.

Esther Boyer College of Music

Degree Programs Offered: *Baccalaureate, master's, doctorate.*

Distinctive Educational Programs: Cooperative music education extern program with School Board of Philadelphia. Work-study in association with Philadelphia Orchestra. Philadelphia woodwind quintet-in-residence. Master class series with international artists. The New School Institute for Ensemble and Instrumental Studies.

School of Pharmacy

Degree Programs Offered: *Baccalaureate* in pharmacy; *master's* in environmental health; *master's, doctorate* in pharmaceutical chemistry, pharmacology, and pharmacy.

School of Social Administration

Degree Programs Offered: *Baccalaureate, master's* in social work.

School of Dentistry

Degree Programs Offered: *First-professional, master's, doctorate.*

Admission: *For first-professional degree:* Baccalaureate which must include 6 hours each of biology, English, inorganic chemistry, organic chemistry, physics; minimum 60 electives.

Degree Requirements: *For first-professional degree:* 2.0 GPA, 4 years in residence, prescribed curriculum.

Distinctive Educational Programs: Cooperative study programs with approved hospitals.

Temple University School of Law

Degree Programs Offered: *First-professional, master's.*

Admission: *For first-professional degree:* Baccalaureate from accredited college or university, LSAT.

Degree Requirements: *For first-professional degree:* 83 credit hours, 2.0 GPA, 24 months in residence, prescribed curriculum.

School of Medicine

Degree Programs Offered: *Master's* in biochemistry, physiology, pathology and biometrics; *doctorate* in anatomy, biochemistry, microbiology, physiology, pathology, medical pharmacology, biometrics.

Admission: Minimum 90 semester hours at an accredited college or university which must include 1 year, each with laboratory, of biology, general physics, inorganic chemistry, organic chemistry.

Degree Requirements: 24 months in residence, prescribed curriculum.

Temple University School of Podiatric Medicine

8th and Race Streets
Philadelphia, Pennsylvania 19107-2496
Tel: (215) 629-0300 **E-mail:** admissions@podiatry.temple.edu
Fax: (215) 627-2815 **Internet:** www.podiatry.temple.edu

Institution Description: Temple University School of Podiatric Medicine, formerly known as The Pennsylvania College of Podiatric Medicine, is a public institution supported in part by the Commonwealth of Pennsylvania. *Enrollment:* 288. *Degrees awarded:* First-professional.

Accreditation: *Regional:* MSA/CHE. *Professional*: podiatry

History: Founded 1963; moved to present location 1973; became a unit of Temple University 2002.

Institutional Structure: *Governing board:* Extrainstitutional representation: 30 trustees. 1 administrator (ex officio), 2 faculty representatives, 2 student representatives. *Composition of institution:* President, executive vice president, vice president for academic affairs, vice president for clinical education, vice president for student affairs. Full-time instructional faculty 30.

Calendar: Trimesters. Academic year Sept. to June.

Admission: Selection is based on academic performance and Medical College Admission Test scores. At the invitation of the College, personal interviews are conducted. *Requirements:* Generally 4 years undergraduate study; minimum requirement 90 hours. Accelerated admissions program available: 3 years preprofessional and 4 years podiatric medical education.

Degree Requirements: Completion of prescribed 4 year curriculum; 2 years in residence; successful completion of Part I of National Board of Podiatry Examiners; must have taken Part II National Broad of Podiatry Examiners.

Distinctive Educational Programs: Special facilities for using telecommunications in lecture rooms. On-site surgical suite, laboratories, Foot and Ankle Institute which serves the Greater Philadelphia Area provides students with the opportunity to learn all aspects of clinical education; Gait Study Center (computer-assisted locomotion analysis).

Degrees Conferred: 68 *first-professional:* podiatric medicine.

Fees and Other Expenses: *Full-time tuition per academic year 2008–09:* contact the institution for current information.

Financial Aid: Aid from institutionally generated funds is provided on the basis of academic merit, financial need, other criteria. Institution has a Program Participation Agreement with the U.S. Department of Education for eligible students to receive Pell Grants and, depending upon the agreement, other federal aid.

Departments and Teaching Staff: *Total instructional faculty:* 122. Degrees held by full-time faculty: doctorate 33%, master's 10%, professional 57%. 93% hold terminal degrees.

Enrollment: Total enrollment 288.

Characteristics of Student Body: *Ethnic/racial makeup:* number of Black non-Hispanic: 24; Asian or Pacific Islander; 36; Hispanic: 12; White non-Hispanic: 299. other: 23.

International Students: 22 nonresident aliens enrolled fall 2008. Students from Europe, Canada. No programs available to aid students whose native language is not English. No financial aid specifically designated for international students.

Student Life: 7-story apartment building adjacent to the College; parking available on private lot. *Student publications: In-Step*, quarterly student newsletter; *Pace*, quarterly public interest newsletter for local distribution; *Strides*, newsletter distributed quarterly to alumni and area podiatrists; *Footage*, weekly in-house newsletter distributed to employees and students. *Surrounding community:* The college is located in the Independence Mall section of Philadelphia.

Library Collections: 40,000 volumes. 300 microforms, 550 videocassettes; 330 current periodical subscriptions. Students have access to online information retrieval services and the Internet.

Most important special holdings include Dr. Stewart E. Reed Historical Collection; archival collection and special podiatric exhibits maintained by the Center for the History of Foot Care and Foot Wear.

Buildings and Grounds: Campus area 1.5 acres.

Chief Executive Officer: Dr. David Adamany, President.

Address admission inquiries to David Martin, Director of Student Services.

Thiel College

75 College Avenue
Greenville, Pennsylvania 16125
Tel: (724) 589-2000 **E-mail:** admissions@thiel.edu
Fax: (724) 589-2850 **Internet:** www.thiel.edu

Institution Description: Thiel College is a private, independent, nonprofit college affiliated with the Evangelical Lutheran Church in America. *Enrollment:* 1,137. *Degrees awarded:* Associate, baccalaureate.

Accreditation: *Regional:* MSA/CHE. *Professional*: chemistry

History: Established at Phillipsburg as Thiel Academy 1866; chartered as Thiel College of Evangelical Lutheran Church, moved to present location, and offered first instruction at postsecondary level 1870; awarded first degree (baccalaureate) 1874; changed name to Thiel College of Pittsburgh Synod of United Lutheran Church in America 1956; adopted present name 1964. *See* Roy H. Johnson, *The History of Thiel College 1866–1974* (Philadelphia, Pa.: Dorrance Publishing Co.) for further information.

Institutional Structure: *Governing board:* Thiel College Board of Trustees. Representation: 45 trustees, including 6 alumni. 2 ex officio. All voting. *Com-*

position of institution: Administrators 18. Academic affairs headed by vice president for academic services. Management/business/finances directed by vice president for administrative services. Full-time instructional faculty 62. Academic governance body, the faculty, meets an average of 9 times per year.

Calendar: Semesters. Academic year Aug. to May. Freshmen admitted Aug., Jan, June, July. Degrees conferred and formal commencement May. Summer session of 2 terms from June to July.

Characteristics of Freshmen: 1,439 applicants (599 female, 840 male). 71% of applicants accepted. 31% of accepted applicants enrolled full-time.

72% (262 students) submitted SAT scores; 33% (120 students) submitted ACT scores. *25th percentile*: SAT Critical Reading 400, SAT Math 400; ACT Composite 16, ACT English 14, ACT 16. *75th percentile*: SAT Critical Reading 520, SAT Math 530; ACT Composite 22, ACT English 22, ACT Math 22.

40% of entering freshmen expected to graduate within 5 years. 66% of freshmen from Pennsylvania. Freshmen from 23 states and 11 foreign countries.

Admission: Rolling admissions plan. For fall acceptance, apply as early as June 1 of previous year. Early acceptance available. *Requirements:* Either graduation from accredited secondary school with 16 units which normally include 4 English, 2 foreign language, 3 mathematics, 2 science, 3 social studies; or GED. *Entrance tests:* College Board SAT or ACT recommended. For foreign students TOEFL is required. *For transfer students:* 2.0 minimum GPA; 94 hours maximum transfer credit; good standing at institution previously attended.

College credit and advanced placement for postsecondary-level work completed in secondary school. College credit for extrainstitutional learning on basis of faculty assessment.

Tutoring available. Remedial courses offered during regular academic year.

Degree Requirements: *For all associate degrees:* 64 credit hours. *For all baccalaureate degrees:* 124 credit hours; 2.0 GPA in major. *For all undergraduate degrees:* 2.0 GPA; final 30 hours in residence; exit competency examination in English; core requirements.

Fulfillment of some degree requirements and exemption from some beginning courses possible by passing College Board CLEP and AP. *Grading system:* A–F; pass-fail; withdraw (carries time limit); incomplete (carries time limit).

Distinctive Educational Programs: Cooperative Education program. Internships, independent studies, special projects, seminars. Off-campus college, evening classes. Accelerated degree programs. Honors program. ESL program. Tutorials. Professional school early acceptance program. Dual-degree program in engineering with Case Western Reserve University (OH) and the University of Pittsburgh (PA) and in environmental management and forestry with Duke University (NC). Interdisciplinary programs in allied health. Junior year abroad through programs sponsored by other institutions or by individual arrangement. Exchange program with Ewha Women's University (Korea). Cooperative programs include Appalachian Semester sponsored by Union College (KY); Argonne National Laboratories Semester (IL) in cooperation with Central States Universities, Inc.; commercial art program with Art Institute of Pittsburgh (PA); art semester and United Nations semester at Drew University (NJ); degree and diploma program with the Pittsburgh Institute of Mortuary Science (PA); the professional Internship Philadelphia Program; Ethical Issues and Public Affairs Semester as part of the Lutheran College Washington Consortium (DC); Washington (DC) Semester Program at American University.

Degrees Conferred: 182 *baccalaureate*. Bachelor's degrees awarded in top five disciplines: business, management, marketing, and related support services 74; education 28; social sciences 23; psychology 17; history 11.

Fees and Other Expenses: *Full-time tuition per academic year 2008–09:* \$21,406. *Books and supplies:* \$1,000. *Room and board per academic year:* \$8,192. *Other expenses:* \$3,000.

Financial Aid: Aid from institutionally generated funds is provided on the basis of academic merit, financial need. Institution has a Program Participation Agreement with the U.S. Department of Education for eligible students to receive Pell Grants and, depending upon the agreement, other federal aid.

Financail aid to first-time, full-time undergraduate students: 100% received some form of aid. Average amount of aid received: federal grants \$4,097; Pell grants \$3,128; other federal aid \$1,279; state/local grants \$2,989; institutional grants \$9,397.

Departments and Teaching Staff: *Total instructional faculty:* 113 (full-time 62, part-time 51). 72% of faculty hold the doctorate, first-professional, or other terminal degree. Student/faculty ratio: 17:1.

Enrollment: Total enrollment 1,137. Undergraduate 1,137 (full-time 94%; female 49%, male 51%). Transfer-in students 39.

Characteristics of Student Body: *Ethnic/racial makeup:* Black non-Hispanic: 6%; Asian or Pacific Islander: 1%; Hispanic: 1%; White non-Hispanic: 63%; unknown: 24%; nonresident alien 5%.

International Students: 55 nonresident aliens enrolled fall 2008. Students from Europe, Asia, Latin America, Africa. Programs available to aid students whose native language is not English: social, cultural. English as a Second Language Program. Financial aid specifically designated for international students: scholarships available annually to qualifying students.

Student Life: On-campus residence halls, including fraternities, house 70% of student body. Residence halls for males constitute 47% of such space, for females 53%. 35% of males join fraternities and 30% of females join sororities; 25% of total Greeks live in fraternity housing and/or Greek Community housing. *Intercollegiate athletics:* male: baseball, basketball, football; female: basketball, softball, tennis, volleyball; both sexes: cross-country, track. *Special regulations:* Cars permitted without restrictions. *Special services:* Learning Resources Center, medical services. Transportation to and from campus and bus station or airport at opening and closing of terms; fee charged. *Student publications, radio: Endymion*, a yearbook; *Thielensian*, a weekly newspaper. Radio station WTGP broadcasts 56 hours per week. *Surrounding community:* Greenville area population 12,000. Pittsburgh, 75 miles from campus, is nearest metropolitan area. Served by airport 20 miles from campus.

Publications: *The Bell*, a semiannual bulletin distributed to alumni, denominational members, and friends of the college.

Library Collections: 187,000 volumes. 305,000 government documents (separate collection); 149,000 microforms; 6,500 audiovisual materials 415 current periodical subscriptions. Students have access to online information retrieval services and the Internet.

Most important special holdings include Lutheran Church in America Synod Archives; United States, Pennsylvania, and United Nations documents.

Buildings and Grounds: Campus area 135 acres.

Chief Executive Officer: Dr. Lance A. Masters, President.

Address admission inquiries to Sonya Kapikas, Chief, Admissions Office.

Thomas Jefferson University

130 South Ninth Street
Philadelphia, Pennsylvania 19107
Tel: (215) 955-6000 **E-mail:** admissions@tju.edu
Fax: (215) 955-7241 **Internet:** www.tju.edu

Institution Description: Thomas Jefferson University is a private, independent, nonprofit institution providing upper division, professional, and graduate degree study. Part-time associate degree program also offered. *Enrollment:* 3,202. *Degrees awarded:* Associate, baccalaureate, first-professional (medicine), master's, doctorate.

Accreditation: *Regional:* MSA/CHE. *Professional*: cytotechnology, dental hygiene, diagnostic medical sonography, medicine, nursing, occupational therapy, physical therapy, radiography

History: Established as Jefferson Medical College and offered first instruction at postsecondary level 1824; awarded first degree (first-professional) 1826; chartered 1838; added College of Allied Health and Sciences, College of Graduate Studies, and adopted present name 1969. *See* George M. Gould, ed., *The Jefferson Medical College of Philadelphia, A History* (New York: The Lewis Publishing Co., 1904) for further information.

Institutional Structure: *Governing board:* The Board of Trustees. Extrainstitutional representation: 37 trustees, 6 trustees emeriti, 3 alumni. 31 voting. *Composition of institution:* Administrators 7. Academic affairs headed by president. Management/business/finances directed by vice president for administration and finance. Full-time instructional faculty 410. Academic governance body, Council of Academic Officers, meets an average of 4 times per year.

Calendar: Semesters. Academic year Sept. to June. Entering students admitted Sept., Jan., Mar. Degrees conferred and formal commencement June. Summer session from June to Aug.

Characteristics of Freshmen: 1,839 applicants (1,392 female, 301 male).

Admission: Rolling admissions process except for physical therapy program for which application deadline is Feb. 15. For fall acceptance, apply as early as Sept. of previous year. *Requirements:* 2 years at an accredited college or university with 6 semester hours English, 8 laboratory biology, 3 mathematics, 3 psychology. Additional requirements for some programs. *For transfer students:* minimum transfer GPA 2.00 with maximum transfer credit limited by residence requirement.

College credit and advanced placement for postsecondary-level work through ACT-PEP and CLEP. Tutoring available. Developmental courses offered throughout entire academic year.

Degree Requirements: *For all associate degrees:* 60 credit hours. *For all baccalaureate degrees:* 120–130 credit hours; comprehensives in individual fields of study. *For all undergraduate degrees:* 2.0 GPA; last 30 credits in residence.

Fulfillment of some degree requirements possible by passing departmental examinations, College Board CLEP. *Grading system:* A–F; withdraw (carries time limit).

Distinctive Educational Programs: *For undergraduates:* Flexible meeting and class schedules available. Most programs available full- or part-time, day and evenings. An off-campus center specializing in BSN for registered nurses in

THOMAS JEFFERSON UNIVERSITY—*cont'd*

operation at Harrisburg Community College (PA). *Other distinctive programs:* Post-certificate program for dental hygienists, advanced placement program in diagnostic imaging, occupational therapy certificate program, cytotechnology post-certificate program, advanced placement program for registered nurses, master of science in nursing (rehabilitation emphasis). For graduate students: developmental biology/teratology.

Degrees Conferred: 88 *associate*; 325 *baccalaureate*; 167 *master's*; 17 *doctorate*; 217 *first-professional*. Bachelor's degrees awarded in top five disciplines: health professions and related clinical sciences 276; biological/life sciences 8.

Fees and Other Expenses: *Full-time tuition per academic year 2008–09:* contact the university for current tuition, fees, and housing expenses. Tuition for medical school and other graduate programs vary.

Financial Aid: Aid from institutionally generated funds is provided on the basis of academic merit, financial need. Institution has a Program Participation Agreement with the U.S. Department of Education for eligible students to receive Pell Grants and, depending upon the agreement, other federal aid.

Financial aid to first-time, full-time undegraduate students: 74% received some form of aid.

Departments and Teaching Staff: *Total instructional faculty:* 407.

Enrollment: Total enrollment 3,202. Undergraduate 1,122 (full-time 69%; female 84%, male 16%). Graduate 2,080 (full-time 74%). Undergraduate transfer-in students 541.

Characteristics of Student Body: *Ethnic/racial makeup:* Black non-Hispanic: 9%; Asian or Pacific islander 6%; Hispanic: 2%; White non-Hispanic: 57%; unknown: 25%; nonresident alien 1%.

International Students: 32 nonresident aliens enrolled fall 2008. No programs available to aid students whose native language is not English. No financial aid specifically designated for international students.

Student Life: On-campus residence halls house 39% of student body; 2% of married population is housed in on-campus residence halls. *Special services:* Medical services. *Surrounding community:* Philadelphia population 1,650,000. Served by mass transit bus and rail systems; airport 10 miles from campus, passenger rail service 1 mile from campus.

Library Collections: 150,000 volumes. 19,000 microforms; 1,360 audiovisual materials; 1,762 current periodical subscriptions. Students have access to online information retrieval services and the Internet.

Most important special holdings include Bland Collection (obstetrics and gynecology); Dr. Peter Herbut Papers (first president of TJU); Jeffersoniana (University faculty and staff publications and manuscripts).

Buildings and Grounds: Campus area 13 acres.

Chief Executive Officer: Dr. Robert L. Barchi, President.

Address admission inquiries to Director of Admissions and Enrollment Management.

Jefferson Medical College

Degree Programs Offered: *First-professional.*

Admission: Baccalaureate degree from accredited U.S. college or university with one year each of general biology or zoology, organic chemistry, inorganic chemistry, general physics (all must include laboratory).

Degree Requirements: 228 credit hours; grade of 70 in each course.

Distinctive Educational Programs: Combined first-professional and doctoral program. 6-year dual-degree program with Pennsylvania State University leading to baccalaureate and first-professional degrees. Cooperative program in medical education with University of Delaware and the Medical Center. Interdepartmental courses in cell and tissue biology, clinical medicine, growth and development, medicine and society, neurosciences. *Other distinctive programs:* Continuing education for physicians. Physician Shortage Area Program for students who plan to practice family medicine in physician shortage areas.

Trinity Episcopal School for Ministry

311 Eleventh Street
Ambridge, Pennsylvania 15003
Tel: (724) 266-3838 **E-mail:** info@tesm.edu
Fax: (724) 266-4617 **Internet:** www.tesm.edu

Institution Description: Trinity Episcopal School for Ministry is a private, Episcopal, professional school offering graduate study only. *Enrollment:* 286. *Degrees awarded:* Master's, first-professional.

Accreditation: *National:* ATS. *Professional*: theology

Institutional Structure: *Composition of institution:* Academic affairs headed by dean of academic affairs. Management/business/finances directed by director of financial affairs.

Calendar: Semesters. Academic year Sept. to May.

Characteristics of Freshmen: 2,350 applicants (1,478 female, 813 male). 49% of applicants admitted. 50% of admitted applicants enrolled full-time.

Admission: *Requirements:* Baccalaureate degree from accredited institution.

Degree Requirements: Completion of prescribed curriculum.

Degrees Conferred: 10 *master's;* 31 *first-professional:* master of divinity; 4 *doctorate*.

Fees and Other Expenses: *Full-time tuition per academic year:* contact the seminary for current rates.

Financial Aid: Aid from institutionally generated funds is provided on the basis of financial need. Institution has a Program Participation Agreement with the U.S. Department of Education for eligible students to receive Pell Grants and, depending upon the agreement, other federal aid.

Departments and Teaching Staff: *Total instructional faculty:* 19. Total tenured faculty: 12. Degrees held by full-time faculty: master's 100%, doctorate 60%.

Enrollment: Total enrollment 286.

Characteristics of Student Body: *Ethnic/racial makeup:* Black non-Hispanic: 1.4%; American Indian or Alaska Native: 11.5%; Asian or Pacific Islander: .7%; Hispanic: .7%; White non-Hispanic: 83.6%.

International Students: 6 nonresident aliens enrolled fall 2008. No programs available to aid students whose native language is not English. Financial aid specifically designated for international students: one scholarship awarded annually.

Student Life: *Special regulations:* Cars permitted without restrictions. *Surrounding community:* Ambridge is located on the Ohio River, 30 miles west of Pittsburgh. Served by airport 20 miles from campus.

Library Collections: 67,000 volumes. 300 current periodical subscriptions. Most important special collection in Biblical Studies.

Chief Executive Officer: Very Rev. Paul F.M. Zaul, President and Dean.

Address admission inquiries to Director of Admissions.

University of the Arts

320 South Broad Street
Philadelphia, Pennsylvania 19102
Tel: (215) 717-6000 **E-mail:** admissions@uarts.edu
Fax: (215) 717-6045 **Internet:** www.uarts.edu

Institution Description: The University of the Arts includes the Philadelphia College of Art and Design (PCAD) and the Philadelphia College of Performing Arts (PCPA), and prepares its students for more than 150 career paths in the visual and performing arts and related fields. *Enrollment:* 2,401. *Degrees awarded:* Associate, baccalaureate, master's. Diplomas also awarded.

Accreditation: *Regional:* MSA/CHE. *Professional*: art, interior design, music

History: Established as Philadelphia Musical Academy and offered first instruction at postsecondary level 1870; awarded first degree (baccalaureate) 1881; chartered 1915; merged with Philadelphia Conservatory of Music 1962; adopted present name 1976; merged with Philadelphia Dance Academy 1977; added School of Theatre 1986; consolidated with Philadelphia College of Art under the name Philadelphia Colleges of the Arts 1986. Pennsylvania Department of Education approval for university status and name changed to The University of the Arts 1987.

Institutional Structure: *Governing board:* Board of Trustees (44 men / 13 women). *Composition of institution:* Chief academic and administrative officer is Provost. Administrative officers: 5 men / 3 women. Full-time instructional faculty 83. Academic governance body, University Senate, meets an average of 10 times per year (13 male / 17 female elected from and by ranks of full- and part-time faculty and staff); 2 primary functions: represent its constituencies in governance of University and advise the Board of Trustees and University President, Provost, Deans, and Directors in creation and implementation of policy.

Calendar: Semesters. Academic year Sept. to May. Freshmen admitted Sept., Jan., June. Degrees conferred and formal commencement May. Summer session from May to Aug.

Characteristics of Freshmen: 2,705 applicants (1,746 female, 959 male). 45% of applicants accepted. 45% of accepted applicants enrolled full-time.

93% (531 students) submitted SAT scores; 13% (75 students) submitted ACT scores. *25th percentile*: SAT Critical Reading 470, SAT Math 450, SAT Writing 460; ACT Composite 20, ACT English 20. *75th percentile*: SAT Critical Reading 580, SAT Math 570; ACT Composite 25, ACT English 25.

43% of freshmen expected to graduate within 5 years. 39% of freshmen from Pennsylvania. Freshmen from 40 states and 43 foreign countries.

Admission: Rolling admissions. Early acceptance available. *Requirements:* GED or graduation from accredited secondary school with minimum of 4 units English, 1 unit social science, 2 units science, 2 units math. *Entrance tests:* College Board SAT (preferred) or ACT Composite; foreign students, TOEFL; performing arts audition, visual arts portfolio or successful completion of 6-week summer program; *For transfer students:* 2.0 minimum GPA; maximum transfer credit limited by residence requirement.

Degree Requirements: *PCAD:* 132 semester hours for all baccalaureate degrees; 48 credits in residence; foundation program. Fulfillment of some degree requirements and exemption from some beginning courses possible through College Board CLEP, AP tests. *PCPA:* 125–143 semester hours depending upon curriculum for baccalaureate degrees; 4 terms in residence; core curriculum; concert attendance; performance requirements. Fulfillment of some degree requirements and exemption from some beginning courses possible through departmental examinations. *For all programs:* Minimum 2.0 GPA. *Grading system:* A–F; pass–fail; option for humanities and elective courses; credit–no credit; withdrawal and incomplete carry time limits.

Distinctive Educational Programs: *Special academic programs:* Accelerated program, honors program, independent study, teacher preparatory program, internships; University affiliates program with Academy of Vocal Arts, American Music Theater Festival, Brooklyn Academy of Music Next Wave Festival, Jacob's Pillow, The Jamison Project, The Painted Bride, Pennsylvania Opera Theater, Small Computers for the Arts Network (SCAN), The Wilma Theater. *Collaborations with other institutions:* Visiting/exchange student program; Mobility Program cross-registration with East Coast Art College Consortium (Parsons School of Design; Pratt Institute; Cooper Union; Nova Scotia College of Art and Design; Rhode Island School of Design; School of Museum of Fine Arts, Boston; Maryland Institute College of Art; Massachusetts College of Art) and Pennsylvania Academy of Fine Arts, Philadelphia College of Textiles and Science; Alliance of Independent Colleges of Art/New York Studio School; domestic off-campus programs with Vermont Studio Center (Johnson, VT) and Springside School (Philadelphia, PA). *Other programs:* Saturday School (children, adult), New Studies (adult), NS Teachers Institute, Continuing Education, CE Papermaking Institute, CE Lecture Series, CE Exhibition Series, A Summer World of Dance (with The Jamison Project), Dance Extension (adult). *Pre-college educational programs.* PREP Studio and Humanities courses for incoming freshmen, New Talent Visual Arts Program for high school juniors and seniors, Summer Intensive Studio and Humanities courses for mid-year admitted students to attain sophomore status. Study abroad in exchange with Brighton Polytechnic in Brighton, England; Ravensbourne College of Design, England; Tokyo School of Art, Japan.

Degrees Conferred: 452 *baccalaureate*; 88 *master's*. Bachelor's degrees awarded in top disciplines: visual and performing arts 369; multidisciplinary studies 23; communication, journalism, and related programs 16; education 13. Master's degrees awarded: various disciplines 88.

Fees and Other Expenses: *Full-time tuition per academic year 2008–09:* $30,600. *Books and supplies:* $2,100. *Room and board per academic year:* $8,712. *Other expenses:* $2,515.

Financial Aid: Aid from institutionally generated funds is provided on the basis of academic merit, financial need, other criteria (talent).

Financial aid to full-time, first-time undergraduate students: 99% received some form of financial aid. Average amount of aid received: federal grants $2,615; Pell grants $2,849; other federal aid: $2,176; state/local grants $3,421; institutional grants $11,254.

Departments and Teaching Staff: *Total instructional faculty:* 83. Student/faculty ratio: 19:1.

Enrollment: Total enrollment 2,401. Undergraduate 2,183 (full-time 98%; female 51%; male 43%). Graduate 218 (full-time 75%). Undergraduate transfer-in students 115.

Characteristics of Student Body: *Ethnic/racial makeup:* Black non-Hispanic: 10%; American Indian or Alaska Native: 1%; Asian or Pacific Islander: 3%; Hispanic: 5%; White non-Hispanic: 64%; unknown: 14%; nonresident alien 4%.

International Students: 96 nonresident aliens enrolled fall 2008. Programs available to aid students whose native language is not English: social, cultural. English as a Second Language Program. No financial aid specifically designated for international students.

Student Life: On-campus apartment-style residence halls and off-campus housing information available. *Special regulations:* Freshmen living beyond commuting distance must live in campus housing; smoking restricted to certain areas. *Special services:* Learning Resources Center, medical services, physical fitness facilities. *Activities:* Choral groups, dance, jazz band, ensembles, musical theater, opera, symphony orchestra, Artists' Christian Fellowship, Afro-American Student Union, Arts Council, Orientation Committee, Society for Ecological Education, intramural volleyball, Student Congress. *Surrounding community:* Campus is located in the heart of Philadelphia's cultural community in Center City; includes 6 classroom buildings, 2 student residence facilities, and the Shubert Theater. The Academy of Music and the proposed sites for the new Philadelphia Orchestra Hall and Wilma Theater are adjacent to campus. Served by mass transit bus and subway system; airport 10 miles from campus; passenger rail service less than 1 mile from campus. Philadelphia population 1,725,000.

Library Collections: 189,000 volumes. 294,000 audiovisual materials. 500 serial subscriptions. Audiovisual materials include phonodisks, compact disks, audiocassettes, reel-to-reel tapes, multimedia, VHS tapes. Visual resources include 103,980 pictures; 149,671 slides. Online catalog. Students have access to online information retrieval services and the Internet.

Most important special holdings include book arts collection; illustrated books; textiles.

Buildings and Grounds: Campus DVD available.

Chief Executive Officer: Miguel Angel Corzo, President.

Address admission inquiries to Susan Gandy, Director of Admissions.

University of Pennsylvania

34th and Spruce Streets
Philadelphia, Pennsylvania 19104
Tel: (215) 898-5000 **E-mail:** info@admissions.upenn.edu
Fax: (215) 898-5756 **Internet:** www.upenn.edu

Institution Description: University of Pennsylvania is a private, state-aided institution. *Enrollment:* 24,107. *Degrees awarded:* Associate, baccalaureate, first-professional (dentistry, law, medicine, veterinary medicine), master's, doctorate.

Member of Consortium on Financing Higher Education.

Accreditation: *Regional:* MSA/CHE. *Professional*: architecture, business, dentistry, engineering, health services administration, landscape architecture, law, medicine, nuclear medicine technology, nursing, planning, practical nursing, psychology internship, social work, teacher education, veterinary medicine

History: Established as Charity School 1740; chartered as Academy and Charity School in the Province of Pennsylvania 1753; changed name to College, Academy and Charitable School in the Province of Pennsylvania and offered first instruction at postsecondary level 1755; awarded first degree (baccalaureate) 1757; changed name to University of the State of Pennsylvania 1779; adopted present name 1791. *See* Edgar Potts Cheyney, *History of the University of Pennsylvania 1740–1940* (Philadelphia, Pa.: University of Pennsylvania Press, 1940) for further information.

Institutional Structure: *Governing board:* The Trustees of the University of Pennsylvania. Representation: 63 trustees, including the president of the university, governor of Pennsylvania, president of general alumni society. 3 ex officio. 44 voting. *Composition of institution:* Administrators 35. Academic affairs headed by provost. Management/business/finances directed by vice president for budget and finance. Full-time instructional faculty 3,221.

Calendar: Semesters. Academic year Sept. to Apr. Freshmen admitted Sept. Degrees conferred May, Aug., Dec. Formal commencement May. Summer session from May to Aug.

Characteristics of Freshmen: 22,935 applicants (11,284 female, 11,851 male). 17% of applicants accepted. 63% of accepted applicants enrolled full-time.

97% (2,321 students) submitted SAT scores; 26% (632 540 students) submitted ACT scores. *25th percentile*: SAT Critical Reading 620, SAT Math 680, SAT Writing 650; ACT Composite 39. *75th percentile*: SAT Critical Reading 720, SAT Math 770, SAT Writing 740; ACT Composite 33.

92% of entering freshmen expected to graduate within 5 years. 17% of freshmen from Pennsylvania. Students from 50 states and 89 foreign countries.

Admission: Early admission plan for state residents. For fall acceptance, apply no later than Jan. 1 of year of enrollment. Students are notified of acceptance Apr. 15. Apply by Nov. 1 for early decision; must limit application to University of Pennsylvania. Early acceptance available. *Requirements:* Graduation from accredited secondary school. Recommend strong academic background, including study in English, foreign language, mathematics, social studies, natural sciences. *Entrance tests:* College Board SAT, 2 subject tests. *For transfer students:* Recommend 3.5 0 minimum GPA; 16 course units maximum transfer credit. Transfer students must have completed 1 full year of postsecondary-level work.

College credit and advanced placement for postsecondary-level work completed in secondary school. Tutoring available. Noncredit developmental courses offered in summer session.

Degree Requirements: 30 to 40 course units; GPA 2.0; 10 units must be in science, humanities, and mathematics; requirements in the major: 12 to 18 units.

Fulfillment of some degree requirements and exemption from some beginning courses by passing International Baccalaureate Examination, College Board AP.

Distinctive Educational Programs: Flexible meeting places and schedules. Facilities and programs for independent research, including honors programs, individual majors, tutorials, and degree programs. Flower and Cook Observatory for astronomical research. Morris Arboretum for botanical and horticultural research. University Museum for study of ancient and primitive man. Study abroad in Bologna, Italy; Beijing or Nanking, China; Munich, Germany; Com-

UNIVERSITY OF PENNSYLVANIA—*cont'd*

peigne, France; Edinburgh, Scotland; London, England; Tokyo, Japan; Madrid, Spain; Ibadan, Nigeria; Paris, France.

ROTC: Army, Navy. Air Force in cooperation with St. Joseph's University; Army with Drexel University.

Degrees Conferred: 1 *associate;* 2,766 *baccalaureate*; 3,019 *master's*; 496 *doctorate*; 666 *first-professional.* Bachelor's degrees awarded in top five disciplines: social sciences and history 252; business and management 612; engineering 241; biological/life sciences 157; health professions and related clinical sciences 148. Master's: various disciplines 2,794. Doctorates awarded: various disciplines 496. First-professional: dentistry 125; law 273; veterinary medicine 110; medicine 158; other health professions 393.

Fees and Other Expenses: *Full-time tuition per academic year 2008–09:* $37,526 undergraduate; contact the university for current graduate/first-professional tuition and other costs that vary by program. *Required fees:* $3,172. *Room and board per academic year:* $10,621. *Books and supplies:* $1,050. *Other expenses:* $2,102.

Financial Aid: Aid from institutionally generated funds is provided on the basis of financial need.

Financial aid to full-time, first-time undergraduate students: 59% received some form of financial aid. Average amount of aid received: federal grants $6,762; Pell grants $3,227; other federal aid $3,535; state/local grants $5,004; institutional grants $25,821.

Departments and Teaching Staff: *Total instructional faculty:* 5,869 (full-time 3,221, part-time 2,648). Student/faculty ratio: 6:1.

Enrollment: Total enrollment 24,107. Undergraduate 11,851 (full-time 87%; female 51%, male 49%). Graeduate 12,256 (full-time 80%).

Characteristics of Student Body: *Ethnic/racial makeup (undergraduate):* Black non-Hispanic: 5%; Asian or Pacific Islander: 16%; Hispanic: 5%; White non-Hispanic: 40%; unknown: 21%; nonresident alien 10%. *Age distribution:* number under 18: 2,299; 18–19: 4,520; 20–21: 2,590; 22–24: 177; 25–29: 108; 30–34: 11; 35–39: 6; 40–49: 66; 50–64: 2.

International Students: 2,410 nonresident aliens enrolled fall 2008. Programs available to aid students whose native language is not English: social, cultural, financial. English as a Second Language Program. Financial aid specifically designated for international students: scholarships available annually.

Student Life: On-campus residence halls house 64% of student body. Residence halls for both sexes constitute 100% of such space. 24% of undergraduate males join and 8% live in fraternity hosuing. 18% of undergraduate females join and live in sorority housing. Housing available for married students. *Intercollegiate athletics:* male: baseball, basketball, football, gymnastics, lacrosse, soccer, swimming, tennis, track, volleyball, wrestling; female: basketball, field hockey, gymnastics, lacrosse, swimming, tennis, track, volleyball; both sexes: sailing. *Special regulations:* Cars permitted without restrictions. *Special services:* Learning Resources Center, medical services, campus bus service, escort service. *Student publications, radio, television: Black Student News*, a newsletter published 6 times a year; *Columns*, a quarterly journal of current events; *Consuming Apartments*, a guide for the off-campus student; *Daily Pennsylvanian*, a newspaper published 5 times a week; *Era*, an annual literary; *Penn Press*, a newspaper published 6 times a year; *Penn Review*, an annual literary magazine; *Penn Triangle*, a quarterly engineering magazine; *Poor Richard's Record*, a yearbook; *Powerline*, a newsletter on energy-related issues; *Punch Bowl*, a biannual humor magazine; *SCUE Course Guide*, an annual course evaluation publication; *A Voyage Out*, an annual women's literary magazine; *Wharton Account*, undergraduate business magazine; *WXPN Program Guide*, a monthly tabloid. Radio station WXPN-FM broadcasts 168 hours per week. TV station UTV broadcasts 40 hours per week. *Surrounding community:* Philadelphia population 1,725,000. Served by mass transit bus and rail system; airport 3 miles from campus; passenger rail service less than 1 mile from campus.

Publications: *American Quarterly, Expedition* (quarterly), *Health Law Project Library Bulletin* (monthly), *Hispanic Review* (quarterly), *International Economics Review* (3 times per year), *Isis* (five times per year), *Journal of Communication* (quarterly), *Journal of Economic Theory, Keystone Folklore* (2–3 times per year), *Orbis* (quarterly), *University of Pennsylvania Law Review* (6 times per year), *The Wharton Magazine* (quarterly).

Library Collections: 5,760,000 volumes. 4.2 million microforms; 89,000 audiovisual materials; 51,000 periodicals available in paper, microform, and via electronic access. Online catalog. Students have access to online information retrieval services and the Internet.

Most important special holdings include Furness Library of Shakespeare and his contemporaries; Lea Library of European Middle Ages, specializing in legal and ecclesiastical history; E. F. Smith Collection on history of chemistry; Dreiser Papers.

Buildings and Grounds: Campus area 269 acres. Campus DVD available.

Chief Executive Officer: Dr. Amy Gutmann, President.

Address admission inquiries to Eric J. Kaplan, Director of Admissions.

School of Arts and Sciences

Degree Programs Offered: *Baccalaureate, master's, doctorate.*

Distinctive Educational Programs: Accelerated 7-year baccalaureate/first-professional degree program with School of Dental Medicine. Accelerated 6-year doctorate/first-professional degree program with School of Veterinary Medicine. Dual-degree programs in engineering, design and structural technology, and science technology and society with School of Engineering and Applied Science. Interdepartmental/interdisciplinary majors, including Afro-American studies, biological basis of behavior, communications, design of the environment, East Asian studies, education, environmental studies, fine arts, international relations, theater arts, urban studies, women's studies. Individualized majors. University scholars program.

School of Engineering and Applied Science

Degree Programs Offered: *Baccalaureate* in applied science, bioengineering, chemical engineering, civil and urban engineering, computer science and engineering, electrical engineering and science, materials science and engineering, mechanical engineering and applied mechanics, systems science and engineering; *master's, doctorate* in bioengineering, chemical and biochemical engineering, civil and urban engineering, computer and information science, electrical engineering and science, materials science and engineering, mechanical engineering and applied mechanics, systems engineering; *master's* in energy engineering.

Distinctive Educational Programs: Interdisciplinary programs in architecture and engineering, city planning and engineering, design theory/structural technology and science/technology/society, management and technology, podiatry/engineering. Study abroad in France, Israel, People's Republic of China, Scotland. *See also* The Wharton School.

School of Nursing

Degree Programs Offered: *Baccalaureate, master's.*

The Wharton School

Degree Programs Offered: *Associate* in business administration; *baccalaureate* in economics; *master's* in accounting, business administration; *doctorate* in finance, industrial relations, marketing, operational research, organizational behavior, social systems science.

Distinctive Educational Programs: Dual undergraduate degree program with School of Engineering and Applied Science. Dual graduate degree programs in Schools of Engineering and Applied Science, Law, Medicine, Social Work. MBA programs for students with extensive business experience and for students interested in careers in health care administration. *See also* School of Dental Medicine.

School of Dental Medicine

Degree Programs Offered: *First-professional.* Certificates in dental hygiene also given.

Admission: Undergraduate study which must include 1 year of English, 1 year college-level mathematics (calculus preferred), 3 semesters of chemistry (including inorganic and organic with laboratories), 2 semesters biology or zoology (with laboratory), 2 semesters physics. DAT. Additional units in anatomy, biochemistry, genetics, organic and physical chemistry, physiology recommended.

Degree Requirements: 1 year in residence, successful completion of all curriculum requirements.

Distinctive Educational Programs: Joint first-professional-M.B.A. program in business with the Leonard Davis Institute of Health Economics of the Wharton School; joint first-professional-M.D. with the School of Medicine. Independent research opportunities through the school's Center for Oral Health Research and the W. D. Miller Clinical Research Center. Certificate programs and postgraduate study through Division of Advanced Dental Education. Continuing education program for practicing professionals. *See also* Faculty of Arts and Sciences.

University of Pennsylvania Law School

Degree Programs Offered: *First-professional, master's, doctorate.*

Distinctive Educational Programs: Joint degree programs in law and city planning, economics, graduate business, public policy analysis. Certificate program in law and Islamic studies.

School of Medicine

Degree Programs Offered: *First-professional.*

Admission: Graduation from accredited institution of higher education with 2 units each in biology, inorganic chemistry, organic chemistry, physics, all with laboratories; 2 algebra.

Degree Requirements: 33 months (36 recommended) in residence; passing scores on parts 1 and 2 of the National Board of Medical Examiners examination; demonstrated interpersonal skills.

Distinctive Educational Programs: *See* Wharton School and School of Dental Medicine.

School of Veterinary Medicine

Degree Programs Offered: *First-professional.*

Admission: 3 years undergraduate study with 90 semester credits, including 6 English, 3 calculus, 9 biology, 12 chemistry, 6 physics, 6 humanities.

Degree Requirements: 90 credit hours, 3.0 GPA, 48 months in residence.

Distinctive Educational Programs: Center for the Interaction of Animals and Society. Multi-disciplinary laboratories. Pennsylvania Embryo Transfer Service. New Bolton Center, a large animal facility.

Annenberg School of Communications

Degree Programs Offered: *Master's, doctorate.*

Graduate School of Education

Degree Programs Offered: *Master's, doctorate.*

Graduate School of Fine Arts

Degree Programs Offered: *Master's, doctorate.*

School of Public and Urban Policy

Degree Programs Offered: *Master's, doctorate*

Distinctive Educational Programs: *See* the University of Pennsylvania Law School.

School of Social Work

Degree Programs Offered: *Master's, doctorate*

Distinctive Educational Programs: *See* The Wharton School.

University of Pittsburgh

4200 Fifth Avenue
Pittsburgh, Pennsylvania 15260
Tel: (412) 624-4141 **E-mail:** oafa@pitt.edu
Fax: (412) 648-8815 **Internet:** www.pitt.edu

Institution Description: The University of Pittsburgh is a nonsectarian, coeducational, state-related, public research university with four regional campuses in addition to the main campus. *Enrollment:* 27,562. *Degrees awarded:* Baccalaureate, first-professional (dentistry, law, medicine, pharmacy), master's, doctorate. Certificates are also awarded.

Accreditation: *Regional:* MSA/CHE. *Professional*: athletic training, audiology, clinical psychology, counseling, cytotechnology, dental hygiene, dental public health, dentistry, dietetics, endodontics, engineering, English language education, health information administration, health services administration, law, librarianship, medicine, nurse anesthesia education, nursing, nursing education, occupational therapy, pediatric dentistry, periodontics, pharmacy, physical therapy, psychology internship, public administration, public health, social work, speech-language pathology, theatre

History: Established and chartered as Pittsburgh Academy 1787; incorporated as Western University of Pennsylvania and offered first instruction at postsecondary level 1819; awarded first degree (baccalaureate) 1823; adopted present name 1908. *See* Robert C. Alberts, *Pitt: The Story of the University of Pittsburgh, 1787–1987* (Pittsburgh: University of Pittsburgh, 1986).

Institutional Structure: *Governing board:* The Board of Trustees of the University of Pittsburgh of the Commonwealth System of Higher Education. The Board of Trustees is comprised of 51 members divided into 5 classes: The Chancellor (ex officio with vote), 17 Term Trustees, elected by the Board on nomination by the university of Pittsburgh Alumni Association; and 12 Commonwealth Trustees (4 appointed by the Governor, with the advice and consent of two-thirds of all the members of the Senate, 4 by President Pro Tempore of the Senate and 4 by the Speaker of the House of Representatives). *Composition of institution:* Academic affairs headed by Provost. Finance headed by the Vice Chancellor for Finance and business headed by the Vice Chancellor for Business. Academic governing bodies: University Senate, Senate Council, Faculty Assembly.

Calendar: Three 15-week terms. Two terms (fall and spring) make up the typical academic year. A 15-week summer term is offered. Numerous summer sessions, varying in length, are also offered. Freshmen admitted Sept., Jan., May, June. Degrees conferred Apr., May, June, Aug, Dec.

Characteristics of Freshmen: 19,056 applicants (10,205 female, 8,851 male). 56% of applicants accepted. 32% of accepted applicants enrolled full-time.

25th percentile: SAT Critical Reading 560, SAT Math 570. *75th percentile*: SAT Critical Reading 570, SAT Math 660.

73% of freshmen expected to graduate within 6 years. 75% of freshmen from Pennsylvania. Undergraduates from 54 states and territories and 43 countries.

Admission: Rolling admissions plan. Early admission available. *Requirements:* College of Arts and Sciences requires 15 secondary school units including 4 units English, 3 units mathematics, 3 units laboratory science, 1 unit social studies, 4 units academic electives (3 of which it is recommended to be in the same foreign language). College of General Studies accepts GED. Requirements for other programs may vary. *Entrance tests:* College Board SAT or ACT composite. *For transfer students:* 3.0 minimum GPA from 4-year and 2-year accredited institutions. A maximum of 90 credits can transfer for credit.

College credit and advanced placement for postsecondary-level work completed in secondary school.

Tutoring available. Credit-bearing developmental and remedial courses offered.

Degree Requirements: *For undergraduate degrees:* For the College of Arts and Sciences, the student must earn a minimum of 120 credits (the last 30 credits must be taken in the College of Arts and Sciences); achieve a QPA no lower than 2.0; satisfy the CAS skills requirements in writing, quantitative and formal reasoning, and foreign language requirement; satisfy the General Education requirements; complete a major.

Fulfillment of some degree requirements and exemption from some beginning courses possible by passing Advanced Placement Examination. College of General Studies offers credit through CLEP. *Grading system:* A–F; incomplete; pass; withdraw.

Distinctive Educational Programs: Weekend and evening classes. Three term calendar allows students, who wish to do so, to complete their baccalaureate degree in less than four years. Honors College. External Studies Program. Self-designed majors. Joint degree program between College of Arts and Sciences and the School of Engineering. Study abroad is available in the following countries: Argentina, Australia, China, Czech Republic, France, Germany, India, Israel, Italy, Japan, Mexico, United Kingdom.

ROTC: Army, Air Force, Navy.

Degrees Conferred: 3,913 *baccalaureate*; 2,006 *master's*; 647 *doctorate*; 516 *first-professional.* Bachelor's degrees awarded in top five disciplines: psychology 356; communications 244; nursing 197; marketing 193; pharmacy 98. Master's degrees awarded: various disciplines 2,006. Doctorates awarded: various disciplines 510. First-professional degrees awarded: dentistry 64; law 227; medicine 125; pharmacy 98.

Fees and Other Expenses: *Full-time tuition per academic year 2008–09:* undergraduate resident $13,642, nonresident $23,290; contact the university for current graduate/first-professional tuition and applicable fees that vary by program. *Required fees:* undergraduate $770; graduate $650. *Room and board per academic year:* $8,600. *Books and supplies:* $1,030. *Other expenses:* $2,840.

Financial Aid: Aid from institutionally generated funds is awarded on the basis of academic merit, financial need, athletic ability, other criteria. Institution has a Program Participation Agreement with the U.S. Department of Education for eligible students to receive Pell Grants and, depending upon the agreement, other federal aid.

Financial aid to full-time, first-time undergraduate students: 80% received some form of aid. Average amount of aid received: federal grants $3,933; Pell grants $2,770; other federal aid $1,251; state/local grants $3,717; institutional grants $10,293.

Departments and Teaching Staff: *Total instructional faculty:* 4,243. Degrees held by full-time faculty: baccalaureate 1%, master's 9%, doctorate 40%, professional 40%. 90% hold terminal degrees.

Enrollment: Total enrollment 27,562. Undergraduate 17,427 (full-time 92%; female 52%, male 48%). Graduate 10,135 (full-time 71%). Undergraduate transfer-in students 861.

Characteristics of Student Body: *Ethnic/racial makeup:* Black non-Hispanic: 8%; Asian or Pacific Islander: 5%; Hispanic: 1%; White non-Hispanic: 80%; unknown 4%; nonresident alien 1%.

International Students: 2,756 nonresident aliens enrolled fall 2008. Students from Europe, Asia, Latin America, Africa, Australia and New Zealand, Middle East. Programs available to aid students whose native language is not English: social, cultural. English as a Second Language. No financial aid specifically designated for international students.

Student Life: On-campus residence halls house 47% of full-time undergraduate students. Residence halls for both males and females. 10% of males join fra-

UNIVERSITY OF PITTSBURGH—*cont'd*

ternities; 9% of females join sororities. *Intercollegiate athletics:* male: baseball, basketball, cross-country, diving, football, soccer, swimming, track and field, wrestling; female: basketball, cross-country, diving, gymnastics, soccer, softball, swimming, tennis, track and field, volleyball. *Special regulations:* Cars permitted without restrictions. Residence hall visitation until 2am weekdays, no limit on weekends. *Special services:* Learning Skills Center, University Placement Service, University Student Health Service, campus bus system. *Student publications, radio: The Pitt News*, a student newspaper published Monday through Thursday; *Night Times*, is the newspaper for College of General Studies students, published monthly; *Panther Prints*, a yearbook. AM/FM radio station WPTS broadcasts 24 hours, 7 days per week. PITT-TV, student run tv station. *Surrounding community:* Campus located in Oakland, Pittsburgh's cultural center. The campus is 3 miles from downtown Pittsburgh. Pittsburgh is served by mass transit bus, air and rail systems.

Publications: University press published 39 new titles and 6 reprints in fiscal year 2006.

Library Collections: 4,9 millionis volumes. 7.6 million microforms; 1.1 million audiovisual materials; 50,000 periodicals including via electronic access. Students have access to the Internet. Computer work stations available campus-wide.

Most important special holdings include Curtis Theatre Collection (theatrical ephemera, archival records of theatre organizations, and the papers of theatre personages); Nietz Textbook Collection (early American primary and secondary schoolbooks published before 1900); Archives of Scientific Philosophy in the 20th Century, including the Rudolf Carnap Collection (the works of one of the most influential philosophers of the 20th century; key figure in the rise of logical positivism).

Buildings and Grounds: Campus area 132 acres.

Chief Executive Officer: Dr. Mark A. Nordenberg, Chancellor and Chief Executive Officer.

Undergraduates address admission inquiries to Betsy A. Porter, Director of Admissions; graduate and/or first-professional inquiries to the appropriate school(s) of interest.

Arts and Sciences

Degree Programs Offered: *Baccalaureate* in actuarial mathematics, Africana studies, anthropology, applied mathematics, architectural studies, biological sciences, business, chemistry, Chinese, classics, computer science, ecology and evolution, economics, English literature, English writing, environmental geology, environmental studies, film studies, French, geology, German, history, history and philosophy of science, history of art and architecture, interdisciplinary studies, Italian, Italian studies, Japanese, linguistics, mathematics - economics, mathematics - neuroscience, mathematics - philosophy, microbiology, molecular biology, music, neuroscience, philosophy, physics, physics and astronomy, Polish, political science, politics and philosophy, psychology, religious studies, rhetoric and communication, Russian, sociology, Spanish, statistics, studio arts, theatre arts, urban studies; *certificates* in children's literature, film studies, Jewish studies, medieval and Renaissance *Master's, doctorate* in anthropology, applied mathematics, applied statistics, astronomy, behavioral neuroscience, behavioral neuroscience - neuroscience, biological sciences, biological sciences - neuroscience, chemistry, classics, communication: communication disorders, communication: rhetoric and communication, computer science, crystallography, geology, intelligent systems, mathematics, physics, psychology, East Asian languages and literatures, East Asian studies, economics, fine arts, French, Germanic languages and literatures, Hispanic languages and literatures, history, history and philosophy of science, Italian, linguistics, music, philosophy, political science, Slavic languages and literatures, sociology, theatre arts. Certificates offered in cultural studies, medieval and renaissance studies, teaching English as another language, scientific computing, and women's studies.

Distinctive Educational Programs: Joint degree programs with School of Law, Joseph M. Katz Graduate School of Business, School of Medicine. A cooperative degree in religion is offered with the Pittsburgh Theological Seminary. Combined major degree programs are offered, BA and BS, and joint degree programs between the College of Arts and Sciences and the School of Engineering, BA/BSE and BS/BSE. A double major is offered in which the Business major is taken in conjunction with any other College of Arts and Sciences major.

School of Education

Degree Programs Offered: *Baccalaureate* in health/physical/recreation education - exercise science, health/physical/recreation education - movement science; *master's, doctorate* in administrative and policy studies, health/physical/recreation education, instructional learning, psychology in education; *doctorate* in administration *master's, doctorate* in education.

Distinctive Educational Programs: An interschool degree program is offered jointly through the School of Education and the Graduate School of Public Health.

School of Engineering

Degree Programs Offered: *Baccalaureate, master's, doctorate*. Degrees offered in bioengineering, chemical engineering, civil and environmental engineering, computer engineering, electrical engineering, engineering physics, industrial engineering, materials science and engineering, mechanical engineering, metallurgical engineering, petroleum engineering.

Distinctive Educational Programs: A dual-degree program with the School of Engineering, (MSChe/MSPE), is offered and joint degree programs are offered between the School of Engineering and the College of Arts and Sciences, BSE/BA and BSE/BS.

School of Health Rehabilitation Sciences

Degree Programs Offered: *Baccalaureate, master's, doctorate, certificate.* Degrees offered in clinical dietetics and nutrition, communication science, health information management, medical technology, occupational therapy, physical therapy, rehabilitation science and technology.

Distinctive Educational Programs: Interdisciplinary baccalaureate program for health professionals with associate degrees. Combined master's-certificate program in records administration and physical therapy.

School of Information Sciences

Degree Programs Offered: *Baccalaureate, master's, doctorate, certificate.* Degrees offered in information science, library and information sciences, telecommunications.

Distinctive Educational Programs: Joint degree program with the Graduate School of Public and International Affairs.

School of Nursing

Degree Programs Offered: *Baccalaureate, master's, doctorate.* Degrees offered in nursing, acute and tertiary care, health and community systems, health promotion and development, and nurse anesthesia.

Distinctive Educational Programs: A joint degree program between the School of Nursing and the Joseph M. Katz Graduate School of Business (MSN/MBA) is offered. The Registered Nurse-MSN program is a specially designed program available to individuals who are practicing RNs. The curriculum expedites the advanced educational preparation of the RN, enabling the individual to receive both the BSN and MSN degrees.

School of Pharmacy

Degree Programs Offered: *Baccalaureate, master's, doctorate.* Degrees offered in pharmaceutical sciences and pharmacy.

School of Social Work

Degree Programs Offered: *Baccalaureate, master's, doctorate, certificate.* Degrees offered in child development and child care, social work.

Distinctive Educational Programs: Also available are joint degree programs between the School of Social Work and the Graduate School of Public Health (PhD/MPH) and between the School of Social Work and the Graduate School of Public and International Affairs (MSW/MPA, MSW/MPIA, MSW/MURP) and cooperative degree programs between the School of Social Work and Pittsburgh Theological Seminary (MSW/MDiv), and between the School of Social Work and Hebrew Union College (MSW/MAJCS).

School of Dental Medicine

Degree Programs Offered: *Master's, doctorate, first-professional.* Degrees offered in dental medicine, endodontics, orthodontics, pediatric dentistry, periodontics, prosthodontics.

Admission: *For first-professional degree:* 90 credits from accredited college including 6 English, 6 biology, zoology, or botany (with 1 laboratory); 6 physics, 8 inorganic chemistry, 6 organic chemistry; DAT; applications must be processed through AADSAS.

Degree Requirements: *For first-professional degree:* Prescribed curriculum, unit and comprehensive examinations, clinical work.

School of Law

Degree Programs Offered: *Master's, doctorate, certificate.* Degrees offered in law, international and comparative law.

Admission: Baccalaureate from accredited college or university, LSAT, LSDAS.

Degree Requirements: 86 credit hours.

Distinctive Educational Programs: Also available are joint degree programs between the School of Law and the Joseph M. Katz Graduate School of Business (JD/MBA), between the School of Law and the Graduate School of Public and International Affairs (JD/MPA, JD/MPIA, and JD/MURP) and between the School of Law and the Graduate School of Public Health (JD/MPH) and cooperative degree programs between the School of Law and Carnegie Mellon University (JD/MS, JD/MAM, and JD/MSIA).

School of Medicine

Degree Programs Offered: *Master's, doctorate, first-professional.* Degrees offered in biochemistry and molecular genetics, cell biology and molecular physiology, cellular and molecular pathology, immunology, molecular pharmacology, molecular virology and microbiology, and neurobiology.

Admission: *For first-professional degree:* 120 semester hours from accredited college or university, MCAT.

Degree Requirements: *For first-professional degree:* Prescribed curriculum.

Joseph M. Katz Graduate School of Business

Degree Programs Offered: *Master's, doctorate.* Degrees offered in business administration, international business, and management of information systems.

Distinctive Educational Programs: A dual-degree program is offered MBA/MS with the Faculty of Arts and Sciences; with the School of Law (MBA/JD) and between the Joseph M. Katz Graduate School of Business and the School of Nursing (MBA/MSN), and a cooperative degree program between the Joseph M. Katz Graduate School of Business and Pittsburgh Theological Seminary (MBA/MDiv). The EMBA is a specially designed program offered to experienced executives.

College of Business Administration

Degree Programs Offered: *Baccalaureate.* Degrees offered in accounting, finance, general management, and marketing.

Departments and Teaching Staff: Courses are taught by faculty who have their primary appointment in the Joseph M. Katz Graduate School of Business.

Graduate School of Public and International Affairs

Degree Programs Offered: *Master's, doctorate, certificate.* Degrees offered in economic and social development, international affairs, public and international affairs, public management and policy, public policy and management.

Distinctive Educational Programs: Also available within the Graduate School of Public and International Affairs are dual-degree programs (MPA/MPIA, MPA/MURP, MPIA/MURP) and joint degree programs between the Graduate School of Public and International Affairs and the School of Law (MPA/JD, MPIA/JD, and MURP/JD) and between the Graduate School of Public and International Affairs and the School of Social Work (MPA/MSW, MPIA/MSW, MURP/MSW).

University Center for International Studies

Degree Programs Offered: The center is the principal administrative mechanism for campus-wide coordination and support of international activities at the University of Pittsburgh.

Distinctive Educational Programs: The center offers certificate programs in the following areas: Asian Studies, East Asian Studies, East European Studies, Latin American Social and Public Policy, Latin American Studies, Russian and East European Studies, Russian Studies, Soviet Studies, and West European Studies.

Graduate School of Public Health

Degree Programs Offered: *Master's, doctorate, certificate.* Degrees offered in behavioral and community health services, biostatistics, environmental and occupational health, epidemiology, genetic counseling, health administration, human genetics, infectious diseases and microbiology, occupational medicine, public health multidisciplinary program.

Distinctive Educational Programs: Also offered is a joint degree program between the Graduate School of Public Health and the School of Social Work (MPH/PhD) and between the Graduate School of Public Health and the School of Law (MPH/JD), and a cooperative degree program between the Graduate School of Public Health and Pittsburgh Theological Seminary. The MHA is an interschool degree offered through both the Graduate School of Public Health and the Joseph M. Katz Graduate School of Business.

University of Pittsburgh at Titusville

Degree Programs Offered: *Associate, certificate.* Degrees offered in accounting, business, business information systems, liberal arts, natural science, occupational therapist assistant program, physical therapist assistant program. Certificates offered in accounting.

University Honors College

Degree Programs Offered: The *Bachelor of Philosophy* degree (BPhil), offered through the Honors College, is available in all baccalaureate degree programs.

Departments and Teaching Staff: Courses in the University Honors College are taught by faculty who have primary appointments in other schools.

Enrollment: Students, while participating in the University Honors College, maintain their enrollment in a "home" undergraduate school.

University of Pittsburgh at Bradford

300 Campus Drive
Bradford, Pennsylvania 16701
Tel: (814) 362-7500 **E-mail:** admissions@pitt.edu
Fax: (814) 362-7578 **Internet:** www.upb.pitt.edu

Institution Description: *Enrollment:* 1,502. *Degrees awarded:* Associate, baccalaureate.

Accreditation: *Regional:* MSA/CHE.

History: Established and offered first instruction at postsecondary level 1963; awarded first degree (baccalaureate) 1976.

Institutional Structure: *Composition of institution:* Administrators 12. Academic affairs headed by dean of academic affairs. Management/business/finances directed by director of financial affairs. Instructional faculty 71. Academic governance body, Faculty Senate, meets an average of 6 times per year.

Calendar: Trimesters. Academic year Sept. to Apr. Freshmen admitted Sept., Jan., May, June. Degrees conferred Apr., Aug., Dec. Formal commencement Apr. Summer session from June to Aug.

Characteristics of Freshmen: 737 applicants (424 female, 313 male). 84% of applicants accepted. 52% of accepted applicants enrolled full-time.

83% (679 students) submitted SAT scores; 13% (107 students) submitted ACT scores. *25th percentile*: SAT Critical Reading 430, SAT Math 430; ACT Composite 17. *75th percentile*: SAT Critical Reading 530, SAT Math 550; ACT Composite 25.

42% of entering freshmen expected to graduate within 5 years. 85% of freshmen from Pennsylvania. Freshmen from 24 states and 5 foreign countries.

Admission: Rolling admissions plan. For fall acceptance, apply as early as Sept. 1 of previous year, but not later than July 1. Apply by Nov. 1 for early decision; need not limit application to University of Pittsburgh at Bradford. Early acceptance available. *Requirements:* Either graduation from accredited secondary school with 4 units English, 2 foreign language, 1 algebra, 1 plane geometry, 1 history, 1 laboratory science, 5 academic electives; or GED. For engineering program, additional 1 unit in chemistry, 1 physics, 1/2 trigonometry. For nursing program, units in laboratory biology and chemistry. Minimum GPA 2.5. *Entrance tests:* College Board SAT or ACT composite. *For transfer students:* 2.5 minimum GPA; from 4- and2-year year accredited institutions 90 semester hours maximum transfer credit.

College credit and advanced placement for postsecondary-level work completed in secondary school. Developmental courses offered in summer session and regular academic year; credit given.

Degree Requirements: *For all associate degrees:* 2.0 GPA; 60 credit hours. *For all baccalaureate degrees:* 2.0 GPA (and 2.0 in major); 120 hours; last 30 credits in residence, distribution requirement.

Fulfillment of some degree requirements and exemption from some beginning courses possible by passing College Board CLEP. *Grading system:* A–F; incomplete; pass, withdraw (carries time limit).

Distinctive Educational Programs: Evening classes. Cross-registration with a number of institutions in northwestern Pennsylvania. Special facilities for using telecommunications in the classroom. Interdisciplinary program in earth and environmental science. Tutorials.

ROTC: Army in cooperation with St. Bonaventure University (NY).

Degrees Conferred: 34 *associate*; 191 *baccalaureate*. Bachelor's degrees awarded in top five disciplines: business, management, marketing, and related support services 46; social sciences 28; English health professions and related clinical sciences 27; security and protective services 20; English 14.

UNIVERSITY OF PITTSBURGH AT BRADFORD—*cont'd*

Fees and Other Expenses: *Full-time tuition per academic year 2008–09:* resident $11,722, nonresident $21,282. *Required fees:* $710. *Room and board per academic year:* $7,050. *Books and supplies:* $1,030. *Other expenses:* $2,840.

Financial Aid: Aid from institutionally generated funds is provided on the basis of academic merit, financial need. Institution has a Program Participation Agreement with the U.S. Department of Education for eligible students to receive Pell Grants and, depending upon the agreement, other federal aid.

Financial aid to full-time, first-time undergraduate students: 98% received some form of aid. Average amount of aid received: federal grants #3,803; Pell grants $2,787; other federal grants $753; state/local grants $4,319; institutional grants $5,783.

Departments and Teaching Staff: *Total instructional faculty:* 124 (full-time 71, part-time 53). Total faculty with doctorate, first-professional, or other terminal degree: 51. Student/faculty ratio: 13:1.

Enrollment: *Total enrollment:* 1,502. Undergraduate 1,502 (full-time 88%; female 56%, male 44%). Transfer-in students 88.

Characteristics of Student Body: *Ethnic/racial makeup:* Black non-Hispanic: 5%; Asian or Pacific Islander: 2%; Hispanic: 1%; White non-Hispanic: 84%; unknown: 7%. *Age distribution:* number under 18: 20; 18–19: 178; 20–21: 344; 22–24: 197; 25–29: 85; 30–34: 60; 35–39: 55; 40–49: 62; 50–64: 44; 18.

International Students: 9 nonresident aliens enrolled fall 2008. Students from Asia, Canada, Middle East. No programs available to aid students whose native language is not English. No financial aid specifically designated for international students.

Student Life: On-campus residence halls house 50% of student body. Residence halls for males constitute 60% of such space, for female 40%. *Intercollegiate athletics:* male: baseball, basketball; female: basketball, volleyball. *Special regulations:* Cars permitted without restrictions. *Special services:* Medical services. *Student publications: Frameworks*, an annual literary magazine; *Horizons*, a monthly student newspaper. *Surrounding community:* Bradford population 10,500. Buffalo (NY), 80 miles from campus, is nearest metropolitan area. Served by airport 18 miles from campus.

Library Collections: 95,000 volumes. 480 current periodical subscriptions. 15,000 microforms; 6,000 audiovisual materials. Students have access to online information retrieval services and the Internet.

Most important holdings include Lowenthal Library of Skepticism.

Buildings and Grounds: Campus area 175 acres.

Chief Executive Officer: Dr. Livingston Alexander, President.

Address admission inquiries to Alexander P. Nazemetz, Director of Admissions.

University of Pittsburgh at Greensburg

1150 Mt. Pleasant Road
Greensburg, Pennsylvania 15601
Tel: (724) 836-7040 **E-mail:** upgadmits@pitt.edu
Fax: (724) 836-7160 **Internet:** www.upg.pitt.edu

Institution Description: *Enrollment:* 1,826. *Degrees awarded:* Baccalaureate. Certificates also awarded.

Accreditation: *Regional:* MSA/CHE.

History: Established and offered first instruction at postsecondary level 1963.

Institutional Structure: *Composition of institution:* Academic affairs headed by dean of academic affairs. Management/business/finances directed by director of financial affairs. Instructional faculty 56.

Calendar: Trimesters. Academic year Sept. to Apr. Freshmen admitted Sept., Jan., May, June. Degrees conferred Apr., Aug., Dec. Formal commencement Apr. Summer session from June to Aug.

Characteristics of Freshmen: 1,425 applicants (750 female, 675 male). 85% of applicants admitted. 40% of applicants admitted and enrolled full-time.

100% (463 students) submitted SAT scores; 12% (57 students) submitted ACT scores. *25th percentile*: SAT Critical Reading 480, SAT Math 450; ACT Composite 17. *75th percentile*: SAT Critical Reading 570, SAT Math 560; ACT Composite 24.

95% of freshmen from Pennsylvania. Freshmen from 6 states and 2 foreign countries.

Admission: Rolling admissions plan. For fall acceptance, apply as early as Sept. 1 of previous year, but not later than July 1. Apply by Nov. 1 for early decision; need not limit application to University of Pittsburgh at Greensbrug. Early acceptance available. *Requirements:* Either graduation from accredited secondary school with 4 units English, 2 foreign language, 1 algebra, 1 plane geometry, 1 history, 1 laboratory science, 5 academic electives; or GED. For engineering program, additional 1 unit in chemistry, 1 physics, 1/2 trigonometry. For nursing program, units in laboratory biology and chemistry. Minimum GPA 2.5. *Entrance tests:* College Board SAT or ACT composite. *For transfer students:* 2.5 minimum GPA; from 4- and2-year year accredited institutions 90 semester hours maximum transfer credit.

College credit and advanced placement for postsecondary-level work completed in secondary school. Developmental courses offered in summer session and regular academic year; credit given.

Degree Requirements: *For all baccalaureate degrees:* 2.0 GPA (and 2.0 in major); 120 hours; last 30 credits in residence, distribution requirement.

Fulfillment of some degree requirements and exemption from some beginning courses possible by passing College Board CLEP. *Grading system:* A–F; incomplete; pass, withdraw (carries time limit).

Distinctive Educational Programs: Evening classes. Cross-registration with a number of institutions in northwestern Pennsylvania. Special facilities for using telecommunications in the classroom.

Degrees Conferred: 306 *baccalaureate:* biological/life sciences 9; business/marketing 62; communications/communication technologies 27;; computer and information sciences 11; English 20; interdisciplinary studies 2; mathematics 7; physical sciences 4; social sciences and history 60; visual and performing arts 68.

Fees and Other Expenses: *Full-time tuition per academic year 2008–09:* resident $11,722, nonresident $21,282. *Required fees:* $714. *Room and board per academic year:* $7,050. *Books and supplies:* $1,030. *Other expenses:* $2,840.

Financial Aid: Aid from institutionally generated funds is provided on the basis of academic merit, financial need. Financial assistance is available in the form of Pell Grants, College Work-Study, Veterans Administration Benefits, National Direct Student Loans, Supplemental Education Opportunity Grants (SEOG), Stafford Loans, other federal aid programs.

Financial aid to first-time, full-time undergraduate students: 87% received some form of aid. Average amount of aid received: federal grants $3,230; Pell grants $2,809; other federal aid $666; state/local grants $3,354; institutional grants $3,111.

Departments and Teaching Staff: *Total instructional faculty:* 140 (full-time 77, part-time 63). Total faculty with doctorate, first-professional, or other terminal degree: 80. Student/faculty ratio: 18:1.

Enrollment: Total enrollment 1,826. Undergraduate 1,826 (full-time 92%; female 50%, male 50%). Transfer-in students 144.

Characteristics of Student Body: *Ethnic/racial makeup:* Black non-Hispanic: 5%; Asian or Pacific Islander: 3%; Hispanic: 1%; White non-Hispanic: 86%; unknown: 4%.

International Students: No programs available to aid students whose native language is not English. No financial aid specifically designated for international students.

Student Life: On-campus residence halls available. *Intercollegiate athletics:* male: baseball, basketball; cross-country, golf, soccer, tennis; female: basketball, cross-country, golf, soccer, softball, volleyball. *Special regulations:* Cars permitted without restrictions. *Special services:* Medical services. *Surrounding community:* Greensburg is located 30 miles east of Pittsburgh.

Library Collections: 79,000 volumes. Current periodical subscriptions: paper 308, microform 9,535, plus thousands via electronic access. Online catalog. 2,986 audio/videotapes; 540 DVD discs. Students have access to online information retrieval services and the Internet.

Buildings and Grounds: Campus area 219 acres.

Chief Executive Officer: Dr. Frank A. Cassell, President.

Address admission inquiries to Brandi S. Darr, Director of Admissions.

University of Pittsburgh at Johnstown

450 Schoolhouse Road
Johnstown, Pennsylvania 15904
Tel: (814) 269-7000 **E-mail:** admissions@upj.pitt.edu
Fax: (814) 269-7044 **Internet:** www.upj.pitt.edu

Institution Description: *Enrollment:* 3,032. *Degrees awarded:* Associate, baccalaureate.

Accreditation: *Regional:* MSA/CHE.

History: Established, chartered as Johnstown College and offered first instruction at postsecondary level 1927; adopted present name 1964; awarded first degree (baccalaureate) 1970. *Composition of institution:* Administrators 20. Academic affairs headed by academic dean. Management/business/finances directed by director of administration and budget. Full-time instructional faculty 133. Academic governance body, Faculty Senate, meets an average of 7 times per year.

Calendar: Trimesters. Academic year Sept. to Apr. Freshmen admitted Sept., Jan., Apr., June. Degrees conferred Apr., June, Aug., Dec. Formal commencement Apr. Summer session from Apr. to Aug.

Characteristics of Freshmen: 1,749 applicants (909 female, 840 male). 88% of applicants accepted. 55% of accepted applicants enrolled full-time.

Average secondary school rank 70th percentile. Mean SAT scores 505 verbal, 560 mathematical.

75% of entering freshmen expected to graduate within 5 years. 99% of freshmen from Pennsylvania. Freshmen from 92 states and 3 foreign countries.

Admission: Rolling admissions plan. For fall acceptance, apply as early as Sept 15 of previous year, but not later than Aug. of year of enrollment. Apply by Nov. 1 for early decision; need not limit application to University of Pittsburgh at Johnstown. Early acceptance available. *Requirements:* Graduation from accredited secondary school with 4 units in English, 2 algebra, 1 plane geometry, 2 foreign language, 1 history, 3 academic electives; or GED. Additional units in physics and trigonometry for engineering program. *Entrance tests:* College Board SAT or ACT composite. *For transfer students:* 2.0 minimum GPA; from 4-year accredited institution 90 credit hours; from 2-year accredited institution 60 hours.

College credit and advanced placement for postsecondary-level work completed in secondary school. Tutoring available.

Degree Requirements: 120 credit hours; 2.0 GPA; last 30 hours in residence, demonstrated proficiency in English; distribution requirements. *Grading system:* A–F; pass-fail; withdraw (carries time limit).

Distinctive Educational Programs: Work-experience programs. Flexible meeting places and schedules, including off-campus centers, weekend and evening classes. Cooperative baccalaureate in anthropology, classics, fine arts, foreign languages, geography, history of religion, music, physics, studio art with Pittsburgh campus. Special facilities for using telecommunications in the classroom. Interdisciplinary programs in American studies. Appalachian regional studies. Facilities and programs for independent research, including individual majors, tutorial. Independent study. Study abroad through Pittsburgh campus.

Degrees Conferred: 21 *associate*; 533 *baccalaureate*. Bachelor's degrees awarded in top five disciplines: business, management, marketing, and related support services 108; education 66; engineering 54; English language/literature 35; social sciences 33.

Fees and Other Expenses: *Full-time tuition per academic year 2008–09:* $11,754 resident, $21,314 nonresident. *Room and board per academic year:* $6,860. *Books and supplies:* $1,030. *Other expenses:* $2,840.

Financial Aid: Aid from institutionally generated funds is provided on the basis of academic merit, financial need.

Financial aid to full-time, first-time undergraduate students: 85% received some form of aid. Average amount of aid received: federal grants $3,692; Pell grants $2,719; other federal aid $1,065; state/local grants $3,526; institutional grants $4,541.

Departments and Teaching Staff: *Total instructional faculty:* 133. Student/faculty ratio: 19:1.

Enrollment: Total enrollment 3,032.. Undergraduate 3,032 (full-time 93%; female 47%, male 53%). Transfer-in students 129.

Characteristics of Student Body: *Ethnic/racial makeup:* Black non-Hispanic: 2%; Asian or Pacific Islander: 1%; Hispanic: 1%; White non-Hispanic: 93%; unknown: 2%.

International Students: No programs available to aid students whose native language is not English. No financial aid specifically designated for international students.

Student Life: On-campus residence halls house 45% of student body. Residence halls for males constitute 45% of such space, for females 51%. *Intercollegiate athletics:* male: baseball, basketball, cross-country, golf, soccer, track; female: basketball, golf, gymnastics, volleyball. *Special regulations:* Cars permitted without restrictions. *Special services:* Learning Resources Center, medical services. *Student publications, radio: Advocate*, a weekly newspaper; *Backroads*, a literary magazine published 4 times per term; *Freshman Record*, a yearbook; *Trails*, a yearbook. Radio station WUPJ broadcasts 84 hours per week. *Surrounding community:* Johnstown population 33,500. Pittsburgh, 75 miles from campus, is nearest metropolitan area. Served by mass transit bus system; airport 5 miles from campus; passenger rail service 8 miles from campus.

Library Collections: 150,000 volumes. 6,600 microforms; 11,500 audiovisual materials; 630 current periodical subscriptions. Students have access to online information retrieval services and the Internet.

Buildings and Grounds: Campus area 635 acres.

Chief Executive Officer: Dr. Albert Etheridge, President.

Address admission inquiries to James F. Gyare, Director of Admissions.

University of the Sciences in Philadelphia

600 South 43rd Street
Philadelphia, Pennsylvania 19104-4495
Tel: (215) 596-8810 **E-mail:** admit@usip.edu
Fax: (215) 895-1100 **Internet:** www.usip.edu

Institution Description: The University of the Sciences in Philadelphia is a private, independent, nonprofit college. *Enrollment:* 3,000. *Degrees awarded:* Baccalaureate, first-professional (pharmacy), master's, doctorate.

Accreditation: *Regional:* MSA/CHE. *Professional*: chemistry, occupational therapy, pharmacy, physical therapy, physician assisting

History: Established as Philadelphia College of Apothecaries and offered first instruction at postsecondary level 1821; chartered, incorporated, and changed name to Philadelphia College of Pharmacy 1822; became coeducational 1876; awarded first degree (baccalaureate) 1920; adopted present name 1998.

Institutional Structure: *Governing board:* Board of Trustees. Representation: 23 trustees, including 9 corporate trustees, 11 trustees at large, 3 alumni. All voting. *Composition of institution:* Administrators 14. Academic affairs headed by dean of faculty. Management/business/finances directed by comptroller and treasurer. Full-time instructional faculty 123. Academic governance body, Faculty Council, meets an average of 10 times per year.

Calendar: Semesters. Academic Sept. to May. Freshmen admitted Aug. Degrees conferred May, Sept., Jan. Formal commencement May. Summer session from June to July.

Characteristics of Freshmen: 3,968 applicants (2,644 female, 1,319 male). 58% of applicants accepted. 21% of accepted applicants enrolled full-time. 91% (544 students) submitted SAT scoares; 11% (63 students) submitted ACT scores.

Admission: Rolling admissions plan. For fall acceptance, apply as early as June following junior year of secondary school, but not later than summer of year of enrollment. *Requirements:* Graduation from accredited secondary school with 4 units English, 3 mathematics, 3 science, 1 American history, 1 social studies or history, 4 academic electives. GED considered. Lowest acceptable secondary school class standing 80th percentile. *Entrance tests:* College Board SAT. *For transfer students:* From 4-year accredited institution 2.5 minimum GPA; hours maximum transfer credit; from 2-year accredited institution 2.8 GPA; maximum transfer credit 70 hours.

Advanced placement for postsecondary-level work completed in secondary school.

Noncredit developmental courses offered during regular academic year.

Degree Requirements: Minimum program requirements are program dependent. Refer to the university catalog for specific information (website).

Distinctive Educational Programs: *For undergraduate and graduate students:* Independent study. Continuing Education Programs, including credit and noncredit evening courses, symposia, seminars for scientists, pharmacists, and other health professionals.

ROTC: Army offered in cooperation with University of Pennsylvania.

Degrees Conferred: 178 *baccalaureate:* biological sciences 11; health professions 86; physical sciences 3; 85 *master's*; 9 *doctorate*; 218 *First-professional.* Master's degrees awarded: various disciplines 85. Doctorates awarded: various disciplines 9. First-professional degrees awarded: pharmacy 215; physical therapy 3.

Fees and Other Expenses: *Full-time tuition and fees per academic year 2008–09:* $28,506 undergraduate; contact the university for current graduate and first-professional tuition/fees that vary by program. *Room and board per academic year:* $11,146. *Books and supplies:* $1,050. *Other expenses:* $2,660.

Financial Aid: Aid from institutionally generated funds is provided on the basis of financial need. Merit awards are available to entering student and are awarded on the basis of academic excellence in high school and comparative scores on the SAT.

Financial aid to first-time, full-time undergraduate students: 100% received some form of aid. Average amount of aid received: federal grants $1,994; Pell grants $3,032; other federal aid $743; state/local grants $3,098; institutional grants $9,129.

Departments and Teaching Staff: *Total instructional faculty:* 250. *Total tenured faculty:* 46. Student/faculty ratio: 14:1. Degrees held by full-time faculty: doctorate or first-professional 75%, master's 17%, baccalaureate 2. 75% hold terminal degrees.

Enrollment: Total enrollment 3,000. Undergreaduate 1,571 (full-time 98%; female 62%. male 38%). Graduate 1,429 (full-time 81%). Undergraduate transfer-in students 83.

Characteristics of Student Body: *Ethnic/racial makeup:* Black non-Hispanic: 6%; Asian or Pacific Islander: 35%; Hispanic: 2%; White non-Hispanic: 48%; unknown: 6%; nonresident alien 2%.

UNIVERSITY OF THE SCIENCES IN PHILADELPHIA—*cont'd*

International Students: 60 nonresident aliens enrolled fall 2008. Programs available to aid students whose native language is not English: social, cultural. English as a Second Language Program. No financial aid specifically designated for international students.

Student Life: Two college-owned residence halls house 75% of freshman students and 44% of student body; 86% live in off-campus housing including fraternity houses. *Intercollegiate athletics:* male: baseball, basketball, cross-country, tennis; female: cross-country, tennis, volleyball; both sexes: cheerleading, rifle. *Special regulations:* Cars permitted; fee charged. Residence hall quiet hours 9pm to 7am Sun.–Thurs, 11pm to 7am Fri. and Sat. *Special services:* medical services. *Student publications: The Elixir*, a literary magazine published once a year; *The Graduate*, a yearbook; *Panacea*, a newspaper published 6 times a year. *Surrounding community:* Philadelphia population 1,650,000. Served by mass transit system; airport 4 miles from campus; passenger rail service 2 miles from campus.

Library Collections: 90,000 volumes. 6,500 electronic subscriptions; 400 current periodicals. Students have access to online information retrieval services and the Internet.

Most important special collections include History of Pharmacy Collection; foreign pharmacy journals; rare and old books on botany, chemistry, and herbs.

Buildings and Grounds: Campus area 25 acres.

Chief Executive Officer: Dr. Philip P. Gerbino, President.

Address admission inquiries to Director of Admissions.

University of Scranton

800 Linden Street
Scranton, Pennsylvania 18510-4629
Tel: (570) 941-7400 **E-mail:** admissions@scranton.edu
Fax: (570) 941-6369 **Internet:** www.scranton.edu

Institution Description: University of Scranton is a private institution conducted by the Society of Jesus, Roman Catholic Church. *Enrollment:* 5,651. *Degrees awarded:* Associate, baccalaureate, master's.

Accreditation: *Regional:* MSA/CHE. *Professional*: business, chemistry, computer science, physical therapy, nursing, rehabilitation counseling, teacher education

History: Established by the Congregation of Christian Brothers as St. Thomas College, a school for men, 1888; offered first instruction at postsecondary level 1921; incorporated 1923; awarded first degree (baccalaureate) 1925; adopted present name 1938; Jesuit fathers assumed control 1942; became coeducational 1972.

Institutional Structure: *Governing board:* Board of Trustees. Extrainstitutional representation: 30 trustees; 1 ex officio, president of the university. All voting. *Composition of institution:* Administrators 57. Academic affairs headed by headed by provost/academic vice president. Other vice-presidential areas include: finance, planning, administrative services, student affairs, development, and campus ministries. Full-time instructional faculty 253. Academic governance body, University Senate, meets an average of 8 times per year. *Faculty representation:* Faculty served by collective bargaining agent, Faculty Affairs Committee.

Calendar: Semesters. Academic year Aug. to May. Freshmen admitted June, Aug. Degrees conferred May, Aug. Formal commencement May. Summer session of 2 terms from June to Aug.

Characteristics of Freshmen: 7,890 applicants (4,500 female, 3,385 male). 66% of applicants accepted. 19% of accepted applicants enrolled full-time. 93% (908 students) submitted SAT scores. *25th percentile*: SAT Critical Reading 510, SAT Math 510. *75th percentile*: SAT Critical Reading 600, SAT Math 610.

83% of entering freshmen expected to graduate within 5 years. 47% of freshmen from Pennsylvania. Freshmen from 25 states and 27 foreign countries.

Admission: Rolling admissions plan. For fall acceptance, apply as early as Oct. of previous year, but not later than Mar. 1 of year of enrollment. Students are notified of acceptance beginning Dec. 1. Apply by Nov. 1 for early decision; need not limit application to University of Scranton. Early acceptance available. *Requirements:* Applicants should be graduates of an accredited secondary school, although in some cases a GED may be accepted. They should complete 18 academic or Carnegie units including 4 years of English, 3 each of college preparatory mathematics and science and 2 each of foreign language, 2 social studies, social science, and electives. *Entrance tests:* College Board SAT or ACT required. Two letters of recommendation are also required. *For transfer students:* 2.5 minimum GPA; 63 hours minimum of credits to be completed at University of Scranton to earn a degree.

College credit and advanced placement for postsecondary-level work completed in secondary school. College credit for extrainstitutional learning on basis of portfolio and faculty assessments; personal interview.

Tutoring available. Developmental courses offered in summer session and regular academic year; credit given.

Degree Requirements: *For all associate degrees:* 60 credit hours. *For all baccalaureate degrees:* 127–147 credit hours; 3 terms in residence; 3 credits physical education. *For all undergraduate degrees:* 2.0 GPA; competency in oral and written communication; distribution requirements.

Fulfillment of some degree requirements and exemption from some beginning courses possible by passing College Board CLEP, APP before entrance. *Grading system:* A–F; satisfactory-unsatisfactory; withdraw (carries time limit); incomplete (carries time limit).

Distinctive Educational Programs: Cooperative baccalaureate in medical technology with approved training institutions. Interdepartmental/interdisciplinary majors in biochemistry, biophysics, Byzantine studies, chemistry-business, electronics-business, international studies, international language-business, medical technology. Five-year physical therapy program resulting in master's degree. Preprofessional programs in law, engineering, and medicine. Direct transfer agreement with engineering schools of Widener University, and special cooperative engineering at the University of Detroit Mercy (MI) for students who have completed the pre-engineering curriculum. Facilities for independent research, including honors programs, individual majors. Study abroad opportunities for students in all majors. In recent years, students representing all colleges in the University have studied in over 50 programs in countries on every continent. Programs for foreign study are available in any language for which the student is adequately prepared. *Available to all students:* Work-experience programs. Evening classes. Accelerated degree programs. Special facilities for using telecommunications in the classroom. Tutorials. *Other distinctive programs:* Degree-granting evening division primarily for adults. Noncredit continuing education enrichment program.

ROTC: Army optional.

Degrees Conferred: 6 *associate*; 869 *baccalaureate*; 616 *master's*; 36 *doctorate*. Bachelor's degrees awarded in top five disciplines: business, management, marketing, and related support services 202; education 100; communication, journalism, and related programs 96; health professions and related clinical sciences 94; biological/life sciences 72. Master's degrees awarded: various disciplines 616. Doctorates awarded: health professions 36.

Fees and Other Expenses: *Full-time tuition per academic year 2008–09:* $31,576. *Books and supplies:* $1,100. *Room and board per academic year:* $10,990. *Other expenses:* $1,850.

Financial Aid: Aid from institutionally generated funds is provided on the basis of academic merit, financial need.

Financial aid to full-time, first-time undergraduate students: 87% received some form of aid. Average amount of aid received: federal grants $3,804; Pell grants $2,614; other federal aid $1,242; state/local grants $1,639; institutional grants $12,771.

Departments and Teaching Staff: *Total instructional faculty:* 509 (full=-time 253, part-time 256). Student/faculty ratio: 11:1. Degrees held by full-time faculty: master's 15%, doctorate 85%.

Enrollment: Total enrollment 5,651. Undergraduate 4,132 (full-time 94%; female 57%, male 43%). Graduate 1,519 (full-time 51%). Undergraduate transfer-in students 83.

Characteristics of Student Body: *Ethnic/racial makeup:* Black non-Hispanic: 1%; Asian or Pacific Islander: 2%; Hispanic: 4%; White non-Hispanic: 86%; unknown: 12%; nonresident alien 1%.

International Students: 57 undergraduate nonresident aliens enrolled fall 2008. Students from Europe, Asia, Latin America, Africa, New Zealand. No programs available to aid students whose native language is not English. No financial aid aid specifically designated for international students.

Student Life: University housing comprises 33 buildings, including 14 traditional dormitories, 17 university houses/apartments, and 2 dorm suites. 49% of the student body live in dormitories and student housing. Male occupancy in university-owned housing 43%, female 57%, *Intercollegiate athletics:* male: baseball, basketball, cross-country, golf, ice hockey, lacrosse, soccer, swimming, wrestling, tennis; female: basketball, field hockey, cross-country, soccer, swimming, softball, volleyball, tennis. *Special regulations:* Registered cars with parking stickers permitted for all but freshmen. Quiet hours from 7pm to 7am. Residence hall visitation from 11am to midnight Sun.–Thurs., 11am to 2am. *Special services:* Learning Resources Center, medical services, commuter services, student volunteer director. *Student publications, radio: Aquinas*, a weekly newspaper; *Esprit*, a semiannual literary journal, *Retrospect*, an annual history journal; *Student Government Newsletter*, published weekly; *Windhover*, a yearbook. Radio station WYRE broadcasts 14 hours per day. FCC license granted to operate a new FM radio station, WSR. *Surrounding community:* Scranton population 88,500. Philadelphia and New York City, both 125 miles from campus, are nearest metropolitan areas. Served by mass transit bus system; airport 8 miles from campus.

Library Collections: 487,000 volumes. 109,000 microforms; 16,000 audiovisual materials; 17,500 periodicals including via electronic access. Online catalog. Students have access to online information retrieval services and the Internet.

Most important special collections include Joseph Polakoff Collection; Buckley Collection; Lackawanna Country and City of Scranton historical materials; University of Scranton Archives.

Buildings and Grounds: Campus area 50 acres.

Chief Executive Officer: Rev. Scott R. Pilarz, S.J., President.

Undergraduates address admission inquiries to Joseph Robach, Dean of Admissions; graduate inquiries to Dean of Graduate School.

Ursinus College

601 East Main Street
P.O. Box 1000
Collegeville, Pennsylvania 19426-1000
Tel: (610) 409-3000 **E-mail:** admissions@ursinus.edu
Fax: (610) 409-0627 **Internet:** www.ursinus.edu

Institution Description: Ursinus College is a private, independent, nonprofit college affiliated with the United Church of Christ. *Enrollment:* 1,680. *Degrees awarded:* Associate, baccalaureate.

Accreditation: *Regional:* MSA/CHE.

History: Established and chartered 1869; offered first instruction at postsecondary level 1870; awarded first degree (baccalaureate) 1873; became coeducational 1881.

Institutional Structure: *Governing board:* Board of Directors of Ursinus College. Representation: 44 directors, including 6 life trustees, 5 alumni, president of the college. *Composition of institution:* Administrators 18. Academic affairs headed by dean of the college. Management/business/finances directed by vice president for business affairs. Full-time instructional faculty 95. Academic governance body, Ursinus College Faculty, meets monthly.

Calendar: Semesters. Academic year Sept. to May. Freshmen admitted May. Degrees conferred and formal commencements May, Nov.

Characteristics of Freshmen: 6,192 applicants (3,459 female, 2,733 male). 55% of applicants accepted. 16% of accepted applicants enrolled full-time.

74% (301 students) submitted SAT scores; 13 students submitted ACT scores. *25th percentile*: SAT Critical Reading 560, SAT Math 540; ACT Composite 22. *75th percentile*: SAT Critical Reading 680, SAT Math 660; ACT Composite 27.

73% of entering freshmen expected to graduate within 5 years. 63% of freshmen from Pennsylvania. Freshmen from 12 states and 2 foreign countries.

Admission: Common Application. Early Decision deadline Dec. 15; Regular Decision deadline Feb. 15. Notified by March 15. *Requirements:* SAT, 2 teacher recommendations, counselor recommendation, official high school transcript, common application essay, Ursinus supplement. Personal interview highly recommended (required for merit scholarship eligibility). ACH recommended. TOEFL required for foreign students. *For transfer students:* 60% acceptance rate; 2.5 GPA required; 64 hours maximum transfer credit.

College credit and advanced placement available for postsecondary-level work and strong Advanced Placement results.

Degree Requirements: *For all associate degrees:* 64 credit hours. *For all baccalaureate degrees:* 128 credit hours; last 2 terms in residence. *For all degrees:* Average grade 2.00; distribution requirements.

Fulfillment of some degree requirements and exemption from some beginning courses possible by passing College Board AP, CLEP subject examinations. *Grading system:* A–F; withdraw (carries penalty after midterm); incomplete (deadline after which A–F assigned).

Distinctive Educational Programs: Programs for independent research, including honors programs, individual majors, tutorials, independent study, research scholars' program. Institutionally-sponsored travel and study abroad in France, Mexico, Costa Rica, and Japan during the summer and winter terms; junior year abroad by individual arrangement. *Other distinctive programs:* degree and nondegree programs through continuing education. Area high school students and senior citizens may enroll in courses for half tuition during fall or spring terms.

Degrees Conferred: 365 359 *baccalaureate*. Bachelor's degrees awarded in top five disciplines: social sciences 83; biological/life sciences 40; English language/literature 38; business, management, marketing, and related support services 35; psychology 33.

Fees and Other Expenses: *Full-time tuition per academic year 2008–09:* $36,710. *Books and supplies:* $1,000. *Room and board per academic year:* $8,800. *Other expenses:* $1,600.

Financial Aid: Aid from institutionally generated funds is provided on the basis academic merit, financial need.

Financial aid to full-time, first-time undergraduate students: 93% received some form of financial aid. Average amount of aid relieved: federal grants $5,336; Pell grants $3,223; other federal aid $2,360; state/local grants $3,079; institutional grants $17,438.

Departments and Teaching Staff: *Total instructional faculty:* 95. Degrees held by full-time faculty: baccalaureate 100%, master's 100%, doctorate 90%, professional 2%. 92% hold terminal degrees.

Enrollment: Total enrollment 1,680. Undergraduate1,680 (full-time 99%; female 55%, male 45%).

Characteristics of Student Body: *Ethnic/racial makeup:* Black non-Hispanic: 6%; Asian of Pacific Islander: 4%; Hispanic: 3%; White non-Hispanic: 72%; unknown 14%; nonresident alien 1%.

International Students: 17 nonresident aliens enrolled fall 2008. Students from Europe, Asia, Latin America. Programs available to aid students whose native language is not English: English as a Second Language Program. No financial aid specifically designated for international students.

Student Life: Characterized by residential living (90% of students) and programs to develop leadership, community service. *Leadership:* Leadership Scholar Program, Ursinus Student Government Association, Resident Assistant Program, Campus Life Committee, Student Activities Committee, Campus Activities Board, Judiciary Board, Campus Planning Group. *Community Service:* Student Environmental Action Coalition, Habitat for Humanity, Norristown Soup Kitchen, Jr. and Sr. High School Tutoring, Alpha Pi Omega (national service fraternity), Alpha Sigma Nu (local service sorority) and Circle K. *Intercollegiate or Club Sports:* Male: only: baseball, basketball, cross-country, football, golf, lacrosse, soccer, swimming, tennis, track and field, wrestling; female: basketball, cross-country, field hockey, gymnastics, lacrosse, soccer, softball, swimming, tennis, track and field, volleyball. *Student Publications: The Grizzly,* a weekly newspaper; *The Lantern,* a biannual literary magazine; *The Ruby,* a yearbook. *Surrounding Community:* Collegeville Borough population 3,200. Philadelphia 25 miles from campus. Campus served by mass transit bus system. Airport 30 miles from campus. Train station 8 miles from campus.

Library Collections: 235,000 volumes. 356,000 microforms; 4,400 audiovisual materials; 1,160 current periodical subscriptions. Students have access to online information retrieval services and the Internet.

Most important holdings include J.H.A. Bomberger Collections; Pennsylvania Folklife Society archives (magazines, books, artifacts); Linda Grace Hoyer Updike Literary Papers (1919–1989), contains the manuscripts and correspondence of Linda Hoyer (1904–1989), Ursinus graduate, writer and mother of John Updike.

Buildings and Grounds: Campus area 140 acres.

Chief Executive Officer: Dr. John R. Strassburger, President.

Address admission inquiries to Robert McCullgh, Dean of Admissions.

Valley Forge Christian College

1401 Charlestown Road
Phoenixville, Pennsylvania 19460
Tel: (610) 935-0450 **E-mail:** admissions@vfcc.edu
Fax: (610) 935-9353 **Internet:** www.vfcc.edu

Institution Description: Valley Forge Christian College is a private institution affiliated with the Assemblies of God. *Enrollment:* 1,201. *Degrees awarded:* Associate, baccalaureate. Certificates also awarded.

Accreditation: *Regional:* MSA/CHE. *National:* ABHE.

History: Established and chartered as Eastern Bible Institute 1939; changed name to Northeast Bible Institute 1962; authorized to grant the Bachelor of Science degree and name changed to Northeast Bible College 1975; adopted present name 1977.

Institutional Structure: *Governing board:* Board of Trustees. *Composition of institution:* Administrators 13. Academic affairs headed by vice president of academic affairs. Management/business/finances directed by vice president of administrative services. Full-time instructional faculty 23.

Calendar: Semesters. Academic year Aug. to May. Freshmen admitted Aug, Jan., May, June. Degrees conferred and formal commencement May. summer session of 2 terms May to June.

Characteristics of Freshmen: 65% of freshmen from Pennsylvania. Freshmen from 20 states.

Admission: Apply at least one month prior to the term of enrollment. Early acceptance available. *Requirements:* Graduation from accredited secondary school or GED. *Entrance tests:* SAT or ACT composite encouraged but not required. For foreign students TOEFL. *For transfer students:* Credit may be granted for comparable courses in which grades of C or higher are earned as they apply toward the degree program entered.

VALLEY FORGE CHRISTIAN COLLEGE—*cont'd*

Degree Requirements: *For associate degrees:* 60–64 credits; 2.0 GPA. *For baccalaureate degrees:* 126–133 credits; 2.0 GPA; completion of the last 30 credits in residence; completion of the minimum number of Student Ministry Department requirements; soundness in doctrine; acceptable deportment and regular chapel attendance; completion of Internship. *Grading system:* A–F.

Fulfillment of some degree requirements may be granted by passing College Board CLEP, APP (to a total of 30 credits) and through life experience (up to 9 credits).

Distinctive Educational Programs: Evangelical Teacher Training Association diploma earned upon completion of curriculum. Student Ministries and Internship program provide opportunities for students to develop proficiency in various student ministries. Extension classes offered in Fairfax (VA) and Richmond (VA).

Degrees Conferred: 6 *associate*; 109 *baccalaureate*. Bachelor's degrees awarded in three disciplines: theology 73; education 26; psychology 8.

Fees and Other Expenses: *Full-time tuition per academic year 2008–09:* contact the college for current tuition, fees, housing, and other costs.

Financial Aid: Aid from institutionally generated funds is provided on the basis of academic merit, financial need, other criteria.

Financial aid to full-time, first-time undergraduate students: 98% received some form of financial aid. Average amount of aid received: federal grants $2,746; state/local grants $2,918; institutional grants $2,046; loans $3,571.

Departments and Teaching Staff: *Total instructional faculty:* 34. Student/faculty ratio: 18.5:1. Degrees held by full-time faculty: baccalaureate 13%, master's 65%, doctorate 22%. 22% hold terminal degrees.

Enrollment: Total enrollment 1,201. Undergradaute 1,187 (full-time 69%; female 55%, male 45%). Graduate 14 (full-time 74%). Undergraduate transfer-in students 74.

Characteristics of Student Body: *Ethnic/racial makeup:* Black non-Hispanic: 8%; Asian or Pacific Islander: 2%; Hispanic: 10; White non-Hispanic: 69%; unknown: 10%; nonresident alien 1%.

International Students: 12 nonresident aliens enrolled fall 2008. Programs available to aid students whose native language is not English: English as a Second Language Program. No financial aid specifically designated for international students.

Student Life: On-campus residence halls house all single students who take a minimum of 9 credit hours. *Varsity athletics:* male: basketball, soccer; female: baseball, basketball, soccer. *Special regulations:* Students are to wear modest clothing, reflecting Christian values; specified attire for gym classes. Cars must be registered with the college. *Special services:* health services, student center. *Surrounding community:* Phoenixville is 25 miles northwest of Philadelphia.

Publications: *The Forge*, a quarterly college publication for constituents and alumni.

Library Collections: 62,000 volumes. Online catalog. Computer work stations available. Students have access to the Internet at no charge.

Most important special collection: Pentecostalism.

Buildings and Grounds: Campus area 77 acres.

Chief Executive Officer: Dr. Don Meyer, President.

Address admission inquiries to William Chenco, Director of Admissions.

Washington and Jefferson College

60 South Lincoln Street
Washington, Pennsylvania 15301-4801
Tel: (724) 223-4400 **E-mail:** admission@washjeff.edu
Fax: (724) 223-6534 **Internet:** www.washjeff.edu

Institution Description: Washington and Jefferson College is a private, independent, nonprofit college. *Enrollment:* 1,519. *Degrees awarded:* Associate, baccalaureate, master's.

Accreditation: *Regional:* MSA/CHE.

History: Established 1865 through a merger of Washington College (established as Washington Academy, a school for men, chartered, incorporated and offered first instruction at postsecondary level 1787) and Jefferson College (chartered as Canonsburg Academy and Library Company 1794; changed name to Jefferson College 1802); became coeducational 1970.

Institutional Structure: *Governing board:* The Board of Trustees. Representation: 36 trustees (including 10 alumni), president of the college. 1 ex officio. 42 voting. *Composition of institution:* Administrators 10. Academic affairs headed by vice president for academic affairs and dean of the faculty. Management/business/finances directed by vice president for business and finance. Full-time instructional faculty 104. Academic governance body, the faculty, meets an average of 10 times per year.

Calendar: Semesters. Academic year Aug. .to May. Freshmen admitted Sept., Aug., Jan., Feb. June. Degrees conferred and formal commencement May. Summer session of 2 terms from June to Aug.

Characteristics of Freshmen: 6,823 applicants (3,612 female, 3,211 male). 38% of applicants accepted. 15% of accepted applicants enrolled full-time.

84% (382 students) submitted SAT scores; 31% (142 students) submitted ACT scores. *25th percentile*: SAT Critical Reading 500, SAT Math 520; ACT Composite 22, ACT English 20, ACT Math 21. *75th percentile*: SAT Critical Reading 600, SAT Math 620; ACT Composite 26, ACT English 27, ACT Math 26.

68% of entering freshmen expected to graduate within 5 years. 75% of freshmen from Pennsylvania. Freshmen from 21 states.

Admission: Rolling admissions plan. For fall acceptance, apply as early as Sept. of previous year, but not later than Mar. of year of enrollment. Students are notified of acceptance beginning in Feb. Apply by Dec. 1 for early decision; need not limit application to Washington and Jefferson. Early acceptance available. *Requirements:* Either graduation from accredited secondary school or GED. Recommend 15 units which include 3 in college preparatory English, 2 in a foreign language, 3 college preparatory mathematics, 1 from among history, natural science or social studies, 6 academic electives. *Entrance tests:* College Board SAT and 3 Achievements (1 English) or ACT composite. For foreign students TOEFL. Essay required. *For transfer students:* 2.5 minimum GPA; 18 courses maximum transfer credit.

College credit and advanced placement for postsecondary-level work completed in secondary school and for extrainstitutional learning (life experience) on basis of individual assessment.

Informal tutoring available.

Degree Requirements: 34 courses minimum; 2.0 GPA; 2 years in residence; 1 physical education course or ROTC; core requirements.

Fulfillment of some degree requirements and exemption from some beginning courses possible by passing College Board CLEP, AP exams. *Grading system:* A–F; pass-fail; withdraw (deadline after which pass-fail is appended to withdraw).

Distinctive Educational Programs: *For undergraduates:* Dual-degree programs in engineering with Case Western Reserve University (OH), Washington University (MO), Columbia University (NY); in optometry with Pennsylvania College of Optometry. Cooperative baccalaureate in medical technology with area hospitals. Interdepartmental program in industrial chemistry and management. Facilities and programs for independent research, including honors programs, individual majors, tutorials. Institutionally arranged study abroad during intersession; junior year abroad through programs offered by other institutions. Cooperative exchange program with universities throughout the world. Entrepreneurial Studies Program.

ROTC: Air Force and Army in cooperation with University of Pittsburgh. .

Degrees Conferred: 366 *baccalaureate*. Bachelor's degrees awarded in top five disciplines: business, management, marketing, and related support services 83; social sciences English 37; psychology 35; biological/life sciences 26, social sciences 26.

Fees and Other Expenses: *Full-time tuition per academic year 2008–09:* $31,496. *Other expenses:* $700. *Room and board per academic year:* $8,488. *Books and supplies:* $800.

Financial Aid: Aid from institutionally generated funds is provided on the basis of academic merit, financial need.

Financial aid to full-time, first-time undergraduate students: 98% received some form of financial aid.

Departments and Teaching Staff: *Total instructional faculty:* 145. Student/faculty ratio: 12:1.

Enrollment: Total enrollment 1,519. Undergradduate 1,519 (full-time 99%; female 46%, male 54%).

Characteristics of Student Body: *Ethnic/racial makeup:* Black non-Hispanic: 3%; Asian or Pacific Islander: 1%; Hispanic: 1%; White non-Hispanic: 85%; unknown: 8%.; nonresident alien 2%.

International Students: 8 undergraduate nonresident aliens enrolled fall 2008. No programs available to aid students whose native language is not English. No financial aid specifically designated for international students.

Student Life: On-campus residence halls house 88% of student body. Residence halls for males constitute 33% of such space, for females 20%, for both sexes 47%. 32% of males join and live in fraternity housing. *Intercollegiate athletics:* male: baseball, basketball, cross-country, football, golf, lacrosse, soccer, swimming and diving, tennis, track and field, water polo. wrestling; female: basketball, cross-country, golf, soccer, softball, track and field, swimming and diving, tennis, volleyball, water polo. *Special regulations:* Cars permitted; no fee charged. *Special services:* medical services. *Student publications: Pandora*, a yearbook; *Red & Black*, campus newspaper. *Surrounding community:* Washington population 16,000. Pittsburgh, 25 miles from campus, is nearest metropolitan area. Served by mass transit bus system; airport 25 miles from campus.

Library Collections: 223,000 volumes including bound books, serial backfiles, electronic documents, and government documents not in separate collections. Online catalog. 15,000 microforms; 10,000 audiovisual materials; 12,000 periodicals including via electronic access. Computer work stations available. Students have access to the Internet at no charge.

Most important special collections include History of Washington and Jefferson College; Walker Collection of art books; Historical Collection (19th century manuscripts on Upper Ohio Valley Region); Joseph F. Guffey Papers.

Buildings and Grounds: Campus area 43 acres.

Chief Executive Officer: Dr. G. Andrew Rembert, President.

Address admission inquiries to Alton Newell, Dean of Enrollment.

Waynesburg University

51 West College Street
Waynesburg, Pennsylvania 15370-1257
Tel: (724) 627-8191 **E-mail:** admissions@waynesburg.edu
Fax: (724) 627-8124 **Internet:** www.waynesburg.edu

Institution Description: Waynesburg University is a private college affiliated with The Presbyterian Church (U.S.A.). *Enrollment:* 2,541. *Degrees awarded:* Associate, baccalaureate.

Member of the consortium Southwestern Pennsylvania Higher Education Council, Inc.

Accreditation: *Regional:* MSA/CHE.

History: Established as Waynesburg College by merger of Greene Academy and Madison College and offered first instruction at postsecondary level 1849; chartered 1850; awarded first degree (baccalaureate) 1853; achieved university status 2007. *See* William H. Dusenberry, *The Waynesburg College Story 1849–1974* (Kent, Ohio: The Kent State University Press, 1975) for further information.

Institutional Structure: *Governing board:* The Board of Trustees of Waynesburg University. Extrainstitutional representation: 33 trustees; including 9 alumni; institutional representation: president of the college. 1 ex officio. All voting. *Composition of institution:* Administrators 42. Academic affairs headed by vice president for academic affairs. Management/business/finances directed by vice president, business and finance. Full-time instructional faculty 62. Academic governance body, the faculty, meets an average of 9 times per year.

Calendar: Semesters. Academic year Aug. to May. Freshmen admitted Aug., Sept., Jan., June, July. Degrees conferred May, July, Aug., Dec. Formal commencement May. Summer session from May to Aug.

Characteristics of Freshmen: 2,310 applicants (1,057 female, 1,253 male). 62% of applicants accepted. 31% of accepted applicants enrolled full-time.

85% (297 students) submitted SAT scores. *25th percentile*: SAT Critical Reading 430, SAT Math 440. *75th percentile*: SAT Critical Reading 550, SAT Math 550.

43% of entering freshmen expected to graduate within 5 years. 77% of freshmen from Pennsylvania. Freshmen from 13 states.

Admission: Rolling admissions plan. For fall acceptance, apply as early as Aug. of previous year, but not later than July of year of enrollment. Early acceptance available. *Requirements:* Either graduation from accredited secondary school with 16 academic units in college preparatory courses or GED. Minimum GPA 2.0. *Entrance tests:* College Board SAT or ACT composite. *For transfer students:* 2.0 minimum GPA; from 4-year accredited institution 90 hours maximum transfer credit; from 2-year accredited institution 60 hours.

College credit and advanced placement for postsecondary-level work completed in secondary school.

Tutoring available. Developmental / remedial courses offered in summer session and regular academic year; credit given.

Degree Requirements: *For all associate degrees:* 60 credit hours. *For all baccalaureate degrees:* 124 hours. *For all undergraduate degrees:* 2.0 GPA (2.25 GPA in major courses); 2 terms in residence; demonstrated proficiency in major; distribution requirements.

Fulfillment of some degree requirements and exemption from some beginning courses possible by passing College Board CLEP, APP. *Grading system:* A–F; pass-fail; withdraw (carries time limit); incomplete (carries time limit).

Distinctive Educational Programs: Evening classes. Cooperative baccalaureate in medical technology with approved schools. Facilities and programs for independent research. Study abroad individually arranged.

Degrees Conferred: 5 *associate*; 413 *baccalaureate*; 233 *master's*. Bachelor's degrees awarded in top five disciplines: health professions and related clinical sciences 73; business, management, marketing, and related support services 64; public administration 29; education 25; communication, journalism, and related programs 23. Master's degrees awarded: various disciplines 233.

Fees and Other Expenses: *Full-time tuition per academic year 2008–09:* undergraduate $17,080; contact the college for current charge per credit hour for graduate study. *Books and supplies:*$1,200. *Room and board per academic year:* $7,060. *Other expenses:* $575.

Financial Aid: Aid from institutionally generated funds is provided on the basis of academic merit, financial need, other criteria.

Financial aid to full-time, first-time undergraduate students: 86% received some form of financial aid. Average amount of aid received: federal grants $2,575; state/local grants %1,475; institutional grants 43,891; loans $3,131.

Departments and Teaching Staff: *Total instructional faculty:* 110. Degrees held by full-time faculty: masters 41%, doctorate 59%, professional .1%. 62% hold terminal degrees.

Enrollment: Total enrollment 2,549. Undergraduate 1,828 (full-time 89%; female 64%, male 36%). Graduate 721 (full-time 13%).

Characteristics of Student Body: *Ethnic/racial makeup:* Black non-Hispanic: 2%; Asian or Pacific Islander 1%; Hispanic 2%; White non-Hispanic 93%; unknown 3%.

International Students: No programs available to aid students whose native language is not English. No financial aid specifically designated for international students.

Student Life: On-campus residence halls house 50% of student body. Residence halls for males constitute 61% of such space, for females 39%. 14% of males join and 6% live in off-campus fraternity housing. Off-campus living available for seniors. *Intercollegiate athletics:* male: baseball, basketball, football, golf, tennis, wrestling, soccer; female: soccer, softball, tennis, volleyball, basketball. *Special regulations:* Registered cars with decals permitted for all but freshmen. Quiet hours during final examinations periods. Dormitory visitation from noon to midnight weekdays, noon to 3am on weekends. *Special services:* Medical services. Limited college van service to Pittsburgh and local hospital. Chapel offered weekly. *Student publications, radio: Green Fuse*, a literary magazine; *The Mad Anthony*, college yearbook; *Yellow Jacket*, college newspaper. Radio station WCYJ-FM; WCYJ-TV. *Surrounding community:* Waynesburg population 4,500. Pittsburgh 50 miles from campus, is nearest metropolitan area. Served by airport 60 miles from campus; passenger rail service 50 miles from campus.

Library Collections: 100,000 volumes. 83,000 microforms; 2,800 audiovisual materials; 395 current periodical subscriptions. Online catalog. Students have access to online information retrieval services and the Internet.

Most important holdings include Honorable John Clark Knox Room; Thomas E. Morgan Archives; Trans-Appalachian Collection.

Buildings and Grounds: Campus area 30 acres.

Chief Executive Officer: Dr. Timothy R. Thyreen, President.

Address admission inquiries to Robin L. King, Dean of Admissions.

West Chester University of Pennsylvania

University Avenue and High Street
West Chester, Pennsylvania 19383
Tel: (610) 436-1000 **E-mail:** ugadmiss@wcupa.edu
Fax: (610) 436-3115 **Internet:** www.wcupa.edu

Institution Description: West Chester University of Pennsylvania, formerly West Chester College, is a state institution. *Enrollment:* 13,619. *Degrees awarded:* Associate, baccalaureate, master's. Certificates also awarded.

Academic offerings subject to approval by statewide coordinating bodies. Budget subject to approval by state governing boards.

Accreditation: *Regional:* MSA/CHE.*Professional*: athletic training, business, music, nursing, nursing education, public health, respiratory therapy, social work, speech-language pathology, teacher education

History: Chartered as West Chester Academy 1812; closed 1869; reopened as West Chester State Normal School 1871; changed name to West Chester State Teachers College and offered first instruction at postsecondary level 1927; awarded first degree (baccalaureate) 1828; became West Chester State College 1960; adopted present name 1983. *See* Russell L. Sturzbecker, *Centennial History of West Chester State College* (West Chester: Tinicum Press, 1971) for further information.

Institutional Structure: *Governing board:* Board of Governors (comprised of 16 members appointed by the governor and confirmed by the senate) with the chancellor for the state system of higher education serving as the chief executive officer; Council of Trustees (8 trustees, 1 student appointed by governor and confirmed by senate). All voting. *Composition of institution:* Administrators 15. Academic affairs headed by provost and academic vice president. Management/business/finances directed by vice president for administrative and fiscal affairs. Full-time instructional faculty 570. Academic governance body, Faculty Senate, meets an average of 12 times per year. *Faculty representation:* Faculty served by collective bargaining agent, Association of Pennsylvania State University Faculty, affiliated with AAUP and AFT.

WEST CHESTER UNIVERSITY OF PENNSYLVANIA—*cont'd*

Calendar: Semesters. Academic year Aug. to May. Freshmen admitted Aug., Jan., June. Degrees conferred May, Aug., Dec. Formal commencement May, Dec. Summer session of 3 terms from June to Aug.

Characteristics of Freshmen: 13,553 applicants (8,337 female, 5,016 male). 47% of applicants accepted. 32% of accepted applicants enrolled full-time.

83% (1,885 students) submitted SAT scores. *25th percentile*: SAT Critical Reading 480, SAT Math 490. *75th percentile*: SAT Critical Reading 570, SAT Math 580.

30% of entering freshmen expected to graduate within 5 years. 87% of freshmen from Pennsylvania. Freshmen from 19 states and 24 foreign countries.

Admission: Rolling admissions plan. For fall acceptance, apply as early as Aug. 1 of previous year, but not later than July 1 of year of enrollment. Early acceptance available. *Requirements:* Either graduation from secondary school or GED. Minimum 2.0 GPA. *Entrance tests:* College Board SAT or ACT composite. For foreign students TOEFL minimum score of 550 required. *For transfer students:* 2.0 minimum GPA; from 4-year accredited institution 90 semester hours maximum transfer credit; from 2-year accredited institution 65 semester hours.

Tutoring available. Developmental courses offered in summer session and regular academic year; credit given.

Degree Requirements: *For undergraduate degrees:* 128 semester hours; 2 semesters in residence; 2 credit hours of physical education courses; general education requirements.

Fulfillment of some degree requirements possible by passing departmental examinations, College Board Subject CLEP, AP. *Grading system:* A–F; pass-fail; withdraw (carries time limit).

Distinctive Educational Programs: Internships. Flexible meeting places and schedules, including off-campus centers (at varying locations according to need) and evening classes. Accelerated degree programs. Dual-degree program in physics and engineering. Special facilities for using telecommunications in the classroom. Interdisciplinary and preprofessional programs. Facilities and programs for independent research, including honors programs, independent study. Institutionally sponsored study abroad in Montpelier, France, and Swansen, Wales. Junior Year Abroad (France). Study also available through programs sponsored by other institutions.

ROTC: Air Force in cooperation with St. Joseph;s University; Army with Widener University.

Degrees Conferred: 2,114 *baccalaureate*; 575 *master's*. Bachelor's degrees awarded in top five disciplines: education 351; business, management, marketing, and related support services 334; liberal arts and sciences, general studies, and humanities 230; health professions and related clinical sciences 228; visual and performing arts 138. Master's degrees awarded in top five disciplines: education 204; health professions 58; public administration and social services 37; psychology 25.

Fees and Other Expenses: *Full-time tuition per academic year 2008–09:* undergraduate resident $6,737, nonresident $14,867; contact the university for current graduate tuition/fees. *Room and board per academic year:* $8,874. *Books and supplies:* $1,296. *Other expenses:* $3,585.

Financial Aid: The university offers a direct lending program. Aid from institutionally generated funds is awarded on the basis of academic merit, financial need, athletic ability, other criteria.

Financial aid to full-time, first-time undergraduate students: 77% received some form of aid. Average amount of aid received: federal grants $3,578; Pell grantss $2,786; other federal aid $866; state/local grants $3,471; institutional grants $2,776.

Departments and Teaching Staff: *Total insructional faculty:* 806 (full-time 570, part-time 236). Student/faculty ratio: 13:1. Degrees held by full-time faculty: baccalaureate 1%, master's 26%, doctorate 73%.

Enrollment: *Total enrollment:* 13,619. Undergraduate 11,482 (full-time 90%; female 61%, male 39%). Graduate 2,137 (full-time 29%). Undergraduate transfer-in students 1,070.

Characteristics of Student Body: *Ethnic/racial makeup:* Black non-Hispanic: 9%; Asian or Pacific Islander: 2%; Hispanic: 3%; White non-Hispanic: 85%. *Age distribution:* number under 18: 172; 18–19: 3,587; 20–21: 3,845; 22–24: 2,086; 25–29: 564; 30–34: 172; 35–39: 104; 40–49: 172; 50–64: 86; 65 and over: 27.

International Students: 76 undergraduate nonresident aliens enrolled fall 2008. Students from Europe, Asia, Latin America, Africa, 8 Canada, Australia, Middle East. No programs available to aid students whose native language is not English. No financial aid specifically designated for international students.

Student Life: On-campus residence halls house 40% of student body. Residence halls for females only constitute 27% of such space, for both sexes 73%. 3% of males join and some live in fraternity housing. *Intercollegiate athletics:* male: baseball, basketball, cross-country, football, golf, gymnastics, lacrosse, soccer, swimming, tennis, track, wrestling; female: badminton, basketball, cross-country, gymnastics, lacrosse, hockey, softball, swimming, tennis, track, volleyball. *Special regulations:* Registered cars permitted for students with 66 credits. Quiet hours and visitation hours vary according to residence hall. *Special services:* Learning Resources Center, medical services, transportation service to and from physical education facilities. *Student publications, radio, television: Daedalus*, an annual literary magazine; *The Quad*, a weekly newspaper; *The Serpentine*, an annual student book. Radio station WCUR broadcasts 80 hours per week. TV station WCSC broadcasts 30 hours per week. *Surrounding community:* West Chester population 18,500. Philadelphia, 27 miles from campus, is nearest metropolitan area. Served by mass transit bus and train systems; airport 28 miles from campus; passenger rail service less than 1 mile from campus.

Library Collections: 1,950,000 volumes including bound books, serial backfiles, electronic documents, and government documents not in separate collections. Online catalog. 882,000 microforms; 78,000 audiovisual materials; 9,300 periodicals including via electronic access. Computer work stations available. Students have access to the Internet at no charge.

Most important special holdings include Chester County Historical Collection, including Darlington Collection of rare scientific and botanical materials; Ehinger Collection of historical material on physical education; Philips Collection of autographed books and letters.

Buildings and Grounds: Campus area 385 acres.

Chief Executive Officer: Dr. Madeleine Wing Adler, President.

Undergraduates address admission inquiries to Marsha Haug, Director of Admissions; graduate inquiries to Dean of Graduate Studies.

Westminster College

319 South Market Street
New Wilmington, Pennsylvania 16172

Tel: (724) 946-8761 **E-mail:** admissions@westminster.edu
Fax: (724) 946-7171 **Internet:** www.westminster.edu

Institution Description: Westminster College is a private, independent, nonprofit college related to the Presbyterian Church (USA). *Enrollment:* 1,516. *Degrees awarded:* Baccalaureate, master's.

Member of East Central College Consortium, Pittsburgh Regional Library Center, and Southwestern Pennsylvania Higher Education Council, Inc.

Accreditation: *Regional:* MSA/CHE. *Professional*: music

History: Established and chartered as Westminster Collegiate Institute and offered first instruction at postsecondary level 1852; awarded first degree (baccalaureate) 1854; adopted present name 1897. *See* Paul Gamble, *History of Westminster College 1852–1977* (New Wilmington: Westminster College, 1977) for further information.

Institutional Structure: *Governing board:* Board of Trustees. Extrainstitutional representation: 34 trustees; 14 alumni. All voting. *Composition of institution:* Administrators 52. Academic affairs headed by vice president for academic affairs and dean of the college. Management/business/finances directed by vice president for finance. Full-time instructional faculty 100. Academic governance body, The Faculty of Westminster College, meets an average of 10 times per year.

Calendar: Semesters. Academic year Aug. to May. Freshmen admitted Aug., Jan., Feb., June, July. Degrees conferred May, July, Aug. Formal commencement May or June. Summer session of 6 weeks from June to July.

Characteristics of Freshmen: 2,945 applicants (1,660 female, 1,285 male). 59% accepted and admitted. 26% of accepted applicants admitted full-time.

88% (277 students) submitted SAT scores; 36% (113 students) submitted ACT scores. *25th percentile*: SAT Critical Reading 470, SAT Math 480, SAT Writing 470; ACT Composite 20, ACT English 19, ACT Math 19. *75th percentile*: SAT Critical Reading 590, SAT Math 590, SAT Writing 570; ACT Composite 25, ACT English 26, ACT Math 25.

78% of entering freshmen expected to graduate within 5 years. 79% of freshmen from Pennsylvania. Freshmen from 20 states and 1 foreign country.

Admission: Rolling admissions plan. For fall acceptance, apply as early as June 1 of junior year of secondary school. Early acceptance available. *Requirements:* Graduation from accredited secondary school with 16 units including 4 English, 2 in foreign language, 3 mathematics, 2 lab sciences, 1 social studies. *Entrance tests:* College Board SAT or ACT composite. *For transfer students:* 2.0 minimum GPA; maximum transfer credit limited only by residence requirement.

College credit and advanced placement for postsecondary-level work completed in secondary school. Advanced placement on basis of faculty assessment.

Degree Requirements: 36 course units required; 2.0 GPA; 2 terms in residence; General Education Curriculum including physical education. Comprehensive exams required for biology, chemistry, psychology, and telecommunications majors.

Fulfillment of some degree requirements and exemption from some introductory courses possible through departmental examinations, College Board AP. *Grading system:* A–F; satisfactory/unsatisfactory; withdraw; withdraw/failure (carries penalty), incomplete (carries time limit).

Distinctive Educational Programs: *For undergraduates:* Internships. Accelerated degree programs. Dual-degree programs in engineering with Case-Western Reserve University, Pennsylvania State University, and Washington University (MO); in nursing with Case-Western Reserve. Interdisciplinary programs in environmental science, industrial relations, information arts, international economics and business, international politics, organizational behavior, and psychobiology. Other special programs include Quest for Human Understanding, a two-year program for freshmen and sophomores. Facilities for independent research, honors programs, individual majors, and tutorials. Study abroad in England through an exchange with Westminster College in Oxford, England; programs available in conjunction with the Council on International Educational Exchange and other accredited programs. Off-campus study in the U.S. including a broad variety of programs through American University's Washington Semester, Sea Semester through the Sea Education Association in Woods Hole, Massachusetts, programs at the Art Institute of Pittsburgh and its related sister institutes in other cities, and the college and university exchange.

ROTC: Army offered in cooperation with Youngstown State University (OH).

Degrees Conferred: 306 *baccalaureate*; 47 *master's*. Bachelor's degrees awarded in top five disciplines: education 63; business, management, marketing, and related support services 61; social sciences 34; communication, journalism, and related programs 33; biological/life sciences 19. Master's degrees awarded: education 47.

Fees and Other Expenses: *Full-time tuition per academic year 2008–09:* $27,000 undergraduate; graduate study charged per credit hour (contact the college for current information). *Books and supplies:* $1,700. *Room and board per academic year:* $8,110. *Other expenses:* $500.

Financial Aid: Aid from institutionally generated funds is provided on the basis of academic merit, financial need, athletic ability, performance.

Financial aid to full-time, first-time undergraduate students: 100% received some form of financial aid. Average amount of aid received: federal grants $3,125; state/local grants $3,246; institutional grants $10,339; loons $5,324.

Departments and Teaching Staff: *Total instructional faculty:* 104. Degrees held by full-time faculty: baccalaureate 7%, master's 16%, doctorate 82%. 82% hold terminal degrees.

Enrollment: Total enrollment 1,516. Undergraduate 1,431 (full-time 97%; female 59%, male 41%). Graduate 77 (full-time 4%).

Characteristics of Student Body: *Ethnic/racial makeup:* Black non-Hispanic: 2%; Asian or Pacific Islander 1%; White non-Hispanic 80%; unknown 17%.

International Students: No programs available to aid students whose native language is not English. No financial aid specifically designated for international students.

Student Life: On-campus residence halls house 85% of student body. Residence halls for males constitute 45% of such space, for females 55%. 50% of males join and 16% live in fraternity housing. 50% of females join sororities. 85% of students live on campus. *Intercollegiate athletics:* male: baseball, basketball, football, golf, soccer, tennis, track; female: basketball, softball, tennis, volleyball; both sexes: cross-country, swimming. *Special regulations:* Registered cars permitted in designated parking areas. Quiet hours 9pm to 9am Sun.–Thurs., 1am to 10am Fri. and Sat. Residence hall visitation hours from 11am to 12am Sun.–Thurs., open visitation hours Fri. and Sat. *Special services:* Career Planning and Placement, Counseling, Learning Skills Center, medical services. *Student publications, radio, television: Argo*, a yearbook; *Westminster Holcad*, a weekly newspaper; *Scrawl*, a biannual literary magazine. Radio station WWNW broadcasts 18 hours a day during the academic year and 12 hours a day during all breaks; TV station WWNW Cable-9 broadcasts 22 hours per week during the academic year. *Surrounding community:* New Wilmington population 3,500. Pittsburgh, 65 miles from campus, is nearest metropolitan area.

Publications: Sources of information about the college include *Westminster Magazine,* sent to Presbyterian Churches, alumni, parents, and friends of the college. Admissions brochures available upon request.

Library Collections: 355,000 volumes. 19,700 microforms; 940 current periodical subscriptions. Students have access to online information retrieval services and the Internet.

Buildings and Grounds: Campus area 300 acres.

Chief Executive Officer: Dr. R. Thomas Williamson, President.

Address admission inquiries to Director of Admissions.

Westminster Theological Seminary

2960 West Church Road
Glenside, Pennsylvania 19038

Tel: (215) 887-5511 **E-mail:** admissions@wts.edu
Fax: (215) 887-5404 **Internet:** www.wts.edu

Institution Description: Westminster Theological Seminary is a private, independent institution with a Reformed and Presbyterian orientation. *Enrollment:* 808. *Degrees awarded:* First-professional (master of divinity), master's, doctorate.

Accreditation: *Regional:* MSA/CHE. *National:* ATS. *Professional*: theology

History: Established 1929; chartered 1930; awarded first degree 1939.

Institutional Structure: *Governing board:* Board of Trustees. Representation: 24 trustees, 7 honorary trustees. *Composition of institution:* Administrators 35. Academic affairs headed by vice president for academic affairs. Development directed by vice president for development. Management/business directed chief operating officer; finances direct4ed by vice president for finance. Full-time instructional faculty 21.

Calendar: Semesters. Academic year Sept. to May. Formal commencement May. Summer session of 3 terms from June to Aug.

Admission: *Requirements:* For M.A., M.A.R., M.Div., baccalaureate degree from approved institutions. Recommend some mastery of English, classical and modern foreign languages, Bible, history, natural sciences, philosophy, social sciences. For Th.M., D.Min., baccalaureate degree and master's degree from approved institutions. For Ph.D., baccalaureate degree and first theological degree from approved institutions. *Entrance tests:* GRE for Ph.D. students. TSE-A for Th.M. and Ph.D. students. For foreign students TOEFL.

Degree Requirements: *For M.A.Mis.:* 36 credit hours plus ministry project. *For M.A.R.:* 55 credit hours. *For M.Div.:* 92 credit hours plus supervised ministry project. For M.A.R., M.Div., proficiency in Greek and Hebrew; 1.8 GPA. For Th.M., Ph.D., D.Min., 2.6 GPA. *Grading system:* A–F.

Distinctive Educational Programs: Facilities for independent research, individually arranged research courses. Training in pastoral counseling through Christian Counseling and Education Foundation (CCEF). Study abroad through Institute of Holy Land Studies in Israel; Institute on the Religious Roots of America - The British Backgrounds: England, Scotland, Wales. Training in urban missions.

Degrees Conferred: 59 *master's*; 14 *doctorate*; 51 *first-professional*: master of divinity.

Fees and Other Expenses: *Full-time tuition per academic year:* contact the seminary for current tuition, fees, and housing information.

Financial Aid: Aid from institutionally generated funds is provided on the basis of academic merit, financial need. Institution has a Program Participation Agreement with the U.S. Department of Education for eligible students to receive Pell Grants and, depending upon the agreement, other federal aid.

Departments and Teaching Staff: *Total instructional faculty:* 63. Degrees held by full-time faculty: baccalaureate 95%, master's 90%, doctorate 80%, professional 80%. 85% hold terminal degrees.

Enrollment: Total enrollment 808.

Characteristics of Student Body: *Ethnic/racial makeup:* number of Black non-Hispanic: 51; American Indian or Alaska Native: 3; Asian or Pacific Islander: 197; Hispanic: 9; White non-Hispanic: 139; unknown: 121.

International Students: 79 nonresident aliens enrolled fall 2008. Financial aid specifically designated for international students: scholarships available annually to qualifying students.

Student Life: Limited on-campus residence halls for single students. *Surrounding community:* Philadelphia metropolitan population 4,725,000. Served by mass transit bus system.

Publications: *The Westminster Theological Journal* (biannually).

Library Collections: 140,000 volumes. 12,000 microforms; 20 audiovisual materials; 760 current periodical subscriptions. Students have access to online information retrieval services and the Internet.

Most important special collections include Bible Texts and Versions; Early Reformed Theology; Biblical Studies.

Buildings and Grounds: Campus area 17 acres.

Chief Executive Officer: Dr. Peter A. Lillback, President.

Address admission inquiries to Dan Cajon, Director of Admissions.

Widener University

One University Place
Chester, Pennsylvania 19013-5792
Tel: (610) 499-4000 **E-mail:** admissions.office@widener.edu
Fax: (610) 876-9751 **Internet:** www.widener.edu

Institution Description: Widener University is an independent, nonprofit comprehensive teaching institution comprised of 8 schools and colleges: Engineering, Arts and Sciences, Business Administration, Nursing, Hospitality Management, University College (part-time non-traditional), Human Services Professions (includes programs in education, doctorate in clinical psychology and social work), and the School of Law which has campuses in Wilmington, Delaware and Harrisburg, Pennsylvania. *Enrollment:* 4,861. *Degrees awarded:* Associate, baccalaureate, first-professional (law), master's, doctorate.

Accreditation: *Regional:* MSA/CHE. *Professional*: chemistry, clinical psychology, engineering, health services administration, law, nursing, physical therapy, psychology internship, social work, teacher education

History: Established as Bullock School 1821; chartered 1843; received collegiate charter 1847; changed name to Hyatt School 1853, to Delaware Military Academy 1859; offered first instruction at postsecondary level and changed name to Pennsylvania Military Academy 1862; offered first degree (baccalaureate) 1867; changed name to Pennsylvania Military College 1892, to PMC Colleges (Pennsylvania Military College and Penn Norton College) 1966, to Widener College 1972; achieved university status 1979. *See* Clarence R. Moll, *A History of Pennsylvania Military College, 1821–1954* (Diss., New York University, 1954) for further information.

Institutional Structure: *Governing board:* Widener University Board of Trustees. Extrainstitutional representation: 24 trustees, 6 trustees emeriti; institutional representation: 1 administrator; 7 alumni, 5 ex officio. 24 voting. *Composition of institution:* Administrators 66. Academic affairs headed by academic vice president and provost. Management/business/finances directed by vice president for finance. Full-time instructional faculty 319. Academic governance bodies, faculties of Schools and Colleges, meet an average of 9 times per year.

Calendar: Semesters. Academic year Sept. to May. Freshmen admitted Sept., Jan. Degrees conferred May, Aug., Dec. Formal commencement May. Summer session of 3 terms.

Characteristics of Freshmen: 69% of applicants accepted. 26% of accepted applicants enrolled.

99% (735 students) submitted SAT scores. *25th percentile*: SAT Critical Reading 440, SAT Math 450. *75th percentile*: SAT Critical Reading 530, SAT Math 560.

58% of entering freshmen expected to graduate within 5 years. 64% of freshmen from Pennsylvania. Freshmen from 21 states and 15 foreign countries.

Admission: Rolling admissions plan. For fall acceptance, apply early in senior year of secondary school, but not later than June 1. Students are notified of acceptance beginning Dec. 31. Apply by Nov. 1 for early decision; need not limit application to Widener. Early acceptance available. *Requirements:* 16 secondary school units from among English, foreign language, history or social studies, mathematics, science. Specific requirements for some programs. Recommend additional units in foreign language, mathematics, science, social science. Minimum 2.5 GPA. Lowest acceptable secondary school class standing 50th percentile. GED accepted. *Entrance tests:* College Board SAT. *For transfer students:* 2.0 minimum GPA; from 4-year accredited institution 90 hours maximum transfer credit; from 2-year accredited institution 30 hours.

College credit and advanced placement for postsecondary-level work completed in secondary school and for extrainstitutional learning on basis of faculty assessment.

Tutoring available. Developmental courses offered in summer session and regular academic year; credit given.

Degree Requirements: *For all associate degrees:* 60–66 credit hours; 15–30 hours in residence. *For all baccalaureate degrees:* 121–138 credit hours; 45 hours in residence; two ½-credit physical education courses; English and distribution requirements. *For all undergraduate degrees:* 2.0 GPA; exit competency examinations (comprehensives in individual fields of study).

Fulfillment of some degree requirements and exemption from some beginning courses possible by passing departmental examinations, College Board CLEP, AP. *Grading system:* A–F; pass-fail; withdraw (carries time limit).

Distinctive Educational Programs: Work-experience programs. Evening classes. Accelerated degree programs. Four-year co-op program. Interdisciplinary (open major) programs. Facilities and programs for independent research, including individual majors, senior team projects. Institutionally arranged study abroad in England, France, Korea, Germany; in Italy, Latin America, Spain through programs offered by other institutions. *Other distinctive programs:* Project Prepare, a summer tutorial and counseling program designed to assist educationally and economically disadvantaged students prepare for college.

ROTC: Army.

Degrees Conferred: 12 *associate*; 590 *baccalaureate*; 170 *master's*; 170 *doctorate*; 475 *first-professional*. Bachelor's degrees awarded in top five disciplines:business, management, marketing, and related support services 179; engineering 65; education 51; psychology 44; social sciences 34. Master's degrees awarded in top five disciplines: public administration and social services 103; education 96; business/marketing 59; health professions and related clinical sciences 41; psychology 34. Doctorates awarded: education 89; health professions 41; law/legal studies 4; psychology 35. First-professional degrees awarded: law 475.

Fees and Other Expenses: *Full-time tuition per academic year 2008–09:* \$30,450 undergraduate; graduate study charged per credit (varies, depending on program). *Books and supplies:* \$1,080. *Required fees:* \$400. *Room and board per academic year:* \$11,400. *Other expenses:* \$1,665.

Financial Aid: Aid from institutionally generated funds is provided on the basis of academic merit, financial need, other criteria.

Financial aid to full-time, first-time undergraduate students: 95% received some form of aid.

Departments and Teaching Staff: *Total instructional faculty:* 471. Student/faculty ratio: 12:1.

Enrollment: Total enrollment 4,861. Undergraduate 3,232 (full-time 82%; female 54%, male 46%). Graduate 1,629. Undergraduate transfer-in students 158.

Characteristics of Student Body: *Ethnic/racial makeup:* Black non-Hispanic: 13%; Asian or Pacific Islander: 2%; Hispanic: 35; White non-Hispanic: 89%; unknown: 10%; nonresident alien 2%. *Age distribution:* number under 18: 44; 18–19: 1,158; 20–21: 911; 22–24: 352; 25–29: 188; 30–34: 122; 35–39: 127; 40–49: 207; 50–64: 90; 65 and over: 14.

International Students: 98 nonresident aliens enrolled fall 2008. Students from Europe, Asia, Latin America, Africa, Canada. Programs available to aid students whose native language is not English: social, cultural, financial. English as a Second Language Program.

Student Life: On-campus residence halls house 55% of student body. Males only residences constitute 14% of such space, for females women only 16%, for both sexes 70%. 27% of males and 10% live in fraternity housing. College-owned housing is provided for sororities and 19% of females affiliate with a sorority. *Intercollegiate athletics:* male: baseball, basketball, cross-country, football, golf, indoor track, lacrosse, outdoor track, soccer, squash, swimming, tennis; female: basketball, cross-country, field hockey, indoor track, lacrosse, outdoor track, softball, swimming, tennis, volleyball. *Honor Societies:* 8 national honor societies have established chapters at Widener to recognize outstanding scholarship in their respective fields. The societies and their fields are Alpha Chi and Phi Kappa Phi, national scholarship honor societies; Alpha Sigma Lambda, adult student honor society; Alpha Psi Omega, dramatics; Omicron Delta Epsilon, economics; Pi Gamma Mu, social science; Sigma Pi Sigma, physics; Tau Beta Pi, engineering; and Sigma Theta Tau, nursing. *Special regulations:* Full-time undergraduate day students required to live on campus unless classified as a commuter; registered cars permitted in designated areas; quiet hours in residence halls. *Special services:* Writing and reading centers, medical services, counseling. Freshman Programs Office and special program for returning adult students. *Student media:* Weekly newspaper, yearbook. Radio station WDNR broadcasts 112 hours per week. *Surrounding community:* Philadelphia 15 miles from campus. Served by mass transit bus system; airport 10 miles from campus; passenger rail service 1 mile from campus.

Publications: *Widener Magazine, Widener Review, Delaware Journal of Corporate Law, Newsletter of the Society of Health Care Administrators, Widener Journal of Public Law, Widener University School of Law Magazine, Journal of Solid Waster Technology and Management.*

Library Collections: 242,000 volumes. 175,000 microforms; 12,000 audiovidual materials; 1,960 current serial subscriptions. Online catalog. Students have access to online information retrieval services and the Internet.

Most important special holdings of Main Library include Wolfgram Collection of English and American Literature; Nursing; Education, Psychology, and Human Services. Law Library: Corporate Law and Finance Collection; U.S. Government Documents Collection; Health Law Collection.

Buildings and Grounds: Campus area 161 acres.

Chief Executive Officer: Dr. James T. Harris, III, President.

Undergraduate students address admission inquiries to M. Hendrick, Jr., Dean of Admissions. graduate inquiries to Assistant Provost for Graduate Studies; Law School inquiries to Marion R. Newbold, Assistant Dean.

Wilkes University

84 West South Street
Wilkes-Barre, Pennsylvania 18766
Tel: (570) 408-5000 **E-mail:** admissions@wilkes.edu
Fax: (570) 408-7820 **Internet:** www.wilkes.edu

Institution Description: Wilkes University is a private, independent, nonprofit comprehensive college. *Enrollment:* 4,687. *Degrees awarded:* Baccalaureate, master's, first-professional.

Accreditation: *Regional:* MSA/CHE. *Professional*: business, engineering, pharmacy, nursing

History: Established as Bucknell University Junior College and offered first instruction 1933; chartered and incorporated as Wilkes College in 1947; awarded first degree (baccalaureate) 1948; achieved university status 1990.

Institutional Structure: *Governing board:* Board of Trustees. *Composition of institution:* Vice presidential structure. College of Science and Engineering; College of Arts, Humanities, and Social Sciences; College of Pharmacy and Nursing; School of Business and Leadership. Academic affairs headed by provost for academic affairs. Management/business/finances directed by vice president for finance and support operations. Fund raising and alumni directed by vice president for development and alumni relations. Administrators 53. Full-time instructional faculty 133.

Calendar: Semesters. Academic year Aug. to May. Freshmen and transfer students admitted Aug., Jan., June. Degrees conferred and formal commencements Aug., Jan., May. Summer sessions.

Characteristics of Freshmen: 73% of applicants accepted. 19% of accepted applicants enrolled.

99% (566 students) submitted SAT scores. *25th percentile*: SAT Critical Reading 460, SAT Math 470. *75th percentile*: SAT Critical Reading 580, SAT Math 600.

52% of entering freshmen expected to graduate within 5 years. 75% of freshmen from Pennsylvania. Freshmen from 10 states and 4 foreign countries.

Admission: Rolling admissions plan. Early acceptance available. *Requirements:* Either graduation from accredited secondary school or GED. *Entrance tests:* College Board SAT preferred; ACT composite accepted. For foreign students TOEFL.

Degree Requirements: 120 credit hours; 2.0 GPA; 30 hours in residence; liberal arts core requirements. *Grading system:* 4.0–0.0.

Distinctive Educational Programs: Individualized studies. 5-year programs (B.A. History/M.A., B.S.-M.S.). Wilkes University/Temple University College of Allied Health Professions Program (physical therapy, occupational therapy, health records administration, medical technology, nursing). Also joint Wilkes University/Temple University programs in dentistry, and pharmacy. Joint Wilkes University/Pennsylvania College of Optometry Program; Wilkes University/Pennsylvania College of Podiatric Medicine Program; Doctor of Pharmacy; Master of Arts in Creative Writing.

ROTC: Air Force; Army in cooperation with King's College or University of Scranton.

Degrees Conferred: 425 *baccalaureate*; 224 >*master's*. Bachelor's degrees awarded in top five disciplines: liberal arts/general studies 64; business, management, marketing, and related support services 57; health professions and related clinical sciences 139; biological/life sciences 36; psychology 31. Master's degrees awarded: business/marketing 48; education 154; engineering 12; health professions and related clinical sciences 15. First-professional degrees awarded: pharmacy 73.

Fees and Other Expenses: *Full-time tuition per academic year 2008–09:* $22,990. *Required fees:* $1,160. *Room and board per academic year:* $10,000.

Financial Aid: Aid from institutionally generated funds is provided on the basis of academic merit, financial need, other criteria.

Departments and Teaching Staff: *Total instructional faculty:* 345 (full-time 133, part-time 312). 88% of faculty hold the doctorate, first-professional, or other terminal degree Student/faculty ratio: 15:1.

Enrollment: Total enrollment 4,687. Undergraduate 2,030.

Characteristics of Student Body: *Ethnic/racial makeup:* number of Black non-Hispanic: 63; American Indian or Alaska Native: 5; Asian or Pacific Islander: 64; Hispanic: 39; White non-Hispanic: 2,056. *Age distribution:* number under 18: 8; 18–19: 847; 20–21: 835; 22–24: 243; 25–29: 51; 30–34: 20; 35–39: 7; 40–49: 6; 50–64: 3.

International Students: 98 nonresident aliens enrolled fall 2008. No programs available to aid students whose native language is not English. No financial aid specifically designated for international students.

Student Life: On-campus residence halls house 54% of undergraduate student body. *Intercollegiate athletics:* male: football, basketball, soccer, wrestling, golf, tennis, baseball; female: field hockey, lacrosse, soccer, tennis, basketball, volleyball, softball. *Special services:* Academic Support Center (free tutoring); access to the main computer available 24 hours a day, 7 days a week, for authorized users; microcomputer laboratories. *Student publications: The Beacon*, a weekly newspaper; *The Manuscript*, a literary magazine published semiannually; *Amnicola*, the student yearbook. *Surrounding community:* Wilkes-Barre population 50,000.

Library Collections: 200,000 volumes. 599,500 microforms; 8,600 audiovisual units; 789 current periodical subscriptions. Students have access to online information retrieval services and the Internet.

Most important special collections include Polish culture and history; northwest Pennsylvania history.

Buildings and Grounds: Campus area 55 acres.

Chief Executive Officer: Dr. Joseph E. Gilmour, President.

Address admission inquiries to Michael Frantz, Vice President of Enrollment Services. Dean of Admissions.

Wilson College

1015 Philadelphia Avenue
Chambersburg, Pennsylvania 17201-1285
Tel: (717) 264-4141 **E-mail:** admissions@wilson.edu
Fax: (717) 264-1578 **Internet:** www.wilson.edu

Institution Description: Wilson College is a private, independent, nonprofit college for women. It is affiliated with the Presbyterian Church (USA). *Enrollment:* 770. *Degrees awarded:* Associate, baccalaureate, master's.

Accreditation: *Regional:* MSA/CHE.

History: Established and chartered as Wilson Female College 1869; offered first instruction at postsecondary level 1870; awarded first degree (baccalaureate) 1874; adopted present name 1920.

Institutional Structure: *Governing board:* Wilson College Board of Trustees. Representation: 26 trustees, including 16 alumnae and president of the college, ex officio. All voting. *Composition of institution:* Administrators 8. Academic affairs headed by vice president for academic affairs;/dean of faculty. Finances directed by vice president for finance and administration. Full-time instructional faculty 38. Academic governance body, the faculty, meets an average of 9 times per year.

Calendar: Semesters. Academic year Sept. to May. Freshmen admitted Sept. Jan. Degrees conferred and formal commencement May or June.

Characteristics of Freshmen: 51% of applicants admitted. 86% of applicants admitted and enrolled.

90% (69 students) submitted SAT scores; 14% (11 students) submitted ACT scores. *25th percentile*: SAT Critical Reading 460, SAT Math 440; ACT Composite 20. *75th percentile*: SAT Critical Reading 560, SAT Math 550; ACT Composite 25.

45% of entering freshmen expected to graduate within 5 years. 62% of freshmen from Pennsylvania. Freshmen from 16 states and 10 foreign countries.

Admission: Rolling admissions plan. For fall acceptance, apply no later than third week of Aug. of year of enrollment. Early acceptance available. *Requirements:* Either graduation from accredited secondary or home school program. . Minimum GPA 2.5. Recommend secondary school class standing no lower than 50th %ile. *Entrance tests:* College Board SAT or ACT Composite. *For transfer students:* 2.0 minimum GPA; from 4-year accredited institution 22 course credits maximum transfer credit; from 2-year accredited institution and for correspondence/extension students 18 course credits.

College credit and advanced placement for postsecondary-level work completed in secondary school. College credit for extrainstitutional learning (life experience) on basis of faculty assessment.

Tutoring available.

Degree Requirements: 36 course credits; 2.0 GPA; 4 terms in residence; 2 semesters physical education and foreign language requirements; distribution requirements.

Fulfillment of some degree requirements and exemption from some beginning courses possible by passing departmental examinations, College Board CLEP, AP. *Grading system:* A–F; withdraw (carries time limit); credit-no credit.

Distinctive Educational Programs: January term internships. Evening classes. Accelerated degree programs. Facilities and programs for independent research, interdisciplinary majors, special majors.

Degrees Conferred: 55 *associate;* 81 *baccalaureate:* agriculture 9; biological/life sciences 4; business and marketing 5; communications/communication technologies 2; education 7; English 3; health professions and related sciences 28; interdisciplinary studies 6; mathematics 1; natural resources/environmental science 4; parks and recreation 2; physical sciences 2; psychology 1; social sciences 6; visual and performing arts 1.

WILSON COLLEGE—*cont'd*

Fees and Other Expenses: *Full-time tuition per academic year 2008–09:* $21,830. *Books and supplies:* $750. *Required fees:* $500. *Room and board per academic year:* $8,500.

Financial Aid: Aid from institutionally generated funds is provided on the basis of academic merit, financial need, other criteria.

Departments and Teaching Staff: *Total instructional faculty:* 77 (full-time 38, part-time 39). Total faculty with doctorate, first-professional, or other terminal degree: 42. Student/faculty ratio: 10:1.

Enrollment: Total enrollment 770. Undergraduate

Characteristics of Student Body: *Ethnic/racial makeup:* number of Black non-Hispanic: 37; Asian or Pacific Islander: 2; Hispanic: 16; White non-Hispanic: 645; unknown: 25. *Age distribution:* number under 18: 14; 18–19: 123; 20–21: 118; 22–24: 85; 25–29: 119; 30–34: 82; 35–39: 71; 40–49: 123; 50–64: 29; 65 and over: 1.

International Students: 40 nonresident aliens enrolled fall 2008. Students from Europe, Asia, Latin America, Africa, Middle East. Programs available to aid students whose native language is not English: English as a Second Language Program. Financial aid specifically designated for international students: 30 scholarships available annually. $516,559 awarded 21006–07.

Student Life: On-campus residence halls house 29% of student body. Residence halls for females constitute 100% of such space. *Intercollegiate athletics:* female: basketball, gymnastics, field hockey, softball, equestrian, soccer, tennis, volleyball. *Special regulations:* Cars permitted without restrictions. *Special services:* medical services. *Student publications: Billboard*, a biweekly newspaper; *Conococheague*, a yearbook. *Surrounding community:* Chambersburg population 17,960. Washington (DC) 97 miles from campus, is nearest metropolitan area.

Library Collections: 177,000 volumes. 2,007 audiovisual materials. Current periodical subscriptions; paper 200; microform 14; via electronic access 14,970. Online catalog. Students have access to online information retrieval services and the Internet.

Most important special collections include Jean Stapleton Archives; Maria Bashkirtseff Collection; Totem Pole Theater (PA) Archives; women's studies; English history.

Buildings and Grounds: Campus area 300 acres.

Chief Executive Officer: Dr. Lorna Dufinney Edmundson, President.

Address admission inquiries to Mary Ann Naso, Assistant Director of Admissions.

York College of Pennsylvania

Country Club Road
York, Pennsylvania 17405-7199
Tel: (717) 846-7788 **E-mail:** admissions@ycp.edu
Fax: (717) 849-1607 **Internet:** www.ycp.edu

Institution Description: York College of Pennsylvania is a private, independent, nonprofit, career-oriented liberal arts college. *Enrollment:* 5,627. *Degrees awarded:* Associate, baccalaureate, master's. Certificates also awarded.

Accreditation: *Regional:* MSA/CHE. *Professional*: business, engineering, medical record technology, respiratory therapy, nursing, recreation and leisure services.

History: Founded as the York Academy 1887; operated jointly by a *Teaching Reciprocal Agreement* with York College after 1929; York Junior College program introduced 1941; chartered as York College of Pennsylvania 1968.

Institutional Structure: *Governing board:* Board of Trustees of York College of Pennsylvania. Representation: 35 trustees, including 4 alumni. All voting. *Composition of institution:* Administrators40. Academic affairs headed by dean. Management/business/finances directed by chief financial officer. Full-time instructional faculty 145. Academic governance body, Academic Senate, meets an average of 10 times per year.

Calendar: Semesters. Academic year Aug. to May. Freshmen admitted Sept., Jan., June, July. Degrees conferred May, Aug., Dec. Formal commencements May and Dec. Summer session of 3 terms from May to Aug.

Characteristics of Freshmen: 66% of applicants admitted. 34% of applicants admitted and enrolled.

87% (949 students) submitted SAT scores. 87% (87 students) submitted ACT scores. *25th percentile*: SAT Critical Reading 610, SAT Math 490; ACT Composite 18. *75th percentile*: SAT Critical Reading 590, SAT Math 570; ACT Composite 24.

61% of entering freshmen expected to graduate within 5 years. 58% of freshmen from Pennsylvania. Freshmen from 30 states and 37 foreign countries.

Admission: Rolling admissions plan. For fall acceptance, apply as early as 1 year prior to enrollment, but not later than Sept. 1 of year of enrollment. Early acceptance available. *Requirements:* Either graduation from accredited secondary school or GED. Recommend 3 units in English, 4 foreign language and/or science, 3 mathematics, 3 social studies, 2 electives. *Entrance tests:* College Board SAT or ACT Composite. For foreign students TOEFL. *For transfer students:* 2.5 minimum GPA; from 4-year accredited institution 90 hours maximum transfer credit; from 2-year accredited institution 75 hours maximum transfer credit.

College credit and advanced placement for postsecondary-level work completed in secondary school. College credit for extrainstitutional learning on basis of faculty assessment. Tutoring available. Developmental courses offered in summer session and regular academic year; credit given.

Degree Requirements: *For all associate degrees:* 62 credit hours; 2 physical education courses. *For most baccalaureate degrees:* 124 credit hours; 4 physical education courses. *For all undergraduate degrees:* 2.0 GPA; 2 semesters in residence; distribution requirements.

Fulfillment of some degree requirements and exemption from some beginning courses possible by passing departmental examinations, College Board CLEP, Achievement Tests, AP. *Grading system:* 4, 3.5, 3, 2.5, 2, 1, 0; pass-fail; withdraw (carries time limit); incomplete (carries time limit).

Distinctive Educational Programs: *For undergraduates:* Internships. Off-campus center (at Hanover, less than 30 miles from main institution). Accelerated degree programs. Cooperative baccalaureate programs in engineering, medical technology and nuclear medicine with approved businesses, schools and hospitals. Pre-Medical Scholars Program in association with York Hospital; early admission agreement with Penn State Medical School at Hershey. Interdepartmental program in engineering management: interdisciplinary program in intercultural studies. Facilities and programs for independent research. Sponsored study abroad in Japan, England, Mexico, Puerto Rico, Korea, Germany.

ROTC: Army in cooperation with Dickinson College.

Degrees Conferred: 38 *associate;* 983 *baccalaureate*; 78 *master's*. Bachelor's degrees awarded in top five disciplines: business, management, marketing, and related support services 169; health professions and related clinical sciences 153; communications/journalism 89; security and protective services 63; parks and recreation 53. Master's degrees awarded: business, management, marketing, and related support services 53; education 6; health professions 19.

Fees and Other Expenses: *Full-time tuition per academic year 2008–09:* undergraduate $13,680, graduate tuition charged per credit hour (contact the college for current information). *Books and supplies:* $1,000. *Room and board per academic year:* $7,800. *Other expenses:* $1,600.

Financial Aid: Aid from institutionally generated funds is provided on the basis of academic merit, financial need. Institution has a Program Participation Agreement with the U.S. Department of Education for eligible students to receive Pell Grants and, depending upon the agreement, other federal aid.

Financial aid to full-time, first-time undergraduate students: 85% received some form of aid.

Departments and Teaching Staff: *Total instructional faculty:* 427 (full-time 145, part-time 282). 71% of faculty hold the doctorate, first-professional, or other terminal degree. Student/faculty ratio: 21:1.

Enrollment: Total enrollment 5,627. Undergraduate 5,329 (full-time 87%; female 56%, male 44%). Graduate 298. Undergraduate transfer-in students 308.

Characteristics of Student Body: *Ethnic/racial makeup:* number of Black non-Hispanic: 105; American Indian or Alaska Native: 8; Asian or Pacific Islander: 77; Hispanic: 92; White non-Hispanic: 4,782; unknown: 289. *Age distribution:* number under 18: 135; 18–19: 1,823; 20–21: 1,775; 22–24: 693; 25–29: 245; 30–34: 137; 35–39: 119; 40–49: 194; 50–64: 71; 65 and over: 8. 34% of student body attend summer sessions.

International Students: 23 nonresident aliens enrolled fall 2008. Students from Europe, Asia, Latin America, Africa, Middle East. No programs available to aid students whose native language is not English. Financial aid specifically designated for international students: 5 scholarships available annually; 5 totaling $2,500 awarded 2008–09.

Student Life: Students may live on or off campus. Co-ed, male and female dormitories; school-owned/operated apartments. Suites, mini-dorms, houses, special-interest housing, fraternity and sorority housing. 45% of students live on campus. *Intercollegiate sports:* male: baseball, basketball, cross-country, golf, lacrosse, soccer, swimming, tennis, track and field, wrestling; female: basketball, cross-country, field hockey, soccer, softball, swimming, tennis, track and field, volleyball. Intramural basketball, flag football, soccer, softball, tennis, volleyball, water polo. *Special regulations:* Cars permitted (20% of students have cars on campus). *Social organizations:* nine fraternities and six sororities. 10% of men join a fraternity and 13% of women join a sorority. *Other student activities:* Undergraduate student council. Radio and TV stations. Choir, madrigal singers, stage band, Circle K, theatre group, debate club, departmental groups, special-interest groups. Catholic Campus Ministry, Intervarsity Christian Fellowship, Hillel, Black Student Union, international students organizations. *Special services:* Learning Resource Center, medical services. *Surrounding community:* York population 45,000. Located in the Pennsylvania Dutch country, York is 4 hours from New York, 2 hours from Philadelphia and Washington (DC), and 1 hour from Baltimore. Served by mass transit bus system; airport and train station 25 miles from campus.

Publications: Sources of information about York College include *The York Scene*, a quarterly magazine distributed to parents, alumni, and friends of the college; *York College Catalog: The Viewbook* for high school students and families; visitors' guide; Academic Excellence brochure.

Library Collections: 300,,000 volumes. Online catalog. 5,000 government documents; 500,000 microforms; 11,000 audiovisual materials; 1500 current periodical subscriptions. Students have access to online information retrieval services and the Internet.

Most important special collections include Abraham Lincoln Collection; 19th-century fiction; 17th and 18th Century Bibles; York County History Collection.

Buildings and Grounds: Campus area 118 acres. Campus DVD available.

Chief Executive Officer: Dr. George W. Waldner, President.

Address admission inquiries to Admissions Office.

Puerto Rico

American University of Puerto Rico

P.O. Box 2037
Bayamon, Puerto Rico 00960-2037
Tel: (787) 620-2040 **E-mail:** admissions@aupr.edu
Fax: (787) 785-7377 **Internet:** www.aupr.edu

Institution Description: American College of Puerto Rico is a private, independent, nonprofit college with a branch campus in Manati. *Enrollment:* 1,528. *Degrees awarded:* Associate, baccalaureate. Certificates also awarded.

Accreditation: *Regional:* MSA/CHE.

History: Established as American Junior College of Puerto Rico and offered first instruction at postsecondary level 1973; awarded first degree 1975; adopted present name 1978.

Institutional Structure: *Governing board:* Board of Trustees. Representation: 9 trustees. All voting. *Composition of institution:* Administrators 8. Academic affairs headed by vice president for academic affairs. Management/business/finances directed by vice president for administrative affairs. Full-time instructional faculty 68. Academic governance body, Academic Council, meets an average of 4 times per year.

Calendar: Semesters. Academic year Aug. to May. Freshmen admitted Aug., Jan. Degrees conferred and formal commencement June. Summer session of 2 terms from early June to late July.

Admission: Rolling admissions plan. *Requirements:* Either graduation from accredited secondary school or GED. *For transfer students:* 2.0 minimum GPA; maximum transfer credit limited only by residence requirement.

College credit and advanced placement for postsecondary-level work completed in secondary school. Tutoring available. Noncredit remedial courses offered in summer session and regular academic year.

Degree Requirements: *For all associate degrees:* 60–69 credit hours. *For all baccalaureate degrees:* 125–127 credit hours. *For all undergraduate degrees:* 2.0 GPA; last 30 credits in residence; general education requirements.

Fulfillment of some degree requirements and exemption from some beginning courses possible by passing College Board CLEP, AP. *Grading system:* A–F; pass-fail; withdraw (carries time limit).

Distinctive Educational Programs: Internships. Weekend and evening classes. Special facilities for using telecommunications in the classroom. Honors programs.

Degrees Conferred: 93 *accociate*; 181 *baccalaureate:* business and management. 5 *master's*: education 5.

Fees and Other Expenses: *Full-time tuition per academic year 2008=09:* $4,435. *Books and supplies:* $900. *Room and board per academic year:* $4,200. *other expenses:* $6,600.

Departments and Teaching Staff: *Total instructional faculty:* 68. Student/faculty ratio: 19:1.

Enrollment: Total enrollment 1,528. Undergraduate 1,464 (full-time 76%; female 62%, male 38%). Graduate 64 (full-time 36%). Undergraduate transfer-in students 70.

Characteristics of Student Body: *Ethnic/racial makeup:* Hispanic: 100%. *Age distribution:* 17–21: 28%; 22–24: 38%; 25–29: 20%; 30–34: 6%; 35–39: 4%; 40–49: 2%; 50–59: 1%; 60–and over 1%.

Student Life: No on-campus housing. *Intercollegiate athletics:* male: basketball, tennis, track and field, volleyball; female: basketball, tennis, track and field, volleyball. *Special regulations:* Cars permitted without restrictions. *Special services:* Learning Resources Center. *Student publications:* Newspaper. *Surrounding community:* Bayamon population 197,000. Served by mass transit bus system; airport 35 miles from campus.

Buildings and Grounds: Campus area 21 acres.

Chief Executive Officer: Juan B. Nazario-Negron, President.

Address admission inquiries to Director of Admissions.

Bayamon Central University

P.O. Box 1725
Bayamon, Puerto Rico 00960-1725
Tel: (787) 786-3030 **E-mail:** admissions@ucb.edu.pr
Fax: (787) 740-2200 **Internet:** www.ucb.edu.pr

Institution Description: Bayamon Central University is a private, Catholic, independent, nonprofit institution. Classes are conducted in Spanish. *Enrollment:* 2,382. *Degrees awarded:* Associate, baccalaureate.

Accreditation: *Regional:* MSA/CHE.

History: Established Bayamon Center of Catholic University of Puerto Rico 1961; chartered 1964; incorporated, offered first instruction at postsecondary level and adopted present name 1970; awarded first degree (baccalaureate) 1972.

Institutional Structure: *Governing board:* Junta de Sindicos de la Universidad Central de Bayamon. Extrainstitutional representation: 10 trustees; institutional representation: president of the university. All voting. *Composition of institution:* Administrators 26. Academic affairs headed by academic dean. Management/business/finances directed by dean of administration and finance. Full-time instructional faculty 62. Academic governance body, University Senate, meets an average of 3 times per year.

Calendar: Semesters. Academic year Aug. to May. Freshmen admitted Aug., Jan. Degrees conferred May, June, July, Dec. Formal commencement May. Summer session of 2 terms from May to July.

Characteristics of Freshmen: 2,586 applicants (female 1,740, male 846). 20% of applicants accepted. 74% of accepted applicants enrolled full-time. 100% of freshmen from Puerto Rico.

Admission: Rolling admissions plan. For fall acceptance, apply as early as 1 year prior to enrollment, but not later than Apr. 15. *Requirements:* Graduation from secondary school or GED. Minimum 2.0 GPA. *Entrance tests:* College Board SAT. *For transfer students:* Maximum transfer credit limited only by residence requirement.

Tutoring available.

Degree Requirements: 125–130 credit hours; 2.0 GPA; 30 credits in residence; 2 credits physical education; core curriculum. *Grading system:* A–F; withdraw (carries time limit).

Distinctive Educational Programs: Tutorials.

Degrees Conferred: 8 *associate;* 280 *baccalaureate*; 126 *master's* Bachelor's degrees awarded in top five disciplines include business and management 128, communications 14, education 72, health professions and related sciences; public administration and services; 126 *master's:* various disciplines 126.

Fees and Other Expenses: *Full-time tuition and fees per academic year 2008–09:* $4,340. *Books and supplies:* $1,250. No on-campus housing. *Other expenses:* $2,850.

Financial Aid: Aid from institutionally generated funds is provided on the basis of academic merit, financial need. Institution has a Program Participation Agreement with the U.S. Department of Education for eligible students to receive Pell Grants and, depending upon the agreement, other federal aid.

Financial aid for full-time, first-time undergraduate students: 925 received some form of aid. Average amount of aid received: federal grants 44,851; Pell grants $3,771; other federal aid $1,285; state/local grants $876.

Departments and Teaching Staff: *Total instructional faculty:* 113. Degrees held by full-time faculty: doctorate 18%, master's 46%. 28% hold terminal degrees.

Enrollment: Total enrollment 2,382. Undergraduate 1,829 (full-time 74%; female 69%, male 31%). Graduate 554. Undergraduate transfer-in students 105.

Characteristics of Student Body: *Ethnic/racial makeup:* Hispanic 100%. *Age distribution:* 17–21: 51%; 22–24: 19%; 25–29: 14%; 30–34: 6%; 35–39: 3.5%; 40–49: 4%; 50–59: .7%; 60–and over: .18%.

International Students: No financial aid specifically designated for international students.

Student Life: No on-campus housing. *Special regulations:* Registered cars permitted in designated areas. *Special services:* Learning Resources Center, medical services. *Surrounding community:* Bayamon population 425,000. Served by mass transit bus system.

Publications: *Cruz Ansata* (annually) first published in 1978.

Library Collections: 55,000 volumes. 6,100 government documents; 3,100 microforms; 900 audiovisual materials; 820 current periodical subscriptions.

Most important special holdings include theology collection; Puerto Rican Collection.

Buildings and Grounds: Campus area 52 acres.

Chief Executive Officer: Fr. Benito Reyes, President.

Address admission inquiries to Christini M. Hernandez, Director of Admissions.

Caribbean University

Road 167 KM21.2 Forest Hills
Bayamon, Puerto Rico 00960-0493
Tel: (787) 758-0070 **E-mail:** carib@caribbean.edu
Fax: (787) 785-0101 **Internet:** www.caribbean.edu

Institution Description: Caribbean University College is a private, independent, nonprofit institution with branch campuses in Carolina, Vega Baja, and Ponce. *Enrollment:* 2,009. *Degrees awarded:* Associate, baccalaureate, master's.

Accreditation: *Regional:* MSA/CHE.

History: Established as Caribbean Junior College and offered first instruction at postsecondary level 1969; adopted present name 1978.

Institutional Structure: Central Administration and 4 academic centers. *Composition of institution:* Administrative personnel 150. Academic affairs headed by vice president. Management/business/finances directed by vice president. Full-time instructional faculty 96. Academic governance body, Faculty of Academic Affairs, meets an average of 12 times per year.

Calendar: Semesters. Academic year Jan. to Dec. Freshmen admitted Jan., Aug. Formal commencement May.

Characteristics of Freshmen: 35% of entering freshmen expected to graduate within 5 years. 99% of freshmen from Puerto Rico. Freshmen from 2 states and 3 foreign countries.

Admission: Open and rolling admissions. *Requirements:* Either graduation from accredited secondary school or GED.

Degree Requirements: *For all associate degrees:* 60–72 credit hours; 15 credit hours in residence, 9 of which must be in concentration. *For all baccalaureate degrees:* 110–177 credit hours; 30 hours in residence, 12 of which must be in concentration. *For all degrees:* 2.0 GPA overall, 2.30 in concentration.

Fulfillment of some degree requirements and exemption from some beginning courses possible by passing departmental examinations. *Grading system:* A–F; withdraw (carries time limit).

Distinctive Educational Programs: Spanish is primary language of instruction. Master of Education program offered. Teachers Certification Program.

ROTC: Army offered in cooperation with the University of Puerto Rico.

Degrees Conferred: 13 *associate*; 105 *baccalaureate*; 4 *master's*. Bachelor's degrees awarded in top five disciplines: business and management 31; education 17; health professions and related sciences 21; protective services 23; public administration and services 13. *Master's:* various disciplines 4.

Fees and Other Expenses: *Full-time tuition per academic year 2008–09:* $4,106.

Financial Aid: Aid from institutionally generated funds is provided on the basis of academic merit, financial need, other criteria.

94% of first-time full-time undergraduate received some form of aid. Average amount of aid received: federal grants $4,164; Pell grants $3,938; other federal aid $373; state/local grants $278; institutional grants $452.

Departments and Teaching Staff: *Total instructional faculty:* 98. Degrees held by full-time faculty: baccalaureate 5%, master's 90%, doctorate 5%. 100% hold terminal degrees.

Enrollment: Total enrollment 2,009. Undergraduate 1,718 (full-time 68%; female 53%, male 47%). Graduate 291. Undergraduate transfer-in students 209.

Characteristics of Student Body: *Ethnic/racial makeup:* Hispanic 100%.

Student Life: No on-campus housing. Student associations; Student Council; various clubs and organizations. Intramural basketball, volleyball.

Publications: *Desde la Presidencia and Laurel*, a magazine.

Library Collections: 38,000 volumes. 200 audiovisual titles; 385 current periodical subscriptions.

Buildings and Grounds: Campus area 16 acres.

Chief Executive Officer: Dr. Ana E. Cucurella, President.

Address admission inquiries to Director of Admissions.

Carlos Albizu University

Tanca St. #151
P.O. Box 9023711
San Juan, Puerto Rico 00902-3711
Tel: (787) 725-6500 **E-mail:** admissions@ccas.edu
Fax: (708) 721-7187 **Internet:** www.ccas.edu

Institution Description: Formerly named the Center for Advanced Studies of Puerto Rico and the Caribbean, the university is a public, independent, nonprofit institution. *Enrollment:* 5,519. *Degrees awarded:* Baccalaureate, master's, doctorate.

Accreditation: *Regional:* MSA/CHE.

History: Established and incorporated as Center for Advanced Studies 1968; offered first instruction at postsecondary level 1971; awarded first degree (master's) 1980; adopted present name 1999.

Institutional Structure: *Governing board:* Board of Trustees. Extrainstitutional representation: 7 trustees; institutional representation: 1 full-time instructional faculty member, 1 student. All voting. *Composition of institution:* Administrators 6. Academic affairs headed by dean. Management/business/finances directed by assistant to the director in charge of administrative affairs. Academic governance body, Committee on Admissions and Academic Affairs, meets an average of 4 times per year.

Calendar: Semesters. Academic year Aug. to May. Degrees conferred as earned. Formal commencement May.

Admission: Rolling admissions plan. *Requirements:* Baccalaureate from recognized college or university, interview, personal statement. Recommend courses on Caribbean history and literature.

Degree Requirements: 33–39 credit hours, according to specialty; 3.0 GPA; 28 hours in residence; comprehensives in individual fields of study; thesis. *Grading system:* A–F; pass; withdraw.

Distinctive Educational Programs: Cooperative programs with the university of Valladolid, and the University of Sevilla, Spain. Special program with Universidad Autonoma de Santo Domingo, Dominican Republic. Cooperative arrangements with University of San Carlos, Guatemala, and several universities and organizations in Puerto Rico.

Degrees Conferred: 16 *baccalaureate:* psychology; 29 *master's:* psychology; 38 *doctorate:* psychology.

Fees and Other Expenses: *Full-time tuition and fees per academic year 2008–09:* contact the university for current information (costs vary for master's/doctoral programs).

Financial Aid: Aid from institutionally generated funds is provided on the basis of academic merit, financial need. Institution has a Program Participation Agreement with the U.S. Department of Education for eligible students to receive Pell Grants and, depending upon the agreement, other federal aid.

Departments and Teaching Staff: The Center's faculty is basically a part-time faculty. They are either retired or teaching full-time at other institutions. Of the 16 professors currently teaching, 14 hold doctorates.

Enrollment: Total enrollment 836.

Characteristics of Student Body: *Ethnic/racial makeup:* Hispanic: 623.

International Students: No financial aid specifically designated for international students.

Student Life: No on-campus housing. *Special regulations:* Cars permitted without restrictions. *Student publications: La Revista. Surrounding community:* San Juan metropolitan area population over 1 million. Served by mass transit bus system; airport 3 miles from campus.

Library Collections: 15,000 volumes. 1,500 audiovisual materials; 30 current periodical subscriptions.

Most important special holdings include specialized Puerto Rican books of archaeology, painting, theater, and literature; books and personal documents donated by The Society of Puerto Rican Authors and other known authors; oral history tape collection (local history); Spanish discovery of the West Indies (books and maps).

Buildings and Grounds: Campus area approximately 44,000 square feet.

Chief Executive Officer: Dr. Jose M. Garcia, President.

Address admission inquiries to Carlos Rodriguez, Director of Student Services.

Columbia Century Universitario

Carretera 183, Km. 1.7
Caguas, Puerto Rico 00726
Tel: (787) 743-4041 **E-mail:** admissions@columbiaco.edu
Fax: (787) 746-5616 **Internet:** www.columbiaco.edu

Institution Description: Columbia Centro Universitario, formerly Caguas City College, is a private institution with branch campuses in Rio Grande and Yauco. *Enrollment:* 1,142. *Degrees awarded:* Associate, baccalaureate. Certificates and diplomas also awarded.

Accreditation: *Regional:* MSA/CHE. *Nonregional:* ACICS.

Calendar: Trimesters.

Degree Requirements: Completion of prescribed curriculum.

Degrees Conferred: 176 *associate;* 144 *baccalaureate:* business and management 113, health professions and related sciences 31.

Fees and Other Expenses: *Full-time tuition per academic year 2008–09:* contact the university for current information.

Financial Aid: Aid from institutionally generated funds is provided on the basis of academic merit, financial need, other criteria. Institution has a Program Participation Agreement with the U.S. Department of Education for eligible students to receive Pell Grants and, depending upon the agreement, other federal aid.

Departments and Teaching Staff: *Total instructional faculty:* 57.

Enrollment: Total enrollment 1,142.

Characteristics of Student Body: *Ethnic/racial makeup:* Hispanic 100%.

Library Collections: 15,000 volumes. 200 serial subscriptions.

Chief Executive Officer: Dr. Alex A. DeJorge, President.

Address admission inquiries to Director of Admissions.

Conservatory of Music of Puerto Rico

350 Rafael Lamar Street
San Juan, Puerto Rico 00918
Tel: (787) 751-0160 **E-mail:** admissions@cmpr.edu
Fax: (787) 787-8268 **Internet:** www.cmpr.edu

Institution Description: Conservatory of Music of Puerto Rico is a public institution. Classes are conducted in Spanish. *Enrollment:* 298. *Degrees awarded:* Baccalaureate.

Accreditation: *Regional:* MSA/CHE. *Professional*: music

History: Established 1959; incorporated and offered first instruction at postsecondary level 1960; awarded first degree (baccalaureate) 1964.

Institutional Structure: *Governing board:* Conservatory of Music of Puerto Rico Governing Board. Extrainstitutional representation: 6 trustees; institutional representation: 1 full-time instructional faculty member. All voting. *Composition of institution:* Administrators 12. Academic affairs headed by dean of students. Management/business/finances directed by dean of administration. Full-time instructional faculty 29. Academic governance body, Academic Senate, meets an average of 8 times per year.

Calendar: Semesters. Academic year Aug. to May. Freshmen admitted Aug. Degrees conferred May. Formal commencement June. No summer session.

Characteristics of Freshmen: 56% of applicants accepted. 86% of accepted applicants enrolled. Freshmen from 6 foreign countries.

Admission: For fall acceptance, apply as early as Feb. 1, but not later than Apr. 15. Students are notified of acceptance in June. *Requirements:* Graduation from accredited secondary school or GED; audition; interview. Minimum 2.0 GPA. *Entrance tests:* College Board SAT and institutional examinations in theory and solfege. *For transfer students:* 2.0 minimum GPA; from 4-year and 2-year accredited institutions, 60 semester hours maximum transfer credit; audition required.

Remedial courses offered during regular academic year.

Degree Requirements: *For baccalaureate degree:* 136 credit hours; 2.0 GPA; normally 4 years in residence; general education requirements and exemption from some beginning courses possible by passing institutional examinations. *Grading system:* A–F; withdraw (carries time limit); incomplete.

Distinctive Educational Programs: Work-experience programs.

Degrees Conferred: 29 *baccalaureate:* visual and performing arts 30.

Fees and Other Expenses: *Full-time tuition per academic year 2008–09:* $2,410. *Room and board per academic year:* $6,000.

Financial Aid: Aid from institutionally generated funds is provided on the basis of academic merit, financial need, talent.

Financial aid to full-time, first-time undergraduate students: need-based scholarships/grants totaling $688,009, self-help $261,503; non-need-based scholarships/grants totaling $19,800.

Departments and Teaching Staff: *Total instructional faculty:* 74 (full-time 42, part-time 32). Total faculty with doctorate, first-professional, or other terminal degree: 3. Student/faculty ratio: 6:1.

Enrollment: *Total enrollment:* 237 (undergraduate).

Characteristics of Student Body: 14 nonresident aliens enrolled fall 2008. No financial aid specifically designated for international students.

Student Life: No on-campus housing. *Special regulations:* Cars with parking permits allowed. *Special services:* Learning Resources Center, medical services. *Surrounding community:* San Juan population 415,000. Served by airport 30 miles from campus.

Library Collections: 24,000 volumes. 101 current periodical subscriptions. 3,499 recordings. 1,212 compact discs. 98 CD-ROMs. Computer work stations available.

Most important special holdings: Puerto Rican Collection; music scores.

Buildings and Grounds: Campus area 3 acres.

Chief Executive Officer: Dr. Maria Del Carmen Gil, Chancellor.

Address admission inquiries to Zulma Palos-Santini, Director of Admissions.

Electronic Data Processing College

108 Domenech Avenue
Hato Rey, Puerto Rico 00919
Tel: (809) 765-3560 **E-mail:** admissions@edpcollege.edu
Fax: (809) 765-2650 **Internet:** www.edpcollege.com

Institution Description: Electronic Data Processing College is a private institution with a branch campus in San Sebastian. *Enrollment:* 512. *Degrees awarded:* Associate, baccalaureate. Certificates are also awarded.

Accreditation: *Nonregional:* ACICS.

Calendar: Courses offered are of varying lengths.

Degree Requirements: Completion of prescribed curriculum.

Degrees Conferred: 43 *associate;* 41 *baccalaureate:* business and management 18, computer and information science 23; *Master's:* business and management 6.

Fees and Other Expenses: *Full-time tuition per academic year* $4,500. *Books and supplies:* $700. No on-campus housing.

Financial Aid: Aid from institutionally generated funds is provided on the basis of academic merit, financial need, other criteria. Institution has a Program Participation Agreement with the U.S. Department of Education for eligible students to receive Pell Grants and, depending upon the agreement, other federal aid.

Percentage of undergraduate first-time full-time students receiving various forms of financial aid: federal scholarships and grants 90% (average $3,000).

Departments and Teaching Staff: *Total instructional faculty:* 28.

Enrollment: Total enrollment 512 (undergraduate).

Chief Executive Officer: Dr. Gladys Nieves, President.

Address admission inquiries to Janet Centino, Recruitin Officer.

Escuela de Artes Plasticas de Puerto Rico

P.O. Box 9021112
Viejo San Juan, Puerto Rico 00902-1112
Tel: (787) 725-8120
Fax: (787) 725-8111 **Internet:** www.edp.edu.pr

Institution Description: The Escuela de Artes Plasticas is a public fine arts college offering programs in painting, sculpture, printmaking, art education, and image and design. *Enrollment:* 461. *Degrees offered:* Baccalaureate.

Accreditation: *Regional:* MSA/CHE.

History: Founded 1966 by Institute of Puerto Rican Culture; chartered in 1971 by Puerto Rican Legislature to grant the baccalaureate degree; obtained full administrative and fiscal autonomy.

Institutional Structure: *Governing board:* Representation: Governing Board of 7 members. *Composition of institution:* Chancellor, dean of studies, dean of students, dean of administration, director of planning and development; 5 heads of departments, librarian, extension program coordinator.

Calendar: Semesters. Trimesters for Adult Program. Academic year Aug. to May. Summer session July. Freshmen admitted in Aug. only; transfer students in Aug. and Jan. Degrees and formal commencement in June.

Characteristics of Freshmen: 44% of applicants accepted. 96% of accepted applicants enrolled. 50% of freshmen expected to graduate within 5 years.

Admission: Based on portfolio, interview, and academic index. Portfolio admission seminars for less experienced art students in March and summer. Applications accepted until May 30. *Requirements:* graduation from secondary school and College Board ACT required, although talent and performance are most important. *For transfer students:* must have a 24 credit minimum of which 15 must be workshops and 2.2 academic index.

College credit and advanced placement for postsecondary-level work completed in secondary school and for extrainstitutional learning on basis of ACE *2006 Guide to the Evaluation of Educational Experiences in the Armed Services.*

Developmental/remedial courses offered in summer session and regular academic year; credit given.

Degree Requirements: *For the baccalaureate degree:* 132 credit hours.

Distinctive Educational Programs: Extension program; free-studies program (nondegree); tutoring program. Internships. Study abroad; off-campus general education courses. Summer camp for children.

ROTC: admissions@edp.edu.pr

Degrees Conferred: 11 *baccalaureate.*

Fees and Other Expenses: *Full-time tuition per academic year 2008–09:* $2,465. *Required fees:* $250. No on-campus housing.

Financial Aid: Aid from institutionally generated funds is provided on the basis of academic merit, financial need.

Financial aid to full-time, first-time undergraduate students: need-based scholarships/grants totaling $900,857, self-help $100,000.

Departments and Teaching Staff: *Total instructional faculty:* 77 (full-time 17,part-time 60). Total faculty with doctorate, first-professional, or other terminal degree: 4. Degrees held by full-time faculty: baccalaureate 36%, master's 55%, doctorate 9%. 26% hold terminal degrees.

Enrollment: Total enrollment 461. Undergraduate: 372 (full-time 208, part-time 164).

Characteristics of Student Body: *Ethnic/racial makeup:* Hispanic 100%. *Age distribution:* number under 18: 2; 18–19: 49; 20–21: 49; 22–24: 66; 25–29: 40; 30–34: 10; 35–39: 10; 40–49: 10; 50–64: 6.

International Students: No financial aid specifically designated for international students.

Student Life: Gallery space for students and faculty. Art shop for students to display their work. Film, theater, and music presentations on campus. Student Council. Counseling services, career planning and employment and professional development. Located in Old San Juan, art capital of the Island, full of galleries and museums.

Library Collections: 214,000 volumes. 78 current periodical subscriptions. 720 recordings; 62 CD-ROMs. Online catalog. Computer work stations available. Students have access to online information retrieval services and the Internet.

Chief Executive Officer: Dr. Marimar Benitez, Chancellor.

Address admissions inquiries to Doris Perez, Director of Admissions.

Evangelical Seminary of Puerto Rico

776 Ponce de Leon Avenue
San Juan, Puerto Rico 00925-2207
Tel: (787) 763-6700 **E-mail:** registro@semevangpr.org
Fax: (787) 751-0847 **Internet:** www.semevangpr.org

Institution Description: The Evangelical Seminary of Puerto Rico is an ecumenical nonprofit graduate school dedicated to the formation of pastors and religious leaders. *Enrollment:* 175. *Degrees awarded:* Master's, first-professional.

Accreditation: *Regional:* MSA. *National:* ATS. *Professional*: theology

History: The seminary was established in 1919 as a joint effort of local historical religious denominations including American Baptist Churches, Christian Church (Disciples of Christ), Methodist Church of Puerto Rico, and the Presbyterian Church (USA).

Institutional Structure: *Governing board:* Board of Directors (34 members) including representatives from sponsoring denominations. Academic affairs headed by dean. Academic governance body includes Academic Council and Committee.

Calendar: Semesters. Academic year Aug. to May. 3 summer sessions. Students admitted Aug, Jan. Degrees conferred May.

Admission: Deadline for August admittance May 31, for January admittance Oct. 31. *Requirements:* Baccalaureate degree; 2 letters of recommendation; health certificate; personal essay; local admissions test; faculty interview.

Degree Requirements: *For all Master of Divinity:* 90 credits including integration essay and colloquial experiences; *M.A.R. degree:* 60 credits including 4 comprehensive examinations.

Distinctive Educational Programs: Continuing education program. Total quality workshops. Center for Women in Ministry Support provides leadership workshops.

Degrees Conferred: 11 *master's:* theology/religious vocations; 22 *first-professional:* master of divinity.

Fees and Other Expenses: *Full-time tuition per academic year 2008–09:* $4,475.

Financial Aid: Aid from institutionally generated funds is provided on the basis of financial need. Institution has a Program Participation Agreement with the U.S. Department of Education for eligible students to receive Pell Grants and, depending upon the agreement, other federal aid.

Institutional funding for graduate students: 8 fellowships and grants totaling $10,650 ($500 to $2,000). *Federal and state funding for undergraduates:* 10 fellowships totaling $12,740 ($250 to $1,500).

Departments and Teaching Staff: *Total instructional faculty:* 17. Degrees held by full-time faculty: doctorate 100%.

Enrollment: Total enrollment 175.

Characteristics of Student Body: *Ethnic/racial makeup:* Black non-Hispanic: 1; Asian or Pacific Islander: 1; Hispanic: 168; White non-Hispanic: 1.

International Students: 5 nonresident aliens enrolled fall 2004. 1 student from Asia, 4 Latin America. No programs available to aid students whose native language is not English. No financial aid specifically designated for international students.

Student Life: On campus residence hall. Fraternal relationship with the University of Puerto Rico and Inter American University.

Publications: Faculty publications. Joint effort with ecumenical groups in publication and *Presencia Magazine.*

Library Collections: 65,000 volumes including bound books, serial backfiles, electronic documents, and government documents not in separate collections. Online catalog. Current serial subscriptions: paper, microform, and electronic. 10 computer work stations. Students have access to the Internet at no charge.

Most import special collections include Protestantism in Puerto Rico Historical Collection; Bible and Theology Collection.

Buildings and Grounds: Urban campus.

Chief Executive Officer: Dr. Sergio Ojeda, President.

Address admission inquiries to Rev. Walter Acevedo, Registrar/Financial Aid Officer.

Inter American University of Puerto Rico, Arecibo University College

P.O. Box 4050
Arecibo, Puerto Rico 00614-4050
Tel: (787) 878-5475 **E-mail:** admissions@arecibo.inter.edu
Fax: (787) 780-1624 **Internet:** www.arecibo.inter.edu

Institution Description: Arecibo University College is a private, nonsectarian institution. *Enrollment:* 5,800. *Degrees awarded:* Associate, baccalaureate.

Accreditation: *Regional:* MSA/CHE.

History: Established 1957.

Institutional Structure: *Composition of institution:* Chancellor, dean of studies, dean of administrative affairs, den of student affairs. Academic affairs headed by dean of studies. Management/business/finance directed by dean of administrative affairs. Full-time instructional faculty 89.

Calendar: Semesters. Academic year Aug. to May.

Characteristics of Freshmen: 941 applicants (female 251, male 684). 96% of applicants admitted. 96% of admitted applicants enrolled full-time.

Admission: Graduation from an accredited secondary school or equivalent with a minimum GPA of 2.00. Satisfactory scores in the Aptitude and English Achievement Tests of the College Board. Students whose first language is English may take the SAT Test. Those whose first language is Spanish, "Prueba de Aptitud Academica."

Degrees Conferred: 62 *associate*; 422 *baccalaureate*; 142 *master's.* Bachelor's degrees awarded in top five disciplines: biological and life sciences 24; business and management 143; education 81; protective services 37; public administration and services 54. Master's degrees awarded: various disciplines 146.

Fees and Other Expenses: *Full-time tuition and fees per academic year 2008–09:* $6,330. *Books and supplies:* $2,310. *Room and board per academic year:* $11,704. *Other expenses:* $6,191.

Financial Aid: Aid from institutionally generated funds is provided on the basis of academic merit, financial need. Institution has a Program Participation Agreement with the U.S. Department of Education for eligible students to receive Pell Grants and, depending upon the agreement, other federal aid.

98% of undergraduate first-time full-time students received some form of financial aid. Average amount of aid received: federal grants $3,328; Pell grants

INTER AMERICAN UNIVERSITY OF PUERTO RICO, ARECIBO UNIVERSITY COLLEGE—*cont'd*

$3,108; other federal aid $683; state/local grants $1,187; institutional grants $590.

Departments and Teaching Staff: *Total instructional faculty:* 249. Degrees held by full-time faculty: doctorate 24%, master's 76%. 100% hold terminal degrees.

Enrollment: Total enrollment 5,800. Undergraduate 5,139 (full-time 53%; female 23%, male 77%). Graduate 661 (full-time 56%). Undergraduate transfer-in students 264.

Characteristics of Student Body: *Ethnic/racial makeup:* Hispanic 100%.

International Students: No financial aid specifically designated for international students.

Library Collections: 82,500 volumes. 1,008 government documents; 7,300 microforms; 28,586 audiovisual materials; 1,500 current periodical subscriptions. Students have access to online information retrieval services and the Internet.

Chief Executive Officer: Dr. Jean Marie Gonzalez, Chancellor.

Address admission inquiries to Delma Barrios, Director of Admissions.

Inter American University of Puerto Rico, Bayamon Campus

500 Road Drive

Bayamon, Puerto Rico 00957

Tel: (787) 279-1912 **E-mail:** calcia@bc.inter.edu

Fax: (787) 279-2205 **Internet:** www.bc.inter.edu

Institution Description: *Enrollment:* 5,337. *Degrees awarded:* Baccalaureate.

Accreditation: *Regional:* MSA/CHE.

History: Established 1912.

Calendar: Semesters.

Characteristics of Freshmen: 88% of applicants accepted. 67% of accepted applicants enrolled. 100 % of freshmen from Puerto Rico.

Degrees Conferred: 372 *baccalaureate:* biological/life sciences 40; business/marketing 193; communications/communication technologies 30; computer and information sciences 15; education 1; engineering 44; mathematics 2; physical sciences 5; trade and industry 42.

Fees and Other Expenses: *Full-time tuition per academic year 2008–09:* $4,602. *Required fees:* $402.

Room and board per academic year: $5,000.

Financial Aid: Aid from institutionally generated funds is provided on the basis of academic merit, financial need. Institution has a Program Participation Agreement with the U.S. Department of Education for eligible students to receive Pell Grants and, depending upon the agreement, other federal aid.

Financial aid to full-time, first-time undergraduate students: need-based scholarships/grants totaling $2,401,267, self-help $4,674,995, parent loans $9,700, tuition waivers $29,655, athletic awards $13,317.

Departments and Teaching Staff: *Total instructional faculty:* 298 (full-time 98, part-time 200). Total faculty with doctorate, first-professional, or other terminal degree: 83.

Enrollment: Total enrollment 5,337. Undergraduate 4,374.

Characteristics of Student Body: *Ethnic/racial makeup:* Hispanic 100%. *Age distribution:* number under 18: 156; 18–19: 1,745; 20–21: 1,253; 22–24: 1,163; 25–29: 559; 30–34: 194; 35–39: 79; 40–49: 83; 50–64: 20; 65 and over: 1.

International Students: 11 nonresident aliens enrolled fall 2004. No financial aid programs available to international students.

Library Collections: 67,000 volumes. 247,500 microforms; 5,100 audiovisual materials. 275 current periodical subscriptions: paper, microform, electronic access. Computer work stations available. Students have access to the Internet at no charge.

Most important special holdings include collections on Puerto Rico and aeronautics.

Chief Executive Officer: Dr. Omar Cueto-Toro, Chancellor.

Address admission inquiries to Carmen Montez Bugos, Director of Admissions.

Inter American University of Puerto Rico, Fajardo Campus

Call Box 7003

Fajardo, Puerto Rico 00738-7003

Tel: (787) 863-2390 **E-mail:** admissions@fajardo.inter.edu

Fax: (787) 860-3470 **Internet:** www.fajardo.inter.edu

Institution Description: *Enrollment:* 2,252. *Degrees awarded:* Associate, baccalaureate.

Accreditation: *Regional:* MSA/CHE.

Calendar: Semesters.

Characteristics of Freshmen: 1,696 applicants (female 1,123, 573 male). 25% of applicants accepted. 96% of accepted applicants enrolled full-time.

Admission: Rolling admissions. *Required:* Graduation from high school or GED.

Degree Requirements: Completion of all requirements as specified for the program in which the student is enrolled.

Degrees Conferred: 16 *associate*; 252 *baccalaureate*; 17 *master's*. Bachelor's degrees awrded: business and management 99; communication, journalism, and related programs 26; computer and information sciences 12; education 70; social sciences and history 45. Master's degrees awarded: education 17.

Fees and Other Expenses: *Full-time tuition per academic year: 2008–09:* $4,212. *Required fees:* $176. *Books and supplies:* $985. *room and board per academic year:* $9,261. *Other expenses:* $3,875.

Financial Aid: Aid from institutionally generated funds is provided on the basis of academic merit, financial need, other criteria.

Financial aid to full-time, first-time undergraduate students: 98% feceived some form of aid. Average amount of aid received: federal grants $2,253; Pell grants $1,986; other federal aid $172; state/local grants $172; institutional grants $308.

Departments and Teaching Staff: *Total instructional faculty:* 151 (full-time 38, part-time 113). Total faculty with doctorate, first-professional, or other terminal degree: 121.

Enrollment: Total enrollment 2,252. Undergraduate 2,223 (full-time 79%; female 67%, male 33%). Graduate 29 (full-time 9%). Undergraduate transfer-in students 308.

Characteristics of Student Body: *Ethnic/racial makeup:* Hispanic 100%.

International Students: No financial aid specifically designated for international students.

Library Collections: 50,000 volumes. 11,005 audiovisual materials; 211 current periodical subscriptions. Computer work stations available. Online catalog. Students have access to online information retrieval services and the Internet.

Most important special holdings include Census Data; Antonio R. Barcelo Personal Papers; Emilio S. Belaval Personal Library.

Chief Executive Officer: Dr. Ismael Suarez Herrero, Chancellor. Address admission inquiries to Ada Caraballo, Director of Admissions.

Inter American University of Puerto Rico, Metropolitan Campus

P.O. Box 191293

Hato Rey, Puerto Rico 00919-1293

Tel: (787) 250-0742 **E-mail:** admissions@metro.inter.edu

Fax: (787) 250-0782 **Internet:** www.metro.inter.edu

Institution Description: *Enrollment:* 10,613. *Degrees awarded:* Associate, baccalaureate, master's, doctorate, first-professional.

Accreditation: *Regional:* MSA/CHE. *Professional*: clinical lab scientist, nursing, optometry, social work

History: Established 1960.

Calendar: Semesters.

Characteristics of Freshmen: 5,159 applicants (female 3,094, male 2,065). 27% of applicants accepted. 77% of accepted applicants enrolled full-time. 100 % of freshmen from Puerto Rico.

Degrees Conferred: 55 *associate*; 782 *baccalaureate*. Bachelor's degrees awarded in top five disciplines: biological/life sciences 96; business and management 375; education 124; protective services 71; psychology 54. *Master's*: various disciplines 649. Doctorates awarded: various disciplines 61.

Fees and Other Expenses: *Full-time tuition per academic year 2008*+09:* $4,212. *Books and supplies:* $894. *Room and board per academic year:* $11,061. *Other expenses:* $3,878.

Financial Aid: Aid from institutionally generated funds is provided on the basis of academic merit, financial need. Institution has a Program Participation Agreement with the U.S. Department of Education for eligible students to receive Pell Grants and, depending upon the agreement, other federal aid.

91% of undergraduate first-time full-time students received some form of financial aid. Average amount of aid received: federal grants $2,028; Pell grants $1,903; other federal aid $331; state/local grants $301; institutional grants $434.

Departments and Teaching Staff: *Total instructional faculty:* 274. Degrees held by full-time faculty: doctorate 32.6%, master's 65.5%, professional 1.9%.

Enrollment: Total enrollment 10,613. Undergraduate 6,951 (full-time 90%; female 54%, male 46%). Graduate 3,682 (full-time 70%). Undergraduate transfer-in students 1,654.

Characteristics of Student Body: *Ethnic/racial makeup:* Hispanic 100%.

Publications: *Homines*, review of social sciences.

Library Collections: 112,000 volumes. 658,000 microforms; 5,000 audiovisual materials; 2,800 836 current periodical subscriptions including via electronic access.

Most important special holdings include Puerto Rico Collections; Emilio S. Belaval Collection; Jaime Benitez Collection.

Chief Executive Officer: Dr. Ivonne Rivera, Chancellor.

Address admission inquiries to Lisette Rivera-Ortiz, Director of Admissions.

Inter American University of Puerto Rico, Ponce Campus

104 Turpo Industrial Park RD 1
Mercedita, Puerto Rico 00715-1602
Tel: (787) 284-1912 **E-mail:** admissions@ponce.inter.edu
Fax: (787) 841-0103 **Internet:** www.ponce.inter.edu

Institution Description: *Enrollment:* 5,963. *Degrees awarded:* Associate, baccalaureate.

Accreditation: *Regional:* MSA/CHE.

History: The Inter American University system was established in 1912 and is the largest educational institution in Puerto Rico.

Institutional Structure: *Composition of institution:* Administrators 6. Academic affairs headed by dean of academic affairs. Management/business/finances directed by dean of administrative affairs. Full-time instructional faculty 76.

Calendar: Semesters. Academic year Aug. to May.

Characteristics of Freshmen: 2,690 applicants (femlae 1,027, male 1,663). 57% of applicants accepted. 71% of accepted applicants enrolled full-time.

Mean SAT scores 425 critical reading, 454 mathematical.

100% of freshmen from Puerto Rico.

Admission: Present evidence of graduation from an accredited secondary school or its equivalent with a minimum grade point index of 2.50; satisfactory scores in the aptitude and English achievement tests of the College Entrance Examination Board.

Degree Requirements: *For associate degree:* general education requirements; GPA 2.0 or higher; cumulative GPA of 2.0 or higher in concentration course requirements; complete no fewer than one-fourth of all credits in residence. *For baccalaureate degree:* 120 credit hours; GPA 2.25 or higher; complete at least 30 credit hours of the last 36 credit hours in residence; general education requirements.

Degrees Conferred: 88 *associate;* 381 *baccalaureate:* biological and life sciences 41, business and management 148, computer and information sciences 42, education 74, law/legal studies 65. Master's degrees awarded: various disciplines 49.

Fees and Other Expenses: *Full-time tuition per academic year 2008–09:* undergraduate $5,026. *Room and board per academic year:* $11,061. *books and supplies:* $686. *Other expenses:* $3,878.

Financial Aid: The university offers a direct lending program. Aid from institutionally generated funds is provided on the basis of academic merit, financial need, athletic ability. Institution has a Program Participation Agreement with the U.S. Department of Education for eligible students to receive Pell Grants and, depending upon the agreement, other federal aid.

Departments and Teaching Staff: *Total instructional faculty:* 199. Degrees held by full-time faculty: doctorate 22%, master's 72%, baccalaureate 3%, professional 4%. 21% hold terminal degrees.

Enrollment: Total enrollment 5,963. Undergraduate 5,880 (full-time 82%; female 62%; male 36%). Graduate 283 (full-time 84%). Undergraduate transfer-in students 744.

Characteristics of Student Body: *Ethnic/racial makeup:* Hispanic 100%.

International Students: No international students enrolled.

Library Collections: 100,000 volumes. 515 government documents; 2,500 audiovisual materials; 565 current periodical subscriptions. Online catalog. Computer work stations. Students have access to online information retrieval services and the Internet.

Chief Executive Officer: Dr. Vilma E. Colon-Acosta, Chancellor.

Address admission inquiries to Franco L. Diaz, Director of Admissions.

Inter American University of Puerto Rico, San German Campus

P.O. Box 5100
San German, Puerto Rico 00683
Tel: (787) 264-1912 **E-mail:** admissions@sg.inter.edu
Fax: (787) 264-0220 **Internet:** www.sg.inter.edu

Institution Description: *Enrollment:* 5,712. *Degrees awarded:* Associate, baccalaureate, master's, doctorate

Accreditation: *Regional:* MSA/CHE. *Professional*: clinical lab scientist, health information technician

History: Established 1912.

Institutional Structure: *Composition of institution:* Administrators 6. Academic affairs headed by dean of academic affairs. Management/business/finances directed by dean of administrative affairs. Full-time instructional faculty 130.

Calendar: Semesters. Academic year Aug. to May.

Characteristics of Freshmen: 1,593 applicants (female 872, male 721). 98% of applicants accepted. 66% of accepted applicants enrolled full-time.

Mean SAT class scores 459 critical reading, 476 mathematical.

99% of freshmen from Puerto Rico.

Admission: Present evidence of graduation from an accredited secondary school or its equivalent with a minimum grade point index of 2.50; satisfactory scores in the aptitude and English achievement tests of the College Entrance Examination Board.

Degree Requirements: *For associate degree:* general education requirements; GPA 2.0 or higher; cumulative GPA of 2.0 or higher in concentration course requirements; complete no fewer than one-fourth of all credits in residence. *For baccalaureate degree:* 120 credit hours; GPA 2.25 or higher; complete at least 30 credit hours of the last 36 credit hours in residence; general education requirements.

ROTC: Air Force, Navy. Offered in cooperation with University of Puerto Rico-Mayaguez Campus.

Degrees Conferred: 40 *associate*; 460 *baccalaureate*; 211 *master's*; 4 *doctorate*. Bachelor's degrees awarded in top five disciplines: business, management, marketing, and related support services 134; education 118; biological/life sciences 71; psychology 44; computer and information sciences 38. Master's degrees awarded: various disciplines 211. Doctorates awarded: business/managment 4.

Fees and Other Expenses: *Full-time tuition per academic year 2008–09:* $4,209 undergraduate; graduate charges per credit (contact the university for current rate). *Room and board per academic year:* $2,500. *books and supplies:* $894. *Other expenses:* $3,878.

Financial Aid: Aid from institutionally generated funds is provided on the basis of academic merit, financial need, athletic ability.

Financial aid to full-time, first-time undergraduate students: 93% received some form of aid. Average amount of aid received: federal grants $2,133; Pell grants $1,921; other federal aid $428; state/local grants $233; Institutional grants $759.

Departments and Teaching Staff: *Total instructional faculty:* 355 (full-time 134, part-time 221). Total faculty with doctorate, first-professional, or other terminal degree: 331.

Enrollment: Total enrollment 5,712. Undergraduate 4,827 (full-time 86%; female 53%, male 47%). Graduate 885. Undergraduate transfer-in students 539.

International Students: 43 nonresident aliens enrolled fall 2008. Programs available to aid students whose native language is not English: English as a Second Language. No financial aid specifically designated for international student.

Student Life: On-campus residence halls house 5% of student body.

Library Collections: 154,000 volumes including bound books, serial backfiles, electronic documents, and government documents not in separate collections. Online catalog. 571,000 microforms; 31,000 audiovisual materials; 3,820 current serial subscriptions. Students have access to the Internet at no charge.

Most important special holdings include Puerto Rican Collection; Dr. Arturo Morales Carrion Collections; historical museum.

Buildings and Grounds: Campus DVD available.

Chief Executive Officer: Prof. Agnes Mojica, Chancellor.

Address admission inquiries to Mildred Camacho, Director of Admissions.

Inter American University of Puerto Rico, School of Law

P.O. Box 70351
San Juan, Puerto Rico 00936-8351
Tel: (787) 751-1912 **E-mail:** admissions@derecho.inter.edu
Fax: (787) 751-2975 **Internet:** www.derecho.inter.edu

Institution Description: *Enrollment:* 782. *Degrees awarded:* Juris Doctor.

Accreditation: *Regional:* MSA/CHE. *Professional*: law

History: The School of Law was established in 1961.

Institutional Structure: Since 1992 the School's governing body has been the Academic Senate, where the entire community has direct participation and input. The Senate meets twice each semester. The work is channeled through five permanent committees: Curricular Affairs and Academic Norms, Faculty Affairs, Students Affairs, Library, and Graduate Studies.

Calendar: Semesters. Entering students admitted fall semester only. Degrees conferred Dec. and June; formal commencement June. Summer session of one term June to July.

Admission: LSAT (130 required; 140 average); minimum GPA of 2.5 (average 3.2); PAEG (575 required).

Degree Requirements: 92 credits; required courses total 62 credits; program exemplifies both the Civil and Common Law traditions.

Distinctive Educational Programs: Emphasis on legal skills development.

Degrees Conferred: 174 *first-professional:* law.

Fees and Other Expenses: *Full-time tuition per academic year 2008–09:* $13,360.

Financial Aid: The university offers a direct lending program. Aid from institutionally generated funds is provided on the basis of academic merit, financial need. Institution has a Program Participation Agreement with the U.S. Department of Education for eligible students to receive Pell Grants and, depending upon the agreement, other federal aid.

Departments and Teaching Staff:
Total instructional faculty: 57. Student/faculty ratio: 16:1. Degrees held by full-time faculty: baccalaureate 100%, master's 77%, doctorate 18%, professional 100%. 100% hold terminal degrees.

Enrollment: Total enrollment 782. First-professional 782.

Characteristics of Student Body: *Ethnic/racial makeup:* Hispanic 100%.

International Students: No international students enrolled.

Library Collections: 180,000 volumes including bound books, serial backfiles, electronic documents, and government documents not in separate collections. Online catalog. Current serial subscriptions: 2,302 paper, 55 microform, 6 electronic. 11 CD-ROMs. Computer work stations available. Students have access to online information retrieval services and the Internet.

Most important special collections include the works of Jose Echeverria-Yanez, Domingo Toledo-Alamo, and Jose Velez-Torres.

Chief Executive Officer: Luis M. Negron-Portello, Dean.

Address admission inquiries to Julio Fontanet-Maldonado, Dean of Students.

Pontifical Catholic University of Puerto Rico

Avenue Las Americas
Suite 564
Ponce, Puerto Rico 00717-0777
Tel: (787) 841-2000 **E-mail:** admisiones@pucpr.edu
Fax: (787) 840-4295 **Internet:** www.pucpr.edu

Institution Description: Pontifical Catholic University of Puerto Rico is a private institution affiliated with the Roman Catholic Church and with 2-year branch campuses at Arecibo and Guayama. The language of instruction for most courses is Spanish. *Enrollment:* 7,413. *Degrees awarded:* Associate, baccalaureate, first-professional (law), master's.

Accreditation: *Regional:* MSA/CHE. *Professional*: clinical lab scientist, law, nursing, social work

History: Established as Universidad Santa Maria and offered first instruction at postsecondary level 1948; incorporated under present name 1949; awarded first degree (associate) 1950; chartered 1959.

Institutional Structure: *Governing board:* Board of Trustees of Pontifical Catholic University of Puerto Rico. Extrainstitutional representation: 19 trustees; institutional representation: 3 administrators, 1 full-time instructional faculty member, 1 student. All voting. *Composition of institution:* Academic affairs headed by vice president for academic affairs. Management/business/finances directed by vice president for financial affairs. Full-time instructional faculty 124. Academic governance body, University Senate, meets an average of 9 times per year.

Calendar: Semesters. Academic year July to June. Freshmen admitted Aug., Jan., June, July. Degrees conferred May, June, July, Dec. Formal commencement May. Summer session of 2 terms from June to July.

Characteristics of Freshmen: 1,540 applicants (female 923, mael 617). 81% of applicants admitted. 72% of applicants admitted and enrolled full-time.

93% (935 students) submitted SAT scores. *25th percentile*: SAT Verbal 396, SAT Math 399. *75th percentile*: SAT Verbal 513, 555 mathematical.

99% of freshmen from Puerto Rico.

Admission: Rolling admissions plan. For fall acceptance, apply as early as Jan. 15, but not later than July 15 of year of enrollment. Early acceptance available. *Requirements:* Either graduation from accredited public secondary school with 3 units in Spanish, 3 English, 2 mathematics, 1 history, 1 natural science; or graduate from an accredited private secondary school with 4 units English, 4 Spanish, 3 mathematics, 2 natural science; or GED. Additional requirements for some programs. Minimum 2.0 GPA. *Entrance tests:* College Board SAT, 3 Achievements. *For transfer students:* 2.0 minimum GPA; maximum transfer credit limited only by residence requirement.

Tutoring available. Developmental/remedial courses offered.

Degree Requirements: *For all associate degrees:* 71–77 credit hours; 1 credit physical education; 4 credits theology. *For all baccalaureate degrees:* 128–140 hours; 2 credits physical education; 8 credits theology. *For all undergraduate degrees:* 2.0 GPA; last 30 hours in residence.

Fulfillment of some degree requirements and exemption from some beginning courses possible by passing College Board AP. *Grading system:* A–F; pass-fail; pass; withdraw (carries time limit).

Distinctive Educational Programs: Tutorials. English Language Institute offers training in communicative English as a second language. Facilities and programs for independent research, including tutorials. Continuing education program.

ROTC: Air Force and Army offered in cooperation with Colegio Unviersitario Technologico de Ponce.

Degrees Conferred: 10 *associate*; 707 *baccalaureate*; 178 *master's*; 46 *doctorate*; 174 *first-professional.* Bachelor's degrees awarded in top five disciplines: business, management, marketing, and related support services 209; education 180; health professions and related clinical 11; liberal arts/general studies 67; protective services/public administration 47. Master's degrees awarded: various disciplines 178. Doctorates awarded: various disciplines 46. First-professional degrees awarded: law 174.

Fees and Other Expenses: *Full-time tuition per academic year 2008–09:* $5,478 undergraduate; contact the university and School of Law for current tuition and applicable fees. *books and supplies:* $600. *Room and board per academic year:* $2,990. *Other expenses* $900.

Financial Aid: Aid from institutionally generated funds is provided on the basis of academic merit, financial need, athletic ability.

Financial aid to full-time, first-time undergraduate students: 99% received some form of financial aid. Average amount of aid received: federal grants $4,414; Pell grants $3,701; other federal aid $893; state/local grants $408; institutional grants $1,351.

Departments and Teaching Staff: *Total instructional faculty:* 360 (full-time 226, part-time 134). Total faculty with doctorate, first-professional, or other terminal degree: 323. Student/faculty ratio: 27:1. Degrees held by full-time faculty: doctorate 16%, master's 62%, baccalaureate 5%, professional 13%, other 2%. 100% hold terminal degrees.

Enrollment: Total enrollment 7,413. Undergraduate 5,273 *(full-time 89%; female 73%, male 37%). Graduate 2,140 (full-time 65%). Undergraduate transfer-in students 183. *Age distribution:* number under 18: 15; 18–19: 951; 20–21: 1,562; 22–24: 1742; 25–29: 736; 30–34: 252; 35–39: 117; 40–49: 111; 50–64: 31.

International Students: 50 nonresident aliens enrolled fall 2008. Students from Europe, Latin America. No programs available to aid students whose native language is not English. No financial aid specifically designated for international students.

Student Life: On-campus residence halls house 2% of student body. *Intercollegiate athletics:* male: soccer; female: track; both sexes: basketball, judo, swimming, tennis, volleyball. *Special regulations:* Registered cars permitted in designated areas. *Special services:* Learning Resources Center, medical services. *Student publications, radio: El Comunicador, El Orbital, La Nao,* newspapers; *Senda*, a yearbook; *Facundo.* Radio station WEUC broadcasts 126 hours per week. *Surrounding community:* Ponce population 186,475. Served by airport 7 miles from campus.

Publications: *Beyond the Business College, Horizontes, Revista de Derecho Puertorriquen, Revista Universidad Catolica.*

Library Collections: 243,000 volumes including bound books, serial backfiles, electronic documents, and government documents not in separate collections. Online catalog. 512,000 microforms; 13,500 audiofisucal materials; 58,200 periodicals including via electronic access. Computer work stations available. Students have access to the Internet at no charge.

Most important holdings include Msgr. Vicente Murga Collection; Dr. Rafael Caldera (former President of Venezuela) Collection.

Buildings and Grounds: Campus area 120 acres. Campus DVD available.

Chief Executive Officer: Marcelina Velez de Santiago, President.

Address admission inquiries to Ana Bonilla, Director of Admissions.

School of Law

Degree Programs Offered: *First-professional, master's.*

Admission: Prelaw curriculum at a college or university, including 6 credits in English, 6 Spanish, 24 humanities, 3 mathematics, 6 natural science, 15 social science.

Departments and Teaching Staff: *Total instructional faculty:* 36. Degrees held by full-time faculty: doctorate 17%, master's 50%, professional 33%.

Universidad Adventista de las Antillas

Box 118
Mayaguez, Puerto Rico 00681-0118
Tel: (787) 834-9595 **E-mail:** admission@uaa.edu
Fax: (787) 834 9597 **Internet:** www.uaa.edu

Institution Description: Universidad Adventista de las Antillas is a private institution affiliated with the Seventh-day Adventist Church. All courses are conducted in Spanish. *Enrollment:* 950. *Degrees awarded:* Associate, baccalaureate.

Accreditation: *Regional:* MSA/CHE.

History: Established in Cuba as Colegio Adventista de las Antillas 1945; transferred to Puerto Rico and named Antillian College 1961; adopted present name 1989.

Institutional Structure: *Governing board:* Board of Trustees of Universidad Adventista de las Antillas. Extrainstitutional representation: 22 trustees; institutional representation: president of the university. 23 voting. *Composition of institution:* Administrators 19.. Academic affairs headed by academic dean. Management/business/finances directed by dean of finances. Full-time instructional faculty 41. Academic governance body, Board of Trustees, meets an average of 2 times per year.

Calendar: Semesters. Academic year Aug. to May. Freshmen admitted Aug., Jan., May. Degrees conferred and formal commencement May. Summer session of 2 terms from May to July.

Characteristics of Freshmen: 400 applicants (female 247, male 153). 55% of applicants accepted. 70% of accepted applicants admitted full-time. 72% of freshmen from Puerto Rico. Freshmen from 15 states and 23 foreign countries.

Admission: Rolling admissions plan. Apply no later than 2 weeks prior to enrollment. *Requirements:* Either graduation from accredited secondary school or GED. Minimum 2.0 GPA. *Entrance tests:* College Board SAT or ACT composite. *For transfer students:* 2.0 minimum GPA; maximum transfer credit limited only by residence requirement.

College credit and advanced placement for postsecondary-level work completed in secondary school. College credit for extrainstitutional learning on basis of ACE *2006 Guide to the Evaluation of Educational Experiences in the Armed Services.*

Tutoring available. Remedial courses offered during regular academic year.

Degree Requirements: *For all associate degrees:* 64–71 credit hours; 16 hours in residence. *For all baccalaureate degrees:* 128 credit hours; 30 hours in residence. *For all degrees:* 2.0 GPA; weekly chapel attendance; 2 hours physical education; general education requirements.

Fulfillment of some degree requirements and exemption from some beginning courses possible by passing departmental examinations, College Board CLEP. *Grading system:* A–F; pass; DP (passing class at time of withdrawal); DF (failing class at time of withdrawal); W (withdraw, carries time limit); incomplete; audit.

Degrees Conferred: 23 *associate;* 101 *baccalaureate:* biological sciences 7; business and management 27; education 141 health professions and related sciences 341 theology/religious vocations 8. Master's degrees awarded: education 9.

Fees and Other Expenses: *Full-time tuition per academic year 2008–09:* $5,506. *Books and supplies:* $1,200. *Room and board per academic year:* $4,025. *Other expenses:* $3,000.

Financial Aid: Aid from institutionally generated funds is provided on the basis of academic merit, financial need. Institution has a Program Participation Agreement with the U.S. Department of Education for eligible students to receive Pell Grants and, depending upon the agreement, other federal aid.

Financial aid to first-time, full-time undergraduate students: 96% received some form of aid. Average amount of aid received: federal grants $3,699; Pell grants $3,357; other federal aid $385; state/local grants $410; institutional grants $1,051.

Departments and Teaching Staff: *Total instructional faculty* 63 (full-time 45, part-time 18). Total faculty with doctorate, first-professional, or other terminal degree 13. Student/faculty ratio: 13:1. Degrees held by full-time faculty: doctorate 15%, master's 76%, baccalaureate .9%.

Enrollment: Total enrollment 950. Undergradaute 883 (full-time 90%; female 56%, male 44%). Graduate 67 (full-time 84%). Undergraduate transfer-in students 78.

Characteristics of Student Body: *Ethnic/racial makeup:* Black non-Hispanic: 3%; Hispanic: 91%; White non-Hispanic: 1%; nonresident alien 5%. *Age distribution:* number under 18: 14; 18–19: 186; 20–21: 190; 22–24: 156; 25–29: 106; 30–34: 77; 35–39: 33; 49; 40–49: 10.

International Students: 50 nonresident aliens enrolled fall 2008. No financial aid specifically designated for international students.

Student Life: On-campus residence halls house 29% of student body. Residence halls for males constitute 12% of such space, for females 15%. Institutionally leased apartments also offer residence space. 2% of married students request institutional housing. *Special regulations:* Registered cars permitted in designated areas. Dress code calls for modest simplicity. Curfews. Quiet hours. Residence hall visitation from 10am to 9:30pm. *Special services:* Learning Resource Center, medical services, van service for nursing students and students doing canvassing. *Student publications: Cumbres*, a biannual magazine; *Flamboyan*, a yearbook; *Mizpa*, a biannual magazine. *Surrounding community:* Mayaguez population 445,000. San Juan, 100 miles from campus, is nearest metropolitan area. Served by airport 10 miles from campus.

Publications: *Publisher:* Antillian College Press.

Library Collections: 88,500 volumes. 2,600 units of microforms; 1,720 audiovisual materials; 392 current periodical subscriptions.

Most important special holdings include collection on nursing; religion; Puerto Rico.

Buildings and Grounds: Campus area 284 acres. Campus DVD available.

Chief Executive Officer: Dr. Myrna Costa, President.

Address admission inquiries to Evelyn del Valle, Director of Admissions.

Universidad Central del Caribe

P.O. Box 60327
Bayamon, Puerto Rico 00960-6032
Tel: (787) 798-3001 **E-mail:** admissions@uccaribe.edu
Fax: (787) 798-6836 **Internet:** www.uccaribe.edu

Institution Description: Universidad Central del Caribe is a private nonprofit coeducational institution established for the development of health sciences educational programs. At present there are programs in medicine, graduate studies in biomedical sciences, radiological technology, and drug abuse. *Enrollment:* 360. *Degrees awarded:* Associate, master's, first-professional.

Accreditation: *Regional*: MSA/CHE. *Professional*: medicine, radiation therapy technology

History: The Universidad Central del Caribe began operating in 1976 and was the first private medical school in Puerto Rico; was first named Universidad del Caribe, Escuela de Medicina de Cayey; in 1984 the University and the Department of Health of the Commonwealth of Puerto Rico established a consortium by which the Government provided the facilities of the Northeastern Regional Hospital in Bayamon and the local Health Centers for use by the medical school as clinical workshops; construction of a new building adjacent to the Regional Hospital integrated all facilities in Bayamon in 1990.

Institutional Structure: Board of trustees. President, deans for hospital affairs, academic affairs, student affairs, administration, school of medicine, radiological technology program.

Calendar: Semesters. Academic year Aug. to May.

Characteristics of Freshmen: 24% of applicants accepted. 71% of accepted applicants enrolled.

96% of entering students from Puerto Rico. Students from 8 states and 4 foreign countries.

Admission: The admission process relies on a combination of objective factors such as performance on the MCAT, PAEG, GRE, CEEB (radiologic technology); previous academic record; personal qualifications of the applicant as they are conveyed by letters of recommendation and personal interviews.

Degree Requirements: Completion of prescribed curriculum with minimum cumulative quality point index (CQPI) of 2.00 for medical students; 2.00 radiology students, and 3.00 for master's students.

Distinctive Educational Programs: The school's curriculum provides examination, analysis, and application of the fundamental concepts in family

UNIVERSIDAD CENTRAL DEL CARIBE—*cont'd*

medicine, preventive medicine and public health, general internal medicine, general pediatrics, and obstetrics-gynecology. The school prepares the graduate to enter an internship or residency in the aforementioned branches of medicine. Graduate studies in the basic biomedical sciences provides the student with a broad background needed to be successful in research in government and private industry, such as the pharmaceutical industry and the field of education. The general objective of the Radiological Technology program is to educate and train professionals for the needs of hospitals, diagnostic centers, and private laboratories.

Degrees Conferred: 28 *associate;* 4 *baccalaureate:* biomedical sciences; 9 *master's:* biomedical sciences. 58 *first-professional:* medicine.

Fees and Other Expenses: *Full-time tuition per and fees academic year 2008–09:* contact the university for current information.

Financial Aid: Aid from institutionally generated funds is provided on the basis of academic merit, financial need. Institution has a Program Participation Agreement with the U.S. Department of Education for eligible students to receive Pell Grants and, depending upon the agreement, other federal aid.

Departments and Teaching Staff: *Total instructional faculty:* 282. Degrees held by full-time faculty: doctorate 10%, master's 3%, professional 87%.

Enrollment: Total enrollment 357.

International Students: No programs available to aid students whose native language is not Spanish. All students are fully conversant in English. No financial aid specifically designated for international students.

Library Collections: 30,000 volumes including bound books, serial backfiles, electronic documents, and government documents not in separate collections. Online catalog. Current serial subscriptions: 320 paper, 700 electronic. 325 recordings; 135 CD-ROMs. Computer work stations available. Students have access to the Internet at no charge.

Most important special collection: Dr. Arana Soto Collection.

Chief Executive Officer: Dr. Nilda Candelario, President.

Address admission inquiries to Irma L. Cordero, Admissions Officer.

Universidad del Este

P.O. Box 2010
Carolina, Puerto Rico 00984-2010
Tel: (787) 257-7373 **E-mail:** admissions@www.suagm.edu/une
Fax: (787) 252-0070 **Internet:** www.suagm.edu

Institution Description: Universidad del Este was formerly named Colegio Universitario del Este. It is a four-year institution offering a baccalaureate degree program. *Enrollment:* 6,647. *Degrees awarded:* Associate, baccalaureate.

Accreditation: *Regional:* MSA/CHE. *Professional*: health information technician

Calendar: Semesters. Academic year Aug. to May.

Characteristics of Freshmen: 66% of entering freshmen expected to graduate within 5 years. 100% of freshmen from Puerto Rico.

Admission: Present evidence of graduation from an accredited secondary school or its equivalent with a minimum grade point index of 2.50; satisfactory scores in the aptitude and English achievement tests of the College Entrance Examination Board.

Degree Requirements: *For associate degree:* general education requirements; GPA 2.0 or higher; cumulative GPA of 2.0 or higher in concentration course requirements; complete no fewer than one-fourth of all credits in residence. *For baccalaureate degree:* 120 credit hours; GPA 2.25 or higher; complete at least 30 credit hours of the last 36 credit hours in residence; general education requirements.

Degrees Conferred: 207 *associate*; 247 *baccalaureate*. Bachelor's degrees awarded in top five disciplines: business and management 135; education 11; health professions and related sciences, protective services, public administration and services 54.

Fees and Other Expenses: *Full-time tuition per academic year 2008–09:* $4,810.

Financial Aid: Aid from institutionally generated funds is provided on the basis of academic merit, financial need. Institution has a Program Participation Agreement with the U.S. Department of Education for eligible students to receive Pell Grants and, depending upon the agreement, other federal aid.

Percentage of undergraduate first-time full-time students receiving various forms of financial aid: federal scholarships and grants 95% (average $1,500); state/local scholarships and grants 1% (average $356); institutional fellowships 3% (average $514); loans 1% (average $521).

Departments and Teaching Staff: *Total instructional faculty:* 292 FTE. Degrees held by full-time faculty: Doctorate 15%, master's 15%.

Enrollment: Total enrollment 9,735.

International Students: No financial aid specifically designated for international students.

Library Collections: 45,000 volumes. 1,400 microforms; 1,560 audiovisual materials; 410 current periodical subscriptions. Students have access to online information retrieval services and the Internet.

Chief Executive Officer: Alberto Maldonado-Ruiz, Chancellor.

Address admission inquiries to Director of Admissions.

Universidad del Turabo

P.O. Box 3030
University Station
Gurabo, Puerto Rico 00778-3030
Tel: (787) 743-7979 **E-mail:** admissions@suagm.edu
Fax: (787) 744-5394 **Internet:** www.suagm.edu

Institution Description: Universidad del Turabo is a private, nonsectarian university for commuter students. *Enrollment:* 16,296. *Degrees awarded:* Associate, baccalaureate, master's.

Accreditation: *Regional:* MSA/CHE.

History: Established 1872.

Institutional Structure: *Composition of institution:* Administrators 11. Academic affairs headed by academic dean. Management/business/finances directed by directed by dean of administration. Full-time instructional faculty 81.

Calendar: Semesters.

Admission: Rolling admissions plan. *Requirements:* Graduation from accredited secondary school; fluency in English and Spanish; minimum 2.0 GPA (2.3 for programs in allied health subjects).

Degree Requirements: *For all associate degrees:* 72 semester hours. *For all baccalaureate degrees:* 129 semester hours. *For all degrees:* 2.0 GPA; 30 hours in residence; general education requirements. *Grading system:* A–F.

Degrees Conferred: 85 *associate*; 926 *baccalaureate*. Bachelor's degrees awarded in top five disciplines: biological/life sciences 27; business and management 283; education 132; social sciences and history 62; public administration and services 48. *Master's:* various disciplines 838. Doctorates awarded: business/management 5.

Fees and Other Expenses: *Full-time tuition per academic year 2008–09:* $4,584. *Books and supplies:* $900. *Room and board per academic year:* $7,315. *Other expenses:* $5,029.

Financial Aid: Aid from institutionally generated funds is provided on the basis of financial need. Institution has a Program Participation Agreement with the U.S. Department of Education for eligible students to receive Pell Grants and, depending upon the agreement, other federal aid.

Percentage of undergraduate first-time full-time students receiving various forms of financial aid: federal scholarships and grants 98% (average $1,488); state/local scholarships and grants 2% (average $224); institutional fellowships 35 (average $941); loans 1% (average $1,359).

Departments and Teaching Staff: *Total instructional faculty:* 364.

Enrollment: Total enrollment 16,296. Undergraduate 13,032 (full-time 79%; female 60%, male 40%). Graduate 3,264 (full-time 45%). Undergraduate transfer-in students 634.

Student Life: *Surrounding community:* Gurabo is located 15 miles south of San Juan.

Buildings and Grounds: 13 acre campus.

Chief Executive Officer: Dennis Aliceo, President.

Address admission inquiries to Director of Admissions.

Universidad Metropolitana

P.O. Box 21150
San Juan, Puerto Rico 00928-1150
Tel: (787) 766-1717 **E-mail:** admissions@suagm.edu/umet
Fax: (787) 759-7663 **Internet:** www.suagm.edu

Institution Description: Universidad Metropolitana, member of the Ana G. Mendez University System (AGMUS), is a private, independent, nonprofit, postsecondary institution. *Enrollment:* 12,369. *Degrees awarded:* Baccalaureate, master's.

Accreditation: *Regional:* MSA/CHE. *Professional.* nursing, respiratory therapy

History: Universidad Metropolitana was established in 1980 as Colegio Universitario Metropolitano. In 1985 it began offering graduate programs and adopted its present name.

Institutional Structure: *Governing Board:* Board of Trustees. 15 members. All voting.

Calendar: Semesters. Academic year Aug. to May. Freshmen admitted Aug.

Characteristics of Freshmen: 65% of accepted applicants enrolled.

Admission: Rolling admissions plan. *Requirements:* Graduation from accredited secondary school. Fluency in English and Spanish. Minimum 2.0 GPA (2.3 for programs in allied health subjects).

Degree Requirements: *For all associate degrees:* 72 semester hours. *For all baccalaureate degrees:* 129 semester hours. *For all degrees:* 2.0 GPA; 30 hours in residence; general education requirements. *Grading system:* A–F.

Degrees Conferred: 70 *associate;* 734 *baccalaureate*; 526 *master's*.

Fees and Other Expenses: *Full-time tuition per academic year 2008–09:* $4,584. *Books and supplies:* $900. *Room and board per academic year:* $7,315. *Other expenses:* $5,029.

Financial Aid: Aid from institutionally generated funds is provided on the basis of academic merit, financial need, athletic ability. Institution has a Program Participation Agreement with the U.S. Department of Education for eligible students to receive Pell Grants and, depending upon the agreement, other federal aid.

Financial aid awarded to first-time, full-time undergraduate students: 99% received some form of aid. Average amount of aid received: federal grants $200; Pell grants $1,998; other federal aid $361; state/local grants $225; institutional grants $1,208.

Departments and Teaching Staff: *Total instructional faculty:* 151. Degrees held by full-time faculty: doctorate 36%, master's 63%, baccalaureate 1%. 63% hold terminal degrees.

Enrollment: Total enrollment 12,369. Undergraduate 9,796 (full-time 80%; female 67%, male 33%). Gradaute 2,593. Undergraduate transfer-in students 514.

Characteristics of Student Body: *Ethnic/racial makeup:* Hispanic 100%.

International Students: No international students enrolled.

Library Collections: 64,000 volumes including bound books, serial backfiles, electronic documents, and government documents not in separate collections. Online catalog. Current serial subscriptions: 1,148 paper, 156 microform, 1,140 electronic. Computer work stations available. Students have access to the Internet at no charge.

Buildings and Grounds: Urban campus.

Chief Executive Officer: Dr. Federico M. Matheu, Chancellor. Address admission inquiries to Evelyn Robledo, Director of Admissions.

Universidad Politecnica de Puerto Rico

377 Ponce de Leon Avenue
P.O. Box 192017
San Juan, Puerto Rico 00919-2017
Tel: (787) 754-8000 **E-mail:** admissions@pupr.edu
Fax: (787) 763-8919 **Internet:** www.pupr.edu

Institution Description: The Universidad Politecnica de Puerto Rico is a nonprofit, private institution. *Enrollment:* 5,800. *Degrees awarded:* Baccalaureate, master's. Certificates also awarded.

Accreditation: *Regional:* MSA/CHE. *Professional*: engineering

History: Established as Technological Lyceum of Puerto Rico 1964; offered first instruction at postsecondary level 1965; awarded first degree (baccalaureate) 1969; adopted present name 1976.

Institutional Structure: *Governing board:* Board of Trustees. Extrainstitutional representation: 9 trustees. *Composition of institution:* President, assistant to the president in academic affairs, dean of administration, dean of engineering faculty, dean of arts and science faculty, dean of student affairs, academic department directors.

Calendar: Trimesters. Academic year Aug. to Aug. Summer session of 1 term.

Characteristics of Freshmen: 941 applicants (female 257, male 684). 96% of applicants accepted. 73% of accepted applicants enrolled full-time.

100% of freshmen from Puerto Rico.

Admission: Rolling admissions plan. *Requirements:* Either graduation from accredited secondary school or GED. Minimum 2.0 GPA. *Entrance tests:* College Board SAT required of all students 23 years of age and younger. *For transfer students:* 2.0 minimum GPA.

Degree Requirements: 120–176 credit hours; 2.0 GPA. *Grading system:* A–F; withdraw; incomplete.

Distinctive Educational Programs: Corrective core courses for educationally disadvantaged, ill-prepared students. Honor-freshmen fellowship for high achievement.

Degrees Conferred: 326 *baccalaureate:* business 31, engineering 267, other 28; 146 *master's:* engineering.

Fees and Other Expenses: *Full-time tuition per academic year 2008–09:* $6,330. *Books and supplies:* $2,310. *Room and board per academic year:* $11,704. *Other expenses:* $6,921.

Financial Aid: Aid from institutionally generated funds is provided on the basis of academic merit, financial need, other criteria. Institution has a Program Participation Agreement with the U.S. Department of Education for eligible students to receive Pell Grants and, depending upon the agreement, other federal aid.

Financial aid to full-time, first-time undergraduate students: 98% received some form of aid. Average amount of aid received: federal grants $3,328; Pell grants $3,100; other federal aid $683; state/local grants $1,187; institutional grants $590.

Departments and Teaching Staff: *Total instructional faculty:* 340. Degrees held by full-time faculty: doctorate 16%, master's 75%, baccalaureate 9%.

Enrollment: Total enrollment 5,800. Undergraduate 5,139 (full-time 55%; female 23%, male 77%). Graduate 661 (full-time 56%). Undergraduate transfer-in students 264.

Characteristics of Student Body: *Ethnic/racial makeup:* Hispanic 100%.

International Students: No international students enrolled.

Student Life: Social and cultural activities available; 6 student associations and student council; various types of team sports and activities.

Library Collections: 104,500 068 volumes including bound books, serial backfiles, electronic documents, and government documents not in separate collections. Online catalog. Current serial subscriptions: 1,743 paper, 11,431 via electronic access. 168 compact discs; 237 recordings; 593 CD-ROMs. Students have access to the Internet at no charge.

Most important special holdings include collections on engineering, architecture, and business administration.

Chief Executive Officer: Ernesto Vasquez-Barquet, President.

Address admission inquiries to Teresa Cardona, Director of Admissions.

University of Puerto Rico

1187 Flamboyan Street
San Juan, Puerto Rico 00936
Tel: (787) 250-000 **E-mail:** admissions@upr.edu
Fax: (787) 259-6917 **Internet:** www.upr.edu

Institution Description: The University of Puerto Rico is a public institution and land-grant college with three campuses, two university colleges, three technological university colleges, and three regional colleges. The Mayaguez, Rio Piedras, and Medical Sciences campuses offer undergraduate, graduate, and first-professional degree programs. The University Colleges of Cayey and Humacao and the Technological University Colleges of Arecibo, Bayamon, and Ponce offer associate and baccalaureate degrees. The University System also includes three regional colleges at Aguadilla, Carolina, and Utuado which offer associate degrees.

Accreditation: *Regional:* MSA–CHE. *Professional*: architecture, chemistry, dental assisting, dentistry, dietetics, engineering, health services administration, law, medical record administration, medicine, nursing, occupational therapy, physical therapy, public health, social work, teacher education

History: Established as Industrial Normal School in Fajardo 1900; incorporated as University of Puerto Rico and moved to Rio Piedras 1903; became land-grant college 1908; established regional colleges system 1962; reorganized as a multiunit institutional system 1966.

Institutional Structure: *Governing board:* Council on Higher Education. Extrainstitutional representation: 8 members appointed by the Governor of Puerto Rico and the State Secretary of Education (an ex-officio member).

Calendar: Semesters (except Carolina Regional College and some programs in the School of Public Health which are on the quarter system). Students admitted Aug., Jan. Degrees conferred June, Dec. Formal commencement June. Summer session.

Admission: For fall acceptance, apply no later than Nov. 30 of previous year. *Requirements:* Either graduation from high school or GED. Demonstrated proficiency in English and Spanish. *Entrance tests:* College Board SAT, 3 Achievements. *For transfer students:* 2.0–2.5 minimum GPA; maximum transfer credit 50% of coursework in major field; good standing at institution previously attended.

Tutoring available. Noncredit remedial courses offered in summer session and regular academic year.

Degree Requirements: *For all associate degrees:* 62–79 credit hours. *For all baccalaureate degrees:* 122–124 credit hours. *For all undergraduate degrees:* 2.0 GPA; final 28 credit hours in residence.

UNIVERSITY OF PUERTO RICO—*cont'd*

Fulfillment of some degree requirements and exemption from some beginning courses possible by passing College Board CLEP, AP. *Grading system:* A–F; withdrawal; incomplete (carries time limit).

Distinctive Educational Programs: Weekend and evening classes. Extension and continuing education programs. Student-exchange programs with several universities in the U.S. mainland, Spain, and Latin America.

ROTC: Army, Air Force. The Rio Piedras and Mayaguez campuses are the ROTC centers in Puerto Rico. Cadets from different units receive their training at these two centers.

Financial Aid: Aid from institutionally generated funds is provided on the basis of academic merit, financial need, athletic ability, other criteria.

Characteristics of Student Body: Extension education offered on campus.

International Students: Programs available to aid students whose native language is not English: English as a Second Language Program.

Publications: Editorial Universitaria is the University press.

Chief Executive Officer: Antonio R. Garcia-Padillo, President.

Address admission inquiries to Director of Academic Affairs, Central Administration, University of Puerto Rico.

University of Puerto Rico, Arecibo Technological University College

P.O. Box 4010
Arecibo, Puerto Rico 00614-4010
Tel: (787) 878-2830 **E-mail:** admissions@upra.edu
Fax: (787) 880-2245 **Internet:** www.upra.edu

Institution Description: *Enrollment:* 4,599. *Degrees awarded:* Associate, baccalaureate.

Accreditation: *Regional:* MSA–CHE. *Professional*: nursing

History: The college was founded in 1967 on the northern coast of Puerto Rico. o\130 *Composition of institution:* Administrators 7. The chancellor is aided by the dean of academic, administrative, and student affairs. Full-time instructional faculty 263. Academic governance body, Academic Senate, meets an average of 24 times per year.

Calendar: Semesters. Academic year Aug. to May. Freshmen admitted in Aug.

Characteristics of Freshmen: 77% of applicants accepted. 80% of accepted applicants enrolled.

100% of freshmen from Puerto Rico.

Admission: Rolling admissions plan. For fall acceptance, apply no later than Nov. 30 of previous year. *Requirements:* School achievement record and test scores. *Entrance tests:* College Board ACT or SAT I and II with 3 achievements in English, Spanish, and mathematics. For fall acceptance apply no later than Nov. 30 of previous year. *For transfer students:* 2.0–2.5 minimum GPA; minimum 24 hours of transferable credit; good standing at institution previously attended.

Degree Requirements: *For all associate degrees:* 62–79 credit hours. *For all baccalaureate degrees:* 122–144 credit hours. *For all degrees:* 2.0 GPA; final 28 hours in residence.

Fulfillment of some degree requirements and exemption from some beginning courses possible by passing College Board CLEP. *Grading system:* A–F; withdraw (carries time limit); incomplete.

ROTC: Army.

Degrees Conferred: 28 *associate;* 408 *baccalaureate:* biological and life sciences 43; business 176; communications 23; computer and information science 22; education 63; engineering 20; health professions 61.

Fees and Other Expenses: *Full-time tuition per academic year 2008–09:* contact the university for current information.

Financial Aid: The university offers a direct lending program. Aid from institutionally generated funds is provided on the basis of financial need. Institution has a Program Participation Agreement with the U.S. Department of Education for eligible students to receive Pell Grants and, depending upon the agreement, other federal aid.

Federal and state funding for undergraduates: 3,449 scholarships and grants totaling $10,722,462 (ranging from $400 to $3,125); 501 loans totaling $1,700,000 (ranging from $3,000 to $3,500); 274 work-study jobs totaling $222,398 (ranging from $800 to $7,500).

Departments and Teaching Staff: *Total instructional faculty:* 245. Student/faculty ratio: 18:1. Degrees held by full-time faculty: doctorate 14%, master's 86%. 14% hold terminal degrees.

Enrollment: Total enrollment 4,599.

Characteristics of Student Body: *Ethnic/racial makeup:* Hispanic 100%.

International Students: No international students enrolled.

Library Collections: 75,000 volumes. 253 microform titles; 1,495 audiovisual materials; 2,460 current periodical subscriptions. 240 computer work stations campus-wide.

Most important special holdings include Coleccion Arecibo; Coleccion Juvenil; Sala de Musica.

Buildings and Grounds: Campus area 50 acres.

Chief Executive Officer: Dr. Edwin Hernandez, Chancellor.

Address admission inquiries to Margarita Saenz, Director of Admissions.

University of Puerto Rico, Cayey University College

Antonio R. Barcelo Avenue
Cayey, Puerto Rico 00633
Tel: (787) 738-2161 **E-mail:** admissions@cayey.upr.edu
Fax: (787) 738-8039 **Internet:** www.cayey.upr.edu

Institution Description: Cayey University College is a separately managed unit of the University of Puerto Rico. *Enrollment:* 3,658. *Degrees awarded:* Baccalaureate.

Accreditation: *Regional:* MSA/CHE.

History: Established, chartered, and incorporated as Cayey Regional College, and offered first instruction at postsecondary level 1967; adopted present name 1969; awarded first degree (baccalaureate) 1972.

Institutional Structure: *Composition of institution:* Chancellor is the chief executive officer. Academic senate, administrative senate, academic dean, administrative dean, student's dean. Full-time instructional faculty 197. Academic governance body, Course and Curriculum Committee, meets an average of 12 times per year.

Calendar: Semesters. Academic year Aug. to May. Freshmen admitted Aug. Degrees conferred June. Summer session of 1 term from June to July.

Characteristics of Freshmen: 78% of applicants accepted. 61% of applicants accepted and enrolled.

96% of entering freshmen expected to graduate within 5 years. 100% of freshmen from Puerto Rico.

Admission: For fall acceptance, apply no later than Nov. 30 of previous year. *Requirements:* Either graduation from high school or GED. Demonstrated proficiency in English and Spanish. *Entrance tests:* College Board SAT, 3 Achievements. *For transfer students:* 2.0–2.5 minimum GPA; maximum transfer credit 50% of coursework in major field; good standing at institution previously attended.

Tutoring available. Noncredit remedial courses offered in summer session and regular academic year.

Degree Requirements: *For all associate degrees:* 62–79 credit hours. *For all baccalaureate degrees:* 122–124 credit hours. *For all undergraduate degrees:* 2.0 GPA; final 28 credit hours in residence.

Fulfillment of some degree requirements and exemption from some beginning courses possible by passing College Board CLEP, AP. *Grading system:* A–F; withdrawal; incomplete (carries time limit).

Distinctive Educational Programs: Weekend and evening classes. Extension and continuing education program. Study abroad at Ortega and Gasset Foundation at Toledo, Spain; National Student Exchange Program.

ROTC: Army.

Degrees Conferred: 3,658 *baccalaureate:* business, management, marketing, and related support services 980; education 1,109; English 31; health professions and related clinical sciences 731; mathematics 63; psychology 74; social sciences and history 570.

Fees and Other Expenses: *Full-time tuition per academic year 2008*09:* $1,4705 (in-state).

Financial Aid: Aid from institutionally generated funds is provided on the basis of academic merit, financial need. Institution has a Program Participation Agreement with the U.S. Department of Education for eligible students to receive Pell Grants and, depending upon the agreement, other federal aid.

Percentage of undergraduate first-time full-time students receiving various forms of financial aid: federal scholarships and grants 87% (average $3,000); state/local scholarships and grants 9% (average $300); 1% loans (average $1,923).

Departments and Teaching Staff: *Total instructional faculty:* 197. Degrees held by full-time faculty: doctorate 35%, master's 65%. 35% hold terminal degrees.

Enrollment: Total enrollment 3,658.

Characteristics of Student Body: *Ethnic/racial makeup:* Hispanic 100%.

International Students: No financial programs specifically designated for international students.

Student Life: No on-campus housing. *Special services:* Medical services. *Surrounding community:* Cayey.

Library Collections: 125,000 volumes. 75 microforms titles; 840 current periodical subscriptions. Students have access to online information retrieval services and the Internet.

Most important special holdings include Miguel Melendez Munoz Hall Puerto Rican Collection; women's studies collection; juvenile collection.

Chief Executive Officer: Dr. Ragael, Aragunde, Chancellor.

Address admission inquiries to Wilfredo Lopez, Director of Admission.

University of Puerto Rico, Humacao University College

100 Road 908
CUH Station
Humacao, Puerto Rico 00791-4300
Tel: (787) 850-0000 **E-mail:** admissions@uprh,edu
Fax: (787) 850-4638 **Internet:** www.uprh.edu

Institution Description: *Enrollment:* 4,744. *Degrees awarded:* Associate, baccalaureate.

Accreditation: *Regional:* MSA/CHE.

History: Established as Humacao Regional College, chartered, offered first first instruction at postsecondary level 1962; awarded first degree (associate) 1969; adopted present name 1973; added baccalaureate degree programs 1974.

Institutional Structure: *Composition of institution:* Administrators 23. Academic affairs headed by dean. Management/business/finances directed by dean of administrative affairs. Full-time instructional faculty 261. Academic and administrative boards. Academic Board meets an average of 12 times per year.

Calendar: Semesters. Academic year Aug. to May. Freshmen admitted Aug. Degrees conferred May, July, Dec. Formal commencement June. Summer session of 1 term from May to June.

Characteristics of Freshmen: 2,929 applicants (female 1,914, male 1,015). 43% of applicants accepted. 91% of accepted applicants enrolled full-time.

(CEEB Spanish Version) SAT class scores 532 verbal, 551 mathematical.

99% of freshmen from Puerto Rico.

Admission: For fall acceptance, apply no later than Nov. 30 of previous year. *Requirements:* Either graduation from high school or GED. Demonstrated proficiency in English and Spanish. *Entrance tests:* College Board SAT, 3 Achievements. *For transfer students:* 2.0–2.5 minimum GPA; maximum transfer credit 50% of coursework in major field; good standing at institution previously attended.

Tutoring available. Noncredit remedial courses offered in summer session and regular academic year.

Degree Requirements: *For all associate degrees:* 65–79 credit hours. *For all baccalaureate degrees:* 128–136 credit hours. *For all undergraduate degrees:* 2.00 GPA; 30 credit hours in residence.

Fulfillment of some degree requirements and exemption from some beginning courses possible by passing CEEB Advance Placement. *Grading system:* A–F; withdrawal; incomplete (carries time limit).

Distinctive Educational Programs: Work-experience programs. Weekend and evening classes. Honors programs. Tutorials. Credit and noncredit continuing education. Study abroad program with National Student Exchange Program. Teacher certification program and internships. Continuing educational credit and noncredit courses.

Degrees Conferred: 123 *associate;* 532 *baccalaureate:* agriculture 9, biological sciences 76, business and management 210, computational mathematics 12, education 50, health professions 39, physical sciences 83, protective services/public administration 53.

Fees and Other Expenses: *Full-time tuition and fees academic year 2008–09:* $1,945 in-state. Nonresident students who are U.S. citizens pay an amount equal to the rate for nonresidents at a state university in their home state. *Books and supplies:* $1,825. *Room and board per academic year (off-campus):* $8,190. *Other expenses* $2,050.

Financial Aid: Aid from institutionally generated funds is provided on the basis of financial need. Institution has a Program Participation Agreement with the U.S. Department of Education for eligible students to receive Pell Grants and, depending upon the agreement, other federal aid.

Financial aid to undergraduate first-time, full-time students: 79% received some form of aid. Average amount of aid received: federal grants $3,794; Pell grants $3,491; other federal aid $801; state/local grants $729.

Departments and Teaching Staff: *Total instructional faculty:* 269. Student/faculty ratio: 15:1. Degrees held by full-time faculty: doctorate 35%, master's 63%, baccalaureate 2%. 35% hold terminal degrees.

Enrollment: Total enrollment 4,744 (yndergraduate).

Characteristics of Student Body: *Ethnic/racial makeup:* Hispanic 100%.

International Students: No international students enrolled.

Student Life: No on-campus housing. *Intercollegiate athletics:* male: basketball, judo, soccer, volleyball, weight lifting, wrestling; both sexes: cross-country, swimming, table tennis, tennis, track and field. *Special regulations:* Cars with parking stickers permitted for all but freshmen. *Special services:* Learning Resources Center, medical services. *Surrounding community:* Humacao, San Juan, 100 miles from campus, is nearest metropolitan area.

Publications: *Exegesis, Que hacer universitario.*

Library Collections: 120,000 volumes including bound books, serial backfiles, electronic documents, and government documents not in separate collections. Online catalog. 18,700 periodicals including via electronic access. 2,468 audiovisual materials. Computer work stations available. Students have access to the Internet at no charge.

Most important special collections include the Puerto Rican Collection; Santiago Iglesias Pantin Personal Papers and Documents.

Buildings and Grounds: Campus area 62 acres.

Chief Executive Officer: Dr. Hilda M. Colon, Chancellor.

Address admission inquiries to Inara Ferrer, Director of Admissions.

University of Puerto Rico, Mayaguez Campus

P.O. Box 9020
Mayaguez, Puerto Rico 00681
Tel: (787) 832-4040 **E-mail:** admissions@uprm.edu
Fax: (787) 834-33031 **Internet:** www.uprm.edu

Institution Description: *Enrollment:* 13,324. *Degrees awarded:* Associate, baccalaureate, master's, doctorate. Certificates also awarded.

Accreditation: *Regional:* MSA/CHE.

History: Established and offered first instruction at postsecondary level 1911; awarded first degree (baccalaureate) 1915.

Calendar: Semesters. Academic year Aug. to May.

Characteristics of Freshmen: 3,364 applicants (female 1,613, male 1,751). 77% of applicants accepted. 95% of accepted applicants enrolled full-time.

SAT scores *25th percentile*: SAT Verbal 535, SAT Math 565. *75th percentile*: SAT Verbal 626, SAT Math 694. Freshmen from 5 states.

Admission: For fall acceptance, apply no later than Nov. 30 of previous year. *Requirements:* Either graduation from high school or GED. Demonstrated proficiency in English and Spanish. *Entrance tests:* College Board SAT, 3 Achievements. *For transfer students:* 2.0–2.5 minimum GPA; maximum transfer credit 50% of coursework in major field; good standing at institution previously attended.

Tutoring available. Noncredit remedial courses offered in summer session and regular academic year.

Degree Requirements: *For all associate degrees:* 62–79 credit hours. *For all baccalaureate degrees:* 122–124 credit hours. *For all undergraduate degrees:* 2.0 GPA; final 28 credit hours in residence.

Fulfillment of some degree requirements and exemption from some beginning courses possible by passing College Board CLEP, AP. *Grading system:* A–F; withdrawal; incomplete (carries time limit).

Distinctive Educational Programs: Work-experience programs in business administration and engineering. Weekend and evening classes. Cooperative baccalaureate in medical technology with approved hospitals. Special facilities for using telecommunications in the classroom. Interdepartmental programs in agricultural sciences. Interdisciplinary program in Hispanic studies. Tutorials. Preprofessional programs in medicine and veterinary medicine. Office of International Programs in Agriculture administers training and research programs in tropical agriculture. *Other distinctive programs:* Agricultural Experiment Station sponsors agro-industrial research. Agricultural Extension Service. Water Resource Research Institute. Center for Energy and Environmental Research. Division of Academic Extension and Community Services offers credit and noncredit continuing education. Engineering Research Center composed of a Construction Institute, a Transportation Institute, a Quality Control Laboratory, and a Technical Information Center.

ROTC: Army, Air Force.

Degrees Conferred: 1,461 *baccalaureate*; 179 *master's*; 19 *doctorate*. Bachelor's degrees awarded in top five disciplines: engineering 648; business, management, marketing, and related support services 221; biological/life sciences 184; agriculture 81; social sciences and history 79. Master's degrees awarded: various disciplines 179. Doctorates awarded: education 19.

Fees and Other Expenses: *Full-time tuition per academic year:* undergraduate resident $1,940, nonresident $3,884. *Books and supplies:* $1,825. *room and board per academic year (off-campus)* $8,180. *Other expenses:* $2,050.

Financial Aid: Aid from institutionally generated funds is provided on the basis of academic merit, athletic ability.

UNIVERSITY OF PUERTO RICO, MAYAGUEZ CAMPUS—*cont'd*

Financial aid to full-time, first-time undergraduate students: 70% received some form of aid.

Departments and Teaching Staff: *Total instructional faculty:* 650. Degrees held by full-time faculty: doctorate 52%, master's 44%, baccalaureate 4%.

Enrollment: Total enrollment 13,324. Undergraduate 12,234 (full-time 93%; female 49%, male 51%). Graduate 1,090 (full-time 85%). Undergraduate transfer-in students 208.

Characteristics of Student Body: *Age distribution:* number under 18: 787; 18–19: 2,063; 20–21: 3,546; 22–24: 3,647; 25–29: 769; 30–34: 110; 35–39: 47; 40–49: 44; 50–64: 16; 65 and over: 1.

International Students: No international students enrolled.

Student Life: No on-campus housing. *Intercollegiate athletics:* male: basketball, soccer, softball, swimming, tennis, track and field, volleyball, water polo; female: basketball, softball, swimming, tennis, track and field, volleyball. *Special regulations:* Cars permitted in designated areas for all but freshmen. *Special services:* Learning Resources Center, medical services, campus transportation system for some off-campus activities. *Surrounding community:* Mayaguez population 83,000. San Juan, 110 miles from campus, is nearest metropolitan area. Served by airport 6 miles from campus.

Library Collections: 784,000 volumes. 487,000 government documents; 345,000 microforms; 43,600 audiovisual materials; 2,170 current periodical subscriptions. Students have access to online information retrieval services and the Internet.

Most important special holdings include the Puerto Rican Collection; Alfred Stern Collection; Marine Sciences Collection.

Buildings and Grounds: Campus area 305 acres.

Chief Executive Officer: Dr. Jrge I. Velez Arocho, Chancellor.

Address admission inquiries to Norma Torres, Admissions Director.

University of Puerto Rico, Medical Sciences Campus

G.P.O. Box 365067
San Juan, Puerto Rico 00936-5067
Tel: (787) 758-2525 **E-mail:** admissions@rcm.upr.edu
Fax: (787) 282-9117 **Internet:** www.rcm.upr.edu

Institution Description: University of Puerto Rico, Medical Sciences Campus is a state institution. *Enrollment:* 2,334. *Degrees awarded:* Associate, baccalaureate, first-professional (dentistry, medicine), master's, doctorate. Certificates also awarded.

Accreditation: *Regional:* MSA/CHE. *Professional*: clinical lab scientist, dentistry, dietetics, medicine, medical record technology, nursing, occupational therapy, physical therapy, public health, radiography, speech-language pathology

History: Established 1912; offered first instruction at postsecondary level 1926; awarded first degree (master's) 1941; adopted present name 1966.

Institutional Structure: *Composition of institution:* Administrators 23. Academic affairs headed by dean for academic affairs. Management/business/finances directed by dean for administration. Total instructional faculty 738. Academic governance body, Academic Senate, meets an average of 12 times per year.

Calendar: Trimesters. Academic year Aug. to May. Freshmen admitted Aug. Degrees conferred June. Summer session of 1 term from June to July.

Admission: Apply no later than Dec. 15. Students are notified of acceptance in May. *Requirements:* For first-professional students 90 semester hours with emphasis in science from accredited institution; MCAT or DAT. For graduate students graduation from accredited institution with 60 semester hours and emphasis in science; GRE.

Degree Requirements: *For first-professional degrees:* medicine: 4,912 contact hours; 2.50 GPA; dentistry: 242.5 credit hours; 2.00 GPA; graduate programs: 50–70 credit hours; 2.50 and 3.00 GPA in field of concentration; undergraduate programs: 125–130 credit hours; 2.00 GPA. *Grading system:* A–F.

Distinctive Educational Programs: The Medical Sciences Campus is the only institution of higher education in Puerto Rico that specializes in the health sciences.

Degrees Conferred: 182 *baccalaureate:* health professions and related sciences; 194 *master's:* health professions; 7 *doctorate:* health professions; 160 *first-professional:* dentistry 45; medicine 115.

Fees and Other Expenses: *Full-time tuition per academic year 2008–09:* in-state undergraduate $30 per credit; graduate $75 per credit. *Required fees:* $1,370.

Financial Aid: Aid from institutionally generated funds is provided on the basis of financial need.

Financial aid to full-time, first-time undergraduate students: need-based scholarships/grants totaling $1,367,026, self-help $263,878. *Graduate aid:* 402 students received $1,894,400 in federal and state-funded fellowships/grants; 685 received $7,195,994 in federal and state-funded loans; 9 students held work-study jobs yielding $8,761.

Departments and Teaching Staff: *Total instructional faculty:* 733 (full-time 569, part-time 164). Total faculty with doctorate, first-professional, or other terminal degree 605. Student/faculty ratio: 4:1.

Enrollment: Total enrollment 2,334. Undergraduate full-time 56 men / 348 women, part-time 13m / 57w; first-professional full-time 295m / 478w, part-time 1m / 4w; graduate full-time 203m / 687w, part-time 38m / 154w.

Characteristics of Student Body: *Ethnic/racial makeup:* Hispanic 100%.

International Students: 29 nonresident aliens enrolled fall 2008. Students from Europe, Asia, Latin America. No financial aid specifically designated for international students.

Student Life: No on-campus housing. The Social and Cultural Activities Program of the Deanship for Student Affairs provides activities for the social and cultural development of students and the campus community. Concerts, conferences, dances, lectures, films, variety shows, and plays are offered throughout the year. Wellness Program. Student health services. Guidance and Counseling Office. *Special regulations:* Cars permitted in designated areas only. *Special services:* Medical services. *Surrounding community:* San Juan, 1 mile from campus, is nearest metropolitan area.

Library Collections: 157,000 volumes. Online catalog. 2,150 audiovisual materials; 1,163 current periodical subscriptions. Access to 27,264 journals via electronic access. Students have access to online information retrieval services.

Most important special holdings include Bailey K. Ashford Memorial Collection; Puerto Rican Health History Collection; Aids Collection.

Buildings and Grounds: Campus area 18 acres.

Chief Executive Officer: Dr. Jose R. Carlo, Chancellor.

Address admission inquiries to Director of Admissions.

University of Puerto Rico, Rio Piedras Campus

P.O. Box 23300
University Station
Rio Piedras, Puerto Rico 00931-3300
Tel: (787) 764-0000 **E-mail:** admissions@rrp.upr.edu
Fax: (787) 764-8799 **Internet:** www.rrp.upr.edu

Institution Description: *Enrollment:* 18,653. *Degrees awarded:* Associate, baccalaureate, first-professional (law), master's, doctorate.

Accreditation: *Regional:* MSA/CHE.

History: Established 1903.

Institutional Structure: *Composition of institution:* Administrators 18. Academic affairs headed by dean of academic affairs. Management/business/finances directed by dean of administration. Full-time instructional faculty 1,299.

Calendar: Semesters. Academic year Aug. to May. Freshmen admitted Aug. Degrees conferred May, Dec., July. Formal commencement June.

Characteristics of Freshmen: 8,196 applicants (female 5,236, male 2,900). 37% of applicants accepted. 92% of accepted applicants enrolled full-time.

99% of freshmen from Puerto Rico.

Distinctive Educational Programs: Individually designed interdisciplinary programs. Honors programs. Tutorials. Study in the United States. Doctorate degrees offered in psychology, education, and history.

Degrees Conferred: 2,405 *baccalaureate*. Bachelor's degrees awarded in top five disciplines: biological and life sciences 248; business and management 631; education 274; psychology 114; social sciences and history 233; Master's degrees awarded: various disciplines 364. Doctorates awarded: various disciplines 196. First-professional degrees awarded: law 111.

Fees and Other Expenses: *Full-time tuition per academic year 2008–09:* $1,272 in-state. *Room and board per academic year:* $6,380. *Books and supplies:* $1,825. *Other expenses:* $2,050. Contact the university for current information regarding graduate and first-professional tuition, fees, and housing.

Financial Aid: Aid from institutionally generated funds is provided on the basis of financial need. Institution has a Program Participation Agreement with the U.S. Department of Education for eligible students to receive Pell Grants and, depending upon the agreement, other federal aid.

Financial aid to first-time, full-time undergraduate students: 595 received some form of aid.

Departments and Teaching Staff: *Total instructional faculty:* 1,357. Student/faculty ratio: 14:1. Degrees held by full-time faculty: doctorate 45.9%, master's 52.7%, baccalaureate 1.4%.

Enrollment: Total enrollment 18,653. Undergraduate 15,186 (full-time 83%; female 66%, male 34%). Graduate 3,467 (full-time 73%). Undergraduate transfer-in students 513.

International Students: 111 nonresident aliens enrolled fall 2008. Students from Europe, Asia, Latin America, Africa, United States.

Student Life: On-campus residence halls available. *Intercollegiate athletics:* male: baseball, basketball, football, softball, swimming, tennis, track, volleyball; female: basketball, softball, swimming, tennis, track, volleyball. *Special regulations:* Cars permitted in designated areas only. *Special services:* Learning Resources Center, medical services. *Student radio:* Radio station WRCU broadcasts 126 hours per week. *Surrounding community:* Rio Piedras. San Juan, 1 mile from campus, is nearest metropolitan area. Served by airport.

Publications: *Dialogo*, Office of the President.

Library Collections: 4,500,000 volumes. 1,300,000 microforms; 275,000 audiovisual materials; 4,035 current periodical subscriptions. Online catalog. Students have access to online information retrieval services and the Internet.

Most important special holdings include Puerto Rican Collection; Caribbean and Latin American Studies Collection; Zenobia and Juan Ramon Jimenez Collection.

Buildings and Grounds: Campus area 281 acres.

Chief Executive Officer: Gladys Escalana-De Motta, Chancellor.

Address admission inquiries to Director, Office of Admissions.

University of the Sacred Heart

Calle Rosales Esq
San Antonio PDA 26-1/2
Santurce, Puerto Rico 00907
Tel: (787) 728-1515 **E-mail:** admissions@sagrado.edu
Fax: (787) 728-1692 **Internet:** www.sagrado.edu

Institution Description: The University of the Sacred Heart (Universidad del Sagrado Corazon) is a private institution affiliated with the Roman Catholic Church. Classes are conducted in Spanish. *Enrollment:* 4,978. *Degrees awarded:* Associate, baccalaureate, master's. Certificates also awarded.

Accreditation: *Regional:* MSA/CHE.

History: Established as Academy Colegio de Sagrado Corazon 1880; chartered and offered first instruction at postsecondary level 1935; awarded first degree (baccalaureate) 1939; adopted present name 1976.

Institutional Structure: *Governing board:* Board of Trustees. Extrainstitutional representation: 25 trustees. All voting. *Composition of institution:* Academic affairs headed by dean of academic affairs. Management/business/finances directed by dean of administration. Full-time instructional faculty 58 men / 102 women. Academic governance body, Academic Council.

Calendar: Semesters. Academic year Aug. to July. Freshmen admitted Aug., Jan., June, July. Degrees conferred and formal commencement May. Summer session of 2 terms from June to July.

Characteristics of Freshmen: 64% of applicants accepted. 66% of accepted applicants enrolled.

99% of freshmen from Puerto Rico.

Admission: Rolling admissions plan. Apply no later than beginning of term. *Requirements:* Either graduation from accredited secondary school or GED. Minimum 2.5 GPA. *Entrance tests:* College Board SAT. *For transfer students:* 2.5 minimum GPA.

Tutoring available. Noncredit remedial courses offered in summer session and regular academic year.

Degree Requirements: *For all associate degrees:* credit hours vary according to concentrations; 21 credits general education requirements. *For all baccalaureate degrees:* credit hours vary according to concentrations; 60 credits general education requirements. *For all degrees:* 2.1 GPA. *Grading system:* A–F; withdraw (carries time limit; deadline after which pass-fail is appended to withdraw).

Distinctive Educational Programs: Weekend and evening classes. Special facilities for using telecommunications in the classroom. Communication Center, Language Laboratory, Academic Computer Center. Tutorials and service for the vision and audio impaired.

Degrees Conferred: 10 *associate;* 533 *baccalaureate.* Bachelor's degrees awarded in top five disciplines: business and management 121; communications 172; protective services 37; psychology 31; marketing 45. *Master's:* various disciplines 39.

Fees and Other Expenses: *Full-time tuition per academic year 2008–09:* $5,800.

Financial Aid: Aid from institutionally generated funds is provided on the basis of academic merit, financial need. Institution has a Program Participation Agreement with the U.S. Department of Education for eligible students to receive Pell Grants and, depending upon the agreement, other federal aid.

Departments and Teaching Staff: *Total instructional faculty:* 336. Degrees held by full-time faculty: doctorate 27%, master's 71%, baccalaureate 1%. 100% hold terminal degrees.

Enrollment: Total enrollment 4,978.

Characteristics of Student Body: *Ethnic/racial makeup:* Hispanic 100%.

International Students: No financial aid specifically designated for international students.

Student Life: On-campus residence halls house 3% of student body. *Intercollegiate athletics:* both sexes: basketball, cross-country, tennis, table tennis, weight lifting, swimming, track, volleyball. *Special regulations:* Registered cars permitted (one car per student). Curfews. *Special services:* Learning Resources Center, medical services. *Surrounding community:* San Juan metropolitan area population 1,100,000. Served by mass transit bus system.

Library Collections: 130,000 volumes. 49,000 microforms; 10,400 audiovisual materials; 1,525 current periodical subscriptions. Online catalog. Access to online information retrieval services and the Internet.

Most important holdings include collection on Puerto Rico; Foundation Center; audiovisual materials.

Buildings and Grounds: Campus area 33 acres. Campus DVD available.

Chief Executive Officer: Dr. Jose J. Rivera, President. Address admission inquiries to Coordinator of Admissions.

Rhode Island

Brown University

One Prospect Street
Providence, Rhode Island 02912-9127
Tel: (401) 863-1000 **E-mail:** admissions@brown.edu
Fax: (401) 863-3700 **Internet:** www.brown.edu

Institution Description: Brown University is a private, independent, nonprofit institution. *Enrollment:* 8,318. *Degrees awarded:* Baccalaureate, first-professional (medicine), master's, doctorate.

Accreditation: *Regional:* NEASC. *Professional*: engineering, medicine

History: Established and chartered as Rhode Island College 1764; offered first instruction at postsecondary level 1765; awarded first degree (baccalaureate) 1769; adopted present name 1804; merged with Pembroke College and admitted women 1971. *See* Walter C. Bronson, *The History of Brown University* (Providence: Brown University, 1914) for further information.

Institutional Structure: *Governing board:* The Corporation of Brown University. Representation: 42 trustees, including 37 alumni; 12 fellows. All voting. *Composition of institution:* Academic affairs headed by provost and dean of the faculty. Management/business/finances directed by senior vice president. Full-time instructional faculty 687. Academic governance body, University Faculty, meets an average of 8 times per year.

Calendar: Semesters. Academic year Sept. to May. Freshmen admitted Sept., Jan. Degrees conferred and formal commencement May.

Characteristics of Freshmen: 20,833 applicants (female 12,518, male 8,115). 14% of applicants admitted. 55% admitted applicants accepted and enrolled.

92% (1,431 students) submitted SAT scores; 30% (464 students) submitted ACT scores. *25th percentile*: SAT Critical Reading 670, SAT Math 680; AC ACT Composite 27, ACT English 28, ACT math 27. *75th percentile*: SAT Critical Reading 760, SAT Math 770; ACT Composite 33, ACT English 34, ACT Math 34.

93% of entering freshmen expected to graduate within 5 years. 3% 5f freshmen from Rhode Island. Freshmen from 47 states and 47 foreign countries.

Admission: For fall acceptance, apply as early as end of junior year of secondary school, but not later than Jan. 1 of year of enrollment. Students notified of acceptance in April. Apply by Nov. 1 for early decision. Early decision notification Dec. 15. Must limit application to Brown University. *Requirements:* Recommend graduation from accredited secondary school with 4 units in English, 3 in a foreign language, 3 mathematics continued through senior year, 4 sciences (3 in lab), 2 history, additional academic electives. *Entrance tests:* College Board SAT Reasoning and any two SAT Subject Tests. Students may substitute the ACT with the Writing Test. *For transfer students:* must have completed one full year of college. Students who have completed more than two dull years of college should not apply as two full years of attendance at Brown are required for the Brown degree. Students may not transfer into the Program in Liberal Medical Education (PLME) continuum. Deadline for both fall and spring admission Mar. 1.

College credit and advanced placement for postsecondary-level work completed in secondary school.

Tutoring available.

Degree Requirements: 30 course credits; 4 semesters in residence; demonstrated proficiency in writing. Concentration programs have specific graduation requirements. Fulfill the requirement of 32 units of tuition. At least four full-time semester in residence. Fulfillment of some degree requirements and exemption from some beginning courses possible by passing departmental examinations, College Board APP. *Grading system:* A–C, credit/no credit.

Distinctive Educational Programs: *For undergraduates:* combined degree programs, including dual baccalaureate programs in arts and sciences; 4-year baccalaureate and master's program; integrated 5-year baccalaureate and master's program. Interdisciplinary concentration programs in Afro-American studies, American civilization, ancient and medieval culture, ancient studies, applied mathematics-biology, applied mathematics-computer science, applied mathematics-economics, aquatic biology, architectural studies, art-semiotics, biochemistry and molecular biology, biomedical engineering, biomedical ethics, biophysics, cognitive science, community health, computational biology, computer science-mathematics, development studies, East Asian studies, educational studies, engineering-economics, engineering-physics, environmental studies, ethnic studies, geology-physics/mathematics, human biology, medieval studies, neuroscience, Old World archaeology and art, public and private sector organizations, Renaissance and Early Modern Studies, semiotics-French, sexuality and society, South Asian studies, statistics, urban studies. Honors programs. Foreign study programs: Brown offers a wide variety of foreign study opportunities including its own programs in Barbados, Brazil, Czech Republic, Denmark, France, Germany, India, Italy, Japan, Mexico, Spain, Sweden, Tanzania, United Kingdom. There are also ample opportunities to use programs sponsored by other approved American or foreign institutions. *For graduate students:* The Graduate School offers courses leading to six degrees. The Doctor of Philosophy is offered in 44 areas. The Master of either Arts or Science is offered in four areas, and there are programs leading to a Master's of Public Policay and Mastr's of Public Affairs. The Master of Medical Science, although awarded through the Graduate School, is restricted to students enrolled in the Program in Medicine. The Program in Medicine: The 8-year medical continuum, the Program in Liberal Medical Education, provides flexibility in curriculum and planning and an interdisciplinary approach to medical education; it combines undergraduate studies and professional medical studies. *Other distinctive programs:* Cooperative program with Tougaloo College (MS) for faculty and students. Resumed Undergraduate Education program offers credit for students who have interrupted their education for 5 years, or who are 25 years old or older.

ROTC: Army in cooperation with Providence College.

Degrees Conferred: 1,542 *baccalaureate*; 348 *master's*; 186 *doctorate*. Bachelor's degrees awarded in top five disciplines: social sciences 326; biological/life sciences 137; psychology business/markeitng 129; history 102; area and ethnic studies 108. Master's degrees awarded in top five disciplines: social sciences 41; physical sciences 34; Rnglish 34; computer and information sciences 27; biological/life sciences 27. Doctoratews awarded in top five disciplines: social sciences 34; physical sciences 34; biological/life sciences 31; mathematics 23; area and ethnic studties 16. First-professional degrees awar4ded: medicine 89.

Fees and Other Expenses: *Full-time tuition per academic year 2008=09:* $37,718. Contact the school for School of Medicine tuition/fees. *Room and board per academic year:* $10,322. *Books and supplies:* $1,230. *Other expenses:* $1,590.

Financial Aid: Aid from institutionally generated funds is awarded on the basis of financial need.

Financial aid to full-time, first-time undergraduate students: 835 received some form of financial aid. Average amount of aid received: federal grants $3,999; Pell grants $3,109; other federal aid $1,764; state/local aid $912; institutional grants $23,255.

Departments and Teaching Staff: *Total instructional faculty:* 823 (full-time 687, part-time 136). Total faculty with doctorate, first-professional, or other terminal degree: 763. Student/faculty ratio: 9:1. Degrees held by full-time faculty: doctorate 97%, master's: 100%.

Enrollment: Total enrollment 8,318. Undergraduate 8,095 (full-time 96%; female 52%, male 48%). Graduate 2,223 (full-time 94%). Undergraduate transfer-in students 80.

Characteristics of Student Body: *Ethnic/racial makeup (undergraduate):* Black non-Hispanic: 7%; American Indian or Alaska Bative: 1%; Asian or Pacific Islander: 16%; White non-Hispanic: 45%; unknown: 15%; nonresident alien 8%. *Age distribution:* number under 18: 129; 18–19: 2,594; 20–21: 2,562; 22–24: 469; 25–29: 32; 30–34: 8, 35–39: 3; 40–49: 2; 50–64: 2.

International Students: 915 nonresident aliens enrolled fall 2008. Students from Europe, Asia, Latin America, Africa, Canada, Australia, New Zealand, Middle East.

Student Life: The Office of Campus Life and Student Services supports Brown's academic mission by providing students with services and opportunities to enhance intellectual, emotion, social, spiritual, and physical development; developing and implementing programs and policies to enhance campus life; providing assistance and guidance during individual and campus crises. The

Vice President for Campus Life and Student Services overseas all student counseling programs and oversees student health services, health education, student activities, psychological services and student disciplinary procedures as well as access for students with disabilities.

On-campus residence halls house 80% of student body. *Intercollegiate athletics:* male: baseball, basketball, football, ice hockey, lacrosse, soccer, swimming, tennis, track; female: basketball, field hockey, ice hockey, soccer, swimming, tennis, track, volleyball. *Special regulations:* Cars permitted without restriction. *Special services:* Medical services. *Student publications, radio: Brown Daily Herald*, a daily newspaper; *Liber Brunensis*, a yearbook. Radio station WBRU. *Surrounding community:* Providence. Served by mass transit bus system; airport 10 miles from campus; passenger rail service 1 mile from campus.

Library Collections: 3,600,000 volumes including bound books, serial backfiles, electronic documents, and government documents not in separate collections. Online catalog. Current serial subscriptions: 8,912 paper, 155 microform, 11,166 electronic. 71,935 recordings. 175 computer work stations available to library users. Students have access to the Internet at no charge.

Most important special holdings include Harris Collection of American Poetry and Plays (200,000 bound volumes, 30,000 broadsides and leaflets, 300,000 pieces of sheet music, 50,000 manuscripts; includes Walt Whitman Collection and Langdon Collection of Pageants); Lownes History of Science and 7 other related collections; Anne S. K. Brown Military Collection.

Buildings and Grounds: Campus area 143acres.

Chief Executive Officer: Dr. Ruth J. Simmons, President.

Address admission inquiries to Admissions Office or Graduate School.

Bryant University

1150 Douglas Pike
Smithfield, Rhode Island 02917-1291
Tel: (401) 232-6000 **E-mail:** admission@bryant.edu
Fax: (401) 232-6319 **Internet:** www.bryant.edu

Institution Description: Bryant University is a private, independent, nonprofit college. *Enrollment:* 3,800. *Degrees awarded:* Baccalaureate, master's.

Accreditation: *Regional:* NEASC. *Professional*: business

History: Established and chartered as Bryant and Stratton Business College 1863; offered first instruction at postsecondary level 1916; awarded first degree (baccalaureate) 1921; adopted name of Bryant College of Business Administration 1935; became Bryant College 1990; adopted present name status 2004.

Institutional Structure: *Governing board:* Board of Trustees, Bryant University. 37 current members including president ex-officio; 17 alumni. Board bylaws allow for 40 members, including president. *Composition of institution:* Academic affairs headed by vice president of academic affairs; business/finances directed by vice president of business affairs. Administrators 143. Full-time instructional faculty 147, Academic governance body through Dean of Faculty and elected bodies. *Faculty representation:* Faculty served by collective bargaining agent, Bryant Faculty Federation, affiliated with AFT.

Calendar: Semesters. Academic year Aug. to May. Freshmen admitted fall and spring semesters. Degrees conferred and formal commencement May. Two undergraduate summer sessions, one graduate.

Characteristics of Freshmen: 5,649 applicants (female 3,277, male 3,372). 44% of applicants admitted. 35% of applicants admitted and enrolled full-time. 100% (853 students) submitted SAT scores; 18% (152 students) submitted ACT scores. *25th percentile*: SAT Critical Reading 500, SAT Math 540; ACT Composite 21. *75th percentile*: SAT Critical Reading 580, SAT Math 620; ACT Composite 25.

62% entering freshmen expected to graduate within 5 years. 16% of freshmen from Rhode Island. Freshmen from 31 states and 46 foreign countries.

Admission: Rolling admissions plan. Apply by Feb. 1. Early decision closing date Nov. 15. early action. *Requirements:* Either graduation from accredited secondary school with 16 units which normally include 4 English, 4 mathematics (must include a year beyond Algebra II with a preference for precalculus or calculus in the senior year), 3 science (2 units must be lab), 2 foreign language, 2 history/social sciences. GED accepted. *Entrance tests:* College Board SAT Reasoning or ACT required. TOEFL is required of international students. *For transfer students:* 2.5 minimum GPA (3.0 recommended) from 4-year accredited institution 92 hours maximum transfer credit; from 2-year accredited institution 62 hours.

Tutoring available. Noncredit remedial courses offered during regular academic year.

Degree Requirements: *For all baccalaureate degrees:* minimum 123 credit hours (18 to 36 hours in area of concentration); 2.0 GPA;

Fulfillment of some degree requirements and exemption from some beginning courses possible by passing departmental examinations, College Board CLEP, AP. *Grading system:* A–F; withdraw (may carry penalty).

Distinctive Educational Programs: Honors program, directed study programs; Learning for Leadership Program; study abroad; exchange programs; consortia; internships; advanced Placement credit. *Special facilities:* Stanton W. and Elizabeth K.Davis Electronic Classroom, Discovery Lab; Learning/Language Lab; Academic Center for Excellence; Writing Center; John H. Chafee Center for International Business; CV Starr Financial Markets Center; Executive Development Center.

ROTC: Army in cooperation with Providence College.

Degrees Conferred: 724 *baccalaureate*; 167 *master's*. Bachelor's degrees awarded: business/marketing 562; communication, journalism, and related programs 20; computer and information sciences 40; English 3; interdisciplinary studies 6; mathematics 18; psychology 7; social sciences 5; other disciplines 63. Master's degrees awarded: business/marketing 121; computer and information sciences 18; other disciplines 28.

Fees and Other Expenses: *Full-time tuition per academic year 2008–9:* $30,511 undergraduate; contact the university ofr current graduate tuition. *Room and board per academic year:* $11,475. *Books and supplies:* $1,200. *Other expenses:* $1,400.

Financial Aid: Aid from institutionally generated funds is provided on the basis of academic merit, athletic ability, financial eed.

Financial aid to first-time, full-time undergraduate students: 96% received some form of financail aid. Average amount of aid received: federal grants $4,251; Pell grants $2,86f; ohter federal aid $1,393; state/local grants $954; institutional grants $14,498.

Departments and Teaching Staff: *Total instructional faculty:* 283 (full-time 147, part-time 126). Total faculty with doctorate, first-professional, or other terminal degree: 166. Student/faculty ratio: 16:1. Degrees held by full-time faculty: baccalaureate 100%, master's 21%, doctorate 74%, professional 5%. 79% hold terminal degrees.

Enrollment: Total enrollment 3,800. Undergraduate 3,515 (full-time 95%; female 43%, male 51%). Graduate 265 (ful-time 14%). Undergraduate transfer-in students 106.

Characteristics of Student Body: *Ethnic/racial makeup:* Black non-Hispanic: 3%; Asian or Pacific Islander: 3%; Hispanic: 4%; White non-Hispanic: 83%; unknown: 3%; nonresident alien 4%. *Age distribution:* number under 18: 67; 18–19: 1,380; 20–21: 1,158; 22–24: 250; 25–29: 68; 30–34: 36; 35–39: 35; 40–49: 40; 50–64: 13.

International Students: 152 nonresident aliens enrolled fall 2008. Students from Europe, Asia, Latin America, Africa, Canada. No programs available to aid students whose native language is not English. No financial aid specifically designated for international students.

Student Life: On-campus residence halls and townhouses house 81% of undergraduate student body. *Intercollegiate athletics:* male: baseball, basketball, cross-country, football, golf, lacrosse, soccer, tennis, track and field, swimming; female: basketball, cross-country, field hockey, lacrosse, soccer, softball tennis, track and field, swimming, volleyball. *Special regulations:* Cars permitted without restrictions. *Activities available:* 79 organizations including choral groups, dance, theater, pep band, student government, special interest and social services organizations. *Special services:* Medical services. *Student publications, radio: The Archway*, a biweekly newspaper; *The Ledger*, a yearbook. Radio station WJMF. *Surrounding community:* Smithfield population 20,000. Providence, 12 miles from campus, is nearest metropolitan area. Served by airport 30 minutes from campus; passenger rail service 12 miles from campus.

Library Collections: 153,000 volumes. Online catalog. 14,500 microforms; 1,300 audiovisual materials. 30,300 periodicals including via electronic access. Computer work stations available. Students have access to online information retrieval services and the Internet.

Most important special holdings include collections on taxation, entrepreneurship, management, and marketing.

Buildings and Grounds: Campus area 392 acres. Campus DVD available.

Chief Executive Officer: Robert K. Machtley, President. Address undergraduate admission inquiries to TTMichelle Brauregard, Director of Admission; graduate inquiries to Kristopher Sullivan, Director, Graduate Programs.

Johnson and Wales University

8 Abbot Park Place
Providence, Rhode Island 02903-3703
Tel: (401) 598-1000 **E-mail:** admissions@jwu.edu
Fax: (401) 598-2345 **Internet:** www.jwu.edu

Institution Description: Johnson and Wales University is a privately supported university and vocational school with branch campuses in Denver, Colorado; Charlotte, North Carolina; Charleston, South Carolina; North Miami, Florida; Norfolk, Virginia. *Enrollment:* 10,488. *Degrees awarded:* Associate, baccalaureate, master's, doctorate. Certificates also awarded.

JOHNSON AND WALES UNIVERSITY—*cont'd*

Accreditation: *Regional:* NEASC.

History: Established 1914.

Calendar: Trimesters.

Characteristics of Freshmen: 13,617 applicants (female 7,705, male 592). 72% of applicants admitted. 24% of admitted applicants enrolled full-time.

Admission: *Requirements:* Graduation from accredited secondary school or equivalent; non-high school graduates considered.

Degree Requirements: Completion of prescribed curriculum.

ROTC: Army.

Degrees Conferred: 1,455 *associate;* 1,523 *baccalaureate*; 409 *master's*; 37 *doctorate*.

Fees and Other Expenses: *Full-time tuition per academic year 2008–09:* $22.385. *Books and supplies:* $1,000. *Room and board per academic year:* $8,892. *Other exepnses:* $1,250.

Financial Aid: Aid from institutionally generated funds is provided on the basis of academic merit, financial need, other criteria. Institution has a Program Participation Agreement with the U.S. Department of Education for eligible students to receive Pell Grants and, depending upon the agreement, other federal aid.

Financial aid to full-time, first-time undergraduate students: 88% received some form of financial aid. Average amount of aid received: federal grants $3,709; Pell grants $2,824; other federal aid $933; state/local grants $864; institutional grants $7,419.

Departments and Teaching Staff: *Total instructional faculty:* 398 (full-time 278, part-time 120). Student/faculty ratio: 27:1.

Enrollment: Total enrollment 10,488. Undergraduate 9,395 (full-time 91%; female 53%, male 47%). Graduate 1,093 (full-time 84%). Undergraduate transfer-in students 507.

Characteristics of Student Body: *Ethnic/racial makeup:* Black non-Hispanic: 7%; Asian or Pacific Islander: 3%; Hispanic: 7%; White non-Hispanic: 55%; unknown: 22%; nonresident alien 6%.

International Students: 629 nonresident aliens enrolled fall 2008.

Library Collections: 109,000 volumes. 3,800 audiovisual materials; 440,000 microforms; 26,200 periodicals including via electronic accesss. Online catalog. Students have access to the online information retrieval services and the Internet.

Chief Executive Officer: Dr. John Bowen, President.

Address admission inquiries to Director of Admissions.

Providence College

549 River Avenue
Providence, Rhode Island 02918-0002
Tel: (401) 865-1000 **E-mail:** pcadmiss@providence.edu
Fax: (401) 865-2826 **Internet:** www.providence.edu

Institution Description: Providence College is a private college affiliated with the Roman Catholic Church. *Enrollment:* 5,085. *Degrees awarded:* Associate, baccalaureate, master's, doctorate.

Accreditation: *Regional:* NEASC. *Professional*: chemistry, social work

History: Chartered and incorporated 1917; offered first instruction at postsecondary level 1919; awarded first degree (baccalaureate) 1923. *See* "Providence College—50th Anniversary 1919–1969," *Providence Visitor*, 9 Sept. 1969 for further information.

Institutional Structure: *Governing board:* Corporation of Providence College. Representation: 29 trustees including 2 full-time faculty members; 2 students; 1 alumni. 2 ex officio. All voting. *Composition of institution:* Academic affairs headed by vice president for academic administration. Management/business/finances directed by vice president for business affairs. Full-time instructional faculty 295. Academic governance body, Faculty Senate, meets an average of 9 times per year.

Calendar: Semesters. Academic year Sept. to May. Freshmen admitted Sept. Degrees conferred and formal commencement May. Summer session of 1 term from June to July.

Characteristics of Freshmen: 8,044 appliants (5,395 female, 3,549 male). 45% of applicants accepted. 25% of accepted applicants enrolled full-time.

92% (910 students) submitted SAT scores; 3-% (297 students) submitted ACT scores. *25th percentile*: SAT Critical Reading 540, SAT Math 560; ACT Composite 23. *75th percentile*: SAT Critical Reading 690, SAT math 650; ACT Composite 28.

87% of entering freshmen expected to graduate within 5 years. 23% of freshmen from Rhode Island. Freshmen from 49 states and 15 foreign countries.

Admission: For fall acceptance, apply as early as 1 year prior to enrollment, but not later than Feb. 15 of year of enrollment. Students are notified of acceptance in Mar. Apply by Dec. 15 for early decision; need not limit application to Providence College. Early acceptance available. *Requirements:* Either graduation from accredited secondary school or GED. Recommend 4 units in English, 3 in a foreign language, 3 mathematics, 2 social studies, 2 laboratory science, 4 more in subjects which meet requirements for graduation. Additional units in mathematics for some programs. *Entrance tests:* College Board SAT or ACT composite. For foreign students TOEFL. *For transfer students:* From 4-year accredited institution minimum recommended 2.5 GPA; from 2-year accredited institution 3.0 GPA; 56 hours maximum transfer credit.

College credit and advanced placement for postsecondary-level work completed in secondary school. Tutoring available.

Degree Requirements: *For all associate degrees:* 66 credit hours; 1.85 GPA. *For all baccalaureate degrees:* 116 credit hours; 2.0 GPA; 8 semesters in residence; distribution requirements; demonstrated proficiency in English.

Fulfillment of some degree requirements and exemption from some beginning courses possible by passing College Board CLEP, APP. *Grading system:* A–F; pass-fail; withdraw (carries time limit).

Distinctive Educational Programs: *For undergraduates:* Work-experience programs. Dual-degree program in engineering with Columbia University (NY), Washington University (MO). Interdisciplinary programs in humanities, liberal arts, public administration, Western civilization may be individually arranged. Facilities for independent research, including honors programs, individual majors. Study abroad at the University of Fribourg (Switzerland); Oxford University (England); Kansai-Gadai University (Japan). *For graduate students:* Flexible meeting places and schedules, including weekend and evening classes. Directed reading. *Available to all students:* Tutorials. *Other distinctive programs:* Degree-granting continuing education.

ROTC: Army.

Degrees Conferred: 6 *associate*; 984 *baccalaureate*; 208 *master's*. Bachelor's degrees awarded top five disciplines: business, management, marketing, and related support services 244; social sciences 144; education 85; history 63; psychology 56. Master's degrees awarded: business/marketing 54; education 120; history 21; philosopht/religious studies 13.

Fees and Other Expenses: *Full-time tuition per academic year 2008–9:* $31,374 undergraduate; graduate tuition varies by program. *Required fees:* $780. *Room and board per academic year:* $10,810. *Books and supplies:* $800. *Other expenses:* $906.

Financial Aid: Aid from institutionally generated funds is provided on the basis of academic merit, financial need, athletic ability, other criteria.

Financial aid to full-time, first-time undergraduate students: 79% received some form of aid. Average amount of aid received: federal grants $8,231; Pell grants $2,806; other federal aid $3,820; state/local grants $1,104; institutional grants $16,597.

Departments and Teaching Staff: *Total instructional faculty:* 379 (full-time 295, part-time 86). Total faculty with doctorate, first-professional, or other terminal degree: 239. Student/faculty ratio: 13:1. Degrees held by full-time faculty: baccalaureate 100%, master's 6%, doctorate 78%, professional 3%. 86% hold terminal degrees.

Enrollment: Total enrollment 5,085. Undergraduate 4,350 (full-time 89%; female 56%, male 44%). Graduate 735 (full-time 21%). Undergraduate transfer-in students 64.

Characteristics of Student Body: *Ethnic/racial makeup:* Black non-Hispanic: 3%; Asian or Pacific Islander: 2%; Hispanic: 2%; White non-Hispanic: 76%; unknown: 14%; nonresident alien 1%. *Age distribution:* number under 18: 80; 18–19: 1,902; 20–21: 1,861; 22–24: 150; 25–29: 2; 30–34: 2; 35–39: 1. 20% of student body attend summer sessions.

International Students: 31 nonresident aliens enrolled fall 2008. Students from Europe, Asia, Latin America, Aftica, Canada, New Zealnd. No programs available to aid students whose native language is not English. No financial aid specifically designated for international students.

Student Life: On-campus residence halls house 97% of student body. *Intercollegiate athletics:* male: baseball, basketball, cross-country, golf, hockey, lacrosse, soccer, swimming, tennis, track; female: basketball, cross-country, field hockey, ice hockey, softball, swimming, tennis, track. *Special regulations:* Cars permitted without restrictions for all but freshmen. Residence hall visitation from 10am to midnight Sun.–Thurs., 10am to 2am Fri.–Sat. *Special services:* Learning Resource Center, medical services, evening shuttle bus service for off-campus students. *Student publications, radio: Alembic*, a quarterly literary magazine; *The Cowl*, a weekly newspaper; *Veritas*, a yearbook. Radio station WDOM broadcasts 133 hours per week. *Surrounding community:* Boston (MA) 40 miles from campus, passenger rail service 3 miles from campus.

Publications: *Biological Notes* (quarterly) first published in 1976, *INTI* (biannually) first published 1974. *Providence Update* (bimonthly newsletter for alumni and friends).

Library Collections: 369,300 volumes. 156,700 government documents; 212,000 microforms; 1,625 current periodical subscriptions; 25,250 via electronic access. Online catalog. Computer work stations available. Students have access to online information retrieval services and the Internet.

Most important special holdings include John E. Fogarty Papers; John O. Pastore Collection; Rhode Island Constitutional Convention Collections; William R. Bonniwell, O.P. Collections.

Buildings and Grounds: Campus area 105 acres.

Chief Executive Officer: Rev. Brian J. Shanley, O.P., President.

Undergraduates address admission inquiries to Christopher Lyden, Dean of Admissions; graduate inquiries to Dr. Thomas F. Flaherty, Graduate Studies Program.

Rhode Island College

600 Mount Pleasant Avenue
Providence, Rhode Island 02908
Tel: (401) 456-8000 **E-mail:** admissions@ric.edu
Fax: (401) 456-8817 **Internet:** www.ric.edu

Institution Description: Rhode Island College is a state college. *Enrollment:* 9,085. *Degrees awarded:* Baccalaureate, master's.

Academic offerings subject to approval by statewide coordinating bodies. Budget subject to approval by state governing boards.

Accreditation: *Regional:* NEASC. *Professional*: art, music, nursing, social work, teacher education

History: Established as Rhode Island State Normal School 1854; name changed to Rhode Island College of Education and offered first instruction at postsecondary level 1920; awarded first degree (baccalaureate) 1922; adopted present name 1960. *See* Thomas Bicknell, *History of the Rhode Island Normal School* (Providence: Publisher unknown, 1911) for further information.

Institutional Structure: *Governing board:* Rhode Island Board of Governors for Higher Education. Extrainstitutional representation: 13 trustees, 2 legislators. All voting. *Composition of institution:* Administrators 26. Academic affairs headed by vice president for academic affairs. Management/business/finances directed by controller. Full-time instructional faculty 313. Academic governance body, Council of Rhode Island College, meets an average of 10 times per year. *Faculty representation:* Faculty served by collective bargaining agent, Rhode Island College/AFT Local 1819.

Calendar: Semesters. Academic year Aug. to May. Freshmen admitted Sept., Jan. Degrees conferred May, Jan. Formal commencement May, Jan. Summer session of two 6-week sessions from end of May to mid-Aug.

Characteristics of Freshmen: 3.636 applicants (2,373 female, 1,263 male). 72% of applicants accepted. 43% of accepted applicants enrolled full-time.

95% (1,075 students) submitted SAT scores. 4% (50 students) submitted ACT scores. *25th percentile*: SAT Critical Reading 410, SAT Math 410. *75th percentile*: SAT Critical Reading 530, SAT Math 530.

36% of entering freshmen expected to graduate within 5 years. 57% of freshmen from Rhode Island. Freshmen from 24 states and 5 foreign countries.

Admission: Rolling admissions plan. For fall acceptance, apply as early as Sept. 1 of previous year, but not later than May 1. Early acceptance available. *Requirements:* Either graduation from accredited secondary school with 4 units English, 2 foreign language, 3 mathematics, 2 laboratory science, 2 social studies, 6 academic electives; or GED. *Entrance tests:* College Board SAT. *For transfer students:* 2.0 minimum GPA; maximum transfer credit limited only by residence requirement.

College credit and advanced placement for postsecondary-level work completed in secondary school and for extrainstitutional learning basis of portfolio assessment; faculty assessment.

Tutoring available. Developmental courses offered in summer session and regular academic year; credit given.

Degree Requirements: 120 credit hours; 2.0 GPA; 2 terms in residence; exit competency examinations in writing and mathematics.

Fulfillment of some degree requirements and exemption from some beginning courses possible by passing College Board CLEP, AP. *Grading system:* A–F; pass-fail; withdraw (carries time limit); incomplete (deadline after which letter grade is assigned).

Distinctive Educational Programs: *For undergraduates:* Interdisciplinary programs in Black, film, and women's studies. Honors programs. Study abroad by individual arrangement through various agencies. Cross-registration and transfer articulation with the Community College of Rhode Island and the University of Rhode Island. *For graduate students:* Interdisciplinary programs in bilingual-bicultural studies and urban education. *Available to all students:* Work-experience programs, including cooperative education, internships. Weekend and evening classes. Facilities and programs for independent research, including individual majors and tutorials.

ROTC: Army available through Providence College ROTC program.

Degrees Conferred: 1.246 *baccalaureate:* 249 *master's;* 7 *doctorate*. Bachelor's degrees awarded in top five disciplines: education 337; education 357; psychology 158; business, management, marketing, and related support services 148; visucal and performing arts 87; communications/journalism 79. Master's degrees awarded: biological/life sciences 3; business/marketing 8; education 141; English 5; history 2; liveral arts/general studies 3; psychology 69; public administration 72; visual and performing arts 6. Doctrorate awarded: education 7.

Fees and Other Expenses: *Full-time tuition per academic year 2008–9:* undergraduate resident $5,771, nonresident $14,482; contact the college for current graduate tuition/fees. *Required fees:* $814. *Books and supplies:* $900. *Room and board per academic year:* $8,250.

Financial Aid: Aid from institutionally generated funds is provided on the basis of academic merit, financial need, other criteria.

Financial aid to full-time, first-time undergraduate students: 79% received some form of aid. Average amount of aid received: federal grants $4,193; Pell grants $2,911; other federal aid $1,402; state/local aid $132; institutional grants $3,248.

Departments and Teaching Staff: *Total instructional faculty:* 657 (full-time 313, part-time 344). Student/faculty ratio: 16:1. Degrees held by full-time faculty: doctorate: 87%, master's 13%. 90% hold terminal degrees.

Enrollment: Total enrollment 9,085. Undergraduate 7,601 (full-time 72%; female 68%, male 32%). Graduate 1,484 (full-time 18%). Undergraduate transfer-in students 617.

Characteristics of Student Body: *Ethnic/racial makeup:* Black non-Hispanic: 6%; Asian or Pacific Islander: 2%; Hispanic: 7%; White non-Hispanic: 71%; unknown 3%. *Age distribution:* number under 18: 212; 18–19: 2,941; 20–21: 21,870; 22–24: 1,593; 25–29: 773; 30–34: 351; 35–39: 254; 40–49: 359; 50–64: 93; 65 and over 3; unknown 29.

International Students: 36 undergraduate nonresident aliens enrolled fall 2008. No programs available to aid students whose native language is not English: No financial aid specifically designated for international students.

Student Life: On-campus residence halls house 12% of student body. *Intercollegiate athletics:* male: baseball, basketball, cross-country, soccer, tennis, track and field, wrestling; female: basketball, cross-country, gymnastics, softball, tennis, track and field, volleyball. *Special regulations:* Cars with decals permitted without restriction. *Special services:* Medical services. *Student publications, radio: The Anchor*, a weekly newspaper; *Exodus*, a yearbook. Radio station WRIC broadcasts 60 hours per week. *Surrounding community:* Providence population 160,000. Boston, 40 miles from campus, is nearest metropolitan area. Served by mass transit system, airport 10 miles from campus, passenger rail service 3 miles from campus.

Library Collections: 645,500 volumes. 1,322,500 microforms; 3,500 audiovisual materials Current serial subscriptions: paper 857; via electronic access: 1,468. Online catalog. Students have access to the Internet and online information retrieval services.

Most important special holdings include Nathaniel T. Bacon Collection (papers of the Pulitzer Prize winning poet Leonard Bacon); Amy Thompson Collection (a selection of early children's books); Charles R. Gross Collection (material of a physician who was the historian of the Black community in Rhode Island).

Buildings and Grounds: Campus area 170 acres.

Chief Executive Officer: Dr. John Nazarian, President.

Undergraduates address admission inquiries Holly Shadoian, Director of Admissions; graduate inquiries to James Turley, Dean of Graduate Studies.

Rhode Island School of Design

2 College Street
Providence, Rhode Island 02903
Tel: (401) 454-6100 **E-mail:** admissions@risd.edu
Fax: (401) 454-6320 **Internet:** www.risd.edu

Institution Description: Rhode Island School of Design is a private, independent, nonprofit institution. *Enrollment:* 2,352. *Degrees awarded:* Baccalaureate, master's.

Accreditation: *Regional:* NEASC. *Professional*: architecture, interior design, landscape architecture

History: Established and chartered 1877; offered first instruction at postsecondary level 1932; awarded first degree (baccalaureate) 1937. *See* Lorraine Hopkins, "RISD Centennial," *The Providence Journal* (special sections), March 20, 1977, 56 pp., for further information.

Institutional Structure: *Governing board:* Board of Trustees. Representation: 42 members, including 6 alumni and president of the institution. 6 ex officio. All voting. *Composition of institution:* Administrators 21. Academic affairs headed by vice president for academic affairs. Management/business/finances directed by vice president for budget and control. Full-time instructional faculty 139. Academic governance body, College Council, meets an average of 6 times

RHODE ISLAND SCHOOL OF DESIGN—*cont'd*

per year. *Faculty representation:* Faculty served by collective bargaining agent affiliated with NEA.

Calendar: Semesters. Academic year Sept. to May. Freshmen admitted Sept. Degrees conferred and formal commencement May.

Characteristics of Freshmen: 3,148 applicatns (female 2,203, male 945). 29% of applicants accepted. 47% of accepted applicants enrolled full-time.

92% (408 students) submitted SAT scores. 8% (36 students) submitted ACT scores. *25th percentile*: SAT Critical Reading 530, SAT Math 570; *75th percentile*: SAT Crictical Reading 650, SAT Math 680.

85% of entering freshmen expected to graduate within 5 years. 6% of freshmen from Rhode Island. Freshmen from 39 states.

Admission: Two deadlines: early action Dec. 15 with notification in last week of Jan.; regular deadline of Feb. 15 with notification Apr. 1. *Requirements:* Either graduation from accredited secondary school or GED. Portfolio required for most programs. For architecture students, additional academic requirements. Minimum GPA 2.0. *Entrance tests:* College Board SAT or ACT composite. *For transfer students:* 2.0 minimum GPA; maximum transfer credit limited only by residence requirement.

Tutoring available. Remedial courses offered during regular academic year; credit given.

Degree Requirements: 126 credit hours; 2.0 GPA; 4 terms in residence; distribution requirements; degree project. *Grading system:* A–F (descriptive reports may be attached); withdraw (carries time limit).

Distinctive Educational Programs: *For undergraduates:* Internships. Institutionally sponsored study abroad in Italy; study abroad also available by individual arrangement. *Available to all students:* Special facilities for using telecommunications in the classroom. Facilities and programs for independent research, including honors programs, individual majors. Cross-registration with Brown University. European Honors Program, Piazza Cenci, Rome, Italy. *Other distinctive programs:* Continuing Education.

Degrees Conferred: 580 *baccalaureate*; 161 *master's*. Bachelors' degrees awarded in top disciplines: visual and performing arts 354; architecture 90; family and consumer sciences 37; precision production 19. Master's degrees awarded: various disciplines: 161.

Fees and Other Expenses: *Full-time tuition per academic year 2008–9:* $34,925. *Room and board per academic year:* $10,260. *Books and supplies* $260. *Other expenses:* $3,475.

Financial Aid: Aid from institutionally generated funds is provided on the basis of academic merit, financial need.

Financial aid to full-time, first-time undergraduate students: 50% received some form of financial aid. Average amount of aid received: federal grants $2,945; Pell grants $3,048; state/local grants $1,033; institutional grants $13,102.

Departments and Teaching Staff: *Total instructional faculty:* 342. Student/faculty ratio: 11:1.

Enrollment: Total enrollment 2,352. Undergraduate 1,926 (full-time 100%; femlae 68%, male 32%). Gradaute 426 (full-time 100%). Undergraduate transfer-in students 85.

Characteristics of Student Body: *Ethnic/racial makeup:* Black non-Hispanic: 4%; Asian or Pacific Islander: 14%; Hispanic: 2%; White non-Hispanic: 38%; unknown: 22%; nonresident alien 16%.

International Students: 285 nonresident aliens enrolled fall 2008. Programs available to aid students whose native language is not English: English as a Second Language Program. No financial aid specifically designated for international students.

Student Life: On-campus residence halls available to 33% of the student body. *Special regulations:* No cars permitted on campus for any student. *Special services:* Learning Resources Center, medical services, campus transportation system. *Student publications: RISD Voice*, a biweekly newspaper. *Surrounding community:* Providence population 160,000. Boston (MA), 35 miles from campus, is nearest metropolitan area. Served by mass transit bus system; airport 10 miles from campus; passenger rail service .5 mile from campus.

Publications: *Museum Notes* (annually) first published 1943.

Library Collections: 120,500 volumes including bound books, serial backfiles, electronic documents, and government documents not in separate collections. Online catalog. 1,900 miocrosorms; 2,100 audiovisual materials; 500 Current serial subscriptions. Computer work stations available. Students have access to the Internet at no charge.

Most important special collections include 900 volumes of artist's books; Lowthorope Collection on Landscape Architecture; picture collection of 463,000 clippings.

Buildings and Grounds: Campus area 13 acres.

Chief Executive Officer: Dr. E. Roger Mandle, President.

Address admission inquiries to Edward Newhall, Director of Admissions.

Roger Williams University

One Old Ferry Road
Bristol, Rhode Island 02809-2921
Tel: (401) 253-1040 **E-mail:** admit@rwu.edu
Fax: (401) 254-3599 **Internet:** www.rwu.edu

Institution Description: Roger Williams University is a private, independent, nonprofit college. *Enrollment:* 4,609. *Degrees awarded:* Associate, baccalaureate, first-professional (law).

Accreditation: *Regional:* NEASC. *Professional*: architecture, business, chemistry, construction technology, engineering, law, teacher education

History: Established as junior college, offered first instruction at postsecondary level, and awarded first degree (associate) 1948; incorporated 1956; became a 4-year college 1967; established Rhode Island's first and only School of Law in 1993.

Institutional Structure: *Governing board:* Board of Trustees. Extrainstitutional representation: 16 trustees; institutional representation: president of the institution; 2 alumni. All voting. *Composition of institution:* Administrators 63. Academic affairs headed by vice president divided into 7 schools each with a dean (business, justice studies, education, engineering, arts and sciences, business, architecture, university college). Full-time instructional faculty 182. *Faculty representation:* Collective bargaining agreement with NEA.

Calendar: Semesters. Academic year Sept. to May. Freshmen admitted Sept., Jan., Feb., June. Degrees conferred and formal commencement May. Summer session of 2 terms from May to Aug.

Characteristics of Freshmen: 8,561 applicants (4,645 female, 3,918 male). 61% of applicants admitted. 18% of applicants admitted and enrolled full-time.

86% (898 students) submitted SAT scores; 20% (194 students) submitted ACT scores. *25th percentile*: SAT Critical Reading 490, SAT Math 510; ACT Composite 21. *75th percentile*: SAT Critical Reading 570, SAT math 600; ACT Composite 25..

52% of entering freshmen expected to graduate within 5 years. 18% of freshmen from Rhode Island. Freshmen from 39 states and 42 foreign countries.

Admission: Rolling admissions plan. For fall acceptance, apply as early as end of junior year in secondary school, but preferably no later than Feb. 1 of senior year. Apply prior to Nov. 1 of senior year for early decision; must limit application to Roger Williams. Early acceptance Nov. 15. *Requirements:* Either graduation from accredited secondary school or GED. Recommend 4 units English, 3 social science, 3 mathematics, 3 science. Additional units recommended for some programs. Minimum 2.0 GPA. *For transfer students:* 2.5 minimum GPA; from 4-year accredited institution 75 hours maximum transfer credit; from 2-year accredited institution and for extension students 60 hours. Student must complete a minimum of 45 credit hours at Roger Williams University to earn a bachelor's degree.

College credit for postsecondary-level work completed in secondary school. College credit for extrainstitutional learning on basis of portfolio and faculty assessments.

Tutoring available. Developmental/remedial courses offered during regular academic year; credit given.

Degree Requirements: *For all associate degrees:* 60 semester credit hours; 2 terms in residence. *For all baccalaureate degrees:* 150 semester credit hours for architecture; 120 semester credit hours for other majors; 2 terms in residence. *For all degrees:* 2.0 GPA; general education requirements. Minimum of 30 credits in major, university core curriculum requirements, Service Learning requirement, complete 45 of the last 60 credits in residence or a Roger Williams University Semester Abroad Program.

Fulfillment of some degree requirements and exemption from some beginning courses possible by passing institutional examinations. *Grading system:* A–F; pass; no credit; withdraw; incomplete.

Distinctive Educational Programs: Work-experience programs, including cooperative education and internships. Flexible meeting places and schedules, including off-campus centers (at Providence, 20 miles away from main institution; at Newport, 20 miles away), and evening classes. Accelerated degree programs. Special facilities for using telecommunications in the classroom. Interdisciplinary program in urban and environmental planning. Facilities and programs for independent research, including individual majors, tutorials. *Other distinctive programs:* Continuing education program in Providence through Evening Division. Study abroad: London Theatre Program; Law in London; Humanities in Greece; Great Cities in History (London, Jerusalem, Paris); Biology in Jamaica; Great Cities Program: England, Belgium, and Holland; Historic Preservation in London; Architecture Program in Prague.

ROTC: Army.

Degrees Conferred: 14 *associate;* 871 *baccalaureate*; 80 *master's*. Bachelor's degrees awarded in top five disciplines: business, management, marketing, and related support services 1,660; security and protective services 120; architecture 80; psychology 78; biological/life sciences 45. Master's degrees awarded: architecture 11; engineering 48; security and protective services 25.

Fees and Other Expenses: *Full-time tuition per academic year 2008–9:* undergraduate $27,718; graduate/first-professional costs vary by program (contact the university for current information). *Required fees:* $1,140. *Room and board per academic year:* $12,140. *Books and supplies:* $900. *Other expenses:* $1,581.

Financial Aid: Aid from institutionally generated funds is provided on the basis of academic merit, financial need.

Financial aid to full-time, first-time undergraduate students: 78% received some form of aid. Average amount of aid received: federal grants $4,418; Pell grants $3,090; other federal aid $2,047; state/local grants $1,045; institutional grants $9,889.

Departments and Teaching Staff: *Total instructional faculty:* 465 (full-time 182, paart-time 283). Total faculty with doctorate, first-professional, or other terminal degree: 217. Student/faculty ratio: 15:1.

Enrollment: Total enrollment 4,609. Undergraduate 4,345 (full-time 89%; female 48%, male 52%). Graduate 264 (full-time 36%). Undergraduate transfer-in students 177.

Characteristics of Student Body: *Ethnic/racial makeup:* Black non-Hispanic: 2%; Asian or Pacific Islander: 1%; Hispanic: 2%; White non-Hispanic: 73%; unknown: 19%; nonresident alien 2%. *Age distribution:* number under 18: 97; 18–19: 1,849; 20–21: 1,190; 22–24: 561; 25–29: 109; 30–34: 103; 35–39: 106; 40–49: 175; 50–64: 50; 65 and over: 3.

International Students: 92 undergraduate nonresident aliens enrolled fall 2008. Students from Europe, Asia, Latin America, Africa, Canada, Middle East. Programs available to aid students whose native language is not English: social, cultural. English as a Second Language Program. Financial aid specifically designated for international students: scholarships available annually for undergraduate students.

Student Life: On-campus residence halls house 65% of full-time student body. *Intercollegiate athletics:* male: baseball, basketball, cross-country, lacrosse, tennis, wrestling and soccer; female: basketball, cross-country, soccer, softball, tennis, volleyball; both sexes: sailing, equestrian. Club sports include crew, track and field; men's rugby, volleyball, cheerleading. *Special regulations:* Cars allowed in designated parking areas. *Special services:* health services, Women's Center; Center for Academic Development. Student radio station WQRI broadcasts 168 hours per week. *Surrounding community:* Bristol population 21,000. Providence, 20 miles from campus, is nearest metropolitan area.

Library Collections: 216,500 volumes. Online catalog. Current serial subscriptions: paper 1,002; microform 156; via electronic access 12,164. Students have access to online information retrieval services and the Internet.

Most important special holdings include Rhode Island Collection; architecture collection; university archives; backfiles of *Bristol Phoenix* (local newspaper).

Buildings and Grounds: Campus area 140 acres.

Chief Executive Officer: Dr. Roy J. Nirschel, President.

Address admission inquiries to Didier Bouvdet, Director of Freshman Admissions; graduate inquiries Suzanne Faubl, Director of Graduate Programs; School of Law inquiries to Director of Admissions.

Salve Regina University

100 Ochre Point Avenue
Newport, Rhode Island 02840-4192
Tel: (401) 847-6650 **E-mail:** sruadmis@salve.edu
Fax: (401) 848-2823 **Internet:** www.salve.edu

Institution Description: Salve Regina University is a private institution affiliated with the Sisters of Mercy, Roman Catholic Church. *Enrollment:* 2,693. *Degrees awarded:* Associate, baccalaureate, master's, doctorate.

Accreditation: *Regional:* NEASC. *Professional*: art, nursing, social work

History: Incorporated 1934; offered first instruction at postsecondary level 1947; awarded first degree (baccalaureate) 1951.

Institutional Structure: *Composition of institution:* Academic affairs headed by vice president/dean of faculty. Management/business/finances directed by executive vice president. Full-time instructional faculty 107.

Calendar: Semesters. Academic year Sept. to May.

Characteristics of Freshmen: 5,952 applicants (4,120 female, 1,832 male). 59% of applicants accepted. 16% of accepted applicants enrolled full-time.

84% (467 students) submitted SAT scores; 16% (90 students) submitted ACT scores. *25th percentile*: SAT Critical Readiong 500, SAT Math 510, SAT Writing 510; ACT Composite 21, ACT English 26, ACT Math 20. *75th percentile*: SAT Critical Reading 590, SAT Math 680, SAT Writing 600; ACT Composite 25, ACT English 24, ACT Math 25.

58% of entering freshmen expected to graduate within 5 years. 15% of freshmen from Rhode Island. Freshmen from 39 states and 12 foreign countries.

Admission: Early acceptance available. *Requirements:* Graduation from secondary school. *For transfer students:* Transfer credit varies.

College credit and advanced placement for postsecondary-level work completed in secondary school. College credit for extrainstitutional learning on basis of nontraditional study, military experiences, CLEP, and departmental examinations.

Tutoring available.

Degree Requirements: *For all baccalaureate degrees:* 128 credit hours; 2.0 GPA; 36 hours in residence; general education requirements.

Fulfillment of some degree requirements and exemption from some beginning courses possible by passing departmental examinations, College Board CLEP, AP. *Grading system:* A–F.

Degrees Conferred: 474 *baccalaureate*; 137 *master's*; 5 *doctorate*; Bachelor's degrees awarded in top five disciplines: business, management, marketing, and related support services 80; education 72; security and protective services 37; English language/literature 28; psychology 27. Master's degrees awarded: various disciplines 137. Doctoates awarded: liberal arts 5.

Fees and Other Expenses: *Full-time tuition per academic year 2008–9:* $29,150. *Room and board per academic year:* $10,700. *Other expenses:* $1,800. Contact the university for graduate tuition and fees.

Financial Aid: Aid from institutionally generated funds is provided on the basis of academic merit, financial need.

Financial aid to full-time, first-time undergraduate students: 81% received some form of financial aid. Average amount of aid received: federal grants $4,263; Pell grants $2,800; other federal aid $1,965; state/local grants $872; institutional grants $13,464.

Departments and Teaching Staff: *Total instructional faculty:* 194. Student/faculty ratio: 14:1. Degrees held by full-time faculty: doctorate 69%, master's 51%. 65% hold terminal degrees.

Enrollment: Total enrollment 2,693. Undergraduate 2,130 (full-time 94%; female 69%' male 31%). Graduate 563 (full-time 21%). Undergraduate transfer-in students 50.

Characteristics of Student Body: *Ethnic/racial makeup:* Black non-Hispanic: 1%; Asian or Pacific Islander: 1%; Hispanic: 3%; White non-Hispanic: 78%; unknown: 16%; nonresident alien 1%.

International Students: 27 nonresident aliens enrolled fall 2008. Programs available to aid students whose native language is not English: English as a Second Language Program. No financial aid specifically designated for international students.

Student Life: On-campus housing available. *Intercollegiate athletics:* Member of NCAA Division III and offers varsity athletic programs for males and females in basketball, cross-country, golf, indoor/outdoor track and field, soccer, tennis. Male baseball, football, ice hockey; female field hockey, softball, and lacrosse. *Special services:* Tutoring, medical services. *Surrounding community:* Newport population 30,000. Providence, 40 miles from campus, is nearest metropolitan area.

Publications: *Mosaic* magazine; academic advising handbook; undergraduate catalog; student handbook; student newspaper.

Library Collections: 139,200 volumes. U.S. Government Documents Depository Library. 43,200 microforms; 19,500 audiovisual materials; 1,050 current periodical subscriptions. Online catalog. Students have access to online information retrieval services and the Internet.

Buildings and Grounds: Campus area 68 acres. Campus DVD available.

Chief Executive Officer: M. Theresa Anton, R.S.M., President.

Address admission inquiries to Dean of Enrollment Management.

University of Rhode Island

14 Upper College Road
Kingston, Rhode Island 02881
Tel: (401) 874-1000 **E-mail:** uriadmit@uri.edu
Fax: (401) 874-5523 **Internet:** www.uri.edu

Institution Description: The University of Rhode Island is a state institution and land-grant college with Narragansett Bay and W. Alton Jones campuses. *Enrollment:* 15,904. *Degrees awarded:* Associate, baccalaureate, first-professional (pharmacy), master's, doctorate.

Academic offerings subject to approval by statewide coordinating bodies. Budget subject to approval by state governing board.

Accreditation: *Regional:* NEASC. *Professional*: accounting, audiology, business, clinical psychology, computer science, dental hygiene, dietetics, engineering, landscape architecture, librarianship, marriage and family therapy, nursing-midwifery, music, nursing, nursing education, pharmacy, physical therapy, planning, school psychology, speech-language pathology, teacher education

UNIVERSITY OF RHODE ISLAND—*cont'd*

History: Established and chartered as State Agricultural School 1888; offered first instruction at postsecondary level as Rhode Island College of Agriculture and Mechanic Arts 1892; awarded first degree (baccalaureate) 1894; changed name to Rhode Island State College 1909; adopted present name 1951. *See* Herman Eschenbacher, *University of Rhode Island* (New York: Appleton Century Crofts, 1967) for further information.

Institutional Structure: *Governing board:* Board of Governors for Higher Education. Representation: 13 members (appointed by governor of Rhode Island), chairman of Board of Regents for Elementary and Secondary Education, chairmen of state House and Senate finance committees. 3 ex officio. All voting. *Composition of institution:* Administrators 130. Academic affairs headed by provost and vice president for academic affairs. Management/business/finances directed by vice president for business and finance. Full-time instructional faculty 574. Academic governance body, Faculty Senate, meets an average of 16 times per year. *Faculty representation:* Faculty served by collective bargaining agent affiliated with AAUP.

Calendar: Semesters. Academic year Sept. to May. Freshmen admitted Sept., Jan. Degrees conferred May, Aug., Dec. Formal commencement May. Summer session from May to July.

Characteristics of Freshmen: 15,658 applicants (9,412 female, 6,244 male). 82% of applicants accepted. 24% of accepted applicants enrolled full-time. 96% (2,926 students) submitted SAT scores. 13% (398 students) submitted ACT scores. *25th percentile*: SAT Critical Reading 490, SAT Math 510. *75th percentile*: SAT Critical Reading 585, SAT Math 610.

61% of freshmen from Rhode Island. Freshmen from 50 states and 54 foreign countries.

Admission: Rolling admissions plan. For fall acceptance, apply as early as Sept. 15 of previous year, but not later than Mar. 1 of year of enrollment. Apply by Nov. 1 for early decision; need not limit application to University of Rhode Island. Early acceptance available. *Requirements:* Either graduation from accredited secondary school with 18 college preparatory units which must include 4 English, 3 college preparatory mathematics, 2 each of science, foreign language, and history or social studies, 5 academic electives; or GED. Additional requirements for some programs. *Entrance tests:* College Board SAT or ACT required. For foreign students TOEFL. *For transfer students:* 90 hours maximum transfer credit. Transfer students must submit transcripts from all colleges or universities attended whether or not credit is desired. Their high school record must also be submitted. A minimum GPA of 2.5 is required. Many programs require higher GPAs.

College credit and advanced placement for postsecondary-level work completed in secondary school and for extrainstitutional learning on basis of assessment by dean of college.

Degree Requirements: *For all associate degrees:* 71–72 hours; 1–2 years in residence. *For all baccalaureate degrees:* 120–161 hours; final year in residence. *For all undergraduate degrees:* 2.0 GPA; general education requirements.

Fulfillment of some degree requirements possible by passing departmental examinations, College Board CLEP. *Grading system:* A–F; pass-fail; withdraw; satisfactory-unsatisfactory; incomplete.

Distinctive Educational Programs: Flexible meeting places and schedules, including continuing education centers (at various locations throughout Rhode Island), weekend and evening classes. Accelerated degree programs. Cooperative program in medicine with Brown University. Special facilities for using telecommunications in the classroom. Facilities and programs for independent research, including honors programs and individual majors. Individually arranged study abroad. The University sponsors exchange programs with the University of Orleans, France; University of Hohneheim, Germany; Seinan Gakuin University, Japan; and the University of East Anglia and Oxford Polytechnic, England. The University is also an active participant in the New England/Quebec Exchange Program, a consortium of the land-grant universities of the region and the ten English and French-speaking universities of Quebec. Through another regional consortium, the University also sponsors study programs in Florence, Italy, Granada, Spain; and an international business program in Grenoble, France. *Other distinctive programs:* New England Regional Student Program admits students from other New England states to certain curricula at University of Rhode Island at reduced cost. Participation in the National Student Exchange Program with state institutions of higher education.

ROTC: Army.

Degrees Conferred: 2,201 *baccalaureate;* 481 *master's*; 68 *doctorate*; *first-professional:* 87. Bachelor's degrees awarded in top five disciplines: business, management, marketing, and related support services 339; communication, journalism, and related programs 240; social sciences and history 194; engineering/engineering technologies 169; education 157. Master's degrees awarded: various disiplines 481. Doctorates awarded: various disciplines 68. First-professional degrees awarded: pharmacy 87.

Fees and Other Expenses: *Full-time tuition per academic year 2008–9:* undergraduate resident $8,678, nonresident $24,716; contact the university for graduate and pharmacy school tuition and fees. *Required fees:* $2,068. *Books and supplies:* $1,200. *Room and board per academic year:* $9,342. *Other expenses:* $1,548.

Financial Aid: Aid from institutionally generated funds is provided on the basis of academic merit, financial need, athletic ability, other criteria. Institution has a Program Participation Agreement with the U.S. Department of Education for eligible students to receive Pell Grants and, depending upon the agreement, other federal aid.

Financial aid to full-time, first-time undergraduate students: Average amount of aid received: federal grants $2,870; Pell grants $2,956; other federal aid $2,526; state/local grants $9,342; institutional grants $1,548.

Departments and Teaching Staff: *Total instructional faculty:* 706 (full-time 674, part-time 32). 91% hold terminal degrees.

Enrollment: Total enrollment 15,904. Undergraduate 12,793 (full-time 88%; female 56%, male 44%). Graduate 3,111 (full-time 51%). Undergraduate transfer-in students 410.

Characteristics of Student Body: *Ethnic/racial makeup:* Black non-Hispanic: 5%; Asia or Pacific Islander: 3%; Hispanic: 5%; White non-Hispanic 73%; unknown 14%;.

International Students: 32 undergraduate nonresident aliens enrolled fall 2008. Programs available to aid students whose native language is not English: social, cultural. English as a Second Language Program. Financial aid specifically designated for international students: scholarships available annually for qualifying undergraduate students.

Student Life: On-campus residence halls number 19, including 2 all-freshmen halls, 1 wellness hall. Housing for 3,400 undergraduates; graduate housing (apartments) is available. *Intercollegiate athletics:* male: baseball, basketball, football, tennis, track and field, cross-country, swimming, soccer; female: basketball, volleyball, gymnastics, field hockey, soccer, softball, swimming, track and field, cross-country, tennis. *Special regulations:* Cars permitted. *Special services:* Counseling, Learning Assistance Center, Health Services, speech and hearing testing, University Chaplains. *Student publications, radio:* Yearbook, *Good 5 Cent Cigar* (student newspaper), literary magazines yearbook, Student Handbook. Radio station WRIU-FM broadcasts 7 days per week. *Surrounding community:* South Kingston population 22,000. Providence, 35 miles from campus, is nearest metropolitan area. Served by mass transit bus system, airport 28 miles from campus, passenger rail service (AMTRAK) 2 miles from campus.

Publications: *American Transcendental Quarterly*, first published at Trinity College (CT) 1969, first published at University of Rhode Island 1978. Member of University Press of New England.

Library Collections: 1,300,000 books, serial backfiles, government documents. 7,966 current serials (titles); 1,655,100 microform units; 11,670 audiovisual units. Online catalog. Students have access to online information retrieval services and the Internet.

Most important special holdings include Marine Sciences (books and journals); Rhode Island political figures (personal papers); fine printing; American poetry.

Buildings and Grounds: Urban campus.

Chief Executive Officer: Dr. Robert L. Carothers, President.

Address admission inquiries to David Taggert, Dean of Admissions and Financial Aid.

College of Arts and Sciences

Degree Programs Offered: *Associate* in science; *baccalaureate* in anthropology, art, biological sciences, computer science, dental hygiene, economics, English, geography and marine affairs, geology, history, journalism, languages, Latin American studies, linguistics, mathematics, medical technology, military science, music, philosophy, physics, political science, psychology, sociology, speech communications, theater. Urban affairs and women's studies; *master's, doctorate* in various fields.

Distinctive Educational Programs: Programs in Latin American studies, marine affairs, medical technology, urban affairs, women's studies.

College of Business Administration

Degree Programs Offered: *Baccalaureate* in accounting, business education, finance, general business administration, insurance management, management information systems, management science, marketing, official administration, production and operations management, urban affairs; *master's, doctorate* in business administration.

Distinctive Educational Programs: Interdepartmental doctoral program in applied mathematical sciences. Bureau of Government Research provides research, consulting, and training in public administration. Research Center in

Business and Economics initiates, conducts, and services faculty research activities.

College of Engineering

Degree Programs Offered: *Baccalaureate* in chemical, chemical and ocean, civil, computer electronics, electrical, industrial, mechanical engineering; *master's* in chemical, civil, electrical, mechanical and ocean engineering.

Distinctive Educational Programs: Research facilities in the fields of chemical, civil, electrical, industrial, mechanical, materials, nuclear, environmental, and ocean engineering. Marine research in cooperation with Graduate School of Oceanography and College of Arts and Sciences, Pharmacy Resource Development.

College of Human Science and Services

Degree Programs Offered: *Baccalaureate* in communicative disorders, consumer affairs, elementary and secondary education; home economics; human development and family studies; human science and services; physical education, health and recreation; textiles, fashion merchandising, and design; textile marketing; *master's* in various fields.

Distinctive Educational Programs: Interdisciplinary programs in consumer affairs, general home economics, gerontology, special populations. Curriculum Research and Development Center conducts sponsored research in the field of education. Institute of Human Science and Services promotes activities in human service areas across all departments of the college.

College of Nursing

Degree Programs Offered: *Baccalaureate, master's* and *doctorate* in nursing.

Degree Requirements: *For baccalaureate:* 128 credits and C or better in major courses. *For master's:* 36-39 credits. *For doctorate:* 43 credits of post-master's courses and dissertation.

College of Pharmacy

Degree Programs Offered: *Baccalaureate* in respiratory therapy; *first-professional* in pharmacy, Doctor of Pharmacy; *master's* in pharmacy administration; *master's, doctorate* in pharmacognosy, pharmacology and toxicology, pharmaceutics.

Degree Requirements: *For first-professional:* 161 credit hours, 2.0 GPA, last year in residence.

Distinctive Educational Programs: Interdisciplinary master's program in environmental health.

College of Resource Development

Degree Programs Offered: *Baccalaureate* in animal science and technology, aquaculture and fishery technology, food science and nutrition, natural resources, plant science and technology, urban affairs; *master's* and *doctorate* in various fields.

Distinctive Educational Programs: Agricultural Experiment Station for investigation in natural and human resources. Cooperative Extension Service provides educational resources throughout Rhode Island. International Center for Marine Resource Development and the Consortium for the Development of Technology provide assistance to foreign countries.

Graduate Library School

Degree Programs Offered: *Master's.*

Distinctive Educational Programs: Dual master's degree in history and library science.

Graduate School of Oceanography

Degree Programs Offered: *Master's, doctorate* in biological, chemical, geological, and physical oceanography.

Distinctive Educational Programs: Research aboard oceangoing vessels. Bay campus shore facilities include Clairborne Pell Marine Science Library, research aquarium, engineering wave tank.

South Carolina

Allen University

1530 Harden Street
Columbia, South Carolina 29204
Tel: (803) 254-4165 **E-mail:** info@allenuniversity.edu
Fax: (803) 376-5709 **Internet:** www.allenuniversity.edu

Institution Description: Allen University is a four-year, coeducational institution of the African Methodist Episcopal Church. *Enrollment:* 725. *Degrees offered:* Baccalaureate.

Accreditation: *Regional:* SACS-Comm. on Coll.

History: The university was founded in 1870.

Calendar: Semesters. Academic year Sept. to May.

Characteristics of Freshmen: 100% of applicants accepted. 85% of accepted applicants enrolled.

Admission: Open admissions. *Requirements:* High school graduation.

College credit and advanced placement for postsecondary-level work completed in secondary school and for extrainstitutional learning. Developmental/remedial courses offered in summer session and regular academic year; credit given.

Degree Requirements: *For all undergraduate degrees:* 128 semester hours. Internship; senior project. *Grading system:* A–F.

Fees and Other Expenses: *Full-time tuition per academic year 2008–09:* $7,884. *Room and board per academic year:* $5,254. *Books and supplies:* $800.

Financial Aid: Aid from institutionally generated funds is provided on the basis of academic merit, financial need. Institution has a Program Participation Agreement with the U.S. Department of Education for eligible students to receive Pell Grants and, depending upon the agreement, other federal aid.

Financial aid to full-time, first-time undergraduate students: 96% received some form of financial aid. Average amount of aid received: federal grants $5,780; Pell grants $2,590; state/local grants $3,100; institutional grants $247.

Departments and Teaching Staff: *Total instructional faculty:* 17. Student/faculty ratio: 20:1.

Enrollment: Total enrollment 725. Undergraduate 99%; female 54%, male 48%.

Characteristics of Student Body: *Ethnic/racial makeup:* Black non-Hispanic: 83%; Hispanic: 1%; unknown: 16%.

International Students: No programs available to aid students whose native language is not English. No financial aid specifically designated for international students.

Student Life: Coed housing available. Students permitted to live off-campus.

Library Collections: 53,000 volumes. 175 current periodical subscriptions. Students have access to online information retrieval services and the Internet.

Chief Executive Officer: Dr. Charles E. Young, President.

Address admissions inquiries to Jason Darby, Director of Admissions.

Anderson College

316 Boulevard
Anderson, South Carolina 29621
Tel: (864) 231-2000 **E-mail:** admissions@ac.edu
Fax: (864) 231-2006 **Internet:** www.ac.edu

Institution Description: Anderson College is a private four-year liberal arts college sponsored by the South Carolina Baptist Convention. *Enrollment:* 2,064. *Degrees awarded:* Baccalaureate.

Accreditation: *Regional:* SACS-Comm. on Coll.

History: Founded 1911.

Calendar: Semesters. Academic year Aug. to May. Freshmen admitted Aug. Degrees conferred and formal commencement May. Summer session of three terms from May to Aug.

Characteristics of Freshmen: 1,547 applicants (female 952, male 595). 80% of applicants admitted. 45% of applicants admitted and enrolled.

89% (342 students) submitted SAT scores; 51% (197 students) submitted ACT scores. *25th percentile*: SAT Critical Reading 450, SAT Math 460; ACT Composite 18, ACT English 16, ACT Math 21. *75th percentile*: SAT Critical Reading 570, SAT Math 570; ACT Composite 23, ACT English 24, ACT Math 25.

82% of freshmen from South Carolina. Freshen from 16 states and 4 foreign countries.

Admission: *Requirements:* High school transcript; SAT I or ACT. TOEFL for foreign students. For fall semester, apply by Aug. 15.

College credit and advanced placement for postsecondary-level work completed in secondary school and for extrainstitutional learning.

Developmental/remedial courses offered in summer session and regular academic year; credit given.

Degree Requirements: *For all baccalaureate degrees:* 128 semester hours. *Grading system:* A–F.

ROTC: Air Force and Army offered in cooperation with Clemson University.

Degrees Conferred: 220 *baccalaureate:* biological/life sciences 7; business 60; communications 5; education 43; English 3; mathematics 1; parks and recreation 15; philosophy/religion/theology 14; psychology 18; social sciences and history 5; visual and performing arts 22. Master's degrees awarded: education 13.

Fees and Other Expenses: *Full-time tuition per academic year 2008–09:* $18,700. *Required fees:* $1,100. *Room and board per academic year:* $7,050. *Books and supplies:* $1,600. *Other expenses:* $3,150.

Financial Aid: Aid from institutionally generated funds is provided on the basis of academic merit.

Financial aid to full-time, first-time undergraduate students: 97% received some form of financial aid. Average amount of aid received: federal grants $1,170; Pell grants $3,105; state/local grants $5,850; institutional grants $8,093.

Departments and Teaching Staff: *Total instructional faculty:* 151 (full-time 69, part-time 82). Total faculty with doctorate, first-professional, or other terminal degree: 62. Student/faculty ratio: 14:1. Degrees held by full-time faculty: 64.7% hold terminal degrees.

Enrollment: Total enrollment: 2,064. Undergraduate 1,974 (full-time 78%; female 66%, male 34%). Graduate 90 (full-time 3%). Undergraduate transfer-in students 125.

Characteristics of Student Body: *Ethnic/racial makeup:* Black non-Hispanic: 11%; Asian or Pacific Islander: 1%; Hispanic: 2%; White non-Hispanic: 83%; unknown 1%; nonresident alien 2%. *Age distribution:* number under 18: 177; 18–19: 559; 20–21: 453; 22–24: 194; 25–29: 80; 30–34: 72; 35–39: 46; 40–49: 66; 50–64: 19.

International Students: 21 nonresident aliens enrolled fall 2008. No programs available to aid students whose native language is not English. Financial aid specifically designated for international students: scholarships are available annually to qualifying students.

Student Life: Intercollegiate and intramural sports. Health services; counseling. Various student organizations for student participation.

Library Collections: 70,000 volumes including bound books, serial backfiles, electronic documents, and government documents not in separate collections. Online catalog. Current serial subscriptions: 314 paper, 7,200 microform, 11,000 via electronic access. 4,868 recordings; 600 compact discs; 87 CD-ROMs. Computer work stations available campus-wide. Students have access to the Internet at no charge.

Buildings and Grounds: Campus area 32 acres.

Chief Executive Officer: Dr. Evans P. Whitaker, President.

Address admissions inquiries to Pam Bryant, Director of Admissions.

Benedict College

1600 Harden Street
Columbia, South Carolina 29204
Tel: (803) 256-4220 **E-mail:** admissions@benedict.edu
Fax: (803) 253-5167 **Internet:** www.benedict.edu

Institution Description: Benedict College is an independent, coeducational, private college founded by the Baptist Church. *Enrollment:* 2,883. *Degrees awarded:* Baccalaureate.

Accreditation: *Regional:* SACS-Comm. on Coll.

History: Established as Benedict Institute 1870; offered first instruction at postsecondary level 1889; chartered, adopted present name, and awarded first degree 1984.

Institutional Structure: *Governing board:* Benedict College Board of Trustees. Extrainstitutional representation: 26 trustees, including 9 alumni; institutional representation: president of the college, 1 full-time instructional faculty member, 1 student. All voting. *Composition of institution:* Administrators 6. Academic affairs headed by dean of academic affairs. Management/business/finances directed by director of business affairs. Full-time instructional faculty 82. Academic governance body, The Faculty Forum and Faculty Promotions and Tenure committees meet of 24 times per year.

Calendar: Semesters. Academic year Aug. to May. Freshmen admitted Aug., Jan., May, June. Degrees conferred and formal commencement May. Summer session of 2 terms from late May to late July.

Characteristics of Freshmen: 78% of applicants accepted. 25% of accepted applicants enrolled.

Admission: Rolling admissions plan. Early acceptance available. *Requirements:* Either graduation from accredited secondary school with 18 units which normally include 4 English, 2 mathematics, 2 natural science, 2 social studies, 8 electives; or GED. Minimum 2.0 GPA. *Entrance tests:* College Board SAT preferred; ACT composite accepted. *For transfer students:* 2.0 minimum GPA; from 4-year accredited institution 90 hours maximum transfer credit; from 2-year accredited institution 65 hours; good standing at institution previously attended.

College credit and advanced placement for postsecondary-level work completed in secondary school. Tutoring available.

Degree Requirements: 125 credit hours; 2.0 GPA; 1 year in residence. Fulfillment of some degree requirements and exemption from some beginning courses possible by passing College Board CLEP and other standardized tests. *Grading system:* A–F; withdraw; incomplete (carries time limit).

Distinctive Educational Programs: Evening classes. Dual-degree programs in engineering with Georgia Institute of Technology and Southern Technical Institute (GA) and in medicine and dentistry with Medical University of South Carolina. Facilities and programs for independent research, including honors programs, individual majors, tutorials.

ROTC: Army.

Degrees Conferred: 343 *baccalaureate.* Bachelor's degrees awarded in top five disciplines: business, management, marketing, and related support services 68; security and protective services 50; family and consumer sciences 48; public administration 36; biological/life sciences 33.

Fees and Other Expenses: *Full-time tuition per academic year 2008–09:* $14,510. *Room and board per academic year:* $6,706. *Books and supplies:* $2,000. *Other expenses:* $1,600.

Financial Aid: Aid from institutionally generated funds is provided on the basis of academic merit, financial need, athletic ability, other criteria. Institution has a Program Participation Agreement with the U.S. Department of Education for eligible students to receive Pell Grants and, depending upon the agreement, other federal aid.

Financial aid to full-time, first-time undergraduate students: 99% received some form of financial aid. Average amount of aid received: federal grants $3,641; Pell grants $3,460; state/local grants $4,458; institutional grants $6,828.

Departments and Teaching Staff: *Total instructional faculty:* 143. Degrees held by full-time faculty: doctorate 48%, master's 50%, professional 2%. 50% hold terminal degrees.

Enrollment: Total enrollment 2,883 (undergraduate).

Characteristics of Student Body: *Ethnic/racial makeup:* Black non-Hispanic: 98%; Hispanic: 1%. unknown 1%.

International Students: No financial aid specifically designated for international students.

Student Life: On-campus residence halls house 64% of student body. Residence halls for males constitute 31% of such space, for females 69%. *Intercollegiate athletics:* male: baseball, football, basketball, cross-country, track; female: basketball, softball, volleyball; both sexes: golf, tennis. *Special regulations:* Cars with decals permitted to park on campus. *Special services:* Learning Resources Center, medical services. *Student publications: Benedictus*, a yearbook; *Tiger*, a biannual newspaper. *Surrounding community:* Columbia population 100,000. Jacksonville (FL), 400 miles from campus, is nearest metropolitan area. Served by mass transit bus system; airport 8 miles from campus; passenger rail service 1 mile from campus.

Library Collections: 120,500 volumes. 14,000 government documents; 164,500 microforms; 6,700 audiovisual materials; 315 current periodical subscriptions. Students have access to online information retrieval services and the Internet.

Most important special collections include Afro-American Collection (11,124 volumes plus vertical file material); Humanities Collection.

Buildings and Grounds: Campus area 20 acres. Campus DVD available.

Chief Executive Officer: Dr. David H. Swinton, President.

Address admission inquiries to Phyllis Thompson, Director of Enrollment Management.

Charleston Southern University

9200 University Boulevard
P.O. Box 118087
Charleston, South Carolina 29423-0087
Tel: (800) 947-7474 **E-mail:** enroll@csuniv.edu
Fax: (843) 863-7070 **Internet:** www.csuniv.edu

Institution Description: Charleston Southern University, formerly Baptist College at Charleston, is a private college affiliated with the Southern Baptist Convention of South Carolina. *Enrollment:* 3,200. *Degrees awarded:* Associate, baccalaureate, master's.

Accreditation: *Regional:* SACS-Comm. on Coll. *Professional*: music

History: Chartered 1960; became Baptist College at Charleston and offered first instruction at postsecondary level 1965; awarded first degree (baccalaureate) 1967; adopted present name 1991.

Institutional Structure: *Governing board:* Board of Trustees. Representation: 25 trustees. *Composition of institution:* Administrators 12. Academic affairs headed by vice president for academic affairs. Management/business/finances directed by vice president for business affairs. Full-time instructional faculty 71.

Calendar: Semesters. Academic year Sept. to May.

Characteristics of Freshmen: 2,966 applicants (female 1,951, male 1,035). 62% of applicants accepted. 34% of accepted applicants enrolled full-time. Average secondary school rank of freshmen: Mean SAT Critical Reading 585, SAT Math 491; ACT Composite 23.

81% of freshmen from South Carolina. Freshmen from 45 states and 36 foreign countries.

Admission: Rolling admissions plan. *Requirements:* Either graduation from accredited secondary school or GED. *Entrance tests:* College Board SAT or ACT composite.

Remedial courses offered.

Degree Requirements: *For baccalaureate degrees:* 125 credit hours; 2.0 GPA; 12 hours in major and 6 in minor in residence; general education requirements. *Grading system:* A–F.

ROTC: Army.

Degrees Conferred: 437 *baccalaureate.* Bachelor's degrees awarded in top five disciplines: education 64; business, management, marketing, and related support services 58; social sciences 41; psychology 36; health professions and related clinical sciences 33. Master's degrees awarded: various disciplines 136.

Fees and Other Expenses: *Full-time tuition per academic year 2008–09:* $18,708. *Room and board per academic year:* $7,178. *Books and supplies:* $1,250.

Financial Aid: Aid from institutionally generated funds is provided on the basis of academic merit, financial need, athletic ability. Institution has a Program Participation Agreement with the U.S. Department of Education for eligible students to receive Pell Grants and, depending upon the agreement, other federal aid.

100% of first-time, full-time freshmen received some form of aid. Average amount of aid received: federal grants $3,770; Pell grants $3,036; other federal aid $998; state/local grants $5,055; institutional grants $7,167.

Departments and Teaching Staff: *Total instructional faculty:* 71. Student/faculty ratio: 17:1. Degrees held by full-time faculty: doctorate 68%, master's 32%. 68% hold terminal degrees.

Enrollment: Total enrollment 3,200. Undergraduate 2,762 (full-time 85%; female 57%, male 62%). Graduate 438 (full-time 5%). Undergraduate transfer-in students 278.

Characteristics of Student Body: *Ethnic/racial makeup:* Black non-Hispanic: 36%; Asian or Pacific Islander: 1%; Hispanic: 2%; White non-Hispanic: 36%; unknown: 8%; nonresident alien 1%.

CHARLESTON SOUTHERN UNIVERSITY—*cont'd*

International Students: Students from Europe, Asia, Latin America, Africa, Canada, Australia. No programs to aid students whose native language is not English. No financial aid specifically designated for international students.

Library Collections: 213,000 volumes. 118,822 government documents; 7,000 audiovisual materials; 213,000 microforms; 9,800 periodicals including via electronic access. Online catalog. Students have access to online information retrieval services and the Internet.

Buildings and Grounds: Campus DVD available.

Chief Executive Officer: Dr. Jairy C. Hunter, Jr., President.

Address admission inquiries to Cheryl Burton, Director of Enrollment Services.

Citadel Military College of South Carolina

171 Moultrie Street
Charleston, South Carolina 29409
Tel: (843) 225-3294 **E-mail:** admissions@citadel.edu
Fax: (843) 953-7036 **Internet:** www.citadel.edu

Institution Description: The Citadel Military College of South Carolina, is a state college. *Enrollment:* 3,328. Males and females are admitted to the undergraduate residential Corps of Cadets. In addition to the day program, undergraduate and graduate programs are offered at the College of Graduate and Professional Studies. *Degrees awarded:* Baccalaureate, master's.

Academic offerings subject to approval by statewide coordinating bodies. Budget subject to approval by state governing boards. Member of Charleston Higher Education Consortium.

Accreditation: *Regional:* SACS-Comm. on Coll. *Professional*: business, chemistry, engineering, teacher education

History: Established as The Citadel and first chartered 1842; offered first instruction at postsecondary level 1843; closed 1865; reopened 1882; changed name to South Carolina Military Academy 1887; present official name (The Citadel, The Military College of South Carolina) adopted 1910; offered first degree (baccalaureate) 1948. *See* Oliver T. Bond, *Story of the Citadel* (Richmond, Va.: Garret and Massic, 1936) for further information.

Institutional Structure: *Governing board:* The Citadel Board of Visitors. Extrainstitutional representation: 11 trustees and 2 emeriti (all alumni); 3 state officials (ex officio), 1 secretary. 14 voting. *Composition of institution:* Administrators 14. Academic affairs headed by provost and dean of the college. Management/business/finances directed by vice president for financial management. Full-time instructional faculty 163. Academic governance body, Academic Board, meets an average of 15 times per year.

Calendar: Semesters. Academic year Sept. to May. Freshmen admitted Aug. Degrees conferred and formal commencements May, Aug. Summer session of 2 terms from June to Aug.

Characteristics of Freshmen: 2,081 applicants (female 264, male 1,817). 579% of applicants admitted. 36% of applicants admitted and enrolled.

80% (451 students) submitted SAT scores; 18% (99 students) submitted ACT scores. *25th percentile*: SAT Critical Reading 490, SAT Math 510; ACT Composite 20. *75th percentile*: SAT Critical Reading 590, SAT Math 600; ACT Composite 23.

63% of entering freshmen expected to graduate within 5 years. 47% of freshmen from South Carolina. Freshmen from 46 states and 27 foreign countries.

Admission: Rolling admissions plan. For fall acceptance, apply as early as Sept. 1 of previous year, but not later than June 30. *Requirements:* Graduation from accredited secondary school with 16 units which must include 4 English, 3 mathematics (including algebra), 3 science (which must include lab), 2 foreign language, 2 social studies, 1 history, 1 academic elective, 1 physical education or ROTC. Minimum 2.0 GPA on a 4.0 scale. Applicants for the Corps of Cadets must be medically approved by The Citadel physician, complete a diagnostic Citadel Physical Fitness Test, be 17–23 years of age, and cannot be married. *Entrance tests:* College Board SAT or ACT composite. *For transfer students:* 2.0 minimum GPA; 60 hours maximum transfer credit from accredited institutions.

College credit and advanced placement for postsecondary-level work completed in secondary school. College credit for CLEP.

Tutoring available. Noncredit developmental courses in English and mathematics offered in summer session.

Degree Requirements: *For all baccalaureate degrees:* minimum 121 credit hours (credit hours may vary by degree); 2.0 GPA; 4 semesters in residence; minimum 2 hours military training per week for 4 years; 4 semesters physical education. Fulfillment of some degree requirements and exemption from some beginning courses including English, foreign languages, and history possible by passing College Board CLEP and APP which should be taken before registering at Citadel. *Grading system:* A–F; pass-fail; withdraw (deadline after which pass-fail is appended to withdraw).

Distinctive Educational Programs: *For graduate students:* Flexible meeting places and schedules. *Available to all students:* Facilities and programs from independent research. Study abroad in France, Ecuador, and Spain (summer only).

ROTC: Army, Navy, Marines, Air Force.

Degrees Conferred: 467 *baccalaureate*; 214 *master's*. Bachelor's degrees awarded in top five disciplines: business marketing 148, engineering 66; security and protective services 53; social sciences 38; education 37. Master's degrees awarded in top five disciplines: education 124; business/marketing 49; psychology 92; biological/life sciences 7; parks and recreation 7.

Fees and Other Expenses: *Full-time tuition per academic year 2008–09:* undergraduate resident $8,428, nonresident $21,031; contact the college for current graduate tuition and applicable fees. *Required fees:* $1,000. *Room and board per academic year:* $5,750. *Other expenses:* $1,089.

Financial Aid: The Citadel offers a direct lending program. Aid from institutionally generated funds is provided on the basis of academic merit, financial need, athletic ability, other criteria.

Financial aid to full-time, first time undergraduate students: 86% received some form of aid.

Departments and Teaching Staff: *Total instructional faculty:* 233 (full-time 163, part-time 70). Total faculty with doctorate, first-professional, or other terminal degree: 182. Student/faculty ratio: 15:1. Degrees held by full-time faculty: 95% hold terminal degrees.

Enrollment: Total enrollment 3,328. Undergraduate 2,288 (full-time 95%; female 8%, male 92%). Graduate 1,040 (full-time 18%). Undergraduate transfer-in students 73.

Characteristics of Student Body: *Ethnic/racial makeup:* Black non-Hispanic: 7%; American Indian or Alaska Native: 1%; Asian or Pacific Islander: 3%; Hispanic: 4%; White non-Hispanic: 83%; nonresident alien 2%.

International Students: 66 nonresident aliens enrolled fall 2008. Students from Europe, Asia, Latin America, Africa. Programs available to aid students whose native language is not English: English as Second Language Program. No financial aid specifically designated for international students.

Student Life: On-campus residence halls house 100% of student body. Residence halls for Corps of Cadets only. *Intercollegiate athletics:* baseball, basketball, cross-country, football, golf, soccer, tennis, track and field, volleyball, wrestling. *Special regulations:* Cars permitted for all but freshmen (fee per semester). Military uniforms required. Quiet hours from 7:30pm to 10:30pm. Sun.–Thurs. *Special services:* Medical services. *Student publications: The Brigadier*, a newspaper published 20 times annually; *The Guidon*, an annual freshman handbook; *The Shako*, a triennial literary magazine; *The Sphinx*, a yearbook. *Surrounding community:* Charleston, population 430,500, is nearest metropolitan area. Served by mass transit bus system; airport 15 miles from campus; passenger rail service 10 miles from campus.

Publications: *Citadel Monograph Series* (published irregularly).

Library Collections: 235,000 volumes including bound books, serial backfiles, electronic documents, and government documents not in separate collections. Online catalog. Current serial subscriptions: 540 paper. 1,200,400 microform. 7,600 audiovisual materials. Students have access to the Internet at no charge.

Most important special collections include General Mark W. Clark Papers; General Ellison Capers Papers.

Buildings and Grounds: Campus area 108 acres. Campus DVD available.

Chief Executive Officer: Lt. Col. John W. Rosa, President.

Address inquiries to Lt. Col. John Powell, Director of Admissions; graduate inquiries to Dr. Raymond S. Jones, Dean of Graduate and Professional Studies.

Claflin University

400 Magnolia Street
Orangeburg, South Carolina 29115
Tel: (803) 535-5097 **E-mail:** admissions@claflin.edu
Fax: (803) 531-2860 **Internet:** www.claflin.edu

Institution Description: Claflin University is a private college affiliated with the United Methodist Church. *Enrollment:* 1,773. *Degrees awarded:* Baccalaureate, master's.

Accreditation: *Regional:* SACS-Comm. on Coll.

History: Chartered and offered first instruction at postsecondary level 1869; merged with Baker Theological Institute and awarded first degree (baccalaureate) 1870.

Institutional Structure: *Governing board:* Trustees of Claflin University and Officers of the Corporation. Extrainstitutional representation: 35 trustees; institutional representation: president of the university. *Composition of institu-*

tion: Administrators 6. Academic affairs headed by vice president of academic affairs. Management/business/finances directed by business manager. Full-time instructional faculty 93. Academic governance body is the Academic Affairs Committee.

Calendar: Semesters. Academic year Aug. to May. Formal commencement May. Summer session from early June to late July.

Characteristics of Freshmen: 2,851 applicants (female 1,799, male 1,058). 40% of applicants accepted. 35% of accepted applicants enrolled.

89% (242 students) submitted SAT scores. *25th percentile*: SAT Critical Reading 430, SAT Math 440. *75th percentile*: SAT Critical Reading 5875 SAT Math 5100.

64% of entering freshmen expected to graduate within 5 years. 91% of freshmen from South Carolina. Freshmen from 19 states and 7 foreign countries.

Admission: For fall enrollment, apply no later than June 30. *Requirements:* Graduation from accredited secondary school with 4 units English, 2 mathematics, 1 natural science, 2 social studies, 1 physical education, 7 electives. GED may be acceptable. *Entrance tests:* College Board SAT or ACT composite. *For transfer students:* 2.0 minimum GPA.

Remedial courses offered.

Degree Requirements: 124 credit hours; 2.0 GPA; last 30 semester hours or 4 consecutive summer session in residence; comprehensives in individual fields of study; distribution requirements.

Fulfillment of some degree requirements possible by passing College Board CLEP. *Grading system:* A–F; withdraw passing; withdraw failing.

Distinctive Educational Programs: Accelerated degree programs.

ROTC: Army offered in cooperation with South Carolina State University.

Degrees Conferred: 274 *baccalaureate*: biological/life sciences 26; business/marketing 53; communications/communication technologies 13; computer and information sciences 16; education 15; engineering 1; English 5; home economics 35; interdisciplinary studies 1; parks and recreation 2; philosophy/religion/theology 2; protective services and public administration 47; social sciences and history 42; visual and performing arts 3. *Master's*: business/marketing 31.

Fees and Other Expenses: *Full-time tuition per academic year 2008–09:* $12,925. undergraduate; contact the university for current graduate tuition. *Required fees:* $1,684. *Room and board per academic year:* $6,806. *Books and supplies:* $1,500. *Other expenses:* $3,200.

Financial Aid: Aid from institutionally generated funds is provided on the basis of academic merit, financial need, athletic ability, other criteria.

Financial aid to full-time, first-time undergraduate students: 98% received some form of financial aid. Average amount of aid received: federal grants $4,645; Pell grants $3,072; state/local grants $4,860; institutional grants $12,709.

Departments and Teaching Staff: *Total instructional faculty:* 133 (full-time 93, part-time 40). Total faculty with doctorate, first-professional, or other terminal degree: 86. Student/faculty ratio: 14:1. Degrees held by full-time faculty: doctorate 43%, master's 57%. 43% hold terminal degrees.

Enrollment: Total enrollment 1,773. Undergraduate 1,698 (full-time 98%; female 68%, male 32%). Graduate 83 (full-time 73%). Undergraduate transfer-in students 97.

Characteristics of Student Body: *Ethnic/racial makeup:* Black non-Hispanic: 94%; White non-Hispanic: 1%; unknown: 1%; nonresident alien 3%.

International Students: 54 nonresident aliens enrolled fall 2008. No programs available to aid students whose native language is not English. No financial aid specifically designated for international students.

Student Life: On-campus residence halls. *Intercollegiate athletics:* Basketball, softball, tennis, track. *Special regulations:* Registered cars permitted without restrictions. *Special services:* Medical services. *Student publications: Les Memoirs*, a yearbook; *The Panther*, a quarterly newspaper. *Surrounding community:* Orangeburg population 15,000.

Library Collections: 161,000 volumes. 64,000 microforms; 1,100 audiovisual materiasl; 450 periodical subscriptions. Online catalog. Computer work stations available. Students have access to online information retrieval services and the Internet.

Most important special holdings include Schomburg Collection; minutes of the 1866 United Methodist Conference; papers of Rev. Matthew McCollum, religious and civic leader.

Buildings and Grounds: Campus area 43 acres.

Chief Executive Officer: Dr. Henry N. Tisdale, President.

Address admission inquiries to Michael Zeigler, Director of Admissions.

Clemson University

Clemson, South Carolina 29634
Tel: (864) 656-2287 **E-mail:** cuadmissions@clemson.edu
Fax: (864) 656-2464 **Internet:** www.clemson.edu

Institution Description: Clemson University is a state institution. *Enrollment:* 18,317. *Degrees awarded:* Baccalaureate, master's, doctorate. Specialist in Education Degree also awarded.

Academic offerings subject to approval by statewide coordinating bodies. Budget subject to approval by state governing boards.

Accreditation: *Regional:* SACS-Comm. on Coll. *Professional*: architecture, business, chemistry, engineering, engineering technology, forestry, nursing, teacher education

History: Established and chartered as Clemson Agricultural College 1889; offered first instruction at postsecondary level 1893; awarded first degree (baccalaureate) 1896; adopted present name 1964. *See* Wright Bryan, *Clemson: An Informal History of the University* (Columbia, SC: R.L. Bryan Co., 1979) for further information.

Institutional Structure: *Governing board:* Board of Trustees. Extrainstitutional representation: 13 trustees (including 6 elected by the state legislature, 7 life members). All voting. *Composition of institution:* Administrators 197. Academic affairs headed by provost. Management/business/finances directed by chief financial officer. Full-time instructional faculty: 1,061. Academic governance body, Faculty Senate, meets an average of 12 times per year.

Calendar: Semesters. Academic year Aug. to May. Freshmen admitted Aug., Jan., May, June. Degrees conferred and formal commencements May, Aug., Dec. Summer session of 2 terms from May to Aug.

Characteristics of Freshmen: 14,255 applicants (female 7,319, male 6,936). 55% of applicants accepted. 22% of accepted applicants enrolled full-time.

88% (2,469 students) submitted SAT scores; 12% (345 students) submitted ACT scores. *25th percentile*: SAT Critical Reading 560, SAT Math 580; ACT Composite 24. *75th percentile*: SAT Critical Reading 640, SAT Math 670; ACT Composite 29.

75% of entering freshmen expected to graduate within 5 years. 68% of freshmen from South Carolina. Freshmen from 49 states and 85 foreign countries.

Admission: Rolling admissions plan. For fall acceptance, apply as early as Sept. of the previous year. *Requirements:* Graduation from accredited secondary school with the following units: English, 4; mathematics, 3; laboratory science, 2; foreign language, 2; other (choose from advanced math, world history or western civilization or geography), 1; U.S. history, 1; economics, ½; government, ½; additional social studies, 1; physical education or ROTC, 1. Grades and class rank are very important. *Entrance tests:* College Board SAT. For foreign students, SAT and TOEFL. *For transfer students:* candidates should have 30 semester (45 quarter) hours of work with a cumulative C plus average (2.5 on a 4.0 scale).

College credit and advanced placement for postsecondary-level work completed in secondary school.

Degree Requirements: *For undergraduates:* 129–143 semester hours, depending on major; 2.0 GPA; 30 of last 36 credits in residence; distribution requirements.

Fulfillment of some degree requirements and exemption from some beginning courses possible by passing departmental examinations, College Board CLEP, AP. *Grading system:* A–F; pass-fail; withdraw (carries time limit).

Distinctive Educational Programs: Accelerated program; cooperative (work-study) program; distance learning; double major; exchange student program (domestic); Honors program; internships; study abroad; teacher certification program.

ROTC: Air Force, Army.

Degrees Conferred: 3,075 *baccalaureate*; 816 *master's*; 145 *doctorate*. Bachelor's degrees awarded in top five disciplines: business, management, marketing, and related support services 534; engineering/engineering technology 476; education 224; social sciences 265; health professions and related clinical sciences 217. Master's degrees awarded in top five disciplines: engineering 226; education 184; business/marketing 147; architecture 60; computer and information sciences 44. Doctorates awarded in top five disciplines: engineering 31; biological/life sciences 21; education 18; physical sciences 15; agriculture 13.

Fees and Other Expenses: *Full-time tuition and fees per academic year 2008–09:* resident undergraduate $10,379, nonresident $23,401; contact the university for current graduate tuition and applicable fees. *Room and board per academic year:* $6,556. *Books and supplies:* $900. *Other expenses:* $4,280.

Financial Aid: Aid from institutionally generated funds is awarded on the basis of academic merit, financial need, athletic ability, other considerations.

Financial aid to full-time, first-time undergraduate students: 90% received some form of aid. Average amount of aid received: federal grants $3,884; Pell

CLEMSON UNIVERSITY—*cont'd*

grants $3,570; other federal aid $927; state/local grants $5,585; institutional grants $5,888.

Departments and Teaching Staff: *Total instructional faculty:* 1,233 (full-time 1,061, part-time 172). Total faculty with doctorate, first-professional, or other terminal degree: 986. Student/faculty ratio: 14:1. Degrees held by full-time faculty: 76% hold terminal degrees.

Enrollment: Total enrollment 18,317. Undergraduate 14,713 (full-time 94%; female 46%; male 54%). Graduate 3,604 (full-time 63%). Undergraduate transfer-in students 960.

Characteristics of Student Body: *Ethnic/racial makeup:* Black non-Hispanic: 7%; Asian or Pacific Islander: 2%; Hispanic: 1%; White non-Hispanic: 82%; unknown 7%; nonresident alien 1%. *Age distribution:* number under 18: 33; 18–19: 2,006; 20–21: 5,864; 22–24: 2,587; 25–29: 3961 30–34: 113; 35–39: 591 40–49: 82; 50–64: 22.

International Students: 183 nonresident aliens enrolled fall 2008. Students from Europe, Asia, Latin America, Africa, Canada, Australia, New Zealand. Programs available to aid students whose native language is not English: social, cultural, financial. English as a Second Language Program. No financial aid specifically designated for international students.

Student Life: On-campus residence halls house 49% of student body. *Intercollegiate athletics:* male: baseball, basketball, cross-country, football, golf, soccer, swimming, tennis, track, wrestling; female: basketball, cross-country, swimming, tennis, track, volleyball. *Activities:* choral groups, concert band, dance, drama/theater, jazz band, literary magazine, marching band, music ensembles, musical theater, pep band, radio station, student government, student newspaper, yearbook, intramural sports. *Special regulations:* Residence hall visitation from 10am to 2am daily. *Special services:* Handicapped, minority, and international programs and counseling and psychological services. *Student publications: Chronicle*, a literary magazine published each semester; *TAPS*, a yearbook; *The Tiger*, a weekly newspaper; *Reveille*, feature magazine published 2 or 3 times per year; *Tiger Town Observer*, a conservative journal. *Surrounding community:* Clemson population 11,096. Atlanta (GA), 135 miles from campus, is nearest metropolitan area. Served by airport 45 miles from campus; passenger rail service 1 mile from campus.

Publications: *Clemson World*, an alumni magazine published quarterly; *Consider Clemson, The Clemson Choice*, and *Tiger Times* are targeted toward potential students.

Library Collections: 1,300,200 volumes including bound books, serial backfiles, electronic documents, and government documents not in separate collections. Online catalog. 1,169,000 microforms; 139,700 audiovisual materials; 11,570 periodicals including via electronic access. Computer work stations available. Students have access to the Internet at no charge.

Most important special collections include political papers of Strom Thurmond, James F. Byrnes, Ben Tillman, and Thomas G. Clemson; Clemson University Archives; South Carolina Textile History Collection.

Buildings and Grounds: Campus area 1,400 acres. Campus DVD available.

Chief Executive Officer: Dr. James F. Barker, President.

Undergraduates address admission inquiries to Robert S. Barkley, Director of Admissions; graduate inquiries to Dr. J. Bruce Rafert, Dean of the Graduate School.

College of Engineering and Science

Degree Programs Offered: *Baccalaureate* in agricultural engineering, ceramic engineering, chemical engineering, civil engineering, computer engineering, electrical engineering, engineering analysis, industrial engineering, mechanical engineering, biochemistry, biological sciences, chemistry, computer information systems, computer science, geology, mathematical sciences, medical technology, microbiology, physics; *master's* in biochemistry, botany, chemistry, computer science, geology, mathematical sciences, microbiology, physics, zoology; *doctorate* in biochemistry, chemistry, computer science, management science, mathematical sciences, microbiology, physics, agricultural engineering, bioengineering, ceramic engineering, chemical engineering, civil engineering, computer engineering, electrical engineering, engineering mechanics, environmental systems engineering, industrial engineering, materials science and engineering, mechanical engineering; *doctorate* in agricultural engineering, bioengineering, ceramic engineering, chemical engineering, civil engineering, computer engineering, electrical engineering, engineering mechanics, environment systems engineering, industrial engineering, materials science and engineering, mechanical engineering.

Admission: All freshmen are admitted to the Freshman Engineering Program. Entrance to the professional programs follows the satisfactory completion of the Freshman Program requirements.

Degree Requirements: Overall GPR of 2.00. 2.00 GPR in all engineering courses.

Distinctive Educational Programs: A wide range of international programs are offered, including overseas internships with major international companies and study abroad linkages with leading technical universities. Special academic options include a biophysics option in physics; a computer science option in math sciences; and minors in all science disciplines, environmental systems engineering, environmental science and policy, and bioengineering. Specialized laboratory facilities in various engineering/scientific fields. Special graduate programs include summer and external masters programs, and a joint doctorate in management science offered by the departments of mathematical sciences and management. Special engineering facilities, including ceramics pilot laboratory, experimental animal surgery and histopathology laboratory, artificial intelligence laboratory, polymer processing and rheology laboratory, experimental thermodynamics laboratory, computer process control laboratory, polymer composites laboratory, molecular simulation facilities, radioactive materials laboratory, hazardous and toxic materials analysis laboratory, microelectronics laboratory, image processing laboratory, speech processing laboratory, microelectronics cleanroom, hydraulics laboratory, fluid mechanics lab, structural laboratory, electro-optics and laser laboratory, antenna and microwave laboratory, semiconductor reliability laboratory, CIM facilities, high-speed cinematography and stroboscopy laboratory, heat-transfer laboratory, solar cell testing and reliability laboratories, materials testing and processing laboratories, robotics laboratory, aerodynamics laboratory, metallurgical laboratories, and shops.

College of Agriculture, Forestry, and Life Sciences

Degree Programs Offered: *Baccalaureate* in agricultural and applied economics, agricultural education, agricultural engineering, agricultural mechanization and business, agronomy, animal industries, aquaculture, fisheries and wildlife biology, biological sciences, entomology, food science, horticulture, packaging science, plant pathology; forest resource management; forest products; parks, recreation and tourism management; *master's* in forestry; parks, recreation and tourism management; agriculture, agricultural and applied economics, agricultural education, agricultural engineering, agronomy, animal and food industries, animal physiology, aquaculture, fisheries and wildlife biology, entomology, horticulture, nutrition, plant pathology; *doctorate* in agriculture engineering, agronomy, animal physiology, applied economics, food technology, plant pathology, plant physiology, forestry; parks, recreation, tourism management.

Distinctive Educational Programs: Reconstituting plastics as fiber materials (recycling) and wood chemistry. The Clemson Experimental Forest (17,000 acres) provides resources for instruction and research. The Belle W. Baruch Forest Science Institute provides facilities for wetlands research and the Archbold Tropical Research Center on Dominica focuses tropical research activities in Dominica, Costa Rica, Panama, and Brazil. Numerous interdisciplinary programs, e.g. packaging science and graphic arts, food safety, rural economic development and genetics;. Campus facilities for aquaculture instruction and research. Nationally recognized programs in turf grass and ornamental horticulture.

College of Architecture, Arts, and Humanities

Degree Programs Offered: *Baccalaureate* in English, history, language and international trade, modern languages, philosophy, political science, psychology, sociology; fine arts, landscape architecture; *master's* in architecture, city and regional planning, construction science and management, visual arts, applied psychology, English, history, construction science and management, design.

Distinctive Educational Programs: Study abroad at the Charles E. Daniel Center for Building Research and Urban Studies in Genoa, Italy, for graduate students in all disciplines for a full semester credit. A semester in Charleston (SC) at Clemson University's College of Architecture Center at the College of Charleston for junior and senior undergraduate students.

College of Health, Education, and Human Development

Degree Programs Offered: *Baccalaureate* in early childhood education, elementary education, graphic communications, industrial education, mathematics teaching, science teaching, secondary education, special education; *master's* in administration and supervision, counseling and guidance services, elementary education, human resources and development, industrial education, reading, secondary education, special education; *doctorate* in administration and supervision, vocational and technical education.

Distinctive Educational Programs: Parks, Recreation, and Tourism Management majors select course work from among several emphasis areas including community leisure services, recreation resource management, therapeutic recreation, and travel and tourism management. Special programs within education include education and undergraduate certification in 12 programs, reading recovery program, the nationally funded Clemson Writing Project, special education undergraduate certification which is a state model program integrated with the Center of Excellence for Recruitment, Training, and Retention of Special Educators in Rural Schools.

College of Business and Public Affairs

Degree Programs Offered: *Baccalaureate* in accounting, economics, financial management, industrial management, management, marketing, textile chemistry, textile management, textile science; *master's* in accounting, business administration, economics, industrial management, textile chemistry, textile science; *doctorate* in applied economics, industrial management, management science, textile and polymer science.

Distinctive Educational Programs: MBA programs offered in Greenville (SC) and international programs in Pordenone, Italy. Joint programs with College of Agriculture, Forestry and Life Sciences. Extensive executive education in the office of Professional Development and the Small Business Development Center. Provides public service outreach. Unique real-world projects and courses offered by the Spiro Center for Entrepreneurial Leadership. Graphic Communication and both Army and Air Force ROTC are provided by the college.

Coastal Carolina University

P.O. Box 261954
Conway, South Carolina 29528-6054
Tel: (843) 347-3161 **E-mail:** admissions@coastal.edu
Fax: (843) 349-2127 **Internet:** www.coastal.edu

Institution Description: Coastal Carolina University, formerly known as University of South Carolina - Coastal Carolina, is a state-supported institution. *Enrollment:* 8,154. *Degrees awarded:* Baccalaureate, master's.

Accreditation: *Regional:* SACS-Comm. on Coll.

History: Established as a branch campus of the College of Charleston 1954; affiliated with the University of South Carolina from 1960 to 1993; state approved independence and became Coastal Carolina University 1993. *See* Edward M. Singleton, *History of Horry County Higher Education Commission* (Conway: Coastal Educational Foundation, 1965) for further information.

Institutional Structure: *Composition of institution:* Academic affairs headed by provost. Management/business/finances directed by executive vice president. Full-time instructional 241. Academic governance body, Faculty Senate, meets an average of 9 times per year.

Calendar: Semesters. Academic year July to June. Freshmen admitted Aug., May, June, July, Jan. Degrees conferred May, Aug., Dec. Formal commencement May, Dec. Summer session of 3 terms from May to Aug.

Characteristics of Freshmen: 6,618 applicants (female 3,533, male 3,085). 68% of applicants admitted. 35% of applicants admitted and enrolled full time.

75% (1,106 students) submitted SAT scores; 24% (359 students) submitted ACT scores. *25th percentile*: SAT Critical Reading 470, SAT Math 430; ACT Composite 20. *75th percentile*: SAT Critical Readding 510, SAT Math 530; ACT Composite 21.

18% of entering freshmen expected to graduate within 5 years. 54% of freshmen from South Carolina. Freshmen from 48 states and 50 foreign countries.

Admission: Rolling admissions plan. For fall acceptance, apply as early as the beginning of senior year of secondary school, but not later than Aug. 15. *Requirements:* Either graduation from accredited secondary school or GED. Additional requirements for some programs. High school preparation should include the following: 4 units in English, 3 mathematics, 3 social studies, 2 laboratory science, 2 foreign language. *Entrance tests:* College Board SAT or ACT composite. *For transfer students:* good standing at institution previously attended and GPA must be in accordance with standards described in Coastal Carolina University catalog.

Degree Requirements: 120 semester hours minimum; 2.0 GPA minimum; last 30 hours in residence; general education requirements.

Fulfillment of some degree requirements and exemption from some beginning courses possible by passing departmental examinations, College Board CLEP; SAT scores, and CEEB Advanced Placement Examinations. *Grading system:* A–F; withdraw (carries time limit).

Distinctive Educational Programs: Flexible meeting places and schedules, including off-campus centers (at Myrtle Beach, 9 miles away from main institution; Litchfield, 30 miles away; and Georgetown, 30 miles away), and evening classes. Special facilities for using telecommunications in the classroom. Interdisciplinary studies program. Individual majors. Study abroad consists of occasional travel seminars. CCU participates in ISEP, exchange program with Deakins University, summer study in London. Nationally recognized Marine Science Program.

Degrees Conferred: 1,076 *baccalaureate*; 86 *master's*. Bachelor's degrees awarded in top five disciplines: business/marketing 296; biological/life sciences 128; education 121; social sciences 64; psychology 60. Master's degrees awarded biological/life science 4; education 82.

Fees and Other Expenses: *Full-time tuition per academic year 2008–09:* undergraduate resident $8,650, nonresident $18,090; contact the university for current graduate tuition and applicable fees. *Room and board per academic year:* $6,970. *books and supplies:* $1,044. *Other expenses:* $4,344.

Financial Aid: Aid from institutionally generated funds is provided on the basis of academic merit, athletic ability.

Financial aid to full-time, first-time undergraduate students: 88% received some form of aid. Average amount of aid received: federal grants $3,825; Pell grants $2,951; other federal aid $952; state/local grants $4,500; institutional grants $4,574.

Departments and Teaching Staff: *Total instructional faculty:* 443 (full-time 241, part-time 202). Total faculty with doctorate, first-professional, or other terminal degree: 241. Student/faculty ratio: 19:1.

Enrollment: Total enrollment 8,154. Undergraduate 7,573 (full-time 91%; female 53%, male 47%). Graduate 581 (full-time 18%). Undergraduate transfer-in students 721.

Characteristics of Student Body: *Ethnic/racial makeup:* Black non-Hispanic: 13%; American Indian or Alaska Native: 1%; Asian or Pacific Islander: 1%; Hispanic: 2%; White non-Hispanic: 91%; unknown: 1%; nonresident alien 1%. *Age distribution:* number under 18: 112; 18–19: 2,384; 20–21: 2,165; 22–24: 1,365; 25–29: 335; 30–34: 112; 35–39: 581 40–49: 87; 50–64: 40; 65 and over: 12.

International Students: 82 nonresident aliens enrolled fall 2008. Students from Europe, Asia, Latin America, Africa, Canada, Australia, New Zealand. No programs available to aid students whose native language is not English. No financial aid specifically designated for international students.

Student Life: On-campus housing designed to accommodate 2,250 students. Off-campus housing information service lists space for approximately 1,000 students. *Intercollegiate athletics:* male: baseball, basketball, football, golf, soccer, tennis, track and field, cross-country; female: basketball, softball, tennis, track and field, volleyball, cross-country, golf. *Special regulations:* Cars permitted in designated ares. *Special services:* Learning Resources Center, medical services. *Student publications: The Archarios*, an annual literary magazine; *Chanticleer*, a biweekly newspaper; a yearbook. *Surrounding community:* Conway population 15,000. Served by airport 12 miles from campus.

Library Collections: 149,990 volumes. Current serial subscriptions: paper 551; microform 17; via electronic access 13,903. 10,432 recordings, compact discs, and CD-ROMs. Computer work stations available. Students have access to online information retrieval services and the Internet.

Most important special holdings include collections on marine science; Waccamaw Region.

Buildings and Grounds: Campus area 240 acres.

Chief Executive Officer: Dr. Ronald R. Ingle, President.

Address admission inquiries to Dr. Judy W. Vost, Vice President, Enrollment Services.

Coker College

300 East College Avenue
Hartsville, South Carolina 29550
Tel: (843) 383-8000 **E-mail:** admission@coker.edu
Fax: (843) 383-8048 **Internet:** www.coker.edu

Institution Description: Coker College is a private, independent, nonprofit college. *Enrollment:* 1,099. *Degrees awarded:* Baccalaureate.

Accreditation: *Regional:* SACS-Comm. on Coll. *Professional*: music

History: Established as Welsh Neck Academy 1896; chartered as Coker College for Women and offered first instruction at postsecondary level 1908; awarded first degree (baccalaureate) 1912; adopted present name 1970.

Institutional Structure: *Governing board:* Coker College Board of Trustees. Extrainstitutional representation: 20 trustees; immediate past chairman of board of trustees; institutional representation: president of the college, treasurer of the college, 2 full-time instructional faculty members, 2 students; 5 alumni. 3 ex officio. 27 voting. *Composition of institution:* Administrators 11. Academic affairs headed by dean of the college. Management/business/finances directed by vice president for business affairs. Full-time instructional faculty 49. Academic governance body, Faculty Senate, meets an average of 10 times per year.

Calendar: Semesters. Academic year Aug. to May. Freshmen admitted on a rolling basis. Degrees conferred and formal commencement May. Summer session of 2 terms from June to July.

Characteristics of Freshmen: 1,112 applicants (female 742, male 390). 61% of applicants accepted. 32% of applicants accepted and enrolled.

COKER COLLEGE—*cont'd*

58% (119 students) submitted SAT scores. *25th percentile*: SAT Critical Reading 430, SAT Math 460. *75th percentile*: SAT Critical Reading 560, SAT Math 560.

52% of entering freshmen expected to graduate within 5 years. 87% of freshmen from South Carolina. Freshmen from 28 states and 7 foreign countries.

Admission: Rolling admissions plan. For fall acceptance, apply as early as spring of junior year of secondary school, but not later than registration day. *Requirements:* Either graduation from accredited secondary school with 18 units which normally include college preparatory English and mathematics; or GED. Minimum 2.0 GPA. *Entrance tests:* College Board SAT or ACT. For foreign students TOEFL. *For transfer students:* 2.0 minimum GPA; 64 hours maximum transfer credit towards graduation at Coker.

College credit and advanced placement for postsecondary-level work completed in secondary school and for College Board CLEP. College credit for extrainstitutional learning on basis of faculty assessment.

Tutoring and writing lab available.

Degree Requirements: 120 credit hours; 2.0 GPA; 30 hours in residence; 6 credit hours foreign language; 6 credit hours rhetoric (oral and written); 6 credit hours in the arts; 6 credit hours in behavioral science; 3 credit hours in mathematics; 7 credit hours in science; plus 30–45 credit hours in the major and 44 credit hours in electives.

Fulfillment of some degree requirements and exemption from some beginning courses possible by passing departmental examination, CLEP, College Board AP. *Grading system:* A–F; pass-fail; withdraw (carries time limit).

Distinctive Educational Programs: Internships. Flexible meeting places and schedule, including off-campus center (in Columbia, 75 miles away from main institution), and evening classes. Cooperative baccalaureate program in medical technology with McLeod Regional Medical Center. Facilities and programs for independent research, including individual majors, tutorials. Institutionally sponsored study abroad at various locations (Susan Coker Watson Scholarship for study abroad in London, Paris, Rome).

Degrees Conferred: 240 *baccalaureate*. Bachelor's degrees awarded in top five disciplines: business, management, marketing, and related support services 67; social sciences 24; education 22; public administration 21; parks and recreation 19.

Fees and Other Expenses: *Full-time tuition per academic year 2008–09:* $19,322. *Books and supplies:* $1,200. *Room and board per academic year:* $6,008. *Other expenses:* $900.

Financial Aid: Aid from institutionally generated funds is provided on the basis of academic merit, financial need, athletic ability, other criteria. Institution has a Program Participation Agreement with the U.S. Department of Education for eligible students to receive Pell Grants and, depending upon the agreement, other federal aid.

Financial aid to full-time, first-time undergraduate students: 100% received some form of financial aid. Average amount of aid received: federal grants $3,967; state/local grants $6,064; institutional grants $4,467.

Departments and Teaching Staff: *Total instructional faculty:* 73. Student/faculty ratio: 12:1. Degrees held by full-time faculty: doctorate 36%, master's 100%. 83.33% hold terminal degrees.

Enrollment: Total enrollment 1,099 (undergrdduate).

Characteristics of Student Body: *Ethnic/racial makeup:* Black non-Hispanic: 41%; Asian or Pacific Islander: 1%; Hispanic: 1%; White non-Hispanic: 55%; nonresident alien 1%.

International Students: 3 nonresident aliens enrolled fall 2008. Students from Asia, Canada. Programs available to aid students whose native language is not English: English as a Second Language Program. Financial aid specifically designated for international students: scholarships available annually to qualifying students.

Student Life: On-campus residence halls house 31% of student body. Residence halls for males constitute 39% of such space, for females 61%. *Intercollegiate athletics:* male: baseball, basketball, golf, soccer, tennis; female: basketball, softball tennis, volleyball. *Special regulations:* Cars permitted without restrictions. Residence hall visitation from 10am to 1am. *Special services:* Medical services. *Student publications: The Periscope*, a quarterly newspaper; *Milestone*, a yearbook. *Surrounding community:* Hartsville population 8,000. Columbia, 75 miles from campus, is nearest metropolitan area.

Library Collections: 85,500 volumes. 35,600 audiovisual materials. 590 serial subscriptions. 3,500 recordings. Online and card catalogs. Computer work stations available. Students have access to online information retrieval services and the Internet.

Most important special collections include Arents Tobacco Collection; Major James Lide Coker's personal collection of first edition histories (1865–1910); record collection of symphonies and operas by Strauss and Wagner.

Buildings and Grounds: Campus area 15 acres.

Chief Executive Officer: Dr. B. James Dawson, President.

Address admission inquiries to Perry Kerrien, Director of Admissions.

College of Charleston

66 George Street
Charleston, South Carolina 29424
Tel: (843) 953-5500 **E-mail:** admissions@cofc.edu
Fax: (843) 953-5505 **Internet:** www.cofc.edu

Institution Description: The College of Charleston is a state institution. *Enrollment:* 11,367. *Degrees awarded:* Baccalaureate, master's.

Academic offerings subject to approval by statewide coordinating bodies. Budget subject to approval by state governing boards.

Accreditation: *Regional:* SACS-Comm. on Coll. *Professional*: business, chemistry, computer science, public administration, teacher education

History: Established 1770; chartered and offered first instruction at postsecondary level 1785; awarded first degree (baccalaureate) 1794; women admitted 1918; became state institution 1970. *See* J. Harold Easterby, *History of the College of Charleston* (Charleston: Scribner Press, 1935) for further information.

Institutional Structure: *Governing board:* State College Board of Trustees. Representation: 17 trustees. All voting. *Composition of institution:* Administrators 52. Academic affairs headed by vice president for academic affairs. Management/business/finances directed by vice president for business affairs. Full-time instructional faculty 515. Academic governance body, the faculty, meets an average of 9 times per year.

Calendar: Semesters. Academic year Aug. to May. Freshmen admitted on a rolling basis. Degrees conferred and formal commencements May, Dec. Maymester (a three-week term) and 4 summer sessions from May to Aug.

Characteristics of Freshmen: 8,941 applicants (female 6,039, male 2,902). 66% of applicants accepted. 37% of accepted applicants enrolled full-time.

78% (1,366 students) submitted SAT scores; 22% (382 students) submitted ACT scores. *25th percentile*: SAT Critical Reading 570, SAT Math 570; ACT Composite 22, ACT English 22, ACT Math 20. *75th percentile*: SAT Critical Reading 650, SAT Math 640; ACT Composite 25m ACT English 26, ACT Math 25.

52% of entering freshmen expected to graduate within 5 years. 62% of freshmen from South Carolina. Freshmen from 49 states and 75 foreign countries.

Admission: Rolling admissions plan. For fall acceptance, apply as early as Sept. 1 of previous year, but not later than July 1 of year of enrollment. Early acceptance available. *Requirements:* 16 specified high school units which should include 4 English, 3 mathematics, 3 laboratory science, 2 foreign language, 1 U.S. history, 3 social studies, advanced mathematics or computer science or a combination of these (or 1 unit of world history, world geography, or Western civilization). *Entrance tests:* College Board SAT or ACT. TOEFL for foreign students. *For transfer students:* 2.3 minimum GPA; 92 semester hours maximum transfer credit from a four-year institution; 60 semester hours from a two-year institution.

College credit and advanced placement for postsecondary-level work completed in secondary school. College credit for extrainstitutional learning (life experience) on basis of faculty assessment.

Tutoring available. Noncredit remedial courses offered in summer session and regular academic year.

Degree Requirements: 122 credit hours; 2.0 GPA; core requirements. Fulfillment of some degree requirements and exemption from some beginning courses possible by passing College Board CLEP General Examinations, APP, and departmental examinations. *Grading system:* A–F; withdraw (carries time limit).

Distinctive Educational Programs: *For undergraduates:* Accelerated degree programs. Dual-degree programs in chemistry and biochemistry and in mathematics and biometry with Medical University of South Carolina; in engineering with Case Western Reserve University (OH), Clemson University, Georgia Institute of Technology, Washington University (MO). Interdisciplinary major in urban studies. Honors programs. Tutorials. Institutionally sponsored summer, semester, and academic year abroad programs available in all major European countries, and in Africa, Asia, Central and South America. Programs with numerous international schools through International Student Exchange Program. Direct exchange programs with Kansai University in Osaka, Japan, and University of St. Andrews, Scotland. Public service internship through the Washington (DC) Center for Learning Alternatives. Sea Education Association Center semester at Woods Hole (MA) and aboard research schooner. *For graduate students:* Early Child Development Center. Marine Biology Program in conjunction with Medical University of South Carolina, Marine Resources, and The Citadel. Off-campus centers at several area schools. Dual-degree programs in education with The Citadel; in public administration with University of South Carolina. Interdisciplinary major in public administration. Facilities and programs for independent research. *Available to all students:* Work-experience programs including internships, cooperative education. Flexible meeting places and schedules including off-campus centers at the George D. Grice Marine Biological Laboratory (at Fort Johnson, on James Island, about 10 miles away from main institution). Weekend and evening classes. *Other distinctive programs:* Continuing education. Community service programs. Governor's School, a 6-week residential honors program for qualified South Carolina secondary school juniors and seniors. Venture program for minority adults. College completion for adults. Professional development. Credit and noncredit off-campus in-house programs for business and government agencies.

ROTC: Air Force in cooperation with Charleston Southern University.

Degrees Conferred: 2,140 *baccalaureate*; 189 *master's*. Bachelor's degrees awarded in top five disciplines include: biological/ sciences 173; business, management, marketing, and related support services 229; communications 200; education 244; social sciences and history 262. <Master's degrees awarded: various disciplines 189.

Fees and Other Expenses: *Full-time tuition per academic year 2008–09:* $8,400 resident, $20,418 nonresident. *Books and supplies:* $1,123. *Room and board per academic year:* $8,899. *Other expenses:* $2,771.

Financial Aid: Aid from institutionally generated funds is provided on the basis of academic merit, financial need, athletic ability, other criteria.

Financial aid to full-time, first-time undergraduate students: 76% received some form of aid. Average amount of aid received: federal grants $4,213; Pell grants $3,132; other federal aid $1,229; state/local grants $4,079; institutional grants $5,998.

Departments and Teaching Staff: *Total instructional faculty:* 858 (full-time 515, part-time 343). Total faculty with doctorate, first-professional, or other terminal degree: 564. Student/faculty ratio: 14:1. Degrees held by full-time faculty: doctorate 81%, master's 18%, baccalaureate 1%. 91% hold terminal degrees.

Enrollment: Total enrollment 11,367. Undergraduate 9,784 (full-time 92%; female 63%, male 37%). Graduate 1,583 (full-time 19%). Undergraduate transfer-in students 707.

Characteristics of Student Body: *Ethnic/racial makeup:* Black non-Hispanic: 6%; Asian or Pacific Islander: 2%; Hispanic: 2%; White non-Hispanic: 83%; unknown: 6%; nonresident alien 1%.

International Students: 114 undergraduate nonresident aliens enrolled fall 2008. Students from Europe, Asia, Latin America, Africa, Canada, New Zealand. Programs available to aid students whose native language is not English: social, cultural. English as a Second Language Program. No financial aid specifically designated for international students.

Student Life: On-campus residence halls house 29% of student body. Residence halls for males constitute 6% of such space, for females 65%, co-ed halls 29%. 15% of males join fraternities; 15% of females join sororities. *Intercollegiate athletics:* male: baseball, basketball, cross-country, golf, soccer, swimming and diving, tennis; female: basketball, cross-country, golf, soccer, softball, swimming and diving, tennis, volleyball; co-ed teams: equestrian and sailing. *Special regulations:* Parking available on a semester basis. Freshmen housed in residence halls may not park on campus. Residence hall visitation from 11am to midnight Mon.–Thurs., 11am to 2am Fri., 9am to 2am Sat., 9am to midnight Sun. *Special services:* student health services; counseling and psychological services, career resource center; services for students with a learning disorder; physically disabled student serves; college skills lab. *Student publications: Miscellany*, an annual literary magazine; *The Comet*, a yearbook; *The Cougar Pause*, a biweekly newspaper. *Surrounding community:* Charleston metropolitan population 507,000. Served by mass transit bus system; airport 10 miles from campus; passenger rail service 7 miles from campus.

Library Collections: 720,000 volumes. 870,000 microforms; 7,500 audiovisual materials; 4,370 periodicals including via electronic access. Online catalog. Students have access to online information retrieval services and the Internet.

Most important special collections include Burnett Rhett Maybank Papers (documents of a U.S. senator from South Carolina); College of Charleston Archives (documents dating back to 1770); Friendly Moralist Society Minutes (documents of an antebellum free Black mutual aid society); Beth Elhoim Collection (historical manuscripts from America's oldest Reform congregation); Audubon/Bould Prints Collection; Levi Pigeon Collection; John Henry Dick Collection (extremely rare and valuable prints, books, and manuscripts in the area of ornithology).

Buildings and Grounds: Campus area 12 acres. Campus DVD available.

Chief Executive Officer: Dr. Conrad Festa, President.

Address undergraduate admission inquiries to Dean of Admissions and Adult Student Services; graduate inquiries to Graduate Studies Coordinator.

Columbia College

1301 Columbia College Drive
Columbia, South Carolina 29203
Tel: (803) 786-3012 **E-mail:** admissions@colacoll.edu
Fax: (803) 736-3674 **Internet:** www.colacoll.edu

Institution Description: Columbia College is a private liberal arts college for women, affiliated with the United Methodist Church. *Enrollment:* 1,445. *Degrees awarded:* Baccalaureate, master's.

Accreditation: *Regional:* SACS-Comm. on Coll. *Professional*: art, dance, music, social work, teacher education

History: Established and chartered as The Columbia Female College 1854; offered first instruction at postsecondary level 1859; awarded first degree (baccalaureate) 1895; adopted present name 1904. *See* Jerold J. Savory, *Columbia College: The Ariail Era* (Columbia: R.L. Bryan Company, 1979) for further information.

Institutional Structure: *Governing board:* The Columbia College Board of Trustees. Representation: 27 trustees. All voting. *Composition of institution:* Administrators 5. Academic affairs headed by provost. Management/business/ finances directed by vice president for finance. Full-time instructional faculty 82. Academic governance body, Academic Affairs Committee of the Board of Trustees, meets an average of 3 times per year.

Calendar: Semesters. Academic year Sept. to May. Freshmen admitted Aug., Jan., May, June, July. Degrees conferred and formal commencements May, Dec. Summer session of 2 terms from June to July.

Characteristics of Freshmen: 1,069 applicants (female 1,068, male 1). 82% of applicants admitted. 24% of admitted applicants enrolled full-time.

87% (226 students) submitted SAT scores; 42% (110 students) submitted ACT scores. *25th percentile*: SAT Critical Reading 450, SAT Math 430; ACT Composite 18, ACT English 18, ACT 17. *75th percentile*: SAT Critical Reading 560, SAT math 540; ACT Composite 23, ACT English 24, ACT Math 22.

48% of freshmen expected to graduate within 5 years. 90% of freshmen from South Carolina. Freshmen from 250 states and 10 foreign countries.

Admission: Early application strongly encouraged and selection is competitive (rolling admissions plan). Early decision available. *Requirements:* Graduation from accredited secondary school or GED. Recommend 4 units in English, 2 in a foreign language, 3 mathematics, 2 laboratory science, 1 U.S. history, 1 world history, 3 science. *Entrance tests:* College Board SAT or ACT composite. For foreign students TOEFL. *For transfer students:* 2.0 minimum GPA; from 2-year accredited institution 72 hours.

College credit and advanced placement for postsecondary-level work completed in secondary school.

Degree Requirements: 127 credit hours; 2.0 GPA on 4.0 scale; 2 terms in residence; general education requirements.

Fulfillment of some degree requirements and exemption from some beginning courses possible by passing departmental examinations, College Board CLEP. *Grading system:* A–F; pass-fail; withdraw (deadline after which pass-fail is appended to withdraw); incomplete.

Distinctive Educational Programs: Evening classes. Interdepartmental program in communication arts. Individual majors. Institutionally sponsored study abroad in Canada, England, France, Mexico, Spain. Graduate programs in divergent learning. and human behavior and conflict management. Dance major offered.

ROTC: Army.

Degrees Conferred: 220 *baccalaureate:* biological sciences 18; business and management 26; communications 5; computer and information science 6; education 34; English 12; foreign languages 6; health professions and related clinical sciences 14; home economics 4; mathematics 5; philosophy/religion/theology 2; physical sciences 3; protective services/public administration 36; psychology 9; social sciences and history 30; visual and performing arts 22. Master's degrees aawarded: education 210.

Fees and Other Expenses: *Full-time tuition per academic year 2008–09:* undergraduate $23,030; graduate tuition varies by program. *Required fees:* $400. *Room and board per academic year:* $6,750. *Books and supplies:* $1,100. *Other expenses:* $7,146.

Financial Aid: Aid from institutionally generated funds is provided on the basis of academic merit, financial need, athletic ability. Institution has a Program Participation Agreement with the U.S. Department of Education for eligible students to receive Pell Grants and, depending upon the agreement, other federal aid.

Financial aid to full-time, first-time undergraduate students: 100% received some form of aid. Average amount of aid received: federal grants $3,536; Pell grants $3,104; other federal aid $951; state/local grants $6,528; institutional grants $10,203.

COLUMBIA COLLEGE—*cont'd*

Departments and Teaching Staff: *Total instructional faculty:* 154 (full-time 82, part-time 72). Total faculty with doctorate, first-professional, or other terminal degree 90. Student/faculty ratio: 12:1.

Enrollment: Total enrollment 1,445. Undergraduate 1,232 (full-time 100%).

Characteristics of Student Body: *Ethnic/racial makeup:* Black non-Hispanic: 44%; American Indian or Alaska Native: 1%; Asian or Pacific Islander: 2%; Hispanic: 2%; White non-Hispanic: 47%; unknown: 4%. *Age distribution:* number under 18: 47; 18–19: 385; 20–21: 272; 22–24: 108; 25–29: 102; 30–34: 78; 35–39: 52; 40–49: 84; 50–64: 16.

International Students: 29 nonresident aliens enrolled fall 2008. Students from Europe, Latin America. Latin America, Africa, Middle East. No programs available to aid students whose native languages not English. Financial aid specifically designated for international students.

Student Life: On-campus residence halls house 66% of student body. Residence halls for females constitute 100% of such space. *Intercollegiate athletics:* female: cross-country, running, tennis, volleyball. *Special regulations:* Cars permitted without restrictions. Curfews and quiet hours. Residence hall visitation from 2pm to 6pm Sat. and Sun. *Special services:* Learning Resources Center, medical services. *Student publications: Columbian*, a yearbook; *Criterion*, a biannual literary magazine; *Postscript*, a biweekly newspaper. *Surrounding community:* Columbia population 107,000. Atlanta (GA), 210 miles from campus, is nearest metropolitan area. Served by mass transit bus system, airport 15 miles from campus, passenger rail service 3 miles from campus.

Library Collections: 170,000 volumes including bound books, serial backfiles, electronic documents, and government documents not in separate collections. Online catalog. 8,400 microforms; 30,000 audiovisual materials; 630 current serial subscriptions. Computer work stations available. Students have access to the Internet at no charge.

Most important special holdings include religious literature for children published before 1850; Peggy Pavis Collection; Barbara F. Johnson Collection.

Buildings and Grounds: Campus area 32 acres.

Chief Executive Officer: Dr. Caroline Whitson, President.

Address admission inquiries to Julie King, Director of Admission.

Columbia International University

P.O. Box 3122
Columbia, South Carolina 29230-3122
Tel: (803) 754-4100 **E-mail:** admissions@ciu.edu
Fax: (803) 786-4209 **Internet:** www.ciu.edu

Institution Description: Columbia International University, formerly known as Columbia Bible College and Seminary, is a private, independent, nonprofit college. *Enrollment:* 923. *Degrees awarded:* Associate, baccalaureate. Columbia Graduate School of Bible and Missions awards first-professional (master of divinity), master's, and doctoral degrees.

Accreditation: *Regional:* SACS-Comm. on Coll. *National:* ABHE; ATS. *Professional*: theology

History: Established as Columbia Bible School, chartered, incorporated, and offered first instruction at postsecondary level 1923; awarded first degree (baccalaureate) 1929; adopted present name 1974. *See* R. Arthur Matthews, *Towers Pointing Upward* (Columbia: Columbia Bible College, 1973) for further information.

Institutional Structure: *Governing board:* The Board of Trustees of Columbia Bible College, Inc. Extrainstitutional representation: 18 trustees; all voting. *Composition of institution:* Administrators 19. Academic affairs headed by provost. Management/business/finances directed by vice president for business and finance. Full-time instructional faculty 60. Academic governance body, Academic Affairs and Curriculum Review Committee (Bible College), Dean's Cabinet (Seminary), meets an average of 12 times per year.

Calendar: Semesters. Academic year late Aug. to mid-May. Freshmen admitted Aug., Jan. Degrees conferred May, Aug., Dec. Formal commencement June. Summer Studies late May to Aug.; Winterim modular courses early Jan.

Characteristics of Freshmen: 216 applicants (female 129, male 87). 77% of applicants accepted. 44% of accepted applicants enrolled.

57% (52 students) submitted SAT scores; 16% (15 students) submitted ACT scores. *25th percentile*: SAT Critical Reading 550, SAT Math 500; ACT Composite 18, ACT English 15, ACT Math 17. *75th percentile*: SAT Critical Reading 650, SAT Math 590; ACT Composite 25, ACT English 28, ACT Math 23.

64% of entering freshmen expected to graduate within 5 years. 30% of freshmen from South Carolina. Freshmen from 18 states.

Admission: Rolling admissions plan. For fall acceptance, apply as early as Aug. 1 of previous year, but no later than Aug. 15 of year of enrollment. Students are notified of acceptance Jan., Mar., May; after June 1, as applications are reviewed. Apply by Jan. 1 for early decision; need not limit application to Columbia Bible. *Requirements:* Either graduation from accredited secondary school GED. Recommend 4 units English, 2 or more foreign language, 2 history, 2 mathematics, 1 natural science. Minimum 2.0 GPA. Lowest acceptable secondary school class standing 25th percentile. Evidence of Christian conversion and commitment to will of God. *Entrance tests:* College Board SAT. For foreign students TOEFL. *For transfer students:* 2.0 minimum GPA.

College credit and advanced placement for postsecondary-level work completed in secondary school.

Degree Requirements: *For all associate degrees:* 63 semester hours, including 23 hours Bible/theology, 4 hours field education. *For all baccalaureate degrees:* 128 semester hours, including 32 hours Bible/theology, 42 hours general education, 18 hours professional studies, 4–8 hours field education; 2.0 GPA; last 15 hours in resident. *For seminary/graduate degrees:* semester hour, residence and curricular requirements based on degree program, ranging from one to three years full-time study. Transfer credit allowed up to one-half of degree program. *For all degree programs:* evidence of Christian character and sound doctrinal views; reading of entire Bible.

Fulfillment of some degree requirements and exemption from some beginning courses possible by passing College Board CLEP, AP (Bible College); advanced standing by examination (Seminary). *Grading system:* A–F; withdraw.

Distinctive Educational Programs: Facilities and programs for independent learning. European study tour; study abroad available through Jerusalem University College; Bible College Division cooperative agreements with Midlands Technical College, Summer Institute of Linguistics (University of North Dakota) and Focus on the Family Institute; Seminary branch campus in Korntal, Germany and cooperative agreements with Willow Creek Leadership Institute, Stephen Olford Center for Biblical Preaching, and University of South Carolina.

Degrees Conferred: 4 *associate;* 118 *baccalaureate*; 111 *master's* ; 10 *doctorate*; 19 *first-professional.* Bachelor's degrees awarded: philosophy/religion 118. Master's degrees awarded: education 46, philosophy/religion 82. Doctorates awarded: philosophy/religion 10. First-professional degrees awarded: master of diviinit 19.

Fees and Other Expenses: *Full-time tuition per academic year 2008–09:* Undergraduate $16,210; contact the university for current gradduate and first-professional tution and applicable fees. *Other fees:* $420. *Room and board per academic year:* $6,110. *Books and supplies:* $600. *Other expenses:* $2,000.

Financial Aid: Aid from institutionally generated funds is provided on the basis of academic merit, financial need, other criteria.

Financial aid to full-time, first-time undergraduate students: 86% received some form of aid.

Departments and Teaching Staff: *Total instructional faculty:* 82 (full-time 42, part-time 40). Student/faculty ratio: 11:1.

Enrollment: Total enrollment 923. Undergraduate 480 (full-time 92%; female 53%, male 47%). Graduate 443 (full-time 47%). Undergraduate transfer-in students 443.

Characteristics of Student Body: *Ethnic/racial makeup:* Black non-Hispanic 7%; Hispanic 2%; White non-Hispanic 80%; unknown 9%; nonresident alien 2%. *Age distribution:* number under 18: 8; 18–19: 148; 20–21: 158; 22–24: 85; 25–29: 38; 30–34: 11; 35–39: 6; 40–49: 11; 50–64: 6.

International Students: 18 nonresident aliens enrolled fall 2008. Students from Europe, Asia, Latin America, Africa, Canada. No programs available to aid students whose native language is not English. Financial aid specifically designated for international students.

Student Life: On-campus residence halls house 40% of student body. Residence halls for males constitute 50% of such space, for females 50%. Housing available for married students. *Special regulations:* Cars must be registered and have parking permit. Student dress must be consistent with Christian standards. Residence hall lobbies close at 12am. Quiet hours begin 10pm. Residence hall visitation is limited to lobbies. *Special services:* Learning Resources Center, medical services. *Student publications, radio: The White Napkin; The Finial*, a yearbook. Radio station WCBC broadcasts irregularly. *Surrounding community:* Columbia metropolitan area population 410,000. Served by mass transit bus system; airport 7 miles from campus; passenger rail service 5 miles from campus.

Library Collections: 128,000 volumes including bound books, serial backfiles, electronic documents, and government documents not in separate collections. Online catalog. Current serial subscriptions: 490 paper; 30 microform; 59 via electronic access. 5,552 recordings; 259 142 CD-ROMs. 9 computer work stations. Students have access to the Internet at no charge.

Most important special holdings include collections on missions, sanctification, and Biblical studies.

Buildings and Grounds: Campus area 350 acres.

Chief Executive Officer: Dr. George W. Murray, President.

Address undergraduate admission inquiries to Julia Genhino, Director of Admissions; graduate and seminary inquiries to June Wolfe, Admissions Office Manager.

Converse College

580 East Main Street
Spartanburg, South Carolina 29302-0006
Tel: (864) 596-9000 **E-mail:** info@converse.edu
Fax: (864) 596-9225 **Internet:** www.converse.edu

Institution Description: Converse College is a private, independent, nonprofit college. *Enrollment:* 2,068. Males may enroll in the graduate programs of the College of Arts and Sciences and through the undergraduate exchange program with Wofford College. *Degrees awarded:* Baccalaureate, master's. Education specialist also awarded.

Accreditation: *Regional:* SACS-Comm. on Coll.*Professional*: music

History: Established and chartered 1889; offered first instruction at postsecondary level 1890; awarded first degree (baccalaureate) 1893. *See* Lillian A. Kibler, *History of Converse College* (Spartanburg: Converse College, 1973) for further information.

Institutional Structure: *Governing board:* Board of Trustees of Converse College. Extrainstitutional representation: 30 trustees; institutional representation: president of the college, president of alumni association. 2 ex officio. 31 voting. *Composition of institution:* Administrators 6. Academic affairs headed by president. Management/business/finances directed by vice president for financial affairs. Full-time instructional faculty 80. Academic governance body, the faculty, meets an average of 9 times per year.

Calendar: Semesters. Academic year Sept. to May. Freshmen admitted Sept., Jan., June, July. Degrees conferred and formal commencements May, Aug. Summer session of 3 terms from June to Aug.

Characteristics of Freshmen: 47% of applicants accepted. 25% of accepted applicants enrolled.

88% (144 students) submitted SAT scores; 54% (86students) submitted ACT scores. *25th percentile*: SAT Critical Reading 490, SAT Math 490; ACT Composite 21, ACT English 21, ACT Math 18. *75th percentile*: SAT Critical Reading 600, SAT Math 590; ACT Composite 25, ACT English 26, ACT Math 25.

62% of entering freshmen expected to graduate within 5 years. 64% of freshmen from South Carolina. Freshmen from 25 states and 5 foreign countries.

Admission: Rolling admissions plan. For fall acceptance, apply as early as spring of previous year, but not later than Aug. 1 of year of enrollment. Students are notified of acceptance starting in Sept. *Requirements:* 16 secondary school units which normally include 4 English, 2 in a foreign language, 1 algebra, 1 geometry, 1 history, 7 electives. Additional requirements for music majors. Minimum 2.0 GPA. *Entrance tests:* College Board SAT preferred; ACT composite accepted. *For transfer students:* 2.0 minimum GPA; from 4-year accredited institution 78 hours maximum transfer credit; from 2-year accredited institution 62 hours; good standing at institution previously attended.

College credit and advanced placement for postsecondary-level work completed in secondary school and for College Board CLEP. Tutoring available.

Degree Requirements: *For Bachelor of Arts:* 120 credit hours; 2.0 GPA; 3 semesters in residence; distribution requirements; major and related subject or minor requirements; exit competency examinations/comprehensives in individual fields of study. *For Bachelor of Music:* varies by major; 122–132 credit hours; 2.0 GPA; 3 semesters in residence; distribution requirements; major and related subject or minor requirements; exit competency examinations/comprehensives in individual fields of study.

Fulfillment of some degree requirements and exemption from some beginning courses possible by passing College Board CLEP, APP. Fulfillment of some degree requirements also possible for those whose formal education has been interrupted by passing CLEP General Examination. Exemption from some beginning courses also possible by passing College Board APP. *Grading system:* A–F; pass-fail; withdraw (carries penalty, time limit, and deadline after which pass-fail is appended to withdraw).

Distinctive Educational Programs: *For undergraduates:* Work-experience programs. Double majors. Internships. Career programs in allied health professions, arts management, criminal justice, and judicial administration, interior design, journalism and media, medical technology, urban planning. Preprofessional programs for law, medicine, dentistry, pharmacy, theology. Extensive teacher education programs at undergraduate and graduate levels; elementary, special, early childhood, secondary, and gifted education. Study abroad: London term in alternating years.

ROTC: Army offered in cooperation with Wofford College.

Degrees Conferred: 116 *baccalaureate*;203 *master's*. Bachelor's degrees awarded: biological sciences 5; business and management 24; computer and information sciences 1; education 37; foreign languages 8; mathematics 1; philosophy/religious studies 5; physical sciences 4; psychology 23; social sciences 13; visual and performing arts 51. *Master's:* education 198.

Fees and Other Expenses: *Full-time tuition academic year 2008–09:* \$24,500. *Room and board per academic year:* \$7,530. *Books and supplies:* \$900. *Other expenses:* \$2,650.

Financial Aid: Aid from institutionally generated funds is provided on the basis of academic merit, financial need, athletic ability.

Financial aid to full-time, first-time undergraduate students: 99% received some form of financial aid. Average amount of aid received: federal grants \$4,384; Pell grants \$3,190; other federal aid \$1,228; state/local grants \$7,451; institutional grants \$12,561.

Departments and Teaching Staff: *Total instructional faculty:* 165 (full-time 75, part-time 90). Total faculty with doctorate, first-professional, or other terminal degree: 76. Student/faculty ratio: 14:1.

Enrollment: Total enrollment 2,068. Undergraduate 7,351 (full-time 87%; female 100%).

Characteristics of Student Body: *Ethnic/racial makeup:* Black non-Hispanic: 13%; Asian or Pacific Islander: 1%; Hispanic: 3%; White non-Hispanic: 68%; unknown: 11%; nonresident alien 2%.

International Students: 42 nonresident aliens enrolled fall 2008. Programs available to aid students whose native language is not English: English as a Second Language Program. No financial aid specifically designated for international students.

Student Life: 8 on-campus residence halls house 92% of student body. *Intercollegiate athletics:* female: basketball, cross-country, volleyball, tennis. *Special regulations:* Cars permitted without restrictions. Quiet hours. Residence hall visitation from 7pm to midnight every other weekend. *Special services:* Study Center, Writing Lab, medical services. *Student publications: Concept*, a biannual literary magazine; *Conversationalist*, a biweekly newspaper; *Y's And Other Y's*, a yearbook. *Surrounding community:* Spartanburg population 44,000. Atlanta (GA), 175 miles from campus, passenger rail service 1 mile from campus.

Library Collections: 155,000 volumes. 13,000 microforms; 17,500 audiovisual materials; 700 current periodical subscriptions. Online and card catalogs. 8 computer work stations. Students have access to online information retrieval services and the Internet.

Most important special holdings include collection of over 13,000 recordings and musical scores; Elizabeth Boatwright Coker Collection of South Caroliniana; A. B. Taylor Collection of School prize volumes.

Buildings and Grounds: Campus area 70 acres. Campus DVD available.

Chief Executive Officer: Dr. Nancy Oliver Gray, President.

Address admission inquiries to Director of Admissions.

Erskine College and Theological Seminary

2 Washington Street
Due West, South Carolina 29639
Tel: (864) 379-2131 **E-mail:** admissions@erskine.edu
Fax: (864) 379-2167 **Internet:** www.erskine.edu

Institution Description: Erskine College and Seminary is a private coeducational liberal arts college with a theological seminary. It is affiliated with the Associate Reformed Presbyterian Church. *Enrollment:* 864. *Degrees awarded:* Baccalaureate, first-professional (master of divinity), doctorate (divinity).

Accreditation: *Regional:* SACS-Comm. on Coll. *National:* ATS. *Professional*: theology

History: Established as The Academy at Due West, a men's institution, 1835; changed name to Clark and Erskine Seminary 1837; offered first instruction at postsecondary level 1837; adopted present name 1842; awarded first degree (baccalaureate) 1842; merged with Erskine Theological Seminary (established 1837) 1926; merged with Due West Female College (established 1860) 1927.

Institutional Structure: *Governing board:* Board of Trustees. Representation: 34 trustees. 4 ex officio. *Composition of institution:* Administrators 7. Academic affairs headed by executive vice president and dean of the college. Management/business/finances directed by chief financial officer. Full-time instructional faculty 40.

Calendar: Semesters. Academic year Sept. to May. Freshmen admitted Sept., Feb., June. Degrees conferred and formal commencement May. Summer session of 1 term June-July.

Characteristics of Freshmen: 895 applicants (female 274, male 421). 69% of applicants accepted. 28% of accepted applicants enrolled.

78% (131 students) submitted SAT scores; 22% (36 students) submitted ACT scores. *25th percentile*: SAT Critical Reading 470, SAT Math 500; ACT Composite 22. *75th percentile*: SAT Critical Reading 590, SAT Math 610; ACT Composite 25.

69% of entering freshmen expected to graduate within 5 years. 73% of freshmen from South Carolina. Freshmen from 15 states and 5 foreign countries.

ERSKINE COLLEGE AND THEOLOGICAL SEMINARY—*cont'd*

Admission: Rolling admissions plan. Apply as early as 15 months prior to enrollment. Early acceptance available. *Requirements:* Graduation from accredited secondary school with 14 units in college preparatory courses which must include 4 English, 2 mathematics. *Entrance tests:* College Board SAT or ACT composite. *For transfer students:* 2.0 minimum GPA; from 4-year accredited institution maximum transfer credit limited only by residence requirement; from 2-year accredited institution 64 hours.

College credit and advanced placement for postsecondary-level work completed in secondary school.

Degree Requirements: 124 credit hours; 2.0 GPA overall and in major; last 30 hours in residence; 48–60 hours general education, including 4 terms physical education; junior-senior writing requirement. Fulfillment of some degree requirements and exemption from some beginning courses possible by passing College Board CLEP, AP, or other standardized tests. *Grading system:* A–F; pass-low, pass-fail; authorized withdrawal without penalty; automatic withdraw-fail after mid-term.

Distinctive Educational Programs: January term includes travel courses, preprofessional externship programs, extensive field experiences, independent study projects, exchange possibilities with other 4-1-4 institutions. Dual-degree programs in engineering with Clemson University and University of Tennessee at Knoxville and in medical technology with Medical University of South Carolina. Facilities and programs for independent research. Study skills and tutoring assistance available. Study abroad: Junior Year Abroad at Mansfield College, Oxford University, England; University of St. Andrews, Scotland; Aix-en-Provence, France. January study trips have been taken to England, Europe, Russia, China, Africa, and South America.

Degrees Conferred: 117 *baccalaureate;* 11 *master's*; 10 *doctorate*; 28 *first-professional*> Bachelor's degrees awarded in top five disciplines: business, management, marketing, and related support services 33; education 20; biological/life sciences 17; psychology 9; philosophy/religion/theology 7. Master's degrees awarded: theology 11. Doctorates awarded: 10 theology. First-professional degrees awarded: master of divinity 28.

Fees and Other Expenses: *Full-time tuition per academic year 2008–09:* $23,165 undergraduate; contact the institution for current graduate and first-professional tuition. *Required fees:* $1,435. *Books and supplies:* $1,250. *Room and board per academic year:* $7,961. *Other expenses:* $3,050.

Financial Aid: Aid from institutionally generated funds is provided on the basis of academic merit, financial need, athletic ability. Institution has a Program Participation Agreement with the U.S. Department of Education for eligible students to receive Pell Grants and, depending upon the agreement, other federal aid.

Financial aid to full-time, first-time undergraduate students: 94% received some form of aid.

Departments and Teaching Staff: *Total instructional faculty:* 68 (full-time 40, part-time 28). Student/faculty ratio: 12:1. Degrees held by full-time faculty: 85% hold terminal degrees.

Enrollment: Total enrollment 864. Undergraduate 566 (full-time 99%; female 54%, male 46%). Graduate 296 (full-time 35%). Undergraduate transfer-in students 17.

Characteristics of Student Body: *Ethnic/racial makeup:* White non-Hispanic: 69%; unknown 22%; nonresident alien 25.

International Students: 16 nonresident aliens enrolled fall 2008. Student from Europe, Africa, Australia. No programs available to aid students whose native language is not English. No financial aid specifically designated for international students.

Student Life: On-campus residence halls house over 90% of student body. *Intercollegiate athletics:* male: baseball, basketball, cross-country, soccer and tennis; female: basketball, soccer, softball, tennis. *Special services:* Medical services. *Student publications: The Arrow*, a yearbook; *The Mirror*, a biweekly newspaper; *The Review*, a semiannual literary magazine; *The Pilot*, an annual student handbook. *Surrounding community:* Due West is a village of 1,400; Anderson and Greenwood 20 minutes away; Greenville (population 100,000) less than 1 hour; and Atlanta (GA) and Charlotte (NC) less than 3 hours.

Library Collections: 264,500 volumes including bound books, serial backfiles, electronic documents, and government documents not in separate collections. Online catalog. 63,400 microforms; 2,000 audiovisual materials; 970 current serial subscriptions. Students have access to the Internet at no charge.

Most important special holdings include genealogical collection; Erskine College historical materials; Associate Reformed Presbyterian materials (including Samuel Agnew diaries).

Buildings and Grounds: Campus area 85 acres.

Chief Executive Officer: Dr. Randy Ruble President. Address admission inquiries to Bart Walyer, Director of Admissions; graduate inquiries to Bruce Cooley, Erskine Theological Seminary.

Francis Marion University

P.O. Box 100547
Florence, South Carolina 29501-0547
Tel: (843) 661-1362 **E-mail:** admission@fmarion.edu
Fax: (843) 661-1165 **Internet:** www.fmarion.edu

Institution Description: Francis Marion University is a state institution. *Enrollment:* 4,020. *Degrees awarded:* Baccalaureate, master's.

Accreditation: *Regional:* SACS-Comm. on Coll.

History: Established and offered first instruction at postsecondary level 1970; chartered and awarded first degree (baccalaureate) 1971.

Institutional Structure: *Governing board:* State College Board of Trustees. Extrainstitutional representation: 17 trustees voting. *Composition of institution:* Administrators 55. Academic affairs headed by the provost. Management/business/finances directed by senior vice president for administration and finance. Full-time instructional faculty 159. Academic governance body, Academic Committee, meets an average of 6 times per year.

Calendar: Semesters. Academic year Aug. to May. Freshmen admitted Aug., Jan., May, June, July. Degrees conferred and formal commencements May, Dec. 3 summer terms from May through Aug.

Characteristics of Freshmen: 2,693 applicants (female 1,860, male 833). 67% of applicants admitted. 44% of applicants admitted and enrolled.

72% (567 students) submitted SAT scores; 26% (224 students) submitted ACT scores. *25th percentile*: SAT Critical Reading 420, SAT Math 440; ACT Composite 15, ACT English 18, ACT Math 16. *75th percentile*: SAT Critical Reading 518, SAT Math 530; ACT Composite 32, ACT English 32, ACT Math 32.

35% of freshmen expected to graduate within 5 years. 95% of freshmen from South Carolina. Freshmen from 31 states and 16 foreign countries.

Admission: Rolling admissions plan. For fall acceptance, apply as early as Sept. of senior year in secondary school, but not later than Aug. 1 of year of enrollment. *Requirements:* Either graduation from accredited secondary school or GED. *Entrance tests:* College Board SAT or ACT (exemption applicants 25 years of age or older). For international students TOEFL and SAT. *For transfer students:* 2.0 minimum GPA; from 4-year accredited institution maximum transfer credit limited only by residence requirement; from 2-year accredited institution 65 hours maximum transfer credit; good standing at institution previously attended.

College credit and advanced placement for postsecondary-level work completed in secondary school. College credit for extrainstitutional learning.

Degree Requirements: *For all baccalaureate degrees:* Minimum of 120 credit hours (specific majors may require more than 120 credit hours). *For all undergraduate degrees:* 2.0 GPA; 36 hours in residence for all programs except Business which requires 50% of hours in residence; general education requirements.

Fulfillment of some degree requirements and exemption from some beginning courses possible by passing departmental examinations, College Board CLEP, AP. *Grading system:* Scale of 1–4; withdraw (carries time limit; deadline after which pass-fail is appended to withdraw).

Distinctive Educational Programs: *For undergraduates:* Dual-degree program in engineering with Clemson University. Cooperative majors. Honors programs. Second baccalaureate may be earned with additional 30 hours credit in appropriate area of concentration. *For graduates:* M.Ed. in Remediation. *Available to all students:* Evening classes. Special facilities for using telecommunications in the classroom. *Other distinctive programs:* Continuing education.

Degrees Conferred: 482 *baccalaureate*: 122 *master's*. Bachelor's degrees awarded: biological sciences 42; business and and management 141; communications 18; computer and information sciences 14; education 53; engineering 1; English 17; foreign languages 1; liberal arts 7; mathematics 8; physical sciences 11; psychology 29; social sciences 69; visual and performing arts 10. *Master's*: business/marketing 59; education 51; psychology 12.

Fees and Other Expenses: *Full-time tuition per academic year 2008–09:* undergraduate residence $7,632, nonresident $14,999; contact the university for current graduate resident/nonresident tuition and fees. *Other fees:* $135. *Room and board per academic year:* $6,024. *Books and supplies:* $1,133. *Other expenses:* $4,888.

Financial Aid: Aid from institutionally generated funds is provided on the basis of academic merit, financial need, athletic ability, other criteria.

Financial aid to full-time, first-time undergraduate students: 96% received some form of financial aid. Average amount of aid received: federal grants $4,345; Pell grants 43,430; other federal aid $923; state/local grants $4,626; institutional grants $2,712.

Departments and Teaching Staff: *Total instructional faculty:* 213 (full-time 176, part-time 43). Total faculty with doctorate, first-professional, or other terminal degree: 153. Student/faculty ratio: 17:1. Degrees held by full-time faculty: master's 78%, baccalaureate 15%. 78% hold terminal degrees.

Enrollment: Total enrollment 4,020. Undergraduate 3,469 (full-time 89%; female 67%; male 33%). Graduate 531 (full-time 9%). Undergraduate transfer-in students 276.

Characteristics of Student Body: *Ethnic/racial makeup:* Black non-Hispanic: 44%; American Indian or Alaska Native: 1%; Asian or Pacific Islander: 1%; Hispanic: 1%; White non-Hispanic: 49%; unknown: 3%; nonresident alien 1%. *Age distribution:* number under 18: 143; 18–19: 1,262; 20–21: 949; 22–24: 516; 25–29: 167; 30–34: 74; 35–39: 41; 40–49: 55; 50–64: 17; 65 and over: 2; unknown: 1.

International Students: 40 nonresident aliens enrolled fall 2003. Students from Europe, Asia, Latin America, Africa, Canada. Programs available to aid students whose native language is not English: social, cultural. English as a Second Language Program. No financial aid specifically designated for international students.

Student Life: On-campus residence halls house 44% of student body. 3% of males join fraternities; 5% of females join sororities. *Intercollegiate athletics:* male: baseball, basketball, cross-country, golf, soccer, tennis, track; female: basketball, softball, tennis, volleyball. *Special regulations:* Registered cars permitted without restrictions. Quiet hours on weekdays, 7pm to 10pm. *Special services:* Counseling and Testing Center; health services, career development. *Student publications: The Second Sun*, a weekly newspaper. *Surrounding community:* Florence County population 115,000. Columbia (SC), 80 miles from campus, and Atlanta (GA), 300 miles from campus, are nearest metropolitan areas. Served by airport 4 miles from campus; passenger rail service 7 miles from campus.

Library Collections: 342,500 including bound books, serial backfiles, electronic documents, and government documents not in separate collections. Online catalog. 580,000 miocroforms; 9,200 audiovisual materials; 27,000 e-books; 1,500 current serial subscriptions. Computer work stations available. Students have access to the Internet at no charge.

Most important special holdings include first editions relating to the Pee Dee Region and to colonial and revolutionary South Carolina; books relating to General Francis Marion; Francis Marion University Archives; the Small Arms Technical Publishing Company imprints.

Buildings and Grounds: Campus area 309 acres. Campus DVD available.

Chief Executive Officer: Dr. Luther F. Carter, President.

Undergraduates address admission inquiries to James Schlimmer, Director of Admission; graduate inquires to Ronnie Gamble, Administrative Manager.

Furman University

3300 Poinsett Highway
Greenville, South Carolina 29613
Tel: (864) 294-2000 **E-mail:** admissions@furman.edu
Fax: (864) 294-2018 **Internet:** www.furman.edu

Institution Description: Furman University is a private, nonprofit, independent liberal arts institution. *Enrollment:* 2,977. *Degrees awarded:* Baccalaureate, master's.

Accreditation: *Regional:* SACS-Comm. on Coll. *Professional*: chemistry, music, teacher education

History: Established and chartered as Furman Academy and Theological Institution (for men) 1826; changed name to Furman Theological Institution 1833; incorporated, rechartered, and adopted present name 1850; offered first instruction at postsecondary level 1851; awarded first degree (baccalaureate) 1852; coordinated with Greenville Woman's College (established 1854) 1933; awarded chapter of Phi Beta Kappa 1973; severed formal ties with South Carolina Baptist Convention 1992.

Institutional Structure: *Governing board:* Furman University Board of Trustees. Extrainstitutional representation: 33 trustees. All voting. *Composition of institution:* Administrators 14. Academic affairs headed by vice president for academic affairs and dean. Management/business/finances directed by vice president for business affairs. Full-time instructional faculty 228. Academic governance body, the faculty, meets an average of 9 times per year.

Calendar: Trimesters. Academic year Sept. to May. Freshmen admitted Sept., Jan., Mar., June, July. Degrees conferred and formal commencements May, Aug. Summer session of 2 terms from June to Aug.

Characteristics of Freshmen: 3,870 applicants (female 2,257, male 1,622). 55% of applicants accepted. 32% of accepted applicants enrolled.

95% (651 students) submitted SAT scores; 51% (346 students) submitted ACT scores. *25th percentile*: SAT Critical Reading 590, SAT Math 590; ACT Composite 25. *75th percentile*: SAT Critical Reading 690, SAT Math 690; ACT Composite 31.

86% of freshmen expected to graduate within 5 years. 24% of freshmen from South Carolina. Freshmen from 38 states and 7 foreign countries.

Admission: Rolling admissions plan. For fall acceptance, apply no later than Jan. 15 of year of enrollment. Students are notified of acceptance by Mar. 15. Apply by Nov. 1 for early decision plan. Students are notified of acceptance by Dec. 15. . Early acceptance available. *Requirements:* Graduation from accredited secondary school with 4 units English, 3 mathematics, 3 social studies, 2 natural science, 2 years in same foreign language. *Entrance tests:* Either College Board SAT of ACT required. *For transfer students:* 3.0 minimum GPA; from 4-year accredited institution 64 hours maximum transfer credit; from 2-year accredited institution 64 hours.

College credit and advanced placement for postsecondary-level work completed in secondary school.

Tutoring available. Noncredit developmental courses offered during regular academic year.

Degree Requirements: 128 credit hours; at least 60 hours at Furman; 2.0 GPA; general education requirements; participation in Cultural Life Program.

Fulfillment of some degree requirements and exemption from some beginning courses possible by passing departmental examinations, College Board AP. *Grading system:* A–F; pass-fail; withdraw (carries time limit).

Distinctive Educational Programs: Engaged learning; experiential learning program, undergraduate research, internships, teaching assistantships, independent study, accelerated degree programs. Dual-degree programs in engineering with Auburn University, Clemson University, Georgia Institute of Technology, North Carolina State University, Washington University (St. Louis); in forestry and environmental studies with Duke University. Interdisciplinary programs in Asian-African studies, urban studies, communication studies, women's studies. Facilities and programs for independent research, including individualized majors, tutorials. Study abroad opportunities annually or every other year in England, France, Germany, Spain, Russia and the Baltics, Africa and the Middle East (Israel, Egypt), Japan, China, Costa Rica, Ecuador. *Available to all students:* Evening classes.

ROTC: Army.

Degrees Conferred: 651 *baccalaureate*; 71 *master's*. Bachelor's degrees awarded in top five disciplines: business, management, marketing, and related support services 85; 68; visual and performing arts63; history 79; 61; foreign languages and literature 56; communications/journalism 50. Master's degrees awarded: education 71.

Fees and Other Expenses: *Full-time tuition per academic year 2008–09:* $34,588 undergraduate; contact the university for current graduate tuition. *Required fees:* $488. *Room and board per academic year:* $8,966. *Books and supplies:* $850. *Other expenses:* $2,636.

Financial Aid: Aid from institutionally generated funds is provided on the basis of academic merit, financial need, athletic ability, other criteria.

Financial aid to full-time, first-time undergraduate students: 81% received some form of aid. Average amount of aid received: federal grants $4,545; Pell grants $2,903; other federal aid $1,642; state/local grants $1,642; institutional grants $17,800.

Departments and Teaching Staff: *Total instructional faculty:* 274 (full-time 228, part-time 46). Total faculty with doctorate, first-professional, or other terminal degree: 242. Student/faculty ratio: 11:1.

Enrollment: Total enrollment 2,977. Undergraduate 2,801 (full-time 96%; female 57%, male 43%). Graduate 176 (full-time 29%). Undergraduate transfer-in students 176.

Characteristics of Student Body: *Ethnic/racial makeup:* Black non-Hispanic: 7%; Asian or Pacific Islander: 3%; Hispanic: 2%; White non-Hispanic: 81%; unknown: 5%; nonresident alien 2%. *Age distribution:* number under 18: 25; 18–19: 239; 20–21: 1,290; 22–24: 18; 25–29: 7; 35–39: 2; 40–49: 2; 50–64: 3. 6% of student body attend summer sessions.

International Students: 60 nonresident aliens enrolled fall 2008. Students from Europe, Asia, Latin America, Africa, Canada, New Zealand, Middle East. Programs available to aid students whose language is not English: social, cultural. Financial aid specifically designated for international graduate students.

Student Life: On-campus residence halls house 91% of student body. Five residence halls for males; seven for females; five coed facilities. *Intercollegiate athletics:* male: baseball, basketball, cross-country, football, golf, soccer, tennis, track and field; female: basketball, cross-country, golf, indoor track, outdoor track and field, soccer, softball, tennis, volleyball. *Special regulations:* Registered cars permitted without restrictions. Quiet hours set by residents in individual halls. Visitation from noon to midnight Sun. through Thurs., noon to 2am Fri. and Sat. *Special services:* Learning Resources Center, medical services, counseling center, career services, minority student services, international student advisor. *Student publications, radio: Bonhomie*, a yearbook; *Echo*, a literary journal published on an average of twice a year; *The Paladin*, a weekly newspaper. Radio station WPLS-FM broadcasts 102 hours per week. *Surrounding com-*

FURMAN UNIVERSITY—*cont'd*

munity: Greenville metropolitan population 450,000. Served by airport 19 miles from campus.

Library Collections: 447,000 volumes including bound books, serial backfiles, electronic documents, and government documents not in separate collections. Online catalog. 862,300 microforms; 9,200 audiovisual materials; 13,2000 periodicals including via electronic access. Computer work stations available. Students have access to the Internet at no charge.

Most important special holdings include Baptist Historical Collection; Furman Family Papers, 1777 to present; Haynesworth Papers.

Buildings and Grounds: Campus area 750 acres. Campus DVD available.

Chief Executive Officer: Dr. David E. Shi, President.

Undergraduates address admission inquiries to Woody O'Cain, Director of Admissions; graduate inquiries to Dr. Hazel Harris, Director of Graduate Studies.

Lander University

320 Stanley Avenue
Greenwood, South Carolina 29649
Tel: (864) 388-8000 **E-mail:** admissions@lander.edu
Fax: (864) 388-8125 **Internet:** www.lander.edu

Institution Description: Lander University is a state institution. *Enrollment:* 2,614. *Degrees awarded:* Baccalaureate, master's.

Academic offerings subject to approval by statewide coordinating bodies. Budget subject to approval by state governing boards.

Accreditation: *Regional:* SACS-Comm. on Coll. *Professional*: business, music, nursing, teacher education

History: Established and chartered as Williamson Female College; offered first instruction at postsecondary level 1872; awarded first degree (baccalaureate) 1873; became part of South Carolina Conference of Methodist Episcopal Church South 1898; adopted present name 1904; admitted men 1943; control assumed by Greenwood County 1951; became state college 1973.

Institutional Structure: *Governing board:* Lander University Board of Trustees. Extrainstitutional representation: 16 trustees. All voting. *Composition of institution:* Administrators 34. Academic affairs headed by vice president for academic affairs. Management/business/finances directed by vice president for business and administration. Full-time instructional faculty 120. Academic governance bodies, five policy-making committees, meet an average of 9 times per year.

Calendar: Semesters. Academic year Aug. to May. Freshmen admitted Aug., Jan., June, July. Degrees conferred and formal commencements May, Dec. Summer session of 3 terms from May to Aug.

Characteristics of Freshmen: 2,230 applicants (female 1,550, male 880). 66% of applicants accepted. 45% of accepted applicants enrolled.

72% (408 students) submitted SAT scores; 28% (161 students) submitted ACT scores. *25th percentile*: SAT Critical Reading 420, SAT Math 435; ACT Composite 17. *75th percentile*: SAT Critical Reading 530, SAT Math 540; ACT Composite 21.

52% of entering freshmen expected to graduate within 5 years. 95% of freshmen from South Carolina. Freshmen from 11 states and 7 foreign countries.

Admission: Rolling admissions plan. Apply at any time. *Requirements:* Either graduation from accredited secondary school or GED. Recommend 4 units English, 2 foreign language, 3 mathematics, 3 lab science, 2 social studies, 1 U.S. history, 1 physical education or ROTC. *Entrance tests:* College Board SAT or ACT composite. *For transfer students:* From 4-year accredited institution maximum transfer credit limited only by residence requirement; from 2-year accredited institution 64 hours; correspondence/extension students 15 hours.

College credit and advanced placement for postsecondary-level work completed in secondary school. College credit for extrainstitutional learning.

Tutoring available. Developmental courses offered in summer session and regular academic year; credit given.

Degree Requirements: *For all baccalaureate degrees:* 125 credit hours; 30 hours in residence; 2 hours physical education. *For all degrees:* 2.0 GPA; general education requirements; students must attend 15 lecture/fine arts program events.

Fulfillment of some degree requirements and exemption from some beginning courses possible by passing departmental examinations, College Board CLEP, AP, other standardized tests. *Grading system:* A–F; withdraw (carries time limit); incomplete (carries time limit).

Distinctive Educational Programs: Cooperative education. Evening classes. Dual-degree program in engineering with Clemson University. Individually designed interdisciplinary programs. Institutionally sponsored study abroad at Trent Polytechnic University, England. *Other distinctive programs:* Continuing education.

ROTC: Army offered in cooperation with Presbyterian College.

Degrees Conferred: 404 *baccalaureate*; 41 *master's*. Bachelor's degrees awarded: biological sciences 9; business and management 109; computer and information sciences 12; education 62; English 9; foreign languages 6; health professions 30; liberal arts/general studies 27; mathematics 2; natural resources 4; parks and recreation 16; physical sciences 10; psychology 36; social sciences 57; visual and performing 29. *Master's*: education 41.

Fees and Other Expenses: *Full-time tuition per academic year 2008–09:* undergraduate resident $9,900, nonresident $17,340; contact the university for current graduate resident/nonresident tuition and fees. *Room and board per academic year:* $6,200. *Books and supplies:* $1,000. *Other expenses:* $4,100.

Financial Aid: Aid from institutionally generated funds is provided on the basis of academic merit, financial need, athletic ability, other criteria.

Financial aid to full-time, first-time undergraduate students: 95% received some form of financial aid. Average amount of aid received: federal grants $3,688; Pell grants $2,901; other federal aid $870; state/local grants $4,493; institutional grants $4,273.

Departments and Teaching Staff: *Total instructional faculty:* 141 (full-time 117, part-time 66). Total faculty with doctorate, first-professional, or other terminal degree: 84. Student/faculty ratio: 20:1.

Enrollment: Total enrollment 2,614. Undergraduate 2,555 (full-time 87%; female 65%, male 35%). Graduate 59 (full-time 29%). Undergraduate transfer-in students 215.

Characteristics of Student Body: *Ethnic/racial makeup:* Black non-Hispanic: 26%; American Indian or Alaska Native: 1%; Asian or Pacific Islander: 1%; Hispanic: 15%; White non-Hispanic: 85%; unknown 4%; nonresident alien 3%. *Age distribution:* number under 18: 83; 18–19: 1,011; 20–21: 811; 22–24: 480; 25–29: 153; 30–34: 81; 35–39: 50; 40–49: 49; 50–64: 15. 38% of student body attend summer sessions.

International Students: 78 nonresident aliens enrolled fall 2008. No programs available to aid students whose native language is not English. No financial aid specifically designated for international students.

Student Life: On-campus residence halls house 40% of student body. *Intercollegiate athletics:* male: baseball, basketball, golf, soccer, tennis; female: basketball, cross-country, soccer, softball, volleyball, tennis. *Special regulations:* Cars permitted without restrictions. Residence hall from noon to 11pm <daily. *Special services:* Learning Resources Center, medical services, academic support center, counseling offices, career planning and placement. *Student publications: The Forum*, a bimonthly newspaper; *Review*, an annual literary magazine. *Surrounding community:* Greenwood population 25,000. Atlanta (GA), 155 miles from campus, is nearest metropolitan area.

Library Collections: 204,000 volumes. 2,459 government documents; 92,388 microforms; 1,408 audiovisual materials; 679 current periodical subscriptions plus 916 microform, 127 via electronic access. Computer work stations available. Students have access to online information retrieval services and the Internet.

Most important special holdings include collections on South Carolina; Welsh language, linguistics, and literature.

Buildings and Grounds: Campus area 75 acres.

Chief Executive Officer: Dr. Daniel W. Ball, President.

Address admission inquiries to Bettie Home, Director of Admissions.

Limestone College

1115 College Drive
Gaffney, South Carolina 29340-3799
Tel: (864) 489-7151 **E-mail:** admiss@limestone.edu
Fax: (864) 487-8706 **Internet:** www.limestone.edu

Institution Description: Limestone College is a private, independent, coeducational four-year liberal arts institution. *Enrollment:* 3,255. *Degrees awarded:* Associate, baccalaureate.

Accreditation: *Regional:* SACS-Comm. on Coll. *Professional*: athletic training, music, teacher education, social work

History: Established as Limestone Springs School for women and chartered 1845; changed name to Cooper-Limestone Institute and offered first instruction at postsecondary level 1881; awarded first degree (baccalaureate) 1883; adopted present name 1899; came under control of State Convention of the Baptist Denomination of South Carolina 1921; became independent 1942; admitted males to all programs 1969. *See* Montague McMillan, *Limestone College, A History, 1845–1970* (Columbia: William Bryan Company, 1970) for further information.

Institutional Structure: *Governing board:* Limestone College Board of Trustees. Representation: 38 trustees, including 18 alumni. All voting. *Compo-*

sition of institution: Administrators 29. Academic affairs headed by vice president for academic and student affairs. Management/business/finances directed by vice president for financial affairs. Full-time instructional faculty 54. Academic governance through the Instruction and Academic Policy Committee of the Board of Trustees.

Calendar: Semesters. Academic year Aug. to May. Freshmen admitted Aug., Jan., June. Degrees conferred and formal commencements May, Dec. Summer session of 3 terms from May to Aug.

Characteristics of Freshmen: 2,011 applicants (female 1,131, male 940). 47% of applicants admitted. 58% of applicants admitted and enrolled full-time.

61% (111 students) submitted SAT scores; 28% (51 students) submitted ACT scores. *25th percentile*: SAT Critical Reading 440, SAT Math 450; ACT Composite 17, ACT English 16, ACT Math 16. *75th percentile*: SAT Critical Reading 530, SAT Math 550; ACT Composite 22, ACT English 21, ACT Math 21.

35% of entering freshmen expected to graduate within 5 years. 50% of freshmen from South Carolina. Freshmen from 21 states and 8 foreign countries.

Admission: Rolling admissions plan. For fall acceptance, apply as early as junior year of secondary school, but not later than Aug. 26 of year of enrollment. Early acceptance available. *Requirements:* Either graduation from accredited secondary school or GED. Recommend 12 academic units. Minimum 2.0 GPA. Lowest acceptable secondary school class standing 50th percentile. *For transfer students:* 2.0 minimum GPA; from 4-year accredited institution unlimited hours transfer credit; from 2-year accredited institution 60 hours.

College credit and advanced placement for postsecondary-level work completed in secondary school. College credit for extrainstitutional learning. Developmental courses offered in summer session and regular academic year; pass/fail on developmental courses.

Degree Requirements: 123 semester credit hours; 2 terms in residence (30 semester credit hour minimum with a minimum of 15 semester credit hours in the major), distribution requirements and exemption from some beginning courses possible by passing College Board CLEP, AP. *Grading system:* A–F.

Distinctive Educational Programs: Flexible meeting places and schedules, including off-campus centers for degree-granting extended campus at 9 locations in South Carolina. Programs for independent research, including individual majors, independent study.

Degrees Conferred: 82 *associate;* 397 *baccalaureate: Bachelor's degrees awarded:* biological/life sciences 4; business and management 33; computer and information science 3; education 48; English q; history 5; law/legal studies 3; liberal arts/general studies 10; mathematics 1; physical sciences 1; parks and recreation 5; public administration and social services 5; science technologies 5; visual and performing arts 8; various other disciplines.

Fees and Other Expenses: *Full-time tuition per academic year 2008–09:* $17,300. *Books and supplies:* $1,870. *Room and board per academic year:* $6,400.

Financial Aid: Aid from institutionally generated funds is provided on the basis of academic merit, financial need, athletic ability

Financial aid to full-time, first-time undergraduate students: 98% received some form of aid. Average amount of aid received: federal grants $1,689; Pell grants $2,258; other federal aid $830; state/local grants $3,958; institutional grants $6,215.

Departments and Teaching Staff: *Total instructional faculty:* 65 (full-time 54, part-time 11). Total faculty with doctorate, first-professional, or other terminal degree: 42. Student/faculty ratio: 13:1. Degrees held by full-time faculty: doctorate 56%, master's 98%, baccalaureate 100%. 76.5% hold terminal degrees.

Enrollment: Total enrollment 3,255. Undergraduate 3,255 (full-time 68%; female 62%, male 38%). Transfer-in students 421.

Characteristics of Student Body: *Ethnic/racial makeup:* Black non-Hispanic: 49%; Asian or Pacific Islander: 1%; Hispanic: 2%; White non-Hispanic: 47%; unknown: 1%. *Age distribution:* number under 18: 2; 18–19: 271; 20–21: 261; 22–24: 120; 25–29: 28; 30–34: 17; 35–39: 8 40–49: 3; 50–64: 2.

International Students: 27 nonresident aliens enrolled fall 2008. Students from Europe, Latin America, Canada. No programs available to aid students whose native language is not English. No financial aid specifically designated for international students.

Student Life: On-campus residence halls house consist of 1.2 male and 2.5 female. *Intercollegiate athletics:* male: baseball, basketball, cross-country, golf, lacrosse, soccer, tennis, wrestling; female: basketball, cross-country, golf, lacrosse, soccer, softball, swimming, tennis, volleyball. *Special regulations:* Cars permitted with parking sticker. Residence hall visitation from 10am to 12 midnight Sun.–Thurs., 10am to 2am Fri. and Sat. *Special services:* Program for learning disabled students (PALS); Student Success Center. *Student publications: Calciid*, an annual; *Candelabra*, an annual literary magazine. *Surrounding community:* Gaffney population 13,000. Charlotte (NC), 50 miles from campus, is nearest metropolitan area.

Library Collections: 123,000 volumes including bound books, serial backfiles, electronic documents, and government documents not in separate collections. Online catalog. Current serial subscriptions: 253 paper, 28 microform. 1,200 recordings; 121 DVD discs. Computer work stations available. Students have access to the Internet at no charge.

Most important special holdings include Curriculum Lab (collection for teacher education); music collection (records and scores); archives.

Buildings and Grounds: Campus area 115 acres.

Chief Executive Officer: Dr. Walt Griffin, President.

Address admission inquiries to Mr. Chris Phenicie, Vice President for Admissions.

Lutheran Theological Southern Seminary

4201 North Main Street
Columbia, South Carolina 29203-5898
Tel: (803) 786-5150 **E-mail:** admissions@ltss.edu
Fax: (803) 786-6499 **Internet:** www.ltss.edu

Institution Description: Lutheran Theological Southern Seminary is a graduate professional school of theology of the Evangelical Lutheran Church in America. *Enrollment:* 146. *Degrees awarded:* First-professional; master's.

Accreditation: *Regional:* SACS-Comm. on Coll. *National:* ATS. *Professional*: theology

History: Established by the Lutheran Synod of South Carolina 1830; present campus in Columbia established 1911.

Institutional Structure: *Governing board:* Board of Trustees with representatives from each of the six supporting synods of Virginia, North Carolina, South Carolina, Southeastern, Florida/Bahamas, and Caribbean.

Calendar: Semesters. Academic year Aug. to May. Seven-week summer Greek course for entering students.

Admission: *Requirements:* Bachelor's degree. Applicants should apply by June 1 prior to entrance in the fall.

Degree Requirements: *For master of divinity degree:* 131 credit hours (99 academic credit hours; 32 internship credit hours); 3 years in residence; one year in internship; 2.5 GPA. *For master of arts in religion:* 64 credit hours; at least 22 credit hours in major area; 2.0 GPA.

Distinctive Educational Programs: Field education in parish and institutional settings; Lutheran Theological Center (Atlanta, Georgia), other off-campus opportunities at Urban Training Organization of Atlanta; National Capital Semester for Seminarians and Luther House of Studies (both in Washington, DC); Appalachian Ministry; internship year program. Evening courses.

Degrees Conferred: 8 *master's:* theology; 27 *first-professional:* master of divinity.

Fees and Other Expenses: *Full-time tuition per academic year 2008–09:* $11,375. *Required fees:* $195. *Room per academic year:* $665 per month.

Financial Aid: Aid from institutionally generated funds is provided on the basis of academic merit, financial need. *Graduate aid:* 62 students received $801,844 in federal and state-funded loans; 103 received $308,447 in other fellowships and grants.

Departments and Teaching Staff: *Total instructional faculty:* 19 (full-time 13, part-tame 6). Degrees held by full-time faculty: doctorate 100%.

Enrollment: Total enrollment 171.

International Students: 3 nonresident aliens enrolled fall 2008. No programs available to aid students whose native language is not English. No financial aid specifically designated for international students.

Student Life: Students and their families are encouraged to get involved in the seminary community through student organizations and committees. *Special services:* Seminary food cooperative. *Student publications: Southern Apology*, a student publication; *LTSS Bulletin*, for friends and alumni of the Seminary; *Taproot*, articles by faculty, student research papers, book reviews; *Weekly Newsletter*, calendar of events plus announcements for upcoming week.

Publications: *Southern Accent*, issue-oriented publication for supporters.

Library Collections: 103,000 volumes including bound books, serial backfiles, electronic documents, and government documents not in separate collections. Online catalog. Current serial subscriptions: 400 paper. 5 compact discs; 7 CD-ROMs. 14 computer work stations. Students have access to the Internet at no charge.

Most important special holdings include Lutheranism in the U.S. South; 16th–18th century German Pietism.

Buildings and Grounds: Campus area 15 acres. *New buildings:* Hillcrest Student Housing completed 2005.

Chief Executive Officer: Rev. Dr. Marcus J. Miller, President.

Address admission inquiries to Rev. Thomas Henderson, Director of Admissions.

Medical University of South Carolina

171 Ashley Avenue
Charleston, South Carolina 29425
Tel: (843) 792-3281 **E-mail:** admissions@musc.edu
Fax: (843) 792-3764 **Internet:** www.musc.edu

Institution Description: Medical University of South Carolina is a state institution offering sophomore-level and upper division baccalaureate, first-professional, and graduate degree study. *Enrollment:* 2,433. *Degrees awarded:* Baccalaureate, first-professional (dentistry, medicine, pharmacy), master's, doctorate.

Academic offerings subject to approval by statewide coordinating bodies. Budget subject to approval by state governing boards. Member of Charleston Higher Education Consortium.

Accreditation: *Regional:* SACS-Comm. on Coll. *Professional*: blood bank technology, cytotechnology, dentistry, health services administration, medicine, nurse anesthesia education, nursing, occupational therapy, ophthalmic medical technology, perfusion, pharmacy, physical therapy, practical nursing, radiation therapy

History: Established and offered first instruction at postsecondary level 1824; awarded first degree (doctorate) 1825; chartered 1832; added college of pharmacy 1881, diploma program in nursing 1883, graduate level and baccalaureate program in nursing 1965, allied health college 1966, and dental school 1967. *See* Kenneth M. Lynch, *Medical Schooling in South Carolina 1823–1969* (Columbia, SC: R.L. Bryan, 1970).

Institutional Structure: *Governing board:* Board of Trustees. Representation: 12 trustees (appointed by state legislature) consisting of 6 medical professionals and 6 nonmedical members from each congressional district in South Carolina, and 4 ex officio (members: governor of the state, designee and appointee-at-large, state senator, state representative). All voting. *Composition of institution:* Administrators 18. Academic affairs headed by vice president for academic affairs and provost. Management/business/finances directed by vice president for finance and administration. Academic governance bodies: President's Council meets weekly; Deans Council meets monthly; Academic Council meets monthly.

Calendar: Semesters. Academic year Aug. to May. Admission dates vary with program. Degrees conferred May, Aug., Dec. Formal commencement May.

Admission: See specific schools below.

Degree Requirements: See specific schools below.

Distinctive Educational Programs: Facilities providing student laboratory experience as well as community services, including children's hospital, family medicine clinic, dental clinic, eye institute, psychiatric institute. *Other distinctive programs:* Professional courses offering continuing education credit. Affiliated medical institutions, include Charleston Memorial Hospital, Veterans Administration Hospital. Cooperating in the statewide medical education extension programs are the Richland Memorial Hospital, Columbia; Greenville Hospital System; Spartanburg Regional Medical Center; McLeod Regional Medical Center, Florence; Self Memorial Hospital, Greenwood; Anderson Memorial Hospital. Among other cooperating institutions are Roper Hospital, St. Francis Xavier Hospital, South Carolina State Hospital. The other colleges of the Medical University as well as the Medical University Hospital maintain various ancillary affiliations with agencies, hospitals, and clinics both in and outside the state. The Medical University's educational role is further enhanced as it reaches out to health facilities throughout the state through its Division of Continuing Education and Area Health Education Center program, and the Charleston Higher Education Consortium.

Degrees Conferred: 182 *baccalaureate:* health professions; 269 *master's:* health professions; 30 *doctorate:* health professions. 239 *first-professional:* dentistry, medicine, pharmacy.

Fees and Other Expenses: Contact the university for current tuition, fees, and other costs.

Financial Aid: Aid from institutionally generated funds is provided on the basis of academic merit, financial need. Institution has a Program Participation Agreement with the U.S. Department of Education for eligible students to receive Pell Grants and, depending upon the agreement, other federal aid.

Departments and Teaching Staff: *See individual colleges below.*

Enrollment: Total enrollment 2,528. Undergradaute 316. Graduate 2,212.

Characteristics of Student Body: *Ethnic/racial makeup:* Black non-Hispanic: 13%; American Indian or Alaska Native: 3%; Asian or Pacific Islander: 1%; Hispanic: 2%; White non-Hispanic: 79%; unknown: 4%.

International Students: 1 undergraduate nonresident alien enrolled fall 2008. Programs available to aid students whose native language is not English: social, cultural. English as a Second Language Program. No financial aid specifically designated for international students.

Student Life: *Special regulations:* Cars permitted as space allows. *Special services:* Center for Academic Excellence; computer lab; counseling and psychological services; health services; bus service to and from parking areas; Office of Diversity; employment services and federal work-study program; escort service; financial aid services; fitness assessment and human performance laboratories, off-campus housing service; international programs and services; legal consultation; MUSC Gives Back Community Service Volunteer Program; Wellness Center; Writing Center. *Student publications: Student Lifelines,* biweekly newsletter; *Semester Highlights,* semester-long calendar of campus dates; *Student Handbook*, annual guide to student support services and student life policies; *Catalyst,* university/medical center weekly newspaper. *Surrounding community:* Charleston metropolitan area population 450,000. Served by airport 10 miles from campus, passenger rail service 9 miles from campus.

Library Collections: 220,000 volumes including bound books, serial backfiles, electronic documents, and government documents not in separate collections. Online catalog. Current serial subscriptions: 2,416 paper, 7 microform, 322 electronic. Computer work stations available. Students have access to the Internet at no charge.

Most important special holdings include Waring Historical Library (including rare books and manuscripts relating to history of medicine); Melvin H. Knisely Rheology Collection; MUSC Archives.

Buildings and Grounds: Campus area 55 acres.

Chief Executive Officer: Dr. Raymond S. Greenberg, M.D., President.

Address admission inquiries to Debra Van Pelt, Director of Admissions.

College of Health Professions

Degree Programs Offered: *Baccalaureate* in extracorporeal circulation technology, health sciences, physician assistant; *master's* in anesthesia for nurses, communication sciences and disorders, cytotechnology, health administration, health information administration, medical technology, occupational therapy, periodontics, physical therapy, physician assistant; *doctorate* in health administration.

Admission: Each discipline has individual admission requirements. Consult the university catalog.

Degree Requirements: Each discipline has individual degree requirements. Consult the university catalog.

College of Nursing

Degree Programs Offered: *Baccalaureate, master's, doctorate.*

Admission: *For undergraduates:* 60 semester hours from accredited university or college which must include hours each in English, biology, chemistry (organic), general psychology, developmental psychology, sociology, anatomy, physiology, microbiology, statistics, humanities and electives. Either graduation from accredited secondary school or GED. A minimum GPA of 2.0. *For graduate students:* Baccalaureate degree in nursing from an NLN accredited program with a minimum GPA of 2.5 with 2.75 in nursing and support courses, registered nurse license, acceptable GRE or MAT scores, 3 semester hours in elementary statistics, competency in physical assessment (clinical majors), clinical experience (requirements vary depending upon major chosen), and evidence of professional liability insurance prior to entering the major.

Degree Requirements: *For baccalaureate degree:* 124 credit hours, with an overall GPA of 2.0. *For master's degree:* 37 semester hours for all majors except Nurse-Midwifery, which requires 50 semester hours, 3.0 GPA. *For doctorate:* GRE General Test (minimum combined score of 1500 on three sections required).

Departments and Teaching Staff: Nursing *professors* 3, *associate professors* 22, *assistant professors* 20, *instructors* 11, *part-time teachers* 1. *Total instructional faculty:* 57. Degrees held by full-time faculty: doctorate 24%, master's 76%. 24% hold terminal degrees.

Distinctive Educational Programs: Baccalaureate completion program for registered nurses.

College of Pharmacy

Degree Programs Offered: *Doctor of Pharmacy*; first-professional; Ph.D.

Admission: *For Doctor of Pharmacy:* 67 semester hours from accredited university or college which must include 6 hours in English (3 composition, 3 literature); 8 in general biology, 8 general chemistry, 8 inorganic chemistry, 6 physics, 6 mathematics [3 calculus], 9 in social sciences or humanities electives, 3 economics, 3 statistics, 4 microbiology, 3 psychology, 3 interpersonal communications. 2.5 GPA. PCAT scores. *For Ph.D.:* B.S. degree in a related science with a GPA of at least 3.0, GRE score of 1600 or better.

Degree Requirements: *For Doctor of Pharmacy:* 164 credit hours, 2.0 GPA, 18 months in residence, core requirements. *For Ph.D.:* 48 hours of coursework, research with thesis.

Departments and Teaching Staff: Pharmacy *professors* 12, *associate professors* 12, *assistant professors* 15. *Total instructional faculty:* 39. Degrees held by full-time faculty: doctorate 94.8%, master's 2.6%, baccalaureate 2.6%.

College of Dental Medicine

Degree Programs Offered: *First-professional.*

Admission: 90 semester hours from accredited university or college which must include 6 hours in English; 8 each (including 2 hours laboratory) biology, inorganic and organic chemistry, physics; 6 mathematics. DAT. Strongly recommend baccalaureate degree.

Degree Requirements: 256 credit hours, 2.0 GPA, 45 months in residence, prescribed curriculum, demonstration of professional ethics, and proficiency in the practice of dentistry.

Departments and Teaching Staff: *Professors* 19, *associate professors* 15, *assistant professors* 13, *part-time faculty* 28. *Total instructional faculty:* 75. *Degrees held by full-time faculty:* Doctorate 5%, professional 100%.

Distinctive Educational Programs: Dual-degree program in dentistry and philosophy with College of Graduate Studies. *Other distinctive programs:* Post-doctoral program for specialization in general dentistry, oral surgery, pedodontics, prosthodontics, periodontics, and advanced education in general dentistry. Private collection of dental books and instruments housed by Macauley Museum of Dental History.

College of Medicine

Degree Programs Offered: *First-professional.* In addition, the College of Medicine, in conjunction with the College of Graduate Studies, offers the Medical Scientist Training Program, leading to an M.D.-Ph.D. degree.

Admission: 90 semester hours from an accredited university or college. MCAT. Credentials must be assembled by AMCAS. Strongly recommend baccalaureate degree. South Carolina residency is of primary importance.

Degree Requirements: 207 credit hours, 2.0 GPA, must be 21 years of age, prescribed curriculum, demonstration of professional ethics, and proficiency in the practice of medicine.

Departments and Teaching Staff: *Professors* 151, *associate professors* 157, *assistant professors* 202, *instructors* 76, *part-time faculty* 50. *Total instructional faculty:* 636. Degrees held by full-time faculty: doctorate 14%, master's 5%, baccalaureate 2%, professional 79%. 93% hold terminal degrees.

Distinctive Educational Programs: Dual-degree program in medicine and philosophy with College of Graduate Studies. Cooperative medical scientist program with College of Graduate Studies.

College of Graduate Studies

Degree Programs Offered: *Master's, doctorate* in basic and clinical immunology and microbiology, biochemistry, biometry, cell biology and anatomy, environmental studies, pathology, pharmacology, physiology; *doctorate* in molecular and cellular biology and pathobiology, and pharmaceutical sciences.

Admission: Requirements vary with program and level.

Degree Requirements: Graduate requirements vary.

Departments and Teaching Staff: All faculty have primary appointments in other colleges within the university. Degrees held by full-time faculty: doctorate 100%.

Morris College

100 West College Street
Sumter, South Carolina 29150-3599
Tel: (803) 934-3200 **E-mail:** admissions@morris.edu
Fax: (803) 773-3687 **Internet:** www.morris.edu

Institution Description: Morris College is a private college affiliated with The Baptist Educational and Missionary Convention of South Carolina. *Enrollment:* 921. *Degrees awarded:* Baccalaureate.

Accreditation: *Regional:* SACS-Comm. on Coll.

History: Established 1908; incorporated and offered first instruction at post-secondary level 1911; awarded first degree (baccalaureate) 1915. *See* Julia E. Wells, *A History of Morris College* (Sumter: Morris College, 1979) for further information.

Institutional Structure: *Governing board:* Morris College Board of Trustees. Extrainstitutional representation: 32 trustees; institutional representation: 1 administrator, 1 full-time instructional faculty member, 1 student; 1 alumnus. 9 ex officio. All voting. *Composition of institution:* Administrators (chief administrative officers) 7. Academic affairs headed by academic dean. Business/finances directed by director of business affairs. Full-time instructional faculty 43. Academic governance body, the faculty, meets an average of 12 times per year.

Calendar: Semesters. Academic year Aug. to May. Freshmen admitted Aug., Jan., May, June. Degrees conferred and formal commencement May. Summer sessions May to July.

Characteristics of Freshmen: 100% of applicants accepted. 39% of accepted applicants enrolled.

30% of entering freshmen expected to graduate within 5 years. 94% of freshmen from South Carolina. Freshmen from 14 states.

Admission: Rolling admissions plan. *Requirements:* Either graduation from accredited secondary school with 24 units which must include 4 English, 4 mathematics, 1 social studies, 3 natural science, 1 computer science, 1 economics, 1 government, 1 foreign language, 7 electives; or GED. *Entrance tests:* For foreign students TOEFL. *For transfer students:* 2.0 minimum GPA; from 4-year accredited institution 96 semester hours maximum transfer credit; from 2-year accredited institution 64 semester hours.

College credit for postsecondary-level work completed in secondary school.

Tutoring available. Developmental courses offered in summer session and regular academic year; credit given.

Degree Requirements: 124 semester hours; 2.0 GPA; 2 semesters in residence; distribution requirements. All freshmen are required to take CIS 101 - Introduction to Computers as part of the general education requirements.

Fulfillment of some degree requirements possible by passing College Board CLEP, DANTES, PEP. *Grading system:* A–F; withdraw (carries time limit); incomplete (carries time limit).

Distinctive Educational Programs: Work-experience programs, including cooperative education, internships. Evening classes. Interdepartmental programs in humanities, liberal studies, social studies. Facilities and programs for independent research, including honors programs, individual majors, tutorials. *Other distinctive programs:* Honors program.

ROTC: Army.

Degrees Conferred: 158 *baccalaureate:* biological sciences 5; business and management 40; communications 15; education 6; English 8; health professions and related sciences 34; mathematics 2; parks and recreation 6; philosophy/religious studies 5; protective services/public administration 23; social sciences and history 30. 5

Fees and Other Expenses: *Full-time tuition per academic year 2008–09:* $9,350. *Other fees:* $235. *Room and board per academic year:* $4,250. *Books and supplies:* $1,700.

Financial Aid: Aid from institutionally generated funds is provided on the basis of academic merit, financial need, athletic ability.

Financial aid to full-time, first-time undergraduate students: 99% received some form of financial aid. Average amount of aid received: federal grants $4,000; state/local grants 2,800; institutional grants $750; loans #2,015.

Departments and Teaching Staff: *Total instructional faculty:* 64 (full-time 48, part-time 16). Total faculty with doctorate, first-professional, or other terminal degree: 34. Student/faculty ratio: 19:1. Degrees held by full-time faculty: doctorate 63%, master's 37%. 63% hold terminal degrees.

Enrollment: Total enrollment 921. Undergraduate 921 (full-time 97%; female 58%, male 42%). Transfer-in students 39.

Characteristics of Student Body: *Ethnic/racial makeup:* ack non-Hispanic: 100%. *Age distribution:* number under 18: 7; 18–19: 355; 20–21: 302; 22–24: 135; 25–29: 41; 30–34: 16; 35–39: 16; 40–49: 18; 50–64: 6; 65 and over: 1.

International Students: No international students enrolled.

Student Life: On-campus residence halls house 72% of student body. Residence halls for males constitute 34% of such space, for females 66%. *Intercollegiate athletics:* male: baseball, basketball, track; female: basketball, softball, track. *Special regulations:* Cars with permits allowed. Curfews vary according to residence hall. *Special services:* Learning Resources Center, medical services. *Student publications: The Heritage*, a monthly newspaper; *The Hornet*, a yearbook; *The Bell Ringer*, a biannual literary magazine. *Surrounding community:* Sumter population 25,000. Atlanta (GA), 265 miles from campus, is nearest metropolitan area. Served by airport 60 miles from campus; passenger rail service 40 miles from campus.

Publications: *Faculty Forum* (annual) first published in 1979.

Library Collections: 103,000 volumes including bound books, serial backfiles, electronic documents, and government documents not in separate collections. Online catalog. Current serial subscriptions: 340; 217,000 microforms; 2,100 audiovisual materials. Computer work stations available. Students have access to the Internet at no charge.

Most important special holdings include Library of American Civilization Collection; Coleman Collections (books by and about African Americans);teacher education curriculum materials.

Buildings and Grounds: Campus area 34 acres.

Chief Executive Officer: Dr. Luns C. Richardson, President.

Address admission inquiries to Deborah Calhoun, Director of Admissions and Records.

Newberry College

2100 College Street
Newberry, South Carolina 29108
Tel: (803) 321-5110 **E-mail:** admissions@newberry.edu
Fax: (803) 321-5627 **Internet:** www.newberry.edu

Institution Description: Newberry College is a private college affiliated with the Evangelical Lutheran Church in America. *Enrollment:* 973. *Degrees awarded:* Baccalaureate.

Accreditation: *Regional:* SACS-Comm. on Coll. *Professional*: music, teacher education

History: Established and chartered 1856; offered first instruction at postsecondary level 1859; awarded first degree (baccalaureate) 1869.

Institutional Structure: *Governing board:* Newberry College Board of Trustees. Extrainstitutional representation: 17 trustees; institutional representation: 2 administrators, 2 full-time instructional faculty members, 4 students; 1 alumnus. 10 ex officio. 35 voting. *Composition of institution:* Administrators 29. (includes professional librarians, does not include coaching staff). Academic affairs headed by vice president for academic affairs. Management/business/ finances directed by vice president for business. Full-time instructional faculty 48. Academic governance body, Newberry College Faculty, meets an average of 8 times per year.

Calendar: Semesters. Academic year Aug. to May. Freshmen admitted Aug., Jan., June, July. Degrees conferred and formal commencement Dec., May, Aug. Summer sessions May to Aug.

Characteristics of Freshmen: 1,618 applicants (female 793, male 825). 64% of applicants accepted. 49% of accepted applicants enrolled full-tie.

81% (215 students) submitted SAT scores; 39% (103 students) submitted ACT score/ *25th percentile*: SAT Critical Reading 430, SAT Math 440; ACT Composite 18, ACT English 16, ACT Math 16. *75th percentile*: SAT Critical Reading 530, SAT Math 560; ACT Composite 26, ACT English 26, ACT Math 26.

22% of entering freshmen are expected to graduate within 5 years.

86% of freshmen from South Carolina. Freshmen from 14 states and 3 foreign countries.

Admission: Rolling admissions plan. For fall acceptance, apply as early as Sept. 1 of previous year, but not later than Aug. 1 of year of enrollment. Early acceptance available. *Requirements:* Either graduation from approved secondary school with 18 units which normally include 16 in academic subjects; or GED. Recommend 4 units English, 2 foreign language, 2 laboratory science, 2 mathematics, 1 history. Minimum GPA 2.0. Lowest acceptable secondary school class standing 25th percentile. *Entrance tests:* College Board SAT or ACT composite. *For transfer students:* 2.0 minimum GPA; from 4-year accredited institution 96 hours maximum transfer credit; from 2-year accredited institution 72 hours.

College credit and advanced placement for postsecondary-level work completed in secondary school. College credit for extrainstitutional learning. Developmental courses offered in summer session and regular academic year; credit given.

Degree Requirements: *For all baccalaureate degrees:* 126 credit hours; 2.0 GPA; 2 semesters in residence; 1 physical education course; core requirements.

Fulfillment of some degree requirements and exemption from some beginning courses possible by passing departmental examinations, College Board CLEP, APP. *Grading system:* A–F; pass-fail; withdraw (deadline after which pass-fail is appended to withdraw).

Distinctive Educational Programs: Veterinary Technology baccalaureate degree program. Work-experience programs, including internships, cooperative education, experiential learning. Evening degree completion programs in business administration and psychology. Dual-degree programs in engineering with Clemson University; in forestry with Duke University (NC). Interdisciplinary general honors program. Cooperative program in medical technology with AMA-approved schools. Special facilities for using telecommunications in the classroom, interdisciplinary programs in international studies, and international government and commerce. Study abroad through Central College of Iowa in Austria, England, France, Mexico, Spain, Wales, Germany, The Netherlands; with South Atlantic States Associations for Asian and Africa Studies at Kansai Gaidai University in Japan; term in China or India. Facilities and programs for independent research, including honors programs, tutorials.

ROTC: Army.

Degrees Conferred: 134 *baccalaureate.* Bachelor's degrees awarded in top five disciplines: education 22; parks and recreation 16; business, management, marketing, and related support services 14; communication, journalism, and related programs 11; history 9.

Fees and Other Expenses: *Full-time tuition per academic year 2008–09:* \$21,560. *Books and supplies:* \$1,500. *Room and board per academic year:* \$7,400. *Other expenses:* \$3,710.

Financial Aid: Aid from institutionally generated funds is provided on basis of academic merit, financial need, athletic ability. Institution has a Program Participation Agreement with the U.S. Department of Education for eligible students to receive Pell Grants and, depending upon the agreement, other federal aid.

Financial aid to full-time, first-time undergraduate students: 100% received some form of aid.

Departments and Teaching Staff: *Total instructional faculty:* 70. Student/ faculty ratio: 12.4: 1. Degrees held by full-time faculty: doctorate 71%, master's 29%. 77% hold terminal degrees.

Enrollment: Total enrollment 973. Undergraduate 973 (full-time 98%; female 42%, male 58%). Transfer-in students 62.

Characteristics of Student Body: *Ethnic/racial makeup:* Black non-Hispanic: 24%; Asian or Pacific Islander: 1%; Hispanic: 2%; White non-Hispanic: 68%.; unknown 1%; nonresident alien 4%.

International Students: 40 nonresident aliens enrolled fall 2008. No programs available to aid students whose native language is not English. No financial aid specifically designated for international students.

Student Life: On-campus residence halls house 70% of student body. Residence halls for males constitute 56% of such space, for females 44%. 24% of males join fraternities; 27% of females join sororities. *Intercollegiate sports:* Member of NCAA III and South Atlantic Conference; baseball, basketball (male and female), football, golf, soccer (male and female), softball and volleyball (female). *Intramural sports:* flag football, basketball, volleyball, biking. Approximately 40 organizations (social, religious, service, academic, leadership, political, honor). Career Services include jobshadowing, internships, part-time and full-time employment, career decisions and preparation. *Special regulations:* Registered cars permitted without restrictions. Quiet hours from 8pm to 8am. Residence hall visitation from noon to midnight. *Special services:* Learning Resources Center, medical services, counseling. *Student publications, radio: The Indian*, a biweekly newspaper; *Kinnikinnick*, an annual literary magazine; *The Newberrian*, a yearbook; *Eklekta*, an annual collection of interdisciplinary student research. Radio stations WKDK. *Surrounding community:* Newberry population 10,000. Columbia, 40 miles from campus, is nearest metropolitan area. Served by airport and passenger rail service, each 40 miles from campus.

Publications: *Studies in Short Fiction* (quarterly); *Advances in Management Accounting.*

Library Collections: 100,000 volumes including bound books, serial backfiles, electronic documents, and government documents not in separate collections. Online catalog. Current serial subscriptions: 419 paper, 3 microform. 10 CD-ROMs. Computer work stations available. Students have access to the Internet at no charge.

Most important special collections include Lutheran Church History; South Caroliniana; Newberry College publications.

Buildings and Grounds: Campus area 60 acres. Campus DVD available.

Chief Executive Officer: Dr. Mitchell M. Zais, President.

Address admission inquiries to Jon Reece, Director of Admissions.

North Greenville University

P.O. Boix 1892
Tigerville, South Carolina 29688-1892
Tel: (864) 977-7000 **E-mail:** admission@ngc.edu
Fax: (864) 977-7021 **Internet:** www.ngc.edu

Institution Description: North Greenville University is affiliated with the South Carolina Baptist Convention. *Enrollment:* 1,944. *Degrees offered:* Associate, baccalaureate.

Accreditation: *Regional:* SACS-Comm. on Coll.

History: The college was founded in1892.

Calendar: Semesters. Academic year Aug. to May.

Characteristics of Freshmen: 1,477 applicants (female 734, male 743). 86% of applicants accepted. 69% of accepted applicants enrolled full-time.

85% (498 students) submitted SAT scores; 44% (210 students) submitted ACT scores. *25th percentile*: SAT Critical Reading 440, SAT Math 430; ACT Composite 17. *75th percentile*: SAT Critical Reading 590, SAT Math 570; ACT Composite 23.

80% of freshmen from South Carolina. Freshmen from 22 states and 8 foreign countries.

Admission: *Requirements:* High school graduation; SAT I or ACT. Test scores used for admission and placement. Preference given to Baptists.

College credit and advanced placement for postsecondary-level work completed in secondary school and for extrainstitutional learning (life experience). Tutoring available.

Degree Requirements: *For all undergraduate degrees:* 129 semester hours; 2 mathematics courses; senior project for honors students and some majors. *Grading system:* A–F.

ROTC: Air Force and Army in cooperation with Furman University.

Degrees Conferred: 262 *baccalaureate:* biological/life sciences 4; business, management, marketing, and related support services 51; communications 23; education 40; English 9; interdisciplinary studies 42; liberal arts/general studies 2; philosophy/religion/theology 78; visual and performing arts 9; other 18.

Fees and Other Expenses: *Full-time tuition per academic year 2008–09:* Tuition per academic year: $11,880. *Books and supplies $1,400. Room and board per academic year:* $6,720. *Other expenses:* $4,700.

Financial Aid: Aid from institutionally generated funds is provided on the basis of academic merit, financial need, athletic ability.

Financial aid to full-time, first-time undergraduate students: 96% received some form of aid.

Departments and Teaching Staff: *Total instructional faculty:* 147 (full-time 73, part-time 74). Student/faculty ratio: 18:1.

Enrollment: Total enrollment 1,944. Undergraduate 1,846 (full-time 88%; female 51%, male 49%). Graduate 98 (full-time 100%). Undergraeduate transfer-in students 108.

Characteristics of Student Body: *Ethnic/racial makeup:* Black non-Hispanic: 151; American Indian or Alaska Native: 5; Asian or Pacific Islander: 7; Hispanic: 13; White non-Hispanic: 1,507; unknown: 54. *Age distribution:* number under 18: 120; 18–19: 758; 20–21: 671; 22–24: 215; 25–29: 52; 30–34: 22; 35–39: 15; 40–49: 21; 50–64: 9; 65 and over: 1.

International Students: 28 nonresident aliens enrolled fall 2008. Students from Europe, Asia, Latin America, Africa, Canada. Programs available to aid students whose native language is not English: social, cultural. English as a Second Language Program. Financial aid specifically designated for international students.

Student Life: Intercollegiate and intramural sports. Drama-theatre group; student newspaper; health services.

Library Collections: 50,000 volumes. 3,000 recordings/tapes; 2,950 microform titles; 536 current periodical subscriptions. Online catalog. 10 computer work stations. Students have access to online information retrieval services and the Internet.

Buildings and Grounds: Campus area 400 acres.

Chief Executive Officer: Dr. James Epting, President.

Address admissions inquiries to Charles W. Freeman, Director of Admissions.

Presbyterian College

503 South Broad Street Clinton
South Carolina 29325
Tel: (864) 833-2820 **E-mail:** admissions@presby.edu
Fax: (864) 833-8481 **Internet:** www.presby.edu

Institution Description: Presbyterian College is a private college affiliated with the Presbyterian Synod of South Atlantic. *Enrollment:* 1,177. *Degrees awarded:* Baccalaureate.

Accreditation: *Regional:* SACS-Comm. on Coll.

History: Established and chartered as Clinton College and offered first instruction at postsecondary level 1880; awarded first degree (baccalaureate) 1883; changed name to Presbyterian College of South Carolina 1890; adopted present name 1928.

Institutional Structure: *Governing board:* Presbyterian College Board of Trustees. Representation: 49 trustees (24 representing Synod of South Atlantic, 9 chosen at-large by board, 3 elected alumni). All voting. *Composition of institution:* Administrators 7; department directors 29. Academic affairs headed by senior vice president for academic affairs. Management/business/finances directed by vice president and treasurer. Full-time instructional faculty 88. Academic governance body, the faculty, meets an average of 8 times per year.

Calendar: Semesters. Academic year Sept. to May. Freshmen admitted Sept., Jan., June, July. Degrees conferred and formal commencement May. Summer session of 2 terms from June to Aug.

Characteristics of Freshmen: 1,403 applicants (female 686, male 717). 77% of applicants admitted. 39% of applicants admitted and enrolled full-time.

96% (346 students) submitted SAT scores; 52% (189 students) submitted ACT scores. *25th percentile*: SAT Critical Reading 500, SAT Math 510; ACT Composite 21. *75th percentile*: SAT Critical Reading 610, SAT Math 620; ACT Composite 26.

76% of entering freshmen expected to graduate within 5 years. 67% of freshmen from South Carolina. Freshmen from 20 states and 11 foreign country.

Admission: Rolling admissions plan. For fall acceptance, apply as early as 1 year prior to enrollment, but not later than July 1. Early decision by Nov. 15. *Requirements:* Either graduation from accredited secondary school or GED. *Entrance tests:* College Board SAT or CCT composite. *For transfer students:* 2.5 minimum GPA; from 4-year accredited institution hours maximum transfer credit limited only by residence requirement; from 2-year accredited institution or correspondence/extension school 68 hours.

College credit and advanced placement for postsecondary-level work completed in secondary school.

Degree Requirements: 122 semester hours with a minimum of 48 hours earned in residence; 2.0 GPA; general education courses; completion of requirements within an area of concentration; requirements for the Cultural Enrichment Program.

Fulfillment of some degree requirements and exemption from some beginning courses possible by passing departmental examinations, College Board CLEP, AP. *Grading system:* A, A-, B+, B-, C+, C-, D+, D, F, pass-fail; withdraw (may carry penalty); incomplete (carries time limit).

Distinctive Educational Programs: Dual-degree programs in engineering with Auburn University (AL), Clemson University (SC), Vanderbilt University (TN), and Mercer University (GA); forestry with Duke University (NC); allied health sciences with College of Nursing, Medical University of South Carolina, and Christian education with Presbyterian School of Christian Education (VA). Honors Program. Russell Program (series of programs on various issues and events dealing with the media). Study abroad programs are scheduled through Central College of Iowa in Austria, England, France, Mexico, Spain, Wales, Germany, and The Netherlands. A Term-in-China or Term-in-India is available through the South Atlantic States Association for Asian and African Studies and at the Kansai Gaidai University in Japan. Other foreign studies may be cleared through the college registrar.

ROTC: Army.

Degrees Conferred: 247 *baccalaureate:*. Bachelor's degrees awarded in top five disciplines: business/marketing 50; social sciences 31; history 30; education 29; biological/life sciences 28.

Fees and Other Expenses: *Full-time tuition per academic year 2008–09:* $27,902. *Required fees:* $2,192. *Room and board per academic year:* $8,064. *Books and supplies:* $580. *Other expenses:* $2,750.

Financial Aid: Aid from institutionally generated funds is provided on the basis of academic merit, financial need, athletic ability, other criteria.

Financial aid to full-time, first-time undergraduate students: 98% received some form of aid.

Departments and Teaching Staff: *Total instructional faculty:* 130 (full-time 83, part-time 47). Total faculty with doctorate, first-professional, or other terminal degree: 87. Student/faculty ratio: 14:1.

Enrollment: Total enrollment 1,177. Undergraduate 1,177 (full-time 96%; female 49%, male 51%). Transfer-in students 23.

Characteristics of Student Body: *Ethnic/racial makeup:* Black non-Hispanic: 8%; Asian or Pacific Islander 1%; Hispanic: 1%; White non-Hispanic: 86%; unknown: 3%. *Age distribution:* number under 18: 49; 18–19: 561; 20–21: 510; 22–24: 771 25–29: 31 30–34: 1; 35–39: 1; 40–49: 3; 65 and over: 1.

International Students: 17 nonresident aliens enrolled fall 2008. Students from Europe, Asia, Latin America, Africa, Canada. No programs available to aid students whose native language is not English. No financial aid specifically designated for international students.

Student Life: On-campus residence halls house 96% of student body. Residence halls for males constitute 50% of such space, for females 50%. 41% of males join and 10% live in fraternity housing. 94% of students live on campus. *Intercollegiate athletics:* male: basketball, cross-country, golf, soccer, tennis; female: basketball, cross-country, golf, soccer, softball, tennis, volleyball. *Special regulations:* Cars permitted without restrictions. Each year each residence hall votes on its own visitation policy based on 2/3 majority. *Special services:* Learning Resources Center, medical services, student activities transcripts, peer connectors (advisors), extensive intramural activities, career planning programs. *Student publications: The Blue Stocking*, a weekly newspaper; *Figs and Thistles*, an annual literary magazine; *PaC SaC*, a yearbook. *Surrounding community:* Clinton population 9,500. Atlanta (GA), 180 miles from campus, is nearest metropolitan area.

Library Collections: 135,800 volumes. 9,300 microforms; 10,000 audiovisual materials; 3,970 periodical subscriptions. Online catalog. Students have access to online information retrieval services and the Internet.

Most important special holdings: Founder's Library; Smith College (Southern history, religion, culture); Jackson-Arnold Collection.

Buildings and Grounds: Campus area 240 acres.

Chief Executive Officer: John V. Griffith, President.

Address admission inquiries to Leni N. Paterson, Dean of Admissions.

South Carolina State University

300 College Avenue, N.E.
Orangeburg, South Carolina 29115
Tel: (803) 536-7000 **E-mail:** admissions@scsu.edu
Fax: (803) 536-8890 **Internet:** www.scsu.edu

Institution Description: South Carolina State College is a state institution. *Enrollment:* 4,888. *Degrees awarded:* Baccalaureate, master's, doctorate. Education specialist also awarded.

Academic offerings subject to approval by statewide coordinating bodies. Budget subject to approval by state governing boards.

Accreditation: *Regional:* SACS-Comm. on Coll. *Professional*: computer science, engineering technology, family and consumer science, music, nursing, speech-language pathology, social work, teacher education

History: Established and chartered as Colored Normal, Industrial, Agricultural and Mechanical College of South Carolina, and offered first instruction at postsecondary level 1896; awarded first degree (baccalaureate) 1897; became South Carolina State College 1954; received university status 1992. *See* John F. Potts, Sr., *The History of South Carolina State College* (Columbia, SC: R. L. Bryan Company, 1978) for further information.

Institutional Structure: *Governing board:* South Carolina State University Board of Trustees. Extrainstitutional representation: 13 trustees; institutional representation: 1 student; 1 alumnus, 1 faculty. 1 ex officio. 13 voting. *Composition of institution:* Administrators 57. President's cabinet consist of 1 senior vice president; 4 vice presidents; 2 executive directors, 1 director. Management/business/finances directed by senior vice president. Academic affairs headed by vice president. Academic governance body, Faculty Senate, meets an average of 9 times per year.

Calendar: Semesters. Academic year Aug. to May. Freshmen admitted Aug., Jan., June. Degrees conferred and formal commencement Dec., May. Summer session of 2 terms from June to July.

Characteristics of Freshmen: 3,245 applicants (female 1,947, male 1,298). 79% of applicants accepted. 43% of accepted applicants enrolled full-time.

64% (560 students) submitted SAT scores; 36% (319 students) submitted ACT scores. *25th percentile*: SAT Critical Reading 370, SAT Math 380; ACT Composite 15. *75th percentile*: SAT Critical Reading 458, SAT Math 470; ACT Composite 18.

465 of entering freshmen expected to graduate within 5 years. 79% of freshmen from South Carolina. Freshmen from 23 states and 5 foreign countries.

Admission: Rolling admissions plan. For fall acceptance, apply as early as 1 year prior to enrollment, but not later than July 31 of year of enrollment. *Requirements:* Graduation from accredited secondary school with 4 units in English, 3 mathematics (algebra I, II, and geometry), 2 science (from biology, chemistry, or physics), 2 of the same foreign language, 2 social studies. GED accepted. *Entrance tests:* SAT or ACT. For first-year foreign students: TOEFL. *For transfer students:* 2.0 minimum GPA; from 4-year and 2-year accredited institutions maximum transfer credit limited only by residence requirement.

Advanced placement credit for grades of 3. College credit for extrainstitutional learning.

Degree Requirements: 120–140 credit hours; 2.0 GPA; 30 hours in residence; 4 courses physical education or ROTC; general education requirements; exit competency examination in English.

Fulfillment of some degree requirements and exemption from some beginning courses possible by passing departmental examinations, College Board CLEP. *Grading system:* A–F; pass-fail; withdraw (deadline after which pass-fail is appended to withdraw); satisfactory-unsatisfactory.

Distinctive Educational Programs: Work-experience programs, including cooperative education, internships. Weekend and evening classes. Accelerated degree programs. Cooperative baccalaureate programs in agriculture and nursing with Clemson University. Preprofessional programs in agriculture, dentistry, medicine, optometry, veterinary medicine. Tutorials. Study abroad.

ROTC: Army.

Degrees Conferred: 554 *baccalaureate*; 115 *master's*; 13 *doctorate*. Bachelors's degrees awarded in top five disciplines: business, management, marketing, and related support services 90; protective engineering technologies 54; biological/life sciences 31; psychology 49; family and consumer sciences 40. *Master's*: agriculture 1; education 66; family and consumer sciences 8; health professions 29; transportation and materials moving 11. Doctorates awarded: education 13.

Fees and Other Expenses: *Full-time tuition per academic year 2008–09:* $7,806 resident, $15,298 nonresident. *Room and board per academic year:* $7,658. *Books and supplies:* $1,200. *Other expenses:* $3,150.

Financial Aid: Aid from institutionally generated funds is provided on the basis of academic merit, financial need, athletic ability, other considerations.

Financial aid to full-time, first-time undergraduate students: 99% received some form of aid. Average amount of aid received: federal grants $4,090; Pell grants $3,425; other federal aid $785; state/local grants $3,020; institutional grants $5,629.

Departments and Teaching Staff: *Total instructional faculty:* 267. Degrees held by full-time faculty: doctorate 63.2%, master's 35%, baccalaureate 1.8%. 63.2% old terminal degrees.

Enrollment: Total enrollment 4,888. Undergraduate 4,153 (full-time 89%; female 55%, male 45%). Graduate 735 (full-time 40%). Undergraduate transfer-in students 209.

Characteristics of Student Body: *Ethnic/racial makeup:* Black non-Hispanic 96%; White non-Hispanic: 2%; unknown 1%. *Age distribution:* number under 18: 28; 18–19: 1,482; 20–21: 1,267; 22–24: 655; 25–29: 122; 30–34: 60; 35–39: 55; 40–49: 81; 50–64: 39.

International Students: 197 nonresident aliens enrolled fall 2008. Students from Europe, Asia, Latin America, Africa, Canada, Middle East. No programs available to aid students whose native language is not English. No financial aid specifically designated for international students.

Student Life: On-campus residence halls house 45% of student body. Residence halls for males constitute 55% of such space, for females 45%. 1% of married students request institutional housing and are so housed. *Intercollegiate athletics:* male: basketball, football, cross-country, golf, tennis, track, female: basketball, soccer, softball, tennis, track, cross-country, volleyball. *Special regulations:* Registered cars permitted on campus. *Special services:* tutorial center, writing lab, health center. *Student publications: Collegian*, a monthly newspaper; *Bulldog*, a yearbook. *Surrounding community:* Metropolitan Orangeburg population 45,000. Columbia (SC), 45 miles away, is nearest metropolitan area.

Library Collections: 1,462,000 volumes. 77,000 federal government documents; 18,400 state government documents; 840,500 microforms; 1,081 current periodical subscriptions. Online catalog. Computer work stations available. Students have access to online information retrieval services and the Internet.

Most important special holdings include books by and about African Americans; Congressman James E. Clyburn Papers; South Carolina State University Archives.

Buildings and Grounds: Campus area 142 acres.

Chief Executive Officer: Dr. Andrew Hugine, Jr., President.

Address admission inquiries to Dorothy L. Brown, Director of Admissions.

Southern Wesleyan University

907 Wesleyan Drive
P.O. Box 1020
Central, South Carolina 29630-1020
Tel: (864) 644-5000 **E-mail:** admissions@swu.edu
Fax: (864) 644-5900 **Internet:** www.swu.edu

Institution Description: Southern Wesleyan University, formerly known as Central Wesleyan College, is a private institution affiliated with The Wesleyan Church of America. *Enrollment:* 2,391. *Degrees awarded:* Associate, baccalaureate, master's.

Member of the Council of Christian College and Universities.

Accreditation: *Regional:* SACS-Comm. on Coll.

History: Established as Wesleyan Methodist College 1906; awarded first degree (baccalaureate) 1908; chartered 1909; adopted present name 1959.

Institutional Structure: *Governing board:* Board of Trustees of Central Wesleyan College. Extrainstitutional representation: 35 trustees; institutional representation: president of the college. 1 ex officio. *Composition of institution:* Administrators 6. Academic affairs headed by academic vice president. Management/business/finances directed by vice president of finance. Full-time instructional faculty 41. Academic governance body, the faculty, meets an average of 8 times per year.

Calendar: Semesters. Academic year Aug. to May. Freshmen admitted Aug., Jan., May. Degrees conferred and formal commencement Aug., Dec., May. Summer session from May to July.

Characteristics of Freshmen: 317 applicants (female 190, male 127). 70% of applicants admitted. 35% of applicants admitted and enrolled full-time.

79% (96 students) submitted SAT scores; 48% (59 students) submitted ACT scores. *25th percentile*: SAT Critical Reading 445, SAT Math 440; ACT Composite 17. *75th percentile*: SAT Critical Reading 560, SAT Math 570; ACT Composite 22.

36% of entering freshmen expected to graduate within 5 years. 82% of freshmen from South Carolina. Freshmen from 26 states and 15 foreign countries.

Admission: Rolling admissions plan. Apply as early as 1 year prior to enrollment, but not later than day of registration. Early acceptance available. *Requirements:* Either graduation from accredited secondary school with 16 units which must include 4 English, 2 mathematics, 2 science, 2 social studies; or GED. Minimum 2.0 GPA. *Entrance tests:* College Board SAT or ACT composite. For foreign students TOEFL. *For transfer students:* From 4-year accredited institution minimum 2.0 GPA, maximum transfer credit limited only by residence requirement; from 2-year accredited institution minimum 2.0 GPA, 68 hours maximum transfer credit.

College credit and advanced placement for postsecondary-level work completed in secondary school.

Tutoring available. Developmental courses offered in regular sessions.

Degree Requirements: 128 semester hours; 2.0 GPA; 32 hours in residence; writing, math, computer competency required; chapel attendance twice weekly. 3 hours physical education; general education requirements.

Fulfillment of some degree requirements and exemption from some beginning courses possible by passing departmental examinations, College Board CLEP, AP. *Grading system:* 1.0–4.0; no credit; incomplete; pass; withdraw.

Distinctive Educational Programs: Cooperative baccalaureate in medical technology and nursing with approved hospitals or schools. Facilities and programs for independent research, including honors programs, tutorials. Limited cross-registration with Clemson University. Leadership Education for the Adult Profession (LEAP) for working adults who wish to obtain Bachelor of Science degree in the Management of Human Resources, Business Administration, or Associate of Science in General Business. Classes meet at night and on weekends throughout South Carolina. Master's degree also offered in this schedule format. Study abroad: Mini-course in England; Council of Christian Colleges and Universities Study Semesters.

Degrees Conferred: 402 *baccalaureate:* biological sciences 3; business and management 175; computer and information sciences 7; education 46; English 8; health professions 1; parks and recreation 6; philosophy/religion/theology 10; physical sciences 2; psychology 8; visual and performing arts. *Master's:* business/marketing 122; education 122; theology 1.

Fees and Other Expenses: *Full-time tuition per academic year 2008–09:* $18,000. *Books and supplies:* $950. *Room and borad per academic year:* $7,450. *Other expenses:* $1,950.

Financial Aid: Aid from institutionally generated funds is provided on the basis of academic merit, financial need, athletic ability, other criteria.

Financial aid to full-time, first-time undergraduate students: 98% received some form of aid. Average amount of aid received: federal grants $4,253; Pell grants $3,079; other federal aid $1,266; state/local grants $8,217; institutional grants $6,904.

Departments and Teaching Staff: *Total instructional faculty:* 246 (full-time 48, part-time 198). Total faculty with doctorate, first-professional, or other terminal degree: 100. Student/faculty ratio: 17:1. Degrees held by full-time faculty: doctorate 75%, master's 25%. 75% hold terminal degrees.

Enrollment: Total enrollment 2,391. Undergraduate 1,631 (full-time 98%; female 63%, male 37%). Graduate 760 (full-time 100%). Undergraduate transfer-in students 53.

Characteristics of Student Body: *Ethnic/racial makeup:* Black non-Hispanic: 29%; American Indian or Alaska Native: 1%; Hispanic: 2%; White non-Hispanic: 29%; unknown: 6%; nonresident alien 1%. *Age distribution:* number under 18: 14; 18–19: 178; 20–21: 71; 22–24: 127; 25–29: 299; 30–34: 346; 35–39: 304; 40–49: 900; 50–64: 128.

International Students: 24 nonresident aliens enrolled fall 2008. No programs available to aid students whose native language is not English. No financial aid specifically designated for international students.

Student Life: On-campus residence halls house 520 students. *Intercollegiate athletics:* male: baseball, basketball, cross-country, golf, soccer; female: cross-country, basketball, softball, volleyball. *Special regulations:* Cars permitted without restrictions. Shirts required. Curfews. Quiet hours. *Special services:* Medical, counseling, Learning Assistance Center. Lifestyle expectations include chapel attendance, modesty in dress, limitation on residence hall visitation, no alcohol or tobacco permitted. *Student publications:* An annual literary magazine; *The Centralian,* a yearbook; annual literary magazine and editorial newspaper offered through courses. *Surrounding community:* Central population 3,000. Atlanta (GA), 125 miles from campus, is nearest metropolitan area. Served by airport 40 miles from campus; passenger rail service 5 miles from campus.

Library Collections: 109,000 volumes including bound books, serial backfiles, electronic documents, and government documents not in separate collections. Online catalog. 2,200 microforms; 4,000 audiovisual materials; 530 current serial subscriptions. Computer work stations available. Students have access to the Internet at no charge.

Most important special collections include Nicholson Collection of Wesleyan Church History; Clayton Genealogical Collection.

Buildings and Grounds: Campus area 200 acres. Campus DVD available.

Chief Executive Officer: Dr. David Spittal, President.

Address admission inquiries to Chad Peters, Director of Admissions.

University of South Carolina - Aiken

471 University Parkway
Aiken, South Carolina 29801
Tel: (803) 648-6851 **E-mail:** admit@aiken.sc.edu
Fax: (803) 641-3362 **Internet:** www.usca.sc.edu

Institution Description: *Enrollment:* 3,232. *Degrees awarded:* Associate, baccalaureate, master's.

Accreditation: *Regional:* SACS-Comm. on Coll. *Professional*: business, engineering, journalism, nursing, teacher education

History: Established as an off-campus center of University of South Carolina (Columbia) 1961; awarded first degree (associate) and became branch campus of University of South Carolina 1968; became 4-year institution 1974; became academically autonomous 1976.

Institutional Structure: *Composition of institution:* Administrators 22. Academic affairs headed by vice chancellor-academic affairs. Management/business/finances directed by associate chancellor. Full-time instructional faculty 148. Academic governance body, faculty assembly, meets an average of 7 times per year.

Calendar: Semesters. Academic year Aug. to May. Degrees conferred May, Aug., Dec. Formal commencement May. Summer session of 2 terms from May to Aug.

Characteristics of Freshmen: 2,422 applicants (female 1,598, male 824). 95% of applicants accepted. 73% of accepted applicants enrolled full-time.

84% (563 students) submitted SAT scores; 33% (222 students) submitted ACT scores. *25th percentile*: SAT Critical Reading 440, SAT Math 460, SAT Writing 430, SAT Essay 6; ACT Composite 18, ACT English 18, ACT Math 16. *75th percentile*: SAT Critical Reading 530, SAT Math 550, SAT Writing 520, SAT Essay 8; ACT Composite 22, ACT English 22, ACT Math 22.

35% of entering freshmen expected to graduate within 5 years. 35% of freshmen from South Carolina. Freshmen from 34 states and 12 foreign countries.

Admission: Various categories of admissions: freshman, readmits, transfer, international students. High school graduation.

Degree Requirements: Completion of prescribed curriculum including general education requirements; minimum of 120 semester credit hours and GPA of at least 2.o are required for the baccalaureate degree.

Distinctive Educational Programs: Work-experience programs. Evening classes. Cooperative master's degree programs with University of South Carolina (Columbia). Interdisciplinary programs.

Degrees Conferred: 25 *associate*; 502 *baccalaureate*; 17 *master's*. Bachelor's degrees awarded in top five disciplines: business, management, marketing, and related support services 161; education 82; health professions and related clinical sciences 41; communication, journalism, and related programs 30; social sciences 29. Master's degrees awar4ded: education 10, psychology 7.

Fees and Other Expenses: *Full-time tuition per academic year 2008–09:* resident $7,382; nonresident $14,946. *Books and supplies:* $1,080. *Room and board per academic year:* $6,940. *Other expenses:* $3,340.

Financial Aid: Aid from institutionally generated funds is provided on the basis of academic merit, financial need, athletic ability, other criteria.] Institution has a Program Participation Agreement with the U.S. Department of Education for eligible students to receive Pell Grants and, depending upon the agreement, other federal aid.

Financial aid to full-time, first-time undergraduate students: 96% received some form of aid. Average amount of aid received: federal grants $3,890; Pell grants $3,059; other federal aid $871; state/local grants $4,317; institutional grants $2,178.

Departments and Teaching Staff: *Total instructional faculty:* 265 (full-time 148, part-time 117). Student/faculty ratio: 14:1. Degrees held by full-time faculty: doctorate 74%, master's 26%. 75% hold terminal degrees.

Enrollment: Total enrollment 3,232. Undergraduate 3,078 (full-time 78%; female 67%, male 23%). Graduate 154 (full-time 10%). Undergraduate transfer-in students 267.

Characteristics of Student Body: *Ethnic/racial makeup:* Black non-Hispanic: 27%; Asian or Pacific Islander:1%; Hispanic: 2%; White non-Hispanic: 64%; unknown: 5%; nonresident alien 2%.

International Students: 64 nonresident aliens enrolled fall 2008. Students from Europe, Asia, Latin America, Canada, Australia, New Zealand. No programs to aid students whose native language is not English. Financial aid specifically designated for international students: Scholarships available annually to qualifying students.

Student Life: No on-campus housing. 10% of student body housed in privately owned and operated residence halls. 53 student organizations; 2 fraternities, 3 sororities; 5 honor societies. *Intercollegiate athletics:* Member NCAA II and charter member of the Peach Belt Athletic Conference. Males compete in:

UNIVERSITY OF SOUTH CAROLINA - AIKEN—*cont'd*

baseball, basketball, cross-country, soccer, tennis, golf; females compete in: basketball, cross-country, softball, volleyball. *Special services:* orientation programs; counseling; career services; disabled student services; math tutoring center; writing center; multicultural affairs office; academic advising. *Student publication: Pacer Times*, published weekly during major semesters. *Surrounding community:* Aiken County population 133,100. Augusta, 14 miles from campus, is nearest metropolitan area. Campus is one hour drive to Columbia, S.C.

Library Collections: 135,000 volumes. 52,000 government documents; 20,500 microforms; 850 current periodical subscriptions. Online catalog. Students have access to online information retrieval services.

Most important special holdings include May Collection of Southern history; U.S. Department of Energy Public Reading Room Documents Collection; Graniteville Co.'s historical files (1845–present).

Buildings and Grounds: Campus area 144 acres.

Chief Executive Officer: Dr. Thomas L. Hallman, Chancellor.

Address undergraduate admission inquiries to Andrew Hendricks, Director of Admissions; graduate inquiries to Coordinator of Graduate Studies.

University of South Carolina - Columbia

Columbia, South Carolina 29208

Tel: (803) 777-7000 **E-mail:** admissions@sc.edu
Fax: (803) 777-0101 **Internet:** www.sc.edu

Institution Description: The University of South Carolina is a state university system of eight campuses. The Columbia campus offers undergraduates, graduate, and first-professional degree study; the campuses at Aiken and Spartanburg offer undergraduate degrees. *Enrollment:* 27,488. *Degrees awarded:* Associate, baccalaureate, first-professional (law, medicine, pharmacy), master's, doctorate.

Member of the consortium Oak Ridge Associated Universities.

Accreditation: *Regional:* SACS-Comm. on Coll. *Professional*: art, business, chemistry, engineering, journalism, law, librarianship, music, nursing, pharmacy, psychology internship, public health, rehabilitation counseling, social work, speech-language pathology, teacher education

History: Established as South Carolina College and chartered 1801; offered first instruction at postsecondary level 1805; awarded first degree (baccalaureate) 1807; changed name to University of South Carolina 1865, to College of Agriculture and Mechanical Arts 1880, to South Carolina College 1882, to University of South Carolina 1887, to South Carolina College 1890; adopted present name 1906. *See* D. W. Hollis, *South Carolina College* (Columbia: University of South Carolina Press, 1951) for further information.

Institutional Structure: *Composition of institution:* Administrators 76. President assisted by a vice president for academic affairs and provost, and vice presidents for advancement, business and finance, human resources and student affairs. Full-time instructional faculty 1,169. Academic governance body, Faculty Senate, meets 10 times per year.

Calendar: Semesters. Academic year Aug. to May. Degrees conferred at formal commencements May, Aug., and Dec. Summer session of 2 terms from June to Aug.

Characteristics of Freshmen: 14,994 applicants (female 8,838, male 6,536). 59% of applicants accepted. 43% of accepted applicants enrolled full-time.

82% (3,057 students) submitted SAT scores; 18% (666 students) submitted ACT scores. *25th percentile*: SAT Critical Reading 520, SAT Math 540; ACT Composite 22. *75th percentile*: SAT Critical Reading 630, SAT Math 640; ACT Composite 27.

61% of entering freshmen expected to graduate within 5 years. 67% of freshmen from South Carolina. Freshmen from 39 states and 14 foreign countries.

Distinctive Educational Programs: Flexible meeting places and schedules, including off-campus centers (at various locations throughout the state), weekend and evening classes. Special facilities for using telecommunications in the classroom. Facilities and programs for independent research, including honors programs, individual majors, small business development center, Social and Behavioral Sciences Laboratory, Southern Studies Facilities. Participant in 56 educational exchange programs.

ROTC: Army, Navy; Air Force in cooperation with Benedict College.

Degrees Conferred: 9 *associate*; 3,459 *baccalaureate*; 1,652 *master's*; 244 *doctorates*; 383 *first-professional*. Bachelor's degrees awarded in top five disciplines: business/marketing 863; social sciences 539; communications/journalism 298; psychology 237;] engineering 196. Master's degrees awarded in top five disciplines: business/marketing 339; education 319; public administration 230; health professions 174; library science 126. Doctorates awarded in top five disciplines: health professions 43; engineering 28; physical sciences 19; psychology 19; social sciences 17. First-professional degrees awarded: pharmacy 71; law 247; medicine 65.

Fees and Other Expenses: *Full-time tuition per academic year 2008–09:* resident $8,838, nonresident $22,908; contact the university for current graduate and first-professional tuition and fees that vary by program. *Required fees:* 400. *Books and supplies:* $936/ *Room and board per academic year:* $7.318. *Other expenses:* $3,955.

Financial Aid: Aid from institutionally generated funds is provided on the basis of academic merit, financial need, athletic ability.

Financial aid to full-time, first-time undergraduate students: 88% received some form of aid. Average amount of aid received: federal grants $4,098; Pell grants $3,090; other federal aid $1,116; state/local grants $5,341; institutional grants $3,545.

Departments and Teaching Staff: *Total instructional faculty:* 1,552 (full-time 1,166, part-time 386). Total faculty with doctorate, first-professional, or other terminal degree: 1,149. Student/faculty ratio: 18:1. Degrees held by full-time faculty: master's 10%, doctorate 85%, professional 4%. 85% hold terminal degrees.

Enrollment: Total enrollment 27,588. Undergraduate 19,785 (full-time 93%; female 55%, male 45%). Graduate 7,723. Undergraduate transfer-in students 1,571.

Characteristics of Student Body: *Ethnic/racial makeup:* Black non-Hispanic: 12%; Asian or Pacific Islander: 3%; Hispanic: 2%; White non-Hispanic: 73%; unknown 8%; nonresident alien 1%.

International Students: 275 undergraduate nonresident aliens enrolled fall 2008. Students from Europe, Asia, Central and south America, Africa, Canada, Australia, Middle East. Programs available to aid students whose native language is not English: social, cultural. English as a Second Language Program. No financial aid specifically designated for international students.

Student Life: On-campus residence halls house 28% of student body. Residence halls for males constitute 13% of such space, for females 13%, for both sexes 74%. 14% of males join fraternities, 43% of the fraternity males live in Greek housing. 15% of females join sororities and 33% of these females live in Greek housing. Apartments are available for married students. *Intercollegiate athletics:* male: baseball, basketball, football, golf, soccer, swimming, tennis, track; female: basketball, golf, softball, swimming, tennis, volleyball. *Special regulations:* Cars must be registered. *Special services:* Learning Resources Center, medical services, campus shuttle bus service, Disabled Student Services. *Student publications, radio: Gamecock*, a newspaper published 3 times per week; *Garnet and Black*, a yearbook; *Portfolio,* a literary magazine published 3 times per year; *South Carolina Law Review*, a quarterly; *Studies in Economic Analysis*, a biannual publication. Radio station WUSC-FM broadcasts 24 hours, 7 days a week. *Surrounding community:* Columbia population over 100,000. Charlotte (NC), 100 miles from campus, is nearest metropolitan area. Served by airport 7 miles from campus and passenger rail service 1 mile from campus.

Publications: Academic journals distributed nationally include *Anthropological Studies Series* (annually) first published in 1974; *ARETE* (social work, biannually) first published 1970; *Business and Economic Review* (6 times a year) first published 1954; *Carolina View* (student affairs, annually) first published 1985, *Criminal Justice Monograph Series* (irregularly) first published 1981, *Essays in Economics* (irregularly) first published 1955; *Essays in International Studies* (irregularly) first published 1967; *French Literature Series* (annually) first published 1974, *Historical Sites Conference Papers* (annually) first published 1967; *The Notebook* (4 times per year) first published in 1969; *Occasional Papers in International Studies* (irregularly) first published 1969; *Occasional Studies* (business administration, irregularly) first published 1972; *Research Manuscript Series* (monthly) first published 1969; *Review of Public Personnel Administration* (3 times per year) first published 1980; *South Carolina Essays in International Business* (2 times a year) first published 1980, *Studies in International Affairs Series* (irregularly) first published 1961, *Update* (music, 3 times a year) first published 1982, *Teaching Education* (2 times a year) first published 1986, *The South Carolina Forum* (4 times a year) first published 1990, *Journal of International Business Studies* (4 times a year) first published 1984, and *Journal of the Freshman Year Experience* (2 times a year) first published 1989. Shorter academic and news publications include *Occasional Papers* (education, 4 times per year) first published 1985, *South Carolina Economic Indicators* (12 times a year) first published 1965, *Tidings* (marine biology and coastal research, 3 times per year) first published 1975, and *The Freshman Year Experience Newsletter* (4 times a year) first published 1988.

Library Collections: 3,500,000 volumes. 4,200,000 microforms; 18,400 periodicals. 41,000 audiovisual materials. Online catalog. Students have access to online information retrieval services and the Internet.

Most important special holdings include collections on South Carolina literature and history; 18th-19th century exploration, travel and natural history, ornithology; 18th-20th century English and American literature, first editions; F. Scott Fitzgerald Collection.

Buildings and Grounds: Campus area 372 acres. Campus DVD available.

Chief Executive Officer: Dr. Andrew A. Sorenson, President.

Address undergraduate admission inquiries to Scott Verzyl, Director of Undergraduate Admissions; graduate inquiries to Graduate Admissions.

College of Humanities and Social Sciences

Degree Programs Offered: *Baccalaureate* in Afro-American studies, anthropology, art, classical studies, contemporary European studies, English, foreign languages, geography, history, interdisciplinary studies, Latin American studies, music, philosophy, political science, psychology, religious studies, sociology, theater and speech; *masters, doctorate* in comparative literature, linguistics, creative writing. Teacher preparation programs.

Distinctive Educational Programs: Interdepartmental major in Afro-American studies. Interdisciplinary programs in comparative literature, Latin American studies, Southern studies. Computer assistance program through social and behavioral sciences laboratory. Bureau of Government Research Services sponsored by department of government and international studies. Joint degree program in economics and law in cooperation with Law School. Joint master's program in English and librarianship. Cooperative program in public administration with College of Charleston.

College of Business Administration

Degree Programs Offered: *Baccalaureate* in accounting, finance, management, management science, marketing, insurance and economic security, international business, business economics, real estate; *master's* in accountancy, business administration, international business, personnel/employment relations, taxation; *doctorate* in business administration, economics.

Distinctive Educational Programs: Joint degree in teaching in cooperation with College of Education. Joint degree programs in cooperation with Law School.

College of Criminal Justice

Degree Programs Offered: *Baccalaureate, master's* in criminal justice.

College of Education

Degree Programs Offered: *Extended baccalaureate* and *post-baccalaureate* certification programs in cooperation with various colleges in early childhood, elementary, and secondary education. *Master's* degrees (M.A., M.Ed., M.A.T.) in teaching fields and support areas including community education, early childhood education, educational administration, educational research, elementary education, elementary school guidance, generic special education, mental retardation, reading, visually handicapped, orthopedically handicapped, rehabilitation counseling, secondary education, secondary school guidance, student personnel services in higher education, testing and measurement, and instructional media. *Education specialist* degrees in counselor education, rehabilitation counseling, and educational administration. *Doctor of Philosophy in Education* with specialization in elementary education (which may include early childhood education), secondary education, educational administration, educational research, foundations of education, counselor education, and reading. *Doctor of Education* in the fields of curriculum and instruction, health education administration, special education administration, and student personnel services in higher education administration. *Baccalaureate, master's, doctorate* in physical education.

Admission: For certification programs, students must pass the Education Entrance Exam and have a 2.5 grade point ratio.

Degree Requirements: The College of Education now has certification programs as mentioned above in lieu of the baccalaureate degree.

Distinctive Educational Programs: *See* College of Business Administration.

College of Engineering

Degree Programs Offered: *Baccalaureate, master's, doctorate* in chemical engineering, civil engineering, computer engineering, electrical engineering, mechanical engineering.

College of Health

Degree Programs Offered: *Master's* in communicative disorders, environmental health, health administration, health education, public health, epidemiology, biostatistics, medical administration; *dual master's degree* in nursing/public health administration; *doctorate* in health administration, epidemiology, biostatistics, health education, environmental health, communicative disorders.

College of Journalism

Degree Programs Offered: *Baccalaureate* in journalism with emphasis in advertising, public relations, broadcasting, news-editorial; *master's* in journalism, mass communication.

Admission: Predicted grade point average of 2.5.

Degree Requirements: Minimum 2.5 grade point average on all USC work attempted, in addition to meeting all academic degree requirements.

College of Nursing

Degree Programs Offered: *Baccalaureate* in nursing; *master's* in community mental health and psychiatric nursing, clinical nursing (parent-child, gerontological, medical-surgical), health nursing, nursing administration; *doctorate* in nursing science.

School of Law

Degree Programs Offered: *First-professional.*

Admission: Baccalaureate from accredited college or university; LSAT.

Degree Requirements: 3 years study, 2 years in residence.

Fees and Other Expenses: Contact the school for current tuition.

Distinctive Educational Programs: *See* College of Humanities and Social Science, College of Business Administration.

School of Medicine

Degree Programs Offered: *First-professional*

Admission: Baccalaureate from accredited college or university (or completion of 90 semester hours outstanding undergraduate work) which must include 6 hours English, 8 biology with laboratory, 8 physics with laboratory, 8 general inorganic chemistry with laboratory, 8 general organic chemistry with laboratory, 6 mathematics; MCAT.

Degree Requirements: 4 years study, 2 years in residence.

Fees and Other Expenses: Contact the school for current tuition.

College of Pharmacy

Degree Programs Offered: *B.S.* (4-years, non-entry level); *B.S. in Pharmacy* (5-year, entry level); *M.S.* in pharmaceutics, medicinal chemistry, pharmacology, pharmacy administration; *Pharm.D.* (6.5-year, entry level); *Ph.D.* in pharmaceutics, medicinal chemistry, pharmacology, pharmacy administration.

Admission: *For pre-pharmacy: See* general university requirements. *For professional program:* 68 hours pre-pharmacy, completed application form. *For Pharm.D. Optional Track:* First 2 professional years and completed application.

Degree Requirements: *For first-professional:* 160 hours, must have 2.0 GPA or higher.

College of Social Work

Degree Programs Offered: *Master's, doctorate.*

Admission: Admission to the master's degree programs on a selective basis and is determined by the academic preparation and personal qualifications of the applicant. The applicant must have a bachelor's degree from an accredited institution. A grade point ratio of 3.0 (on a 4.0 scale) on all advanced undergraduate courses began with the Fall 1987 semester. A grade point ratio of 2.75 will be utilized for students applying for the advanced standing program in Summer (1987) and to students beginning the program in Spring or Summer (1987). It is also expected that the applicant will have a sound educational foundation with a liberal arts perspective. Intellectual maturity, emotional stability, and motivation and capacity to work with people are essential qualifications. An interview with a member of the faculty may also be required. An applicant who has not attained the required undergraduate grade point ration but who meets all other criteria will be admitted upon submitting a score of 800 on the general portion of the Graduate Record Examination as additional evidence of capacity to pursue graduate study.

Degree Requirements: The College of Social Work offers a number of options in obtaining the M.S.W. degree. Such options include full-time study, part-time study, telecommunication courses, course waivers.

College of Applied Professional Sciences

Degree Programs Offered: *Bachelor of Science* in office administration; hotel, restaurant, and tourism; retailing; sports administration; *Bachelor of Media Arts; Bachelor of Arts in Interdisciplinary Studies; master's* in media arts; hotel, restaurant, tourism.

UNIVERSITY OF SOUTH CAROLINA - COLUMBIA—*cont'd*

College of Library and Information Science

Degree Programs Offered: *Master's.* Specialist certificates also awarded.

Admission: Undergraduate GPA of 2.50; GRE (Quant. and Verbal) of 800 or MAT of 35.

Degree Requirements: *For master's:* 36 hours. *For specialist:* 30 hours beyond the master's.

Distinctive Educational Programs: *See* College of Humanities and Social Sciences.

College of Science and Mathematics

Degree Programs Offered: *Baccalaureate* in biology, chemistry, computer science, geology, marine science, mathematics, medical technology, physics, statistics; *master's* in biology, chemistry, computer science, earth sciences, geology, marine science, mathematics, physics, statistics; *doctorate* in biology, chemistry, computer science, geology, marine science, mathematics, physics, statistics.

University of South Carolina - Upstate

800 University Way
Spartanburg, South Carolina 92303
Tel: (864) 503-5000 **E-mail:** admissions@uscupstate.edu
Fax: (864) 503-5201 **Internet:** www.uscupstate.edu

Institution Description: The University of South Carolina Upstate was formerly known as University of South Carolina Spartanburg. *Enrollment:* 5,063. *Degrees awarded:* Baccalaureate, master's.

Accreditation: *Regional:* SACS-Comm. on Coll. *Professional*: business, computer science, nursing, teacher education

History: Established as Spartanburg Regional Campus and offered first instruction at postsecondary level 1967; chartered and awarded first degree (associate) 1969; became 4-year institution 1975; adopted present name 2006.

Institutional Structure: *Composition of institution:* Administrators 15. Academic affairs headed by executive vice-chancellor. Management/business/finances directed by associate chancellor for administration. Full-time instructional faculty 196. Academic governance body, The University Faculty, meets an average of 2 times per year.

Calendar: Semesters. Academic year Aug. to May. Maymester. Freshmen admitted Aug., Jan., June, July. Degrees conferred May, Aug., Dec. Formal commencement May, Dec. Summer session of 2 terms from June to Aug.

Characteristics of Freshmen: 2,505 applicants (female 1,639, male 866). 66% of applicants admitted. 44% of applicants admitted and enrolled full-time.

71% (532 students) submitted SAT scores; 47% (352 students) submitted ACT scores. *25th percentile*: SAT Critical Reading 460, SAT Math 460; ACT Composite 18. *75th percentile*: SAT Critical Reading 540, SAT Math 560; ACT Composite 21.

30% of entering freshmen expected to graduate within 5 years. 93% of freshmen from South Carolina. Freshmen from 15 states and 12 foreign countries.

Admission: *Requirements:* Freshmen are required to have a high school diploma or GED certificate. Students who graduated form high school in 2001 or after are required to have successfully completed the following college preparatory high school units: 4 English, 3 mathematics, 3 laboratory science, 2 foreign language, 1 U.S. history, 2 social studies, 1 physical education, 4 electives. Students under the age of 22 are required to submit SAT or ACT test scores. High school GPA average and SAT or ACT scores are reviewed to determine eligibility. Transfer students are required to have a cumulative GPA of 2.0 and must be eligible to return to the last institution attended.

Degree Requirements: Completion of the prescribed curriculum; minimum 120 hours; 2.0 GPA.

Distinctive Educational Programs: Evening classes. Special facilities for using telecommunications in the classroom. Interdisciplinary degree program. Facilities and programs for independent research, including individual majors, tutorials. B.A. in Graphic Design; BSN Nursing; Information Management and Systems; International Studies; B.S. in Engineering Technology Management. Study abroad in England, France, Germany, Italy, Spain.

ROTC: Army in cooperation with Wofford College.

Degrees Conferred: 927 *baccalaureate*; 12 *master's*. Bachelor's degrees awarded in top five disciplines: health professions and related clinical sciences 195; education 194; business/marketing 153; liberal arts/general studies 86; psychology 55. Master's degrees awarded: education 12.

Fees and Other Expenses: *Full-time tuition per academic year 2008–09:* undergraduate resident $8,512, nonresident $16,854; contact the university for current graduate tuition. *Other fees:* $386. *Room and board per academic year:* $8,400. *Books and supplies:* $1,000. *Other expenses:* $200.

Financial Aid: Aid from institutionally generated funds is provided on the basis of academic merit, athletic ability, other criteria.

Financial aid to full-time, first-time undergraduate students: 96% received some form of aid. Average amount of aid received: federal grants $4,002; Pell grants $3,083; other federal aid $983; state/local grants $4,163; institutional grants $3,925.

Departments and Teaching Staff: *Total instructional faculty:* 352 (full-time 196, part-time 145). Total faculty with doctorate, first-professional, or other terminal degree: 161. Student/faculty ratio: 16:1.

Enrollment: Total enrollment 5,063. Undergraduate 4,999 (full-time 83%; female 65%, male 35%). Graduate 64 (full-time 5%). Undergraduate transfer-in students 780.

Characteristics of Student Body: *Ethnic/racial makeup:* Black non-Hispanic: 24%; Asian or Pacific Islander: 2%; Hispanic: 3%; White non-Hispanic: 55%; unknown: 13%; nonresident alien 2%.

International Students: 102 nonresident aliens enrolled fall 2008. Students from Europe, Asia, Latin America, Africa, Canada, Australia. Programs available to aid students whose native language is not English: social, cultural. No financial aid specifically designated for international students.

Student Life: Housing on-campus for 700 students. *Intercollegiate athletics:* male: baseball, basketball, golf, soccer, tennis; female: basketball, golf, soccer, softball, volleyball. *Special regulations:* Cars with parking stickers permitted. *Special services:* Learning Resources Center. *Student publications: Carolinian*, a weekly newspaper; *USC Update Literary Journal, A Near Miss, Writer's Inc. Surrounding community:* Spartanburg population 45,000. Charlotte (NC), 70 miles from campus, is nearest metropolitan area. Served by airport 25 miles from campus; passenger rail service 6 miles from campus.

Library Collections: 227,000 volumes including bound books, serial backfiles, electronic documents, and government documents not in separate collections. Online catalog. 57,000 microforms; 7,000 audiovisual materials; 26,900 periodicals including via electronic access. Computer work stations available. Students have access to the Internet at no charge.

Buildings and Grounds: Campus area 298 acres.

Chief Executive Officer: Dr. John C. Stockwell, Chancellor.

Address admission inquiries to Donette Stewart, Director of Admissions.

Voorhees College

481 Porter Drive
Denmark, South Carolina 29042
Tel: (803) 793-3351 **E-mail:** admission@voorhees.edu
Fax: (803) 793-4584 **Internet:** www.voorhees.edu

Institution Description: Voorhees College is a private college affiliated with The Episcopal Church. *Enrollment:* 568. *Degrees awarded:* Associate, baccalaureate.

Accreditation: *Regional:* SACS-Comm. on Coll.

History: Established as Denmark Industrial School 1897; incorporated and changed name to Voorhees Industrial School 1902; offered first instruction at postsecondary level and changed name to Voorhees Normal and Industrial School 1929; changed name to Voorhees School and Junior College 1947; became 4-year institution and adopted present name 1962; awarded first degree (baccalaureate) 1969.

Institutional Structure: *Governing board:* Voorhees College Board of Trustees. Extrainstitutional representation: 35 trustees, including 2 alumni; institutional representation: 1 administrator, 1 full-time instructional faculty member, 1 student. All voting. *Composition of institution:* Administrators 9. Academic affairs headed by president. Management/business/finances directed by director of financial services. Full-time instructional faculty 40. Academic governance body, Academic Policies Council, meets an average of 6 times per year.

Calendar: Semesters. Academic year Aug. to May. Freshmen admitted Aug., Jan., June, July. Degrees conferred and formal commencement May. Summer session from May to Aug.

Characteristics of Freshmen: 40% of applicants accepted. 13% of accepted applicants enrolled.

37% (57 students) submitted SAT scores; 34% (52 students) submitted ACT scores. *25th percentile*: SAT Critical Reading 340, SAT Math 310, SAT Writing 300; ACT Composite 14, ACT English 11, ACT Math 14. *75th percentile*: SAT Critical Reading 430, SAT Math 450, SAT Writing 420; ACT Composite 18, ACT English 17, ACT Math 17.

45% of entering freshmen expected to graduate within 5 years. 78% of freshmen from South Carolina. Freshmen from 200 states and 6 foreign countries.

Admission: Rolling admissions plan. For fall acceptance, apply as early as Sept. of previous year, but not later than Aug. of year of enrollment. *Requirements:* Either graduation from accredited secondary school or approved adult school with academic units which must include 4 English, 3 foreign language, 4 mathematics, 2 science, 2 social studies, 3 electives. Minimum GPA 2.0. Lowest acceptable secondary school class standing 10th percentile. *Entrance tests:* College Board SAT or ACT Composite. For foreign students TOEFL. *For transfer students:* 2.0 GPA; from 4-year accredited institution maximum transfer credit limited by residence requirement; correspondence/extension students 9 semester hours.

College credit for postsecondary-level work completed in secondary school and for extrainstitutional learning on basis.

Tutoring available. Noncredit developmental courses offered in summer session and regular academic year.

Degree Requirements: *For all baccalaureate degrees:* 124–130 hours. *For all degrees:* 2.0 minimum GPA; final year in residence; twice weekly chapel attendance; 2 credit hours of physical education courses; exit competency examination in writing. General education, distribution requirements. Additional requirements for some programs.

Fulfillment of some degree requirements possible by passing departmental examinations. *Grading system:* A–F; withdraw (carries penalty, carries time limit).

Distinctive Educational Programs: Work-experience programs. Evening classes. Cooperative associate program in engineering with Denmark Technical College. Facilities and programs for independent research, including individual majors, tutorials. *Other distinctive programs:* Credit and noncredit continuing education.

ROTC: Army in cooperation with South Carolina State College.

Degrees Conferred: 189 *baccalaureate*. Bachelor's degrees awarded in top five disciplines: business, management, marketing, and related support services 100; social sciences 16; security and protective services 12; biological/life sciences 9; parks and recreation 4.

Fees and Other Expenses: *Full-time tuition per academic year 2008–09:* $9,034. *Books and supplies:* $1,500. *Room and board per academic year:* $5,796. *Other expenses:* $250.

Financial Aid: Aid from institutionally generated funds is provided on the basis of academic merit, financial need, athletic ability. Institution has a Program Participation Agreement with the U.S. Department of Education for eligible students to receive Pell Grants and, depending upon the agreement, other federal aid.

Financial aid to full-time, first-time undergraduate students: 100% received some form of financial aid. Average amount of aid received: $4,653; state/local grants $5,885; institutional grants $2,926; loans $4,223.

Departments and Teaching Staff: *Total instructional faculty:* 40. Student/faculty ratio: 17:1. Degrees held by full-time faculty: doctorate 60%, master's 100%. 60% hold terminal degrees.

Enrollment: Total enrollment 568. Transfer-in students 28.

Characteristics of Student Body: *Ethnic/racial makeup:* Black non-Hispanic: 95%; American Indian or Alaskan Native 1%; Hispanic: 1%; nonresident alien 2%.

International Students: 12 nonresident aliens enrolled fall 2008. No programs available to aid students whose native language is not English. No financial aid specifically designated for international students.

Student Life: On-campus residence halls house 79% of student body. Residence halls for males constitute 36% of such space, for females 64%. *Intercollegiate athletics:* male: baseball, basketball, tennis, track; female: basketball, track. *Special regulations:* Cars permitted without restrictions. Curfews. Quiet hours. Residence hall visitation from 6pm to 11pm Sun.–Thurs., 6pm to 11:30pm Fri. and Sat. *Special services:* Learning Resources Center, medical services, motor pool scheduled for various trips away from campus. *Student publications: The Tiger*, a yearbook; *The Voorhees Vista*, a quarterly newspaper. *Surrounding community:* Denmark population 5,000. Columbia, 50 miles from campus, is nearest metropolitan area. Served by airport 50 miles from campus; passenger rail service 2 miles from campus.

Library Collections: 135,500 volumes. 32,000 microforms; 29,500 audiovisual materials; 465 current periodical subscriptions. 1,003 recordings; 102 CD-ROMs. Computer work stations available. Students have access to the Internet at no charge.

Most important holdings include Library of American Civilization on microfiche (20,000 volumes, papers, and documents); personal papers of Elizabeth Evelyn Wright that include communication with Booker T. Washington; African American Collection.

Buildings and Grounds: Campus area 350 acres. Campus DVd available.

Chief Executive Officer: Dr. E. Lee Monroe, President.

Address admission inquiries to Director of Admissions.

Winthrop University

701 Oakland Avenue
Rock Hill, South Carolina 29733
Tel: (803) 323-2211 **E-mail:** admissions@winthrop.edu
Fax: (803) 323-2137 **Internet:** www.winthrop.edu

Institution Description: Winthrop University is a state institution. *Enrollment:* 6,249. *Degrees awarded:* Baccalaureate, master's. Specialist degree in education and school psychology also awarded.

Academic offerings subject to approval by statewide coordinating bodies. Budget subject to approval by state governing boards. Member of Charlotte Area Educational Consortium.

Accreditation: *Regional:* SACS-Comm. on Coll. *Professional*: art, business, computer science, dance, dietetics, interior design, journalism, music, psychology internship, social work, teacher education, theatre

History: Established as Winthrop Training School for Teachers, chartered, and offered first instruction at postsecondary level 1886; became state supported and changed name to The South Carolina Industrial and Winthrop Normal College 1891, to Winthrop Normal and Industrial College of South Carolina 1893; awarded first degree (baccalaureate) 1898; changed name to Winthrop College, the South Carolina College for Women 1920; became coeducational and adopted name of Winthrop College 1974; became Winthrop University 1992.

Institutional Structure: *Governing board:* Winthrop University Board of Trustees. Extrainstitutional representation: 7 trustees, governor of South Carolina, state superintendent, representative of state Senate Committee on Education, representative of state House Committee on Education (governor's appointee); institutional representation: 1 full-time instructional faculty member, 1 student; 2 alumni. 4 ex officio. 13 voting. *Composition of institution:* Administrators 71. Academic affairs headed by vice president. Management/business/finances directed by vice president for finance and business. Full-time instructional faculty 273. Academic governance body, Faculty Conference, meets an average of 4 times per year.

Calendar: Semesters. Academic year Aug. to May. Freshmen admitted Aug., Jan., June. Degrees conferred May, Aug., Dec. Formal commencements May, Dec. Summer session of 4 terms from May to Aug.

Characteristics of Freshmen: 3,996 applicants (female 2,702, male 1,294). 75% of applicants accepted. 42% of accepted applicants enrolled full-time.

74% (878 students) submitted SAT scores; 25% (294 students) submitted ACT scores. *25th percentile*: SAT Critical Reading 510, SAT Math 510, ACT Composite 24. *75th percentile*: SAT Critical Reading 570, SAT Math 480; ACT 20.

50.2% of entering freshmen expected to graduate within 5 years. 87.5% of freshmen from South Carolina. Freshmen from 21 states and 9 foreign countries.

Admission: For fall enrollment, apply by May 1. *Requirements:* Either graduation from accredited secondary school or GED. *Entrance tests:* College Board SAT or ACT composite. For foreign students TOEFL. *For transfer students:* 2.2 minimum GPA; from 4-year accredited institution 90 semester hours maximum transfer credit; from 2-year accredited institution 65 semester hours.

College credit and advanced placement for postsecondary-level work completed in secondary school and for extrainstitutional learning. Tutoring available.

Degree Requirements: *For baccalaureate degree:* 124 semester hours; 2.0 GPA; 30 hours in residence; distribution requirements; exit competency examination in writing.

Fulfillment of some degree requirements and exemption from some beginning courses possible by passing College Board CLEP, AP, other standardized tests. *Grading system:* A–F; satisfactory-unsatisfactory.

Distinctive Educational Programs: *For undergraduates:* Cooperative baccalaureate in medical technology with approved hospitals. *Available to all students:* Evening classes. Institutionally sponsored summer study abroad in Denmark, Netherlands, Scotland, Ireland, England, France, Peru, and Spain.

ROTC: Army.

Degrees Conferred: 930 *baccalaureate*; 262 *master's*. Bachelor's degrees awarded in top five disciplines: business, management, marketing, and related support services 197; education 155; visual and performing arts 124; social sciences and history 90; communication, journalism, and related programs 68; psychology 62. Master' degrees awarded: in top five disciplines: education 135; business/marketing 93; visual and performing arts 18; psychology 8; liberal arts/general studies 7.

Fees and Other Expenses: *Full-time tuition per academic year 2008–09:* $11,060 resident undergraduate, $20,610 nonresident; contact the university for current graduate tuition and applicable fees. *Room and board per academic year:* $8,320. *Books and supplies* $976. *Other expenses:* $2,832.

Financial Aid: Aid from institutionally generated funds is provided on the basis of academic merit, financial need, athletic ability, other criteria. Financial

WINTHROP UNIVERSITY—*cont'd*

assistance is available in the form of Pell Grants, College Work-Study, Veterans Administration Benefits, National Direct Student Loans, Supplemental Education Opportunity Grants (SEOG), Stafford Loans, other federal aid programs.

Financial aid for first-time, full-time undergraduate students: 99% received some form of aid. Average amount of aid received: federal grants $4,049; Pell grants $3,110; other federal aid $1,049; state/local grants $1,049; institutional grants $8,779.

Departments and Teaching Staff: *Total instructional faculty:* 453 (full-time 273, part-time 700). Total faculty with doctorate, first-professional, or other terminal degree: 277. Student/faculty ratio: 15:1. Degrees held by full-time faculty: baccalaureate 4%, master's 15.7%, doctorate 83.5%. 83% hold terminal degrees.

Enrollment: Total enrollment 6,249. Undergraduate 5,068 (full-time 89%, female 69%, male 31%). Graduate 1,181 (full-time 34%). Undergraduate transfer-in students 330.

Characteristics of Student Body: *Ethnic/racial makeup:* Black non-Hispanic: 27%; American Indian or Alaska Native: 1%; Asian or Pacific Islander: 2%; Hispanic: 2%; White non-Hispanic: 86%; nonresident alien 2%. *Age distribution:* number under 18: 258; 18–19: 1,7671 20–21: 1,789; 22–24: 852; 25–29: 233; 30–34: 86; 35–39: 84; 40–49: 89; 50–64: 25; 65 and over: 4.

International Students: 126 undergraduate nonresident aliens enrolled fall 2008. Students from Europe, Asia, Latin America, Africa, Canada, Australia, New Zealand, Middle East. Programs available to aid students whose native language is not English: social, cultural. Some financial aid specifically designated for international students.

Student Life: On-campus residence halls house 45.5% of student body. Residence halls for males constitute 30% of such space, for females 70%. Housing available for married students. *Intercollegiate athletics:* male: baseball, basketball, cross-country, golf, soccer, tennis; female: basketball, cross-country, golf, softball, tennis, volleyball. *Special regulations:* Cars permitted without restrictions. *Special services:* Medical services. *Student publications: The Anthology,* an annual literary magazine; *The Johnsonian*, a weekly newspaper; *The Tatler*, a yearbook. *Surrounding community:* Rock Hill population 60,000. Charlotte (NC), 20 miles from campus, is nearest metropolitan area. Served by airport 20 miles from campus; passenger rail service 2 miles from campus.

Library Collections: 425,999 volumes including bound books, serial backfiles, electronic documents, and government documents not in separate collections. Online catalog. Current serial subscriptions: paper 946; microform 197; via electronic access 23,749. 1,739 recordings; 1,798 compact discs; 117 CD-ROMs. Ccomputer work stations available. Students have access to the Internet at no charge.

Most important special holdings include Eliza Ragsdale Wylie Manuscript; the Knox-Wise Family Papers; Mary Elizabeth Massey Papers.

Buildings and Grounds: Campus area 418 acres. Campus DVD available.

Chief Executive Officer: Dr. Anthony DiGiorgio, President.

Address admission inquiries to Deborah Barber, Director of Admissions.

Wofford College

429 North Church Street
Spartanburg, South Carolina 29303-3663
Tel: (864) 597-4000 **E-mail:** admissions@wofford.edu
Fax: (864) 597-4219 **Internet:** www.wofford.edu

Institution Description: Wofford College is a private college affiliated with the United Methodist Church of South Carolina. *Enrollment:* 1,429. *Degrees awarded:* Baccalaureate.

Accreditation: *Regional:* SACS-Comm. on Coll.

History: Established 1850; chartered 1851; offered first instruction at postsecondary level 1854; awarded first degree (baccalaureate) 1856; first women resident students admitted 1976. *See* David Duncan Wallace, *History of Wofford College, 1854–1949* (Nashville, Tenn.: Vanderbilt University Press, 1951) for further information.

Institutional Structure: *Governing board:* Wofford College Board of Trustees. Representation: 30 trustees. All voting. *Composition of institution:* Administrators/professional staff 61. Academic affairs headed by president and 12 cabinet members. Full-time instructional faculty 98. Academic governance body, the faculty, meets an average of 10 times per year.

Calendar: Semesters. Academic year Sept. to May. Degrees conferred May, Aug., Feb. Formal commencement May. Summer sessions June to Aug.

Characteristics of Freshmen: 2,218 applicants (female 1,085, male 2,278). 59% of applicants admitted. 31% of applicants admitted and enrolled full-time.

56% (212 students) submitted SAT scores; 44% (166 students) submitted ACT scores. *25th percentile*: SAT Critical Reading 560, SAT Math 540; ACT Composite 22. *75th percentile*: SAT Critical Reading 670, SAT math 680; ACT Composite 27.

70% of entering freshmen expected to graduate within 5 years. 60% of freshmen from South Carolina. Freshmen from 34 states and 10 foreign countries.

Admission: All persons seeking admission must complete an application form and forward transcripts of previous academic work and a secondary school report form. Either ACT or SAT scores are acceptable (achievement tests recommended but not required). The deadline for admission to the fall semester is Feb. 1. Those who apply prior to Dec. 1 will receive early notification by Dec. 15. (This is not an early decision program; students who are offered admission are not required to make an early commitment, but can pay their deposits any time before May 1). Those who are accepted for admission may reserve space in the student body and college housing by making a deposit on or before May 1. *Requirements:* Either recommend 20 secondary school units which normally include 4 English, 3 foreign language, 3 science with lab, 4 mathematics, 2 social studies, 1 history, 3 electives; or GED. Students with 14 secondary school units considered on individual basis. 1–2 additional units foreign language, 1 science or mathematics recommended. Lowest acceptable secondary school class standing 50th percentile. *For transfer students:* 3.0 minimum GPA; from 4-year accredited institution 90 semester hours maximum transfer credit; from 2-year accredited institution 62 hours.

College credit and advanced placement for postsecondary-level work completed in secondary school. College credit for DANTES, and for extrainstitutional learning. Tutoring available.

Degree Requirements: 124 semester hours which must include at least 4 January Interim projects. General education requirements. Fulfillment of some degree requirements and exemption from some beginning courses possible by passing College Board CLEP General and Subject Examinations, AP (score of 3), other standardized tests. *Grading system:* A–F, except during Interim, where projects are graded normally pass with honors, pass and fail. It is possible to earn a grade of withdrawal-passing before a certain published deadline each semester.

Distinctive Educational Programs: Cooperative education. Dual-degree programs in engineering with Columbia University (NY) and Clemson University. Individually designed interdepartmental majors. Facilities for independent research including honors programs, individual majors and independent interim study. Wofford students can study in 21 countries in Europe, Asia or Latin America through one of three foreign study consortia. Institutionally-sponsored foreign study available during interim and summer programs. Special Presidential International Scholarship program for one student each year. Cross-registration and cooperative majors with Converse College. Wofford Library Press is used to instruct students in book arts during interim.

ROTC: Army.

Degrees Conferred: 296 *baccalaureate*:. Bachelor's degrees awarded in top five disciplines: business/marketing 76; biological/life sciences 54; social science 33; English 30; history 21.

Fees and Other Expenses: *Full-time tuition per academic year 2008–09:* $29,465. *Room and board per academic year:* $7,920. *Books and supplies:* $1,050. *Other expenses:* $2,400.

Financial Aid: Aid from institutionally generated funds is provided on the basis of academic merit, financial need, athletic ability, other criteria.

Financial aid to full-time, first-time undergraduate students: 89% received some form of aid. Average amount of aid received: federal grants $4,085; Pell grants $1,504; other federal aid $1,504; state/local grants $8,380; institutional grants $15,332.

Departments and Teaching Staff: *Total instructional faculty:* 129 (full-time 98, part-time 31). Total faculty with doctorate, first-professional, or other terminal degree:107. Student/faculty ratio: 11:1.

Enrollment: Total enrollment 1,429. Undergraduate 1,429 (full-time 98%; female 49%, male 51%). Transfer-in students 17.

Characteristics of Student Body: *Ethnic/racial makeup:* Black non-Hispanic: 6%; Asian or Pacific Islander: 2%; Hispanic: 6%; White 87%; unknown 2%; nonresident alien 1%. *Age distribution:* number under 18: 11; 18–19: 579; 20–21: 521; 22–24: 47.

International Students: 2 nonresident aliens enrolled fall 2008. No programs available to aid students whose native language is not English. No financial aid specifically designated for international students.

Student Life: Campus housing for 1,141 students. *Intercollegiate athletics:* (NCAA Division IAA) male: football, basketball, baseball, golf, soccer, tennis, cross-country, track; female: basketball, volleyball, tennis, cross-country, golf, soccer, track. Club sports (open to males and females) include fencing. *Special regulations:* Cars permitted; fee charged. Quiet hours begin 5pm starting week before examinations and continuing through examination week. Residence hall visitation from noon to midnight Sun.–Thurs., noon to 2am Fri. and Sat. *Special services:* Learning Resources Center, medical services. *Student publications: Bohemian*, a yearbook; *The Journal*, an annual literary magazine; *The Old Gold and Black*, a biweekly newspaper. *Religious life:* Baptist Student Union, Episcopal Canterbury Club, Newman Club, Presbyterian Student Association, Fellowship of Christian Athletes, Wesley Fellowship. *Greek life:* 6 national men's fraternities and 4 national women's sororities. 4 NPHC groups represented. *Surrounding community:* Spartanburg County population over 250,000.

Library Collections: 197,000 volumes including bound books, serial backfiles, electronic documents, and government documents not in separate collections. Online catalog. 38,000 microforms; 4,300 audiovisual materials; 49,000 periodicals including via electronic access. Students have access to the Internet at no charge.

Most important special holdings include South Carolina United Methodist Archives; Sandor Teszler Collection of Hungarian Art; Littlejohn Rare Book Room (books, maps, art); college archives.

Buildings and Grounds: Campus area 170 acres. Campus DVD available.

Chief Executive Officer: Dr. Benjamin B. Dunlap, President.

Address admission inquiries to Brand R. Stille, Director of Admissions.

South Dakota

Augustana College

2001 South Summit Street
Sioux Falls, South Dakota 57197
Tel: (605) 336-0770 **E-mail:** info@augie.edu
Fax: (605) 336-5518 **Internet:** www.augie.edu

Institution Description: Augustana College is a private institution affiliated with the Evangelical Lutheran Church in America. *Enrollment:* 1,734. *Degrees awarded:* Baccalaureate, master's.

Member of Lutheran College Washington Consortium, Higher Education Consortium for Urban Affairs, Upper Midwest Association for Intercultural Education.

Accreditation: *Regional:* NCA. *Professional*: chemistry, music, nursing, social work, teacher education

History: Established in Chicago as Augustana College and Seminary 1860; moved to Paxton, IL, incorporated, and offered first instruction 1863; awarded first degree (baccalaureate) 1888; moved to Marshall, WI, and changed name to Augsberg Seminary and Marshall Academy 1869; moved to Beloit, IA, and changed name to Augustana Seminary and Academy 1881; moved to Canton, SD, and changed name to Augustana College 1884; moved to Sioux Falls, merged with Lutheran Normal School (established 1889), and changed name to Augustana College and Normal School 1918; adopted present name 1926.

Institutional Structure: *Governing board:* Board of Regents, Augustana College Association. Extrainstitutional representation: 26 regents; institutional representation: president of the college (ex officio). All voting. *Composition of institution:* Administrators 81. Academic affairs headed by vice president for academic affairs. Management/business/finances directed by vice president for financial affairs. Full-time instructional instructors 135. Academic governance body, the faculty, meets an average of 10 times per year.

Calendar: Semesters. Academic year Sept. to May. Freshmen admitted Sept., Jan., Feb. Degrees conferred and formal commencement May. Summer session of 2 terms from June to Aug.

Characteristics of Freshmen: 1,168 applicants (723 female, 483 male). 21% of applicants accepted. 45% of accepted applicants enrolled full-time.

Mean SAT scores Critical Reading 570, Math 580 .

63% of entering freshmen expected to graduate within 5 years. 46% of freshmen from South Dakota. Freshmen from 19 states and 9 foreign countries.

Admission: Rolling admissions plan. For fall acceptance, apply as early as second semester of junior year of secondary school, but not later than Aug. 15 of year of enrollment. Early acceptance available. *Requirements:* Either graduation from accredited secondary school or GED. Lowest recommended secondary school class standing 50th percentile. *Entrance tests:* For foreign students TOEFL. *For transfer students:* 2.0 minimum GPA; from 4-year accredited institution hours maximum transfer limited only by residence requirement; from 2-year accredited institution 65 semester hours.

Tutoring available. Developmental courses offered during regular academic year; credit given.

Degree Requirements: *For all associate degrees:* 66 credit hours. *For all baccalaureate degrees:* 130 credit hours; 6 credits religion. *For all undergraduate degrees:* 2.0 GPA; last 30 credits in residence; 2 credits physical education courses; core requirements.

Fulfillment of some degree requirements and exemption from some beginning courses possible by passing departmental examinations, College Board CLEP, AP. *Grading system:* A–F; withdraw (carries time limit); satisfactory-unsatisfactory; in progress.

Distinctive Educational Programs: Internships. Dual-degree programs in most engineering fields with Columbia University (NY), Washington University (MO); in divinity with North American Baptist Seminary; occupation therapy with Washington University (MO) and Boston University (MA). Special facilities for using telecommunications in the classroom. Interdepartmental-interdisciplinary self-designed programs in biological chemistry, biophysics, engineering physics, environmental studies, minority studies, music merchandising. Preprofessional programs include architecture, chemical engineering, dentistry, law, medicine, mortuary science, occupational therapy, optometry, pharmacy, physical therapy, theology, veterinary science. Facilities and programs for independent research, including honors programs, individual majors, tutorials. Study abroad in Austria, France, Spain, West Germany, United Kingdom, and elsewhere; year, semester, interim programs available. Domestic off-campus study includes Minneapolis-St. Paul Urban Studies Term, San Francisco Studies Term, semester in Washington, DC. Cross-registration with University of Sioux Falls, North American Baptist Seminary. *Other distinctive programs:* Evaluation of extrainstitutional learning for adult students through Center for Evaluation of Experiential learning. Center for Western Studies.

Degrees Conferred: 341 *baccalaureate*; 12 *master's*. Bachelor;s degrees awarded: biological sciences 25; business and management 69; communications 13; computer and information sciences 3; education 66; English 15; foreign languages 10; health professions and related sciences 50; mathematics 7; parks and recreation 6; philosophy/religion/theology 9; physical sciences 8; protective services/public administration 10; psychology 20; social sciences and history 25; visual and performing arts 18. Master's degrees awarded: health professions 3; education 9.

Fees and Other Expenses: *Full-time tuition per academic year 2008–09:* undergraduate $22,450; contact the college for current graduate tuition. *Room and board per academic year:* $5,920. *Books and supplies:* $1,000. *Other expenses:* $1,400.

Financial Aid: Aid from institutionally generated funds is provided on the basis of academic merit, financial need, athletic ability, other criteria.

Financial aid to full-time, first-time undergraduate students: 100% received some form of financial aid. Average amount of aid received: federal grants $5,850; Pell grants $3,070; other federal aid $2,248; state/local grants $1,000; institutional grants $11,160.

Departments and Teaching Staff: *Total instructional faculty:* 176 (full-time 109, part-time 67). Total faculty with doctorate, first-professional, or other terminal degree: 97. Student/faculty ratio: 13:1. Degrees held by full-time faculty: doctorate 67.5%, master's 26.6%, baccalaureate 5.9%. 70.4% hold terminal degrees.

Enrollment: Total enrollment 1,754. Undergraduate 1,733 (full-time 94%; female 64%, male 36%). Graduate 21 (full-time 5%). Undergraduate transfer-in students 79.

Characteristics of Student Body: *Ethnic/racial makeup:* Black non-Hispanic: 1%; Asian or Pacific Islander: 2%; White non-Hispanic: 94%; nonresident alien 2%. *Age distribution:* number under 18: 6; 18–19: 676; 20–21: 699; 22–24: 210; 25–29: 30; 30–34: 11; 35–39: 6; 40–49: 14; 50–64: 1; 65 and over: 1,653.

International Students: 17 nonresident aliens enrolled fall 2008. Students from Europe, Asia, Africa, Canada. No programs available to aid students whose native language is not English. Financial aid specifically designated for international students.

Student Life: On-campus residence halls house 70% of student body. Residence halls for both sexes 100%. Housing available for married students, or students with dependent children. *Intercollegiate athletics:* male: baseball, basketball, cross-country, football, golf, tennis, track, wrestling; female: softball, basketball, cross-country, golf, soccer, tennis, track, volleyball. *Special regulations:* On-campus housing required of freshmen and sophomores. Limited parking. *Special services:* Day Care Center; health and counseling services, comprehensive recreation/intramural program. *Student publications, radio: The Augustana MIRROR*, a weekly newspaper; *EDDA*, a yearbook; *Venture*, an annual literary magazine. Radio station KAUR-FM broadcasts 100 hours per week. *Surrounding community:* Sioux Falls population 110,000. Minneapolis-St. Paul (MN), 250 miles from campus, is nearest metropolitan area. Served by mass transit bus system, airport 3 miles from campus.

Library Collections: 280,000 volumes including bound books, serial backfiles, electronic documents, and government documents not in separate collections. Online catalog. Current serial subscriptions: 595 paper, 31,345 microform, over 5,000 via electronic access. 5,637 recordings; 1,965 compact discs; 1,655 80 CD-ROMs. Computer work stations available. Students have access to the Internet at no charge.

Most important special holdings include Center for Western Studies; Dakota Collection; Norwegian Collection.

Buildings and Grounds: Campus area 100 acres.

Chief Executive Officer: Dr. Bruce Halverson, President.

Address undergraduate admission inquiries to Nancy L. Davidson, Vice President for Enrollment.

Black Hills State University

1200 University Avenue
Spearfish, South Dakota 57799-9500
Tel: (605) 642-6011 **E-mail:** admissions@bhsu.edu
Fax: (605) 642-6022 **Internet:** www.bhsu.edu

Institution Description: Black Hills State University is a state institution. *Enrollment:* 4,016. *Degrees awarded:* Associate, baccalaureate, master's.

Academic offerings subject to approval by statewide coordinating bodies. Budget subject to approval by state governing boards.

Accreditation: *Regional:* NCA. *Professional*: music, teacher education

History: Established and chartered as Dakota Territorial Normal School 1881; changed name to Spearfish Normal School 1883; offered first instruction at postsecondary level 1885; awarded first degree (baccalaureate) 1926; changed name to Black Hills Teachers College 1941; became Black Hills State College 1964; adopted present name 1989. *See* LeRoye C. Carlson, *A History of the Founding and Operation of the Black Hills Teachers College* (Spearfish, S.D.: Black Hills State College, 1966) for further information.

Institutional Structure: *Governing board:* South Dakota Board of Regents. Extrainstitutional representation: 10 regents, including 1 student. 9 voting. *Composition of institution:* Administrators 18. Academic affairs headed by vice president for academic affairs. Management/business/finances directed by business manager. Full-time instructional faculty 105. Academic governance body, Council of Division Chairmen, meets an average of 25 times per year.

Calendar: Semesters. Academic year July to June. Freshmen admitted Sept., Aug., Jan., June, July. Degrees conferred May, Aug., Dec. Formal commencement May.

Characteristics of Freshmen: 2,182 applicants (female 1,343, male 839). 93% of applicants accepted. 28% of accepted applicants enrolled full-time.

91% (529 students) submitted ACT scores. *25th percentile:* ACT Composite 118, ACT English 16, ACT Math 17. *75th percentile:* ACT Composite 23, ACT English 23, ACT Math 23.

25% of entering freshmen expected to graduate within 5 years. 81% of freshmen from South Dakota. Freshmen from 32 states and 8 foreign countries.

Admission: Rolling admissions plan. For fall acceptance, apply as early as end of junior year of secondary school, but not later than 2 weeks after registration. Early acceptance available. *Requirements:* Either graduation from accredited secondary school or GED. Lowest acceptable secondary school class standing 33rd percentile. *Entrance tests:* Minimum ACT composite score 20. *For transfer students:* 2.0 minimum GPA; from 4-year accredited institution maximum transfer credit limited only by residence requirement; from 2-year accredited institution 64 hour; correspondence/extension students 32 hours.

College credit for postsecondary-level work completed in secondary school and for extrainstitutional learning on basis of portfolio assessment.

Tutoring available. Noncredit developmental courses offered during regular academic year.

Degree Requirements: *For all associate degrees:* 64–68 semester hours; 2 hours physical activity courses. *For all baccalaureate degrees:* 128 hours; 4 hours physical activity courses; distribution requirements; exit competency exam in English. *For all undergraduate degrees:* 2.0 GPA; 32 hours in residence (includes on-campus course requirements); general education requirements.

Fulfillment of some degree requirements and exemption from some beginning courses possible by passing institutional examinations, College Board CLEP Subject Examinations. *Grading system:* A–F; pass-fail; withdraw (deadline after which pass-fail is appended to withdraw); incomplete (carries time limit).

Distinctive Educational Programs: *For undergraduates:* Work-experience programs. Off-campus centers (at O'Neil Pass, less than 30 miles away from main institution, and Douglas, 55 miles away). Joint academic programs with South Dakota School of Mines and Technology. Tutorials. *Available to all students:* Evening and weekend classes. Interdepartmental program in American Indian studies.

ROTC: Army offered in cooperation with South Dakota School of Mines and Technology.

Degrees Conferred: 32 *associate*; 394 *baccalaureate*; 35 *master's*. Bachelor's degrees awarded in top five disciplines: education 113 business, management, marketing, and related support services 96; psychology 32; social sciences 27; public administration 26. Master's degrees awarded: various disciplines 35.

Fees and Other Expenses: *Full-time tuition per academic year 2008–09:* undergraduate resident $6,269, nonresident $12,411; contact the university for graduate tuition/fees. *Room and board per academic year:* $4,380. *Books and supplies:* $800. *Other expesnes:* $2,800.

Financial Aid: Aid from institutionally generated funds is provided on the basis of academic merit, athletic ability, other criteria.

Financial aid to full-time, first-time undergraduate students: 87% received some form of financial aid. Average amount of aid received: federal grants $4,055; Pell grants $3,077; other federal aid $1,457; state/local grants $1,856; institution grants $1,363.

Departments and Teaching Staff: *Total instructional faculty:* 105. Student/faculty ratio: 14:1. 55% hold terminal degrees.

Enrollment: Total enrollment 4,016. Undergraduate 3,686 (full-time 68%; female 64%, male 36%). Graduate 330 (full-time 1%). Undergraduate transfer-in students 312.

Characteristics of Student Body: *Ethnic/racial makeup:* Black non-Hispanic: 1%; American Indian or Alaska Native: 4%; Asian or Pacific Islander: 1%, Hispanic: 2%, White non-Hispanic: 85%; unknown: 6%; nonresident alien 1%.

International Students: 40 nonresident aliens enrolled fall 2008. Students from Europe, Asia, Africa, Canada. No programs available to aid students whose native language is not English. No financial aid specifically designated for international students.

Student Life: On-campus residence halls house 30% of student body. Residence halls for males constitute 28% of such space, for females 18%, for both sexes 54%. 2% of males join and 1% live off campus in fraternity housing. *Intercollegiate athletics:* male: football, basketball, cross-country, track; female: basketball, cross-country, track, volleyball. *Special regulations:* Registered cars permitted without restrictions. Residence hall visitation from 10am to 12 midnight every night. *Special services:* Learning Resources Center, medical services. *Student publications, radio: The Ecochia*, a yearbook; *Today*, a weekly newspaper. Radio station KBHU broadcasts 124 hours per week. *Surrounding community:* Spearfish population 5,250. Denver (CO), 400 miles from campus, is nearest metropolitan area. Served by airport 60 miles from campus.

Library Collections: 235,000 volumes. 70,500 government documents; 355,000 microforms; 1,300 audiovisual materials; 1,800 current periodical subscriptions. Computer work stations available. Online catalog. Students have access to online information retrieval services and the Internet.

Most important holdings include Case Library for Western Historical Studies; E.Y. Berry Congressional Collection; Szalay Map Collection.

Buildings and Grounds: Campus area 123 acres.

Chief Executive Officer: Dr. Thomas O. Flickema, President.

Address admission inquiries to Admissions Officer.

Dakota State University

820 North Washington Avenue
Madison, South Dakota 57042-1799
Tel: (605) 256-5111 **E-mail:** dsuinfo@dsu.edu
Fax: (605) 256-5020 **Internet:** www.dsu.edu

Institution Description: Dakota State University is a state institution. *Enrollment:* 2,675. *Degrees awarded:* Associate, baccalaureate.

Academic offerings subject to approval by statewide coordinating bodies. Budget subject to approval by state governing boards.

Accreditation: *Regional:* NCA. *Professional*: health information administration, respiratory therapy, teacher education

History: Established as Dakota Normal School 1881; offered first instruction at postsecondary level 1883; awarded first degree (associate) 1885; changed name to Eastern State Normal School 1921, General Beadle State Teachers College 1947, General Beadle State College 1964; became Dakota State College 1969; in 1984, the State Legislature mandated that Dakota State College become a model for the development and offering of programs that utilize the latest technologies for the enhancement of education; adopted present name 1989.

Institutional Structure: *Governing board:* South Dakota Board of Regents. Representation: 10 regents, including 1 student. 9 voting. *Composition of institution:* Administrators 16. Academic affairs headed by vice president for academic affairs. Management/business/finances directed by business manager. Full-time instructional faculty 37. Academic governance body, Faculty Senate, meets an average of 12 times per year. *Faculty representation:* Faculty served by collective bargaining agents, Council of Higher Education and South Dakota Education Association, affiliated with NEA.

Calendar: Semesters. Academic year Sept. to May. Freshmen admitted on a rolling basis. Degrees conferred May, July, Dec. Formal commencement May. Summer session May to Aug.

DAKOTA STATE UNIVERSITY—*cont'd*

Characteristics of Freshmen: 509 5 applicants (247 female, 262 male). 96% of applicants accepted. 58% of applicants enrolled full-time.

88% (248 students) submitted ACT scores. *25th percentile*: ACT Composite 116, ACT English 17, ACT Math 18. *75th percentile*: ACT Composite 24, ACT English 23, ACT Math 25.

35% of freshmen from South Dakota. Freshmen from 18 states and 3 foreign countries.

Admission: Rolling admissions plan. For fall acceptance, apply as early as 1 year prior to enrollment, but not later than 2 weeks after beginning of semester. Early acceptance available. *Requirements:* Either graduation from accredited secondary school or GED. Secondary school class rank in top two thirds or minimum ACT composite 20 or 2.0 GPA on core curriculum. *Entrance tests:* ACT composite. *For transfer students:* 2.0 minimum GPA; from 4-year accredited institution 96 hours maximum transfer credit; from 2-year accredited institution 64 hours; correspondence/extension students 30 hours.

College credit and advanced placement for postsecondary-level work completed in secondary school and for extrainstitutional learning on basis of portfolio assessment.

Tutoring available. Developmental courses offered during regular academic year; no credit given.

Degree Requirements: *For all associate degrees:* 64 credit hours. For some programs, physical activity courses. *For all baccalaureate degrees:* 128 credit hours; 2 hours physical activity courses. *For all degrees:* 2.0 GPA; 2 semesters in residence; distribution requirements.

Fulfillment of some degree requirements and exemption from some beginning courses possible by passing departmental examinations, College Board CLEP, AP. *Grading system:* A–F; pass-fail; withdraw (deadline after which A–F is appended to withdraw); incomplete (carries time limit).

Distinctive Educational Programs: Internships. Cooperative associate programs in child development-elementary education with South Dakota State University; elementary-special education and education-industrial arts with Northern State College. Individual majors. Study abroad in London for student teachers.

Degrees Conferred: 44 *associate;* 194 *baccalaureate*; 46 *master's*. Bachelor's degrees awarded in top five disciplines: business and management 35, computer and information science 23, education 50, English 6, health professions and related sciences 7. Master's degrees awarded: various disciplines 46.

Fees and Other Expenses: *Full-time tuition per academic year 2008–09:* resident $5,816, nonresident $17,136. *Books and supplies:* $900. *Room and board per academic year:* $4,880. *Other expenses:* $3,818.

Financial Aid: Aid from institutionally generated funds is provided on the basis of academic merit, financial need, athletic ability, other criteria.

Financial aid to full-time, first-time undergraduate students: 96% received some form of financial aid. Average amount of aid received: federal grants $3,848; Pell grants $2,776; other federal aid $166; state/local grants $160; institutional grants $1,764.

Departments and Teaching Staff: *Total instructional faculty:* 65. Degrees held by full-time faculty: doctorate 55%, master's 38%, baccalaureate 7%. 57.5% hold terminal degrees.

Enrollment: Total enrollment 2,675. Undergraduate 2,296 (full-time 48%; female 64%, male 46%). Graduate 379 (full-time 15%). Undergraduate transfer-in students 167.

Characteristics of Student Body: *Ethnic/racial makeup:* Black non-Hispanic: 2%; American Indian or Alaska Native: 1%; Asian or Pacific Islander: 1%; Hispanic: 1%; White non-Hispanic: 85%; unknown: 8%; nonresident alien 1%.

International Students: 27 nonresident aliens enrolled fall 2008. Programs available to aid students whose native language is not English: English as a Second Language Program. No financial aid specifically designated for international students.

Student Life: On-campus residence halls house 32% of student body (4 residence halls: 1 male, 1 female, 2 coed). *Intercollegiate athletics:* male: basketball, cross-country, football, track, golf, baseball; female: basketball, cross-country, softball, track, volleyball. *Special regulations:* Residence hall visitation from 10am to 2am. *Special services:* Learning Resources Center, medical services. *Student publications: Eastern*, a bimonthly newspaper; *Trojan*, a yearbook; *Dakota Access*, a biweekly newspaper. *Surrounding community:* Madison population 6,500. Omaha (NE), 219 miles from campus, is nearest metropolitan area.

Library Collections: 126,000 volumes. 15,500 microforms; 450 current periodical subscriptions. Students have access to online information retrieval services and the Internet.

Most important special holdings include education collection; early South Dakota history collection (microfilm); Senator Karl E. Mundt Archives Collection.

Buildings and Grounds: Campus area 54 acres.

Chief Executive Officer: Dr. Douglas D. Knowlton, President. Address admission inquiries to High School Relations Director.

Dakota Wesleyan University

1200 West University Avenue
Mitchell, South Dakota 57301
Tel: (605) 995-2600 **E-mail:** admissions@dwu.edu
Fax: (605) 995-2699 **Internet:** www.dwu.edu

Institution Description: Dakota Wesleyan University is a private institution affiliated with the United Methodist Church. *Enrollment:* 730. *Degrees awarded:* Associate, baccalaureate, master's.

Accreditation: *Regional:* NCA. *Professional*:

History: Chartered as Dakota University 1883; rechartered and offered first instruction at postsecondary level 1885; awarded first degree (baccalaureate) 1888; adopted present name 1904.

Institutional Structure: *Governing board:* Board of Trustees. Representation: 33 trustees. 7 ex officio. All voting *Composition of institution:* Administrators 6. Academic affairs headed by vice president for academic affairs and academic dean. Management/business/finances directed by vice president of finance and administration. Full-time instructional faculty 54. Academic governance body, the faculty, meets an average of 10 times per year.

Calendar: Semesters. Academic year Aug. to May. Degrees conferred May, Aug., Dec. Formal commencement May. Summer session from May to Aug.

Characteristics of Freshmen: 523 applicants (243 female, 280 male). 75% of applicants accepted. 42% of accepted applicants enrolled full-time.

13% (22 students) submitted SAT scores; 82% (135 students) submitted ACT scores. *25th percentile*: SAT Critical Reading 433, SAT Math 372; ACT Composite 18, ACT English 16l SAT Math 17. *75th percentile*: SAT Critical Reading 540, SAT Math 517; ACT Composite 23, ACT English 22, ACT Math 24.

42% of entering freshmen expected to graduate within 5 years. 69% of freshmen from South Dakota. Freshmen from 27 states and 4 foreign countries.

Admission: Rolling admissions plan. For fall acceptance, apply as early as Oct. 1 of previous year, but not later than Sept. 1 of year of enrollment. *Entrance tests:* College Board SAT or ACT composite. For foreign students TOEFL. *For transfer students:* 2.0 minimum GPA, 68 semester hours maximum transfer credit.

College credit and advanced placement for postsecondary-level work completed in secondary school. College credit for extrainstitutional learning on basis of faculty assessment.

Tutoring available. Developmental courses offered in summer session and regular academic year; credit given.

Degree Requirements: *For all associate degrees:* 62–68 semester hours. *For all baccalaureate degrees:* 125 semester hours; 2 semesters in residence; 2 semester hours physical education; general education requirements; demonstrated competency in reading, writing, mathematics. *For all degrees:* 2.0 GPA.

Fulfillment of some degree requirements and exemption from some beginning courses possible by passing departmental examinations, College Board CLEP; AP. *Grading system:* A–F; pass-fail; withdraw (deadline after which pass-fail is appended to withdraw).

Distinctive Educational Programs: Work-experience programs, including internships, practicums. Evening classes. Dual-degree program in engineering with South Dakota State University. Special facilities for using telecommunications in the classroom. Interdisciplinary summer programs. Preprofessional programs in allied health fields and engineering. Facilities and programs for independent research, including honors programs, individual majors, tutorials. Study abroad and off-campus study in U.S. by individual arrangement. Travel interim. Urban experience programs. *Other distinctive programs:* Dakota Wesleyan University Daycare Center. McGovern Center - Public Service and Leadership Program.

Degrees Conferred: 66 *associate;* 102 *baccalaureate:* biological sciences 11; business/marketing 21; communications 1; education 22; English 3; foreign languages 2; history 4; law/legal studies 7; mathematics 1; parks and recreation 4; personal and miscellaneous services 3; philosophy/religion 2; physical sciences 2; psychology 4; science technologies 2; visual and performing arts 1. Master's degrees awarded: education 9. Master's degrees awarded: education 17.

Fees and Other Expenses: *Full-time tuition per academic year 2008–09:* $18,500. *Room and board per academic year:* $5,800. *books and supplies:* $920. *Other expenses:* $2,700.

Financial Aid: Aid from institutionally generated funds is provided on the basis of academic merit, financial need, athletic ability, other criteria.

Financial aid to full-time, first-time undergraduate students: 100% received some form of aid.

Departments and Teaching Staff: *Total instructional faculty:* 99 (full-time 54, part-time 454). Total faculty with doctorate, first-professional, or other terminal degree: 40. Student/faculty ratio: 10:1.

Enrollment: Total enrollment 730. Undergraduate 702 (full-time 91%; female 59%, male 41%). Graduate 28 (full-time 29%). Undergraduate transfer-in students 98.

Characteristics of Student Body: *Ethnic/racial makeup:* Black non-Hispanic: 3%; American Indian or Alaska Native: 1%; Asian or Pacific Islander: 4%; Hispanic: 3%; White non-Hispanic: 87%; unknown 2%; nonresident alien 1%. *Age distribution:* number 18–19: 200; 20–21: 150; 22–24: 150; 25–29: 50; 30–34: 50; 35–39: 6; 40–49: 5; 50–64: 10; 65 and over: 1.

International Students: 7 nonresident aliens enrolled fall 2008. Programs available to aid students whose native language is not English: social, cultural. Financial aid specifically designated for international students. f\260 On-campus residence halls house 43% of student body. Residence halls for males constitute 50% of such space, for females 50%. *Intercollegiate athletics:* male: baseball, basketball, cross-country, football, golf, soccer, track, wrestling; female: basketball, cross-country, golf, soccer, softball, track, volleyball. *Special regulations:* Cars permitted without restrictions. Quiet hours from 11pm to 10am. Residence halls visitation from 10am to 1am weekdays; 10am to 3am weekends. *Special services:* student support services, health services, counseling services, wellness program, career planning and placement. *Student publications: Phreno Cosmian*, a monthly newspaper; *Prairie Winds*, an annual literary magazine. *Surrounding community:* Mitchell population 14,000. Sioux Falls (SD), 65 miles from campus, is nearest metropolitan area. Served by airport 5 miles from campus.

Library Collections: 73,000 including bound books, serial backfiles, electronic documents, and government documents not in separate collections. Online catalog. 72,500 mciroforms; 3,700 audiovisual materials; 620 current serial subscriptions. Computer work stations available. Students have access to the Internet at no charge.

Most important special holdings include the Jennewein Collection (4,000 monographs, 200 maps, and several thousand photographs, including rare and old materials, pertaining to the history and culture of the Dakota region); Senator Francis Case Collection (personal and political papers, books and memorabllla of Case's more than 30 years in Congress); Senator George McGovern's Collection (2,000 volumes and a partial collection of personal and political papers).

Buildings and Grounds: Campus area 50 acres.

Chief Executive Officer: Dr. Robert Duffett, President.

Address admission inquiries to Amy Novak, Director of Enrollment and Retention.

Mount Marty College

1105 West 8th Street
Yankton, South Dakota 57078

Tel: (605) 668-1011 **E-mail:** mmcadmit@mtmc.edu
Fax: (605) 668-1607 **Internet:** www.mtmc.edu

Institution Description: Mount Marty College is a private institution affiliated with the Sisters of St. Benedict of Sacred Heart Monastery, Roman Catholic Church. *Enrollment:* 1,880. *Degrees awarded:* Associate, baccalaureate, master's. Certificates also awarded.

Accreditation: *Regional:* NCA. *Professional*: nurse Anesthesia education, nursing, teacher education

History: Established as Mount Marty Junior College and offered first instruction at postsecondary level 1936; awarded first degree (associate) 1938; became 4-year institution and adopted present name first degree awarded 1985.

Institutional Structure: *Governing board:* Mount Marty College Board of Trustees and President. Extrainstitutional representation: 28 trustees; institutional representation: 5 administrators. 1 ex officio. 28 voting. *Composition of institution:* Administrators 7. Academic affairs headed by dean for academic affairs. Management/business/finances directed by chief financial officer. Full-time instructional faculty 35. Academic governance body, Academic Affairs Council, meets an average of 9 times per year.

Calendar: Semesters. Academic year Aug. to May. Freshmen admitted Sept., Jan, May, July, Aug. Degrees conferred May, Dec., Aug. Formal commencement May. Summer session of 4 terms from early June to late July.

Characteristics of Freshmen: 375 applicants (213 female, 162 male). 78% of applicants admitted. 55% of applicants admitted and enrolled full-time.

5% (7 students) submitted SAT scores; 95% (127 students) submitted ACT scores. *25th percentile*: SAT Critical Reading 340, SAT Math 340; ACT Composite 19, ACT English 17, ACT Math 19. *75th percentile*: SAT Critical Reading 50, SAT Math 680; ACT Composite 24, ACT English 24, ACT Math 22.

42% of entering freshmen expected to graduate within 5 years. 60% of freshmen from South Dakota. Freshmen from 251 states and 5 foreign countries.

Admission: Rolling admissions plan. Apply as early as the summer following junior year in secondary school. *Requirements:* Either graduation from accredited secondary school or GED with minimum ACT score of 18. 2.0 GPA.

Advanced placement for postsecondary-level work completed in secondary school. College credit for extrainstitutional learning on basis of faculty assessment.

Tutoring available. Developmental courses offered in summer session and regular academic year; elective credit given.

Degree Requirements: *For all associate degrees:* 64 hours. *For all baccalaureate degrees:* 128 hours. *For all undergraduate degrees:* 2.0 minimum GPA; last 32 hours in residence; distribution requirements.

Fulfillment of some degree requirements and exemption from some beginning courses possible by passing departmental examinations and College Board CLEP. *Grading system:* A–F; pass-fail.

Distinctive Educational Programs: Work-experience programs. Flexible meeting places and schedules, including evening classes and off-campus center (at Watertown, 165 miles from main institution). Preprofessional programs in dentistry, seminary training, veterinary medicine, medical school, occupational therapy, physical therapy. Individually designed programs. Tutorials. Study-travel abroad.

Degrees Conferred: 26 *associate;* 169 *baccalaureate*l 44 *master's*. Bachelor's degrees awarded: biological sciences 12; business and management 31; computer and information sciences 12; education 261; English 4; liberal arts 17; mathematics 7; philosophy/religion/theology 3; public administration 2; psychology 1; social sciences and history 5. *Master's:* philosophy/religion 44.

Fees and Other Expenses: *Full-time tuition per academic year 2008–09:* $16,250. *Other fees:* $1,682. *Room and board per academic year:* $5,210. *Books and supplies:* $920. *Other expenses:* $1,704.

Financial Aid: Aid from institutionally generated funds is provided on the basis of academic merit, financial need, athletic ability, talent (vocal, instrumental). Institution has a Program Participation Agreement with the U.S. Department of Education for eligible students to receive Pell Grants and, depending upon the agreement, other federal aid.

Financial aid to full-time, first-time undergraduate students: 100 received some form of financial aid. Average amount of aid received: federal grants $3,375; state/local grants $7,000; institutional grants $7,480; loans $6,073.

Departments and Teaching Staff: *Total instructional faculty:* 54 (full-time 54). Total faculty with doctorate, first-professional, or other terminal degree: 28. Student/faculty ratio: 13:1. Degrees held by full-time faculty: doctorate 64%, master's 63%, baccalaureate 3%. 43% hold terminal degrees.

Enrollment: Total enrollment 1,180. Undergraduate 1,046 (full-time 58%; female 62%, male 38%). Graduate 134 (full-time 100%). Undergraduate transfer-in students 47.

Characteristics of Student Body: *Ethnic/racial makeup:* Black non-Hispanic: 2%; American Indian or Alaska Native: 4%; Asian or Pacific Islander: 1%; Hispanic: 2%; White non-Hispanic: 2%; unknown: 3%. *Age distribution:* number under 18: 85; 18–19: 267; 20–21: 221; 22–24: 170; 25–29: 108; 30–34: 58; 35–39: 51; 40–49: 91; 50–64: 21; 65 and over: 3.

International Students: No programs available to aid students whose native language is not English. No financial aid specifically designated for international students.

Student Life: On-campus residence halls house 60% of student body. *Intercollegiate athletics:* male: baseball, basketball, cross-country, soccer, track; female: basketball, cross-country, softball, track, volleyball. *Special regulations:* Cars permitted without restrictions. Quiet hours from 7pm to 10:30pm. Residence hall visitation from 8am to 1am. *Special services:* Learning Resources Center, medical services, special advisement. *Student publications: The Midstream,* a semiannual literary magazine; *The Moderator,* a bimonthly newspaper. *Surrounding community:* Yankton population 12,000. Sioux Falls (SD), 80 miles, Sioux City (IA), 60 miles and Omaha (NE), 160 miles from campus, are the nearest metropolitan areas. Served by airport 3 miles from campus.

Library Collections: 79,500 volumes including bound books, serial backfiles, electronic documents, and government documents not in separate collections. Online catalog. 11,700 microforms; 8,500 audiovisual materials; 440 current serial subscriptions. Computer work staations available. Students have access to the Internet at no charge.

Most important special holdings include general works on Catholicism; theology collection; Southeast Asia collection; rare books collection; anesthesia theses from master's degree students.

Buildings and Grounds: Campus area 20 acres.

Chief Executive Officer: Dr. James T. Barry, President.

Address admission inquiries to Director of Admission.

National American University

5301 S. Hwy 16
Suite 200
Rapid City, South Dakota 57701
Tel: (605) 394-4800 **E-mail:** apply@national.edu
Fax: (605) 394-4871 **Internet:** www.national.edu

Institution Description: National American University, formerly named National College, is a private college with branch programs in Bloomington, MN; Brooklyn Center MN; Albuquerque NM, Colorado Springs CO; Denver CO; Ellsworth AFB, SD; Independence MO; Oakland Park KS; Rapid City SD; Rio Hondo NM; Roseville MN; Sioux Falls SD. Selected Internet courses are available, allowing students to take online classes anywhere in the world. *Enrollment:* 1,837 (Rapid City). *Degrees awarded:* Associate, baccalaureate. Diplomas also awarded.

Accreditation: *Regional:* NCA. *Professional*: medical assisting, medical record technology, veterinary technology

History: Established and incorporated as National School of Business 1941; offered first instruction at postsecondary level 1942; awarded first degree (associate) and changed name to National College of Business 1965; named National College 1979; adopted present name 1997.

Institutional Structure: *Governing board:* Board of Governors. Extrainstitutional representation: 13 governors; institutional representation: 2 administrators. All voting. *Composition of institution:* Administrators 6. Academic affairs headed by dean of academic affairs. Management/business/finances directed by director of business affairs. Full-time instructional faculty 26. Academic governance body, Curriculum Council, meets an average of 12 times per year.

Calendar: Quarters. Academic year Sept. to May. Degrees conferred and formal commencement May. Summer session from early June to mid-Aug.

Characteristics of Freshmen: Open enrollment. 43% of accepted applicants enrolled full-time. 66 % of freshmen from South Dakota.

Admission: Rolling admissions plan. For fall acceptance, apply as early as 1 year prior to enrollment, but not later than first day of classes. Early decision available; need not limit application to National American University College. Early acceptance available. *Requirements:* Graduation from secondary school or GED. *Entrance tests:* ACT composite. *For transfer students:* 2.0 GPA; from 4-year accredited institution 144 hours maximum transfer credit; from 2-year accredited institution 96 hours.

Advanced placement for postsecondary-level work completed in secondary school. College credit on basis of portfolio assessment; faculty assessment personal interview.

Tutoring available. Remedial courses offered during regular academic year; credit given.

Degree Requirements: *For all associate degrees:* 93 credit hours; 32 hours in residence. *For all baccalaureate degrees:* 186 credit hours; 48 hours in residence. *For all undergraduate degrees:* 2.0 GPA.

Fulfillment of some degree requirements and exemption from some beginning courses possible by passing departmental examinations, College Board CLEP. *Grading system:* A–F; pass-fail; withdraw (deadline after which pass-fail is appended to withdraw); incomplete (carries time limit).

Distinctive Educational Programs: Evening classes. Complete on-line degree programs.

ROTC: Army offered in cooperation with South Dakota School of Mines and Technology.

Degrees Conferred: 70 *associate;* 158 *baccalaureate*. Bachelor's degrees awarded: business and management 158. Master's degrees awarded: business and management 40.

Fees and Other Expenses: *Full-time tuition per academic year 2008–09:* varies from campus to campus. Contact the campus of interest for current information.

Financial Aid: Aid from institutionally generated funds is provided on the basis of academic merit, financial need, other criteria. Financial assistance is available in the form of Pell Grants, College Work-Study, Veterans Administration Benefits, National Direct Student Loans, Supplemental Education Opportunity Grants (SEOG), Stafford Loans, other federal aid programs.

Enrollment: Total enrollment 1,837. Undergraduate 1,413 (full-time 27%; female 67%, male 33%). Graduate 224 (full-time 46%). Undergraduate transfer-in students 221.

International Students: 42 nonresident aliens enrolled fall 2008. Programs available to aid students whose native language is not English: English as a Second Language Program. No financial aid specifically designated for international students.

Student Life: On-campus residence halls house 10% of student body. Residence halls for both sexes constitute 100% of such space. *Special regulations:* Cars permitted, parking limited. *Special services:* Medical services. *Student publications: Maverick Tales*, a newspaper. *Surrounding community:* Rapid City population 60,000. Denver (CO), 400 miles from campus, is nearest metropolitan area. Served by airport 10 miles from campus.

Library Collections: 45,000 volumes. 300 audiovisual titles; 450 current periodical subscriptions; electronic access to various online databases; 10,150 e-Books through Netlibrary. Online catalog. Students have access to online information retrieval services and the Internet.

Most important special holdings include collections on law and management; veterinary medicine; travel hospitality; data processing.

Buildings and Grounds: Campus area 7.5 acres.

Chief Executive Officer: Dr. Jerry Gallentine, President.

Address inquiries to Angela Beck, Director of Admissions.

Northern State University

1200 South Jay Street
Aberdeen, South Dakota 57401
Tel: (605) 626-2544 **E-mail:** admissions@northern.edu
Fax: (605) 626-2431 **Internet:** www.northern.edu

Institution Description: Northern State University is a state institution. *Enrollment:* 2,927. x*Degrees awarded:* Associate, baccalaureate, master's.

Academic offerings subject to approval by statewide coordinating bodies. Budget subject to approval by state governing boards.

Accreditation: *Regional:* NCA. *Professional*: music, teacher education

History: Established and chartered as Normal Northern and Industrial School 1901; offered first instruction at postsecondary level 1902; awarded first degree (baccalaureate) 1921; changed name to Northern State Teachers College 1939; became Northern State College 1963; adopted present name 1988.

Institutional Structure: *Governing board:* South Dakota Board of Regents. Representation: 9 regents, including 1 student. *Composition of institution:* Academic affairs headed by vice president. Management/business/finances directed by vice president. Full-time instructional faculty 93. Academic governance body, Faculty Senate, meets an average of 10 times per year. *Faculty representation:* Faculty served by collective bargaining agents, Council of Higher Education and South Dakota Education Association, affiliated with NEA.

Calendar: Semesters. Academic year Aug. to May. Freshmen admitted Aug., Jan., June, July. Degrees conferred and formal commencement May, Dec., Aug. Summer session of 2 terms from early June to late July.

Characteristics of Freshmen: 915 applicants (499 female, 415 male). 92% of applicants accepted. 48% of accepted applicants enrolled full-time. 94% (383 students) submitted ACT scores.

25th percentile: mean ACT Composite 18. *75th percentile:* mean ACT Composite 24.

80% of freshmen from South Dakota. Freshmen from 32 states and 17 foreign countries.

Admission: Rolling admissions plan. For fall acceptance, apply no later than Aug. 15. Early acceptance available. *Requirements:* C average in high school courses of 4 years English, 3 laboratory science, 3 mathematics (algebra or advanced), 3 social studies, 1/2 fine arts; Students who have not completed the required high school courses can be admitted provisionally and satisfy the deficiency by completing an appropriate college course in that area; a deficient course must be satisfied within 2 years and will be earned above and beyond any degree program requirements; or take the required high school courses and score 18 or above on the ACT; or have taken the required high school courses and rank in the top 60% of their graduating class. *Entrance tests:* ACT composite. *For transfer students:* 2.0 minimum GPA; from 4-year accredited institution 96 hours maximum transfer credit; from 2-year accredited institution 64 hours; correspondence/extension students 32 hours. Good standing at institution previously attended.

College credit and advanced placement for postsecondary-level work completed in secondary school. College credit for extrainstitutional learning on basis of faculty assessment; personal interviews.

Tutoring available. Remedial courses offered in summer session and regular academic year; credit given.

Degree Requirements: *For all associate degrees:* 64 credit hours. *For most baccalaureate degrees:* 128 credit hours. *For all undergraduate degrees:* 2.0 GPA; 1 year in residence; physical education (requirements vary with program); general education requirements.

Fulfillment of some degree requirements and exemption from some beginning courses possible by passing College Board CLEP; fulfillment of degree requirements also possible by passing departmental examinations. *Grading system:* A–F; pass-fail (for some internships); withdraw (carries time limit).

Distinctive Educational Programs: *For undergraduates:* Interdisciplinary program in environmental science. Cross-registration with other South Dakota state universities. *Available to all students:* Work-experience programs, including cooperative education, internships. Flexible meeting places, including off-campus centers (at varying locations within South Dakota). Evening classes. Facilities and programs for independent research. *Other distinctive programs:* Degree and nondegree granting continuing education program. E-Learning, Banking and financial services. Sports marketing and administration. International business major; professional accountancy degree program. Student/faculty exchange programs with institutions in China, Germany, Mexico, Poland.

Degrees Conferred: 14 *associate*; 263 *baccalaureate*; 56 *master's*. Bachelor's degrees awarded in top five disciplines: business, management, marketing, and related support services 97; education 92; social sciences 29; visual and performing arts 16; psychology 13. Master's degrees awarded: computer and information sciences 3; education 53. Master's degrees awarded: various disciplines 81.

Fees and Other Expenses: *Full-time tuition per academic year 2008–09:* resident undergraduate $5,712, nonresident $11,470; contact the university for current graduate tuition and applicable fees. *Room and board per academic year:* $4,864. *Books and supplies:* $900. *Other expenses:* $3,200.

Financial Aid: Aid from institutionally generated funds is provided on the basis of academic merit, financial need, athletic ability, other criteria. 97% received some form of aid. Aveage amount of aid received: federal grants $3,964; Pell grants $2,871; other federal aid $1,392; state/local grants $1,923; institutional grants $1,843.

Departments and Teaching Staff: *Total instructional faculty:* 93. Student/faculty ratio: 20:1. Degrees held by full-time faculty: doctorate 72%, master's 22%. 78% hold terminal degrees.

Enrollment: Total enrollment 2,927. Undergraduate 2,412 (full-tmie 72%; female 58%, male 42%). Graduate 515 (full-time 7%). Undergraduate transfer-in students 269.

Characteristics of Student Body: *Ethnic/racial makeup:* number of Black non-Hispanic: 34; American Indian or Alaska Native: 20; Asian or Pacific Islander: 127; Hispanic: 20; White non-Hispanic: 1,806; unknown 138.

International Students: 24 nonresident aliens enrolled fall 2008. Students from Europe, Asia, Latin America. Programs available to aid students whose native language is not English: social, cultural. English as a Second Language Program. No financial aid specifically designated for international students.

Student Life: All unmarried students under 21 years of age who are not veterans are required to live on campus. On-campus residence halls house 33% of student body. *Intercollegiate athletics:* male: baseball, basketball, cross-country, football, golf, tennis, track, wrestling; female: basketball, cross-country, golf, tennis, track, volleyball, softball. *Special regulations:* Cars with permits (fee charged) allowed. *Special services:* Learning Resources Center, medical services. *Student publications: Northern Exponent*, a bimonthly newspaper; *Pasque*, a yearbook; *What's Up*, published 3 times weekly. *Surrounding community:* Aberdeen population 28,000. Minneapolis-St. Paul, 285 miles from campus, is nearest metropolitan area. Served by airport 4 miles from campus.

Library Collections: 199,000 volumes. 28,455 government documents. Current periodical subscriptions: paper 1,100; microform 205,000; via electronic access 150. Online catalog. Computer work stations available. Students have access to online information retrieval services and the Internet.

Most important special holdings include collections on Indians of the Great Plains (2,000 volumes); the history of South Dakota (1,000 volumes); the history of Aberdeen and of Brown County. All three collections include some rare books.

Buildings and Grounds: Campus area 18 square blocks.

Chief Executive Officer: Dr. Patrick Schloss, President.

Address admission inquiries to alan Vogel, Director of Admissions.

Oglala Lakota College

Piya Wiconi Road
P.O. Box 490
Kyle, South Dakota 57752
Tel: (605) 455-2321 **E-mail:** admissions@olc.edu
Fax: (605) 455-2787 **Internet:** olc.edu

Institution Description: Oglala Lakota College is a tribally controlled school. *Enrollment:* 1,531. *Degrees awarded:* Associate, baccalaureate, master's.

Accreditation: *Regional:* NCA.

Calendar: Semesters.

Admission: High school graduation or GED; certification of degree of Indian blood from the tribal census office is required.

Degree Requirements: *For baccalaureate degree:* 128 credit hours; 22 credit hours in core curriculum; 15 credit hours in Lakota studies; Lakota language proficiency; GPA 2.0.

Degrees Conferred: 84 *associate*; 42 *baccalaureate*; 18 *master's*. Bachelor's degrees awarded in top five disciplines: business, management, marketing, and related support services 16; social sciences 15; natural resources 5; education 4; area and ethnic studies 2.

Fees and Other Expenses: *Full-time tuition per academic year 2008–09:* contact the college for current tuition and fees.

Financial Aid: Aid from institutionally generated funds is provided on the basis of academic merit, athletic ability, financial need, other criteria. Financial assistance is available in the form of Pell Grants, College Work-Study, Veterans Administration Benefits, National Direct Student Loans, Supplemental Education Opportunity Grants (SEOG), Stafford Loans, other federal aid programs.

Departments and Teaching Staff: *Total instructional faculty:* 19.

Enrollment: Total enrollment 1,531. Undergraduate 1,479 (full-time 52%; female 69%, male 31%_). Graduate 52 (full-time 50%).

Characteristics of Student Body: *Ethnic/racial makeup:* American Indian or Alaska Native: 90%.; White non-Hispanic: 9%; unknown: 1%.

Student Life: Located on the Pine Ridge Indian Reservation in southwestern South Dakota.

Library Collections: Learning Resource Center maintains the archives, audio-video studio, and an American Indian collection.

Chief Executive Officer: Dr. Thomas H. Shortbull, President.

Address admission inquiries to William K. Hornbeck, Registrar.

Presentation College

1500 North Main Street
Aberdeen, South Dakota 57401
Tel: (605) 225-1634 **E-mail:** admit@presentation.edu
Fax: (605) 229-8332 **Internet:** www.presentation.edu

Institution Description: Presentation College is an independent college primarily for women and affiliated with the Roman Catholic Church. *Enrollment* 733. *Degrees offered:* Associate, baccalaureate.

Accreditation: *Regional:* NCA. *Professional:* nursing, social work

History: The college was founded in 1951.

Calendar: Semesters. Academic year Sept. to May.

Characteristics of Freshmen: 100% of applicants accepted. 60% of accepted applicants enrolled.

Admission: *Requirements:* Secondary school graduation; ACT. *For transfer students:* High school/college transcript; 2.0 GPA; TOEFL for international students.

College credit and advanced placement for postsecondary-level work completed in secondary school and for extrainstitutional learning.

Developmental/remedial courses offered in summer session and regular academic year; credit given.

Degree Requirements: *For all associate degrees:* 60 credit hours. *For baccalaureate degrees:* 120 semester hours.

Degrees Conferred: 33 *associate*; 131 *baccalaureate*. Bachelor's degrees awarded in top three disciplines: health professions and related clinical sciences 40; public administration 7; business, management, marketing, and related support services 4;

Fees and Other Expenses: *Full-time tuition per academic year:* $12,951. *Books and supplies:* $1,388. *Room and board per academic year:* $4,875. *Books and supplies:* $1,388. *Other expenses:* $3,105.

Financial Aid: Aid from institutionally generated funds is provided on the basis of academic merit, financial need. Institution has a Program Participation Agreement with the U.S. Department of Education for eligible students to receive Pell Grants and, depending upon the agreement, other federal aid.

Financial aid to full-time, first-time undergraduate students: 100% received some form of aid.

Departments and Teaching Staff: *Total instructional faculty:* 31. Total tenured faculty: 12. Degrees held by full-time faculty: doctorate 19%, master's 62%, baccalaureate 19%.

Enrollment: Total enrollment 733.

Characteristics of Student Body: *Ethnic/racial makeup:* Black non-Hispanic: 1%; American Indian or Alaska Native: 1%; Asian or Pacific Islander: 1%; Hispanic: 1%; White non-Hispanic: 71%; unknown: 17%.

International Students: 1 nonresident alien enrolled fall 2008.

Student Life: Student newspaper; personal-psychological counseling; National Student Nursing Association; choral group; theater group. Intramural sports activities.

Library Collections: 34,000 volumes. 220 current periodical subscriptions.

Buildings and Grounds: Campus area 100 acres.

Chief Executive Officer: Dr. Lorraine Hale, President.

Address admissions inquiries to Joddy Meidinger, Director of Admissions.

Sinte Gleska College

150 East 2nd Street
P.O. Box 105
Mission, South Dakota 57555-0105
Tel: (605) 656-8100 **E-mail:** admissions@sinte..edu
Fax: (605) 656-5401 **Internet:** www.sinte.edu

Institution Description: Sinte Gleska College is a tribally controlled institution. *Enrollment:* 1,012. *Degrees awarded:* Associate, baccalaureate, master's.

Accreditation: *Regional:* NCA.

Calendar: Semesters. Academic year Sept. to July.

Characteristics of Freshmen: 100% of applicants accepted. 100% of accepted applicants enrolled. 99% of freshmen from South Dakota. Freshmen from 2 states.

Degree Requirements: Completion of prescribed curriculum.

Degrees Conferred: 21 *associate*; 20 *baccalaureate*; 1 *master's*. Bachelor's degrees awarded in top five disciplines: education 10; business, management, marketing, and related support services 3; security and protective services 3; health professions and related clinical sciences 2; visual and performing arts 1.

Fees and Other Expenses: *Full-time tuition per academic year 2008–09:* contact the school for current information. 300.

Financial Aid: Aid from institutionally generated funds is provided on the basis of academic merit, athletic ability, financial need, other criteria.

Financial assistance is available in the form of Pell Grants, College Work-Study, Veterans Administration Benefits, National Direct Student Loans, Supplemental Education Opportunity Grants (SEOG), Stafford Loans, other federal aid programs.

Departments and Teaching Staff: *Total instructional faculty:* 17.

Enrollment: Total enrollment 1,012. Undergraduate 848 (full-time 49%; female 69%, male 31%). Graduate 164 (full-time 9%).

Characteristics of Student Body: *Ethnic/racial makeup:* American Indian or Alaska Native: 85%; White non-Hispanic: unknown: 15%.

Chief Executive Officer: Dr. Lionel R. Bordeaux, President.

Address admission inquiries to Michelle Zophier, Registrar.

Sioux Falls Seminary

1525 South Grange Avenue
Sioux Falls, South Dakota 57105
Tel: (605) 336-6588 **E-mail:** train@nabs.edu
Fax: (605) 335-9090 **Internet:** www.nabs.edu

Institution Description: Sioux Falls Seminary, formerly named North American Baptist Seminary, is a private graduate school of theological education affiliated with the North American Baptist Conference. *Enrollment:* 117. *Degrees awarded:* First-professional (master of divinity), master's, doctorate.

Accreditation: *Regional:* NCA. *National:* ATS. *Professional*: theology

History: Established as German department of Rochester Theological Seminary 1858; chartered and offered first instruction at postsecondary level 1858; incorporated 1877; changed name to German Baptist Seminary circa 1930, to Rochester Baptist Seminary 1935; adopted present name 1944; awarded first degree (first-professional) 1951.

Institutional Structure: *Governing board:* Board of Trustees. Extrainstitutional representation: 25 trustees, including 8 elected clergy, 8 elected laity, up to 8 appointed. institutional representation: president of the seminary, 1 student. 1 ex officio. 25 voting. *Composition of institution:* Administrators 9. Academic affairs headed by academic vice president. Business/finances directed by administrative vice president for business operations. Full-time instructional faculty 11. Academic governance body, the faculty, meets an average of 10 times per year.

Calendar: Semesters (4-1-4 plan). Academic year Sept. to Aug. Entering students admitted Sept., Jan., Feb. Degrees conferred and formal commencement May.

Admission: Rolling admissions plan. *Requirements:* Baccalaureate degree from accredited institution with liberal arts curriculum. Minimum GPA 2.50.

Degree Requirements: *For first-professional degree:* 94 semester hours; 5 hours field of education; 2.5 GPA. *For one master's degree:* 73 semester hours; 14 hours of practicum; 3.0 GPA. *For other master's degrees:* 62 semester hours, 4–6 hours of practicum, 2.25 GPA. *For academic master's degrees:* 62 semester hours; 2.25 GPA. *For doctor of ministry degree:* 30 semester hours.

Distinctive Educational Programs: Flexible degree programs. Internships. Flexible scheduling with evening, weekend, and block classes. Partnership with First Priority of Sioux Falls for youth ministry training. 3–3 Program (a combined bachelor of arts and master of divinity that can be completed in six years in partnership with 3 undergraduate institutions). Reciprocal agreement with 2 local colleges. Annual lectureship featuring outstanding Christian scholars. On-site cross-cultural studies in Mexico, inner-city Minneapolis, or Indian reservation. Studies in the Holy Land at Jerusalem University College.

Degrees Conferred: 10 *master's:* theology; 2 *doctorate:* ministry; 15 *first-professional:* master of divinity.

Fees and Other Expenses: *Full-time tuition per academic year:* contact the seminary for current tuition/fees.

Financial Aid: Aid from institutionally generated funds is provided on the basis of academic merit, financial need, other criteria. Institution has a Program Participation Agreement with the U.S. Department of Education for eligible students to receive Pell Grants and, depending upon the agreement, other federal aid.

Departments and Teaching Staff: *Total instructional faculty:* 16. *Degrees held by full-time faculty:* Doctorate 73%, master's 45%, baccalaureate 100%, professional 100%. 100% hold terminal degrees.

Enrollment: Total enrollment 117.

Characteristics of Student Body: *Ethnic/racial makeup:* Black non-Hispanic: 2%; American White non-Hispanic: 98%.

International Students: Programs available to aid students whose native language is not English: social, cultural, Financial aid specifically designated for international students: 1 scholarship available annually.

Student Life: On-campus residence apartments consisting of 3 buildings, 35 one- and 22 two-bedroom apartments available to single or married students. Use of the nearby wellness center at the University of Sioux Falls available to students. *Surrounding community:* Sioux Falls population approximately 120,000. Omaha NE, 175 miles from campus and Minneapolis-St. Paul MN, 250 miles from campus, are nearest metropolitan areas. Served by airport 3 miles from campus.

Library Collections: 68,000 volumes including bound books, serial backfiles, electronic documents, and government documents not in separate collections. Online catalog. Current serial subscriptions: 304 paper, 743 microform. 1,771 recordings; 4 compact. Computer work stations available. Students have access to the Internet at no charge.

Most important special holdings include the Harris Homiletics Collection.

Buildings and Grounds: Urban campus.

Chief Executive Officer: Dr. G. Michael Hagan, President.

Address admission inquiries to Director of Admissions.

South Dakota School of Mines and Technology

501 East Saint Joseph Street
Rapid City, South Dakota 57701-3995
Tel: (605) 394-2400 **E-mail:** admissions@sdsmt.edu
Fax: (605) 394-1268 **Internet:** www.sdsmt.edu

Institution Description: South Dakota School of Mines and Technology is a state institution. *Enrollment:* 2,061. *Degrees awarded:* Baccalaureate, master's, doctorate. Academic offerings subject to approval by statewide coordinating bodies. Budget subject to approval by state governing boards.

Accreditation: *Regional:* NCA. *Professional*: chemistry, engineering

History: Established as Dakota School of Mines early 1885; changed name to South Dakota School of Mines late 1885; offered first instruction at postsecondary level 1886; awarded first degree 1888; adopted present name 1943.

Institutional Structure: *Governing board:* South Dakota Board of Regents. Representation: 10 regents, including 1 student. 9 voting. *Composition of institution:* Administrators 5. Academic affairs headed by president. Management/business/finances directed by controller. Full-time instructional faculty 104. Academic governance body, the faculty, meets an average of 9 times per year. *Faculty representation:* Faculty served by collective bargaining agents, Council of Higher Education and South Dakota Education Association, affiliated with NEA.

Calendar: Semesters. Academic year Sept. to May. Freshmen admitted Sept., Jan. Degrees conferred and formal commencements May, Dec. Summer session.

Characteristics of Freshmen: 691 applicants (214 female, 677 male). 83% of applicants accepted. 42% of accepted applicants enrolled full-time.

15% (48 students) submitted SAT scores. 93% (296 students) submitted ACT scores. *25th percentile*: ACT Composite 28, ACT English 20, ACT Math 24. *75th percentile*: ACT Composite 28, ACT English 28, ACT Math 28.

43% of entering freshmen expected to graduate within 5 years. 67% of freshmen from South Dakota. Freshmen from 34 states and 13 foreign countries.

Admission: Rolling admissions plan. For fall acceptance, apply as early as Sept. of previous year, but not later than Aug. 1 of year of enrollment. *Require-*

ments: Graduation from accredited secondary school with C or better in 4 years English, 3 mathematics (algebra-level or higher), 3 laboratory science, 3 social science, ½ fine arts, ½ computer science. *Entrance tests:* ACT composite. For foreign students TOEFL. *For transfer students:* 2.0 minimum GPA; from 4-year accredited institution hours maximum transfer credit limited only by residence requirement; from 2-year accredited institution 68 hours.

Degree Requirements: 128 or 136 credit hours; 2.0 GPA; 2 terms in residence; 2 hours physical education; distribution requirements.

Fulfillment of some degree requirements and exemption from some beginning courses possible by passing departmental examinations, College Board CLEP, AP (score of 3). *Grading system:* A–F; pass-fail; withdraw (deadline after which pass-fail is appended to withdraw); incomplete (carries time limit).

Distinctive Educational Programs: *For undergraduates:* Weekend classes. 5-year double-degree program. Institutionally arranged study abroad in England, France, Ireland, Italy, West Germany. Qualified seniors may earn graduate credit for graduate-level courses. Cross-registration with Black Hills State College. *For graduate students:* Cooperative master's program in engineering management with University of South Dakota (Vermillion campus). *Available to all students:* Evening classes. Individual majors. Black Hills Natural Science Field Station, located on campus, offers summer field courses. *Other distinctive programs:* Continuing education program.

ROTC: Army.

Degrees Conferred: 9 *associate*; 250 *baccalaureate*; 73 *master's*; 2 *doctorate*. Bachelor's degrees awarded in top five disciplines: engineering 171, multidisciplinary studies 131; computer and information sciences; physical sciences 9; mathematics 3. Master's degrees awarded: various disciplines 73. Doctorates awrded: engineering 1; physical sciences 1.

Fees and Other Expenses: *Full-time tuition per academic year 2008–09:* undergraduate resident $6,280, nonresident $10,520. *books and supplies:* $1,200. *Room and board per academic year:* $4,770. *Other expenses:* $3,850.

Financial Aid: Aid from institutionally generated funds is provided on the basis of academic merit, financial merit, athletic ability.

Financial aid to full-time, first-time undergraduate students: 92% received some form of financial aid. Average amount of aid received: federal grants $4,549; Pell grants $2,632; ohter federal aid $2,436; state/local grants $2,172; institutional grants $1,933.

Departments and Teaching Staff: *Total instructional faculty:* 104. Total tenured faculty: 50. Degrees held by full-time faculty: doctorate 74%, master's 26%, 76% hold terminal degrees.

Enrollment: Total enrollment 2,061. Undergraduate 1,817 (full-time 78%; female 30%, male 70%). Graduate 244 (full-time 59%). Undergraduate transfer-in students 72.

Characteristics of Student Body: *Ethnic/racial makeup:* Black non-Hispanic: 1%; American Indian or Alaska Native: 3%; Asian or Pacific Islander: 1%; Hispanic: 5%; White non-Hispanic: 88%; unknown: 5%; nonresident alien 1%.

International Students: 21 nonresident aliens enrolled fall 2008. No programs available to aid students whose native language is not English. No financial aid specifically designated for international students.

Student Life: On-campus residence halls house 27% of student body. Residence halls for males constitute 81% of such space, for females 19%. 11% of males and 7% of females join fraternities and sororities. *Intercollegiate athletics:* male: basketball, cross-country, football, track; female: basketball, cross-country, track, volleyball. *Special regulations:* Cars with decals permitted on college-owned lots; fee charged. Residence hall visitation from noon to midnight. *Special services:* Learning Resources Center, medical services. *Student publications, radio: The Engineer,* a yearbook; *The Tech,* a biweekly newspaper. Radio station KTEQ broadcasts 80 hours per week. *Surrounding community:* Rapid City population 60,000. Denver (CO), 400 miles from campus, is nearest metropolitan area. Served by airport 10 miles from campus.

Library Collections: 301,000 volumes including bound books, serial backfiles, electronic documents, and government documents not in separate collections. Online catalog. Current serial subscriptions: 461 paper. 255,784 microform units. 3,046 recordings. Computer work stations available. campus-wide. Students have access to online information retrieval services and the Internet. Most important special holdings include South Dakota Collection; government documents; mining and Black Hills area archives.

Buildings and Grounds: Campus area 120 acres.

Chief Executive Officer: Dr. Charles P. Ruch, President.

Address admission inquiries to Director of Admissions.

South Dakota State University

Box 2201
Brookings, South Dakota 57007
Tel: (800) 952-3541 **E-mail:** admissions@sdstate.edu
Fax: (605) 688-6891 **Internet:** www.sdstate.edu

Institution Description: South Dakota State University is a state institution and land-grant college. *Enrollment:* 11,995. *Degrees awarded:* Associate, baccalaureate, master's, doctorate.

Budget subject to approval by state governing boards.

Accreditation: *Regional:* NCA. *Professional*: athletic training, chemistry, counseling, dietetics, engineering, family and consumer science, journalism, music, nursing, pharmacy, teacher education, veterinary technology

History: Established and chartered as Agricultural College of South Dakota 1881; offered first instruction at postsecondary level 1884; awarded first degree (baccalaureate) 1886; changed name to State College of Agriculture and Mechanic Arts 1907; adopted present name 1964. *See* J. Howard Kramer, *History of South Dakota State University* (Brookings: South Dakota State University Foundation, 1977) for further information.

Institutional Structure: *Governing board:* South Dakota Board of Regents. Representation: 10 regents, including 1 student. 10 voting. *Composition of institution:* 7 administrators, 15 deans and associate deans: 32. Academic affairs headed by provost. Administration headed by executive vice-president. Full-time instructional faculty 423. Academic governance body, Academic Senate, meets an average of 18 times per year. *Faculty representation:* Faculty served by collective bargaining agents, Council of Higher Education and South Dakota Education Association, affiliated with NEA.

Calendar: Semesters. Academic year Sept. to May. Freshmen admitted June, July, Aug., Jan. Degrees conferred May, Aug., Dec. Formal commencement May, Dec. Summer session.

Characteristics of Freshmen: 3,961 applicants (2,014 female, 1,947 male). 93% of applicants accepted. 57% of accepted applicants enrolled full-time.

97% (2,044 students) submitted ACT scores. *25th percentile*: ACT Composite 20, ACT English 19, ACT Math 19. *75th percentile*: ACT Composite 25, ACT English 25, ACT Math 26.

49% of entering freshmen expected to graduate within 5 years. 70% of freshmen from South Dakota. Freshmen from 39 states and 26 foreign countries.

Admission: Rolling admissions plan. *Requirements:* Either graduation from accredited secondary school with 2.0 GPA in the following courses: 4 years of English, 3 laboratory science, 3 social science, 3 mathematics, 1/2 year computer science, 1/2 year fine arts. South Dakota and Minnesota students not meeting course requirements may be admitted provisionally if class rank is upper one-half or ACT composite score is 22. Out-of-state students not meeting course requirements may be admitted provisionally if class rank is upper one-half or ACT composite score is 23. TOEFL required of foreign students. *For transfer students:* 2.0 minimum GPA; from 4-year and 2-year accredited institutions 64 hours maximum transfer credit.

College credit and advanced placement for postsecondary-level work completed in secondary school. Tutoring available.

Degree Requirements: *For all associate degrees:* 64 credit hours; 2.0 GPA; 16 hours in residence. *For all baccalaureate degrees:* Completion of at least 128 semester credit hours (see individual professional college requirements); 2.0 GPA; 32 hours in residence. Some programs have varying degree requirements.

Fulfillment of some degree requirements and exemption from some beginning courses possible by passing departmental examinations, College Board CLEP, AP, other standardized tests. *Grading system:* A–F; pass-fail; withdraw (carries time limit).

Distinctive Educational Programs: Work-experience programs, including cooperative education, internships. Accelerated degree programs. Cooperative teacher education certification programs with Black Hills State University, Dakota State University. Special facilities for using telecommunications in the classroom. Interdepartmental programs in environmental management, European studies, international agriculture, Latin American area studies, women's studies. Facilities and programs for independent research, including Honors College, individual majors. Institutionally sponsored study abroad in Bolivia, China, England, France, India, Japan, Malaysia, Republic of Korea, Germany, Russia, Sweden, Egypt, Jordan, Turkey, Canada, Australia, North Korea, Poland, and the Cooperative Center for Study Abroad which has many other international options. Spain. *Other distinctive programs:* Continuing education; community service. New Ph.D. programs in electrical engineering, nursing, computational science, geological engineering, wildlife and fisheries.

ROTC: Air Force, Army.

Degrees Conferred: 16 *associate*; 1,884 *baccalaureate*; 275 *master's*; 24 *doctorate*; 59 *first-professional*. Bachelor's degrees awarded in top five disciplines: health professions and related clinical sciences 330; social sciences 178;

SOUTH DAKOTA STATE UNIVERSITY—*cont'd*

agriculture 155; engineering 111, family and consumer sciences 92. Master's degrees awarded: various disciplines 253. *First-professional:* pharmacy 59.

Fees and Other Expenses: *Full-time tuition per academic year 2008–09:* undergraduate resident $5,808, nonresident $7,143; contact the university for current graduate and first-professional tuition and any applicable fees. *Other fees:* vary by program. *Required fees:* $2,670. *Room and board per academic year:* $5,423. *Books and supplies:* $1,014. *Other expenses:* $3,494.

Financial Aid: Aid from institutionally generated funds is provided on the basis of academic merit, financial need, athletic ability.

Financial aid to full-time, first-time undergraduate students: 93% received some form of aid. Average amount of aid received: federal grants $3,989; Pell grants $2,765; other federal aid $1,600; state/local grants $1,767; institutional grants $1,892.

Departments and Teaching Staff: *Total instructional faculty:* 598 (full-time 425, part-time 175). Total faculty with doctorate, first-professional, or other terminal degree: 347. Student/faculty ratio: 17.6:1. Degrees held by full-time faculty: baccalaureate 21%, master's 30.5%, doctorate 67.4%. 70% hold terminal degrees.

Enrollment: Total enrollment 11,995. Undergraduate 10,532 (full-time 79%; female 52%, male 48%). Graduate 1,483 (full-time 29%). Undergraduate transfer-in students 790.

Characteristics of Student Body: *Ethnic/racial makeup:* Black non-Hispanic: 1%; American Indian or Alaska Native: 2%; Asian or Pacific Islander: 1%; Hispanic: 1%; White non-Hispanic: 88%; unknown 6%; nonresident alien 1%. *Age distribution:* number under 18: 25; 18–19: 3,037; 20–21: 3,206; 22–24: 2,017; 25–29: 649; 30–34: 260; 35–39: 149; 40–49: 193; 50–64: 78.

International Students: 120 nonresident aliens enrolled fall 2008. Students from Europe, Asia, Latin America, Africa, Canada, Middle East. Programs available to aid students whose native language is not English: social, cultural. English as a Second Language Program. No financial aid specifically designated for international students.

Student Life: On-campus co-ed residence halls house 39% of the student body. Special-interest housing is available for male engineering students and for all students desiring intensive study halls. 4% of males join fraternities; 3% of females join sororities. 12% of married students are housed in campus housing. *Intercollegiate athletics:* male: baseball, basketball, cross-country, football, golf, swimming, tennis, track, wrestling; female: golf, basketball, cross-country, soccer, softball, swimming, tennis, track, volleyball. *Intramural and recreational sports:* 24 intramural athletic programs and 46 sports clubs. *Special regulations:* Cars permitted without restrictions. *Special services:* Medical services, counseling services, Native American Advisor, Disabled Student Advisor, International Student Advisor. *Student organizations:* 170 recognized campus organizations provide a variety of educational, social, cultural, service, and recreational programs for the campus community. *Student publications, radio, television: Collegian*, a weekly newspaper; *Jackrabbit*, a yearbook; *Oakwood*, a quarterly literary publication. Radio station KESD-FM, television station KESD; each broadcasts 126 hours per week. *Surrounding community:* Brookings population 16,500. Minneapolis (MN), 200 miles from campus, is nearest metropolitan area. Served by airport 2 miles from campus.

Library Collections: 1,027,000 volumes bound books and serial backfiles; 2,562 electronic documents; 297,162 government documents. Online catalog. 1,011,000 microforms; 3,300 audiovisual materials; 29,400 periodicals including via electronic access. Computer work stations available. Students have access to online information retrieval services and the Internet.

Most important special holdings include collections on South Dakota history; George Norby Collection of Local History; Thomas A, Daschle Congressional papers; Elizabeth Cook-Lynn Papers; Margahab Rare Book Collection and Personal Papers; nursing and pharmacy.

Buildings and Grounds: Campus area 260 acres.

Chief Executive Officer: Dr. David Chicoine, President.

Undergraduates address admission inquiries to Megan Dombek, Director of Admissions; graduate inquiries to Dr. Kevin Kephart, Dean of Graduate School.

University of Sioux Falls

1101 West 22nd Street
Sioux Falls, South Dakota 57105-1699
Tel: (605) 331-5000 **E-mail:** admissions@usiouxfalls.edu
Fax: (605) 331-6615 **Internet:** www.usiouxfalls.edu

Institution Description: The University of Sioux Falls, formerly known as Sioux Falls College, is a private institution affiliated with the American Baptist Churches, U.S.A. *Enrollment:* 1,589. *Degrees awarded:* Associate, baccalaureate, master's.

Member of the consortium Council of Christian Colleges and Universities and Colleges of Mid-America.

Accreditation: *Regional:* NCA. *Professional*: business, social work, teacher education

History: Established as Dakota Collegiate Institute, chartered, and offered first instruction at postsecondary level 1883; reorganized and changed name to Sioux Falls University 1885; awarded first degree (baccalaureate) 1904; merged with Grand Island College of Nebraska and adopted present name 1931; added graduate level 1980; current name adopted 1995.

Institutional Structure: *Governing board:* University of Sioux Falls Board of Trustees. Extrainstitutional representation: 25 trustees; institutional representation: 1 full-time instructional faculty member, 1 student; 12 alumni. All voting. *Composition of institution:* Administrators 7 including president, vice president for academic affairs/provost, vice president of student services, vice president of development, vice president for professional studies, vice president for administration and human resources, chief operations officer. Full-time instructional faculty 61. Academic governance body, University of Sioux Falls Faculty, meets an average of 9 times per year.

Calendar: Semesters. Academic year Sept. to May. Freshmen admitted Sept., Feb., June. Degrees conferred and formal commencement May. Summer session from June to Aug.

Characteristics of Freshmen: 752 applicants (379 female, 373 male). 97% of applicants admitted. 40% of applicants admitted and enrolled full-time.

3% (9 students) submitted SAT scores; 97% (277 students) submitted ACT scores. *25th percentile*: SAT Critical Reading 500, SAT Math 460; ACT Composite 19, ACT English 18, ACT Math 18. *75th percentile*: SAT Critical Reading 600, SAT Math 660; ACT Composite 25, ACT English 25, ACT Math 26.

45% of entering freshmen expected to graduate within 5 years. 67% of freshmen from South Dakota. Freshmen from 28 states and 6 foreign countries.

Admission: Rolling admissions plan. For fall acceptance, apply as early as Aug. of previous year, but not later than Aug. of year of enrollment. Early acceptance available. *Requirements:* Either graduation from accredited secondary school or GED. Submit ACT, SAT or GED official reports along with an official high school transcript. *For transfer students:* 2.5 minimum GPA. From 4-year institution 96 hours maximum transfer credit; from 2-year institution 64 hours.

College credit for extrainstitutional learning on basis of portfolio assessment.

Degree Requirements: *For all associate degrees:* 64 semester hours; last 14 semester hours in residence. *For all baccalaureate degrees:* 128 semester hours; last 30 semester hours in residence. *For all undergraduate degrees:* 2.0 GPA; 2.6 GPA for students entering teaching majors.

Fulfillment of some degree requirements possible by passing College Level Examination Program tests (CLEP). *Grading system:* A–F; P-NC.

Distinctive Educational Programs: *For undergraduates:* Weekend classes. Interdepartmental majors available. Degree Completion Program for adults. Facilities for independent research. Honors program, individual majors, and tutorials. Reciprocal registration available with North American Baptist Seminary and Augustana College. Evening classes available for both graduate and undergraduate students. Latin American, Russian, Middle East Studies Programs. Study abroad through Council of Christian Colleges and Universities. Two students per semester may attend Hong Kong Baptist University.

Degrees Conferred: 262 *baccalaureate*; 107 *master's*. Bachelor's degrees awarded in top five disciplines: business, management, marketing, and related support services 123; education 31; health professions and related clinical sciences 20; social sciences 16; biological/life sciences 12. Master's degrees awarded: business/marketing 15; education 74; other disciplines 18.

Fees and Other Expenses: *Full-time tuition per academic year 2008–09:* $19,325; undergraduate; graduate tuition charged per credit hour depending on program. *Room and board per academic year:* $6,376. *Required fees:* $320. *Books and supplies:* $800. *Other expenses:* $1,000.

Financial Aid: Aid from institutionally generated funds is provided on the basis of academic merit, financial need, athletic ability.

Financial aid to full-time, first-time undergraduate students: 100% received some form of aid. Average amount of aid received: federal grants $3,630; Pell grants $2,896; other federal aid $1,018; state/local grants $956; institutional grants $7,993.

Departments and Teaching Staff:

Total instructional faculty: 136. Total faculty with doctorate, first-professional, or other terminal degree: 43. Student/faculty ratio: 17:1. Degrees held by full-time faculty: master's 15%, doctorate 75%, professional 10%. 85% hold terminal degrees.

Enrollment: Total enrollment 1,589. Undergraduate 1,244 (full-time 83%; female 53%, male 47%). Graduate 347 (part-time 100%). Undergraduate transfer-in students 35.

Characteristics of Student Body: *Ethnic/racial makeup:* Black non-Hispanic: 2%; Hispanic: 2%; White non-Hispanic: 95%. *Age distribution:* number

18–19: 132; 20–21: 398; 22–24: 381; 25–29: 101; 30–34: 49; 35–39: 22; 40–49: 44; 50–64: 11; 65 and over: 1. 78% of student body attend summer sessions.

International Students: 4 nonresident aliens enrolled fall 2008. Students from Asia, Latin America, Canada. No programs available to aid students whose native language is not English. Financial aid specifically designated for international students: 10 scholarships available annually to qualifying students.

Student Life: On-campus residence halls house 54% of the student body. Residence halls for males constitute 45% of such space, for females 55%. Housing is available for married students. *Intercollegiate athletics:* male: basketball, cross-country, football, soccer, tennis, track; female: basketball, cross-country, soccer, softball, tennis, track, volleyball. *Special regulations:* Registered cars permitted on campus; no fee charged. Quiet hours from 11pm to 8am. Residence hall visitation from 12m to 11pm. *Special services:* Learning Resources Center, Career and Academic Planning Center, Tutorial Assistance Program, medical services. *Student publications, radio: The Vessel,* a biweekly newspaper. College owned radio station, KCFS broadcasts 80 hours per week. *Surrounding community:* Sioux Falls, population 135,000. Minneapolis, MN, 240 miles from campus, is nearest metropolitan area. Sioux Falls is served by mass transit bus system; airport 5 miles from campus.

Library Collections: 89,500 volumes including bound books, serial backfiles, electronic documents, and government documents not in separate collections. Online catalog. Current serial subscriptions: 290 paper, 22 microform. 867 audio/videotapes; 24 DVD discs. Computer work stations available. Students have access to online information retrieval services and the Internet.

Buildings and Grounds: Campus area includes 8 square blocks with 2 administrative/classroom buildings, science facility, fine arts facility, library, wellness/athletic facility, 4 residence halls (one of which is available to married students), and student union/dining area. The oldest building was erected in 1908.

Chief Executive Officer: Dr. Mark Benedetto, President.

Undergraduates address admission inquiries to Gregory Fritz, Vice President for Enrollment; graduate inquires to Director, Graduate Education.

University of South Dakota

414 East Clark Street
Vermillion, South Dakota 57069-2390
Tel: (605) 677-5434 **E-mail:** admiss@usd.edu
Fax: (605) 677-6323 **Internet:** www.usd.edu

Institution Description: University of South Dakota is a state institution. *Enrollment:* 9,291. *Degrees awarded:* Associate, baccalaureate, first-professional (law, medicine), master's, doctorate.

Budget subject to approval by state governing boards.

Accreditation: *Regional:* NCA. *Professional*: art, business, chemistry, dental hygiene, counseling, health services administration, journalism, law, medicine, music, nursing, clinical psychology, social work, teacher education, physical therapy, occupational therapy, physician assisting, psychology internship, public administration, speech-language pathology, theatre

History: Established and chartered as University of Dakota 1862; offered first instruction at postsecondary level 1882; awarded first degree (baccalaureate) 1884; changed name to University of South Dakota 1891, to State University of South Dakota 1959; readopted present name 1963. *See* Cedric Clisten Cummins, *The University of South Dakota* (Vermillion: Dakota Press, 1975) for further information.

Institutional Structure: *Governing board:* South Dakota Board of Regents. Representation: 10 regents, including 1 student. 9 voting. Academic affairs headed by Vice President of Academic Affairs. Admission, Financial Aid, Registrar, Resident Services headed by Dean of Student Life. Athletics, Alumni and Media Relations headed by Vice President of University Relations. Facilities, Auxiliary Services, Personnel, Finance and Administration headed by Vice President of Finance and Administration. Full-time instructional faculty 287. Academic governance body, University Senate, meets an average of 11 times per year. *Faculty representation:* Faculty served by collective bargaining agent affiliated with COHE.

Calendar: Semesters. Academic year Sept. to May. Freshmen admitted Aug., Jan., June. Degrees conferred Dec., May. Summer sessions.

Characteristics of Freshmen: 2,345 applicants (2,058 female, 1,287 male). 83% of applicants accepted. 42% of accepted applicants enrolled full-time.

4% (48 students) submitted SAT scores; 93% (1,087 students) submitted ACT scores. *25th percentile*: SAT Critical Reading 460, SAT Math 470; ACT Composite 20, ACT English 19, ACT Math 18. *75th percentile*: SAT Critical Reading 580, SAT Math 620; ACT Composite 25, ACT English 25, ACT Math 25.

43% of entering freshmen expected to graduate within 5 years. 76% of freshmen from South Dakota. Freshmen from 43 states and 11 foreign countries.

Admission: Rolling admissions plan. Students may apply any time after the junior year of high school. Early acceptance available to students in senior year of high school based on ACT score, class rank, or cumulative GPA.. *Requirements:* Graduation from accredited secondary school with 4 years English, 3 social sciences, 3 mathematics (algebra, geometry, trigonometry, or other advanced mathematics), 3 laboratory science (biology, chemistry, or physics with at least one regular laboratory period per week), 1 semester computer science, 1 semester fine arts. *Entrance tests:* ACT or SAT. For foreign students TOEFL. *For transfer students:* 2.0 minimum GPA; from 4-year accredited institution hours maximum transfer credit limited only by residence requirement; credit; from 2-year accredited institution 64 semester hours maximum transfer credit; for correspondence/extension students 30 hours.

College credit and advanced placement for postsecondary-level work completed in secondary school. College credit for extrainstitutional learning on basis of faculty assessment.

Tutoring available. Remedial courses offered during regular academic year; credit given.

Degree Requirements: *For all associate degrees:* 68 semester hours. *For all baccalaureate degrees:* 120 hours. *For all undergraduate degrees:* 2.0 GPA; 30 hours in residence.

Fulfillment of some degree requirements and exemption from some beginning courses possible by passing College Board CLEP, AP, departmental examinations. *Grading system:* A–F; pass-fail; withdraw (deadline after which pass-fail appended to withdraw).

Distinctive Educational Programs: Off-campus centers (at Sioux Falls, 55 miles away from main institution; Rapid City, 500 miles away). Evening classes. Special facilities for using telecommunications in the classroom. Interdisciplinary baccalaureate program in liberal studies, master's in selected studies. Facilities and programs for independent research, including honors programs, tutorials. Study abroad in England, France, German, and Sweden. *Other distinctive programs:* Continuing education.

ROTC: Army.

Degrees Conferred: 284 *associate*; 819 *baccalaureate*; 448 *master's*; 49 *doctorate*; 126 *first-professional*. Bachelor's degrees awarded in top five disciplines: business/marketing 153; psychology 101; health professions and related sciences 85; education 86; security and protective services 61. Master's degrees awarded: various disciplines 448; doctorates awarded: 49; first-professional degrees awarded: law 85; medicine 51.

Fees and Other Expenses: *Full-time tuition per academic year 2008–09:* undergraduate resident $5,828, nonresident $7,148; contact the university for current graduate and first-professional tuition and applicable fees. *Books and supplies:* $900. *Other expenses:* $3,577. *Room and board per academic year:* $5,492.

Financial Aid: Aid from institutionally generated funds is provided on the basis of academic merit, financial need, athletic ability.

Financial aid to full-time, first-time undergraduate students: 945 received some form of aid. Average amount of aid received: federal grants $3,821; Pell grants $2,765; other federal aid $1,561; state/local grants $1,854; institutional grants $2,595.

Departments and Teaching Staff: *Total instructional faculty:* 375 (full-time 287, part-time 48). Total faculty with doctorate, first-professional, or other terminal degree: 244. Student/faculty ratio: 15:1. Degrees held by full-time faculty: baccalaureate 5%, master's 22%, doctorate 58%, professional 15%. 86% hold terminal degrees.

Enrollment: Total enrollment 8,746. Undergraduate

Characteristics of Student Body: *Ethnic/racial makeup:* number of Black non-Hispanic: 99; American Indian or Alaska Native: 147; Asian or Pacific Islander: 81; Hispanic: 57; White non-Hispanic: 5,614; unknown: 449. *Age distribution:* number under 18: 37; 18–19: 1,153; 20–21: 1,094; 22–24: 1,111; 25–29: 763; 30–34: 380; 35–39: 260; 40–49: 2651 50–64: 1571 65 and over: 3. 29% of student body attend summer sessions.

International Students: 144 nonresident aliens enrolled fall 2008. No programs to aid students whose native language is not English. No financial aid specifically designated for international students.

Student Life: On-campus residence halls house 34% of student body. Co-ed housing, fraternities, sororities, and housing for married students are all available. *Intercollegiate athletics:* male: baseball, basketball, cross-country, football, swimming and diving, tennis, track; female: basketball, softball, swimming and diving, tennis, track, volleyball. *Special regulations:* Cars with parking permit allowed. Quiet hours vary according to residence hall. *Special services:* Medical services. *Student publications, television:* A quarterly literary magazine, *Volante,* a weekly student newspaper. TV station KYOT. 138 active clubs and organizations. *Surrounding community:* Vermillion population 10,100. Sioux Falls (SD) 50 miles from campus and Omaha (NE), 130 miles from campus, are nearest metropolitan areas.

Library Collections: 912,000 volumes. 297,355 government documents. 760,000 microforms; 24,000 audiovisual materials; 3,200 current periodical subscriptions. Online catalog. Students have access to online information retrieval services and the Internet.

UNIVERSITY OF SOUTH DAKOTA—*cont'd*

Most important special holdings include Herman P. Chilson Western Americana Collection; Richardson Archives; University Archives (USD).

Buildings and Grounds: Campus area 216 acres.

Chief Executive Officer: James W. Abbott, President.

Undergraduates address admission inquiries to Director of Admissions; graduate inquiries to Dean of Graduate School.

College of Arts and Sciences

Degree Programs Offered: *Associate* in criminal justice studies; *baccalaureate* in anthropology, biology, chemistry, classical humanities, classics, communication disorders, computer science, contemporary media and journalism, criminal justice studies, earth sciences, economics, English, French, German, Greek, history, Latin, liberal studies, mathematics, philosophy, physics, political science, psychology, sociology. *Master's, doctorate* available in selected areas.

Distinctive Educational Programs: Indian studies, integrated humanities, women's studies programs. Preprofessional programs in selected areas.

School of Business

Degree Programs Offered: *Baccalaureate* in accounting, economics, finance, health services administration, management. *Master's* in accounting, business administration.

School of Education

Degree Programs Offered: *Baccalaureate, master's*in education (elementary, secondary, special), library media, recreation.

College of Fine Arts

Degree Programs Offered: *Baccalaureate* in art, history of musical instruments, music, theater; *master's* in art, history of musical instruments, music, theatre.

School of Law

Degree Programs Offered: *Juris Doctorate.*

Admission: Graduation from approved college or university with a satisfactory GPA; LSAT.

Degree Requirements: 90 credit hours, 2.0 GPA, 6 semesters in residence.

Fees and Other Expenses: Contact the school for current information.

Distinctive Educational Programs: Clinical law work-experience program. Joint J.D.-master's degree programs with College of Arts and Sciences, School of Business, School of Education. Dual-degree program in law and agriculture with South Dakota State University.

School of Medicine

Degree Programs Offered: *Associate* in nursing; *baccalaureate* in alcohol and drug abuse, medical technology, anesthesia, medicine; *master of science* in microbiology, biochemistry, physiology, pharmacology, anatomy, medical science, social work; *doctorate* in medicine.

Admission: *For first-professional:* 12 hours in English, 8 mathematics, 8 biology, 14-18 chemistry, 6 behavioral science. MCAT.

Degree Requirements: *For first-professional:* 167 credit hours; 2.00/4.00 GPA; passing score, as a candidate, on the Part I and Part II examinations of the National Board of Medical Examiners.

Fees and Other Expenses: Contact the school for current information.

Graduate School

Degree Programs Offered: *Master's* in accounting, adult and higher education, art, biochemistry, biology, business administration, business education, chemistry, communication, computer science, economics, educational administration, educational psychology and counseling, elementary education, English, history, management information systems, mathematics, microbiology, music, occupational therapy, physical education, physical therapy, political science, psychology, public administration, secondary education, sociology, special education, technology management, theater; *doctorate* in adult and higher education, anatomy, biochemistry, biology, educational administration, elementary education, microbiology, physiology and pharmacology, psychology, secondary education.

Departments and Teaching Staff: Teaching staff is provided by specific schools and colleges.

Division of Continuing Education

Degree Programs Offered: *Master's* in business administration in Rapid City, in Aberdeen in cooperation with Northern State University and in Sioux City, Iowa; *licensed practical nurse* Upward Mobility Program in nursing in Sioux Falls; *associate* in criminal justice in Rapid City; *master's* in business administration, political science, and public administration in Rapid City; *master's* in technology management in Rapid City in conjunction with South Dakota School of Mines and Technology.

Distinctive Educational Programs: Off-campus programs, University Telecourses, independent study courses, conferences and institutes.

Tennessee

American Baptist College

1800 Baptist World Center
Nashville, Tennessee 37207-4996
Tel: (615) 228-7877 **E-mail:** admissions@abcnash.edu
Fax: (615) 226-7855 **Internet:** www.abcnash.edu

Institution Description: American Baptist College is a coeducational Christian college offering preparation in Biblical-theological studies, church vocations, and humanities. The college is affiliated with the National Baptist Convention, USA Inc. and the Southern Baptist Convention. *Enrollment:* 106. *Degrees awarded:* Baccalaureate.

Accreditation: *National:* ABHE.

History: Founded under the name and charter of the American Baptist Theological Seminary 1924; became an accredited 4-year undergraduate Bible college 1971.

Institutional Structure: *Governing board:* Board of Trustees. Academic affairs headed by president. Management/business/finances directed by business manager. Full-time instructional faculty 7.

Calendar: Semesters. Academic year mid-Aug. to early May. Freshmen admitted Aug. Degrees conferred and formal commencement May. Summer session of 2 terms.

Characteristics of Freshmen: 90% of entering freshmen expected to graduate within 5 years.

Admission: Open enrollment. *Requirements:* Completion of 16 units in secondary school including 4 English, 3 mathematics, 2 foreign language, 2 social science, 2 natural science. *Entrance tests:* College Board SAT or ACT. Non-high school graduates considered for admission under certain circumstances.

Degree Requirements: *For baccalaureate degree:* completion of prescribed curriculum.

Degrees Conferred: 1 *associate;* 19 *baccalaureate:* theology and religious vocations.

Fees and Other Expenses: *Full-time tuition per academic year 2008–09:* $4,800. *Books and supplies:* $900. *Room and board per academic year:* $5,000. *Other expenses:* $2,725.

Financial Aid: Aid from institutionally generated funds is provided on the basis of financial need. Institution has a Program Participation Agreement with the U.S. Department of Education for eligible students to receive Pell Grants and, depending upon the agreement, other federal aid.

Departments and Teaching Staff: *Total instructional faculty:* 15 (several professors serve in more than one division). Student/faculty ratio: 10:1. Degrees held by full-time faculty: doctorate 60%, master's 40%, baccalaureate 1%. 80% hold terminal degrees.

Enrollment: Total enrollment 106 (undergraduate).

Characteristics of Student Body: *Ethnic/racial makeup:* Black non-Hispanic: 100%.

International Students: No programs available to aid students whose native language is not English. No financial aid specifically designated for international students.

Student Life: *Student publications: The Watchman*, a newsletter for students since 1985.

Publications: *The Vision*, a newsletter for students and alumni since 1986.

Library Collections: 43,000 volumes. 200 current periodical subscriptions.

Most important special holdings include collections on biblical-theological, pastoral ministries; Black studies; history (American, Black, church, Baptist).

Chief Executive Officer: Dr. Forrest E. Harris, Sr., President.

Address admission inquiries to the Registrar.

Aquinas College

4210 Harding Road
Nashville, Tennessee 37205-2005
Tel: (615) 297-7545
Fax: (615) 297-3892

Institution Description: Aquinas College, formerly Aquinas Junior College, is a private, Catholic college administered by the Dominican Sisters of the St. Cecilia Congregation. *Enrollment:* 847. *Degrees awarded:* Associate, baccalaureate.

Accreditation: *Regional:* SACS-Comm. on Coll. *Professional*: nursing

History: Established 1928 as a normal school for the education of the sisters; was affiliated with the Catholic University in America 1929; replaced with Aquinas Junior College and opened to the public 1961; name changed to Aquinas College 1993 when baccalaureate degree program was introduced; achieved accreditation for baccalaureate offering in liberal arts and nursing 1996.

Institutional Structure: *Governing board:* Aquinas Board of Directors. Extrainstitutional representation: 13 voting members; institutional representation: president of the college, non-voting. *Composition of institution:* Administrators 7. Academic affairs headed by academic dean and associate academic dean. Management/business/finances directed by the campus business manager. Full-time instructional faculty 22.

Calendar: Semesters. Academic year Sept. to May. May term and 2 summer terms (June and July). Formal commencement May.

Characteristics of Freshmen: 233 applicants (194 female, 39 male). 85% of applicants admitted. 34% of admitted applicants enrolled full-time.

12% (1 student) submitted SAT scores; 50% (16 students) submitted ACT scores. *25th percentile*: SAT I Critical Reading 370, SAT Math 370; ACT Composite 18, ACT English 17, ACT Math 16. *75th percentile*: SAT Critical Reading 600, SAT Math 620; ACT Composite 21, ACT English 22, ACT Math 20.

Admission: Rolling admissions. *Requirements:* Graduation from an accredited secondary school. Liberal arts applicants must have an overall GPA of 2.0. GED recipients must have a GED score of 50 or above. Applicants for nursing program must have overall GPA of 2.5 and elementary teacher educator must have overall GPA of 2.6. *Entrance tests:* ACT enhanced composite of 18 for liberal arts applicants and nursing applicants. Elementary teacher education applicants must have a passing score on PPST or a score of 22 on the enhanced ACT.

Degree Requirements: Minimum 64 semester hours for the associate of arts in liberal arts; 144 semester hours for the bachelor of arts in liberal arts (teacher education); 71 semester hours for the associate of science in nursing and 124 semester hours for the bachelor of science in nursing.

Distinctive Educational Programs: Adult education degree.

ROTC: Air Force offered in cooperation with Tennessee State University and Army in cooperation with Vanderbilt University. Academic credit is granted for completion of the program.

Degrees Conferred: 101 *associate;* 78 *baccalaureate:* business, management, marketing, and related support services education 46; education 18; health professions and related clinical sciences

Fees and Other Expenses: *Full-time tuition per academic year 2008–09:* $16,100. *Required fees:* $300. *Room and board per academic year:* $12,700. *Books and supplies:* $1,000. *Other expenses:* $4,000.

Financial Aid: Aid from institutionally generated funds is provided on the basis of academic merit, other criteria.

Financial aid to full-time, first-time undergraduate students: 96% received some form of financial aid. Average amount of aid received: federal grants $2,029; state/local grants $2,059; institutional grants #1,422; loans $2,585.

Departments and Teaching Staff: *Total instructional faculty:* 69 (full-time 29, part-time 40). Total faculty with doctorate, first-professional, or other terminal degree: 17. Student/faculty ratio: 12:1. Degrees held by full-time faculty: doctorate 29%, master's 71%. 29% hold terminal degrees.

AQUINAS COLLEGE—*cont'd*

Enrollment: Total enrollment 847. Undergraduate 824 (full-time 38%; female 81%, male 19%). Graduate 23 (full-time 70%). Undergraduate transfer-in students 171.

Characteristics of Student Body: *Ethnic/racial makeup:* Black non-Hispanic: 15%; Asian or Pacific Islander: 3%; Hispanic: 3%; White non-Hispanic: 65%; unknown: 13%.

Student Life: Aquinas College is a commuter college consisting of traditional and nontraditional college students. The student body is offered membership in the President's Council and the Phi Theta Kappa honor society. A weekly Mass is offered during the fall and spring semesters.

Publications: *The Torch* is a newsletter for the regular student and *The Weekender* is a newsletter for the Weekend College students. *The White House Paper* is a quarterly publication mailed to the alumni.

Library Collections: 45,800 volumes. Online catalog. 300 current serial subscriptions. 141,000 microforms; 1,820 audiovisual materials; Students have access to online information retrieval services and the Internet.

Most important special holdings include the Flanagan Papers; Muehlenkamp U.S. Civil War Memorabilia; Freolac Club (lecture series cassettes).

Buildings and Grounds: Campus area 91 acres.

Chief Executive Officer: Sr. Mary Evelyn Potts, O.P., President.

Address admissions inquiries to Diane C. LeJeune, Director of Admissions.

Austin Peay State University

601 College Street
Clarksville, Tennessee 37040

Tel: (931) 221-7011 **E-mail:** admissions@apsu.edu
Fax: (931) 221-6168 **Internet:** www.apsu.edu

Institution Description: Austin Peay State University is a member of the State University and Community College System of Tennessee. *Enrollment:* 9,401. *Degrees awarded:* Associate, baccalaureate, master's. Specialist certificates also awarded.

Academic offerings subject to approval by statewide coordinating bodies. Budget offerings subject to approval by statewide coordinating bodies.

Accreditation: *Regional:* SACS-Comm. on Coll. *Professional*: art, chemistry, music, nursing, teacher education

History: Established as Austin Peay Normal School 1927; offered first instruction at postsecondary level 1929; added upper division 1939; awarded first degree (baccalaureate) 1942; changed name to Austin Peay State College 1943; adopted present name 1967. *See* Charles M. Waters, *The First 50 Years of Austin Peay State University* (Clarksville: Austin Peay State University, 1977) for further information.

Institutional Structure: *Governing board:* Tennessee Board of Regents of the State University and Community College System. Extrainstitutional representation: 17 regents, including 1 student (appointed by governor of Tennessee), governor, commissioner of education, commissioner of agriculture, executive director of Tennessee Higher Education Commission. 4 ex officio. 16 voting. *Composition of institution:* Administrators 169. Academic affairs headed by provost and vice president for academic and student affairs. Management/business/finances directed by vice president for finance and administration. Full-time instructional faculty 278. Academic governance body, Academic Council, meets an average of 4 times per year.

Calendar: Semesters. Academic year Aug. to May. Freshmen admitted Aug., Jan., June. Degrees conferred May, Aug., Dec. Formal commencements May, Aug., Dec. Summer session of 2 terms from June to Aug.

Characteristics of Freshmen: 2,575 applicants (1,544 female, 1,031 male). 91% of applicants accepted. 58% of accepted applicants enrolled full-time.

.5% (7 students) submitted SAT scores; 82.6% (1,067 students) submitted ACT scores. *25th percentile:* SAT Critical Reading 465, SAT Math 420; ACT Composite 19, ACT English 19, ACT math 18. *75th percentile*: SAT Critical Reading 575, SAT math 525; ACT Composite 24, ACT English 25, ACT Math 23.

25% of entering freshmen expected to graduate within 5 years. 95% of freshmen from Tennessee. Freshmen from 18 states and 5 foreign countries.

Admission: Rolling admissions plan. Early acceptance available. *Requirements:* Either graduation from accredited secondary school or GED. Minimum 2.75 GPA. *Entrance tests:* ACT minimum composite score 19. For foreign students TOEFL. *For transfer students:* Maximum transfer credit limited only by residence requirement. Must be in good standing at institution previously attended.

College credit and advanced placement for postsecondary-level work completed in secondary school. Developmental courses offered in summer session and regular academic year; credit given.

Degree Requirements: *For all associate degrees:* 64 semester hours. *For all baccalaureate degrees:* 128 semester hours; 2.0 GPA; 32 semester hours in residence; physical education courses; general education requirements. *For all undergraduate degrees:* A–F; pass-fail; withdraw (carries time limit).

Distinctive Educational Programs: Flexible meeting places and schedules, including off-campus center (at Fort Campbell, KY, 11 miles away from main institution) and evening classes. Cooperative baccalaureate in medical technology with approved hospitals. Interdepartmental programs in African American studies, urban and regional planning, women's studies. Preprofessional programs in clinical microbiology, dental hygiene, dentistry, medicine, optometry, pharmacy, physical therapy, radiological technology. Facilities and programs for independent research, including honors programs, individual majors. *Other distinctive programs:* Continuing education. Study abroad in Africa, Asia (China, Japan, Taiwan), Europe (England, German, Ireland, France, Greece, Spain, Sweden), Canada, Mexico.

ROTC: Army.

Degrees Conferred: 108 *associate*; 1,159 *baccalaureate*; 215 *master's*. Bachelor's degrees awarded in top five disciplines: business, management, marketing, and related support services 246; health professions and related clinical sciences 101; multidisciplinary studies 74; liberal arts/general studies 61; social sciences 56. Master's degrees awarded: biological/life sciences 8; business/marketing 50; communications 16; education 90; English 9; health professions 1; parks and recreation 29; psychology 5; visual and performing arts 7.

Fees and Other Expenses: *Full-time tuition per academic year 2008–09:* resident undergraduate $5,528, nonresident $16,418; contract the university for current graduate tuition/fees. *Books and supplies:* $1,550. *Required fees:* $1,009; *Room and board per academic year:* $5,870. *Other expenses:* $2,000.

Financial Aid: Aid from institutionally generated funds is provided on the basis of academic merit, financial need, other criteria.

Financial aid to full-time, first-time undergraduate students: 94% received some form of aid. Average amount of aid received: federal grants $3,550; Pell grants $3,127; other federal aid $744; state/local grants $4,342; institutional grants $4,258.

Departments and Teaching Staff: *Total instructional faculty:* 494 (full-time 278, part-time 216). Student/faculty ratio: 17:1. Degrees held by full-time faculty: doctorate 77%, master's 22%, professional 1%. 91% hold terminal degrees.

Enrollment: *Total enrollment:* 9,401. Undergraduate 8,573 (full-time 76%; female 52%, male 38%). Graduate 828 (full-time 28%). Undergraduate transfer-in students 724.

Characteristics of Student Body: *Ethnic/racial makeup:* Black non-Hispanic: 18%; American Indian or Alaska Native: 1%; Asian or Pacific Islander: 3%; Hispanic: 4%; White non-Hispanic: 62%; unknown: 12%; nonresident alien 1%. *Age distribution:* number under 18: 25; 18–19: 1,705; 20–21: 1,565; 22–24: 1,511; 25–29: 1,341; 30–34: 798; 35–39: 520l 40–49: 583; 50–64: 182; 65 and over: 6.

International Students: 94 nonresident aliens enrolled fall 2008. Students from Europe, Asia, Latin America, Africa, Canada, Australia. Programs available to aid students whose native language is not English: social, cultural. English as a Second Language Program. No financial aid specifically designated for international students.

Student Life: On-campus residence halls house 15% of student body. Residence halls for males constitute 33% of such space, for females 33%, for both sexes 34%. 6% of males join fraternities; 3% of females join sororities. Housing available for married students. *Intercollegiate athletics:* male: baseball, basketball, cross-country, football, golf, tennis; female: basketball, cross-country, golf, riflery, softball, track, volleyball. *Special regulations:* Cars permitted without restrictions. *Special services:* Learning Resources Center, medical services. *Student publications: The All State*, a weekly newspaper; *The Tower*, an annual literary magazine. *Surrounding community:* Clarksville population 132,000. Nashville, 45 miles from campus, is nearest metropolitan area. Served by airport 10 miles from campus.

Library Collections: 216,500 volumes including bound books, serial backfiles, electronic documents, and government documents not in separate collections. Online catalog. 669,000 microforms; 5,530 audiovisual materials; 15,000 periodicals including via electronic access. Computer work stations available. Students have access to the Internet at no charge.

Most important special collections include Dorothy Dix Collection; Dr. Joseph Milton Henry Papers; Hillman Papers.

Buildings and Grounds: Campus area 158 acres.

Chief Executive Officer: Dr. Sherry L. Hoppe, President.

Address admission inquiries to Ryan Forsythe, Director of Admissions.

Belmont University

1900 Belmont Boulevard
Nashville, Tennessee 37212-3757
Tel: (615) 460-6000 **E-mail:** buadmission@belmont.edu
Fax: (615) 460-6446 **Internet:** www.belmont.edu

Institution Description: Belmont University is a private institution affiliated with the Tennessee Baptist Convention. *Enrollment:* 4,991. *Degrees awarded:* Baccalaureate, master's, doctorate.

Accreditation: *Regional:* SACS-Comm. on Coll. *Professional*: music, nursing, occupational therapy, physical therapy, teacher education

History: Chartered as Ward-Belmont, Inc. and offered first instruction at postsecondary level 1951; became Belmont College 1952; awarded first degree (baccalaureate) 1955; became Belmont University 1991.

Institutional Structure: *Governing board:* Board of Trustees. Representation: 32 trustees. All voting. *Composition of institution:* Academic affairs headed by academic vice president. Management/business/finances directed by chief financial officer. Full-time instructional faculty 221.

Calendar: Semesters. Academic year Aug. to Aug. Freshmen admitted Aug., Jan., May, June, July. Degrees conferred and formal commencement May, Dec. Summer session of 2 terms from early June to mid-Aug.

Characteristics of Freshmen: 3,060 applicants (1,890 female, 1,170 male). 69% of applicants admitted. 34% of applicants admitted and enrolled.

56% (427 students) submitted SAT scores; 76% (582 students) submitted ACT scores. *25th percentile*: SAT Critical Reading 540, SAT Math 530; ACT Composite 23, ACT English 24, ACT Math 22. *75th percentile*: SAT Critical Reading 690, SAT Math 640; ACT Composite 28, ACT English 30; ACT Math 27.

56% of entering freshmen expected to graduate within 5 years. 44% of freshmen from Tennessee. Freshmen from 46 states and 48 foreign countries.

Admission: Rolling admissions plan. *Requirements:* Graduation from accredited secondary school or GED. Recommend 4 units English, 3 mathematics, 2 natural science, 2 social studies, recommend 2 foreign language units. Minimum 2.0 GPA. *Entrance tests:* College Board SAT or ACT Composite.

College credit and advanced placement for postsecondary-level work completed in secondary school. College credit for extrainstitutional learning.

Degree Requirements: *For all baccalaureate degrees:* 128 credit hours. *For all degrees:* 2.0 GPA; 24 hours in residence; 4 hours physical education; distribution requirements; 60 cultural life/community service units as designated in university convocation program.

Fulfillment of some degree requirements and exemption from some beginning courses possible by passing departmental examinations, College Board CLEP, AP. *Grading system:* A–F; pass-fail; withdraw (pass-fail is appended to withdraw).

Distinctive Educational Programs: Work-experience programs, including cooperative education, internships. Weekend classes. Dual-degree program in engineering with Auburn University (AL), University of Tennessee at Knoxville; American Management Association Extension Institute. Study abroad in China, Ireland, Scotland, France, Germany, Mexico, Russia. *Other distinctive programs:* Continuing education. Occupational therapy; physical therapy; music business.

ROTC: Army and Navy in cooperation with Vanderbilt University.

Degrees Conferred: 975 *baccalaureate*; 246 *master's*; 37 *doctorate*. Bachelor's degrees awarded in top five disciplines: visual and performing arts 233; business, management, marketing, and related support services 109; health professions and related clinical sciences 37; liberal arts/general studies 33; philosophy/religion/theology 28.

Fees and Other Expenses: *Full-time tuition per academic year 2008–09:* undergraduate $21,110; graduate costs vary by program. *Other fees* $950. *Room and board per academic year:* $10,000. *Books and supplies:* $1,200. *Other expenses:* $3,900.

Financial Aid: Aid from institutionally generated funds is provided on the basis of academic merit, financial need, athletic ability, other criteria.

Financial aid to full-time, first-time undergraduate students: 80% received some form of aid. Average amount of aid received: federal grants $3,883; Pell grants $2,884; other federal aid $1,245 state/local grants $4,474; institutional grants $8,922.

Departments and Teaching Staff: *Total instructional faculty:* 466 (full-time 221, part-time 295). Total faculty with doctorate, first-professional, or other terminal degree: 133. Student/faculty ratio: 13:1.

Enrollment: Total enrollment 4,991. Undergraduate 4,174 (full-time 92%; female 58%, male 42%). Graduate 717 (full-time 50%). Undergraduate transfer-in students 393.

Characteristics of Student Body: *Ethnic/racial makeup:* Black non-Hispanic: 4%; Asian or Pacific Islander: 2%; Hispanic: 2%; White non-Hispanic: 87%; unknown: 4%; nonresident alien 1%. *Age distribution:* number under 18: 32; 18–19: 1,251; 20–21: 1,131; 22–24: 508; 25–29: 166; 30–34: 88; 35–39: 55; 40–49: 62; 50–64: 23; 65 and over: 1.

International Students: 50 nonresident aliens enrolled fall 2008. Students from Europe, Asia, Latin America, Africa, Canada, Australia. Programs available to aid students whose native language is not English: social, cultural. English as a Second Language Program. Financial aid specifically designated for international students.

Student Life: On-campus residence halls available for single and married students. *Surrounding community:* Nashville metropolitan population over 1,000,000. Served by airport 12 miles from campus.

Library Collections: 263,000 volumes including bound books, serial backfiles, electronic documents, and government documents not in separate collections. Online catalog. 24,000 microforms; 35,000 audiovisual materials; 4,150 current serial subscriptions. Computer work stations available campus-wide. Students have access to the Internet at no charge.

Most important special collections in: religion, music, business.

Buildings and Grounds: Campus area 30 acres. Campus DVD available.

Chief Executive Officer: Dr. Robert Fisher, President.

Address admission inquiries to Dr. Kathryn H. Baugher, Dean of Enrollment Services.

Bethel College

325 Cherry Avenue
McKenzie, Tennessee 38201
Tel: (731) 352-4000 **E-mail:** admissions@bethel-college.edu
Fax: (731) 352-4069 **Internet:** www.bethel-college.edu

Institution Description: Bethel College is a private college affiliated with the Cumberland Presbyterian Church. *Enrollment:* 2,408. *Degrees awarded:* Baccalaureate, master's.

Accreditation: *Regional:* SACS-Comm. on Coll.

History: Established as Bethel Seminary and offered first instruction at postsecondary level 1842; chartered and awarded first degree (baccalaureate) 1847; adopted present name 1850; admitted women 1872.

Institutional Structure: *Governing board:* Board of Trustees of Bethel, College, Inc. Extrainstitutional representation: 24 trustees. All voting. *Composition of institution:* Administrators 13. Academic affairs headed by academic dean. Management/business/finances directed by business manager. Full-time instructional faculty 32. Academic governance body, Faculty Organization, meets an average of 8 times per year.

Calendar: Semesters. Academic year Aug. to May. Freshmen admitted Aug., Jan., June. Degrees conferred Dec., May. Formal commencement May. Summer semester of 2 four-week terms.

Characteristics of Freshmen: 955 applicants (492 female, 955 male). 64% of accepted applicants enrolled. 30% of accepted applicants enrolled full-time.

Mean ACT Composite score 21.

19% of entering freshmen expected to graduate within 5 years. 55% of freshmen from Tennessee. Freshmen from 20 states and 6 foreign countries.

Admission: Rolling admissions plan. Early acceptance available. *Requirements:* Either graduation from accredited secondary school or GED. *Entrance tests:* ACT. *For transfer students:* from 4-year accredited institution maximum transfer credits limited only by resident requirement; from 2-year accredited institution up to 68 hours; correspondence students 9 hours.

College credit and advanced placement for postsecondary-level work completed in secondary school. College credit for extrainstitutional learning on basis of portfolio and faculty assessments; personal interview.

Tutoring available. Noncredit developmental courses offered during regular academic year.

Degree Requirements: 128 credit hours; 2.0 GPA; completion of 32 of last 38 hours in in residence; 18 hours in major; 9 hours in minor (if required) OR complete 40 semester hours in adult degree completion major; 1 hour physical education in core requirements (some majors require 2 hours).

Fulfillment of some degree requirements and exemption from some beginning courses possible by passing College Board CLEP, AP. *Grading system:* A–F; withdraw (deadline after which pass-fail is appended to withdraw).

Distinctive Educational Programs: Internships. Flexible meeting places, schedules, evening classes. Accelerated degree programs. Dual degree program in engineering with Tennessee Technological University. Special facilities for using telecommunications in the classroom. Interdisciplinary programs may be individually designed. Preprofessional programs in cytotechnology, dentistry, engineering, medical record administration, medical technology, medicine,

BETHEL COLLEGE—*cont'd*

nursing, optometry, pharmacy, physical therapy, radiologic technology. Study abroad by individual arrangement.

Degrees Conferred: 372 *baccalaureate*; 68 *master's*. Bachelor's degrees awarded in top five disciplines: business, management, marketing, and related support services 206; education 12; biological/life sciences 11; public administration 10; parks and recreation 7. biological sciences 6, business and management 108, education 11, English 1, liberal arts 2, mathematics 1, parks and recreation 2, psychology 4, social sciences and history 6, other 1; 39 *master's:* education 68.

Fees and Other Expenses: *Full-time tuition per academic year 2008–09:* $112,242 undergraduate; contact the college for current graduate tuition/fees. *Books and supplies:* $1,000. *Room and board per academic year:* $6,926. *Other expenses:* $4,150.

Financial Aid: Aid from institutionally generated funds is provided on the basis of academic merit, financial need, athletic ability, other criteria.

Financial aid to full-time, first-time undergraduate students: 98% received dome form of aid. Average amount of aid received: federal grants $2,052; Pell grants $1,720; other federal aid $404; state/local grants $2,756; institutional grants $3,806.

Departments and Teaching Staff: *Total instructional faculty:* 66. Student/faculty ratio: 14:1. Degrees held by full-time faculty: doctorate 20%, master's 100%. 59% hold terminal degrees.

Enrollment: Total enrollment 2,408. Undergraduate 2,128 (full-time 83%; female 59%, male 41%). Graduate 282 (full-time 41%). Undergraduate transfer-in students 56.

Characteristics of Student Body: *Ethnic/racial makeup:* Black non-Hispanic: 53%; Hispanic: 1%; White non-Hispanic: 54%; nonresident alien 2%.

International Students: 48 nonresident aliens enrolled fall 2008. No programs available to aid students whose native language is not English. No financial aid specifically designated for international students.

Student Life: On-campus residence halls house 53% of student body. Residence halls for males constitute 45% of such space, for females 55%. *Intercollegiate athletics:* male: baseball, basketball, football, golf, soccer; female: basketball, soccer, softball, tennis. *Special regulations:* Cars permitted without restrictions. Quiet hours from 10pm to 7am. Residence hall visitation at specified times. *Special services:* Academic Skills Center. *Student publications: Bethel Beacon*, a weekly newspaper; *Log Cabin*, a yearbook. *Surrounding community:* McKenzie population 5,500. Memphis and Nashville, 120 miles from campus, are nearest metropolitan areas.

Publications: Sources of information about Bethel include *The Cumberland Presbyterian*, a denominational magazine featuring biweekly columns about Bethel.

Library Collections: 101,000 volumes including bound books, serial backfiles, electronic documents, and government documents not in separate collections. Online catalog. Current serial subscriptions: 254 paper, 2,600 microform, 1,200 electronic. 2,380 recordings; 45 CD-ROMs. Computer work stations available. Students have access to the Internet at no charge.

Most important special holdings include collections on Cumberland Presbyterian Church; Bethel College; religion.

Buildings and Grounds: Campus area 100 acres.

Chief Executive Officer: Dr. Robert D. Proser, President.

Address admission inquiries to Tona Hedges, Director of Admissions.

Bryan College

Bryan Drive
Box 7000
Dayton, Tennessee 37321-7000
Tel: (423) 775-2041 **E-mail:** admiss@bryan.edu
Fax: (423) 775-7330 **Internet:** www.bryan.edu

Institution Description: Bryan College, formerly known as William Jennings Bryan College, is a private, independent, nonprofit college. *Enrollment:* 1,079. *Degrees awarded:* Associate, baccalaureate.

Accreditation: *Regional:* SACS-Comm. on Coll.

History: Established, chartered as William Jennings Bryan University, and offered first instruction at postsecondary level 1930; awarded first degree (baccalaureate) 1934; adopted name, William Jennings Bryan College, 1958; became Bryan College 1993.

Institutional Structure: *Governing board:* Board of Trustees. Extrainstitutional representation: 24 trustees; institutional representation: president of the college. 1 ex officio. 24 voting. *Composition of institution:* Administrators 19. Academic affairs headed by vice president for academic affairs. Management/business/finances directed by vice president for business affairs. Full-time instructional faculty 32. Academic governance body, the faculty, meets an average of 10 times per year.

Calendar: Semesters. Academic year Aug. to May. Freshmen admitted Aug., Jan., May. Degrees conferred May, Aug., Dec. Formal commencement May.

Characteristics of Freshmen: 532 applicants (258 female, 274 male). 82% of applicants accepted. 40% of accepted applicants enrolled full-time.

Average secondary school rank of freshmen top 25th percentile. Mean SAT class score 1150. Mean ACT class score 23.

52% of entering freshmen expected to graduate within 5 years. 40% of freshmen from Tennessee. Freshmen from 33 states and 6 foreign countries.

Admission: Rolling admissions plan. For fall acceptance, apply as early as end of junior year of secondary school, but not later than Aug. 1 of year of enrollment. Early acceptance available. *Requirements:* Either graduation from accredited secondary school with 15 units which must include 3 English, 1 U.S. history, 1 science, 5 academic electives in English, foreign language, mathematics, science, and social studies; or GED. Minimum GPA 2.0. *Entrance tests:* ACT composite preferred; College Board SAT accepted. For foreign students minimum TOEFL score 200 (computer board). *For transfer students:* 2.0 minimum GPA; from 4-year accredited institution 94 hours maximum transfer credit; from 2-year accredited institution 64 hours; correspondence / extension students 31 hours.

College credit and advanced placement for postsecondary-level work completed in secondary school. For extrainstitutional learning on basis of faculty assessment.

Tutoring available. Developmental courses offered during regular academic year; credit given.

Degree Requirements: 124 credit hours; 2.0 GPA; 31 hours in residence; chapel attendance 3 days per week; Bible study requirements.

Fulfillment of some degree requirements and exemption from some beginning courses possible by passing departmental examinations, College Board CLEP, AP. *Grading system:* A–F; withdraw (carries time limit).

Degrees Conferred: 247 *baccalaureate.* Bachelors' degrees awarded in top five disciplines: business, management, marketing, and related support services 33; communication, journalism, and related programs 16; education 15; psychology 9; social sciences and history 9. Master's degrees awarded: business/management 11.

Fees and Other Expenses: *Full-time tuition per academic year 2008–09:* $17,020. *Books and supplies:* $1,200. *Room and board per academic year:* $5,095. *Other expenses:* $2,500.

Financial Aid: Aid from institutionally generated funds is provided on the basis of academic merit, financial need, athletic ability, other criteria. Institution has a Program Participation Agreement with the U.S. Department of Education for eligible students to receive Pell Grants and, depending upon the agreement, other federal aid.

Departments and Teaching Staff: *Total instructional faculty:* 54. Student/faculty ratio: 14:1. Degrees held by full-time faculty: doctorate 86.6%, master's 100%. 87% hold terminal degrees.

Enrollment: Total enrollment 1,079. Undergraduate 1,034 (full-time 93%; female 53%, male 47%). Graduate 43 (full-time 100%). Undergraduate transfer-in students 32.

Characteristics of Student Body: *Ethnic/racial makeup:* Black non-Hispanic: 5%; Asian or Pacific Islander: 1%; Hispanic: 2%; White non-Hispanic: 90%; nonresident alien 2%.

International Students: 22 nonresident aliens enrolled fall 2008. Some financial aid available for international students.

Student Life: On-campus residence halls house 82% of student body. Residence halls for males constitute 50% of such space, for females 50%. *Intercollegiate athletics:* male: basketball, soccer, tennis; female: basketball, soccer, tennis, volleyball. *Special regulations:* Cars permitted without restrictions. Dress code based on generally accepted standards. *Student publications: Commoner*, a yearbook; *Triangle*, a weekly newspaper. *Surrounding community:* Dayton population 6,000. Chattanooga, 40 miles from campus, is nearest metropolitan area. Served by municipal airport 2 miles from campus; major airport 40 miles from campus.

Publications: Sources of information about Bryan include a quarterly magazine, *Bryan Life*, distributed to Alumni and others.

Library Collections: 150,000 volumes. 135,000 microforms; 3,675 audiovisual materials; 10,000 periodicals including via electronic access. Online catalog. Students have access to online information retrieval services and the Internet.

Most important holdings include Alma F. Radar Bible and Rare Book Collection; Anna Trentham Collection (books and memorabilia pertaining to state history).

Buildings and Grounds: Campus area 106 acres. Campus DVD available.

Chief Executive Officer: Dr. Stephen D. Livesay, President.

Address admission inquiries to Michael Sapienza, Director of Admissions.

Carson-Newman College

1646 South Russell Avenue
Jefferson City, Tennessee 37760
Tel: (865) 471-2000 **E-mail:** admissions@cncadm.cn.edu
Fax: (865) 471-3502 **Internet:** www.cn.edu

Institution Description: Carson-Newman College is a private college affiliated with the Tennessee Baptist Convention. *Enrollment:* 2,032. *Degrees awarded:* Associate, baccalaureate, master's.

Accreditation: *Regional:* SACS-Comm. on Coll. *Professional*: art, dietetics, family and consumer science, interior design, music, nursing, teacher education

History: Chartered as Mossy Creek Baptist Seminary and offered first instruction at postsecondary level 1851; awarded first degree (baccalaureate) 1855; changed name to Mossy Creek Baptist College 1856, to Carson College 1880; adopted present official name, Carson-Newman College of the Tennessee Baptist Convention, 1889.

Institutional Structure: *Governing board:* Board of Trustees. Representation: 36 trustees. All voting. *Composition of institution:* Administrators 37. President, provost/vice president for academic affairs, vice president for finance, vice president for advancement. Full-time instructional faculty 131. Academic governance body, the faculty, meets an average of 9 times per year.

Calendar: Semesters. Academic year Aug. to May. Freshmen admitted June, Aug., Jan. Degrees conferred and formal commencement July, Dec., May. Summer session of 4 terms from mid-May to late July.

Characteristics of Freshmen: 2,815 applicants (1,393 female, 1,222 male). 65% of applicants admitted. 30% of applicants admitted and enrolled full-time.

25th percentile: ACT Composite 19. *75th percentile*: ACT Composite 25.

61% of entering freshmen expected to graduate within 5 years. 64% of freshmen from Tennessee. Freshmen from 33 states and 7 foreign countries.

Admission: Rolling admissions plan. Early acceptance available. *Requirements:* Either graduation from accredited secondary school or GED. *Entrance tests:* ACT composite. *For transfer students:* Good standing at institution previously attended; 2.0 minimum GPA; from 4-year accredited institution maximum transfer credit limited only by residence requirement; from 2-year accredited institution 68 hours maximum transfer credit.

College credit and advanced placement for postsecondary-level work completed in secondary school.

Developmental courses offered in summer session and regular academic year; credit given but does not count toward graduation.

Degree Requirements: 128 credit hours; 2.0 GPA; last 32 semester hours in residence; general education requirements, and satisfaction of specific major requirement.

Fulfillment of some degree requirements and exemption from some beginning courses possible by passing departmental examinations, College Board CLEP, AP. *Grading system:* A–F; pass-fail; withdraw (deadline after which pass-fail is appended to withdraw).

Distinctive Educational Programs: Dual-degree programs with approved schools in engineering, medical technology, pharmacy, and physician's assistant. Preprofessional programs in dentistry, law, medicine, optometry, and veterinary medicine. Transfer programs in health information management, physical therapy, and occupational therapy. Internships including summer work-at-home opportunities. Freshman year and academic success seminars. Tutorials, study skills training, and a support service for learning disabled students. Interdisciplinary studies in such areas as Chinese studies, film study, gerontology, athletic training, marketing, military leadership, and international relations. Innovative studies in such areas as athletic training, photography, broadcasting, computers, nutrition, nursing, and long-term health care management. Facilities and programs for independent research in such areas as psychology, physics, and the honors program. Centers of excellence in the areas of Baptist studies, church music, wellness, and educational service to Appalachia. Evening/Weekend College, and off-campus courses of study for working adults in general studies, business, and human services. Special interest study opportunities through Individual Directions and the Washington Semester. Study abroad includes London Term (London, England); Oxford Term (London, England); and foreign travel study (varied: Morocco, Australia, Korea, and other possibilities).

Degrees Conferred: 401 *baccalaureate:* biological and life 41, business and management 75, computer and information sciences 4, education 76, English 15, fine and applied arts 17, foreign languages 2, health professions 23, home economics 29, liberal arts 10, mathematics 3, parks and recreation 4, physical sciences 7, psychology 34, social sciences and history 50, visual and performing arts 21, other 9; 69 *master's:* education 56 health professions and related clinical science 10; psychology 3.

Fees and Other Expenses: *Full-time tuition per academic year 2008–09:* $17,800 undergraduate; graduate study charged per credit hour (contact the college for current rate). *Other fees:* $780. *Room and board per academic year:* $5,450. *Books and supplies:* $1,000. *Other expenses:* $2,500.

Financial Aid: Aid from institutionally generated funds is provided on the basis of academic merit, financial need, athletic ability, other criteria.

Financial aid to full-time, first-time undergraduate students: 100% received some form of aid. Average amount of aid received: federal grants $3,037; Pell grants $2,979; other federal aid $3,016; state/local grants $3,033; institutional grants $6,006.

Departments and Teaching Staff: *Total instructional faculty* 131. Student/faculty ratio: 13:1. Degrees held by full-time faculty: master's 32%, doctorate 68%. 68% hold terminal degrees.

Enrollment: Total enrollment 2,032. Undergraduate 1,829 (full-time 94%; female 58%, male 42%). Graduate 209 (full-time 54%). Undergraduate transfer-in students 123.

Characteristics of Student Body: *Ethnic/racial makeup:* Black non-Hispanic: 8%; Asian or Pacific Islander: 1%; 8; Hispanic: 1%; White non-Hispanic: 82%; unknown: 3%; nonresident alien 3%. *Age distribution:* number under 18: 13; 18–19: 638; 20–21: 651; 22–24: 382; 25–29: 88; 30–34: 49=0; 35–39: 34; 40–49: 33; 50–64: 9; 65 and over: 1.

International Students: 60 nonresident aliens enrolled fall 2008. Students from Europe, Asia, Latin America, Africa. No programs available to aid students whose native language is not English. No financial aid specifically designated for international students.

Student Life: On-campus residence halls house 50% of student body. Housing available for married students. *Intercollegiate athletics:* male: baseball, basketball, cross-country, football, golf, soccer, tennis, track, wrestling; female: basketball, cross-country, soccer, softball, tennis, track, volleyball. *Special regulations:* Cars permitted without restrictions. *Special services:* Learning Resources Center, medical services. *Student publications: The Appalachian*, a yearbook; *Orange and Blue*, a biweekly newspaper. *Surrounding community:* Jefferson City population 6,100. Knoxville, 35 miles from campus, is nearest metropolitan area. Served by airport 50 miles from campus.

Library Collections: 300,000 volumes. 90,400 government documents (separate collection); 222,000 microforms; 15,000 audiovisual materials; 2,000 current periodical subscriptions. Computer work stations available. Online catalog. Students have access to online information retrieval services and the Internet.

Most important special holdings include Baptist History and Archives Collection; Carson-Newman College Archives; Dr. R. Lofton Hudson Collection on Marriage and Family Counseling.

Buildings and Grounds: Campus area 88 acres. Campus DVD available.

Chief Executive Officer: Dr. James S. Netherton, President.

Undergraduates address admission inquiries to Sheryl M. Gray, Director of Undergraduate Admissions; graduate inquiries to Jean Love, Graduate Admissions and Services Advisor.

Christian Brothers University

650 East Parkway South
Memphis, Tennessee 38104
Tel: (901) 321-3000 **E-mail:** admissions@cbu.edu
Fax: (901) 321-3494 **Internet:** www.cbu.edu

Institution Description: Christian Brothers University is a private institution affiliated with the Brothers of the Christian Schools, Roman Catholic Church. *Enrollment:* 1,869. *Degrees awarded:* Baccalaureate, master's. Member of Greater Memphis Area Consortium.

Accreditation: *Regional:* SACS-Comm. on Coll. *Professional*: business, engineering

History: Established and offered first instruction at postsecondary level 1871; chartered 1872; awarded first degree (baccalaureate) 1878; became a university 1990.

Institutional Structure: *Governing board:* Board of Trustees. Extrainstitutional representation: 35 trustees, including 11 alumni and provincial of the order; institutional representation: president of the college. 2 ex officio. All voting. *Composition of institution:* Administrators 5. Academic affairs headed by vice president for academic affairs. Management/business/finances directed by vice president for administrative affairs. Full-time instructional faculty 92. Academic governance body, Academic Council, meets an average of 25 times per year.

Calendar: Semesters. Academic year Aug. to May. Freshmen admitted Aug., Oct., Jan., Mar., June, July. Degrees conferred May, Aug., Dec. Formal commencement May. Summer session of 3 terms from early June to early Aug.

Characteristics of Freshmen: 1,360 applicants (821 female, 539 male). 64% of applicants admitted. 37% of applicants admitted and enrolled full-time.

6% (16 students) submitted SAT scores; 95% (267 students) submitted ACT scores. *25th percentile*: SAT Critical Reading 510, SAT Math 460; ACT Com-

CHRISTIAN BROTHERS UNIVERSITY—*cont'd*

posite 22. *75th percentile*: SAT Critical Reading 580, SAT Math 590; 630; ACT Composite 27.

59% of entering freshmen expected to graduate within 5 years. 78% of freshmen from Tennessee. Freshmen from 16 states and 4 foreign countries.

Admission: Rolling admissions plan. Apply as early as 1 year prior to enrollment, but not later than week of registration. Early acceptance available. *Requirements:* Either graduation from accredited secondary school or GED. Lowest acceptable secondary school class standing in upper two thirds. *Entrance tests:* College Board SAT or ACT Composite. For foreign students TOEFL. *For transfer students:* maximum transfer credit if credits fulfill requirements of student's program.

College credit and advanced placement for postsecondary-level work completed in secondary school. College credit for extrainstitutional learning.

Tutoring available.

Degree Requirements: *For all baccalaureate degrees:* 121–139 credit hours; *For all degrees:* 2.0 GPA; distribution requirements.

Fulfillment of some degree requirements and exemption from some beginning courses possible by passing departmental examinations, College Board CLEP Subject Examinations, AP. *Grading system:* A–F; pass-fail; withdraw (carries time limit).

Distinctive Educational Programs: Flexible meeting places and schedules, weekend and evening classes. Double degree programs available. Degree-granting evening school. Master's degree program in business administration, engineering management, education, Catholic studies, executive leadership.

ROTC: Air Force, Army, and Navy in cooperation with University of Memphis.

Degrees Conferred: 208 *baccalaureate:* biological sciences 16; business and management 96; computer and information science 3; education 15; engineering 33; English 12; philosophy/religion/theology 3; physical sciences 18; psychology 61, Master's degrees awarded: business/marketing 69; educator 57; engineering 18.

Fees and Other Expenses: *Full-time tuition per academic year 2008–09:* $22,600 undergraduate; contact the institution for current graduate tuition. *Required fees:* $520. *Room and board per academic year:* $6,050. *Books and supplies:* $1,100. *Other expenses:* $520.

Financial Aid: Aid from institutionally generated funds is provided on the basis of academic merit, financial need, athletic ability.

Financial aid to full-time, first-time undergraduate students: 100% received some form of aid.

Departments and Teaching Staff: Total faculty with doctorate, first-professional, or other terminal degree: 124. Student/faculty ratio: 13:1. Degrees held by full-time faculty: doctorate 80.5%, master's 19.5%. 80.5% hold terminal degrees.

Enrollment: Total enrollment 1,869. Undergraduate 1,420 (full-time 85%; female 55%, male 45%). Graduate 449 (full-time 14%). Undergraduate transfer-in students 83.

Characteristics of Student Body: *Ethnic/racial makeup:* Black non-Hispanic: 32%; Asian or Pacific Islander: 5%; Hispanic: 35; White non-Hispanic: 32%; unknown 6%; nonresident alien 2%. *Age distribution:* number under 18: 17; 18–19: 452; 20–21: 397; 22–24: 152; 25–29: 120; 30–34: 103; 35–39: 84; 40–49: 74; 50–64: 21.

International Students: 38 nonresident aliens enrolled fall 2008. Students from Europe, Asia, Latin America, Africa, Canada, Australia. No programs available to aid students whose native language is not English. No financial aid specifically designated for international students.

Student Life: On-campus residence halls house 27% of the entire student body. Co-ed, male and female dorms. *Intercollegiate athletics:* male: baseball, basketball, cross-country, golf, soccer, tennis; female: basketball, cross-country, golf,soccer, softball, tennis, volleyball. *Special regulations:* Cars with parking permits allowed. Dormitory visitation from noon to midnight Sun.–Thurs., noon to 2am Fri. and Sat. *Special services:* Medical services. *Student publications: Castings*, a literary magazine. *Surrounding community:* Memphis population 650,000. Served by mass transit bus system; airport 5 miles from campus; passenger rail service 10 miles from campus.

Library Collections: 154,000 volumes including bound books, serial backfiles, electronic documents, and government documents not in separate collections. Online catalog. Current serial subscriptions: 548 paper. Computer work stations available. Students have access to the Internet at no charge.

Most important special holdings include: Leslie H. Kuehner Napoleon Collection; Higgins Collection on the History of Bolivia; De La Salle Christian Brothers Midwest Province Archival Record and Museum Collections.

Buildings and Grounds: Campus area 75 acres.

Chief Executive Officer: Br. Vincent Malham, F.S.C., President.

Address undergraduate admission inquiries to Tracey Dysart, Dean of of Admissions; graduate inquiries to Dr. Neal Jackson, Director of Graduate Education Program; MBA program inquiries to Dr. Bev Pray, Director.

Crichton College

255 North Highland
Memphis, Tennessee 38111-1375
Tel: (901) 367-9800 **E-mail:** info@crichton.edu
Fax: (901) 367-3866 **Internet:** www.crichton.edu

Institution Description: Crichton College, formerly Mid-South Bible College, is a private, Christian liberal arts, coeducational, interdenominational college. *Enrollment:* 1,016. *Degrees awarded:* Baccalaureate.

Accreditation: *Regional:* SACS-Comm. on Coll.

History: Formed as Mid-South Bible Center 1941; established institute program 1948; established four-year college program 1960; present name adopted by the Board of Trustees 1987.

Institutional Structure: *Governing board:* Independent board with 29 trustees; institutional representation: president of the college. *Composition of institution:* Administrators 6. Vice presidents: academic affairs, business/finance, student development, institutional management, enrollment management. Full-time instructional faculty 39. Academic governance body meets 10 times per year.

Calendar: Semesters. Academic year Aug. to July. Freshmen admitted continually. Degrees conferred and formal commencement May,

Characteristics of Freshmen: 499 applicants (248 female, 246 male). 8% (15 students) submitted SAT scores; 93% (179 students) submitted ACT scores. *25th percentile*: SAT Critical Reading 402, SAT Math 422; ACT Composite 16. *75th percentile*: SAT Critical Reading 495, SAT Math 500; ACT Composite 22.

22% of entering freshmen expected to graduate within 5 years. 87% of freshmen from Tennessee. Freshmen from 15 states and 14 foreign countries.

Admission: *Requirements:* Either graduation from accredited secondary school or GED. Selection criteria: school achievement record, test scores, interview, references. ACT minimum of 18. *For transfer students:* must be eligible to return to previous school; transfer credits reviewed.

Degree Requirements: Completion of course requirements for respective program; 2.0 GPA (teacher education program 2.75 GPA).

Distinctive Educational Programs: Accelerated Degree Program for adult students; high school senior program. Memphis Center for Urban Theological Studies; Urban Youth Studies Program; Teacher Education Program.

Degrees Conferred: 167 *baccalaureate:* business and management 88; education 38; law/legal studies English 4; history 4; interdisciplinary studies 1; psychology 10; theology and religious vocations 15.

Fees and Other Expenses: *Full-time tuition per academic year 2008–09:* $12,114. *Required fees:* $18 per credit hour. *Books and supplies:* $1m032. *Room and board per academic year:* $8,332. *Other expenses:* $3,562.

Financial Aid: Aid from institutionally generated funds is provided on the basis of academic merit, financial need.

Financial aid to full-time, first-time undergraduate students: 100% received some form of aid.

Departments and Teaching Staff: *Total instructional faculty:* 79 (full-time 39, part-time 40). Student/faculty ratio: 18:1. Degrees held by full-time faculty: doctorate 54%, master's 46%. 54% hold terminal degrees.

Enrollment: Total enrollment 1,016. Undergraduate 929 (full-time 98%; female 67%, male 33%). Graduate 96 (full-time 42%). Undergraduate transfer-in students 224.

Characteristics of Student Body: *Ethnic/racial makeup:* Black non-Hispanic: 71%; Hispanic: .4%; White non-Hispanic: 21%; unknown: 3%; nonresident alien 2%.

International Students: 20 nonresident aliens enrolled fall 2008. Students from Europe, Asia, Latin America, Canada, Middle East. No programs available to aid students whose native language is not English. Some financial aid specifically designated for international students.

Student Life: College-leased apartments for males and females. Varsity baseball; club-level basketball; intramural flag football, basketball, softball, volleyball. *Surrounding community:* Suburban campus in Memphis.

Library Collections: 53,000 volumes. 32,000 microforms; 2,210 audiovisual materials; 175 current periodical subscriptions. Students have access to online information retrieval services and the Internet.

Most important special collections include papers and notes of Dr. James Crichton; Bible and theology collection (books); teacher education, psychology.

Chief Executive Officer: Dr. Larry B. Lloyd, President.

Address admission inquiries to Ashley Burns, Director of Admissions.

Cumberland University

One Cumberland Square

Lebanon, Tennessee 37087-3554

Tel: (615) 444-2562 **E-mail:** admissions@cumberland.edu
Fax: (615) 444-2569 **Internet:** www.cumberland.edu

Institution Description: Cumberland University is a private institution. *Enrollment:* 1,351. *Degrees awarded:* Associate, baccalaureate, master's.

Accreditation: *Regional:* SACS-Comm. on Coll.

History: Founded 1842.

Institutional Structure: *Governing board:* Board of Trustees. Academic affairs headed by president. Management/business/finances directed by business manager. Full-time instructional faculty 48.

Calendar: Semesters. Academic year Aug. to May. Freshmen admitted Aug. Degrees conferred and formal commencement May.

Characteristics of Freshmen: 592 applicants (283 female, 309 male). 69% of applicants admitted. 32% of applicants admitted and enrolled.

13% (25 students) submitted SAT scores; 87 (164 students) submitted ACT scores. *25th percentile*: SAT Critical Reading 410, SAT Math 500, ACT Composite 18. *75th percentile*: SAT Critical Reading 5000, SAT Math 520; ACT Composite 22.

37% of entering freshmen expected to graduate within 5 years. 84% of freshmen from Tennessee. Freshmen from 26 states and 28 foreign countries.

Admission: *Requirements:* High school graduation or GED; ACT; minimum GPA 2.5.

Degree Requirements: *For baccalaureate degree:* 128 credit hours.

Degrees Conferred: 2 *associate;* 193 *baccalaureate*; 240 *master's*. Bachelor's degrees awarded in top five disciplines: business, management, marketing, and related support services 44; education 33; health professions and related clinical sciences 24; psychology 15; public administration 11. *Master's*: business 10; education 195; public administration and social services 35.

Fees and Other Expenses: *Full-time tuition per academic year 2008–09:* $16,730. *Books and supplies:* $1,260. *Room and board per academic year:* $5,840. *Required fees:* $840.

Financial Aid: Aid from institutionally generated funds is provided on the basis of academic merit, financial need.

Financial assistance is available in the form of Pell Grants, College Work-Study, Veterans Administration Benefits, National Direct Student Loans, Supplemental Education Opportunity Grants (SEOG), Stafford Loans, other federal aid programs.

Financial aid to full-time, first-time undergraduate students: 100% received some form of aid.

Departments and Teaching Staff: *Total instructional faculty:* 90 (full-time 48, part-time 42). Total faculty with doctorate, first-professional, or other terminal degree: 48. Student/faculty ratio: 15:1.

Enrollment: Total enrollment 1,351. Undergraduate 1,055 (full-time 85%; female 54%, male 48%). Graduate 296 (full-time 20%). Undergraduate transfer-in students 166.

Characteristics of Student Body: *Ethnic/racial makeup:* Black non-Hispanic: 11%; American Indian or Alaska Native: 1%; Asian or Pacific Islander: 1%; Hispanic: 2%; White non-Hispanic: 75%; unknown: 7%; nonresident alien 4%.

International Students: 52 nonresident aliens enrolled fall 2008. Students from Europe, Latin America, Africa, Canada, Australia. No programs available to aid students whose native language is not English. No financial aid specifically designated for international students.

Student Life: College-sponsored housing includes single-sex and co-ed dormitories. On-campus housing available on a first available basis. Intramural sports activities.

Library Collections: 75,000 volumes. Current periodical subscriptions 391 paper; 5 microform; 30 via electronic access. 250 compact discs. Computer work stations available.

Most important special collections include Heydel Noble Collection; Stockton Collection; Tennessee and Wilson County History.

Chief Executive Officer: Dr. Harvill Eaton, President.

Address admission inquiries to James Snider, Director of Admissions.

East Tennessee State University

807 University Parkway
Johnson City, Tennessee 37614
Tel: (423) 439-1000 **E-mail:** go2etsu@etsu.edu
Fax: (423) 439-4630 **Internet:** www.etsu.edu

Institution Description: *Enrollment:* 13,646. *Degrees awarded:* baccalaureate, first-professional (medicine), master's, doctorate.

Academic offerings subject to approval by statewide coordinating bodies. Budget subject to approval by state governing boards. Member of Appalachian Consortium.

Accreditation: *Regional:* SACS-Comm. on Coll. *Professional*; biomedical, chemistry, computer science, dental hygiene, dental laboratory technology, engineering technology, industrial technology, journalism, medicine, music, nursing, social work, teacher education

History: Established and chartered as East Tennessee State Normal School 1909; offered first instruction at postsecondary level 1911; changed name to East Tennessee State Teachers College 1925; awarded first degree (baccalaureate) 1926; changed name to East Tennessee State College 1944; adopted present name 1963. *See* David Sinclair Burleson, *History of East Tennessee State College* (Johnson City: East Tennessee State College, 1947) and Frank Broyles Williams, *East Tennessee State University: A University's Story, 1911–1980* (Johnson City: East Tennessee State University) for further information.

Institutional Structure: *Governing board:* State Board of Regents of the State University and Community College System. Representation: 18 regents, including 1 student (appointed by governor of Tennessee), governor, commissioner of agriculture, executive director of Tennessee Higher Education Commission. 4 ex officio. 17 voting. *Composition of institution:* Administrators 65.. Academic affairs headed by vice president for academic affairs. Management/business/finances directed by vice president for business and finance. Full-time instructional faculty 659. Academic governance body, Academic Council, meets an average of 26 times per year.

Calendar: Semesters. Academic year Aug. to May. Freshmen admitted Aug, Jan., June. Degrees conferred May, Aug., Dec. Formal commencements May, Dec.

Characteristics of Freshmen: 4,514 applicants (2,858 female, 1,936 male). 91% of applicants admitted. 48% of applicants admitted and enrolled.

17% (302 students) submitted SAT scores; 93% (1,624 students) submitted ACT scores. *25th percentile*: SAT Critical Reading 450, SAT Math 450, SAT Writing 440; ACT Composite 20, ACT English 19, ACT Math 17. *75th percentile*: SAT Critical Reading 560, SAT Math 580, SAT Writing 540; ACT Composite 25, ACT English 25, ACT Math 24.

30% of entering freshmen expected to graduate within 5 years. 89% of freshmen from Tennessee. Freshmen from 38 states and 47 foreign countries.

Admission: Rolling admissions plan. Apply as early as 1 year prior to enrollment, but not later than beginning of term. Early acceptance available. *Entrance tests:* ACT or SAT. TOEFL required for international students. High school units, grade point average, and test scores considered in freshman admission. *For transfer students:* 2.0 GPA on transferable courses from regionally accredited institutions.

Advanced placement of the College Board available to those successfully completing examinations. CLEP credit accepted on basis of examination results. Military credit based on American Council on Education guidelines. Admission available each semester.

Tutoring available.

Degree Requirements: *For all baccalaureate degrees:* 120 semester hours minimum; 2 hours physical education; general education core requirements. *For all undergraduate degrees:* 2.0 GPA.

Fulfillment of some degree requirements and exemption from some beginning courses possible by passing departmental examinations, College Board CLEP. *Grading system:* A–F; pass-fail; withdraw (deadline after which pass-fail is appended to withdraw).

Distinctive Educational Programs: Work-experience programs. Flexible meeting places and schedules, including off-campus centers (at Bristol, Elizabethton, Greenville, Kingsport, Oak Ridge, Mountain City) all less than 30 miles away from main institution, and evening classes. Special facilities for using telecommunications in the classroom. Facilities for independent research, including honors programs, tutorials. Study abroad in Australia, China, Ecuador, England, France, Germany, Hungary, Scotland, Spain.

ROTC: Army.

Degrees Conferred: 1,694 *baccalaureate*; 506 *master's*; 30 *doctorate*. Bachelor's degrees awarded in top five disciplines: business, management, marketing, and related support services 282; health professions and related clinical sciences 240; liberal arts 124; protective services/public administration 123; interdisciplinary studies 90. *First-professional:* medicine 58.

EAST TENNESSEE STATE UNIVERSITY—*cont'd*

Fees and Other Expenses: *Full-time tuition per academic year:* undergraduate resident $5,201, nonresident $16,093; contact the university for current graduate and first-professional tuition and fees. *Room and board per academic year:* $5,322. *Books and supplies:* $1,030. *Other expenses:* $6,803.

Financial Aid: Aid from institutionally generated funds is provided on the basis of academic merit, athletic ability, other criteria.

Financial aid to full-time, first-time undergraduate students: 86% received some form of financial aid. Average amount of aid received: federal grants $2,342; Pell grants $2,803; other federal aid $807; state/local grants $3,558; institutional grants $3,696.

Departments and Teaching Staff: *Total instructional faculty:* 760 (full-time 476, part-time 284). Total faculty with doctorate, first-professional, or other terminal degree: 401. Student/faculty ratio: 17:1.

Enrollment: Total enrollment 13,646. Undergraduate 11,028 (full-time 83%; female 37%, male 43%). Graduate 2,618 (full-time 61%). Undergraduate transfer-in students 1,010.

Characteristics of Student Body: *Ethnic/racial makeup:* Black non-Hispanic: 45; Asian or Pacific Islander: 2%; Hispanic: 2%; White non-Hispanic: 87%; unknown: 3%; nonresident alien 1%. *Age distribution:* number under 18: 24; 18–19: 2,261; 20–21: 2,995; 22–24: 2,090; 25–29: 1,102; 30–34: 609; 35–39: 359; 40–49: 495; 50–64: 204; 65 and over: 3.

International Students: 136 nonresident aliens enrolled fall 2008. Students from Europe, Asia, Latin America, Africa, Canada, other. Programs available to aid students whose native language is not English: social, cultural. English as a Second Language Program.

Student Life: On-campus residence halls house 20% of student body. Residence halls for males constitute 40% of such space, for females 60%. 5% of married students request institutional housing; 2% are so housed. *Intercollegiate athletics:* male: baseball, basketball, cross-country, golf, tennis, track; female: basketball, cross-country, golf, tennis, soccer, softball, track, volleyball. *Special services:* Advisement, Resources, Career Center; tutoring, written and oral communication lab, math lab, medical services, campus transportation system, disability services, counseling. *Student publications: East Tennessean*, published biweekly; *Mockingbird*, annually. Radio station WETS-FM broadcasts 24 hours daily, 7 days per week. *Surrounding community:* Johnson City population approximately 50,000. Nashville, 250 miles from campus, is nearest metropolitan area. Served by mass transit bus system; airport 25 miles from campus.

Library Collections: 1,100,000 volumes including bound books, serial backfiles, electronic documents, and government documents not in separate collections. Online catalog. Current serial subscriptions: 8,5213 paper, 1,684,938 microform. Computer work stations available. Students have access to the Internet at no charge.

Most important special holdings include collections on Southern Appalachia Culture; American Literature; American History.

Buildings and Grounds: Campus area 366 acres. Campus DVD available.

Chief Executive Officer: Dr. Paul E. Stanton, Jr. President.

Undergraduates address admission inquiries to Dr. Nancy Dishner, Vice Provost; graduate inquiries to Wesley Brown, Dean of Graduate Studies; medical school inquiries to E. Doug Taylor, Assistant Dean for Admissions and Records.

College of Arts and Sciences

Degree Programs Offered: *Baccalaureate* in art, biology, chemical physics, chemistry, city management, clinical psychology, criminal justice, English, foreign languages, geography, geology, history, humanities, mass communications, mathematics, microbiology, music, music education, philosophy, physics, political science, preprofessional programs, psychology, social sciences, social work, sociology, speech.

Distinctive Educational Programs: Interdisciplinary programs in American studies, general science, medical technology. Preprofessional programs in dentistry, medicine, optometry, pharmacy, physical therapy.

School of Applied Science and Technology

Degree Programs Offered: *Baccalaureate* in applied human sciences, computer and information sciences, geography, engineering technology, surveying and mapping; *master's* in clinical computer and information sciences, technology.

College of Business

Degree Programs Offered: *Baccalaureate* in accountancy, economics, finance, management, marketing. Secretarial certificates also given.

School of Continuing Studies

Degree Programs Offered: *Baccalaureate* in general studies; *master's* in liberal studies.

Admission: Baccalaureate degree from a regionally accredited institution; cumulative GPA 2.5; admission interview.

Degree Requirements: For master of liberal studies: 10 hours of core curriculum; 18–21 hours in plan of study; 3 hours thesis or special project.

College of Education

Degree Programs Offered: *Baccalaureate, master's* in early childhood, elementary, and special education. *Baccalaureate* in physical education, exercise and sports science. Approved elementary and secondary teacher preparation and programs at the undergraduate and graduate levels. *Master's* degree programs in reading, including reading education and storytelling and in counseling, including school counseling, marriage and family counseling, and community agency counseling. *Master's, doctorate* programs in school administration, teacher leadership, and postsecondary and private sector leadership.

School of Nursing

Degree Programs Offered: *Baccalaureate, master's.*

Departments and Teaching Staff: Adult nursing *professors* 1, *associate professors* 2, *assistant professors* 9, *instructors* 2, part-time teachers 4; family and community health nursing 5, 5, 9, 0, 3; professional roles and mental health 2, 3, 4, 2, 5.

College of Public and Allied Health

Degree Programs Offered: *Baccalaureate* in environmental health, health sciences, physical therapy, public health; *master's* in communicative disorders, environmental health, physical therapy, public health, microbiology.

James H. Quillen College of Medicine

Degree Programs Offered: *First-professional.*

Admission: 90 semester hours at accredited college or university which must include 9 semester hours communication skills, 8 biology, 8 general chemistry, 8 organic chemistry, 8 physics; MCAT.

Degree Requirements: 2.0 GPA, at least 2 years of 4-year program in residence.

Fees and Other Expenses: Contact the college for current tuition.

School of Graduate Studies

Degree Programs Offered: *Master's* in accounting, art and design, biology, biomedical science, business administration, chemistry, city management, clinical nutrition, communication (professional), communicative disorders, computer and information sciences, counseling, criminal justice, early childhood education, educational leadership, elementary education, English, environmental health, history, liberal studies, mathematical sciences, media services, music education, nursing, physical education, physical therapy, psychology, public health, public management, reading, secondary education, sociology, special education, technology; *doctorate* in biomedical science, educational leadership. *Specialist certificates* in educational leadership. *Graduate certificates* in business, health care management, nursing (advanced practice).

Departments and Teaching Staff: Faculty of the Graduate School is drawn from other colleges and schools.

Fisk University

1000 17th Avenue North
Nashville, Tennessee 37208-3051
Tel: (615) 329-8500 **E-mail:** admissions@fisk.edu
Fax: (615) 329-8576 **Internet:** www.fisk.edu

Institution Description: Fisk University is a private institution affiliated with the United Church of Christ. *Enrollment:* 726. *Degrees awarded:* Baccalaureate, master's.

Member of the consortia Nashville University Center and Oak Ridge Associated Universities.

Accreditation: *Regional.* SACS-Comm. on Coll. *Professional:* chemistry, music

History: Established as Fisk School 1865; incorporated and adopted present name 1967; offered first instruction at postsecondary level 1871; awarded first degree (baccalaureate) 1875. *See* Joe M. Richardson, *A History of Fisk Univer-*

sity, 1865–1946 (University, Ala.: The University of Alabama Press) for further information.

Institutional Structure: *Governing board:* Board of Trustees. Representation: 21 trustees including 14 alumni. All voting. *Composition of institution:* Administrators 20. Academic affairs headed by dean of the university. Management/business/finances directed by vice president for finance and budget. Full-time instructional faculty 63. Academic governance body, Faculty Assembly, meets an average of 9 times per year.

Calendar: Semesters. Academic year Aug. to Apr. Freshmen admitted Aug., Jan. Degrees conferred and formal commencement May.

Characteristics of Freshmen: 928 applicants (689 female, 239 male). 68% applicants accepted. 22% of accepted applicants enrolled.

52% (142 students) submitted SAT scores; 56% (154 students) submitted ACT scores. *25th percentile*: SAT Critical Reading 450, SAT Math 440; ACT Composite 19, ACT English 19, ACT Math 17. *75th percentile*: SAT Critical Reading 556, SAT Math 540; ACT Composite 23, ACT English 24, ACT Math 22.

50% of entering freshmen expected to graduate within 5 years. Freshmen from 33 states.

Admission: Rolling admissions plan. For fall acceptance, apply as early as Oct. of previous year, but not later than June 15. Early acceptance available. *Requirements:* Either graduation from accredited secondary school or GED. Recommend 15 units, including 4 English, 1 foreign language, 1 algebra, 1 geometry, 1 history, 1 laboratory science. *Entrance tests:* College Board SAT or ACT composite strongly recommended. *For transfer students:* 2.0 minimum GPA; from 2-year and 4-year accredited institution 60 hours maximum transfer credit.

College credit and advanced placement for postsecondary-level work completed in secondary school. Tutoring available. Noncredit developmental courses offered during regular academic year.

Degree Requirements: 120 credit hours; 2.0 GPA; 4 semesters, including last 30 hours, in residence; core courses.

Fulfillment of some degree requirements and exemption from some beginning courses possible by passing departmental examinations, College Board AP. *Grading system:* A–F; pass-fail; withdraw (carries time limit).

Distinctive Educational Programs: Work-experience programs. Accelerated degree programs. Dual-degree programs in engineering and management with Vanderbilt University; pharmacy with Howard University. Facilities and programs for independent research, including honors programs, individual majors, tutorials. Study abroad in various countries.

ROTC: Army, Navy in cooperation with Vanderbilt University; Air Force with Tennessee State University.

Degrees Conferred: 107 *baccalaureate*; 16 *master's*. Bachelor's degrees awarded in top five disciplines: psychology 52; business, management, marketing, and related support services 23; visual and performing arts 21; social sciences 21; biological/life sciences 17. Master's degrees awarded: physical sciences 8; psychology 8.

Fees and Other Expenses: *Full-time tuition per academic year 2008–09:* $16,240. *Books and supplies:* $1,400. *Room and board per academic year:* $7,725. *Other expenses:* $3,350.

Financial Aid: Aid from institutionally generated funds is provided on the basis of academic merit.

Financial aid to full-time, first-time undergraduate students: 96% received some form of financial aid. Average amount of aid relieved: federal grants $3,732; state/local grants $2,487; institutional grants $4,898; loans $7,660.

Departments and Teaching Staff: *Total instructional faculty:* 71. Student/faculty ratio: 12:1. Degrees held by full-time faculty: doctorate 70%, master's 30%. 70% hold terminal degrees.

Enrollment: Total enrollment 726. Undergraduate 683 (full-time 96%; female 68%, male 32%). Graduate 43 (full-time 51%). Undergraduate transfer-in students 4.

Characteristics of Student Body: *Ethnic/racial makeup:* Black non-Hispanic: 82%; Asian or Pacific islander 1%; unknown 5%; nonresident alien 12%.

International Students: 29 nonresident aliens enrolled fall 2008. Students from Asia, Africa. Programs available to aid students whose native language is not English: English as a Second Language Program. No financial aid specifically designated for international students.

Student Life: On-campus residence halls house 80% of student body. Residence halls for males constitute 30% of such space, for females 70%. *Intercollegiate athletics:* male: baseball, basketball, cross-country, football, tennis, track; female: basketball, cross-country, tennis, track, volleyball. *Special regulations:* Cars must be registered and display parking permits. Quiet hours. Residence hall visitation from 6pm to midnight. *Special services:* Learning Resources Center, medical services. Transportation system between Fisk and Vanderbilt Universities, Meharry Medical College, and Scarritt College for Christian Workers. *Student publications, radio: Fisk Herald*, an annual literary magazine; *Fisk Forum*, a biweekly newspaper; *Oval*, a yearbook. Radio station WFSK broadcasts 105 hours per week. *Surrounding community:* Nashville metropolitan area population 1,000,000. Served by mass transit bus system; airport 11 miles from campus.

Publications: *Fisk News*, an alumni magazine; *Fisk Newsletter*, faculty staff newsletter; *President's Report to the Board of Trustees*.

Library Collections: 218,000 volumes. 190,500 government documents (separate collection); 3,600 microforms; 3,000 audiovisual materials; 169 current periodical subscriptions. Online and card catalogs. Computer work stations avaukabke campus-wide. Students have access to online information retrieval services and the Internet.

Most important special collections include Gershwin Collection; Rosenwald Archives; W.E.B. DuBois Collection; Stieglitz Collection (artworks of Alfred Stieglitz and Georgia O'Keefe).

Buildings and Grounds: Campus area 40 acres.

Chief Executive Officer: Dr. John L. Smith, President.

Address admission inquiries to William Carter, Director of Admissions.

Free Will Baptist Bible College

3606 West End Avenue
Nashville, Tennessee 37205-0117
Tel: (615) 844=5000 **E-mail:** recruit@fwbbc.edu
Fax: (615) 269-6028 **Internet:** www.fwbbc.edu

Institution Description: Free Will Baptist College is a private, nonprofit institution owned and operated by the National Association of Free Will Baptists. *Enrollment:* 317. *Degrees awarded:* Associate, baccalaureate, master's.

Accreditation: *National:* ABHE. *Regional:* SACS.

History: Founded as a two-year college and offered first courses 1942; third year added 1949 and fourth year added 1950; first baccalaureate degrees awarded 1951.

Institutional Structure: *Governing board:* Board of trustees with 9 members elected by the denomination. 1 ex officio (president of the college). *Composition of institution:* Administrators 7. Academic affairs headed by provost. Business/finances directed by vice president for financial affairs. Full-time instructional faculty 21. Academic governance body, the faculty, meets monthly.

Calendar: Semesters. Academic year Aug. to May. Freshmen admitted Aug., Jan., May. Degrees conferred May. Summer session of 5 weeks from May to June.

Characteristics of Freshmen: 94% of applicants accepted. 56% of accepted applicants enrolled.

10.6% (6 students) submitted SAT scores; 77.3% (58 students) submitted ACT scores.

Mean ACT Composite class score 20.3.

39% of freshmen expected to graduate within 5 years. 36% of freshmen from Tennessee. Freshmen from 16 states and 1 foreign country.

Admission: Rolling admissions plan. For fall acceptance, apply no later than July 15. *Requirements:* Either graduation from secondary school or GED; medical examination; 3 letters of reference verifying Christian faith and character. *Entrance tests:* ACT.

Degree Requirements: Minimum of 124 hours with 2.0 (of 4.00) average overall and in each major for baccalaureate degrees; 30 hours residence including last semester before graduation.

Fulfillment of some degree requirements possible by passing College Board CLEP, AP. *Grading system:* A–F; withdraw (deadline after which pass-fail is appended to withdraw).

Distinctive Educational Programs: All educational programs offered in a context of Bible-centered academics and strong Christian standards. Every student majors in Bible, but may select from a number of areas for second major (or minor), including individually designed major. Christian perspective and service undergird all programs of work.

ROTC: Air Force available through cooperative program with Tennessee State University; Army available through cooperative program with Vanderbilt University.

Degrees Conferred: 66 *baccalaureate*: business/marketing 17; education 21; English 1; psychology 5; theology and religious vocations 19; visual and performing arts 1.

Fees and Other Expenses: *Full-time tuition per academic year 2008–09:* $13,086. *Books and supplies:* $788. *Required fees:* $696. *Room and board per academic year:* $5,352. *Other expenses:* $4,895.

Financial Aid: Aid from institutionally generated funds is provided on the basis of financial need, other criteria.

Financial aid to full-time, first-time undergraduate students: 98% received some form of aid.

FREE WILL BAPTIST BIBLE COLLEGE—*cont'd*

Departments and Teaching Staff: *Total instructional faculty:* 42 (full-time 21, part-time 21). Student/faculty ratio: 14.3:1. Degrees held by full-time faculty: doctorate 37%, master's 63%.

Enrollment: Total enrollment 317.

Characteristics of Student Body: *Ethnic/racial makeup:* Black non-Hispanic: 8%; American Indian or Alaska Native 1%; Hispanic: 25; White non-Hispanic: 82%; nonresident alien 9%. *Age distribution:* number under 18: 2; 18–19: 108; 20–21: 124; 22–24: 63; 25–29: 40; 30–34: 26; 35–39: 4; 40–49: 11; 50–64: 11; 65 and over: 6. 28% of student body attend summer sessions.

International Students: 6 nonresident aliens enrolled fall 2008. No programs to aid students whose native language is not English. No financial aid specifically designated for international students.

Student Life: All single students either commute from their homes or live in college residence halls (currently about 68% of students are in residence halls). *Intramural athletics:* male: softball, tennis, swimming, basketball, volleyball, soccer; female: badminton. *Special regulations:* Registered cars permitted. Dress and conduct regulations. *Student publications: The Lumen*, a yearbook.

Publications: *ONE Magazine*, the official college public relations/news publication.

Library Collections: 77,000 volumes. 1,640 microforms; 2,500 audiovisual materials; 388 current periodical subscriptions. Students have access to online information retrieval services and the Internet.

Most important special holdings include Free Will Baptist Historical Collection; Education Curriculum Lab; Biblical/theological collection; music collection.

Buildings and Grounds: Campus area 10 acres.

Chief Executive Officer: J. Matthew Pinson, President.

Address admission inquiries to Registrar.

Freed-Hardeman University

158 East Main Street
Henderson, Tennessee 38340-2399
Tel: (731) 989-6648 **E-mail:** admissions@fhu.edu
Fax: (731) 989-6650 **Internet:** www.fhu.edu

Institution Description: Freed-Hardeman University is an independent university affiliated with the Churches of Christ. *Enrollment:* 2,061. *Degrees awarded:* Baccalaureate, master's.

Accreditation: *Regional:* SACS-Comm. on Coll. *Professional*: business, social work, teacher education

History: Predecessor established and chartered as Henderson Male and Female Institute 1869; offered first instruction at postsecondary level 1870; changed name to Henderson Masonic Male and Female Institute 1877; changed name to West Tennessee Christian College 1885, to George Robertson Christian College 1897; awarded first degree (baccalaureate) circa 1875; closed 1907. Present institution chartered as National Teachers Normal and Business College 1907; offered first instruction 1908; adopted present name 1919; became 4-year institution 1976. *See* M. Norvel Young, *A History of Colleges Established and Controlled by Members of Churches of Christ* (Kansas City, Mo.: Old Paths Book Club, 1949) for further information. Graduate offerings leading to the M.Ed., M.Min. began 1989; name changed to Freed-Hardeman University 1990.

Institutional Structure: *Governing board:* Freed-Hardeman University Board of Trustees. Extrainstitutional representation: 40 trustees, including 14 alumni; institutional representation: none. All voting. *Composition of institution:* Administrators: president and five vice presidents. Academic affairs headed by vice president for academic affairs. Management/business/finances directed by vice president for business affairs. Full-time instructional faculty 112. Academic governance body, The Faculty of Freed-Hardeman University, meets an average of 5 times per year.

Calendar: Semesters. Academic year Aug. to May. Freshmen admitted Aug., Jan., May, June, July. Degrees conferred May, Aug., Dec. Formal commencement May. Summer session of 2 terms from June to Aug.

Characteristics of Freshmen: 2,420 applicants (1,459 female, 961 male). 38% of applicants accepted. 37% of accepted applicants enrolled full-time.

Mean ACT composite class score 22.6.

44% of entering freshmen expected to graduate within 5 years. 25% of freshmen from Tennessee. Freshmen from 25 states and 2 foreign countries.

Admission: Rolling admissions plan. For fall acceptance, apply no later than close of registration. Early acceptance available. *Requirements:* Either graduation from accredited secondary school or GED. For unrestricted admission, minimum high school GPA 2.25. *Entrance tests:* ACT composite. For unrestricted admission, score of 16 on ACT composite. For foreign students TOEFL. *For transfer students:* 1.40–2.00 minimum GPA for unqualified good standing, depending upon hours earned.

College credit for postsecondary-level work completed in secondary school. College credit for extrainstitutional learning.

Tutoring available. Developmental courses offered in summer session and regular academic year; credit given.

Degree Requirements: *For all baccalaureate degrees:* 132 hours; 33 hours in residence; comprehensives in individual fields of study. *For all degrees:* 2.0 GPA; daily chapel attendance; general education requirements; Bible courses; exit competency examinations or minimum grades in writing, speech communication, and mathematics.

Fulfillment of some degree requirements and exemption from some beginning courses possible by passing departmental examinations, College Board CLEP, AP (score of 3); ACT standardized tests. *Grading system:* A–F; pass-fail; pass; withdraw.

Distinctive Educational Programs: Work-experience programs, including cooperative education, field study. Accelerated degree programs. Special facilities for using telecommunications (voice, data, and video networks) in classrooms and residence hall rooms. Interdisciplinary programs in American studies, world culture, missions, and by individual arrangement. Facilities and programs for independent research, including honors programs, individual majors, tutorials, independent study. Cross-registration with Lambuth University and Union University. Program allowing students admitted to accredited schools of dentistry, engineering, law, or medicine after 3 years of undergraduate study to receive baccalaureate degree following completion of first year of professional study. *Other distinctive programs:* Continuing education.

Degrees Conferred: 252 *baccalaureate:* agriculture 12; biological sciences 18; business, management, marketing, and related support services 87; communication, journalism, and related programs 18; computer and information sciences 11; education 40; English 7; mathematics 4; philosophy/religion/theology 40; physical sciences 6; psychology 25; social sciences and history 10; visual and performing arts 8. Master's degrees awarded: various disciplines 117. First-professional degree awrded: philosophy/religion/theology 14.

Fees and Other Expenses: *Full-time tuition per academic year 2008–09:* $14,550. *books and supplies:* $1,800. *Room and board per academic year:* $6,970. *Other expenses:* $3,650.

Financial Aid: Aid from institutionally generated funds is provided on the basis of academic merit, financial need, athletic ability,

Financial aid to full-time, first-time undergraduate students: 99% received some form of aid. Average amount of aid received: federal grants $4,053; Pell grants $3,042; other federal aid $1,154; state/local grants $5,782; institutional grants $3,650.

Departments and Teaching Staff: *Total instructional faculty:* 136 (full-time 99, part-time 37). Total faculty with doctorate, first-professional, or other terminal degree: 93. Student/faculty ratio: 15:1. Degrees held by full-time faculty: doctorate 60%, master's 38%, baccalaureate 2%. 60% hold terminal degrees.

Enrollment: Total enrollment 2,061. Undergraduate 1,534 (full-time 92%; female 55%, male 45%). Graduate 527 (full-time 16%). Undergraduate transfer-in students 74.

International Students: 30 nonresident aliens enrolled fall 2008. Students from Europe, Asia, Latin America, Africa, Canada. No programs available to aid students whose native language is not English. No financial aid specifically designated for international students.

Student Life: On-campus residence halls house 80% of student body. Residence halls for males constitute 44% of such space, for females 56%. *Intercollegiate athletics:* male: baseball, basketball, golf, tennis; female: basketball, tennis, volleyball. *Special regulations:* Registered cars permitted in designated areas. Curfews midnight to 6am Sun.–Thurs.; 12:30am to 6am Fri. and Sat. Residence hall visitation hours vary according to residence hall. *Special services:* Medical services. *Student publications, radio: The Bell Tower*, a semimonthly newspaper; *The Treasure Chest*, a yearbook. Radio station WFHC-FM broadcasts 130 hours per week. *Surrounding community:* Henderson population 5,000. Jackson, 15 miles north, is regional medical, entertainment, and shopping center. Memphis, 90 miles from campus, is nearest metropolitan area. Served by airport 25 miles from campus.

Library Collections: 176,000 volumes. 240,000 microforms; 43,000 audiovisual materials; 1,650 current periodical subscriptions. Online catalog. Students have access to online information retrieval services and the Internet.

Most important special collections include Restoration Library (books, microforms, periodicals pertaining to history of the Church of Christ in the U.S.); collection of U.S. War Department Civil War records.

Buildings and Grounds: Campus area 100 acres. Campus DVD available.

Chief Executive Officer: Dr. Milton Sewell, President.

Address admission inquiries to Belinda Anderson, Director of Admissions.

Harding University Graduate School of Religion

1000 Cherry Road
Memphis, Tennessee 38117-5499
Tel: (901) 761-1353 **E-mail:** admissions@hugsr.edu
Fax: (901) 761-1358 **Internet:** www.hugsr.edu

Institution Description: Harding University Graduate School of Religion is a private institution affiliated with the Church of Christ. The school is a branch of Harding University, Searcy, Arkansas. *Enrollment:* 221. *Degrees awarded:* First-professional (theology), master's, doctorate.

Accreditation: *Regional:* NCA (parent university in Arkansas). *National:* ATS. *Professional*: theology

History: Established as the graduate department of religious studies at Harding University (established 1924) 1952; moved to present location, became a branch school and changed name to Harding Graduate School of Bible and Religion 1958; awarded first degree (first-professional) 1959; adopted present name 1966.

Institutional Structure: *Governing board:* Harding University Board of Trustees. Extrainstitutional representation: 24 trustees; institutional representation: president of the university. 1 ex officio. 24 voting. *Composition of institution:* Administrators 5. Academic affairs and finances headed by vice president/ dean. Management/business/finances directed by vice president for finance. Full-time instructional faculty 8/ Academic governance body, Faculty Association, meets an average of 10 times per year.

Calendar: Semesters. Academic year Aug. to May. Freshmen admitted Sept., Jan., May, June, July, Aug. Degrees conferred and formal commencement May. Summer session of 4 terms from May to Aug.

Admission: Rolling admissions plan. *Requirements:* For first-professional students, 2.0 GPA. For master's students, 2.7 minimum GPA; 21 semester hours in Bible and related coursework. For both degrees, baccalaureate from accredited college or university; 4 character references. Recommend interview. *Entrance tests:* National standardized psychological personality test. For foreign students TOEFL. *For transfer students:* For first-professional students minimum 2.5 GPA; 54 semester hours maximum transfer credit; for master's students minimum 3.0 GPA; 6 hours maximum transfer credit.

Degree Requirements: *For first-professional degree:* 84 credit hours; 2.5 GPA; 6 hours field education. *For master's degrees:* 57 credit hours; 3.0 GPA; minor requirement. *For both degrees:* 1 year in residence; core requirements. *Grading system:* A–F; pass-fail; withdraw (carries time limit).

Distinctive Educational Programs: Work-experience programs, including internships, practicums. Tutorials. Independent study. *Other distinctive programs:* W. B. West, Jr. lecture series features Christian scholars and current church-related issues.

Degrees Conferred: 9 *master's:* theology; 3 *doctorate*: theology; 15 *first-professional:* master of divinity.

Fees and Other Expenses: *Tuition per academic year:* contact the university for current tuition, fees, and housing costs.

Financial Aid: Aid from institutionally generated funds is provided on the basis of academic merit, financial need. Institution has a Program Participation Agreement with the U.S. Department of Education for eligible students to receive Pell Grants and, depending upon the agreement, other federal aid.

Departments and Teaching Staff: *Total instructional faculty:* 14. Student/ faculty ratio: 10:1. Degrees held by full-time faculty: doctorate 100%.

Enrollment: Total enrollment 221.

International Students: 3 nonresident aliens enrolled fall 2008. No programs available to aid students whose native language is not English. Some financial aid specifically designated for international students.

Student Life: On-campus university-owned apartments house 13% of student body. *Special regulations:* Cars permitted without restrictions. *Student publications:* a monthly student newsletter. *Surrounding community:* Memphis metropolitan area population over 1 million. Served by mass transit bus system; airport 10 miles from campus; passenger rail service 12 miles from campus.

Library Collections: 125,000 volumes including bound books, serial backfiles, electronic documents, and government documents not in separate collections. Current serial subscriptions: 630 paper, 50 microform. 47 recordings; 5 CD-ROMs. Computer work stations available. Students have access to the Internet at no charge.

Most important special collections in Biblical Studies; Restoration History; Missions.

Buildings and Grounds: Campus area 23 acres.

Chief Executive Officer: Dr. Everett W. Huffard, Dean/Executive Director.

Address admission inquiries to Mark parker, Director of Admissions.

Johnson Bible College

7900 Johnson Drive
Knoxville, Tennessee 37998
Tel: (865) 251-2346 **E-mail:** jbc@jbc.edu
Fax: (865) 579-2336 **Internet:** www.jbc.edu

Institution Description: Johnson Bible College is a private, independent, nonprofit college related the Christian Churches-Churches of Christ. *Enrollment:* 801. *Degrees awarded:* Associate, baccalaureate, master's.

Accreditation: *Regional:* SACS-Comm. on Coll. *National:* ABHE.

History: Established as School of the Evangelists and offered first instruction at postsecondary level 1893; awarded first degree (baccalaureate) 1897; chartered 1901; adopted present name 1909. *See* L. Thomas Smith, *Above Every Other Desire* (available from Johnson Bible College) for further information.

Institutional Structure: *Governing board:* Johnson Bible College Board of Trustees. Extrainstitutional representation: 12 trustees, including 7 alumni; institutional representation: president of the college. 1 ex officio. 11 voting. *Composition of institution:* Administrators 9. Academic affairs headed by academic dean. Management/business/finances directed by business manager. Full-time instructional faculty 20. Academic governance body, the faculty, meets an average of 34 times per year.

Calendar: Semesters. Academic year Aug. to May. Freshmen admitted Aug., Jan. Degrees conferred and formal commencement May. Summer session from May to June.

Characteristics of Freshmen: 213 applicants (115 female, 98 male). 83% of applicants admitted. 80% of applicants admitted and enrolled.

45% (64 students) submitted SAT scores; 69% (98 85 students) submitted ACT scores. *25th percentile*: SAT Critical Reading 450, SAT Math 480; ACT Composite 23, ACT English 21, ACT Math 24. *75th percentile*: SAT Critical Reading 580, SAT Math 580; ACT Composite 31, ACT English 36, ACT Math 35.

34% of entering freshmen expected to graduate within 5 years. Freshmen from 15 states and 2 foreign countries.

Admission: Apply as early as 1 year prior to enrollment. Early acceptance available. *Requirements:* Either graduation from accredited secondary school with 16 units, 12 of which must be in academic subjects; or GED. *Entrance tests:* ACT composite. For foreign students TOEFL. *For transfer students:* From 4-year accredited institution 100 semester hours maximum transfer credit; from 2-year accredited institution 66 semester hours; correspondence/extension students 18 hours.

College credit and advanced placement for postsecondary-level work completed in secondary school. College credit for extrainstitutional learning.

Developmental courses offered during regular academic year; no credit given.

Degree Requirements: *For all baccalaureate degrees:* 132 credit hours; 2.0 GPA; senior year in residence; daily chapel attendance; 2 semesters physical education; general education requirements.

Fulfillment of some degree requirements and exemption from some beginning courses possible by passing College Board CLEP, AP. *Grading system:* A–F; pass-fail; withdraw (deadline after which pass-fail is appended to withdraw).

Distinctive Educational Programs: Internships and field experience. Special facilities for using telecommunications in the classroom.

Degrees Conferred: 21*associate;* 139 *baccalaureate:* education 23; theology 105; 29 *master's:* education 25, theology 12.

Fees and Other Expenses: *Full-time tuition per academic year 2008–09:* $7,780. *Books and supplies:* $1,300. *Room and board per academic year:* $4,890. *Other expenses:* $3,650.

Financial Aid: Aid from institutionally generated funds is provided on the basis of academic merit, financial need.

Financial aid to full-time, first-time undergraduate students: 100% received some form of financial aid. Average amount of aid received: federal grants $2,501; state/local grants $4,300; institutional grants $1,958; loans $2,803.

Departments and Teaching Staff: *Total instructional faculty:* 58 (full-time 26, part-time 32). Total faculty with doctorate, first-professional, or other terminal degree 22. Student/faculty ratio: 22:1. Degrees held by full-time faculty: doctorate 55%, master's 45%. 55% hold terminal degrees.

Enrollment: Total enrollment 801. Undergraduate 685 (full-timre 94%; female 49%, male 51%). Graduate 116 (full-time 30%). Undergraduate transfer-in students 40.

Characteristics of Student Body: *Ethnic/racial makeup:* Black non-Hispanic: 1%; Asian or Pacific Islander: 1%; Hispanic: 3%; White non-Hispanic: 92%; nonresident alien 1%. *Age distribution:* number under 18: 6; 18–19: 291; 20–21: 238; 22–24: 82; 25–29: 43; 30–34: 21; 35–39: 14; 40–49: 23; 50–64: 16; 65 and over: 1.

JOHNSON BIBLE COLLEGE—*cont'd*

International Students: 8 nonresident aliens enrolled fall 2008. Students from Europe, Asia, Latin America, Africa, Australia. No programs available to aid students whose native language is not English. Financial aid specifically designated for international students: scholarships available annually to qualifying students.

Student Life: On-campus residence halls, duplex housing, and mobile homes house 95% of student body. *Intercollegiate athletics:* male: baseball, basketball; female: basketball, volleyball; both sexes: soccer. *Special regulations:* Registered cars permitted. Curfews from 11pm to 6am Mon.–Thurs., 1am to 6am Fri.–Sun. *Surrounding community:* Knoxville metropolitan area population 500,000. Served by airport 20 miles from campus.

Publications: Sources of information about Johnson Bible College include *Blue and White*, a monthly publication with information on alumni, students, faculty research, and institutional activities.

Library Collections: 105,000 volumes. 10,500 audiovisual materials. 450 current periodical subscriptions. Online catalog. Students have access to online information retrieval services and the Internet.

Most important special collection in Restoration History.

Buildings and Grounds: Campus area 50 acres.

Chief Executive Officer: Dr. David L. Eubanks, President.

Address admission inquiries to Tim Wingfield, Admissions Director.

King College

1350 King College Road
Bristol, Tennessee 37620-2699
Tel: (423) 968-1187 **E-mail:** admissions@king.edu
Fax: (423) 968-4456 **Internet:** www.king.edu

Institution Description: King College is a private college affiliated with the Presbyterian Church (USA). *Enrollment:* 1,702. *Degrees awarded:* Baccalaureate, master's.

Member of the Council of Christian Colleges and Universities.

Accreditation: *Regional:* SACS-Comm. on Coll.

History: Established as a college for men 1867; chartered and offered first instruction at postsecondary level 1869; awarded first degree (baccalaureate) 1870; admitted women 1931.

Institutional Structure: *Governing board:* Board of Trustees of King College, Incorporated. Extrainstitutional representation: 33 trustees; institutional representation: president of the college, 1 full-time instructional faculty member, 1 student; 2 alumni members. 1 ex officio. 14 voting. *Composition of institution:* Administrators 101. Academic affairs headed by dean of the faculty. Management/business/finances directed by business manager. Full-time instructional faculty 60. Academic governance body, the faculty, meets an average of 10 times peryear.

Calendar: Semesters. Academic year Aug. to May. Freshmen admitted Aug., Jan., Feb. Degrees conferred May, Aug., Dec. Formal commencement May. Summer session.

Characteristics of Freshmen: 898 applicants (489 female, 409 male). 95% of applicants admitted. 39% of applicants admitted and enrolled.

49% (102 students) submitted SAT scores; 65% (135 118 students) submitted ACT scores. *25th percentile*: SAT Critical Reading 450, SAT Math 480; ACT Composite 21, ACT English 20, ACT Math 18. *75th percentile*: SAT Critical Reading 540, SAT Math 568; ACT Composite 25, ACT English 26, ACT Math 25.

59% entering freshmen expected to graduate within 5 years. 59% of freshmen from Tennessee. Freshmen from 27 states and 20 foreign countries.

Admission: Rolling admissions plan. For fall acceptance, apply as early as Sept. of previous year, but not later than 1 month prior to enrollment. Early acceptance available. *Requirements:* Either graduation from accredited secondary school with 16 units which must include 4 English; 5 from among history, social studies, foreign languages; 4 from among natural sciences, mathematics, other academic electives; 2 algebra; 1 geometry; or GED. *Entrance tests:* College Board SAT or ACT composite. *For transfer students:* 2.0 minimum GPA; 80 semester hours maximum transfer credit.

Degree Requirements: 124 semester hours; 2.0 GPA; 50 hours in residence; weekly chapel attendance; 3 hours physical education; distribution requirements; comprehensives in individual fields of study; demonstrated proficiency in a foreign language.

Fulfillment of some degree requirements and exemption from some beginning courses possible by passing College Board CLEP, APP. *Grading system:* A–F; pass-fail; withdraw (deadline after which pass-fail is appended to withdraw); incomplete (carries time limit).

Distinctive Educational Programs: Internships. Cooperative education. Study abroad may be individually arranged and also offered during May term and summer session (Israel, Mexico, France, England, Spain, Germany, Russia, New Guinea, Puerto Rico, other locations). Off-campus study in U.S. for May term and summer interim by individual arrangement. Cross-registration with Virginia Intermont College.

Degrees Conferred: 368 *baccalaureate:* degrees awarded in top five disciplines: biological/life sciences 7; English language and literature 14; psychology 6; social sciences and history 42; philosophy/religious studies 6. Master's degrees awarded: various disciplines 90.

Fees and Other Expenses: *Full-time tuition per academic year 2008–09:* $20,582. *Room and board per academic year:* $6,900. *Required fees:* $1,054. *Books and supplies:* $900. *Other expenses:* $3,000.

Financial Aid: Aid from institutionally generated funds is provided on the basis of academic merit, financial need, athletic ability, other criteria.

Financial aid to full-time, first-time undergraduate students: 87% received some form of aid. Average amount of aid received; federal grants $2,733; Pell grants $3,618; other federal aid $1,000; state/local grants $1,000; institutional grants $3,000.

Departments and Teaching Staff: *Total instructional faculty:* 122 (full-time 60, part-time 62). Total faculty with doctorate, first-professional, or other terminal degree: 49. Student/faculty ratio: 14:1. Degrees held by full-time faculty: doctorate 88%, master's 100%, baccalaureate 100%. 88% hold terminal degrees.

Enrollment: Total enrollment 1,702. Undergraduate 1,441 (full-time 90%; female 65%, male 35%). Graduate 261 (full-time 27%). Undergraduate transfer-in students 337.

Characteristics of Student Body: *Ethnic/racial makeup:* Black non-Hispanic: 2%; Hispanic: 2%; White non-Hispanic: 65%; unknown: 28%; nonresident alien 3%.

International Students: 52 nonresident aliens enrolled fall 2008. Students from Europe, Asia, Latin America, Africa, Australia. Programs available to aid students whose native language is not English: English as a Second Language Program. No financial aid specifically designated for international students.

Student Life: On-campus residence halls house 80% of student body. Residence halls for males constitute 43% of such space, for females 55%. *Intercollegiate athletics:* male: baseball, basketball, cross-country, golf, soccer, tennis; female: basketball, cross-country, golf, soccer, tennis, softball, volleyball. *Special regulations:* Cars permitted on campus in designated areas only. *Special services:* Medical services. *Student publications: Kayseean*, a bimonthly newspaper; *Tornado*, a yearbook; *King's Herald*, a twice-yearly magazine. *Surrounding community:* Bristol population 46,000. Knoxville, 120 miles from campus, is nearest metropolitan area. Served by airport 20 miles from campus.

Library Collections: 115,000 volumes. 15,000 government documents; 59,539 microforms; 4,300 audiovisual materials; 605 current periodical subscriptions. Online catalog. Students have access to online information retrieval services and the Internet.

Most important special collections include Southern Presbyterian history; classics; history of printing.

Buildings and Grounds: Campus area 135 acres.

Chief Executive Officer: Dr. Gregory D. Jordan, President.

Address admission inquiries to Melinda Clark, Associate Vice President for Enrollment Management.

Lambuth University

705 Lambuth Boulevard
Jackson, Tennessee 38301
Tel: (731) 425-2500 **E-mail:** admit@lambuth.edu
Fax: (731) 425-3496 **Internet:** www.lambuth

Institution Description: Lambuth University is a private liberal arts and sciences institution affiliated with the United Methodist Church. *Enrollment:* 815. *Degrees awarded:* Baccalaureate.

Accreditation: *Regional:* SACS-Comm. on Coll. *Professional*: business

History: Established and chartered as Memphis Conference Female Institute and offered first instruction at postsecondary level 1843; rechartered as coeducational college and became Lambuth College 1923; awarded first degree (baccalaureate) 1928; became Lambuth University 1991. *See* Sarah V. Clement, *A College Grows... MCFI - Lambuth* (Jackson: McCowat-Mercer Press, 1972) for further information.

Institutional Structure: *Governing board:* Board of Trustees. Extrainstitutional representation: 46 trustees, including 12 alumni; institutional representation: president of the university. 9 ex officio. 39 voting. *Composition of institution:* Administrators 22. Academic affairs headed by executive vice president and academic dean. Management/business/finances directed by vice president for business affairs. Full-time instructional faculty 48. Academic governance body, Council of Deans, meets weekly.

Calendar: Semesters. Academic year Aug. to Apr. Freshmen admitted Aug., Jan., June. Degrees conferred and formal commencement May. May term. Summer session of 2 terms from June to Aug.

Characteristics of Freshmen: 679 042 applicants (female 295, male 384). 62% of applicants admitted. 49% of applicants admitted and enrolled full-time.

18% (30 students) submitted SAT scores; 12% (52 students) submitted ACT scores. *25th percentile*: SAT Critical Reading 450, SAT Math 480; ACT Composite 20, ACT English 20, ACT Math 18. *75th percentile*: SAT Critical Reading 603, SAT 600 560; ACT Composite 26, ACT English 27, ACT Math 25.

40% of entering freshmen expected to graduate within 5 years. 81% of freshmen from Tennessee. Freshmen from 25 states and 3 foreign countries.

Admission: Rolling admissions plan. For fall acceptance, apply as early as June 1 of previous year, but not later than Aug. 15 of year of enrollment. Early acceptance available. *Requirements:* Either graduation from approved secondary school with units in foreign languages, mathematics, natural science, social studies; or GED. Minimum 2.0 GPA. *Entrance tests:* College Board SAT or ACT composite. For foreign students TOEFL or equivalent examination. *For transfer students:* 2.0 minimum GPA; from 4-year accredited institution maximum transfer credit limited by residence requirement; from 2-year accredited institution 68 hours; correspondence/extension students 8 hours.

College credit for postsecondary-level work completed in secondary school and for extrainstitutional learning on basis of ACE *2006 Guide to the Evaluation of Educational Experiences in the Armed Services*.

Tutoring available. Developmental courses offered in summer session and regular academic year; credit given.

Degree Requirements: *For baccalaureate degrees:* 128 semester hours; 2.0 GPA; last 32 hours in residence; 2 semesters physical education; 2 fine arts; general education requirements.

Fulfillment of some degree requirements and exemption from some beginning courses possible by passing College Board CLEP, AP, other standardized tests. *Grading system:* A–F; pass-fail; withdraw (carries time limit).

Distinctive Educational Programs: Work-experience programs, including cooperative education, internships. Evening classes. Accelerated degree programs. Interdisciplinary majors by individual arrangement. Facilities and programs for independent research, Lambuth Scholars, individual majors, tutorials. *Other distinctive programs:* Summer program in biology at Gulf Coast Research Laboratory (MS). Study abroad: Lambuth at Oxford Program at Westminster College, Oxford, England.

Degrees Conferred: 152 *baccalaureate:* biological/life sciences 11; business and management 18; communications 9; computer and information sciences 2; education 13; English 3; foreign language 9; health professions 3; home economics 3; interdisciplinary studies 5; mathematics 3; parks and recreation 9; philosophy/religion 4; psychology 13; social sciences and history 44, visual and performing arts 9.

Fees and Other Expenses: *Full-time tuition per academic year 2008–09:* $17,450. *Other fees:* $300. *Books and supplies:* $1,200. *Room and board per academic year:* $7,510. *Other expenses:* $4,000.

Financial Aid: Aid from institutionally generated funds is awarded on the basis of academic merit, financial need, athletic ability, other criteria.

Financial aid to full-time, first-time undergraduate students: 98% received some form of financial aid. Average amount of aid received: federal grants $3,038; state/local grants $4,231; institutional grants $9,157; loans $3,184.

Departments and Teaching Staff: *Total instructional faculty:* 93 (full-time 53, part-time 40). Total faculty with doctorate, first-professional, or other terminal degree: 44. Student/faculty ratio: 12:1. Degrees held by full-time faculty: doctorate 70%, master's 28%, professional 2%. 72% hold terminal degrees.

Enrollment: Total enrollment 815. Undergraduate 815 (full-time 91%; female 48%, male 52%). Transfer-in students 86.

Characteristics of Student Body: *Ethnic/racial makeup:* Black non-Hispanic: 20%; Asian or Pacific Islander: 2%; Hispanic: 2%; White non-Hispanic: 73%; unknown: 2%; nonresident alien 2%. *Age distribution:* number under 18: 3; 18–19: 285; 20–21: 263; 22–24: 173; 25–29: 40; 30–34: 17; 35–39: 5; 40–49: 11; 50–64: 4; 65 and over: 1. 20% of student body attend summer sessions.

International Students: 16 nonresident aliens enrolled fall 2008. Students from Europe, Asia, Latin America, Canada. Programs available to aid students whose native language is not English: English as a Second Language Program. No financial specifically designated for international students.

Student Life: On-campus residence halls house 66% of student body. 35% of males and 25% of females join fraternities and sororities. *Intercollegiate athletics:* male: baseball, basketball, football, soccer, tennis; female: basketball, softball, tennis, volleyball. *Special regulations:* Cars permitted without restrictions. Quiet hours vary according to residence hall. Residence hall visitation from 6pm to 11pm. Wed., 6pm to midnight Fri. and Sat., 2pm to 5pm Sun. *Special services:* Learning Enrichment Center, medical services. *Student publications, radio: The Lantern*, a yearbook; *The Vision*, a monthly newspaper; *Coffeehouse Papers*, a literary publication. Radio station WLAM broadcasts irregularly. *Surrounding community:* Jackson, Madison County, population 87,100. Memphis, 80 miles from campus, is nearest metropolitan area. Served by mass transit bus system; airport 3 miles from campus.

Library Collections: 292,500 volumes. Online catalog. 4,000 government documents. 207,300 microfroms; 3,250 audiovisual materials; 15,200 periodicals including via electronic access. Computer work stations available. Students have access to online information retrieval services and the Internet.

Most important special holdings include archives section for United Methodist Church-Memphis Conference. Library is a partial depository for government documents.

Buildings and Grounds: Campus area 50 acres.

Chief Executive Officer: Dr. R. Fred Zuker, President.

Address admission inquiries to Lisa Warmath, Director of Admissions.

Lane College

545 Lane Avenue
Jackson, Tennessee 38301-4598

Tel: (731) 426-7500 **E-mail:** admissions@lanecollege.edu
Fax: (731) 427-3987 **Internet:** www.lanecollege.edu

Institution Description: Lane College is a private institution affiliated with the Christian Methodist Episcopal Church. *Enrollment:* 1,981. *Degrees awarded:* Baccalaureate.

Accreditation: *Regional:* SACS-Comm. on Coll.

History: Established as Colored Methodist Episcopal High School 1882; changed name to Lane Institute 1883; chartered 1884; adopted present name 1895; awarded first degree (baccalaureate) 1899.

Institutional Structure: *Governing board:* Board of Trustees. Representation: 16 trustees. 1 ex officio. 15 voting. *Composition of institution:* Administrators 12. Academic affairs headed by dean of the college. Management/business/finances directed by director of business and finance. Full-time instructional faculty 43.

Calendar: Semesters. Academic year Aug. to May. Freshmen admitted Aug., Jan., May. Degrees conferred and formal commencement May. Summer session of 2 terms from Apr. to June.

Characteristics of Freshmen: 5,095 applicants (2,906 female, 2,189 male). 33 of applicants accepted. 37% of accepted applicants enrolled.

Mean ACT Composite class score 16.

57% of entering freshmen expected to graduate within 5 years. 56% of freshmen from Tennessee. Freshmen from 30 states.

Admission: Regulated admissions. *Requirements:* Either graduation from accredited secondary school with 4 units English, 2 mathematics, 2 science, 2 social studies, 5 academic electives; or GED. *For transfer students:* 2.0 GPA minimum; from 4-year accredited institution 96 hours maximum transfer credit.

Tutoring available. Developmental courses offered in summer session and regular academic year; credit given.

Degree Requirements: 124 credit hours; 2.0 GPA; last 31 hours in residence; 2 physical activity courses; foundation program requirements. *Grading system:* A–F.

Distinctive Educational Programs: Evening classes. Dual-degree program in computer science with Jackson State University (MS), in engineering with Tennessee State University Center for Academic Development.

Degrees Conferred: 88 *baccalaureate:* biological/life sciences 10; business and management 11; communications 2; computer and information science 12; English 5; interdisciplinary studies 16; law/legal studies 9; mathematics 5; physical sciences 2; social sciences and history 6; visual and performing arts 2; other 7.

Fees and Other Expenses: *Full-time tuition per academic year 2008–09:* $7,770. *Other fees:* $600. *Room and board per academic year:* $5,520. *books and supplies:* $1,000. *Other expenses:* $1,450.

Financial Aid: Aid from institutionally generated funds is provided on the basis of academic merit, financial need, other criteria.

Financial aid to full-time, first-time undergraduate students: 840% received some form of financial aid. Average amount of aid received: federal grants $4,428; Pell grants $3,801; other federal aid $1,059; state/local grants $4,751; institutional grants $2,563.

Departments and Teaching Staff: *Total instructional faculty:* 52 (full-time 51, part-time 1). Total faculty with doctorate, first-professional, or other terminal degree 30.Student/faculty ratio: 15:1. Degrees held by full-time faculty: doctorate 58%, master's 100%, professional 7%. 63% hold terminal degrees.

Enrollment: Total enrollment 1,981. Undergraduate 1,981 (full-time 98%; female 52%, male 48%). Transfer-in students 120.

Characteristics of Student Body: *Ethnic/racial makeup:* Black non-Hispanic: 99%; unknown 1%.

LANE COLLEGE—*cont'd*

International Students: No programs available to aid students whose native language is not English. No financial aid specifically designated for international students.

Student Life: On-campus residence halls house 85% of student body.

Library Collections: 115,000 volumes including bound books, serial backfiles, electronic documents, and government documents not in separate collections. Online catalog. Current serial subscriptions: 260 paper, 59 microform, 210 via electronic access. Computer work stations available. Students have access to the Internet at no charge.

Most important special holdings include Negro Heritage Collection; Childrens Literature Collection; curriculum library.

Chief Executive Officer: Dr. Wesley Cornelius McClure, President.

Address admission inquiries to Kelly Boyd, Director of Admissions.

Lee University

120 North Ocoee Street
P.O. Box 3450
Cleveland, Tennessee 37320-3450
Tel: (423) 614-8500 **E-mail:** admissions@leeuniversity.edu
Fax: (423) 614-8533 **Internet:** www.leeuniversity.edu

Institution Description: Lee University, formerly Lee College, is a private college affiliated with the Church of God. *Enrollment:* 4,147. *Degrees awarded:* Baccalaureate, master's.

Accreditation: *Regional:* SACS-Comm. on Coll.

History: Established in Cleveland as Bible Training School 1918; purchased Murphy Collegiate Institute and moved to Sevierville 1938; offered first instruction at postsecondary level 1941; returned to Cleveland and became Lee College 1947; chartered 1950; became 4-year Bible college 1953; awarded first degree (baccalaureate) 1958; initiated liberal arts curriculum 1968; achieved university status 1997.

Institutional Structure: *Governing board:* Board of Directors. Representation: 13 directors. 1 ex officio. All voting. *Composition of institution:* Administrators 8. Academic affairs headed by dean of the college. Management/business/finances directed by director of business and finance. Full-time instructional faculty 158. Academic governance body, Academic Council, meets weekly.

Calendar: Semesters. Academic year Sept. to May. Freshmen admitted Sept., Jan., June, July. Degrees conferred and formal commencement May, Aug. Summer session of 2 terms from June to Aug.

Characteristics of Freshmen: 1,674 applicants (975 female, 679 male). 67% of applicants accepted. 52% of accepted applicants enrolled.

46% (371 students) submitted SAT scores; 75% (608 students) submitted ACT scores. *25th percentile*: SAT Critical Reading 570, SAT Math 450; ACT Composite 20, ACT English 20, ACT M8th 17. *75th percentile*: SAT Critical Reading 600, SAT Math 600; ACT Composite 27, ACT English 28, ACT Math 25.

47% of freshmen expected to graduate within 5 years. 36% of freshmen from Tennessee. Freshmen from 48 states and 42 foreign countries.

Admission: Rolling admissions plan. Early acceptance available. *Requirements:* Either graduation from accredited secondary school or GED. Minimum 3.5 GPA. *Entrance tests:* ACT Composite. For foreign students TOEFL. *For transfer students:* 2.0 minimum GPA; from 4-year accredited institution 100 semester hours maximum transfer credit; from 2-year accredited institution 70 semester hours.

College credit and advanced placement for postsecondary-level work completed in secondary school and for extrainstitutional learning (life experience) on basis of USAFI. Tutoring available. Developmental courses offered during regular academic year; credit given.

Degree Requirements: 130 credit hours; 2.0 GPA; 30 hours in residence; chapel attendance 3 times weekly; 4 semester hours physical education; core courses in religion; general education requirements.

Fulfillment of some degree requirements and exemption from some beginning courses possible by passing departmental examinations, College Board CLEP, AP. *Grading system:* A–F; pass-fail; withdraw (carries time limit).

Distinctive Educational Programs: Facilities for independent research, including honors programs, independent study. Study abroad by individual arrangement. *Other distinctive programs:* Degree-granting continuing education program prepares students for ministries in the church. Lee houses the Pentecostal Research Center.

Degrees Conferred: 577 *baccalaureate*; 121 *master's*. Bachelor's degrees awarded in top five disciplines: education 130; theology and religious vocations 102; business/marketing 81; psychology 531 communications/journalism 50. Master's degrees awarded: education 82; psychology 27; theology and religious vocations 8; visual and performing arts 3.

Fees and Other Expenses: *Full-time tuition per academic year 2008–09:* $11,314. *Room and board per academic year:* $5,880. *Required fees:* $370. *Books and supplies:* $900. *Other expenses:* $2,906.

Financial Aid: Aid from institutionally generated funds is provided on the basis of academic merit, financial need, athletic ability, music performance.

Financial aid to full-time, first-time undergraduate students: 91% received some form of aid. Average amount of aid received: federal grants $3,643; Pell grants $3,045; other federal aid $850; state/local grants $4,872; institutional grants $7,051.

Departments and Teaching Staff: *Total instructional faculty:* 320 (full-time 158, part-time 162). Student/faculty ratio: 17:1. Degrees held by full-time faculty: doctorate 33%, master's 33%. 50% hold terminal degrees.

Enrollment: Total enrollment 4,147. Undergraduate 3,447 (full-time 87%; female 56%, male 44%). Graduate 300 (full-time 38%). Undergraduate transfer-in students 266.

Characteristics of Student Body: *Ethnic/racial makeup:* Black non-Hispanic: 4%; Asian or Pacific Islander: 1%; Hispanic: 3%; White non-Hispanic: 80%; unknown: 5%; nonresident alien 5%.

International Students: 205 nonresident aliens enrolled fall 2008. Students from Europe, Asia, Latin America, Africa, Canada, New Zealand, Middle East. Programs available to aid students whose native language is not English: English as a Second Language Program. No financial aid specifically designated for international students.

Student Life: On-campus residence halls house 62% of student body. Residence halls for males constitute 44% of such space, for females 56%. Off-campus institutional housing available for married students. 20% of married students request institutional housing; 13% are so housed. *Intercollegiate athletics:* male: basketball, soccer; female: basketball, softball; both sexes: tennis, golf. *Special regulations:* Registered cars permitted in designated areas. Modest dress is required. Curfew begins 11pm Sun.–Thurs., 1am Fri. and Sat. Quiet hours from 7pm to 8am Mon.–Fri. Residence hall visitation from 8am to 11pm. *Special services:* Learning Resources Center, medical services. *Student publications: Collegian*, a student newspaper; *Vindagua*, a yearbook; *What's Happening*, a weekly with news and announcements. *Surrounding community:* Cleveland population 26,000. Atlanta (GA), 130 miles from campus, is nearest metropolitan area. Served by airport 30 miles from campus.

Library Collections: 158,000 volumes. 52,000 microforms; 2,000 audiovidual materials; 28,300 periodicals including via electronic access. catalog. Students have access to online information retrieval services and the Internet.

Pentecostal Collection is the most important special collection.

Buildings and Grounds: Campus area 20 acres.

Chief Executive Officer: Dr. Charles Paul Conn, President.

Address admission inquiries to Phil Cook, Director of Admissions.

LeMoyne-Owen College

807 Walker Avenue
Memphis, Tennessee 38126
Tel: (901) 774-9090 **E-mail:** admissions@loc.edu
Fax: (901) 942-3572 **Internet:** www.loc.edu

Institution Description: LeMoyne-Owen College is a private college affiliated with the United Church of Christ and the Tennessee Baptist Convention. *Enrollment:* 893. *Degrees awarded:* Baccalaureate.

Member of the Greater Memphis Consortium.

Accreditation: *Regional:* SACS-Comm. on Coll.

History: Established as LeMoyne Normal and Commercial School 1871; offered first instruction at postsecondary level 1924; became 4-year institution 1930; awarded first degree (baccalaureate) 1932; changed name to LeMoyne College 1934; merged with Owen College (established 1946) and adopted present name 1968. *See* Margaret C. McCulloch, *Fearless Advocate of the Right* (Boston: The Christopher Publishing House, 1941) for further information.

Institutional Structure: *Governing board:* LeMoyne-Owen College Board of Trustees. Representation: 45 trustees, 5 emeritus, 12 alumni (regular and emeritus). The 45 regular trustees vote. *Composition of institution:* Administrators 29. Academic affairs headed by provost. Management/business/finances directed by chief financial officer/treasurer. Student affairs headed by dean of students. Development headed by chief advancement officer. Full-time instructional faculty 54. Academic governance body, Academic Council, meets an average of 12 times per year.

Calendar: Semesters. Academic year Sept. to May. Freshmen admitted Sept., Jan., May. Degrees conferred and formal commencement May.

Characteristics of Freshmen: 446 applicants (290 female, 156 male). 48% of applicants accepted. 36% of accepted applicants enrolled.

3% (3 students) submitted SAT scores; 45% (40 students) submitted ACT scores. *25th percentile*: SAT Critical Reading 325, SAT Math 350; ACT Composite 12. *75th percentile*: SAT Critical Reading 350, SAT Math 350; ACT Composite 20.

89% of freshmen from Tennessee. Freshmen from 15 states and 4 foreign countries.

Admission: Rolling admissions plan. For fall acceptance, apply as early as 1 year prior to enrollment, but not later than Apr. 15 of year of enrollment. *Requirements:* Either graduation from accredited secondary school with 21 units or GED. Recommend 4 units English, 3 mathematics, 3 science, 3 social studies, 1 lifetime wellness, 2 foreign language, 1 fine arts, 4 electives. *Entrance tests:* College Board ACT (preferably) or SAT. *For transfer students:* 2.0 minimum GPA; maximum transfer credit limited only by residence requirement.

College credit and advanced placement for postsecondary-level work completed in secondary school.

Tutoring available. Developmental and remedial courses offered in summer session and regular academic year; credit given.

Degree Requirements: 120 credit hours; 2.0 GPA; 2 terms in residence; 2 physical education courses; general education requirement; 3 terms cooperative education. Fulfillment of some degree requirements and exemption from some beginning courses possible by passing departmental examinations, College Board CLEP, AP. *Grading system:* A–F; pass-fail; withdraw (deadline after which pass-fail is appended to withdraw).

Distinctive Educational Programs: The Freshman Seminar. The Service Learning Program. TRIO Programs. The Cooperative Education/Internships. International Studies Program. Dual degree programs and collaborative programs. Dual degree programs in pharmacy with Xavier University; in optometry with Southern College of Optometry; in engineering with Christian Brothers University in Memphis, Tuskegee University (AL), and Southern Illinois University in Carbondale; in mass communication with Rust College. Interdepartmental/interdisciplinary programs in art, humanities, philosophy, and religion. Facilities and programs for independent research, including honors programs, independent study. Study abroad in Israel, Great Britain, France, Spain, Japan, South Africa, Zimbabwe. Off-campus study in the U.S. includes Washington (DC) semester at American University. Cross-registration through consortium. *Other distinctive programs:* Humanities enrichment program for position of leadership and management in voluntary not-for-profit youth and human services.

ROTC: Students can participate in either Air Force, Army, or Navy crosstown programs based at the University of Memphis.

Degrees Conferred: 100 *baccalaureate*. Bachelor's degrees awarded in top five disciplines: business, management, marketing, and related support services 38; education 31; security and protective services 16; biological/life sciences 12; social sciences 12.

Fees and Other Expenses: *Full-time tuition per academic year 2008–09:* $10,298. *Required fees:* $200. *Room and board per academic year:* $4,852. *Books and supplies:* $1,200. *Other expenses:* $750.

Financial Aid: Aid from institutionally generated funds is provided on the basis of financial need.

Financial aid to full-time, first-time undergraduate students: 100% received some form of aid.

Departments and Teaching Staff: *Total instructional faculty:* 72 (full-time 54, part-time 18), Student/faculty ratio: 15:1. Degrees held by full-time faculty: doctorate 56%, master's 44%.

Enrollment: Total enrollment 893. Undergradudate 893 (full-time 85%; female 66%, male 34%). Transfer-in students 84.

Characteristics of Student Body: *Ethnic/racial makeup:* Black non-Hispanic: 99%; unknown 1%. *Age distribution:* number under 18: 2; 18–19: 153; 20–21: 170; 22–24: 142; 25–29: 123; 30–34: 74; 35–39: 45; 40–49: 61; 50–64: 29.

International Students: No programs available to aid students whose native language is not English. Financial aid specifically designated for international students: special scholarships available to qualifying students; variable number annually.

Student Life: On-campus housing. 16% of student body live in campus housing. *Intercollegiate athletics:* male: baseball, basketball, cross-country, golf, tennis; female: basketball, cross-country, golf, softball, tennis, volleyball. *Special regulations:* Cars permitted in designated areas; fee charged. *Special services:* Academic Skills Center, medical services, swimming pool, weight room, game room, outdoor track, tennis court, basketball facilities. All recognized black Panhellenic sororities and fraternities. *Student publications: The Magician*, a monthly newspaper; *The Observer*, a bimonthly newsletter. *Surrounding community:* Memphis and Shelby County population approximately 800,000. Served by mass transit bus system; airport 10 miles from campus; passenger rail service 5 miles from campus.

Publications: *The Beacon* , a magazine published 3 times per year.

Library Collections: 95,000 volumes. 7,000 microforms; 4,800 audiovisual materials; 276 current periodical subscriptions. Computer work stations available. Card Catalog. Students have access to the Internet at no charge.

Most important special holdings include the Sweeney Collection (more than 4,000 books by Black authors about Black history and culture).

Chief Executive Officer: Dr. Johnnie B. Watson, President.

Address admission inquiries to Director of Admissions.

Lincoln Memorial University

6965 Cumberland Gap Parkway
Harrogate, Tennessee 37752

Tel: (423) 869-3611 **E-mail:** admissions@lmunet.edu
Fax: (423) 869-6250 **Internet:** www.lmunet.edu

Institution Description: Lincoln Memorial University is a private, independent, nonprofit institution offering undergraduate and graduate degrees in the fine arts and selected professional areas. *Enrollment:* 3,365. *Degrees awarded:* Associate, baccalaureate, master's. Educational specialist also awarded.

Accreditation: *Regional:* SACS-Comm. on Coll. *Professional*: clinical lab scientist, veterinary technology

History: Established and chartered 1897; offered first instruction at postsecondary level 1899; awarded first degree (baccalaureate) 1906.

Institutional Structure: *Governing board:* Board of Trustees. The university is owned and controlled by an independent,self-perpetuating Board of Trustees. *Composition of institution:* The president appoints vice presidents of the administrative and academic units who supervise their operation. Academic affairs headed by the vice president and dean of the faculty. Business/finance is directed by the senior vice president for finance. Full-time faculty 86.

Calendar: Semesters. Academic year Aug. to May. Formal commencement May. Summer session of 2 terms from early June to early Aug.

Characteristics of Freshmen: 1,080 applicants (736 female, 344 male). 69% of applicants admitted. 44% of applicants admitted and enrolled.

13% (33 students) submitted SAT scores; 68% (177 students) submitted ACT scores. *25th percentile*: SAT Critical Reading 450, SAT Math 450; ACT Composite 18, ACT English 18, ACT Math 16. *75th percentile*: SAT Critical Reading 560, SAT Math 540; ACT Composite 23, ACT English 24, ACT Math 22.

51% of entering freshmen expected to graduate within 5 years. 67% of freshmen from Tennessee. Freshmen from 25 states and 23 foreign countries.

Admission: Rolling admissions plan. *Requirements:* Either graduation from accredited or state-approved high school with 4 units English, 2 natural/physical sciences, 1 social studies, 1 U.S. history; minimum GPA of 2.3; or GED. *Entrance test:* ACT or SAT. TOEFL required for international students. *For transfer students:* 2.0 minimum GPA; from 2-year accredited institution 68 semester hours transfer credit.

College credit for extrainstitutional learning (life experience) on basis of portfolio and faculty assessments.

Tutoring is available in most academic areas.

Degree Requirements: *For all associate degrees:* 64–75 semester hours. *For all baccalaureate degrees:* 128 semester hours. *For all degrees:* 2.0 GPA; 30 hours in residence; 2 hours physical education courses; general education requirement.

Fulfillment of some degree requirements and exemption from some beginning courses possible by passing College Board CLEP. *Grading system:* A–F; pass-no credit; incomplete (carries time limit).

Distinctive Educational Programs: Internships in selected fields of study. Off-campus graduate and undergraduate centers within the tri-state area. Programs in medical technology, environmental science, athletic training, and veterinary technology with excellent facilities.

Degrees Conferred: 139 *associate;* 140 *baccalaureate:* biological sciences 5; business and management 42; communications 7; computer and information sciences 1; education 44; English 6; health professions 9; mathematics 4; natural resources/environmental science 13; parks and recreation 17; psychology 4; social sciences and history 18; visual and performing arts 2. 216 *master's:* business 16; education 144; 721 *educational specialist.*

Fees and Other Expenses: *Full-time tuition per academic year 2008–09:* $15,720 undergraduate; contact the university for current graduate tuition. *Books and supplies:* $1,200. *Room and board per academic year:* $7,051. *Other expenses:* $4,310.

Financial Aid: Aid from institutionally generated funds is provided on the basis of academic merit, financial need, athletic ability. Institution has a Program Participation Agreement with the U.S. Department of Education for eligible students to receive Pell Grants and, depending upon the agreement, other federal aid.

Financial aid to full-time, first-time undergraduate students: 100 received some form of financial aid. Average amount of aid received: federal grants

LINCOLN MEMORIAL UNIVERSITY—*cont'd*

$4,153; Pell grants $3,270; other federal aid $1,200; state/local grants $5,594; institutional grants $7,315.

Departments and Teaching Staff: *Total instructional faculty:* 159 (full-time 103, part-time 56). Total faculty with doctorate, first-professional, or other terminal degree: 108. Student/faculty ratio: 18:1. Degrees held by full-time faculty: doctorate 55%, master's 41%, baccalaureate 4%. 55% hold terminal degrees.

Enrollment: Total enrollment 3,365. Undergraduate 1,429 (full-time 81%; female 69%, male 31%). Graduate 1,936 (full-time 30%). Undergraduate transfer-in students 194.

Characteristics of Student Body: *Ethnic/racial makeup:* Black non-Hispanic: 4%; Asian or Pacific Islander: 1%; Hispanic: 1%; White non-Hispanic: 83%; unknown: 7%; nonresident alien 4%. *Age distribution:* number under 18: 13; 18–19: 240; 20–21: 247; 22–24: 227; 25–29: 160; 30–34: 141; 35–39: 89; 40–49: 91; 50–64: 18; 65 and over: 2.

International Students: 132 nonresident aliens enrolled fall 2008. Programs available to aid students whose native language is not English: social, cultural. English as a Second Language Program. No financial aid specifically designated for international students.

Student Life: On-campus housing available. Housing available for married students. *Intercollegiate athletics:* male: baseball, basketball, cross-country, golf, soccer, tennis; female: basketball, cross-country, softball, tennis, volleyball. *Special regulations:* Registered cars permitted without restrictions. *Publications: Railsplitter,* a yearbook; *Blue and Gray,* a newspaper. *Surrounding community:* Harrogate is unincorporated and located in Claiborne County, population 27,000. Knoxville, 50 miles from campus, is nearest metropolitan area.

Library Collections: 200,000 volumes including bound books, serial backfiles, electronic documents, and government documents not in separate collections. 160,000 microforms; 300 audiovisual materials; 900 current serial subscriptions. Students have access to the Internet at no charge.

Most important special holdings include Abraham Lincoln Collection; Jesse Stuart Collection; personal papers of Cassius Clay, Gen. O.O. Howard, and John Warden.

Chief Executive Officer: Dr. Nancy B. Moody, President.

Address admission inquiries to Conrad Daniels, Dean of Admissions.

Lipscomb University

3901 Granny White Pike
Nashville, Tennessee 37204-3951
Tel: (615) 269-1000 **E-mail:** admissions@lipscomb.edu
Fax: (615) 269-1804 **Internet:** www.lipscomb.edu

Institution Description: Lipscomb University, formerly named David Lipscomb University, is a private institution affiliated with the Churches of Christ. *Enrollment:* 3,073. *Degrees awarded:* Baccalaureate, master's.

Accreditation: *Regional:* SACS-Comm. on Coll. *Professional*: business, chemistry, dietetics, engineering, music, teacher education, social work

History: Established as Nashville Bible School and offered first instruction at postsecondary level 1891; incorporated 1901; adopted present name 1918; became 4-year college 1947; awarded first degree (baccalaureate) 1948.

Institutional Structure: *Governing board:* Board of Directors. Extrainstitutional representation: 26 directors; institutional representation: 4 administrators; 12 alumni; 1 ex officio. *Composition of institution:* Administrators 8. Academic affairs headed by provost. Management/business/finances directed by Vice President for Business Affairs. Full-time instructional faculty 96. Academic governance body, Academic Affairs Committee, meets an average of 25 times per year.

Calendar: Semesters. Academic year Aug. to May. Freshmen admitted Aug., Jan., May. Degrees conferred and formal commencements May, Dec. Summer session of two 5-week terms and one 10-week session.

Characteristics of Freshmen: 2,028 applicants (1,195 female, 833 male). 74% of applicants accepted. 48% of accepted applicants enrolled.

35% (202 students) submitted SAT scores; 85% (487 students) submitted ACT scores. *25th percentile*: SAT Critical Reading 500, SAT Math 500, SAT Writing 490; ACT Composite 21, ACT English 21, ACT Math 20. *75th percentile*: SAT Critical Reading 620, SAT Math 600, SAT Writing 600; ACT Composite 27, ACT English 29, ACT Math 26.

Admission: Rolling admission plan. For fall acceptance, apply as early as the end of the junior year in secondary school. Early acceptance available. *Requirements:* Applicants must meet at least two of the following three criteria for unconditional admission: (1) a high school GPA of 2.25 on a 4.0 scale; (2) a minimum of 12 academic units of high school credit; these credits must consist of 4 units of English, 2 units of mathematics (preferably algebra I, II), 2 units of natural science, 2 units of history/social science, and 2 academic electives (selected from natural sciences, mathematics, foreign languages or social sciences); (3) a composite score of 19 or more on the ACT or a total score of 810 or more on the SAT. This testing should be done no later than the end of the senior year of high school; the requirement may be waived is the applicant has been graduated from high school for five years or more. Conditional admission is granted to the select applicants who do not qualify for unconditional admission. Students admitted on this basis are admitted on the condition that they meet certain requirements in their first year at Lipscomb. The specific requirements for each student will be based on that student's need as determined by the Student Development Services staff. *Entrance tests:* SAT or ACT composite. *For transfer students:* 2.0 minimum GPA; from 4-year accredited institution 102 semester hours maximum transfer credit; from 2-year accredited institution 68 semester hours; correspondence (one course)/ extension combined hours 20 semester hour maximum. Transfer students must be eligible to return to last institution attended.

College credit for postsecondary-level work completed in secondary school if validated by standardized test, and for extrainstitutional learning on basis of faculty assessment. Evidence of good health and moral character are also expected. Advanced Placement (AP) and CLEP credit are accepted.

Noncredit remedial courses offered. Tutoring available.

Degree Requirements: 132 semester hours; 2.0 GPA; last 30 hours in residence; daily chapel attendance; daily Bible class; 2 activity courses in physical education; general education requirements. Additional requirements for teacher education program.

Fulfillment of some degree requirements and exemption from some beginning courses possible by passing departmental examinations. Fulfillment of some degree requirements also possible by passing College Board CLEP, AP. *Grading system:* A–F; pass-fail; withdraw (deadline after which pass-fail is appended to withdraw). Deadline for withdrawing from course enforced.

Distinctive Educational Programs: Dual-degree programs in engineering with Auburn University (AL), Georgia Institute of Technology, Tennessee Technological University, University of Tennessee at Knoxville, Vanderbilt University. Interdisciplinary programs in American studies, business management-chemistry, fashion merchandising, food services, government and public administration, health-physics, history-communication, political science-communication, urban studies. Preprofessional programs in dentistry, engineering, law, medical technology, medicine, nursing, pharmacy, veterinary medicine.

ROTC: Army offered in cooperation with Vanderbilt University; Air Force with Tennessee State University.

Degrees Conferred: 443 *baccalaureate*; 68 *master's.* Bachelor's degrees awarded in top five disciplines: business, management, marketing, and related support services 160; education 50; psychology 45; biological/sciences 34; communication, journalism, and related programs 24. *Master's* business and management 31; education 27; philosophy/religion/theology 16. *First-professional:* master of divinity 7.

Fees and Other Expenses: *Full-time tuition per academic year 2008–09:* $18,580. *Books and supplies:* $1,000. *Room and board per academic year:* $7,200. *Other expenses:* $2,500.

Financial Aid: Aid from institutionally generated funds is provided on the basis of academic merit, financial need, athletic ability, other criteria.

96% of full-time, first-time undergraduate students received some form of aid. Average amount of aid received: federal grants $3,551; Pell grants $3,053; other federal aid $697; state/local grants $4,806; institutional grants $6,994.

Departments and Teaching Staff: *Total instructional faculty:* 194 (full-time 116, part-time 78). Total faculty with doctorate, first-professional, or other terminal degree: 104. Student/faculty ratio: 13:

Enrollment: Total enrollment 3,073. Undergraduate 2,439 (full-time 92%; female 57%, male 43%). Graduate 634 (full-time 64%). Undergraduate transfer-in students 106.

Characteristics of Student Body: *Ethnic/racial makeup:* Black non-Hispanic: 5%; Asian or Pacific Islander: 2%; Hispanic: 3%; White non-Hispanic: 83%; unknown: 4%; nonresident alien 2%. *Age distribution:* number under 18: 37; 18–19: 893; 20–21: 854; 22–24: 356; 25–29: 70; 30–34: 33; 35–39: 27; 40–49: 23; 50–64: 11; 65 and over: 1.

International Students: 62 nonresident aliens enrolled fall 2008. No programs available to aid students whose native language is not English. Financial aid specifically designated for international students: Varying number of scholarships available annually.

Student Life: On-campus residence halls house 62% of student body. Residence halls for males constitute 40% of such space, for females 60%. *Intercollegiate athletics:* male: baseball, basketball, cross-country, golf, soccer, tennis; female: basketball, cross-country, golf, soccer, softball, tennis, track and field (indoor and outdoor), volleyball. *Special regulations:* Registered cars with decals permitted. Dress must be modest and appropriate. Curfews from midnight to 6am Fri.–Sun. *Student publications: The Babbler,* a biweekly newspaper; *The Backlog*, a yearbook. *Surrounding community:* Nashville-Davidson population 500,000. Served by mass transit bus system; airport 8 miles from campus.

Library Collections: 255,500 volumes. 46,000 microforms; 6,800 audiovisual materials; 1,000 current periodical subscriptions. Online catalog. Students have access to online information retrieval services and the Internet.

Most important special holdings include Bailey Hymnology Collection; C.E.W. Dorris Collection; Herald of Truth Videotapes.

Buildings and Grounds: Campus area 65 acres.

Chief Executive Officer: Dr. Stephen Flatt, President.

Address admission inquiries to Director of Admissions.

Martin Methodist College

433 West Madison Street
Pulaski, Tennessee 38478-2799
Tel: (931) 363-9804 **E-mail:** admit@martinmethodist.edu
Fax: (931) 363-9818 **Internet:** www.martinmethodist.edu

Institution Description: Martin Methodist College is a four-year coeducational, United Methodist-related institution. *Enrollment:* 953. *Degrees awarded:* Associate, baccalaureate.

Accreditation: *Regional:* SACS-Comm. on Coll. *Professional*: business, English language education, teacher education

History: Established 1870 as a four-year boarding college for women with an elementary division for young people; became coeducational 1938; became a four-year institution 1993.

Institutional Structure: *Governing board:* Martin Methodist College Board of Trustees. *Composition of institution:* Administrators 8. Full-time instructional faculty 25.

Calendar: Semesters. Academic year Sept. to May; for Evening Classes Aug. to June. Degrees conferred and formal commencement May. Evening College commencement June.

Characteristics of Freshmen: 554 applicants (321 female, 233 male). 100% of applicants accepted. 98% of accepted applicants enrolled.

Mean ACT Composite score 19.92.

40% of entering freshmen expected to graduate within 5 years. 84% of freshmen from Tennessee. Freshmen from 8 states and 7 foreign countries.

Admission: Rolling admissions. For fall acceptance, apply as early as the beginning of senior year in high school. *Requirements:* Graduation from high school or successful completion of the high school level GED test. Student must have two of the following three: composite score of 18 or above on the ACT or 750 or above on the combined SAT; 2.00 or above GPA in high school work OR graduation in the top 50th percentile. *For transfer students:* 2.00 or above GPA.

Degree Requirements: *For all associate degrees:* 62 hours with at least 32 semester hours at Martin. *For baccalaureate degrees:* minimum of 132 hours with at least 36 hours earned at Martin and the completion of departmental requirements in the program of concentration with a 2.0 GPA or higher. *Grading system:* A–F; pass-fail; withdraw (carries time limit).

Distinctive Educational Programs: Evening, summer, and daytime programs for adult students.

Degrees Conferred: 15 *associate*; 105 *baccalaureate*. Bachelor's degrees awarded in top five disciplines: business, management, marketing, and related support services 49; psychology 18; education 13; public administration 12; English language/literature 7.

Fees and Other Expenses: *Full-time tuition per academic year 2008–09:* $17,626. *Books and supplies:* $1,000. *Room and board per academic year:* $6,100. *Other expenses:* 42,500.

Financial Aid: Aid from institutionally generated funds is provided on the basis of academic merit, financial need, athletic ability, other criteria.

Financial aid to full-time, first-time undergraduate students: 95% received some form of financial aid. Average amount of aid received: federal grants $3,660; state/local grants $2,356; institutional grants $7,747; loans $3,217.

Departments and Teaching Staff: *Total instructional faculty:* 52. Student/faculty ratio: 18:1. Degrees held by full-time faculty: doctorate 45%, master's 55%. 45% hold terminal degrees.

Enrollment: Total enrollment 953. Undergraduate 953 (full-time 83%; female 61%, male 39%). Transfer-in students 61.

Characteristics of Student Body: *Ethnic/racial makeup:* Black non-Hispanic: 12%; White non-Hispanic: 80%; nonresident alien 7%.

International Students: 63 nonresident aliens enrolled fall 2008. Programs available to aid students whose native language is not English: English as Second Language Program. No financial aid specifically designated for international students.

Student Life: On-campus residence halls house 35% of student body. Traditional-style halls for each sex constitute 100% of such space. Cars permitted without restrictions. *Student publications: Marinaier*, a yearbook. Clubs and organizations including co-curricular, student government, creative, and performing arts, special interests groups. *Surrounding community:* Pulaski, population 7,500. Nashville is approximately 1 hour north of Pulaski and Huntsville is 1 hour south.

Library Collections: 82,500 volumes including bound books, serial backfiles, electronic documents, and government documents not in separate collections. Online catalog. Current serial subscriptions: 50 paper, 200 microform, 2 electronic. 500 recordings; 50 compact discs; 50 CD-ROMs. computer work stations available. Students have access to the Internet at no charge.

Most important special collections include Methodist Reference and Rare Books; local history; Gregory McDonald manuscripts.

Chief Executive Officer: Dr. Ted R. Brown, President.

Address admissions inquiries to Director of Admissions.

Maryville College

502 East Lamar Alexander Parkway
Maryville, Tennessee 37804-5907
Tel: (865) 981-8000 **E-mail:** info@maryvillecollege.edu
Fax: (865) 981-5907 **Internet:** www.maryvillecollege.edu

Institution Description: Maryville College is a private college affiliated with the Presbyterian Church (U.S.A.). *Enrollment:* 1,114. *Degrees awarded:* Baccalaureate.

Accreditation: *Regional:* SACS-Comm. on Coll. *Professional*: music

History: Established as The Southern and Western Theological Seminary 1819; offered first instruction at postsecondary level 1821; chartered and adopted present name 1842; awarded first degree (baccalaureate) 1825. *See* Ralph Waldo Lloyd, *Maryville College: A History of 150 Years—1819–1969* (Maryville: The Maryville College Press, 1969) and Carolyn Blair and Arda Walker, *By Faith Endowed: The Story of Maryville College 1819–1994* (Maryville: The Maryville College Press, 1994) for further information.

Institutional Structure: *Governing board:* Maryville College Board of Directors. Extrainstitutional representation: 36 directors; institutional representation: president of the college. 1 ex officio. 36 voting. *Composition of institution:* Principle administrative officers 57. Vice Presidents for academic affairs, admissions and enrollment, business affairs, development, student development. Elected faculty chair. Full-time instructional faculty 53. Academic governance body, Academic Life Council, meets an average of 12 times per year.

Calendar: 4-1-4 plan. Academic year Sept. to May. Freshmen admitted Sept., Jan., Feb., June. Degrees conferred at end of each term. Formal commencement May. Summer sessions May to July.

Characteristics of Freshmen: 1,624 applicants (782 female, 839 male). 78% of applicants accepted. 30% of accepted applicants enrolled.

40% (118 students) submitted SAT scores; 91% (270 students) submitted ACT scores. *25th percentile*: SAT Critical Reading 490, SAT Math 480, SAT Writing 470; ACT Composite 22, ACT English 21, ACT Math 20. *75th percentile*: SAT Critical Reading 600, SAT Math 610, SAT Writing 610; ACT Composite 28, ACT English 28, ACT Math 26.

49% of entering freshmen expected to graduate within 5 years. 66% of freshmen from Tennessee. Freshmen from 19 states and 3 foreign countries.

Admission: Rolling admissions plan. Application deadlines: Early decision Nov. 15, scholarship candidates Jan. 15, regular application Mar. 1, transfer students Apr. 15. *Requirements:* High school graduates must have satisfactorily completed at least 15 academic units including 4 English, 2 science (including 1 of laboratory science), 3 mathematics (including 1 year of algebra and 2 above algebra I). Home schooled students, those with a GED, and international students are evaluated on the basis of a portfolio. Transfer students: minimum 2.5 GPA required.

College credit and advanced placement for postsecondary-level work completed in secondary school. For extrainstitutional learning college credit on basis of portfolio and faculty assessment.

Tutoring available. Noncredit developmental/remedial courses offered during regular academic year.

Degree Requirements: 128 semester hours; 2.00 GPA; 45 hours in residence; distribution requirements; exit competency examination in writing; comprehensives in individual fields of study; research paper required of all students (senior thesis).

Fulfillment of some degree requirements and exemption from some beginning courses possible by passing College Board CLEP, AP. *Grading system:* A–F; pass-fail; withdraw (carries time limit); incomplete (carries time limit).

Distinctive Educational Programs: The centerpiece of a Maryville education is the general education curriculum, the common set of courses for all students. Features of the curriculum include a series of courses designed for freshmen only, an emphasis on interdisciplinary coursework and attention to values and ethical decision-making across the curriculum. All students complete senior theses. Comprehensive examinations in the discipline, experiential education, internships, and practica. Study abroad is encouraged and the college maintains direct exchange programs with 10 overseas institutions (England, France, Ire-

MARYVILLE COLLEGE—*cont'd*

land, Japan, Puerto Rico). The college promotes many other study abroad opportunities through cooperative arrangements with Kalamazoo College and Alma College. Mountain Challenge Program.

Degrees Conferred: 214 *baccalaureate*. Bachelor's degrees awarded in top five disciplines: education 44; business, management, marketing, and related support services 43; psychology 25; biological/life sciences 25; social sciences 18.

Fees and Other Expenses: *Full-time tuition per academic year 2008–09:* $28,949. *Books and supplies:* $800. *Room and board per academic year:* $8,2400. *Other expenses:* $1,770.

Financial Aid: Aid from institutionally generated funds is provided on the basis of academic merit, financial need.

Financial aid to full-time, first-time undergraduate students: 100% received some form of financial aid. Average amount of aid received: federal grants $3,946; state/local grants $1,297; institutional grants $13,385; loans $5,957.

Departments and Teaching Staff: *Total instructional faculty:* 58. Student/faculty ratio: 13:1. Degrees held by full-time faculty: baccalaureate 100%, master's 19%, doctorate 81%. 87% hold terminal degrees.

Enrollment: Total enrollment 1,114 (undergraduate).

Characteristics of Student Body: *Ethnic/racial makeup:* Black non-Hispanic: 5%; Asian or Pacific Islander: 1%; Hispanic: 2%; White non-Hispanic: 86%, unknown: 1%; nonresident alien 4%.

International Students: 11 nonresident aliens enrolled fall 2008. Students from Europe, Asia, Latin America, Africa, Canada. Programs available to aid students whose native language is not English: social, cultural. English as a Second Language Program. Financial aid specifically designated for international students: variable number of scholarships available annually.

Student Life: On-campus residence halls house 75% of student body. Residence halls include 1 residence for females; 1 residence for males; 5 co-ed residences. *Intercollegiate athletics:* male: baseball, basketball, football, soccer; female: basketball, soccer, softball, volleyball; male and female: equestrian. Club sports: cheerleading. *Special regulations:* Cars permitted without restrictions. Residence hall visitation from 10:30am to 11pm Sun.–Thurs., 10:30am to 1am Fri. and Sat. *Special services:* On-campus clinic with nurse and campus physician. *Campus activities:* 35 student clubs and organizations; intramural sports; Student Programming Board. *Student publications: The Chilhowean*, a yearbook; *The Highland Echo*, a weekly newspaper; *Impressions*, an irregularly published poetry magazine. *Surrounding community:* Maryville population 18,500. Knoxville (TN), 15 miles from campus, is nearest metropolitan area. Served by airport 5 miles from campus.

Library Collections: 134,000 volumes including bound books, serial backfiles, electronic documents, and government documents not in separate collections. Online catalog. Current serial subscriptions: 615 paper, 180 electronic. Students have access to the Internet at no charge.

Most important holdings include 19th-century songsters/hymnbooks; Appalachian materials; Maryville College history.

Buildings and Grounds: Campus area 325 acres.

Chief Executive Officer: Dr. Gerald W. Gibson, President.

Address admission inquiries to Vice President for Admissions and Enrollment.

Meharry Medical College

1005 B. Todd Boulevard
Nashville, Tennessee 37208
Tel: (615) 327-6111 **E-mail:** admissions@mmc.edu
Fax: (615) 327-6228 **Internet:** www.mmc.edu

Institution Description: Meharry Medical College is a private, independent, nonprofit institution. *Enrollment:* 730. *Degrees awarded:* First-professional (dentistry, medicine), master's, doctorate.

Accreditation: *Regional:* SACS-Comm. on Coll. *Professional*: dental hygiene, dentistry, medicine

History: The college was founded in 1876 as the Meharry Medical Department of Central Tennessee College by the Freedmen's Aid Society of the Methodist Episcopal Church.

Institutional Structure: *Governing board:* Board of Trustees. Representation: 35 trustees. All voting. *Composition of institution:* Administrators 18. Academic affairs headed by vice president for academic affairs. Management/business/finances directed by vice president for business and finance. Full-time instructional faculty 194. Academic governance body, Academic Council, meets an average of 12 times per year.

Calendar: Semesters. Academic year Aug. to May. Students admitted Aug., June. Degrees conferred and formal commencement May. Summer session from early June to early Aug.

Admission: Rolling admissions plan. For fall acceptance, apply as early as May 1 of previous year, but not later than Jan. 2 of year of enrollment. *Requirements:* For first-professional programs, 90 semester hours from accredited institution, including 2 semesters English, 2 biology with lab, 2 each general chemistry and organic chemistry with lab, 2 physics with laboratory. Minimum GPA 2.0. For medical program, interview and MCAAT. For dental program, DAT. Minimum GPA 2.0. *For transfer students:* Transfer possible only in first 2 years. Must be in good academic standing and must have passed all courses.

Tutoring available. Noncredit developmental courses offered in summer session.

Degree Requirements: *For all first-professional degrees:* Prescribed 4-year curriculum; clinical requirement. *Grading system:* A–F.

Distinctive Educational Programs: Special facilities for using telecommunications in the classroom.

Degrees Conferred: 11 *master's:* health professions; 10 *doctorate:* biological sciences; 102 *first-professional:* dentistry 40, medicine 72.

Fees and Other Expenses: *Full-time tuition per academic year 2008–09:* contact the college for current tuition and fees for graduate and first-professional programs.

Financial Aid: *Institutional funding:* scholarships and loans available to qualifying students.

Departments and Teaching Staff: *Full-time instructional faculty:* 214.

Enrollment: Full-time enrollment 730.

Characteristics of Student Body: *Ethnic/racial makeup:* Black non-Hispanic: 79%; American Indian or Alaska Native: 1%; Asian or Pacific Islander: 7%; Hispanic: 5%; White non-Hispanic: 8%

International Students: No programs available to aid students whose native language is not English. No financial aid specifically designated for international students.

Student Life: On-campus residence halls available. *Special regulations:* Cars permitted without restrictions. *Special services:* Learning Resources Center, medical services. *Student publications: Foebia*, a newspaper; a yearbook. *Surrounding community:* Nashville population 500,000. Served by mass transit bus system; airport 10 miles from campus.

Library Collections: 90,000 volumes.

Chief Executive Officer: Dr. John E. Maupin, President.

Address admission inquiries to Director of Admissions Records.

Memphis College of Art

1940 Poplar Avenue
Overton Park 1930 Poplar Avenue
Memphis, Tennessee 38104-2764
Tel: (901) 272-5100 **E-mail:** info@mca.edu
Fax: (901) 272-5104 **Internet:** www.mca.edu

Institution Description: Memphis College of Art, formerly the Memphis Academy of Arts, is a private, independent, nonprofit institution. *Enrollment:* 404. *Degrees awarded:* Baccalaureate, master's.

Member of Greater Memphis Area Consortium.

Accreditation: *Regional:* SACS-Comm. on Coll. *Professional*: art

History: Established, chartered, and offered first instruction at postsecondary level 1936; awarded first degree (baccalaureate) 1950.

Institutional Structure: *Governing board:* Board of Trustees. Extrainstitutional representation: 25 trustees. *Composition of institution:* Administrators 6. Academic affairs headed by vice-president. Management/business/finances directed by vice-president for business affairs. Instructional faculty 24 full-time, 13 part-time. Academic governance body, the faculty, meets an average of 9 times per year.

Calendar: Semesters. Academic year Sept. to May. Freshmen admitted Aug., Jan., June. Degrees conferred May, Dec. Formal commencement May. Summer session from June to July.

Characteristics of Freshmen: 664 applicants (414 female, 250 male). 68% of applicants accepted. 13% of applicants accepted and enrolled.

8% of applicants submitted SAT scores; 92% submitted ACT scores. *25th percentile*: ACT Composite 18. *75th percentile*: ACT Composite 24.

39% of entering freshmen expected to graduate within 5 years. 45% of freshmen from Tennessee. Freshmen from 25 states and 4 foreign countries.

Admission: Rolling admissions plan. For fall acceptance, apply as early as Jan. 1 of previous year, but not later than Aug. 1 of year of enrollment. *Requirements:* Either graduation from accredited secondary school or GED. Portfolio of artwork must be submitted. *Entrance tests:* ACT composite recommended. *For transfer students:* 2.0 minimum GPA.

College credit and advanced placement for postsecondary-level work completed in secondary school and for extrainstitutional learning (life experience) on basis of portfolio and faculty assessment.

Degree Requirements: 120 semester hours; 2.0 GPA; course requirements; presentation of portfolio. *Grading system:* A–F; withdraw (deadline after which pass-fail is appended to withdraw).

Distinctive Educational Programs: Individual majors. Cross-registration through consortium.

Degrees Conferred: 53 *baccalaureate:* visual and performing arts; 6 *master's:* visual and performing arts.

Fees and Other Expenses: *Full-time tuition per academic year 2008–09:* $21,500. *Required fees:* $560. *Books and supplies:* $1,600. *Room and board per academic year:* $7,800. *Other expenses:* $2,840.

Financial Aid: Aid from institutionally generated funds is provided on the basis of academic merit, financial need, portfolio awards. Financial assistance is available in the form of Pell Grants, College Work-Study, Veterans Administration Benefits, National Direct Student Loans, Supplemental Education Opportunity Grants (SEOG), Stafford Loans, other federal aid programs.

Financial aid to full-time, first-time undergraduate students: 100% received some form of aid.

Departments and Teaching Staff: *Total instructional faculty:* 37 (full-time 24, part-time 13). Total faculty with doctorate, first-professional, or other terminal degree: 20. Student/faculty ratio: 10:1. Degrees held by full-time faculty: master's 59%, baccalaureate 100%. 59% hold terminal degrees.

Enrollment: Total enrollment 404. Undergraduate 322 (full-time 93%; female 51%, male 43%). Gradaute 82 (full-time 24%). Undergraduate transfer-in students 33.

Characteristics of Student Body: *Ethnic/racial makeup:* Black non-Hispanic: 19%; Asian or Pacific Islander: 2%; Hispanic: 3%; White non-Hispanic: 74%; nonresident alien 2%.

International Students: 8 nonresident aliens enrolled fall 2008. Students from Europe, Asia, Africa. No programs available to aid students whose native language is not English. No financial aid specifically designated for international students.

Student Life: On-campus housing; off-campus arranged by admissions office; limited on-campus housing in The Parkview and Metz Hall. Exhibitions scheduled for student work; student council-sponsored events include weekly film series, field trips, special events. *Special regulations:* Cars permitted without restriction. *Student publications: MCA Newsletter*, published 3 times yearly. *Surrounding community:* Memphis area population over 1 million. Served by airport 6 miles from campus; passenger rail service 8 miles from campus.

Library Collections: 20,000 volumes. 30,000 slides; 140 current periodical subscriptions.

Buildings and Grounds: Campus area 3 acres. *New buildings:* Metz Hall (student housing) completed 2006.

Chief Executive Officer: Jeffrey D. Nesin, President.

Address admission inquiries to Annette Moore, Director of Admissions.

Memphis Theological Seminary

168 East Parkway South
Memphis, Tennessee 38104-4395
Tel: (901) 458-8232 **E-mail:** admissions@mtscampus.edu
Fax: (901) 452-4051 **Internet:** www.mtscampus.edu

Institution Description: Memphis Theological Seminary is a related to the Cumberland Presbyterian Church and offers graduate study only. *Enrollment:* 280. *Degrees awarded:* First-professional, master's, doctorate.

Accreditation: *Regional:* SACS. *National:* ATS. *Professional*: theology

History: The seminary was founded in 1852. The purpose of the seminary is to provide graduate, professional education as preparation for persons seeking ordination to the ministry and to lay persons who want to serve in positions in the church. The seminary is owned and operated by the Cumberland Presbyterian Church and moved to its present location 1964.

Calendar: Semesters. Academic year Aug. to July. Summer term.

Admission: *Requirements:* Bachelor's degree from accredited college or university.

Degree Requirements: Completion of prescribed curriculum.

Degrees Conferred: 11 *master's:* theology; 6 *doctorate* theology; 45 *first-professional:* master of divinity.

Fees and Other Expenses: *Full-time tuition per academic year:* contact the seminary for current tuition, fees, and housing costs.

Financial Aid: Aid from institutionally generated funds is provided on the basis of academic merit, financial need. Institution has a Program Participation Agreement with the U.S. Department of Education for eligible students to receive Pell Grants and, depending upon the agreement, other federal aid.

Departments and Teaching Staff: *Total instructional faculty:* 13. Degrees held by full-time faculty: doctorate 93%, baccalaureate 100%. 77% hold terminal degrees.

Enrollment: Total enrollment 280.

Characteristics of Student Body: *Ethnic/racial makeup:* Black non-Hispanic: 33%; Asian or Pacific Islander: 1%; White non-Hispanic: 65%.

International Students: 4 nonresident aliens enrolled fall 2008. No programs available to aid students whose native language is not English. No financial aid specifically designated for international students.

Student Life: Ecumenical worship services; morning prayers daily; chapel service on Thursdays. *Surrounding community:* The seminary is located in the section of Memphis (population 650,000) called Mid-Town.

Library Collections: 82,000 volumes. 50 current periodical subscriptions.

Special collection of Martin Luther King, Jr. speeches; rare books; Black Studies Collection.

Chief Executive Officer: Dr. Timothy P. Weber, President.

Address admission inquiries to Director of Admissions.

Mid-America Baptist Theological Seminary

2216 Germantown Road, South
Germantown, Tennessee 38138
Tel: (901) 751-8453 **E-mail:** info@mabts.edu
Fax: (901) 751-8454 **Internet:** www.mabts.edu

Institution Description: Mid-America Baptist Theological Seminary is a private, independent institution. Although the institution is neither owned or controlled by, nor has any formal affiliation with the Southern Baptist Convention, the Seminary is committed to Southern Baptist churches, and the scholastic program and curriculum are geared directly to Southern Baptist churches and missions. *Enrollment:* 349. *Degrees awarded:* master's, first-professional (master of divinity), doctorate.

Accreditation: *Regional:* SACS-Comm. on Coll.

History: Established 1972; moved to new campus 1996.

Institutional Structure: *Governing board:* Board of Trustees. Representation: 8 trustees. *Composition of institution:* Administration by president and 4 vice presidents (executive vice president, vice president for academic affairs, vice president for business affairs, vice president for development and public relations). Administrative staff: 43. Full-time instructional faculty 22.

Calendar: Semesters. Academic year Aug. to May. Students admitted Aug., Oct., Jan., Mar, May, June. Graduation ceremonies Dec., May. Summer session of 2 terms from May to July.

Admission: Rolling admissions plan. Applications should be submitted at least 30 days prior to registration. *Requirements:* For associate degree program, high school diploma or equivalency certificate; for master's degree programs, baccalaureate degree from accredited college or university with 60 hours in liberal arts; for doctoral program, master of divinity degree with specified hours in Greek and Hebrew.

Degree Requirements: *For all master's degrees:* 64 credit hours. *For first-professional degree:* 96 credit hours, including Greek and Hebrew. *For doctoral degree:* Latin and German proficiency examinations; 32 credit hours of doctoral seminars; graduate colloquia dissertation, oral examination. *For all degrees:* 1.0 GPA on a 3.0 scale (minimum 2.0 GPA in doctoral program); mission assignments; personal witnessing requirements; demonstrated proficiency in English.

Advanced standing in survey courses available, based upon previous academic courses and/or examinations. *Grading system:* A–F; incomplete (with time limit); withdrawal.

Distinctive Educational Programs: Independent study. Summer missions program in the United States and abroad.

Degrees Conferred: 14 *associate of divinity*; 14 *master's:* religious education; 14 *doctorate:* philosophy/ministries. 28 *first-professional:* master of divinity.

Fees and Other Expenses: *Full-time tuition per academic year 2008*09:* contact the institution for current tuition, fees, and housing costs.

Financial Aid: Aid from institutionally generated funds is provided on the basis of academic merit, financial need. Institution has a Program Participation Agreement with the U.S. Department of Education for eligible students to receive Pell Grants and, depending upon the agreement, other federal aid.

Departments and Teaching Staff: *Total instructional faculty:* 35 (full-time 15, part-time 20). Total faculty with doctorate, first-professional, or other terminal degree: 21. Degrees held by full-time faculty: doctorate 100%.

Enrollment: Total enrollment 349.

MID-AMERICA BAPTIST THEOLOGICAL SEMINARY—*cont'd*

Characteristics of Student Body: *Ethnic/racial makeup:* number of Black non-Hispanic: 2; White non-Hispanic: 56.

International Students: No programs available to aid students whose native language is not English. No financial aid specifically designated for international students.

Student Life: Apartments are available for students. Student services office assists students with regard to housing, off-campus and on-campus employment, children's schooling, health needs. Placement Office assists students with regard to church-related vocational service. *Surrounding community:* Memphis metropolitan population over 1 million.

Publications: *Mid-America Theological Journal* published semiannually.

Library Collections: 128,000 volumes including bound books, serial backfiles, electronic documents, and government documents not in separate collections. Online catalog. Current serial subscriptions: 897 paper, 1 microform. Computer work stations available. Students have access to the Internet at no charge.

Most important special collections include Biblical studies; missions; Hebraica.

Buildings and Grounds: The seminary campus was relocated to in 1996 to a new site in Germantown, a suburb of Memphis.

Chief Executive Officer: Dr. Michael R. Spradlin, President.

Address admission inquiries to Kim Powers, Admissions Counselor.

Middle Tennessee State University

1301 East Main Street
Murfreesboro, Tennessee 37132
Tel: (615) 898-2300 **E-mail:** admissions@mtsu.edu
Fax: (615) 898-5478 **Internet:** www.mtsu.edu

Institution Description: Middle Tennessee State University is a member of the State University and Community College System. *Enrollment:* 23,872. *Degrees awarded:* Associate, baccalaureate, master's, doctorate. Specialist certificates in education also awarded.

Academic offerings subject to approval by statewide coordinating bodies. Budget subject to approval by state governing boards.

Accreditation: *Regional:* SACS-Comm. on Coll. *Professional*: aviation technology, business, chemistry, computer science, engineering technology, family and consumer science, industrial technology, interior design, journalism, music, nursing, recreation and leisure services, social work, teacher education

History: Chartered as Middle Tennessee State Normal School 1909; offered first instruction at postsecondary level 1911; changed name to Middle Tennessee State Teachers College and awarded first degree (baccalaureate) 1926; changed name to State Teachers College, Murfreesboro, 1929, to Middle Tennessee State College 1943; adopted present name 1965. *See* Homer Pittard, *The First Fifty Years* (Murfreesboro: Middle Tennessee State College, 1961) for further information.

Institutional Structure: *Governing board:* Tennessee Board of Regents (State University and Community College System of Tennessee). Representation: 17 regents, including 1 student (appointed by governor of Tennessee), governor, commissioner of education, commissioner of agriculture, executive director of Tennessee Higher Education Commission. 4 ex officio. 16 voting. *Composition of institution:* Administrators 349. Academic affairs headed by Vice President for Academic Affairs; Management/business/finances directed by Vice President for Finance and Administration; student affairs headed by Vice President for Student Affairs; public relations and development headed by Vice President for Development and University Relations. Full-time instructional faculty 708.

Calendar: Semesters. Academic year Aug. to May. Freshmen admitted Aug., Jan., May, June, July. Degrees conferred and formal commencements May, Aug., Dec. Summer session from mid-May to mid-Aug.

Characteristics of Freshmen: 9,585 applicants (5,148 female, 4,457 male). 77% of applicants accepted. 61% of accepted applicants enrolled.

12% (384 students) submitted SAT scores; 88% (3,178 students) submitted ACT scores. *25th percentile*: SAT Critical Reading 470, SAT Math 470; ACT Composite 19, ACT English 19, ACT Math 17. *75th percentile*: SAT Critical Reading 580, SAT Math 560; ACT Composite 24, ACT English 25, ACT Math 23.

39% of entering freshmen expected to graduate within 5 years. 93% of freshmen from Tennessee. Freshmen from 33 states and 20 foreign countries.

Admission: Rolling admissions plan. Apply no later than day of registration. Early acceptance available. *Requirements:* Graduation from secondary school with 2.8 GPA or ACT composite score of 20 or greater (SAT score of 950) and completion or required high school units. For candidates 18 years or older, GED (score of 45) also accepted. *Entrance tests:* For foreign students TOEFL. *For transfer students:* 2.0 minimum GPA; from 4-year accredited institution 102 semester hours maximum transfer credit; from 2-year accredited institution 72 hours; correspondence/extension students 66 hours.

College credit and advanced placement for postsecondary-level work completed in secondary school. College credit for extrainstitutional learning.

Tutoring available.

Degree Requirements: *For all associate degrees:* 65–72 credit hours; 2 semester in residence. *For all baccalaureate degrees:* 132 credit hours; 2 semesters in last 2 years, including final semester, in residence; 4 semester hours physical education; general studies requirements. Additional requirements for some programs. *For all undergraduate degrees:* 2.0 GPA.

Fulfillment of some degree requirements and exemption from some beginning courses possible by passing College Board CLEP, AP, other standardized tests. *Grading system:* A–F; pass-fail; withdraw.

Distinctive Educational Programs: Flexible meeting places and schedules, including weekend and evening classes. Dual-degree program in criminal justice with Tennessee State University; in engineering with Georgia Institute of Technology, University of Tennessee, Tennessee Technological University, University of Memphis, and Vanderbilt University. Cooperative baccalaureate in medical technology with approved hospitals. Special facilities for using telecommunications in the classroom. Interdisciplinary programs in Asian studies, Black studies, early modern European studies, environmental science and technology, aging studies, Latin American studies, medieval studies, twentieth-century European studies, urban planning. Preprofessional programs in agricultural engineering, architecture, dental hygiene, dentistry, engineering, forestry, medical record administration, medicine, nursing, pharmacy, physical therapy, radiologic technology, veterinary medicine. Programs in horse science, aerospace, historic preservation, and recording industry. Centers of Excellence in historic preservation and popular music. Honors program. *Other distinctive programs:* Continuing education courses; summer honors program for secondary school students.

ROTC: Army; Air Force in cooperation with Tennessee State University.

Degrees Conferred: 3 *associate*; 3,547 *baccalaureate*; 606 *master's*. Bachelor's degrees awarded in top five disciplines: business, management, marketing, and related support services 609; visual and performing arts 456; multidisciplinary studies 271; communication, journalism, and related programs 270; social sciences 141. Master's degrees awarded: various disciplines 606.

Fees and Other Expenses: *Full-time tuition per academic year 2008–09:* undergraduate resident $5,700, nonresident $16,592; contact the university for current graduate tuition/fees. *Room and board per academic year:* $6,453. *Books and supplies:* $1,000. *Other expenses:* $2,800.

Financial Aid: The university offers a direct lending program. Aid from institutionally generated funds is provided on the basis of academic merit, financial need, athletic ability.

Financial aid to full-time, first-time undergraduate students: 92% received some form of financial aid. Average amount of aid received: federal grants $3,394; Pell grants $3,035; other federal aid $721; state/local grants $4,434; institutional grants $3,269.

Departments and Teaching Staff: *Total instructional faculty:* 749. Student/faculty ratio: 23:1. Degrees held by full-time faculty: baccalaureate 6.6%, master's 26.5%, doctorate 65.5%, professional 1.1%. 74% hold terminal degrees.

Enrollment: Total enrollment 23,872. Undergraduate 21,252 (full-time 85%; female 52%, male 48%). Graduate 2,820 (full-time 30%). Undergraduate transfer-in students 1,935.

Characteristics of Student Body: *Ethnic/racial makeup:* Black non-Hispanic: 15%; Asian or Pacific Islander: 3%; Hispanic: 2%; White non-Hispanic: 78%; unknown: .1%; nonresident alien 1%.

International Students: 239 nonresident aliens enrolled fall 2008. Students from Europe, Asia, Latin America, Africa, Canada, Australia, New Zealand. No programs available to aid students whose native language is not English. No financial aid specifically designated for international students.

Student Life: 3,400 students reside in residence halls and apartments. 230 students reside in fraternity houses. *Intercollegiate athletics:* male: baseball, basketball, football, tennis, track; female: basketball, soccer, softball, tennis, track, volleyball. *Special regulations:* Registered cars permitted ($45 fee per year). *Special services:* Learning Resources Center, Student Health Services, Disabled Student Services, Adult Student Services, Multicultural Affairs, Women's Center. *Student publications, radio: Collage*, a biannual creative magazine; *Midlander*, a yearbook; *Sidelines*, a biweekly newspaper. Radio station WMOT-FM (public radio) and WMTS-FM (student station). *Surrounding community:* Murfreesboro population 70,000. Nashville, 30 miles from campus, is nearest metropolitan area. Served by airport and passenger rail service, each 30 miles from campus.

Library Collections: 703,000 volumes. 36,922 government documents collections; 1,300,000 microforms; 3,800 current periodical subscriptions. Computer work stations available. Students have access to online information retrieval services and the Internet.

Most important special holdings include Tennesseana; Albert Gore, Sr., Papers; Center for Popular Music.

Buildings and Grounds: Campus area 497 acres.

Chief Executive Officer: Dr. Sidney A. McFee, President.

Address admission inquiries to Lynn M. Palmer, Director of Admissions; graduate inquiries to Dr. Donald L. Curry, Dean, College of Graduate Studies.

Milligan College

Main Street
P.O. Box 50
Milligan College, Tennessee 37682
Tel: (423) 461-8700 **E-mail:** admissions@milligan.edu
Fax: (423) 461-8755 **Internet:** www.milligan.edu

Institution Description: Milligan College is a private, independent, nonprofit institution affiliated with the Christian Church (Independent). *Enrollment:* 1,018. *Degrees awarded:* Baccalaureate, master's.

Accreditation: *Regional:* SACS-Comm. on Coll. *Professional*: nursing, occupational therapy, teacher education

History: Chartered as Buffalo Male and Female Institute 1886; offered first instruction at postsecondary level and adopted present name 1881; awarded first degree (baccalaureate) 1882.

Institutional Structure: *Governing board:* Board of Trustees. Representation: 32 trustees. *Composition of institution:* Academic affairs headed by academic dean. Management/business/finances directed by senior vice-president. business manager. Full-time instructional faculty 71.

Calendar: Semesters. Academic year Aug. to May. Freshmen admitted Aug., Jan. Formal commencement May, Aug., Dec. Summer session from mid-June to mid-Aug.

Characteristics of Freshmen: 580 applicants (345 female, 235 male). 74% of applicants accepted. 32% of accepted applicants enrolled. 56% (92 students) submitted SAT scores; 75% (124 students) submitted ACT scores. *25th percentile*: SAT Critical Reading 490, SAT Math 480; ACT Composite 22, ACT English 21, ACT Math 19. *75th percentile*: SAT Critical Reading 600, SAT Math 580; ACT Composite 27, ACT English 28, ACT Math 26.

51% of entering freshmen expected to graduate within 5 years. 44% of freshmen from Tennessee. Freshmen fro 23 states and 4 foreign countries.

Admission: Early acceptance available. *Requirements:* Graduation from accredited secondary school or GED. Recommend college preparatory English, college preparatory mathematics, 1 unit history and/or 1 social studies, 1 science, foreign language, coursework in art, music, speech. *Entrance tests:* College Board SAT or ACT composite. For foreign students TOEFL. *For transfer students:* 2.0 minimum GPA.

College credit and advanced placement for postsecondary-level work completed in secondary school.

Noncredit developmental and remedial courses offered.

Degree Requirements: *For all baccalaureate degrees:* 128 credit hours; Undergraduate Record Examination. *For all undergraduate degrees:* 2.0 GPA; 45 units in residence; general education requirements.

Fulfillment of some degree requirements and exemption from some beginning courses possible by passing College Board CLEP, AP. *Grading system:* A–F.

Distinctive Educational Programs: Summer tour of Europe. Off-campus programs available through the Coalition of Christian Colleges and Universities.

ROTC: Army in cooperation with East Tennessee State University.

Degrees Conferred: 170 *baccalaureate:*; 91 *master's*. Bachelor;s degrees awarded in top five disciplines: business/marketing 32; education 41; health professions and related clinical sciences 18.

Fees and Other Expenses: *Full-time tuition per academic year 2008–09:* $20,560 undergraduate; contact the college for current graduate tuition/fees. *Required fees:* $520. *Room and board per academic year:* $5,650. *Books and supplies:* $800. *Other expenses:* $2,800.

Financial Aid: Aid from institutionally generated funds is provided on the basis of academic merit, financial need, athletic ability.

Financial aid to full-time, first-time undergraduate students: 98% received some form of aid.

Departments and Teaching Staff: *Total instructional faculty:* 99 (full-time 67, part-time 32). Total faculty with doctorate, first-professional, or other terminal degree: 52. Student/faculty ratio: 11:1. Degrees held by full-time faculty: doctorate 62%, master's 38%. 64% hold terminal degrees.

Enrollment: Total enrollment 1,018. Undergraduate 799 (full-time 96%; female 59%, male 41%). Graduate 219 (full-time 74%). Undergraduate transfer-in students 110.

Characteristics of Student Body: *Ethnic/racial makeup:* Black non-Hispanic: 8%; Asian or Pacific Islander: 1%; Hispanic: 2%; White non-Hispanic: 88%; unknown 1%; nonresident alien 2%. *Age distribution:* number under 18: 1; 18–19: 259; 20–21: 277; 22–24: 112; 25–29: 30; 30–34: 23; 35–39: 16; 40–49: 22; 50–64: 6.

International Students: 20 nonresident aliens enrolled fall 2008. Students from Europe, Asia, Africa, Canada, Australia. No programs available to aid students whose native language is not English. No financial aid specifically designated for international students.

Student Life: On-campus residence halls. Housing available for married students. *Intercollegiate athletics:* baseball, basketball, soccer, softball, tennis, track and field, volleyball. *Special regulations:* Registered cars permitted; fee charged. *Special services:* Learning Resources Center, medical services. *Student publications: The Buffalo*, a yearbook; *Phoenix*, an annual literary magazine; *The Stampede*, a newspaper. *Surrounding community:* Knoxville, 90 miles from campus, is nearest metropolitan area.

Library Collections: 213,000 volumes including bound books, serial backfiles, electronic documents, and government documents not in separate collections. Online catalog. 494,000 microforms; 4,000 audiovisual materials. Current serial subscriptions: 416 paper, 10,445 via electronic. Computer work stations available. Students have access to the Internet at no charge.

Most important special collections include Restoration Movement History; Josephus Hopwood Paper (founder and first president of the college); Henry J. Derthick Papers (president of the college 1917–40); Milligan College archives; juvenile literature.

Buildings and Grounds: Campus area 135 acres.

Chief Executive Officer: Dr. Donald R. Jeanes, President.

Address admission inquiries to Tracy Brinn, Director of Undergraduate Admissions; graduate inquiries to Carrie Davidson, Director of Graduate Admissions.

O'More College of Design

423 South Margin Street
Franklin, Tennessee 37064
Tel: (615) 794-4254 **E-mail:** admissions@omorecollege.edu
Fax: (615) 790-1662 **Internet:** www.omorecollege.edu

Institution Description: O'More College of Design is a private nonprofit institution, formerly known as O'More School of Design. *Enrollment:* 202. *Degrees awarded:* Associate, baccalaureate.

Accreditation: *National:* ACCSCT. *Professional*: interior design

History: Chartered 1970.

Institutional Structure: *Governing board:* Board of Trustees. Full-time instructional faculty 7.

Calendar: Semesters. Academic year Aug. to May.

Admission: Rolling admissions plan. *Requirements:* High school transcript and/or college transcript; picture and interview required. GED accepted.

Degree Requirements: *For associate degrees:* 76–118 credits. *For baccalaureate degrees:* 127–137 credits. *For all degrees:* 2.0 minimum GPA.

Distinctive Educational Programs: Intensive programs in interior design, historic preservation, and fashion merchandising and design. Instructors and teachers are professionals in the fields in which they teach.

Degrees Conferred: 21 *baccalaureate:* visual and performing arts 15; business, management, marketing, and related support services 8.

Fees and Other Expenses: *Full-time tuition per academic year 2008–09:* $17,160. *Books and supplies:* $550. *Rooma and board per academic year:* $6,000. *Other expenses:* $4,800.

Departments and Teaching Staff: *Total instructional faculty:* 9. Degrees held by full-time faculty: master's 2%, baccalaureate 100%.

Enrollment: Total enrollment 202.

Characteristics of Student Body: *Ethnic/racial makeup:* Black non-Hispanic: 9%; Asian or Pacific Islander: 4%; Hispanic: 5%; White non-Hispanic: 83%.

International Students: No programs available to aid students whose native language is not English. No financial aid specifically designated for international students.

Student Life: *Special services:* Personal counseling and career counseling. Student chapter of American Society of Interior Designers.

Library Collections: 7,000 volumes. 3,000 audiovisual materials; 75 current periodical subscriptions.

Buildings and Grounds: O'More College is housed in 2 historic mansions listed on the National Register of Historic Places and located on 6 acres in the center of a small suburban town only 15 miles from Nashville (TN).

Chief Executive Officer: Dr. Mark Hilliard, President.

O'MORE COLLEGE OF DESIGN—*cont'd*

Address admission inquiries to Director of Admissions.

Rhodes College

2000 North Parkway
Memphis, Tennessee 38112-1690
Tel: (901) 843-3000 **E-mail:** adminfo@rhodes.edu
Fax: (901) 843-3084 **Internet:** www.rhodes.edu

Institution Description: Rhodes College, formerly Southwestern at Memphis, is a private liberal arts institution affiliated with the Presbyterian Church (USA). *Enrollment:* 1,678. *Degrees awarded:* Baccalaureate, master's.

Member of Associated Colleges of the South.

Accreditation: *Regional:* SACS-Comm. on Coll.

History: Established in Clarksville as Montgomery University of Tennessee 1848; offered first instruction at postsecondary level 1849; awarded first degree (baccalaureate) 1853; changed name to Stewart College 1855; chartered and changed name to Southwestern Presbyterian University 1875; changed name to Southwestern 1924; affiliated with Alabama, Louisiana, Mississippi, and Tennessee synods and moved campus to Memphis 1925; changed name to Southwestern at Memphis 1945; adopted present name 1984 in honor of President Emeritus Peyton Rhodes.

Institutional Structure: *Governing board:* The Board of Trustees. Extrainstitutional representation: 42 trustees, 7 life trustees; institutional representation: president of the college, 3 full-time instructional faculty members, 3 students. 1 ex officio. 42 voting. *Composition of institution:* Administrators 79. Academic affairs headed by Dean of Academic Affairs. Day-to-day management, business and finances directed by Executive Vice President. Long-range planning and overall responsibility of college falls to president. Full-time instructional faculty 144. Academic governance body, the Faculty of Rhodes College, meets an average of 9 times per year.

Calendar: Semesters. Academic year Aug. to May. Freshmen admitted Aug., Jan. Degrees conferred May, Aug. Formal commencement May.

Characteristics of Freshmen: 3,747 applicants (2,084 female, 1,683 male). 68% of applicants accepted. 28% of accepted applicants enrolled.

57% (271 students) submitted SAT scores; 43% (203 students) submitted ACT scores. *25th percentile*: SAT Critical Reading 600, SAT Math 590; ACT Composite 25, ACT English 26, ACT Math 24. *75th percentile*: SAT Critical Reading 690, SAT Math 680; ACT Composite 30, ACT English 32, ACT Math 28. 6 National Merit Scholars.

79% of entering freshmen expected to graduate within 5 years. 26% of freshmen from Tennessee. Freshmen from 37 states and 5 foreign countries.

Admission: For fall acceptance apply no later than Feb. 1. Apply by Nov. 15 for early decision. Early acceptance available. *Requirements:* Normally require graduation from accredited secondary school (this can be waived with appropriate high school courses, scores, and grades). 16 units required, normally including 4 English, 2 of same foreign language, 3 mathematics. *Entrance tests:* College Board SAT or ACT composite. For foreign students TOEFL. *For transfer students:* 56 hours maximum transfer credit.

Tutoring available.

Degree Requirements: 112 credit hours; 2.00 GPA; 2 years, including senior year, in residence; distribution requirements; exit competency examinations; senior seminar in the major department.

Fulfillment of some degree requirements and exemption from some beginning courses possible by passing AP (score of 4). *Grading system:* A–F; pass-fail; withdraw (carries time limit).

Distinctive Educational Programs: Interdisciplinary programs in economics and international studies, economics and math, computer science/math, international studies and a foreign language, political science and psychology, American studies, Asian studies, Latin American studies, Russian/Soviet studies, and others; or individually arranged. Facilities and programs for independent research, including honors programs, individualized majors, tutorials. Institutionally sponsored study abroad in England, France, Germany, Spain, Latin America; other study abroad individually arranged. Off-campus study in U.S. at Oak Ridge National Laboratory, Gulf Coast Research Laboratory, and in Washington (DC).

ROTC: Air Force and Army in cooperation with University of Memphis.

Degrees Conferred: 407 *baccalaureate*; 18 *master's*. Bachelor's degrees awarded in top five disciplines: social sciences 115; biological/life sciences 37; English 34; psychology 28; philosophy/religion 26. Master's degrees awarded: business/management 14.

Fees and Other Expenses: *Full-time tuition per academic year 2008–09:* $32,446. *Required fees:* $310. *Books and supplies:* $1,020. *Room and board per academic year:* $7,842. *Other expenses:* $2,372.

Financial Aid: Aid from institutionally generated funds is provided on the basis of academic merit, financial need, special achievement.

Financial aid to full-time, first-time undergraduate students: 86% received some form of aid. Average amount of aid received: federal grants $4,480; Pell grants $2,708; other federal aid $1,953; state/local grants $5,053; institutional grants $14,577.

Departments and Teaching Staff: *Total instructional faculty:* 180 (full-time 144, part-time 136). Student/faculty ratio: 11:1.

Enrollment: Total enrollment 1,678. Undergraduate 1,669 (full-time 99%; female 58%, male 42%). Graduate 9 (full-time 100%). Undergraduate transfer-in students 8.

Characteristics of Student Body: *Ethnic/racial makeup:* Black non-Hispanic: 7%; Asian or Pacific Islander: 5%; Hispanic: 2%; White non-Hispanic: 79%; unknown: 5%; nonresident alien 2%. *Age distribution:* number under 18: 5; 18–19: 551; 20–21: 783; 22–24: 264; 25–29: 4; 30–34: 3; 40–49: 3; 50–64: 2; unknown: 18.

International Students: 34 nonresident aliens enrolled fall 2008. Programs available to aid students whose native language is not English: social, cultural. No financial aid specifically designated for international students.

Student Life: On-campus residence halls house 76% of student body. Residence halls for males constitute 47% of such space, for females 53%. 55% of males join and 0% live in fraternity housing. 63% of females join and 0% live in sorority housing. *Intercollegiate athletics:* male: baseball, soccer, golf, football, basketball, tennis, track, cross-country; female volleyball, basketball, tennis, soccer, track and cross-country. *Special regulations:* Registered cars with decals permitted on campus in designated areas. Visitation hours vary according to residence hall. *Special services:* Career counseling and job placement, medical services and insurance, personal counseling, academic advising, interdenominational religious offerings. *Student publications: Lynx*, a yearbook; *Sou'Wester*, a weekly newspaper; *Currents*, a literary magazine; *Freshman Handbook*. *Surrounding community:* Memphis area population over 1 million. Served by mass transit bus system; airport 7 miles from campus; passenger rail service 6 miles from campus.

Library Collections: 278,500 volumes. 33,751 books. 95,000 microforms; 10,600 audiovisual materials; 1,685 periodical subscriptions. Online catalog. Computer work stations available. Students have access to online information retrieval services and the Internet.

Most important special collections include the Halliburton Collection; the Walter Armstrong Rare Book Collection.

Buildings and Grounds: Campus area 100 acres.

Chief Executive Officer: Dr. William E. Troutt, President.

Address admission inquiries to David Wottle, Dean of Admissions and Financial Aid.

Southern Adventist University

P.O. Box 370
Collegedale, Tennessee 37315-0370
Tel: (423) 236-2000 **E-mail:** admissions@southern.edu
Fax: (423) 236-1000 **Internet:** www.southern.edu

Institution Description: Southern Adventist University, formerly known as Southern College of Seventh-day Adventists, is a private university owned by the Southern Union Conference of Seventh-day Adventists. *Enrollment:* 2,777. *Degrees awarded:* Associate, baccalaureate, master's.

Accreditation: *Regional:* SACS-Comm. on Coll. *Professional*: music, nursing, social work, teacher education

History: Established as Graysville Academy 1892; changed name to Southern Industrial School 1896; changed name to Southern Training School 1901; moved to present location and changed name to Southern Junior College 1916; chartered as junior college and offered first instruction at postsecondary level 1917; awarded first degree (associate) 1918; became 4-year college and changed name to Southern Missionary College 1944; changed name to Southern College of Seventh-day Adventists 1982; adopted present name 1996. *See* Elva Gardner, *A School of His Planning* (Chattanooga, Tenn.: Starkey Printing Co., 1962) for further information.

Institutional Structure: *Governing board:* Board of Trustees of Southern College of Seventh-day Adventists. Representation: 37 trustees. 13 ex officio. All voting. *Composition of institution:* Administrators 55. Academic affairs headed by vice president for academic administration. Management/business/finances directed by vice president for financial administration. Full-time instructional faculty 129. Academic governance body, Faculty Senate, meets an average of 7 times per year.

Calendar: Semesters. Academic year Aug. to May. Summer sessions from May to Aug. Freshmen admitted Aug., Jan., May, June, July. Degrees conferred each month. Formal commencement May, July, Dec. Summer session of 3 terms from May to Aug.

Characteristics of Freshmen: 1,510 applicants (869 female, 641 male). 80% of applicants admitted. 40% of applicants admitted and enrolled.

43% (242 students) submitted SAT scores; 81% (459 students) submitted ACT scores. *25th percentile*: SAT Critical Reading 410, SAT Math 4210; ACT Composite 19, ACT English 17, ACT Math 19. *75th percentile*: SAT Critical Reading 540, SAT Math 560; ACT Composite 25, ACT English 25, ACT Math 26.

40% of entering freshmen expected to graduate within 5 years. 22% freshmen from Tennessee. Freshmen from 46 states and 43 foreign countries.

Admission: Rolling admissions plan. For fall acceptance, apply no later than Aug. 1. Early acceptance available. *Requirements:* Either graduation from approved secondary school or 18 secondary school units (14 in academic subjects) or GED. Recommend 4 units English, 2 in a foreign language, 3 mathematics (including algebra), 3 science, 2 social studies, 1 typing. Additional requirements for nursing and music education majors. Minimum 2.0 GPA for secondary school graduates; 3.0 for nongraduates. *Entrance tests:* ACT of SAT. For foreign students English language proficiency test. *For transfer students:* 2.0 minimum GPA; from 4-year accredited institution 94 hours maximum transfer credit; from 2-year accredited institution 72 hours.

College credit and advanced placement for postsecondary-level work completed in secondary school.

Remedial courses offered in summer session and regular academic year; some are noncredit.

Degree Requirements: *For all associate degrees:* 64–66 credit hours; 2 terms in residence; 2 semesters physical education. *For all baccalaureate degrees:* 124–128 credit hours; 2.25 GPA in major; 2 terms in residence; 1 semester physical education; 2.5 GPA for nursing and education. *For all degrees:* 2.0 GPA; chapel attendance once weekly; distribution requirements. Additional requirements for some majors.

Fulfillment of some degree requirements and exemption from some beginning courses possible by passing departmental examinations, College Board CLEP, AP. *Grading system:* A–F; withdraw.

Distinctive Educational Programs: Work-experience programs. Accelerated degree programs. Special facilities for using telecommunications in the classroom. Preprofessional programs in dental hygiene, dentistry, dietetics, medical records administration, medicine, occupational therapy, optometry, pharmacy, physical therapy, public health science, radiology technology, respiratory therapy, veterinary medicine, long-term care administration. Facilities for independent research, including honors programs, individual majors, tutorials. Study abroad in Austria, France, Italy, Germany, Spain, and Argentina through Adventist Colleges Abroad.

Degrees Conferred: 131 *associate;* 302 *baccalaureate*; 33 *master's*. Bachelor's degrees awarded in top five disciplines: business and management 50; health professions and related clinical sciences 44; visual and performing arts 32; education 29; psychology 20. Master's degrees awarded: business/marketing 9; computer and information sciences 21; health professions 22; philosophy and religious studies 2; psychology 5; theology and religious vocations 1.

Fees and Other Expenses: *Full-time tuition per academic year 2008–09:* undergraduate $16,550; contact the university for graduate tuition/fees. *Room and board per academic year:* $4,900. *Books and supplies:* $1,000. *other expenses:* $4,000.

Financial Aid: Aid from institutionally generated funds is provided on the basis of academic merit, financial need, other criteria.

Financial aid to full-time, first-time undergraduate students: 91% received some form of aid. Average amount of aid received: federal grants $3,422; Pell grants $2,938; other federal aid $966; state/local grants $2,810; institutional grants $4,545.

Departments and Teaching Staff: *Total instructional faculty:* 216 (full-time 129, part-time 87). Total faculty with doctorate, first-professional, or other terminal degree: 117. Student/faculty ratio: 16:1. Degrees held by full-time faculty: doctorate 56%, master's 41%, baccalaureate 3%. 56% hold terminal degrees.

Enrollment: Total enrollment 2,777. Undergraduate 2,574 (full-time 84%; female 56%, male 42%). Graduate 203 (full-time 29%). Undergraduate transfer-in students 175.

Characteristics of Student Body: *Ethnic/racial makeup:* Black non-Hispanic: 11%; American Indian or Native Alaskan: 1%; Asian or Pacific Islander 5%; Hispanic: 15%; White non-Hispanic: 83%; nonresident aliens 6%. *Age distribution:* 17–21: 71%; 22–24: 16%; 25–29: 6%; 30–34: 2%; 35–39: 1%; 40–49: 20%; 50–up: 1%; 60–up: .5%.

International Students: 168 nonresident aliens enrolled fall 2008. Programs available to aid students whose native language is not English: English as a Second Language Program. Financial aid specifically designated for international students.

Student Life: On-campus residence halls house 61% of student body. Residence halls for males constitute 50% of such space, for females 50%. 75% of married students request institutional housing and are so housed. 75% of students live on-campus. *Special regulations:* Cars permitted without restrictions. *Special services:* Medical services, campus transportation service. *Student publications: Joker*, an annual roster; *Southern Accent*, a weekly newspaper; *Southern Memories*, a yearbook. *Surrounding community:* Collegedale, population 5,000, is located in Chattanooga metropolitan area. Served by airport 12 miles from campus.

Library Collections: 169,000 volumes including bound books, serial backfiles, electronic documents, and government documents not in separate collections. Online catalog. 484,000 microforms; 7,000 audiovisual materials; 21,000 periodicals including via electronic access. Computer work stations available. Students have access to the Internet at no charge.

Special collections include Seventh-day Adventist Heritage Collection; Thomas Memorial Lincoln/Civil War Collection; Religion Center Collection.

Buildings and Grounds: Campus area 1,000 acres.

Chief Executive Officer: Dr. Gordon Bietz, President.

Address admission inquiries to Marc Grundy, Vice President for Marketing and Enrollment Services.

Southern College of Optometry

1245 Madison Avenue
Memphis, Tennessee 38104-3211
Tel: (901) 722-3228 **E-mail:** admissions@sco.edu
Fax: (901) 722-3328 **Internet:** www.sco.edu

Institution Description: Southern College of Optometry is a private, independent, nonprofit institution. *Enrollment:* 483. *Degrees awarded:* Baccalaureate, first-professional (optometry).

Accreditation: *Regional:* SACS-Comm. on Coll. *Professional*: optometry

History: Chartered, incorporated, and offered first instruction at postsecondary level 1932; awarded first degree (first-professional) 1934.

Institutional Structure: *Governing board:* Board of trustees. Extrainstitutional representation: 14 trustees; institutional representation: 1 faculty ex officio member, 1 student voting member. *Composition of institution:* Administrators 14. Academic affairs headed by vice president of academic affairs. Management/business/finances directed by vice president of finance. Full-time instructional faculty 43. Academic governance body, the faculty, meets an average of 3 times per year.

Calendar: Quarters. Academic year June to May. Entering students admitted Aug. Degrees conferred and formal commencement June. Summer quarter June to Aug.

Characteristics of Freshmen: 25% of applicants accepted. 17% of accepted applicants enrolled.

Average secondary school rank of freshmen 40th percentile.

98% of entering students expected to graduate within 5 years. 15% of entering students from Tennessee. Students from 32 states and 1 foreign country.

Admission: Rolling admission with applications received as early as one year in advance. Early application recommended. *Requirements:* at least 3 years of pre-optometry courses at an accredited undergraduate institution and a competitive level of performance. Courses must include English (1 year), biology with laboratory (1 year), microbiology (1 semester), mathematics through differential calculus, general chemistry with laboratory (1 year), organic chemistry with laboratory (1 year), general physics with laboratory (1 year), general psychology (1 semester), statistics (1 semester), social sciences (1 year). Letters of recommendation from optometrist and pre-professional advisor required. Interview required. *Entrance tests:* OAT.

Degree Requirements: *For first-professional degree:* 232 quarter hours; 2.0 GPA; final year in residence; clinic competency evaluation; prescribed curriculum; clinical externship. *Grading system:* A–F; withdraw (deadline after which pass-fail is appended to withdraw); incomplete.

Distinctive Educational Programs: Off-campus preceptorship program for two quarters of fourth year.

Degrees Conferred: 125 *first-professional:* optometry.

Fees and Other Expenses: *Full-time tuition per academic year 2008–09:* contact the college for current tuition, fees, and off-campus housing costs.

Financial Aid: Aid from institutionally generated funds is provided on the basis of academic merit, financial need. Institution has a Program Participation Agreement with the U.S. Department of Education for eligible students to receive Pell Grants and, depending upon the agreement, other federal aid.

Departments and Teaching Staff: *Total instructional faculty:* 44 FTE. Degrees held by full-time faculty: doctorate 100%, master's 52%, baccalaureate 81%, professional 100%. 100% hold terminal degrees.

Enrollment: Total enrollment 483.

SOUTHERN COLLEGE OF OPTOMETRY—*cont'd*

Characteristics of Student Body: *Ethnic/racial makeup:* Black non-Hispanic: 3%; Asian or Pacific Islander: 5%; Hispanic: 1%; White non-Hispanic: 87%; unknown 3%.

International Students: 5 nonresident aliens enrolled fall 2008. No programs available to aid students whose native language is not English. No financial aid specifically designated for international students.

Student Life: No on-campus housing. *Special regulations:* Ample parking for registered vehicles. *Special services:* Major medical group insurance furnished to students at minimal cost. On-campus clinic available to students at no additional cost. *Student publications: Scope*, a yearbook. *Surrounding community:* Memphis metropolitan population over 1 million. Served by mass transit bus system; airport 8 miles from campus; passenger rail service 3 miles from campus.

Library Collections: 22,000 volumes. 529 microforms; 1,151 audiovisual materials; 175 current periodical subscriptions. Students have access to online information retrieval services.

Most important special holdings include British theses in vision science; oral history series (pioneers in optometry).

Buildings and Grounds: Campus area 1 square block.

Chief Executive Officer: Dr. William E. Cochran, President.

Address admission inquiries to Elizabeth Darke, Director of Records and Admissions.

Tennessee State University

3500 John A. Merritt Boulevard
Nashville, Tennessee 37209-1561
Tel: (615) 963-5111 **E-mail:** admissions@tnstate.edu
Fax: (615) 963-5108 **Internet:** www.tnstate.edu

Institution Description: Tennessee State University is a state institution and land-grant college and a member of the Tennessee State University and Community College System. *Enrollment:* 8,254. *Degrees awarded:* Associate, baccalaureate, master's, doctorate.

Academic offerings subject to approval by statewide coordinating bodies. Budget subject to approval by state governing boards.

Accreditation: *Regional:* SACS-Comm. on Coll. *Professional*; engineering, family and consumer science, medical record administration, music, nursing, respiratory therapy, social work, speech-language pathology, teacher education

History: Incorporated 1909; established as Agricultural and Industrial State Normal School 1912; offered first instruction at postsecondary level 1922; awarded first degree (baccalaureate) and changed name to Agricultural and Industrial State Normal College 1924; changed name to Agricultural and Industrial State College 1927; to Tennessee Agricultural and Industrial State University 1951; adopted present name 1969; merged with University of Tennessee at Nashville 1979.

Institutional Structure: *Governing board:* State Board of Regents of the State University and Community College System of Tennessee. Representation: 17 regents, including 1 student (appointed by governor of Tennessee), governor, commissioner of agriculture, executive director of Tennessee Higher Education Commission. 4 ex officio. 16 voting. *Composition of institution:* Administrators 31. Academic affairs headed by vice president for academic affairs. Management/business/finances directed by vice president for business affairs. Full-time instructional faculty 406. Academic governance bodies, Academic Affairs Council and Faculty Senate, meet an average of 52 times per year.

Calendar: Semesters. Academic year Aug. to May. Freshmen admitted Aug., Jan., June. Degrees conferred and formal commencement May, Aug. Summer session from May to Aug.

Characteristics of Freshmen: 3,227 applicants (2,255 female, 972 male). 46% of applicants accepted. 69% of accepted applicants enrolled.

16% (759 students) submitted SAT scores; 95% (4,530 students) submitted ACT scores. *25th percentile*: SAT Critical Reading 400, SAT Math 400; ACT Composite 18, ACT English 18, ACT Math 18. *75th percentile*: SAT Critical Reading 500, SAT Math 500; ACT Composite 20, ACT English 20, ACT Math 20.

40% of entering freshmen expected to graduate within 5 years. 60% of freshmen from Tennessee. Freshmen from 40 states and 20 foreign countries.

Admission: Rolling admissions plan. For fall acceptance, apply as early as beginning of senior year of secondary school, but not later than final day of registration. Early acceptance available. *Requirements:* In-state applicants are required to graduate from approved secondary schools with a minimum 2.0 GPA and earn a composite score of 14 on the ACT. Out-of-state applicants are required to graduate from an approved secondary school and have a composite ACT score of 16. Students not meeting above requirements may be admitted under regulated program of study. *Entrance tests:* College Board SAT or ACT composite. *For transfer students:* 2.0 minimum GPA; from 4-year and 2-year accredited institutions 100 semester hours maximum transfer credit.

College credit and advanced placement for postsecondary-level work completed in secondary school and for extrainstitutional learning.

Tutoring available. Developmental courses offered in summer session and regular academic year; credit given.

Degree Requirements: *For all associate degrees:* 73 semester hours; clinical experience. *For all baccalaureate degrees:* 128–134 semester hours; project writing; English proficiency examination. *For all undergraduate degrees:* 2.0 GPA; 2 terms in residence; 6 hours physical education; general education core requirements. Additional requirements for some programs.

Fulfillment of some degree requirements and exemption from some beginning courses possible by passing departmental examination, College Board CLEP. *Grading system:* A–F; pass-fail; withdraw (carries time limit).

Distinctive Educational Programs: Work-experience programs. Cluster colleges. Flexible meeting places and schedules, including off-campus centers, weekend and evening classes. Doctorate in educational administration in cooperation with Peabody College of Vanderbilt University. Doctorate program in public administration. Cooperative programs in allied health with Meharry Medical College; in speech and audiology with Vanderbilt Hospital. Special facilities for using telecommunications in the classroom. Interdisciplinary programs in developmental studies, government and political affairs, sociology. Honors programs. Individual majors. Center for Urban and Public affairs in cooperation with Middle Tennessee State University. *Other distinctive programs:* Continuing education.

ROTC: Air Force.

Degrees Conferred: 149 *associate*; 942 *baccalaureate*; 471 *master's*; 44 *doctorate*. Bachelor's degrees awarded in top five disciplines: business, management, marketing, and related support services 226; liberal arts and sciences, general studies, and humanities 131, health professions and related clinical sciences 111; engineering 111; psychology 76.

Fees and Other Expenses: *Full-time tuition per academic year 2008–09:* $5,192 resident, $16,042 nonresident; contact the university for current graduate tuition/fees. *Room and board per academic year:* $3,990. *Books and supplies:* $1,600. *Other expenses:* $3,900.

Financial Aid: Aid from institutionally generated funds is provided on the basis of academic merit, athletic ability, other criteria.

Financial aid to full-time, first-time undergraduate students: 94% received some form of financial aid. Average amount of aid relieved: federal grants $3,945; Pell grants $3,334; other federal aid $1,135; state/local grants $3,966; institutional grants $3,888.

Departments and Teaching Staff: *Total instructional faculty:* 295. Degrees held by full-time faculty: doctorate 61%, master's 36%, baccalaureate 3%. 61% hold terminal degrees.

Enrollment: Total enrollment 8,254. Undergraduate 6,431 (full-time 80%; female 64%, male 36%). Graduate 1,823 (full-time 34%). Undergraduate transfer-in students 498.

Characteristics of Student Body: *Ethnic/racial makeup:* nBlack non-Hispanic: 80%; Asian or Pacific Islander: 1%; Hispanic: 1%; White non-Hispanic: 16%; unknown 2%.

International Students: No programs available to aid students whose native language is not English. No financial aid specifically designated for international students.

Student Life: On-campus residence halls house 27% of student body. *Special regulations:* Cars permitted without restrictions. *Special services:* Learning Resources Center, medical services. *Student publications, radio: Accent*, a monthly publication; *Cupolian*, published 2 times per year; *Meter*, a weekly publication; *Tennessean*, an annual publications. Radio station WTSU broadcasts 35 hours per week. *Surrounding community:* Nashville population 500,000. Served by mass transit bus system; airport 12 miles from campus.

Library Collections: 586,000 volumes. 34,000 government documents (separate collection); 24,000 audiovisual materials; 132,000 microform units; 1,254 periodicals. Online catalog. Students have access to online information retrieval services.

Most important special collections include McKissack architectural designs; Tennessee State University Historical Documents; Thomas E. Poag Papers.

Buildings and Grounds: Campus area 538 acres.

Chief Executive Officer: Dr. James A. Hefner, President.

Address admission inquiries to Director of Admissions.

Tennessee Technological University

1000 North Dixie Avenue
Cookeville, Tennessee 38505-0001
Tel: (931) 372-3888 **E-mail:** admissions@tntech.edu
Fax: (931) 372-6250 **Internet:** www.tntech.edu

Institution Description: Tennessee Technological University is a member of the State University and Community College System. *Enrollment:* 9,733. *Degrees awarded:* Associate, baccalaureate, master's, doctorate. Specialist degree in education also awarded.

Academic offerings subject to approval by statewide coordinating bodies. Budget subject to approval by state governing boards. Member of Oak Ridge Associated Universities.

Accreditation: *Regional:* SACS-Comm. on Coll. *Professional*: business, chemistry, engineering, music, nursing, teacher education

History: Established, chartered, and incorporated as Tennessee Polytechnic Institute 1915; offered first instruction at postsecondary level 1916; awarded first degree (bachelor of science) 1929; bachelor of arts authorized in 1964; TPI gained university status and changed its name to Tennessee Technological University in 1965; specialist in education degree authorized in 1970; doctor of philosophy in engineering authorized in 1971; the master's in business administration authorized in 1976; the associate degree in criminal justice authorized in 1977; in 1980 the B.S. degree in nursing was offered; B.S. and B.F.A. in crafts and fine arts offered in 1980; and the B.S. in Technical Communications offered in 1986. *See* Harvey G. Neufeldt and W. Calvin Dickinson, *The Search for Identity: A History of Tennessee Technological University, 1915–1985* (Memphis: Memphis State University Press, 1991); *see also* Austin Wheeler Smith, *The Story of Tennessee Tech* (Nashville: McQuiddy Printing Company, 1957) for further information.

Institutional Structure: *Governing board:* Tennessee Board of Regents of the State University and Community College System of Tennessee. Representation: 17 regents, including 1 student (appointed by governor of Tennessee), Governor, Commissioner of Education, Commissioner of Agriculture, Executive Director of Tennessee Higher Education Commission, 4 ex officio, 16 voting. *Composition of institution:* Administrators 24. Academic affairs headed by Vice President for Academic Affairs. Business/finances directed by Vice President for Business and Fiscal Affairs. Student affairs headed by Vice President for Student Services. Full-time instructional faculty 373. Academic governance body, The University Assembly, meets an average of 2 times per year.

Calendar: Semesters. Academic year Aug. to May. Freshmen admitted Sept., Jan., Mar., June. Degrees conferred and formal commencements June, Aug., Dec., Mar.

Characteristics of Freshmen: 2,937 applicants (1,274 female, 1,663 male). 92% of applicants accepted. 56% of accepted applicants enrolled.

9% (142 students) submitted SAT scores; 96% (1,489 students) submitted ACT scores. *25th percentile*: SAT Critical Reading 500, SAT Math 530; ACT Composite 20, ACT English 20, ACT Math 19. *75th percentile*: SAT Critical Reading 630, SAT Math 640; ACT Composite 25, ACT English 26, ACT Math 25.

34% of entering freshmen expected to graduate within 5 years. 96% of freshmen from Tennessee. Freshmen from 20 states and 10 foreign countries.

Admission: Rolling admissions plan. Apply as early as 11 months, but not later than 2 weeks, prior to beginning of semester. Early acceptance available. *Requirements:* Graduation from approved or accredited secondary school, or GED. Minimum GPA 2.5. *Entrance tests:* ACT composite (score of 19). *For transfer students:* From 4-year accredited institution 102 semester hours maximum transfer credit; from 2-year accredited institution 60 hours; for correspondence/extension and credit for examination students, 2.00 minimum GPA; 33 hours maximum transfer credit. Out-of-state admission requirements are the same as in-state requirements.

College credit and advanced placement for postsecondary-level work completed in secondary school. College credit for extrainstitutional learning on basis of university requirements.

Tutoring available. Developmental/remedial courses offered in summer session and regular academic year; credit given.

Degree Requirements: *For associate degree in criminal justice:* 64 semester hours. *For all baccalaureate degrees:* 132 semester hours; 2 terms in residence; American history course requirement. *For all undergraduate degrees:* 2.0 GPA. *Grading system:* A–F.

Distinctive Educational Programs: Three Centers of Excellence in the College of Engineering emphasize interdisciplinary research by engineering, biology, chemistry, agriculture, foreign languages, and business faculty and students. The foci are water resources utilization and management, electric power simulation and control, and manufacturing technology. The heavy involvement of students with individualized faculty members, faculty teams, and the Centers of Excellence in interdisciplinary research serves as a remarkable launching pad into the business/professional world. A B.F.A. degree is offered in art in conjunction with the Joe L. Evins Appalachian Center for Crafts. The program includes a staff of 6 artists-in-residence/instructors at the Center, which is located 25 miles from the main campus. *Other distinctive programs:* Work experience programs; off-campus centers (35–88 miles away), evening classes; special facilities for using telecommunications in the classroom; interdisciplinary honors program; credit and noncredit continuing education programs.

ROTC: Air Force, Army (in cooperation with Tennessee State University).

Degrees Conferred: 1,294 *baccalaureate*; 532 *master's*; 13 *doctorate*. Bachelor's degrees awarded in top five disciplines: business, management, marketing, and related support services 345; engineering 267; education 225; social sciences and history 77; agriculture 54. Master's degrees awarded: business 45; health professions 1; mathematics 5; physical sciences 5. Doctorates awarded: education 3; engineering 4; environmental science 2.

Fees and Other Expenses: *Full-time tuition per academic year 2008–09:* undergraduate resident $4,580, nonresident $14,256; contact the university for current graduate tuition/fees. *Books and supplies:* $1,300. *Room per academic year:* $7,000.

Financial Aid: Aid from institutionally generated funds is provided on the basis of academic merit, financial need, athletic ability, other criteria.

Financial aid to full-time, first-time undergraduate students: 90% received some form of financial aid. Average amount of aid received: federal grants $2,855; state/local grants $3,918; institutional grants $4,376; loans $3,359.

Departments and Teaching Staff: *Total instructional faculty:* 554 (full-time 372, part-time 172). Total faculty with doctorate, first-professional, or other terminal degree: 362. Student/faculty ratio: 18:1. Degrees held by full-time faculty: baccalaureate 100%, master's 99.8%, doctorate 78.3%. 78.3% hold terminal degrees.

Enrollment: Total enrollment 9,733.

Characteristics of Student Body: *Ethnic/racial makeup:* number of Black non-Hispanic: 203; American Indian or Alaska Native: 19; Asian or Pacific Islander: 83; Hispanic: 62; White non-Hispanic: 6,357; unknown: 370.

International Students: 200 nonresident aliens enrolled fall 2008. Programs available to aid students whose native language is not English: English as a Second Language Program. Financial aid specifically designated for international students: scholarships available annually to qualifying students.

Student Life: On-campus residence halls house 31% of student body. Residence halls for males constitute 55% of such space, for females 45%. Some males live in fraternity housing. Housing available for married students. *Intercollegiate athletics:* male: baseball, basketball, cross-country, football, golf, tennis; female: basketball, cross-country, golf, softball, tennis, track and field, volleyball; both sexes: rifle. *Special regulations:* Registered cars permitted in designated areas only. *Special services:* Learning Resources Center, Macintosh Lab, D.W. Mattson Computer Center, medical services, University Recreation and Fitness Center. *Student publications, radio: The Eagle*, a yearbook; *Homespun*, an annual literary magazine; *The Oracle*, a weekly newspaper. Radio station WTTU broadcasts 117 hours per week. *Surrounding community:* Cookeville population 22,000. Nashville, 80 miles from campus, is nearest metropolitan area. Served by airport 3 miles from campus.

Publications: *Tech Times* (biweekly faculty and staff newsletter); *The Alumnus* (quarterly alumni newsletter); *President's Report* (annually); *Undergraduate Catalog* (biannually); and *Graduate School Catalog* (biannually).

Library Collections: 395,000 volumes. 145,000 government documents; 990,000 microforms; 8,100 audiovisual materials; 3,000 current serial subscriptions. Students have access to online information retrieval services and the Internet.

Most important special holdings include Joe L. Evins Collection; Harding Studies Collection; Cordell Hull Collection.

Buildings and Grounds: Campus area 204 acres.

Chief Executive Officer: Dr. Robert Bell, President.

Address admission inquiries to Vanessa Palmer, Director of Admissions.

College of Arts and Sciences

Degree Programs Offered: *Associate* in criminal justice; *baccalaureate* in biochemistry, biology, chemistry, computer science, criminal justice, English, foreign language, geology, history, journalism, mathematics, physics, political science, psychology, social work, sociology, technical communications, wildlife and fisheries science; *master's* in biology, chemistry, English, mathematics.

Distinctive Educational Programs: The Cooperative Fisheries Unit, funded by the Tennessee Technological University, the U.S. Fish and Wildlife Agency, and the Tennessee Wildlife Resources Agency, offers graduate-level study in fish management and water quality and also provides research for various agencies.

TENNESSEE TECHNOLOGICAL UNIVERSITY—*cont'd*

College of Agriculture and Home Economics

Degree Programs Offered: *Baccalaureate* in agriculture, home economics.

Distinctive Educational Programs: Preprofessional program in veterinary medicine, forestry. Specialized research and public service facility for nurseries, to study plant diseases and propagation.

College of Business Administration

Degree Programs Offered: *Baccalaureate, master's, 5-year accounting program.*

Distinctive Educational Programs: Division of Management Programs offers consultative services to business and industry. Case study format in MBA program. Entrepreneurial Training Program. College houses two Chairs of Excellence in information systems and operations management.

College of Education

Degree Programs Offered: *Baccalaureate* in elementary, secondary, early childhood, special, health and physical, art, music education and psychology, music therapy and art; *master's* in curriculum, elementary, early childhood, secondary, special, health and physical, reading, administration and supervision, counselor education and school psychology; *specialist degree* in all master's areas except health and physical education.

Admission: *For admission to Level 2 of programs leading to Teacher Licensure:* Successful completion of Pre-Professional Skills Test; overall quality point average of 2.50.

Degree Requirements: *For programs leading to teacher licensure:* student must complete the National Teacher Examinations including Core Battery and Specialty Area Test.

Distinctive Educational Programs: B.F.A. offered in art in conjunction with the Crafts Center.

College of Engineering

Degree Programs Offered: *Baccalaureate, master's,* and *doctorate* in chemical engineering, civil engineering, electrical engineering, industrial engineering and mechanical engineering; *baccalaureate* in industrial technology.

Distinctive Educational Programs: Cooperative education. The College of Engineering administers 3 Centers of Excellence: the Electric Power Center, the Manufacturing Center, and the Water Resources Center.

School of Nursing

Degree Programs Offered: *Baccalaureate.*

Distinctive Educational Programs: School's 4-year program is designed for health care delivery in rural and semi-rural communities. Emphasis on public health care.

Tennessee Temple University

1815 Union Avenue
Chattanooga, Tennessee 37404-3587
Tel: (423) 493-4100 **E-mail:** ttuinfo@tntemple.edu
Fax: (423) 493-4497 **Internet:** www.tntemple.edu

Institution Description: Tennessee Temple University is a private, nonprofit institution affiliated with Highland Park Baptist Church in Chattanooga. *Enrollment:* 716. *Degrees awarded:* Associate, baccalaureate, master's.

Accreditation: *National:* Transnational Association of Christian Colleges and Schools.

History: Organized as junior college and Bible college 1946; restructured as baccalaureate-level college 1950; achieved university status 1978.

Institutional Structure: *Governing board:* Board of Trustees. Full-time instructional faculty 82.

Calendar: Semesters. Academic year Aug. to May.

Characteristics of Freshmen: 683 applicants (298 female, 375 male). 24% of applicants admitted. 84% of applicants admitted and enrolled.

43% of applicants submitted SAT scores; 66% ACT scores. *25th percentile:* SAT Critical Reading 410, SAT Math 430, SAT Writing 400; ACT Composite 17, ACT English 17, ACT Math 16. *75th percentile:* SAT Critical Reading 500, SAT Math 480, SAT Writing 500; ACT Composite 21, ACT English 22, ACT Math 20.

38% entering freshmen expected to graduate within 5 years. 29% of freshmen from Tennessee. Freshmen from 33 states and 10 foreign countries.

Admission: Rolling admissions plan. For fall acceptance, apply as early as end of junior year of secondary school, but not later than one month prior to beginning of semester. *Entrance tests:* SAT or ACT scores required.

Degree Requirements: *For all baccalaureate degrees:* 128–133 hours minimum; 2.0 GPA; minimum of 40 upper division hours.

Distinctive Educational Programs: Distance learning program offered online. Evening classes.

Degrees Conferred: 3 *associate;* 74 *baccalaureate:* business, management, marketing, and related support services 23; communications/communication technologies 1; education 14; English 2; foreign language 6; liberal arts 8; mathematics 1; philosophy/religion/theology 27; psychology 13; social sciences and history 4; visual and performing arts 4. Master's degrees awarded: education 41.

Fees and Other Expenses: *Full-time tuition per academic year 2008–09:* $8,11,172. *Books and supplies:* $1,400. *Room and board per academic year:* $5,950. *Other expenses:* $3,800.

Financial Aid: Aid from institutionally generated funds is provided on the basis of academic merit, financial need, and other criteria.

Financial aid to full-time, first-time undergraduate students: 92$ received some form of financial aid. Average amount of aid received: federal grants $3,308; institutional grants $3,060; loans $6,791.

Departments and Teaching Staff: *Total instructional faculty:* 49 (full-time 26, part-time 23). Total faculty with doctorate, first-professional, or other terminal degree: 13. Student/faculty ratio: 9:1. Degrees held by full-time faculty: doctorate 20.6%, master's 79.4%. 20.6% hold terminal degrees.

Enrollment: Total enrollment 716. Undergraduate 543 (full-time 79%; female 46%, male 54%). Graduate 173 (full-time 34%). Undergraduate transfer-in students 75.

Characteristics of Student Body: *Ethnic/racial makeup:* Black non-Hispanic: 12%; American Indian or Alaska Native: 1%;; Asian or Pacific Islander: 1%; Hispanic: 6%; White non-Hispanic: 79%; unknown 1%; nonresident alien 1%. *Age distribution:* number under 18: 2; 18–19: 145; 20–21: 142; 22–24: 87; 25–29: 22; 30–34: 5; 35–39: 4; 40–49: 6; 50–64: 1.

International Students: 7 nonresident aliens enrolled fall 2008. No programs available to aid students whose native language is not English. No financial aid specifically designated for international students.

Student Life: On-campus residence halls house 70% of student body. *Intercollegiate athletics:* Baseball, basketball, soccer, and volleyball. *Special regulations:* Registered vehicles permitted for all students.

Library Collections: 195,000 volumes. Card catalog. 62,000 microforms; 8,935 audiovisual materials; 194 current periodical subscriptions. 500 recodings. Computer work stations available.

Most important special collections include the Roberson and Faulkner Collection; Revis Educational Collection.

Chief Executive Officer: Dr. Danny Lovett, President.

Address admission inquiries to Chris Walker, Director of Enrollment Services.

Tennessee Wesleyan College

P.O. Box 40
Athens, Tennessee 37371-0040
Tel: (423) 745-7504 **E-mail:** admissions@twcnet.edu
Fax: (423) 745-9968 **Internet:** www.twcent.edu

Institution Description: Tennessee Wesleyan College is a private, independent, nonprofit college affiliated with The Holston Conference of The United Methodist Church. *Enrollment:* 988. *Degrees awarded:* Baccalaureate.

Accreditation: *Regional:* SACS-Comm. on Coll.

History: Established as Athens Female College 1857; offered first instruction at postsecondary level and changed name to East Tennessee Wesleyan College 1866; changed name to East Tennessee Wesleyan University 1867; changed name to Grant Memorial University 1886, to U.S. Grant University 1889, to Athens School of the University of Chattanooga 1906; adopted present name 1925; awarded first baccalaureate degree 1957.

Institutional Structure: *Governing board:* Board of Governors (34 members). *Composition of institution:* Administrators 7. Academic affairs headed by academic dean. Management/business/finances directed by chief financial officer. Full-time instructional faculty 44. Academic governance body, the faculty, meets an average of 9 times per year.

Calendar: Semesters. Academic year Aug. to July. Freshmen admitted Aug., Jan., May. Degrees conferred May, Aug., Dec. Formal commencement May. Summer session of 3 terms from May to Aug.

Characteristics of Freshmen: 833 applicants. 86% of applicants accepted. 48% of accepted applicants enrolled full-time.

47% (7 students) submitted SAT scores; 924% (148 students) submitted ACT scores. *25th percentile*: SAT Critical Reading 440, SAT Math 450; ACT Composite 18, ACT English 17, ACT Math 17. *75th percentile*: SAT Critical Reading 530, SAT Math 510; ACT Composite 23, ACT English 22, ACT Math 24.

37% of entering freshmen expected to graduate within 5 years. 91% of freshmen from Tennessee. Freshmen from 22 states and 11 foreign countries.

Admission: Rolling admissions plan. For fall acceptance, apply as early as Sept. 15 of previous year, but not later than first day of classes of year of enrollment. Early acceptance available. *Requirements:* Graduation from accredited secondary school with 4 units English, 2 or more mathematics, 2 biological/natural science, 1 or more of social studies, 1 history; grade of C or higher. Students who have attained the GED are also considered for admission; these students are asked to interview with the Admissions Review Committee to determine their readiness for enrollment. *Entrance tests:* College Board SAT or ACT composite.

Tutoring available.

Degree Requirements: 128 semester hours; 2.0 GPA overall; last 30 semester hours in residence; participation in at least 10 cultural events or religious services per year; completion of all college requirements; last 32 semester hours in residence; completion of the Writing Proficiency Examination.

Fulfillment of some degree requirements and exemption from some beginning courses possible by passing College Board CLEP, AP. *Grading system:* A–F; pass-fail; pass; withdraw (carries time limit); SP/UP (satisfactory progress/ unsatisfactory progress).

Distinctive Educational Programs: Internships. Flexible meeting places and schedules, including off-campus centers (at Knoxville) and evening classes at the main campus.

Degrees Conferred: 216 *baccalaureate*.

Fees and Other Expenses: *Full-time tuition per academic year 2008–09:* $17,050. *Books and supplies:* $1,000. *Required fees:* $550. *Room and board per academic year:* $5,800. *Other expenses:* $1,500.

Financial Aid: Aid from institutionally generated funds is provided on the basis of academic merit, financial need, athletic ability.

Financial aid to full-time, first-time undergraduate students: need-based scholarships/grants totaling $3,651,676, self-help $2,399,940, parent loans $129,081, tuition waivers $86,955, athletic awards $892,678; non-need based scholarships/grants totaling $583,582, self-help $638,689, parent loans $252,887, tuition waivers $86,955, athletic awards $582,287.

Departments and Teaching Staff: *Total instructional faculty:* 88 (full-time 44, part-time 44). Total faculty with doctorate, first-professional, or other terminal degree: 39. Student/faculty ratio: 13:1. Degrees held by full-time faculty: doctorate 63%, master's 28%, professional 9%. 72% hold terminal degrees.

Enrollment: Total enrollment 988. Undergraduate 988 (full-time 86%; female 61%, male 39%). Transfer-in students 175.

Characteristics of Student Body: *Ethnic/racial makeup:* Black non-Hispanic: 3%; Asian or Pacific Islander: 1%; Hispanic: 2%; White non-Hispanic: 80%; unknown: 12%; nonresident alien 2%.

International Students: 20 nonresident aliens enrolled fall 2008. Students from Europe, Asia, Latin America, Africa. Programs available to aid students whose native language is not English: English as a Second Language Program. Financial aid specifically designated for international students.

Student Life: On-campus residence halls available. *Intercollegiate athletics:* male: baseball, basketball, soccer, golf; female: basketball, tennis, soccer, softball, volleyball. *Special regulations:* Registered cars with decals permitted; no fee charged. Quiet hours from 9pm to 9am. *Special services:* Medical services. *Student publications: The New Exponent*, a twice quarterly news magazine; *The Nocatula*, a yearbook; *The Springs of Helicon*, an annual literary magazine. *Student activities:* 2 sororities and 1 fraternity; 22 campus clubs and organizations. *Surrounding community:* Athens population 13,500. Atlanta (GA), 150 miles from campus, is nearest metropolitan area; Knoxville 50 miles from campus. Served by airport 60 miles from campus.

Library Collections: 154,000 volumes including bound books, serial backfiles, electronic documents, and government documents not in separate collections. Online catalog. 9,700 microforms; 3,560 audiovisual materials; 9,665 current serial subscriptions. Computer work stations available. Students have access to the Internet at no charge.

Most important holdings include Methodist Historical Collection (1,765 volumes from mid-18th century to present on regional and national history of Methodism); Holston Papers (correspondence and other personal papers of prominent East Tennessee family c.1650); Bolton Papers (memoirs and personal papers of David A. Bolton, historian and college alumnus).

Buildings and Grounds: Campus area 40 acres.

Chief Executive Officer: Dr. Steven Condon, President.

Address admission inquiries to Stan Harrison, Director of Admissions.

Trevecca Nazarene University

333 Murfreesboro Road
Nashville, Tennessee 37210
Tel: (615) 248-1200 **E-mail:** admissions@trevecca,edu
Fax: (615) 248-7728 **Internet:** www.trevecca.edu

Institution Description: Trevecca Nazarene University is a private institution affiliated with the Church of the Nazarene. *Enrollment:* 2,266. *Degrees awarded:* Associate, baccalaureate, master's, doctorate.

Accreditation: *Regional:* SACS-Comm. on Coll. *Professional*: physician assisting, music

History: Established as Literary and Bible Training School 1901; chartered, incorporated, offered first instruction at postsecondary level, and changed name to Trevecca College 1915; became 2-year college and changed name to Trevecca Nazarene College 1935; awarded first degree (baccalaureate) 1942; adopted present name 1996. *See* Mildred Wynkoop, *The Trevecca Story* (Nashville: Trevecca Press, 1976) for further information.

Institutional Structure: *Governing board:* Board of Trustees of Trevecca Nazarene University. Representation: 42 trustees, including 2 alumni; president of college. 1 ex officio. All voting. *Composition of institution:* Administrators 79. Academic affairs headed by dean of the university. Management/business/ finances directed by chief fiscal officer. Full-time instructional faculty 82. Academic governance body, Academic Council, meets an average of 9 times per year.

Calendar: Semesters. Academic year Aug. to May. Freshmen admitted Aug., Jan., May. Degrees conferred and formal commencement May. Summer session from early May to late July.

Characteristics of Freshmen: 821 applicants (510 female, 311 male). 88% of applicants accepted. 44% of accepted applicants enrolled.

25th percentile: SAT Critical Reading 470, SAT Math 550; ACT Composite 19, ACT English 17, ACT Math 18. *75th percentile*: SAT Critical Reading 590, SAT Math 590; ACT Composite 25, ACT English 24, ACT Math 25.

29% of entering freshmen expected to graduate within 5 years. 38% of freshmen from Tennessee. Freshmen from 23 states and 4 foreign countries.

Admission: Rolling admissions plan. Early acceptance available. *Requirements:* Freshmen must meet one of two conditions; a minimum ACT composite 18 (860 SAT combined) or 2.5 high school GPA based on a 4.0 scale. *Entrance tests:* ACT composite (students with scores of less than 15 will be admitted through academic enrichment program). For foreign students TOEFL. *For transfer students:* evidence of good standing from former institution attended. Maximum of 64 hours maximum transfer credit accepted from 2-year accredited institution.

College credit and advanced placement for postsecondary-level work completed in secondary school and for extrainstitutional learning on basis of portfolio and faculty assessments, personal interview.

Tutoring available. Developmental courses offered during regular academic year; credit does not count toward degree.

Degree Requirements: *For all associate degrees:* 64 semester hours. *For all baccalaureate degrees:* 128 semester hours; completion of 59-hour general education curriculum (varies for teacher education, business, allied health programs). *For all degrees:* minimum 2.0 GPA.

Fulfillment of some degree requirements and exemption from some beginning courses possible by passing departmental examinations, College Board CLEP, AP. *Grading system:* A+–F; pass-fail; withdraw (deadline after which pass-fail is appended to withdraw).

Distinctive Educational Programs: Internships. Flexible meeting places and schedules, including weekend and evening classes in certain programs. An accredited physician assistant program (the only such accredited program in Tennessee). Preprofessional programs in dentistry, engineering, medicine, nursing, pharmacy. A post-baccalaureate program that provides continuing education for teachers (credit does not count toward another degree).

ROTC: Army in cooperation with Vanderbilt University.

Degrees Conferred: 2 *associate*; 334 *baccalaureate*; 385 *master's*; 24 *doctorate*. Bachelor's degrees awarded in top five disciplines: business, management, marketing, and related support services 203; philosophy/religion 30; education 24; communication, journalism, and related programs 19; biological/life sciences 15. Master's degrees awarded: various disciplines 385. Doctorates awareded: education 25.

Fees and Other Expenses: *Full-time tuition per academic year 2008–09:* $16,288; contact the university ofr current graduate tuition. *Books and supplies:* $917. *Room and board per academic year:* $7,134. *Other expenses:* $2,386.

Financial Aid: Aid from institutionally generated funds is provided on the basis of academic merit, financial need, athletic ability, other criteria.

TREVECCA NAZARENE UNIVERSITY—*cont'd*

Financial aid for first-time, full-time undergraduate students: 100% received some form of aid. Average amount of aid received: federal grants $3,415; Pell grants $2,135; other federal aid $1,604; state/local grants $4,415; institutional grants $6,443.

Departments and Teaching Staff: *Total instructional faculty:* 219 (full-time 82, part-time 137). Total faculty with doctorate, first-professional, or other terminal degree: 51. Student/faculty ratio: 17:1. Degrees held by full-time faculty: doctorate 58%, master's 38%, baccalaureate 2%.

Enrollment: Total enrollment 2,366. Undergraduate 1,271 (full-time 90%; female 56%, male 44%). Graduate 1,095 (full-time 85%). Undergraduate transfer-in students 108.

Characteristics of Student Body: *Ethnic/racial makeup:* Black non-Hispanic: 10%; American Indian or Alaska Native: 1%; Asian or Pacific Islander: 2%; Hispanic: 2%; White non-Hispanic: 82%; unknown: 2%; nonresident alien 1%. *Age distribution:* number under 18: 2; 18–19: 551; 20–21: 313; 22–24: 186; 25–29: 88; 30–34: 67; 35–39: 55; 40–49: 76; 50–64: 24.

International Students: 24 nonresident aliens enrolled fall 2008. Students from Europe, Asia, Latin America, Africa, Canada, Australia. No programs available to aid students whose native language is not English. No financial aid specifically designated for international students.

Student Life: On-campus residence halls house 71% of traditional undergraduates. Residence halls for males constitute 45% of such space; for females 55%. Married student housing available. *Intercollegiate athletics:* male: baseball, basketball, golf; female: softball, basketball, golf, volleyball. *Special regulations:* Cars permitted without restrictions. Appropriate dress required. Curfews. *Special services:* medical services, career counseling. *Student publications, radio:* Newspaper; yearbook. Radio station WNAZ broadcasts 24 hours a day, 7 days per week. *Surrounding community:* Nashville population 1,000,000. Served by mass transit bus system; airport 6 miles from campus.

Library Collections: 111,000 volumes including bound books, serial backfiles, electronic documents, and government documents not in separate collections. Online catalog. 308,000 microforms; 4,600 audiovisual materials; 485 current serial subscriptions. Students have access to the Internet at no charge.

Most important special collections include university history, Church of the Nazarene history.

Buildings and Grounds: Campus area 75 acres.

Chief Executive Officer: Dr. Donald Boone, President.

Address admission inquiries to Patty Cook, Director of Admissions.

Tusculum College

Greeneville, Tennessee 37743
Tel: (423) 636-7300 **E-mail:** admissions@tusculum.edu
Fax: (423) 638-9166 **Internet:** www.tusculum.edu

Institution Description: Tusculum College is a private college affiliated with the Presbyterian Church (USA). *Enrollment:* 2,241. *Degrees awarded:* Baccalaureate, master's.

Accreditation: *Regional:* SACS-Comm. on Coll.

History: Established and chartered as Greeneville College, and offered first instruction at postsecondary level 1794; awarded first degree (baccalaureate) 1799; merged with Tusculum College (established 1818), and changed name to Greeneville and Tusculum College 1868; adopted present name 1912. *See* Allen Edgar Ragan, *A History of Tusculum College 1794–1944* (Greeneville: Tusculum Sesquicentennial Committee, 1945) and Joseph T. Fuhrmann, *The Life and Times of Tusculum College* (Greeneville: Tusculum College, 1987) for further information.

Institutional Structure: *Governing board:* Tusculum College Board of Trustees. Representation: 25 trustees, 20 alumni, 1 ex officio. All voting. *Composition of institution:* Administrators 11. Academic affairs headed by dean of faculty. Management/business/finances directed by director of planning and budget. Full-time instructional faculty 66. Academic governance body, Faculty Affairs Committee, meets an average of 9 times per year.

Calendar: Semesters. Academic year Aug. to May. Students take one course at a time; each block course lasting 18 days. Freshmen admitted Aug., Jan. Degrees conferred and formal commencement Dec., May. Summer session of 2 terms from June to July.

Characteristics of Freshmen: 1,868 applicants (female 861, male 1,001). 74% of applicants accepted. 21% of accepted applicants enrolled.

42% (102 students) submitted SAT scores; 73% (180 students) submitted ACT scores. *25th percentile*: SAT Critical Rending 410, SAT Math 440; ACT Composite 18, ACT English 17, ACT Math 17. *75th percentile*: SAT Critical Reading 530, SAT math 523; ACT Composite 23, ACT English 23, ACT Math 23.

40% of entering freshmen expected to graduate within 5 years. 39% of freshmen from Tennessee. Freshmen from 24 states and 5 foreign countries.

Admission: Rolling admissions plan. Applicants are reviewed for admission three times each year: end of Nov., end of Jan., and end of Mar. Early acceptance available. *Requirements:* Graduation from accredited secondary school or GED; minimum 2.0 GPA. Lowest acceptable secondary school class standing 50th percentile. *Entrance tests:* College Board SAT or ACT composite. For international students minimum TOEFL score of 550 or demonstrated proficiency in English. *For transfer students:* 2.0 minimum GPA; maximum transfer credit limited only by residence requirement.

College credit and advanced placement for postsecondary-level work completed in secondary school. College credit for extrainstitutional learning (life experience) on basis of portfolio assessment.

Developmental courses offered during regular academic year; credit given.

Degree Requirements: 128 credit hours; 2.0 GPA; 32 hour residency; completion of general education core; demonstrated proficiency in 9 competencies in foundation skills and civic virtue skills.

Fulfillment of some degree requirements possible by passing College Board CLEP. Exemption from some beginning courses possible by passing other standardized tests. *Grading system:* A–F; pass; credit-no credit; withdraw (carries penalty and time limit).

Distinctive Educational Programs: Work-experience programs, including cooperative education, internships. Accelerated degree programs. Cooperative baccalaureate in medical technology with approved hospitals. Facilities and programs for independent research, including individual majors, tutorials, independent study. Tusculum College has a productive exchange program with Universidad Latina in Costa Rica, University of Edinburgh in Scotland, and Derby University in England.

Degrees Conferred: 592 *baccalaureate*; 196 *master's*. Bachelor's degrees awarded in top five disciplines: business, management, marketing, and related support services 395; education 52; psychology 16; health professions and related clinical sciences 9; communication, journalism, and related programs 6. Master's degrees awarde: various disciplines 90.

Fees and Other Expenses: *Full-time tuition per academic year 2008–09:* undergraduate $18,870; graduate charged per semester hour (contact the college for current rate). *Books and supplies:* $960 *Room and board per academic year:* $7,120. *Other expenses:* $2,800.

Financial Aid: Aid from institutionally generated funds is provided on the basis of academic merit, financial need, athletic ability, other criteria.

Financial aid to full-time, first-time undergraduate students: 93% received some form of financial aid. Average amount of aid received: federal grants $3,954; Pell grants $3,000; other federal aid $1,480; state/local grants $4,141; institutional grants $8,256.

Departments and Teaching Staff: *Total instructional faculty:* 110. Student/faculty ratio: 10:1. Degrees held by full-time faculty: doctorate 84%, master's 100%. 84% hold terminal degrees.

Enrollment: Total enrollment 2,241. Undergraduate 2,010 (full-time 99%; female 62%, male 38%). Graduate 171 (full-time 99%). Undergraduate transfer-in students 48.

Characteristics of Student Body: *Ethnic/racial makeup:* Black non-Hispanic: 11%; Hispanic: 2%; White non-Hispanic: 11%; unknown: 1%; nonresident alien 2%.

International Students: 44 nonresident aliens enrolled fall 2008. Students from Europe, Canada, Australia, New Zealand, Jamaica, Trinidad, Bahamas. Programs available to aid students whose native language is not English: English as a Second Language Program. No financial aid specifically designated for international students.

Student Life: On-campus residence halls house 64% of campus-based students. 162 males and 124 females occupy the residence halls. *Intercollegiate athletics:* male: baseball, basketball; cross-country, soccer, golf, tennis; female: basketball, softball, cross-country, golf, soccer, tennis, volleyball. *Special regulations:* Registered cars permitted without restrictions. Dormitory visitation according to posted times. *Special services:* Learning Resources Center. *Student publications: Pioneer*, a monthly newspaper; *Tusculana*, a yearbook. *Surrounding community:* Greeneville population 14,000. Knoxville, 80 miles from campus, is nearest metropolitan area. Served by airport 30 miles from campus.

Library Collections: 71,000 volumes including bound books, serial backfiles, electronic documents, and government documents not in separate collections. Card catalog. Current serial subscriptions: 1,000 paper. 231,687 microform units. Computer work stations available. Students have access to the Internet at no charge.

Most important special holdings include The Charles Coffin Collection; College Archives (1794 to present); The Andrew Johnson Collection.

Chief Executive Officer: Dr. Dolphus E. Henry, President.

Address admission inquiries to Amy Yeazel, Vice President for Enrollment Services.

Union University

1050 Union University Drive
Jackson, Tennessee 38305
Tel: (731) 668-1818 **E-mail:** info@uu.edu
Fax: (731) 661-5444 **Internet:** www.uu.edu

Institution Description: Union University is a private institution affiliated with the Tennessee Baptist Convention (Southern Baptist). *Enrollment:* 2,910. x*Degrees awarded:* Associate, baccalaureate, master's.

Accreditation: *Regional:* SACS-Comm. on Coll. *Professional*: music, nursing, social work, teacher education

History: Established as Jackson Male Academy, chartered and offered first instruction at postsecondary level 1825; awarded first degree 1828; rechartered as West Tennessee College 1844, as Southwestern Baptist University 1875; adopted present name 1907. *See* Richard Hiram Ward, *A History of Union University* (Jackson: Union University Press, 1975) for further information.

Institutional Structure: *Governing board:* Union University Board of Trustees. Extrainstitutional representation: 48 trustees; institutional representation: president of the college. 1 ex officio. 48 voting. Academic affairs headed by provost. Management/business/finances directed by vice president for business affairs. Full-time instructional faculty 133. Academic governance body, the faculty, meets an average of 10 times per year.

Calendar: Semesters. Academic year Sept. to May. Freshmen admitted Sept., Jan., Feb., June. Degrees conferred and formal commencement May, Dec. Summer session from June to July.

Characteristics of Freshmen: 1,703 applicants (687 female, 416 male). 83% of applicants admitted. 47% of applicants admitted and enrolled.

26% (111 students) submitted SAT scores; 87% (378 students) submitted ACT scores. *25th percentile*: SAT Critical Reading 520, SAT Math 500; 490; ACT Composite 21, ACT English 21, ACT Math 19. *75th percentile*: SAT Critical Reading 660, SAT Math 640; ACT Composite 27, ACT English 29, ACT Math 26.

55% of entering freshmen expected to graduate within 5 years. 76% of freshmen from Tennessee. Freshmen from 34 states and 10 foreign countries.

Admission: Rolling admissions plan. Early acceptance available. *Requirements:* Either graduation from accredited secondary school with 10 units from among English, foreign language, history, mathematics, natural sciences, social studies, or GED. Minimum 2.0 GPA. ACT composite score of 20 or comparable score on a similar examination; for nursing program ACT composite score of 20. *Entrance tests:* ACT composite preferred; College Board SAT accepted. *For transfer students:* 2.0 minimum GPA; from 4-year accredited institution 96 hours maximum transfer credit; from 2-year accredited institution 72 hours; correspondence/extension students 8 hours.

College credit and advanced placement for postsecondary-level work completed in secondary school; college credit for extrainstitutional learning on basis of faculty assessment.

Degree Requirements: *For all associate degrees:* 66 credit hours; 1 term in residence. *For all baccalaureate degrees:* 128 credit hours; 2 terms in residence; 2 hours physical education; demonstrated proficiency in English. *For all degrees:* 2.0 GPA; weekly chapel attendance; core requirements.

Fulfillment of some degree requirements possible by passing College Board CLEP, AP; exemption from some beginning courses possible by passing departmental examinations, College Board CLEP. *Grading system:* A–F; pass-fail; withdraw (carries time limit).

Distinctive Educational Programs: Evening classes. Accelerated degree programs. Cooperative baccalaureate with approved hospitals. Honors programs. *Other distinctive programs:* Rising High School Senior Program allows secondary school students to attend summer terms at Union. Study abroad at multiple locations.

Degrees Conferred: 7 *associate*; 399 *baccalaureate*; 312 *master's*; 22 *doctorate*. Bachelor's degrees awarded in top five disciplines: business, management, marketing, and related support services 119; health professions and related clinical sciences 64; education 55; philosophy/religion/theology 46; psychology 25.

Fees and Other Expenses: *Full-time tuition per academic year 2008–09:* undergraduate $17,790; graduate tuition/fees differ by program. *Other fees:* $500. *Room and board per academic year:* $6,250.

Financial Aid: Aid from institutionally generated funds is provided on the basis of academic merit. Institution has a Program Participation Agreement with the U.S. Department of Education for eligible students to receive Pell Grants and, depending upon the agreement, other federal aid.

Financial aid to full-time, first-time undergraduate students: 98% received some form of financial aid. Average amount of aid received: federal grants $3,212; state/local grants $4,377; institutional grants $1,262; loans $3,971.

Departments and Teaching Staff: *Total instructional faculty:* 151. Student/faculty ratio: 12:1. Degrees held by full-time faculty: 68% hold terminal degrees.

Enrollment: Total enrollment 2,910.

Characteristics of Student Body: *Ethnic/racial makeup:* number of Black non-Hispanic: 170; American Indian or Alaska Native: 3; Asian or Pacific Islander: 20 Hispanic: 17; White non-Hispanic: 1,789; unknown: 27.

International Students: 60 nonresident aliens enrolled fall 2008. Students from Europe, Asia, Latin America, Africa, Canada. No programs available to aid students whose native language is not English. No financial aid specifically designated for international students.

Student Life: On-campus residence halls house 53% of student body. Housing for married students; 5% of married students request institutional housing; 5% are so housed. *Athletics:* male: baseball, basketball, golf, soccer, tennis; female: basketball, softball, tennis, volleyball. *Special regulations:* Registered cars permitted in designated areas. Curfews. Residence hall visitation permitted on special occasions under supervision. *Special services:* Medical services, counseling, job placement. *Student publications: Cardinal and Cream*, a monthly newspaper; *Lest We Forget*, a yearbook; *Torch*, an annual literary magazine. *Surrounding community:* Jackson population 50,000. Memphis, 80 miles from campus, is nearest metropolitan area. Served by airport 5 miles from campus.

Library Collections: 150,000 volumes including bound books, serial backfiles, electronic documents, and government documents not in separate collections. Online catalog. Current serial subscriptions: 2,653 paper, 2,005 electronic. 440,297 microform units. 5,573 recordings; 649 compact discs. Computer work stations available campus-wide. Students have access to the Internet at no charge.

Most important special collections include the Lee Library; Bateman Collection; Baptist History Collection (rare books); Union University Archives.

Buildings and Grounds: Campus area 190 acres.

Chief Executive Officer: Dr. David S. Dockery, President.

Address admission inquiries to Richard Gumm, Vice President for Enrollment Management; graduate education inquiries to Dr. Tom Rosebrough, Dean, School of Education; MBA inquiries to Barbara Perry, Director of MBA Program.

University of Memphis

Memphis, Tennessee 38152
Tel: (901) 678-2000
Fax: (901) 678-3299 a\108 recruitment@memphis.edu**Internet:** www.memphis.edu

Institution Description: The University of Memphis, formerly known as Memphis State University, is a member of the State University and Community College System. *Enrollment:* 20,220. *Degrees awarded:* Baccalaureate, first-professional (law), master's, doctorate. Specialist degree in education also awarded.

Academic offerings subject to approval by statewide coordinating bodies. Budget subject to approval by state governing boards.

Accreditation: *Regional:* SACS-Comm. on Coll. *Professional*: business, chemistry, engineering, engineering technology, journalism, law, medical record administration, music, nursing, psychology internship, rehabilitation counseling, social work, speech-language pathology, teacher education, theatre

History: Established as West Tennessee State Normal School and offered first instruction at postsecondary level 1912; became senior college, changed name to West Tennessee State Teacher's College, and awarded first degree (baccalaureate) 1929; changed name to Memphis State College 1941; added graduate school 1951; became Memphis State University 1957; adopted present name 1994.

Institutional Structure: *Governing board:* Tennessee Board of Regents of the State University and Community College System of Tennessee. Representation: 18 regents (including 13 appointed by governor of Tennessee), 4 ex officio members: the governor, commissioner of education, commissioner of agriculture, and executive director of the Tennessee Higher Education Commissions, and on statutory member. One member is appointed from each of the state's nine congressional districts, and three are approved at-large from different geographic areas of the state. A student regent is appointed from one of the system institutions for a one-year term. *Composition of Institution:* Administrators 109. Academic affairs headed by vice provost for academic affairs. Management/business/finances directed by vice president for business and finance. Full-time instructional faculty 755. Academic governance body, Academic Senate, meets an average of 11 times per year.

Calendar: Semesters. Academic year Aug. to May. Freshmen admitted Sept., Jan., June. Degrees conferred and formal commencements Dec., May, Aug. Summer session of 2 terms, from June to Aug.

Characteristics of Freshmen: 6,625 applicants (3,495 female, 2,530 male). 66% of applicants admitted. 51% of admitted applicants enrolled.

UNIVERSITY OF MEMPHIS—*cont'd*

5% (104 students) submitted SAT scores; 92% (1,928 students) submitted ACT scores. *25th percentile*: SAT Critical Reading 460, SAT Math 470; ACT Composite 19, ACT English 19, ACT Math 17. *75th percentile*: SAT Critical Reading 620, SAT Math 590; ACT Composite 24, ACT English 25, ACT Math 24.

29% of freshmen expected to graduate within five years. 92% of freshmen from Tennessee. Freshmen from 24 states and 19 foreign countries.

Admission: Rolling admissions plan. For fall acceptance, apply no later than July. 1. Early acceptance available. *Requirements:* Either graduation from accredited secondary school or GED; or ACT minimum score 19. *Entrance tests:* ACT composite preferred; College Board SAT or institutional examination accepted. For foreign students TOEFL. *For transfer students:* 1.4 minimum GPA.

College credit for postsecondary-level work completed in secondary school and for extrainstitutional learning based on portfolio assessment; *2006 Guide to the Evaluation of Educational Experiences in the Armed Services.*

Tutoring available.

Degree Requirements: *For all undergraduate degrees:* 120 credit hours; 2.0 GPA; 1 year in residence; 2 semesters physical education courses; general education requirements. Additional requirements for some programs.

Fulfillment of some degree requirements and exemption from some beginning courses possible by passing departmental examinations and College Board CLEP. *Grading system:* A–F; credit-no credit; withdraw (carries time limit).

Distinctive Educational Programs: Work experience programs. Off-campus centers. Weekend and evening classes. Dual degree programs in medical technology; in nursing with approved hospitals. Special facilities for using telecommunications in the classroom. Interdepartmental-interdisciplinary programs in African studies, international studies, Latin American studies, urban studies. Facilities and programs for independent research, including honors programs, individual majors, tutorials. *Other distinctive programs:* Center for Instructional Service and Research. Center for Nuclear Studies. Credit and noncredit continuing education, including conferences. Tuition discounts for senior citizens and disabled students.

ROTC: Army, Navy, Air Force.

Degrees Conferred: 2,432 *baccalaureate;* 870 *master's;* 68 doctorate; 125 *first-professional:* law.Bachelor's degrees awarded in top five disciplines: communication technologies 484; education 171; communications/journalism 155; health professions and related clinical sciences 147; social sciences 128. Master's degrees awarded in top five disciplines: education 241; communication technologies 144; health professions 94; engineering 41; social sciences 31. Doctorates awarded: biological/life sciences 3; communication/journalism 5; communication technologies 6; education 14; engineering 4; English 2; health professions 7; history 1; mathematics 7; physical sciences 4; psychology 24; visual and performing arts 9.

Fees and Other Expenses: *Full-time tuition per academic year 2008–09:* undergraduate resident $6,128, nonresident $17,714; contact the university for current graduate and Law School tuition and applicable fees. *Required fees:* $868 (undergraduate). *Room and board per academic year:* $7,014. *Books and supplies:* $1,100. *Other expenses:* $4,213.

Financial Aid: Aid from institutionally generated funds is provided on the basis of academic merit, financial need, athletic ability, other criteria. Institution has a Program Participation Agreement with the U.S. Department of Education for eligible students to receive Pell Grants and, depending upon the agreement, other federal aid.

Financial aid to first-time, full-time undergraduate students: 95% received some form of aid. Average amount of aid received: federal grants $3,863; Pell grants $3,783; state/local grants $4,547; institutional grants $4,771.

Departments and Teaching Staff: *Total instructional faculty:* 1,279 (full-time 735, part-time 534). Total faculty with doctorate, first-professional, or other terminal degree: 623. Degrees held by full-time faculty: master's 15.8%, doctorate 84.2%. 86.8% hold terminal degrees.

Enrollment: Total enrollment 20,220. Undergraduate 15,823 (full-time 75%; female 82%; male 38%). Graeduate 4,397 (full-time 49%). Undergraduate transfer-in students 1,207.

Characteristics of Student Body: *Ethnic/racial makeup:* Black non-Hispanic: 39%; Asian or Pacific Islander: 3%; Hispanic: 2%; White non-Hispanic: 54%; unknown 1%; nonresident alien 1%. *Age distribution:* under 18: 252; 18–19: 3,927; 22–24: 3,309; 25–29: 193; 30–34: 971; 35–39: 693; 40–49: 905; 50–59: 278; 60–up: .6. 36% of student body attend summer sessions.

International Students: 202 nonresident aliens enrolled 2008. Students from Europe, Asia, Central and South America, Africa, Canada, Australia, New Zealand, Middle East. Programs available to aid students whose native language is not English: social, cultural. English as a Second Language Program. Financial aid specifically designated for international students.

Student Life: On-campus residence halls available. 1% of males live in fraternity housing. Housing available for married students. 11% of students live on campus. *Intercollegiate athletics:* male: baseball, basketball, football, golf, gymnastics, tennis, track; female: basketball, golf, gymnastics, tennis, track, volleyball. *Special regulations:* Cars with decals permitted in designated parking areas; fee charged. *Special services:* Learning Resources Center, medical services. *Student publications, radio, television: Helmsman*, a daily newspaper; *DeSoto*, a yearbook; a student handbook. Radio stations WKNO-FM, WSMS-AM, each broadcasts 126 hours per week. TV station WKNO broadcasts 130 hours per week; programs are of an educational nature. *Surrounding community:* Memphis metropolitan area population over 1 million. Served by mass transit bus system, airport and passenger rail service, each 15 miles from campus.

Library Collections: 1,700,000 volumes. 470,000 government documents; 3,495,312 microforms; 30,390 audiovisual materials; 15,643 current periodical subscriptions. Online catalog. Students have access to online information retrieval services and the Internet.

Most important special holdings include Mississippi Valley Collection; Church Family Papers; Martin Luther King Collection.

Buildings and Grounds: Campus area 1,160 acres. Campus DVD available.

Chief Executive Officer: Dr. Shirley C. Raines, President.

Undergraduates address admission inquiries to David Wallace, Director of Admissions; graduate inquiries to Director of Graduate and International Admissions.

College of Arts and Sciences

Degree Programs Offered: *Baccalaureate* in anthropology, biology, chemistry, comparative literature, criminal justice, economics, English, foreign languages, geography, geology, history, mathematics, medical technology, philosophy, physics, political science, psychology, sociology, social work; *master's* in anthropology, biology, chemistry, city and regional planning, criminal justice, English, geography, geology, history, individual studies, mathematics, mathematical sciences, natural science, physics, psychology, political science, public administration, Romance languages, school psychology, sociology; *doctorate* in biology, chemistry, history, mathematics, psychology.

Distinctive Educational Programs: Interdisciplinary program in comparative literature. Institute of Government Studies and Research.

Fogelman College of Business and Economics

Degree Programs Offered: *Baccalaureate* in accounting, business economics, finance, insurance, international business, management, management information systems, marketing, office administration; *master's* accounting, business administration, business education and office management, economics, finance, individual studies, management, management information systems, marketing; *doctorate* in business administration.

Distinctive Educational Programs: Interdisciplinary program in international business. Bureau of Business and Economic Research. Center for Manpower Studies.

College of Communication and Fine Arts

Degree Programs Offered: *Baccalaureate* in art, art history, journalism, music, theater, theater and communication arts; *master's* in art, art history, communication, journalism, music, music education, theater; *doctorate* in communication, music.

College of Education

Degree Programs Offered: *Baccalaureate* in consumer science, and education, exercise and sport science, sport and leisure studies, human development and learning, special education; *master's* in consumer science and education, clinical nutrition, counseling and personnel services, educational psychology and research, human movement science, instruction and curriculum leadership, leadership and policy studies; *specialist* in education; *doctorate* in counseling and personnel services, counseling psychology, educational psychology and research, instruction and curriculum leadership, leadership and policy studies, and higher and adult education.

Distinctive Educational Programs: Bureau of Education Research and Services. Center for Study of Higher Education. Duration Children's Program (ages 3-6). University Campus School (grades 1-6).

Herff College of Engineering

Degree Programs Offered: *Baccalaureate* in civil engineering, industrial and systems engineering, electrical engineering, mechanical engineering, architectural technology, computer engineering technology, electronics engineering technology, manufacturing engineering technology; *master's* in biomedical engineering, civil engineering, electrical engineering, engineering technology, mechanical engineering, industrial and systems engineering; *doctorate* in engineering.

Distinctive Educational Programs: Combined pre-medical and engineering curriculum. Institute for Engineering Research.

C. C. Humphreys School of Law

Degree Programs Offered: *First-professional.*

Admission: Baccalaureate in appropriate discipline from accredited college or university, LSAT.

Degree Requirements: *See* general requirements. *For first-professional:* 90 semester hours, 28 hours in residence.

University College

Degree Programs Offered: *Baccalaureate* in liberal studies, professional studies.

Departments and Teaching Staff: Faculty members are drawn from other schools within the University.

Distinctive Educational Programs: Flexible, individualized programs for nontraditional studies. Interdisciplinary programs in Black studies, women's studies.

School of Nursing

Degree Programs Offered: *Baccalaureate* in nursing.

Admission: In addition to meeting the general requirements for admission to the University, the following requirement must be met: associate degree in nursing, declaration of nursing as a major, license as an R.N., GPA of 2.00, interview with advisor and filing of intent form.

Degree Requirements: 132 semester hours meeting the lower and upper division requirements.

University of the South

735 University Avenue
Sewanee, Tennessee 37383-1000
Tel: (931) 598-1000 **E-mail:** admission@sewanee.edu
Fax: (931) 598-3248 **Internet:** www.sewanee.edu

Institution Description: The University of the South is an independent institution affiliated with The Episcopal Church. *Enrollment:* 1,562. *Degrees awarded:* Baccalaureate, first-professional (master of divinity), doctorate of ministry.

Member of the consortium Southern College and University Union.

Accreditation: *Regional:* SACS-Comm. on Coll. *National:* ATS. *Professional*: theology

History: Established 1857; incorporated 1858; offered first instruction at postsecondary level 1868; awarded first degree (baccalaureate) 1874. *See* George R. Fairbanks, *History of the University of the South at Sewanee, Tennessee* (Jacksonville, Fla.: The H. and W. B. Drew Company, 1905) and Arthur Benjamin Chitty, Jr., *Reconstruction at Sewanee: The Founding of the University of the South and Its First Administration, 1857–1872* (Sewanee: The University Press, 1954) for further information.

Institutional Structure: *Governing board:* Board of Trustees. Extrainstitutional representation: 131 trustees (including 7 alumni), 22 honorary trustees; institutional representation: 1 administrator, 3 full-time faculty members. 131 voting. *Composition of institution:* Administrators 18. Academic affairs headed by dean of the College of Arts and Sciences and dean of the School of Theology, both of whom report to the provost as chief academic officer. Management/business/finances directed by the provost. Full-time instructional faculty 123. Academic governance body, the faculty, meets an average of 11 times per year.

Calendar: Semesters. Academic year Aug. to May. Freshmen admitted Aug., Jan. Degrees conferred and formal commencement May. Summer session of 1 term from June to July.

Characteristics of Freshmen: 2,488 applicants (1,267 female, 1,221 male). 64% of applicants accepted. 26% of accepted applicants enrolled.

83% (240 students) submitted SAT scores; 56% (231 students) submitted ACT scores. *25th percentile*: SAT Critical Reading 570, SAT Math 560, SAT Writing 570; ACT Composite 25, ACT English 25, ACT Math 23. *75th percentile*: SAT Critical Reading 570, SAT Math 650, SAT Writing 668; ACT Composite 29, ACt English 31, ACT Math 28.

84% of entering freshmen expected to graduate within 5 years. 14% of freshmen from Tennessee. Freshmen from 36 states and 5 foreign countries.

Admission: The university admission process is very selective. Prospective students must apply by Feb. 1 for fall admissions. Deadline for early decision Nov. 15. Under this plan, students must be willing to accept admission if offered and to immediately withdraw applications from other schools. *Requirements:* GED or graduation from accredited secondary school with 13 units which must include 4 English, 2 or more in a foreign language, 3 or more mathematics, 1 social studies, academic electives. Minimum recommended GPA 3.0 on a 4-point scale. *Entrance tests:* SAT or ACT. College Board SAT or ACT composite. *For transfer students:* 3.00 minimum GPA; maximum transfer credit limited only by residence requirement.

College credit and advanced placement for postsecondary-level work completed in secondary school and for extrainstitutional learning on basis of faculty assessment; advanced placement.

Degree Requirements: 128 semester hours or 32 full courses; 2.0 GPA; 4 semesters in residence; 2 semesters physical education courses; distribution requirement; comprehensive examination in individual majors.

Fulfillment of some degree requirements and exemption from some beginning courses possible by passing institutional examinations, College Board CLEP, AP. *Grading system:* A–F.

Distinctive Educational Programs: Work-experience programs. Accelerated degree programs. Dual-degree programs with Columbia University (NY), Georgia Institute of Technology, Rensselaer Polytechnic Institute (NY), Vanderbilt University, Washington University (MO), Cambridge University (England); in forestry with Duke University (NC) and Yale University. Interdepartmental-interdisciplinary programs in American studies, comparative literature, medieval studies, Russian and Soviet studies, social science-foreign language, Third World studies. Student-initiated courses. Language houses for French, German, Spanish. Facilities and programs for independent research, including honors programs, individual majors, tutorials. Study abroad opportunities in Germany; British Studies at Oxford and International Studies in London with Rhodes College in affiliation with the Associated Colleges of the South and Vanderbilt University; Sewanee-Oxford at Herford College, Oxford University; European Studies in Britain and on the Continent, jointly sponsored by Rhodes College and the University of the South; Study in Spain in conjunction with the Vanderbilt-in-Spain program; Study in Japan under an exchange program with Rikkyo University and the University of the South; Asian Studies in Singapore at the National University of Singapore; Semester in Liberia sponsored by the Lutheran Church in America; Japanese Studies in Nagoya at Nanzan University in Japan sponsored by the Institute of European Studies/Institute of Asian Studies; Studies in Europe in cooperation with the Institute of European Studies/Institute of Asian Studies (programs located at Durham and London, England; Freiberg, Germany; Madrid, Spain; Milan, Italy; Nantes and Paris, France; and Vienna, Austria). Off-campus study at Oak Ridge National Laboratories through consortium. Institutional summer internships in public affairs and in economics.

Degrees Conferred: 346 *baccalaureate*; 3 *master's*; 5 *doctorate*. Bachelor's degrees awarded in top five disciplines: social sciences 73; English language/literature 48; visual and performing arts 34; history 27; biological/life sciences 27. *First-professional:* master of divinity 28.

Fees and Other Expenses: *Full-time tuition per academic year 2008–09:* undergraduate $32,760; contact the university for current graduate/first-professional tuition/fees. *Books and supplies:* $800. *Room and board per academic year:* $8,360. *Other expenses:* $1,100.

Financial Aid: Aid from institutionally generated funds is provided on the basis of academic merit and financial need.

Financial aid to full-time, first-time undergraduate students: 63% received some form of financial aid. Average amount of aid received: federal grants $2,123; Pell grants $2,664; other federal grants $1,562; state/local grants $2,993; institutional grants $18,300.

Departments and Teaching Staff: *Total instructional faculty:* 140. Student/faculty ratio: 11:1. Degrees held by full-time faculty: master's 5%, doctorate 95%. 95% hold terminal degrees.

Enrollment: Total enrollment 1,611.

Characteristics of Student Body: *Ethnic/racial makeup:* Black non-Hispanic: 4%; American Indian or Alaska Native: 1%; Asian or Pacific Islander: 3%; Hispanic: 4%; White non-Hispanic: 88%; nonresident alien 2%.

International Students: 32 nonresident aliens enrolled fall 2008. Students from Europe, Asia, Latin America, Africa, Canada. Programs available for students whose native language is not English: social, cultural, financial. Financial aid specifically designated for international students: scholarships available annually to qualifying students.

Student Life: On-campus residence halls house 90% of student body. Residence halls for males constitute 38% of such space, for females 35%; for both sexes 20%. Three language houses serve as residence halls. 90% of married students request institutional housing and are so housed. *Intercollegiate athletics:* (NCAA Division III) male: baseball, basketball, cross-country, football, golf, soccer, swimming, tennis, track; female: basketball, cross-country, field hockey, soccer, softball, swimming, tennis, track, volleyball. Club sports that compete intercollegiately include canoe, cycling, fencing, lacrosse, rugby, and skiing for men; canoe, equestrian, lacrosse, and skiing for women. *Special regulations:*

UNIVERSITY OF THE SOUTH—*cont'd*

Cars permitted in designated areas. Quiet hours. Visitation in dormitories from 9am to midnight Sun.–Thurs., 9am to 1am Fri. and Sat. *Special services:* Medical services, counseling, career services. *Student publications, radio:* A literary magazine, a newspaper, yearbook, and a scholarly journal. Radio station WUTS broadcasts 80 hours per week. *Surrounding community:* Sewanee population 3,500. Chattanooga, 56 miles from campus, is nearest metropolitan area. Served by airport 60 miles from campus.

Publications: *The Sewanne Review,* America's oldest literary quarterly, and the *Sewanee Theological Review* are published by the University of the South.

Library Collections: 649,000 volumes. 308,520 government documents (separate collection); 328,000 microforms; 73,000 audiovisual materials; 3,400 current serial subscriptions. Students have access to online information retrieval services and the Internet.

Most important special collections include Sewaneeana (letters, manuscripts, personal papers, official records of the University of the South); Episcopal Church History and Theology; Southern History and Theology; limited editions books.

Buildings and Grounds: Campus area 10,000 acres. Campus DVD available.

Chief Executive Officer: Dr. Joel Cunningham, President.

Address admission inquiries to David Lesesne, Dean of Admissions.

University of Tennessee

System Administration
Knoxville, Tennessee 37916
Tel: (865) 974-1000 **E-mail:** info@utk.edu
Fax: (865) 974-3753 **Internet:** www.utk.edu

Institution Description: The University of Tennessee, a state university system and land-grant college, has primary campuses at Chattanooga, Knoxville, Martin, and Memphis. Undergraduate and graduate programs are offered at all four campuses. At UT Memphis all degree programs are in the health sciences. Professional programs are offered at Knoxville and Memphis.

Institutional Structure: *Governing board:* The University of Tennessee Board of Trustees. 19 trustees, including 1 student, appointed by the governor of Tennessee; governor; commissioner of education; commissioner of agriculture; president of the university; executive director of the Tennessee Higher Education Commission. 5 ex officio. 23 voting.

Admission: For fall acceptance, apply as early as senior year of secondary school, but not later than Aug. 1 of year of enrollment. *Requirements:* Set by each campus. Entering high school graduates are considered on basis of ACT (SAT may be accepted), grade point average, and high school units completed. Inquire directly to the campus. Adult and transfer students should also inquire to individual campuses for admissions requirements.

Distinctive Educational Programs: Cooperative education programs at all campuses. Honors programs at Chattanooga, Knoxville, and Martin. Study abroad through Knoxville campus available to students at other system campuses. Agriculture Extension Service and Agriculture Experiment Stations offer programs and services throughout the state. UT Space Institute conducts research and graduate study programs in engineering and physical sciences. The Institute for Public Service coordinates assistance programs for state and local governments and industry. The Division of Continuing Education offers the Center for Extended Learning, Radio and Television Services.

Chief Executive Officer: Dr. John D. Petersen, President.

Address admission inquiries to individual campuses.

University of Tennessee at Chattanooga

615 McCallie Avenue
Chattanooga, Tennessee 37403
Tel: (423) 755-4111 **E-mail:** admin/ug@utc.edu
Fax: (423) 755-4157 **Internet:** www.utc.edu

Institution Description: *Enrollment:* 9,807. *Degrees awarded:* Baccalaureate, master's, doctorate. Educational specialist certificate also awarded.

Accreditation: *Regional:* SACS-Comm. on Coll. *Professional*: business, chemistry, engineering, journalism, music, nursing, physical therapy, public administration, social work, teacher education

History: Established as Chattanooga University by the Methodist Episcopal Church 1866; awarded first degree (baccalaureate) 1888; changed name to Grant University 1889; changed name to University of Chattanooga 1907; became independent of church 1909; merged with University of Tennessee and Chattanooga City College 1969.

Institutional Structure: *Composition of institution:* Administrators 100. Academic affairs headed by provost. Management/business/finances directed by vice chancellor for finance and administration. Full-time instructional faculty 375. Academic governance body, Faculty Council, meets an average of 15 times per year.

Calendar: Semesters. Academic year Aug. to May. Freshmen admitted Aug., Jan., May, June, July. Degrees conferred and formal commencements May, Dec., Aug. Summer session of 5 terms from May to Aug.

Characteristics of Freshmen: 5,849 applicants (3,481 female, 2,360 male). 79% of applicants admitted. 45% of applicants admitted and enrolled.

7% (127 students) submitted SAT scores; 92% (1,642 students) submitted ACT scores. *25th percentile*: ACT Composite 17, ACT English 18, ACT Math 17. *75th percentile*: ACT Composite 23, ACT English 26, ACT Math 25.

30% of entering freshmen expected to graduate within 5 years. 94% of freshmen from Tennessee. Freshmen from 25 states and 11 foreign countries.

Admission: Students with a 2.00 high school GPA or ACT 16 (SAT 900) and required high school units in English, mathematics, laboratory science, American history, social sciences, and foreign language are admitted as regular students. Applicants below those standards may be admitted as conditional.

College credit and advanced placement for postsecondary-level work completed in secondary school and college credit for extrainstitutional learning on basis of faculty assessment.

Tutoring available. Developmental/remedial courses offered in summer session and regular academic year; credit given.

Degree Requirements: 128 credit hours; 2.0 GPA; last 30 hours in residence; 2 physical education courses; general education requirements.

Fulfillment of some degree requirements and exemption from some beginning courses possible by passing departmental and institutional examinations, College Board CLEP, AP. *Grading system:* A–F; pass-fail; withdraw (carries time limit).

Distinctive Educational Programs: Flexible meeting places and schedules, including off-campus centers, weekend and evening classes. Accelerated degree programs. Dual-degree programs in political science or public administration with the University of Tennessee at Knoxville, communications, environmental studies, humanities. Preprofessional programs in nursing, pharmacy, physical therapy. *Other distinctive programs:* The Cadek Conservatory of Music provides music education in students of all ages who are not enrolled at university level. Credit and noncredit continuing education offers weekend and evening classes both on- and off-campus. University offers senior citizens and disabled persons the opportunity to audit classes free of charge.

Degrees Conferred: 1,258 *baccalaureate*; 355 *master's*; 27 *doctorate*. Bachelor's degrees awarded in top five disciplines: business, management, marketing, and related support services 347; education 173; psychology 92; health professions and related clinical sciences 80; biological/life sciences 53. Master's degrees awarded: business/marketing 91; computer and information sciences 4; education 123; engineering 2; engineering tedchnologies 2; English 15; health professions 29; natural resources and environmental science 9; parks and recreation 21; psychology 7; public administration and social services 14; security and protective services 7; visual and performing arts 1. Doctorates awarded: education 1; health professions 26.

Fees and Other Expenses: *Full-time tuition per academic year 2008–09:* undergraduate resident $5,310, nonresident $15,810; contact the university for current graduate tuition and applicable fees. *Room and board per academic year:* $8,100. *Required fees:* $940. *Books and supplies:* $1,000. *Other expenses:* $3,032.

Financial Aid: Aid from institutionally generated funds is provided on the basis of academic merit.

Financial aid to full-time, first-time undergraduate students: 96% received some form of aid. Average amount of aid received: federal grants $2,507; Pell grants $3,741; other federal aid $738; state/local grants $5,041; institutional grants $3,655.

Departments and Teaching Staff: *Total instructional faculty:* 637 (full-time 375, part-time 262). Total faculty with doctorate, first-professional, or other terminal degree: 345. Student/faculty ratio: 14:1. Degrees held by full-time faculty: doctorate 81%, master's 19%. 83% hold terminal degrees.

Enrollment: Total enrollment 9,801. Undergraduate 8,405 (full-time 88%; female 56%, male 44%). Graduate 1,402 (full-time 42%). Undergraduate transfer-in students 667.

Characteristics of Student Body: *Ethnic/racial makeup:* Black non-Hispanic: 17%; Asian or Pacific Islander: 2%; Hispanic: 2%; White non-Hispanic: 77%; nonresident alien 1%. *Age distribution:* number under 18: 39; 18–19: 2,468, 20–21: 2,130; 22–24: 1,619; 25–29: 659; 30–34: 241; 35–39: 144; 40–49: 189; 50–64: 55; 65 and over: 4.

International Students: 98 nonresident aliens enrolled fall 2008. Students from Europe, Asia, Latin America, Africa; Canada, Australia, Middle East. Programs available to aid students whose native language is not English: English as a Second Language Program. No financial aid specifically designated for international students.

Student Life: 30% of students live on campus. Eight national fraternities and seven national sororities are offered, student governance is available in the Student Government Association. Religious life is offered through the Baptist Student Union, United Methodist Student Center, Catholic Center, Presbyterian Campus Ministry, and Church of Christ Center with centers on campus. *Intercollegiate athletics:* male: basketball, football, tennis, wrestling, golf, cross-country; female: basketball, golf, softball, tennis, volleyball. *Special services:* Counseling and Career Center, Health Services, tutorial and study skills programs, University Housing, Food Services, Career Placement, Job Location and Development, Adult Services Center, Developmental Studies. *Student publications, radio: The Echo,* a student newspaper; *The Moccasin,* a yearbook; *Sequoya Review,* a semiannual literary magazine. Radio station WUTC. *Surrounding community:* Chattanooga population 175,000. Served by mass transit bus system; airport 10 miles from campus.

Publications: *Poetry Miscellany* (annually) first published 1971.

Library Collections: 503,000 volumes. 1,400,000 microforms; 2,770 current serial subscriptions. Online catalog. 146,500 audiovisual materials. Students have access to online information retrieval services and the Internet.

Most important special holdings include Civil War History Collection; local historical manuscripts collection; newspapers on microfilm.

Buildings and Grounds: Campus area 116.5 acres.

Chief Executive Officer: Dr. Roger Brown, Chancellor.

Undergraduates address admission inquiries to Yancy Freeman, Director of Admissions; graduate inquiries to Dr. Deborah Arfken, Director of Graduate Admissions.

University of Tennessee at Knoxville

800 Andy Holt Tower
Knoxville, Tennessee 37996
Tel: (865) 974-2184 **E-mail:** admissions@utk.edu
Fax: (865) 974-5341 **Internet:** www.utk.edu

Institution Description: *Enrollment:* 30,410. *Degrees awarded:* Baccalaureate, first-professional (law, veterinary medicine), master's (some programs offered at branches in Nashville and Memphis, as well as Knoxville); doctorate.

Member of the consortium Oak Ridge Associated Universities.

Accreditation: *Regional:* SACS-Comm. on Coll. *Professional*: architecture, art, business, chemistry, counseling, engineering, interior design, journalism, law, librarianship, music, nursing, planning, psychology internship, public health, recreation and leisure services, social work, speech-language pathology, teacher education, veterinary medicine

History: Established and chartered as Blount College 1794; offered first instruction at postsecondary level 1795; awarded first degree (baccalaureate) 1806; changed name to East Tennessee College 1807, East Tennessee University 1840; adopted present name 1879. *See* James Riley Montgomery, *The Threshold of a New Day* (Knoxville: The University of Tennessee, 1971) for further information.

Institutional Structure: *Composition of institution:* Administrators 28. Academic affairs headed by chancellor. Management/business/finances directed by vice chancellor for business and finance. Full-time instructional faculty 1,540. Academic governance body, Faculty Senate, meets an average of 11 times per year.

Calendar: Semesters. Academic year Aug. to May. Freshmen admitted Aug., Jan., June. Degrees conferred and formal commencements May, Aug., Dec. Summer session of 2 terms from June to Aug.

Characteristics of Freshmen: 12,824 applicants (6,882 female, 5,942 male). 71% of applicants admitted. 48% of applicants admitted and enrolled.

37% (1,555 students) submitted SAT scores; 89% (3,783 students) submitted ACT scores. *25th percentile*: SAT Critical Reading 520, SAT Math 530; ACT Composite 23, ACT English 23, ACT Math 23. *75th percentile*: SAT Critical Reading 630, SAT Math 640; ACT Composite 28, ACT English 27, ACT Math 29.

55% of entering freshmen expected to graduate within 5 years. 86% of freshmen from Tennessee. Freshmen from 36 states and 17 foreign countries.

Admission: The university's admissions policy for incoming freshmen weights entrance test scores, high school grade point average, class rank, and writing samples as admissions factors. In addition, high school coursework must include 4 units English, 3 mathematics (1 of which must be geometry, trigonometry, advanced math, or calculus), 2 natural science science (including at least on year of biology, chemistry, or physics), 2 of a single foreign language, 1 visual or performing arts, 1 American history, 1 European history or world geography.

Degree Requirements: 180–240 credit hours; 2.0 GPA; final year in residence; general education requirements, 1 unit American history on secondary school level or 9 quarter hours on postsecondary level.

Fulfillment of some degree requirements and exemption from some beginning courses possible by passing departmental examinations, College Board CLEP. *Grading system:* A–F; satisfactory-no credit; withdraw.

Distinctive Educational Programs: Flexible meeting places and schedules, including off-campus centers, evening classes. Accelerated degree programs. Special facilities for using telecommunications in the classroom. Interdisciplinary programs in African and Afro-American studies, American studies, ancient Mediterranean civilizations, Asian studies, business education, comparative literature, home economics education, Latin American studies, linguistics, medieval studies, Russian and East European studies, urban studies, women's studies. Facilities and programs for independent research, including honors programs, individual majors, tutorials. *Other distinctive programs:* Continuing education. Students can spend a semester or academic year abroad in one of more than 100 universities in more than 30 countries worldwide.

ROTC: Army, Air Force.

Degrees Conferred: 3,655 *baccalaureate*; 1,556 *master's*; 319 *doctorate*; 556 *first-professional*. Bachelor's degrees awarded in top five disciplines: business, management, marketing, and related support services 666; psychology social sciences 557; psychology 410; communications/journalism 335; health professions and related clinical sciences 241. Master's degrees awarded in top five disciplines: education 302; business 242; security and protective services 203; engineering 166; health professions 203. Doctorates awarded in top five disciplines: engineering 43; education 42; biological/life sciences 35; physical sciences 30; psychology 23. First-professional degrees awarded: dentistry 77; pharmacy 120; veterinary medicine 65; law 147; medicine 147.

Fees and Other Expenses: *Full-time tuition per academic year 2008–09:* undergraduate $6,250, nonresident $19,208; contact the university for graduate and first-professional tuition and applicable fees. Professional school tuition and fees vary. *Room and board per academic year:* $6,888. *Books and supplies:* $1,326. *Other expenses:* $5,154.

Financial Aid: Aid from institutionally generated funds is provided on the basis of academic merit, financial need, athletic ability, other criteria.

Financial aid to full-time, first-time undergraduate students: 92% received some form of aid. Average amount of aid received: federal grants $3,175; Pell grants $3,017; other federal aid $1,110; state/local grants $4,706; institutional grants $3,550.

Departments and Teaching Staff: *Total instructional faculty:* 1,625 (full-time 1,540, part-time 85). Total faculty with doctorate, first-professional, or other terminal degree: 1,3'19. Student/faculty ratio: 15:1. Degrees held by full-time faculty: doctorate 77%, master's 15%, professional 6%. 83% hold terminal degrees.

Enrollment: Total enrollment 30,410. Undergraduate 21,717 (full-time 94%; female 50%, male 50%). Graduate 8,693 (full-time 74%). Undergraduate transfer-in studnets 1,320.

Characteristics of Student Body: *Ethnic/racial makeup:* Black non-Hispanic: 8%; Asian or Pacific Islander: 3%; Hispanic: 2%; White non-Hispanic: 85%; unknown: 1%; nonresident alien 1%. *Age distribution:* number under 18: 18–19: 6,766; 20–21: 7,414; 22–24: 4,259.

International Students: 1,199 nonresident aliens enrolled fall 2008. No programs available to aid students whose native language is not English. Financial aid specifically designated for international students.

Student Life: On-campus residence halls house 34% of student body. Residence halls for males constitute 23% of such space, for females 28%, for both sexes 49%. 13% of males join fraternities; 19% of females join sororities. *Intercollegiate athletics:* male: baseball, basketball, football, golf, swimming, tennis, track, wrestling; female: basketball, swimming, tennis, track, volleyball. *Special regulations:* Registered cars permitted without restrictions. *Special services:* Learning Resources Center, medical services, campus bus service. *Student publications, radio: The Daily Beacon,* a newspaper; *The Phoenix,* a quarterly literary magazine; *The Portfolio,* an annual architecture journal; *The Tennessee Engineer,* a quarterly engineering publication; *The Tennessee Farmer,* a quarterly agricultural publication; *The Tennessee Law Review,* a quarterly. Radio station WUOT broadcasts 133 hours per week. *Surrounding community:* Knoxville metropolitan area population 500,000. Served by mass transit bus system; airport 8 miles from campus.

Library Collections: 3,300,000 volumes. 4,356,422 units of microforms; 33,769 audiovisual materials; 16,656 serial subscriptions. 41,913 audio/videotapes. 173,009 recordings. Computer work stations available campus-wide. students have access to online information retrieval services and the Internet.

Most important holdings include Estes Kefauver collection; personal papers of William Blount and John Sevier; Cherokee Phoenix collection (early 19th-century newspaper by and for the Cherokee); Alex Haley Papers; Howard Baker, Jr. Papers; Jane Austen Collection.

Buildings and Grounds: Campus area 417 acres.

Chief Executive Officer: Dr. John Peterson, President.

UNIVERSITY OF TENNESSEE AT KNOXVILLE—*cont'd*

Undergraduates and first-professional students address admission inquiries to Nancy McGlasson, Director of Asmissions; graduate inquiries to Dr. Carolyn Hodges, Dean of Graduate School.

College of Liberal Arts

Degree Programs Offered: *Baccalaureate* in ecology, economics, human services; *master's, doctorate* in radiation biology; *baccalaureate, master's, doctorate* in anthropology, art, audiology and speech pathology, biochemistry, biology, botany, chemistry, classics, computer science, cultural science, English, geography, geological sciences, Germanic and Slavic languages, history, mathematics, microbiology, music, philosophy, physics and astronomy, political science, psychology, religious studies, Romance languages, sociology, speech and theater, statistics, zoology.

Distinctive Educational Programs: Work-experience program in chemistry. Preprofessional programs in dentistry, dental hygiene, medicine, medical record administration, medical technology, nursing, pharmacy, physical therapy. Individual majors.

College of Agricultural Sciences and Natural Sciences

Degree Programs Offered: *Baccalaureate, master's, doctorate* in agricultural economics and rural sociology, agricultural and extension education, agricultural engineering, agricultural mechanization, animal science, entomology and plant pathology, food science and technology, forestry, ornamental horticultural and landscape design, plant and soil science, wildlife and fisheries.

Distinctive Educational Programs: Work-experience program. Preprofessional program in veterinary medicine.

College of Architecture and Planning

Degree Programs Offered: *Baccalaureate, master's, first-professional.*

Admission: Admission to undergraduate programs is competitive, based on high school record, test scores, and optional portfolio.

Degree Requirements: Vary by program.

Distinctive Educational Programs: Work-experience programs and community field studies. Institutionally sponsored study in Poland, Italy, Portugal, and other locations. Internships. Urban Design Center in Chattanooga. Interdisciplinary design studios. Public lecture series.

College of Business Administration

Degree Programs Offered: *Baccalaureate, master's, doctorate* in business, management.

Distinctive Educational Programs: Innovative cross functional business education programs primarily in management development (nondegree institutes), MBA 21-month full-time, and executive education MBA (1 year in six residence periods).

College of Communications

Degree Programs Offered: *Baccalaureate, master's, doctorate* in communications with a concentration in advertising, broadcasting, journalism, public relations, and science communications.

Distinctive Educational Programs: Work-experience programs, including internships.

College of Education

Degree Programs Offered: *Baccalaureate, master's, educational specialist, doctorate.*

Distinctive Educational Programs: Field experience available in professional development schools and many cooperating agencies.

College of Engineering

Degree Programs Offered: *Baccalaureate, master's, doctorate* in aerospace engineering, biomedical engineering, chemical engineering, civil engineering, electrical engineering, engineering physics, engineering science, environmental engineering, industrial engineering, mechanical engineering, materials science and engineering (metallurgical and polymer), nuclear engineering.

Distinctive Educational Programs: Cooperative engineering and minority engineering programs. Training and work experience through Maintenance and Reliability Center integrated into engineering degree program.

College of Human Ecology

Degree Programs Offered: *Baccalaureate* in child and family studies, community health education, recreation and leisure studies, business/marketing education, industrial education, hotel and restaurant administration, nutrition, retail and consumer science; *master's* in child and family studies, health promotion and health education, human resource development, nutrition, public health, recreation and leisure studies, safety education and service, textiles retailing, and consumer sciences; *doctorate* in child and family studies, nutrition, textile science, retail and consumer science, human resource development, health education.

Distinctive Educational Programs: Internships and field-based experiences. Teacher education programs in family and consumer science, business education, marketing education, technology education, and early childhood education.

College of Nursing

Degree Programs Offered: *Baccalaureate, master's.*

Degree Requirements: *For baccalaureate:* 123 semester hours. *Master's* for nurses with BSN: 36 semester hours; *master's* for non-nurses with college degree: 77 semester hours; *for doctorate:* 72 semester hours.

College of Law

Degree Programs Offered: *First-professional.*

Admission: Baccalaureate from accredited college or university; LSAT.

Degree Requirements: 89 credit hours; 2.0 GPA; 6 semesters in residence.

Distinctive Educational Programs: The Legal Clinic, the Center for Advocacy, and the Center for Entrepreneurial Law.

College of Veterinary Medicine

Degree Programs Offered: *First-professional.*

Admission: Admission of new students for the fall semester each year. Priority is given to qualified Tennessee residents. Baccalaureate from accredited college or university with 66 hours of required pre-veterinary program which must include 6 units in English, 18 humanities,/social sciences; 8 physics, 8 general chemistry, 8 organic chemistry, 8 general biology, 3 genetic, 3 cellular biology, 4 of cellular and comparative biochemistry.

Degree Requirements: 152 semester hours; 2.0 GPA; 9 semesters in residence.

Distinctive Educational Programs: Residency training programs in various clinical specialties.

Graduate School of Biomedical Sciences

Degree Programs Offered: *Master's, doctorate.*

Distinctive Educational Programs: Joint facilities with Oak Ridge National Laboratory.

School of Information Sciences

Degree Programs Offered: *Master's.*

Admission: Minimum undergraduate GPA of 3.0 or a satisfactory graduate degree GPA; total GRE score of 1500 or better unless a graduate degree has been completed prior to application for admission; three recommendations.

Degree Requirements: 43 semester hours, 16 of which form a core curriculum; final examination; culminating experience.

College of Social Work

Degree Programs Offered: *Master's.*

Admission: Beginning in 1997, the GRE scores are required for the general section. No minimum score specified. Baccalaureate degree from accredited college or university; GPA 2.7 or higher; personal qualifications acceptable for entrance into the professional practice of social work.

Degree Requirements: Minimum 60 semester hours including foundation courses and field practice; 30 hours of coursework and field practice in the clinical social work practice concentration or the social welfare management and community practice concentration; overall GPA 3.0 or better; comprehensive examination or successful defense of a thesis.

Distinctive Educational Programs: Field experience. Branch campuses in Memphis, Nashville. *Other distinctive program:* Continuing education.

University of Tennessee Space Institute

Degree Programs Offered: *Master's, doctorate* in aerospace engineering, electrical engineering, engineering science, mechanical engineering, metallurgical engineering and physics; *master's* in aviation systems, chemical engineering, computer science, industrial engineering, mathematics.

Distinctive Educational Programs: Arnold Engineering Development Center provides research opportunities and facilities.

University of Tennessee at Martin

University Street
Martin, Tennessee 38238
Tel: (731) 587-7000 **E-mail:** admitme@utm.edu
Fax: (731) 587-7503 **Internet:** www.utm.edu

Institution Description: *Enrollment:* 7,574. *Degrees awarded:* Baccalaureate, master's.

Academic offerings subject to approval by statewide coordinating bodies.

Accreditation: *Regional:* SACS-Comm. on Coll. *Professional*: business, chemistry, engineering, engineering technology, family and consumer science, music, nursing, social work, teacher education

History: The University of Tennessee at Martin traces it origin to Hall-Moody Institute, established by the Baptists of Martin in 1900. it gained junior college status in 1927 and was named University of Tennessee Junior College; became 4-year institution and changed name to University of Tennessee Martin Branch 1953; adopted present name 1967.

Institutional Structure: *Composition of institution:* Administrators 136. Academic affairs, finance and administration, university advancement, student affairs all directed by vice chancellors. Full-time instructional faculty 252. Academic governance body, Faculty Senate, meets 6 times per year.

Calendar: Semesters. Academic year Aug. to May. Freshmen admitted Aug., Jan., May, June. Degrees conferred and formal commencements May, Aug., Dec. Summer session of 2 terms from June to Aug.

Characteristics of Freshmen: 3,833 applicants (1,951 female, 1,376 male). 76% of applicants admitted. 55% of applicants admitted and enrolled.

89% (1,091 students) submitted ACT scores. *25th percentile*: ACT Composite 19, ACT English 19, ACT Math 17. *75th percentile*: ACT Composite 24, ACT English 25, ACT Math 24.

37% of entering freshmen expected to graduate within 5 years. 94% of freshmen from Tennessee. Freshmen from 17 states and 8 foreign countries.

Admission: UTM requires an ACT score of 20 and high school GPA of 2.40 or ACT score of 17 and 2.75 GPA. Special programs are available for students who do not meet these requirements.

Degree Requirements: *For all baccalaureate degrees:* 124–134 semester hours; last 2 terms in residence. *For all undergraduate degrees:* 2.0 GPA; general education requirements.

Fulfillment of some degree requirements and exemption from some beginning courses possible by passing College Board CLEP. *Grading system:* A–F; pass-fail; withdraw (carries time limit).

College credit and advanced placement for postsecondary-level work completed in secondary school. For extrainstitutional learning college credit.

Tutoring available. Developmental/remedial courses offered in summer session and regular academic year; credit given.

Distinctive Educational Programs: Accelerated program. Cooperative education program. Cross-registration. Distance Learning. Double Major. Dual enrollment. Exchange student program (domestic). Honors Program; independent study, internships, student-designed majr. Study abroad. Teacher certification program. English as a second language.

ROTC: Army. 8 commissions awarded 2006.

Degrees Conferred: 998 *baccalaureate*; 142 *master's*. Bachelor's degrees awarded in top five disciplines: business/marketing 178; interdisciplinary studies 118; education 84; parks and recreation 48; natural resources/environmental science 21. Master's degrees awarded: agriculture 8; business/marketing 44; education 84; family and consumer science 6.

Fees and Other Expenses: *Full-time tuition per academic year 2008–09:* undergraduate resident $5,285, nonresident $15,877; contact the university for current graduate tuition/fees. *Required fees:* $749. *Room and board per academic year:* $4,806. *Books and supplies:* $1,200. *Other expenses:* $3,380.

Financial Aid: Aid from institutionally generated funds is provided on the basis of academic merit, financial need, athletic ability, other criteria.

Financial aid to full-time, first-time undergraduate students: 95% received some form of aid. Average amount of aid recieved: federal grants $3,514; Pell grants $3,149; other federal aid $726; state/local grants $4,920; institutional grants $3,019.

Departments and Teaching Staff: *Total instructional faculty:* 446 (full-time 252, part-time 194). Total faculty with doctorate, first-professional, or other terminal degree: 224. Student/faculty ratio: 17:1. Degrees held by full-time faculty: master's 16%, doctorate 74%. 81 hold terminal degrees.

Enrollment: Total enrollment 7,514. Undergraduate 7,123 (full-time 77%; female 57%; male 43%). Graduate 451 (full-time 18%). Undergraduate transfer-in students 427.

Characteristics of Student Body: *Ethnic/racial makeup:* Black non-Hispanic: 145; Asian or Pacific Islander: 1%; Hispanic: 1%; White non-Hispanic: 82%; nonresident alien 2%. *Age distribution:* number under 18: 518; 18–19: 1,761, 20–21: 1,697; 22–24: 1,077; 25–29: 439; 30–34: 196; 35–39: 159; 40–49: 185; 50–64: 81; 65 and over: 7. 21% of study body attend summer sessions.

International Students: 150 nonresident aliens enrolled fall 2008. Students from Europe, Asia, Latin America, Africa, Canada, Middle East. Programs available to aid students whose native language is not English: social, cultural. English as a Second Language Program. No financial aid specifically designated for foreign students.

Student Life: On-campus residence halls house 31% of student body. Apartment-style housing accounts for 35% of campus housing. *Intercollegiate athletics:* male: baseball, basketball, mixed rifle, cross-country, football, tennis, rodeo, golf; female: basketball, cross-country, women's rifle, soccer, tennis, volleyball, rodeo. *Special regulations:* Cars permitted in designated areas. Quiet hours. Residence hall visitation is differentiated; student can choose any of four types of visitation. *Special services:* Medical services, computer labs, child care. *Student publications, radio: PACER*, a weekly newspaper; *Spirit*, a yearbook; *Bean Switch*, an annual literary magazine. Radio station WUTM (AM and FM) broadcasts 90 hours per week. *Surrounding community:* Martin population 10,151. Memphis, 125 miles from campus, is nearest metropolitan area. Served by major bus system.

Publications: *Business and Economic Perspectives* (biannually) first published in 1976.

Library Collections: 508,000 volumes including bound books, serial backfiles, electronic documents, and government documents not in separate collections. Online catalog. 705,000 microforms; 14,000 audiovisual materials; 1,200 current serial subscriptions. Computer work stations available. Students have access to the Internet at no charge.

Most important special holdings include Congressman Ed Jones Papers; former Governor Ned McWhether Papers; Holland McCombs Papers; Tennessee Collection.

Buildings and Grounds: Campus area 900 acres.

Chief Executive Officer: Nick Donagan, Chancellor.

Undergraduates address admission inquiries to Judy Rayburn, Director of Admissions; graduate inquiries to Linda Arant, Director of Graduate Studies.

University of Tennessee Health Science Center

800 Monroe Avenue
Memphis, Tennessee 38163
Tel: (901) 448-5560 **E-mail:** admissions@utmem.edu
Fax: (901) 448-7772 **Internet:** www.utmem.edu

Institution Description: The University of Tennessee Health Science Center was formerly named The University of Tennessee at Memphis. It is a state institution. *Enrollment:* 2,116. *Degrees awarded:* Baccalaureate, first-professional (dentistry, medicine, pharmacy), master's, doctorate.

Academic offerings subject to approval by statewide coordinating bodies Budget subject to approval by state governing boards.

Accreditation: *Regional:* SACS-Comm. on Coll. *Professional*: cytotechnology, dental hygiene, dentistry, medical record administration, medicine, nursing, occupational therapy, pharmacy, physical therapy, psychology internship, social work.

History: Established in Memphis as the University of Tennessee Medical Units and offered first instruction at postsecondary level 1911; awarded first degree (first-professional) 1912; became the University of Tennessee Center for the Health Sciences in 1974; adopted present name in 1985. *See University of Tennessee Record*, Vol. 49, vol. 74, no. 1 (1946): vol. 64, no. 3 (1961); vol. 69, no. 6 (1966); vol. 74, no. 6 (1971), vol. 8, no. 1 (1986) for further information.

Institutional Structure: *Composition of institution:* Academic affairs headed by vice-chancellor. Management/business/finances directed by vice-chancellor. Academic governance body, Administrative Council, meets an average of 50 times per year.

Calendar: Semesters. Academic year Aug. to June. Degrees conferred and formal commencements June, Dec.

See specific schools for admission and degree requirements.

Degrees Conferred: 252 *baccalaureate;* 34 *master's;* 5 *doctorate;* 281 *first-professional.*

Fees and Other Expenses: *Full-time tuition per academic year:* contact the center for current tuition, fees, and housing costs.

Departments and Teaching Staff: *Total instructional faculty:* 715.

SITY OF TENNESSEE HEALTH E CENTER—*cont'd*

Enrollment: Total enrollment 2,067.

Characteristics of Student Body: *Ethnic/racial makeup:* Black non-Hispanic 10%, Asian or Pacific Islander 3%, Hispanic 1%.

Student Life: On-campus residence halls house 27% of student body. *Special regulations:* Cars permitted in designated areas only. *Special services:* Learning Resources Center, Computer Center, medical services, Fitness Center, Center for Health Promotion. *Surrounding community:* Memphis population 650,000. Served by mass transit bus system; airport 10 miles from campus; passenger rail service 3 miles from campus.

Publications: *The Record*, a campus newspaper; *Asklepieion*, a yearbook; alumni magazines.

Library Collections: 160,000 volumes. 2,100 current periodical subscriptions. Students have access to online information retrieval services and the Internet. Most important special holdings include Wallace Collection of works by university faculty.

Buildings and Grounds: Campus area 75 acres.

Chief Executive Officer: William R. Rice, Chancellor.

Address admission inquiries to Director of Admissions.

College of Allied Health Sciences

Degree Programs Offered: *Baccalaureate* in cytotechnology, dental hygiene, health information management, occupational therapy, medical technology; *master's* in physical therapy, clinical laboratory sciences. Certificate in immunohematology also given.

Admission: 2–3 years prescribed preprofessional courses. Dental Hygiene Admission Test for dental hygiene program.

Degree Requirements: 120 and up semester hours, 2.0 GPA, 12–24 months in residence.

College of Nursing

Degree Programs Offered: *Master's, doctorate.*

College of Pharmacy

Degree Programs Offered: *First-professional (Pharm.D.), master's, doctorate.*

Admission: *For first-professional:* 60 semester hours from accredited college or university which must include 18 in English, 24 chemistry (including a complete course in organic), 12 biological sciences (general, zoology), 12 social sciences, 12 physics, 3 statistics, 3 calculus, 3 psychology; all science courses with laboratory; 2.5 GPA. Pharmacy College Admission Test; preprofessional evaluation.

Degree Requirements: *For first-professional degree:* 2.5 GPA, 4 academic years of professional study.

College of Dentistry

Degree Programs Offered: *First-professional* in dentistry; *master's* in orthodontics, pediatric dentistry. Certificates in oral surgery, periodontics also given.

Admission: *For first-professional:* 90 semester hours from an accredited college or university which must include 9 English composition; 12 general biology; 12 general chemistry; 12 organic chemistry; 12 physics; 78 electives; 2.5 GPA; DAT.

Degree Requirements: *For first-professional degree:* 172 semester hours, 2.0 GPA, 40 months in residence.

Distinctive Educational Programs: Double-degree programs with basic sciences department. Work-experience programs with hospitals and private practices. Honors program in comprehensive patient care. Research facilities in departments of biomaterials, oral pathology, periodontics.

College of Medicine

Degree Programs Offered: *First-professional.*

Admission: 90 semester hours which must include 1 year English, 1 year biology, 1 year general chemistry, 1 year organic chemistry, 1 year physics; 2.5 GPA; MCAT; Tennessee or contiguous state residency; or children of University of Tennessee alumni regardless of residence.

Degree Requirements: 9 full-time semesters of credit.

College of Graduate Health Sciences

Degree Programs Offered: *Master's* in microbiology and immunology, physiology and biophysics, medicinal chemistry, pharmaceutics, pharmacy administration; *doctorate* in anatomy, biochemistry, microbiology and immunology, pharmacology, physiology and biophysics, medicinal chemistry and pharmaceutics.

Admission: Baccalaureate from an accredited college or university, 3.0 GPA, GRE score of 1,000 or higher (SAT Critical Reading and quantitative), 3 letters of recommendation. Foreign applicants must provide evidence of proficiency in English, or a TOEFL score of 525 or higher.

Degree Requirements: *For master's:* All requirements must be completed within a period of 6 consecutive years, minimum residency requirement of 2 full-time semesters of study, minimum of 30 semester hours of approved graduate courses, must pass a general oral examination, successful completion of research and thesis. *For doctorate:* Doctoral program must be completed within a period of 5 years after admission to candidacy, not less than 6 semesters of full-time study beyond the bachelor's degree or its equivalent, must pass a general oral examination, research accomplishment and dissertation.

Vanderbilt University

2305 West End Avenue
Nashville, Tennessee 37240
Tel: (615) 322-7311 **E-mail:** admissions@vanderbilt.edu
Fax: (615) 343-7765 **Internet:** www.vanderbilt.edu

Institution Description: Vanderbilt University is a private, independent, nonprofit institution. *Enrollment:* 12,903. *Degrees awarded:* Baccalaureate, first-professional (law, master of divinity, medicine), master's, doctorate. Specialist certificate in education also awarded.

Member of Consortium on Financing Higher Education, Nashville University Center, Southern College University Union (SCUUI).

Accreditation: *Regional:* SACS-Comm. on Coll. *Professional*: business, chemistry, cytotechnology, dietetics, engineering, law, librarianship, medicine, music, nursing, psychology internship, respiratory therapy, speech-language pathology, teacher education, theology

History: Established and chartered as The Central University of Methodist Episcopal Church, South, 1872; changed name to Vanderbilt University 1873; offered first instruction at postsecondary level 1875; awarded first degree (baccalaureate) 1877. *See* Robert A. McGaw, *A Brief History of Vanderbilt University* (Nashville: Vanderbilt University Press, 1973) for further information.

Institutional Structure: The general government of Vanderbilt University is vested in its Board of Trust. The Board consists of a maximum of 41 regular members, one of whom is the Chancellor, plus such additional members as may be elected to serve as Life Trustees. The chief officer of the University is the Chancellor, who may delegate authority to assisting officers, faculties, and others within the University. The Chancellor appoints assisting officers, including general officers and deans of colleges and schools, as necessary, for the orderly administration of the University.

Calendar: Semesters. Academic year Aug. to May. Freshmen admitted Sept., Jan., June. Degrees conferred and formal commencement May. Summer school includes Maymester plus 2 terms.

Characteristics of Freshmen: 16,944 applicants (female 9,131, male 7,813). 25% of applicants accepted. 37% of accepted applicants enrolled.

69% (1,445 students) submitted SAT scores; 53% (885 students) submitted ACT scores. *25th percentile*: SAT Critical Reading 630, SAT Math 650; ACT Composite 28, ACT English 29, ACT Math 27. *75th percentile*: SAT Critical Reading 720, SAT Math 740; ACT Composite 23, ACT English 24, ACT Math 33.

83% of entering freshmen expected to graduate within 5 years. 14% of freshmen from Tennessee. Freshmen from 46 states and 34 foreign countries.

Admission: For fall acceptance, apply as early as fall of senior year of secondary school, but not later than Jan. 15 of year of enrollment. Students are notified of acceptance by April 1. Apply by Nov. 1 for early decision. Early decision is binding. Early acceptance available. *Requirements:* Either graduation from accredited secondary school with a minimum of 15 units including 4 English, 2 foreign language, 3 mathematics; or GED. Natural science and social science units recommended. *Entrance tests:* College Board SAT and ACT (SAT preferred); results of SAT-IIs recommended. For foreign students TOEFL. *For transfer students:* From 4- and 2-year accredited institutions 60 semester hours maximum transfer credit.

College credit and advanced placement for postsecondary-level work completed in secondary school.

Degree Requirements: *For all baccalaureate degrees:* 120 semester hours with 2.0 average on four point scale; special core curriculum defines liberal education.

Fulfillment of some degree requirements and exemption from some beginning courses possible by passing departmental examinations and College Board AP. *Grading system:* A–F; pass-fail; withdraw (carries time limit).

Distinctive Educational Programs: Dual-degree programs in engineering with Fisk University; B.A./M.B.A.; J.D./M.B.A.; M.D./Ph.D.; B.A./M.S.N. Accelerated program enables the student to earn the bachelor's degree in 3 regular academic years and 2 summer sessions; the program can even be shorter with Advanced Placement and Advanced Credit. Up to 30 hours of advanced placement may be received (additional hours only by positive response to petition). Departmental Honors Programs are available for juniors and seniors. Students may earn Honors or High Honors in their majors. The College Scholars Program in available to highly qualified freshmen and sophomores (appointments are based on records before or after enrollment), providing Honors work and involvement in the Center for College Scholars. College Scholars may pursue Honors in the College of Arts and Science. The Senior Scholar Program is available to seniors pursuing an entire year of projects of their own devising. Study abroad: Vanderbilt has its own direct credit program in England (University of Leeds), France (Aix-en-Provence), Germany (University of Regensburg), and Spain (Madrid). Students regularly participate in Vanderbilt approved programs in Israel (Tel Aviv University) and the Intercollegiate Center for Classical Studies in Rome. Vanderbilt has its own summer programs in Spain and France as well as a Theatre-in-London course. May session course in European studies in Caen, France. *Other distinctive programs:* Directed study and independent study programs are available to students. Freshman Seminars offer small classes of scholarly study under the leadership of senior faculty members. Joint Programs offer special courses in Vanderbilt's professional schools (Blair School of Music, etc). Area Studies offer special programs in African-American, East Asian, European, Latin American and Iberian, and Slavic Languages. Theme Dorms are available to students (e.g., art and philosophy residences are available). French, German, Russian and Spanish are spoken in McTyeire International House. Vanderbilt awards 25 summer research grants of $3,000 every year for 10-week intensive study. Students write the grants, often with the help of a professor, and conduct their own study with the help of faculty. Undergraduate students from all schools are eligible.

ROTC: Army, Navy; Air Force in cooperation with Tennessee State University.

Degrees Conferred: 1,342 *baccalaureate (B)*; 1,044 *master's (M)*; 650 *doctorate (D)*; 334 *first-professional.* Degrees awarded: area studies 31 (B), 5 (M); biological sciences 88 (B), 10 (M), 42 (D); business and management 359 (M), 3 (D); computer and information sciences 42 (B), 15 (M); education 109 (B), 125 (M), 32 (D); engineering 311 (B), 83 (M), 19 (D); English 91 (B), 13 (M), 9 (D); foreign languages 80 (B), 19 (M), 4 (D); health professions 240 (M), 3 (D); liberal arts 7 (M); mathematics 98 (B), 7 (M), 1 (D); physical sciences 38 (B), 18 (M), 7 (D); psychology 157 (B), 30 (M), 20 (D); social sciences and history 608 (B), 36 (M), 17 (D); other 98 (B), 27 (M)< 29 (D). 539 *first-professional:* law 180, medicine 101, theology 41, nursing 217.

Fees and Other Expenses: *Full-time tuition per academic year 2008–09:* $37,005. Contact the university for current graduate and professional school tuition and fees. *Other undergraduate fees:* $780. *Books and supplies:* $1,208. *Room and board per academic year:* $12,698. *Other expenses:* $2,062.

Financial Aid: Aid from institutionally generated funds is provided on the basis of academic merit, financial need, athletic ability.

Financial aid to full-time, first-time undergraduate students: 65% received some form of financial aid. Average amount of aid received: federal grants $5,709; Pell grants $2,941; other federal aid $3,296; state/local grants $5,545; institutional grants $28,014.

Departments and Teaching Staff: *Total instructional faculty:* 2,263. Student/faculty ratio: 19:1 (undergraduate). Degrees held by full-time faculty: 93% hold terminal degrees.

Enrollment: Total enrollment 12,093. Undergraduate 6,631 (full-time 99%; female 52%, male 48%). Graduate 5,456 (full-time 87%). Undergraduate transfer-in students 172.

Characteristics of Student Body: *Ethnic/racial makeup:* Black non-Hispanic: 9%; Asian or Pacific Islander: 7%; Hispanic: 6%; White non-Hispanic: 59%; unknown: 15%; nonresident alien 3%.

International Students: 363 nonresident aliens enrolled fall 2008. Programs available to aid students whose native language is not English: social, cultural, financial. English as a Second Language Program. No financial aid specifically designated for international students.

Student Life: On-campus residence halls house 85% of student body. Housing available for married students. Mayfield Living/Learning Lodges are set aside for groups of 10 students who wish to establish their own special-interest houses (i.e., arts, community service, computers, environment, world religions, music). *Intercollegiate athletics:* male: baseball, basketball, cross-country, football, golf, soccer, tennis; female: basketball, cross-country, golf, lacrosse, track, soccer, swimming and diving, tennis. *Special regulations:* Registered cars with decals permitted in designated areas; limitations on parking for freshmen. *Special services:* Center for Learning, Center for Teaching, Peer Counseling, medical services. *Student publications, radio: The Commodore*, a yearbook; *The Vanderbilt Review*, annual literary magazine; *The Vanderbilt Hustler*, a biweekly newspaper; *Versus*, a monthly literary magazine; *Vanderbilt Video Publications; Slightly Amusing,* a humor publication. Radio station WRVU broadcasts 168 hours per week. *Surrounding community:* Nashville population approximately 500,000. Served by mass transit bus system, airport 10 miles from campus.

Library Collections: 2,883,000 volumes. 228,500 government documents; 2,967,000 microforms; 29,000 audiovisual materials; 29,200 periodicals including via electronic access. Students have access to online information retrieval services and the Internet.

Most important special holdings include Fugitive/Agrarian Collection (U.S. Southern literature, history, MSS); Baudelaire Center (French literature and literary criticism); Judaica Collection (Hebrew, Greek, and related literature, MSS); extensive archive of television news.

Buildings and Grounds: Campus area 333 acres. Campus DVD available.

Chief Executive Officer: Dr. E. Gordon Gee, Chancellor.

Undergraduates address admission inquiries to Undergraduate Admissions Office; graduate inquiries to Owen Graduate School; first-professional inquiries to Divinity School, Peabody Professional School, Law School, or Graduate School.

College of Arts and Science

Degree Programs Offered: *Baccalaureate* in anthropology, biology, chemistry, classical languages, classics, economics, English, fine arts, French, geology, German, history, mathematics, molecular biology, philosophy, physics, physics and astronomy, political science, Portuguese, psychology, religious studies, Russian, sociology, Spanish, theatre; *interdisciplinary majors* in African-American studies, American studies, communication, East Asian studies, European studies, Latin American and Iberian studies, public policy studies.

Distinctive Educational Programs: College Scholars Program for students with outstanding academic records; freshman seminars; area studies in African-American, East Asian, European, Latin American and Iberian, and Slavic; exchange program with Howard University; overseas study in England, France, Germany, Israel, Spain; early acceptance to Vanderbilt University School of Medicine.

School of Engineering

Degree Programs Offered: *Baccalaureate* in biomedical engineering, chemical engineering, civil and environmental engineering, computer science, electrical engineering, engineering science, mechanical engineering; *master's* in biomedical engineering, chemical engineering, civil engineering, computer science, electrical engineering, environmental and water resources engineering, management of technology, materials science, mechanical engineering.

School of Nursing

Degree Programs Offered: *Master's.* MS/MBA with Owen Graduate School of Management.

Admission: *For MSN-MEO:* (master of science in nursing-multiple entry option) requires MAT or GRE exam, 3.0/4.0 GPA.

Degree Requirements: *For MSN-MEO:* 72 hours of transfer work, 49 hours of 200 level courses and 39 hours of 300 level courses. *For MSN:* 39 hours of 300 level courses.

Distinctive Educational Programs: Interdisciplinary program in medical ethics in cooperation with the Divinity School, the School of Law, and the School of Medicine. Prison Program, a field-based clinical experience for nurses.

Peabody College

Degree Programs Offered: *Baccalaureate* in cognitive studies, early childhood education, elementary education, secondary education, special education, child development, human and organizational development, interdisciplinary majors; *master's* in college student personnel services, curriculum and supervision, early childhood education, elementary education, English education, general administrative leadership, health promotion, higher education administration, human development, human development counseling, human resource development, institutional advancement, mathematics education, policy development and program evaluation, reading education, science education, school administration, secondary education, social studies education, special education; *doctorate* in curriculum and supervision, early childhood education, elementary education, English education, general administrative leadership, higher education administration, mathematics education, policy development and program evaluation, reading education, science education, school administration, social studies education, special education; *specialist certificates* in curriculum

VANDERBILT UNIVERSITY—*cont'd*

and supervision, general administrative leadership, higher education administration, school administration, special education.

Admission: *For M.Ed., M.P.P. degrees:* 3.0 GPA (on a 3.0 scale) for last 2 years of undergraduate study. *For Ed.D. degree:* 3.4 GPA.

Degree Requirements: *For M.Ed. degree:* 30 credit hours (48 credit hours in human development counseling). *For M.P.P. degree:* 39 credit hours. *For Ed.D. degree:* 84 credit hours.

Divinity School

Degree Programs Offered: *First-professional* (master of divinity, master of theological studies, doctor of ministry); *joint programs* in divinity and law, public policy.

Admission: *For M.Div. degree:* Baccalaureate from accredited college, B-average or 2.9 G.P.A. (on a 4.0 scale).

Degree Requirements: *See also* general requirements. *For M.T.S. degree:* 51 credit hours; 2.0 GPA (on a 4.0 scale). *For M.Div. degree:* 84 credit hours; 2.0 GPA (on a 4.0 scale). *For D.Min. degree:* 30 credit hours; 3.0 G.P.A. (on a 4.0 scale).

School of Law

Degree Programs Offered: *First-professional.*

Admission: *For first-professional:* Graduation from accredited college or university, LSAT; letters of recommendation.

Degree Requirements: 88 credit hours, 1.7 GPA or above; 6 semesters in residence.

Distinctive Educational Programs: M.B.A.-J.D. with Owen Graduate School of Management; M.T.S.-J.D., M.Div.-J.D. with Divinity School; M.P.P.-J.D. with Peabody College.

School of Medicine

Degree Programs Offered: *First-professional* (Doctor of Medicine); joint M.D./Ph.D. program; Summer Research Fellowship Program; M.P.H. program.

Admission: Baccalaureate degree with 8 semester hours biology, 8 general chemistry, 8 organic chemistry, 8 physics and 6 English and composition.

Degree Requirements: Prescribed curriculum, 24 months in residence.

Distinctive Educational Programs: Joint M.D.-Ph.D. program. Summer Research Fellowship program.

The Graduate School

Degree Programs Offered: *Master's* in anthropology, art history, astronomy, geology, Latin American studies, Portuguese; *master's, doctorate* in biochemistry, biomedical engineering, cell biology, chemical engineering, chemistry, civil engineering, classics, comparative literature, computer science, economics, education and human development, electrical engineering, English, environmental and water resources engineering, French, biology, German, hearing and speech sciences, history, materials science, mathematics, mechanical engineering, microbiology and immunology, molecular biology, pathology, philosophy, physics, political science, psychology, psychology and human development, religion, sociology, Spanish; *doctorate* in anthropology, management, molecular physiology and biophysics, Spanish and Portuguese. *Other programs* include graduate program in economic development, master's in teaching, joint medical scientist training program with School of Medicine.

Departments and Teaching Staff: Faculty for the Graduate School is drawn from other schools within the University.

Owen Graduate School of Management

Degree Programs Offered: *Master's* in business administration; *doctorate* in management. *Joint programs* in management and law, management and the College of Arts and Science, management and engineering, management and Fisk University, management and nursing. *Executive M.B.A. program.*

Admission: GMAT; 2 letters of recommendation; interview required.

Degree Requirements: *For M.B.A. degree:* 60 credit hours. *For Ph.D. degree:* 72 credit hours; dissertation presentation.

Distinctive Educational Programs: Center for Latin American and Iberian Studies.

Blair School of Music

Degree Programs Offered: *Baccalaureate* in composition/theory, musical arts, or performance, with majors in any instrument of the orchestra or band, piano, organ, guitar, voice. *Special programs* include double majors, liberal arts major, minors in music and music history, adult offerings, second instrument or voice, and pre-college program including a certificate program, youth orchestras, and out-of-school credit.

Admission: High school units required include 4 units of English, 2 of algebra, 1 of geometry, 1 of history, 2 of single foreign language (students who do not meet the language requirement may complete it a Vanderbilt). Audition is required except for composition/theory applicants, who submit a portfolio of compositions and interview.

Degree Requirements: 126 credit hours, including 27 hours minimum in liberal arts; a music core of theory, keyboard harmony, music literature/history, conducting, individual performance instruction, and ensemble; and electives.

Texas

Abilene Christian University

ACU Box 29000
Abilene, Texas 79699
Tel: (325) 674-2650 **E-mail:** info@admissions.acu.edu
Fax: (325) 674-2130 **Internet:** www.acu.edu

Institution Description: Abilene Christian University (Abilene Christian College until 1976) is a private, nonprofit institution affiliated with the Church of Christ. *Enrollment:* 4,669. *Degrees awarded:* Associate, baccalaureate, first-professional, master's, doctorate.

Accreditation: *Regional:* SACS-Comm. on Colleges. *Professional*: business, chemistry, dietetics, family and consumer science, journalism, music, nursing, social work, speech-language pathology, teacher education, theology

History: Established as Childers Classical Institute and first charter issued 1906; offered first instruction at postsecondary level 1912; awarded first degree (associate) 1916; name changed to Abilene Christian College 1920; graduate school established 1953; adopted present name 1976.

Institutional Structure: *Governing board:* Board of Trustees. Extrainstitutional representation: 90 trustees, 71 alumni. 53 voting. *Composition of institution:* Administrators 9. Academic affairs, student retention, counseling, discipline, and security headed by provost. Financial management, financial aid, human resources, and information services led by vice president for finance. Admission/recruiting, alumni, public relations and university events led by vice president for university and alumni relations. Full-time instructional faculty 223. Academic governance body, the faculty Senate, meets once a month during the fall and spring semesters.

Calendar: Semesters. Academic year Aug. to May. Freshmen admitted Aug., Jan., June, July. Degrees conferred and formal commencement May, Aug., Dec. Summer session of 3 terms from May to Aug.

Characteristics of Freshmen: 3,897 applicants (2,308 female, 1,589 male). 47% of applicants admitted. 53% of applicants admitted and enrolled.

52% (497 students) submitted SAT scores; 48% (462 students) submitted ACT scores. *25th percentile*: SAT Critical Reading 480, SAT Math 490; ACT Composite 20, ACT English 19, ACT Math 20. *75th percentile*: SAT Critical Reading 620, SAT Math 630; ACT Composite 27, ACT English 26, ACT Math 28. 12 National Merit Scholars.

52% of entering freshmen expected to graduate within 5 years. 81% of freshmen from Texas. Freshmen from 39 states and 21 foreign countries.

Admission: Rolling admissions plan. For fall acceptance, apply as early as one year prior to year of enrollment. Early acceptance available. *Requirements:* Either graduation from accredited secondary school with 12 units which must include 4 English, 3 mathematics, 2 lab sciences, 1 non-lab science, 2 foreign language; or GED. Lowest acceptable secondary school class standing 50th percentile. *Entrance tests:* SAT. *For transfer students:* 2.0 minimum GPA. Maximum hours transfer credit 66 hours from 2-year school; 96 hours from 4-year school.

Advanced placement for postsecondary-level work completed in secondary school.

Tutoring available. Developmental courses offered in summer sessions and academic year.

Degree Requirements: *For all associate degrees:* 64 hours; 2.0 GPA; 2 hours physical education. *For all baccalaureate degrees:* 128-138 credit hours; 2.0–2.5 GPA; daily chapel attendance; 4 hours physical education; 33 hours minimum upper division; 30 hours minimum major. *For all undergraduate degrees:* 32 hours in residence.

Fulfillment of some baccalaureate degree requirements possible by taking achievement tests for maximum credit of 30 hours. In baccalaureate degree program, exemption from American history, biology, chemistry, English, European history, foreign language, mathematics, music, physics is possible by passing departmental exams (offered during academic year), or College Board CLEP, (offered before classes start in fall). *Grading system:* A–F; pass-fail (for non-major electives); withdraw (if failing, carried penalty).

Distinctive Educational Programs: *For undergraduates:* Preprofessional programs in dentistry, medicine, medical technology, optometry, veterinary medicine. *For all students:* Limited evening classes. Interdisciplinary programs. Intercollege enrollment plan allows students to take courses for credit at Hardin-Simmons University and McMurry University. *For graduate students:* Off-campus centers at Dallas. Study abroad at permanent location in Oxford, England and Montevideo, Uruguay. Travel courses available: Central Europe, Central America, Far East. Adult Degree Completion Program.

Degrees Conferred: 3 *associate*; 850 *baccalaureate*; 144 *master's*; 6 *doctorate*. Bachelor's degrees awarded in top five disciplines: business, management, marketing, and related support services 160; education 99; interdisciplinary studies 76; visual and performing arts 64; health professions and related clinical sconces 56. Master's degrees awarded: business/marketing 16; communications/journalism 1; education 13; health professions 37; history 1; interdisciplinary studies 18; psychology 18; theology and religious vacations 22. Doctorates awarded: theology 6. *First-professional:* master of divinity 25.

Fees and Other Expenses: *Full-time tuition per academic year 2008–09:* undergraduate $18,930; contact the university for current graduate and first-professional tuition and applicable fees. *Other fees:* $700. *Room and board per academic year:* $7,236. *Books and supplies:* $1,150. *Other expenses:* $3,184.

Financial Aid: Aid from institutionally generated funds is provided on the basis of academic merit, financial need, athletic ability, other considerations.

Financial aid to full-time, first-time undergraduate students: 96% received some form of aid. Average amount of aid received: federal grants $4,028; Pell grants $3,049; other federal aid $1,360; state/local grants $3,741; institutional grants $7,210.

Departments and Teaching Staff: *Total instructional faculty:* 378 (full-time 223, part-time 155). Total faculty with doctorate, first-professional, or other terminal degree: 203. Student/faculty ratio: 16:1. Degrees held by full-time faculty: baccalaureate 1.5%, master's 35.8%, doctorate 59.9%, professional 2.9%. 72% hold terminal degrees.

Enrollment: Total enrollment 5,669. Undergraduate 3,906 (full-time 93%; female 54%, male 46%). Graduate 763 (full-time 763). Undergraduate transfer-in students 173.

Characteristics of Student Body: *Ethnic/racial makeup:* Black non-Hispanic: 8%; American Indian or Alaska Native: 1%; Asian or Pacific Islander: 1%; Hispanic: 6%; White non-Hispanic: 78%; unknown: 2%; nonresident alien 4%. *Age distribution:* number under 18: 67; 18–19: 1699; 20–21: 1,552; 22–24: 609; 25–29: 112; 30–34: 57; 35–39: 23; 40–49: 68; 50–64: 21; 65 and over: 1.

International Students: 188 nonresident aliens enrolled fall 2008. Students from Europe, Asia, Latin America, Africa, Canada, Australia, New Zealand. Programs available to aid students whose native language is not English: English as a Second Language Program. Financial aid specifically designated for international students: 98 scholarships totaling $203,958 awarded 20064–07.

Student Life: On-campus residence halls house 42% of student body and another 10% in on-campus apartments. Residence halls for males constitute 44% of such space, for females 55%, married housing 1%. *Intercollegiate athletics:* male: baseball, basketball, cross-country, football, golf, tennis, track; female: basketball, cross-country, softball, tennis, track, volleyball. *Special regulations:* Cars allowed with permit. Freshman curfew 11:30pm weekdays, 1am weekends. *Special services:* Medical services. *Student publications, radio: The Optimist*,a twice weekly newspaper; *The Shineery Review*, an annual literary magazine; *Visions*, a video yearbook. Radio station KACU; KACU-FM, National Public Radio station for Abilene and west Texas. KUF-TV, local television with The Learning Channel affiliation. *Surrounding community:* Abilene population 109,000. Fort Worth, 150 miles from campus, is nearest metropolitan area. Airport 5 miles from campus.

Library Collections: 511,000 volumes including bound books, serial backfiles, electronic documents, and government documents not in separate collections. Online catalog. Current serial subscriptions: 2,425 paper, 12,000 electronic. 60,000 audiovisual materials. Computer work stations available. Students have access to online information retrieval services and the Internet.

Most important holdings include Omar Burleson Congressional Papers (U.S. representative, 17th District); Robbins Railroad Collection; ACU Archives; Center for Restoration Studies (Stone-Campbell Movement in 20th Century).

ABILENE CHRISTIAN UNIVERSITY—*cont'd*

Buildings and Grounds: Campus area 208 acres.

Chief Executive Officer: Dr. Royce Money, President.

Address admission inquiries to Hayley Webb, Director of Admissions.

Amberton University

1700 Eastgate Drive
Garland, Texas 75041
Tel: (972) 279-6511 **E-mail:** admissions@amberton.edu
Fax: (972) 279-9773 **Internet:** www.amberton.edu

Institution Description: Amberton University (formerly known as Amber University) is a private, independent, Christian (nondenominational), commuter institution offering specialized upper division and graduate level programs to working adults. *Enrollment:* 1,537. *Degrees awarded:* Baccalaureate, master's.

Accreditation: *Regional:* Regional: SACS-Comm. on Coll.

History: Established in 1971 as a branch of Abilene Christian College; awarded first degree (associate) 1972; Amber University incorporated as an independent, accredited institution in 1982.

Institutional Structure: *Governing board:* Board of Trustees of Amber University. Representation: Self-perpetuating board of from 9 to 29 members. *Composition of institution:* Administrators 5. President, dean for strategic planning and control, vice president business services vice president academic services, dean for student services. Academic governance body, Faculty Council, meets an average of 5 times per year. Full-time instructional faculty 16.

Calendar: Four sessions per year; each session 10 weeks in duration. Summer semester June to August; fall semester Sept. to Nov.; winter semester Dec. to Feb.; spring semester March to May.

Admission: *Undergraduate requirements:* Applicant must be a citizen of the United States, 21 years of age or older, and have an academic transcript from a college or university accredited by a regional association of colleges and schools within the United States that reflect a GPA of at least 2.0 (C). *Graduate requirements:* The applicant must be a citizen of the United States, 21 years of age or older, and have an academic transcript from a college or university accredited by a regional association of colleges and schools within the United States that reflects a baccalaureate degree and: (1) have a grade point average (GPA) of 3.0 or higher on a 4.0 scale, on the last 30 semester hours taken, or (2) have scored 30 or higher on the Miller Analogies Test, GRE (800), or GMAT (400).

Degree Requirements: *For all undergraduate degrees:* A minimum of 126 credit hours with a 2.0 GPA; last 30 hours must be in residency. *For all graduate degrees:* A minimum of 36 credit hours with a 3.0 GPA; last 24 hours must be in residency.

Distinctive Educational Programs: Weekend and evening classes. Interdisciplinary programs in professional development and human relations and business.

Degrees Conferred: 42 *baccalaureate*; 199 *master's*. Bachelor's degrees awarded in top five disciplines: business, management, marketing, and related support services 31; multidisciplinary studies 11.

Fees and Other Expenses: *Full-time tuition per academic year 2008–09:* $4,800.

Financial Aid: Aid from institutionally generated funds is provided on the basis of academic merit, financial need. Institution has a Program Participation Agreement with the U.S. Department of Education for eligible students to receive Pell Grants and, depending upon the agreement, other federal aid.

Departments and Teaching Staff: *Total instructional faculty:* 54. Student/faculty ratio: 25:1. Degrees held by full-time faculty: doctorate 95%, master's 5%. 95% hold terminal degrees.

Enrollment: Total enrollment 1,537.

International Students: No programs available to aid students whose native language is not English. No financial aid specifically designated for international students.

Student Life: The university caters exclusively to commuting adults. The average age of the student is 37 years. The student body is equally divided between male and female and upper and graduate level students. Amber University does not offer many of the social activities found on the traditional college campus: football, intramurals, student center, band, etc. The student body of Amber University perceives the institution more like that of a professional school; the entire emphasis is on academics.

Library Collections: 22,000 volumes (specialized holdings restricted to business and human behavior). 3,000 microforms; 650 audiovisual materials; 210 current periodical subscriptions. Online catalog. Students have access to online information retrieval services and the Internet.

Special collections on contemporary management; counseling.

Buildings and Grounds: Campus area 5 acres.

Chief Executive Officer: Dr. Douglas W. Warner, President.

Address admission inquiries to Registrar.

Angelo State University

2601 West Avenue N
San Angelo, Texas 76909
Tel: (325) 942-2555 **E-mail:** admissions@angelo.edu
Fax: (325) 942-2078 **Internet:** www.angelo.edu

Institution Description: Angelo State University is a state institution. *Enrollment:* 6,155. *Degrees awarded:* Associate (nursing), baccalaureate, master's.

Academic offerings subject to approval by statewide coordinating body. Budget subject to approval by state governing board.

Accreditation: *Regional:* SACS-Comm. on Coll. *Professional*: athletic training, business, music, nursing, physical therapy

History: Established as San Angelo Junior College and offered first instruction at postsecondary level 1928; became 4-year institution and changed name to Angelo State College 1965; awarded first degree (baccalaureate) 1967; adopted present name 1969.

Institutional Structure: *Governing board:* Board of Regents, Texas State University System. Representation: 9 members (appointed by governor of Texas). All voting. *Composition of institution:* Administrators 38. Academic affairs headed by vice president for academic and student affairs. Management/business/finances directed by vice president for fiscal affairs. Full-time instructional faculty 235.

Calendar: Semesters. Academic year Sept. to May. Freshmen admitted Aug., Jan., May, or June. Degrees conferred May, Aug., Dec. Formal commencements May, Aug, Dec. Summer session of 2 terms.

Characteristics of Freshmen: 2,566 applicatns (female 149, male 1,147). 99% of applicants admitted. 48% of applicants admitted and enrolled.

59% (357 students) submitted SAT scores; 65% (944 students) submitted ACT scores. *25th percentile*: SAT Critical Reading 410, SAT Math 420; ACT Composite 14, ACT English 16, ACT Math 17. *75th percentile*: SAT Critical Reading 520, SAT Math 550, ACT Composite 22, ACT English 22, ACT Math 22.

34% of entering freshmen expected to graduate within 5 years. 96% of freshmen from Texas. Freshmen from 42 states and 20 foreign countries.

Admission: Rolling admissions plan. Apply no later than 2 weeks prior to enrollment. Early acceptance available. *Requirements:* An applicant from an accredited high school must meet one of the following requirements to be eligible for regular admission: rank in the top half of the senior class at the time of application or graduate in the top half of the graduating class, or graduate advanced, advanced honors, or Texas scholar; *or* present a composite score of 30 on the ACT or a combined verbal and math score of 1270 on the SAT; no minimum scores for those in top half of high school class; or have the probability of earning an overall C average during the freshmen year at Angelo State University as computed from the student's high school grades and ACT or SAT scores. *Entrance tests:* ACT composite or SAT combined math and verbal. For foreign students TOEFL score 550 minimum or minimum ACT English score of 17 or 430 verbal SAT I. *For transfer students:* Minimum 2.00 GPA for students with 1–17 college level hours and must meet admission criteria for high school graduates; minimum 2.00 GPA for students with 18 or more hours college level credit.

College credit and advanced placement for postsecondary-level work completed in secondary school. College credit for extrainstitutional learning.

Tutoring available. Remedial courses offered in English and mathematics during regular academic year; credit given but does not count toward graduation.

Degree Requirements: *For all associate degrees:* 68 credit hours; exit competency examinations (clinical and standardized tests). *For all baccalaureate degrees:* 130 hours; 2 hours of physical education courses. *For all undergraduate degrees:* 2.0 GPA; overall and in major 30 hours in residence; general education requirements.

Fulfillment of some degree requirements and exemption from some beginning courses possible by passing departmental examinations, College Board CLEP, AP. Fulfillment of some degree requirements also possible by passing ACT subject examinations. *Grading system:* A–F; withdraw (deadline after which pass-fail is appended to withdraw).

Distinctive Educational Programs: *For undergraduates:* cooperative baccalaureate in medical technology and nursing with approved hospitals. Preprofessional programs in allied health, engineering, home economics. *Available to all students:* Intern programs. Evening classes. Institutionally sponsored summer study-travel abroad in France, Germany, Mexico; international studies program in United Kingdom. The university provides over 1,000 Carr Academic Scholarships annually totaling more than $2 million for worthy and deserving students with outstanding academic records. *Other distinctive programs:* Degree-completion program for registered nurses. Student laboratory experience and community services available through Child Development Center. Up[and Coming

Scholars program for area high school students. Small Business Development Center. Continuing education.

ROTC: Air Force.

Degrees Conferred: 61 *associate*; 780 *baccalaureate*. Bachelor's degrees awarded in top five disciplines: business, management, marketing, and related support services 177; parks and recreation 116; education 107; psychology 79; social sciences 61. Master's degrees awarded: various disciplines 143.

Fees and Other Expenses: *Full-time tuition per academic year 2008–09:* undergraduate resident $4,598, nonresident $11,340; contacat the university for current graduate tuition and applicable fees. *Room and board per academic year:* $6,407. *Other expenses:* $3,820.

Financial Aid: Aid from institutionally generated funds is provided on the basis of academic merit, financial need, athletic ability. Institution has a Program Participation Agreement with the U.S. Department of Education for eligible students to receive Pell Grants and, depending upon the agreement, other federal aid.

Financial aid to first-time, full-time undergraduate students: 85% received some form of aid. Average amount of aid received: federal grants $3,416; Pell grants $2,750; other federal aid $794; state/local grants $3,421; institutional grants $2,556.

Departments and Teaching Staff: *Total instructional faculty:* 394 (full-time 235, part-time 109). Total faculty with doctorate, first-professional, or other terminal degree: 187. Student/faculty ratio: 20:1. Degrees held by full-time faculty: doctorate 64%, master's 36%. 66% hold terminal degrees.

Enrollment: Total enrollment 6,155. Undergraduate 5,662 (full-time 85%; female 54%, male 46%). Graduate 493 (full-time 41%). Undergraduate transfer-in students 377.

Characteristics of Student Body: *Ethnic/racial makeup:* Black non-Hispanic: 24%; American Indian or Alaska Native: 1%; Asian or Pacific Islander: 1%; Hispanic: 8%; White non-Hispanic: 65%; nonresident alien 1%. *Age distribution:* number under 18: 2; 18–19: 948; 20–21: 1,804; 22–24: 1,753; 25–29: 800; 30–34: 289; 35–39: 183; 40–49: 236; 50–64: 111; 65 and over: 11.

International Students: 62 nonresident aliens enrolled fall 2008. Students from Europe, Asia, Latin America, Africa, Canada. Programs available for students whose native language is not English: social. Financial aid specifically designated for international students: variable number of scholarships available annually for qualifying students.

Student Life: On-campus residence halls and single-students apartments house 26% of student body. Residence halls for males constitute 47% of such space, for females 53%. *Intercollegiate athletics:* male: baseball, basketball, cross-country, football, track; female: basketball, soccer, softball, cross-country, track, volleyball. *Special regulations:* Registered cars permitted. Quiet hours in some residence halls. Visitation hours set within specified limits by residents in individual halls. *Special services:* Medical services. *Student publications:* Weekly newspaper, yearbook. *Surrounding community:* San Angelo population 90,000. San Antonio, 215 miles from campus, is nearest metropolitan area. Served by mass transit bus system; airport 5 miles from campus.

Library Collections: 521,500 volumes including bound books, serial backfiles, electronic documents, and government documents not in separate collections. Online catalog. 974,000 microforms; 18,000 audiovisual materials; 21,600 periodicals including via electronic access. Computer work stations available. Students have access to the Internet at no charge.

Most important special holdings include genealogy books in the West Texas Collection; Tom Green County Historical Society materials in the West Texas Collection; the Hiram Phillips books in the West Texas Collection.

Buildings and Grounds: Campus area 268 acres. Campus DVD available.

Chief Executive Officer: Dr. Joseph Rallo, President.

Address undergraduate admission inquiries to Lorrie Moore, Director of Admissions; graduate inquiries to Dr. Carol Diminnie, Dean of Graduate School.

Arlington Baptist College

3001 West Division Street
Arlington, Texas 76012-3497
Tel: (817) 461-8741 **E-mail:** jhall@abconline.edu
Fax: (817) 274-1138 **Internet:** www.abconline.edu

Institution Description: Arlington Baptist College is a private, independent, nonprofit institution sponsored by the World Baptist Fellowship. *Enrollment:* 140. *Degrees awarded:* Baccalaureate.

Accreditation: *National:* ABHE.

History: Chartered as the Fundamental Baptist Bible Institute 1939; awarded first degree 1939; adopted present name 1972.

Institutional Structure: *Governing board:* 11 directors and college president. Only directors vote. *Composition of institution:* Administrators 11. Academic affairs headed by academic dean. Business affairs directed by business manager. Full-time instructional faculty 9.

Calendar: Semesters. Academic year Aug. to May. Degrees conferred May. Formal commencement May. Summer session of 2 terms.

Characteristics of Freshmen: 100% of applicants accepted. 85% of accepted applicants enrolled.

20% of entering freshmen expected to graduate within 5 years. 75% of freshmen from Texas. Freshmen from 15 states and 3 foreign countries.

Admission: Rolling admissions plan. Applications deadline 1 month before semester begins. Open policy for applicants with strong Christian background. Recommend 3 years high school English, 2 social studies, 2 mathematics, 1 year science. *Entrance tests:* College Board SAT or ACT recommended.

Degree Requirements: *For baccalaureate degrees:* 128 hours minimum; 2.0 GPA; 30 hours in residence; core curriculum.

Fulfillment of some degree requirements and exemption from some beginning courses possible by passing College Board CLEP, AP. *Grading system:* A–F; pass/no pass; incomplete; withdraw.

Distinctive Educational Programs: All programs built on Bible studies major. Training for church vocations. Double majors in music and elementary education. Preseminary program. Evening classes.

Degrees Conferred: 33 *baccalaureate:* education 22 philosophy/religion/theology 11.

Fees and Other Expenses: *Full-time tuition per academic year 2008–09:* $7,340. *Other fees:* $540. *Room and board per academic year:* $7,600. *Books and supplies:* $750. *Other expenses:* $5,000.

Financial Aid: Aid from institutionally generated funds is provided on the basis of financial need. Institution has a Program Participation Agreement with the U.S. Department of Education for eligible students to receive Pell Grants and, depending upon the agreement, other federal aid.

Financial aid to first-time, full-time undergraduate students: 74% received some form of aid.

Departments and Teaching Staff: *Total instructional faculty:* 21. Student/faculty ratio: 15:1. Degrees held by full-time faculty: master's 88%, baccalaureate 12%. 88% hold terminal degrees.

Enrollment: Total enrollment 140.

Characteristics of Student Body: *Ethnic/racial makeup:* Black non-Hispanic: 7%; Asian or Pacific islander 1%; Hispanic: 4%; White non-Hispanic: 84%; nonresident alien 4%.

International Students: 18 nonresident aliens enrolled fall 2008. Students from Asia. No programs available to aid students whose native language is not English. No financial aid specifically designated for international students.

Student Life: 50% of students live in 2 residence halls, 1 for males and 1 for females. *Intercollegiate athletics:* male: basketball, baseball, soccer, cross-country; female: basketball, volleyball, softball. *Special regulations:* Residence hall visiting hours noon to 10:30pm. Quiet hours. *Student publications, radio: Media,*a monthly publication; *The Patriot Focus,*a student quarterly; *The Torch,* a yearbook. *Surrounding community:* Dallas/Fort Worth metropolitan area population 3 million. Located 20 minutes from DFW airport.

Library Collections: 35,000 volumes. 400 microform titles; 800 audiovisual materials; 188 current periodical subscriptions.

Most important special holdings include J. Frank Norris Papers; Fundamentalist Papers.

Buildings and Grounds: Campus area 35 acres.

Chief Executive Officer: Dr. David Bryant, President.

Address admission inquiries to Janice Taylor, Registrar.

Austin College

900 North Grand Avenue
Sherman, Texas 75090-4400
Tel: (903) 813-2000 **E-mail:** admission@austincollege.edu
Fax: (903) 813-3198 **Internet:** www.austincollege.edu

Institution Description: Austin College is a private college affiliated with the Presbyterian Church, U.S.A. *Enrollment:* 1,298. *Degrees awarded:* Baccalaureate, master's.

Member of the consortium Association for Higher Education in North Texas.

Accreditation: *Regional:* SACS-Comm. on Coll.

History: Established, chartered, and offered first instruction 1849; awarded first degree (baccalaureate) 1854. *See* George L. Landolt, *Search for the Summit: Twelve Decades of Austin College History* (Austin: Von Boeckman-Jones Co., 1970) for further information.

Institutional Structure: *Governing board:* Board of Trustees of Austin College. Extrainstitutional representation: 39 trustees (including 23 alumni). 32 voting. *Composition of institution:* president, vice president for academic affairs, vice president for student affairs, vice president for business affairs, vice presi-

AUSTIN COLLEGE—*cont'd*

dent for development, vice president for institutional enrollment. Full-time instructional faculty 93. Academic governance body, Governing Council, meets an average of 9 times per year.

Calendar: 4-1-4 plan. Academic year Aug. to May. Freshmen admitted Feb., June, Sept. Degrees conferred May, Aug., Jan. Formal commencement May.

Characteristics of Freshmen: 1,526 applicants (851 female, 609 male). 69% of applicants accepted. 94% of applicants accepted and enrolled.

69% of entering freshmen expected to graduate within 5 years. 90% of freshmen from Texas. Freshmen from 13 states and 3 foreign countries.

5 National Merit Scholars.

Admission: Acceptance announcements for fall term made on Dec. 15, Feb. 15, and April 1; on a rolling basis thereafter. Early admission available. *Requirements:* Either 15 secondary school units, which should include 12 academic; or GED. Applicants should rank in top one half of secondary school class. *Entrance tests:* College Board SAT or ACT. *For transfer students:* 2.0 minimum GPA; from 4-year accredited institution 94 hours maximum transfer credit; from 2-year accredited institution 66 hours.

College credit for postsecondary-level work completed in secondary school. Tutoring available.

Degree Requirements: *For all baccalaureate degrees:* 34 courses; 2.0 GPA; 2 years in residence; 1 physical fitness course.

Fulfillment of some degree requirements possible by passing departmental examinations, College Board CLEP or APP, offered throughout the academic year. *Grading system:* A–F; pass-fail.

Distinctive Educational Programs: Four-course core curriculum consisting of a freshman seeming and a 3-course heritage of western culture sequence. January term provides concentrated involvement in one area of study, and a greater emphasis on exploration and experiential learning. 3-2 dual-degree programs in engineering available with Washington University in St. Louis, Columbia University, Texas A&M University, and the University of Texas at Dallas. Interdepartmental/interdisciplinary studies, cognitive science, environmental studies, leadership studies, and gender studies. Individual majors. Austin College emphasizes international education of its students and arranges a variety of experiences throughout the world.

Degrees Conferred: 336 *baccalaureate*; 17 *master's*. Bachelor's degrees awarded in top five disciplines: social sciences and history 107; psychology 48; physical science 47; business, management, marketing, and related support services 47; biological/life sciences 34. Master's degrees awarded: education 17.

Fees and Other Expenses: *Full-time tuition per academic year 2008–09:* $26,330. *Books and supplies:* $1,000. *Room and board per academic year:* $8,651. *Other expenses:* $1,000.

Financial Aid: Aid from institutionally generated funds is provided on the basis of academic merit, financial need, other criteria.

Financial aid to full-time, first-time undergraduate students: 97% received some form of aid.

Departments and Teaching Staff: *Total instructional faculty:* 132. Student/faculty ratio: 12:1. Degrees held by full-time faculty: master's 12%, doctorate 88%. 96% hold terminal degrees.

Enrollment: Total enrollment 1,298. Undergraduate 1,263 (full-time 99%; female 55%, male 45%). Graduate 35 (full-time 97%). Undergraduate transfer-in students 41.

Characteristics of Student Body: *Ethnic/racial makeup:* Black non-Hispanic: 2%; American Indian or Alaska Native: 1%; Asian or Pacific Islander: 16%; Hispanic: 9%; White non-Hispanic: 89%; nonresident alien 2%.

International Students: 26 nonresident aliens enrolled fall 2008. Students from Europe, Asia, Latin America, Africa. Programs available to aid students whose native language is not English: social, cultural. Financial aid specifically designated for international students: scholarships available to qualifying new freshmen annually.

Student Life: On-campus residence halls house 72% of student body. Residence halls for males constitute 33% of such space, for females 33%, for both sexes 33%. 28% of student body lives off campus in rented units or with parents. *Intercollegiate athletics:* male: basketball, baseball, football, golf, soccer, swimming, tennis, track; female: basketball, soccer tennis, track, volleyball, swimming. *Special regulations:* Cars permitted without restrictions. Residence hall visitation and quiet hours set by each residence hall. *Special services:* Learning Resources Center, medical services. *Student publications: The Chromoscope*, a yearbook; *The Observer*, a biweekly newspaper. *Surrounding community:* Sherman population 35,000. Dallas, 65 miles from campus, is nearest metropolitan area. Served by airport 65 miles from campus.

Library Collections: 213,000 volumes including bound books, serial backfiles, electronic documents, and government documents not in separate collections. Online catalog. Current serial subscriptions: 642 paper; 176 microform; 1,870 via electronic access. 7,303 recordings; 14 compact discs. Computer work stations available. Students have access to the Internet at no charge.

Most important special holdings include Berzunza Collection (Alexander the Great); Pate Texana Collection; Joyce Pate Viet Nam War Collection; Hoard Texas Collection.

Buildings and Grounds: Campus area 25 square blocks.

Chief Executive Officer: Dr. Oscar C. Page, President. Address admission inquiries to Office of Admissions.

Austin Graduate School of Theology

1909 University Avenue
Austin, Texas 78705
Tel: (512) 476-2772 **E-mail:** admissions@austingrad.edu
Fax: (512) 476-3919 **Internet:** www.austingrad.edu

Institution Description: Austin Graduate School of Theology, formerly names Institute for Christian Studies, is a private, independent, nonprofit institution affiliated with the Church of Christ. It offers programs in the upper division only. *Enrollment:* 101. *Degrees awarded:* Baccalaureate, master's.

Accreditation: *Regional:* SACS-Comm. on Colleges.

History: Established circa 1920 as a Bible Chair with the University of Texas at Austin.

Institutional Structure: *Governing board:* Trustees with the administrative/development Board. Business/finances directed by vice president for financial affairs. Full-time instructional faculty 5.

Calendar: Semesters. Academic year Aug. to May.

Admission: New students are accepted Sept., June, Jan. It is recommended that those who enter in Sept. should apply no later than June 1. Those planning to enter in Jan. should apply by Dec. 1. Those planning to enter in June should apply by April 1.

Degree Requirements: *Bachelor of Arts degree:* 54 hours general coursework; 65 hours upper division; ICS curriculum. University offers the master's of arts degree in religion. *Grading system:* Courses may be taken for credit or audited.

Distinctive Educational Programs: Evening classes offered; excellent for continuing education/career changes. Large research library.

Degrees Conferred: 9 *baccalaureate:* religion, 7 *master's:* religion.

Fees and Other Expenses: *Full-time tuition per academic year 2008–09:* contact the school for current tuition, housing, and other costs.

Financial Aid: Aid from institutionally generated funds is provided on the basis of academic merit, financial need. Institution has a Program Participation Agreement with the U.S. Department of Education for eligible students to receive Pell Grants and, depending upon the agreement, other federal aid.

Departments and Teaching Staff: *Total instructional faculty:* 11. Degrees held by full-time faculty: doctorate 100%.

Enrollment: Total enrollment 66, Undergraduate

Characteristics of Student Body: *Ethnic/racial makeup:* Black non-Hispanic: 44.8%; Hispanic 3.4%; White non-Hispanic: 51.7%.

International Students: No programs available to aid students whose native language is not English. No financial aid specifically designated for international students.

Student Life: On-campus dormitory housing available. *Student activities:* Austin hike and bike trails; sports and cultural events. *Student publications:* Student Association Newsletter.

Publications: *Christian Studies* and *Things That Matter*, faculty publications.

Library Collections: 25,000 volumes. 128 microforms; 14 audiovisual materials; 78 current periodical subscriptions. 625 recordings. Computer work stations available. Students have access to online information retrieval services and the Internet.

Most important special holding is the Showalter Collection.

Chief Executive Officer: Dr. Stanley G. Reid, President.

Address admission inquiries to Beverly Martin, Registrar/Director of Admissions.

Austin Presbyterian Theological Seminary

100 East 27th Street
Austin, Texas 78705-5797
Tel: (512) 472-6736
Fax: (512) 479-0738

Institution Description: Austin Presbyterian Theological Seminary is a private institution affiliated with the Presbyterian Church (U.S.A.). *Enrollment:* 275. *Degrees awarded:* First-professional (master of divinity), master's, doctorate.

Accreditation: *Regional:* SACS-Comm. on Coll. *National:* ATS. *Professional*: theology

History: Chartered 1900; established and offered first instruction at postsecondary level 1902; awarded first degree (master's) 1905. *See* Thomas White Currie, Jr., *Austin Presbyterian Theological Seminary: A Seventy-Fifth Anniversary History* (San Antonio: Trinity University Press, 1978) and James S. Currie, *Austin Presbyterian Theological Seminary: Completing a Century of Service* (Austin, Eakin Press, 2002) for further information.

Institutional Structure: *Governing board:* Board of Trustees, Austin Presbyterian Theological Seminary. Representation: 30 trustees, including 5 alumni. All voting. *Composition of institution:* Administrators 9. Academic affairs headed by academic dean. Management/business/finances directed by vice president for business affairs. Full-time instructional faculty 19. Academic governance body, the faculty, meets an average of 10 times per year.

Calendar: Semesters. Academic year Sept. to Aug. Students admitted Sept. Degrees conferred May. Formal commencement May.

Admission: For fall acceptance, apply no later than Feb. 15 for early consideration; May 15 for later consideration. Students are notified of acceptance Apr., June. *Requirements:* Bachelor degree from an accredited university or college of liberal arts and science. Evidence of full communion with some branch of the Christian Church. On-campus interview. Minimum GPA 2.5

Degree Requirements: *For first-professional degree:* 92 semester hours (184 credits); 2.0 GPA; 3 years in residence. *Grading system:* A–F; pass-fail; withdraw (carries time limit); incomplete (carries time limit).

Distinctive Educational Programs: Internships. Teaching Church Program. Facilities and programs for independent research, including directed and independent study, international travel seminars, cross-registration with Episcopal Theological Seminary of the Southwest. Continuing education. First-professional (Master of Divinity) degree courses offered at Austin Seminary Extension Program in Houston during fall and spring terms.

Degrees Conferred: 9 *master's:* theology; 5 *doctorate* theology; 48 *first-professional*: master of divinity.

Fees and Other Expenses: *Full-time tuition per academic year 2008–09:* $9,685. *Room per academic year:* avaialble on a per month basis (off campus).

Financial Aid: Aid from institutionally generated funds is provided on the basis of academic merit, financial need. *Graduate aid:* 52 students received $453,594 in federal and state-funded loans; 53 received $88,851 for work-study jobs; 32 received $74,323 for college-assigned jobs; 153 received other fellowships/grants totaling $898,508; 15 teaching assistantships awarded totaling $9,786; 6 research assistantships totaling $4,793.

Departments and Teaching Staff: *Total instructional faculty:* 35. Degrees held by full-time faculty: doctorate 89%, professional master's 11%.

Enrollment: Total enrollment 275.

International Students: 6 nonresident aliens enrolled fall 2008. Students from Asia, Latin America, Africa. No programs available to aid students whose native language is not English. Financial aid specifically designated for international students: 1 scholarship worth $18,640 awarded 2008–09.

Student Life: On-campus residence halls and apartments house 96% of student body. *Special regulations:* Cars permitted in designated areas only; permit required. *Surrounding community:* Austin metropolitan area population over 1 million. Served by airport and rail service, each 5 miles from campus.

Publications: *INSIGHTS*, faculty journal published semiannually.

Library Collections: 160,000 volumes. 11,297 microforms; 3,500 audiovisual materials; 585 current periodical subscriptions. Computer work stations available.

Most important special collections include the Robert Louis Dabney Collection; Stitt Archives.

Buildings and Grounds: Campus area 12 acres plus 14 added units off-campus as student housing.

Chief Executive Officer: Dr. Theodore J. Wardlaw, President.

Address admission inquiries to Jack Barden, Director of Admissions.

Baptist Missionary Association Theological Seminary

1530 East Pine Street
Jacksonville, Texas 75766-5407
Tel: (903) 586-2501 **E-mail:** admissions@bmats.edu
Fax: (903) 586-0378 **Internet:** www.bmats.edu

Institution Description: Baptist Missionary Association Theological Seminary is a private institution affiliated with the Baptist Missionary Association of America. *Enrollment:* 140 *Degrees awarded:* Associate, baccalaureate, master's, first-professional.

Accreditation: *Regional:* SACS-Comm. on Coll.

History: Founded 1954.

Institutional Structure: *Governing board:* 15 trustees.

Calendar: Semesters. Academic year Aug. to May.

Admission: *Requirements:* Transcripts of previous work; 3 letters giving character recommendation; statement of church approval; all paperwork must be received at least 4 weeks before start of the semester.

Degree Requirements: Associate of divinity: 66 semester hours; bachelor of arts in religion: 66 semester hours; master of arts in religion: 69 semester hours; master of divinity: 90 semester hours.

Distinctive Educational Programs: Some evening and summer classes.

Degrees Conferred: 5 *baccalaureate:* theology, 7 9 *master's:* theology; 7 *first-professional:* master of divinity.

Fees and Other Expenses: *Full-time tuition per academic year 2008–09:* $3,310. *Books and supplies:* $350. *Room and board per academic year:* $3,580. *Other expenses:* $650.

Financial Aid: Aid from institutionally generated funds is provided on the basis of financial need. Institution has a Program Participation Agreement with the U.S. Department of Education for eligible students to receive Pell Grants and, depending upon the agreement, other federal aid.

Departments and Teaching Staff: *Total instructional faculty:* 20. Degrees held by full-time faculty: doctorate 82%, master's 9%, professional 9%. 91% hold terminal degrees.

Enrollment: Total enrollment 140. Undergraduate 77 (full-time 23%; female 33%, male 11%). Graduate 83 (full-time 44%).

Characteristics of Student Body: *Ethnic/racial makeup:* Black non-Hispanic: 43%; White non-Hispanic: 43%; Hispanic 1%; nonresident alien 10%.

International Students: 14 nonresident aliens enrolled falll 2008. No programs available to aid students whose native language is not English. No financial aid specifically designated for international students.

Student Life: 20 campus apartments. Chapel service twice a week. *Challenge* published twice a year.

Library Collections: 68,000 volumes. 930 microforms; 4,834 audiovisual materials; 330 current periodical subscriptions. Computer work stations available. Students have access to the Internet at no charge.

Buildings and Grounds: Campus area 17 acres.

Chief Executive Officer: Dr. Charley Holmes, President.

Address admissions inquiries to Phillip Atterbery, Dean of Admissions.

Baylor College of Medicine

One Baylor Plaza
Houston, Texas 77030
Tel: (713) 798-4951 **E-mail:** admissions@bcm.edu
Fax: (713) 798-5555 **Internet:** www.bcm.edu

Institution Description: Baylor College of Medicine is a private, independent nonprofit professional health science center also offering an upper-division baccalaureate and graduate programs. *Enrollment:* 1,385. *Degrees awarded:* Baccalaureate, first-professional (medicine), master's, doctorate. Certificates are also awarded.

Accreditation: *Regional:* SACS-Comm. on Coll. *Professional*: medicine, nurse anesthesia education, physician assisting

History: Established as University of Dallas Medical Department, chartered, and offered first instruction at postsecondary level 1900; awarded first degree (first-professional) 1901; changed name to Baylor University College of Medicine 1903; separated from Baylor University and adopted present name 1969. *See* Walter H. Moursund, *A History of Baylor University College of Medicine 1900–1953* (Houston: Gulf Publishing Company, 1956) for further information.

Institutional Structure: *Governing board:* Board of Trustees. Representation: 44 trustees. All voting. *Composition of institution:* Chief Executive Officer-President; Academic affairs headed by Executive Vice President and Dean of Medicine; management/business/finance directed by vice president. Full-time instructional faculty 1,323. Academic governance body, Executive Faculty Committee, meets an average of 22 times per year.

Calendar: Quarters. Academic year varies with type of program. Entering medical school class Aug. to July. Formal commencement May.

Admission: *Medical School:* For fall acceptance, students should apply as early as June but not later than Nov. 1 of previous year. Students are notified of acceptance beginning Nov. 15. Apply by Aug. 1 for early decision; must limit application to Baylor. *Requirements:* Satisfactory completion of 90 semester hours at accredited U.S. institution, with 1 year English, 1 year general physics (including laboratory), 1 year each of general and organic chemistry (including laboratory), 1 year general biology. *Entrance tests:* MCAT. *For transfer students:* Students considered for acceptance only after completion of basic science curriculum at accredited medical school in U.S.

BAYLOR COLLEGE OF MEDICINE—*cont'd*

Graduate School: For fall acceptance, Feb. 15 is the target date for completed applications. Applicants must hold a bachelor's degree or a more advanced degree or must be in the final stages of a program leading to a bachelor's degree or the equivalent. *Requirements:* 1 year each general biology, physics, mathematics, inorganic chemistry and organic chemistry, all with a B average or better. *Entrance tests:* GRE or MCAT for M.D./Ph.D. applicants.

Tutoring available.

Degree Requirements: *First-professional degree:* satisfactory completion of 4-5 years of academic program; Ph.D. 5-7 years; master's 2.5 years.

Distinctive Educational Programs: *Honors Premedical Academy:* Baylor/Rice University 6-week summer program for minority undergraduate students. *Medical Scholars Program:* Baylor/Rice University program accepting high school graduates into an 8-year program leading to M.D. degree. *Summer Medical Training Program (SMART):* Graduate School 10-week summer program offering laboratory experiences in biomedical sciences.

Degrees Conferred: 49 *master's*; 45 *doctorate*; 170 *first-professional*.

Fees and Other Expenses: *Full-time tuition per academic year:* contact the college for current information regarding tuition, fees, and other expenses.

Financial Aid: Aid from institutionally generated funds is provided on the basis of academic merit, financial need, other criteria (total indebtedness).

Departments and Teaching Staff: *Total instructional faculty:* 1,353. Degrees held by full-time faculty: baccalaureate 2%, master's 4%, doctorate 34%, professional 60%. 94% hold terminal degrees.

Enrollment: Total enrollment 1,385.

International Students: 267 nonresident aliens enrolled. Students from Europe, Asia, Latin America, Canada. No financial aid specifically designated for international students.

Student Life: Limited Texas Medical Center housing. *Special services:* Learning Resources Center, medical services. *Surrounding community:* Houston metropolitan area population 4 million. Served by airport 15 miles from campus.

Library Collections: 255,000 volumes. 600 microforms; 2,000 audiovisual materials; 4,500 current periodical subscriptions. Access to online information retrieval systems.

Most important special holdings include Burbank Collection on Arthritis, Rheumatism, and Gout; Mading Collection on Public Health; McGovern History, Medicine Collection.

Buildings and Grounds: Medical Center campus area 35 acres. *New buildings:* Baylor Clinic-Adult Ambulatory Care Center.

Chief Executive Officer: Peter Traber, President.

Address medical school admission inquiries to Admissions Office. address graduate school admission inquiries to Office of Graduate Sciences.

Baylor University

Waco, Texas 76798

Tel: (254) 755-1011 **E-mail:** admissions@baylor.edu
Fax: (254) 710-3557 **Internet:** www.baylor.edu

Institution Description: Baylor University is a private institution that is affiliated with the Baptist General Convention of Texas. *Enrollment:* 14,541. *Degrees awarded:* Baccalaureate, first-professional (law), master's, doctorate.

Accreditation: *Regional:* SACS-Comm. on Coll. *Professional*: accounting, business, chemistry, computer science, dietetics, engineering, family and consumer science, health services administration, journalism, law, music, nursing, physical therapy, psychology internship, social work, teacher education

History: Established and chartered as Baylor University 1845; offered first instruction at postsecondary level 1847; awarded first degree (baccalaureate) 1854; added graduate programs ca. 1900. *See* Lois Smith Murray, *Baylor at Independence (1845–1886)* (Waco: Baylor Press, 1972) for further information.

Institutional Structure: *Governing board:* Board of Regents. Representation: 36 Regents. All voting. *Composition of institution:* Academic affairs headed by executive vice president for academic affairs. Management/business/finances directed by executive vice president for administrative affairs. Total instructional faculty 920. Academic governance body, Faculty Senate, meets once a month.

Calendar: Semesters. Academic year Aug. to May. Freshmen admitted Aug., Jan., June. Degrees conferred and formal commencements May, Aug., Dec.

Characteristics of Freshmen: 25,501 applicants (female 15,329, male 10,158). 43% of applicants admitted. 31% of applicants admitted and enrolled.

67% (1,860 students) submitted SAT scores; 33% (923 students) submitted ACT scores. *25th percentile*: SAT Critical Reading 540, SAT Math 560; ACT Composite 23, ACT English 22, ACT Math 22. *75th percentile*: SAT Critical Reading 650, SAT Math 660; ACT Composite 28, ACT English 28, ACT Math 27.

89% of entering freshmen expected to graduate within 5 years. 81% of freshmen from Texas. Freshmen from 45 states and 29 foreign countries.

Admission: For fall acceptance, apply as early as Aug. before senior year of secondary school but not later than Mar. 1 of year of enrollment. Early acceptance available. *Requirements:* Graduation from accredited secondary school with 16 units which must include 4 English, 3 mathematics, 2 natural science (both with laboratory), 1 social studies, 1 history, 2 foreign language, 2 academic electives. Additional requirements for some programs. Lowest acceptable secondary school standing 50th percentile. *Entrance tests:* College Board SAT or ACT composite. *For transfer students:* 2.5 minimum GPA; 70 semester hours maximum transfer credit from a junior college. TOEFL may be required of applicants for whom English is a second language.

College credit and advanced placement for postsecondary-level work completed in secondary school. College credit and advanced placement on basis of faculty assessment. Tutoring available.

Degree Requirements: *For all undergraduate degrees:* 124–144 credit hours; 2.0 GPA; 60 semester hours, including last 30, in residence; 2 semesters biweekly chapel-forum attendance; 4 semesters physical education; distribution requirements.

Fulfillment of some degree requirements and exemption from some beginning courses possible through the Credit by Examination program. The CBE program includes approved examinations from The College Board SAT II Subject Tests, The College Board Advanced Placement (AP) Examinations, The College-Level Examination Program (CLEP) Subject Examinations, Baylor course examinations, International Baccalaureate. Refer to the current Credit by Examination brochure for a complete list of approved examinations, minimum score requirements, additional requirements, and corresponding Baylor courses. *Grading system:* A–F; pass-fail (limited to electives).

Distinctive Educational Programs: *Available to all students:* Facilities and programs for independent research, including honors programs, individual majors. Study abroad in Africa (Kenya), Austria, Belize, British Isles, China, Egypt, Germany, Guatemala, Israel, Italy, Scandinavia, Spain, Thailand, Turkey.

ROTC: Air Force.

Degrees Conferred: 2,445 *baccalaureate*; 136 *master's*; 362 *doctorate*. Bachelor's degrees awarded in top five disciplines: business, management, marketing, and related support services 665; communication, journalism, and related programs 281; health professions 208; biological/life sciences 196; education 92. *first-professional:* law 152; master of divinity 74.

Fees and Other Expenses: *Full-time tuition per academic year 2008–09:* undergraduate $26,239; contact the university for graduate and first-professional program tuition/fees. *Other fees:* $1,070. *Room and board per academic year:* $7,563. *Books and supplies:* $1,634. *Other expenses:* $3,840.

Financial Aid: Aid from institutionally generated funds is provided on the basis of academic merit, financial need, athletic ability, other considerations.

Financial aid to full-time, first-time undergraduate students: 93% received some form of aid. Average amount of aid received: federal grants $4,011; Pell grants $3,088; other federal aid $1,008; state/local grants $7,563; insitutional grants $3,840.

Departments and Teaching Staff: *Total instructional faculty:* 928 (full-time 767, part-time 161). Student/faculty ratio: 16:1.

Enrollment: Total enrollment 14,541. Undergraduate 1,2162 (full-time 98%; female 58%; male 42%). Graduate 2,319 (full-time 85%). Undergraduate transfer-in students 404.

Characteristics of Student Body: *Ethnic/racial makeup:* Black non-Hispanic: 7%; American Indian or Alaska Native: 1%; Asian or Pacific Islander: 1%; Hispanic: 1%; White non-Hispanic: 71%; unknown 2%; nonresident alien 2%. *Age distribution:* number under 18: 167; 18–19: 4,893; 20–21: 4,607; 22–24: 1,555; 25–29: 206; 30–34: 58; 35–39: 55; 40–49: 44; 50–64: 14; 65 and over: 1.

International Students: 291 nonresident aliens enrolled fall 2008. Programs available to aid students whose native language is not English: English as as a Second Language Program. No financial aid specifically designated for international students.

Student Life: On-campus residence halls house 30% of student body. Residence halls for males constitute 40% of such space, for females 60%. Housing available for married students. *Intercollegiate athletics:* male: baseball, football; female: soccer, softball, volleyball; males and females: basketball, cross-country, golf, lacrosse, sailing, soccer, tennis, track, water skiing. *Special regulations:* Cars permitted without restrictions. Curfews and quiet hours in each residence hall. *Special services:* Learning Resources Center, medical services. *Student publications, radio: Lariat*, a daily newspaper; *Up*,a yearbook. Radio station KWBU broadcasts 120 hours per week; public television station KCTF. *Surrounding community:* Waco population 110,000. Dallas, 90 miles from campus, is nearest metropolitan area. Served by mass transit bus system, airport 10 miles from campus.

Publications: *Baylor Browning Interests* (irregularly) first published in 1927, *Baylor Business Review* (biannually) first published 1982; *Baylor Educator*

(biannually) first published 1976; *Baylor Geological Studies* (annually) first published 1961; *Baylor Law Review* (quarterly) first published 1948; *The Baylor Messenger for Texas Baptists* (quarterly) first published 1991; *Baylor News* (monthly) first published 1991; *Docket Call* (5 times yearly) first published 1975; *Edmonson Historical Lectures* (annually) first published 1978, *Entrepreneurship: Theory and Practice* (quarterly) first published 1959; *Journal of Church and State* (quarterly) first published 1959, *Studies in Browning and His Circle* (annually) first published 1931; *The Pedagogue* (biannual); *Strecker Museum News; Baylor Line*, published for alumni.

Library Collections: 2,166,000 volumes. 595,000 government documents; 2,059,300 microforms; 83,200 audiovisual materials; 18,940 periodicals including via electronic access. Computer work stations available campus-wide. Online catalog. Students have access to online information retrieval services and the Internet.

Most important special holdings include Armstrong Browning Library; Texas Collection Library; Poage Legislative Library.

Buildings and Grounds: Campus area 508 acres. Campus DVD available.

Chief Executive Officer: Dr. John M. Lilley, President and Chief Executive Officer. Address admission inquiries to Jennifer Carron, Director of Admissions; first-professional inquiries to Dean of Law School or Dean of the Truett Seminary; graduate inquiries to Dean of Graduate Studies and Research.

College of Arts and Sciences

Degree Programs Offered: *Baccalaureate* in acting, anthropology, architecture, art, art history, aviation sciences, biology, business administration, chemistry, child and family studies, communication disorders, communication specialist, computer science, dentistry, design and directing, dietetics, earth science, economics, engineering, English, fashion design, fashion merchandising, foreign service, forestry, French, geology, geophysics, German, Greek, history, home economics (general), interior design, journalism, Latin, law, mathematical sciences, mathematics, medical technology and biology, medicine, music, optometry, philosophy, physics, political science, professional writing, psychology, religion, Russian, social work, sociology, Spanish, speech communication, studio art, telecommunication, theater arts. *Master's* in biology, chemistry, communication disorders, communication studies, computer science, earth science, economics, English, environmental biology, environmental chemistry, geology, history, international journalism, international relations, mathematics, philosophy, physics, political science, religion, sociology, speech pathology and audiology, theater arts. *Doctorate* in behavioral statistics, clinical psychology, English, geology, general-experimental psychology, neuroscience, physics, religion.

Distinctive Educational Programs: Aviation sciences, professional writing. Interdisciplinary programs in business administration, foreign service, law, and music. Preprofessional programs in dentistry, medical technology and biology, medicine, optometry. Dual-degree programs in forestry with Duke University (NC), and architecture with Washington University (MO).

Hankamer School of Business

Degree Programs Offered: *Baccalaureate* in accounting, administrative information systems, basic business, business-broadcasting, business-journalism, computer information systems, economics, entrepreneurship, finance, financial services/planning, human resources management, insurance, international business, law, management, marketing, operations management, public administration, quantitative business analysis, real estate, regional/urban studies. *Master's* in business administration, economics, information systems management, international management, taxation.

Distinctive Educational Programs: Entrepreneurship. Interdisciplinary programs in business-broadcasting, business-journalism.

School of Education

Degree Programs Offered: *Baccalaureate* in art, biology, business administration, chemistry, church recreation, computer information systems, earth science, economics, education, English, French, German, health, history, interdisciplinary studies, journalism, Latin, life-earth science, mathematics, physical education, physical science, physics, political science, recreation, science, social studies, sociology, Spanish, speech and language therapy, speech communications, theater arts. *Master's* in curriculum and instruction, education, educational administration, educational psychology, health/physical education and recreation. *Education Specialist* and *doctorate* in curriculum and instruction, educational administration, educational psychology. *Professional Teacher Certificate* for elementary teacher, secondary teacher, all-level teacher, master teacher. *Professional Service Certificate* for mid-management administrator, superintendent, counselor, educational diagnostician, instructional supervisor, special education supervisor, reading specialist, school psychologist, associate school psychologist. *Endorsements* for early childhood (pre-kindergarten/kindergarten), driver education, English as a Second Language, gifted and talented (all-level), special education counselor.

School of Music

Degree Programs Offered: *Baccalaureate* in applied music, choral music, church music, composition, instrumental music, music history and literature, pedagogy, theory. *Master's* in choral conducting, church music, composition, music education, music history and literature, music theory, performance, piano pedagogy and performance, woodwind instruments.

School of Nursing

Degree Programs Offered: *Baccalaureate* in nursing. *Master's* in patient care management, family nurse practitioner.

Distinctive Educational Programs: Patient care management.

School of Law

Degree Programs Offered: *First-professional:* Juris Doctorate.

Admission: Baccalaureate from an accredited institution, or 90 semester hours in theory; LSAT.

Degree Requirements: 120 quarter hours; 1.0 GPA on a 3.0 scale; 27 months in residence.

Graduate School

Degree Programs Offered: In cooperation with the Baylor College of Dentistry, Dallas, Texas, *master's* in anatomy, biochemistry, microbiology, oral biology, pharmacology, physiology. In affiliation with the U.S. Army Academy of Health Sciences, Fort Sam Houston, Texas, *master's* in health care administration, physical therapy.

Institutes and Special Studies

Degree Programs Offered: *Baccalaureate* in American studies, archaeology, Asian studies, biblical and related languages, environmental studies, Latin American studies, museum studies, Slavic studies, university scholars. *Master's* in American studies, biomedical studies, church-state studies, clinical gerontology, environmental economics, environmental studies, gerontology. *Doctorate* in biomedical studies, statistics.

Truett Seminary

Degree Programs Offered: *Master of Divinity.*

Concordia University at Austin

3400 Interstate 35 North
Austin, Texas 78705-2799
Tel: (512) 452-7661 **E-mail:** admissions@concordia.edu
Fax: (512) 459-8517 **Internet:** www.concordia.edu

Institution Description: Concordia University at Austin, formerly named Concordia Lutheran College, is a private 4-year college owned and operated by the Lutheran Church-Missouri Synod. *Enrollment:* 2,260. *Degrees awarded:* Associate, baccalaureate.

Accreditation: *Regional:* SACS. *Professional*: teacher education

History: Established in 1926 as a preparatory academy for young men; junior college added in 1951; junior college became coeducational in 1955; first baccalaureate degrees awarded in 1982; adopted present name 1995.

Institutional Structure: *Governing board:* 9 member Board of Regents. *Composition of institution:* Administrative council of president and 6 vice presidents operate the university. Administration heads faculty, and business affairs; vice president for college advancement heads development and public relations activities. Full-time instructional faculty 35.

Calendar: Semesters. Academic year Aug. to Aug. Formal commencements Dec., May. Summer sessions of varying lengths.

Characteristics of Freshmen: 812 applicatns (female 485, male 332). 90% of applicants accepted. 31% of accepted applicants enrolled.

Mean SAT scores of freshmen class 482 verbal, 493 mathematical. Mean ACT Composite score 21.

34% of freshmen expected to graduate within five years. 93% of freshmen from Texas. Freshmen from 7 states and 3 foreign countries.

Admission: Rolling admissions plan. For fall acceptance, apply as early as the end of the junior year in secondary school. *Requirements:* Either graduation

CONCORDIA UNIVERSITY AT AUSTIN—*cont'd*

from secondary school with a 2.5 average or GED. *Entrance tests:* College Board SAT or ACT. *For transfer students:* eligibility determined by Registrar.

Degree Requirements: 128 credit hours; 2.0 GPA, 2.25 in major, except elementary education, which requires a 2.50; 30 of final 36 credit hours in residence. *Grading system:* A–F; credit by examination through CLEP and PEP.

Distinctive Educational Programs: Prime Time Education, degree programs in the evening; Mini-Courses, usually involving travel, during twice yearly mini-course weekends. Mexican-American Studies major includes a semester of study in Mexico. Distance learning course offered via cable television or videotape rental; Adult Degree Program offers 13 sequential module over 18 months for 40 semester hours of credit toward BA degree in business management; CUENet offers compressed video courses with members of Concordia University System.

ROTC: Air Force Reserve Training and Army Reserve training offered in conjunction with The University of Texas.

Degrees Conferred: 142 *baccalaureate*. Bachelor's degrees awarded in top five disciplines: business, management, marketing, and related support services 871 education 23; communication, journalism, and related programs 12; social sciences 9; theology 9.

Fees and Other Expenses: *Full-time tuition per semester 2008–09:* $20,410. *Books and supplies:* $1,200. *Room and board per academic year:* $7,800. *Other expenses:* $1,930.

Financial Aid: Aid from institutionally generated funds is provided on the basis of academic merit, financial need, other criteria.

Financial aid to full-time, first-time undergraduate students: 100% received federal grants averaging $3,105; 44% state/local grants averaging $4,123; 69% institutional grants averaging $7,000; 79% received loans averaging $4,265.

Departments and Teaching Staff: *Total instructional faculty:* 49.67 FTE. Student/faculty ratio: 13:1. Degrees held by full-time faculty: doctorate 60%, master's 34%, professional 6%. 69% hold terminal degrees. 47% hold terminal degrees.

Enrollment: Total enrollment 2,260. Undergraduate 1,172 (full-time 76%; female 57%, male $43%). Graduate 154 (full-time 3%). Undergraduate transfer-in students 154.

Characteristics of Student Body: *Ethnic/racial makeup:* Black non-Hispanic: 11%; American Indian or Alaska Native: 1%; Asian or Pacific Islander: 2%; Hispanic: 18%; White non-Hispanic: 62%; unknown: 6%.

International Students: Students from Asia, Latin America, Africa, Canada. No programs available for students whose native language is not English. No financial aid specifically designated for international students.

Student Life: On-campus residence halls house 31% of student body. *Intercollegiate athletics:* male: baseball, golf, soccer; female: softball, volleyball; both sexes: basketball, golf, soccer, tennis. *Special services:* Daily, optional chapel services. *Student publications: Crossroads,* a literary magazine. *Surrounding community:* Austin population 480,000.

Publications: *Connections,* alumni magazine published 2 times yearly.

Library Collections: 56,000 volumes including bound books, serial backfiles, electronic documents, and government documents not in separate collections. Online catalog. Current serial subscriptions: 611 paper, 290 microform. 2,075 recordings; 28 compact discs; 13 CD-ROMs. Computer work stations available. Students have access to the Internet at no charge.

Most important special collections include Martin Luther's works (German and English, 6 volumes printed in 1500s); William S. Grey Collection in Reading (microfiche); Harpers (periodical) June 1866 –Dec. 1913, June 1936–Dec. 1967 plus more recent volumes.

Buildings and Grounds: Campus area 23 acres.

Chief Executive Officer: Dr. Thomas E. Cedel, President.

Address admission inquiries to Dr. Michael Mqgavero, Vice President of Enrollment Services.

Criswell College

4010 Gaston Avenue
Dallas, Texas 75246
Tel: (800) 899-0012 **E-mail:** admissions@@criswell.edu
Fax: (214) 818-1310 **Internet:** www.criswell.edu

Institution Description: Criswell College is a private institution affiliated with the Baptist Church. *Enrollment:* 459. *Degrees awarded:* Associate, baccalaureate, master's, first-professional.

Accreditation: *Regional:* SACS-Comm. on Coll.

Calendar: Semesters. Academic year Aug. to May.

Characteristics of Freshmen: 83% of applicants accepted. 76% of accepted applicants enrolled.

Degree Requirements: Completion of prescribed curriculum.

Degrees Conferred: 12 *associate;* 26 *baccalaureate:* theology; 22 *master's:* theology 22. 5 *first-professional:* master of divinity.

Fees and Other Expenses: *Full-time tuition per academic year 2008–09:* contact the college for tuition, fees, and housing costs.

Financial Aid: Aid from institutionally generated funds is provided on the basis of academic merit, financial need, other criteria.

Financial assistance is available in the form of Pell Grants, College Work-Study, Veterans Administration Benefits, National Direct Student Loans, Supplemental Education Opportunity Grants (SEOG), Stafford Loans, other federal aid programs.

Departments and Teaching Staff: *Total instructional faculty:* 27. Student/faculty ratio: 20:1. Degrees held by full-time faculty: doctorate 53.8%, master's 46.2%.

Enrollment: Total enrollment 459. Undergraduate

Characteristics of Student Body: *Ethnic/racial makeup:* Black non-Hispanic: 92; American Indian or Native Alaskan: 3; Asian or Pacific Islander: 35; Hispanic: 37; White non-Hispanic 251.

International Students: No programs available to aid students whose native language is not English. No financial aid specifically designated for international students.

Library Collections: 96,000 volumes. 500 current periodical subscriptions.

Chief Executive Officer: Jerry A. Johnson, President.

Address admission inquiries to Vice President for Enrollment Services.

Dallas Baptist University

3000 Mountain Creek Parkway
Dallas, Texas 75211-9299
Tel: (214) 333-7100 **E-mail:** admiss@dbu.edu
Fax: (214) 333-5115 **Internet:** www.dbu.edu

Institution Description: Dallas Baptist University is a private college affiliated with the Baptist General Convention of Texas. *Enrollment:* 5,297. *Degrees awarded:* Associate, baccalaureate, master's, doctorate.

Accreditation: *Regional:* SACS-Comm. on Coll. *Professional*: business, music, teacher education

History: Established and chartered as Decatur Baptist College, a junior college 1898; moved to Dallas and adopted present name 1965; became 4-year institution 1968; awarded first degree (baccalaureate) 1970; obtained university status in 1985.

Institutional Structure: *Governing board:* Dallas Baptist University Board of Trustees. Extrainstitutional representation: 36 trustees. All voting. *Composition of institution:* Administrators 8. Academic affairs headed by vice president and dean of academic affairs. Management/business/finances directed by vice president. Full-time instructional faculty 111. Academic governance body, Faculty Council, meets an average of 8 times per year.

Calendar: Semesters. 4-1-4 plan. Academic year Aug. to May. Degrees conferred May, Aug., Dec. Formal commencement May, Dec. Summer session May to Aug.

Characteristics of Freshmen: 1,305 applicants (female 753, male 532). 55% of applicants admitted. 59% of applicants admitted.

52% (889 students) submitted SAT scores; 38% (171 students) submitted ACT scores. *25th percentile*: SAT Critical Reading 480, SAT Math 478; ACT Composite 19. *75th percentile*: SAT Critical Reading 582, SAT Math 587; ACT Composite 23.

90% of freshmen from Texas. Freshmen from 172 states and 3 foreign countries.

Admission: Rolling admissions plan. For fall acceptance, apply as early as 24 months prior to enrollment, but not later than last day of registration. *Requirements:* Graduation from accredited secondary school; GED accepted for students over 18 years of age. *Entrance tests:* ACT or SAT; For foreign students TOEFL. *For transfer students:* From 4-year accredited institution maximum transfer credit limited only by degree and residence requirement; from 2-year accredited institution 66 semester hours.

Degree Requirements: 126 semester hours; 2.0 GPA; 32 hours in residence; weekly chapel attendance; 2 physical education courses; 2–4 religion courses; distribution requirements; exit competency examination in English.

Fulfillment of some degree requirements and exemption from some beginning courses possible by passing departmental examinations, College Board CLEP, AP. *Grading system:* A–F; withdraw (carries time limit); incomplete (carries time limit).

Distinctive Educational Programs: Internships. Flexible meeting places and schedules, including off-campus centers and evening classes. Special facilities for using telecommunications in the classroom. Study abroad in China, Costa Rica, England, Egypt, Russian, Taiwan.

ROTC: Army offered in cooperation with University of Texas at Arlington. Air Force offered in cooperation with Texas Christian University.

Degrees Conferred: 1 *associate*; 811 *baccalaureate*; 562 *master's*; 1 *doctorate*. Bachelor's degrees awarded in top five disciplines: business, management, marketing, and related support services 309; liberal arts/general studies 133; communication, journalism, and related programs 63; philosophy/religion/theology 61; psychology 59.

Fees and Other Expenses: *Full-time tuition per academic year 2008–09:* undergraduate $16,440; contact the university for current graduate tuition and applicable fees. *Room and board per academic year:* $5,409. *Books and supplies:* $1,800. *Other exepnses:* $2,322.

Financial Aid: Aid from institutionally generated funds is provided on the basis of academic merit, financial need, athletic ability, other criteria.

Financial aid to full-time, first-time undergraduate students: 89% received some form of aid. Average amount of aid received: federal grants $3,156; Pell grants $2,334; other federal aid $1,851; state/local grants $1,851; institutional grants $6,884.

Departments and Teaching Staff: *Total instructional faculty:* 488 (full-time 111, part-time 377). Total faculty with doctorate, first-professional, or other terminal degree: 181. Student/faculty ratio: 17:1.

Enrollment: Total enrollment 5,297. Undergraduate 3,515 (full-time 62%; female 58%, male 42%). Graduate 1,722 (full-time 31%). Undergraduate transfer-in students 275.

Characteristics of Student Body: *Ethnic/racial makeup:* Black non-Hispanic: 15%; American Indian or Alaska Native: 2%; Asian or Pacific Islander: 2%; Hispanic: 9%; nonresident alien 8%.

International Students: 404 nonresident aliens enrolled fall 2008. Programs available to aid students whose native language is not English: English as a Second Language Program. No financial aid specifically designated for international students.

Student Life: On-campus residence halls house 37% of student body. Residence halls for males constitute 43% of such space, for females 57%. *Intercollegiate athletics:* male: baseball; males and female: cross-country, golf, soccer, tennis, track and field, soccer, volleyball. *Special regulations:* Cars permitted without restrictions. Dress in keeping with Christian standards of the college. Curfews begin midnight Sun.–Thurs., 1am Fri.–Sat. Quiet hours from 10pm to 8am. Residence hall visitation from 6pm to 9pm Sun.–Thurs. *Special services:* Learning Resources Center, medical services. *Student publications: The Summit*, a yearbook. *Surrounding community:* Campus is located 13 miles from downtown Dallas. Served by airport 12 miles from campus; passenger rail service 18 miles from campus.

Library Collections: 316,000 volumes including bound books, serial backfiles, electronic documents, and government documents not in separate collections. Online catalog. 517,000 microforms; 6,700 audiovisual materials. Current serial subscriptions: 402 paper, microform 598,421.

Most important special holdings include Bain Library; ERIC Microfiche Collection; The Microbook Libraries of American Civilization and English Literature.

Buildings and Grounds: Campus area 293 acres.

Chief Executive Officer: Dr. Gary R. Cook, President.

Address admission inquiries to Erin Spivey, Director of Undergraduate Admissions; graduate inquiries to Kit Montgomery, Director, Graduate Programs.

Dallas Christian College

2700 Christian Parkway
Dallas, Texas 75234-7299
Tel: (972) 241-3371 **E-mail:** dcc@dallas.edu
Fax: (972) 241-8021 **Internet:** www.dallas.edu

Institution Description: Dallas Christian College is affiliated with the Christian Churches. *Enrollment:* 315. *Degrees awarded:* Associate, baccalaureate.

Accreditation: *National:* ABHE.

History: The college was established in 1950 in downtown Dallas; relocated to present location in 1967.

Calendar: Semesters. Academic year Aug. to May.

Characteristics of Freshmen: 309 applicants (female 161, male 142). 89% of applicants admitted. 89% of applicants admitted and enrolled.

84% (43 students) submitted SAT scores; 31% (16 students) submitted ACT scores. *25th percentile*: SAT Critical Reading 348, SAT Math 374; ACT Composite 16, ACT English 14, ACT Math 17. *75th percentile*: SAT Critical Reading 603, SAT Math 634; ACT Composite 22, ACT English 23, ACT Math 24.

100% of freshmen are expected to graduate within 5 years. 92% of freshmen from Texas. Freshmen from 5 states.

Admission: *Requirements:* Graduation from accredited secondary school. ACT or SAT entrance tests.

Degree Requirements: Completion of prescribed curriculum.

Distinctive Educational Programs: Quest Degree Completion Program for adult students who have earned approximately two years of college experience. Online degree completion also available. ACCESS program available for alternative state teacher certification.

Degrees Conferred: 1 *associate; 59 baccalaureate:* business/marketing 103; education 7, theology 49.

Fees and Other Expenses: *Full-time tuition per academic year 2008–09:* $10,908. *Other fees:* $600. *Room and board per academic year:* $6,250. *Books and supplies:* $900. *Other expenses:* $3,200.

Financial Aid: Aid from institutionally generated funds is provided on the basis of academic merit, financial need.

Financial aid to full-time, first-time undergraduate students: 100% received some form of aid.

Departments and Teaching Staff: *Total instructional faculty:* 78 (full-time 78, part-time 60). Total faculty with doctorate, first-professional, or other terminal degree: 22. Student/faculty ratio: 16.3:1. Degrees held by full-time faculty: doctorate 30%, master's 84%, baccalaureate 95%.

Enrollment: Total enrollment 315. Undergraduate 301 (full-time 63%; female 45%, male 55%). Graduate 14 (full-time 100%). Transfer-in students 40.

Characteristics of Student Body: *Ethnic/racial makeup:* Black non-Hispanic: 18%; American Indian or Alaska Native: 3%; Asian or Pacific Islander: 1%; Hispanic: 11%; White non-Hispanic: 65%; unknown: 2%. *Age distribution:* number under 18: 6; 18–19: 78; 20–21: 51; 22–24: 47; 25–29: 49; 30–34: 19; 35–39: 40; 40–49: 45; 50–64: 20; 65 and over: 1.

International Students: 1 international student enrolled fall 2008. No programs available to aid students whose native language is not English. No financial aid specifically designated for international students.

Student Life: On-campus residence halls available.

Library Collections: 50,000 volumes. 980 audiovisual titles. Current periodical subscriptions: 3,514 paper, microform, electronic access. Students have access to online information retrieval services and the Internet.

Chief Executive Officer: Dustin D. Rubeck, President.

Address admission inquiries to Eric Hinton, Director of Admissions.

Dallas Theological Seminary

3909 Swiss Avenue
Dallas, Texas 75204
Tel: (214) 824-3094 **E-mail:** admissions@dts.edu
Fax: (214) 841-3664 **Internet:** www.dts.edu

Institution Description: Dallas Theological Seminary is a private nondenominational institution. *Enrollment:* 1,937. *Degrees awarded:* Master's, doctorate. Certificates also awarded.

Accreditation: *Regional:* SACS-Comm. on Coll. *National:* ATS. *Professional*: theology

History: Established as Evangelical Theological College and offered first instruction at postsecondary level 1924; chartered and awarded first degree (master's) 1925; changed name to Dallas Theological Seminary and Graduate School of Theology 1936; adopted present name 1969. *See* Rudolph A. Renfer, "A History of Dallas Theological Seminary" (Ph.D. diss., University of Texas at Austin, 1959) for further information. *See also* John D. Hannah, "The Social and Intellectual Origins of the Evangelical Theological College" (Ph.D. diss., University of Texas at Dallas, 1988).

Institutional Structure: *Governing board:* Board of Incorporate Members. Extrainstitutional representation: 30 directors (including 10 members of Board of Regents and 11 members of Board of Trustees); institutional representation: president of the seminary; 7 alumni. All voting. *Composition of institution:* Executive Committee: president, assistant to the president; executive vice president and vice presidents for academics, advancement, business, and student services meets biweekly. Academic affairs headed by dean. Business/finance/physical plant headed by vice president, director of finance and director of auxiliary services. Full-time faculty 40. Academic governance body, Faculty, meets about 45 time per year.

Calendar: Semesters. Academic year Sept. to May. Degrees conferred and formal commencement May. Summer session of 6 terms from May to Aug.

Admission: Rolling admissions plan. Apply as early as 15 months, but not later than 2 months, prior to enrollment. *Requirements:* Baccalaureate from an accredited or recognized school, preferably with at least 60 semester hours in liberal arts and sciences. Recommend minimum 5 semesters in English, 4 foreign language (1 year of Greek and additional work in French, German, or Latin), 2

DALLAS THEOLOGICAL SEMINARY—*cont'd*

history, 2 natural science, 2 psychology, 2 social science, 1 speech. Additional requirements for some programs. *Entrance tests:* GRE in some cases. *For transfer students:* Credits earned in a seminary or graduate school of theology are individually evaluated.

Degree Requirements: *For master's degrees:* 32–122 semester hours; 2.0–2.5 GPA; 26–62 hours in residence; chapel attendance 4 times weekly. Additional requirements for some programs. *For Certificate of Graduate Studies:* 30 semester hours; 2.0 GPA; 24 hours in residence; chapel attendance 4 times weekly.

Grading system: A–F; withdraw (carries time limit).

Distinctive Educational Programs: Field education, including local and off-campus internships. Evening classes. Accelerated degree programs. Facilities and programs for independent research. *Other distinctive programs:* Lay Institute offers adult education courses; Center for Christian Leadership. 30-hour Certificate of Graduate Studies Program. Extension programs in Philadelphia (PA) and San Antonio (TX). Jerusalem University College (Israel) graduate program.

Degrees Conferred: 158 *master's;* 182 *doctorate:* theology. 121 *first-professional:* master of theology.

Fees and Other Expenses: *Full-time tuition per academic year 2008–09:* contact the seminary for current tuition, fees, and housing costs.

Financial Aid: Aid from institutionally generated funds is provided on the basis of financial need. Institution has a Program Participation Agreement with the U.S. Department of Education for eligible students to receive Pell Grants and, depending upon the agreement, other federal aid.

Departments and Teaching Staff: *Total instructional faculty:* 71. Degrees held by full-time faculty: master's 100%, doctorate 80%, professional 85%. 83% hold terminal degrees.

Enrollment: Total enrollment 1,937. Undergraduate

Characteristics of Student Body: *Ethnic/racial makeup:* Black non-Hispanic: 9%; American Indian or Alaska Native: .5%; Asian or Pacific Islander: 5.9%; Hispanic: 2.9%; White non-Hispanic: 69.6%; unknown: 4.2%.

International Students: 148 nonresident aliens enrolled fall 2008. Students from Europe, Asia, Latin America, Africa, Canada, Australia, New Zealand. Programs available to aid students whose native language is not English: social, cultural. English as a Second Language Program. Financial aid specifically designated for international students: scholarships available annually to qualifying students.

Student Life: On-campus residence halls house 110 single males; 113 seminary-owned apartments house married couples and single females. 24 apartments permit children and 9 are reserved for internationals. Spiritual Life is encouraged through chapel programs. Spiritual Formation Groups, and a variety of programs for non-student spouses. Daycare is not available. Counseling services are provided by professional staff or through contracted referrals. Student newspaper *threshing Floor* published monthly. Activity Fee provides access to the nearby Baylor Fitness Center. *Surrounding community:* Dallas population over 1.2 million. Campus location: urban neighborhood, ethnically diverse; served by mass transit, rail and bus; airports: international 24 miles from campus; regional 8 miles from campus.

Publications: Sources of information about Dallas Theological Seminary include *Kindred Spirit* magazine. *Bibliotheca Sacra* (quarterly) first published in 1843 and by Dallas Theological Seminary since 1934.

Library Collections: 165,000 volumes. 44,000 microforms; 14,600 audiovisual materials; 960 current periodical subscriptions. Students have access to online information retrieval services and the Internet.

Most important special holdings include personal papers of Lewis Sperry Chafer, Seminary founder and first president; archives/papers of International Council on Biblical Inerrancy (ICBI).

Buildings and Grounds: Campus area 17 acres.

Chief Executive Officer: Dr. Mark L. Bailey, President.

Address admission inquiries to Director of Admissions.

East Texas Baptist University

1209 North Grove Avenue
Marshall, Texas 75670-1498
Tel: (903) 935-7963 **E-mail:** admissions@etbu.edu
Fax: (903) 938-7798 **Internet:** www.etbu.edu

Institution Description: East Texas Baptist University is a private institution owned by the Baptist General Conference of Texas. *Enrollment:* 1,210. Degrees awarded: Associate, baccalaureate.

Accreditation: *Regional:* SACS-Comm. on Coll. *Professional*: music, nursing

History: Established as College of Marshall, chartered, and offered first instruction at postsecondary level 1917; awarded first degree (baccalaureate) 1945; adopted present name 1984.

Institutional Structure: *Governing board:* Board of Trustees. Representation: 48 trustees. All voting. *Composition of institution:* Admnistrators 9. Academic affairs headed by vice president for academic affairs. Management/business/finances directed by vice president for administration and finance. manager. Full-time instructional faculty 66. Academic governance body, the faculty, meets an average of 10 times per year.

Calendar: 4-4-1 calendar. Academic year June to May. Freshmen admitted Aug., Jan., May, June, July. Degrees conferred and formal commencement May, Dec. Summer session June term and July term.

Characteristics of Freshmen: 970 applicants (female 504, male 970). 86% of applicants accepted. 52% of accepted applicants enrolled.

35% (188 students) submitted SAT scores; 71% (243 students) submitted ACT scores. *25th percentile*: SAT Critical Reading 400, SAT Math 420; ACT Composite 18, ACT English 16, ACT Math 17. *75th percentile*: SAT Critical Reading 500, SAT Math 530; ACT Composite 23, ACT English 23, ACT Math 23.

90% of freshmen from Texas. Freshmen from 7 states and 3 foreign countries.

Admission: Rolling admissions plan. Early acceptance available. *Requirements:* Either graduation from accredited secondary school with 16 units or GED. Recommend 4 units English, 2 mathematics, 2 natural science, 2.5 social studies, .5 economics, 1.5 physical education, .5 health education, 1 technology applications. .5 speech, 1 academic elective. *Entrance tests:* ACT minimum (unconditional admission) 15. For foreign students TOEFL. *For transfer students:* 2.0 minimum GPA; from 4-year accredited institution 90 semester hours maximum transfer credit; from 2-year accredited institution 66 hours,

College credit and advanced placement for postsecondary-level work completed in secondary school. For extrainstitutional learning college credit and advanced placement on basis of portfolio and faculty assessments; personal interview.

Tutoring available.

Degree Requirements: *For all associate degrees:* 66 semester hours. *For all baccalaureate degrees:* 120 hours; *For all degrees:* 2.0 GPA; weekly chapel attendance; distribution requirements.

Fulfillment of some degree requirements and exemption from some beginning courses possible by passing departmental examinations, College Board CLEP, AP. *Grading system:* A–F; withdraw (carries penalty).

Distinctive Educational Programs: Internships. Evening classes. Accelerated degree programs. Preprofessional programs in dentistry, medicine, nursing, occupational therapy, pharmacy, physician assistant, physical therapy, radiological technology, respiratory therapy, veterinary medicine. Facilities and programs for independent research, including honors programs, Study at the Amusable Institute, Asheville, NC; Chicago; Colorado Springs, CO; Los Angles CA; Martha's Vineyard MA; Washington DC; Wheaton IL. Study abroad in Hong Kong, Australia, Central America, China, Costa Rica, Egypt, England, Israel, New Zealand, Russia, Uganda.

Degrees Conferred: 258 *baccalaureate*. Bachelor's degrees awarded in top five disciplines: education 56; business/marketing 24; theology and religious vocations 34; health professions and related clinical sciences 22; psychology 18.

Fees and Other Expenses: *Full-time tuition per academic year 2008–09:* $16,140. *Room and board per academic year:* $4,913. *Books and supplies:* $866. *Other expenses:* $2,212.

Financial Aid: Aid from institutionally generated funds is provided on the basis of financial need. 99% of first-time, full-time undergraduate students received some form of financial aid.

Departments and Teaching Staff: *Total instructional faculty:* 102 (full-time 66, part-time 36). Total faculty with doctorate, first-professional, or other terminal degree: 61. Student/faculty ratio: 16:1. Degrees held by full-time faculty: master's 37%, doctorate 63%. 63% hold terminal degrees.

Enrollment: Total enrollment 1,210 (ndergraduate).

Characteristics of Student Body: *Ethnic/racial makeup:* Black non-Hispanic: 18%; Asian or Pacific Islander: 2%; Hispanic: 5%; White non-Hispanic: 72%; nonresident alien 1%. *Age distribution:* number under 18: 42; 18–19: 531; 20–21: 421; 22–24: 271; 25–29: 72; 30–34: 29; 35–39: 17; 40–49: 29; 50–64: 9.

International Students: 12 nonresident aliens enrolled fall 2008. Students from Europe, Asia, Latin America, Africa. Programs available to aid students whose native language is not English: social, cultural. English as a Second Language Program. Financial aid specifically designated for international students: >scholarships available annually to qualifying students.

Student Life: On-campus residence halls house 72% of student body. Residence halls for males constitute 51% of such space, for females 49%. 72% of students live on campus. *Intercollegiate athletics:* male: baseball, basketball, cross-country, football, soccer; female: basketball, cross-country, soccer, softball, volleyball. *Special regulations:* Cars permitted with proper parking permits. Curfew begins at 12:30pm. Quiet hours from 8pm to 8am. Residence hall lobbies open 8am to midnight. *Special services:* Learning Resources Center. *Student publications: The Compass*,a monthly newspaper; *The Martian*,a yearbook. *Surrounding community:* Marshall population 25,000. Shreveport (LA), 40 miles from campus, is nearest metropolitan area. Served by airport 45 miles from campus (Shreveport); passenger rail service 1 mile from campus.

Library Collections: 228,000 volumes including bound books, serial backfiles, electronic books and serials and government documents not in separate collections. Online catalog. Current serial subscriptions: 300 paper, 20 microform. 15,000 fulltext and electronic journals. Computer work stations available. Students have access to the Internet at no charge.

Most important holdings include local history collection (Marshall and Harrison County); Texas Baptist History; Texana.

Buildings and Grounds: Campus area 200 acres.

Chief Executive Officer: Dr. Bob E. Riley, President.

Address admission inquiries to Melissa Fitts, Director of Admissions.

Episcopal Theological Seminary of the Southwest

606 Rathervue Place
Austin, Texas 78705-2247
Tel: (512) 472-4133 **E-mail:** jliro@etss.edu
Fax: (512) 472-3098 **Internet:** www.etss.edu

Institution Description: The Episcopal Theological Seminary of the Southwest prepares students for the Christian ministry. *Enrollment:* 75. *Degrees awarded:* Master's, first-professional. Certificates also awarded.

Accreditation: *Regional:* SACS-Comm. on Coll. *National:* ATS. *Professional*: theology

Calendar: Semesters. 4-1-4 calendar. Academic year Sept. to May.

Admission: *Requirements:* Bachelor's degree.

Degree Requirements: Completion of prescribed curriculum.

Degrees Conferred: 37 *first-professional:* master of divinity. *Honorary degrees awarded 2006:* Doctor of Humane Letters 1, Doctor of Divinity 1.

Fees and Other Expenses: *Full-time tuition per academic year 2008–09:* $13,150. *Room and board per academic year:* $5,586.

Financial Aid: Aid from institutionally generated funds is provided on the basis of financial need. Institution has a Program Participation Agreement with the U.S. Department of Education for eligible students to receive Pell Grants and, depending upon the agreement, other federal aid.

Departments and Teaching Staff: *Total instructional faculty:* 47 (full-time 10, part-time 37). Total faculty with doctorate, first-professional, or other terminal degree 27. Student/faculty ratio: 6:1. Degrees held by full-time faculty: doctorate 80%, professional 1%, *master's* 1%. 80% hold terminal degrees.

Enrollment: Total enrollment 75.

International Students: 1 nonresident alien enrolled fall 2008 Programs available to aid students whose native language is not English: English as a Second Language Program. Some financial aid specifically designated for international students.

Library Collections: 102,000 volumes including bound books, serial backfiles, electronic documents, and government documents not in separate collections. Online catalog. Current serial subscriptions: 275 paper, 50 via electronic access. 1,158 audio/videotapes; 509 DVD discs. Computer work stations available. Students have access to the Internet at no charge.

Most important special holdings include liturgies; theology.

Buildings and Grounds: Urban campus.

Chief Executive Officer: Rev. Dr. Philip Turner, Dean and President.

Address admission inquiries to Joseph Liro, Director of Admissions.

Hardin-Simmons University

2200 Hickory Street
Abilene, Texas 79698
Tel: (325) 670-1206 **E-mail:** enroll@hsutx.edu
Fax: (325) 670-2115 **Internet:** www.hsutx.edu

Institution Description: Hardin-Simmons University is a private institution affiliated with the Baptist General Convention of Texas. *Enrollment:* 2,387. *Degrees awarded:* Baccalaureate, master', doctorate.

Member of University Consortium of Abilene, Inc.

Accreditation: *Regional:* SACS-Comm. on Coll. *Professional*: business, music, nursing, physical therapy, social work, teacher education, theology

History: Established and chartered 1891; offered first instruction at postsecondary level 1892; awarded first degree (baccalaureate) 1895. *See* Rupert Richardson, *Famous Are Thy Halls,* 2nd Edition (Abilene: HSU Press, 1976) for further information.

Institutional Structure: *Governing board:* Hardin-Simmons University Board of Trustees. Representation: 36 trustees. All voting. *Composition of institution:* Administrators 6. Academic affairs headed by provost. Management/business/finances directed by the vice president for finance and management. Full-time instructional faculty 129. Academic governance body, the faculty, meets an average of 8 times per year.

Calendar: Semesters. Academic year Aug. to May. Freshmen admitted Sept., Jan., June. Degrees conferred and formal commencements May, Dec. Summer session of 2 terms and a May term.

Characteristics of Freshmen: 1,816 applicants (female 1,075, male 801). 55% of applicants admitted. 29% of applicants admitted and enrolled.

62% (248 students) submitted SAT scores; 71% (282 students) submitted ACT scores. *25th percentile*: SAT Critical Reading 440, SAT Math 450; ACT Composite 19, ACT English 18, ACT Math 18. *75th percentile*: SAT Critical Reading 570, SAT Math 560; ACT Composite 24, ACT English 24, ACT Math 24.

76% of entering freshmen expected to graduate within 5 years. 95% of freshmen from Texas. Freshmen from 12 states and 2 foreign countries.

Admission: Rolling admissions plan. Early acceptance available. *Requirements:* Either graduation from accredited secondary school with 3 units English, 2 mathematics, 2 social science, 2 science, 7 electives (maximum of 3 vocational units); or GED. Minimum 2.0 GPA. *Entrance tests:* College Board SAT or ACT composite. *For transfer students:* 2.0 minimum GPA; from 4-year accredited institution 94 hours maximum transfer credit; from 2-year accredited institution 66 hours maximum transfer credit; correspondence/extension students 30 hours, 2.0 minimum GPA.

College credit for postsecondary-level work completed in secondary school. Remedial courses in English and mathematics offered.

Degree Requirements: *For undergraduate degree:* 124 credit hours; 2.0 GPA; 2 terms (25% of total hours) in residence; weekly chapel attendance; 4 semester hours physical education courses.

Fulfillment of some degree requirements and exemption from some beginning courses possible by passing departmental examinations, College Board CLEP (with score at or above 50th percentile), AP (with score of 3, 4, or 5 for most programs). *Grading system:* A–F; withdraw (carries penalty if failing at time of withdrawal).

Distinctive Educational Programs: Weekend and evening classes. Dual-degree programs with Abilene Christian University, McMurry University. Special facilities for using telecommunications in the classroom. Semester abroad programs are offered at Harlaxton College, England; Salzburg College, Austria; and Altea, Spain. Travel courses are offered by a range of academic disciplines, including: international business, English, Spanish, sociology, art, music, and biblical archaeology. Different faculty members lead the travel courses which change year by year, and are generally offered during spring break, May, and summer terms.

Degrees Conferred: 380 *baccalaureate*; 100 *master's*; 26 *doctorate*. Bachelor's degrees awarded in top five disciplines: business/marketing 57; education 49; parks and recreation 35; psychology 25. Mastger's degrees awarded: business/marketing 23; education 41; English 4; health professions 5; natural resources/environmental science 2; parks and recreation 15; philosophy and religious studies 3 psychology 6; visual and performing arts 1. Doctorates awarded: health professions 26. *First-professional*: theology (master of divinity) 13.

Fees and Other Expenses: *Full-time tuition per academic year 2008–09:* undergraduate $18,380; contact the university for current graduate and first-professional tuition and other applicable fees. *Other fees:* $896. *Room and board per academic year:* $5,180. *Other exepnses:* $2,562.

Financial Aid: Aid from institutionally generated funds is provided on the basis of academic merit, financial need.

Financial aid to full-time, first-time undergraduate students: 97% received some form of aid. Average amount of aid received: federal grants $1,998; Pell grants $2,868; other federal aid $1,003; state/federal aid $3,359; institutional grants $5,899.

Departments and Teaching Staff: *Total instructional faculty:* 184 (full-time 1298, part-time 55). Total faculty with doctorate, first-professional, or other terminal degree 110. Student/faculty ratio: 15:1. Degrees held by full-time faculty: master's 27%, doctorate 70%; professional 3%. 74% hold terminal degrees.

Enrollment: Total enrollment 2,387. Undergraduate 1,934 (full-time 90%; female 58%, male 42%). Graduate 453 (full-time 53%). Undergraduate transfer-in students 155.

Characteristics of Student Body: *Ethnic/racial makeup:* Black non-Hispanic: 5%; American Indian or Alaska Native: 1%; Asian or Pacific Islander: 1%; Hispanic: 10%; White non-Hispanic: 75%; unknown: 5%; nonresident alien 1%. *Age distribution:* number under 18: 13; 18–19: 717; 20–21: 674; 22–24: 326; 25–29: 117; 30–34: 32; 35–39: 23; 40–49: 28; 50–64: 11; 65 and over: 1.

HARDIN-SIMMONS UNIVERSITY—*cont'd*

International Students: 24 nonresident aliens enrolled fall 2008. Students from Europe, Asia, Latin America, Africa. No programs available to aid students whose native language is not English. No financial aid specifically designated for international students.

Student Life: On-campus residence halls house 43% of student body. 9% live in married student housing; apartments available. *Intercollegiate athletics:* male: baseball, basketball, football, golf, soccer, tennis; female: : softball, tennis, basketball, volleyball, golf, soccer. *Special regulations:* Cars permitted without restrictions. *Special services:* Medical services. *Student publications: The Brand*, a weekly newspaper; *The Bronco*, a yearbook; *The Corral*, an annual literary magazine. *Surrounding community:* Abilene population 115,930.. Served by mass transit system; airport 8 miles from campus.

Library Collections: 263,000 volumes including bound books, serial backfiles, electronic documents, and government documents not in separate collections. Online catalog. Current serial subscriptions: 658 paper, 29 microform, 35,567 via electronic access. 2,703 audio/videotapes; 342 DVD discs; 2,773 CD-ROMs. Computer work stations available. Students have access to the Internet at no charge. Total 2008–09 budget for books, periodicals, audiovisual materials, microforms: $367,500.

Most important special holdings include Carl Hertzog Collection of Fine Printing; R.N. Richardson Research Center - Crane Collection of Texana; Morrison Collection of Hymnody; Abilene Photographic Collections (over 10,000 photos indexed).

Buildings and Grounds: Campus area 120 acres. Campus DVD available.

Chief Executive Officer: Dr. W. Craig Turner, President.

Undergraduates address admission inquiries to Vicki House, Director of Admissions; graduate inquiries to Dr. Gary Stanake, Dean of Graduate Studies.

Houston Baptist University

7502 Fondren Road
Houston, Texas 77074-3298
Tel: (281) 649-3000 **E-mail:** unadm@hbu.edu
Fax: (281) 649-3209 **Internet:** www.hbu.edu

Institution Description: Houston Baptist University (formerly Houston Baptist College) is a private institution affiliated with the Baptist General Convention of Texas. *Enrollment:* 2,364. *Degrees awarded:* Associate, baccalaureate, master's.

Accreditation: *Regional:* SACS-Comm. on Coll. *Professional*: nursing, social work

History: Chartered 1960; offered first instruction at postsecondary level 1963; awarded first degree (baccalaureate) 1967.

Institutional Structure: *Governing board:* Board of Trustees. Representation: 21 trustees. *Composition of institution:* Administrators 21. Academic affairs headed by vice president for academic affairs. Management/business/finances directed by vice president for financial affairs. Full-time instructional faculty 125.

Calendar: Quarters. Academic year June to May. Formal commencement May.

Characteristics of Freshmen: 8,532 applicants (female 4,127, male 2,116). 46% of applicants admitted. 18% of admitted applicants enrolled full-time. Mean SAT scores 550 verbal, 560 mathematical. Mean ACT Composite score 22.

Admission: Early acceptance available. *Requirements:* Graduation from accredited secondary school. GED accepted. Minimum acceptance requirements depend on combination of class rank and admission test scores. *Entrance tests:* College Board SAT or ACT composite. For foreign students TOEFL. *For transfer students:* 2.0 minimum GPA.

College credit for postsecondary-level work completed in secondary school.

Degree Requirements: 130–137 semester hours; 2.0 GPA; 32 semester hours in residence; 4 semester hours in physical education; general education requirements, attendance at convocations; English proficiency examination.

Fulfillment of some degree requirements possible by passing College Board CLEP, AP, and other standardized test. *Grading system:* A–F; pass-fail; withdraw (carries time limit); satisfactory progress, work incomplete; unsatisfactory progress, work incomplete.

Distinctive Educational Programs: Evening classes. Preprofessional programs in medicine, dentistry, optometry, physical therapy, veterinary medicine, physician's assistant. Joint programs in nuclear medicine technology and medical technology with various approved schools. Interdepartmental/interdisciplinary programs in Culture and Human Experience, and Great Issues of the 20th Century. Study abroad in England, Mexico, Middle Eastern and European countries.

ROTC: Army, Navy; offered in cooperation with Rice University.

Degrees Conferred: 5 *associate*; 333 *baccalaureate*; 111 *master's*. Bachelor's degrees awarded in top five disciplines: business, management, marketing, and related support services 113; biological and life sciences 48; philosophy/religion 33; education 32; communication, journalism, and related programs 28. Master's degrees awarded: various disciplines 111.

Fees and Other Expenses: *Full-time tuition per academic year 2008–09:* $19,970. *Books and supplies:* $1,230. *Room and board per academic year:* $5,710. *Other expenses:* $2,734.

Financial Aid: Aid from institutionally generated funds is provided on the basis of academic merit, athletic ability.

Financial aid to full-time, first-time undergraduate students: 94% received some form of aid. Average amount of aid received: federal grants $3,780; Pell grants $365; other federal aid $1,039; state/local grants $3,231; institutional grants $7,853.

Departments and Teaching Staff: *Total instructional faculty:* 125. Student/faculty ratio: 14:1. Degrees held by full-time faculty: doctorate 67%, master's 32%, baccalaureate 100%. 67% hold terminal degrees.

Enrollment: Total enrollment 2,564. Undergraduate 2,208 (full-time 86%; female 65%, male 35%). Graduate 356 (full-time 32%). Undergraduate transfer-in students 252.

Characteristics of Student Body: *Ethnic/racial makeup:* Black non-Hispanic: 26%; Asian or Pacific Islander: 145; Hispanic: 20%; White non-Hispanic: 35%; unknown: 3%; nonresident alien 6%.

International Students: 51 nonresident aliens enrolled fall 2008. No programs available to aid students whose native language is not English. No financial aid specifically designated for international students.

Student Life: On-campus residence halls available. *Intercollegiate athletics:* basketball, golf, gymnastics, tennis, track. *Special regulations:* Registered cars permitted without restrictions. All unmarried students, except Houston residents living at home, must live in university residence halls. *Student publications: Collegian*, student-run newspaper; *Ornogah*, student-produced yearbook. *Surrounding community:* Houston population 1,600,000. Served by mass transit bus system.

Library Collections: 265,000 volumes including bound books, serial backfiles, electronic documents, and government documents not in separate collections. Online catalog. Current serial subscriptions: 1,040 paper, microform, and electronic. Computer work stations available. Students have access to the Internet at no charge.

Most important special holdings include Bradley Collection (military history, Victorian literature); A. S. Johnston Confederate History Collection; Hicks Collection (Texas history and politics).

Buildings and Grounds: Campus area 158 acres.

Chief Executive Officer: Dr. Jack O.Carlson, President.

Address admission inquiries to Eduardo Borges, Director of Admissions.

Howard Payne University

1000 Fisk Avenue
Brownwood, Texas 76801
Tel: (325) 646-2502 **E-mail:** enroll@hputx.edu
Fax: (325) 649-8901 **Internet:** www.hputx.edu

Institution Description: Howard Payne University is a private college affiliated with the Baptist General Convention of Texas. *Enrollment:* 1,388. *Degrees awarded:* Associate, baccalaureate, master's..

Accreditation: *Regional:* SACS-Comm. on Coll. *Professional*: business, music, social work

History: Established and chartered as Howard Payne College 1889; offered first instruction at postsecondary level 1890; awarded first degree (baccalaureate) 1895; merged with Daniel Baker College (established 1888) 1953; adopted present name 1974.

Institutional Structure: *Governing board:* Howard Payne University Board of Trustees. Extrainstitutional representation: 32 trustees. All voting. *Composition of institution:* Administrators 4. Academic affairs headed by vice president. Management/business/finances directed by vice president. Full-time instructional faculty 73,. Academic governance body, the faculty, meets an average of 7 times per year.

Calendar: Semesters. Academic year June to May. Freshmen admitted Aug., Jan., June. Degrees conferred and formal commencement May. Summer session from June to Aug.

Characteristics of Freshmen: 874 applicants (405 female, male 469). 65% of applicants admitted. 57% of applicants admitted and enrolled.

55% (231 students) submitted SAT scores; 45% (185 students) submitted ACT scores. *25th percentile*: SAT Critical Reading 448, SAT Math 458; ACT Composite 18, ACT English 17, ACT Math 17. *75th percentile*: SAT Critical

Reading 588, SAT Math 588; ACT Composite 25, ACT English 26, ACT Math 25.

98% of freshmen from Texas. Freshmen from 6 states.

Admission: Rolling admissions plan. Early acceptance available. *Requirements:* Either graduation from accredited secondary school with 22 units which must include 4 English, 3 mathematics or 2 science, 1.5 social studies; or GED. Minimum GPA 3.0. *Entrance tests:* College Board SAT or ACT Composite.

College credit and advanced placement for postsecondary-level work completed in secondary school.

Tutoring available. Remedial course offered in summer session and regular academic year; credit given.

Degree Requirements: *For all baccalaureate degrees:* 128 credit hours; 3 terms in residence; weekly chapel attendance; 2 hours physical education; distribution requirements. For master's degree in youth ministry: 42 hours (non-thesis).

Fulfillment of some degree requirements and exemption from some beginning courses possible by passing departmental examinations, College Board CLEP. *Grading system:* A–F; withdraw (carried time limit).

Distinctive Educational Programs: *Available to all students:* Flexible meeting places and schedules, including off-campus centers at Corpus Christi, El Paso, Ft. Worth, Harlingen, and Midland. Evening classes. Interdisciplinary programs. Preprofessional programs in dentistry, medicine, medical technology. Honors programs. *Other distinctive program:* Degree- and non-degree-granting continuing education program for adults. Study abroad programs in Israel and England (Oxford University).

Degrees Conferred: 247 *baccalaureate*: education 49; theology and religious vocations 42; business/marketing 31; social sciences 24; liberal arts/general studies 16. Master's degrees awarded: theology 3.

Fees and Other Expenses: *Full-time tuition per academic year 2008–09:* $17,480. *Other fees:* $1,030. *Room and board per academic year:* $4,940. *Books and supplies:* $1,200. *Other expenses:* $2,400.

Financial Aid: Aid from institutionally generated funds is provided on the basis of academic merit, financial need, athletic ability, and other criteria.

Financial aid to full-time, first-time undergraduate students: 98% received some form of aid.

Departments and Teaching Staff: *Total instructional faculty:* 147 (full-time 73, part-time 74). Total faculty with doctorate, first-professional, or other terminal degree: 62. Student/faculty ratio: 12:1.

Enrollment: Total enrollment 1,388. Undergraduate 1,371 (full-time 78%; female 49%, male 31%). Graduate 17 (full-time 245). Undergraduate transfer-in students 92.

Characteristics of Student Body: *Ethnic/racial makeup:* Black non-Hispanic: 7%; American Indian or Alaska Native: 1%; Asian or Pacific Islander: 1%; Hispanic: 15%; White non-Hispanic: 69%; unknown 6%; nonresident alien 1%. *Age distribution:* number under 18: 3; 18–19: 403; 20–21: 372; 22–24: 21; 25–29: 42; 30–34: 20; 35–39: 5; 40–49: 13; 50–64: 2; 65 and over: 1.

International Students: 2 nonresident aliens enrolled fall 2008. No programs available to aid students whose native language is not English. No financial aid specifically designated for international students.

Student Life: On-campus residence halls house 85% of student body. Residence halls for males constitute 54% of such space, for females 46%. *Intercollegiate athletics:* male: baseball, basketball, cross-country, football, golf, tennis, track; female: basketball, cross-country, golf, softball, tennis, track, volleyball. *Special services:* Medical services. *Student publications: The Swarm*, a yearbook; *The Yellow Jacket*, a weekly newspaper. *Surrounding community:* Brownwood population 19,500. Fort Worth, 130 miles from campus, is nearest metropolitan area. Served by airport 5 miles from campus.

Library Collections: 121,264 volumes including bound books, serial backfiles, electronic documents, and government documents not in separate collections. Online catalog. Current serial subscriptions: paper 419; via electronic access 66,107. 279,911 microforms. 6,800 recordings. Students have access to the Internet at no charge.

Most important holdings include Burress Genealogical Collection; U.S. Government Documents Depository Collection; Douglas MacArthur Museum.

Buildings and Grounds: Campus area 10 square blocks.

Chief Executive Officer: Dr. Lanny Hall, President.

Address all admission inquiries to Cheryl Mangrum, Director of Admissions.

Huston-Tillotson University

900 Chicon Street
Austin, Texas 78702-2795
Tel: (512) 505-3000 **E-mail:** admissions@htu.edu
Fax: (512) 505-3190 **Internet:** www.htu.edu

Institution Description: Huston-Tillotson University is a private college affiliated with The United Methodist Church and The United Church of Christ. *Enrollment:* 785. *Degrees awarded:* Baccalaureate.

Member of Texas Association of Developing Colleges.

Accreditation: *Regional:* SACS-Comm. on Coll.

History: Established as Tillotson Collegiate and Normal Institute 1875; chartered 1877; offered first instruction at postsecondary level 1881; changed name to Tillotson College 1874; incorporated and awarded first degree (baccalaureate) 1909; became 4-year college 1931; merged with Samuel Hutson College (established 1876); became Huston-Tillotson College 1952; achieved university status 2005.

Institutional Structure: *Governing board:* Board of Trustees. Extrainstitutional representation: 27 trustees, 12 trustees emeriti; institutional representation: 1 administrator. 13 ex officio. 27 voting. *Composition of institution:* Administrators 16. Academic affairs headed by vice president for academic affairs. Full-time instructional faculty 37. Academic governance body, Educational Policy Council, meets an average of 9 times per year.

Calendar: Semesters. Academic year Aug. to May. Freshmen admitted Aug., Jan., June. Degrees conferred and formal commencement May. Summer session from June to July.

Characteristics of Freshmen: 743 applicants (female 318, male 425). 100% of applicants accepted. 78% of accepted applicants enrolled.

68% (109 students) submitted SAT scores; 35% (65 students) submitted ACT scores. *25th percentile*: SAT Critical Reading 350, SAT Math 350; ACT Composite 14, ACT English 12, ACT Math 15. *75th percentile*: SAT Critical Reading 450, SAT Math 470l; ACT Composite 18, ACT English 17, ACT Math 17.

16% of entering freshmen expected to graduate within 5 years. 26% of freshmen from Texas. Freshmen from 22 states and 15 foreign countries.

Admission: Rolling admissions plan. *Requirements:* Either graduation from accredited secondary school with 15 units which normally include 3 English, 2 mathematics, 2 social studies (including 1 history), 1 science, 7 electives (including at least 3 academic); or GED. *Entrance tests:* College Board SAT or ACT composite. For foreign students TOEFL. *For transfer students:* Maximum transfer credit limited only by residence requirement.

College credit and advanced placement for extrainstitutional learning.

Tutoring available. Developmental courses offered in summer session and regular academic year; credit given.

Degree Requirements: 120 credit hours; 2.0 GPA; last 24 hours in residence; exit competency examination in writing; 4 hours physical education. *Grading system:* A–F; withdraw (carries time limit and penalty).

Distinctive Educational Programs: Work-experience programs. Cluster colleges. Evening classes. Special facilities for using telecommunications in the classroom. Interdisciplinary programs in business education, physical education, music education. Facilities and programs for independent research, including honors programs, tutorials. Distance and online learning courses offered.

Degrees Conferred: 93 *baccalaureate*. Bachelor's degrees awarded in top five disciplines: business, management, marketing, and related support services 13; computer and information sciences 81 social sciences 7; parks and recreation 7; multidisciplinary studies 7.

Fees and Other Expenses: *Full-time tuition per academic year 2008–09:* $11,184. *Books and supplies:* $900. *Required fees:* $470. *Room and board per academic year:* $6,400. *Other expenses:* $3,000.

Financial Aid: Aid from institutionally generated funds is provided on the basis of academic merit, financial need, other criteria.

Financial aid to full-time, first-time undergraduate students: 69% received some form of aid.

Departments and Teaching Staff: *Total instructional faculty:* 67. Student/faculty ratio: 14:1.

Enrollment: Total enrollment 785. Undergraduate 725 (full-time 93%; female 495, male 51%). Graduate 60 (part-time 100%). Undergraduate transfer-in students 90.

Characteristics of Student Body: *Ethnic/racial makeup:* Black non-Hispanic: 78%; Hispanic: 11%; White non-Hispanic: 6%; unknown 1%; nonresident alien 3%. *Age distribution:* number under 18: 30; 18–19: 239; 20–21: 159; 22–24: 25–29: 131; 30–34: 25; 35–39: 14; 40–49: 21; 50–64: 11.

International Students: 27 nonresident aliens enrolled fall 2008. Programs available to aid students whose native language is not English: Intensive English

HUSTON-TILLOTSON UNIVERSITY—*cont'd*

language study. No financial aid specifically designated for international students.

Student Life: On-campus residence halls house 47% of student body. *Intercollegiate athletics:* male: baseball, basketball, golf, soccer, track and field; female: basketball, track and field, volleyball. *Special regulations:* Cars with parking stickers permitted; fee charged. Curfews. Residence hall visitation from 6pm to 10pm Wed. and Sun. *Special services:* Learning Resources Center, medical services. *Student publications: Rams Voice*, a weekly newsletter. *Surrounding community:* Austin metropolitan area population 550,000. Served by mass transit bus system; airport 5 miles from campus; passenger rail service 3 miles from campus.

Library Collections: 93,000 volumes. 70,000 microforms; 9,500 audiovisual materials; 2,350 current periodical subscriptions.

Buildings and Grounds: Campus area 23 acres.

Chief Executive Officer: Dr. Larry L. Earvin, President.

Address all admission inquiries to Antonio Hooloway, Dean of Enrollment Management.

Jarvis Christian College

U.S. Highway 80 East
P.O. Drawer 1470
Hawkins, Texas 757651470

Tel: (903) 769-5700 **E-mail:** admissions@jarvis.edu
Fax: (903) 769-4842 **Internet:** www.jarvis.edu

Institution Description: Jarvis College is a private college affiliated with the Christian Church (Disciples of Christ). *Enrollment:* 728. *Degree awarded:* Baccalaureate.

Accreditation: *Regional:* SACS-Comm. on Coll.

History: Established as Jarvis Christian Institute, an elementary school, 1912; adopted present name and offered first instruction at postsecondary level 1937; chartered 1938; awarded first degree (baccalaureate) 1939.

Institutional Structure: *Governing board:* Board of Trustees. Extrainstitutional representation: 21 trustees; institutional representation: president of the college, 1 full-time instructional faculty member, 1 student; 4 alumni. 1 ex officio. All voting. *Composition of institution:* Administrators 37. Academic affairs headed by dean of academic affairs. Management/business/finances directed by director for fiscal affairs. Full-time instructional faculty 32. Academic governance body, Academic Affairs Committee, meets an average of 9 times per year.

Calendar: Semesters. Academic year Aug. to May. Freshmen admitted Aug. Degrees conferred and formal commencement May. No summer session.

Characteristics of Freshmen: 51% of applicants admitted. 29% of accepted applicants enrolled.

Average secondary school rank of freshmen top 50th percentile. Mean ACT Composite score 15.

21% of freshmen expected to graduate within 5 years. 79% of freshmen from Texas. Freshmen from 9 states.

Admission: Rolling admissions plan. For fall acceptance, apply as early as junior year of secondary school, but not later than 30 days prior to enrollment. Early acceptance available. *Requirements:* Either graduation from accredited secondary school with 3 units English, 3 social studies, 2 mathematics, 1 science, 7 electives; or GED. Minimum GPA 2.0. *Entrance tests:* ACT composite. *For transfer students:* 2.0 minimum GPA; from 4-year accredited institution maximum transfer credit limited only by residence requirement; from 2-year accredited institution 65 hours.

Tutoring available. Remedial courses offered during regular academic year; credit given.

Degree Requirements: *For all baccalaureate degrees:* 124 credit hours; last 30 hours in residence; 2 hours physical education; GRE. *For all degrees:* 2.0 GPA; weekly chapel attendance; sophomore comprehensive examination; faculty approval.

Fulfillment of some degree requirements possible by passing College Board CLEP. *Grading system:* A–F; withdraw; incomplete (carries time limit).

Distinctive Educational Programs: Cooperative education. Honors programs, individual majors. Summer enrichment program for entering students. *Other distinctive programs:* Degree-granting and noncredit continuing education.

Degrees Conferred: 86 *baccalaureate:* biological sciences 9. business 23; computer and information science 7; education 10; health professions 8; history 1; interdisciplinary studies 13; physical sciences 5; social sciences 15.

Fees and Other Expenses: *Full-time tuition per academic year 2008–09:* $8,208. *Required fees:* $770. *Room and board per academic year:* $4,954. *Books and supplies:* $800. *Other expenses:* $1,750.

Financial Aid: Aid from institutionally generated funds is provided on the basis of academic merit, financial need, athletic ability.

Financial aid to full-time, first-time undergraduate students: 88% received some form of aid.

Departments and Teaching Staff: *Total instructional faculty:* 41 (full-time 32, part-time 9). Student/faculty ratio: 16:1. Degrees held by full-time faculty: doctorate 57%, master's 43%. 57% hold terminal degrees. *Faculty development:* $140,000 in grants for research.

Enrollment: Total enrollment 728 (undergraduate).

Charaeteristics of Student Body: *Ethnic/racial makeup:* Black non-Hispanic: 96%; Hispanic: 4%; White non-Hispanic: 1%. *Age distribution:* number 18–19: 226; 20–21: 148; 22–24: 124; 25–29: 20; 30–34: 7; 35–39: 9; 40–49: 4; 50–64: 5.

International Students: No programs available to aid students whose native language is not English. No financial aid specifically designated for international students.

Student Life: On-campus residence halls house 75% of student body. Housing available for married students. 15% of married students request institutional housing; 8% are so housed. *Intercollegiate athletics:* male: baseball, basketball; female: basketball, volleyball. *Special regulations:* Cars permitted in designated areas only, parking permit required; fee charged. Residencc hall visitation from 1pm to midnight Sun.–Thurs., 1pm to 1am Fri. and Sat. *Special services:* Learning Resources Center, medical services. Vans provided for field trips and special events. *Student publications: The Bulldog*, a yearbook; *The Expression*, a monthly newspaper. *Surrounding community:* Hawkins, population 1,300. Dallas, 100 miles from campus, is nearest metropolitan area.

Library Collections: 59,000 volumes including bound books, serial backfiles, electronic documents, and government documents not in separate collections. Online catalog. Current serial subscriptions: 121 paper; 135 microform. Computer work stations available. Students have access to the Internet at no charge.

Most important holdings include 1,500 volumes by and about Black people; young adult collection of 2,500 volumes, including juvenile literature, career information, self-help books.

Buildings and Grounds: Campus area 245 acres.

Chief Executive Officer: Dr. Sebetha Jenkins, President.

Address admission inquiries to Felicia Tyska, Director of Admissions.

Lamar University

4400 Martin Luther King, Jr. Parkway
Beaumont, Texas 77710

Tel: (409) 880-7011 **E-mail:** admissions@lamar.edu
Fax: (409) 880-8463 **Internet:** www.lamar.edu

Institution Description: Lamar University is A component of the Texas State University System. *Enrollment:* 15,465. *Degrees awarded:* Associate, baccalaureate, master's, doctorate.

Academic offerings subject to approval by statewide coordinating bodies. Budget subject to approval by state governing boards.

Accreditation: *Regional:* SACS-Comm. on Coll. *Professional*: audiology, business, chemistry, dietetics, engineering, music, nursing, radiography, respiratory therapy, social work, speech-language pathology, social work, teacher education

History: Established, chartered, incorporated, and offered first instruction at postsecondary level as South Park Junior College 1940; changed name to Lamar College 1932, to Lamar Junior College 1940; became 4-year institution and changed name to Lamar State College of Technology 1951; awarded first degree (baccalaureate) 1953; added doctorate program and changed name to Lamar University 1971; legislative action caused Lamar University System to be crated in 1983, with Lamar University being the major component; the College of Technical Arts was separated from Lamar University in 1990 and became the fourth component of the Lamar University System; in 1995 the Lamar University System was merged with the Texas State University System.

Institutional Structure: *Governing board:* Board of Regents of Texas State University System. Representation: 9 regents. All voting. *Composition of institution:* Administrators 26. Academic affairs headed by executive vice president. Finance and student affairs headed by vice president. Information Systems headed by assistant vice president. Physical Plant headed by director. Full-time instructional faculty 340. Academic governance body, Faculty Senate, meets an average of 9 times per year.

Calendar: Semesters. Academic year late Aug. to May. Freshmen admitted Aug., Jan., May, July. Degrees conferred and formal commencements May, Aug., Dec. Summer session from May to Aug.

Characteristics of Freshmen: 5,190 applicants (female 3,995, male 2,195). 62% of applicants admitted. 41% of applicants admitted and enrolled.

84% (1,255 students) submitted SAT scores; 16% (237 students) submitted ACT scores. *25th percentile*: SAT Critical Reading 400, SAT Math 400; ACT Composite 16, ACT English 14, ACT Math 15. *75th percentile*: SAT Critical Reading 520, SAT Math 530; ACT Composite 20, ACT English 20, ACT Math 21.

98% of freshmen from Texas. Freshmen from 11 states and 4 foreign countries.

Admission: Rolling admissions plan. For fall acceptance, apply as early as 1 year, but not later than 1 week, prior to semester of enrollment. Early acceptance available. *Requirements:* Graduation from accredited secondary school and successful completion of 14 high school units in college preparatory courses including 4 units in college preparatory English courses, 3 units of college preparatory mathematics courses (algebra I, II, geometry, or higher level mathematics courses), 2 units of laboratory science courses (any 2 units from biology I, II, chemistry I, II, physics I, II, or geology), 2–1/2 units of social science courses (U.S. history 1 unit, U.S. government ½ unit, world history studies 1 unit or world geography studies 1 unit), 2* 1/2 units of approved college preparatory course electives. In addition, students must graduate in the top half of their high school class or achieve a composite score on the SAT of 700 for those with class rank in third quarter, 800 in fourth quarter. Students who graduate from an accredited high school or who hold a GED but who fail to meet the foregoing requirements for regular admission will be permitted to attend on a provisional basis. General admission standards do not apply to students entering associate degree, vocational, or technical programs. Applicants over 25 years of age will be granted full admission with proof of high school graduation or GED completion. In addition to the general admission standards, preprofessional and professional programs may require separate, more rigorous standards commensurate with the demands of the various programs.

Degree Requirements: *For all associate degrees:* 70 credit hours; 2 semesters physical education; course and distribution requirements. *For all baccalaureate degrees:* 120–145 credit hours; 4 semesters physical education; general education requirements. *For all undergraduate degrees:* 2.0 GPA, 30 semester hours in residence.

Exemption from some beginning courses possible by passing departmental examinations, College Board CLEP. *Grading system:* A–F; pass-fail; withdraw (carries time limit).

Distinctive Educational Programs: Evening classes. Double-degree associate and baccalaureate programs. Facilities and programs for independent research, including honors programs, individual majors, tutorials. Study abroad in England, Italy.

Degrees Conferred: 39 *associate*; 1,191 *baccalaureate*; 412 *master's*; 35 *doctorate*. Bachelor's degrees awarded in top five disciplines: business, management, marketing, and related support services 271; interdisciplinary studies 203; health professions 110; liberal arts/general studies 109; engineering 90.

Fees and Other Expenses: *Full-time tuition per academic year 2008–09:* undergraduate/graduate resident $8,014, nonresident $14,444; contact the university for graduate tuition/fees. *Required fees:* $1,154. *Room and board per academic year:* $6,290. *Books and supplies:* $1,440. *Other expenses:* $4,284.

Financial Aid: Aid from institutionally generated funds is provided on the basis of academic merit, financial need, athletic ability, other criteria.

Financial aid to full-time, first-time undergraduate students: 78% received some form of aid. Average amount of aid received: federal grants $1,721; Pell grants $1,733; other federal aid $1,381; state/local grants $2,453; institutional grants $1,216.

Departments and Teaching Staff: *Total instructional faculty:* 490 (full-time 340, part-time 158). Total faculty with doctorate, first-professional, or other terminal degree: 282. Student/faculty ratio: 18:1.

Enrollment: Total enrollment 15,465. Undergraduate 8,993 (full-time 70%; female 61%, male 39%). Graduate 4,472 (full-time 15%). Undergraduate transfer-in students 650.

Characteristics of Student Body: *Ethnic/racial makeup:* Black non-Hispanic 29%; Asian or Pacific Islander: 4%; Hispanic: 7%; White non-Hispanic: 53%; unknown: 3%; nonresident alien 1%. *Age distribution:* number under 18: 248; 18–19: 2,261; 20–21: 2,224; 22–24 2,163; 25–29: 1,175; 30–34: 572; 35–39: 390; 40–49: 508; 50–64: 179; 65 and over: 6.

International Students: 504 nonresident aliens enrolled fall 2008. Students from Europe, Asia, Latin America, Africa, Canada, Middle East. Programs available to aid students whose native language is not English: social, cultural. English as a Second Language Program. No financial aid specifically designated for international students.

Student Life: On-campus residence halls house 8% of student body. 2% of males join fraternities; 1.5% of females join sororities. *Intercollegiate athletics:* male: baseball, basketball, cross-country, golf, tennis, track and field; female basketball, cross-country, golf, tennis, track and field, volleyball. *Special services:* Medical services. *Student publications, radio: UP*, a biweekly newspaper; *The Pulse.* Radio station KVLU. *Surrounding community:* Beaumont population 120,000. Houston, 90 miles from campus, is nearest metropolitan area. Served by mass transit bus system.

Library Collections: 900.000 volumes including bound books, serial backfiles, electronic documents, and government documents not in separate collections. Online catalog. 2,800 current serial subscriptions: paper, microform, and electronic. Computer work stations available. Students have access to the Internet at no charge.

Most important special holdings include collections on engineering, and cookery (17th–19th centuries); Peter Wells Texana Collection; Congressional Papers of Jack B. Brooks.

Buildings and Grounds: Campus area 200 acres. Campus DVD available.

Chief Executive Officer: Dr. James M. Simmons, President.

Undergraduates address admission inquiries to James Rush, Director of Admissions.

College of Arts and Sciences

Degree Programs Offered: *Associate* in nursing; *baccalaureate* in chemistry, English, French, history, political science, sociology, Spanish, liberal arts, biology, criminal justice, energy resource management, environmental science, geology, medical technology, oceanographic technology, physics, political science, social work; *master's* in English, history, nursing, political science, biology, chemistry, public administration, applied criminology, psychology. .

College of Business

Degree Programs Offered: *Baccalaureate* in accounting, office administration, management information systems, economics, finance, management, human resources management, marketing.

Admission: Newly entering freshmen who meet general entrance requirements will be admitted to the College of Business in a 'pre-business' classification only. Major declared after completion of 45 semester hours with a GPA of at least 2.0 (course requirements within the 45 hours). Transfer students with grade point deficiency classified as "pre-business." No enrollment in 400 level business courses until GPA is at least 2.0.

Distinctive Educational Programs: Baccalaureate concentrations in advertising, computer science, industrial engineering, law, retail merchandising.

College of Education and Human Development

Degree Programs Offered: *Baccalaureate* in deaf education/habilitation, music education, art education, education (elementary, secondary and special), health education, home economics, physical education; *master's* in elementary education, guidance and counseling, kinesiology, school administration, secondary education, special education, supervision.

Admission: Overall GPA of 2.0, successful completion of 60 semester hours (required courses included), completion of Pre-Professional Skills Test in accordance with state policy.

Distinctive Educational Programs: Cooperative doctorate in educational administration with Texas A&M University.

College of Engineering

Degree Programs Offered: *Baccalaureate* in computer science, chemical engineering, civil engineering, electrical engineering, industrial engineering, mechanical engineering, industrial engineering; *master's* in computer science, engineering science, engineering, engineering management; *doctorate* in engineering.

Admission: High school course requirements. GPA of 2.25 to remain in program and 2.0 GPA in major courses. Completion of 51 semester hours with GPA of 2.25 on all required courses for admission to engineering program. Approved electives.

Distinctive Educational Programs: Work-experience programs.

College of Fine Arts and Communication

Degree Programs Offered: *Baccalaureate* in secondary art, speech, speech pathology and audiology, theatre, fine arts-graphic design, fine arts-studio art, music, music education, communication, graphic design, mass communication, studio art; *baccalaureate* and *master's* in music, music education, audiology, public address, speech, speech pathology/audiology, theatre.

LeTourneau University

2100 Moberly Avenue
P.O. Box 7001
Longview, Texas 75607-7001
Tel: (800) 759-8811 **E-mail:** admissions@letu.edu
Fax: (903) 233-3411 **Internet:** www.letu.edu

Institution Description: LeTourneau University is a private, independent, nonprofit, Christian institution. *Enrollment:* 3,662. *Degrees awarded:* Associate, baccalaureate, master's.

Accreditation: *Regional:* SACS-Comm. on Coll. *Professional:* Business, engineering.

History: Established as LeTourneau Technical Institute, chartered, incorporated, offered first instruction at postsecondary level and awarded first degree (associate) 1946; became 4-year institution and adopted the name LeTourneau College in 1961; became LeTourneau University 1995.

Institutional Structure: *Governing board:* Trustees of LeTourneau University. Representation: 24 trustees, including President. *Composition of institution:* President and 7 Cabinet Officers. Academic affairs headed by Vice President for Academic Affairs. Business/finance directed by Vice President for Business and Finance. Full-time instructional faculty: 56. Academic governance body, Academic Council, meets an average of 25 times per year.

Calendar: Semesters. Academic year Aug. to May. Freshmen admitted Aug., Jan., May. Degrees conferred May, July, Dec. Formal commencements May and Dec. Summer sessions from May to Aug.

Characteristics of Freshmen: 910 Applicants (female 332, male 638). 66% pf applicants admitted. 51% of accepted applicants enrolled full-time.

75% (254 students) submitted SAT scores; 49% (166 students) submitted ACT scores.

42% of entering freshmen expected to graduate within 5 years. 55% of freshmen from Texas. Freshmen from 49 states and 19 foreign countries.

Admission: Rolling admissions plan. For fall acceptance, apply as early as spring of junior year of secondary school, but not later than July 1 of year of enrollment. *Requirements:* Either graduation from accredited secondary school with 16 units which normally include 4 English, 3 mathematics, 3 social studies, 1 computer skills, 1 foreign language, 1 fine arts; or GED. Additional requirements for engineering program. Minimum GPA 2.5. Lowest acceptable secondary school class standing 50th %ile. *Entrance tests:* ACT composite or College Board SAT accepted. For foreign students TOEFL. *For transfer students:* 2.0 minimum GPA; from 4-year accredited institution 94 hours maximum transfer credit; from 2-year accredited institution 72 hours.

College credit and advanced placement for postsecondary-level work completed in secondary school and for extrainstitutional learning (life experience).

Degree Requirements: *For all associate degrees:* 74 credit hours; 2.0 GPA; 2 semesters in residence; chapel attendant; general education requirements. *For baccalaureate degrees:* 124 credit hours; 2.0 GPA; 2 semesters in residence; chapel attendance; general education requirements. *For master's degree:* 3.0 GPA; one year in residence; minimum 39 credit hours; no more than 2 grades of C. Fulfillment of some degree requirements and exemption from some beginning courses possible by passing College Board CLEP. Exemption from courses also possible by passing departmental examinations, CLEP. *Grading system:* A–F; withdraw (carries time limit).

Distinctive Educational Programs: Honors Program; distance learning; preprofessional programs in health science; cooperative learning; adult education for working professionals. Study abroad: China, Costa Rica, Egypt, England, Russia. Special facilities for using telecommunications in the classroom. Preprofessional program in health sciences. *Other distinctive programs:* The Longview Citizens' Resource Center, a teaching-learning facility. LeTourneau Education for Adult Professionals (LEAP) enables adults with at least 60 hours of transferable college credit to earn a B.S. in Business Management in only 18 months by attending classes one night a week.

Degrees Conferred: 631 *baccalaureate:* biological and life sciences 10; business and management 371; computer and information science 9; engineering 78; mathematics 3; physical sciences 3; psychology 9; social sciences and history 7; other disciplines 25. 112 *master's:* business and management.

Fees and Other Expenses: *Full-time tuition per academic year 2008–09:* undergraduate $19,140; contact the university for current graduate tuition and other applicable fees. *Room and board per academic year:* $7,500. *Books and supplies:* $1,600. *Other expenses:* $2,200.

Financial Aid: Aid from institutionally generated funds is provided on the basis of academic merit, financial need, other criteria.

Financial aid to first-time, full-time undergraduate students: 97% received some form of financial aid. Average amount of aid received: federal grants $3,469; Pell grants $2,642; other federal aid $953; state/local grants $3,016; institutional grants $6,050.

Departments and Teaching Staff: *Total instructional faculty:* 199. *Student/faculty ratio:* 15:1. *Degrees held by full-time faculty:* Baccalaureate 100%, master's 24%, doctorate 71%. 71% hold terminal degrees.

Enrollment: Total enrollment 3,662. Undergraduate 3,376 (full-time 91%; female 56%, male 44%). Graduate 291 (full-time 100#). Undergraduate transfer-in students 117.

Characteristics of Student Body: *Ethnic/racial makeup:* Black non-Hispanic 19%; Asian and Pacific islander 1%; Hispanic 8%; White non-Hispanic 67%; unknown 3%; nonresident alien 1%. *Age distribution:* 17–21 28%, 22–24 7%, 25–29 15%, 30–34 14%, 35–39 15%, 40–49 17%, 50–64 3%, 65–up 1%.

International Students: 37 nonresident aliens enrolled fall 2008. Students from Europe, Asia, Latin America, Africa, Canada. No programs available to aid students whose native language is not English. No financial aid specifically designated for international students.

Student Life: On-campus residence halls, apartments, and society houses are home to 87% of student body. Housing available for married students. *Intercollegiate athletics:* male: baseball, basketball, cross-country, soccer; female: basketball, cross-country, volleyball. *Intramural athletics:* A variety of team and individual events are offered for both males and females in 25 different competitive and recreational sports. *Special regulations:* Cars with registration stickers are permitted; quiet hours begin at 7pm. *Special services:* Medical services, career planning and placement services, counseling services. *Student publications: Pioneer*, the yearbook; *Yellowjacket*, the biweekly newspaper. *Spiritual life:* Chapel program meets 3 days each week; opportunities for outreach through variety of campus ministry programs. *Surrounding community:* Longview population 71,000. Dallas, 125 miles from campus. Passenger rail, bus and air service available locally.

Publications: Sources of information about LeTourneau include *NOW*, an institutional publication for friends of the college.

Library Collections: 139,000 volumes including bound books, serial backfiles, electronic documents, and government documents not in separate collections. Online and card catalogs. 51,000 micaroforms; 3,150 audiovisual materials; 380 current serial subscriptions. Computer work stations available. Students have access to the Internet at no charge.

Most important holdings include memorabilia of R. G. LeTourneau (founder of college and industrialist who invited God into his business); Abraham Lincoln Collection (150 volumes, including rare books, about Lincoln); Billy Sunday Collection (scrapbook and Bible of the early 20th century evangelist).

Buildings and Grounds: Campus area 160 acres. Campus DVD available.

Chief Executive Officer: Alvin O. Austin, President. Address admission inquiries to James Townsend, Director of Admissions.

Lubbock Christian University

5601 19th Street
Lubbock, Texas 79407-2099
Tel: (800) 933-7601 **E-mail:** admissions@lcu.edu
Fax: (806) 720-7162 **Internet:** www.lcu.edu

Institution Description: Lubbock Christian University is a private, independent, nonprofit university affiliated with the Church of Christ. *Enrollment:* 1,868. *Degrees awarded:* Baccalaureate, master's. Certificates also awarded.

Accreditation: *Regional:* SACS-Comm. on Coll.

History: Established, chartered, and offered first instruction at postsecondary level 1957; awarded first degree (associate) 1959; awarded first baccalaureate degree 1972.

Institutional Structure: *Governing board:* Board of Trustees. Extrainstitutional representation: 45 trustees, including 7 alumni. All voting. *Composition of institution:* Administrators 9. Academic affairs headed by academic vice president. Management/business/finances directed by business vice president. Full-time instructional faculty 83. Academic governance body, Academic Policy Committee, meets an average of 12 times per year.

Calendar: Semesters. Academic year Aug. to May. Freshmen admitted May, June, July, Aug., Jan. Degrees conferred May, Aug., Dec. Formal commencement May, Dec. One mini-session Dec. –Jan. Three summer sessions May, June, July.

Characteristics of Freshmen: 1,099 applicatns (female 731, male 366). 75% of applicants admitted. 35 of applicants admitted and enrolled.

58% (185 students) submitted SAT scores; 75% (238 students) submitted ACT scores. *25th percentile*: SAT Critical Reading 450, SAT Math 440; ACT Composite 18. *75th percentile*: SAT Critical Reading 582, SAT Math 572; ACT Composite 24.

17% of entering freshmen expected to graduate within 5 years. 87% of freshmen from Texas. Freshmen from 12 states.

Admission: Rolling admissions plan. For fall acceptance, apply as early as one year prior to enrollment, but not later than registration period. Early acceptance available. *Requirements:* Either graduation from accredited secondary school or GED. *Entrance tests:* ACT composite or SAT and the Texas Academic Skills Program (TASP) test to be taken either before or during the first semester in college. For foreign students TOEFL. *For transfer students:* 2.0 minimum GPA; 102 hours maximum transfer credit.

College credit and advanced placement for postsecondary-level work completed in secondary school and for extrainstitutional learning on basis of Admissions Committee if enrolled as Organizational Management major.

Tutoring available. Developmental and remedial courses offered during regular academic year; credit given.

Degree Requirements: *For all associate degrees:* 64 credit hours (general studies 20 hours; kinesiology 2 hours; biblical studies 8 hours; major 26 hours; supporting courses 6 hours; elective 2 hours); 1 term in residence. *For all baccalaureate degrees:* 126 semester hours, of which at least 42 must be advanced upper division courses. *For all undergraduate degrees:* Completion of requirements in general education, biblical studies, the major, supporting courses, and electives; minimum 2.25 overall grade point average with a 2.50 in the major subject area; 32 hours in residence after achieving senior status. *For all master's degrees:* M.A., 30 hours which includes a thesis; M.S., 36 hour, a non-thesis program.

Fulfillment of some degree requirements and exemption from some beginning courses possible by passing departmental examinations, College Board CLEP, AP, or other standardized tests. *Grading system:* A–F; Pass-fail; withdraw (carries time limit).

Distinctive Educational Programs: *Available to all students:* Work-experience programs. Evening classes. Cooperative baccalaureate in programs in engineering, broad-field social science education, broad-field science education, agriculture education, and early childhood education with Texas Tech University. Pre-professional programs in dentistry, law, medicine, veterinary science, and pharmacy. Concurrent registration with Texas Tech University and South Plains College (TX). *Other distinctive programs:* Organizational Management Program for working adults.

ROTC: Air Force and Army in cooperation with Texas Tech University.

Degrees Conferred: 360 *baccalaureate*; 59 *master's*. Bachelor's degrees awarded in top five disciplines: business, management, marketing, and related support services 101; education 71; health professions and related clinical sciences 37; theology and religious vocations 26; biological/life sciences 18. Master's degrees awarded: education 55; theology and religious vocations 14.

Fees and Other Expenses: *Full-time tuition per academic year 2008–09:* undergraduate $14,100; contact the university for current graduate tuition/fees. *Required fees:* $1,156 undergraduate. *Room and board per academic year:* $5,884.

Financial Aid: Aid from institutionally generated funds is provided on the basis of academic merit, financial need, athletic ability, other criteria.

Financial aid to full-time, first-time undergraduate students: 95 received some form of aid. Average amount of aid received: federal grants $3,790; Pell grants $2,816; other federal aid $1,067; state/local aid $3,267; institutional grants $4,505.

Departments and Teaching Staff: *Total instructional faculty:* 149 (full-tine 83, part-time 66). Total faculty with doctorate, first-professional, or other terminal degree: 69. Student/faculty ratio: 15:1. Degrees held by full-time faculty: master's 52%, doctorate 40%, baccalaureate 6%, professional 1%. 41.79% hold terminal degrees.

Enrollment: Total enrollment 1,868. Undergraduate 1,564 (full-time 82%; female 58%, male 42%). Graduate 304 (full-time 14%). Undergraduate transfer-in students 183.

Characteristics of Student Body: *Ethnic/racial makeup:* Black non-Hispanic: 5%; Hispanic: 16%; White non-Hispanic: 77%; nonresident alien 1%. *Age distribution:* number under 18: 49; 18–19: 445; 20–21: 458; 22–24: 299; 25–29: 212; 30–34: 119; 35–39: 73; 40–49: 95; 50–64: 27; 65 and over: 1.

International Students: 19 nonresident aliens enrolled fall 2008. Students from Europe, Asia, Latin America, Africa, Canada. Programs available to aid students whose native language is not English: social, cultural. No financial aid specifically designated for international students.

Student Life: On-campus residence halls house 22% of student body. Residence halls for males constitute 46% of such space, for females 52%. 5% of student body lives on campus in college-operated apartments. Housing available for married students. *Intercollegiate athletics:* male: baseball, basketball, track; female: basketball, volleyball. *Special regulations:* Cars with parking stickers permitted in designated areas. Curfews: 1am Sun. through Sat. Residence hall visitation varies according to facility. *Student publications: Duster,* an online newspaper; *El Explorador*, a yearbook. *Surrounding community:* Dallas, 350 miles; Albuquerque 325 miles; Denver, 550 miles from campus. Served by mass transit bus system; modern airport with major airline companies serving Lubbock, 15 miles from campus.

Library Collections: 120,000 volumes. Online and card catalogs. Current serial subscriptions: 572 paper; 96,871 microform; 73 via electronic access. Computer work stations available. Students have access to online information retrieval services and the Internet.

Most important special holdings include religious materials.

Buildings and Grounds: Campus area 90 acres. Campus DVD available.

Chief Executive Officer: Dr. L. Ken Jones, President.

Address admission inquiries to Brad Rogers, Director of Admissions.

McMurry University

South 14th and Sayles Boulevard
Abilene, Texas 79697
Tel: (325) 793-3800 **E-mail:** admissions@mcmurry.edu
Fax: (325) 793-4718 **Internet:** www.mcm.edu

Institution Description: McMurry University is a private institution affiliated with the United Methodist Church. *Enrollment:* 1,515. *Degrees awarded:* Baccalaureate.

Member of University Consortium of Abilene.

Accreditation: *Regional:* SACS-Comm. on Coll. *Professional*: nursing, teacher education

History: Chartered 1920; established 1922; offered first instruction at post-secondary level 1923; awarded first degree (baccalaureate) 1926; merged with Dallas Institute of Vocal and Dramatic Art (established 1946) 1947.

Institutional Structure: *Governing board:* Board of Trustees. Extrainstitutional representation: 29 trustees, 5 church officials; institutional representation: president of the college. 5 ex officio. 29 voting. *Composition of institution:* Aministrators 80. Academic affairs headed by vice president for academic affairs. Management/business/finances directed by vice president for financial affairs. Full-time instructional faculty 79. Academic governance body, the faculty, meets an average of 6 times per year.

Calendar: Semesters. 4-4-1 plan. Academic year Aug. to May. Freshmen admitted Aug., Jan., June, July. Degrees conferred May, Aug., Dec. Formal commencement May, Dec. Summer session of 2 terms June to Aug.

Characteristics of Freshmen: 1,448 applicants (female 621, male 521). 63% of applicants admitted. 24% of applicants admitted and enrolled.

65% (199 students) submitted SAT scores; 61% (185 students) submitted ACT scores. *25th percentile*: SAT Critical Reading 410, SAT Math 420; ACT Composite 18, ACT English 16, ACT Math 17. *75th percentile*: SAT Critical Reading 530, SAT Math 560; ACT Composite 23, ACT English 23, ACT Math 24.

43% of entering freshmen expected to graduate within 5 years. 94% of freshmen from Texas. Freshmen from 8 states and 2 foreign countries.

Admission: Rolling admissions plan. For fall acceptance, apply as early as completion of junior year in secondary school, but not later than Aug. 15 of year of enrollment. Early acceptance available. *Requirements:* Either graduation from accredited secondary school or GED. Required 4 units English, 4 social studies, 3 mathematics, 3 science. 25% of total hours must be earned at McMurry to earn the bachelor's degree. *Entrance tests:* College Board SAT or ACT composite. For foreign students TOEFL. *For transfer students:* 2.0 minimum GPA; from 2-year accredited institution minimum 66 hours.

College credit for postsecondary-level work completed in secondary school and for extrainstitutional learning evaluated individually basis.

Tutoring available. Developmental courses offered in summer session and regular academic year.

Degree Requirements: *For all baccalaureate degrees:* 120 credit hours; 25% of total hours in residence. *For all undergraduate degrees:* 2.0 GPA; core curriculum.

Fulfillment of some degree requirements possible by passing departmental examinations, College Board CLEP, AP. *Grading system:* A–F; withdraw (WP/WF after deadline).

Distinctive Educational Programs: Flexible meeting places and schedules, including off-campus center (at Dyess Air Force Base, less than 10 miles away from main institution), and evening classes. Interdisciplinary programs. Preprofessional programs in athletic training, dentistry, engineering, law, medical technology, nursing, pharmacy, physical therapy, veterinary medicine. Cross-registration with Abilene Christian University and Hardin-Simmons University. *Other distinctive programs:* Servicemembers' Opportunity College, Abilene Intercollegiate School of Nursing, Honors Program, Servant Leadership. Study abroad opportunities available.

ROTC: Air Force in cooperation with Angelo State University.

Degrees Conferred: 226 *baccalaureate*. Bachelor's degrees awarded in top five disciplines: education 61; business/marketing 40; health professions and related clinical sciences 23; communications/journalism 31; biological/life sciences 35.

MCMURRY UNIVERSITY—*cont'd*

Fees and Other Expenses: *Full-time tuition per academic year 2008–09:* $18,135. *Other fees:* $200. *Room and board per academic year:* $6,651. *Books and supplies:* $1,200. *Other expenses:* $2,800.

Financial Aid: Aid from institutionally generated funds is provided on the basis of academic merit, financial need. Institution has a Program Participation Agreement with the U.S. Department of Education for eligible students to receive Pell Grants and, depending upon the agreement, other federal aid.

Financial aid to full-time, first-time undergraduate students: 100% received some form of aid.

Departments and Teaching Staff: *Total instructional faculty:* 132 (full-time 79, part-time 53). *Student/faculty ratio:* 13:1. Degrees held by full-time faculty: doctorate 76%, master's 21%, professional 3%. 84% hold terminal degrees.

Enrollment: Total enrollment 1,515. Undergraduate 1,515 (full-time 80%; female 50%, male 50%). Transfer-in students 181.

Characteristics of Student Body: *Ethnic/racial makeup:* Black non-Hispanic: 14%; American Indian or Alaska Native: 1%; Asian or Pacific Islander: 1%; Hispanic: 16%; White non-Hispanic: 64%; unknown: 4%; nonresident alien 1%. *Age distribution:* number under 18: 9; 18–19: 456; 20–21: 440; 22–24: 220; 25–29: 89; 30–34: 65; 35–39: 26; 40–49: 63; 50–64: 16; 65 and over: 2.

International Students: 15 nonresident aliens enrolled fall 2008. Students from Europe, Asia, Latin America, Africa, Australia. No programs available to aid students whose native language is not English. Financial aid specifically designated for international students: 4 scholarships available annually.

Student Life: On-campus residence halls house 41% of full-time student body. *Intercollegiate athletics:* male: baseball, basketball, cross-country, football, golf, tennis, soccer, swimming/diving, track and field; female: basketball, cross-country, golf, tennis, soccer, swimming/diving, track and field, volleyball. *Special regulations:* Registered cars permitted in designated areas. Quiet hours. *Special services:* Learning Resources Center, medical services. Computer network linked to rooms in residence halls. *Student publications: The Galleon*, an annual literary magazine; *Totem*, a yearbook; *The War Whoop*, a biweekly newspaper. *Surrounding community:* Abilene population 116,000. Dallas, 180 miles from campus, is nearest metropolitan area. Served by mass transit bus system; airport 7 miles from campus.

Library Collections: 156,500 volumes including bound books, serial backfiles, electronic documents, and government documents not in separate collections. Online and card catalogs. Current serial subscriptions: 403 paper, 3 microform, 201 electronic. 418 recordings; 401 compact discs; 47 CD-ROMs. Computer work stations available. Students have access to the Internet at no charge.

Most important holdings include the J.W. Hunt Library of Texana and the Southwest; Archives of the Northwest Texas Methodist Church; E.L. and A.W. Yeats Collection.

Chief Executive Officer: Dr. John H. Russell, President.

Address admission inquiries to Amy Weyant, Director of Admission.

Midwestern State University

3400 Taft Boulevard
Wichita Falls, Texas 76308-2099
Tel: (940) 397-4334 **E-mail:** admissions@mwsu.edu
Fax: (940) 397-4672 **Internet:** www.mwsu.edu

Institution Description: Midwestern State University is a state institution. *Enrollment:* 6,093. *Degrees awarded:* Associate, baccalaureate, master's.

Academic offerings subject to approval by statewide coordinating bodies. Budget subject to approval by state governing boards.

Accreditation: *Regional:* SACS-Comm. on Coll. *Professional*: chemistry, dental hygiene, music, nursing, radiography, respiratory therapy

History: Established as Wichita Falls Junior College and offered first instruction at postsecondary level 1922; awarded first degree (associate) 1924; changed name to Hardin Junior College 1937; adopted 4-year program and changed name to Hardin College 1946, to Midwestern University 1950; became state institution 1961: adopted present name 1975.

Institutional Structure: *Governing board:* Midwestern State University Board of Regents. Representation: 9 regents appointed by the governor of Texas. *Composition of institution:* Administrators 55. Academic affairs headed by provost. Management/business/finances directed by vice president for administration and finance. Full-time instructional faculty 206. Academic governance body, Academic Council, meets and average of 15 times per year.

Calendar: Semesters. Academic year Aug. to May. Freshmen admitted Aug., Jan., June, July. Degrees conferred May, Aug., Dec. Formal commencement May. Dec., Summer session of two terms from May to Aug.

Characteristics of Freshmen: 2,982 applicants (female 1,740, male 1,232). 83% of applicants accepted. 56% of accepted applicants enrolled.

796% (541 students) submitted SAT scores; 73% (495 students) submitted ACT scores. *25th percentile*: SAT Critical Reading 440, SAT Math 450; ACT Composite 18, ACT English 17, ACT Math 18. *75th percentile*: SAT Critical Reading 550, SAT Math 560; ACT Composite 23, ACT English 23, ACT Math 24.

34% of entering freshmen expected to graduate within 5 years. 96% of freshmen from Texas. Freshmen from 14 states and 7 foreign countries.

Admission: Rolling admissions plan. For fall acceptance, apply by Aug. 7. Early acceptance available. *Requirements:* Either graduation from accredited high school or GED. Admission fro academically deficient students possible through Advised Admission if student meets criteria. *Entrance tests:* College Board SAT combined or ACT composite, excluding writing scores. Writing scores required. For foreign students TOEFL. *For transfer students:* 2.0 minimum GPA; from 4-year accredited institution hours maximum transfer credit limited only by residence requirement; from 2-year accredited institution 69 semester hours; correspondence/extension students 30 hours (18 correspondence).

MSU will accept up to 60 hours of credit by examination, limiting CLEP, DANTES, and proficiency exams to a maximum of 30 hours. College credit and advanced placement for postsecondary-level work completed in secondary school. College credit for extrainstitutional learning.

Tutoring available. Developmental courses offered in summer session and regular academic year; nondegree credit given.

Degree Requirements: *For all baccalaureate degree:* 124 hours; 3 hours physical education; 24 hours in residence; general education requirements including coursework in English, math, science, history, and government of U.S. and Texas. Additional requirements for some programs.

Fulfillment of some degree requirements and exemption from some beginning courses possible by passing departmental examinations, College Board CLEP. *Grading system:* A–F; withdraw.

Distinctive Educational Programs: Flexible meeting places and schedules, Evening classes. Special facilities for telecommunications in classroom. Interdisciplinary programs in geophysics, chemistry, public management. Facilities and programs for independent research, including honors programs, tutorials. *Other distinctive programs:* noncredit continuing education. Study abroad in England, France, Mexico, Spain.

ROTC: Air Force in cooperation with University of North Texas.

Degrees Conferred: 38 *associate*; 974 *baccalaureate*; 122 *master's*. Bachelor's degrees awarded in top five disciplines: business/marketing 180; interdisciplinary studies 176; health professions and related clinical sciences 161; education 76; security and protective services 45. Master's degrees awarded in top five disciplines: education 85; business/marketing 24; health professions and related clinical sciences 18; psychology 14; history 5.

Fees and Other Expenses: *Full-time tuition per academic year 2008–09:* undergraduate resident $4,806, nonresident $5,526; contact the university for current graduate tuition and fees. *Room and board per academic year:* $6,121. *Books and supplies:* $960. *Other expenses:* $1,379.

Financial Aid: Aid from institutionally generated funds is provided on the basis of academic merit, financial need, athletic ability, other criteria.

Financial aid to full-time, first-time undergraduate students: 44% received some form of aid. Average amount of aid received: federal grants $3,736; Pell grants $3,168; other federal aid $792; state/local grants $3,843; institutional grants $2,102.

Departments and Teaching Staff: *Total instructional faculty:* 314. Student/faculty ratio:13:1. Degrees held by full-time faculty: doctorate 60%, master's 39%, baccalaureate 1%. 72% hold terminal degrees.

Enrollment: Total enrollment 6,093. Undergraduate 5,361 (full-time 74%; female 51%, male 49%). Graduate 732 (full-time 28%). Undergraduate transfer-in students 718.

Characteristics of Student Body: *Ethnic/racial makeup:* Black non-Hispanic: 14%; American Indian or Alaska Native: 1%; Asian or Pacific Islander: 1%; Hispanic: 10%; White non-Hispanic: 86%; unknown: 1%; nonresident alien 6%.

International Students: 345 undergraduate nonresident aliens enrolled fall 2008. Students from Europe, Asia, Latin America, Africa. Programs available to aid students whose native language is not English: social. English as a Second Language Program. No financial aid specifically designated for international students.

Student Life: On-campus residence halls house 18% of student body. Residence halls for males constitute 48% of such space, for females 52%. *Intercollegiate athletics:* male: baseball, basketball, golf, soccer, tennis; female: basketball, cross-country, soccer, softball, tennis, volleyball. *Special regulations:* Cars permitted without restrictions. *Special services:* Medical services. *Student publications: The Wai-kun*, a yearbook; *The Wichitan*, a weekly newspaper; *Voices*, an annual literary magazine. *Surrounding community:* Wichita Falls population 114,000. Dallas/Fort Worth, 125 miles from campus, is nearest metropolitan area. Served by airport 8 miles from campus.

Library Collections: 349,749 volumes including bound books, serial backfiles, electronic documents, and government documents not in separate collections. Online catalog. Current serial subscriptions: 936 paper, 250 microform, 33,961 electronic. 6,791 audio/videotapes; 1,473 DVD discs; 142 CD-ROMs. Computer work stations available. Students have access to the Internet at no charge. Total 2008–09 budget for books and materials $574,693.

Most important special collections include Nolan A. Moore, III Heritage of Print Collection; Americana; education.

Buildings and Grounds: Campus area 255 acres.

Chief Executive Officer: Dr. Jesse W. Rogers, President.

Address admission inquiries to Barbara Merkle, Director of Admissions.

Oblate School of Theology

285 Oblate Drive
San Antonio, Texas 78216-6693
Tel: (210) 341-1366 **E-mail:** registrar@ost.edu
Fax: (210) 341-4519 **Internet:** www.ost.edu

Institution Description: Oblate School of Theology is a private college affiliated with the Roman Catholic Church. The School's name was changed in 1982 from Oblate College of the Southwest. *Enrollment:* 198. *Degrees awarded:* First-professional (master of divinity), master's, doctorate. Certificates also awarded.

Accreditation: *Regional:* SACS-Comm. on Coll. *National:* ATS. *Professional*: theology

History: Established as the San Antonio Philosophical and Theological Seminary and offered first instruction at postsecondary level 1903; changed name to The Sacred Heart Scholasticate 1920, to DeMazenod Scholasticate 1927; to Oblate College of the Southwest in 1962; chartered 1950; awarded first degree (baccalaureate) 1951; added graduate-level program 1968; adopted present name 1982.

Institutional Structure: *Governing board:* The Board of Trustees. Representation: 20 trustees, including president of the school, 4 alumni. 1 ex officio. President does not vote. Full-time instructional faculty 18. Academic governance body, The Faculty, meets an average of 8 times per year.

Calendar: Semesters. Academic year Aug. to May. Entering students admitted Aug., Jan, June. Degrees conferred at formal commencement in May. Summer session of 2 terms June to July.

Characteristics of Freshmen: 58% of new students from Texas. New students from 5 states and 3 foreign countries.

Admission: *Requirements:* Baccalaureate from accredited institution. For first-professional degree, 18 credit hours in philosophy with minimum GPA of 2.0. Applicants must be in a recognized formation program or submit 3 letters of recommendation from ecclesiastical authorities, and an autobiographical account. Recommended reading knowledge of Spanish and one or more of the following languages: French, German, Greek, Hebrew, Latin. For master's degree 2.5 GPA. *For transfer students:* First-professional students 2.0 minimum GPA, 53 hours maximum transfer credit from accredited institution; graduate students 12 hours from accredited institution.

Degree Requirements: *For first-professional degree:* 104 semester hours, 2.5 GPA; field education 2 years full-time study at Oblate School of Theology; complete Interdisciplinary Seminar in Theological Studies, write major paper, pastoral competence in Spanish; degree program must be completed within 7 years after matriculation. *For master's degree:* 36 semester hours, 2.5 GPA, practicum, thesis, comps; degree program must be completed within 5 years of matriculation. *Grading system:* A–F; pass; withdraw (carries time limit).

Distinctive Educational Programs: Certificate of Pastoral Studies; Lay Ministry Institute preparing laity for pastoral ministry; Ministry to Ministers, a 4-month renewal period for priests and religious; Instituto de Formacion Pastoral, a Spanish program to prepare laity for pastoral ministry.

Degrees Conferred: 20 *master's:* theology; 13 *first-professional:* master of divinity; 5 *doctorate*: theology.

Fees and Other Expenses: *Tuition for academic year 2008–09:* $10,406. *Required fees:* $345.

Financial Aid: Aid from institutionally generated funds is provided on the basis of financial need. Institution has a Program Participation Agreement with the U.S. Department of Education for eligible students to receive Pell Grants and, depending upon the agreement, other federal aid. *Graduate aid:* 3 students received $27,750 in federal and state-funded loans; 18 other fellowships and grants awarded totaling $16,094.

Departments and Teaching Staff: *Total instructional faculty:* 26 (full-time 19, part-time 7). Total faculty with doctorate, first-professional, or other terminal degree: 23. Student/faculty ratio: 4:1. Degrees held by full-time faculty: master's 22%, doctorate 68%, professional 10%. 79% hold terminal degrees.

Enrollment: Total enrollment 198.

International Students: 41 nonresident aliens enrolled fall 2008. Students from Europe, Asia, Latin America, Africa. No programs available to aid students whose native language is not English. No financial aid specifically designated for international students.

Student Life: No on-campus housing. *Special regulations:* Cars permitted without restrictions. *Surrounding community:* San Antonio population 790,000. Served by mass transit bus system; airport 2 miles from campus; passenger rail service 8 miles from campus.

Library Collections: 164,000 volumes. 9,000 audiovisual materials, 360 current periodical subscriptions. Computer work stations available. Students have access to online information retrieval services and the Internet.

Most important special holdings include Oblate Mission Collection; Roman Catholic Theological Collection; faculty dissertations.

Buildings and Grounds: Campus area 20 acres.

Chief Executive Officer: Rev. Ronald Rolheiser, O.M,I. President.

Address admission inquiries to James Oberhausen, Registrar.

Our Lady of the Lake University

411 S.W. 24th Street
San Antonio, Texas 78207-4689
Tel: (210) 434-6711 **E-mail:** admissions@ollusa.edu
Fax: (210) 436-4036 **Internet:** www.ollusa.edu

Institution Description: Our Lady of the Lake University (Our Lady of the Lake College until 1975) is a private institution affiliated with the Sisters of Divine Providence, Roman Catholic Church. *Enrollment:* 2,642. *Degrees awarded:* Baccalaureate, master's, doctorate.

Member of the consortium United Colleges of San Antonio.

Accreditation: *Regional:* SACS-Comm. on Coll. *Professional*: family and consumer science, social work, speech-language pathology, teacher education

History: Established and chartered as Our Lady of the Lake Academy, a women's institution, 1896; offered first instruction at postsecondary level 1911; changed name to Our Lady of the Lake College 1912; became 4-year institution and awarded first degree (baccalaureate) 1919; added master's program 1942; became coeducational 1969; adopted present name 1975. *See* Sr. Generosa Callahan, *Mother Angelique Ayers, Dreamer and Builder of Our Lady of the Lake University* (Austin, TX.: Jenkins Press, 1981) for further information.

Institutional Structure: *Governing board:* Board of Trustees. Extrainstitutional representation: 27 trustees; institutional representation: president of the university, 1 full-time instructional faculty member, president of the student association; 1 alumna. 4 ex officio. 30 voting. *Composition of institution:* Administrators 18. Academic affairs headed by provost. Management/business/finances directed by vice president for finance and facilities. Full-time instructional faculty 105. Academic governance body, Faculty Assembly, meets an average of 7 times per year.

Calendar: Semesters for traditional students; trimesters for Weekend College. Academic year Aug. to May. Freshmen admitted Aug. Jan., June, July. Degrees conferred May, July, Aug., Dec. Formal commencements May, Aug., Dec.

Characteristics of Freshmen: 2,054 applicants (female 1,446, male 568). 55% of applicants accepted. 11% of accepted applicants enrolled.

Mean SAT scores class 490 verbal, 472 mathematical.

13% of entering freshmen expected to graduate within 5 years. 93% freshmen from Texas. Freshmen from 16 states and 2 foreign countries.

Admission: Rolling admissions plan. Early acceptance available. *Requirements:* Either graduation from accredited secondary school with 16 academic units which must include 4 English, 2 laboratory natural science, 2 mathematics, 2 social studies, 2 foreign language (or 2 additional units in English, mathematics, social studies, or natural science); or GED. Minimum GPA 2.75. *Entrance tests:* College Board SAT or ACT composite. For foreign students minimum TOEFL score 500. *For transfer students:* 2.0 minimum GPA; from 4-year accredited institution 98 hours maximum transfer credit; from 2-year accredited institution 66 hours; correspondence/extension students 30 hours.

College credit and advanced placement for postsecondary-level work completed in secondary school for USAFI/DANTES, and for extrainstitutional learning on basis of portfolio and faculty assessments; personal interview.

Tutoring available. Noncredit developmental courses offered in summer session and regular academic year.

Degree Requirements: *For all undergraduate degrees:* 128 semester hours; 2.0 GPA; 30 hours in residence; general education requirements; exit competency examinations (College Outcome Measures Project of the American College Testing Program).

Fulfillment of some degree requirements and exemption from some beginning courses possible by passing departmental examination and College Board CLEP. *Grading system:* A–F; pass-fail; withdraw (carries time limit, deadline after which pass-fail is appended to withdraw); incomplete (carries time limit).

OUR LADY OF THE LAKE UNIVERSITY—*cont'd*

Distinctive Educational Programs: *For undergraduates:* Interdisciplinary majors in American studies, fine arts, human sciences, liberal studies, management, media communication arts, natural sciences, public administration, social science, speech and drama, theater management. *For graduate students:* Cooperative master's program in English with Incarnate Word College and St. Mary's University. Counseling psychology program (master's, doctorate). *Available to all students:* Work-experience programs, including internships and practicums, weekend and evening classes. Accelerated degree programs. Special facilities for using telecommunications in the classroom. Independent study. Institutionally sponsored study tours abroad. Cross-registration through consortium. Laboratory and clinical experience available at the Jersig Center for communications and learning disorders and St. Martin Hall, an elementary school. Training for bilingual-bicultural social workers and community health services provided by El Centro del Barrio. Intercultural Institute for Training and Research promotes multicultural academic programs and community interaction. *Other distinctive programs:* Degree-granting Weekend College for adults; credit and noncredit continuing education programs; MBA featuring decision science using Decision Theatre. Servicemembers Opportunity College.

Degrees Conferred: 318 *baccalaureate*; 346 *master's*; 9 *doctorate*. Bachelor's degrees awarded in top five disciplines: business, management, marketing, and related support services 77; liberal arts psychology 41; education 36; public administration and social services 34. Master's degrees awarded: various disciplines 346. Doctorates awarded; business/management 5; psychology 4.

Fees and Other Expenses: *Full-time tuition per academic year 2008–09:* $20,232. *Books and supplies:* $1,200. *Room and board per academic year:* $6,238. *Other expenses:* $3,300.

Financial Aid: Aid from institutionally generated funds is provided on the basis of academic merit, financial need.

Financial aid to full-time, first-time undergraduate students: 98% received some form of aid.

Departments and Teaching Staff: *Total instructional faculty:* 120. Degrees held by full-time faculty: master's 24%, doctorate 76%. 69% hold terminal degrees.

Enrollment: Total enrollment 2,642. Undergraduate 1,563 (full-time 74%; female 74%; male 26%). Graduate 1,819 (full-time 22%). Undergraduate transfer-in students 140.

Characteristics of Student Body: *Ethnic/racial makeup:* Black non-Hispanic: 7%; Asian or Pacific Islander: 1%; Hispanic: 72%; White non-Hispanic: 12%; unknown 6%; nonresident alien 1%.

International Students: 26 nonresident aliens enrolled fall 2008. Programs available to aid students whose native language is not English: English as a Second Language Program. No financial aid specifically designated for international students.

Student Life: On-campus residence halls house 14% of student body. Residence halls for males constitute 30% of such space, for females 70%. *Special regulations:* Cars with decals permitted. Quiet hours. *Special services:* Learning Resources Center, medical services, Student Development Center, computer laboratories. *Student publications: The Thing Itself*, an annual literary magazine published in cooperation with consortium members. *Surrounding community:* San Antonio population 788,000. Served by mass transit system; airport 10 miles from campus; passenger rail service 7 miles from campus.

Library Collections: 148,000 volumes. 5,600 microforms. Students have access to online information services and the Internet.

Most important holdings include Old Spanish Missions Historical Research Library; Texana Collection.

Buildings and Grounds: Campus area 75 acres.

Chief Executive Officer: Dr. Tessa M. Pollack, President.

Address admission inquiries to Dr. Mary Kay Cooper, Dean of Enrollment Management.

Paul Quinn College

3837 Simpson Stuart Road
Dallas, Texas 75241
Tel: (214) 376-1000 **E-mail:** admissions@pqc
Fax: (214) 302-3613 **Internet:** www.pgc.edu

Institution Description: Paul Quinn College is a private college affiliated with the African Methodist Episcopal Church. *Enrollment:* 445. *Degrees awarded:* Baccalaureate.

Accreditation: *Regional:* SACS-Comm. on Coll.

History: Established and offered first instruction at postsecondary level 1872.

Institutional Structure: *Governing board:* Board of Trustees. Representation: 32 trustees. All voting. *Composition of institution:* Administrators 14. Academic affairs headed by provost. Management/business/finances directed by business manager. Full-time instructional faculty 27.

Calendar: Semesters. Academic year Aug. to May. Formal commencement May.

Characteristics of Freshmen: 1,279 applicants (female 705, male 574). 11% of applicants admitted. 56% of admited applicants enrolled full-time.

Admission: Rolling admissions plan. *Requirements:* Either graduation from secondary school or GED. *Entrance tests:* ACT composite.

Degree Requirements: *For all baccalaureate degrees:* 124 semester hours; 2.0 GPA; 30 hours in residence; 2 hours in physical education requirements. *Grading system:* A–F; withdraw (pass-fail appended to withdraw).

Distinctive Educational Programs: *Available to all students:* Work-experience programs, including cooperative education, internships.

Degrees Conferred: 132 *baccalaureate*. Bachelor's degrees awarded in top five disciplines: business, management, marketing, and related support services 66; education 16; security and protective services 12; social sciences 9; biological/life sciences 7.

Fees and Other Expenses: *Full-time tuition/fees per academic year 2008–09:* $9,630. *Books and supplies:* $1,200. *Room and board per academic year:* $5,170. *Other expenses:* $500.

Financial Aid: Aid from institutionally generated funds is provided on the basis of academic merit, financial need.

Financial aid to full-time, first-time undergraduate students: 100% received some form of aid.

Departments and Teaching Staff: *Total instructional faculty:* 48. Student/faculty ratio: 14:1. Degrees held by full-time faculty: 49% hold terminal degrees.

Enrollment: Total enrollment 445. Undergraduate 441 (full-time 92%; female 51%, male 49%). Graduate 4 (full-time 100%). Transfer-in students 59.

Characteristics of Student Body: *Ethnic/racial makeup:* Black non-Hispanic: 89%; nonresident alien 7%; unknown 4%.

International Students: 35 nonresident aliens enrolled fall 2007. No programs available to aid students whose native language is not English. No financial aid specifically designated for international students.

Student Life: On-campus housing available. *Surrounding community:* Waco population over 100,000.

Library Collections: 232,000 volumes. 2,000 government documents; 35,000 microforms; 55 current periodical subscriptions. Online catalog. Computer work stations available. Students have access to the Internet at no charge.

Most important special holdings include A.M.E. Church Collection; Ethnic Cultural Center Collection.

Buildings and Grounds: Urban campus.

Chief Executive Officer: Dr. Douglas J. Fennell, President.

Address all admission inquiries to Ralph Spencer, Jr., Director of Admissions.

Prairie View A & M University

P.O. Box 3089
Prairie View, Texas 77446
Tel: (936) 857-3111 **E-mail:** admissions@pvamu.edu
Fax: (936) 857-2699 **Internet:** www.pvamu.edu

Institution Description: Prairie View A & M University is a state institution and land-grant university, and a member of the Texas A & M University System. *Enrollment:* 8,203. *Degrees awarded:* Associate, baccalaureate, master's.

Academic offerings subject to approval by statewide coordinating bodies. Budget subject to approval by state governing boards.

Accreditation: *Regional:* SACS-Comm. on Coll. *Professional*: computer science, dietetics, engineering, engineering technology, nursing, social work, teacher education

History: Established and chartered as Alta Vista Agricultural College 1876; offered first instruction at postsecondary level 1878; name changed to Prairie View State Normal and Industrial College 1895; awarded first degree (baccalaureate) 1902; name changed to Prairie View University 1945, to Prairie View Agricultural and Mechanical College of Texas 1947, to Prairie View Agricultural and Mechanical University 1971; adopted present name 1973.

Institutional Structure: *Governing board:* Texas A & M University System Board of Regents. Representation: 9 members (appointed by governor of Texas). All voting. *Composition of institution:* Administrators 42. Academic affairs headed by vice president for academic affairs. Management/business/finances directed by vice president for finance and administration. Full-time instructional faculty 378.

Calendar: Semesters. Academic year Aug. to May. Freshmen admitted Aug., Jan., June, July. Degrees conferred May, Aug., Dec. Formal commencements May, Aug.

Characteristics of Freshmen: 5,899 applicants (female 3,496, male 3,463). 82% of applicants accepted. 45% of accepted applicants enrolled.

Mean SAT scores 450 verbal, 436 mathematical.

87% of freshmen from Texas. Freshmen from 43 states and 38 foreign countries.

Admission: Open admissions. *Requirements:* Either graduation from accredited secondary school with 16 units which must include 3 English, 3 history and civics, 3 mathematics, 1 laboratory science; or GED. Additional requirements for engineering school applicants. Graduates of nonaccredited secondary schools may take an entrance examination. Minimum GPA 2.0. *Entrance tests:* College Board SAT (minimum score 800) or ACT (minimum score 18); counselor recommendation form. Transfer applicants must submit transcripts from all previous colleges attended and present evidence of good standing at the last institutions attended. International applicants are required to meet all of the above university standards as well as university and U.S. Immigration requirements. International applicants must also submit a notarized Affidavit of Financial Support. Applications must be filed by Aug. 1. Applicants should note that the Texas Academic Skills Program (TASP) is in effect. See the university catalog for particulars.

College credit and advanced placement for postsecondary-level work completed in secondary school.

Tutoring available. Developmental courses offered in summer session and regular academic year; credit given, but not toward a degree.

Degree Requirements: To qualify for a baccalaureate degree, the student must complete the core curriculum requirement in addition to the specific course requirements for the degree program selected. The university requires a minimum of 120 semester credit hours and 2.0 cumulative GPA for graduation with a grade of C in each major area course. Individual degree program requirements may be higher. *Grading system:* A–F; pass-fail; withdraw; incomplete (carries time limit).

Distinctive Educational Programs: The university offers a variety of pre-college and pre-freshman year programs for college-bound students. These programs represent a major part of the university's outreach effort that is designed to increase the pool of students who are academically prepared and motivated to succeed in studies in science, engineering, the health professions, business, and liberal arts. The Pre-College Institute sponsors a series of on-campus residential career development workshops for academically talented high school students. Pre-Freshman programs include: The Engineering and Science Concepts Institute, Pre-Medical Concepts Institute, and the Academy for Collegiate Excellence and Student Success.

ROTC: Army, Navy.

Degrees Conferred: 758 *baccalaureate*; 699 *master's*; 10 *doctorate*. Bachelor's degrees awarded in top five disciplines: health professions and related clinical sciences 115; biological/life sciences 100; business, management, marketing, and related support services 85; engineering 54; multidisciplinary studies 51. Master's degrees awarded: various disciplines 699. Doctorates awarded: education 5; security services 5.

Fees and Other Expenses: *Full-time tuition per academic year 2008–09:* $5,492 resident; $13,186 nonresident. *Books and supplies:* $1,500. *Room and board per academic year:* $8,500. *Other expenses:* $4,000.

Financial Aid: Aid from institutionally generated funds is provided on the basis of academic merit, financial need.

Financial aid to full-time, first-time undergraduate students: 75% received federal grants averaging $3,500; 14% state/local grants averaging $1,500; 8% institutional grants averaging $1,000; 33% received loans averaging $2,000.

Departments and Teaching Staff:

Total instructional faculty: 329. Student/faculty ratio: 18:1. Degrees held by full-time faculty: doctorate 54%, master's 42%, baccalaureate 4%. 46% hold terminal degrees.

Enrollment: Total enrollment 8,203. Undergraduate 6,278 (full-time 90%; female 51%, male 43%). Graduate 1,925 (full-time 29%). Transfer-in students 260.

Characteristics of Student Body: *Ethnic/racial makeup:* Black non-Hispanic: 88%; Asian or Pacific Islander: 2%; Hispanic: 4%; White non-Hispanic: 3%; unknown 1%; nonresident alien 1%.

International Students: 82 nonresident aliens enrolled fall 2008. No programs available to aid students whose native language is not English. No financial aid specifically designated for international students.

Student Life: On-campus residence halls house 50% of student body. Residence halls for males constitute 50% of such space, for females 50%. New apartment-style housing was completed in 1996. *Intercollegiate athletics:* male: baseball, basketball, football, golf, tennis, track; female: basketball, track. *Special regulations:* Registered cars permitted for resident upperclassmen with minimum 2.0 GPA. *Special services:* Learning Resources Center, medical services. *Student publications, radio: The Panther*, a bimonthly newspaper. Radio station KPVU broadcasts 120 hours per week. *Surrounding community:* Prairie View population 4,000. Houston, 47 miles from campus, is nearest metropolitan area. Served by airport 53 miles from campus; passenger rail service 48 miles from campus.

Publications: *Faculty Research Journal* (biannual) first published in 1976.

Library Collections: 362,000 volumes including bound books, serial backfiles, electronic documents, and government documents not in separate collections. Online catalog. Books, serial backfiles, government documents: 222,965 paper, 595,730 microform. 33 electronic. Current serial subscriptions 1,027 paper and microform; 3,208 electronic; 5,900 audiovisual materials. Students have access to the Internet and online information retrieval services.

Most important special holdings include W.D. Lawless Afro-American Collection; Children's Literature Collection; Prairie View A&M University Archives; Black Heritage of the West; Blacks in the U.S.A. Military.

Buildings and Grounds: Campus area 1,369 acres. Campus DVD available.

Chief Executive Officer: Dr. George C. Wright, President.

Address admission inquiries to Dr. Doris Price, Director of Admissions.

Rice University

6100 South Main Street
Houston, Texas 77005

Tel: (713) 349-7423 **E-mail:** admission@rice.edu
Fax: (713) 348-5952 **Internet:** www.rice.edu

Institution Description: Rice University (official name William Marsh Rice University) is a private, independent, nonprofit institution. *Enrollment:* 5,351. *Degrees awarded:* Baccalaureate, first-professional (architecture), master's, doctorate.

Member of the consortia Associated Western Universities and Gulf Universities Research Corporation.

Accreditation: *Regional:* SACS-Comm. on Coll. *Professional:* architecture, engineering

History: Established as William M. Rice Institute and chartered 1891; offered first instruction at postsecondary level 1912; awarded first degree (baccalaureate) 1916; adopted present official name, William Marsh Rice University 1960.

Institutional Structure: *Governing board:* Rice University Board of Governors. Representation: 7 trustees, 8 term governors, 4 alumni governors. All voting. *Composition of institution:* Administrators 19. Academic and financial affairs headed by president. Business and physical plant directed by vice president. Full-time instructional faculty 567.

Calendar: Semesters. Academic year Aug. to May. Freshmen admitted Aug. Degrees conferred and formal commencement May. Summer session early June to mid July.

Characteristics of Freshmen: 9,812 applicants (female 4655, male 5,151). 24% of applicants admitted.

96% (640 students) submitted SAT scores; 38% (233 students) submitted ACT scores. *25th percentile*: SAT Critical Reading 650, SAT Math 680; ACT Composite 30. *75th percentile*: SAT Critical Reading 760, SAT Math 780; ACT Composite 34.

02% of entering freshmen expected to graduate within 5 years. 47% of freshmen from Texas. Freshmen from 50 states and 47 foreign countries.

Admission: Applicants for the freshman class must choose to apply under one of three application decision plans. Consult the university catalog for detailed information. Early decision (binding) due Nov. 1; interim decision due Dec. 1; or regular decision due Jan 10. *Requirements:* Graduation from accredited secondary school with 16 units which must include 4 English, 2 in a foreign language, 3 college preparatory mathematics, 2 laboratory science, 2 social studies. Interview. Audition for music majors. For science and engineering students trigonometry and 1 additional unit mathematics. *Entrance tests:* College Board SAT with 3 Achievements, including English composition; science and engineering majors must also offer mathematics, and chemistry or physics. *For transfer students:* 3.2 minimum GPA, 68 hours maximum transfer credit.

College credit and advanced placement for postsecondary-level work completed in secondary school. Tutoring available.

Degree Requirements: *For all undergraduate degrees:* 120–137 credit hours; 4 semesters in residence; 2 physical education courses; distribution requirements. Additional requirements for some programs.

Fulfillment of some degree requirements and exemption from some beginning courses possible by AP (score of 4). *Grading system:* A–F; pass-fail; withdraw (carries time limit).

Distinctive Educational Programs: Internships. Interdepartmental programs for undergraduates, including behavioral science, computer science, linguistics, managerial studies. For graduate students, bioengineering, solid-state electronics, and materials science. Extensive study abroad opportunities.

ROTC: Air Force and Army in cooperation with University of Houston.

Degrees Conferred: 792 *baccalaureate*; 512 *master's*; 196 *doctorate*.

RICE UNIVERSITY—*cont'd*

Fees and Other Expenses: *Full-time tuition per academic year 2008–09:* $30,486; contact the university for current graduate tuition and fees. *Required fees:* $500. *Room and board per academic year:* $10,750. *Books and supplies:* $800. *Other expenses:* $1,550.

Financial Aid: Aid from institutionally generated funds is provided on the basis of academic merit, financial need, athletic ability.

Financial aid to full-time, first-time undergraduate students: 84% received some form of aid. Average amount of aid received: federal grants $4,279; Pell grants $2,092; other federal aid $1,589; state/local grants $3,716; institutional grants $22,586.

Departments and Teaching Staff: *Total instructional faculty:* 701 (full-time 567, part-time 134). Total faculty with doctorate, first-professional, or other terminal degree: 612. Student/faculty ratio: 5:1. Degrees held by full-time faculty: doctorate 92%, master's 7%, baccalaureate .5%, professional .5%. 92% hold terminal degrees.

Enrollment: Total enrollment 5,351. Undergraduate 3,120 (full-time 99%; female 48%, male 52%). Graduate 2,387 (full-time 96%). Undergraduate transfer-in students 2,337.

Characteristics of Student Body: *Ethnic/racial makeup:* Black non-Hispanic: 7%; Asian or Pacific Islander: 21%; Hispanic: 12%; White non-Hispanic: 48%; unknown: 5%; nonresident alien 7%.

International Students: 378 nonresident aliens enrolled fall 2008. No programs available to aid students whose native language is not English. Financial aid specifically designated for international students.

Student Life: On-campus residence halls house 70% of student body. Residence halls for males constitute 12.5% of such space, for females 12.5%, coed 75%. *Intercollegiate athletics:* male: baseball, basketball, football, golf, swimming, tennis, track; female: basketball, swimming, tennis, track, volleyball. *Special regulations:* Cars permitted without restrictions. *Special services:* Medical services. *Student publications, radio:* A weekly newspaper; a yearbook. Radio station KTRU-FM broadcasts 40 hours per week. *Surrounding community:* Houston metropolitan population 4 million. Served by mass transit bus system; airport 25 miles from campus; passenger rail service 4 miles from campus.

Publications: *Journal of Southern History* (quarterly) first published in 1959; *Papers of Jefferson Davis* (irregularly) first published 1971; *Rice University Studies* (quarterly) first published 1915; *Studies in English Literature* (quarterly) first published 1961; Rice University Press (numerous volumes).

Library Collections: 2,315,000 volumes. Online catalog. 3,075,000 microforms; 40,100 audiovisual materials; 36,900 periodicals including via electronic access. Computer work stations available. Students have access to online information retrieval services and the Internet.

Most important special holdings include Julian Huxley Papers; NASA Collection (Manned Spacecraft Program); Axon Collection (18th-Century English Drama).

Buildings and Grounds: Campus area 285 acres.

Chief Executive Officer: Dr. David W. Leebron, President.

Address admission inquiries to Julie Browning, Director of Undergraduate Enrollment; graduate inquiries to department of interest.

St. Edward's University

3001 South Congress Avenue
Austin, Texas 78704-6489
Tel: (512) 448-8400 **E-mail:** admit@stedwards.edu
Fax: (512) 448-8492 **Internet:** www.stedwards.edu

Institution Description: St. Edward's University is a private, independent, nonprofit institution affiliated with the Roman Catholic Church. *Enrollment:* 5,348. *Degrees awarded:* Baccalaureate, master's.

Accreditation: *Regional:* SACS-Comm. on Coll. *Professional*: social work

History: Founded by Father Edward Sorin, founder of Notre Dame University. Established as St. Edward's Academy in 1878 and offered first instruction at postsecondary level 1885 under the chartered name St. Edward's College; awarded first degree (baccalaureate) 1886; received university charter and adopted present name 1925; became coeducational 1966.

Institutional Structure: *Governing board:* Board of Trustees 35. Edward's University, Inc. Extrainstitutional representation: 27 trustees (voting), 9 of whom are are alumni, 9 trustees emeriti; institutional representation: president of the university, chairperson of the Alumni Board of Directors, president of the Students' Association, all 4 being ex-officio with voice but no vote; Chairperson, National Alumni Association. *Composition of institution:* Administrators 47. Academic affairs headed by executive vice-president/provost. Management/business/finances/physical plant headed by vice-president for financial affairs. Full-time instructional faculty 166. Academic governance body, Academic Council, meets an average of 8 times per year. The Faculty Collegium also meets an average of 8 times per year.

Calendar: Semester plan. Academic year Aug. to Aug. Freshmen admitted Aug., Jan. Degrees conferred May, Aug., Dec. Formal commencement May.

Characteristics of Freshmen: 2,766 applicants (female 1,800, male 966). 66% of applicants accepted. 45% of accepted applicants enrolled.

77% (537 students) submitted SAT scores; 21% (150 students) submitted ACT scores. *25th percentile*: SAT Critical Reading 510, SAT Math 510; ACT Composite 21, ACT English 21, ACT Math 20. *75th percentile*: SAT Critical Reading 620, SAT Math 610; ACT Composite 26, ACT English 27, ACT Math 25.

49% of entering freshmen expected to graduate within 5 years. 91% of freshmen from Texas. Freshmen from 39 states and 40 foreign countries.

Admission: Rolling admissions plan. For fall acceptance, apply as early as Sept. 1 of previous year, but not later than May 1 of year of enrollment. *Requirements:* Either graduation from secondary school or GED. Vast majority of students accepted are in top half of class. *Entrance tests:* College Board SAT or ACT composite. For foreign students TOEFL score 500. *For transfer students:* 2.5 minimum GPA for all college-level work attempted (credit give only for grades of C or better); from 4-year accredited institution 90 hours maximum transfer credit; from 2-year accredited institution 66 hours.

College credit and advanced placement for postsecondary-level work completed in secondary school, USAFI-DANTES, and for extrainstitutional learning on basis of portfolio assessment.

Tutoring available. Noncredit developmental courses offered during regular academic year.

Degree Requirements: 120 credit hours; 2.0 GPA; last 30 hours in residence; 57 hours in general education requirement; demonstrated proficiency in reading, listening, writing, and mathematics.

Fulfillment of some degree requirements and exemption from some beginning courses possible by passing departmental examinations, College Board CLEP, AP. *Grading system:* A–F; pass-fail; withdraw; incomplete (carries time limit).

Distinctive Educational Programs: *For undergraduates:* Internships. Honors programs. Liberal arts/career combination. Preprofessional programs in dentistry, engineering, medicine, pre-law, pre-physical therapy. *Available to all students:* Evening classes. Interdisciplinary programs in freshmen studies, general studies, global studies. *Other distinctive programs:* New College, a flexible adult degree program. Member of International Student Exchange Program: students may study in any country if approved by the university.

Degrees Conferred: 921 *baccalaureate*; 306 *master's*; 53 *doctorate*. Bachelor's degrees awarded in top five disciplines: business, management, marketing, and related support services 289; communication, journalism, and related programs 65; psychology 69; social sciences 64; visual and performing arts 42. Master's degrees awarded: business/marketing 169; health professions and related clinical sciences 77; liberal arts/general studies 20; public administration and social services 27. Doctorates awarded: various disciplines 53.

Fees and Other Expenses: *Full-time tuition per academic year 2008–09:* undergraduate $22,550; contact the university for current graduate tuition/fees. *Room and board per academic year:* $8,158. *Books and supplies:* $1,100. *Other expenses:* $3,392.

Financial Aid: Aid from institutionally generated funds is provided on the basis of academic merit, financial need, athletic ability.

Financial aid to full-time, first-time undergraduate students: 90% received some form of aid. Average amount of aid received: federal grants $4,752; Pell grants $3,094; other federal aid $1,975; state/local grants $3,760; institutional grants $10,217.

Departments and Teaching Staff: *Total instructional faculty:* 472. Student/faculty ratio: 15:1. Degrees held by full-time faculty: baccalaureate 100%, master's 100%, doctorate 70%. 70% hold terminal degrees.

Enrollment: Total enrollment 5,348. Undergraduate 4,383 (full-time 79%; female 60%, male 40%). Graduate 965 (full-time 17%). Undergraduate transfer-in students 455.

Characteristics of Student Body: *Ethnic/racial makeup:* Black non-Hispanic: 5%; American Indian or Alaska Native: 1%; Asian or Pacific Islander: 2%; Hispanic: 31%; White non-Hispanic: 57%; unknown: 5%; nonresident alien 17%.

International Students: 108 nonresident aliens enrolled fall 2008. Students from Europe, Asia, Latin America, Africa, Canada, Australia, Middle East. Programs available to aid students whose native language is not English: Social. No financial aid specifically designated for international students.

Student Life: On-campus residence halls and apartments house 35% of the undergraduate student body. Female only halls house 12%; co-ed 58% (separate wings); apartments 30%. *Intercollegiate athletics:* male: baseball, basketball, cross-country, golf, tennis, soccer; female: basketball, cross-country, tennis, volleyball, softball, soccer. *Special regulations:* Registered cars permitted on campus in designated areas only. *Special services:* Instructional Technology Center, Student Support Center. *Student publications: Sorin Oak Review,* a biennial literary magazine; *Horizon,*, a daily e-newsletter. *Surrounding community:* Austin metropolitan area population 1 million. Served by mass transit bus system; airport 7 miles from campus, passenger rail service 5 miles from campus.

Publications: The St. Edward's marketing department publishes a quarterly alumni magazine that is distributed worldwide to more than 24,000. The university newsletter, *Hilltopics*, is published monthly and distributed electronically via the university's website.

Library Collections: 188,000 volumes. 85,300 microforms; 3,400 audiovisual materials; 962 current periodical subscriptions. Online catalog. Computer work stations available. Students have access to online information retrieval services and the Internet.

Buildings and Grounds: Campus area 155 acres.

Chief Executive Officer: Dr. George E. Martin, President.

Undergraduates address admission inquiries to deborah Gustafson, Director of Undergraduate Admissions; graduate inquiries to Tom Evans, Director, Center for Academic Progress.

St. Mary's University

One Camino Santa Maria
San Antonio, Texas 78228-8503
Tel: (210) 436-3126 **E-mail:** uadm@stmarytx.edu
Fax: (210) 431-6742 **Internet:** www.stmarytx.edu

Institution Description: St. Mary's University of San Antonio is a private institution owned by the Society of Mary, Roman Catholic Church. *Enrollment:* 4,110. *Degrees awarded:* Baccalaureate, first-professional (law), master's.

Member of the consortium United Colleges of San Antonio.

Accreditation: *Regional:* SACS-Comm. on Coll. *Professional* counseling, law, music, engineering

History: Established as St. Mary's Institute 1852; changed name to St. Louis College and offered first instruction at postsecondary level 1894; adopted present name 1923; chartered 1926; awarded first degree (baccalaureate) 1927. *See* Joseph Schmitz, S.M., *History of the Society of Mary in Texas* (San Antonio: The Naylor Co., 1951) for further information.

Institutional Structure: *Governing board:* Corporation and Board of Trustees (31 members). University administration: President, 5 Vice Presidents (Academic Affairs, Financial Administration, Student Services, Enrollment Management, Institutional Advancement), Assistant to President for Planning and Institutional Research, and 5 Academic Deans (Humanities and Social Sciences; Science, Engineering, and Technology; Business and Administration; Law; Graduate School).

Calendar: Semesters. Academic year Aug. to May. Freshmen admitted Aug., Jan., June, July. Degrees conferred May, Dec. Formal commencement May. Summer session of 2 terms June to Aug.

Characteristics of Freshmen:

74% of applicants accepted. 45% of accepted applicants enrolled.

80% (374 students) submitted SAT scores; 45%% (210 students) submitted ACT scores. *25th percentile*: SAT Verbal 480, SAT Math 480; ACT Composite 19, ACT English 18, ACT Math 18. *75th percentile*: SAT Verbal 590, SAT Math 590; ACT Composite 24, ACT English 25, ACT Math 24.

90% of freshmen from Texas. Freshmen from 11 states and 14 foreign countries.

Admission: Rolling admissions plan. For fall acceptance, apply as early as end of junior year of secondary school, but not later than 2 weeks prior to registration. Early acceptance available. *Requirements:* Either graduation from accredited secondary school with 4 units English, 3 mathematics, 2 laboratory science, 2 social studies, 2 foreign language, 3 academic electives; or GED. For science and engineering programs, 4 mathematics including trigonometry and analysis, and 3 laboratory science, including physics. Minimum GPA 2.0 Lowest acceptable secondary school class standing 50th percentile. *Entrance tests:* College Board SAT or ACT composite (upper 50th %ile). For foreign students minimum TOEFL transfer credit limited only by residence requirements. Junior College students limited to 66 hours.

College credit and advanced placement for postsecondary-level work completed in secondary school for USAFI/DANTES, for extrainstitutional learning on basis of ACE *2006 Guide to the Evaluation of Educational Experiences in the Armed Services.*

Tutoring available. Noncredit developmental/remedial courses offered in summer session and regular academic year.

Degree Requirements: *For baccalaureate degrees:* 128–136 semester hours; 2.0 GPA; 30 semester hours, including last 24, and 12 in advanced work in major, in residence; general education requirements.

Fulfillment of some degree requirements and exemption from some beginning courses possible by passing departmental examinations, College Board CLEP, AP, other standardized tests. *Grading system:* A–F; pass-no pass; withdraw (deadline after which pass-fail appended to withdraw).

Distinctive Educational Programs: *For undergraduates:* Honors program, internships, independent study, interdisciplinary programs in computer science and engineering, multinational organizational studies, English communication arts, biotechnology, international relations, public justice, urban studies. Washington Semester. Study abroad through London Semester.

ROTC: Army offered in cooperation with Alamo Community District.

Degrees Conferred: 473 *baccalaureate*; 242 *master's*; 9 *doctorate*; Bachelor's degrees awarded in top five disciplines: business, management, marketing, and related support services 138; social sciences 59; biological and biomedical sciences 57; psychology 33; communication, journalism, and related programs 21. 179 *first-professional:* law.

Fees and Other Expenses: *Full-time tuition per academic year 2008=09* $19,934; conntact the university for current undergraduate, graduate, and law school tuition and fees. *Room and board per academic year:* $7,000.

Financial Aid: Aid from institutionally generated funds is provided on the basis of academic merit, financial need, athletic ability, other criteria. Financial aid to full-time, first-time undergraduate students: need-based scholarships/grants totaling $11,786,189, self-help $8,893,474; non-need-based scholarships/grants totaling $12,775,488, self-help $6,049,834, parent loans $1,053,523, tuition waivers $1,521,523, athletic awards $1,645,737.

Departments and Teaching Staff: *Total instructional faculty:* 177. *Student-to-faculty ratio:* 18:1. *Degrees held by full-time faculty:* Baccalaureate 2%, master's 16%, doctorate 61%, professional 19%. 81% hold terminal degrees.

Enrollment: Total enrollment 4,110. Undergraduate 2,049 (full-time 1,807, part-time 242).

Characteristics of Student Body: *Ethnic/racial makeup:* number of Black non-Hispanic: 87; American Indian or Alaska Native: 6; Asian or Pacific Islander: 6; Hispanic: 1,724; White non-Hispanic: 516; unknown: 14.

International Students: 118 undergraduate nonresident aliens enrolled fall 2008. Programs available to aid students whose native language is not English: social, cultural. English as a Second Language Program. No financial specifically designated for international students.

Student Life: On-campus residence halls house 45% of undergraduates. *Intercollegiate athletics:* male: baseball, basketball, soccer, tennis, female: basketball, softball, tennis, volleyball. Both sexes, golf. *Special regulations:* Cars with parking stickers permitted in designated areas only; fee charged. *Special services:* Learning Resources Center, medical services. Full range of campus activities and organizations, including fraternities and sororities, campus ministry, learning assistance center. *Student publications: Diamondback*, a yearbook; *Law Journal*, a quarterly magazine; *Rattler*, campus newspaper, *Panache*, literary and art magazine, *The Witan*, a law school newspaper published irregularly. *Surrounding community:* San Antonio metropolitan population 1.2 million. Served by mass transit system, airport.

Library Collections: 481,200 volumes. 175,000 government documents; 165,000 microforms; 14,500 audiovisual materials; 1,220 serial subscriptions. Online catalog. Students have access to online information retrieval services and the Internet.

Most important special collections include Spanish Archives of Laredo; microfilmed archives of San Luis Potosi; Oxford Dons Book Collection.

Buildings and Grounds: Campus area 135 acres.

Chief Executive Officer: Fr. John H. Moder, S.M., President.

Address admission inquiries to Director of Admissions.

Sam Houston State University

1700 Sam Houston Avenue
Huntsville, Texas 77340
Tel: (936) 294-1589 **E-mail:** admissions@shsu.edu
Fax: (936) 294-11993758**Internet:** www.shsu.edu

Institution Description: Sam Houston State University is a state institution. *Enrollment:* 16,662. *Degrees awarded:* Baccalaureate, master's, doctorate.

Accreditation: *Regional:* SACS-Comm. on Coll. *Professional*: business, chemistry, dietetics, music, teacher education

History: Chartered as Sam Houston normal Institute 1879; became 4-year institution and offered first instruction at postsecondary level 1918; awarded first degree (baccalaureate) 1920; changed name to Sam Houston State Teachers College 1923, to Sam Houston State College 1965; adopted present name 1969.

Institutional Structure: *Governing board:* Board of Regents, Texas State University System. Representation: 9 members (appointed by governor of Texas). All voting. *Composition of institution:* Administrators 56. Administration is comprised of president, vice presidents for academic affairs, finance and operations, student services and deans of colleges of arts and sciences, business administration, criminal justice, education and applied science. Full-time instructional faculty 600.

Calendar: Semesters. Academic year Sept. to Aug.

SAM HOUSTON STATE UNIVERSITY—*cont'd*

Characteristics of Freshmen: 9,256 applicants (female 5,475, male 3,981). 62% of applicants accepted. 46% of accepted applicants enrolled.

59% (8,169 students) submitted SAT scores; 34% (4,644 students) submitted ACT scores. *25th percentile*: SAT Math 420; ACT Composite 17. *75th percentile*: SAT Math 520; ACT Composite 22.

21% of freshmen expected to graduate within 5 years. 98% of freshmen from Texas. Freshmen from 17 states and 15 foreign countries.

Admission: Rolling admissions plan. *Requirements:* Graduation from accredited secondary school. GED accepted for students over 21 years of age. Consult the university catalog for specific requirements. *Entrance tests:* College Board SAT (minimum combined score of 900) or ACT composite (minimum score 21). For foreign students TOEFL. *For transfer students:* 2.0 minimum GPA; from 2-year accredited institution 66 semester hours maximum transfer credit.

Degree Requirements: *For all baccalaureate degrees:* 128 semester hours; 2.0 GPA; core curriculum. *Grading system:* A–F.

Distinctive Educational Programs: College of Criminal Justice, doctoral program, Criminal Justice Center for professional, continuing education programs, one of largest in the U.S. Has George J. Betto endowed chair. Journalism has Philip G. Warner endowed chair, one of few journalism endowed chairs in the U.S.

Degrees Conferred: 2,695 *baccalaureate;* 696 *master's;* 28 *doctorate.*

Fees and Other Expenses: *Full-time tuition for academic year 2008*09:* undergraduate resident $5,910, nonresident $14,360; contact the university for current graduate tuition and applicable fees. *Required fees:* $1,296. *Room and board per academic year:* $6,046. *Books and supplies:* $1,038. *Other expenses:* $1,288.

Financial Aid: Aid from institutionally generated funds is provided on the basis of academic merit, financial need.

Financial aid to full-time, first-time undergraduate students: 47% received some form of aid. Average amount of aid received: federal grants $4,918; Pell grants $2,655; other federal aid $3,250; state/local grants $4,644; institutional grants $2,269.

Departments and Teaching Staff: *Total instructional faculty:* 920. Student/faculty ratio: 20:1. Degrees held by full-time faculty: 67.9% hold terminal degrees.

Enrollment: Total enrollment 16,662. Undergraduate 14,392 (full-time 84%; female 51%, male 43%). Graduate 2,360 (full-time 26%). Undergraduate transfer-in students 1,760.

Characteristics of Student Body: *Ethnic/racial makeup:* Black non-Hispanic: 15%; American Indian or Alaska Native: 1%; Asian or Pacific Islander: 1%; Hispanic: 13%; White non-Hispanic: 69%; nonresident alien 1%.

International Students: 166 nonresident aliens enrolled fall 2008. Students from Europe, Asia, Latin America, Africa, Canada, Australia, Middle East. No programs available to aid students whose native language is not English. No financial aid specifically designated for international students.

Student Life: On-campus residence halls house 19% of student body. Residence halls for males constitute 36% of such space, for females 45%, for married students 2%. *Intercollegiate athletics:* NCAA Division I in all sports but football (Division 1AA). Intercollegiate competition in football, basketball, baseball, golf, tennis, cross-country, soccer for males; volleyball, basketball, track, cross-country, tennis for females; club teams in rugby, lacrosse, rodeo. Intramurals: 106,000 participations in 56 events. *Surrounding community:* Huntsville, population 34,592. *Student publications: Houstonian*, student newspaper; *Alcalde* yearbook.

Publications: *Texas Review* quarterly literary magazine; *Sam Today* alumni newspaper published quarterly; *SHSU Newsletter* published monthly.

Library Collections: 1,255,000 volumes including bound books, serial backfiles, electronic documents, and government documents not in separate collections. Online catalog. Current serial subscriptions: 2,272 paper, 72 microform, 4,831 electronic. 6,811 recordings; 3,452 compact discs; 1,438 CD-ROMs. Computer work stations available. Students have access to the Internet at no charge.

Most important special collections are John W. Thomas Collection; Clark Texas Collection; Porter Collection of Civil War Broadsides; Shettles Collection.

Buildings and Grounds: Campus area 237 acres.

Chief Executive Officer: Dr. James F. Gaertner, President.

Address undergraduate admission inquiries to Trevor Thom, Director of Admissions.

Schreiner University

2100 Memorial Boulevard
Kerrville, Texas 78028
Tel: (830) 896-5411 **E-mail:** admissions@schreiner.edu
Fax: (830) 896-3232 **Internet:** www.schreiner.edu

Institution Description: Schreiner University is an independent institution related by choice and covenant to the Presbyterian Church (U.S.A.). *Enrollment:* 974. *Degrees awarded:* Associate, baccalaureate. Certificates also awarded.

Accreditation: *Regional:* SACS-Comm. on Coll.

History: Founded 1923; became coeducational for day students 1832, for boarding students 1971; became four-year college 1983.

Institutional Structure: *Governing board:* Board of Trustees. 36 trustees plus president (ex officio). *Composition of institution:* Administrative Council comprised of the president, provost, and 3 vice president.

Calendar: Semesters. Academic year Aug. to May. Summer session June to July.

Characteristics of Freshmen: 1,028 applicants (female 961, male 467). 49.6% of applicants admitted. 27% of applicants admitted and enrolled.

77% (195 students) submitted SAT scores; 92% (132 students) submitted ACT scores. *25th percentile*: SAT Critical Reading 460, SAT Math 430; ACT Composite 18. *75th percentile*: SAT Critical Reading 546, SAT Math 550; ACT Composite 23.

98% of freshmen from Texas. Freshmen from 3 states and 4 foreign countries.

Admission: Rolling admissions plan. Students must have graduated from an accredited high school or receive a high school equivalency certificate. Applicants must have completed 4 years English, 2 social science, 2 laboratory science, and 3 mathematics. *Entrance tests:* College Board SAT or ACT. *For transfer students:* 2.0 minimum GPA.

Degree Requirements: 128 credit hours; students must satisfy distribution requirements from a specific core curriculum; completion of 10 hours in interdisciplinary studies; attend 2 winter terms; cumulative 2.0 GPA.

Distinctive Educational Programs: Teacher education; vocational nursing program; learning support services program; interdisciplinary studies.

Degrees Conferred: 137 *baccalaureate*; 12 *master's*. Bachelor's degrees awarded in top five disciplines: business, management, marketing, and related support services 20; psychology 17; education 14; biological/life sciences 8; English 4. Master's degrees awarded: education 12.

Fees and Other Expenses: *Full-time tuition per academic year 2008–09:* $17,992 undergraduate; contact the university for current graduate tuition. *Room and board per academic year:* $7,952. *Books and supplies:* $1,000. *Other expenses:* $2,016.

Financial Aid: Aid from institutionally generated funds is provided on the basis of academic merit, financial need, athletic ability, other criteria. Institution has a Program Participation Agreement with the U.S. Department of Education for eligible students to receive Pell Grants and, depending upon the agreement, other federal aid.

Financial aid to full-time, first-time undergraduate students: 100% received some form of aid.

Departments and Teaching Staff: *Total instructional faculty:* 84 (full-time 52, part-time 32). Student/faculty ratio: 13:1. Degrees held by full-time faculty: master's 95%, doctorate 65%. 67% hold terminal degrees.

Enrollment: Total enrollment 974. Undergraduate 953 (full-time 95%; female 58%, male 42%). Graduate 21 (full-time 100%). Transfer-in students 73.

Characteristics of Student Body: *Ethnic/racial makeup:* Black non-Hispanic: 4%; American Indian or Alaska Native: 1%; Asian or Pacific Islander: 1%; Hispanic: 21%; White non-Hispanic: 73%. *Age distribution:* number under 18: 10; 18–19: 275; 20–21: 183; 22–24: 121; 25–29: 77; 30–34: 43; 35–39: 27; 40–49: 39; 50–64: 16; 65 and over: 2. 17% of student body attend summer sessions.

International Students: 7 nonresident aliens enrolled fall 2008. Programs available to aid students whose native language is not English: social, cultural. English as a Second Language Program. No financial aid specifically designated for international students.

Student Life: On-campus residence halls and apartments. *Athletics:* male: basketball, baseball, cross-country, golf, soccer, tennis; female basketball, cross-country, golf, soccer, softball, tennis, volleyball. *Special regulations:* Residence hall visitation noon to 11pm. Quiet hours begin at 7:30pm. *Special services:* College store, student center and recreation room; health care for students living in college-owned facilities. *Student publications: The Mountaineer*, biweekly student newspaper; *The Muse*, literary magazine. *Surrounding community:* Kerrville, population 25,000.

Library Collections: 120,000 volumes. 52,000 microforms; 1,100 audiovisual materials. Current serial subscriptions: paper 200; via electronic access

19,579. Online catalog. Computer work stations available. Students have access to online information retrieval services and the Internet.

Most important special holdings include Hill Country Collection; Schreiner College Archives; Texana.

Buildings and Grounds: Campus area 175 acres. Campus DVD available.

Chief Executive Officer: Dr. C. Timothy Summerlin, President.

Address admission inquiries to Sandy Speed, Director of Admissions and Financial Aid.

South Texas College of Law

1303 San Jacinto Street
Houston, Texas 77002-7000
Tel: (713) 659-8040 **E-mail:** acramer@stcl.edu
Fax: (713) 659-2217 **Internet:** www.stcl.edu

Institution Description: South Texas College of Law is a private, nonprofit, independent institution. *Enrollment:* 1,262. *Degrees awarded:* First-professional (law). Continuing legal education and institutes also offered.

Accreditation: *National:* American Bar Association. *Professional*: law

History: Founded by leading members of the Houston bench and bar 1923 as the South Texas School of Law - YMCA until 1964 when it separated from the YMCA and reorganized in its present legal status.

Institutional Structure: *Governing board:* Board of Directors with 18 members; executive authority delegated to the president and dean who is the same person. *Composition of institution:* 2 associate deans who are vice presidents and tenured professors; four additional vice president, one of whom is a tenured professor and director of the law library. Full-time instructional faculty 58.

Calendar: Semesters. Academic year Aug. to May. Optional 8-week summer session. Degrees conferred and formal commencement Dec., May.

Characteristics of Freshmen: 57% of applicants accepted. 42% of accepted applicants enrolled.

Admission: Application must be made by Feb. 25 for fall admission and by Oct. 1 for spring. All applicants are required to take the LSAT and to register with Law School Data Assembly Service (LSDAS). If admitted, applicants must have earned a baccalaureate degree from an accredited college or university.

Degree Requirements: *For first-professional degree:* Minimum of 90 semester hours earned within six years of the date of first enrollment; cumulative grade average of C or better; complete all required courses including the substantial writing component in residence. *Grading system:* The college uses the alphabetical systems of grading; honors pass, pass or fail.

Distinctive Educational Programs: Day and evening classes, all open to full-time and part-time students. Advocacy program resulting in more than 50 national titles; clinical studies offering live-client clinics in disability entitlement, HIV and the Law Issues and in Mediation, as well as civil, criminal, and judicial externships. Extensive summer abroad study opportunities available in Brazil, England, India, Malta, Turkey. Semester abroad exchange program in Aarhus, Denmark.

Degrees Conferred: 352 *first-professional:* law.

Fees and Other Expenses: *Full-time tuition per academic year 2008–09:* $22,440.

Financial Aid: Aid from institutionally generated funds is provided on the basis of academic merit, financial need, other criteria. Institution has a Program Participation Agreement with the U.S. Department of Education for eligible students to receive Pell Grants and, depending upon the agreement, other federal aid.

Departments and Teaching Staff: Law *professors* 39, *associate professors* 5, *assistant professors* 11, *part-time faculty* 35.

Total instructional faculty: 90. Student/faculty ratio: 20.2:1. Degrees held by full-time faculty: master's 40%, doctorate 7%, baccalaureate 100%, professional 100%. 100% hold terminal degrees.

Enrollment: Total enrollment 1,254.

Characteristics of Student Body: *Ethnic/racial makeup:* Black non-Hispanic: 4.6%; American Indian or Alaska Native: .6%; Asian or Pacific Islander: 7.7%; Hispanic: 9.4%; White non-Hispanic: 77.5%.

International Students: No programs available to aid students whose native language is not English. No financial aid specifically designated for international students.

Student Life: The college does not maintain living accommodations for students. Numerous student organizations are active on campus and in the community. *Surrounding community:* Houston is the fourth largest city in the U.S. Served by mass transit bus system; 2 airports.

Publications: *Annotations* is the student-run newspaper published four times per semester. *Corporate Counsel Review* is the journal of the Corporate Counsel section of the State Bar of Texas. *Currents* is the international trade journal published semiannually. *South Texas Review* is a scholarly periodical edited and published by second-year and third-year law students who are selected for membership of the basis of outstanding scholarship or writing abilities; appears four times per year.

Library Collections: 390,000 volumes. 4,263 serial subscriptions (paper, microform, electronic). Computer work stations available. Online catalog. Students have access to the Internet and online information retrieval services.

Most important special holdings include rare law book collection; South Texas College of Law Archives; Pennzoil Papers; international law collection; Texas Law Practice Skills collection; Jesse James Special Collections and Archives; maritime law.

Buildings and Grounds: Campus area 1 city block; includes 11-story South Texas College of Law Tower; Spurgeon E. Bell Conference Center, and Cullen Building. The facilities include the largest courtroom in Texas. The college is home to Texas' First and Fourteenth Courts of Appeals and is the only American law school to house two appellate courts on a permanent basis.

Chief Executive Officer: James J. Alfini, President and Dean. Address admission inquiries to Alicia K. Cramer, Assistant Dean for Admissions.

Southwestern Baptist Theological Seminary

2001 West Seminary Drive
P.O. Box 22000
Fort Worth, Texas 76122
Tel: (817) 923-1921 **E-mail:** admissions@swbts.edu
Fax: (817) 921-8761 **Internet:** www.swbts.edu

Institution Description: Southwestern Baptist Theological Seminary is a private institution affiliated with the Southern Baptist convention. *Enrollment:* 2,588. *Degrees awarded:* First-professional (master of divinity), master's, doctorate. Diplomas also awarded.

Accreditation: *Regional:* SACS-Comm. on Coll. *National:* ATS. *Professional*: music, theology

History: Established as part of Baylor University 1901; adopted present name 1907; chartered, offered first instruction at postsecondary level, and awarded first degrees (baccalaureate and master's) 1908. *See* L. R. Scarborough, *A Modern School of the Prophets* (Nashville, Tenn.: Broadman Press, 1939) and Robert A. Baker, *Tell the Generations Following* (Nashville, Tenn.: Broadman Press, 1983) for further information.

Institutional Structure: *Governing board:* Board of Trustees. Extrainstitutional representation: 37 trustees; institutional representation: 6 administrators, including president of the institution. 37 voting. *Composition of institution:* Administrators 5. Academic affairs headed by vice president for academic affairs and provost. Management/business/finances directed by vice president for business affairs. Full-time instructional faculty 83. Academic governance body, faculty, meets an average of 10 times per year.

Calendar: Semesters. Academic year Aug. to May. Entering students admitted Aug., Jan., May. Degrees conferred and formal commencements May, July, Dec. Summer session May to July.

Characteristics of Freshmen: 83.2% of applicants accepted.

Admission: Rolling admissions plan. Apply no later than 8 weeks before classes begin. *Requirements:* Baccalaureate from accredited college or university; church endorsement; biographical information on spouse. For first-professional students, preseminary curriculum, including biblical and modern classical languages. Additional requirements for some programs. *Entrance tests:* For master of music program GRE. *For transfer students:* From accredited graduate institution 16 hours maximum transfer credit toward music program; transfer credit maximum 33 hours in other master's programs.

Tutoring available. Noncredit remedial courses offered in summer session and regular academic year.

Degree Requirements: *For all first-professional degrees:* 88 semester hours; field education. *For all master's degrees:* 60–66 hours. *For all degrees:* 2.0–3.0 GPA. Additional requirements for some programs.

Exemption from some courses in master's program possible by passing departmental examinations. *Grading system:* A–F; withdraw.

Distinctive Educational Programs: Field education. Flexible meeting places and schedules, including off-campus centers (at Houston, 263 miles from main institution; at San Antonio, 266 miles away; at Shawnee, OK, 300 miles away) and evening classes. Cooperative master of religious education (gerontology concentration) with Baylor University. *Other distinctive programs:* Annual conferences on college missions and church administration. Lay theological studies. Study abroad: Oxford Summer Program, England; Tel Batesh (Timnah) Archaeology Program, Israel.

Degrees Conferred: 10 *baccalaureate;* 430 *master's:* various disciplines; 36 *doctorate:* various disciplines; 220 *first-professional:* theology.

[WESTERN BAPTIST THEOLOGICAL SEMINARY—*cont'd*

Fees and Other Expenses: *Full-time tuition per academic year 2008–09:* $5,618. *Books and supplies:* $1,000. *Room and board per academic year:* $4,200. *Other expenses:* $1,500.

Financial Aid: Aid from institutionally generated funds is provided on the basis of academic merit, financial need. Institution has a Program Participation Agreement with the U.S. Department of Education for eligible students to receive Pell Grants and, depending upon the agreement, other federal aid.

financial aid for first-time, full-time undergraduate students: 88% received some form of aid.

Departments and Teaching Staff: *Total instructional faculty:* 158. Degrees held by full-time faculty: baccalaureate 100%, master's 100%, first-professional 20%. 90% hold terminal degrees.

Enrollment: Total enrollment 2,588. Undergraduate 384.

Characteristics of Student Body: *Ethnic/racial makeup:* Black non-Hispanic: 5%; American Indian or Alaska Native 1%; Asian or Pacific Islander: 5%; Hispanic: 6%; White non-Hispanic: 77%; unknown: 1%; nonresident alien 4%.

International Students: 104 nonresident aliens enrolled fall 2004. Programs available to aid students whose native language is not English: social, cultural. Financial aid specifically designated for international students: scholarships available to qualifying students.

Publications: *Southwestern News*, a monthly news magazine; *Southwestern Journal of Theology*, a theological journal published 3 times annually; *Scroll*, a weekly news bulletin for students.

Library Collections: 420,000 volumes. 16,717 microforms; 48,407 audiovisual materials; Students have access to online information retrieval services and the Internet.

Most important holdings include Texas Baptist Historical Collection; World Missions and Evangelism Periodicals Collection; Church Hymnal and Music Collection; papers of Texas Baptist leaders (L.R. Scarborough, B.H. Carroll, George Truett).

Buildings and Grounds: Campus area 200 acres.

Chief Executive Officer: Dr. Paige Patterson, President. Address admission inquiries to Director of Admissions.

Southern Methodist University

6425 Boaz Street
Dallas, Texas 75275-0296

Tel: (214) 768-2000 **E-mail:** ugadmission@smu.edu
Fax: (214) 768-2103 **Internet:** www.smu.edu

Institution Description: Southern Methodist University is a private, nonsectarian institution affiliated with The United Methodist Church. *Enrollment:* 10,765. *Degrees awarded:* Baccalaureate, first-professional (law, theology), other professional (MBA, MMUS, MFA, DE), master's, doctorate.

Member of the Oak Ridge Associated Universities, Southwest Conference Humanities Consortium.

Accreditation: *Regional:* SACS-Comm. on Coll. *Professional*: art, business, chemistry, dance, engineering, law, music, teacher education, theology

History: Established and chartered 1911; offered first instruction at postsecondary level 1915; awarded first degree (baccalaureate) 1916. *See* Mary Martha Hosford Thomas, *Southern Methodist University, Founding and Early Years* (Dallas: Southern Methodist University Press, 1974) for further information.

Institutional Structure: *Governing board:* Board of Trustees. *Composition of institution:* Administrators 31. Academic affairs headed by vice president and provost. Management/business/finances directed by vice president for finance and administration. Full-time instructional faculty 576. Academic governance body, Faculty Senate, meets an average of 9 times per year.

Calendar: Semesters. Academic year Aug. to May. Freshmen admitted Aug., Jan., June, July. Degrees conferred May, Aug., Dec. Formal commencement May. Summer session of 3 terms from May to Aug.

Characteristics of Freshmen: 8,210 applicants (female 4,596, male 3,574). 64% of applicants admitted. 32% of applicants admitted and enrolled.

83% (1,091 students) submitted SAT scores; 46% (599 students) submitted ACT scores. *25th percentile*: SAT Critical Reading 540, SAT Math 560; ACT Composite 24, ACT English 23, ACT Math 23. *75th percentile*: SAT Critical Reading 640, SAT Math 660; ACT Composite 28, ACT English 29, ACT Math 28.

69% of entering freshmen expected to graduate within 5 years. 58% of freshmen from Texas. Freshmen from 50 states and 19 foreign countries.

Admission: For fall acceptance, apply as early as completion of junior year of secondary school, but not later than Apr. 1 of year of enrollment; for spring acceptance, apply by Jan. 15. *Requirements:* Graduation from accredited secondary school with 15 units. Recommend 4 units in English, 3 natural sciences (including 2 laboratory science); 2 in a foreign language, 3 mathematics, 3 social studies. *Entrance tests:* College Board SAT and/or ACT composite. For foreign students TOEFL. *For transfer students:* 2.7 minimum GPA; 62 semester hours maximum transfer credit. Tutoring available.

Degree Requirements: Minimum of 120 semester credit hours, including 41 hours in the Common Educational Experience; 2.0 GPA; 60 hours in residence; 42 advanced hours (3000 level or above); minimum of 2 non-credit hours in 1-hour physical education courses.

Credit by examination is possible in some areas. *Grading system:* A–F, plus-minus scale; pass-fail; withdraw (deadline after which pass-fail is appended to withdraw); no credit; incomplete.

Distinctive Educational Programs: Work-experience programs. Flexible meeting places and schedules, including off-campus centers, weekend and evening classes. Special facilities for using telecommunications in the classroom. Interdisciplinary programs in African-American studies, German area studies, Latin American civilization, Italian area studies, linguistics, medieval studies, Mexican-American studies, Russian area studies, women's studies. Facilities and programs for independent research, including honors programs, individual majors, tutorials. Study abroad in Australia, Austria, Denmark, Egypt, England, France, Greece, Israel, Italy, Japan, Mexico. *Other distinctive programs:* Continuing education. Industrial Information Services assists business firms in obtaining scientific, technical, business, and marketing information.

ROTC: Air Force in cooperation with University of North Texas; Army in cooperation with University of Texas at Arlington.

Degrees Conferred: 1,541 *baccalaureate*; 1,267 *master's*; 61 *doctorate*; 332 *first-professional*. Bachelor's degrees awarded in top five disciplines: business, management, marketing, and related support services 406; social sciences and history 233; communication, journalism, and related programs 180; psychology 149; visual and performing arts 122. Master's degrees awarded: various disciplines 1,267. Doctorates awarded: various disciplines 61. First-professional degrees awarded: law 282; master of divinity 50.

Fees and Other Expenses: *Full-time tuition per academic year 2008–09:* undergraduate $33,170; contact the university for current graduate/first-professional tuition/fees. *Room and board per academic year:* $11,805. *Books and supplies:* $800. *Other expenses:* $1,600.

Financial Aid: Aid from institutionally generated funds is provided on the basis of academic merit, financial need, athletic ability, other criteria.

Financial aid to full-time, first-time undergraduate students: 785 received some form of aid. Average amount of aid received: federal grants $5,248; Pell grants $3,306; other federal aid $2,260; state/local grants $3,682; institutional grants $14,660.

Departments and Teaching Staff: *Total instructional faculty:* 889 (full-time 576, part-time 313). Total faculty with doctorate, first-professional, or other terminal degree: 645. Student/faculty ratio: 12:1. Degrees held by faculty: master's 10.1%, doctorate 73.6%, baccalaureate 1.9%, professional 14.4%. 89.5% hold terminal degrees.

Enrollment: Total enrollment 10,765. Undergraduate 6,240 (full-time 95%; female 64%, male 46%). Graduate 4,725 (full-time 47%). Undergraduate transfer-in students 290.

Characteristics of Student Body: *Ethnic/racial makeup:* Black non-Hispanic: 5%; American Indian or Alaska Native: 1%; Asian or Pacific Islander: 6%; Hispanic: 8%; White non-Hispanic: 74%; unknown 1%; nonresident alien 6%. *Age distribution:* number under 18: 75; 18–19: 2,439; 20–21: 2,529; 22–24: 789; 25–29: 177; 30–34: 80; 35–39: 40; 40–49: 45; 50–64: 33; 65 and over: 1.

International Students: 658 nonresident aliens enrolled fall 2008. Students from Europe, Asia, Latin America, Africa, Canada, Australia. Programs available to aid students whose native language is not English: social, cultural. English as a Second Language Program. No financial aid specifically designated for international students.

Student Life: On-campus residence halls and Greek housing provide residence for 40% student body. 29% of males join fraternities and live in fraternity housing; 35% of females join and 12% live in sorority housing. Housing available for married students. *Intercollegiate athletics:* male: basketball, football, golf, soccer, swimming, tennis, track; female: basketball, golf, soccer, swimming, tennis, track. *Special regulations:* Registered cars permitted. *Special services:* Medical services. *Student publications, radio: Advocate*, a weekly law newspaper; *Daily Campus*, a newspaper; *Espejo*, a biannual literary magazine; *Peruna Express*, an annual handbook; *Rotunda*, a yearbook; *Student Directory*, an annual publication. Radio station KSMU and SMU-TV channel 7. *Surrounding community:* Dallas population over 1 million. Served by 2 airports; one 15 miles from campus, the other 20 miles from campus.

Publications: *Journal of Air Law and Commerce* (quarterly) first published 1930; *Perkins Perspective* (first date published unknown); *Southwestern Law Journal* (4 times per year) first published 1947; *Southwest Review* first published 1915; *The International Lawyer* (quarterly) first published 1987. University Press published 68 titles from 1986 to present.

Library Collections: 2,900,000 volumes. 579,671 government documents; 1,757,660 microforms; 24,432 recordings; 7,981 compact discs; 1,610 CD-ROMs. 11,216 serial subscriptions (paper, microform, electronic). Online catalog. Students have access to online information retrieval services and the Internet.

Most important holdings include Jerry Bywaters - Hamon Library; DeGoyler Western and Earth Sciences collections; 15th- and 20th-century fine printing collections.

Buildings and Grounds: Campus area 175 acres. Campus DVD available.

Chief Executive Officer: R. Gerald Turner, President.

Address admission inquiries to Nancy Peterson, Associate Director of Admissions.

Dedman College

Degree Programs Offered: *Baccalaureate* in English, creative writing, African American, Mexican American, German area, Italian area, Russian area, French, German, Russian, Spanish, foreign languages, history, philosophy, religious studies, Latin American studies, anthropology, economics, economics with systems analysis, economics with finance, political science, psychology, sociology, biological sciences, chemistry, geology, geophysics, mathematics, physics, statistical science; *Evening program:* humanities, social science. *Master's* in English, creative writing, history, religious studies, Latin American studies, anthropology, medical anthropology, economics, psychology, clinical and counseling, biological sciences, chemistry, geological sciences, applied geophysics, mathematics, physics, statistical science; *Evening program:* liberal arts. *Doctorate* in religious studies, anthropology, economics, psychology, biological sciences, geological sciences, mathematics, statistical science.

Meadows School of the Arts

Degree Programs Offered: *Baccalaureate* in art, art history, dance, music education, music performance, music theory, music composition, music therapy, piano pedagogy, theatre, advertising, cinema, journalism, public relations, TV/radio (includes broadcasting). *Master's* in art, art history, music education, music performance, music composition, music therapy, piano pedagogy, coral conducting, music history and literature, instrumental conducting, sacred music, theatre, TV/radio (includes broadcasting), arts administration.

Edwin L. Cox School of Business

Degree Programs Offered: *Baccalaureate* in general business, accounting, finance, MIS, marketing, organizational behavior, real estate and finance. *Master's* in general business.

School of Education and Human Development

Degree Programs Offered: *Baccalaureate* in humanities, social sciences; *master's* in bilingual education-gifted concentration, education.

School of Engineering and Applied Science

Degree Programs Offered: *Baccalaureate* in mechanical engineering, computer science, computer engineering, management science, electrical engineering. *Master's* in computer science, computer engineering, engineering management, operations research, electrical engineering, telecommunications, material science and engineering, hazardous and waste materials management, applied science. *Doctorate* in computer science, computer engineering, engineering management, operations research, electrical engineering, telecommunications, applied science.

Dedman School of Law

Degree Programs Offered: *JD, SJD* in taxation law (LLM), comparative and international law (LLM).

Admission: *For first-professional degree:* Baccalaureate from accredited institution; LSAT. Graduate requirements vary with level.

Degree Requirements: *For first-professional degree:* 90 credit hours; 70 GPA on scale of 100; 6 residence credits. Graduate requirements vary.

Perkins School of Theology

Degree Programs Offered: Religious education (MRE); theology (MTS); ministry (M.Div., D.Min.).

Admission: *For first-professional degree:* Baccalaureate from accredited institution. Graduate requirements vary with program and level.

Degree Requirements: *For first-professional degree:* 72 credit hours; 70 GPA on scale of 100; 42 hours in residence. Graduate requirements vary.

Southwestern Adventist University

100 West Hillcrest
Keene, Texas 76059
Tel: (817) 645-3921 **E-mail:** admissions@swau.edu
Fax: (817) 556-4744 **Internet:** www.swau.edu

Institution Description: Southwestern Adventist University is a private institution affiliated with the Seventh-day Adventist Church. *Enrollment:* 821. *Degrees awarded:* Associate, baccalaureate, master's.

Accreditation: *Regional:* SACS-Comm. on Coll. *Professional*: business, nursing, social work

History: Established as Keene Academy 1893; changed name to Southwestern Junior College and offered first instruction at postsecondary level 1916; awarded first degree (associate) 1918; changed name to Southwestern Union College 1967; became Southwestern Adventist College 1977; adopted present name 1996.

Institutional Structure: *Governing board:* Board of Trustees. Representation: 35 trustees; including president of the college. All voting. *Composition of institution:* Administrators 16. Academic affairs headed by vice president for academic affairs. Student Affairs head by Dean of Students. Management/business/finances directed by vice president for financial affairs. Full-time instructional faculty 48. Academic governance body, Academic Policies Committee, meets an average of 20 times per year.

Calendar: Semesters. Academic year early Sept. to early May. Freshmen admitted Aug., Jan., June, July. Degrees conferred May, Dec. Formal commencements May. Summer session early May to early Aug.

Characteristics of Freshmen: 759 applicants (female 463, male 294). 92% of applicants accepted. 47% of accepted applicants enrolled.

Average secondary school rank of freshmen 55th percentile. Mean SAT scores 499 verbal, 468 mathematical. Mean ACT Composite score 20.

22% of entering freshmen expected to graduate within 5 years. 25% of fresmen from Texas. Freshmen from 28 states and 18 foreign countries.

Admission: Rolling admissions plan. For fall acceptance, apply as early as June of junior year of secondary school, but not later than 12th day of classes. *Requirements:* Either graduation from accredited secondary school or GED. Recommend 16 college preparatory units from among English, a foreign language, mathematics, natural sciences, social studies. Additional requirements for some programs. *Entrance tests:* ACT or SAT minimum combined score of 800. For foreign students TOEFL. *For transfer students:* 2.0 minimum GPA; from 4-year accredited institution 98 hours maximum transfer credit; from 2-year accredited institution 64 hours; correspondence/extension students 12 hours.

College credit for extrainstitutional learning. Remedial courses offered during regular academic year; credit given for some courses.

Degree Requirements: *For all associate degrees:* 64 semester hours; 2.0 GPA; 1 physical activity course; 15 hours general education courses. *For all baccalaureate degrees:* 128 hours; GPA in major field: 2.25 in upper division work; 2 physical activity courses; 50 hours general education courses; Undergraduate Assessment Program examination. *For all degrees:* 2 semesters in residence; chapel attendance weekly.

Fulfillment of some degree requirements and exemption from some beginning courses possible by passing College Board CLEP, AP. *Grading system:* A–F; pass; withdraw (carries time limit).

Distinctive Educational Programs: Personalized degree program. Study abroad in Austria, Argentina, France, Kenya, Spain through Adventist Colleges Abroad (ACA). Credit transfer agreement with Home Study Institute. *Other distinctive program:* Adult Degree Program offers baccalaureate based primarily on study at home.

Degrees Conferred: 31 *associate*; 103 *baccalaureate*; 10 *master's*. Bachelor's degrees awarded in top five disciplines: education 36; business, management, marketing, and related support services 34; communication, journalism, and related programs 18; psychology 12; theology 9. Master's degrees awarded: business/management 3; education 7.

Fees and Other Expenses: *Full-time tuition per academic year 2008–09:* undergraduate $15,236; contact the university for current graduate tuition/fees. *Books and supplies:* $936. *Room and board per academic year:* $6,742. *Other expenses:* $2,276.

Financial Aid: Aid from institutionally generated funds is provided on the basis of academic merit, financial need, athletic ability.

Financial aid to full-time, first-time undergraduate students: 99% received some form of aid. Average amount of aid received: federal grants $3,371; state/local grants $2,543; institutional grants $4,433; loans $3,595.

SOUTHWESTERN ADVENTIST UNIVERSITY—*cont'd*

Departments and Teaching Staff: *Total instructional faculty:* 60. Student/faculty ratio: 18:1. Degrees held by full-time faculty: doctorate 58%, master's 42%. 60% hold terminal degrees.

Enrollment: Total enrollment 821. Undergraduate 799 (full-time 89%; female 57%; male 43%). Graduate 22% (full-time 36%). Transfer-in students 57.

Characteristics of Student Body: *Ethnic/racial makeup:* Black non-Hispanic: 16%; American Indian or Alaska Native: 1%; Asian or Pacific Islander: 4%; Hispanic: 28%; White non-Hispanic: 33%; unknown: 5%; nonresident alien 18%.

International Students: 16 nonresident aliens enrolled fall 2008. Students from Europe, Asia, Latin America, Africa, Canada. Programs available to aid students whose native language is not English: social, cultural. English as a Second Language Program. No financial aid specifically designated for international students.

Student Life: On-campus residence halls house 55% of student body. Residence halls for males constitute 44% of such space, for females 56%. 7% of student body housed on campus in college-owned cottages and apartments. *Special regulations:* Cars permitted for sophomores, juniors, seniors; special conditions apply for freshmen. Curfews from 10:30pm to 5am Sun.–Fri., 12:30am to 5:30am Sat. Quiet hours for freshmen from 7:30pm to 9:30pm Sun.–Thurs. *Special services:* Medical services. *Student publications, radio: Mizpan*, a yearbook; *Southwesterner*, a biweekly newspaper. Radio station KSUC broadcasts 18 hours per week; programs are of an inspirational nature. *Surrounding community:* Keene population 3,000. Fort Worth, 30 miles from campus, is nearest metropolitan area. Served by airport 60 miles from campus.

Publications: Sources of information about Southwestern Adventist include denominational publications.

Library Collections: 115,000 volumes. 382,533 microforms; 4,400 audiovisual materials; 465 current periodical subscriptions. Students have access to the Internet at no charge.

Most important special holdings include Ellen G. White books; Seventh-day Adventist Church in Texas; Haddock collection of Religious books.

Buildings and Grounds: Campus area 120 acres.

Chief Executive Officer: Dr. Eric D. Anderson, President.

Address admission inquiries to Tina Bottsford, Director of Enrollment.

Southwestern Assemblies of God University

1200 Sycamore Street
Waxahachie, Texas 75165
Tel: (972) 937-4010 **E-mail:** admissions@sagu.edu
Fax: (972) 923-0488 **Internet:** www.sagu.edu

Institution Description: Southwestern Assemblies of God University is a private, independent, nonprofit institution affiliated with the Assemblies of God in the United States of America. *Enrollment:* 1,659. *Degrees awarded:* Associate, baccalaureate.

Accreditation: *Regional:* SACS-Comm. on Coll. *National:* ABHE.

History: Founded 1941 with the merger of three Bible schools (one in Enid, Oklahoma founded 1927; one in Amarillo, Texas founded 1931; and one in Baytown, Texas 1931); moved to present location 1943.

Institutional Structure: *Governing board:* Extrainstitutional representation: 35 member Board of Regents; institutional representation: 1. *Composition of institution:* Administrators 4. Academic affairs headed by academic dean. Student Services headed by dean of student services. Business/Finances directed by business administrator. Full-time instructional faculty 45. Academic governance body, the college faculty, meets biweekly during the school year.

Calendar: Semesters. Academic year May 21 to May 8. Freshmen admitted Aug., Jan., May. Degrees conferred May, Aug., Dec. Formal commencement May. Summer session of 2 terms from May to July.

Characteristics of Freshmen: Average secondary school rank 63rd percentile. Mean ACT Composite score 18.6.

72% of freshmen from Texas. Freshmen from 15 states.

Admission: For fall acceptance, apply as early as end of junior year of secondary school. Early acceptance available. *Requirements:* Either graduation from secondary school or GED. *Entrance tests:* ACT composite. *For transfer students:* 2.0 minimum GPA on all transfer work.

College credit by examination available. Credit granted for appropriate scores on ACT. Extrainstitutional learning (life experience) credit granted on basis of faculty assessment in BCA program.

Degree Requirements: 125–129 credit hours; 2.0 GPA; 30 credit hours in residence; general education requirements.

Fulfillment of some degree requirements and exemption from some beginning courses possible by passing departmental examinations, College Board CLEP, appropriate ACT scores. *Grading system:* A–F; credit-no credit; withdraw (pass-fail is appended to withdraw after deadline).

Distinctive Educational Programs: Facilities and programs for independent research. Some evening classes. *Other distinctive programs:* degree-granting continuing education; credit and noncredit correspondence courses.

Degrees Conferred: 77 *associate*; 270 *baccalaureate*; 42 *master's*. Bachelor's degrees awarded in top five disciplines: theology 109; liberal arts/general studies 59; education 30; psychology 28; business, management, marketing, and related support services 23,

Fees and Other Expenses: *Full-time tuition per academic year 2008–09:* $10,930. *Books and supplies:* $674. *Room and board per academic year:* $4,900.

Financial Aid: Aid from institutionally generated funds is provided on the basis of academic merit, other criteria.

Financial aid to full-time, first-time undergraduate students: 46% received federal grants averaging $2,886; 31% state/local grants averaging $2,791; 57% institutional grants averaging $2,573; 86% received loans averaging $4,495.

Departments and Teaching Staff: *Total instructional faculty:* 45. Degrees held by full-time faculty: Master's 44%, doctorate 56%. 56% hold terminal degrees.

Enrollment: Total enrollment 1,659.

Characteristics of Student Body: *Ethnic/racial makeup:* Black non-Hispanic: 5%; American Indian or Alaska Native: 2.4%; Asian or Pacific Islander: 1.1%; Hispanic: 16.2%; White non-Hispanic: 73.6%; unknown: .6%.

International Students: 18 nonresident aliens enrolled fall 2008. No programs available to aid students whose native language is not English. No financial aid specifically designated for international students.

Student Life: On-campus residence halls house 48% of student body. Residence halls for males constitute 26% of such space, for females 22%, for both sexes 48%. *Intercollegiate athletics:* male: basketball; female: volleyball. *Special regulations:* Registered cars permitted for all students by registering with the Department of Security. Quiet hours set for each residence hall 9pm to 7am. Visitation from 9am until curfew for each residence hall. *Student publications: Outlook*, a monthly publication; *Southwesterner*, a yearbook; *The Image*, a literary magazine published annually. *Surrounding community:* Dallas is 35 miles north of campus. Love Field and Dallas-Fort Worth International airports are approximately 40 miles from the campus.

Library Collections: 115,000 volumes. 500 government documents; 32,680 microforms; 4,350 audiovisual materials; 632 current periodical subscriptions. Students have access to online information retrieval services and the Internet.

Most important special holdings include William Burton McCafferty Pentecostal Periodical Collection; Pentecostal Authors Collection.

Buildings and Grounds: Campus area 70 acres.

Chief Executive Officer: Dr. Kermit S. Bridges, President.

Address admission inquiries to Director of Admissions.

Southwestern Baptist Theological Seminary

2001 West Seminary Drive
P.O. Box 22000
Fort Worth, Texas 76122
Tel: (817) 923-1921 **E-mail:** admissions@swbts.edu
Fax: (817) 921-8761 **Internet:** www.swbts.edu

Institution Description: Southwestern Baptist Theological Seminary is a private institution affiliated with the Southern Baptist convention. *Enrollment:* 2,588. *Degrees awarded:* First-professional (master of divinity), master's, doctorate. Diplomas also awarded.

Accreditation: *Regional:* SACS-Comm. on Coll. *National:* ATS. *Professional*: music, theology

History: Established as part of Baylor University 1901; adopted present name 1907; chartered, offered first instruction at postsecondary level, and awarded first degrees (baccalaureate and master's) 1908. *See* L. R. Scarborough, *A Modern School of the Prophets* (Nashville, Tenn.: Broadman Press, 1939) and Robert A. Baker, *Tell the Generations Following* (Nashville, Tenn.: Broadman Press, 1983) for further information.

Institutional Structure: *Governing board:* Board of Trustees. Extrainstitutional representation: 37 trustees; institutional representation: 6 administrators, including president of the institution. 37 voting. *Composition of institution:* Administrators 5. Academic affairs headed by vice president for academic affairs and provost. Management/business/finances directed by vice president for business affairs. Full-time instructional faculty 83. Academic governance body, faculty, meets an average of 10 times per year.

Calendar: Semesters. Academic year Aug. to May. Entering students admitted Aug., Jan., May. Degrees conferred and formal commencements May, July, Dec. Summer session May to July.

Characteristics of Freshmen: 83.2% of applicants accepted.

Admission: Rolling admissions plan. Apply no later than 8 weeks before classes begin. *Requirements:* Baccalaureate from accredited college or university; church endorsement; biographical information on spouse. For first-professional students, preseminary curriculum, including biblical and modern classical languages. Additional requirements for some programs. *Entrance tests:* For master of music program GRE. *For transfer students:* From accredited graduate institution 16 hours maximum transfer credit toward music program; transfer credit maximum 33 hours in other master's programs.

Tutoring available. Noncredit remedial courses offered in summer session and regular academic year.

Degree Requirements: *For all first-professional degrees:* 88 semester hours; field education. *For all master's degrees:* 60–66 hours. *For all degrees:* 2.0–3.0 GPA. Additional requirements for some programs.

Exemption from some courses in master's program possible by passing departmental examinations. *Grading system:* A–F; withdraw.

Distinctive Educational Programs: Field education. Flexible meeting places and schedules, including off-campus centers (at Houston, 263 miles from main institution; at San Antonio, 266 miles away; at Shawnee, OK, 300 miles away) and evening classes. Cooperative master of religious education (gerontology concentration) with Baylor University. *Other distinctive programs:* Annual conferences on college missions and church administration. Lay theological studies. Study abroad: Oxford Summer Program, England; Tel Batesh (Timnah) Archaeology Program, Israel.

Degrees Conferred: 74 *baccalaureate*; 297 *master's:* various disciplines; 53 *doctorate:* various disciplines; 197 *first-professional:* theology.

Fees and Other Expenses: *Full-time tuition per academic year 2008–09:* contact the seminary for current tuition, fees, and housing costs.

Financial Aid: Aid from institutionally generated funds is provided on the basis of academic merit, financial need. Institution has a Program Participation Agreement with the U.S. Department of Education for eligible students to receive Pell Grants and, depending upon the agreement, other federal aid.

Departments and Teaching Staff: *Total instructional faculty:* 184. Degrees held by full-time faculty: baccalaureate 100%, master's 100%, first-professional 20%. 90% hold terminal degrees.

Enrollment: Total enrollment 2,588. Undergraduate 384 (full-time 51%; female 37%, male 63%). Graduate 2,264 (full-time 43%). Undergraduate transfer-in students 84.

Characteristics of Student Body: *Ethnic/racial makeup:* Black non-Hispanic: 5%; American Indian or Alaska Native 1%; Asian or Pacific Islander: 5%; Hispanic: 6%; White non-Hispanic: 77%; unknown 1%; nonresident alien 4%.

International Students: 96 nonresident aliens enrolled fall 2008. Programs available to aid students whose native language is not English: social, cultural. Financial aid specifically designated for international students: scholarships available to qualifying students.

Publications: *Southwestern News*, a monthly news magazine; *Southwestern Journal of Theology*, a theological journal published 3 times annually; *Scroll*, a weekly news bulletin for students.

Library Collections: 827,000 volumes. Current serial subscriptions: paper 145; microform 24; via electronic access 19. 3,146 audiovisual materials. Students have access to online information retrieval services and the Internet. Computer work stations available.

Most important holdings include Texas Baptist Historical Collection; World Missions and Evangelism Periodicals Collection; Church Hymnal and Music Collection; papers of Texas Baptist leaders (L.R. Scarborough, B.H. Carroll, George Truett).

Buildings and Grounds: Campus area 200 acres.

Chief Executive Officer: Dr. Paige Patterson, President.

Address admission inquiries to Dr. Thomas White, Director of Admissions.

Southwestern Christian College

200 Bowser Circle
P.O. Box 10
Terrell, Texas 75160-4812
Tel: (972) 524-3341 **E-mail:** admissions@swcc.edu
Fax: (972) 563-7133 **Internet:** www.swcc.edu

Institution Description: Southwestern Christian College is a private liberal arts institution affiliated with the Church of Christ. *Enrollment:* 203. *Degrees awarded:* Associate, baccalaureate.

Accreditation: *Regional:* SACS-Comm. on Coll.

History: Chartered 1949.

Calendar: Academic year Aug. to May.

Characteristics of Freshmen: 100% of applicants accepted. 64% of accepted applicants enrolled.

98% of freshmen expected to graduate within 5 years. 42% of freshmen from Texas. Freshmen from 13 states and 1 foreign country.

Admission: High school graduation or GED; 3 units of English, 12 academic subjects; interview recommended.

Degree Requirements: 124–133 credit hours; general distribution requirements; GPA 2.25.

Degrees Conferred: 31 *associate;* 8 *baccalaureate:* theology/religious vocations.

Fees and Other Expenses: *Full-time tuition per academic year 2008–09:* \$6,185. *Books and supplies:* \$630. *Room and board per academic year:* \$3,813. *Other expenses:* \$1,140.

Financial Aid: Aid from institutionally generated funds is provided on the basis of academic merit, financial need, athletic ability, other criteria.

Financial aid to full-time, first-time undergraduate students: 76% received some form of aid.

Departments and Teaching Staff: *Total instructional faculty:* 18. Degrees held by full-time faculty: doctorate 22%, master's 67%, baccalaureate 11%. 22% hold terminal degrees.

Enrollment: Total enrollment 203. Undergraduate 203 (full-time 96%; female 40%; male 60%).

Characteristics of Student Body: *Ethnic/racial makeup:* Black non-Hispanic: 92%; Hispanic 1%; White non-Hispanic: 1%; nonresident alien 6%.

International Students: 23 nonresident aliens enrolled fall 2008. No programs available to aid students whose native language is not English. No financial aid specifically designated for international students.

Student Life: Campus residence halls available.

Library Collections: 31,000 volumes. 16,800 microforms; 5,000 audiovisual materials; 135 current periodical subscriptions. Students have access to online information retrieval services and the Internet.

Most important special holdings include the Bible and Religious Education Studies; Black Studies Collection.

Buildings and Grounds: Urban campus.

Chief Executive Officer: Dr. Jack Evans, President.

Address admission inquiries to Director of Admissions.

Southwestern University

1001 East University Avenue
Georgetown, Texas 78626
Tel: (512) 863-6511 **E-mail:** admission@southwestern.edu
Fax: (512) 863-5788 **Internet:** www.southwestern.edu

Institution Description: Southwestern University is a private, independent, nonprofit institution affiliated with the United Methodist Church. *Enrollment:* 1,270. *Degrees awarded:* Baccalaureate.

Accreditation: *Regional:* SACS-Comm. on Coll. *Professional*: music

History: Established as Rutersville College, chartered, and offered first instruction at postsecondary level 1840; awarded first degree (baccalaureate) 1844; incorporated charters of Methodist institutions McKenzie and Wesleyan Colleges and Soule University, and changed name to Texas University 1873; adopted present name 1876. *See* William B. Jones, *To Survive and Excel, The Story of Southwestern University 1840–2000,* (Austin, TX.: Jenkins Publishing Company, 2004) for further information.

Institutional Structure: *Governing board:* Board of Trustees. Extrainstitutional representation: 48 trustees; institutional representation: president of the university; 3 alumni. 7 ex officio. All voting. *Composition of institution:* Administrators 7. Academic affairs headed by provost. Management/business/finances directed by vice president for fiscal affairs. Full-time instructional faculty 120. Academic governance body, General Faculty, meets an average of 6 times per year.

Calendar: Semesters. Academic year Aug. to May. Freshmen admitted Aug., Jan., May, June. Degrees conferred and formal commencements May. Summer session of 2 terms May to July.

Characteristics of Freshmen: 1,923 applicatns (female 1,188; male 735). 67% of applicants accepted. 24% of accepted applicants enrolled.

Mean SAT scores 622 verbal, 522 mathematical. Mean ACT Composite score 26.7.

70% of entering freshmen expected to graduate within 5 years. 95% of freshmen from Texas. Freshmen from 33 states and 10 foreign countries.

Admission: Rolling admissions plan. For fall acceptance, apply as early as end of junior year of secondary school but no later than April of year of enrollment. Early Decision Round I, apply by Nov. 1; admission decision by Dec. 1; candidate reply date of Jan. 1. Early Decision Round II, apply by Jan. 1; admis-

SOUTHWESTERN UNIVERSITY—*cont'd*

sion decision by Feb. 1; candidate reply date of March. 1. Regular decision Feb. 15. Early admissions available. *Requirements:* Either graduation from accredited secondary school with 4 years of English, 4 mathematics, 3 social science and/or history; 3 science, 2 foreign language, 1 academic elective. Preference given to students in top 25% of secondary school class. *Entrance tests:* College Board SAT or ACT composite. For foreign students TOEFL score 550. *For transfer students:* 3.0 GPA recommended; from 4-year accredited institution 90 hours maximum transfer credit; from 2-year accredited institution 60 hours.

College credit and advanced placement for postsecondary-level work completed in secondary school. College credit for extrainstitutional learning.

Degree Requirements: 122 credit hours; 2.00 GPA; 60 hours in senior college; last 30 hours in residence; general education requirements, 39 hours; integrative or capstone experience; computer literacy; exit competency examinations (comprehensives in individual fields of study).

Fulfillment of some degree requirements and exemption from some beginning courses possible by passing institutional examinations, College Board CLEP, AP. *Grading system:* A–F; pass-fail; withdraw (carries time limit).

Distinctive Educational Programs: Dual-degree programs in cooperation with professional engineering schools. Interdisciplinary programs include American studies, animal behavior, religious education, international studies, social sciences, University Studies program, feminist's studies, environmental studies, Latin American studies. Facilities and programs for independent research, including honors programs, individual majors, tutorials. Study abroad in London, France, Spain, Japan, Mexico, China and elsewhere through ISEP (International Student Exchange Program).

Degrees Conferred: 305 *baccalaureate*. Bachelor's degrees awarded in top five disciplines: social sciences and history 52; business, management, marketing, and related support services 39; communication, journalism, and related programs 38; visual and performing arts 34; biological/life sciences 31.

Fees and Other Expenses: *Full-time tuition per academic year 2008–09:* $27,940. *Books and supplies:* $1,000. *Room and board per academic year:* $8,380. *Other expenses:* $1,220.

Financial Aid: Aid from institutionally generated funds is provided on the basis of academic merit, financial need, other criteria.

Financial aid to full-time, first-time undergraduate students: 91% received some form of aid. Average amount of aid received: federal grants $3,511; state/local grants $3,593; institutional grants $7,654; loans $5,338.

Departments and Teaching Staff: *Total instructional faculty:* 166. Student/faculty ratio: 10:1. Degrees held by full-time faculty: master's 12%, doctorate 88%. 94% hold terminal degrees.

Enrollment: Total enrollment 1,270. Undergraduate 1,270 (full-time 98%; female 61%, male 39%). Transfer-in student 28.

Characteristics of Student Body: *Ethnic/racial makeup:* Black non-Hispanic: 3%; American Indian or Alaska Native: 1%; Asian or Pacific Islander: 4%; Hispanic: 15%; White non-Hispanic: 75%; unknown: 2%.

International Students: No programs available to aid students whose native language is not English. No financial aid specifically designated for international students.

Student Life: On-campus residence halls and fraternities house 83% of student body. Residence halls for males constitute 29% of such space, for females 27%, co-ed 44%. *Intercollegiate athletics:* male: baseball, basketball, cross-country, golf, soccer, tennis; female: basketball, cross-country, golf, soccer, tennis, volleyball. *Special regulations:* Registered cars with decals permitted. Quiet hours. Residence hall visitation 10am to midnight Sun.–Thurs., 10am to 2am Fri. and Sat. *Special services:* Learning Resources Center, medical services. Academic Support Services using peer counselors trained by learning specialists. Psychologists (2) for personal counseling. Career services, religious life, health services, wellness and leisure, intramurals, student activities, police all staffed by full-time qualified personnel. *Student publications: The Megaphone*, a weekly newspaper; *Southwestern Magazine*, a semiannual literary publication; *Sou'wester*, a yearbook. *Surrounding community:* Georgetown corporate area population 18,000. Austin, 28 miles from the campus, is nearest metropolitan area.

Library Collections: 350,000 volumes including bound books, serial backfiles, electronic documents, and government documents not in separate collections. Online catalog. 57,000 microrms; 12,000 audiovisudal materials; 1,370 periodical subscriptions. Students have access to the Internet at no charge.

Most important special holdings include Ambassador Edward A. Clark Texana Collection; John Goodwin Tower Archives; J. Frank Dobie Collection; Methodist Materials Collection.

Buildings and Grounds: Campus area 75 acres.

Chief Executive Officer: Dr. Jake B. Schrum, President.

Address admission inquiries to Thomas J. Olliver, Vice President for Enrollment Services.

Stephen F. Austin State University

1936 North Street
Box 13051, SFA Station
Nacogdoches, Texas 75962
Tel: (936) 468-2011 **E-mail:** admissions@sfasu.edu
Fax: (936) 468-3849 **Internet:** www.sfasu.edu

Institution Description: Stephen F. Austin State University is a state institution. *Enrollment:* 12,000. *Degrees awarded:* Baccalaureate, master's, doctorate.

Academic offerings subject to approval by statewide coordinating bodies. Budget subject to approval by state governing boards.

Accreditation: *Regional:* SACS-Comm. on Coll. *Professional*: business, forestry, family and consumer science, interior design, music, social work, teacher education

History: Chartered as Stephen F. Austin Teachers College 1921;; offered first instruction at postsecondary level 1923; awarded first degree (baccalaureate) 1924; changed name to Stephen F. Austin College 1948; adopted present name 1969.

Institutional Structure: *Governing board:* Board of Regents. Representation: 9 regents. All voting. *Composition of institution:* academic affairs headed by provost/vice president for academic affairs. Management/business/finances directed by vice president for fiscal affairs. Full-time instructional faculty 434. Academic governance body, Deans Council, meets an average of 24 times per year.

Calendar: Semesters. Academic year Aug. to May. Freshmen admitted Aug., Jan., June, July. Degrees conferred and formal commencements May, Aug., Dec. Summer session June through August.

Characteristics of Freshmen: 7,870 applicants (female 4,851, male 2,959). 75% of applicants admitted. 29% of applicants admitted and enrolled.

81% (1,780 students) submitted SAT scores; 51% (1,127 students) submitted ACT scores. *25th percentile*: SAT Critical Reading 440, SAT Math 450; ACT Composite 18. *75th percentile*: SAT Critical Reading 540; SAT Math 550; ACT Composite 23.

31% of entering freshmen expected to graduate within 5 years. 98% of freshmen from Texas. Freshmen from 45 states and 49 foreign countries.

Admission: Modified rolling admissions plan. For fall acceptance, apply as early as Sept. of senior year of secondary school, but not later than day of registration. Early acceptance available. Consult the university catalog for specific information; general information follows. *Requirements:* Graduation from accredited secondary school. *Entrance tests:* College Board SAT or ACT Composite. For foreign students TOEFL. *For transfer students:* 2.0 minimum GPA; from 4-year accredited institution unlimited hours maximum transfer credit; from 2-year accredited institution 66 hours; correspondence/extension students 12 hours.

Tutoring available.

Degree Requirements: 130 credit hours; 2.0 GPA; 42 semester hours in residence; 4 semester hours physical education; general education requirements.

Exemption from some beginning courses possible by passing departmental examinations, College Board CLEP, AP. *Grading system:* A–F; pass-fail; withdraw (deadline after which pass-fail is appended to withdraw).

Distinctive Educational Programs: Internships. Flexible meeting places and schedules; evening classes. Facilities and programs for independent research, including honors programs, individual majors. *Other distinctive programs:* Online elementary education certification program; online master's degree programs in music education and resource interpretation.

ROTC: Army.

Degrees Conferred: 1,783 *baccalaureate*; 454 *master's*; 16 *doctorate*. Bachelor's degrees awarded in top five disciplines: business, management, marketing, and related support services 396; interdisciplinary studies 264; health professions and related clinical sciences 124; communication, journalism, and related programs 104; visual and performing arts 92. Master's degrees awarded: various disciplines 454. Doctorates awarded: natural resources and environmental studis 1; education 15.

Fees and Other Expenses: *Full-time tuition per academic year 2008–09:* undergraduate resident $48,432, nonresident $14,562; contact the university for current graduate resident/nonresident tuition and applicable fees. *Room and board per academic year:* $7,022. *Books and supplies:* $1,020. *Other expenses:* $4,174.

Financial Aid: Aid from institutionally generated funds is provided on the basis of academic merit, financial need, athletic ability.

Financial aid to full-time, first-time undergraduate students: 71% received some form of aid. Average amount of aid received: federal grants $2,067; Pell grants $1,698; other federal aid $421; state/local grants $2,547; institutional grants $1,379.

Departments and Teaching Staff: *Total instructional faculty:* 667 (full-time 434, part-time 148). Total faculty with doctorate, first-professional, or other terminal degree: 388. Student/faculty ratio: 18:1. Degrees held by full-time faculty: doctorate 70%, master's 100%. 75% hold terminal degrees.

Enrollment: Total enrollment 12,000. Undergraduate 10,476 (full-time 87%; female 60%, male 40%). Graduate 1,524 (full-time 70%). Undergraduate transfer-in students 841.

Characteristics of Student Body: *Ethnic/racial makeup:* Black non-Hispanic: 21%; American Indian or Alaska Native: 15; Asian or Pacific Islander: 1%; Hispanic: 9%; White non-Hispanic: 66%; unknown: 1%; nonresident alien 1%. *Age distribution:* number under 18: 137; 18–19: 3,004; 20–21: 3,010; 22–24: 2,093; 25–29: 692; 30–34: 256; 35–39: 135; 40–49: 197; 50–64: 43; 65 and over: 1.

International Students: 120 nonresident aliens enrolled fall 2008.

Student Life: On-campus residence halls house 35% of student body. Housing available for married students. *Intercollegiate athletics:* male: basketball, cross-country, football, golf, track; female: basketball, cross-country, soccer, softball, tennis, track, volleyball. *Special regulations:* Registered cars permitted in designated areas only. Quiet hours. Residence hall visitation from 2pm to midnight daily. *Special services:* Learning Resources Center, medical services, bus service to and from parking lot and main campus. *Student publications, radio, television: Pine Log,* a biweekly newspaper. Radio station KSAU. TV station SFA. *Surrounding community:* Nacogdoches population 30,000. Houston, 140 miles from campus, is nearest metropolitan area.

Library Collections: 1,805,000 volumes. 240,000 government documents; 852,000 microforms; 24,000 audiovidual materials; 1,540 current periodical subscriptions. Online catalog. Students have access to online information retrieval services and the Internet.

Most important special holdings include Forest History Collection; Crockett Local History; Regional Historical Resource Depository Collection; Congressman Charles Wilson Papers.

Buildings and Grounds: Main campus area 360 acres. Campus DVD available.

Chief Executive Officer: Dr. Baker Pattillo, President.

Address admission inquiries to Moniaque Cossich, Director of Enrollment Management.

College of Liberal Arts

Degree Programs Offered: *Baccalaureate* in English, French, geography, gerontology, history, humanities, political science, psychology, public administration, sociology, Spanish; *master's* in various fields.

College of Applied Arts and Sciences

Degree Programs Offered: *Baccalaureate* in applied studies, criminal justice, general communications, journalism, radio/TV, social work, speech communications; *master's* in various fields.

College of Business

Degree Programs Offered: *Baccalaureate* in accounting, business economics, computer information systems, computer science, economics, finance, general business, international business, management, marketing; *master's* in various fields.

College of Education

Degree Programs Offered: *Baccalaureate* in child development and family living, dance, family and consumer sciences, fashion merchandising, food and nutrition/dietetics,health science, hearing impaired, hospitality administration, interdisciplinary studies (elementary education), interior design, kinesiology, orientation and mobility, rehabilitation services, speech and hearing therapy; *master's* in various fields.

School of Fine Arts

Degree Programs Offered: *Baccalaureate* in art, music, theatre; *master's* in various fields.

School of Forestry

Degree Programs Offered: *Baccalaureate* in agribusiness, agriculture development, agriculture machinery, agronomy, animal science (general), environmental science, forestry, forest management, forest recreation management, forest wildlife management, general agriculture, horticulture, poultry science; *master's* in various fields.

School of Sciences and Mathematics

Degree Programs Offered: *Baccalaureate* in biology, chemistry, geology, mathematics, nursing, physics; *master's* in various fields.

Sul Ross State University

400 North Harrison
Alpine, Texas 79832
Tel: (432) 837-8011 **E-mail:** admissions@sulross.edu
Fax: (432) 837-8431 **Internet:** www.sulross.edu

Institution Description: Sul Ross State University is a state institution. *Enrollment:* 2,772. *Degrees awarded:* Baccalaureate, master's. Certificates also awarded.

Academic offerings subject to approval by statewide coordinating bodies. Budget subject to approval by state governing boards.

Accreditation: *Regional:* SACS-Comm. on Coll.

History: Established as Sul Ross Normal School for Teachers 1917; offered first instruction at postsecondary level 1920; changed name to Sul Ross State Teachers College 1924; awarded first degree (baccalaureate) 1925; changed name to Sul Ross State College 1949; began master's program 1935; adopted present name 1969.

Institutional Structure: *Governing board:* Board of Regents, Texas State University System. Representation: 9 members (appointed by governor of Texas). All voting. *Composition of institution:* Administrators 30. Academic affairs headed by vice president for academic affairs. Management/business/finances directed by vice president for business affairs. Full-time instructional faculty 76. Academic governance body, Academic Policy Council, meets twice monthly.

Calendar: Semesters. Academic year Aug. to May. Freshmen admitted Aug., Jan., June. Degrees conferred May, Aug., Dec. Formal commencement May, Aug., Dec. Summer session of 2 terms from May to Aug.

Characteristics of Freshmen: Mean SAT class scores 429.5 verbal, 229.5 mathematical. Mean ACT Composite score 17.4.

53% of entering freshmen expected to graduate within 5 years. 97% of freshmen from Texas. Freshmen from 18 states and 7 foreign countries.

Admission: Rolling admissions plan. For fall acceptance, apply no later than end of registration period of term of enrollment. *Requirements:* Either graduation from accredited secondary school or GED. *Entrance tests:* College Board SAT or ACT composite. For foreign students TOEFL. *For transfer students:* 2.0 minimum GPA; from 4-year accredited institution 100 credit hours maximum transfer credit; from 2-year accredited institution 66 hours; correspondence/extension students 18 hours.

College credit for USAFI/DANTES and for military service. Tutoring available. Remedial courses offered during regular academic year; nondegree credit given.

Degree Requirements: 130 credit hours; 2.0 GPA; 30 hours including last 24 in residence; 2 hours physical education; distribution requirements.

Fulfillment of some degree requirements and exemption from some beginning courses possible by passing College Board CLEP, other standardized tests. *Grading system:* A–F; withdraw (deadline after which pass-fail is appended to withdraw).

Distinctive Educational Programs: An extensive weekend format graduate courses in education give public school teachers the opportunity to continue their education. The Department of Languages and Literature and Department of Behavioral and Social Sciences offer support courses on the weekend. The Department of Business Administration gives students at the undergraduate and graduate levels extensive experience in international trade with Mexico; white the public administration curriculum is tailored to provide administrators for cities in the border region. Students in range animal science, biology, and geology have one of the best natural laboratories in the world in which to study.

Degrees Conferred: 9 *associate*; 361 *baccalaureate*; 196 *master's*. Bachelor's degrees awarded in top five disciplines: multidisciplinary studies 93; English language/literature 38; security and protective services 33; business, management, marketing, and related support services 30; psychology 22. Master's degrees awarded: various disciplines 196.

Fees and Other Expenses: *Full-time tuition per academic year 2008–09:* undergraduate resident $4,202; contact the university for current resident/nonresident graduate tuition and fees. *Books and supplies:* $1,111. *Room and board per academic year:* $6,190. *Other expenses:* $3,019.

Financial Aid: Aid from institutionally generated funds is provided on the basis of academic merit, financial need, other considerations.

Financial aid to full-time, first-time undergraduate students: 85% received fome form of aid. Average amount of aid received: federal grants $4,230; Pell grants $3,155; other federal aid $1,025; state/local grants $2,948; institutional grants $839.

SUL ROSS STATE UNIVERSITY—*cont'd*

Departments and Teaching Staff: *Total instructional faculty:* 129. Degrees held by full-time faculty: doctorate 68%, master's 27%, baccalaureate 1%, professional 4%. 72% hold terminal degrees.

Enrollment: Total enrollment 2,772. Undergraduate 1,974 (full-time 65%; female 57%, male 43%). Graduate 798 (full-time 24%). Undergraduate transfer-in students 264.

Characteristics of Student Body: *Ethnic/racial makeup:* Black non-Hispanic: 5%; American Indian or Alaska Native: 1%; Asian or Pacific Islander: 1%; Hispanic: 62%; White non-Hispanic: 31%; nonresident alien 1%.

International Students: 28 nonresident aliens enrolled fall 2008. Students from Europe, Asia, Latin America, Canada. No programs available to aid students whose native language is not English. No financial aid specifically designated for international students.

Student Life: On-campus residence halls house 21% of student body. Residence halls for males constitute 25% of such space, for females 14%, for both sexes 39%. University-owned apartments also offer residence space. Housing available for married students. 29% of student body lives on campus. *Intercollegiate athletics:* male: basketball, football, golf, track; female: basketball, track, volleyball; both sexes: tennis. *Special regulations:* Registered cars permitted; parking fee charged. Residence hall visitation from 4pm to 10pm Sun.–Thurs., 4pm to midnight Fri. and Sat. *Special services:* Learning Resources Center, medical services. *Student publications: Brand*, a yearbook; *Sage*, an annual literary magazine; *Skyline*, a weekly newspaper. *Surrounding community:* Alpine population 6,000. El Paso, 200 miles from campus, is nearest metropolitan area.

Library Collections: 311,000 volumes. 483,000 microforms; 14,000 audiovisual materials; 1,210 current periodical subscriptions. Online catalog. Students have access to online information retrieval services and the Internet.

Most important special holdings include archives of the Big Bend (11,724 volumes); curriculum library (1,390 volumes); Sul Ross State University Master's Theses (1,300) volumes; curricular and juvenile collections; Texas State Document Collection.

Buildings and Grounds: Campus area 124 acres.

Chief Executive Officer: R. Victor Morgan, President.

Address admission inquiries to Robert C. Collins, Registrar.

Tarleton State University

1333 West Washington Street
Tarleton Station
Stephenville, Texas 76402-4168
Tel: (254) 968-9125 **E-mail:** uadm@tarleton.edu
Fax: (254) 968-9951 **Internet:** www.tarleton.edu

Institution Description: Tarleton State University is a state institution and land-grant college. The institution is a member of the Texas A&M University system. *Enrollment:* 9,633. *Degrees awarded:* Associate, baccalaureate, master's.

Academic offers subject to approval by statewide coordinating bodies. Budget subject to approval by state governing boards.

Accreditation: *Regional:* SACS-Comm. on Coll. *Professional*: social work, teacher education

History: Chartered as John Tarleton College 1899; offered first instruction at postsecondary level 1906; changed name to John Tarleton Agricultural College 1917; became 4-year college and name to Tarleton State College 1959; awarded first baccalaureate degree 1963; awarded first master's degree 1970; adopted present name 1973; in 1999 opened Tarleton University System Center in Killeen, Texas.

Institutional Structure: *Governing board:* Texas A&M Board of Regents. Representation: 9 members (appointed by governor of Texas). All voting. *Composition of institution:* Administrators 19. Academic affairs headed by vice president for academic affairs. Management/business/finances directed by vice president for business affairs. Full-time instructional faculty 265. Academic governance body, Academic Council, meets an average of 10 times per year.

Calendar: Semesters. Academic year Aug. to Aug. Degrees conferred and formal commencement May, Aug., Dec. Summer session of 2 terms from June to Aug.

Characteristics of Freshmen: 3,545 applicants (female 1,949, male 1,594). 54% of applicatns admitted. 63% of admitted applicants enrolled full-time.

68% (875 students) submitted SAT scores; 62% (795 students) submitted ACT scores. *25th percentile*: SAT Critical Reading 420, SAT Math 440; ACT Composite 18, ACT English 17, ACT Math 18. *75th percentile*: SAT Critical Reading 520, SAT Math 450; ACT Composite 22, ACT English 22, ACT Math 23.

42% of entering freshmen expected to graduate within 6 years. 95% of freshmen from Texas. Freshmen from 46 states and 23 foreign countries.

Admission: Rolling admissions plan. *Requirements:* For in-state residents graduation from secondary school. For out-of-state students and graduates of unaccredited secondary schools evaluation is on individual basis. *Entrance tests:* College Board SAT or ACT. TASP is required before students have completed 15 units of college work. For foreign students TOEFL.

Degree Requirements: 128 credit hours; 2.0 GPA; 30 hours in residence; general education requirements. *Grading system:* A–F.

Distinctive Educational Programs: BS degree program in hydrology, horse production, agriculture education. Bachelor's degree in social work; bachelor of science degree in nursing with RN certification; bachelor's degree in agriculture with various concentrations; cooperative 2-year pre-engineering program with Texas A&M University; bachelor's degree in criminal justice; certification program for holders of non-education bachelor's degree.

ROTC: Army.

Degrees Conferred: 6 *associate*; 1,706 *baccalaureate*; 437 *master's*; 12 *doctorate*. Bachelor's degrees awarded in top five disciplines: business, management, marketing, and related support services 425; agriculture 173; interdisciplinary studies 134; parks and recreation 101; protective services/public administration 87. Master's degrees awarded: various disciplines 437. Doctorates awarded: education 12.

Fees and Other Expenses: *Full-time tuition per academic year 2008–09:* $4,613 resident, $11,351 nonresident; contact the institution for current graduate tuition/fees. *Room and board per academic year:* $6,152. *Books and supplies:* $1,200. *Other expenes:* $3,500.

Financial Aid: Aid from institutionally generated funds is provided on the basis of academic merit, financial need. Institution has a Program Participation Agreement with the U.S. Department of Education for eligible students to receive Pell Grants and, depending upon the agreement, other federal aid.

81% of first-time, full-time undergraduate students received some form of aid. Average amount of aid received: federal grants $3,314; Pell grants $3,700; other federal aid $1,200; state/local grants $4,239; institutional grants $4,277.

Departments and Teaching Staff: *Total instructional faculty:* 528 (full-time 265, part-time 265). Total faculty with doctorate, first-professional, or other terminal degree: 235. Student/faculty ratio: 18:1. Degrees held by full-time faculty: baccalaureate 8%, master's 38%, doctorate 54%. 43% hold terminal degrees.

Enrollment: Total enrollment 9,633. Undergraduate 7,886 (full-time 74%; female 57%, male 43%). Graduate 1,747 (full-time 16%). Undergraduate transfer-in students 1,044.

Characteristics of Student Body: *Ethnic/racial makeup:* Black non-Hispanic: 9%; American Indian or Alaska Native: 1%; Asian or Pacific Islander: 1%; Hispanic: 10%; White non-Hispanic: 78%; nonresident alien 1%. *Age distribution:* number under 18: 41; 18–19: 1,772; 20–21: $685; 22–24: 1,685; 25–29: 758; 30–34: 435; 35–39: 288; 40–49: 408; 50–64: 99; 65 and over: 1.

International Students: 96 nonresident aliens enrolled fall 2008. Students from Europe, Asia, Latin America, Africa, Canada, Australia, Middle East. No programs available to aid students whose native language is not English. No financial aid specifically designated for international students.

Student Life: *Surrounding community:* Stephenville, 67 miles southwest of Fort Worth, has a population of 16,000.

Library Collections: 408,000 volumes. 22,200 government documents; 920,000 microforms; 22,200 audiovisual materials. Current periodical subscriptions: paper 800; microform 34; 18,000 via electronic access. Computer work stations available. Students have access to online information retrieval services and the Internet.

Most important special holdings include Texas and Southwest history; agricultural reports; education; audiovisual materials.

Buildings and Grounds: Campus area 123 acres.

Chief Executive Officer: Dr. Dennis P. McCabe, President.

Undergraduates address admission inquiries to Cindy Hess, Director of Admissions; graduate inquiries to Dr. Linda Jones, Director of Graduate Admissions.

Texas A & M International University

5201 University Boulevard
Laredo, Texas 78041-1900
Tel: (956) 326-2001 **E-mail:** enroll@tamiu.edu
Fax: (956) 326-2249 **Internet:** www.tamiu.edu

Institution Description: Texas A & M International University, formerly Laredo State University, offers four-year and master's degree programs. It has the authority to develop joint degree programs with Mexico and Canada. *Enrollment:* 5,856. *Degrees awarded:* Baccalaureate, master's, doctorate.

Academic offerings subject to approval by statewide coordinating bodies.

Accreditation: *Regional:* SACS-Comm. on Coll. *Professional*: business, nursing

History: Established as Texas A & I University at Laredo 1969; offered first instruction at postsecondary level 1970; awarded first degree (baccalaureate) 1972; became Laredo State University 1977; became part of the Texas A & M System in 1989; adopted present name 1993.

Institutional Structure: *Composition of institution:* Executive Council composed of president, provost, vice president for academic affairs, vice president for finance and administration, associate vice president for student affairs. 3 colleges headed by deans, 1 school of nursing, 12 academic departments report to the deans. Full-time instructional faculty 170.

Calendar: Semesters. Academic year Aug. to May. Entering students admitted Aug., Jan., May, July. Degrees conferred Dec., May, Aug. Formal commencements Dec., May. Summer session of 3 terms from May to Aug.

Characteristics of Freshmen: 2,621 applicants (female 1,450, male 1,171). 63% of applicants admitted. 39% of applicants admitted and enrolled.

76% (803 409 students) submitted SAT scores; 41% (431 students) submitted ACT scores. *25th percentile*: SAT Critical Reading 300, SAT Math 400; ACT Composite 15, ACT English 14, ACT Math 15. *75th percentile*: SAT Critical Reading 500, SAT Math 500; ACT Composite 19, ACT English 20, ACT Math 19.

30.7% of entering freshmen expected to graduate within 5 years. 94.4% of entering class from Texas. Entering students from 1 state and2 foreign countries. 5 foreign countries.

Admission: Rolling admissions plan. *Requirements:* High school transcript with class ranking. *Transfer students:* official transcript. *Graduate:* official transcript with degree posted; transcripts from all colleges attended; GRE or GMAT.

Noncredit developmental courses offered in summer session and regular academic year.

Degree Requirements: *For all undergraduate degrees:* 125–139 credit hours; 2.0 GPA; 24 of last 30 hours in residence; written and oral proficiency examinations in English. *Grading system:* A–F; withdraw (deadline after which pass-fail is appended to withdraw).

Distinctive Educational Programs: *Available to all students:* Flexible meeting places and schedules, including weekend and evening classes. Special facilities for using telecommunications in the classroom. Interdisciplinary programs, including one in international trade. Exchange student program with school in Germany. Other study abroad programs in France and Mexico.

Degrees Conferred: 684 *baccalaureate*; 295 *master's*. Bachelor's degrees awarded in top five disciplines: education 167; business/marketing 149; public administration and social services 70; psychology 44; health professions and related clinical sciences 32. Master's degrees awarded: business/marketing 85; computer and information sciences 36; education 122; English 4; history 1; psychology 2; public administration and social services 22; social sciences 1.

Fees and Other Expenses: *Full-time tuition per academic year 2008–09:* $4,497 resident, $11,241 nonresident; contact the institution for current graduate tuition and applicable fees. *Books and supplies:* $1,300. *Other expenses:* $2,205.

Financial Aid: Aid from institutionally generated funds is provided on the basis of academic merit, financial need.

Financial aid to full-time, first-time undergraduate students: 94% received some form of aid. Average amount of aid received: federal grants $4,044; Pell grants $3,812; other federal aid $910; state/local grants $4,918; institutional grants $2,311.

Departments and Teaching Staff: *Total instructional faculty:* 310 (full-time 170, part-time 140). Total faculty with doctorate, first-professional, or other terminal degree: 136. Student/faculty ratio: 14:1. Degrees held by full-time faculty: 80% hold terminal degrees.

Enrollment: Total enrollment 5,856. Undergraduate 4,794 (full-time 64%; female 62%; male 38%). Graduate 1,062 (full-time 18%). Undergraduate transfer-in students 378.

Characteristics of Student Body: *Ethnic/racial makeup:* Black non-Hispanic: 1%; Hispanic: 93%; White non-Hispanic: 2%; nonresident alien 4%. *Age distribution:* number under 18: 109; 18–19: 804; 20–21: 1731; 22–24: 704; 25–29: 487; 30–34: 258; 35–39: 116; 40–49: 117; 50–64: 21; 65 and over: 3.

International Students: 236 nonresident aliens enrolled fall 2008. Students from Europe, Asia, Latin America, Africa. No financial aid specifically designated for international students.

Student Life: Over 34 student organizations active on campus, 3 with most membership are Student Ambassadors, Association of International Students, and Tau Sigma Chi (criminal justice). *Special services:* New student orientation, academic enrichment center, counseling, health services, international student services, on-campus housing available at University Village. *Student newspaper: The Bridge. Surrounding community:* Laredo population 160,000. San Antonio, 150 miles from campus, is nearest metropolitan area. Served by mass transit bus system; airport 9 miles from campus; passenger rail service less than 1 mile from campus.

Library Collections: 875,500 volumes. 440,000 microf subscriptions. Online catalog. Computer work stations. avail access to online information retrieval services and the Interr

Most important holdings include Laredo and South Texas local histo Texas newspapers; National Criminal Justice Reference Service.

Buildings and Grounds: Campus area 146 acres.

Chief Executive Officer: Dr. Ray M. Keck, III, President.

Address admission inquiries to Rosie Dickinson, Director of Admissions.

Texas A & M University

College Station, Texas 77843-1246

Tel: (979) 845-3741 **E-mail:** admissions@tamu.edu

Fax: (979) 847-8737 **Internet:** www.tamu.edu

Institution Description: Texas A & M University is a state institution. *Enrollment:* 48,039. *Degrees awarded:* Baccalaureate, first-professional (veterinary medicine), master's, doctorate.

Accreditation: *Regional:* SACS-Comm. on Coll. *Professional:* In various fields.

History: Established and offered first instruction at postsecondary level 1876; awarded first degree 1878.

Institutional Structure: *Governing board:* Board of Regents. Representation: 9 members. *Composition of institution:* Academic affairs headed by executive vice president and provost. Management/business/finances directed by vice president for finance and controller. Full-time instructional faculty 1,922.

Calendar: Semesters. Academic year Aug. to May. Summer session of 2 terms from June to Aug.

Characteristics of Freshmen: 20,881 applicants (female 10,245, male 10,642). 70% of applicants admitted. 55% of applicants admitted and enrolled.

78% (6,080 students) submitted SAT scores; 22% (1,705 students) submitted ACT scores. *25th percentile*: SAT Critical Reading 520, SAT Math 550; ACT Composite 23, ACT English 22, ACT Math 23. *75th percentile*: SAT Critical Reading 630, SAT Math 660; ACT Composite 28, ACT English 28, ACT Math 28.

36

4% of entering freshmen expected to graduate within 5 years. 95% of freshmen from Texas. Freshmen from 50 states and 116 foreign countries.

Admission: Rolling admissions plan. For fall and summer acceptance, apply no later than Feb. 15; for spring acceptance, apply by Oct. 15. Early decision and early acceptance available. *Requirements:* Graduation from accredited secondary school with 16 units which must include 4 English, 2 ½ social studies, 2 algebra, 1 geometry, 2 science, 4 ½ electives. *Entrance tests:* SAT or ACT with minimum scores as follows: if applicant's rank in high school graduating class is in the top 10%, no minimum SAT/ACT; in 1st quarter, 1000 SAT/24 ACT; 2nd quarter, 1100/27; 3rd and 4th quarters 1200/29. For foreign students, TOEFL. *For transfer students:* If transferring 30 or less semester hours, must meet freshman admission requirements, 3.0 GPR on all college work attempted and each of the 2 most recent semesters attended; 30–45 semester hours requires 3.0 GPR on all college work attempted and each of the 2 most recent semesters attended; 46–60 semester hours requires 2.5 GPR on all college work attempted and each of the 2 most recent semesters attended; 61 or more and a Texas resident requires 2.0 GPR on all college work attempted and each of the 2 most recent semesters attended; 61 or more and not a Texas resident requires 2.5 GPR on all college work attempted and each of the 2 most recent semesters attended. Applicant's with bachelor's degrees and non-degree seeking applicants must obtain individual approval by Office of Transfer Admissions and appropriate college.

Degree Requirements: *For all undergraduate degrees:* 128 credit hours; 2.0 GPA; 30 of last 36 credits in residence; courses in American history, political science.

Fulfillment of some degree requirements and exemption from some beginning courses possible by passing departmental examinations, College Board CLEP, AP, or superior scores on specified College Board Achievement tests. *Grading system:* A–F; pass; satisfactory-unsatisfactory; withdraw (deadline after which pass-fail is appended to withdraw).

Distinctive Educational Programs: Cooperative education. Texas A & M University offers study abroad programs for academic credit as developed in each college or department. Study abroad in Italy, Mexico, Pacific Asia, France, Spain, Latin America and many other locations. Interdisciplinary programs in education, engineering, agriculture. Honors programs. Corps of Cadets program.

ROTC: Army, Navy, Air Force.

Degrees Conferred: 8,152 *baccalaureate*; 1,930 *master's*; 626 *doctorate*; 125 *first-professional. master's*. Bachelor's degrees awarded in top five disciplines: business, management, marketing, and related support services 1,389; engineering/engineering technologies 1,226; agriculture 991; social sciences

TEXAS A & M UNIVERSITY—*cont'd*

and history 851; biological/life sciences 738. Master's degrees awrded: various disciplines 626. First-professional degrees awarded: veterinary medicine 126.

Fees and Other Expenses: *Tuition and fees per academic year 2008–09:* undergraduate resident $7,844, nonresident $22,184; contact the university for current graduate and first-professional tuition and applicble fees. *Room and board per academic year:* $8,000. *Other expenses:* $2,851.

Financial Aid: Aid from institutionally generated funds is provided on the basis of academic merit, financial need, athletic ability, other criteria.

Financial aid to full-time, first-time undergraduate students: 72% received some form of aid. Average amount of aid received: federal grants $4,000; Pell grants $3,028; other federal aid $1,636; state/local grants $5,001; institutional grants $4,623.

Departments and Teaching Staff: *Total instructional faculty:* 2,320 (full-time 1,922, part-time 398). Total faculty with doctorate, first-professional, or other terminal degree: 1,927. Student/faculty ratio: 20:1. Degrees held by full-time faculty: baccalaureate 4.5%, master's 13.3%, doctorate 74.3%, professional 7.9%. 83.8% hold terminal degrees.

Enrollment: Total enrollment 48,039. Undergraduate 38,430 (full-time 92%; female 48%, male 52%). Graduate 4,609 (full-time 78%). Undergraduate transfer-in students 1,588.

Characteristics of Student Body: *Ethnic/racial makeup:* Black non-Hispanic: 3%; American Indian or Alaska Native: 1%; Asian or Pacific Islander: 5%; Hispanic: 13%; White non-Hispanic: 76%; nonresident alien 2%. *Age distribution:* number under 18: 75; 18–19: 11,087; 20–21: 14,388; 22–24: 8,963; 25–29: 906; 30–34: 178; 35–39: 71; 40–49: 89; 50–64: 21; 65 and over: 4.

International Students: 3,554 nonresident aliens enrolled fall 2008. Students from Europe, Asia, Latin America, Africa, Canada, Australia, New Zealand, Middle East. Programs available to aid students whose native language is not English: social, cultural. English as a Second Language Program. No financial aid specifically designated for international students.

Student Life: On-campus residence halls. Housing available for married students. *Special services:* Medical services, legal services. *Student publications: Aggieland*, a yearbook; *The Battalion*, a daily newspaper. *Surrounding community:* College Station population 59,000. Houston, 90 miles from campus, is nearest metropolitan area. Served by university-operated shuttle bus system.

Library Collections: 3,600,000 volumes including bound books, serial backfiles, electronic documents, and government documents not in separate collections. Online catalog. 3.500,000 microforms; 46,000 audiovisual materials; 46,000 periocicals including via electronic access. Computer work stations available. Students have access to online information retrieval services and the Internet.

Most important special holdings include Science Fiction Research Collection; Jeff Dykes Range Livestock Collection; Ragan Military History Collection; Roger Asselineau Walt Whitman Collection.

Chief Executive Officer: Dr. Robert Gates, President.

Address admission inquiries to Dr. Scott McDonald, Director of Admissions.

Texas A & M University - Baylor College of Dentistry

3302 Gaston Avenue
Dallas, Texas 75246
Tel: (214) 828-8100 **E-mail:** info@bcd.tamhsc.edu
Fax: (214) 828-8496 **Internet:** www.bdc.tamhsc.edu

Institution Description: Texas A & M University - Baylor College of Dentistry is a public institution providing professional study. It also provides upper division study through the Caruth School of Dental Hygiene. All degrees are awarded by Texas A & M University. *Enrollment:* 537. *Degrees awarded:* First-professional (dentistry), baccalaureate (dental hygiene). Programs leading to master's degree awarded by Baylor University. Postgraduate certificates given in endodontics, oral and maxillofacial surgery, orthodontics, pediatric dentistry, periodontics, prosthodontics.

Accreditation: *Regional:* SACS-Comm. on Coll. *Professional*: dental hygiene, dentistry

History: Established as State Dental College, chartered, and offered first instruction at postsecondary level 1905; awarded first degree (first-professional) 1906; became Baylor University College of Dentistry 1918; separated from Baylor University 1971; became the Texas A & M University -Baylor College of Dentistry 1996.

Institutional Structure: Independent campus of the Texas A & M University System. *Governing board:* Board of Regents. President directs full campus. Dean of Dental School directs academic affairs. Business/finances directed by vice-president. Full-time instructional faculty 106. Administrative council is academic governing body and meets monthly.

Calendar: Semesters. Academic year Sept. to May. Entering students admitted Sept. Degrees conferred and formal commencement June. Summer session from June to Aug.

Admission: First-Professional students: rolling admissions plan. For fall acceptance, apply as early as June 1 of previous year. Students are notified of acceptance Dec. *Requirements:* 60 semester hours from accredited college or university which must include 6 hours English, 8 biology, 8 each in organic and inorganic chemistry, 9 physics. Recommend baccalaureate from accredited college or university; courses in foreign language, business management, embryology, mechanical drawing, psychology, reading improvement, sociology. *Entrance tests:* DAT.

Degree Requirements: *For first-professional degrees:* 127 semester hours; 2.0 GPA; prescribed curriculum. *Grading system:* A–F; pass-fail; withdraw; incomplete.

Distinctive Educational Programs: Special facilities for using telecommunications in the classroom. Summer patient treatment clinic. Media resources unit. *Other distinctive programs:* Continuing education for practicing dentists and dental auxiliaries.

Degrees Conferred: 351 *first-professional:* dentistry.

Fees and Other Expenses: *Full-time tuition per academic year 2008–09:* contact the school for current graduate (resident, nonresident) tuition and fees.

Financial Aid: Aid from institutionally generated funds is provided on the basis of financial need. Institution has a Program Participation Agreement with the U.S. Department of Education for eligible students to receive Pell Grants and, depending upon the agreement, other federal aid.

Departments and Teaching Staff: *Total instructional faculty:* 220 (includes 114 part-time faculty). Degrees held by full-time faculty: doctorate 26%, master's 66%, baccalaureate 79%, professional 75%. 93.4% hold terminal degrees.

Enrollment: Total enrollment 537.

International Students: No programs available to aid students whose native language is not English. No financial aid specifically designated for international students.

Student Life: No on-campus housing. *Special regulations:* Cars permitted; parking fee charged. *Surrounding community:* Served by mass transit bus system; airport 10 miles from campus.

Publications: *Baylor Dental Journal* (semiannually) first published 1951.

Library Collections: 32,000 volumes. 2,630 microforms; 285 audiovisual materials; 660 current periodical subscriptions; access to computerized information retrieval systems.

Most important holdings include Ruth and Lyle Sellars Medical Collection: personal collection of early/rare books, particularly in otolaryngology.

Buildings and Grounds: Campus area ½ block.

Chief Executive Officer: Dr. James S. Cole, Dean.

Address admission inquiries to Director of Admissions.

Caruth School of Dental Hygiene

Degree Programs Offered: *Baccalaureate* in dental hygiene.

Admission: 62 semester hours from accredited college or university which must include 12 hours English, 8 hours each biology and chemistry (with laboratory), 6 government, 6 history, 4 physical education, 3 mathematics, 3 psychology, 3 sociology, 3 speech. Dental Hygiene Candidate Admissions Test.

Degree Requirements: 126 semester hours, 2.0 GPA, 6 quarters in residence, prescribed curriculum.

Texas A & M University - Commerce

200 South Neal
P.O. Box 3011
Commerce, Texas 75429-3011
Tel: (903) 886-5081 **E-mail:** admissions@tamu-commerce.edu
Fax: (903) 468-3201 **Internet:** www.tamu-commerce.edu

Institution Description: Texas A & M University - Commerce, formerly known as East Texas State University, is a state institution within the Texas A & M System. *Enrollment:* 8,725.. *Degrees awarded:* Baccalaureate, master's, doctorate.

Academic offers subject to approval by statewide coordinating bodies. Budget subject to approval by state governing boards. Member of the consortium North Texas Area Federation.

Accreditation: *Regional:* SACS-Comm. on Coll. *Professional*: business, music, teacher education

History: Established as East Texas Normal College and offered first instruction at postsecondary level 1889; awarded first degree (baccalaureate) 1891;

chartered as a state institution and changed name to East Texas State Normal College 1917; changed name to East Texas State Teachers College 1923; added graduate level 1935; changed name to East Texas State College 1957; adopted present name in 1996 after joining the Texas A & M System.

Institutional Structure: *Governing board:* Board of Regents of the Texas A & M System. Representation: 9 regents. All voting. *Composition of institution:* Administrators 10. Academic affairs headed by provost and vice president of academic and student affairs. Management/business/finances directed by vice president for business and administration. Full-time instructional faculty 286. Academic governance body, Faculty Senate, meets an average of 4 times per year.

Calendar: Semesters. Academic year Aug. to May. Freshmen admitted Aug., Jan., June. Degrees conferred and formal commencement May, Aug., Dec. Summer session of 2 terms from June to Aug.

Characteristics of Freshmen: 3,072 applicants (female 1,811, male 1,246). 50% of applicants admitted. 54% of applicants admitted and enrolled.

81 (481 students) submitted SAT scores; 72% (428 students) submitted ACT scores. *25th percentile*: SAT Critical Reading 400, SAT Math 410; ACT Composite 16, ACT English 15, ACT math 16. *75th percentile*: SAT Critical Reading 530, SAT Math 540; ACT Composite 22, ACT English 22, ACT Math 22.

22% of entering freshmen expected to graduate within 5 years. 97% of freshmen from Texas. Freshmen from 12 states and 3 foreign countries.

Admission: Rolling admissions plan. Early acceptance available. For fall admission, apply by Aug. 1; spring Jan. 1. *Requirements:* Either graduation from accredited secondary school or GED. *Entrance tests:* College Board SAT or ACT composite (minimum score 20). For foreign students TOEFL. *For transfer students:* 2.0 minimum GPA; maximum transfer credit limited only by residence requirement.

College credit and advanced placement for postsecondary-level work completed in secondary school and for extrainstitutional learning on basis of portfolio and faculty assessments; personal interview.

Tutoring available. Developmental courses offered in summer session and regular academic year; credit given.

Degree Requirements: *For all baccalaureate degrees:* at least 126 credit hours; 2.0 GPA; 30 hours in residence; 4 hours physical education; distribution requirements; exit competency examination in writing. Additional requirements for some programs.

Fulfillment of some degree requirements and exemption from some beginning courses possible by passing College Board CLEP, AP. *Grading system:* A–F; pass-fail.

Distinctive Educational Programs: Work-experience programs. Flexible meeting places and schedules, including off-campus center (at Dallas, 65 miles away from main institution and Mesquite, 50 miles from the campus), and weekend and evening classes. Interdisciplinary programs, including ethnic studies, general studies, Latin American studies. Preprofessional programs, including allied health, engineering. Cross-registration through consortium. New Center for Learning offers individually designed degree plans and emphasizes independent study, team teaching, and experiential learning. International Studies Program. British Studies Program. Study abroad opportunities in Australia, Austria, Ireland, Mexico, New Zealand, Scotland, Spain. *Other distinctive programs:* MBA program offered at the Universities Center of Dallas, and MBA program offered online. For military personnel at Carswell Air Force Base in Fort Worth, degree in industry-technology-business. Speech and hearing center provides student laboratory experience as well as community service. Credit and enrichment continuing education.

Degrees Conferred: 1,280 *baccalaureate*; 948 *master's*; 38 *doctorate*. Bachelor's degrees awarded in top five disciplines: business/marketing 133; English 38; psychology 38; history 24; social sciences 20. Master's degree awarded in top five disciplines: business/marketing 139; education 139; computer and information sciences 13; psychology 14; English 8. Doctorates awarded: education 19; English 3; psychology 16.

Fees and Other Expenses: *Full-time tuition per semester 2008–09:* undergraduate resident $5,130, nonresident $13,580; contact the university for current graduate tuition and applicable fees. *Required fees:* $1,106 (undergraduate). *Room and board per academic year:* $6,540. *Books and supplies:* $1,300. *Other expenses:* $3,140.

Financial Aid: Aid from institutionally generated funds is provided on the basis of financial need.

Financial aid to full-time, first-time undergraduate students: 90% received some form of aid. Average amount of aid received: federal grants $3,943; Pell grants $3,259; other federal aid $1,275; state/local grants $4,294; institutional grants $3,085.

Departments and Teaching Staff: *Total instructional faculty:* 317. *Student/faculty ratio:* 17:1. Degrees held by full-time faculty: doctorate 81%, master's 18%, baccalaureate 1%. 87% hold terminal degrees.

Enrollment: Total enrollment 8,725. Undergraduate 4,913 (full-time 78%; female 635, male 37%). Graduate 3,812 (full-time 25%).

Characteristics of Student Body: *Ethnic/racial makeup:* Black non-Hispanic: 18%; American Indian or Alaska Native: 1%; Asian or Pacific Islander: 2%; Hispanic: 10%; White non-Hispanic: 68%; nonresident alien 1%. *Age distribution:* number under 18: 87; 18–19: 1,065; 20–21: 1,387; 22–24: 1,257; 25–29: 593; 30–34: 349; 35–39: 226; 40–49: 321; 50–64: 96; 65 and over: 3.

International Students: 425 nonresident aliens enrolled fall 2008. No programs available to aid students whose native language is not English. No financial aid specifically designated for international students.

Student Life: 25% of student body live in institutionally controlled residence halls and apartments for married students. *Intercollegiate athletics:* male: basketball, football, golf, track; female: basketball, soccer, track, volleyball. *Special regulations:* Registered cars with parking permits allowed; fee charged. *Special services:* Learning Resources Center, medical services. *Student publications, radio: The East Texan*, a weekly newspaper; *ETSU Special*, a quarterly feature magazine; *Forthcoming*, a quarterly literary magazine. Radio station KETR broadcasts 126 hours per week; affiliated with National Public Radio. *Surrounding community:* Commerce population 10,000. Dallas, 65 miles from campus, is nearest metropolitan area. Served by airport 70 miles from campus.

Library Collections: 1,222,600 volumes including bound books, serial backfiles, electronic documents, and government documents not in separate collections. Online catalog. 7,198 current serial subscriptions include paper, microform, and electronic. 14,240 recordings; 947 compact discs; 1,650 CD-ROMs. Computer work stations available. Students have access to the Internet at no charge.

Most important special holdings include East Texas History; Poetry Society of Texas; Political Archives: Ambassador Fletcher Warren; Congressman Ray Roberts.

Buildings and Grounds: Campus area 140 acres. Campus DVD available.

Chief Executive Officer: Dr. Keith McFarland, President.

Address admission inquiries to Judy Tod Hunter Director of Admissions.

Texas A & M University - Corpus Christi

6300 Ocean Drive
Corpus Christi, Texas 78412-5599
Tel: (361) 825-5700 **E-mail:** admissions@tamucc.edu
Fax: (361) 825-5887 **Internet:** www.tamucc.edu

Institution Description: Texas A & M University - Corpus Christi (formerly Corpus Christi State University) provides lower and upper division study. *Enrollment:* 9,007. *Degrees awarded:* Baccalaureate, master's, doctorate.

Accreditation: *Regional:* SACS-Comm. on Coll. *Professional*: business, music, nursing

History: Chartered as Texas A & I University at Corpus Christi 1971; became Corpus Christi State University 1977; adopted present name 1993.

Institutional Structure: *Composition of institution:* Administrators 11. President, provost, vice presidents for finance and advancement, associate vice president for planning and institutional effectiveness, deans, department chairs, faculty senate. Full-time instructional faculty 216. Academic governance body, Academic Council, meets an average of 9 times per year.

Calendar: Semesters. Academic year Aug. to Aug. Entering students admitted Aug., Jan, June, July. Degrees conferred and formal commencements May, Aug., Dec. Summer session from June to Aug.

Characteristics of Freshmen: 76% of applicants accepted. 37% of accepted applicants enrolled.

Average secondary school rank of freshmen 71st percentile. Mean SAT class scores 497 verbal, 497 mathematical. Mean ACT composite class score 21.

32% of entering freshmen expected to graduate within 5 years. 98% of freshmen from Texas. Freshmen from 20 states and 5 foreign countries.

Admission: Open admissions. Applications are accepted during registration. *Requirements:* 60 semester hours from regionally accredited college or university, 2.0 GPA, and eligible to return to last school attended. *Entrance tests:* For foreign students 550 minimum TOEFL score plus other requirements.

Degree Requirements: *For all undergraduate degrees:* minimum 124 semester hours; 2.0 GPA; 245 of last 30 semester hours in residence; minimum 54 semester hours upper-division credit; general education requirements; maximum 15 semester hours correspondence/extension credit granted (only 6 of 15 may be correspondence). Additional requirements for some programs.

Grading system: A–F; CR; NC; withdraurrent periodical subscriptions.

Most important holdings include Peace Studies collection (with materials dealing with disarmament and the Middle East conflict); International Development collection (relating to social and economic development of Third-World countries); Languages and Linguistics collection (consisting primarily of language instruction methodology materials.)

Buildings and Grounds: Campus area 200 acres.

Chief Executive Officer: Dr. James A. Cramer, President.

TEXAS A & M UNIVERSITY - CORPUS CHRISTI—*cont'd*

Address admission inquiries to Admissions Department.

Texas A & M University - Galveston

200 Sea Wolf Parkway
P.O. Box 1675
Galveston, Texas 77554
Tel: (409) 740-4400 **E-mail:** admissions@tamug.edu
Fax: (409) 740-4709 **Internet:** www.tamug.edu

Institution Description: Texas A & M University at Galveston, is a state-operated, coeducational, marine and maritime institution offering U.S. Coast Guard license option programs. *Enrollment:* 1,672. *Degrees awarded:* Baccalaureate.

Accreditation: *Regional:* SACS-Comm. on Coll. *Professional*: engineering

History: Established as Moody College and offered first instruction at post-secondary level 1971; awarded first degree 1974; changed name to Moody College of Marine Science and Maritime Resources 1975; became Texas A & M University at Galveston 1979; adopted present name 1991. *See* J.C. Calhoun, Jr. and Linda J. Whitson, *Texas A & M University at Galveston—Profile* (College Station: Texas A & M, 1979) for further information.

Institutional Structure: *Composition of institution:* Administrators 9. Academic affairs headed by assistant vice president for academic affairs. Management/business/finances directed by director of operations. Full-time instructional faculty 45. Academic governance body, Academic Council, meets an average of 5 times per year.

Calendar: Semesters. Academic year Sept. to May. Freshmen admitted Sept., Jan., June, July. Degrees conferred and formal commencement May, Aug., Dec.

Characteristics of Freshmen: 1,236 applicants (female 522, male 714). Average secondary school rank of freshmen 75th percentile. Mean SAT class scores 473 verbal, 521 mathematical. Mean ACT Composite class score 24.

25% of freshmen from Texas. Freshmen from 45 states.

Admission: Rolling admissions plan. For fall acceptance, apply as early as Oct. 1 of previous year, but not later than week before start of classes. Apply by end of junior year of secondary school for early decision. Early acceptance available. Early admission. *Requirements:* Graduation from accredited secondary school, acceptable score on SAT or ACT. Marine biology majors must have 2.25 cumulative GPA. *For transfer students:* 2.25 cumulative GPA each of last two semesters; from 4-year accredited institution, maximum transfer credit limited only by residence requirement; from 2-year approximately 2 years of credit accepted; correspondence-extension students 12 credits.

College credit and advanced placement for postsecondary-level work completed in secondary school. Tutoring available. Noncredit developmental courses offered in summer session and regular academic year.

Degree Requirements: 133–151 credit hours; 2.0 GPA; 30 of last 36 hours in residence; for license curricula last 2 years of training in residence in Corps of Cadets; political science and American history course requirements.

Fulfillment of some degree requirements and exemption from some beginning courses possible by passing departmental examinations, College Board CLEP. *Grading system:* A–F; withdraw (deadline after which pass-fail is appended to withdraw).

Distinctive Educational Programs: U.S. Coast Guard license option programs. Work-experience programs. Off-campus centers (at Mitchell Campus on Pelican Island and Fort Crockett campus on Galveston Island). Evening classes. Accelerated degree programs. Facilities and programs for independent research, including honors programs, tutorials, individual majors. Majors include marine biology, marine fisheries, marine science, marine engineering, marine transportation, maritime administration, marine systems engineering. *Other distinctive programs:* Training Ship the T/S TEXAS CLIPPER serves as a floating classroom for the summer training cruise of U.S. maritime cadets and provides laboratory facilities during regular academic year. Summer school at sea for entering freshmen. Naval Reserve Commission program. Coastal Zone Laboratory coordinates research, advisory, and extension activities; operates the Marine Radar Simulator Training Facility.

ROTC: Navy.

Degrees Conferred: 257 *baccalaureate*; 5 *master's*. Bachelor's degrees awarded in top five disciplines: biological/life sciences 64; business, management, marketing, and related support services 64; transportation and movement of materials 34; engineering 23; natural resources/environmental sciences 23. Master's degrees awarded: natural resourece/environmental sciences 5.

Fees and Other Expenses: *Full-time tuition per academic year 2008–09:* resident $6,511, nonresident $13,423. *Books and supplies:* $1,200. *Room and board per academic year:* $5,508. *Other expenses:* $2,160.

Financial Aid: Aid from institutionally generated funds is provided on the basis of academic merit, financial need, other considerations.

Financial aid to full-time, first-time undergraduate students: 50% received some form of aid.

Departments and Teaching Staff: *Total instructional faculty:* 67. Student/faculty ratio: 15:1. Degrees held by full-time faculty: doctorate 64%, master's 24%, baccalaureate 12%, professional 5%.

Enrollment: Total enrollment 1,652. Undergraduate 1,566 (full-time 90%; female 40%, male 60%). Graduate 46 (full-time 9%). Transfer-in students 122.

Characteristics of Student Body: *Ethnic/racial makeup:* Black non-Hispanic: 3%; American Indian or Alaska Native: 1%; Asian or Pacific Islander: 2%; Hispanic: 2%; White non-Hispanic: 80%; unknown: 1%; nonresident alien 1%.

International Students: 18 nonresident aliens enrolled fall 2008. No programs available to aid students whose native language is not English. No financial aid specifically designated for international students.

Student Life: All students are required to live on campus until the residence halls are filled. *Intercollegiate athletics:* Sailing. *Special regulations:* Cars permitted without restriction. *Special services:* Medical services. *Student publications:* *Channel Chatter*, a weekly newspaper; *Sea Spray*, an annual literary magazine; *Voyager*, a yearbook. *Surrounding community:* Galveston population 65,000. Houston, 45 miles from campus, is nearest metropolitan area. Served by airport 4 miles from campus.

Library Collections: 65,000 volumes. 40,000 microforms; 1,200 current periodical subscriptions. Online catalog. Students have access to online information retrieval services and the Internet.

Most important special holdings include marine information.

Buildings and Grounds: Campus area 100 acres. Campus DVD available.

Chief Executive Officer: Dr. R. Bowen Loftin, President.

Address all admission inquiries to Susan Trombley, Director of Admissions.

Texas A & M University - Kingsville

955 University Boulevard
Kingsville, Texas 78363
Tel: (361) 593-2315 **E-mail:** admissions@tamuk.edu
Fax: (361) 593-2195 **Internet:** www.tamuk.edu

Institution Description: Texas A & M University - Kingsville was formerly known as Texas A & I University. *Enrollment:* 7,133. *Degrees awarded:* Baccalaureate, master's, doctorate.

Academic offerings subject to approval by statewide coordinating bodies. Budget subject to approval by state governing boards.

Accreditation: *Regional:* SACS-Comm. on Coll. *Professional*: business, chemistry, music, engineering

History: Chartered as South Texas State Teachers College and offered first instruction at postsecondary level 1925; awarded first degree (baccalaureate) 1926; changed name to Texas College of Arts and Industries 1929; adopted present name 1967; became part of Texas A&M University System 1989.

Institutional Structure: *Composition of institution:* Administrators 39. Academic affairs headed by Provost. Management/business/finances directed by comptroller and chief fiscal officer. Student affairs headed by vice president for student affairs. Full-time instructional faculty 245. Academic governance body, Faculty Senate, meets and average of 10 times per year.

Calendar: Semesters. Academic year Aug. to May. Freshmen admitted Aug., Jan., June. Degrees conferred and formal commencement May, Aug., Dec. Summer session of 2 terms from June to Aug.

Characteristics of Freshmen: 3,297 applicants. 12% of high school graduating class in top 10%; 32% in top quarter; 63% in top half.

35% of entering freshmen expected to graduate within 5 years. 95% of freshmen from Texas. Freshmen from 35 states and 45 foreign countries.

Admission: For fall acceptance, apply as early as April 1 of previous year, but not later than day of registration. *Requirements:* Either graduation from accredited secondary school with recommended 24 units to include 4 English, 3 foreign language, 3 mathematics, 4 social studies, 3 science, 3 academic electives. *Entrance tests:* College Board SAT (minimum combined score of 800) or ACT (minimum composite score of 18); exceptions possible. For foreign students TOEFL. *For transfer students:* minimum GPA 1.5-2.0 according to number of hours transferred; from 4-year accredited institution maximum transfer credit limited only by residence requirement; from 2-year accredited institution 60 hours maximum transfer credit; correspondence/extension students 30 hours.

College credit and advanced placement for postsecondary-level work completed in secondary school. College credit for extrainstitutional learning.

Tutoring available. Developmental courses offered in summer session and regular academic year; credit given.

Degree Requirements: *For all undergraduate degrees:* 128 credit hours; 2.0 GPA; 30 hours in residence; 4 hours physical education for those under 23 years of age; general education requirements.

Fulfillment of some degree requirements and exemption from some beginning courses possible by passing departmental examinations, College Board CLEP, AP. *Grading system:* A–F; withdraw (deadline after which pass-fail is appended to withdraw).

Distinctive Educational Programs: Work-experience programs, including internships, cooperative education. Flexible meeting places and schedules, including off-campus center (in Kingsville), weekend and evening classes. Special facilities for using telecommunications in the classroom. Interdisciplinary studies program. Preprofessional programs in dentistry, medicine, nursing, pharmacy, veterinary medicine. College I freshman program. Facilities for independent research, including honors programs, tutorials.

ROTC: Army.

Degrees Conferred: 916 *baccalaureate*; 514 *master's*; 37 *doctorate*. Bachelor's degrees awarded in top five disciplines: business, management, marketing, and related support services 155; multidisciplinary studies 125; engineering 90; agriculture 57; social sciences 49.

Fees and Other Expenses: *Full-time tuition per academic year 2008–09:* $5,000 resident, nonresident $6,000. *Books and supplies:* $1,100. *Room and board per academic year:* $4,800. *Other expenses:* $2,400.

Financial Aid: Aid from institutionally generated funds is provided on the basis of academic merit, financial need, athletic ability, and other criteria.

Financial aid to full-time, first-time undergraduate students: 82% received some form of aid. Average amount of aid received: federal grants $3,534; Pell grants $3,139; other federal aid $742; state/local grants $3,961; institutional grants $2,385.

Departments and Teaching Staff: *Total instructional faculty:* 311. Student/faculty ratio: 15:1.

Enrollment: Total enrollment 7,133. Undergraduate 5,338 (full-time 71%; female 50%, male 50%). Graduate 1,995 (full-time 45%). Undergraduate transfer-in students 789.

Characteristics of Student Body: *Ethnic/racial makeup:* Black non Hispanic: 5%; Asian or Pacific Islander: 1%; Hispanic: 66%; White non-Hispanic: 25%; nonresident alien 2%.

International Students: 142 nonresident aliens enrolled fall 2008. Students from Europe, Asia, Latin America, Africa, Canada, Australia. Programs available to aid students whose native language is not English: English as a Second Language Program. No financial aid specifically designated for international students.

Student Life: On-campus residence halls house 20% of student body. Residence halls for males constitute 40% of such space, for females 34%, for both sexes 26% Housing available for married students. *Intercollegiate athletics:* male: football, tennis, track. female: tennis, track, volleyball. *Special regulations:* Cars permitted for full-time students. Quiet hours. Residence hall visitation from 6pm to 11:3pm Mon.–Fri.; 2pm to 11:30pm Sat.–Sun. *Special services:* medical services. *Student publications, radio: South Texan*, a weekly newspaper. Radio station KTAI. *Surrounding community:* Kingsville population 29,000. Corpus Christi, 45 miles from campus, is nearest metropolitan area. Served by airport 35 miles from campus.

Library Collections: 360,000 volumes. 194,583 government documents; 3,229 audiovisual materials; 2,304 serial subscriptions (paper, microform, electronic). 200,000 microforms; 3,500 audiovisual materials; 2,400 current periodical subscriptions. Online catalog. Students have access to online information retrieval services and the Internet.

Most important holdings include McGill Collection of Books on Texas and the American West; the Runyon Collection of books and journals on botany.

Buildings and Grounds: Campus area 138 acres.

Chief Executive Officer: Dr. Rumaldo Z. Juarez, President.

Address admission inquiries to Joe Estrada, Director of Admissions.

Texas A & M University - Texarkana

P.O. Box 5518

Texarkana, Texas 75505-0518

Tel: (903) 223-3069 **E-mail:** admission@tamut.edu
Fax: (903) 223-3140 **Internet:** www.tamut.edu

Institution Description: Texas A & M University - Texarkana, formerly known as East Texas State University at Texarkana, offers programs leading to the baccalaureate and master's degrees. *Enrollment:* 1,666. *Degrees awarded:* Baccalaureate, master's. Specialist certificates in education also awarded.

Accreditation: *Regional:* SACS-Comm. on Coll.

History: Established as a branch campus of East Texas State University and chartered 1971; offered first instruction at postsecondary level; became a separate unit of Texas A & M University 1996.

Institutional Structure: *Composition of institution:* Administrators 25. Academic affairs headed by vice president for academic affairs. Management/business/finances directed by vice president for finance and administration. Full-time instructional faculty 31. Academic governance body, Faculty Senate, meets an average of 6 times per year.

Calendar: Semesters. Academic year Aug. to Aug. Entering students admitted Aug., Jan., June, July. Degrees conferred and Formal commencements May, Dec.

Admission: Rolling admissions plan. *Requirements:* high school graduation from an accredited school or GED. 0. *For transfer students:* 2.0 minimum GPA; from 4-year accredited institution; from 2-year accredited institution 75 hours; extension students 30 hours; correspondence students 18 hours.

College credit for postsecondary-level work completed in secondary school. College credit for extrainstitutional learning on basis of portfolio and faculty assessments.

Developmental/remedial courses in composition-grammar offered during regular academic year; credit given.

Degree Requirements: *For undergraduate degrees:* 126 credit hours (varies by program); 2.0 GPA; 30 hours in residence; distribution requirements. Additional requirements for some programs.

Fulfillment of some degree requirements possible by passing College Board CLEP, AP. *Grading system:* A–F; S/U; DP; DF; withdraw.

Distinctive Educational Programs: Flexible meeting places and schedules; evening classes. Special facilities for using telecommunications in the classroom. Interdisciplinary programs, including general studies. Individual majors.

Degrees Conferred: 334 *baccalaureate*; 175 *master's*. Bachelor's degrees awarded in top five disciplines: multidisciplinary studies 78 business, management, marketing, and related support services 112; business/marketing 67; liberal arts/general studies 43; psychology 20; history 15. Master's degrees awarded: business/marketing 149; education 39; English 5; interdisciplinary studies 11; psychology 15.

Fees and Other Expenses: *Full-time tuition per academic year 2008–09:* contacat the university for current information regarding tuition, fees, and housing costs.

Financial Aid: Aid from institutionally generated funds is provided on the basis of academic merit, financial need. Institution has a Program Participation Agreement with the U.S. Department of Education for eligible students to receive Pell Grants and, depending upon the agreement, other federal aid.

Financial aid to full-time, first-time undergraduate students: 75% received some form of aid.

Departments and Teaching Staff: *Total instructional faculty:* 115. Student/faculty ratio: 14:1. Degrees held by full-time faculty: 87% hold terminal degrees.

Enrollment: Total enrollment 1,666. Undergraduate 1,046 (full-time 41%; female 71%, male 29%). Graduate 620 (full-time 8%). Transfer-in students 282.

Characteristics of Student Body: *Ethnic/racial makeup:* Black non-Hispanic: 15%; American Indian or Alaska Native: 1%; Asian or Pacific Islander: 1%; Hispanic 6%; White non-Hispanic: 76%. *Age distribution:* number under 18: 4; 18–19: 20–21: 6; 22–24: 135; 25–29: 200; 30–34: 139; 35–39: 114; 40–49: 149; 50–64: 56; 65 and over: 4.

International Students: No programs available to aid students whose native language is not English. No financial aid specifically designated for international students.

Student Life: No on-campus housing. *Special regulations:* Cars with decals permitted; fee charged. *Special services:* Learning Resources Center. *Surrounding community:* Texarkana population 32,000. Dallas, 177 miles from campus, is nearest metropolitan area. Served by airport 6 miles from campus, passenger rail service 4 miles from campus.

Library Collections: 135,000 volumes. Current serial subscription: paper 945; microform 569; via electronic access 5,047. 27 audio/videotapes; 47 DVD discs; 286 CD-ROMs. Computer work stations available. Students have access to online information retrieval services and the Internet.

Most important special holdings include nursing, education, and business collections.

Buildings and Grounds: Campus area 2 acres.

Chief Executive Officer: Dr. Stephen Hensley, President.

Address admission inquiries to Patrica Black, Director of Admissions and Registrar.

Texas Chiropractic College

5912 Spencer Highway
Pasadena, Texas 77505-1699
Tel: (281) 487-1170 **E-mail:** shughes@txchiro.edu
Fax: (281) 487-0329 **Internet:** www.txchiro.edu

Institution Description: The Texas Chiropractic College is a private, nonprofit institution offering the first-professional degree. *Enrollment:* 569. *Degrees awarded:* First-professional.

Accreditation: *Regional:* SACS-Comm. on Coll. *Professional*: chiropractic education

History: Established in San Antonio, Texas 1908; chartered 1913; adopted present name 1925; moved to Pasadena, Texas 1965.

Institutional Structure: *Governing board:* Board of Regents. Extrainstitutional representation: 25 regents, 1 honorary. *Composition of institution:* Administrators 23. Academic affairs headed by vice president for academic affairs. Business affairs directed by dean of business affairs. Full-time instructional faculty 33.

Calendar: Trimesters. Academic year Sept. to Aug. Students admitted Jan., May, Sept. Degrees conferred Apr. Dec., Aug.

Admission: Modified rolling admissions plan. For acceptance, it is recommended that students apply one year in advance. *Requirements:* minimum 60 semester hours college credit including 6 hours each in English, biology, chemistry, organic chemistry, physics; 3 hours psychology, 15 hours social science/humanities; minimum 2.0 GPA.

Degree Requirements: *For first-professional degree:* completion of professional curriculum; 2.0 GPA.

Distinctive Educational Programs: Clinical internship last 3 trimesters. Clinical preceptorship the last trimester. Continuing and extension education for field doctors and students.

Degrees Conferred: 20 *baccalaureate*: biological/life sciences; 118 *first-professional:* doctor of chiropractic.

Fees and Other Expenses: *Full-time tuition per academic year 2008–09:* contact the college for current information regarding tuition, fees, and other costs.

Financial Aid: Aid from institutionally generated funds is provided on the basis of academic merit, financial need.

Departments and Teaching Staff: *Total instructional faculty:* 43 (full-time 33, part-time 10). Student/faculty ratio: 12:1. Degrees held by full-time faculty: doctorate 29%, professional 71%. 100% hold terminal degrees.

Enrollment: Total enrollment 369.

Characteristics of Student Body: *Ethnic/racial makeup:* Black non-Hispanic: 25%; Asian or Pacific Islander: 8%; Hispanic: 8%; White non-Hispanic: 58%. *Age distribution:* number 18–19: 2; 20–21: 18; 22–24: 14; 25–29: 5; 30–34: 6; 35–39: 8; 40–49: 2.

International Students: No programs available to aid students whose native language is not English. No financial aid specifically designated for international students.

Student Life: No residence halls, but apartments, trailer parks, and homes are nearby. *Athletic and recreation activities:* basketball, softball, and other competitive activities available as warranted by student interest. Swimming facilities for students and families. *Special services:* Chiropractic health services provided for all students; special rates for families. Group health insurance available. *Surrounding community:* Pasadena/Houston metropolitan area population over 4,000,000. Gulf of Mexico 40 miles from campus. No public transportation.

Library Collections: 17,000 volumes. 3,100 microforms; 590 audiovisual materials; 174 serial subscriptions. Computer work stations available. Students have access to online information retrieval services and the Internet.

Most important special holdings include chiropractic collection (rare chiropractic material).

Buildings and Grounds: Campus area 18 acres.

Chief Executive Officer: Dr. Richard G. Brassard, President.

Address admission inquiries to Sandra Hughes, Director of Admissions.

Texas Christian University

2800 South University Drive
Fort Worth, Texas 76129
Tel: (817) 257-7000 **E-mail:** frogmail@tcu.edu
Fax: (817) 257-7490 **Internet:** www.tcu.edu

Institution Description: Texas Christian University is a private institution affiliated with the Christian Church (Disciples of Christ). *Enrollment:* 8,696. *Degrees awarded:* Baccalaureate, first-professional (divinity), master's, doctorate. Certificates in piano and ranch management also awarded.

Member of the consortium The Association for Higher Education of North Texas.

Accreditation: *Regional:* SACS-Comm. on Coll. *Professional*: business, chemistry, computer science, dietetics, engineering, interior design, journalism, music, nurse anesthesia education, nursing, social work, speech-language pathology, theology

History: Established as AddRan Male and Female College and offered first instruction at postsecondary level 1873; incorporated 1874; awarded first degree (baccalaureate) 1876; changed name to AddRan Christian College 1889; adopted present name 1902.

Institutional Structure: *Governing board:* Board of Trustees. Extrainstitutional representation: 46 trustees, *Composition of institution:* Vice Chancellors for Academic Affairs; Finance and Administration; Marketing and Communication; Administrative Services; Student Affairs; and University Advancement. Full-time instructional faculty 478. Academic governance body, University Council, meets an average of 9 times per year.

Calendar: Semesters. Academic year Aug. to May. Freshmen admitted Aug., Jan., June. Degrees conferred Aug., Dec., May. Formal commencement Dec., May. Summer session of 4 terms from May to Aug.

Characteristics of Freshmen: 12,212 applicants (female 7,304, male $4,908). 63% of applicants accepted. 30% of accepted applicants enrolled.

65% (1,067 students) submitted SAT scores; 35% (575 students) submitted ACT scores. *25th percentile*: SAT Critical Reading 530, SAT Math 540; ACT Composite 23. *75th percentile*: SAT Critical Reading 630, SAT Math 640; ACT Composite 28.

68% of entering freshmen expected to graduate within 5 years. 73% of freshmen from Texas. Freshmen from 38 states and 25 foreign countries.

Admission: For fall acceptance, apply as early as end of junior year of secondary school, but not later than beginning of semester. Early acceptance available. *Requirements:* Graduation from accredited secondary school. Recommend 17 units to include 4 units English, 3 mathematics 3 units science (including 1 laboratory science), 3 units social studies, 2 units foreign language, 2 academic electives in fine arts or computer science. *Entrance tests:* College Board SAT or ACT composite. For foreign students TOEFL or demonstrated proficiency in English. *For transfer students:* 2.0 minimum GPA; from 4-year accredited institution maximum transfer credit limited only by residence requirement; from 2-year accredited institution 66 hours.

College credit and advanced placement for postsecondary-level work completed in secondary school. College credit for extrainstitutional learning on basis of portfolio and faculty assessments.

Tutoring available. Noncredit developmental courses offered in summer session and regular academic year.

Degree Requirements: University Core Curriculum Requirement; refer to www.rcore.tcu.edu. for complete information. In addition to the curricular requirements, each candidate for a bachelor's degree is required to successfully complete at least 124 semester hours of credit; earn, under the point system of the university, a cumulative GPA of at least 2.0 in all work attempted at TCU, and earn a cumulative GPA of at least 2.0 in all courses attempted in the department(s) of the major (some major and minor programs may require a GPA greater than 2.0); do residence work in this University earning at least 45 semester hours applicable to the degree program in addition to any number accepted from other schools (the last 45 semester hours for the degree must be taken at TCU except as provided for in the Bachelor of General Studies degree, the combination degree with medicine, dentistry); successfully complete at least 42 of the total hours required for graduation in advanced courses numbered 3000 or above (or the equivalent level at other senior colleges and universities); successfully complete at TCU at least 12 semester hours of advanced work in the field of the major and at least 3 semester hours of advanced work in the field of the minor if the degree plan requires a minor.

Fulfillment of some degree requirements and exemption from some beginning courses possible by passing College Board CLEP, AP. *Grading system:* A–F; pass/fail; withdraw; incomplete; no credit; audit.

Distinctive Educational Programs: Work-experience programs. Evening classes. Accelerated degree programs. Special facilities for using telecommunications in the classroom. Facilities and programs for independent research, including honors programs, individual majors. Institutionally sponsored study abroad in Argentina, Australia, Austria, Belgium, Brazil, Chile, China, Costa Rica, Czech Republic, Dominican Republic, France, Germany, Ghana, Hungary, Indonesia, Italy, Japan, Mexico, The Netherlands, Poland, Russia, Spain, Taiwan, Thailand, United Kingdom, Viet Nam.

ROTC: Army, Air Force.

Degrees Conferred: 1,564 *baccalaureate*; 482 *master's*; 28 *doctorate*. Bachelor's degrees awarded in top five disciplines: business, management, marketing, and related support services 452; communication, journalism, and related programs 228; health professions and related clinical sciences 128; education 111;

social sciences 106. Master's degrees awarded: various disciplines 482. *First-professional:* master of divinity 25.

Fees and Other Expenses: *Full-time tuition per academic year 2008–09:* undergraduate $26,948; contact the university for current graduate and and first-professional school tuition and fees. *Books and supplies*: $880. *Room and board per academic year:* $9,600. *Other expenses:* $1,500.

Financial Aid: Aid from institutionally generated funds is provided on the basis of academic merit, financial need, athletic ability, other criteria.

Financial aid to full-time, first-time undergraduate students: 83% received some form of aid. Average amount of aid received: federal grants $4,830; Pell grants $3,018; other federal aid $2,156; state/local grants $2,342; institutional grants $12,056.

Departments and Teaching Staff: *Total instructional faculty:* 803 (full-time 478, part-time 325). Total faculty with doctorate, first-professional, or other terminal degree: 415.Student/faculty ratio: 14:1. Degrees held by full-time faculty: baccalaureate 0.6%, master's 15.82%, doctorate 83%, professional 0.6%. 95% hold terminal degrees.

Enrollment: Total enrollment 8,696. Undergraduate 7,471. Gradaute 1,225. Transfer-in students 409.

Characteristics of Student Body: *Ethnic/racial makeup:* Black non-Hispanic: 5%; Asian or Pacific Islander: 3%; Hispanic: 8%; White non-Hispanic: 5%; unknown: 4%; nonresident alien 5%.

International Students: 435 nonresident aliens enrolled fall 2008. Students from Europe, Asia, Latin America, Africa, Canada, Australia. Programs available to aid students whose native language is not English: social, cultural, financial. English as a Second Language Program. No financial aid specifically designated for international students.

Student Life: On-campus residence halls house 50% of the undergraduate student body. 37% of males belong to fraternities and 39% of females belong to sororities. *Intercollegiate athletics:* male: baseball, basketball, cross-country, football, golf, soccer, swimming, tennis, track; female: tennis, track, volleyball. Offer athletic scholarships for football, basketball, golf, baseball, swimming, tennis, and track. *Special regulations:* Registered cars permitted in designated areas only. Quiet hours.Residence hall hours vary according to residence hall. *Special services:* Career planning and placement, counseling center, health services, university ministries, legal services. *Student publications, radio: The Daily Skiff*, a newspaper published 4 times a week; *Image*, a magazine published 4 times a year by journalism students; *The TCU Magazine,* published 4 times a year. Radio station KTCU-FM. *Surrounding community:* Fort Worth population approximately 450,000. Served by mass transit bus system; airport 25 miles from campus.

Publications: Texas Christian University Press.

Library Collections: 2,148,000 books, serial backfiles, electronic documents, and government documents (titles). Current serial subscriptions: paper 32,017; microform 642,706. 55,246 audiovisual materials. Online catalog. Students have access to online information retrieval services and the Internet.

Most important special holdings include the Cliburn International Piano Competition Archive; William Luther Lewis Collection; Speaker Jim Wright Collection.

Buildings and Grounds: Campus area 268 acres.

Chief Executive Officer: Dr. Victor J. Boschini, Jr., Chancellor.

Address undergraduate admission inquiries to Raymond A. Brown, Dean of Admissions; graduate inquiries to the Office of the Dean for each tcollege/school of interest.

Texas College

2404 North Grand Avenue
P.O. Box 4500
Tyler, Texas 75712-4500
Tel: (903) 593-8311 **E-mail:** admit@texascollege.edu
Fax: (903) 593-0588 **Internet:** www.texascollege.edu

Institution Description: Texas College is a private, coeducational, independent, nonprofit college affiliated with the Christian Methodist Episcopal Church. *Enrollment:* 807. *Degrees awarded:* Associate, baccalaureate.

Member of the Texas Association of Developing Colleges.

Accreditation: *Regional:* SACS-Comm. on Coll.

History: Established under its present name 1894; offered first instruction at postsecondary level 1895; chartered 1907; awarded first degree (baccalaureate) and changed name to Phillips University 1909; readopted present name 1912.

Institutional Structure: *Governing board:* 27 members at large, 5 elected from five CME Annual Conferences, bishop of Eighth Episcopal District, president of the college, ex-officio. *Composition of institution:* Administrators 11. women. President is chief executive officer assisted by executive vice president and 4 vice presidents for academic affairs, student affairs, business and finance, and development. Full-time instructional faculty 27. Academic governance body, the faculty, meets regularly 9 times per year.

Calendar: Semesters. Academic year Aug. to May. Freshmen admitted Sept., Jan., June. Degrees conferred May. Formal commencement May. Summer session late May to late June.

Characteristics of Freshmen: 61% of freshmen from Texas. Freshmen from 14 states and 3 foreign countries.

Admission: Rolling admissions plan. For fall acceptance, apply as early as one year prior to enrollment, but not later than registration. *Requirements:* Either graduation from accredited secondary school with 4 units language arts, 2 social science, 2 mathematics, 2 science, 6 electives; or GED. Additional requirements for some programs. *Entrance tests:* College Board SAT or ACT composite. For foreign students TOEFL or demonstrated proficiency in English. *For transfer students:* 2.0 minimum GPA; from 4-year accredited institution 94 hours maximum transfer credit; from 2-year accredited institution 60 hours.

Tutoring available. Developmental support program offered.

Degree Requirements: 124–138 credit hours; 2.0 GPA; 25% of total required hours in residence. Additional requirements for some programs.

Grading system: A–F; withdraw (carries time limit).

Distinctive Educational Programs: Facilities and programs for independent research, including individual majors. Personalized Alternatives for Career Experience allows students to work in career setting while studying at Texas College and other institutions. Interdisciplinary Academic Reinforcement.

Degrees Conferred: 105 *baccalaureate*. Bachelor's degrees awarded in top five disciplines: business, management, marketing, and related support services 60; social sciences 11; parks and recreation 9; biological/life sciences 8; computer and information science 6.

Fees and Other Expenses: *Full-time tuition per academic year 2008–09:* $7,920. *Other expenses:* $3,390. *Room and board per academic year:* $4,800. *Books and supplies:* $900.

Financial Aid: Aid from institutionally generated funds is provided on the basis of academic merit, financial need.

Financial aid to full-time, first-time undergraduate students: 83% received federal grants averaging $5,000; 68% state/local grants averaging $3,500; 24% institutional grants averaging $5,000; 65% received loans averaging $2,500.

Departments and Teaching Staff: *Total instructional faculty:* 38. Student/faculty ratio: 8:1. Degrees held by full-time faculty: doctorate 50%, master's 45%. 53% hold terminal degrees.

Enrollment: Total enrollment 807.

Characteristics of Student Body: *Ethnic/racial makeup:* Black non-Hispanic: 97%; American Indian or Alaska Native: 1%; Hispanic: 2%; White non-Hispanic: 1%.

International Students: 5 nonresident aliens enrolled. No programs available to aid students whose native language is not English. No financial aid specifically designated for international students.

Student Life: On-campus residence hall house 60% of student body. Housing available for married students. *Intercollegiate athletics:* male: baseball, basketball; female basketball, volleyball. *Special regulations:* Cars permitted without restrictions. Curfews and quiet hours. *Special services:* Academic Development Center, medical services. *Student publications: The Steer's Horn*, a weekly activities listing. *Surrounding community:* Tyler population 75,000. Dallas, 100 miles from campus, is nearest metropolitan area. Served by mass transit bus system; airport 10 miles from campus.

Library Collections: 75,000 volumes including bound books, serial backfiles, electronic documents, and government documents not in separate collections. Online and card catalogs. Current serial subscriptions: 113 paper, 207 microform. 1,372 recordings; 15 CD-ROMs. Computer work stations available. Students have access to the Internet at no charge.

Most important special holdings include Black Studies; rare books; Church-College history memorabilia.

Buildings and Grounds: Campus area 25 acres.

Chief Executive Officer: Dr. Billy C. Hawkins, President.

Address admission inquiries to Lena J. Carter, Director, Enrollment Services.

Texas Lutheran University

1000 West Court Street
Seguin, Texas 78155-5999
Tel: (830) 372-8000 **E-mail:** admissions@tlu.edu
Fax: (830) 372-8096 **Internet:** www.tlu.edu

Institution Description: Texas Lutheran University is a private institution associated with the Evangelical Lutheran Church in America. *Enrollment:* 1,429. *Degrees awarded:* Baccalaureate.

Accreditation: *Regional:* SACS-Comm. on Coll.

TEXAS LUTHERAN UNIVERSITY—*cont'd*

History: Established and incorporated in Brenham as Evangelical Lutheran school 1891; moved to present location 1912; offered first instruction at postsecondary level 1928; merged with Trinity College of Round Rock and awarded first degree (associate) 1929; became Texas Lutheran College 1932; adopted present name 1996. became senior college 1948; merged with Clifton College 1954. *See* A. G. Wiederaenders, *Coming of Age* (San Antonio: Paul Anderson Co., 1978) and Wiederaenders, *TLC's First Century: An Age of Growing Excellence 1891–1991* (Lubbock: Craftsman Printers Inc., 1990) for further information.

Institutional Structure: *Governing board:* Board of Regents. Extrainstitutional representation: 25 regents; institutional representation: 1 administrator, 1 full-time instructional faculty member, 1 student, 1 alumnus. 15 advisory. 25 voting. *Composition of institution:* Administrators 45. Academic affairs headed by vice president for academic affairs. Management/business/finances directed by vice president for fiscal affairs. Full-time instructional faculty 77. Academic governance body: faculty.

Calendar: Semesters. Academic year Aug. to May. Freshmen admitted Sept., Jan., June, July. Degrees conferred May and Dec. Formal commencement May and Dec. Summer session from May to Aug.

Characteristics of Freshmen: 71% of applicants admitted. 34% of applicants admitted and enrolled.

90% (347 students) submitted SAT scores; 45% (174 students) submitted ACT scores. *25th percentile*: SAT Critical Reading 420, SAT Math 500; ACT Composite 19, ACT English 12, ACT Math 23. *75th percentile*: SAT Critical Reading 540, SAT Math 590; ACT Composite 24, ACT English 20, ACT Math 26.

60% of entering freshmen expected to graduate within 5 years. 96% of freshmen from Texas. Freshmen from 10 and 2 foreign countries.

Admission: Rolling admissions plan. For fall acceptance, apply no later than Aug. 1. Early acceptance available. *Requirements:* Either graduation from accredited secondary school with 21 units which must include 16 academic, or GED. Lowest acceptable secondary school class standing 50th percentile. *Entrance tests:* College Board SAT or ACT composite. *For transfer students:* 2.0 minimum GPA; 68 semester hours maximum transfer credit.

Advanced placement for postsecondary-level work completed in secondary school. College credit for extrainstitutional learning. Tutoring available.

Degree Requirements: *For all baccalaureate degrees:* 124 credit hours; 33 semester hours in residence; 30 semester hours upper division credit. *For all associate degrees:* 64 credit hours; 18 semester hours in residence. *For all undergraduate degrees:* 2.0 GPA; 6 hours theology. *Grading system:* A–F; credit,no credit; withdraw.

Distinctive Educational Programs: Preprofessional courses of study to qualify students to apply for admission to professional programs in dentistry, law, medicine, the ministry, nursing, pharmacy, physical therapy, and veterinary medicine. Strong programs in business administration and teacher education. Facilities and programs for independent research. Honors programs. Individual majors. Study abroad opportunities under ISEP membership in: Japan, Germany, Mexico. World Capitals Program. Semester in Washington (DC). 50 Texas Lutheran scholars selected on basis of academic achievement to design own curricula and participate in cultural enrichment program. Texas Lutheran is a Servicemembers Opportunity College as designated by the Federal Government.

ROTC: Air Force and Army in cooperation with Texas State University.

Degrees Conferred: 2 *associate;* 290 *baccalaureate:* biological sciences 31; business and management 78; communications 14; computer and information sciences 8; education 13l English 13; foreign languages and literature 2; mathematics 5; parks and recreation 31; philosophy/religion 17; psychology 16; social sciences 88; visual and performing arts 20; other 2.

Fees and Other Expenses: *Full-time tuition per academic year 2008–09:* $19,940. *Required fees:* $120. *Room per academic year:* $3,700. *Board per academic year:* $3,060.

Financial Aid: Aid from institutionally generated funds is provided on the basis of academic merit, financial need, other criteria.

Financial aid to full-time, first-time undergraduate students: need-based scholarships/grants totaling $9,530,448, self-help $7,044,477, parent loans $2,313,564, tuition waivers $219,482; non-need-based scholarships/grants totaling $1,929,935, self-help $1,404,819, parent loans $1,104,819, tuition waivers $144,070.

Departments and Teaching Staff: *Total instructional faculty:* 143 (full-time 77, part-time 66). Total faculty with doctorate, first-professional, or other terminal degree: 88. Student/faculty ratio: 14:1. 70% of full-time faculty hold terminal degrees.

Enrollment: Total enrollment 1,429.

Characteristics of Student Body: *Ethnic/racial makeup:* number of Black non-Hispanic: 130; American Indian or Alaska Native: 6; Asian or Pacific Islander: 19; Hispanic: 251; White non-Hispanic: 9,80; unknown: 32. *Age distribution:* number under 18: 23; 18–19: 576; 20–21: 501; 22–24: 203; 25–29: 30; 30–34: 18; 35–39: 13; 40–49: 17; 50–64: 6.

International Students: 11 nonresident aliens enrolled fall 2008. Students from Europe, Asia, Latin America. Programs available to aid students whose native language is not English: social, cultural. English as a Second Language Program. No financial aid specifically designated for international students.

Student Life: On-campus residence halls and apartment complexes house 65% of student body. Residence halls for males constitute 34% of such space, for females only 36%, for both sexes 30%. 35% of student body live off campus. *Intercollegiate athletics:* male: baseball, basketball, football, golf, soccer, tennis; female: basketball, cross-country, softball, tennis, track and field, volleyball. *Special regulations:* Cars with permits allowed in designated areas only. *Special services:* Medical and International Student services. *Student publications: Ethos*, a literary magazine; *Growl*, a yearbook; *Lone Star Lutheran*, a weekly newspaper. *Campus organizations:* 14 honor societies, 12 social and service societies, 28 special interest groups, 9 religious groups. *Surrounding community:* Seguin population 23,000. San Antonio, 32 miles from campus, is nearest metropolitan area; Austin, 60 miles from campus. Served by airport 35 miles from campus; passenger rail service 35 miles from campus.

Library Collections: 172,285 volumes including bound books, serial backfiles, electronic documents, and government documents not in separate collections. Online and card catalogs. Current serial subscriptions: 551 paper; 97 microform; 9,000 via electronic access. 4,302 audio/videotapes; 1,079 CD=ROMs. Computer work stations available. Students have access to the Internet at no charge.

Buildings and Grounds: Campus area 160 acres.

Chief Executive Officer: Dr. Jon Moline, President.

Address admission inquiries Norman Jones, Vice President of Enrollment Services.

Texas Southern University

3100 Cleburne Avenue
Houston, Texas 77004

Tel: (713) 313-7011 **E-mail:** admissions@tsu.edu
Fax: (713) 313-7318 **Internet:** www.tsu.edu

Institution Description: Texas Southern University is a state institution. *Enrollment:* 9,102. *Degrees awarded:* Baccalaureate, first-professional (law, pharmacy), master's, doctorate. Certificates also awarded.

Academic offerings subject to approval by statewide coordinating bodies. Budget subject to approval by state governing boards.

Accreditation: *Regional:* SACS-Comm. on Coll. *Professional*: chemistry, clinical lab scientist, dietetics, engineering, health information administration, industrial technology, law, medical record technology, pharmacy, respiratory therapy, social work, teacher education

History: Established as Texas State University, incorporated, and offered first instruction at postsecondary level 1947; awarded first degree (baccalaureate) 1948; added School of Pharmacy 1949; adopted present name 1951; established School of Business 1955, School of Education 1971; added School of Public Affairs 1974, School of Communication 1975. *See* Ira B. Bryant, *Texas Southern University* (Houston: 1975) for further information.

Institutional Structure: *Governing board:* Board of Regents. Representation: 9 regents, including 1 alumnus; 9 administrators. 9 voting. *Composition of institution:* Administrators 55. Academic affairs headed by president. Management/business/finances directed by vice president, fiscal affairs. Full-time instructional faculty 331. Academic governance body, Faculty Assembly, meets an average of 5 times per year.

Calendar: Semesters. Academic year Sept. to Aug. Freshmen admitted Aug., Jan., June, July. Degrees conferred and formal commencement May, Aug. Summer session from May to Aug.

Characteristics of Freshmen: 6,110 applicants (female 3,613, male 2,491). 92% of applicants accepted. 46% of accepted applicants enrolled. 64% (831 students) submitted SAT scores. 44% (588 students) submitted SAt scores.

96% of freshmen from Texas. Freshmen from 21 states and 8 foreign countries.

Admission: Rolling admissions plan. Apply following graduation from secondary school, but no later than Aug. 8 of year of enrollment. *Requirements:* Either graduation from accredited secondary school or GED. Lowest acceptable secondary school class standing 50th percentile for schools of business and pharmacy. *Entrance tests:* College Board SAT or ACT composite. *For transfer students:* 2.0 minimum GPA, 61 semester hours maximum transfer credit.

Tutoring available. Remedial courses offered in summer session and regular academic year; nondegree credit given.

Degree Requirements: 124–128 semester hours; 2.0 GPA; last 30 hours in residence; 2 credit hours physical education; distribution requirements.

Fulfillment of some degree requirements possible by passing departmental examinations. *Grading system:* A–F; withdraw (carries penalty).

Distinctive Educational Programs: Work-experience programs. Weekend and evening classes. Accelerated degree programs. Dual-degree program in engineering with Rice University. Cooperative baccalaureate programs in medical record administration, medical technology, physical therapy with approved schools. Preprofessional programs in dentistry and medicine. Interdisciplinary program in public affairs. Facilities and programs for independent research, including honors programs, tutorials. *Other distinctive programs:* Weekend college offering degree and certificate programs, professional career training.

ROTC: Army in cooperation with University of Houston.

Degrees Conferred: 807 *baccalaureate*; 212 *master's*; 25 *doctorate*; 307 *first-professional*. Bachelor's degrees awarded in top five disciplines: business, management, marketing, and related support services 106; history 49; biological/life sciences 49; family and consumer science 33; security and protective services 32. 239 Master's degrees awrded: various disciplines 25. *first-professional:* law 186, pharmacy 126.

Fees and Other Expenses: *Full-time tuition per academic year 2008–09:* $6,401 resident, $14,831 nonresident; contact the university vor current graduate and first-professional tuition and fees. *Books and supplies:* $1,228. *Room and board per academic year:* $6,514. *Other expenses:* $3,202.

Financial Aid: Aid from institutionally generated funds is provided on the basis of academic merit, financial need.

Financial aid to full-time, first-time undergraduate students: 92% received some form of aid. Average amount of aid received: federal grants $4,158; Pell grants $3,706; other federal aid $902; state/local grants $3,183; institutional grants $4,258.

Departments and Teaching Staff: *Total instructional faculty:* 331. Student/faculty ratio: 18:1. . Degrees held by full-time faculty: doctorate 46%, master's 17.7%, baccalaureate 2.9%, professional 9%. 55% hold terminal degrees.

Enrollment: Total enrollment 9,102. Undergraduate 7,131 (full-time 81%; female 58%, male 42%). Graduate 1,971 (full-time 61%). Undergraduate transfer-in students 588.

Characteristics of Student Body: *Ethnic/racial makeup:* Black non Hispanic: 90%; Asian or Pacific Islander: 2%; Hispanic: 3%; White 1%; nonresident alien 3%.

International Students: 273 aliens enrolled fall 2008. No programs available to aid students whose native language is not English. No financial aid specifically designated for international students.

Student Life: On-campus residence halls house 15% of student body. Housing available for married students. *Intercollegiate athletics:* male: baseball, basketball, football, golf, soccer, track; female: basketball, track, volleyball; both sexes: tennis. *Special regulations:* Cars with decals permitted; fee charged. Curfews. Quiet hours. Residence hall visitation from 2pm to 11pm Sun.–Thurs., 2pm to 2am Fri. and Sat. *Special services:* Learning Resources Center, medical services, campus transportation system. *Student publications, radio: Herald*, a bimonthly newspaper; a yearbook. Radio station KTSU broadcasts 189 hours per week. *Surrounding community:* Houston metropolitan area population 4 million. Served by mass transit bus system; 2 airports 5 and 30 miles from campus.

Library Collections: 915,000 volumes including bound books, serial backfiles, electronic documents, and government documents not in separate collections. Online and card catalogs. Current serial subscriptions: 1,715 paper, 20 microform. 15,259 recordings; 11 CD-ROMs. Computer work stations available. Students have access to the Internet at no charge.

Most important special collections include Barbara Jordan Archives; Heartman Collection; University Archives.

Buildings and Grounds: Campus area 71 acres.

Chief Executive Officer: Dr. Bobby L. Wilson, President.

Address admission inquiries to Joyce Waddell, Director of Admissions; Graduate School inquiries to Dr. Joseph Jones, Dean; Law School admission inquiries to Edward Rene; Pharmacy School admission inquiries to Dr. Tyrone Felder.

Texas State University - San Marcos

601 University Drive
San Marcos, Texas 78666

Tel: (512) 245-2111 **E-mail:** admissions@txstate.edu
Fax: (512) 245-8044 **Internet:** www.txstate.edu

Institution Description: Texas State University - San Marcos was formerly named Southwest Texas State University. *Enrollment:* 29,105. *Degrees awarded:* Baccalaureate, master's, doctorate.

Accreditation: *Regional:* SACS-Comm. on Coll. *Professional*: athletic training, chemistry, health information administration, health services administration, family and consumer science, interior design, music, physical therapy, public administration, respiratory therapy, social work, speech-language pathology, teacher education

History: Established and chartered as Southwest Texas State Normal School 1889; offered first instruction at postsecondary level 1903; awarded first degree (baccalaureate) 1919; changed name to Southwest Texas State College 1959; achieved university status 1969; changed to present name 2003. *See* Ronald C. Brown, *Beacon on the Hill* (Dallas: Taylor, 1979) for further information.

Institutional Structure: *Governing board:* Board of Regents, Texas State University System. 9 members (appointed by governor of Texas). All voting. *Composition of institution:* Full-time administrator 102 men / 64 women. Academic affairs headed by vice president for academic affairs. Management/business/finances directed by vice president for finance and support services. Full-time instructional faculty 841. Academic governance body, Faculty Senate, meets an average of 10 times per year.

Calendar: Semesters. Academic year Aug. to May. Freshmen admitted Aug., Jan., June July. Degrees conferred and formal commencements May, Aug., Dec. Summer sessions offered.

Characteristics of Freshmen: 11,422 applicants (female 6,710, male 4,712). 73% of applicants admitted. 41% of applicants admitted and enrolled.

76% (2,261 students) submitted SAT scores; 24% (715 students) submitted ACT scores. *25th percentile*: SAT Critical Reading 480, SAT Math 500; ACT Composite 21, ACT English 20, ACT Math 19. *75th percentile*: SAT Critical Reading 570, SAT Math 590; ACT Composite 25. ACT English 25, ACT Math 24.

53% of entering freshmen expected to graduate within 5 years. 98% of freshmen from Texas. Freshmen from 46 states and 51 foreign countries.

Admission: Rolling admissions plan. Early acceptance available. *Requirements:* Either graduation from accredited secondary school or GED if 18 or older. If H.S. rank in top 10%, no minimum SAT or ACT scores; next 15%, 920 SAT or 20 ACT; 2nd quarter, 1010 SAT or 22 ACT; 3rd quarter, 1180 SAT or 26 ACT; 4th quarter, 1270 SAT or 29 ACT; or, completion of 30 credit hours transfer with 2.25 GPA. *Entrance tests:* Either SAT I or ACT accepted. For foreign students TOEFL score of 550. *For transfer students:* 2.25 minimum GPA; from 4-year accredited institution 98 semester hours maximum transfer credit; from 2-year institution 66 hours; correspondence/extension students 30 hours.

College credit and advanced placement for postsecondary-level work completed in secondary school. Tutoring available.

Degree Requirements: *For all baccalaureate degrees:* 128 semester hours which includes a minimum of 49 semester hours of general studies curriculum. *For all undergraduate degrees:* 2.0 GPA; 24 of last 30 hours in residence; distribution requirements; demonstrated proficiency in English. Additional requirements for some programs.

Fulfillment of some degree requirements and exemption from some beginning courses possible by passing departmental examinations, College Board CLEP. *Grading system:* A–F; pass-fail; withdraw (carries time limit, deadline after which fail is appended if student failing at time of withdraw); incomplete (carries time limit).

Distinctive Educational Programs: *For undergraduates:* Professional programs in allied health, engineering, communication disorders, geography and planning, aquatic wildlife and marine biology, speech communication, theatre arts. Honors programs. Study abroad program. Academic Semester Abroad, Short Term Study Abroad, European Internships: England, Germany, Japan, Puerto Rico, Poland, Costa Rica, Spain, Scotland, France, Austria. *Available to all students:* Work-experience program. Weekend and evening classes. Interdisciplinary programs. *Other distinctive programs:* Individualized degree-granting program in occupational education, and applied arts and sciences primarily for adults. Off-campus extension by individual arrangement. Noncredit continuing education. For qualified secondary students, enrollment in courses during summer session (juniors) or regular academic year (seniors).

ROTC: Air Force, Army.

Degrees Conferred: 5,033 *baccalaureate*; 1,163 *master's*; 9 *doctorate*. Bachelor's degrees awarded in top five disciplines: business, management, marketing, and related support services 1,032; interdisciplinary studies 546; social sciences and history 346; visual and performing arts 291; communication, journalism, and related programs 277. Master's degrees awrded: various disciplines 1,163. Doctorates awarded: education 9.

Fees and Other Expenses: *Full-time tuition per academic year 2008–09:* undergraduate resident $5,776, nonresident $12,520; contact the university for current graduate tuition and applicable fees. *Other fees:* $1,512. *Room and board per academic year:* $6,960. *Other expenses:* $3,460.

Financial Aid: The university offers a direct lending program. Aid from institutionally generated funds is provided on the basis of academic merit, financial need.

Financial aid to full-time, first-time undergraduate students: 75% received some form of aid. Average amount of aid received: feeral grants $4,096; Pell grants $2,976; other federal aid $1,000; state/local grants $1,209; institutional grants $3,306.

TEXAS STATE UNIVERSITY - SAN MARCOS—*cont'd*

Departments and Teaching Staff: *Total instructional faculty:* 1,773 (full-time 841, part-time 830). Total faculty with doctorate, first-professional, or other terminal degree: 771. Student/faculty ratio: 21:1. Degrees held by full-time faculty: doctorate 56%, master's 32%, baccalaureate 9%, professional 2%. 59% hold terminal degrees.

Enrollment: Total enrollment 29,105. Undergraduate 24,810 (full-time 81%; female 55%, male 49%). Graduate 4,295 (full-time 44%). Undergraduate transfer-in students 3,190.

Characteristics of Student Body: *Ethnic/racial makeup:* Black non-Hispanic: 3%; American Indian or Alaska Native: 1%; Asian or Pacific Islander: 2%; Hispanic: 23%; White non-Hispanic: 67%; unknown: 1%; nonresident alien 1%. *Age distribution:* number under 18: 25; 18–19: 4,602; 20–21: 6,723; 22–24: 7,062; 25–29: 2,362; 30–34: 767; 35–39: 304; 40–49: 454; 50–64: 120; 65 and over: 3.

International Students: 406 nonresident aliens enrolled fall 2008. Students from Europe, Asia, Latin America, Africa, Canada, Australia, Middle East. Programs available to aid students whose native language is not English: social, cultural. English as a Second Language Program. Financial aid specifically designated for qualifying international students.

Student Life: On-campus residence halls house 20% of student body. 8% of students are affiliated with Greek organizations. *Intercollegiate athletics:* men only: baseball, basketball, cross-country, football, golf, track; women only: basketball, cross-country, soccer, softball, tennis, track, volleyball. *Special regulations:* Cars permitted without restrictions. Quiet hours. *Student publications: University Star*, 4 issues per week newspaper; *Persona*, an annual literary magazine. *Surrounding community:* San Marcos population 25,000. Austin, the capital of Texas, is 32 miles away; San Antonio (TX) is 56 miles from campus. Served by shuttle bus to Austin and San Antonio; airport 35 miles from campus.

Publications: *Hillviews* (general interest magazine published monthly by students); *Persona* (annual literary journal published by the English Department).

Library Collections: 3,700,000 volumes. 1,900,000 microforms; 280,000 audiovisual materials. 11,000 periodicals including via electronic access. Computer work stations available. Students have access to online information retrieval services and the Internet.

Most important special holdings include Southwestern Writers Collection; John Wesley Hardin Collection; T.E. Lawrence Collection.

Buildings and Grounds: Campus area 427 acres. *New*

Chief Executive Officer: Dr. Denise M. Trauth, President.

Undergraduates admission inquiries to Ms. Christy Kangas, Director of Admissions; graduate inquiries to Dr. J. Michael Willoughby, Dean of the Graduate School.

Texas Tech University

P.O. Box 45005
Lubbock, Texas 79409-2005
Tel: (806) 742-2011 **E-mail:** admissions@ttu.edu
Fax: (806) 742-0062 **Internet:** www.ttu.edu

Institution Description: Texas Tech University is a state institution. *Enrollment:* 28,001. *Degrees awarded:* Baccalaureate, first-professional (law), master's, doctorate.

Academic offerings subject to approval by statewide coordinating bodies.

Accreditation: *Regional:* SACS-Comm. on Coll. *Professional*: architecture, art, business, chemistry, computer science, dietetics, engineering, engineering technology, family and consumer science, interior design, journalism, landscape architecture, law, marriage and family therapy, music, psychology internship, social work, teacher education, theatre

History: Established as Texas Technological College 1923; offered first instruction at postsecondary level 1925; awarded first degree (baccalaureate) 1927; adopted present name 1969. *See* Jane G. Rushing and Kline A. Knall, *Evolution of a University: Texas Tech's First Fifty Years* (Austin, TX: Madura Press, 1975) for further information.

Institutional Structure: *Governing board:* Board of Regents, Texas Tech University System. Extrainstitutional representation: 9 members (appointed by governor of Texas). All voting. *Composition of institution:* Administrators 432. Academic affairs headed by vice president for academic affairs. Management/business/finances directed by vice president for administration and finance. Full-time instructional faculty 1,096. Academic governance body, Faculty Senate, meets monthly.

Calendar: Semesters. Academic year Sept. to Aug. Freshmen admitted Aug., Jan., June, July. Degrees conferred May, Aug., Dec. Formal commencement May, Aug., Dec. Summer session of two terms from June to Aug.

Characteristics of Freshmen: 67% of applicants admitted. 44% of applicants admitted and enrolled.

64% (2,339 students) submitted SAT scores; 34% (1,393students) submitted ACT scores. *25th percentile*: SAT Critical Reading 500, SAT Math 520; ACT Composite 21, ACT English 21, ACT Math 20. *75th percentile*: SAT Critical Reading 600, SAT Math 620; ACT Composite 26, ACT English 26, ACT Math 26. 9 National Merit Scholars.

48% of entering freshmen expected to graduate within 5 years. 92% of freshmen from Texas. Freshmen from 24 states and 87 foreign countries.

Admission: Rolling admissions plan. Applications should be on file by Mar. 1 for summer or fall admissions, Nov. 1 for spring admission. Early acceptance available. *Requirements:* graduation from accredited secondary school with 4 units English, 3 mathematics, 2 laboratory science, 2 foreign language. *Entrance tests:* College Board SAT or ACT Composite. *For transfer students:* 2.5 cumulative GPA required for students transferring 12–23 hours; 2.25 required for 24 hours or more. Tutoring available.

Degree Requirements: *For all undergraduate degrees:* minimum 120 semester hours; 2.0 GPA; 2 terms in residence; history and political science courses (under Texas state law); core curriculum requirements.

Fulfillment of some degree requirements and exemption from some beginning courses possible by passing departmental examinations and College Board CLEP, AP. *Grading system:* A, B, C, D, F; P, passing; PR, in progress; I, incomplete; W, withdrawal; WF, withdraw failing; CR, credit; NC, no credit.

Distinctive Educational Programs: Accelerated program; cooperative (work-study) program; cross-registration; distance learning; off-campus educational sites: Abilene, Amarillo, Fredericksburg, Highland Lakes and Junction; double major; dual enrollment; English as a Second Language; exchange student program (domestic); external degree program; honors program; independent study; internships; liberal arts/career combination; student-designed major; study abroad; teacher certification program.

ROTC: Army, Air Force.

Degrees Conferred: 3,918 *baccalaureate*; 1,045 *master's*; 175 *doctorate*. Bachelor's degrees awarded in top five disciplines: business, management, marketing, and related support services 1,214; home economics and vocational home economics 506; engineering and engineering technologies 295; English 216; social sciences and history 209. *First-professional:* law 210.

Fees and Other Expenses: *Full-time tuition per academic year 2008–09:* undergraduate resident $8,459, nonresident $14,430; contact the university for current graduate resident/nonresident tuition. *Room and board per academic year:* $6,900.

Financial Aid: Aid from institutionally generated funds is provided on the basis of academic merit, financial need, athletic ability.

Financial aid to full-time, first-time undergraduate students: need-based scholarships/grants totaling $24,022,596, self-help $27,463,501, parent loans $25,368,497; non-need-based scholarships/grants totaling $8,231,300, self-help $25,651,757, athletic awards $2,845,449. *Graduate aid:* 938 teaching assistantships totaling $11,817,467; 479 research assistantships totaling $5,815,423.

Departments and Teaching Staff: *Total instructional faculty:* 1,111 (full-time 1,087, part-time 84). Total faculty with doctorate, first-professional, or other terminal degree: 980. Student/faculty ratio: 19:1. Degrees held by full-time faculty: baccalaureate 77%, master's 13.89%, doctorate 82.03%, professional 3.31%. 93% hold hold terminal degrees.

Enrollment: Total enrollment 28,325.

Characteristics of Student Body: *Ethnic/racial makeup:* number of Black non-Hispanic: 733; American Indian or Alaska Native: 157; Asian or Pacific Islander: 543; Hispanic: 2,621; White non-Hispanic: 18,965; unknown: 79. *Age distribution:* number under 18: 54; 18–19: 6,725; 20–21: 8,664; 22–24: 6,000; 25–29: 1,135; 30–34: 274; 35–39: 112; 40–49: 116; 50–64: 41; 65 and over: 6; unknown: 2.

International Students: 1,110 nonresident aliens enrolled fall 2008. Students from Europe, Asia, Latin America, Africa, Canada, Australia, New Zealand. Programs available to aid students whose native language is not English: English as a Second Language Program. No financial aid specifically designated for international students.

Student Life: On-campus residence halls house 24% of student body; housing consists of female, male, and co-ed dormitories offering themed floors and halls. Apartments available for single students. *Intercollegiate athletics:* male: baseball, basketball, cross-country, golf, football, tennis; female: basketball, cross-country, golf, soccer, softball, tennis, track and field, volleyball. *Special regulations:* Cars permitted in designated areas only. Dormitory visitation hours set by residents in individual residence halls. *Special services:* Access TECH Disability Support Program; Career Center, High Tech Computer Store; Parent Relations; student government; medical, judicial, legal services; Techniques Center; Ombudsman; bus system. *Student publications, radio, television: La Ventana*, a yearbook; *Texas Tech Law Review*, a quarterly journal; *The Daily Toreador* (newspaper); literary and special interest magazines, published irregularly. Radio station KTXT-FM. TV station KTXT public broadcasting system programming and televised extension courses. *Surrounding community:* Lubbock has a population of approximately 201,000. Dallas, 325 miles from campus, is nearest metropolitan area. Served by mass transit but system, airport 11 miles from campus.

Publications: Texas Tech University Press publishes five journals per year; *William Carlos Williams Review* (two issues per year).

Library Collections: 4,900,000 volumes including bound books, serial backfiles, electronic documents, and government documents not in separate collections. Online catalog. 2,400,000 microforms; 86,000 audiovisual materials; 23,000 serials including via electronic access. Computer work stations available. Students have access to the Internet at no charge.

Most important holdings include the Southwest Collection; Vietnam Conflict Archives; Archive of Turkish Oral Narrative.

Buildings and Grounds: Campus area 1,839 acres.

Chief Executive Officer: Dr. Donald R. harragan, Chancellor.

Address undergraduate admission inquiries to Robvert Shindell, Director Admissions; graduate and first-professional inquires to appropriate school.

College of Agriculture and Natural Sciences

Degree Programs Offered: *Baccalaureate* in agribusiness, agricultural economics, agricultural systems management, agriculture, agricultural communications, horticulture science and management, agronomy management and science, integrated pest management, entomology, animal science, animal production, animal business, food technology, landscape architecture, fisheries management, range management, wildlife and fisheries management, environmental conservation of natural resources, interdisciplinary agriculture.

Distinctive Educational Programs: Laboratory field research and study facilities on campus.

College of Architecture

Degree Programs Offered: *Baccalaureate* in architecture, architecture - design, architecture - structures.

College of Arts and Sciences

Degree Programs Offered: *Baccalaureate* in Latin American and Iberian studies, general studies, design communication, art, studio arts, art history, biology, microbiology, zoology, biochemistry, Russian language and area studies, German, French, Spanish, Latin, communication studies, economics, international economics, geography, English, geoscience, geology, geophysics, recreation and leisure services, exercise and sport sciences, athletic training, school health, history, mathematics, philosophy, physics, political science, psychology, social work, anthropology, sociology, theatre arts, advertising, journalism, news/editorial, broadcast journalism, photo communication, public relations, telecommunications, music, music performance, music theory, music composition.

College of Business Administration

Degree Programs Offered: *Baccalaureate* in general business, petroleum land management, accounting, finance, management information systems, management, marketing.

College of Education

Degree Programs Offered: *Baccalaureate* in multidisciplinary science in biology, chemistry, geoscience, physics; multidisciplinary studies; hearing impairment.

College of Engineering

Degree Programs Offered: *Baccalaureate* in engineering, engineering physics, chemical engineering, civil engineering, environmental engineering, computer science, electrical engineering, textile engineering, engineering technology, construction technology, electrical/electronics technology, mechanical technology, industrial engineering, mechanical engineering, petroleum engineering.

College of Human Sciences

Degree Programs Offered: *Baccalaureate* in early childhood, food and nutrition, restaurant/hotel and institutional management, human development, family studies, interior design, clothing, textiles and merchandising, family financial planning, family and consumer sciences.

School of Law

Degree Programs Offered: *First-professional* law.

Admission: Baccalaureate from an accredited college or university; LSAT.

Degree Requirements: *For first-professional degree:* 90 credit hours, 70 average on scale of 100; 6 semester hours in residence.

Graduate School

Degree Programs Offered: *Master's, doctorate* in agricultural and natural resources, agronomy, anatomy, animal science, biology, business administration, chemical engineering, civil engineering, computer science, consumer economics and environmental design, communications, economics, educational leadership, educational psychology, electrical, engineering, English, family and consumer sciences, education, fine arts, fisheries science, food and nutrition, geosciences, health professions, home economics, mathematics, physical sciences, psychology, public affairs and services, social sciences, interdisciplinary studies. *See* college catalog for a complete listing of graduate school subject offerings.

Admission: Graduate requirements vary with programs and level.

Degree Requirements: Graduate requirements vary.

Departments and Teaching Staff: The faculty are drawn from the other Texas Tech University colleges.

Texas Tech University Health Science Center

3601 4th Street
Lubbock, Texas 79430

Tel: (806) 743-2300 **E-mail:** admissions@ttuhsc.edu
Fax: (806) 743-2307 **Internet:** www.ttuhsc.edu

Institution Description: Texas Tech University Health Science Center is a state institution. *Enrollment:* 2,272. *Degrees awarded:* Baccalaureate, master's, doctorate, first-professional.

Accreditation: *Regional:* SACS-Comm. on Coll. *Professional* clinical lab scientist, medicine, nursing, occupational therapy, pharmacy, physical therapy, speech-language pathology

Institutional Structure: *Governing board:* coordinating board; Board of Regents, president, executive committee.

Calendar: Semesters. Academic year Aug. to May.

Admission: All qualified applicants are carefully evaluated by the appropriate committee with regard to their potential for successfully completing a professional curriculum. *Required:* transcripts, test scores, and other application information constitute the core factors for admission.

Degree Requirements: Completion of prescribed program. *See* college catalog for specifics.

Degrees Conferred: 266 *baccalaureate:* health professions and related sciences 266; 225 *master's:* health professions; 10 *doctorate:* health professions; 208 *first-professional:* medicine.

Fees and Other Expenses: *Full-time tuition per academic year 2008–09:* undergraduate contact the center for current graduate and professional tuition and fees that vary by program. *Room and board per academic year:* $10,500.

Financial Aid: Aid from institutionally generated funds is provided on the basis of academic merit, financial need. Institution has a Program Participation Agreement with the U.S. Department of Education for eligible students to receive Pell Grants and, depending upon the agreement, other federal aid.

Departments and Teaching Staff: *Total instructional faculty:* 527. Degrees held by full-time faculty: doctorate 35.7%, master's 29.3%, baccalaureate 6.2%, professional 28.8%. 53.9% hold terminal degrees.

Enrollment: Total enrollment 2,272.

Characteristics of Student Body: *Ethnic/racial makeup:* Black non-Hispanic: 6%; American Indian or Alaska Native: 76%; Asian or Pacific Islander: 3%; Hispanic: 13%; White non-Hispanic: 76%; unknown: 2%.

International Students: No programs available to aid students whose native language is not English. No financial aid specifically designated for international students.

Library Collections: 238,800 volumes. 13,000 materials. 79,500 audiovisual materials. 21,360 serial subscriptions. Online catalog. Students have access to online information retrieval services and the Internet.

Chief Executive Officer: Dr. M. Roy Wilson, President.

Address admission inquiries to: Medicine: Dr. James Chappell; Allied Health: Rob Shive; Biomedical Sciences: Karen Rolan; Pharmacy: Summer Balcer; Nursing: Exa Jackson.

Texas Wesleyan University

1201 Wesleyan Street
Fort Worth, Texas 76105-1536
Tel: (817) 531-4444 **E-mail:** info@txwesleyan.edu
Fax: (817) 531-4425 **Internet:** www.txwesleyan.edu

Institution Description: Texas Wesleyan University is a private, independent, nonprofit institution affiliated with the United Methodist Church. *Enrollment:* 3,202. *Degrees awarded:* Baccalaureate, master's, juris doctor.

Member of the consortium Association for Higher Education of North Texas.

Accreditation: *Regional:* SACS-Comm. on Coll. *Professional*: law, music, nursing, teacher education

History: Established and chartered as Polytechnic College, a coeducational institution, and offered first instruction at postsecondary level 1891; awarded first degree (baccalaureate) 1892; became Texas Women's College 1914; resumed coeducational status as Texas Wesleyan College. In 1988, the name was changed to Texas Wesleyan University.

Institutional Structure: *Governing board:* Board of Trustees. Extrainstitutional representation: 41 trustees; institutional representation: president of the college. All voting. *Composition of institution:* Academic affairs headed by provost. Business/finances directed by vice president for administration. Full-time instructional faculty 122. Academic governance body, Faculty Assembly, meets an average of 8 times per year.

Calendar: Semesters. Academic year Aug. to May. Freshmen admitted Aug., Jan., June, July. Degrees conferred and formal commencements Dec., May. 2 summer terms. May miniterm.

Characteristics of Freshmen: 1,674 applicants (female 1,113, male 561). 83% of applicants accepted. 44% of accepted applicants enrolled.

Mean SAT score 497 verbal, 492 mathematical. Mean ACT Composite class score 20.

92% of freshmen from Texas. Freshmen from 24states and 21 foreign countries.

Admission: Rolling admissions plan. For fall acceptance, apply as early as one year prior to enrollment, but not later than day of registration. Early acceptance available. *Requirements:* Either graduation from accredited secondary school or GED. Recommend 4 units English, 4 mathematics, 3 social science (including 1 American history), 7 electives. *Entrance tests:* College Board SAT or ACT composite. For international students minimum TOEFL score 550. *For transfer students:* 2.0 minimum GPA; from 4-year accredited institution maximum transfer credit limited only by residence requirement (last 30 hours for degree must be taken at Texas Weselyan).

College credit and advanced placement for postsecondary-level work completed in secondary school. College credit for extrainstitutional learning.

Tutoring available. Remedial courses offered in summer session and regular academic year; credit given.

Degree Requirements: *For all undergraduate degrees:* 124 semester hours; 2.0 GPA; 2 terms in residence; 4 hours physical education courses; distribution requirements; foreign language requirement.

Fulfillment of some degree requirements and exemption from some beginning courses possible by passing departmental examinations, College Board CLEP, AP. *Grading system:* A–F; pass-fail; withdraw (deadline after which pass-fail is appended to withdraw).

Distinctive Educational Programs: *Available to all students:* Evening classes. Special facilities for using telecommunications in the classrooms. Interdepartmental/interdisciplinary programs in business-psychology, environmental sciences, international business. Pre-professional, pre-engineering, sports management programs. *Graduate programs:* education, health science in nurse anesthesia. *Other distinctive programs:* Intensive program in English as a Second Language; Weekend University; master's degree program in distance learning. Study abroad in England, Ireland, Italy, Russia, Thailand.

Degrees Conferred: 263 *baccalaureate*; 161 *master's*. Bachelor's degrees awarded in top five disciplines: business, management, marketing, and related support services 51; interdisciplinary studies 44; social sciences and history 41; education 33; visual and performing arts 21. Master's degrees awarded: various disciplines: 161. Doctorates awarded: education 27. First-professional: law 153.

Fees and Other Expenses: *Full-time tuition per academic year 2008–09:* undergraduate $16,736; contact the university for current graduate and first-professional tuition and fees.. *Required fees:* $1,050. *Room and board per academic year:* $5,650. *Other expenses:* $2,862.

Financial Aid: Aid from institutionally generated funds provided on the basis of academic merit, financial need, athletic ability, other considerations.

Financial aid to full-time, first-time undergraduate students: 56% received some form of aid. Average amount of aid received: federal grants $4,071; Pell grants $3,423; other federal aid $3,135; state/local grants $3,155; institutional grants $4,462.

Departments and Teaching Staff: *Total instructional faculty:* 238. Student/faculty ratio: 15:1. Degrees held by full-time faculty: doctorate 60%, master's 19%, professional 21%. 81% hold terminal degrees.

Enrollment: Total enrollment 3,202. Undergraduate 1,708 (full-time 66%; female 66%, male 34%). Graduate 1,494 (full-time 67%). Undergraduate transfer-in students 283.

Characteristics of Student Body: *Ethnic/racial makeup:* Black non-Hispanic: 18%; American Indian or Alaska Native: 1%; Asian or Pacific Islander: 1%; Hispanic: 19%; White non-Hispanic: 38%; unknown 22%; nonresident alien 2%. *Age distribution:* number under 18: 17; 18–19: 246; 20–21: 290; 22–24: 300; 25–29: 201; 30–34: 232; 35–39: 310; 40–49: 150; 50–64: 49; 65 and over: 1.

International Students: 64 nonresident aliens enrolled fall 2008. Programs available to aid students whose native language is not English: English as a Second Language Program. No financial aid specifically designated for international students.

Student Life: On-campus residence halls house 10% of full-time student body. *Intercollegiate athletics:* male: baseball, basketball, golf, soccer, tennis; female: basketball, volleyball, softball, tennis. *Special regulations:* Registered cars permitted on campus in designated areas only. Residence hall visitation 4on to midnight Mon.–Thurs., 1pm to midnight Fri. Sun. *Special services:* Student Guidance Center, Career Placement Center; disability services, internships, Health Center (nurse on staff, doctor and hospitals immediately available). *Student publications: The Rambler*, a weekly newspaper; *The Ram's Horn*, a yearbook; *Aries*, a literary magazine. *Surrounding community:* Fort Worth population approximately 500,000. Served by international airport 20 miles from campus; passenger rail service 3 miles from campus.

Library Collections: 298,000 volumes including bound books, serial backfiles, electronic documents, and government documents not in separate collections. Online catalog. Current serial subscriptions: 4,157 paper. 853, 389 microform units. 5,804 recordings. Computer work stations available. Students have access to the Internet at no charge.

Most important holdings include Carl Hertzog Collection; William S. Gray Research Collection in Reading.

Buildings and Grounds: Campus area 50 acres.

Chief Executive Officer: Dr. Harold G. Jeffcoat, President.

Address admission inquiries to Dean of Admissions; Law School inquiries to Law School Admission, 1515 Commerce Street, Fort Worth TX 76102-6509.

Texas Woman's University

304 Administration Drive
Denton, Texas 76201
Tel: (940) 898-2000 **E-mail:** admissions@twu.edu
Fax: (940) 898-3198 **Internet:** www.twu.edu

Institution Description: Texas Woman's University is a state institution. *Enrollment:* 12,465. Men are admitted to General Division, Institute Health Sciences, and Graduate School. *Degrees awarded:* Baccalaureate, master's, doctorate.

Academic offerings subject to approval by statewide coordinating bodies. Budget subject to approval by state governing boards. Member of the consortium Federation of North Texas Area Universities.

Accreditation: *Regional:* SACS-Comm. on Coll. *Professional*: dental hygiene, dietetics, health services administration, journalism, librarianship, music, nursing, occupational therapy, physical therapy, psychology internship, social work, speech-language pathology, teacher education

History: Established as Girl's Industrial College 1901; chartered and offered first instruction at postsecondary level 1903; changed name to College of Industrial Arts 1905; awarded first degree (baccalaureate) 1915; began graduate program 1930; changed name to Texas State College for Women 1935; adopted present name 1957. *See* Joyce Thompson, *Marking a Trail* (Denton: Texas Woman's University Press, 1982) for further information.

Institutional Structure: *Governing board:* Board of Regents. Representation: 9 regents. All voting. *Composition of institution:* Administrators 20. Academic affairs headed by provost and vice president for academic affairs. Management/business/finances directed by vice president for finance and administration. Full-time instructional faculty 444. Faculty Senate meets monthly.

Calendar: Semesters. Academic year Aug. to Aug. Freshmen admitted Aug., Jan., June, July. Degrees conferred and formal commencement May, Aug., Dec. Summer session of 2 terms June to Aug.

Characteristics of Freshmen: 3,649 applicants (female 2,829, male 231). 56% of applicants accepted. 53% of accepted applicants enrolled.

Mean SAT scores 467 verbal, 450 mathematical.

93% of freshmen from Texas. Freshmen from 28 states and 26 foreign countries.

Admission: Rolling admissions plan. Apply no later than day of registration. Early acceptance available. *Requirements:* Graduation from accredited secondary school with 22 units which must include 4 English, 3 mathematics (1 algebra), 2 science with 2 labs, 3 social studies, 3 academic electives; or GED. Minimum GPA 2.0. *Entrance tests:* College Board SAT or ACT composite. For foreign students TOEFL. *For transfer students:* 2.0 minimum GPA; from 2-year accredited institution 72 semester hours maximum transfer credit. *For all undergraduates:* TASP.

College credit and advanced placement for postsecondary-level work completed in secondary school and for extrainstitutional learning on basis of faculty assessment.

Tutoring available. Remedial courses offered in summer session and regular academic year; credit given (does not satisfy graduation requirements).

Degree Requirements: 124 credit hours; 2.0 GPA; 30 of last 36 hours in residence; 4 hours physical education; general education requirements. exit competency examinations in writing.

Fulfillment of some degree requirements and exemption from some beginning courses possible by passing departmental examinations, College Board CLEP, AP, other standardized tests. *Grading system:* A–F; withdraw (deadline after which pass-fail is appended to withdraw).

Distinctive Educational Programs: Work-experience programs. Flexible meeting places and schedules, including off-campus centers (2 in Dallas, 40 miles away from main institution and one in Houston), weekend and evening classes. Accelerated degree programs. Cross-registration through consortium. Interdisciplinary programs in criminal justice, ethnic studies, marriage and family counseling, women's studies. Health sciences programs in nursing, occupational therapy, physical therapy, dental hygiene, health care administration, health sciences instruction, medical records administration, medical technology, education of the hearing impaired, speech/language pathology. Facilities and programs for independent research, including honors programs, individual majors, tutorials. Study abroad in Greece and Mexico.

Degrees Conferred: 1,446 *baccalaureate*; 1,390 *master's*; 67 *doctorate*. Bachelor's degrees awarded in top five disciplines: health professions and related clinical sciences 427; multidisciplinary studies 96; business, management, marketing, and related support services 66; visual and performing arts 43; parks and recreation services 43. Master's degrees awarded: various disciplines 1,390. Doctorates awarded: various disciplines 67.

Fees and Other Expenses: *Full-time tuition per academic year 2008–09:* undergraduate resident $6,540, nonresident $14,880; contact the university for current graduate tuition and fees. *Books and supplies:* $960. *Room and board per academic year:* $5,697. *Other expenses:* $2,692.

Financial Aid: Aid from institutionally generated funds is provided on the basis of academic merit, financial need, athletic ability, talent.

Financial aid to full-time, first-time undergraduate students: 81% received some form of aid. Average amount of aid received: federal grants $3,391; Pell grants $3,206; other federal aid $1,047; state/local grants $2,699; institutional grants $2,815.

Departments and Teaching Staff: *Total instructional faculty:* 482. Student/faculty ratio: 12:1. Degrees held by full-time faculty: baccalaureate 3.7%, master's 28.6%, doctorate 62%. 69% hold terminal degrees.

Enrollment: Total enrollment 12,465. Undergraduate 7,420 (full-time 68%; female 93%, male 7%). Graduate 5,045 (full-time 35%). Undergraduate transfer-in students 1,068.

Characteristics of Student Body: *Ethnic/racial makeup:* Black non-Hispanic: 21%; American Indian or Alaska Native:1%; Asian or Pacific Islander: 8%; Hispanic: 18%; White non-Hispanic: 51%; nonresident alien 2%.

International Students: 249 nonresident aliens enrolled fall 2008. Students from Europe, Asia, Latin America, Africa, Canada, Australia, New Zealand. No programs available to aid students whose native language is not English. No financial aid specifically designated for international students.

Student Life: On-campus residence halls house 12% of student body. Residence halls for females constitute 27% of such space, for both sexes 68%, and for family housing 5%. *Intercollegiate athletics:* female: basketball, gymnastics, softball, tennis, volleyball. *Special regulations:* Registered cars permitted without restrictions. Quiet hours. Residence hall visitation 6pm to 11:15pm Mon.–Thurs.; 3pm to 12:45am Fri.; 10am to 12:45am Sat.; 10am to 11:15pm Sun. *Special services:* Learning Resources Center, Child Development Center, Student Health Services, Disability Support Services. *Student publications: Lass-O*, a daily newspaper. *Surrounding community:* Denton population 72,000.

Publications: TWU Library, *Finder's Guide to the Texas Women: A Celebration of History Exhibit Archives*, 1984.

Library Collections: 725,000 volumes. 1,514,002 microforms. 2,687 periodicals. 400 computer work stations available throughout the campus. Online catalog. Students have access to the Internet at no charge.

Most important special holdings include Woman's Collection (includes books, periodicals, manuscripts); Women's Air Force Service Pilot Archives; Nursing Collection.

Buildings and Grounds: Denton campus area 270 acres.

Chief Executive Officer: Dr. Ann Stuart, President and Chancellor.

Undergraduates address admission inquiries to Emma N. Nieto, Director of Admissions; graduate admission inquiries to Coordinator of Graduate Admissions.

Trinity University

One Trinity Place
San Antonio, Texas 78213-7200
Tel: (210) 999-7011 **E-mail:** admissions@trinity.edu
Fax: (210) 999-8164 **Internet:** www.trinity.edu

Institution Description: Trinity University is a private, independent, nonprofit institution. *Enrollment:* 2,703. *Degrees awarded:* Baccalaureate, master's.

Accreditation: *Regional:* SACS-Comm. on Coll. *Professional*: engineering, health services administration, teacher education

History: Established and chartered in Tehuacana and offered first instruction at postsecondary level 1869; awarded first degree (baccalaureate) 1871; moved to Waxahachie 1902; moved to San Antonio and absorbed University of San Antonio 1942, moved to present location 1952. *See* Donald Everett, *Trinity University: Record of One Hundred Years* (San Antonio: Trinity University Press, 1968) and R. Douglas Brackenridge, *Trinity University: A Tale of Three Cities* (San Antonio: Trinity University Press, 2005) for further information.

Institutional Structure: *Governing board:* Board of Trustees. Extrainstitutional representation: 36 trustees. *Composition of institution:* Administrators 36. Academic affairs headed by vice president for academic affairs. Management/business/finances directed by vice president for fiscal affairs. Full-time instructional faculty 219. Academic governance body, Faculty Senate, meets an average of 12 times per year.

Calendar: Semesters. Academic year Aug. to May. Freshmen admitted Aug., Jan., June. Degrees conferred and formal commencements May, Aug., Dec.

Characteristics of Freshmen: 3,754 applicants. 60% of applicants admitted. 16% of applicants admitted and enrolled.

77% (483 students) submitted SAT scores; 23% (146 students) submitted ACT scores. *25th percentile*: SAT Critical Reading 600, SAT Math 600; ACT Composite 27, ACT English 26, ACT Math 26. *75th percentile*: SAT Critical Reading 690, SAT Math 690; ACT Composite 31; ACT English 31; ACT Math 30.

69% of entering freshmen expected to graduate within 5 years. 45% of freshmen from Texas.

Admission: For fall acceptance, apply as early as Sept. of previous year, but not later than July 25. Apply by Nov. 1 for early decision; Dec. 15 for early action; Feb 1 for regular decision. *Requirements:* 4 secondary school units in English, 2 in a foreign language, 3 mathematics, 2 laboratory sciences, and 2 social studies; or GED. 3 additional units recommended. Minimum 2.5 GPA except in rare cases. *Entrance tests:* College Board SAT or ACT composite. *For transfer students:* From 4-year accredited institution 2.0 minimum GPA, 64 hours maximum transfer credit; from 2-year accredited institution 2.5 minimum GPA, 64 hours maximum transfer credit.

College credit and advanced placement for postsecondary-level work completed in secondary school.

Degree Requirements: *For all baccalaureate degrees:* 124 credit hours; 2.0 GPA; final 2 terms in residence; basic competence in English; 42 hours in general education courses. For engineering degree, 131 credit hours.

Distinctive Educational Programs: *For undergraduates:* Honors programs. Individually arranged study abroad in Europe, Asia, England. *For graduate students:* External degree programs in health care administration with on-the-job study at various U.S. hospitals. *Available to all students:* Evening classes. Facilities and programs for independent research.

ROTC: Air Force.

Degrees Conferred: 544 *baccalaureate*; 105 *master's*. Bachelor's degrees awarded in top five disciplines: social sciences and history 156; business, management, marketing, and related support services 151; foreign languages and literature 55; biological/life sciences 48; communication, journalism, and related programs 43. Master's degrees awarded: various disciplines 105.

Fees and Other Expenses: *Full-time tuition per academic year 2008–09:* $26,834. *Books and supplies:* $950. *Room and board per academic year:* $9,687. *Other expenses:* $950.

Financial Aid: Aid from institutionally generated funds is provided on the basis of academic merit, financial need. Institution has a Program Participation Agreement with the U.S. Department of Education for eligible students to receive Pell Grants and, depending upon the agreement, other federal aid.

TRINITY UNIVERSITY—*cont'd*

89% of first-time, full-time undergraduate students received some form of aid. Average amount of aid received: federal grants $6,155; Pell grants $2,887; other federal aid $3,468; state/local grants $3,491; insitutional grants $11,823.

Departments and Teaching Staff: *Full-time instructional faculty:* 280 (full-time 219, part-time 61). Total faculty with doctorate, first-professional, or other terminal degree: 214. Student/faculty ratio: 10:1.

Enrollment: Total enrollment 2,703. Undergraduate 2,489.

Characteristics of Student Body: *Ethnic/racial makeup:* Black non-Hispanic: 4%; American Indian or Alaska Native: 1%; Asian or Pacific Islander: 11%; Hispanic: 4%; White non-Hispanic: 60%; unknown: 11%; nonresident alien 6%.

International Students: 135 nonresident aliens enrolled fall 2008. No programs available to aid students whose native language is not English. No financial aid specifically designated for international students.

Student Life: On-campus residence halls house 47% of student body. Residence halls for males constitute 44% of such space, for females 45%, for both sexes 8% 3% of student body lives on campus in university-owned apartments. *Intercollegiate athletics:* male: baseball, basketball, cross-country, football, golf, soccer, swimming/diving, tennis, track and field; female: basketball, cross-county, golf, soccer, softball, swimming/diving, tennis, track and field, volleyball. *Special regulations:* Registered cars permitted on campus in designated areas only. Quiet hours 24 hours a day. Residence hall visitation from noon to midnight Sun.–Thurs. and noon to 2am Fri. and Sat. *Special services:* Medical services. *Student publications, radio: Mirage*, a yearbook; *Trinitonian*, a weekly newspaper; *Trinity Review*, a biannual literary magazine. Radio station KRTU(FM) broadcasts 18 hours a day. *Surrounding community:* San Antonio metropolitan area population 1,100,000. Served by mass transit bus system; airport 5 miles from campus; passenger rail service 5 miles from campus.

Library Collections: 928,000 volumes. 302,000 microforms; 27,000 audiovisual materials; 198,000 government documents; 2,735 serial subscriptions. Online catalog. Computer work stations available. Students have access to the Internet and online information retrieval services.

Buildings and Grounds: Campus area 107 acres.

Chief Executive Officer: Dr. John R. Brazil, President.

Address admission inquiries to Christopher Elbertson, Dean of Admissions.

University of Dallas

1845 East Northgate Drive
Irving, Texas 75062-4799
Tel: (972) 721-5000 **E-mail:** ugadmis@udallas.edu
Fax: (972) 721-5109 **Internet:** www.udallas.edu

Institution Description: University of Dallas is a private institution affiliated with the Roman Catholic Church. *Enrollment:* 2,977. *Degrees awarded:* Baccalaureate, master's, doctorate.

Accreditation: *Regional:* SACS-Comm. on Coll.

History: Established 1955; offered first instruction at postsecondary level 1956; awarded first degree (baccalaureate) 1960.

Institutional Structure: *Governing board:* Board of Trustees of the University of Dallas. Extrainstitutional representation: 36 trustees; institutional representation: 1 administrator ex officio. All voting. *Composition of institution:* Administrators 13. Academic affairs headed by dean of individual college. Management/business/finances directed by vice president for finance and administration. Full-time instructional faculty 120. Academic governance body, Faculty Senate, meets monthly.

Calendar: Semesters. Academic year Aug. to May. Freshmen admitted Aug., Jan. Degrees conferred May, Aug., Dec. formal commencement May. Summer session from early June to mid-Aug. Interterm and Mayterm.

Characteristics of Freshmen: 1,060 applicatns (female 613, male 447). 85% of applicants admitted. 42% of applicants admitted and enrolled.

89% (280 students) submitted SAT scores; 43% (134 students) submitted ACT scores. *25th percentile*: SAT Critical Reading 560, SAT Math 540; ACT Composite 24, ACT English 23, ACT Math 23. *75th percentile*: SAT Critical Reading 690, SAT Math 650; ACT Composite 29, ACT English 27, ACT Math 32.

65% of freshmen expected to graduate within 5 years. 51% of freshmen from Texas. Freshmen from 36 states and 3 foreign countries.

Admission: Rolling admissions plan. For fall acceptance, submit application by Feb. 15 of year of enrollment. Apply by Dec. 1 for early action. Early acceptance available. *Requirements:* Graduation from secondary school or home school program. Recommend 4 units in English, 3 foreign language, 4 mathematics, 4 science, 3 social studies, 2 history, 1 elective. *Entrance tests:* College Board SAT or ACT composite. For foreign students TOEFL; minimum 550 score. *For transfer students:* 2.5 minimum GPA; from 2-year accredited institution 60 credit hours maximum transfer credit.

College credit and advanced placement for postsecondary-level work completed in secondary school.

Degree Requirements: 120 credit hours; 2.0 GPA; 38 credit hours upper level courses in residence; core curriculum requirements, including foreign language requirement. Successful completion of a comprehensive examination in the major field of study.

Fulfillment of some degree requirements and exemption from some beginning courses possible by passing College Board AP. *Grading system:* A–F; pass-fail (up to 4 credits); withdraw (carries penalty, time limit).

Distinctive Educational Programs: Special facilities for using telecommunications in the classroom. Preprofessional program in architecture, engineering, law, medicine, dentistry, physical therapy, allied health sciences, teacher education, and priesthood. 5-year plan for degree/MBA; philosophy degree/MBA; psychology degree/MPA or MPsy. The university has developed a core curriculum based on the "great books" and specifically includes and in-depth study of Western civilization. Facilities and programs for independent research, including honors programs, individual majors. Study abroad program; students with sophomore standing spend one semester at the university's campus in Rome, Italy. The Constantin Scholars Programs (interdisciplinary curriculum) and The Classics Major (language and literature of Greek and Latin classics).

ROTC: Air Force in cooperation with University of North Texas; Army with the University of Texas at Arlington.

Degrees Conferred: 227 *baccalaureate*; 504 *master's*; 2 *doctorate*. Bachelor's degrees awarded in top five disciplines: English 48; biological/live sciences 22; business/marketing 22; history 22; social sciences 19; Master's degrees awarded in top five disciplines: business/marketing 470; English 16; theology and religious vocations 15; liberal arts/general studies 13; philosophy and religious studies 5. Doctorates awarded: social sciences 2.

Fees and Other Expenses: *Full-time tuition per academic year 2008–09:* undergraduate $24,770; graduate charged per per credit hour (contact the university for current rate). *Other fees:* $1,025. *Room and board per academic year:* $7,885. *Books and supplies:* $1,700. *Other expenses:* $3,600.

Financial Aid: Aid from institutionally generated funds is provided on the basis of academic merit, financial need.

Financial aid to full-time, first-time undergraduate students: 97% received some form of aid. Average amount of aid received: federal grants $3,307; Pell grants $2,985; other federal aid $941; state/local grants $3,406; institutional grants $12,000.

Departments and Teaching Staff: *Total instructional faculty:* 233 (full-time 120, par-time 113). Total faculty with doctorate, first-professional, or other terminal degree: 136. Student/faculty ratio: 10:1. Degrees held by full-time faculty: doctorate 59%, master's 40%, baccalaureate 1%. 90% hold terminal degrees.

Enrollment: Total enrollment 2,977. Undergraduate 1,249 (full-time 97%; female 52%, male 48%). Graduate 1,678 (full-time 23%). Undergraduate transfer-in students 55.

Characteristics of Student Body: *Ethnic/racial makeup:* Black non-Hispanic: 16%; Asian or Pacific Islander: 5%; Hispanic: 16%; White non-Hispanic: 68%; unknown: 7%; nonresident alien 2% *Age distribution:* number under 18: 20; 18–19: 476; 20–21: 439; 22–24: 113; 25–29: 86; 30–34: 12; 35–39: 10; 40–49: 27; 50–64: 26; 65 and over: 5.

International Students: 60 nonresident aliens enrolled fall 2008. Students from Europe, Asia, Latin America, Africa, Canada. Programs available to aid students whose native language is not English: English as a Second Language Program. No financial aid specifically designated for international students.

Student Life: 61% of the undergraduate student body live in college-owned housing on the Irving campus. *Intercollegiate athletics:* male: baseball, basketball, cross-country, soccer, track; female: basketball, cross-country, lacrosse, soccer, softball, tennis, track, volleyball. *Special services:* Medical services, minibus service to shopping centers, cultural events. All students have a personal e-mail address and Internet access. An introductory program for freshmen into the Dallas environment. Campus mass offered on campus twice daily, one Sunday vigil mass, and three times on Sunday. Arrangements are made for students of other faiths to attend church services in the city of Irving. *Student publications: University News*, weekly campus newspaper; *Crusader* (annual yearbook); *The Constantin Review* (annual review of undergraduate works edited by Phi Beta Kappa members); *Rostrum* (biannual publication edited by students that features university-wide original works of fiction and poetry). *Surrounding community:* Irving, population 192,000, is located in Dallas-Fort Worth metropolitan area. Served by airport 12 miles from campus.

Publications: *Publisher:* University press.

Library Collections: 234,000 volumes including bound books, serial backfiles, electronic documents, and government documents not in separate collections. Online catalog. 76,000 microforms; 1,650 audiovisual materials; 580 current serial subscriptions. Computer work stations available. Students have access to the Internet at no charge.

Most important special holdings include Wilmoore Kendall Collection.

Buildings and Grounds: Campus area 750 acres. Campus DVD available.

Chief Executive Officer: Dr. Frank M. Lazarus, President.

Address undergraduate admission inquiries to Sr. Mary Brian Bole, Dean of Admissions; Graduate School of Liberal Arts inquiries to Assistant Dean of Enrollment Management.

University of Houston - Clear Lake

2700 Bay Area Boulevard
Houston, Texas 77058-1098
Tel: (281) 283-7600 **E-mail:** admissions@cl.uh.edu
Fax: (281) 283-2530 **Internet:** www.cl.uh.edu

Institution Description: University of Houston - Clear Lake provides upper division baccalaureate and graduate study only. *Enrollment:* 7,853. *Degrees awarded:* Baccalaureate, master's. Certificates also awarded.

Accreditation: *Regional:* SACS-Comm. on Coll. *Professional*: accounting, business, health services administration, teacher education

History: Chartered 1971; offered first instruction at postsecondary level 1974.

Institutional Structure: *Composition of institution:* Administrators 49. Academic affairs headed by provost and vice president for academic affairs. Management/business/finances directed by vice president for administration and finance. Full-time instructional faculty 191.

Calendar: Semesters. Academic year Aug. to May. Entering students admitted Aug., Jan., June. Formal commencements May, Dec. Summer session of 6 terms.

Admission: Rolling admissions plan. *Requirements:* Associate degree or 54 semester hours from accredited college or university with minimum grade of C. College algebra required. Good standing at institution previously attended. *Entrance tests:* For foreign students TOEFL (minimum score 550). Texas Academic Skills Program test must be passed by residents before admission.

Degree Requirements: *For undergraduate degrees:* 123 hours; minimum grade of C or better or at least 30 hours of resident upper level work; final 30 hours (and 12 hours in field of concentration) in residence.

Fulfillment of some degree requirements possible by passing College Board CLEP. *Grading system:* A–F; withdraw.

Distinctive Educational Programs: Environmental Management; Studies of the Future; Healthcare Administration; weekend MBA.

Degrees Conferred: 1,059 *baccalaureate*; 915 *master's*. Bachelor's degrees awarded in top five disciplines: business, management, marketing, and related support services 343; multidisciplinary studies 199; psychology 83; computer and information science 58; history 48.

Fees and Other Expenses: *Full-time tuition/fees per academic year 2008–09:* contact the university for current information regarding tuition, fees, and other costs.

Financial Aid: Aid from institutionally generated funds is provided on the basis of academic merit, financial need. Institution has a Program Participation Agreement with the U.S. Department of Education for eligible students to receive Pell Grants and, depending upon the agreement, other federal aid.

Departments and Teaching Staff: *Total instructional faculty:* 363. Student/faculty ratio: 25:1. Degrees held by full-time faculty: 86% hold terminal degrees.

Enrollment: Total enrollment 7,853.

Characteristics of Student Body: *Ethnic/racial makeup:* Black non-Hispanic: 7%; American Indian or Alaska Native: 1%; Asian or Pacific Islander: 5%; Hispanic: 16%; White non-Hispanic: 68%.

International Students: 112 undergraduate nonresident aliens enrolled fall 2008. Students from Europe, Asia, Latin America, Africa, Canada. No programs available to aid students whose native language is not English. No financial aid specifically designated for international students.

Student Life: On-campus apartments available. *Special services:* Learning Resources Center, medical services, placement center, counseling and testing center, multicultural services, disability services, Student Information and Assistance. center. *Student publications: UHCLidian,* a student newspaper published throughout fall and spring semesters biweekly. *Bayousphere,* a literary magazine published annually. *Surrounding community:* Houston metropolitan area population 4 million. Served by mass transit bus system; airport.

Publications: *Egret*, university-wide publication published twice yearly; *Bayou Buzz*, employee publication issued 9 times per year.

Library Collections: 410,000 volumes including bound books, serial backfiles, electronic documents, and government documents not in separate collections. Online catalog. Current serial subscriptions: 173 paper, 3,154 microform. 404 CD-ROMs. Computer work stations available. Students have access to the Internet at no charge.

Most important special holdings include Early English Books 1475–1700; History of Women (Radcliffe/Smith Core Collection); Congressional Information Service and American Statistics Index.

Buildings and Grounds: Campus area 487 acres.

Chief Executive Officer: Dr. William A. Staples, President.

Address admission inquiries to Dan Garcia, Director of Enrollment Services.

University of Houston - Downtown

One Main Street
Houston, Texas 77002
Tel: (713) 221-8000 **E-mail:** uhadmit@dt.uh.edu
Fax: (713) 221-8157 **Internet:** www.dt.uh.edu

Institution Description: *Enrollment:* 12,283. *Degrees awarded:* Baccalaureate, master's.

Accreditation: *Regional:* SACS-Comm. on Coll.

History: Established as a result of expansion of University of Houston Downtown School (established 1934) and acquisition of South Texas Junior College (established 1923), chartered, and offered first instruction at postsecondary level 1974; awarded first degree (baccalaureate) 1975.

Institutional Structure: *Composition of institution:* Administrators 39. Academic affairs headed by vice president for academic affairs. Management/business/finances directed by vice chancellor for finance and operations. Total instructional faculty 459. Academic governance body, Faculty Senate, meets an average of 20 times per year.

Calendar: Semesters. Academic year Aug. to May. Freshmen admitted Aug., Jan., May or June, July. Degrees conferred May, Aug., Dec. Formal commencement May. Summer session from May to Aug.

Characteristics of Freshmen: 100% of applicants accepted. 53.3% of accepted applicants enrolled.

Admission: Rolling admissions plan. For fall acceptance, apply as early as Jan. of year of enrollment, but not later than Aug. *Requirements:* Either graduation from accredited secondary school with 22 units including 4 English, 4 social studies, 4 mathematics, 4 sciences, 3 foreign language, 3 academic electives; or GED. *Entrance tests:* For foreign students TOEFL. *For transfer students:* 4-and 2-year accredited institutions with less than 2.0 GPA admitted on probationary status; 25% of the total hours required for degree must be from UHD.

College credit for postsecondary-level work completed in secondary school. Tutoring available. Developmental/remedial courses offered in summer session and regular academic year; credit given.

Degree Requirements: 120–135 credit hours; 2.0 GPA; at least 25% of semester credit hours must be earned at UHD; core requirements for individual programs.

Fulfillment of some degree requirements and exemption from some beginning courses possible by passing departmental examination, College Board CLEP Subject Examination. *Grading system:* A–F; withdraw (deadline after which pass-fail is appended to withdraw).

Distinctive Educational Programs: Internships. Weekend and evening classes. Interdisciplinary program in general studies. Facilities and programs for independent research, including individual majors, tutorials. *Other distinctive programs:* minimesters, distance education, continuing education; urban education; criminal justice; computer science; computer information systems.

Degrees Conferred: 2,002 *baccalaureate*; 36 *master's*. Bachelor's degrees awarded in top five disciplines: business, management, marketing, and related support services 665; liberal arts/general studies 289; security and protective services 107; psychology 101; English 78. Master's degrees awarded: various disciplines 36.

Fees and Other Expenses: *Full-time tuition per academic year 2008=09:* in-state $4,190, out-of-state $10,934; contact the university for current graduate tuition and fees. *Books and supplies:* $1,076. *Room and board per academic year:* $8,800. *Other expenses:* $7,000.

Financial Aid: Aid from institutionally generated funds is provided on the basis of academic merit, financial need.

Financial aid to full-time, first-time undergraduate students: 88% received federal grants averaging $2,481; 18% state/local grants averaging $2,719; 15% institutional grants averaging $1,364; 31 % received loans averaging $2,248.

Departments and Teaching Staff: *Total instructional faculty:* 440.

Enrollment: Total enrollment 12,283. Undergraduate 12,134 (full-time 48%; female 61%, male 39%). Graduate 149 (full-time 8%).

Characteristics of Student Body: *Ethnic/racial makeup:* Black non-Hispanic: 10%; Asian or Pacific Islander: 10%; Hispanic: 28%; White non-Hispanic: 35%; nonresident alien 5%.

International Students: *Student publications: Bayou Review* and a monthly newspaper. *Surrounding community:* Houston metropolitan population 4 mil-

UNIVERSITY OF HOUSTON - DOWNTOWN—*cont'd*

lion. Served by mass transit bus system; airport 20 miles from campus; passenger rail service 2 miles from campus.

Publications: *Signature, New Horizons.*

Library Collections: 269,000 books, serial backfiles, electronic documents, and government documents (titles) accessible through the library's catalog. 1,876 current serial subscriptions (paper, microform, electronic). 149,000 microforms; 2,270 audiovisual materials.

Most important holdings include energy information collection, oral history collection.

Buildings and Grounds: Campus area 23 acres.

Chief Executive Officer: Dr. Max Castillo, President.

Address all admission inquiries to Jose Cantu, Director of Admissions.

University of Houston - University Park

212 Ezekiel Cullen Building
Suite 212
Houston, Texas 77204
Tel: (713) 743-1000 **E-mail:** admissions@uh.edu
Fax: (713) 743-8837 **Internet:** www.uh.edu

Institution Description: *Enrollment:* 36,104. *Degrees awarded:* Baccalaureate, first-professional (law, optometry, pharmacy), master's, doctorate.

Accreditation: *Regional:* SACS-Comm. on Coll. *Professional*: architecture, business, chemistry, computer science, engineering, music, law, optometry, pharmacy, social work, construction technology, electronic technology, manufacturing technology

History: Established, chartered, and incorporated as Houston Junior College and offered first instruction at postsecondary level 1927; became 4-year institution and changed name to University of Houston 1934; awarded first degree (baccalaureate) 1935; became state institution 1963.

Institutional Structure: *Composition of institution:* Administrators 32. Academic affairs headed by Executive Vice President for Academic Affairs. Management, business/finances directed by Senior Vice President for Administration and Finance. Total instructional faculty 1,613. Academic governance bodies include Faculty Senate (meets an average of 6 times per year), Undergraduate Council (17 times per year), Graduate and Professional Council (9 times per year).

Calendar: Semesters. Academic year Aug. to May. Freshmen admitted Aug., Jan., June, July. Degrees conferred May, Aug., Dec. Formal commencement May. Summer session June to Aug.

Characteristics of Freshmen: 11,694 applicants (female 6,251, male 5,443). 70% of applicants accepted. 57% of accepted applicants enrolled.

Average secondary school rank of freshmen 70th percentile. Mean SAT scores 508 verbal, 524 mathematical. Mean ACT Composite score 21.

27% of entering freshmen expected to graduate within 5 years. 94% of freshmen from Texas. Freshmen from 31 states and 41 foreign countries.

Admission: Rolling admissions plan. For fall acceptance, apply as early as 1 year prior to enrollment, but not later than June 1 of year of enrollment. Students are notified of acceptance beginning May. Early acceptance available. *Requirements:* Recommend graduation from accredited secondary school with 4 units English, 3 mathematics, 2 natural science, 3 social studies; 2 units in a foreign language strongly recommended but not required. GED accepted. Additional units mathematics and science recommended for Cullen College of Engineering and College of Natural Science and Mathematics. Audition and music theory examination normally required for School of Music. Minimum GPA 2.0. *Entrance tests:* College Board SAT or ACT composite. For foreign students minimum TOEFL score 550. *For transfer students:* 2.5 minimum GPA between 15-29 hours, 2.0 GPA between 30-59 hours; from 4-year accredited institution maximum transfer credit limited only by residence requirement; from 2-year accredited institution 66 hours; correspondence/extension students 30 hours.

College credit and advanced placement for postsecondary-level work completed in secondary school. College credit for extrainstitutional learning.

Tutoring available.

Degree Requirements: *For all undergraduate degrees:* 122 credit hours; 2.0 GPA; 30 hours in residence; core curriculum; exit competency examination in writing. Texas Academic Skills Program examination must be successfully passed by the time the student has acquired 60 hours.

Fulfillment of some degree requirements and exemption from some beginning courses possible by passing departmental examinations, College Board CLEP, AP, other standardized tests. *Grading system:* A–F; pass-fail; withdraw (deadline after which pass-fail is appended to withdraw).

Distinctive Educational Programs: *Available to all students:* work-experience programs. Flexible meeting places and schedules, including off-campus centers, weekend and evening classes. Facilities for independent research, including individual majors, tutorials. Study abroad in France (architecture); Madrid, Spain, and Puebla, Mexico (Spanish); Munich (German). London Program. *Other distinctive programs:* The University of Houston superconductivity lab; Creative Writing Program. The Graduate-Level Interinstitutional Agreement is a reciprocal arrangement with other universities in the Houston area that enables enrolled, full-time graduate students from participating institutions to take a maximum six hours of graduate-level course work per semester at the University of Houston for residence credit. Similar benefits are available to University of Houston students at participating institutions. Language and Culture Center; Cooperative Education Program. PROMES (Program for Minority Engineering Students) provides support in the academic, social, and financial areas, with a strong emphasis on making students' first year in college a success. Upward Bound Program. Division of Continuing Education provides a broad array of programs, courses, and activities to meet the needs of learners in areas other than formal degree programs.

ROTC: Army; Navy in cooperation with Rice University.

Degrees Conferred: 4,759 *baccalaureate*; 1,448 *master's*; 343 *doctorate.* Bachelor's degrees awarded in top five disciplines: business, management, marketing, and related support services 1,691; psychology 363; social sciences 261; communication, journalism, and related programs 244; engineering 219. 466 *first-professional:* law 317, optometry 112, pharmacy 37.

Fees and Other Expenses: *Full-time tuition per academic year 2008–09:* undergraduate resident $6,658, nonresident $13,402; contact the university for current graduate and first-professional tuition and fees. *Required fees:* $2,649. *Books and supplies:* $1,100. *Room and board per academic year:* $6,935. *Other expenses:* $4,324.

Financial Aid: Aid from institutionally generated funds is provided on the basis of academic merit, financial need, athletic ability.

Financial aid to full-time, first-time undergraduate students: 73% received some form of aid. Average amount of aid received: federal grants $3,873; Pell grants $3,345; other federal aid $931; state/local grants $4,579; institutional grants $3,504.

Departments and Teaching Staff: *Total instructional faculty:* 1,823 (full-time 204, part-time 619). Student/faculty ratio: 21:1. Degrees held by full-time faculty: baccalaureate 4.7%, master's 10.4%, doctorate 82.4%, professional 2.5%. 87% hold terminal degrees.

Enrollment: Total enrollment 36,104. Undergraduate 28,800 (full-time 72%; female 51%, male 49%). Graduate 1,304 (full-time 61%). Undergraduate transfer-in students 3,312.

Characteristics of Student Body: *Ethnic/racial makeup:* Black non-Hispanic: 15%; Asian or Pacific Islander: 22%; Hispanic: 23%; White non-Hispanic: 34%; unknown 2%; nonresident alien 4%.

International Students: 1,414 nonresident aliens enrolled fall 2008. Students from Europe, Asia, Latin America, Africa, Canada, Australia, New Zealand. Programs available to aid students whose native language is not English: social, cultural. English as a Second Language. No financial aid specifically designated for international students.

Student Life: On-campus residence halls house 10% of student body. Housing is co-ed. 34% of males and 36% of females join, and some live in, fraternity and sorority housing. *Intercollegiate athletics:* male: baseball, basketball, cross-country, football, golf, track; female: basketball, cross-country, swimming, tennis, track, volleyball. *Special regulations:* Cars permitted without restrictions. *Special services:* Learning Resources Center, medical services, handicapped services, computer network available. *Student publications, radio, television: Daily Cougar*, a newspaper published 5 times per week; *Houstonian*, a yearbook; *Student Handbook*, published annually. Radio station KUHF-FM broadcasts classical music and NPR news. Television station KUHT was the first public broadcast station in the nation. *Surrounding community:* Houston metropolitan area population 4 million. Served by mass transit bus system; airport 15 miles from campus; passenger rail service 8 miles from campus.

Publications: *Publisher:* Arte Publico Press.

Library Collections: 2,040,100 volumes including bound books, serial backfiles, electronic documents, and government documents not in separate collections. Online catalog. Current serial subscriptions: 12,689 paper, 44 microform, 1,511 electronic. 3,961 recordings. Computer work stations available. Students have access to the Internet at no charge.

Most important special holdings include Creative Writing Collection (Larry McMurtry papers); James V. Allred Archive (former governor of Texas); George Fuermann City of Houston Collection; British and American Authors Collection; History of Science Collection.

Chief Executive Officer: Dr. G. J. Gogue, President. Address undergraduate admission inquiries to Ed Apodaca, Director of Admissions; graduate inquiries to the graduate or professional school of interest.

College of Humanities, Fine Arts, and Communication

Degree Programs Offered: *Baccalaureate* in art, art history, classical studies, communication disorders, drama, English, French, German, German area studies, Italian studies, history, journalism, music, philosophy, radio-television, Spanish, speech-communications; *master's* in communication, communication disorders, drama, English, French, German, history, philosophy, Spanish, speech communication, art, music; *doctorate* in English, history, music. Minor programs offered in all the above areas and in Afro-American studies, Mexican-American studies, and women's studies.

Distinctive Educational Programs: Interdisciplinary doctorates. Honors programs. Study abroad through the departments of English, French, and Modern and Classical Languages.

College of Architecture

Degree Programs Offered: *Baccalaureate* in environmental design; *baccalaureate and master's* in architecture.

Distinctive Educational Programs: The Sasakawa International Center for Space Architecture provides opportunities for students and faculty to work together on research and design projects specializing in space architecture as well as planning for other extreme environments. The Environmental Center of Houston accomplishes architectural design, programming, urban design, and urban and regional planning. Saintes Program is the Center for the Study of Architecture and Urbanism in Saintes, France. The College's facility was designed by Philip Johnson.

College of Business Administration

Degree Programs Offered: *Baccalaureate* in accountancy, operations management, management information systems, statistics and operations research, finance, management, marketing, entrepreneurship; *master's* in business administration, accountancy; *doctorate* in business administration.

Distinctive Educational Programs: Centers for advanced study and research include Management Development Center, Information System Research Center, Center for Health Care Marketing, Small Business Development Center, Southwest Center for International Business. Computer support for students, faculty, and staff through Research and Instructional Computing Service in new state-of-the-art facility.

College of Education

Degree Programs Offered: *Baccalaureate* in health, kinesiology, interdisciplinary studies; *master's* in elementary education, exercise science, educational psychology, secondary education, art education, bilingual education, early childhood education, gifted and talented, instructional technology, mathematics education, music education, reading and language arts education, science education, social studies education, teaching, counseling, health education; *master's* and *doctorate* in administration and supervision, higher education, historical social and cultural foundations, curriculum and instruction, special education, allied health education, physical education; *doctorate* in counseling psychology, educational psychology, individual differences.

Degree Requirements: Undergraduate: 122 credit hours; 2.0 GPA; 2 semesters in residence. Fulfillment of some degree requirements and exemption from some beginning courses possible by passing department examinations, College Board CLEP, AP, other standardized tests. *Grading system:* A–F; pass-fail; withdraw (deadline after which pass-fail is appended to withdraw).

Cullen College of Engineering

Degree Programs Offered: *Baccalaureate, master's*, and *doctorate* in chemical engineering, civil engineering, electrical engineering, industrial engineering, and mechanical engineering; *master's* in biomedical engineering, petroleum engineering; *master's* and *doctorate* in aerospace, computer systems, environmental engineering, materials engineering, systems engineering.

Distinctive Educational Programs: University-industry cooperative education offering 5-year work-study program for qualified students. Honors programs.

Conrad N. Hilton College of Hotel and Restaurant Management

Degree Programs Offered: *Baccalaureate* in hotel and restaurant management; *master's* in hospitality management.

Distinctive Educational Programs: Student-run University Hilton Hotel on campus.

College of Natural Sciences and Mathematics

Degree Programs Offered: *Baccalaureate, master's*, and *doctorate* in biology, chemistry, computer sciences, geology, geophysics, mathematics, physics; *baccalaureate* in interdisciplinary sciences, biomedical technology, earth science, mathematics - applied analysis, physics - geophysics, biochemical and biophysical sciences; *master's* in applied mathematics; *master's* and *doctorate* in biochemistry.

Distinctive Educational Programs: Cooperative baccalaureate in medical technology with approved hospitals; in nuclear medical technology with Baylor College of Medicine School of Nuclear Medicine Technology. Preprofessional programs in dentistry, medicine, physical therapy, veterinary medicine. Numerous institutes (housed at least in part within the college) add to the interdisciplinary experience available to students: Allied Geophysical Laboratories (Geosciences, Computer Science, Engineering), Institute for Molecular Design (Chemistry), Institute for Beam Particle Dynamics (Physics), Institute for Theoretical Engineering Sciences (Chemistry, Engineering, Mathematics, Physics), Space Vacuum Epitaxy Center (Physics), Texas Center for Superconductivity at the University of Houston (Physics, Chemistry, Engineering).

College of Pharmacy

Degree Programs Offered: *Baccalaureate* in pharmacy; *master's* in pharmaceutics, pharmacology, medicinal chemistry/pharmacognosy, hospital pharmacy, pharmacy administration; *doctorate* in pharmacology, pharmaceutics; *first-professional* in pharmacy.

Distinctive Educational Programs: Honors program.

College of Social Sciences

Degree Programs Offered: *Baccalaureate* in political science, sociology, psychology, anthropology, economics, Russian studies; *master's* in anthropology, economics, political science, psychology, sociology, public administration; *doctorate* in economics, political science, psychology.

Distinctive Educational Programs: Center for Public Policy; Congressional internships.

College of Technology

Degree Programs Offered: *Baccalaureate* in electrical technology, computer technology, CADD, manufacturing technology, information systems technology, industrial distribution, consumer science, nutrition, construction management technology, human development and family studies, occupational technology, industrial studies; *master's* in construction management technology, manufacturing technology, microcomputer systems technology, occupational technology.

University of Houston Law Center

Degree Programs Offered: *First-professional* (J.D.), *Master of Laws.*

Admission: Baccalaureate, LSAT, LSDAS.

Degree Requirements: *For master's degree:* 24 credit hours, writing requirements. *For first-professional degree:* 88 credit hours, 22 months in residence, senior writing requirements.

College of Optometry

Degree Programs Offered: *First-professional* (O.D.); *master's* and *doctorate* in physiological optics.

Admission: *For first-professional degree:* preprofessional program in optometry, 2.7 GPA, OAT and California Psychological Inventory, 3 recommendations.

Degree Requirements: *For first-professional:* baccalaureate, 4-year prescribed program, C average, externships.

Graduate School of Social Work

Degree Programs Offered: *Master's, doctorate* in social work.

University of Houston - Victoria

2506 East Red River
Victoria, Texas 77901-4450
Tel: (361) 576-4848 **E-mail:** admissions@vic.uh.edu
Fax: (361) 573-0017 **Internet:** www.vic.uh.edu

Institution Description: University of Houston - Victoria is a public upper-level and graduate institution with selected bachelor's and master's programs on

UNIVERSITY OF HOUSTON - VICTORIA—*cont'd*

campus, at off-campus centers, and online. *Enrollment:* 2,491. *Degrees awarded:* Baccalaureate, master's.

Academic offers subject to approval by statewide coordinating bodies. Budget subject to approval by state governing boards.

Accreditation: *Regional:* SACS-Comm. on Coll. *Professional*: business

History: Established and offered first instruction at postsecondary level 1973; awarded first degree (baccalaureate) 1976.

Institutional Structure: *Composition of institution:* Administrators 8. Academic affairs headed by dean of faculties. Management/business/finances directed by director of finance and operations. Full-time instructional faculty 72. Academic governance body, Academic Council, meets weekly.

Calendar: Semesters. Academic year Aug. to May. Degrees conferred May, Aug., Dec. Formal commencement May. Summer session from June to Aug.

Admission: *Requirements:* undergraduate transfer students 54 semester hours with 2.0 minimum GPA and good standing at previous institutions; graduate 60 semester hours and minimum of 800 on GRE verbal and quantitative combined; 3.0 A. Graduate programs: bachelor's degree; 3.0 minimum GPA; GRE General Test or GMAT.

College credit for extrainstitutional learning.

Degree Requirements: 122 credit hours; 2.0 GPA; 54 of the 122 semester hours are to be advanced and at least 18 of these 54 advanced semester hours must be in the student's major. *Grading system:* A–F; withdraw (deadline after which pass-fail is appended to withdraw).

Distinctive Educational Programs: UHV provides extensive course offerings, selected programs, learning supports, and many students services entirely online.

Degrees Conferred: 265 *baccalaureate* (B), 271 147 *master's* (M): biological/life science 8 (B); business 41 (B), 128 (M); communication, journalism, and related programs 9 (B); computer and information sciences 40 (B); education 73 (B), 115 (M); English 15 (B); interdisciplinary studies 23; liberal arts 34 (B); mathematics 2 (B); psychology 24 (B), 5 (M); other 19 (B).

Fees and Other Expenses: *Full-time tuition per academic year:* undergraduate resident $4,290, nonresident $13,350; graduate resident $4,584, nonresident $10,680.

Financial Aid: Aid from institutionally generated funds is provided on the basis of academic merit, financial need.

Financial aid to full-time, first-time undergraduate students: need-based scholarships/grants totaling $2,023,791, self-help $2,551,676, parent loans $3,194, tuition waivers $210,185; non-need-based scholarships/grants totaling $218,086, self-help $779,692; parent loans $4,494, tuition waivers $33,164. *Graduate aid:* 244 students received $161,281 in federal and state-funded fellowships/grants; 418 received $3,165,950 in federal and state-funded loans; 3 held work-study jobs worth $13,533.

Departments and Teaching Staff: *Total instructional faculty:* 122 (full-time 72, part-time 50). Total faculty with doctorate, first-professional, or other terminal degree: 72. Student/faculty ratio: 16:1. Degrees held by full-time faculty: 95% hold terminal degrees.

Enrollment: Total enrollment 2,491. Undergraduate

Characteristics of Student Body: *Ethnic/racial makeup:* Black non-Hispanic: 92; American Indian or Alaska Native: 6; Asian or Pacific Islander: 42; Hispanic: 247; White non-Hispanic: 810. *Age distribution:* number 18–19: 6; 20–21: 131; 22–24: 295; 25–29: 259; 30–34: 145; 35–39: 115; 40–49: 194; 50–64: 63.

International Students: 60 nonresident aliens enrolled fall 2008. Students from Europe, Asia, Latin America, Africa, Canada. Programs available to aid students whose native language is not English: social, cultural. Some financial aid designated for qualifying international students.

Student Life: No on-campus housing. *Special regulations:* Registered cars permitted. *Special services:* Child care drop-in service offered at minimal cost to students while they attend class or study. *Student publications: UH-Voice*, a monthly newspaper. *Surrounding community:* Victoria population 52,000. Houston, 125 miles from campus, is nearest metropolitan area. Served by airport 4 miles from campus.

Publications: *UH-Victoria Newsletter* published monthly.

Library Collections: 600,000 volumes. Online catalog. Current serial subscriptions: paper 460; 53,000 microform; 10,000 via electronic access. Computer work stations available. Students have access to online information retrieval services and the Internet.

Most important special holdings include collections on Texas and local history; local archives; regional historical resources depository. The library is a joint library serving both UH-Victoria and Victoria College (junior).

Buildings and Grounds: The UH-Victoria campus is located in Victoria, including University Center, completed in 2000 and University West which contains classroom and office. UHV's teaching centers are located in Sugar Land and Cisco Ranch in Fort Bend County near Houston.

Chief Executive Officer: Dr. Timothy Hudson, President.

Address admission inquiries to Office of Admissions.

University of the Incarnate Word

4301 Broadway
San Antonio, Texas 78209
Tel: (210) 829-6001 **E-mail:** admissions@uiw.edu
Fax: (210) 829-1220 **Internet:** www.uiw.edu

Institution Description: University of the Incarnate Word, formerly known as Incarnate Word College, is a private institution conducted by the Sisters of Charity of the Incarnate Word, Roman Catholic Church. *Enrollment:* 6,361. *Degrees awarded:* Baccalaureate, master's, doctorate.

Member of the consortium United Colleges of San Antonio.

Accreditation: *Regional:* SACS-Comm. on Coll. *Professional*: Nuclear medicine technology, nursing, teacher education

History: Established and chartered as a normal school 1881; became Academy of the Incarnate Work 1901; offered first instruction at postsecondary level 1904; became Incarnate Word College 1909; awarded first degree (baccalaureate) 1910; adopted present name 1995. *See* Sr. Clement Eagen, *A History of Incarnate Word College* (San Antonio: Incarnate Word College Press, 1981) for further information.

Institutional Structure: *Governing board:* Board of Trustees of University of Incarnate Word. Extrainstitutional representation: 17 trustees; institutional representation: 1 administrator, 1 full-time instructional faculty member, 1 student. All voting. *Composition of institution:* Administrators 14. Academic affairs headed by academic dean. Management/business/finances directed by chief financial officer. Full-time instructional faculty 175. Academic governance body, Faculty Senate, meets an average of 8 times per year.

Calendar: Semesters. Academic year Aug. to May. Freshmen admitted Aug., Jan., June, July. Degrees conferred May. Formal commencement May, Aug. Summer session from early June to early Aug.

Characteristics of Freshmen: 3,390 applicants (female 2,203, male 1,187). 71% of applicants accepted. 35% of accepted applicants enrolled.

25th percentile: SAT Critical Reading 430, SAT Math 420; ACT Composite 17, ACT English 15, ACT Math 15. *75th percentile*: SAT Critical Reading 550, SAT Math 550; ACT Composite 23, ACT English 22, ACT Math 22.

35% of entering freshmen expected to graduate within 5 years. 95% of freshmen from Texas. Freshmen from 20 states and 13 foreign countries.

Admission: Rolling admissions plan. Apply no later than first day of class. Early acceptance available. *Requirements:* Graduation from accredited secondary school with 4 units in English; 3 social science, 3 mathematics, 2 natural science, 2 foreign language, 1 fine arts. GED also accepted. Minimum 2.0 GPA. Lowest acceptable secondary school class standing 50th percentile. *Entrance tests:* College Board SAT or ACT composite. For foreign students TOEFL. *For transfer students:* 2.5 minimum GPA; 66 hours maximum transfer credit; correspondence/extension students 30 hours.

College credit and advanced placement for postsecondary level work completed in secondary school.

Tutoring available. Developmental courses offered in summer session and regular academic year; nondegree credit given.

Degree Requirements: 128 credit hours; 2.0 GPA; last 24 hours in residence; 2 semester hours physical education; core curriculum and integrative seminar.

Fulfillment of some degree requirements and exemption from some beginning courses possible by passing departmental examinations, College Board CLEP, AP. *Grading system:* A–F; pass-fail; withdraw (carries time limit); incomplete (carries time limit).

Distinctive Educational Programs: *For undergraduates:* Cooperative education. Interdisciplinary programs in communication arts, human relations, native American studies. *For graduate students:* Cooperative program in English through consortium. Multidisciplinary studies program. *Available to all students:* Internships. Evening classes. Interdisciplinary program in child care work. Facilities and programs for independent research. Institutionally sponsored study abroad in England, France, Greece, Italy, Mexico, Spain. University of Incarnate Word campus in China, Mexico, Honduras. Cross-registration through consortium. *Other distinctive programs:* Noncredit continuing education program. Women in Education, New Careers, Opportunities, Experiences (WENCOE) program offers educational counseling for women who wish to recommence or begin college careers. UIW campus in Quangchou, China.

ROTC: Army offered in cooperation with St. Mary's University.

Degrees Conferred: 10 *associate*; 802 *baccalaureate*; 315 *master's*; 18 *doctorate*. Bachelor's degrees awarded in top five disciplines: business, management, marketing, and related support services 295; liberal arts/general studies 73; health professions and related clinical sciences 65; visual and performing arts 64; communication, journalism, and related programs 36. Master's degrees awarded: various disciplines 315. Doctorates awarded: education 18.

Fees and Other Expenses: *Full-time tuition per academic year 2008–09:* undergraduate $20,280; contact the university for current graduate tuition/fees. *Books and supplies:* $1,000. *Room and board per academic year:* $7,380. *Other expenses:* $2,470.

Financial Aid: Aid from institutionally generated funds is provided on the basis of academic merit, financial need, athletic ability.

Financial aid to full-time, first-time undergraduate students: 95% received some form of aid. Average amount of aid received: federal grants 43,182; Pell grants $3,082; other federal aid $1,492; state/local grants $3,785; institutional grants $6,454.

Departments and Teaching Staff: *Total instructional faculty:* <445 (full-time 175, part-time 270). Student/faculty ratio: 14:1. Degrees held by full-time faculty: doctorate 60%. 56% hold terminal degrees.

Enrollment: Total enrollment 6,361. Undergraduate 5,110 (full-time 65%; female 66%, male 54%). Graduate 1,251 (full-time 35%). Undergraduate transfer-in students 539.

Characteristics of Student Body: *Ethnic/racial makeup:* Black non-Hispanic: 7%; Asian or Pacific Islander: 2%; Hispanic 57%; White non-Hispanic: 24%; unknown: 1%; nonresident alien 2%.

International Students: 128 nonresident aliens enrolled fall 2008. Programs available to aid students whose native language is not English: English as a Second Language Program. No financial aid specifically designated for international students.

Student Life: On-campus residence halls house 23% of student body. Residence halls for males constitute 26% of such space, for females 74%. *Intercollegiate athletics:* male: baseball, basketball, soccer, tennis, track; female: basketball, softball, synchronized swimming, tennis, volleyball. *Special regulations:* Cars permitted without restrictions. Residence hall visitation hours vary. *Special services:* Learning Resources Center, medical services. *Student publications: Logos*, a monthly newspaper. *Surrounding community:* San Antonio population over 1 million. Served by mass transit bus system; airport 5 miles from campus; passenger rail service 2 miles from campus.

Library Collections: 261,000 volumes including bound books, serial backfiles, electronic documents, and government documents not in separate collections. Online catalog. 273,000 microforms; 13,000 audiovisual materials; 19,000 peridocials including via electronic access. Computer work stations available. Students have access to the Internet at no charge.

Most important special holdings include Special Collections Room; Texana Room; 19th-Century Literature; Nursing Collection; Adina De Zavala Papers.

Buildings and Grounds: Campus area 200 acres. Campus DVD available.

Chief Executive Officer: Dr. Louis Agnese, President.

Address admission inquiries to Andrea Cyterski, Dean of Admissions.

University of Mary Hardin-Baylor

900 College Street
Box 8004 UMHB Station
Belton, Texas 76513-2599
Tel: (800) 727-8642 **E-mail:** admission@umhb.edu
Fax: (254) 295-4535 **Internet:** www.umhb.edu

Institution Description: University of Mary Hardin-Baylor is a private institution affiliated with the Baptist General Convention of Texas. *Enrollment:* 2,648. *Degrees awarded:* Baccalaureate, master's, doctorate.

Accreditation: *Regional:* SACS-Comm. on Coll. *Professional*: counseling, music, nursing, rehabilitation counseling, social work

History: Established as women's division of Baylor University and offered first instruction at postsecondary level 1845; awarded first degree (baccalaureate) 1855; changed name to Baylor Female College 1866, to Baylor College for Women 1924, to Mary Hardin-Baylor College 1934; became coeducational 1971; adopted present name 1978.

Institutional Structure: *Governing board:* Board of Trustees. Representation: 42 trustees. All voting. *Composition of institution:* Administrators 7. Academic affairs, business and finance, athletics, enrollment management, external affairs, student life: each of these functional areas headed by a vice president. Full-time instructional faculty 134. Academic governance body, Faculty Assembly.

Calendar: Semesters. Academic year Aug. to May. Freshmen admitted Aug., Jan., June, July. Degrees conferred and formal commencement May, Aug., Dec. Summer session from late May to early Aug.

Characteristics of Freshmen: 3,703 applicants. 71% of applicants admitted. 40% of applicants admitted and enrolled. >pr62% (294 students) submitted SAT scores; 59% (279 students) submitted ACT scores. *25th percentile*: SAT Critical Reading 470, SAT Math 470; ACT Composite 20,. *75th percentile*: SAT Critical Reading 570, SAT Math 570; ACT Composite 25.

30% of entering freshmen expected to graduate in 5 years. 97% of freshmen from Texas. Freshmen from 20 states and 9 foreign countries.

Admission: Rolling admissions plan. *Requirements:* Freshmen must: rank in top half of high school graduating class or score a minimum SAT of 950 or a minimum ACT of 20; OR rank in lower half of graduating class and score a minimum SAT of 990 or a minimum ACT of 21 OR rank in top 10% of graduating class; have graduated form an accredited high school with 22 units or received GED with a 50 composite score; 9.5 units from high school must include 4 English, 2.5 social science, and 3 mathematics. Conditional admission may be possible. *For transfer students:* 2.0 minimum GPA; from 4-year accredited institution maximum transfer credit limited only by residence requirement; from 2-year accredited institution 66 hours.

College credit and advanced placement for postsecondary-level work completed in secondary school. College credit for extrainstitutional learning.

Tutoring available. Developmental-remedial courses offered in summer session and regular academic year; credit given.

Degree Requirements: Minimum of 124 credit hours; 2.0 GPA; 31 hours in residence; 36 hours upper-level (courses intended for juniors/seniors); 18 of final 30 hours must be completed in residence or 24 of 31 residency hours must be upper-level; weekly chapel attendance for 4 semesters; 2 physical activity courses; core curriculum.

Fulfillment of some degree requirements and exemption from some beginning courses possible by passing departmental examinations, College Board CLEP, other standardized tests. *Grading system:* A–F; withdraw (carries time limit, deadline after which pass-fail is appended to withdrawal).

Distinctive Educational Programs: Field experience programs. Flexible meeting places and schedules, including off-campus centers (at Fort Hood, 16 miles from main campus; Rio Grande Valley, 350 miles away). evening classes. Cooperative baccalaureate in nursing with local hospital. Facilities and programs for independent research, including honors programs, independent study. Servicemembers Opportunity College (SOC); evaluation and credit for military service possible.

ROTC: Air Force in cooperation with Baylor University.

Degrees Conferred: 500 *baccalaureate*; 64 *master's*. Bachelor's degrees awarded in top five disciplines: education 85; health professions and related clinical sciences 72; communications/journalism 51; computer and information sciences 47; liberal arts/general studies 44. Master's degrees awarded: business/marketing 9; computer and information sciences 2; education 13; health professions 9; philosophy and religious studies 1; psychology 10.

Fees and Other Expenses: *Full-time tuition per academic year 2008–09:* undergraduate $18,340; contact the university for current graduate tuition and applicable fees. *Room and board per academic year:* $5,350. *Books and supplies:* $1,200. *Other expenses:* 43,696.

Financial Aid: Aid from institutionally generated funds is provided on the basis of academic merit, financial need.

Financial aid to full-time, first-time undergraduate students: 80% received some form of aid. Average amount of aid received: federal grants $3,544; Pell grants $2,875; other federal aid $810; state/local grants $3,678; institutional grants $4,770.

Departments and Teaching Staff: *Total instructional faculty:* 211 full-time 134, part-time 77). Total faculty with doctorate, first-professional, or other terminal degree: 109. Student/faculty ratio: 14:1. Degrees held by full-time faculty: doctorate 52.7%, master's 47.3%, baccalaureate 100%. 66% hold terminal degrees.

Enrollment: Total enrollment 2,648. Undergraduate 2,460 (full-time 90%; female 63%, male 37%). Graduate 188 (full-time 54%). Undergraduate transfer-in students 274.

Characteristics of Student Body: *Ethnic/racial makeup:* Black non-Hispanic: 11%; American Indian or Alaska Native: 1%; Asian or Pacific Islander: 2%; Hispanic: 13%; White non-Hispanic: 68%; unknown 4%; nonresident alien 1%. *Age distribution:* number under 18: 24; 18–19: 844; 20–21: 690; 22–24: 454; 25–29: 204; 30–34: 135; 35–39: 72; 40–49: 117; 50–64: 24; 65 and over: 1.

International Students: 26 nonresident aliens enrolled fall 2008. Students from Europe, Asia, Latin America, Africa, Canada, Australia. Programs available to aid students whose native language is not English: social, cultural. English as a Second Language Program. No financial aid specifically designated for international students.

Student Life: On-campus residence halls and apartments house 42% of student body. *Intercollegiate athletics:* male: baseball, football; female: softball, volleyball; male and female: basketball, golf, soccer, tennis. *Special regulations:* Insured and registered cars permitted. *Special services:* Nursing services. *Student publications:* Biweekly student newspaper; a yearbook. *Surrounding community:* Belton population 15,000. Austin, 60 miles from campus, is nearest metropolitan area. Served by mass transit system; airport 6 miles from campus.

UNIVERSITY OF MARY HARDIN-BAYLOR—*cont'd*

Library Collections: 237,000 volumes including bound books, serial backfiles, electronic documents, and government documents not in separate collections. Online catalog. 58,000 microforms; 7,000 audiovisual materials; 900 vurrent serial subscriptions. Computer work stations available. Students have access to the Internet at no charge.

Most important special holdings include the University Archives; Bell County Local History Collection; David B, McFadden Texas and Mexican History Collection.

Buildings and Grounds: Campus area 120 acres.

Chief Executive Officer: Dr. Jerry G. Bawcom, President.

Address admission inquiries to Robbin Steen, Director of Admissions and Recruiting.

University of North Texas

P.O. Box 311425
Denton, Texas 76203-1425

Tel: (940) 565-2681 **E-mail:** admissions@unt.edu
Fax: (940) 565-2408 **Internet:** www.unt.edu

Institution Description: University of North Texas is a state institution. *Enrollment:* 34,30. *Degrees awarded:* Baccalaureate, master's, doctorate.

Academic offerings subject to approval by statewide coordinating body. Budget subject to approval by state governing board. Member of Federation of North Texas Area Universities, Association for Higher Education.

Accreditation: *Regional:* SACS-Comm. on Coll. *Professional*: business, chemistry, computer science, counseling, engineering, health services administration, psychology internship, interior design, journalism, librarianship, music, manufacturing technology, psychology internship, public administration, recreation and leisure services, rehabilitation counseling, social work, speech-language pathology

History: Established and chartered as Texas Normal College and offered first instruction at postsecondary level 1890; rechartered as North Texas State Normal College 1894; awarded first degree (baccalaureate) 1919; changed name to North Texas State Teachers College 1923; added graduate program 1935; changed name to North Texas State College 1949; authorized doctorate 1950; name changed to North Texas State University 1961; adopted present name May 1988. *See* James L. Rogers, *The Story of North Texas* (Denton: North Texas State University, 1965) for further information.

Institutional Structure: *Governing board:* Board of Regents of University of North Texas. Representation: 9 regents (appointed by governor of Texas). All voting. *Composition of institution:* Administrators 30. Academic affairs overseen by provost and executive vice president. Management/business/finances directed by vice president for financial and business affairs. Full-time instructional faculty 919. Academic governance body, Faculty Senate, meets an average of 10 times per year.

Calendar: Semesters. Academic year Aug. to Aug. Freshmen admitted Aug., Jan., May or June, July. Degrees conferred May, Aug., Dec. Formal commencements May, Aug., Dec. May minimester available. Summer session of 2 terms June to Aug.

Characteristics of Freshmen: 12,150 applicants (female 7,400, male 5,750). 71% of applicants admitted. 35% of applicants admitted and enrolled.

88% (3,291 students) submitted SAT scores; 41% (606 students) submitted ACT scores. *25th percentile*: SAT Critical Reading 490, SAT Math 490; ACT Composite 20. *75th percentile*: SAT Critical Reading 620, SAT Math 620; ACT Composite 25.

40% of entering freshmen expected to graduate within 5 years. 93% of freshmen from Texas. Freshmen from 49 states and 12 foreign countries.

Admission: Rolling admissions plan. For fall acceptance, apply as early as 11 months prior to enrollment, but not later than Aug. 16; for spring acceptance, apply by Jan. 3. Early acceptance available. *Requirements:* Either graduation from accredited secondary school with recommended units to include 4 English, 4 mathematics (2 must be algebra or higher math), 4 social science, 3 natural science, 3 foreign language; 1/2 health; 1 fine arts; 1-1/2 physical education and 1 computer science. *Entrance tests:* SAT or ACT. For foreign students TOEFL minimum 550. *For transfer students:* Minimum GPA from 2.0 to 2.5, depending on number of hours; from 4-year accredited institution number hours maximum transfer credit limited only by residence requirement; from 2-year accredited institution 66 semester hours.

Advanced placement available for postsecondary-level work completed in secondary school; for College Board Advanced Placement Examination scores of 3, 4, or 5; for some military training schools.

Tutoring available.

Degree Requirements: *For all undergraduate degrees:* Minimum 124 credit hours; 2.0 GPA; 24 of last 30 hours in residence; 42 semester hours of advanced work minimum; distribution requirements; proficiency in English composition as certified by the Student Use of English exam or satisfactory grade of C or above in English composition courses.

Fulfillment of some degree requirements and exemption from some beginning courses possible by passing institutional examinations, College Board CLEP, APP, other standardized tests. *Grading system:* A–F; pass-fail; withdraw (carries time limit); incomplete (carries time limit).

Distinctive Educational Programs: Work-experience programs. Flexible meeting places and schedules, including weekend and evening classes. Honors programs. Exchange programs available in England, France, Germany. Study abroad in London (one semester in humanities, one in business); 3 summer programs (in Spanish language in Mexico; in art and classic learning core, both in Switzerland); other countries include Austria, Japan, Ghana, People's Republic of China, Ireland, Egypt, Italy.

ROTC: Air Force.

Degrees Conferred: 5,183 *baccalaureate*; 1,524 *master's*; 200 *doctorate*. Bachelor's degrees awarded in top five disciplines: business, management, marketing, and related support services 1,152; interdisciplinary studies 475; social sciences and history 448; visual and performing arts 386; communication, journalism, and related programs 287. Master's degrees awarded: various disciplines 1,524. Doctorates awarded: various disciplines 200.

Fees and Other Expenses: *Full-time tuition per academic year 2008–09:* undergraduate resident $46,467, nonresident $13,211; contact the university for current graduate tuition and fees. *Other fees:* $1,870. *Room and board per academic year:* $6,026. *Books and supplies:* $1,210. *Other expenses:* $2,670.

Financial Aid: Aid from institutionally generated funds is provided on the basis of academic merit, financial need.

Financial aid to full-time, first-time undergraduate students: 51% received some form of aid. Average amount of aid received: federal grants $3,875; Pell grants $4,366; other federal aid $1,326; state/local grants $3,765; institutional grants $2,007.

Departments and Teaching Staff: it<Total instructional faculty: 1,520 (full-time 913, part-time 607). Student/faculty ratio: 18:1. Degrees held by full-time faculty: baccalaureate 2%, master's 17%, doctorate 80%, professional 1%. 86% hold terminal degrees.

Enrollment: Total enrollment 34,830. Undergraduate 27,812 (full-time 77%; female 54%, male 46%). Graduate 7,018 (full-time 36%). Undergraduate transfer-in students 4,148.

Characteristics of Student Body: *Ethnic/racial makeup:* Black non-Hispanic: 14%; American Indian or Alaska Native: 1%; Asian or Pacific Islander: 5%; Hispanic: 12%; White non-Hispanic: 64%; unknown: 1%; nonresiddent alien 3%. *Age distribution:* number under 18: 152; 18–19: 2,121, 20–21: 6,449; 22–24: 6,449; 25–29: 4,139; 30–34: 968; 35–39: 495; 40–49: 526; 50–64: 185; 65 and over: 3.

International Students: 1,045 nonresident aliens enrolled fall 2008. Students from Europe, Asia, Latin America, Africa, Canada, Australia. Programs available to aid students whose native language is not English: social, cultural. English as a Second Language Program. No financial aid specifically designated for international students.

Student Life: On-campus residence halls house 16% of student body. Residence halls for females constitute 17% of such space, co-ed 83%. Limited housing available for married students. *Intercollegiate athletics:* male: basketball, football, golf, track; female: basketball, golf, soccer, tennis, track, volleyball. *Special regulations:* Cars permitted without restrictions. *Special services:* medical and wellness services; counseling and testing services; local transportation services. *Student publications, radio: The North Texas Daily*, a newspaper published 4 days per week; *NT Review*, an annual literary magazine. Radio station KNTU broadcasts 126 hours per week. *Surrounding community:* Denton population 90,000. Dallas-Fort Worth-Metroplex 35 miles from campus. Served by airport 26 miles from campus.

Library Collections: 2,134,500 volumes. 369,562 government documents; 2,902,046 microforms; 65,142 audiovisual materials; 6,557 current periodicals (114 microform; 11,960 via electronic access). Online catalog. Computer work stations available. Students have access to online information retrieval services and the Internet.

Most important holdings include Rare Books and Texana Collection; University Archives; Stan Kenton Collection; Sara Hughes Collection; Oppenheimer Collection (in process).

Buildings and Grounds: Campus area 498 acres. Campus DVD available.

Chief Executive Officer: Dr. Norval F. Pohl, President.

Address admission inquiries to Marcilla Collinsworth, Director, Office of Admissions; graduate inquiries to Donna Hughes, Director, Graduate Admissions.

University of North Texas Health Science Center at Fort Worth

3500 Camp Bowie Boulevard
Fort Worth, Texas 76107
Tel: (817) 735-2000 **E-mail:** admissions@hsc.unt.edu
Fax: (817) 735-2486 **Internet:** www.hsc.unt.edu

Institution Description: The University of North Texas Health Science Center at Fort Worth was formerly known as the Texas College of Osteopathic Medicine. It is a public university comprised of three schools, Texas College of Osteopathic Medicine (TCOM), the Graduate School of Biomedical Sciences, and the School of Public Health. *Enrollment:* 1,225. *Degrees awarded:* Baccalaureate, master's, doctorate, first-professional.

Accreditation: *Regional:* SACS-Comm. on Coll. *Professional*: health services administration, osteopathy, public health

History: Chartered 1966; first class enrolled 1970; awarded first degree (first-professional) 1974; became a state institution 1975; adopted present name 1993; became part of University of North Texas System 1999. *See* R.S. Rafes, *The Historical Development of the Texas College of Osteopathic Medicine as a State Medical School, 1960–1975* (health science center library).

Institutional Structure: *Governing board:* University of North Texas System Board of Regents. President of the health sciences center serves as chief operating officer. Advisory Council appointed by Board of Regents including representatives from Texas Osteopathic Medical Association, Alumni Association, and community representatives. All voting. *Composition of institution:* Administrators 35. Academic affairs headed by vice president for health affairs and executive dean. Administrative affairs and fiscal affairs headed by vice presidents. Full-time faculty 190.

Calendar: Semesters. Academic year Aug. to May. Medical students admitted Aug.; biomedical science and public health students admitted 3 times per year; physician assistant students admitted for program of 34 months beginning in September. Degrees conferred and formal commencement June.

Admission: The university participates in the American Association of Colleges of Osteopathic Medicine Application Service. For fall acceptance, apply no] later than Dec. 1 of year prior to enrollment. For early decision program, applicant must be a Texas resident, have exceptional GPA and MCAT scores, apply only to TCOM, and submit all application materials before Aug. 1. *Requirements:* MCAT; 3 years of college (90 semester hours); 1 year of biology, physics, and expository writing, 2 years of chemistry. For the graduate school, rolling admissions with deadlines June 1, Nov. 1, and Apr. 1 for the following terms. *Requirements:* baccalaureate degree or equivalent from regionally accredited institution, GRE (combined 1100 for master's degree, 1200 for doctorate), TOEFL for international students with score of 550 or better.

Degree Requirements: Varies by program.

Distinctive Educational Programs: TCOM is one of 19 institution offering osteopathic medicine in the U.S. and the only one in Texas. The master's program in public health is one of three public health programs in Texas.

Degrees Conferred: 130 *master's:* health professions; 12 *doctorate:* biological sciences. 117 *first-professional:* osteopathic medicine.

Fees and Other Expenses: *Full-time tuition per academic year 2008–09:* contact the university for current tuition, fees, and other costs.

Financial Aid: Aid from institutionally generated funds is provided on the basis of financial need.

Institution has a Program Participation Agreement with the U.S. Department of Education for eligible students to receive Pell Grants and, depending upon the agreement, other federal aid.

Departments and Teaching Staff: *Total instructional faculty:* 177. Student/faculty ratio: 3:1. Degrees held by full-time faculty: doctorate 46.1%, master's 10.3%, baccalaureate 2.5%, professional 41.1%. 97% hold terminal degrees.

Enrollment: Total enrollment 1,225.

Characteristics of Student Body: *Ethnic/racial makeup:* number of Black non-Hispanic: 578; American Indian or Alaska Native: 10; Asian or Pacific Islander: 208; Hispanic 116; White non-Hispanic: 600; unknown 22. 10% of student body attend summer sessions.

International Students: 45 nonresident alien enrolled fall 2008. No programs available to aid students whose native language is not English. No financial aid specifically designated for international students.

Student Life: No on-campus housing. *Special services:* Learning Resources Center, medical services. *Student publications: The Speculum,* a yearbook; student serves as editor for *Pulse*, national osteopathic student newsletter. 30 clubs and organizations on campus including student government and special interest groups. *Surrounding community:* Fort Worth population over 500,000. Surrounding area includes 6 colleges and universities. Located adjacent to the city's museum complex and 30 miles from Dallas. >

Publications: it<Health and Science Quarterly.

Library Collections: 150,000 volumes including bound books, serial backfiles, electronic documents, and government documents not in separate collections. Online catalog. Current serial subscriptions: 2,203 paper, 63 electronic. 4,619 recordings; 308 CD-ROMs. Computer work stations available. Students have access to the Internet at no charge.

Most important special holdings: Osteopathic Medicine Rare Book Collection; William G. Sutherland Collection (personal papers); Texas Osteopathic Medical Association Archives.

Buildings and Grounds: Campus area 15.3 acres.

Chief Executive Officer: Dr. Scott Ransom, President.

Address admission inquiries to Joel Daboub, Director of Medical Admissions; Biomedical Sciences inquiries to Dr. Thomas Yorio, Dean; Public Health inquiries to Dr. Fernando Trevino, Dean; Physician's Assistant Program inquiries to Hank Lemke, Director.

University of St. Thomas

3800 Montrose Boulevard
Houston, Texas 77006-4696
Tel: (713) 522-7911 **E-mail:** admissions@stthom.edu
Fax: (713) 525-2125 **Internet:** www.stthom.edu

Institution Description: University of St. Thomas is an independent, private, coeducational Catholic institution of higher learning. *Enrollment:* 3,165. *Degrees awarded:* Baccalaureate, first-professional (master of divinity), master's, doctorate.

Accreditation: *Regional:* SACS-Comm. on Coll. *National:* ATS. *Professional*: business, theology

History: Founded by the Basilian Fathers in 1947; awarded first degree (baccalaureate) 1951.

Institutional Structure: *Governing board:* Board of Directors. Extrainstitutional representation: 31 directors; institutional representation: 8 administrators. All voting. *Composition of institution:* Administrators 49. Academic affairs headed by vice president for academic affairs. Management/business/finances directed by vice president for finance. Full-time instructional faculty 129. Academic governance body, Faculty Council, meets an average of 8 times yearly.

Calendar: Semesters. Academic year Aug. to May. Freshmen admitted Jan., June, Aug. Degrees conferred May, July, Aug., Dec. Formal commencement May. Summer session of 2 terms from June to July.

Characteristics of Freshmen: 810 applicants (female 550, male 260). 90% of applicants admitted. 38% of applicants admitted and enrolled.

77% (234 students) submitted SAT scores; 18% (53 students) submitted ACT scores. *25th percentile*: SAT Critical Reading 510, SAT Math 510; ACT Composite 23, ACT English 21, ACT Math 21. *75th percentile*: SAT Critical Reading 630, SAT Math 640; ACT Composite 27, ACT English 28, ACT Math 27.

43% of entering freshmen expected to graduate within 5 years. 97% of freshmen from Texas. Freshmen from 5 states and 2 foreign countries.

Admission: Rolling admissions plan. Apply as early as 1 year prior to enrollment, but not later than 2 weeks prior to registration. Early acceptance available. *Requirements:* Either graduation from accredited secondary school or GED. Recommend 4 units English, 2 foreign language, 3 mathematics (algebra, geometry, trigonometry, or calculus); 2 social studies, 3 science (2 must be lab), 1 history, 3 academic electives. Additional requirements for some programs. *Entrance tests:* College Board SAT or ACT Composite. For foreign students TOEFL score 550 (paper) or 213 (computer). *For transfer students:* 2.5 minimum GPA; from 4-year accredited institution 90 hours maximum transfer credit; from 2-year accredited institution 72 hours.

College credit and advanced placement for postsecondary-level work completed in secondary school.

Tutoring available. Remedial courses offered during regular academic year; credit given.

Degree Requirements: 126 credit hours; 2.0 GPA; at least 36 hours in upper-division credits; core curriculum; final 36 hours in residence.

Fulfillment of some degree requirements and exemption from some beginning courses possible by passing departmental examinations, College Board CLEP. *Grading system:* A–F; withdraw (deadline after which A–F is appended to withdraw).

Distinctive Educational Programs: Dual-degree program in engineering with University of Notre Dame (IN) University of Houston, and Texas A&M University; interdepartmental program in international studies. Preprofessional programs in dentistry, medical technology, medicine, nutrition and dietetics, physical therapy. Facilities for independent research, including honors programs, individual majors, tutorials. Study abroad programs: Merida Summer Study Program in Mexico; Edge Hill College, England; Institution Robin, Vienne, France; University of Reading (summer program). The University of St.

UNIVERSITY OF ST. THOMAS—*cont'd*

Thomas is a member of three study abroad consortia administered by the Council on International Exchange (CIEE). *Available to all students:* Evening classes.

ROTC: Army offered in cooperation University of Houston.

Degrees Conferred: 346 *baccalaureate*; 381 *master's:*; 17 *doctorates*. bachelor's degrees awarded in top five disciplines: business/marketing biological/life sciences 10 (B); business/marketing 105; liberal arts/general studies 79; social sciences 50; communications/journalism 22; biological/life sciences 22. Master's degrees awarded: business/marketing 217; education 76; liberal arts/general studies 52; theology and religious vocations 21. Doctorates awarded: theology 14; philosophy/religious studies 3.

Fees and Other Expenses: *Full-time tuition per academic year 2008–09:* undergraduate $20,510; contact the university for current graduate tuition/fees. *Books and supplies:* $1,030. *Room and board per academic year:* $7,700. *Other expenses:* $3,614.

Financial Aid: Aid from institutionally generated funds is provided on the basis of academic merit, financial need.

Financial aid to full-time, first-time undergraduate students: 83% received some form of aid. Average amount of aid received: federal grants $4,731; Pell grants $3,416; other federal aid $923; state/local grants #3,935; institutional grants $8,588.

Departments and Teaching Staff: *Total instructional faculty:* 275 (full-time 129, part-time 146). Total faculty with doctorate, first-professional, or other terminal degree: 199. Student/faculty ratio: 13:1. Degrees held by full-time faculty: doctorate 41%, master's 17%, baccalaureate 42%. 41% hold terminal degrees.

Enrollment: Total enrollment 3,165. Undergraduate 1,698 (full-time 76%; female 59%, male 41%). Graduate 1,467 (full-time 19%). Undergraduate transfer-in students 171.

Characteristics of Student Body: *Ethnic/racial makeup:* Black non-Hispanic: 5%; American Indian or Alaska Native: 1%; Asian or Pacific Islander: 11%; Hispanic: 33%; White non-Hispanic: 34%; 737; unknown: 11%; nonresident alien 5%. *Age distribution:* number under 18: 29; 18–19: 483; 20–21: 470; 22–24: 360; 25–29: 181; 30–34: 78; 35–39: 51; 40–49: 117; 50–64: 112; 65 and over: 13.

International Students: 156 nonresident aliens enrolled fall 2008. Students from Europe, Asia, Latin America, Africa, Canada, Australia. No programs available to aid students whose native language is not English. No financial aid specifically designated for international students.

Student Life: On-campus residence halls and apartment complex house 14% of undergraduates. *Special regulations:* Cars permitted without restrictions.Dormitory visitation from Sun.–Thurs 9am to midnight; Fri. and Sat. 9am to 2am. *Special services:* 24-hour security; on-site computer facility; game room; weekly activities for residents. *Student publications: The Cauldron*, a newspaper; *Laurels*, literary magazine. *Surrounding community:* Houston, metropolitan area population 4 million. Served by mass transit system; airport 12 miles from campus; intonational airport 21 miles from campus; Greyhound and passenger bus service 2 miles from campus.

Library Collections: 254,000 volumes. Online catalog. 579,000 microforms; 1,716 audiovisual materials; 600 current serial subscriptions. Computer work stations available. Students have access to online information retrieval services and the Internet.

Most important special holdings include Hugh Roy Marshall Graduate Philosophy Library.

Buildings and Grounds: Campus area 24.5 acres. Campus DVD available.

Chief Executive Officer: Dr. Robert Ivany, President.

Address admission inquiries to Eduardo Prieto, Dean of Admissions.

University of Texas at Arlington

701 South Nedderman Drive
Arlington, Texas 76019

Tel: (817) 272-2011 **E-mail:** admissions@uta.edu
Fax: (817) 272-3435 **Internet:** www.uta.edu

Institution Description: *Enrollment:* 25,084. *Degrees awarded:* Baccalaureate, master's, doctorate.

Accreditation: *Regional:* SACS-Comm. on Coll. *Professional*: accounting, architecture, business, chemistry, engineering, interior design, landscape architecture, music, nursing, planning, public administration, social work

History: Established as Arlington College 1895; changed name to Carlisle Military Institute 1901, to Arlington Training School 1913; became junior college branch of Agricultural and Mechanical College and changed name to Grubbs Vocational College 1917; changed name to North Texas Junior Agricultural, Mechanical and Industrial College 1923, to Arlington State College 1949; became 4-year college 1959; awarded first baccalaureate 1961; became part of University of Texas System 1965; adopted present name 1967.

Institutional Structure: *Composition of institution:* Administrators 79. Academic affairs headed by senior vice president for academic affairs. Management/business/finances directed by senior vice president for finance and administration. Full-time instructional faculty 758. Academic governance bodies, Undergraduate Assembly and Graduate Assembly, meet an average of 6 times per year each.

Calendar: Semesters. Academic year Aug. to Aug. Freshmen admitted Aug., Jan., June, July. Degrees conferred May, July, Aug., Dec. Formal commencements May, Dec. Winter and May intercessions. Summer session June to Aug.

Characteristics of Freshmen: 8,179 applicants (female 4,382, male 3,797). 72% of applicants admitted. 53% of applicants admitted and enrolled.

87% (1,942 students) submitted SAT scores; 37% (823 students) submitted ACT scores. *25th percentile*: SAT Critical Reading 470, SAT Math 480; ACT Composite 19, ACT English 18, ACT Math 18. *75th percentile*: SAT Critical Reading 580, SAT Math 590; ACT Composite 24, ACT English 24, ACT Math 25.

95% of freshmen from Texas. Undergraduates from 36 states and 64 foreign countries.

Admission: Rolling admissions plan. Apply no later than day before registration. Early acceptance available. *Requirements:* To be eligible for admission to the university, a student must be a high school graduate and have completed 4 units English, 3 mathematics, 3 science, 2 foreign language, 3 social studies, 5 academic electives. The General Education Development Test is not considered as the equivalent of graduation from a high school. The College of Engineering and the School of Architecture have higher admission requirements. *Entrance tests:* College Board SAT or ACT composite. For foreign students TOEFL. *For transfer students:* 2.25 minimum GPA; from 4-year accredited institution maximum transfer credit limited only by residence requirement; from 2-year accredited institution 72 semester hours; correspondence/extension students 30 hours.

College credit and advanced placement for postsecondary-level work completed in secondary school.

Degree Requirements: *For all undergraduate degrees:* 120 semester hours minimum; 2.0 GPA; 30 hours in residence; general education requirements.

Fulfillment of some degree requirements and exemption from some beginning courses possible by passing departmental examinations, College Board CLEP, AP. *Grading system:* A–F; pass-fail; withdraw (carries time limit).

Distinctive Educational Programs: Work-experience programs, including cooperative education, internships. Evening classes. Accelerated degree program. Dual-degree program in biomedical engineering with University of Texas Health Science Center at Dallas. Cooperative baccalaureate in medical technology with approved hospitals. Special facilities for using telecommunications in the classroom. Interdisciplinary programs in the humanities, Soviet and East European studies, urban studies. Preprofessional programs in dentistry, engineering, medicine. Facilities and programs for independent research, including honors programs, individual majors. Study abroad available in 40 countries worldwide. Community service learning programs are stressed in many disciplines across the university.

ROTC: Army. Air Force in cooperation with Texas Christian University.

Degrees Conferred: 3,835 *baccalaureate* (B); 1,663 *master's* (M); 142 *doctorate* (D); 33 *first-professional*. Degrees awarded: architecture 103 (B), 77 (M); biological/life sciences 163, (B), 19 (M), 2 (D); business/marketing 1,032 (B), 499 (M); 9 (D); communications/communication technologies 188 (B); computer and information sciences 8 (B), 47 (M); education 127 (M); engineering and engineering technologies 284 (B), 548 (M); 20 (D); English 116 (B), 6 (M); foreign languages and literature 55 (B), 11 (M), 3 (D); health professions and related sciences 312 (B), 70 (M); home economics and vocational home economics 2 (B); interdisciplinary studies 276 (B), 19 (M); liberal arts/general studies 2 (M), 1 (D); mathematics 16 (B), 10 (M), 5 (D); parks and recreation 66 (B); philosophy/religion/theology 9 (B); physical sciences 23 (B), 11 (M), 6 (D); protective services/public administration 142 (B), 266 (M); 8 (D); psychology 99 (B), 8 (M), 4 (D); social sciences and history 193 (B), 32 (M); visual and performing arts 124 (B).

Fees and Other Expenses: *Full-time tuition per academic year 2008–09:* undergraduate resident $7,780, contact the university for current resident/nonresident graduate tuition. *Other fees:* 1,670 undergraduate, $1,264 graduate. *Room and board per academic year:* $8,412. *Books and supplies:* $882. *Other expenses:* $3,850.

Financial Aid: Aid from institutionally generated funds is provided on the basis of academic merit, financial need, athletic ability.

Financial aid to full-time, first-time undergraduate students: 52% received some form of aid. Average amount of aid received: federal grants $3,269; Pell grants $2,960; other federal aid $871; state/local grants $4,108; institutional grants $2,286.

Departments and Teaching Staff: *Total instructional faculty:* 1,081 (full-time 758, part-time 323). Total faculty with doctorate, first-professional, or other terminal degree: 750. Student/faculty ratio: 22:1. Degrees held by full-time faculty: master's 23%, doctorate 74.6%, baccalaureate 1.2%, professional 1.2%. 82.5% hold terminal degrees.

Enrollment: *Total enrollment:* 25,084. Undergraduate 18,985 (full-time 70%; female 52%, male 48%). Graduate 6,099 (full-time 49%). Undergraduate transfer-in students 3,088.

Characteristics of Student Body: *Ethnic/racial makeup:* Black non-Hispanic: 15%; American Indian or Alaska Native: 1%; Asian or Pacific Islander: 12%; Hispanic: 18%; White non-Hispanic: 48%; unknown: 2%; nonresident alien 4%. *Age distribution:* number under 18: 238; 18–19: 3,935; 20–21: 4,872; 22–24: 4,762; 25–29: 2,527; 30–34: 1,218; 35–39: 632; 40–49: 697; 50–64: 221; 65 and over: 12.

International Students: 1,003 nonresident aliens enrolled fall 2008. Students from Europe, Asia, Latin America, Africa, Canada, Australia, New Zealand. Programs available to aid students whose native language is not English: English as a Second Language Program. No financial aid specifically designated for international students.

Student Life: On-campus residence halls house 14% of undergraduate student body. Available housing includes residence halls, married/family housing, Greek housing, on-campus apartments. 5% of males join fraternities; 4% of females join sororities. *Intercollegiate athletics:* male: baseball, golf; female: softball, volleyball. *Student activities:* Over 400 student organizations. *Special regulations:* Cars permitted without restrictions. *Special services:* Medical services. *Student publications: Shorthorn*, a newspaper; *UTA* , a magazine. *Surrounding community:* Arlington population 300,000. Served by airport 15 miles from campus.

Library Collections: 1,135,500 volumes including bound books, serial backfiles, electronic documents, and government documents not in separate collections. Online catalog. Current serial subscriptions: 37,062 paper, 1,472,120 microform, 229 via electronic access. Computer work stations available campus-wide. Students have access to the Internet at no charge.

Most important special holdings include Mexican American War Collection; American fiction of the late 19th century; Virginia Garrett Cartographic History Library; Minority Cultures Collection.

Buildings and Grounds: Campus area 395 acres. Campus DVD available.

Chief Executive Officer: Dr. James Spaniolo, President.

Undergraduates address admission inquiries to George Norton, Director of Admissions; graduate inquiries to Raymond L. Jackson, Associate Dean of Graduate Studies.

University of Texas at Austin

University Station
Austin, Texas 78712-1111
Tel: (512) 471-8102 **E-mail:** www.applytexas.org
Fax: (512) 475-7475 **Internet:** www.utexas.edu

Institution Description: *Enrollment:* 49,984. *Degrees awarded:* Baccalaureate, first-professional (law, pharmacy), master's, doctorate.

Member of the Gulf Universities Research Consortium and Oak Ridge Associated Universities.

Accreditation: *Regional:* SACS-Comm. on Coll. *Professional*: accounting, architecture, business, dietetics, engineering, engineering technology, family and consumer science, interior design, journalism, law, librarianship, music, nursing, pharmacy, planning, psychology internship, public administration, rehabilitation counseling, social work, speech-language pathology, teacher education

History: Established as University of Texas, Main University 1881; offered first instruction at postsecondary level 1883; awarded first degree (baccalaureate) 1884; adopted present name 1967.

Institutional Structure: *Composition of institution:* Administrators 817. Academic affairs headed by executive vice president and provost. Management/business/finances directed by vice president for business affairs. Full-time instructional faculty 2,090. Academic governance body, University Council, meets an average of 12 times per year.

Calendar: Semesters. Academic year early Sept. to late May. Freshmen admitted Sept., Jan., June. Degrees conferred May, Aug., Dec. Formal commencement May. Summer session from early June to mid-Aug.

Characteristics of Freshmen: 29,501 applicants (female 15,094, male 14,407). 65% of applicants accepted. 39% of accepted applicants enrolled.

95% (6,483 students) submitted SAT scores; 32% (2,160 students) submitted ACT scores. *25th percentile*: SAT Critical Reading 540, SAT Math 570; ACT Composite 23, ACT English 24, ACT Math 22. *75th percentile*: SAT Critical Reading 660, SAT Math 680; ACT Composite 28, ACT English 29; ACT Math 29.

54% of entering freshmen expected to graduate within 5 years. 90% of freshmen from Texas. Freshmen from 44 states and 37 foreign countries.

Admission: Rolling admissions plan. Apply as early as 1 year, but not later than 1 month, before enrollment. *Requirements:* Graduation from accredited secondary school with 15.5 units which must include 4 English, 2 foreign language, 3 mathematics, 2 science, 3 social studies, 1.5 academic electives. Additional requirements for some programs. *Entrance tests:* College Board SAT, with acceptable score dependent on secondary school class rank. *For transfer students:* 2.0 minimum GPA; from 4-year accredited institution 90 hours maximum transfer credit; from 2-year accredited institution 60 hours.

Advanced placement for postsecondary-level work completed in secondary school.

Degree Requirements: *For undergraduate degrees:* 120 credit hours; 2.0 GPA; 30 semester hours in residence; general education requirements; demonstrated proficiency in a foreign language; exit competency examination in American history and government. *Grading system:* A–F; pass-fail; withdraw.

Distinctive Educational Programs: Special facilities for using telecommunications in the classroom. Interdisciplinary programs. Honors programs. Study abroad in Brazil, France, Italy, Peru.

ROTC: Army, Navy, Air Force in cooperation with Saint Edwards University.

Degrees Conferred: 8,669 *baccalaureate;* 2,975 *master's;* 862 *doctorate;* 597 *first-professional.* Bachelor's degrees awarded in top five disciplines: social sciences 1,310; business, management, marketing, and related support services 1,210; communication, journalism, and related programs 1,187; engineering 912; biological and biomedical sciences 623. Master's degrees awarded: various disciplines 2,975. Doctorates awarded: various disciplines 862. First-professional degrees awarded: law 471; pharmacy 126.

Fees and Other Expenses: *Full-time tuition per academic year 2008–09:* undergraduate resident $8,532, nonresident $27,760; contact the university for graduate and first-professional tuition/fees. *Room and board per academic year:* $9,246. *Books and supplies:* $818. *Other expenses:* $3,316.

Financial Aid: Aid from institutionally generated funds is provided on the basis of academic merit, financial need.

Financial aid to full-time, first-time undergraduate students: 87% received some form of aid. Average amount of aid received: federal grants $4,070; Pell grants $3,179; other federal aid $1,060; state/local grants $4,373; institutional grants $4,083.

Departments and Teaching Staff: *Total instructional faculty:* 2,721 (full-time 2,467, part-time 254). Total faculty with doctorate, first-professional, or other terminal degree: 2,414. Student/faculty ratio: 18:1.

Enrollment: Total enrollment 49,984. Undergraduate 37,369 (full-time 93%; female 52%, male 48%). Graduate 12,615 (full-time 87%). Undergraduate transfer-in students 2,270.

Characteristics of Student Body: *Ethnic/racial makeup:* Black non-Hispanic: 5%; Asian or Pacific Islander: 18%; Hispanic: 18%; White non-Hispanic: 55%; nonresident alien 4%).

International Students: 1,999 nonresident aliens enrolled fall 2008. Programs available to aid students whose native language is not English: English as a Second Language Program. No financial aid specifically designated for international students.

Student Life: On-campus residence halls house 12% of student body. Residence halls for males constitute 18% of such space, for females 26%, for both sexes 56%. Some students live on campus in cooperative housing. Housing available for married students. *Intercollegiate athletics:* male: baseball, basketball, football, golf, swimming, tennis, track; female: basketball, golf, gymnastics, soccer, swimming, tennis, track, volleyball. *Special regulations:* Registered cars with decals permitted. *Special services:* Learning Resources Center, medical services, bus service between campus and most areas of Austin. *Student publications, radio, television: Cactus*, a yearbook; *Daily Texas*, a newspaper; *Law Forum*, a monthly magazine; *UT Most*, a quarterly magazine. Radio station KUT-FM broadcasts 140 hours per week. Television station KLRU broadcasts 115 hours per week. *Surrounding community:* Austin population 350,000. San Antonio, 75 miles from campus, is nearest metropolitan area. Served by mass transit bus system; airport 5 miles from campus; passenger rail service 3 miles from campus.

Publications: *Journal of Library History* (quarterly) first published in 1966; *Research in African Literature* (quarterly) first published 1970; *Social Science Quarterly* first published 1961; *Texas Law Review* (published 8 times per year) first published 1922.

Library Collections: 8,230,000 volumes. 665,000 government documents; 6,084,000 microforms; 992,000 audiovisual materials; 50,000 periodicals including via electronic access.

Most important special holdings include Lyndon B. Johnson Presidential Papers; Benson Latin American Collection; Humanities Research Center holdings.

Buildings and Grounds: Campus area 1,464 acres.

Chief Executive Officer: Dr. Stephen A. Monti, President.

Address admission inquiries to Shirley F. Binder, Director of Admissions.

UNIVERSITY OF TEXAS AT AUSTIN—*cont'd*

College of Liberal Arts

Degree Programs Offered: *Baccalaureate* in American studies, anthropology, archeological studies, architectural studies, Asian studies, classics/classical languages, Czech, economics, English, ethnic studies, humanities, history, Italian, Latin, Latin American studies, linguistics, Middle Eastern studies, Oriental and African languages and literatures, philosophy, Portuguese, psychology, Russian, Scandinavian languages and literature, sociology, Spanish; *master's, doctorate* in various fields.

School of Architecture

Degree Programs Offered: *Baccalaureate, master's* in architecture; *master's* in community and regional planning.

College of Business Administration

Degree Programs Offered: *Baccalaureate* in accounting, actuarial science, business education/teacher certification, data processing and analysis, engineering-business; finance, general business, insurance, international business, management, marketing, office administration, petroleum land management, real estate, statistics, transportation; *master's, doctorate* in various fields.

College of Communication

Degree Programs Offered: *Baccalaureate* in advertising, journalism, radio-television-film; speech; *master's* in advertising; *master's, doctorate* in communication, journalism; radio-television-film, speech.

College of Education

Degree Programs Offered: *Baccalaureate* in elementary education, physical and health education, secondary education; *master's, doctorate* in cultural foundations of education, curriculum and instruction, educational administration, educational psychology, foreign language education, math and science education, math education, physical and health education, science education, special education.

College of Engineering

Degree Programs Offered: *Baccalaureate* in aerospace engineering, architectural engineering, chemical engineering, civil engineering, electrical engineering, engineering science, mechanical engineering, petroleum engineering; *master's, doctorate* in various fields.

College of Fine Arts

Degree Programs Offered: *Baccalaureate* in applied music, art, art education, art history, composition, dance, drama, drama education, drama production, music, music education, music literature, music theory, pedagogy, playwriting, studio art; *master's, doctorate* in various fields.

College of Natural Sciences

Degree Programs Offered: *Baccalaureate* in astronomy, biochemistry, biology-biological sciences, botany, chemistry, child development, clothing and textiles, computer science, dietetics, geology, home economics, home economics education, interior design, mathematics, medical technology, microbiology, nutrition, physics, zoology; *master's, doctorate* in various fields.

School of Nursing

Degree Programs Offered: *Baccalaureate, master's, doctorate.*

College of Pharmacy

Degree Programs Offered: *Baccalaureate, first-professional, master's, doctorate.*

School of Social Work

Degree Programs Offered: *Baccalaureate, master's, doctorate.*

School of Law

Degree Programs Offered: *First-professional; master's* in comparative jurisprudence, law.

Admission: *For first-professional:* Graduation from accredited college or university; 2.2 GPA; LSAT.

Degree Requirements: *For first-professional:* 84 credit hours; 65 GPA on 100-point scale; 3 years in residence.

Graduate School of Library and Information Science

Degree Programs Offered: *Master's, doctorate.*

Lyndon B. Johnson School of Public Affairs

Degree Programs Offered: *Master's.*

University of Texas at Brownsville

80 Fort Brown
Brownsville, Texas 78520-4991
Tel: (905) 544-8200 **E-mail:** admissions@utb.edu
Fax: (905) 982-0115 **Internet:** www.utb.edu

Institution Description: The University of Texas at Brownsville is a state-supported, upper-level institution and shares a campus with Texas Southmost College, a two-year institution. *Enrollment:* 11,560. *Degrees offered:* Baccalaureate, master's.

Accreditation: *Regional:* SACS-Comm. on Coll. *Professional*: business, clinical lab technology, nursing, respiratory therapy

History: Founded 1973.

Institutional Structure: *Governing board:* Representation: Senior administrators, president, vice presidents of academic affairs, business affairs, student affairs and administration, university affairs. Full-time instructional faculty 197.

Calendar: Semesters. Academic year Aug. to May.

Characteristics of Freshmen: 95% of accepted applicants enrolled.

Admission: Open admissions. Application deadline Aug. 1. *Requirements:* High school transcript, college transcript (if a transfer student applicant); TOEFL for foreign students. SAT or ACT. Test scores used for admission.

College credit and advanced placement for postsecondary-level work completed in secondary school and for extrainstitutional learning.

Developmental/remedial courses offered in summer session and regular academic year; credit given.

Degree Requirements: 124 semester hours; 8 semester hours of laboratory science, 6 semester hours foreign language. *Grading system:* A–F.

Fees and Other Expenses: *Full-time tuition per academic year 2008–09:* resident $4,425; contact the university for current nonresident tuition/fees. *Books and supplies:* $600. *Room and board per academic year:* $5,200.

Financial Aid: Aid from institutionally generated funds is provided on the basis of academic merit, financial need, athletic ability, other criteria.

Financial aid to full-time, first-time undergraduate students: 78% received federal grants averaging $3,370; 29% state/local grants averaging $2,792; 35% institutional grants averaging $762; 31% received loans averaging $2,516.

Departments and Teaching Staff: *Total instructional faculty:* 197.

Enrollment: Total enrollment 11,560.

Characteristics of Student Body: *Ethnic/racial makeup:* Black non-Hispanic: .1%; American Indian or Alaska Native: .1%; Asian or Pacific Islander: .2%; Hispanic: 90.8%; White non-Hispanic: 5.1%; unknown: .3%.

Student Life: *Intramural sports:* basketball, football, golf, gymnastics, sailing, soccer, swimming and diving, tennis, volleyball. *Special services:* Career planning, health services, computer center, counseling.

Library Collections: 150,000 volumes. 617,000 microforms; 4,450 serial subscriptions. 1,000 audiovisual materials. Online catalog. Students have access to online information retrieval services and the Internet.

Chief Executive Officer: Dr. Juliet V. Garcia, President.

Address admissions inquiries to Director of Enrollment.

University of Texas at Dallas

P.O. Box 830688
Richardson, Texas 75083-0688
Tel: (972) 883-2111 **E-mail:** enrollment@utdallas.edu
Fax: (972) 883-6803 **Internet:** www.utdallas.edu

Institution Description: The University of Texas at Dallas offers a strong research orientation at the graduate level and an interdisciplinary approach to undergraduate education. Focus is on sciences, mathematics and engineering. Callier Center for Communications Disorders provides assessment, treatment, education, and social services for the communicatively handicapped. *Enrollment:* 14,913. *Degrees awarded:* Baccalaureate, master's, doctorate.

Accreditation: *Regional:* SACS-Comm. on Coll. *Professional*: audiology, engineering technology, speech-language pathology

History: Established 1969 (precursor institution Southwest Center for Advanced Studies founded 1961) as a graduate research institution; first upper division undergraduates admitted 1975; first lower division undergraduates admitted 1990; awarded first degree (Ph.D., physics) 1973.

Institutional Structure: *Composition of institution:* Senior administrators: president, vice president for business affairs; provost and vice president for academic affairs; vice president for student, alumni, and external affairs. Executive director of information resources; executive director of development. *Academic structure:* Seven academic schools organized around programs of study rather than traditional departments by faculty discipline. Academic governance bodies, Academic Senate and Academic Council, meet an average of 12 times a year.

Calendar: Semesters. Academic year Aug. to May. Admission accepted Aug., Jan., May, July. Degrees conferred May, Aug., Jan. Formal commencement Jan., May, Aug. 12-week and 8-week summer sessions beginning May.

Characteristics of Freshmen: 4,937 applicants (femlae 2,360, male 2,556). 53% of applicants admitted. 44% of applicants admitted and enrolled.

96% (1,100 students) submitted SAT scores; 39% (445 students) submitted ACT scores. *25th percentile*: SAT Critical Reading 550, SAT Math 580; ACT Composite 24, ACT English 23, ACT Math 24. *75th percentile*: SAT Critical Reading 660, SAT Math 680; ACT Composite 29, ACT English 29, ACT Math 30.

51% of entering freshmen expected to graduate within 5 years. 90% of freshmen from Texas. Freshmen from 43 states and 29 foreign countries.

Admission: Freshmen, sophomore transfers, and executive MBA students admitted for fall term only. Rolling admission for all others for fall, spring, and summer terms. Conditional admission available. *Application deadlines:* For priority processing, applications due July 1 for fall, Nov. 1 for spring, Apr. 1 for summer; international students apply by June 1 for fall, Oct. 1 for spring, Apr. 1 for summer. *Requirements:* Freshmen/sophomores, graduation from an accredited secondary school with 4 units in language arts (including 1 in writing); 3.5 mathematics (beginning with Algebra I and including Trigonometry); 3 laboratory science beyond physical science; 3 social science; 2 same foreign language; .5 fine arts; 1.5 general education. Freshmen transfers, 3.0 GPA. Sophomore/junior/senior transfers, 2.5 GPA. Graduate students, bachelor's degree from an accredited institution in the U.S. or its equivalent; adequate subject preparation; 3.0 GPA in upper division undergraduate work and any graduate work completed. *Entrance tests:* freshmen/sophomores, SAT or ACT; graduate management applicants, GMAT; all other graduate applicants, GRE; foreign applicants, TOEFL (550 minimum paper exam, 215 computerized exam). Undergraduates must take TASP prior to registration.

Degree Requirements: *All undergraduate degrees:* 120 semester hours (51 in upper division courses); 2.0 GPA of last 30 hours, including 6 hours of advanced courses in major, in residence; completion of state mandated core curriculum; maximum of 12 hours by examination (CLEP or AP) may be used to satisfy lower division requirements. *Master's degrees:* number of hours varies by degree program from 33–60; all requirements must be completed within 6 years; up to 15 hours of graduate coursework may be transferred from another institution. *Doctoral degrees:* most 90 semester graduate hours; some vary; requirements must be completed in one 10-year period; up to one half semester credit hours required for a doctoral degree may be transferred from another institution.

Grading system: A–F, pass/fail, withdraw (time limit), incomplete (time limit).

Distinctive Educational Programs: Extensive evening classes, weekend classes; non-credit continuing education and professional/career development courses. Accelerated degree programs; fast track bachelor's/master's degree programs; student-designed majors; Independent research and study encouraged; facilities, tutorials available. *Unique degree programs:* Interdisciplinary Studies, Human Development and Communications Sciences, Applied Cognition and Neurosciences, Microelectronics, Telecommunications, Political Economy, International Management, B.S. Telecommunication Engineering, Clark Foundation Summer Research Participation Program, Teacher certification, certificate endorsements and Master of Arts in Teaching degrees offered. *Other:* Member of Academic Common Market (in-state tuition to graduate students from participating U.S. states). Concurrent enrollment (tuition savings) with components of The University of Texas System (all levels) and The Texas A&M University System (graduate level).

ROTC: Air Force offered in cooperation with North Texas State University; Army in cooperation with University of Texas at Arlington.

Degrees Conferred: 2,384 *baccalaureate* (B), 1,395 *master's* (M), 121 *doctorate* (D): area and ethnic studies 6 (B); biological/life sciences 89 (B), 11 (M), 3 (D); business/marketing 597 (B), 631 (M), 6 (D); computer and information sciences 266 (B), 218 (M), 6 (D); education 13 (M); engineering and engineering technologies 131 (B), 215 (M), 18 (D); foreign languages and literature 53 (B); health professions and related sciences 44 (B), 93 (M), 5 (D); interdisciplinary studies 239 (B), 25 (M); liberal arts/general studies 5 (B), 60 (M), 7 (D); mathematics 15 (B), 12 (M); 1 (D); physical sciences 24 (B), 25 (M), 4 (D); protective services/public administration 11 (B), 20 (M), 4 (D); psychology 128 (B), 13 (M); social sciences and history 173 (B), 25 (M). First-professional degrees awarded: various disciplines 146.

Fees and Other Expenses: *Full-time tuition per academic year 2008–09:* undergraduate resident $9,052, nonresident $18,000; contact the university for current graduate tuition/fees. *Room and board per academic year:* $8,828. *Books and supplies:* $1,200. *Other expenses:* $4170.

Financial Aid: Aid from institutionally generated funds is provided on the basis of academic merit, financial need.

Financial aid to full-time, first-time undergraduate students: 85% received some form of aid. Average amount of aid received: federal grants $3,577; Pell grants $3,354; other federal aid $1,955; state/local grants $5,452; institutional grants $7,108.

Departments and Teaching Staff: *Total instructional faculty:* 627 (full-time 432, part-time 195). Total faculty with doctorate, first-professional, or other terminal degree 509. Student/faculty ratio: 23:1. Degrees held by full-time faculty: doctorate 84%, master's 7%, baccalaureate 1%. 95% of faculty hold terminal degrees.

Enrollment: Total enrollment 14,913. Undergraduate 9,393. Graduate 5,320. Undergraduate transfer-in students 1,804.

Characteristics of Student Body: *Ethnic/racial makeup:* Black non-Hispanic: 8%; American Indian or Alaska Native: 1%; Asian or Pacific Islander: 21%; Hispanic: 11%; White non-Hispanic: 34%; unknown: 1%; nonresident alien 4%.

International Students: 597 nonresident aliens enrolled fall 2008. Programs available to aid students whose native language is not English: English as a Second Language Program; Campus Club meeting. No financial aid specifically designated for international students.

Student Life: On-campus apartments, privately owned/operated. *Special regulations:* Cars permitted without restrictions. Alcohol permitted in apartments and on-campus for special functions. *Special services:* Orientation, international student services, minority student services, disabled student services, veteran's services, Student Health Center, Student Counseling Center, Learning Resource Center (tutoring, math lab, test preparation, etc.). *Student publications: UTD Mercury*, a biweekly newspaper. *Student activities:* Intramural sports, individual sports facilities, various student social, honor, and service organizations, limited fraternities/sororities. *Surrounding community:* Dallas metropolitan area population 3 million. Served by airports 16 and 26 miles from campus, rail 18 miles, and bus 5 miles. Dallas Area Rapid Transit.

Publications: *Management* (biennial) first published 1997; *UTD Network* (biennial) first published 1997; *Translation Review* (triennial) first published 1978; *Issues in Science and Technology* (quarterly) first cooperatively published with UTD 1993; *Sojourn* first published 1994.

Library Collections: 1,400,000 volumes including bound books, serial backfiles, electronic documents, and government documents not in separate collections. Online catalog. 2,800,000 microforms; 5,100 audiovisual materials; 36,500 periodicals including via electronic access. Computer work stations available. Students with ID have access to the Internet at no charge.

Most important special holdings include History of Aviation Collection; Wineburgh Philatelic Research Library; Belsterling Collection of Natural History.

Buildings and Grounds: Campus area 455 acres.

Chief Executive Officer: Dr. David E. Daniel, President.

Address admission inquiries to Office of Admissions.

University of Texas at El Paso

500 West University Avenue
El Paso, Texas 79968-0500
Tel: (915) 747-5000 **E-mail:** admissions@utep.edu
Internet: www.utep.edu

Institution Description: *Enrollment:* 20,458. Baccalaureate, master's, doctorate.

Accreditation: *Regional:* SACS-Comm. on Coll. *Professional*: chemistry, engineering, music, nursing

History: Established as Texas State School of Mines and Metallurgy 1913; offered first instruction at postsecondary level 1914; awarded first degree (baccalaureate) 1916; became department of mines and metallurgy, a branch of the University of Texas 1919; changed name to Texas College of Mines and Metallurgy 1920, to Texas Western College 1949; adopted present name 1967. *See*

UNIVERSITY OF TEXAS AT EL PASO—*cont'd*

Francis Fugate, *Frontier College: The First Fifty Years* (El Paso: Texas Western Press, 1964) for further information.

Institutional Structure: *Composition of institution:* Administrators 125. Academic affairs headed by vice president for academic affairs. Management/ business/finances directed by vice president for finance and administration. Total faculty 792. Academic governance body, Faculty Senate, meets an average of 10 times per year.

Calendar: Semesters. Academic year Aug. to July. Freshmen admitted Sept., Jan., June, July. Degrees conferred Dec., May, Aug. Formal commencement May. Summer session June to Aug.

Characteristics of Freshmen: 5,147 applicants (female 2,874, male 2,353). 98% of applicants admitted. 65% of applicants admitted and enrolled.

74% (1,833 students) submitted SAT scores; 52% (573 students) submitted ACT scores. *25th percentile*: SAT Critical Reading 400, SAT Math 400; ACT Composite 15, ACT English 14, ACT Math 15; *75th percentile*: SAT Critical Reading 520, SAT Math 510; ACT Composite 22, ACT English 21, ACT Math 21.

13% of entering freshmen expected to graduate within 5 years. 86% of freshmen from Texas.

Admission: Rolling admissions plan. For fall acceptance, apply as early as end of junior year in secondary school, but not later than Aug. 15 of year of enrollment. Early acceptance available. *Requirements:* Graduation from accredited secondary school with 4 units English, 2 in a foreign language (or in another science), 3 mathematics (including 1 algebra for science and nursing applicants), 3 natural science (chemistry and physics for nursing applicants), 3 social studies. Additional requirements for college of engineering. GED accepted for students 18 years and older with average standard score of 45. *Entrance tests:* College Board SAT or ACT composite. For foreign students minimum TOEFL score 500. *For transfer students:* 2.0 minimum GPA; from 4-year accredited institution maximum transfer credit limited only be resident requirement; from 2-year accredited institution 66 semester hours; for correspondence/extension students 30 hours.

College credit and advanced placement for postsecondary-level work completed in secondary school. College credit for extrainstitutional learning.

Tutoring available. Developmental courses offered in summer session and regular academic year; credit given.

Degree Requirements: *For all undergraduate degrees:* 125–135 semester hours; 2.0 GPA; 30 credit hours in residence; general education and core course requirements. Fulfillment of some degree requirements and exemption from some beginning courses possible by passing College Board CLEP. *Grading system:* A–F; pass-fail; withdraw (carried time limit, deadline after which pass-fail is appended to withdraw); in progress.

Distinctive Educational Programs: Evening classes. Accelerated degree programs. Cooperative baccalaureate in medical technology with approved hospital programs. Special facilities for using telecommunications in the classroom. Interdepartmental and interdisciplinary programs in inter-American studies, Chicano studies; interdisciplinary master's programs. Preprofessional programs in occupational therapy, optometry, pharmacy, physical therapy. Physician's assistant program. Honors program. *Other distinctive programs:* Continuing education.

ROTC: Army. Air Force in cooperation with New Mexico State University.

Degrees Conferred: 2,631 *baccalaureate* (B), 744 *master's* (M), 37 *doctorate* (D): area and ethnic studies 6 (B), 3 (M); biological sciences 85 (B), 13 (M) 1 (D); business 342 (B), 132 (M); communications 96 (B), 6 (M); computer and information sciences 51 (B), 43 (M); education 288 (B), 229 (M), 6 (D); engineering 158 (B), 98 (M), 2 (D); English 45 (B), 18 (M); foreign languages 29 (B), 7 (M); health professions 275 (B), 45 (M); mathematics 11 (B), 12 (M); philosophy/religion/theology 8 (B); physical sciences 24 (B), 16 (M), 2 (D); psychology 83 (B), 3 (D); social sciences and history 97 (B), 25 (M); visual and performing arts 66 (B), 8 (M), 10 (D).

Fees and Other Expenses: *Full-time tuition per academic year 2008–09:* resident $6,121, nonresident $14,621. *Required fees:* $866. *Room and board per academic year:* $6,942. *Books and supplies:* $890. *Other expenses:* $3,240.

Financial Aid: Aid from institutionally generated funds is provided on the basis of academic merit, financial need, athletic ability, other criteria.

Financial aid to full-time, first-time undergraduate students: 75% received some form of aid. Average amount of aid received: federal grants $4,098; Pell grants 43,523; other federal aid $860; state/local grants $4,810; institutional grants $2,209.

Departments and Teaching Staff: *Total instructional faculty:* 949 (full-time 632, part-time 317).

Enrollment: Total enrollment 20,458. Undergraduate 16,976 (full-time 65%; female 55%, male 45%). Graduate 3,482 (full-time 32%). Undergraduate transfer-in students 1,394.

Characteristics of Student Body: *Ethnic/racial makeup:* Black non-Hispanic: 3%; Asian or Pacific Islander: 1%; Hispanic: 78%; White non-Hispanic: 9%; nonresident alien 9%. *Age distribution:* number under 18: 267; 18–19: 4,103; 20–21: 3,500; 22–24: 3,578; 5–29: 2,000; 30–34: 871; 35–39: 517; 40–49: 590; 50–64: 142; 65 and over: 24.

International Students: 1,841 nonresident aliens enrolled fall 2008. Students from Europe, Asia, Latin America, Africa, Canada, Australia, New Zealand,. Programs available to aid students whose native language is not English: English as a Second Language Program. No financial aid specifically designated for international students.

Student Life: On-campus residence halls for both males and females house 5% of student body. 2% of males join and some live in fraternity housing. 2% of females join and some live in sorority housing. Housing available for married students. *Intercollegiate athletics:* male: baseball, basketball, football, rifle, soccer, track; female: basketball, gymnastics, track, volleyball. *Special regulations:* Cars permitted in designated areas only; fee charged. *Special services:* Learning Resources Center, medical services. *Student publications, radio: Amphora Review*, a biannual literary magazine; *Headframe*, a general interest magazine; *Prospector*, a biweekly newspaper. Radio station WVOF-AM broadcasts 70 hours per week, KTEP-FM broadcasts 24 hours a day. *Surrounding community:* El Paso population 425,000. Served by mass transit bus system, airport 8 miles from campus, passenger rail service 1 mile from campus.

Publications: *Bulletin of the Cross-Cultural Southwest Ethnic Study Center at U.T. El Paso* (quarterly), *El Paso Economic Review* (quarterly), *Southwest Business and Economic Review* (quarterly) first published 1964, *Southwestern Studies* (quarterly) first published 1963.

Library Collections: 1,100,000 volumes. 1,800,000 microforms; 10,000 audiovisual materials; 3,000 current periodical subscriptions. Online catalog. Students have access to online information retrieval services and the Internet.

Most important special holdings include J. Carl Hertzog collection of materials on print, books, and book design; Mexican and Southwestern Collection; S.L.A. Marshall Military History Collection.

Buildings and Grounds: Campus area 333 acres. Campus DVD available.

Chief Executive Officer: Dr. Diana S. Natalicio, President.

Undergraduates address admission inquiries to Irma Nu'ez Rubio, Director of Admissions; graduate inquiries to Patricia A. Caracena, Director, Graduate Student Services.

College of Liberal Arts

Degree Programs Offered: *Baccalaureate* in anthropology, art, broadcasting, creative writing, criminal justice, drama, education for deaf and/or severely hard of hearing, English and American literature, French, German, history, journalism, linguistics, music, philosophy, political science, psychology, social work, sociology, Spanish; speech, hearing, and language disorders; *master's* in anthropology, applied English linguistics, creative writing, drama, English and American literature, history, interdisciplinary studies, political science, professional writing and rhetoric, psychology, public administration, sociology, Spanish, speech pathology and audiology.

College of Business

Degree Programs Offered: *Baccalaureate* in accounting, business administration, economics, finance; *master's* in business administration, economics.

College of Education

Degree Programs Offered: *Baccalaureate* in elementary education, secondary education curriculum and instruction; *master's* in counseling, curriculum and instruction educational administration and supervision, educational psychology and guidance, elementary and secondary supervision, elementary education, health and physical education professional school administration, secondary education.

College of Engineering

Degree Programs Offered: *Baccalaureate* in computer science; *baccalaureate and master's* in civil, electrical, industrial, mechanical, and metallurgical engineering.

College of Nursing

Degree Programs Offered: *Baccalaureate, master's.*

College of Science

Degree Programs Offered: *Baccalaureate* in biology, botany, chemistry, geology, mathematics, microbiology, physics, zoology; *master's* in general chemistry, geology, mathematics, physics; *doctorate* in geology.

Distinctive Educational Programs: Research program for advanced students through biological sciences and chemistry departments. Biological sciences department maintains collection of arid lands flora and fauna for teaching and research purposes.

University of Texas at San Antonio

6900 North Loop 1604 West
San Antonio, Texas 78249-0617
Tel: (210) 458-4706 **E-mail:** admissions@utsa.edu
Fax: (210) 458-4708 **Internet:** www.utsa.edu

Institution Description: *Enrollment:* 28,413. *Degrees awarded:* Baccalaureate, master's, doctorate.

Academic offerings subject to approval by statewide coordinating bodies. Budget subject to approval by state governing boards.

Accreditation: *Regional:* SACS-Comm. on Coll. *Professional*: accounting, art, business, engineering, histologic technology, interior design, music, nursing

History: Established 1969; offered first instruction at postsecondary level 1973; awarded first degree (master's) 1974.

Institutional Structure: *Composition of institution:* 7 Executive Offices with 8 men / 5 women administrators plus 4 colleges with 22 men / 2 women administrators. Academic affairs headed by vice president for academic affairs. Management/business/finances directed by vice president for business affairs. Full-time instructional faculty 372. Academic governance bodies, University Assembly and Council on Graduate Education.

Calendar: Semesters. Academic year Aug. to May. Freshmen admitted Aug., Jan., June. Degrees conferred May, Aug., Dec. Formal commencement May and Dec. Summer session of 2 terms from June to Aug with May 1 application deadline.

Characteristics of Freshmen: 10,929 applicants (femlae 5,631, male 4,298). 99% of applicants accepted. 49% of accepted applicants enrolled.

17% of entering freshmen expected to graduate within 5 years. 97% of freshmen from Texas. Freshmen from 34 states and 23 foreign countries.

Admission: Rolling admissions plan. For fall acceptance, apply as early as beginning of senior year in secondary school, but not later than Aug. 1 of year of enrollment. $20 application fee must accompany all applications for admission. Early acceptance available. *Requirements:* Either graduation from accredited secondary school with 14 units; or GED. Recommend 4 units English, 2 in a foreign language, 3 mathematics, 2 laboratory science, 2 social studies, 1 fine arts. For out-of-state applicants lowest acceptable secondary school class standing 50th percentile. *Entrance tests:* College Board SAT or ACT Composite. For foreign students TOEFL score 550. *For transfer students:* 2.0 minimum GPA; from 4-year accredited institution 96 semester hours maximum transfer credit; from 2-year accredited institution 66 semester hours; correspondence/extension students 30 hours.

College credit and advanced placement for postsecondary-level work completed in secondary school.

Tutoring available. Developmental courses offered in summer session and regular academic year; credit given.

Degree Requirements: 120-146 semester hours; 2.0 GPA; 30 hours in residence; general education and core requirements.

Fulfillment of some degree requirements possible by passing departmental examinations, College Board CLEP. *Grading system:* A–F; pass-fail; credit-no credit; withdraw (deadline after which pass-fail appended to withdraw).

Distinctive Educational Programs: Work-experience programs. Evening classes. Degree program in mechanical, electrical, and civil engineering. Cooperative baccalaureate programs in medical technology, occupational therapy, and physical therapy with the University of Texas Health Science Center at San Antonio; medical technology also available with approved hospitals. Special facilities for using telecommunications in the classroom. Interdisciplinary programs in bicultural-bilingual studies, environmental management. Preprofessional programs in dentistry, medicine, nursing. Study abroad in Australia, Canada, England, Japan, Mexico, France, Spain, Italy. *Other distinctive programs:* Research opportunities. Continuing education. Gifted and Talented Student Program for high school students. Honors Program. Economic Development Centers.

ROTC: Army, Air Force.

Degrees Conferred: 3,553 *baccalaureate*; 886 *master's*; 57 *doctorate*. Bachelor's degrees awarded in top five disciplines: business, management, marketing, and related support services 852; multidisciplinary studies 265; psychology 212; biological/life sciences 207; security and protective services 182. Master's degrees awarded: various disciplines 886. Doctorates awarded: various disciplines 57.

Fees and Other Expenses: *Full-time tuition per academic year 2008–09:* undergraduate resident $6,056, nonresident $12,850; contact the university for current graduate tuition/fees. *Books and supplies*$1,000. *Room and board per academic year:* $7,770. *Other expenses:* $2,630.

Financial Aid: Aid from institutionally generated funds is provided on the basis of academic merit, financial need, other considerations.

Financial aid to full-time, first-time undergraduate students: 65% received some form of aid. Average amount of aid received: federal grants $3,826; Pell grants $3,231; other federal aid $743; state/local grants $4,906; institutional grants $2,051.

Departments and Teaching Staff: *Total instructional faculty:* 866. Student/faculty ratio: 19:1. Degrees held by full-time faculty: 99% hold terminal degrees.

Enrollment: Total enrollment 28,413. Undergraduate 24,848 (full-time 79%; female 51%, male 49%). Graduate 3,765 (full-time 38%). Undergraduate transfer-in students 2,362.

Characteristics of Student Body: *Ethnic/racial makeup:* Black non-Hispanic: 8%; Asian or Pacific Islander: 7%; Hispanic: 44%; White non-Hispanic: 39%; nonresident alien 2%.

International Students: 568 nonresident aliens enrolled fall 2008. Students from Europe, Asia, Latin America, Mexico, Africa, Canada, Australia. Programs available to aid students whose native language is not English: social. English as a Second Language Program. No financial aid specifically designated for international students.

Student Life: On-campus residence halls and apartments. *Special regulations:* Registered cars permitted on campus; fee charged. *Special services:* Learning Assistance Center; state-of-the-art computer labs. Disabled Student Services. Medical Services. 112 registered student organizations. Fraternities, sororities, and national honor societies. Career, academic, and psychological counseling services. *Student publications: The Paisano,* a student-owned newspaper published weekly. *Surrounding community:* San Antonio population 786,000. Served by mass transit bus system; airport and passenger rail service each 16 miles from campus.

Publications: *The Roadrunner,* a university newsletter published weekly; *The Sombrilla,* the official alumni newsletter published 3 times a year.

Library Collections: 778,000 volumes including bound books, serial backfiles, electronic documents, and government documents not in separate collections. Online catalog. 3,200,000 microforms; 48,000 audiovisual materials; 35,000 periodicals including via electronic access. Computer work stations available. Students have access to the Internet at no charge.

Most important special holdings include John Peace Collection (Texana); Richard D. Warden Collection (Southwest and Northwest Americana); Ralph Haywood Collection (architecture).

Buildings and Grounds: Campus area 600 acres located 16 miles northwest of the center of San Antonio.

Chief Executive Officer: Dr. Ricardo Romo, President.

Address admission inquiries to Jennifer Ehlers, Dirctor of Admissions.

University of Texas at Tyler

3900 University Boulevard
Tyler, Texas 75799
Tel: (903) 566-7000 **E-mail:** admissions@uttyl.edu
Fax: (903) 565-5705 **Internet:** www.uttyl.edu

Institution Description: The University of Texas at Tyler provides upper division and master's degree study only. *Enrollment:* 6,117. *Degrees awarded:* Baccalaureate, master's.

Accreditation: *Regional:* SACS-Comm. on Coll. *Professional*: business, clinical lab scientist, industrial technology, nursing

History: Established as Tyler State College 1971; offered first instruction at postsecondary level 1973; awarded first degree (baccalaureate) 1974; changed name to Texas Eastern University 1975; adopted present name 1979.

Institutional Structure: *Composition of institution:* Administrators 15. Academic affairs headed by vice president for academic affairs. Management/business/finances directed by vice president for fiscal affairs. Administrative and Student Services headed by vice president for administration. Full-time instructional faculty 234. Academic governance body, Deans Council, meets an average of 36 times per year.

Calendar: Semesters. Academic year Aug. to May. Students admitted Aug., Jan., May, July. Degrees conferred and formal commencement May, Aug.

Characteristics of Freshmen: 1,411 applicants (female 800, male 511). 80% of applicants admitted. 52% of admitted applicants enrolled full-time. 69% (419 students) submitted SAT scores; 58% (350 students) submitted ACT scores.

UNIVERSITY OF TEXAS AT TYLER—*cont'd*

Admission: Rolling admissions plan. Apply no later than registration. *Requirements:* Graduation from accredited community or junior college, or 42 semester hours from accredited postsecondary-level institution; 2.0 minimum GPA; course work must include 6 hours freshman grammar and/or composition or advanced composition, 6 humanities and liberal arts from at least 2 disciplines, 3 literature, 9 science and mathematics (including laboratory science and mathematics or computer science), 6 U.S. history, 6 federal and state government. *Entrance tests:* For foreign students TOEFL. *For transfer students:* From 4-year accredited institution 1 year upper division maximum transfer credit; correspondence/extension students 6 hours.

Degree Requirements: *For all undergraduate degrees:* 124 semester hours; 2.0 GPA; 20 hours in residence. *Grading system:* A–F; pass; withdraw.

Distinctive Educational Programs: Internships. Flexible meeting places and schedules, including off-campus centers (at various locations in east Texas), evening classes. Cooperative master's in social work with the University of Texas at Arlington. Interdepartmental program in general studies. Travel/Study International Programs offers study in such countries as France, Russia, England. Cultural/study exchange with the University of Metz, France.

Degrees Conferred: 1,028 *baccalaureate*; 28 *master's*. Bachelor's degrees awarded in top five disciplines: multidisciplinary studies 128 business, management, marketing, and related support services 127 health professions and related clinical sciences 125; English language/literature 40; psychology 39. Master's degrees awarded: education 28.

Fees and Other Expenses: *Full-time tuition per academic year 2008–09:* resident $4,764, nonresident $11,508; contact the university for current graduate tuition and applicable fees. *Room and board per academic year (off campus):* $7,510. *Books and supplies:* $920. *Other expenses:* $1,920.

Financial Aid: Aid from institutionally generated funds is provided on the basis of academic merit, financial need.

Financial aid to full-time, first-time undergraduate students: 77% received some form of aid. Average amount of aid received: federal grants $3,656; Pell grants $3,153; other federal aid $754; state/local grants $3,967; institutional grants $2,841.

Departments and Teaching Staff: *Total instructional faculty:* 378 (full-time 234, part-time 144). Degrees held by full-time faculty: 90% hold terminal degrees.

Enrollment: Total enrollment 6,117. Undergraduate 5,091 (full-time 76%; female 59%; male 41%). Graduate 1,026 (full-time 25%). Undergraduate transfer-in students 816.

Characteristics of Student Body: *Ethnic/racial makeup:* Black non-Hispanic: 10%; American Indian or Alaska Native: 1%; Asian or Pacific Islander: 25; Hispanic: 1%; White non-Hispanic: 10%; unknown: 1%; nonresident alien 1%.

International Students: 61 nonresident aliens enrolled fall 2008. Students from Europe; Asia, Latin America, Africa, Canada, Australia. No programs available to aid students whose native language is not English. No financial aid specifically designated for international students.

Student Life: No on-campus housing. Student Association, official student government organization, and more than 30 other organizations for specific interests and areas of study. *Special regulations:* Cars with parking permits allowed. *Special services:* Learning Resources Center. *Student publication: The University of Texas Patriot*, a biweekly newspaper. *Surrounding community:* Tyler population 70,000. Dallas, 90 miles from campus, is nearest metropolitan area. Served by airport 16 miles from campus.

Publications: *The Forum*, university magazine published by the Information Office.

Library Collections: 220,000 volumes including bound books, serial backfiles, electronic documents, and government documents not in separate collections. Online catalog. Current serial subscriptions: 1,484 paper, 28 electronic. Computer work stations available. Students have access to the Internet at no charge.

Most important special holdings include Sarah McClendon Papers; Camp Ford Collection; Tyler and East Texas Civil War Collection.

Buildings and Grounds: Campus area 207 acres.

Chief Executive Officer: Dr. Rodney H. Mabry, President.

Address admission inquiries to Jim Hutto, Dean, Enrollment Management.

University of Texas Health Science Center at Houston

1100 Holcombe Boulevard
P.O. Box 20036
Houston, Texas 77225
Tel: (713) 500-3333 **E-mail:** admin4@uthsc.edu
Fax: (713) 794-5701 **Internet:** www.uthsc.edu

Institution Description: The University of Texas Health Science Center at Houston is part of the 355-acre Texas Medical Center, a complex of over 20 public and private institutions including health care facilities and schools. It offers upper division, graduate and first-professional study only. *Enrollment:* 3,587. *Degrees awarded:* Baccalaureate, first-professional (dentistry, medicine), master's, doctorate. Certificates also awarded.

Accreditation: *Regional:* SACS-Comm. on Coll. *Professional*: blood bank technology, clinical lab scientist, dental assisting, dental hygiene, dentistry, dietetics, histologic technology, medicine, nurse anesthesia education, nursing, perfusion, public health, radiography, respiratory therapy

History: Consists of 6 component schools established between 1905 and 1973 and administratively combined under the umbrella of a health science center in 1972.

Institutional Structure: *Composition of institution:* Administrators 11. Academic affairs headed by vice president for educational services, interprofessional education, and international programs. Management/business/finances directed by executive vice president for administration and finance. Full-time instructional faculty 824. Interdisciplinary faculty advisory body, Interfaculty Council, meets an average of 10 times per year.

Calendar: Semesters. Academic year Sept. to Aug. Formal commencement June.

Admission: For foreign students TOEFL. Tutoring available.

Distinctive Educational Programs: Education, research, and clinical practice opportunities at The University of Texas System Cancer Center and other hospitals and institutions of the Texas Medical Center. Study abroad in University of London King's College, England; Tokyo Dental College, Japan; Capital Institute of Medicine, Beijing, People's Republic of China.

Degrees Conferred: 152 *baccalaureate:* health professions and related sciences; 337 *master's* health professions and related sciences; 98 *doctorate:* health professions and related sciences; 250 *first-professional:* dentistry, medicine,

Fees and Other Expenses: *Full-time tuition per academic year 2008–09:* contact the university center for current tuition, fees, and housing costs.

Financial Aid: Aid from institutionally generated funds is provided on the basis of financial need. Institution has a Program Participation Agreement with the U.S. Department of Education for eligible students to receive Pell Grants and, depending upon the agreement, other federal aid.

Departments and Teaching Staff: *Total instructional faculty:* 1,046.

Enrollment: Total enrollment 3,587.

Characteristics of Student Body: *Ethnic/racial makeup:* Black non-Hispanic: 7%; American Indian or Alaska Native: 1%; Asian or Pacific Islander: 17%; Hispanic: 14%; White non-Hispanic: 53%; unknown: 6%.

International Students: 10 undergraduate nonresident aliens enrolled fall 2008. No programs available to aid students whose native language is not English. No financial aid specifically designated for international students.

Student Life: Approximately 13% of student body live in the university apartment complex, located 1 mile from campus. *Special regulations:* Evening and weekend parking available on campus in designated areas. *Special services:* Learning Resources Center, medical services, psychological counseling, child care center, shuttle bus serving buildings throughout the Texas Medical Center and outlying parking areas; special bus service to and from the university apartment complex and the Texas Medical Center. *Student publications, television:* bimonthly student newsletter; bimonthly medical student newsletter; biennial student guide; monthly dental student television broadcast; campus-wide televised student calendar. *Surrounding community:* Houston area population 4 million. Served by one major airport and one smaller airport, 24 and 10 miles respectively from campus.

Library Collections: 250,000 volumes. 600 microforms, 1,800 audiovisual materials, 4,500 current periodical subscriptions. Access to online information retrieval services and the Internet.

Most important holdings include arthritis, rheumatism, and government book and manuscript collection; Harris County Medicine-Local History Collection; Space Life Sciences Archive from NASA.

Buildings and Grounds: Campus area 97 acres.

Chief Executive Officer: Dr. James T. Willerson, President.

Address admission inquiries to Registrar.

School of Allied Health Sciences

Degree Programs Offered: *Baccalaureate* in nutrition and dietetics, medical technology, perfusion technology, respiratory therapy; *certificate* in biomedical communications, cytogenetics, nurse anesthesia, radiologic technology.

Admission: *For baccalaureate:* in medical technology, 90 semester hours from an accredited college or university; in nutrition and dietetics, 60 semester hours from an accredited college or university, Allied Health Professions Test; in perfusion technology, 60 semester hours from an accredited college or university; in respiratory therapy, 60 semester hours from an accredited college or university. *For all degrees:* Science requirements and coursework in English, mathematics, U.S. history and government, humanities and social studies.

Degree Requirements: 182–210 quarter hours, 2.0 GPA, 36 quarter credits in residence.

Distinctive Educational Programs: The University of Texas School of Allied Health Sciences has provided special leadership in a number of areas: the Program in Medical Technology has one of the first programs in cytogenetics in the country and the only program in Texas to offer a structured educational program in cytogenetics; the Program in Biomedical Communications has a special orientation toward instructional design and evaluation in the health care setting; the Perfusion Technology Program is one of the first in the U.S. that offered an academic program leading to a baccalaureate degree. Other programs offer unique opportunities within the state: the Program in Nutrition and Dietetics has the only coordinated undergraduate program with an emphasis on community nutrition; the Respiratory Therapy program was one of the first to offer a baccalaureate degree in respiratory therapy; the Nurse Anesthesia Program, in collaboration with the University of Texas School of Nursing, awards the only Master of Science in Nursing with a connection in anesthesia. The School of Allied Health Sciences currently has an agreement with the University of Houston whereby the graduates of the Biomedical Communications Program in the school are given credit for their certificate work toward a Master of Education at the University of Houston.

School of Nursing

Degree Programs Offered: *Baccalaureate, master's.*

Admission: For baccalaureate: 60 semester hours from an accredited college or university in prenursing curriculum, 2.5 GPA, ACT or SAT.

Degree Requirements: *See* general requirements. *For baccalaureate:* 193 quarter hours, 2.0 GPA, 36 hours in residence.

Distinctive Educational Programs: Continuing education for nurses.

Dental Branch

Degree Programs Offered: *First-professional* in dentistry; *master's* in biomedical sciences; *certificate* in dental assisting, dental hygiene. Specialist certificates also awarded.

Admission: *For first-professional:* Minimum 60 semester hours from college or university with 1 year in English, 2 biology (1 laboratory), 1 each general chemistry, organic chemistry, and physics, all with laboratory; DAT.

Degree Requirements: *For first-professional:* 265.4 hours; 32 months in residence; 2.0 GPA; core curriculum; comprehensive examination.

Distinctive Educational Programs: Continuing education course for dental practitioners.

University of Texas Medical School at Houston

Degree Programs Offered: *First-professional.*

Admission: 90 hours academic work from accredited institution with 1 year English; 1 biology; 1 each general biology, general chemistry, organic chemistry, physics (all with laboratory); 1/2 calculus. Applicants must have grade of C or better in above courses. MCAT.

Degree Requirements: 4 academic years, core curriculum, clinical clerkship.

Distinctive Educational Programs: Students may take courses at Baylor College of Medicine, Rice University, and other Health Science Center schools. Joint M.D.-Ph.D. in cooperation with Graduate School of Biomedical Sciences. Joint M.D.-Master's in cooperation with School of Public Health.

Graduate School of Biomedical Sciences

Degree Programs Offered: *Master's* in biomedical sciences, medical physics, nuclear physics; *doctorate* in biomedical sciences, immunology, reproductive biology, virology.

Distinctive Educational Programs: Individualized or specialized programs of study and research in 22 areas of concentration in biomedical science. Centers for study of cancer, sensory sciences, medical genetics, demographic and population genetics. Cooperative agreements with Baylor College of Medicine, Rice University, University of Houston.

School of Public Health

Degree Programs Offered: *Master's* in community health/community health sciences; *doctorate* in community health/community health sciences.

Admission: TOEFL needed for students whose prior university coursework has not been in English.

Degree Requirements: Semester.

Distinctive Educational Programs: Teaching-research units explore public health issues, including disease control, health policy, international and rural health, nutrition, occupational health. *See* Medical School.

University of Texas Health Science Center at San Antonio

7703 Floyd Curl Drive
San Antonio, Texas 78284-3900
Tel: (210) 567-2621 **E-mail:** admin4@uthscsa.edu
Fax: (210) 567-2025 **Internet:** www.uthscsa.edu

Institution Description: The University of Texas Health Science Center at San Antonio is a state institution. *Enrollment:* 2,781. *Degrees awarded:* Baccalaureate, first-professional (dentistry, medicine), master's, doctorate. Certificates also awarded.

Academic offerings subject to approval by statewide coordinating bodies. Budget subject to approval by state governing boards.

Accreditation: *Regional:* SACS-Comm. on Coll. *Professional*: blood bank technology, dental assisting, dental hygiene, dental laboratory technology, dentistry, EMT-paramedic, medicine, nursing, occupational therapy, psychology internship

History: Established 1959; offered first instruction at postsecondary level 1966; awarded first degree (first-professional) 1970; adopted present name 1972.

Institutional Structure: *Composition of institution:* Administrators 12. Academic affairs headed by president. Management/business/finances directed by executive vice president for administration and business affairs. Full-time instructional faculty 725. Academic governance body, Faculty Council, meets and average of 10 times per year.

Calendar: Semesters. Calendar system may vary with school.

Distinctive Educational Programs: Special facilities for using telecommunications in the classroom. Independent study. Off-campus electives individually arranged by medical students in other health programs in the United States and abroad. *Other distinctive programs:* Continuing education.

Degrees Conferred: 318 *baccalaureate:* health professions; 131 *master's:* health professions; 34 *doctorate:* health professions; 281 *first-professional:* dentistry, medicine.

Fees and Other Expenses: *Full-time tuition per academic year:* contact the university for current tuition, fees, and housing costs.

Financial Aid: Aid from institutionally generated funds is provided on the basis of academic merit, financial need.

Institution has a Program Participation Agreement with the U.S. Department of Education for eligible students to receive Pell Grants and, depending upon the agreement, other federal aid.

Departments and Teaching Staff: *Total instructional faculty:* 935. Degrees held by full-time faculty: doctorate 27.9%, master's 11.0%, baccalaureate 3.3%, professional 57.8%. 91% hold terminal degrees.

Enrollment: Total enrollment 2,781. Undergraduate

Characteristics of Student Body: *Ethnic/racial makeup:* Black non-Hispanic: 4.6%; American Indian or Alaska Native: .3%; Asian or Pacific Islander: 6%; Hispanic: 37%; White non-Hispanic: 42.9%; unknown: 7.8%.

International Students: 10 undergraduate nonresident aliens enrolled fall 2008. No programs available to aid students whose native language is not English. No financial aid specifically designated for international students.

Student Life: *Special regulations:* Registered cars permitted; fee charged. *Special services:* Learning Resources Center, medical services. *Surrounding community:* San Antonio population 786,000. Served by airport 10 miles from campus.

Library Collections: 178,000 volumes. 3,600 audiovisual materials; 3,143 current periodical subscriptions. Students have access to online information retrieval services and the Internet.

Most important special holdings include P.I. Nixon Library of Rare Medical Books; University Archives, 1965 to present; Bexar County Medical Society Archives, 1900–present.

Buildings and Grounds: Campus area 100 acres.

Chief Executive Officer: Dr. Francisco Cigarroa, President.

Address admission inquiries to Director of Admissions.

UNIVERSITY OF TEXAS HEALTH SCIENCE CENTER AT SAN ANTONIO—*cont'd*

School of Allied Health Sciences

Degree Programs Offered: *Associate* in dental health, *baccalaureate* in occupational therapy. Certificates in dental assisting and dental laboratory technology also awarded.

Admission: Graduation from accredited secondary school with minimum overall grade average of C plus; must have 3 units English, 2 mathematics, 1 biology and 1 chemistry with grade of C in these units; or GED, DHAT, and ACT or SAT. *For baccalaureate:* 55 semester hours of lower-division work including general education requirements; 2.8 GPA.

Degree Requirements: *For associate:* 83 credit hours, 2 years in residence. *For baccalaureate:* 154 credit hours; 2 years in residence; field work.

School of Nursing

Degree Programs Offered: *Baccalaureate; master's* through Graduate School of Biomedical Science.

Admission: *For baccalaureate degree:* Must have completed 60 hours of general coursework at accredited college or university; 2.0 GPA overall (2.3 in prenursing courses); SAT or ACT.

Degree Requirements: *See* general requirements. *For baccalaureate degree:* 120 credit hours; 2.0 GPA; 24 of last 30 hours in residence.

Distinctive Educational Programs: Evening and weekend hours for some classes.

Dental School

Degree Programs Offered: *First-professional*

Admission: 60 semester hours from accredited college or university, including 1 English, 2 biology (1 with laboratory), 1 physics (with laboratory), 2 chemistry (1 general, 1 organic).

Degree Requirements: 4-year prescribed curriculum; 112 credits in residence. Clinical experience. 3.0 GPA recommended.

Distinctive Educational Programs: Double-degree programs (M.S.-D.D.S., Ph.D.-D.D.S). Interdisciplinary courses.

Medical School

Degree Programs Offered: *First-professional.*

Admission: 90 semester hours from accredited college or university, including 1 year English, 2 biology, 1/2 calculus, 1 physics with laboratory, 2 chemistry (1 general, 1 organic with laboratory) with 2.0 GPA.

Degree Requirements: 4-year prescribed curriculum; 2.0 GPA; entire program in residence; clinical experience; passing score on Parts I and II of National Board examinations.

Distinctive Educational Programs: Double-degree programs (M.D.-M.S.; M.D.-Ph.D.).

Graduate School of Biomedical Sciences

Degree Programs Offered: *Master's, doctorate* in anatomy, biochemistry, microbiology, pharmacology, physiology.

Admission: *For master's:* Baccalaureate from accredited college or university with 3.0 GPA; GRE; TOEFL for foreign students.

Degree Requirements: *For master's:* 30 credit hours; 3.0 GPA; 2 semesters in residence; thesis. *For doctorate:* 2 semesters in residence; dissertation.

Distinctive Educational Programs: Joint doctoral program in pharmacy offered with University of Texas at Austin.

University of Texas Medical Branch at Galveston

301 University Boulevard
Galveston, Texas 77555-0129
Tel: (409) 772-1215 **E-mail:** admissions@utma.edu
Fax: (409) 772-4466 **Internet:** www.utmb.edu

Institution Description: The University of Texas Medical Branch at Galveston offers upper division, first-professional and graduate study only. It is one of the operating components of the University of Texas System. Education of health-care professionals is accomplished through 4 schools, 2 institutes, and 7 hospitals. *Enrollment:* 2,172. *Degrees awarded:* Baccalaureate, first-professional (medicine), master's, doctorate.

Accreditation: *Regional:* SACS-Comm. on Coll. *Professional*: blood bank technology, clinical lab scientist, medicine, nursing, occupational therapy, physical therapy, physician assisting, psychology internship, respiratory therapy

History: Established 1881; offered first instruction at postsecondary level 1891; awarded first degree (first-professional) 1892. School for Nurses (now School of Nursing) opened 1890 and became university affiliated in 1896. Graduate programs started 1952; separate Graduate School 1969; became the Graduate School of Biomedical Sciences 1972. School of Allied Health Sciences opened 1968; Marine Biomedical Institute 1969; Institute for the Medical Humanities 1973. See *The University of Texas Medical Branch at Galveston, A Seventy-five Year History by the Faculty and Staff* (Austin, Texas: University of Texas Press, 1967) for further information.

Institutional Structure: *Composition of institution:* Chief Executive Officer, President. Academic affairs headed by vice president for academic affairs. Hospital management headed by vice president for hospital affairs. Professional fee management headed by vice president for medical profession affairs. Management/business/finances directed by executive vice president for administration and business affairs.

Calendar: Semesters. Academic year begins Aug. Entering students admitted summer or fall depending on program. For School of Medicine: year one, Aug.-June, year two June-June; year three, June-June; year four, June-May. Degrees conferred May, Aug., Dec. Formal commencement May, depending on program.

Admission: For fall acceptance, apply no later than Oct. 15 of the year prior to enrollment. Students are notified of acceptance beginning Jan. 15. *Requirements:* The university prefers that the student have an undergraduate degree from an accredited college or university in the United States. Students must have 1 year of college English, 2 biology with 1 year of lab, 1 general chemistry with lab, 1 organic chemistry with lab, 1 physics with lab, and a half year of calculus. All science courses required must be for science majors. *Entrance tests:* MCAT. Tutoring available to medical students.

Degree Requirements: Basic science core, years 1 and 2; clinical science core, year 3; clinical science electives, year 4.

Distinctive Educational Programs: Combined M.D./Ph.D. program: 1st year, basic science core plus graduate school seminars; next 2 years, graduate work and medical science research final 2 years, clinical core; after successful completion, both M.D. and Ph.D. are awarded.

Degrees Conferred: 240 *baccalaureate*, 114 *master's*, 38 *doctorate:* all in health professions; 190 *first-professional:* medicine.

Fees and Other Expenses: *Full-time tuition per academic year 2008–09:* contact the university for current tuition, fees, and other costs.

Financial Aid: The university offers a direct lending program. Aid from institutionally generated funds is provided on the basis of academic merit, financial need.

Departments and Teaching Staff: *Total instructional faculty:* 102. Degrees held by full-time faculty: 99% hold terminal degrees.

Enrollment: Total enrollment: 2,172.

Characteristics of Student Body: *Ethnic/racial makeup:* number of Black non-Hispanic: 49; American Indian or Alaska Native: 5; Asian or Pacific Islander: 46; Hispanic: 79; White non-Hispanic: 303; unknown: 12. *Age distribution:* number 18–19: 2; 20–21: 77; 22–24: 127; 25–29: 222; 30–34: 57; 35–39: 38; 40–49: 78; 50–64: 20; 65 and over: 1.

International Students: 120 nonresident aliens enrolled fall 2008. No programs available to aid students whose native language is not English. No financial aid specifically designated for international students.

Student Life: The four schools of the university have an active cocurricular program with student government association and director of campus life, as well as an ombudsman; comprehensive intramural program; symphonic series; 5 medical fraternities and 50 student professional organizations. Residence hall; fitness center; newspaper; student yearbook.

Publications: *Syndrome*, the student yearbook is produced through the Office of Campus Life. *Omni*, a quarterly newsletter of the Student Government Association and student news.

Library Collections: 250,000 volumes including bound books, serial backfiles, electronic documents, and government documents not in separate collections. Online catalog. Current serial subscriptions: 2,176 paper, 150 electronic. Computer work stations available. Students have access to the Internet at no charge.

Most important holdings include the Truman G. Blocker, Jr. History of Medicine Collections.

Chief Executive Officer: Dr. John D. Stobo, M.D., President.

Address inquiries to the Registrar.

School of Medicine

Degree Programs Offered: *Doctor of Medicine.*

Admission: For fall acceptance, apply no later than Oct. 15 of year prior to enrollment. Students are notified of acceptance beginning Jan. 15. *Requirements:* For first-professional students 90 semester hours from an accredited college or university with 1 year English, 2 biology, 2 chemistry (organic and general), 1 physics, ½ mathematics. Recommend completion of baccalaureate requirements and additional units in foreign languages, philosophy, history, social sciences. *Entrance tests:* MACT. Tutoring available.

Degree Requirements: Basic Science Core, years 1 & 2; Clinical Science Core, year 3; Clinical Science Electives, year 4.

Distinctive Educational Programs: Combined M.D./Ph.D. program: 1st year, basic science core plus graduate school seminars; next 2 years., graduate work and medical science research; final 2 years., clinical core; after successful completion, both M.D. and Ph.D. are awarded.

School of Nursing

Degree Programs Offered: *Baccalaureate, master's, doctorate.*

Admission: *For baccalaureate degree:* 60 semester hours college-level course work to include 6-8 anatomy and physiology, 3-4 microbiology, 6-8 chemistry, 3 nutrition, 3 intro sociology, 3 growth and development, 3 statistics, 3 behavioral science elective, 6 English, 6 U.S. history, 6 U.S. government, 4–9 free elective credit, first aid and CPR certification; 2.0 GPA; higher GPAs given first acceptance. *For master's degree:* baccalaureate degree in nursing from an NLN accredited school; score of 45 on Millers Analogy Test or score of 1000 on GRE; 3.0 GPA. A statistics course must have been completed within 5 years prior to acceptance. Proof of licensure in the U.S.

Degree Requirements: *Baccalaureate:* 127 semester hours, including Pre-professional work; 2.0 GPA; 24 of last 30 hours in residence. *Master's:* primary care practitioner in areas of adult health, pediatrics 42 semester hours.

Distinctive Educational Programs: Flexible option track with the baccalaureate program for registered nurses.

School of Allied Health Sciences

Degree Programs Offered: *Baccalaureate* in health information management, medical technology, occupational therapy, physician's assistant studies; health care administration, *certificate* in physician's assistant studies.

Admission: *For baccalaureate degree:* Requirements vary among the various professional courses of study in the school. In general, a minimum of 60 to 65 semester hours in specific courses or their equivalent when entering at the junior level; a minimum of 82 semester hours at the senior level. Minimum 2.0 to 2.8 GPA required on all prerequisite coursework with minimum acceptable grade-points stipulated for designated courses for some areas of study. 6 semester hours in American and Texas government, 6 in American history; 3 in Texas history may be substituted for ½ of the history requirement; other specific requirements vary by program.

Degree Requirements: *For the baccalaureate degree:* Requirements vary from 127 to 164 semester hours depending upon professional course of study.

Distinctive Educational Programs: Master of Science in Allied Health Sciences is offered through the Graduate School of Biomedical Sciences. Concentrated study may be pursued in health education and clinical gerontology. In cooperation with Galveston College (a 2-year community college) associate in applied science degree/certificate programs and postassociate degree/advanced certificate programs are offered in a variety of specialties.

University of Texas - Pan American

1201 West University Drive
Edinburg, Texas 78539-2999
Tel: (956) 381-2100 **E-mail:** admissions@utpa.edu
Fax: (956) 381-2150 **Internet:** www.utpa.edu

Institution Description: The University of Texas - Pan American (formerly Pan American University) is a state institution. *Enrollment:* 17,534. *Degrees awarded:* Associate, baccalaureate, master's, doctorate.

Academic offers subject to approval by statewide coordinating bodies. Budget subject to approval by state governing boards.

Accreditation: *Regional:* SACS-Comm. on Coll. *Professional*: business, chemistry, clinical lab scientist, dietetics., engineering, nursing, occupational therapy, physician assisting, rehabilitation counseling, social work, speech-language pathology, teacher education

History: Established and chartered as Edinburg Junior College, and offered first instruction at postsecondary level 1927; changed name to Edinburg Regional College 1948, to Pan American College 1951; became 4-year college 1952; became Pan American University 1971; became part of University of Texas system 1989.

Institutional Structure: *Governing board:* University of Texas System Board of Regents. Representation: 9 regents. All voting. *Composition of institution:* Asminlstrators 78. Academic affairs headed by provost. Management/business/finances directed by vice president for business affairs. Full-time instructional faculty 579. Academic governance body, Council of Deans, meets an average of 12 times per year.

Calendar: Semesters. Academic year Sept. to Aug. Freshmen admitted Aug., Jan., June, July. Degrees conferred May, Aug., Dec. Formal commencements May, Dec. Summer session from June to Aug.

Characteristics of Freshmen: 7,613 applicants (female 4,233, male 3,380). 68% of applicants admitted. 59% of applicants admitted and enrolled.

40% (1,131 students) submitted SAT scores; 100% (2,807 students) submitted ACT scores. *25th percentile*: SAT Critical Reading 400, SAT Math 420; ACT Composite 16. *75th percentile*: SAT Critical Reading 510, SAT Math 530; ACT Composite 21.

23% of entering freshmen expected to graduate within 5 years. 96% of freshmen from Texas. Freshmen from 14 states and 10 foreign countries.

Admission: Rolling admissions plan. Apply no later than the first week of registration. Early acceptance available. *Requirements:* Either graduation from accredited secondary school with 24 units which must include 4 English, 3 mathematics, 3 science, 3.5 social studies, .5 economics, 1.5 physical education, l5 health education, 2 foreign language, 1 fine arts. .5 speech, 1 technology application, 3.5 electives; or GED. *Entrance tests:* ACT Composite of at least 15. *For transfer students:* 2.0 minimum GPA; from 4-year and 2-year accredited institutions maximum transfer credit 94 credit hours; correspondence/extension students 45 hours.

Tutoring available. Developmental courses offered in summer session and regular academic year; credit given.

Degree Requirements: *For all baccalaureate degrees:* 124 hours; 30 hours in residence; 4 hours physical education courses; core requirements. *For all undergraduate degrees:* 2.0 GPA.

Fulfillment of some degree requirements and exemption from some beginning courses possible by College Board CLEP. *Grading system:* A–F; pass; withdraw (deadline after which pass-fail is appended to withdraw).

Distinctive Educational Programs: Work-experience programs. Accelerated degree programs. Dual degree program. Special facilities for using telecommunications in the classroom. Interdisciplinary programs in inter-American studies, Mexican-American heritage. Facilities and programs for independent research, including honors programs, tutorials.

ROTC: Army,

Degrees Conferred: 2,405 *baccalaureate*; 643 *master's*; 9 *doctorate*. Bachelor's degrees awarded in top five disciplines: interdisciplinary studies 406; business/marketing 365; health professions and related clinical sciences 228; biological/life sciences 143; engineering 104. Master's degrees awarded in top five disciplines: education 271; health professions 92; business/marketing 50; parks administration and social services 41; computer and information sciences 20. Doctorates awarded business/marketing 2; education 7.

Fees and Other Expenses: *Full-time tuition per academic year 2008–09:* undergraduate resident $4,304, nonresident $11,008; contact the university for current graduate tuition/fees. *Required fees:* $748. *Room and board per academic year:* $6,038. *Books and supplies:* $1,000. *Other expenses:* $2,452.

Financial Aid: Aid from institutionally generated funds is provided on the basis of academic merit, financial need, athletic ability.

Financial aid to full-time, first-time undergraduate students: 86% received some form of aid. Average amount of aid received: federal grants $4,074; Pell grants $3,540; other federal aid $706; state/local grants $5,102; institutional grants $1,893.

Departments and Teaching Staff: *Total instructional faculty:* 740 (full-time 572, part-time 168). Student/faculty ratio: 21.1:1. Degrees held by full-time faculty: doctorate 62%, master's 37%, baccalaureate 1%. 62% hold terminal degrees.

Enrollment: Total enrollment 17,534. Undergraduate 15,336 (full-time 73%; female 58%, male 42%). Graduate 7,198 (full-time 30%). Undergraduate transfer-in students 795.

Characteristics of Student Body: *Ethnic/racial makeup:* Black non-Hispanic: 1%; Asian or Pacific Islander 1%; Hispanic: 88%; White non-Hispanic: 5%. *Age distribution:* number under 18: 395; 18–19: 4,331; 20–21: 3,200; 22–24: 3,049; 25–29: 1,908; 30–34: 883; 35–39: 433; 40–49: 385; 50–64: 101; 65 and over: 3.

International Students: 789 nonresident aliens enrolled fall 2008. Programs available to aid students whose native language is not English: English as a Second Language Program. No financial aid specifically designated for international students.

Student Life: On-campus residence halls house 4% of student body. *Special services:* Learning Resources Center, medical services. *Student publications: El Bronco*, a yearbook; *Pan American*, a weekly newspaper. *Surrounding community:* Edinburg population 55,000. San Antonio, 220 miles from campus, is near-

UNIVERSITY OF TEXAS - PAN AMERICAN—*cont'd*

est metropolitan area. Served by mass transit bus system; airport 10 miles from campus.

Library Collections: 916,000 volumes including bound books, serial backfiles, electronic documents, and government documents not in separate collections. Current serial subscriptions: paper 1,915; microform 1,083,562; via electronic access 32,469. Online catalog. Computer work stations available. Students have access to the Internet at no charge.

Most important special holdings include collections on Lower Rio Grande Valley, Kika de la Garza Collection; Shary Collections.

Buildings and Grounds: Campus area 200 acres. *New buildings:* Child Development Center; Wellness Center; Health Clinic.

Chief Executive Officer: Dr. Blandina Cardenas, President.

Address undergraduate admission inquiries to Madalena Williams, Dean of Admissions; graduate inquires to Dr. Teofilo Ozuma, Associate Vice President for Graduate Studies.

University of Texas of the Permian Basin

4901 East University Boulevard
Odessa, Texas 79762-0001
Tel: (432) 552-2020 **E-mail:** admissions@utpb.edu
Fax: (432) 552-2374 **Internet:** www.utpb.edu

Institution Description: The University of Texas of the Permian Basin is a four-year comprehensive university. *Enrollment:* 3,406. Degrees awarded: Baccalaureate, master's.

Accreditation: *Regional:* SACS-Comm. on Coll.

History: Authorized 1969; offered first instruction at postsecondary level 1973; awarded first degrees (baccalaureate and master's) 1974; received authority in 1991 to offer instruction at lower division level; first freshman class fall 1991.

Institutional Structure: *Composition of institution:* Administrators 28. Executive functions carried out by president, vice president for academic affairs, vice president for business, vice president for student services. Deans lead College of Arts and Sciences, School of Business, School of Education. Full-time instructional faculty 113. Academic governance body, Faculty Senate, meets and average of 8 times per year.

Calendar: Semesters. Academic year Sept. to May. Entering students admitted at fall and spring semesters and at summer terms. Degrees conferred May, Aug., Dec. Formal commencements May, Aug., Dec.

Characteristics of Freshmen: 93% of applicants admitted. 51% of applicants admitted and enrolled.

33% (193 students) submitted SAT scores; 27% (72 students) submitted ACT scores. *25th percentile*: SAT Critical Reading 430, SAT Math 430; ACT Composite 19, ACT English 18, ACT Math 18. *75th percentile*: SAT Critical Reading 560, SAT Math 560; ACT Composite 24, ACT English 25, ACT Math 25.

17% of entering freshmen expected to graduate within 5 years. 98.3% of freshmen from Texas, Freshmen from 3 states and 4 foreign countries.

Admission: Rolling admissions plan. For fall acceptance, apply as early as 1 year prior to enrollment, but not later than registration day. *Requirements:* high school transcript with class rank or equivalent; scores from SAT or ACT. Transfers must provide college transcripts. TOEFL required for foreign students.

Degree Requirements: *For undergraduate degrees:* 120 credit hours; 2.0 GPA; 30 credits in residence; 6 hours Texas history and government, 6 American history and government, 6 English; English writing requirement. *Grading system:* A–F; pass-fail; withdraw; Z grade for progress in self-paced courses.

Distinctive Educational Programs: Internships. Evening classes. Master of Professional Accountancy. Interdisciplinary Bachelor of Arts in Humanities. Independent Study. UT Telecampus degrees. Self-paced instruction program.

Degrees Conferred: 409 *baccalaureate*; 109 *master's*. Bachelor's degrees awarded in top five disciplines: social sciences and history 89; home economics and vocational home economics 66; business/marketing 63; English 34; foreign languages and literature 31.

Fees and Other Expenses: *Full-time tuition per academic year 2008–09:* undergraduate resident $4,519, nonresident $12,550. *Books and supplies:* $750. *Required fees:* $877. *Room and board per academic year:* $4,000.

Financial Aid: Aid from institutionally generated funds is provided on the basis of academic merit, financial need.

Financial aid to full-time, first-time undergraduate students: need-based scholarships/grants totaling $3,853,067, self-help $4,160,209, tuition waivers $87,545; non-need-based scholarships/grants totaling $2,108,874, self-help $2,994,232,parent loans $21,825, tuition waivers $145,085, athletic awards $142,186.

Departments and Teaching Staff: *Total instructional faculty:* 195 (full-time 113, part-time 82). Total faculty with doctorate, first-professional, or other terminal degree: 124. Student/faculty ratio: 17:1. Degrees held by full-time faculty: doctorate 80%, master's 100%. 82% hold terminal degrees.

Enrollment: Total enrollment 3,406.

Characteristics of Student Body: *Ethnic/racial makeup:* number of Black non-Hispanic: 118; American Indian or Alaska Native: 13; Asian or Pacific Islander: 19; Hispanic: 937; White non-Hispanic: 1,477; unknown: 13.

International Students: No programs available to aid students whose native language is not English. No financial aid specifically designated for international students.

Student Life: Variety of living options; new apartment-style housing opened fall 1996. Student government; Student Senate; Program Board. *Intercollegiate athletics:* women: softball, volleyball; men's: soccer. Club sports. Student newspaper; student literary magazine. Office of Student Life provides Leadership Training, Freshman Orientation, Transfer Orientation. Other student activities and organizations. *Special regulations:* Cars must have parking permit. *Special services:* PASS Office, Writing Center. Center for Behavioral Analysis provides counseling and some psychological services. Fort Worth, 350 miles from campus, is nearest metropolitan area. Served by airport 10 miles from campus.

Library Collections: 466,000 volumes. 1,200,000 microforms; 4,600 audiovisual materials; 840 current periodical subscriptions. Online catalog. Students have access to online information retrieval services and the Internet.

Most important special holdings include U.S. Presidential Papers; John Ben Shepperd Papers; John A. Styker Photographs; J. Frank Dobie Collection; collection of manuscripts and books of Texas writers.

Buildings and Grounds: Campus area 640 acres.

Chief Executive Officer: Dr. W. David Watts, President.

Address admission inquiries to Director of Admissions.

University of Texas Southwestern Medical Center at Dallas

5323 Harry Hines Boulevard
Dallas, Texas 75235-9013
Tel: (214) 688-3111 **E-mail:** admissions@swmed.edu
Fax: (214) 648-7503 **Internet:** www.swmed.edu

Institution Description: The University of Texas Southwestern Medical Center at Dallas offers upper division undergraduate instruction, graduate studies, and medical school curricula. *Enrollment:* 2,350. *Degrees awarded:* Baccalaureate, master's, doctorate, first-professional (M.D.). Certificates in certain allied health programs also awarded. UT Southwestern also supervises instruction of medical residents and post-doctoral fellows training and multiple hospital and research sites.

Accreditation: *Regional:* SACS-Comm. on Coll. *Professional*: blood bank technology, clinical lab scientist, clinical pastoral education, dietetics, EMT-paramedic, medical illustration, medicine, nursing, nursing-midwifery, physical therapy, physician assisting, psychology internship, rehabilitation counseling

History: Established as Southwestern Medical School 1943. Changed name to Southwestern Medical School of The University of Texas, 1949; changed again to University of Texas Southwestern Medical School at Dallas, 1954; to the University of Texas Health Science Center at Dallas, 1972; to current name, The University of Texas Southwestern Medical Center at Dallas, 1987.

Institutional Structure: *Composition of institution:* The institution is comprised of 3 schools (Southwestern Medical School, Southwestern Graduate School of Biomedical Sciences, and Southwestern Allied Health Sciences School) each headed by a Dean reporting to the President. Management/business/financial affairs directed by Executive Vice President for Business Affairs. Full-time instructional faculty 844.

Calendar: Semesters. Academic year Sept. to Aug. Medical residency training year begins July 1.

Admission: *Requirements:* Medical, 90 sem. hrs,. Graduate, baccalaureate degree or its equivalent from an accredited institution in the United States or proof of equivalent training at a foreign university. Allied Health, of 60 semester hours (except as defined for individual programs, i.e., physical therapy, 90 hours; medical technology, 90 hours; post-baccalaureate certificate which includes specialist in blood bank technology, bachelor degree). Specific requirements vary by program. *Entrance tests:* For medical school, Medical College Admission Test (MCAT); for graduate school, Graduate Record Examination (GRE); for foreign students, TOEFL. Some programs require individual entrance examinations. *For transfer students:* Transfer credits available for medical technology students.

Degree Requirements: *For all baccalaureate degrees:* 120 semester hours; 2.0 GPA; 30 hours in residence; core curriculum.

Grading system: A–F; pass-fail; withdraw (carries time limit).

Distinctive Educational Programs: Affiliation with 75 area hospitals and facilities. Continuing education for professionals in rehabilitation and human service agencies. Medical Scientist Training Program is 6-year minimum program leading to combined M.D./Ph.D. degrees.

Degrees Conferred: 61 *baccalaureate:* health professions, 84 *master's:* health professions; 62 *doctorate* biological/life sciences 3; engineering 3; health professions 78. 204 *first-professional:* medicine.

Fees and Other Expenses: *Full-time tuition per academic year:* contact the university for current tuition, fees, and other costs.

Financial Aid: Aid from institutionally generated funds is provided on the basis of academic merit, financial need, other criteria.

Financial aid to full-time, first-time undergraduate students: need-based scholarships/grants totaling $187,947, self-help $1,009,058. *Graduate aid:* 11 students received $244,812 in federal and state-funded fellowships/grants; 2,356 received $19,813,116 in federal and state-funded loans; 78 held work-study jobs paying a total of $173,000; 877 other fellowships/grants totaling $2,185,505.

Departments and Teaching Staff: *Total instructional faculty:* 1,703 (full-time 1,464, part-time 239). Total faculty with doctorate, first-professional, or other terminal degree 1,645. Degrees held by full-time faculty: baccalaureate less than 1%, master's less than 1%, doctorate 99%. 99% hold terminal degrees.

Enrollment: Total enrollment 2,350.

Characteristics of Student Body: *Ethnic/racial makeup:* number of Black non-Hispanic: 15; American Indian or Alaska Native: 1; Asian or Pacific Islander: 15; Hispanic: 18; White non-Hispanic: 68; 8. *Age distribution:* number 18–19: 2; 20–21: 39; 22–24: 718; 25–29: 859; 30–34: 416; 35–39: 173; 40–49: 95; 50–64: 15. 95% of student body attend summer sessions.

International Students: 410 nonresident aliens enrolled fall 2008. No programs available to aid students whose native language is not English. No financial aid specifically designated for international students.

Student Life: UT Southwestern has no on-campus housing, but does offer on-campus activities and recreation facilities. *Special regulations:* special clothing or uniforms required for some programs.

Publications: *Center Times* (monthly); *Biologue* (semiannually).

Library Collections: 250,058 volumes. Partial government depository library; 3,078 audiovisual materials; 285 current paper periodical subscriptions; access to 6,420 via electronic access. Computer work stations available. Students have access to online information retrieval services and the Internet.

Most important special holdings include History of the Health Sciences with Infectious Diseases as focus.

Buildings and Grounds: Campus DVD available.

Chief Executive Officer: Dr. Kern Wildenthal, President.

Address admission inquiries to Dr. Scott Wright, Director of Admissions.

Wayland Baptist University

1900 West Seventh Street
Plainview, Texas 79072
Tel: (806) 291-1000 **E-mail:** admityou@wbu.edu
Fax: (806) 291-1960 **Internet:** www.wbu.edu

Institution Description: Wayland Baptist University (Wayland Baptist College until 1981) is a private institution affiliated with the Southern Baptist General Convention of Texas. *Enrollment:* 6,031. *Degrees awarded:* Baccalaureate, master's.

Accreditation: *Regional:* SACS-Comm. on Coll.

History: Established and chartered as Wayland Literary and Technical Institution 1908; changed name to Wayland Baptist College and offered first instruction at postsecondary level 1910; awarded first degree (associate) 1911; became 4-year college 1947; adopted present name 1981.

Institutional Structure: *Governing board:* Wayland Baptist University Board of Trustees. Extrainstitutional representation: 36 trustees. 36 voting. *Composition of institution: >rmAAdministrators 5. Four divisions, each administered by a vice president. Full-time instructional faculty 107. Academic governance body, Academic Council, meets an average of 10 times per year.*

Calendar: Semesters (4-1-4 plan). Academic year Aug. to July. Freshmen admitted Sept., Jan., June. Degrees conferred May, Aug., Dec. Formal commencement May, Dec. Summer session from May to Aug.

Characteristics of Freshmen: 288 applicants (female 153, male 123). 98% of applicants admitted. 86% of applicants admitted and enrolled.

35% (76 students) submitted SAT scores; 83% (179 students) submitted ACT scores. *25th percentile*: SAT Critical Reading 430, SAT Math 450;ACT Composite 18, ACT English 16, ACT Math 17. *75th percentile*: SAT Critical Reading 570, SAT Math 590; ACT Composite 24, ACT English 25, ACT Math 25.

20% of entering freshmen expected to graduate within 5 years. 80% of freshmen from Texas. Freshmen from 10 states and 2 foreign countries.

Admission: Rolling admissions plan. For fall acceptance, apply as early as Nov. of previous year, but not later than 1 day before registration. Early acceptance available. *Requirements:* Either graduation from accredited secondary school with 3 units English, 2 mathematics, 2 social studies, 2 science, no more than 4 vocational subjects; or GED. 2 units foreign language recommended. Graduates of unaccredited secondary schools or those in bottom 30% of graduating class may be admitted on basis of examination scores. *Entrance tests:* ACT composite. *For transfer students:* 2.0 minimum GPA; from 4-year accredited institution 94 hours maximum transfer credit; from 2-year accredited institution 72 hours; correspondence/extension students 12 hours.

College credit and advanced placement for postsecondary-level work completed in secondary school. For occupational education majors, college credit for extrainstitutional learning on basis of portfolio and faculty assessments.

Tutoring available.

Degree Requirements: 124 credit hours with minimum of 31 credit hours completed in residence; minimum GPA of 2.0; minimum of 42 credit hours in upper division courses; completion of general education core; comprehensive examination in major field.

Fulfillment of some degree requirements and exemption from some beginning courses possible by passing departmental examinations; College Board CLEP, APP, other standardized tests. *Grading system:* A–F; withdraw (deadline after which pass-fail is appended to withdraw); incomplete (carries time limit).

Distinctive Educational Programs: Flexible meeting places and schedules, including external campuses at Wichita Falls, Lubbock, Amarillo, San Antonio plus Hawaii, Alaska, Arizona, New Mexico, and Oklahoma. The Bachelor of Science in Occupational Education is offered to provide a flexible course format to permit fully-employed adults to pursue a degree program consistent with past work experience and vocational goals. Preprofessional programs including nursing and optometry. Facilities for independent research, including honors programs, and tutorials. Cooperation with the U.S. Military Services facilitates participation in Operation Bootstrap and other similar opportunities for military service personnel.

Degrees Conferred: 255 *associate*; 1,452 *baccalaureate*; 311 *master's*. Baccalaureate degrees: biological sciences 5; business and management 638, communications 5; education 765; English 3; foreign languages and literature 2; interdisciplinary studies 2; mathematics 5; philosophy/religion/theology 31; physical sciences 1; psychology 19; social sciences and history 263; visual and performing arts 6.

Fees and Other Expenses: *Full-time tuition per academic year 2008–09:* $9,956. *Books and supplies:* $1,248. *Room and board per academic year:* $4,050. *Other expenses:* $2,852.

Financial Aid: Aid from institutionally generated funds is provided on the basis of academic merit, financial need, athletic ability, other criteria.

Financial aid to full-time, first-time undergraduate students: 81% received some form of aid. Average amount of aid received: federal grants $3,247; Pell grants $2,808; other federal aid $849; state/local grants $3,090; institutional grants $5,806.

Departments and Teaching Staff: *Total instructional faculty:* 478 (full-time 107, part-time 371). Total faculty with doctorate, first-professional, or other terminal degree: 80. Student/faculty ratio: 12:1. Degrees held by full-time faculty: doctorate 70%, master's 30%. 75% hold terminal degrees.

Enrollment: Total enrollment 6,031. Undergraduate 4,752 (full-time 80%; female 49%, male 51%). Graduate 1,279 (full-time 7%). Undergraduate transfer-in students 74.

Characteristics of Student Body: *Ethnic/racial makeup:* Black non-Hispanic: 145; American Indian or Alaska Native: 1%; Asian or Pacific Islander: 3%; Hispanic: 15%; White non-Hispanic: 52%; unknown: 11%; nonresident alien 1%. *Age distribution:* number under 18: 77; 18–19: 327; 20–21: 388; 22–24: 559; 25–29: 922; 30–34: 915; 35–39: 843; 40–49: 1,080; 50–64: 245; 65 and over: 8.

International Students: 60 nonresident aliens enrolled fall 2008. Students from Europe, Asia, Latin America, Africa, Canada, New Zealand, Middle East. No programs available to aid students whose native language is not English. No financial aid specifically designated for international students.

Student Life: On-campus residence halls house 46% of Plainview campus student body. Family housing is available for married students and single-parents with dependents. *Intercollegiate athletics:* male: baseball, basketball, cross-country, golf, track; female: basketball, cross-country, track, volleyball. Wayland also offers intramural sports that are student-governed and open to all students. The program includes flag football, volleyball, basketball, golf, and several other activities. *Special regulations:* Registered cars permitted without restrictions. There are no curfews in the residence halls. Quiet hours from 11pm to 8am daily. Residence hall visitation in both rooms and lounge at posted times. *Special services:* Counseling services, tutoring, health services, career planning, placement services. *Student publications, radio: The Trailblazer*, a weekly newspaper; *The Traveler*, a yearbook. Radio station KWLD. *Surrounding com-*

WAYLAND BAPTIST UNIVERSITY—*cont'd*

munity: Plainview population 25,000. Dallas, 325 miles from campus, is nearest metropolitan area.

Library Collections: 128,000 volumes including bound books, serial backfiles, electronic documents, and government documents not in separate collections. Online catalog. 282,000 microforms; 12,000 audiovisual materials; 530 current serial subscriptions. Students have access to the Internet at no charge.

Most important holdings include Baptist Collection; Texas Collection; Wayland Archives.

Buildings and Grounds: Campus area 80 acres.

Chief Executive Officer: Dr. Paul Armes, President

Address admission inquiries to Cimmaron Ainsworth, Director of Admissions.

West Texas A & M University

2501 Fourth Avenue
P.O. Box 997, W.T. Station
Canyon, Texas 79016-0001
Tel: (806) 651-2000 **E-mail:** admissions@wtamu.edu
Fax: (806) 651-2096 **Internet:** www.wtamu.edu

Institution Description: West Texas A & M University, formerly known as West Texas State University, is a state institution and member of the Texas A & M University System. *Enrollment:* 7,535. *Degrees awarded:* Baccalaureate, master's. Certificates also awarded.

Academic offerings subject to approval by statewide coordinating bodies. Budget subject to approval by state governing boards.

Accreditation: *Regional:* SACS-Comm. on Coll. *Professional*: business, music, nursing, social work, teacher education

History: Established as West Texas State Normal College 1909; offered first instruction at postsecondary level 1910; awarded first degree (baccalaureate) 1919; changed name to West Texas State Teachers College 1923, to West Texas State College 1949; became West Texas State University 1963; became part of Texas A & M University System 1990; adopted present name 1993. *See* Joseph A. Hill, *More Than Brick and Mortar* (Amarillo, TX: Russell Stationery Co., 1959) for further information.

Institutional Structure: West Texas State University is a part of the Texas A&M University System. *Governing board:* Board of Regents. Representation: 9 regents. All voting. *Composition of institution:* Academic affairs headed by provost/vice president for academic affairs. Management/business/finances directed by vice president for business and finance. Full-time instructional faculty 239. Academic governance body, Faculty Senate, meets an average of 18 times per year.

Calendar: Semesters. Academic year Sept. to July. Freshmen admitted Aug., Jan., June, July. Degrees conferred and formal commencement Dec., May, Aug. Summer session from early June to mid-Aug.

Characteristics of Freshmen: 2,940 applicants (female 1,583, male 1,377). 71% of applicants accepted. 60% of accepted applicants enrolled.

35% (334 students) submitted SAT scores; 74% (704 students) submitted ACT scores. *25th percentile*: SAT Critical Reading 440, SAT Math 440; ACT Composite 18, ACT English 17, ACT Math 17. *75th percentile*: SAT Critical Reading 560, SAT Math 560; ACT Composite 23, ACT English 23, ACT Math 23.

32% of freshmen expected to graduate within five years. 89% of freshmen from Texas. Freshmen from 18 states and 8 foreign countries.

Admission: Rolling admissions plan. For fall acceptance, apply as early as 1 year prior to enrollment, but not later than Aug. 15 of year of enrollment. Early acceptance available. *Requirements:* Graduation from accredited secondary school or GED. Recommend 4 years English-language arts, 2 college preparatory mathematics, 2 social studies, 1 laboratory science. *Entrance tests:* College Board SAT or ACT composite. For foreign students TOEFL. *For transfer students:* 2.0 minimum GPA; from 4-year accredited institution 94 hours maximum transfer credit; from 2-year accredited institution 66 hours.

College credit and advanced placement for postsecondary-level work completed in secondary school and for extrainstitutional learning.

Tutoring available. Developmental courses offered in summer session and regular academic year; credit given.

Degree Requirements: 130 credit hours; 2.0 GPA; 30 semester hours in residence; 2 hours physical education; general education requirements; core course requirements.

Fulfillment of some degree requirements and exemption from some beginning courses possible by passing departmental examinations, College Board CLEP, AP, other standardized tests. *Grading system:* A–F; pass-fail; withdraw (deadline after which pass-fail is appended to withdraw).

Distinctive Educational Programs: *For undergraduates:* Work-experience programs. Evening classes. Cooperative master's programs in plant science with Texas A&M University, in social work with University of Texas at Arlington. Interdepartmental and interdisciplinary programs in biomedical sciences, criminal justice administration, public administration. Fire safety and protection, animal science/equine industry, Harrington String Quartet Performance Certificate. Preprofessional programs in dentistry, medicine, pharmacy, occupational therapy, physical therapy, veterinary medicine. Facilities and programs for independent research, including honors programs, individual majors. *Other distinctive programs:* Continuing education. Distance education Internet courses in nursing, fire safety and protection; baccalaureate program with teacher certification; master's program in agriculture; master's program in educational diagnostician and administration.

Degrees Conferred: 1.188 *baccalaureate*; 387 *master's*; 2 *doctorate*. Bachelor's degrees awarded in top five disciplines: business, management, marketing, and related support services 179; liberal arts and sciences, general studies, and humanities 144; multidisciplinary studies 137; visual and performing arts 59; biological/life sciences 51. Master's degrees awarded: various disciplines 387. Doctorates awarded: agriculture 2.

Fees and Other Expenses: *Full-time tuition per academic year 2008–09:* $5,340. *Books and supplies:* $1,000. *Room and board per academic year:* $5,728. *Other expenses:* 3,340.

Financial Aid: Aid from institutionally generated fund is provided on the basis of academic merit, financial need, athletic ability, other criteria.

Financial aid to full-time, first-time undergraduate students: 55% received some form of aid. Average amount of aid received: federal grants $1,176; Pell grants $1,146; state/local grants $689; institutional grants $216.

Departments and Teaching Staff: *Total instructional faculty:* 312 (full-time 239, part-time 73). Student/faculty ratio: 24:1. Degrees held by full-time faculty: doctorate 42.6%, master's 53.5%, baccalaureate 13.9%. 46% hold terminal degrees.

Enrollment: Total enrollment 7,535. Undergraduate 6,287 (full-time 76%; female 55%, male 45%). Graduate 1,298 (full-time 25%). Undergraduate transfer-in students 809.

Characteristics of Student Body: *Ethnic/racial makeup:* Black non-Hispanic: 5%; American Indian or Alaska Native: 1%; Asian or Pacific Islander: 2%; Hispanic: 19%; White non-Hispanic: 72%; nonresident alien 2%.

International Students: 151 undergraduate nonresident aliens enrolled fall 2008. Programs available to aid students whose native language is not English: social, cultural. English as a Second Language Program. No financial aid specifically designated for international students.

Student Life: Nine on-campus residence halls house 28% of undergraduate student body. On-campus housing required for students with fewer than 60 semester hours and under the age of 21. Quiet and visitation hours established. *Organizations:* 100 student organizations including fraternities, sororities, sports clubs, professional and honor societies, special interest groups. *Intercollegiate athletics:* Member of the NCAA with participation in football, soccer, basketball, baseball, tennis, cross-country competition for males and in basketball, volleyball, soccer, equestrian, cross-country competition for females. *Special services:* personal counseling, student medical services, wellness services, testing, tutoring, child care. *Student radio:* KWTS student radio station. *Student publication: The Prairie*, a weekly newspaper. *Surrounding community:* Canyon population 13,000. Dallas, 372 miles from campus, is nearest metropolitan area. Served by airport 27 miles from campus.

Library Collections: 1,096,000 volumes including bound books, serial backfiles, electronic documents, and government documents not in separate collections. Online catalog. 1,200,000 microforms; 2,000 audiovisual materials; 17,000 periodicals including via electronic access. Computer work stations available. Students have access to the Internet at no charge.

Most important holdings include Sheffy Southwestern American Collection; WTAMU Archives; Louella Grace Erdman Papers.

Buildings and Grounds: Campus area 135 acres. Campus DVD available.

Chief Executive Officer: Dr. J. Patrick O'Brien, President.

Address admission inquiries to Lila Vars, Director of Admissions.

Wiley College

711 Wiley Avenue
Marshall, Texas 75670
Tel: (903) 927-3300 **E-mail:** admissions@wileyc.edu
Fax: (903) 938-8100 **Internet:** www.wileyc.edu

Institution Description: Wiley College is a private college affiliated with the United Methodist Church. *Enrollment:* 967. *Degrees awarded:* Associate, baccalaureate.

Accreditation: *Regional:* SACS-Comm. on Coll.

History: Established as Wiley University and offered first instruction at postsecondary level 1873; chartered 1882.

Institutional Structure: *Governing board:* Board of Trustees. Extrainstitutional representation: 39 trustees; institutional representation: 1 faculty member. 1 ex officio. 40 voting. *Composition of institution:* Administrators 8. Academic affairs headed by academic vice president. Management/business/finances directed by vice president for fiscal affairs. Full-time instructional faculty 43. Academic governance body, Academic Policy Council, meets an average of 9 times per year.

Calendar: Semesters. Academic year Sept. to May. Freshmen admitted Sept., Jan., June. Degrees conferred and formal commencement May. Summer session from early June to early July.

Admission: Rolling admissions plan. For fall acceptance, apply as early as 1 year prior to enrollment, but not later than 2 weeks after beginning of classes. Early acceptance available. *Requirements:* Either graduation from accredited secondary school or GED. *For transfer students:* 2.0 minimum GPA; maximum transfer credit limited only by residence requirement.

College credit and advanced placement for postsecondary-level work completed in secondary school.

Tutoring available. Developmental courses offered in summer session and regular academic year; credit given.

Degree Requirements: *For all baccalaureate degrees:* 124 credit hours; 2.0 GPA; 30 hours in residence; 3 semesters physical education; general education requirements.

Fulfillment of some degree requirements and exemption from some beginning courses possible by passing departmental examinations, College Board CLEP, AP. *Grading system:* A–F; withdraw (carries time limit).

Distinctive Educational Programs: Work-experience programs, including cooperative education, internships. Evening classes. Interdisciplinary studies major. Honors programs.

Degrees Conferred: 157 *baccalaureate*. Bachelor's degrees awarded in top five disciplines: business, management, marketing, and related support services 77; security and protective services 14; education 11; computer and information science 7; social sciences 6.

Fees and Other Expenses: *Full-time tuition per academic year:* $9,970. *Books and supplies:* $266. *Room and board per academic year:* $5,620. *Other expenes:* $1,580.

Financial Aid: Aid from institutionally generated funds is provided on the basis of academic merit, financial need, other criteria.

Financial aid to full-time, first-time undergraduate students: 97% received some form of aid. Average amount of aid received: federal grants $5,044; Pell grants $3,452; other federal aid $1,813; state/local grants $4,029; institutional grants $3,425.

Departments and Teaching Staff: *Total instructional faculty:* 43.

Enrollment: Total enrollment 815. Undergraduate

Characteristics of Student Body: *Ethnic/racial makeup:* Black non-Hispanic: 91%; Hispanic: 4%; White non-Hispanic: 25; nonresident alien 3%.

International Students: 30 nonresident aliens enrolled fall 2008. No programs available to aid students whose native language is not English. No financial aid specifically designated for international students.

Student Life: On-campus residence halls house 50% of student body. Residence halls for males constitute 50% of such space, for females 50%. Housing available for married students. *Intercollegiate athletics:* male: baseball, basketball, track; female: basketball, softball, track, volleyball. *Special regulations:* Cars permitted without restrictions. *Special services:* Learning Resources Center, medical services. *Student publications, radio:* Newspaper, yearbook. Radio station KWBC broadcasts 60 hours per week. *Surrounding community:* Marshall population 25,000. Dallas, 150 miles from campus, is nearest metropolitan area. Served by airport 40 miles from campus; passenger rail service 2 miles from campus.

Buildings and Grounds: Campus area 63 acres.

Chief Executive Officer: Dr. Haywood L. Strickland, President.

Address admission inquiries to Bioshop B. Curry, Director of Admissions.

Utah

Brigham Young University

Provo, Utah 84602
Tel: (801) 422-4636 **E-mail:** admissions@byu.edu
Fax: (801) 422-0586 **Internet:** www.byu.edu

Institution Description: Brigham Young University is a private institution affiliated with The Church of Jesus Christ of Latter-day Saints. *Enrollment:* 34,244. *Degrees awarded:* Baccalaureate, first-professional (law), master's, doctorate.

Accreditation: *Regional:* MWCCU. *Professional*: accounting, art, athletic training, audiology, business, chemistry, clinical lab scientist, computer science, construction education, counseling, dance, engineering, engineering technology, journalism, law, librarianship, marriage and family therapy, music, nursing, psychology internship, recreation and leisure services, social work, speech-language pathology, teacher education, theatre, veterinary technology

History: Established as Brigham Young Academy 1875; awarded first degree (baccalaureate) 1892; adopted present name 1903. *See* Ernest L. Wilkinson, *BYU-The First One Hundred Years* (Provo: Brigham Young University Press, 1975) for further information.

Institutional Structure: *Governing board:* Board of Trustees of Brigham Young University. Representation: 9 trustees. All voting. *Composition of institution:* Administrators 1,365. Academic affairs headed by academic vice president. Management/business/finances directed by administrative vice president and chief executive officer. Full-time instructional faculty 1,300. Academic advisory body, Faculty Advisory Council, meets an average of 10 times per year.

Calendar: Semesters (4-4-2-2 plan). Academic year Aug. to Aug. Freshmen admitted Aug., Jan., Apr., June. Degrees conferred Dec., Apr., Aug. Formal commencements Apr., Aug. Summer session of 2 terms from May to Aug.

Characteristics of Freshmen: 10,681 applicants (female 5,709, male 4,372). 76% of applicants admitted. 60% of applicants admitted and enrolled.

42% (2,302 students) submitted SAT scores; 94% (5,206 students) submitted ACT scores. *25th percentile*: SAT Verbal 550, SAT Math 570; ACT Composite 25, ACT English 24, ACT Math 24. *75th percentile*: SAT Verbal 660, SAT Math 670; ACT Composite 29, ACT English 30, ACT Math 29.

70% of entering freshmen expected to graduate within 6 years. 18% of freshmen from Utah. Freshmen from 50 states and 124 foreign countries.

Admission: Rolling admissions plan. For fall and summer acceptance for freshmen, apply as early as 1 year prior to enrollment, but no later than Feb. 15 of year of enrollment. Early acceptance available. *Requirements:* Graduation from accredited secondary school with recommendation from bishop or clergyman. Students are evaluated according to their cumulative grade point average, the grade point average in their college preparatory subjects, the percentage of college preparatory classes taken, the results of the American College Test (ACT), and a written essay. AP and honors classes are given additional weighting. GED accepted. *Entrance tests:* American College Test (ACT). *For transfer students:* 50% general education subjects; 3.0 minimum grade point average cumulative. 50% solid academic subjects.

College credit and advanced placement for postsecondary-level work completed in secondary school. College credit for extrainstitutional learning.

Degree Requirements: *For all baccalaureate degrees:* 120 credit hours with a minimum 30 semester hours n residence. *For all undergraduate degrees:* 2.0 GPA; completion of university core requirements; religion courses.

Fulfillment of some degree requirements possible by passing College Board CLEP, AP (score of 3). *Grading system:* A–F; pass-fail; withdraw (deadline after which pass-fail is appended to withdraw).

Distinctive Educational Programs: Academic internships. Flexible meeting places and schedules, including off-campus centers (at Salt Lake City, 45 miles away from main institution); evening classes. Honors program. Study abroad programs in Africa, Asia, Austria, England, France, Italy, New Zealand, Poland, Russia, Spain. Washington (DC) seminar internship program. *Other distinctive programs:* Credit and noncredit continuing education. American Indian Services and Research Center, Resource Center on Adult Development and Aging. Museum of Archaeology and Ethnology. Online courses offered.

ROTC: Army, Air Force.

Degrees Conferred: 6,834 *baccalaureate;* 1,079 *master's;* 67 *doctorate*; *first-professional* 163. Bachelor's degrees awarded in top five disciplines: business, management, marketing, and related support services 1,079; social sciences and history 986; education 596; visual and performing arts 467; home economics and vocational home economics 420; engineering and engineering technologies 385. Master's degrees awarded: various disciplines 1,079; First-professional degrees awarded: law 163.

Fees and Other Expenses: *Full-time tuition per academic year 2008–09:* undergraduate $4,080; contact the university for current graduate and first-professional tuition and applicable fees. *Room and board per academic year:* $6,550. *Books and supplies:* $1,000. *Other expenses:* $3,700.

Financial Aid: Aid from institutionally generated funds is provided on the basis of academic merit, financial need, athletic ability, other criteria.

Financial aid to full-time, first-time undergraduate students: 48% received some form of aid. Average amount of aid received: federal grants $3,203; Pell grants $3,011; other federal aid $772; institutional grants $2,704.

Departments and Teaching Staff: *Total instructional faculty:* 1,744 (full-time 1,300, part-time 444). Total faculty with doctorate, first-professional, or other terminal degree: 1,203. student/faculty ratio: 20:1. Degrees held by full-time faculty: baccalaureate 3%, master's 17.3%, doctorate 79.7%. 81.9% hold terminal degrees.

Enrollment: Total enrollment 34,244. Undergraduate 30,912 (full-time 91%; female 49%, male 51%). Graduate 3,362 (full-time 59%) Undergraduate transfer-in students 1,035.

Characteristics of Student Body: *Ethnic/racial makeup:* American Indian or Alaska Native: 1%; Asian or Pacific Islander: 4%; Hispanic: 4%; White non-Hispanic: 87%; unknown: 2%; nonresident alien 2%. *Age distribution:* number under 18: 491; 18–19: 8,427; 20–21: 7,328; 22–24: 11,696; 25–29: 4,117; 30–34: 656; 35–39: 233; 40–49: 325; 50–64: 151; 65 and over: 3. 29% of student body attend summer sessions.

International Students: 685 nonresident aliens enrolled fall 2008. Students from Europe, Asia, Latin America, Africa, Canada, Australia, New Zealand, Trust Territories. Programs available to aid students whose native language is not English: social, cultural. financial. English as a Second Language Program.

Student Life: On-campus residence halls and apartments house 20% of student body. Housing available for married students. *Intercollegiate athletics:* male: baseball, basketball, cross-country, football, golf, swimming and diving, tennis, track and field, volleyball; female: basketball, cross-country, golf, gymnastics, soccer, softball, swimming, tennis, track and field, volleyball. *Special regulations:* Registered cars permitted. Neat and clean attire and grooming required; shoes must be worn in public campus areas; shorts may be worn only in specified areas. *Special services:* Learning Resources Center, medical services, services for students with disabilities, international student services, Service Learning Center, Counseling and Career Center. *Student radio, television:* Radio station KBYU-FM broadcasts 168 hours per week. TV station KBYU broadcasts 118 hours per week. *Surrounding community:* Provo population 115,000. Salt Lake City, 45 miles from campus, is nearest metropolitan area. Served by airport 50 miles from campus.

Publications: *BYU Studies* (quarterly) first published in 1959; *Family Perspectives* (quarterly) first published 1966; *Brigham Young Magazine*, first published in 1968.

Library Collections: 3,400,000 volumes including bound books, serial backfiles, electronic documents, and government documents not in separate collections. Online catalog. 3,300,000 microforms; 196,000 audiovisual materials; 199,000 peridoicals including via electronic access. Computer work stations available. Students have access to the Internet at no charge.

Most important special holdings include collections on Mormon Americana, American West, history of printing.

Buildings and Grounds: Campus area 557 acres. Campus DVD available.

Chief Executive Officer: Dr. Cecil O. Samuelson, President.

Address admission inquiries to Thoma Gourley, Admissions Office; Law School inquiries to Law School Admissions.

College of Biology and Agriculture

Degree Programs Offered: *Baccalaureate* in agronomy, horticulture, animal science, biology teaching, botany, botany premedical-predental, range science, food science and nutrition, microbiology, premedicine-predentistry microbiology, clinical laboratory science, zoology, entomology, nutritional sciences, dietetics, molecular biology, conservation biology, wildlife and range resources; *master's* in agronomy, horticulture, animal science, biological science education, botany, genetics, wildlife and range resources, range science, food science and nutrition, microbiology, medical technology, zoology, entomology; *doctorate* in botany, genetics, wildlife and range resources, microbiology, zoology, entomology.

School of Education

Degree Programs Offered: *Baccalaureate* in special education, elementary education, middle education, composite teaching, audiology, speech/language pathology; *master's* in speech/language pathology, clinical audiology, educational psychology, special education, teaching and learning, reading, instructional science, community education leadership, counseling and guidance, educational psychology; *doctorate* in curriculum and instruction, educational leadership, higher education, counseling psychology, educational psychology, instructional science, instructional psychology, public school leadership, counseling and personnel services, reading. *Specialist* certificates in community education leadership and public school leadership also given.

College of Engineering and Technology

Degree Programs Offered: *Baccalaureate* in chemical engineering, civil engineering, construction management, electrical engineering, industrial arts teacher education, industrial education, physical plant administration, mechanical engineering, electronics engineering technology, manufacturing engineering technology; *master's* in chemical engineering, civil engineering, electrical engineering, industrial education, mechanical engineering, computer-integrated manufacturing, engineering management, technology management; *doctorate* in chemical engineering, civil engineering, electrical engineering, mechanical engineering.

College of Family, Home, and Social Science

Degree Programs Offered: *Associate* in genealogy, tourism; *baccalaureate* in anthropology (liberal education), anthropology (preprofessional), anthropology teaching, fashion design, economics, history, family and community history studies, political science, public policy, American studies, Asian studies, Canadian studies, European studies, international relations, Latin American studies, Near Eastern studies, fashion merchandising, general clothing and textiles, early childhood education, family sciences, human development, resource management, geography, cartography, geography teaching, planning, home economics, home economics education family life, psychology, psychology teaching, social work, sociology, sociology teaching; *master's* in anthropology, applied economics, family sciences, marriage and family therapy, cartography, geography, planning, history, psychology, social work, sociology; *doctorate* in family science, family studies, marriage and family therapy, history, clinical psychology, psychology, sociology; *certificate* in school psychology.

College of Fine Arts and Communications

Degree Programs Offered: *Associate* in church music; *baccalaureate* in art education, art history, art studio general, broadcast communication, advertising and public relations, journalism, design, music, speech, theatre arts, theatre arts education, interior design, industrial design, graphic design, illustration, photography, musical dance theatre, film, music (composition and theory, education, pedagogy, performance), journalism education, speech education; *master's* in art education, art history, communications, music education, musicology, theater and film, film, ceramics, painting, printmaking, sculpture, theatre design and technology, music (composition, education, pedagogy, performance); *doctorate* in musicology, theatre and cinematic arts.

College of Humanities

Degree Programs Offered: *Associate* in English, library technician, university studies; *baccalaureate* in Chinese, classical studies, comparative literature, Japanese, Korean, Latin teaching, English, English teaching, French, French teaching, Italian, German, German teaching, Russian, Russian teaching, humanities, humanities teaching, linguistics, philosophy, Portuguese, Spanish, Spanish teaching, Spanish translation, university studies; *master's* in English, comparative literature, language acquisition (Arabic, Chinese, Japanese, Korean, French, German, Russian, Scandinavian, Spanish, Portuguese), literature (German, Spanish, Portuguese), humanities, general linguistics, TESL, Spanish teaching, library science.

J. Reuben Clark Law School

Degree Programs Offered: *Master's of Comparative Law* and *Juris Doctorate.*

Admission: Baccalaureate from accredited college or university, LSAT.

Degree Requirements: 87 credit hours, minimum GPA 66 on a 90-point scale, 4 semesters in residence.

College of Nursing

Degree Programs Offered: *Baccalaureate, master's.*

College of Physical and Math Sciences

Degree Programs Offered: *Baccalaureate* in chemistry (premedical/predental emphasis), mathematics education, physics, physics teaching, chemistry, earth science teaching, engineering geology, geology, mathematics, applied physics, physics (computer science), statistics, statistics (computer science), statistics (business), biochemistry, molecular biology, computer science, computer science teaching, statistics-quality; *master's* in computer science, mathematics, mathematics education, chemistry, biochemistry, geology, physics, statistics; *doctorate* in chemistry, biochemistry, computer science, mathematics, physics, physics and astronomy.

College of Physical Education

Degree Programs Offered: *Baccalaureate* in health sciences, dance education, dance, music dance theater, P.E.-sports with emphasis in athletic training, public school teaching, commercial physical education, exercise science, recreation management and youth leadership; *master's* in health sciences, dance, physical education, exercise science and athletic training, recreation management and youth leadership; *doctorate* in P.E. administration, curriculum and instruction, corrective physical education and rehabilitation, therapeutic recreation, exercise physiology.

College of Religious Education

Degree Programs Offered: No degrees are offered in this area.

J. Willard and Alice S. Marriott School of Management

Degree Programs Offered: *Baccalaureate* in general business, finance, marketing, operations management, retailing, finance-international business, marketing-international business, general business-international business, business teacher, accounting; *master's* in managerial economics, accountancy, organizational behavior, business administration, public administration.

Brigham Young University - Hawaii Campus

See separate exhibit under *Hawaii.*

Dixie State College of Utah

225 South 700 East
St. George, Utah 84770-3876
Tel: (435) 652-7500 **E-mail:** admissions@dixie.edu
Fax: (435) 652-4005 **Internet:** www.dixie.edu

Institution Description: Dixie State College of Utah is an undergraduate institution offering baccalaureate programs. *Enrollment:* 6,088.

Accreditation: *Regional:* NWCCU. *Professional*: nursing, teacher education

History: Established by the LDS Church of Salt Lake and St. George Stake Academy; opened 1911; renamed Dixie Normal College 1916; became Dixie Junior College1923; renamed Dixie College 1970; adopted present name 2000.

Institutional Structure: Governing Board - Disxie State College of Utah Board of Trustees.

Calendar: Semesters. Academic year Aug. to May.

Characteristics of Freshmen: Open enrollment. 4% (39 students) submitted SAT scores. 96% (1,029 students) submitted ACT scores.

25th percentile: SAT Critical Reading 425, SAT Math 405; ACT Composite 18, ACT English 17, ACT Math 17. *75th percentile:* SAT Critical Reading 500, SAT Math 505; ACT Composite 23, ACT English 23, ACT Math 23.

87% of freshmen from Utah. Freshmen from 24 states and 6 foreign countries.

Degree Requirements: Graduation from an accredited secondary institution; letters of recommendation.

Distinctive Educational Programs: Completion of required curriculum Contact the college for precise requirements.

DIXIE STATE COLLEGE OF UTAH—*cont'd*

Degrees Conferred: 150 *baccalaureate:* business/marketing 54; computer and information sciences 21; education 29; health professions and related clinical sciences 14; other disciplines 32.

Fees and Other Expenses: *Full-time tuition per academic year 2008&=09:* resident $2,893, nonresident $10,063. *Required fees:* $392. *Room and board per academic year:* $3,398. *Books and supplies:* $950. *other expenses:* $5,928.

Financial Aid: Aid from institutionally generated funds is provided on the basis of academic merit, financial need.

Financial aid to full-time, first-time students: 86% received some form of aid. Average amount of aid received: federal grants $3,108; Pell grants $2,799; other federal aid $660; state/local grants $2,645; institutional grants $1,097.

Departments and Teaching Staff: *Total instructional faculty:* 337 (full-time 113, part-time 224). Total number with doctorate, first-professional, or other terminal degree: 84. student/faculty ratio: 22:1.

Enrollment: *Total enrollment* 6,088. Undergraduate 6,088 (full-time 57%, female 52%, male 48%). Transfer-in students 391.

Characteristics of Student Body: *Ethnic/racial makeup:* Black non-Hispanic 1%; American Indian or Native Alaskan 1%; Asian or Pacific Islander 2%; Hispanic 5%; White non-Hispanic 88%; unknown 2%.

International Students: 27 nonresident aliens enrolled fall 2008. Students from Asia, Central and South America; Africa, Canada, Australia. No programs available to aid students whose native language is not English. No financial aid specifically designated for international students.

Student Life: Intercollegiate athletics: male: basketball, baseball, football, golf; female: basketball, soccer, softball, tennis, volleyball; coed-cross-country.

Cars are allowed on campus for all students. *Student publications: Dixie Sun,* published weekly during the fall and spring of the academic year.

Library Collections: 135,000 volumes. Current periodical subscriptions: paper 309; 43 titles via electronic access. 5,069 audio/videotapes; 838 DVD discs; 1880 CD-ROMs. Computer work stations available. Online catalog.

Most important special collections: James Goodson Blake Collection; oral history collection; Juanita Brooks Collection.

Buildings and Grounds: Campus area: 110 acres.

Chief Executive Officer: Dr. Lee Caldwell, President.

Address admission inquiries to David Roos, Executive Director, Enrollment Management.

ITT Technical Institute

920 West Levoy Drive
Murray, Utah 84123-2500
Tel: (801) 263-3313 **E-mail:** admit@itt-tech.edu
Fax: (801) 263-3497 **Internet:** www.itt-tech.edu

Institution Description: ITT Technical Institute is owned and operated by ITT Educational Services, Inc. of Indianapolis, Indiana.

Accreditation: *National:* ACICS.

Calendar: Quarters.

Admission: The student must provide documented proof of his or her high school diploma or recognized equivalency certificate.

Degree Requirements: Student must attain an overall 2.0 cumulative grade point average for the entire program pursued; must successfully complete all courses specified in the catalog for the program.

Degrees Conferred: 95 *associate;* 17 *baccalaureate:* engineering and engineering-related technologies 111; visual and performing arts 6.

Fees and Other Expenses: *Full-time tuition per academic year 2008–09:* contact the institute for current tuition, fees, and other costs.

Financial Aid: Aid from institutionally generated funds is provided on the basis of academic merit, financial need.

Institution has a Program Participation Agreement with the U.S. Department of Education for eligible students to receive Pell Grants and, depending upon the agreement, other federal aid.

Financial aid to full-time, first-time undergraduate students: 45% received federal grants averaging $2,414; 94% received loans averaging $4,875.

Departments and Teaching Staff: *Total instructional faculty:* 34. Degrees held by full-time faculty: baccalaureate 71%, master's 14%, professional 21%.

Enrollment: *Total enrollment* 706.

International Students: No programs available to aid students whose native language is not English. No financial aid specifically designated for international students.

Library Collections: 3,000 volumes. 75 audiovisual title; 75 current periodical subscriptions.

Chief Executive Officer: Rene Champagne, President/Chairman of the Board.

Address admissions inquiries to Carol Meneck, Director of Recruitment.

Southern Utah University

351 West Center Street
Cedar City, Utah 84720
Tel: (801) 586-7700 **E-mail:** adminfo@suu.edu
Fax: (801) 865-8223 **Internet:** www.suu.edu

Institution Description: Southern Utah University is a state institution. *Enrollment:* 7,516. *Degrees awarded:* Associate, baccalaureate, master's. Certificates also awarded.

Academic offerings subject to approval by statewide coordinating bodies. Budget subject to approval by state governing boards. Member of Northern Rockies Consortium of Higher Education.

Accreditation: *Regional:* NWCCU. *Professional*: business, music, teacher education

History: Established and chartered as Branch Normal School, a part of State Normal School, 1897; became part of Utah State Agricultural College, changed name to Branch Agricultural College, and offered first instruction of postsecondary level 1916; awarded first degree (baccalaureate) 1948; changed name to College of Southern Utah 1953; gained independent status 1965; became Southern Utah State College 1969; adopted present name 1987. *See* William R. Palmer, *The BNS-BAC Alumni Historical Booklets* (Cedar City, Utah: Alumni Association, 1940) for further information.

Institutional Structure: *Governing board:* Utah State Board of Regents. Extrainstitutional representation: 16 regents, all voting. *Composition of institution:* Administrators 11. Academic affairs headed by provost. Management/business/finances directed by executive vice president for financial affairs. Full-time instructional faculty 217. Academic governance body, the Dean's Council, meets an average of 43 times per year.

Calendar: Quarters. Academic year Sept. to June. Freshmen admitted prior to the beginning of each quarter for which admission is desired. Degrees conferred and formal commencement June. Summer session from June to Aug.

Characteristics of Freshmen: 2,774 applicants (female 1,715, male 1,059). 98% of applicants accepted. 52% of applicants accepted and enrolled.

Mean SAT scores 498 verbal, 487 mathematical. Mean ACT Composite score 21.54.

80% of freshmen from Utah. Freshmen from 22 states and 16 countries.

Admission: Rolling admissions plan. For fall acceptance, apply as early as 1 year prior to enrollment, but not later than July 1. Early acceptance available. *Requirements:* Either graduation from accredited secondary school or GED. Admissions index which is a combination of ACT/SAT scores and high school GPA is used to determine admissions for new students. Non graduates whose high school classes have graduated may also be accepted upon meeting published criteria. Early admission for high school students (concurrent enrollment) is also possible. Require competency in material contained in following high school courses (15 units): 4 English, 3 mathematics (one of which is algebra), 2 science, 2 social sciences, 4 core electives. Competency assessed by ACT scores, high school grades. *For transfer students:* 2.25 minimum GPA from credits over 40 hours; from 2-year accredited institution 123 hours maximum transfer credit; correspondence/extension students 45 hours.

College credit for postsecondary-level work completed in secondary school and for extrainstitutional learning based on departmental examinations.

Tutoring available. Developmental courses offered during regular academic year; credit given.

Degree Requirements: 183 credit hours; 2.0 GPA; 30 upper division credit hours and 50% of major courses in residence; 2 hours physical education; 7 to 15 hours skills courses; general education distribution requirement (40 hours).

Fulfillment of some degree requirements and exemption from some beginning courses possible by passing College Board CLEP, APP, ACT, or departmental examinations. *Grading system:* A–F; pass-fail; withdraw (carries time limit).

Distinctive Educational Programs: Work-experience programs. Flexible meeting places and schedules, including weekend and evening classes. Cooperative associate degree program in nursing with Weber State University. Study-travel programs in U.S. and abroad. Upward Bound and Special Services programs sponsor Assistance in Learning and Talent Advancement (ALTA) for minority and economically disadvantaged youth in Southern Utah area.

Degrees Conferred: 209 *associate*; 870 *baccalaureate*; 262 *master's*. Bachelor's degrees awarded in top five disciplines: education 232; business, management, marketing, and related support services 119; communication, journalism, and related programs 81; security and protective services 59; psychology 49. Master's degrees awarded: various disciplines 262.

Fees and Other Expenses: *Full-time tuition per academic year 2008–09:* resident $4,028, nonresident $12,082. *Books and supplies:* $1,036. *Room and board per academic year:* $5,400. *Other expenses:* $3,550.

Financial Aid: Aid from institutionally generated funds is provided on the basis of academic merit, financial need, athletic ability, other criteria. Institution has a Program Participation Agreement with the U.S. Department of Education for eligible students to receive Pell Grants and, depending upon the agreement, other federal aid.

Financial aid to full-time, first-time undergraduate students: 72% received some form of aid. Average amount of aid received: federal grants $3,084; Pell grants $2,875; other federal aid $449; state/local grants $831; institutional grants $3,028.

Departments and Teaching Staff: *Total instructional faculty:* 201. Degrees held by full-time faculty: doctorate 52.8%, master's 45.5%, baccalaureate 1.7%. 60% hold terminal degrees.

Enrollment: Total enrollment 7,516. Undergraduate 6,784 (full-time 76%; female 58%, male 42%). Graduate 732 (full-time 19%).

Characteristics of Student Body: *Ethnic/racial makeup:* Black non-Hispanic: 1%; American Indian or Alaska Native: 2%; Asian or Pacific Islander: 2%; Hispanic: 4%; White non-Hispanic: 87%; unknown: 3%; nonresident alien 1%.

International Students: 75 nonresident aliens enrolled fall 2008. Students from Europe, Asia, Latin America, Canada. Programs available to aid students whose native language is not English: English as a Second Language Program. No financial aid specifically designated for international students.

Student Life: On-campus residence halls house 9% of student body. Residence halls for both sexes constitute 100% of such space. Some single-sex floors and wings. Computer labs in several buildings with over 300 computers available for student use. *Intercollegiate athletics:* male: baseball, basketball, cross-country, football, golf, track; female: basketball, gymnastics, softball, track, volleyball. *Special regulations:* Cars must have parking permits. Quiet hours after 10pm Sun.–Thurs. *Special services:* Learning Resources Center, medical services. *Student publications, radio: Tailwind*, an annual literary magazine. Radio station KGSU broadcasts 84 hours per week. *Surrounding community:* Cedar City population 20,000. Las Vegas, 150 miles from campus, is nearest metropolitan area. Served by airport 2 miles from campus.

Library Collections: 205,000 volumes. 674,000 microforms; 18,000 audiovisual materials; 1,100 current periodical subscriptions. Online catalog. Students have access to online information retrieval services and the Internet.

Most important special holdings include William R. Palmer Collection of books and manuscripts concerning the Paiute Indians; Seymour Collection; picture collection from many donors; Grace Tanner Collection.

Buildings and Grounds: Campus area 114 acres.

Chief Executive Officer: Dr. Gregory R. Stauffer, President.

Address admission inquiries to David Sonton, Director of Admissions.

University of Utah

201 South Presidents Circle
Salt Lake City, Utah 84112-9008
Tel: (801) 581-7200 **E-mail:** admissions@sa.utah.edu
Internet: www.utah.edu

Institution Description: The University of Utah is a state institution. *Enrollment:* 28,211. *Degrees awarded:* Baccalaureate, first-professional (law, medicine, pharmacy), master's, doctorate.

Accreditation: *Regional:* NWCCU. *Professional*: accounting, architecture, audiology, business, dentistry, dietetics, engineering,journalism, law, medicine, music, nursing, nursing-midwifery, pharmacy, occupational therapy, physical therapy, physician assisting, psychology internship, public health, radiation therapy, rehabilitation counseling, social work, speech-language pathology, teacher education

History: Chartered as University of Deseret by provisional government of Deseret, and offered first instruction at postsecondary level 1850; awarded first degree (baccalaureate) 1886; adopted present name 1892. *See* Elizabeth Haglund, ed., *Remembering: The University of Utah* (Salt Lake City: University of Utah Press, 1981) for further information.

Institutional Structure: *Governing board:* Utah State Board of Regents. Representation: 15 regents. *Composition of institution:* Administrators 29. Academic affairs headed by provost. Management/business/finances directed by vice president for administrative services. Full-time instructional faculty 1,214. Academic governance body, Academic Senate, meets an average of 9 times per year.

Calendar: Semesters. Academic year May to Aug. Freshmen admitted year round. Degrees conferred Dec., May, Aug. Formal commencement May. Summer session May to Aug.

Characteristics of Freshmen: 7,244 applicants (female 3,709, male 3,525). 81% of applicants admitted. 45% of applicants admitted and enrolled full-time.

20% (517 students) submitted SAT scores; 89% (2,361 students) submitted ACT scores. *25th percentile*: SAT Math 500; ACT Composite 21, ACT English 20, ACT Math 20. *75th percentile*: SAT Math 640; ACT Composite 26, ACT English 27, ACT Math 27.

41% of entering freshmen expected to graduate within 5 years. 69% of freshmen from Utah. Freshmen from 50 states and 108 foreign countries.

Admission: Rolling admissions plan. Early acceptance available. *Requirements:* Graduation from accredited secondary school and required core courses including 4 years English emphasizing composition and literature, 2 years mathematics beyond algebra 1, 3 years biological and/or physical science (1 with laboratory), 1 year U.S. history, 2 years of same foreign language, 4 years of additional core courses. *Entrance tests:* ACT scores required. College Board SAT accepted. For foreign students TOEFL. Non-high school graduates will be considered with the GED. *For transfer students:* 2.6 minimum GPA; maximum transfer credit limited only by residence requirement.

College credit and advanced placement for postsecondary-level work completed in secondary school.

Tutoring available. Developmental courses offered in summer session and regular academic year; credit given.

Degree Requirements: *For all baccalaureate degrees:* 122 semester hours; 2.0 minimum GPA; 30 hours in residence; general education requirements.

Fulfillment of some degree requirements and exemption from some beginning courses possible by passing College Board CLEP, AP. *Grading system:* A–FE; pass-fail.

Distinctive Educational Programs: Cooperative education and internships. Evening classes. Facilities for independent research, including honors programs, individual majors. Institutionally sponsored study abroad in Argentina, Costa Rica, Finland, France, Hong Kong, India, Ireland, Italy, Japan, Korea, Mexico, Spain, Sweden, Switzerland, United Kingdom, Turkey.

ROTC: Army, Navy, Air Force.

Degrees Conferred: 4,882 *baccalaureate*; 1,611 *master's*; 590 *doctorate*; 277 *first-professional*. Bachelor's degrees awarded in top five disciplines: social sciences and history 1,074; business, management, marketing, and related support services 776; communication, journalism, and related programs 452; visual and performing arts 309; engineering and engineering technologies 292. Master's degrees awarded: various disciplines 1,611. Doctorates awrded: various disciplines 590. First-professiona degrees awarded: law 131, medicine 102, pharmacy 44.

Fees and Other Expenses: *Full-time tuition per academic year 2008–09:* undergraduate resident $5,284, nonresident $16,800; contact the university for current graduate and first-professional tuition and applicable fees. *Required fees:* $690. *Room and board per academic year:* $6,469. *Other expenses:* $5,580.

Financial Aid: Aid from institutionally generated funds is provided on the basis of academic merit, financial need, athletic ability.

Financial aid to full-time, first-time undergraduate students: 51% received some form of aid. Average amount of aid recieved: federal grants $3,278; Pell grants $2,850; other federal aid $800; state/local grants $1,138; institutional grants $5,487.

Departments and Teaching Staff: *Total instructional faculty:* 1,687 (full-time 1,175, part-time 512). Total faculty with doctorate, first-professional, or other terminal degree: 1,206. Student/faculty ratio: 15:1. Degrees held by full-time faculty: baccalaureate 2.1%, master's 7.6%, doctorate 90%, professional 90%. 90% hold terminal degrees.

Enrollment: Total enrollment 28,211. Undergraduate 21,526 (full-time 67%; female 45%, male 55%). Graduate 6,885 (full-time 76%). Undergraduate transfer-in students 1,780.

Characteristics of Student Body: *Ethnic/racial makeup:* Black non-Hispanic: 1%; American Indian or Alaska Native: 1%; Asian or Pacific Islander: 6%; Hispanic: 5%; White non-Hispanic: 78%; unknown: 6%; nonresident alien 3%. *Age distribution:* number under 18: 101; 18–19: 3,405; 20–21: 4,381; 22–24: 7,064; 25–29: 5,454; 30–34: 4,410; 35–39: 665; 40–49: 880; 50–64: 586; 65 and over: 190.

International Students: 2,532 nonresident aliens enrolled fall 2008. Students from Europe, Asia, Latin America, Africa, Canada, Australia, New Zealand. No programs available to aid students whose native language is not English. No financial aid specifically designated for international students.

Student Life: On-campus residence halls house 12.5% of undergraduates. Fraternities and sororities also offer residence space. Housing available for married students. *Intercollegiate athletics:* male: baseball, basketball, cross-country, running, diving, football, golf, skiing, swimming, tennis, track and field; female: basketball, cross-country running, diving, gymnastics, softball, skiing, swimming, tennis, track and field, volleyball. *Special regulations:* Cars allowed with permit. *Special services:* Learning Resources Center, medical services, shuttle bus service. *Student publications, radio, television: Daily Utah Chronicle*, a

UNIVERSITY OF UTAH—*cont'd*

newspaper. Radio station KUER broadcasts 126 hours per week. TV station KUED broadcasts 100 hours per week. *Surrounding community:* Salt Lake City metropolitan area population over 1 million. Served by mass transit bus system and train (light rail); airport 12 miles from campus; passenger rail service 10 miles from campus.

Library Collections: 3,219 volumes. Online catalog. 765,759 government documents collection; 3,610,000 microforms; 80,000 audiovisual materials; 41,000 periodicals including via electronic access. Students have access to online information retrieval services and the Internet.

Most important special holdings include extensive files in both medicine and law.

Buildings and Grounds: Campus area 1,422 acres.

Chief Executive Officer: Dr. Michael K. Young, President.

Address admission inquiries to Timothy Ebner, Director of Admissions.

Utah State University

1400 Old Main Hall
Logan, Utah 84322-1400
Tel: (435) 797-1000 **E-mail:** admit@usu.edu
Fax: (435) 797-3900 **Internet:** www.usu.edu

Institution Description: *Enrollment:* 21,388. *Degrees awarded:* Baccalaureate, master's, doctorate. Specialist certificates also awarded.

Academic offerings subject to approval by statewide coordinating bodies. Budget subject to approval by state governing boards. Member of the consortium Western Interstate Commission for Higher Education.

Accreditation: *Regional:* NWCCU. *Professional*: business, chemistry, dietetics, engineering, family and consumer science, landscape architecture, nursing, psychology internship, social work, teacher education

History: Established as Agricultural College of Utah 1888; offered first instruction at postsecondary level 1890; awarded first degree 1894; changed name to Utah Agricultural College 1929; adopted present official name Utah State University.

Institutional Structure: *Governing board:* Utah State University Board of Trustees. Extrainstitutional representation: 8 directors; institutional representation: 1 student; 1 alumnus. All voting. *Composition of institution:* Administrators 29. Academic affairs headed by provost. Management/business/finances directed by vice president of administrative services. Full-time faculty 752. Academic governance body, Faculty Senate, meets an average of 12 times per year.

Calendar: Semesters. Academic year Aug. to May. Freshmen admitted Aug., Jan., Mar., June. Degrees conferred and formal commencement June. Summer session of 1 term from June to Aug.

Characteristics of Freshmen: 91.5% of applicants accepted. 48.6% of accepted applicants enrolled. 8% (180 students) submitted SAT scores; 94% (2,042 students) submitted ACT scores. *25th percentile*: SAT Verbal 490, SAT Math 500; ACT Composite 21, ACT English 21, ACT Math 20. *75th percentile*: SAT Verbal 610, SAT Math 610; ACT Composite 27, ACT English 27, ACT Math 27.

68% of freshmen from Utah.

Admission: Rolling admissions plan. Apply at anytime, but not later than 2 months before beginning of semester. Early acceptance available. *Requirements:* Either graduation from secondary school or GED. *Entrance tests:* ACT composite. For foreign students TOEFL. *For transfer students:* 2.2 minimum GPA; from 4-year accredited institution 90 semester hours maximum transfer credit; from 2-year accredited institution 60 semester hours.

College credit and advanced placement for postsecondary-level work completed in secondary school and for extrainstitutional learning .

Tutoring available. Remedial courses offered in summer session and regular academic year.

Degree Requirements: 120 semester credits; 2.0 GPA; 30 hours in residence; general education requirements.

Fulfillment of some degree requirements and exemption from some beginning courses possible by passing departmental examinations, College Board CLEP. *Grading system:* A–F; pass-fail.

Distinctive Educational Programs: Work-experience programs, including cooperative education, internships. Flexible meeting places and schedules, including off-campus centers (at Moab, 314 miles away from main institution; at Roosevelt, 230 miles away). Accelerated degree programs. Cooperative baccalaureate program in nursing with Weber State College. Special facilities for using telecommunications in the classroom. Interdepartmental programs in physical ecology, plant ecology, aquatic ecology, forest range and geology; interdisciplinary program in watershed science. Facilities and programs for independent research, including honors programs, individual majors, tutorials. Institutionally sponsored Study Abroad programs in Mexico, France, Germany and USSR. International Student Exchange Programs offer more than 100 study sites throughout the world (Africa, Asia, Australia, Australasia, United Kingdom, Canada, Europe, Latin America).

ROTC: Air Force, Army.

Degrees Conferred: 1,677 *baccalaureate*; 1,881 *master's*; 195 *doctorate*. Bachelor's degrees awarded in top five disciplines: business, management, marketing, and related support services 415; education 330; engineering 185; family and consumer sciences/human sciences 161. Master's degrees awarded: various disciplines 1,881. Doctorates awarded: various disciplines 195.

Fees and Other Expenses: *Full-time tuition per academic year 2008–09:* undergraduate resident $3,856, nonresident $11,161; contact the university for current graduate tuition/fees. *Books and supplies* $1,280. *Room and board per academic year:* $6,634. *Other expenses:* $4,412.

Financial Aid: Aid from institutionally generated funds is provided on the basis of academic merit, financial need, other criteria.

Institution has a Program Participation Agreement with the U.S. Department of Education for eligible students to receive Pell Grants and, depending upon the agreement, other federal aid.

Financial aid to full-time, first-time undergraduate students: 62% received some form of aid. Average amount of aid received: federal grants $2,371; Pell grants $2,601; other federal aid $1,56; state/local grants $1,356; institutional grants $2,599.

Departments and Teaching Staff: *Total instructional faculty:* 870. Total faculty with doctorate, first-professional, or other terminal degree: 641. Student/faculty ratio: 19:1.

Enrollment: Total enrollment 27,388. Undergraduate 20,870. Graduate 518 (full-time 39%). Undergraduate transfer-in students 992.

Characteristics of Student Body: *Ethnic/racial makeup:* Black non-Hispanic: 1%; American Indian or Alaska Native: 1%; Asian or Pacific Islander: 2%; Hispanic: 5%; White non-Hispanic: 64%; unknown 26%; nonresident alien 1%. *Age distribution:* 17–21: 43%; 22–24: 25%; 25–29: 14%; 30–34: 5%; 35–39: 4%; 40–49: 6%; 50–59: 3%.

International Students: 1,200 nonresident aliens enrolled fall 2008. Programs available to aid students whose native language is not English: social, cultural. English as a Second Language Program. No financial aid specifically designated for international students.

Student Life: On-campus residence halls available for males and females. Some males join and live in fraternity housing; some females join and live in sorority housig. Housing available for married students. *Intercollegiate athletics:* male: basketball, football, golf, tennis, track; female: soccer, gymnastics, softball, tennis, track, volleyball. *Special regulations:* Cars with permits allowed; fee charged. *Special services:* Learning Resources Center, medical services, shuttle bus between central campus and outlying dormitories. *Student publications, radio, television: Crucible*, an annual literary journal; *Utah Statesman*, a triweekly newspaper. Radio station KUSU-FM broadcasts 126 hours per week. TV station KUSU-TV broadcasts 2 hours per week. *Surrounding community:* Logan population 50,000. Salt Lake City, 80 miles from campus, is nearest metropolitan area. Served by airport 5 miles from campus.

Publications: *Utah Science* (quarterly), *Western American Literature* (quarterly), *Western Historical Quarterly.*

Library Collections: 1,575,000 volumes (including government documents). 2,649,000 microforms; 16,500 audiovisual materials; 12,400 current serial subscriptions including via electronic access. Online catalog. Students have access to online information retrieval services and the Internet.

Most important special holdings include Fife Folklore Collection; Gunn McKay Congressional Records; material on Utah Mormons and Southern Idaho; Jack London Collection.

Buildings and Grounds: Campus area 450 acres.

Chief Executive Officer: Dr. Stan Albrecht, President.

Address undergraduates inquiries to Jenn Putnam, Director of Admissions; graduate inquiries to KayDawn Sorenson, Staff Assistant.

Utah Valley University

800 West 1200 south
Orem, Utah 84058-5999
Tel: (801) 222-8000 **E-mail:** admissions@uvsc.edu
Fax: (801) 226-5207 **Internet:** www.uvsc.edu

Institution Description: Utah Valley University, formerly named Utah Valley State College, is a public institution. *Enrollment:* 26,696. *Degrees awarded:* Associate, baccalaureate. Certificates and diplomas also awarded.

Academic offerings subject to approval by statewide coordinating bodies. Budget subject to approval by state governing boards.

Accreditation: *Regional:* NWCCU. *Professional*: business, dental hygiene, engineering, nursing

History: Founded as Central Utah Vocational School 1941; became a state institution 1945; relocated to Provo 1948; changed name to Utah Trade Technical Institute 1953; moved to Orem and new campus 1977; became Utah Valley State College 1993; achieved university status 2008.

Institutional Structure: *Governing board:* Representation: Utah Board of Regents. 16 regents, all voting. Board of Trustees. Extrainstitutional representation: 8 members appointed by governor; institutional representation: president of study body, president of alumni association, 2 ex officio. All voting. *Composition of institution:* Administrators 21. Academic affairs headed by vice president for academic affairs. Management/business/finances directed by vice president for institutional advancement and the executive director of budgets. Full-time instructional faculty 409.. Academic governance body, Faculty Senate, meets an average of 14 times per year.

Calendar: Semesters. Academic year Aug. to Apr. Freshmen admitted Aug., Jan., May, June. Degrees conferred and formal commencement Apr. Summer term of 7 sessions from Apr. to Aug.

Characteristics of Freshmen: 100% of applicants accepted. 80% of accepted applicants enrolled.

4% (116 students) submitted SAT scores; 57% (1,168 students) submitted ACT scores. *25th percentile:* SAT Math 420; ACT Composite 19. *75th percentile:* SAT Math 540; ACT Composite 23.

79% of freshmen from Utah. Freshmen from 46 states and 23 foreign countries.

Admission: Apply 1 week prior to registration; trades program students may apply later. Early acceptance available. *Requirements:* Either graduation from accredited secondary school or GED preferred; basically open admission. *Entrance tests:* ACT composite can waive assessment/placement tests. For international students TOEFL (500) or Michigan (80) test. Advanced placement for postsecondary-level work completed in secondary school. College credit for experiential credit through faculty assessment possible.

Degree Requirements: *For all associate degrees:* 64–72 credit hours; 20 hours in residence. *For baccalaureate degrees:* 128 credit hours; 30 hours in residence; 40 hours upper division. *For all degrees:* 2.0 GPA. *Grading system:* A–F.

Distinctive Educational Programs: Cooperative education work-experience program. Ethics Across the Curriculum includes required ethics course for degrees. B.S. in Technology Management. High school concurrent enrollment and accelerated programs. Utah Fire Academy. International students and study center. Evening and weekend programs.

ROTC: Army; Air Force in cooperation with Brigham Young University.

Degrees Conferred: 1,716 *associate*; 1,532 *baccalaureate*. Bachelor's degrees awarded in top five disciplines: business, management, marketing, and related support services 928; psychology 218; education 142; computer and information sciences 122; transportation and movement services 86.

Fees and Other Expenses: *Full-time tuition per academic year 2008–09:* resident $3,752, nonresident $11,514. *Required fees:* $496. *Room and board per academic year:* $8,352. *Books and supplies:* $1,630. *Other expenses:* $5,076.

Financial Aid: Aid from institutionally generated funds is provided on the basis of academic merit, financial need, athletic ability, other criteria. Institution has a Program Participation Agreement with the U.S. Department of Education for eligible students to receive Pell Grants and, depending upon the agreement, other federal aid.

Financial aid to full-time, first-time undergraduate students: 59% received some form of aid. Average amount of aid received: federal grants $3,840; Pell grants $3,385; other federal aid $919; state/local grants $758; institutional grants $3,047.

Departments and Teaching Staff: *Total instructional faculty:* 1,256. student/faculty ratio: 22:1. Degrees held by full-time faculty: doctorate 21%, master's 56%, baccalaureate 10%. 22% hold terminal degrees.

Enrollment: Total enrollment 26,696. Undergraduate 26,676. Graduate 20. Transfer-in students 1,986.

Characteristics of Student Body: *Ethnic/racial makeup:* Black non-Hispanic: 1%; American Indian or Alaska Native: 1%; Asian or Pacific Islander: 3%; Hispanic: 5%; White non-Hispanic: 86%; unknown 3%; nonresident alien 2%.

International Students: 534 nonresident aliens enrolled fall 2008. Students from Europe, Asia, Latin America, Africa, Canada, Australia, New Zealand. Programs available to aid students whose native language is not English: social, cultural. English as a Second Language Program. No financial aid specifically designated for international students.

Student Life: No college residence halls. *Intercollegiate athletics:* male: baseball, basketball, cross-country, golf, track, rodeo; female: basketball, cross-country, rodeo, softball, track, volleyball. *Special regulations:* Cars permitted by permit. *Special services:* Learning Resources Center including developmental classes; Accessibility Services Department; Fellness Center; Tutoring Services; open computer labs. *Student publications: The College Times*, weekly newspaper; *Arete'*, yearly artistic/literary magazine. *Surrounding community:* Orem (91,000)/Provo (100,000). Served by bus system, local airport 9 miles, Salt Lake International Airport 45 miles.

Library Collections: 212,000 volumes. Current periodical subscriptions: paper 642; via electronic access 19,806. Audio/visual materials 10,916; DVD discs 3,531; CD-ROMs 810. Online catalog. Computer work stations available. Students have access to online information retrieval services and the Internet.

Buildings and Grounds: Campus area 211 acres.

Chief Executive Officer: Dr. William A. Sederburg, President.

Address admissions inquiries to Director of Admissions.

Weber State University

1103 University Circle
Ogden, Utah 84408-1103
Tel: (801) 626-6000 **E-mail:** admissions@weber.edu
Fax: (801) 626-6679 **Internet:** www.weber.edu

Institution Description: Weber State University is a public institution. *Enrollment:* 21,288. *Degrees awarded:* Associate, baccalaureate, master's. Certificates and diplomas also awarded.

Academic offerings subject to approval by statewide coordinating bodies. Budget subject to approval by state governing boards.

Accreditation: *Regional:* NWCCU. *Professional*: business, chemistry, dental hygiene, engineering technology, music, nursing, practical nursing, radiography, respiratory therapy, social work, teacher education

History: Established as Weber Stake Academy by The Church of Jesus Christ of Latter-day Saints 1889; chartered 1896; changed name to Weber Academy 1908; offered first instruction at postsecondary level 1916; changed name to Weber Normal College 1918; changed name to Weber College and awarded first degree (associate) 1923; became state institution 1933; became 4-year institution 1959; became Weber State College 1963; became Weber State University 1991.

Institutional Structure: *Governing board:* Utah Board of Regents. Representation: 15 regents and 1 student; lieutenant governor. 1 ex officio. All voting. Board of Trustees. Extrainstitutional representation: president of student body, president of alumni association. 2 ex officio. All voting. *Composition of institution:* Administrators 26. Academic affairs headed by provost. Management/business/finances directed by vice president for business affairs. Full-time instructional faculty 460. Academic governance body, Faculty Senate, meets an average of 9 times per year.

Calendar: Semesters. Academic year Aug. to May. Freshmen admitted year-round. Fall and spring have terms of 16 weeks; summer term is 12 weeks, May to Aug. Degrees conferred at formal commencement Dec., May.

Characteristics of Freshmen: 100% of applicants accepted. 69% of accepted applicants enrolled.

72% (1,768 students) submitted ACT scores. Mean ACT Composite score 22.

30% of entering freshmen expected to graduate within 5 years. 98% of freshmen from Utah. Freshmen from 11 states and 16 foreign countries.

Admission: Rolling admissions plan. Apply by 30 days prior to registration. *Requirements:* All prospective students must have a high school diploma or GED equivalent; index score of 85 with probationary admission for those below 85. ACT or SAT recommended but not required for admission.

Degree Requirements: *For all associate degrees:* 60 semester hours (20 hours in resident) with math and English requirements. *For all baccalaureate degrees:* 120 semester hours (40 hours in residence) with 40 hours of upper division credit; Math, English, history, and computer competency must be satisfied.

Distinctive Educational Programs: Work-experience programs. Flexible meeting places and schedules including off-campus centers (at various statewide locations), weekend and evening classes. Accelerated degree programs. Interdepartmental programs in American studies, Asian studies, Latin American studies, urban planning. Facilities and programs for independent research, including honors programs, individual majors, tutorials. Institutionally sponsored study abroad to Mexico, Spain, and other countries. *Other distinctive programs:* Technical sales; criminal justice; business, education, nursing, musical theatre, automotive programs. Online courses offered.

ROTC: Army, Air Force, Navy.

Degrees Conferred: 1,671 *associate*; 1,881 *baccalaureate*; 195 *master's*. Bachelor's degrees awarded in top five disciplines: business, management, marketing, and related support services 480; health professions and related clinical sciences 263; education 269; computer and information sciences 167; security and protective services 138. Master's degrees awarded: various disciplines 195.

Fees and Other Expenses: *Full-time tuition per academic year 2008–09:* undergraduate resident $3,856, nonresident $11,181; contact the univesrity for current graduate tuition and applicable fees. *Required fees:* $640. *Books and supplies:* $1,200. *Other expenses:* $4,412.

WEBER STATE UNIVERSITY—*cont'd*

Financial Aid: Aid from institutionally generated funds is provided on the basis of academic merit, financial need, athletic ability, other criteria. Institution has a Program Participation Agreement with the U.S. Department of Education for eligible students to receive Pell Grants and, depending upon the agreement, other federal aid.

Financial aid to full-time, first-time undergraduate students: 62% received some form of aid. Average amount of aid received: federal grants $2,311; Pell grants $2,601; other federal aid $1,156; state/local grants $1,356; institutional grants $2,599.

Departments and Teaching Staff: *Total instructional faculty:* 904. student/faculty ratio: 19:1. Degrees held by full-time faculty: 80% hold terminal degrees.

Enrollment: Total enrollment 21,388. Undergraduate 20,870 (full-time 45%; female 52%, male 48%). Graduate 578 (full-time 39%). Undergraduate transfer-in students 992.

Characteristics of Student Body: *Ethnic/racial makeup:* Black non-Hispanic: 1%; Americn Indian or Alaska Native: 1%; Asian or Pacific Islander: 2%; Hispanic: 5%; White non-Hispanic: 64%; unknown: 26%; nonresident alien 1%.

International Students: 214 nonresident aliens enrolled fall 2008. Students from Europe, Asia, Latin America, Canada, Australia. Programs available to aid students whose native language is not English: social, cultural. English as a Second Language Program. No financial aid specifically designated for international students.

Student Life: On-campus residence halls house 5% of student body. Residence halls for males and females constitute 100% of such space. *Club sports:* basketball, hockey, soccer, softball. *Division athletics:* male: basketball, football, golf, tennis, track; female: basketball, golf, soccer, tennis, track, volleyball. *Special regulations:* Cars permitted without restrictions. *Special services:* Learning Resources Center, medical services. Over 130 clubs and organizations. Student government, leadership scholarships. *Student publications, radio: Signpost*, a twice weekly newspaper. Radio station KWCR broadcasts 168 hours per week (24 hours a day). *Surrounding community:* Ogden population 90,000. Salt Lake City, 35 miles from campus, is nearest metropolitan area. Served by mass transit bus system, airport 5 miles from campus, passenger rail service 3 miles from campus.

Library Collections: 525,000 volumes including bound books, serial backfiles, electronic documents, and government documents not in separate collections. Online catalog. 255,000 microforms; 7,500 audiovisual materials; 3,700 current serial subscriptions. Computer work stations available. Students have access to the Internet at no charge.

Most important special holdings include James A. Howell Literature Collection; Lawrence Burton Congressional Collection; Mark E. Austad Collection.

Buildings and Grounds: Campus area 400 acres.

Chief Executive Officer: Dr. F. Ann Millner, President.

Address admission inquiries to Christopher Rivera, Director of Admissions.

Westminster College of Salt Lake City

1840 South 1300 East
Salt Lake City, Utah 84105
Tel: (801) 484-7651 **E-mail:** info@westminstercollege.edu
Fax: (801) 466-6916 **Internet:** www.westminstercollege.edu

Institution Description: Westminster College of Salt Lake City is a private, nonprofit institution. *Enrollment:* 2,479. *Degrees awarded:* Baccalaureate, master's.

Accreditation: *Regional:* NWCCU. *Professional*: business, nursing, teacher education

History: Established as Salt Lake Collegiate Institute 1875; chartered 1892; offered first instruction at postsecondary level 1898; merged with Sheldon Jackson College (established 1895) and adopted Westminster College name 1902; awarded first degree (baccalaureate) 1946; reorganized January 1983.

Institutional Structure: *Governing board:* Board of Trustees. Extrainstitutional representation: 30 trustees; institutional representation: president of the college. All voting. *Composition of institution:* Administrators 13. Academic affairs headed by provost and dean of faculty. Business/finances directed by executive vice president and treasurer. Full-time instructional faculty 119. Academic governance body, full faculty and Faculty Senate meetings, meet an average of 6 times per year.

Calendar: Semesters (4-4-1 plan). Academic year Aug. to April. Freshmen admitted Sept., Jan., June. Degrees conferred and formal commencement June. Summer session from early June to early Aug.

Characteristics of Freshmen: 1,348 applicants (female 702, male 846). 79% of applicants admitted. 40% of applicants admitted and enrolled.

34% (128 students) submitted SAT scores; 78% (291 students) submitted ACT scores. *25th percentile*: SAT Critical Reading 507.5, SAT Math 490; ACT Composite 21, ACT English 19, ACT Math 20. *75th percentile*: SAT Verbal 640, SAT Math 610; ACT Composite 26; ACT English 25; ACT Math 27.

55% of entering freshmen expected to graduate within 5 years. 67% of freshmen from Utah. Freshmen from 20 states.

Admission: Rolling admissions plan. *Requirements:* Either graduation from accredited secondary school or GED. Minimum GPA 2.0. *Entrance tests:* College Board SAT or ACT composite recommended. For foreign students TOEFL. *For transfer students:* 2.5 minimum GPA; 88 semester hours maximum transfer credit from 4-year institution; 72 maximum from 2-year institution.

College credit and advanced placement for postsecondary-level work completed in secondary school. For extrainstitutional learning on basis of portfolio assessment.

Tutoring available. Noncredit developmental courses offered regular academic year.

Degree Requirements: 124 credit hours; 2.0 GPA; 40 hours in upper division courses numbered 300 or above from a 4-year institution. Fulfill all liberal education requirements; 2.0 GPA or above; meet all course requirements and GPA in the major and minor; fulfill residency requirement currently in effect.

Fulfillment of some degree requirements and exemption from some beginning courses possible by passing departmental examinations, College Board CLEP, AP. *Grading system:* A–F; pass-fail; withdraw (carries time limit).

Distinctive Educational Programs: Work-experience programs including cooperative education, internships. Weekend and evening classes. Interdisciplinary programs in behavioral science, environmental science, human resources, physical science. Individual majors. Individually arranged study abroad. University of Cambridge International Summer School, England.

ROTC: Army, Navy, Air Force in cooperation with University of Utah.

Degrees Conferred: 397 *baccalaureate:* biological/life sciences 30; business, management, marketing, and related support services 198; communications/communication technologies 23; computer and information sciences 17; education 33; English 21; health professions and related sciences 53; mathematics 9; philosophy/religion/theology 3; physical sciences 9; psychology 33; social sciences and history 40; trade and industry 22; visual and performing arts 14. 203 *master's*: business, management, marketing, and related support services 72; communication, journalism, and related programs 13; education 12; health professions 1.

Fees and Other Expenses: *Full-time tuition per academic year 2008–09:* $23,790 undergraduate; graduate tution per credit hour (contact the college for current rate). *Required fees:* $390. *Room and board per academic year:* $6,672. *Books and supplies:* .$1,200. *Other expenses:* $1,225.

Financial Aid: Aid from institutionally generated funds is provided on the basis of academic merit, financial need.

Financial aid to full-time, first-time undergraduate students: federal grants $4,103; Pell grants $3,222; other federal aid $791; state/local grants $791; institutional grants $11,074.

Departments and Teaching Staff: *total instructional faculty:* 246. Total faculty with doctorate, first-professional, or other terminal degree: 110. student/faculty ratio: 11:1. Degrees held by full-time faculty: doctorate 69%, master's 16%, baccalaureate 100%, professional 15%. 84% hold terminal degrees.

Enrollment: Total enrollment 2,859. Undergraduate 2,131 (full-time 91%; female 56%, male 44%). Graduate 728 (full-time 49%). Undergraduate transfer-in students 192.

Characteristics of Student Body: *Ethnic/racial makeup:* Black non-Hispanic: 1%; Asian or Pacific Islander: 3%; Hispanic: 6%; White non-Hispanic: 75%; unknown: 12%; nonresident alien 2%. *Age distribution:* number under 18: 10; 18–19: 536; 20–21: 456; 22–24: 372; 25–29: 292; 30–34: 103; 35–39: 36; 40–49: 64; 50–64: 25; 65 and over: 2.

International Students: 59 nonresident aliens enrolled fall 2008. Students from Europe, Asia, Latin America. No programs available to aid students whose native language is not English. No financial aid specifically designated for international students.

Student Life: All on-campus co-ed residence hall house 21% of the students body. *Special regulations:* Residential parking available on a first-come, first-served basis. *Special services:* START Center. *Student publications: The Ellipsis*, a literary magazine; *The Forum*, a weekly newspaper. *Surrounding community:* Salt Lake City metropolitan area population 1,500,000. Served by bus system; airport 12 miles from campus; passenger rail service 4 miles from campus.

Library Collections: 163,069 volumes. Online catalog. Current periodical subscriptions: 4,394 paper; 248,793 microform; 32 via electronic access. 6,067 recordings. 567 compact discs. 32 CD-ROMs. Computer work stations available. Students have access to online information retrieval services and the Internet.

Most important special holdings include Utah landscape collection, theology of the nuclear arms race.; religious history of the relationship between Presbyterian/LDS Church in Utah; Utah history; women's studies.

Buildings and Grounds: Campus area 27 acres.

Chief Executive Officer: Dr. Michael S. Bassis, President.

Address admission inquiries to Christine Taelves, Director of Admissions.

Vermont

Bennington College

One College Drive
Bennington, Vermont 05201-9993
Tel: (800) 933-6845 **E-mail:** admissions@bennington.edu
Fax: (802) 442-4320 **Internet:** www.bennington.edu

Institution Description: Bennington College is a private, independent, nonprofit college. *Enrollment:* 759. *Degrees awarded:* Baccalaureate, master's.

Accreditation: *Regional:* NEASC.

History: Established and chartered 1925; offered first instruction at postsecondary level 1932; awarded first degree (baccalaureate) 1936. *See* Barbara Jones, *Bennington College: The Development of an Educational Idea* (New York: Harper and Brothers, 1946) for further information.

Institutional Structure: *Governing board:* Board of Trustees of Bennington College Corporation. Representation: 34 trustees, including 1 administrator, 23 alumni. All voting. *Composition of institution:* Administrators 8. Academic affairs headed by Dean of Faculty. Management/business/finances directed by vice president for finance and administration. Full-time instructional faculty 62. Academic governance body, Academic Council, meets an average of 28 times per year.

Calendar: Semesters. Academic year Sept. to June. Freshmen admitted Sept., Mar. Degrees conferred and formal commencement June. No summer session.

Characteristics of Freshmen: 1,057 applicants (female 692, male 365). 66% of applicants admitted. 24% of applicants admitted and enrolled.

80% (102 students) submitted SAT scores; 23% (2 students) submitted ACT scores. *25th percentile*: SAT Critical Reading 570, SAT Math 520; ACT Composite 23, ACT English 21, ACT Math 25. *75th percentile*: SAT Critical Reading 700, SAT Math 620; ACT Composite 29, ACT English 27, ACT Math 29. 59% of entering freshmen expected to graduate within 5 years. 5% of freshmen from Vermont. Freshmen from 23 states and 1 foreign country.

Admission: Rolling admissions plan. For fall acceptance, apply as early as Sept. 15 of previous year, but not later than Aug. 1 of year of enrollment. Students notified of acceptance Jan. to July. Apply by Nov. 15 for early decision. Early acceptance available. *Requirements:* Either graduation from accredited secondary school or GED; personal statement, interview. *Entrance tests:* College Board SAT or ACT composite encouraged. For foreign students TOEFL.

College credit for postsecondary-level work completed in secondary school. Advanced placement for extrainstitutional learning on basis of portfolio assessment.

Degree Requirements: Successful completion of work in area of specialization as judged by appropriate division and evaluative committee. *Grading system:* Pass-fail, descriptive comments.

Distinctive Educational Programs: *For undergraduates:* Work experience programs. Facilities for independent research. Study abroad programs in England, Germany, The Netherlands. Post-baccalaureate pre-medical and allied health science program. Bennington College - Bank Street College program for certification in either early childhood/elementary education or junior high education. *Available to all students:* Flexible meeting times and schedules. Individualized majors, tutorials.

Degrees Conferred: 145 *baccalaureate*; 60 *master's*. Bachelor's degrees awarded: architecture 2; biological/life sciences 1; communications/communication1; education 2; English 16; family and consumer sciences 1; foreign languages 6; mathematics 3; natural resources/environmental science 1; philosophy and religious studies 2; physical sciences 2; psychology 1; visual and performing arts 61; other disciplines 32. Master's degrees awarded: education 20; English 39; visual and performing arts 1.

Fees and Other Expenses: *Full-time tuition per academic year 2008–09:* $38,270. undergraduate; graduate study varies by program. *Other fees:* $910. *Room and board per academic year:* $10,680. *Books and supplies:* $800. *Other expenses:* $2,200.

Financial Aid: Aid from institutionally generated funds is provided on the basis of academic merit, financial need.

Financial aid to full-time, first-time undergraduate students: 81% received some form of aid. Need-based scholarships/grants totaling $7,650,163, self-help $1,946,282, parent loans $864,385, tuition waivers $66,980; non-need-based scholarships/grants totaling $300,514, self-help $523,858, parent loans $950,253.

Departments and Teaching Staff: *Total instructional faculty:* 89 (full-time 62, part-time 27).

Enrollment: Total enrollment 759. Undergraduate 618 (full-time 99%; female 66%, male 34%). Graduate 141. Transfer-in students 34.

Characteristics of Student Body: *Ethnic/racial makeup:* Black non-Hispanic: 2%; Asian or Pacific Islander: 2%; Hispanic: 3%; White non-Hispanic: 83%; unknown: 7%; nonresident alien 4%.

International Students: 32 nonresident aliens enrolled fall 2008. Students from Europe, Asia, Latin America, Africa, Canada. No programs available to aid students whose native language is not English. Some financial aid specifically designated for international students.

Student Life: On-campus residence halls house 100% of student body. *Student athletics:* co-ed soccer team; numerous intramural sports. *Special regulations:* Cars permitted in designated areas only. *Special services:* Learning Resources Center, medical services. *Student publication: SILO*, a literary magazine. *Surrounding community:* Bennington population 16,000. Boston, 150 miles from campus, is nearest metropolitan area. Served by mass transit bus system; airport 5 miles from campus.

Publications: *Bennington*, is published twice each year and features stories on the work of alumni, faculty, and students. In the two quarters that *Bennington* is not published, *NOTES,* a tabloid newsletter featuring alumni, faculty, and student news is mailed to alumni and friends of the college.

Library Collections: 121,500 volumes including bound books, serial backfiles, electronic documents, and government documents not in separate collections. Online catalog. Current serial subscriptions: 13,000 print and online access. 4,000 recordings. Computer work stations available. Students have access to the Internet at no charge.

Most important special holdings include collection of important signed photographs (Adams, Weston, Stroud, etc.); collection of materials related to Bennington School of the Dance; Collection of American first editions.

Buildings and Grounds: Campus area 650 acres.

Chief Executive Officer: Dr. Elizabeth Coleman, President.

Address admission inquiries to Ken Himmelman, Dean of Admissions.

Burlington College

95 North Avenue
Burlington, Vermont 05401-8477
Tel: (802) 862-9616 **E-mail:** admissions@burlcol.edu
Fax: (802) 658-0071 **Internet:** www.burlcol.edu

Institution Description: Burlington College is a private, independent, nonprofit college. *Enrollment:* 167. *Degrees awarded:* Associate, baccalaureate.

Accreditation: *Regional:* NEASC.

History: Established as Vermont Institute of Community Involvement, chartered, incorporated, and offered first instruction at postsecondary level 1972; awarded first degree (associate) 1974; adopted present name 1979.

Institutional Structure: *Governing board:* Board of Trustees. Extrainstitutional representation: 20 trustees; institutional representation: president 1 faculty, 2 student, 1 staff. All voting. *Composition of institution:* Administrators 16. Academic affairs headed by academic dean. Management/business/finances directed by Business Manager. Academic governance bodies: Academic Review Committee meets an average of 26 times per year; the Academic Programs Committee meets an average of 4 times per year.

Calendar: Semesters. Academic year Sept. to May. Freshmen admitted Sept., Jan., June.

Characteristics of Freshmen: 93 applicants (female 40, male 53). 36% of applicants accepted. 53% of accepted applicants enrolled.

24% of entering students expected to graduate within 5 years. 61% of freshmen from Vermont. Freshmen from 11 states. countries.

Admission: Rolling admissions plan. Early acceptance available. *Requirements:* Graduation from secondary school or GED. *For transfer students:* From 4-year accredited institution 90 hours maximum transfer credit; from 2-year accredited institution 60 hours; C- minimum grade required for transfer courses.

College credit for postsecondary-level work completed in secondary school and for extrainstitutional learning on basis of portfolio assessment.

Tutoring available.

Degree Requirements: *For all associate degrees:* 60 credit hours; minimum 18 hours in residence. *For all baccalaureate degrees:* 120 credit hours; minimum 30 hours in residence. *For all degrees:* Distribution requirements; satisfactory completion of 75% of work undertaken toward degree; 6-credit final project; approval of Academic Review Committee. *Grading system:* Credit-no credit; withdraw (deadline after which no credit is appended to withdraw); low pass; written evaluation system.

Distinctive Educational Programs: Flexible, self-designed degree programs, independent study options, and small classes and personalized support for adult learners. Designed Degree Programs include Psychology, Transpersonal Psychology, Human Services, Cinema Studies and Humanities, with concentrations in literature and writing, gender studies, fine arts, history, cinema studies, interdisciplinary studies. Low residency B.A. Program: Independent Degree Program with majors in psychology, transpersonal psychology, literature and writing, fine arts, cinema studies and human services. Professional Certificates in Paralegal Studies and Cinema Studies.

Degrees Conferred: 3 *associate*; 37 *baccalaureate*: English 5; interdisciplinary studies 12; liberal arts/general studies 2, psychology 8; visual and performing 10

Fees and Other Expenses: *Full-time tuition per academic year 2008–09;* $19,640. *Books and supplies:* $990. *Room and board per academic year:* $6,750. *Other expenses:* $3,600.

Financial Aid: Aid from institutional generated funds is provided on the basis of academic merit, financial need. Institution has a Program Participation Agreement with the U.S. Department of Education for eligible students to receive Pell Grants and, depending upon the agreement, other federal aid.

Financial aid to full-time, first-time undergraduate students: 81% received some form of aid.

Departments and Teaching Staff: *Total instructional faculty:* 62 (full-time 5, part-time 57). Degrees held by full-time faculty: doctorate 21%, professional 7%, baccalaureate 11.7%, master's 60.5%.

Enrollment: Total enrollment 167. Undergraduate 167 (full-time 65%; female 46%, male 54%). Transfer-in students 27.

Characteristics of Student Body: *Ethnic/racial makeup:* Black non-Hispanic: 2%; American Indian or Alaska Native: 1%; Asian or Pacific Islander 2%; Hispanic: 2%; White non-Hispanic: 80%; unknown: 11%; nonresident alien 2%.

International Students: 4 nonresident aliens enrolled fall 2008. No programs available to aid students whose native language is not English. No financial aid specifically designated for international students.

Student Life: *Surrounding community:* Burlington population 40,000. Montreal, Canada, 90 miles from campus, is nearest metropolitan area. Served by mass transit bus system; airport 4 miles from campus; passenger rail service 7 miles from campus.

Library Collections: Students use collections and facilities of Trinity College library and the University of Vermont. *Special collections:* Frank Michael Film Study Collection; Institute for Social Ecology Collection.

Buildings and Grounds: Campus area 1 building.

Chief Executive Officer: Dr. Jane O'Meara-Sanders, President.

Address admission inquiries to Admissions Director.

Castleton State College

62 Alumni Drive
Castleton, Vermont 05735

Tel: (802) 468-5611 **E-mail:** info@castleton.edu
Fax: (802) 468-5237 **Internet:** www.castleton.edu

Institution Description: Castleton State College is a state institution. *Enrollment:* 1,971. *Degrees awarded:* Associate, baccalaureate, master's, certificate of advanced graduate study (CAGS).

Academic offerings subject to approval by statewide coordinating bodies. Budget subject to approval by state governing boards. Member of Consortium of Vermont Colleges, Consortium of Vermont State Colleges.

Accreditation: *Regional:* NEASC. *Professional*: nursing, social work

History: Established and chartered as Rutland County Grammar School 1787; changed name to Vermont Classical High School 1828; readopted name Rutland County Grammar School (also known as Castleton Academy and Castleton Seminary) 1830; changed name to Castleton Normal School 1867, to Castleton Teachers College 1947; adopted present name 1962.

Institutional Structure: *Governing board:* Board of Trustees of Vermont State Colleges. Extrainstitutional representation: 15 trustees, including governor; institutional representation: 1 student. 1 ex officio. 15 voting. *Composition of institution:* Administrators 46. Academic affairs headed by academic dean. Management/business/finances directed by dean of business administration; Admissions and financial aid directed by dean of enrollment; student affairs directed by dean of students; institutional development directed by dean of institutional advancement. Full-time instructional faculty 88. Academic governance body, Faculty Assembly meets an average of 8 times per year. *Faculty representation:* Faculty is served by collective bargaining agent, Vermont Federation of Teachers, affiliated with AFT.

Calendar: Semesters. Academic year Aug. to May. Freshmen admitted Aug., Jan. Degrees conferred and formal commencement May.

Characteristics of Freshmen: 65% of applicants accepted. 48% of applicants accepted and enrolled.

36% of entering freshmen expected to graduate within 5 years. 55.6% of freshmen from Vermont. Freshmen from 30 states and 4 foreign countries.

Admission: Rolling admissions plan. Early acceptance available. *Requirements:* Either graduation from accredited secondary school with 16 academic units which normally include 4 English, 2 foreign language, 2 science, 2 social studies, 3 mathematics. *Entrance tests:* College Board SAT or ACT composite. *For transfer students:* 2.0 minimum GPA; from 4-year accredited institution 90 hours maximum transfer credit; from 2-year accredited institution 60 hours.

College credit and advanced placement for postsecondary-level work completed in secondary school, and for extrainstitutional learning on basis of ACE *2006 Guide to the Evaluation of Educational Experiences in the Armed Services*; portfolio; faculty assessments.

Tutoring available. Developmental/remedial courses offered during regular academic year.

Degree Requirements: *For all associate degrees:* 64 credit hours. *For all baccalaureate degrees:* 128 credit hours. *For all undergraduate degrees:* 2.0 GPA, minimum 30 credits in residence.

Grading system: A–E; withdraw (carried time limit).

Distinctive Educational Programs: *For undergraduates:* Facilities for independent research, including honors programs, tutorials. First year seminar program; programs in England and Latin America. Independent study in most departments. Contract majors. Work experience programs. Flexible meeting places and schedules, including an off-campus center and evening classes.

Degrees Conferred: 187 *baccalaureate*. Bachelor's degrees awarded in top five disciplines: business, management, marketing, and related support services 41; communication, journalism, and related programs 20; multidisciplinary studies 15; visual and performing arts 14; parks and recreation 13.

Fees and Other Expenses: *Full-time tuition per academic year 2008–09:* undergraduate resident $6,828; nonresident $14,426; contact the college for current graduate tuition/fees. *Books and supplies* $850. *Room and board per academic year:* $8,522.

Financial Aid: The college offers a direct lending program. Aid from institutionally generated funds is provided on the basis of academic merit, financial need, other criteria.

Financial aid to full-time, first-time undergraduate students: 36% received federal grants averaging $2,611; 30% state/local grants averaging $1,262; 9% institutional grants averaging $2,565; 73% received loans averaging $4,835.

Departments and Teaching Staff: *Total instructional faculty:* 176. Student/faculty ratio: 16:1. Degrees held by full-time faculty: master's 6%, doctorate 70%, professional 24%. 94% hold terminal degrees.

Enrollment: Total enrollment 1,971. Undergraduate 1,796 (female 59%, male 41%).

Characteristics of Student Body: *Ethnic/racial makeup:* Black non-Hispanic: 1%; American Indian or Alaska Native: 1%; Asian or Pacific Islander: 1%; Hispanic: 1%; White non-Hispanic: 90%; unknown: 7%.

International Students: 2 undergraduate nonresident aliens enrolled fall 2008. No programs available to aid students whose native language is not English. Some financial aid available for international students.

Student Life: On-campus residence halls house 34% of student body. *Intercollegiate athletics:* meale: baseball, basketball, cross-country, lacrosse, skiing, soccer, tennis; female: basketball, cross-country, field hockey, lacrosse, skiing, soccer, softball, tennis. *Special regulations:* Cars permitted without restrictions. Quiet hours and quiet floors; residence hall visitation requires a guest contract. *Student organizations:* Freshman academic honor society; upperclass academic honor society; active outing club. *Special services:* Medical services. *Student publications, radio: Spartacus*, a yearbook; *Spartan*, a weekly newspaper. Radio station WIUV broadcasts 119 hours per week. *Surrounding community:* Castleton population 5,000. Albany (NY), 80 miles from campus, is nearest metropol-

CASTLETON STATE COLLEGE—*cont'd*

itan area. Served by airport 14 miles from campus; passenger rail service 12 miles from campus.

Publications: Castleton English students and faculty publish *The Vermont Literary Review.*

Library Collections: 186,000 volumes including bound books, serial backfiles, electronic documents, and government documents not in separate collections. Online catalog. 586,000 microforms; 5,200 audiovisual materials; 720 current serial subscriptions. Computer work stations available. Students have access to the Internet at no charge.

Most important special holdings include Vermont Collection; Calvin Coolidge Papers (on microfilm).

Buildings and Grounds: Campus area 130 acres.

Chief Executive Officer: Dr. David S. Wolk, President. Address admission inquiries to Dean of Enrollment.

Champlain College

163 South Willard Street
Burlington, Vermont 05402-0670
Tel: (802) 860-2727 **E-mail:** admissions@champlain.edu
Fax: (802) 860-2767 **Internet:** www.champlain.edu

Institution Description: Champlain College is a private, coeducational institution. *Enrollment:* 2,891. *Degrees offered:* Associate, baccalaureate, master's.

Accreditation: *Regional:* NEASC. *Professional*: radiation therapy technology

History: Founded 1878. The college offers 29 majors covering business fields, computer programming and networking systems, allied health, human services, legal fields, electronic gaming, digital forensics, education, professional writing. Students may earn an associate degree on the path to a bachelor of science degree.

Calendar: Semesters. Academic year Aug. to Apr.

Characteristics of Freshmen: 2,980 applicants (female 1,404, male 1,576). 98% applicants submitted SAT scores; 8% ACT scores. *25th percentile*: SAT Verbal 500, SAT Math 500; ACT Composite 18. *75th percentile*: SAT Verbal 560, SAT Math 570; ACT Composite 20.

Freshmen from 23 states and 19 foreign countries.

Admission: Rolling admissions.

Degree Requirements: Completion of prescribed curriculum.

Distinctive Educational Programs: Electronic gaming and interactive development program; computer forensics and information security.

ROTC: Army in cooperation with University of Vermont.

Degrees Conferred: 405 *associate;* 99 *baccalaureate:* business and management 63; computer and information sciences 9; education 10; liberal arts/general studies; psychology 1; visual and performing arts 7.

Fees and Other Expenses: *Full-time tuition per academic year 2008–09:* $24,355. *Required fees:* $50. *Room and board per academic year:* $9,900. *Books and supplies:* $600. *Other expenses:* $600.

Financial Aid: Aid from institutionally generated funds is provided on the basis of academic merit, financial need, athletic ability.

Financial aid to full-time, first-time undergraduate students: 92% received some form of aid. Average amount of aid received: federal grants $3,446; Pell grants $2,591; other federal aid $955; state/local frants $,393; institutional grants $2,880.

Departments and Teaching Staff: *Total instructional faculty:* 256 (full-time 65, part-time 191). Total faculty with doctorate, first-professional, or other terminal degree: 73. Student/faculty ratio: 17:1. Degrees held by full-time faculty: doctorate 11%, master's 35%, baccalaureate 2%, professional 52%.

Enrollment: Total enrollment 2,891. Undergraduate 2,754 (full-time 76%; female 44%, male 56%). Graduate 137 (full-time 5%). Transfer-in students 192.

Characteristics of Student Body: *Ethnic/racial makeup:* Black non-Hispanic: 1%; Asian or Pacific Islander: 2%; Hispanic: 2%; White non-Hispanic: 61%; unknown 34%.

International Students: 10 nonresident aliens enrolled fall 2008. Programs available to aid students whose native language is not English: social, No financial aid specifically designated for international students.

Student Life: Various intramural sports. Opportunities for skiing, snowboarding, hiking, canoeing, sailing. Book club, peer tutoring, international club. Community service; study abroad. Campus newspaper and literary magazine.

Library Collections: 40,000 volumes. 17,625 microforms; 1,600 audiovisual materials; 1,775 current periodical subscriptions. Students have access to online information retrieval services and the Internet.

Most important special collections include College Archives; business collections; children's literature.

Buildings and Grounds: Campus area 19 acres.

Chief Executive Officer: Dr. David F. Finney, President.

Address admissions inquiries to Laryn Ranco, Director of Admissions.

College of St. Joseph

71 Clement Raod
Rutland, Vermont 05701-3899
Tel: (802) 773-5900 **E-mail:** admissions@csj.edu
Fax: (802) 773-5900 **Internet:** www.csj.edu

Institution Description: The College of St. Joseph is a private, independent, nonprofit college. *Enrollment:* 428. *Degrees awarded:* Associate, baccalaureate, master's.

Accreditation: *Regional:* NEASC.

History: Established and chartered as St. Joseph's Teachers College and offered first instruction at postsecondary level 1954; awarded first degree (baccalaureate) 1960; adopted present official name, The College of St. Joseph, Inc., 1986.

Institutional Structure: *Governing board:* Board of Trustees. Representation: 31 trustees, including 9 representatives of the Sisters of St. Joseph, president of the college, 1 priest, 1 full-time faculty member, 1 student. All voting. *Composition of institution:* Administrators 26. Full-time instructional faculty 13.

Calendar: Semesters. Academic year late Aug. to mid-May. Freshmen admitted Aug., Jan., May. Degrees conferred and formal commencement May.

Characteristics of Freshmen: 100 applicants. 93% of applicants accepted. 61% of freshmen from Vermont. Freshmen from 9 states.

Admission: Rolling admissions plan. Early acceptance available. *Requirements:* Either graduation from accredited secondary school or GED. Recommend 4 units English, 2 social studies, 2 algebra, 1 geometry, 1 science, 7 academic electives. Minimum GPA 2.0. *For transfer students:* 2.0 minimum GPA; 97 hours maximum transfer credit.

Advanced placement for postsecondary-level work completed in secondary school.

Degree Requirements: *For all associate degrees:* 60 credit hours; 15 hours in residence. *For all baccalaureate degrees:* 127 credit hours; 30 hours in residence. *For all undergraduate degrees:* 2.0 GPA; distribution requirements. *Grading system:* A–F; pass-fail; withdraw (carried time limit).

Distinctive Educational Programs: *For graduate students:* Weekend classes.

Degrees Conferred: 16 *associate*; 59 *baccalaureate*; 64 *master's*. Bachelor's degrees awarded in top five disciplines: business, management, marketing, and related support services 19; education 18; psychology 10; liberal arts/general studies 7; public administration 6. Naster;s degrees aawarded various disciplines 64.

Fees and Other Expenses: *Full-time tuition per academic year 2008–09:* undergraduate $16,790; contact the college for current graduate rates. *Books and supplies:* $1,000. *Room and board per academic year:* $8,150. *Other expenses:* $2,000.

Financial Aid: Aid from institutionally generated funds is provided on the basis of academic merit, financial need, athletic ability.

Financial aid to full-time, first-time undergraduate students: 94% received federal grants averaging $2,611; 46% state/local grants averaging $2,176; 97% institutional grants averaging $4,434; 87% received loans averaging $2,162.

Departments and Teaching Staff: *Total instructional faculty:* 30. Student/faculty ratio: 12:1. Degrees held by full-time faculty: doctorate 54%, master's 100%. 62% hold terminal degrees.

Enrollment: Total enrollment 428. Undergraduate 250 (full-time 62%, female 54%, male 48%). Graduate 178 (full-time 27%). Transfer-in students 19.

Characteristics of Student Body: *Ethnic/racial makeup:* Black non-Hispanic: 6%; American Indian or Alaska Native 1%; Hispanic: 3%; White non-Hispanic: 6%.

International Students: No programs available to aid students whose native language is not English. No financial aid specifically designated for international students.

Student Life: On-campus residence halls house 45% of student body. *Intercollegiate athletics:* basketball, soccer. *Special regulations:* Cars permitted without restrictions. *Special services:* Learning Resources Center. *Student publications: Cairn*, a yearbook. *Surrounding community:* Rutland population 25,000. Albany, NY, 140 miles from campus, is nearest metropolitan area. Served by airport 10 miles from campus; passenger rail service 20 miles from campus.

Library Collections: 65,000 volumes including bound books, serial backfiles, electronic documents, and government documents not in separate collections. Online catalog. Current serial subscriptions: 256 paper, 101 microform.

992 recordings; 64 CD-ROMs. Computer work stations available. Students have access to the Internet at no charge.

Most important special holdings include Kyran McGrath Irish Studies Collection; Sr. St. George Vermont Collection; educational and psychological tests.

Buildings and Grounds: Campus area 99 acres.

Chief Executive Officer: Dr. Frank G. Miglorie, Jr., President.

Address admission inquiries to Tracy Gallip0, Director of Admissions.

Goddard College

123 Pitkin Place
Plainfield, Vermont 05667-9432
Tel: (802) 454-8311 **E-mail:** admissions@goddard.edu
Fax: (802) 454-1029 **Internet:** www.goddard.edu

Institution Description: Goddard College is a private, independent, nonprofit college. *Enrollment:* 731. *Degrees awarded:* Baccalaureate, master's.

Accreditation: *Regional:* NEASC.

History: Established as Green Mountain Central Institute, Barre, a secondary school, by a group of Universalists 1863; changed name to Goddard Seminary and offered first instruction at postsecondary level 1870; changed name to Goddard Seminary and Junior College 1935; reincorporated as Goddard College, a 4-year institution, moved to present location, and offered first instruction at senior college level 1938; awarded first baccalaureate 1943.

Institutional Structure: *Governing board:* Board of Trustees. Representation: 20 trustees. All voting. *Composition of institution:* Academic affairs headed by president. Management/business/finances directed by comptroller. Full-time instructional faculty 12. Academic governance body, the Goddard community, meets an average of 16 times per year.

Calendar: Modified semester plan. Academic year Sept. to May. Freshmen admitted Sept., Jan., May. Degrees conferred May, Aug., Dec. Formal commencement May.

Admission: Rolling admissions plan. Early acceptance available. *Requirements:* Either graduation from accredited secondary school or GED. *Entrance tests.* College Board SAT or ACT composite. For foreign students TOEFL. *For transfer students:* 75 hours maximum transfer credit.

College credit and advanced placement for postsecondary-level work completed in secondary school and for extrainstitutional learning (life experience) on basis of faculty assessment.

Developmental courses offered during regular academic year; credit given.

Degree Requirements: 120 semester hours; 2 terms in residence. Fulfillment of some degree requirements and exemption from some beginning courses possible by passing College Board CLEP.

Distinctive Educational Programs: Internships. Weekend and evening classes. Interdepartmental program in women's studies. Individual majors. Tutorials. Individually arranged study abroad.

Degrees Conferred: 51 *baccalaureate*; 158 *master's*. Bachelor's degrees awarded in top disciplines: liberal arts/general studies 59; health professions and related clinical sciences 14; education 12. 124 *master's:* various disciplines 158.

Fees and Other Expenses: *Full-time tuition per academic year 2008–09:* $12,752. Other fees may apply. *Books and supplies:* $1,334. *Room and board per academic year:* housing costs vary; contact the college for current information.

Financial Aid: Aid from institutionally generated funds is provided on the basis of academic merit, financial need.

Institution has a Program Participation Agreement with the U.S. Department of Education for eligible students to receive Pell Grants and, depending upon the agreement, other federal aid.

Departments and Teaching Staff: *Total instructional faculty:* 12.

Enrollment: Total enrollment 731. Undergraduate 252 (female 71%, male 29%). Graduate 479. Transfer-in students 69.

Characteristics of Student Body: *Ethnic/racial makeup:* Black non-Hispanic: 3%; American Indian or Alaska Native: 1%; Hispanic: 6%; White non-Hispanic: 69%; unknown: 21%.

International Students: 17 nonresident aliens enrolled fall 2004. No financial aid specifically designated for international students.

Student Life: On-campus residence halls house 80% of student body. Residence halls for both sexes constitute 100% of such space. *Special regulations:* Cars must be registered. *Special services:* Learning Resources Center. *Student publications, radio:* Newspaper. Radio station WGDR broadcasts 60 hours per week. *Surrounding community:* Plainfield population 600. Boston, 175 miles from campus, is nearest metropolitan area. Served by airport and passenger rail service, both 10 miles from campus.

Library Collections: 62,000 volumes. 225 serial subscriptions. 4,390 audiovisual materials. Online catalog. Students have access to online information retrieval services and the Internet.

Buildings and Grounds: Campus area 250 acres.

Chief Executive Officer: Dr. Mark Schulman, President.

Address admission inquiries to Brenda Hawkins, Director of Admissions.

Green Mountain College

1 College Circle
Poultney, Vermont 05764-1199
Tel: (802) 287-8000 **E-mail:** admiss@greenmtn.edu
Fax: (802) 287-8099 **Internet:** www.greenmtn.edu

Institution Description: Green Mountain College is a private, independent, nonprofit college. *Enrollment:* 861. *Degrees awarded:* baccalaureate, master's/baccalaureate.

Academic offerings subject to approval by statewide coordinating bodies.

Accreditation: *Regional:* NEASC. *Professional*: recreation and leisure services

History: Established by the United Methodist Church as Troy Conference Academy, a preparatory school 1834; changed name to Ripley Female College and offered first instruction at postsecondary level 1863; awarded first degree (baccalaureate) 1866; resumed operation as Troy Conference Academy 1874; became coeducational junior college 1931; reorganized as a women's junior college and adopted present name 1943; became independent 1970; returned to coeducational status, added baccalaureate programs 1975. The college refocused its mission on environmental liberal arts in 1995.

Institutional Structure: *Governing board:* The Board of Trustees of Green Mountain College. Extrainstitutional representation: 22 trustees; institutional representation: 1 chair; 3 alumni. 1 ex officio. 26 voting. *Composition of institution:* Administrators 26. Academic affairs headed by provosts. Management/business/finances directed by chief financial officer. Full-time instructional faculty 47. Academic governance body, Green Mountain College Faculty Association, meets an average of 9 times per year.

Calendar: Semesters. Academic year Aug. to May. Freshmen admitted Sept., Jan. Degrees conferred and formal commencement May. Summer session.

Characteristics of Freshmen: 1,519 applicants (female 853, male 726). 85% of applicants accepted. 28% of accepted applicants enrolled.

89% (170 students) submitted SAT scores; 9% (19 students) submitted ACT scores. *25th percentile*: SAT Verbal 460, SAT Math 430; ACT Composite 18. *75th percentile*: SAT Verbal 580, SAT Math 560; ACT Composite 25.

14% of freshmen from Vermont. Freshmen from 21 states and 2 foreign countries.

Admission: Rolling admissions plan. For fall acceptance, apply as early as Sept. 15. Apply by Nov. 1 for early decision; need not limit application to Green Mountain. Early acceptance available. *Requirements:* Either graduation from accredited secondary school with 16 units or GED. 4 additional units recommended. *Entrance tests:* College Board SAT or ACT composite. *For transfer students:* From 4-year accredited institution 90 hours maximum transfer credit; from 2-year accredited institution 60 hours.

College credit and advanced placement for postsecondary-level work completed in secondary school. For extrainstitutional learning (life experience) college credit and advanced placement on basis of portfolio and faculty assessments, personal interview.

Tutoring available.

Degree Requirements: *For all associate degrees:* 60–67 credit hours. *For all baccalaureate degrees:* 120–128 credit hours. *For all degrees:* 2.00 GPA; minimum of last 30 semester hours in residence.

Fulfillment of some degree requirements and exemption from some beginning courses possible by passing College Board CLEP, APP. *Grading system:* A–F; pass-fail; withdraw (deadline after which pass-fail is appended to withdraw).

Distinctive Educational Programs: Work-experience programs. Evening classes. Independent study option. Learning Center. Study abroad in Wales through the University of Wales at Abergswyth; study abroad in Korea through Nanaam University; semester abroad program in Nanjing, China.

Degrees Conferred: 131 *baccalaureate:* business/marketing 12; communications/journalism 1; education 7; English 3; health professions and related clinical sciences 3; history 5; interdisciplinary studies 6; liberal arts/general studies 8; natural resources/environmental science 19; parks and recreation 15; philosophy and religious studies 3; psychology 6; social sciences 5; visual and performing arts 4. Master's degrees awarded: business 9.

Fees and Other Expenses: *Full-time tuition per academic year 2008–09:* $25,838. *Required fees:* $720. *Room and board per academic year:* $9,522. *Books and supplies:* $1,100. *Other expenses:* $1,470.

Financial Aid: Aid from institutionally generated funds is provided on the basis of academic merit, financial need, athletic ability.

Financial aid to full-time, first-time undergraduate students: 88% received some form of aid. Average amount of aid received: federal grants $5,775; Pell

GREEN MOUNTAIN COLLEGE—*cont'd*

grants $2,649; other federal aid $2,587; state/local grants $2940; institutional grants $11,570.

Departments and Teaching Staff: *Total instructional faculty:* 67 (full-time 41, part-time 37). Total faculty with doctorate, first-professional, or other terminal degree: 33. Student/faculty ratio: 14:1. Degrees held by full-time faculty: doctorate 83%, master's 100%, professional 7%. 90% hold terminal degrees.

Enrollment: Total enrollment 867. Undergraduate 780 (female 51%, male 49%). Graduate 87 (full-time 99%). Transfer-in students 55.

Characteristics of Student Body: *Ethnic/racial makeup:* Black non-Hispanic: 3%; American Indian or Alaska Native: 1%; Asian or Pacific Islander: 1%; Hispanic: 2%; White non-Hispanic: 89%; unknown 24%. *Age distribution:* number under 18: 11; 18–19: 242; 20–21: 216; 22–24: 135; 25–29: 22; 30–34: 5; 35–39: 2; 50–64: 3.

International Students: 10 nonresident aliens enrolled fall 2008. Programs available to aid students whose native language is not English: social, cultural. English as a Second Language Program. No financial aid specifically designated for international students.

Student Life: On-campus residence halls house 90% of student body. There are a number of special interest floors designed by students. *Intercollegiate athletics:* male: basketball, cross-country running, golf, lacrosse, skiing, tennis; female: basketball, skiing, soccer, softball, tennis, volleyball. *Special regulations:* Parking is available for all students; no permit fee required. *Special services:* Medical services. *Student publications: The Mountaineer*, a monthly newspaper; *The Reverie,* art and literary magazine. *Surrounding community:* Poultney Village population 3,500. Albany (NY), 90 miles from campus, is nearest metropolitan area. Served by airport 75 miles from campus; passenger rail service 25 miles from campus.

Library Collections: 90,500 volumes including bound books, serial backfiles, electronic documents, and government documents not in separate collections. Online catalog. Current serial subscriptions: 292 paper, 8,600 via electronic access. Computer work stations available. Students have access to the Internet at no charge. Total budget for books, periodicals, audiovisual materials, microforms 2008–09: $73,000.

Most important special holdings include the Welsh Collection; Ramsay Collection of Early American Decorations; Microbook Library of American Civilization.

Buildings and Grounds: Campus area 155 acres. Campus DVD available.

Chief Executive Officer: Dr. John F. Brennan, President.

Address admission inquiries to Sandra Bartholomew, Dean of Enrollment Management.

Johnson State College

337 College Hill
Johnson, Vermont 05656-9464
Tel: (800) 635-2356 **E-mail:** admission@jsc.vsc.edu
Fax: (802) 635-1230 **Internet:** www.jsc.vsc.edu

Institution Description: Johnson State College is a four-year, coeducational, public, liberal arts science institution. *Enrollment:* 1,898. *Degrees awarded:* Associate, baccalaureate, master's.

Academic offerings subject to approval by statewide coordinating bodies. Budget subject to approval by state governing boards.

Accreditation: *Regional:* NEASC.

History: Established as Johnson Academy 1828; chartered 1832; incorporated as Lamoille County Grammar School 1836; changed name to Johnson Normal School and offered first instruction at postsecondary level 1866; changed name to Johnson Teachers College 1947; awarded first degree (baccalaureate) 1948; adopted present name 1961.

Institutional Structure: *Governing board:* Vermont State Colleges Board of Trustees. Representation: 15 trustees, including governor, 1 student. 1 ex officio. 15 voting. *Composition of institution:* Executive officers: academic dean, dean of administration, dean of students, registrar, associate dean of enrollment services, director of development and alumni affairs (all reporting to the president). Academic governance body, Faculty Assembly, meets an average of 9 times per year. *Faculty representation:* Faculty served by collective bargaining agent affiliated with AFT.

Calendar: Semesters. Academic year Aug. to May. Freshmen admitted fall and spring. Degrees conferred and formal commencement May. Summer courses available.

Characteristics of Freshmen: 1,033 applicants (female 566, male 467). 87% of applicants admitted. 40% of applicants admitted and enrolled.

93% (224 students) submitted SAT scores; 8% (20 students) submitted ACT scores. *25th percentile*: SAT Verbal 440, SAT Math 430. *75th percentile*: SAT Verbal 550, SAT Math 530.

37% of entering freshmen expected to graduate within 5 years. 63% of freshmen from Vermont. Freshmen from 23 states and 7 foreign countries.

Admission: Rolling admissions plan. For fall acceptance, apply as early as 1 year prior to enrollment; priority application deadline for fall Mar. 1, for spring Dec. 1. *Requirements:* graduation from secondary school with 4 units English, 2 mathematics, 2 science with at least 1 lab, 3 social science. Recommended GPA of 2.5 on a 4.0 scale. *Entrance tests:* College Board SAT preferred, will accept ACT. Noncredit developmental courses offered. Tutoring available. GED accepted; letter of recommendation. *For transfer students:* minimum GPA 2.0 on 4.0 scale; will accept credits from accredited institutions for college level course work completed with a C- or better.

Degree Requirements: *For all associate degrees:* minimum 60 semester hours. *For baccalaureate degrees:* minimum of 120 semester hours. Completion of general education program; proficiency on writing competency exam.

Fulfillment of some degree requirements and exemption from some beginning courses possible by passing College Board CLEP, AP (score of 3), other standardized tests. *Grading system:* A–F; pass-fail; incomplete.

Distinctive Educational Programs: Internship programs; independent study; tutorials. Weekend and evening classes offered through the External Degree Program (EDP). National Student Exchange (NSE) participant.

Degrees Conferred: 12 *associate;* 270 *baccalaureate:* biological and life sciences 2; business 59; communications 2; education 32; English 14; health professions 8; liberal arts 29; mathematics 1; natural resources 12; parks and recreation 20; psychology 43; social sciences and history 20; visual and performing arts; 28; 72 *master's:* education 54; psychology 30; visual and performing arts 8.

Fees and Other Expenses: *Full-time tuition per academic year 2008–09:* undergraduate resident $8,184, nonresident $16,848; contact the institution for graduate tuition/fees. *Required fees:* $166. *Room and board per academic year:* $7,509. *Books and supplies:* $1,000. *Other expenses:* $1,250.

Financial Aid: Aid from institutionally generated funds is provided on the basis of academic merit, financial need.

Financial aid to full-time, first-time undergraduate students: 885 received some form of aid. Average amount of aid received: federal grants $3,494; Pell grants $2,872; other federal aid $1,377; state/local grants $1,891; institutional grants $1,744.

Departments and Teaching Staff: *Total instructional faculty:* 177 (full-time 54, part-time 123). Total faculty with doctorate, first-professional, or other terminal degree: 87. Student/faculty ratio: 10:1. Degrees held by full-time faculty: 92% hold terminal degrees.

Enrollment: Total enrollment 1,898. Undergraduate 1,619 (full-time 66%; female 62%, male 38%). Graduate 279 (full-time 20%). Transfer-in students 159.

Characteristics of Student Body: *Ethnic/racial makeup:* Black non-Hispanic: 2%; American Indian or Alaska Native: 1%; Asian or Pacific Islander: 1%; Hispanic: 2%; White non-Hispanic: 87%; unknown 8%. *Age distribution:* number under 18: 20; 18–19: 186; 20–21: 359; 22–24: 352; 25–29: 222; 30–34: 100; 35–39: 74; 40–49: 152; 50–64: 54; 65 and over: 3.

International Students: 4 nonresident aliens enrolled fall 2008. Students from Europe, Asia, Latin America. Programs available to aid students whose native language is not English: social, cultural. English as a Second Language Program. No financial aid specifically designated for international students.

Student Life: On-campus residence halls house 27% of student body; all coeducational. Intercultural student housing; chemical-free living options. Apartments available for married students and families. *Intercollegiate athletics:* male: basketball, cross-country, lacrosse, soccer, tennis; female: basketball, cross-country, soccer, softball, tennis. *Special regulations:* Registered cars permitted. *Special services:* Academic Support Services; Learning Resource Center; Career Center; Counseling Center; Health Center; Academic Advising. *Student publications, radio: Basement Medicine*, a biweekly newspaper; *Gihan River Review*, an annual literary magazine. Radio station WJSC-FM broadcasts 70 hours per week. *Surrounding community:* Johnson population 3,150. Boston (MA), 200 miles from campus, is nearest metropolitan area. Burlington (VT) is 1 hour away by car, Montreal (Canada) 2 hours.

Library Collections: 109,600 volumes including bound books, serial backfiles, electronic documents, and government documents not in separate collections. Online catalog. Current serial subscriptions: 500 paper; 9,613 via electronic access. 7,500 recordings; 450 compact discs; 235 CD-ROMs. Computer work stations available. Students have access to the Internet at no charge.

Most important special holdings include collections on art, children's literature.

Buildings and Grounds: Campus area 330 acres.

Chief Executive Officer: Dr. Barbara E. Murphy, President.

Address admission inquiries to Penny P. Howrigan, Dean of Enrollment Services.

Lyndon State College

1001 College Road
Lyndonville, Vermont 05851-0919
Tel: (802) 626-6200 **E-mail:** admissions@lsc.vsc.edu
Fax: (802) 626-9770 **Internet:** www.lsc.vsc.edu

Institution Description: Lyndon State College is a public institution. *Enrollment:* 1,384. *Degrees awarded:* Associate, baccalaureate, master's.

Academic offerings subject to approval by statewide coordinating bodies. Budget subject to approval by state governing boards.

Accreditation: *Regional:* NEASC. *Professional*: recreation and leisure services

History: Established as Lyndon Training Center, chartered, offered first instruction at postsecondary level 1911; awarded first degree (baccalaureate) 1944; changed name to Lyndon Teachers College 1949; adopted present name and became part of Vermont State Colleges, Inc. 1962.

Institutional Structure: *Governing board:* Vermont State Colleges Board of Trustees. Representation: 15 trustees, including governor, 1 student. 1 ex officio. 15 voting. *Composition of institution:* Administrators 9. Academic affairs headed by dean of academic affairs. Management/business/finances directed by dean of business affairs. Full-time instructional faculty 58. Academic governance bodies, Faculty Assembly, Board of Trustees, and College Deans' Council, meet an average of 8, 10, and 20 times per year, respectively. *Faculty representation:* Faculty served by collective bargaining agent, Local 3180 of AFT.

Calendar: Semesters. Academic year Sept. to May. Degrees conferred May, Oct., Feb. Formal commencement May.

Characteristics of Freshmen: 1,081 applicants (female 484, male 597). 93% of applicants accepted. 37% of applicants accepted and enrolled.

80% (284 students) submitted SAT scores. *25th percentile*: SAT Critical Reading 400, SAT Math 400. *75th percentile*: SAT Critical Reading 520, SAT Math 510.

39% of entering freshmen expected to graduate within 5 years. 56% of freshmen from Vermont. Freshmen from 12 states.

Admission: Rolling admissions plan. Early acceptance available. *Requirements:* Recommend graduation from accredited secondary school with academic units which include 4 English, 2 mathematics, 2 history, 2 science. GED also acceptable. *Entrance tests:* College Board SAT or ACT composite. *For transfer students:* From 4-year accredited institution 92 semester hours maximum transfer credit; from 2-year accredited institution 62 hours; correspondence/extension students 60 hours.

College credit and advanced placement for postsecondary-level work completed in secondary school. College credit for extrainstitutional learning on basis of portfolio assessment; course sponsored by Vermont State Colleges' Office of External Programs.

Tutoring available. Noncredit remedial courses offered during regular academic year.

Degree Requirements: *For all associate degrees:* 62 semester hours. *For all baccalaureate degrees:* 122 hours. *For all undergraduate degrees:* 2.0 minimum GPA; 2 terms in residence; exit competency examinations in writing, quantitative reasoning, information literacy, oral communication; general education requirements.

Fulfillment of some degree requirements and exemption from some beginning courses possible by passing College Board CLEP, APP (score of 3). *Grading system:* A–F; withdraw (carries time limit); credit-no credit.

Distinctive Educational Programs: *For undergraduates:* Weekend classes. Interdisciplinary programs in American studies, behavioral sciences, environmental science, humanities, social sciences. Study abroad in Nice and Paris through Vermont Overseas Study Program; also, by individual arrangement. Domestic study at The School for International Training. Other off-campus study through New England Board of Higher Education Regional Student Program. *For graduate students:* Individual majors. *Available to all students:* Cooperative education. Evening classes. Special facilities for using telecommunications in the classroom. Independent study.

ROTC: Air Force offered in cooperation with St. Michael's College.

Degrees Conferred: 17 *associate;* 280 *baccalaureate:* business 27; communications 25; computer and information sciences 5; education 21; English 5; liberal arts/general studies 8; mathematics 4; parks and recreation 5; physical sciences 15; psychology 33; social sciences and history 5; visual and performing arts 16. *Master's:* education 6. Master's degrees awarded: education 2.

Fees and Other Expenses: *Full-time tuition per academic year 2008–09:* $8,284 undergraduate resident, $16,948 nonresident; contact the college for current graduate tuition and applicable fees. *Required fees:* $70. *Room and board per academic year:* $7,509. *Books and supplies:* $1,000. *Other expenses:* $1,200.

Financial Aid: The college offers a direct lending program. Aid from institutionally generated funds is provided on the basis of academic merit, financial need, other criteria. Institution has a Program Participation Agreement with the U.S. Department of Education for eligible students to receive Pell Grants and, depending upon the agreement, other federal aid.

Departments and Teaching Staff: *Total instructional faculty:* 162 (full-time 58, part-time 104). Total faculty with doctorate, first-professional, or other terminal degree: 83. Student/faculty ratio: 21:1. Degrees held by full-time faculty: doctorate 61%, master's 39%. 61% hold terminal degrees.

Enrollment: Total enrollment 1,384. Undergraduate 1,356 (full-time 88%; female 47%, male 53%). Graduate 28 (full-time 100%). Transfer-in students 85.

Characteristics of Student Body: *Ethnic/racial makeup:* Black non-Hispanic: 2%; American Indian or Alaska Native: 1%; Asian or Pacific Islander: 1%; Hispanic: 2%; White non-Hispanic: 92%; unknown: 2%. *Age distribution:* number under 18: 21; 18–19: 247; 20–21: 22–24: 440; 25–29: 367; 30–34: 29; 35–39: 28; 40–49: 48; 50–64: 16.

International Students: 2 nonresident aliens enrolled fall 2008. Students from Europe, Asia, No programs available to id students whose native language is not English. No financial aid specifically designated for international student.

Student Life: On-campus residence halls house 50% of student body. Residence halls for males constitute 9% of such space, for both sexes 85%. 2% of student body live on campus in college-owned houses. *Intercollegiate athletics:*male: baseball, basketball, soccer, tennis; female: basketball, soccer, softball, volleyball; both sexes: cross-country, Nordic skiing. *Special regulations:* Registered cars permitted in designated areas. Quiet hours from 9pm to 7am. *Special services:* Learning Resources Center, medical services, shuttle bus to and from town. *Student publications, radio: Critic,* a weekly newspaper. Radio station WWLR broadcasts 130 hours per week. *Surrounding community:* Lyndonville population 5,000. Montreal, 125 miles from campus, is nearest metropolitan area. Served by mass transit bus system.

Publications: Sources of information about Lyndon State include *Twin Tower Topics*, a quarterly publication distributed to alumni, friends of the college, and the general public.

Library Collections: 106,000 volumes. 6,000 microforms; 3,100 audiovisual materials; 500 current periodical subscriptions. Computer work stations available. Online catalog. Students have access to online information retrieval services and the Internet.

Most important special holdings include Vermontiana.

Buildings and Grounds: Campus area 174 acres.

Chief Executive Officer: Dr. Carol A. Moore, President.

Address admission inquiries to Bernard Harshhorn, Associate Director of Admissions. Assistant Dean of Admissions.

Marlboro College

P.O. Box A
South Road
Marlboro, Vermont 05344-9999
Tel: (802) 257-4333 **E-mail:** admissions@marlboro.edu
Fax: (802) 257-4154 **Internet:** www.marlboro.edu

Institution Description: Marlboro College is a private, independent, nonprofit college. *Enrollment:* 326. *Degrees awarded:* Baccalaureate.

Accreditation: *Regional:* NEASC.

History: Established and incorporated 1946; offered first instruction at postsecondary level 1947; awarded first degree (baccalaureate) 1948.

Institutional Structure: *Governing board:* The Corporation of Marlboro College. Extrainstitutional representation: 198 voting trustees, 8 honorary members; institutional representation: 1 administrator, 2 faculty delegates, 3 student delegates. *Composition of institution:* Administrators: 9. Academic affairs headed by dean of faculty. Management/business/finances directed by chief resource and planning officer. Full-time instructional faculty 38. Academic governance body, the faculty, meets an average of 12 times per year.

Calendar: Semesters. Academic year Sept. to May. Freshmen admitted Sept., Jan. Degrees conferred Dec, May. Formal commencement May. No summer session.

Characteristics of Freshmen: 472 applicants (female 266, male 206). 68% of applicants accepted. 46% of accepted applicants enrolled.

Mean SAT scores class 650 verbal, 650 mathematical.

99% of freshmen from Vermont. Freshmen from 25 states.

Admission: Most interviews conducted by faculty. *Requirements:* graduation from accredited secondary school, writing sample and autobiographical statement; letter of recommendation. *Entrance tests:* College Board SAT or ACT. For foreign students TOEFL. *For transfer students:* 2.0 minimum GPA.

Credit given for AP examinations.

MARLBORO COLLEGE—*cont'd*

Degree Requirements: Writing proficiency requirement; completion of Plan of Concentration with a final grade of C- or better; completion of 120 credits.

Grading system: A–F; withdraw (deadline after which pass-fail is appended to withdraw).

Distinctive Educational Programs: The Plan of Concentration is a 2-year individualized program of study completed by all students, culminating in the presentation of a body of academic work evaluated by a committee of Marlboro faculty and an outside examiner. Emphasis on tutorials and independent study; internships and field trips. The World Studies Program offered in cooperation with the School for International Training requires a living and working internship in another culture.

Degrees Conferred: 74 *baccalaureate*. Bachelor's degrees awarded in top five disciplines: visual and performing arts 17; social sciences 10; natural resources and conservation 7; history 6; biological/biomedical sciences 4.

Fees and Other Expenses: *Full-time tuition per academic year 2008–09:* $32,180. *Required fees:* $890. *Books and supplies:* $950. *Room and board per academic year:* $9,040. *Other expenses:* $250.

Financial Aid: Aid from institutionally generated funds is provided on the basis of academic merit, financial need. Institution has a Program Participation Agreement with the U.S. Department of Education for eligible students to receive Pell Grants and, depending upon the agreement, other federal aid.

Financial aid to full-time, first-time undergraduate students: 81% received some form of aid. Need-based scholarships/grants totaling $4,244,832, self-help $1,843,309, parent loans $1,256,393.

Departments and Teaching Staff: Marlboro faculty are unranked. *Total instructional faculty:* 58 (full-time 38, part-time 20). Total tenured faculty: 37. Student/faculty ratio: 8:1. Degrees held by full-time faculty: 84% hold terminal degrees. *Faculty development:* 9 faculty members awarded sabbaticals 2008–09.

Enrollment: Total enrollment 326. Undergraduate 326 (full-time 97%; female 49%, male 51%). Transfer-in students 15.

Characteristics of Student Body: *Ethnic/racial makeup:* Black non-Hispanic; 1%; American Indian or Alaska Native: 1%; Asian or Pacific Islander: 3%; Hispanic: 3%; White non-Hispanic; 80%; unknown 11%; nonresident alien 1%.

International Students: 3 nonresident aliens enrolled fall 2008. No programs available to aid students whose native language is not English. Limited need-based financial aid available to international students.

Student Life: On-campus residence halls house 78% of student body. Residence halls for females constitute 5% of such space, for both sexes 95%. 16% of student body live in cooperative apartments, cabins, or cottages. Housing available for married students. *Special regulations:* Cars must be registered with the Business Office. *Special services:* Health Center, counseling services, Student Learning Center. *Student publications: Citizen,* published weekly. *Surrounding community:* Marlboro population 1,000. Boston (MA), 120 miles from campus, is nearest metropolitan area.

Library Collections: 66,000 volumes including bound books, serial backfiles, electronic documents, and government documents not in separate collections. Online catalog. Current serial subscriptions: 188 paper. 20,000 via electronic access. Computer work stations available. Students have access to the Internet at no charge.

Most important special holdings include Otis Guernsey Rudyard Kipling Collection.

Buildings and Grounds: Campus area 350 acres.

Chief Executive Officer: Dr. Ellen McCulloch Lovell, President.

Address all admission inquiries to Alan Young, Dean of Enrollment.

Middlebury College

Old Chapel
Middlebury, Vermont 05753-6200
Tel: (802) 443-3000 **E-mail:** admissions@middlebury.edu
Fax: (802) 443-2056 **Internet:** www.middlebury.edu

Institution Description: Middlebury College is an independent, coeducational, four-year liberal arts institution. Besides the baccalaureate programs offered during the academic year, the college offers 6 programs abroad. Undergraduate and graduate programs in 8 foreign languages, graduate programs in English, and the Bread Loaf Writers' Conference are offered during the summer. *Enrollment:* 2,455. *Degrees awarded:* Baccalaureate, master's, doctorate.

Accreditation: *Regional:* NEASC.

History: Established and chartered 1800; offered first degree (baccalaureate) 1802; admitted women 1883. *See* David Stameshkin, *The Town's College: Middlebury College, 1800–1915* (Ann Arbor, Mich., University Microfilms, 1980) for further information.

Institutional Structure: *Governing board:* The President and Fellows of Middlebury College. Representation: 10 charter trustees, 9 term trustees, president of the college, 6 alumni. All voting. *Composition of institution:* Administrators 10. Academic affairs headed by vice president for academic affairs. Management/business/finances directed by treasurer. Full-time instructional faculty 231. Academic governance body, The Faculty Council, meets an average of 18 times per year.

Calendar: Semesters (4-1-4 plan). Academic year Sept. to May. Freshmen admitted Sept., Jan. Degrees conferred March, May (baccalaureate), Aug. (master's, doctorate). Formal commencement May (baccalaureate), Aug. (master's, doctorate).

Characteristics of Freshmen: 7,180 applicants (female 4,175, male 3,005). 29% applicants accepted. 39% of accepted applicants enrolled.

50% (290 students) submitted SAT scores; 23% (134 students) submitted ACT scores. *25th percentile*: SAT Verbal 690, SAT Math 690; ACT Composite 28. *75th percentile*: SAT Verbal 750, SAT Math 750; ACT Composite 32.

89% of freshmen are expected to graduate within 5 years. 7% of freshmen from Vermont. Freshmen from 45 states and 76 foreign countries.

Admission: For fall acceptance, apply as early as summer following junior year of secondary school, but not later than Jan. 1 of year of enrollment. Students are notified of acceptance Apr. Apply by Nov. 15 for early decision; need not limit application to Middlebury. *Requirements:* Recommend 16 units, including 4 English, 4 foreign language, 4 mathematics, 3 laboratory science, 3 social studies. *Entrance tests:* Students may select one of 3 options: SAT plus 3 Achievements; ACT; 5 Achievements (AP may also be used in lieu of Achievements). *For transfer students:* 3.0 minimum GPA; 54 hours maximum transfer credit.

Degree Requirements: *For all undergraduate degrees:* 36 course credits; 2 years in residence; 5 seasons in lifetime sports, swimming test; core and distribution requirements; comprehensives in individual fields of study for some majors.

Fulfillment of some degree requirements and exemption from some beginning courses possible by passing College Board AP (score of 4). *Grading system:* A–F; pass-fail-honors (winter term only); credit (winter term and off-campus independent courses only).

Distinctive Educational Programs: *For undergraduates:* Internships during winter term. Interdisciplinary programs in American studies, classical studies, East Asian studies, environmental studies, literary studies, Northern studies. Facilities and programs for independent research, including honors programs, individual majors, tutorials. Junior year abroad at Middlebury Language Schools in England, France, Germany, Italy, Russia, China, Spain. Washington (DC) semester at American University. *For graduate students:* Independent study. Summer programs abroad at Middlebury Language Schools. Summer program in writing for secondary school teachers at the Bread Loaf School of English. Literature program at Lincoln College, Oxford, through the Bread Loaf School of English. *Available to all students:* Special facilities for using telecommunications in the classroom. *Other distinctive programs:* The Bread Loaf Writers' Conference in August.

ROTC: Army in cooperation with University of Vermont.

Degrees Conferred: 636 *baccalaureate*; 267 *master's*; 5 *doctorate*.

Fees and Other Expenses: *Comprehensive fee per academic year 2008–09:* $45,000.

Financial Aid: Aid from institutionally generated funds is provided on the basis of financial need. Institution has a Program Participation Agreement with the U.S. Department of Education for eligible students to receive Pell Grants and, depending upon the agreement, other federal aid.

Financial aid to full-time, first-time undergraduate students: 50% received some form of aid. Average amount fo aid received: federal grants $5,701; Pell grants $3,175; other federal aid $2,534; state/local grants $1,088; institutional grants $29,471.

Departments and Teaching Staff: *Total instructional faculty:* 242 (full-time 231, part-time 11). Total faculty with doctorate, first-professional, or other terminal degree: 220. Student/faculty ratio: 11:1.

Enrollment: Total enrollment 2,455. Undergraduate 2,455 (full-time 99%; female 51%, male 49%).

Characteristics of Student Body: *Ethnic/racial makeup:* Black non-Hispanic: 3%; American Indian or Alaska Native: 1%; Asian or Pacific Islander: 9%; Hispanic: 6%; White non-Hispanic: 84%; unknown: 6%; nonresident alien 11%.

International Students: 192 nonresident aliens enrolled fall 2008.

Student Life: On-campus residence halls house 97% of student body. Housing available for married students. *Intercollegiate athletics:* male: baseball, basketball, football, hockey, lacrosse, skiing, soccer, swimming, tennis, track; female: basketball, hockey, lacrosse, skiing, soccer, squash, swimming, tennis, track. *Special regulations:* Cars permitted in designated areas for all but students on disciplinary probation. *Special services:* Medical services. *Student publications, radio: The Campus*, a weekly newspaper; *Frontiers*, a semiannual literary magazine; *Kaleidescope*, a yearbook. Radio station WRMC-FM broadcasts 168 hours per week; 90 hours during the summer. *Surrounding community:* Middlebury population 8,000. Burlington, 35 miles from campus, is nearest metropolitan area. Served by mass transit bus system; airport 35 miles from campus.

Publications: *Section 8*, art newspaper.

Library Collections: 925,000 volumes. 247,900 government documents; 398,000 microforms; 45,000 audiovisual materials; 9,900 serial subscriptions including via electronic access. Online catalog. Students have access to online information retrieval services and the Internet.

Most important special holdings include Abernethy American Literature collection; Flanders Ballad collection; Vermont collection.

Buildings and Grounds: Campus area 350 acres. Campus DVD available.

Chief Executive Officer: Dr. Ronald Liebowitz, President.

Address admission inquiries to Robert S. Clagett, Dean of Admissions.

Norwich University

15 Harmon Drive
Northfield, Vermont 05663
Tel: (802) 485-2001 **E-mail:** nuadm@norwich.edu
Fax: (802) 485-2580 **Internet:** www.norwich.edu

Institution Description: Norwich University is a private, independent, nonprofit institution. *Enrollment:* 3,309. *Degrees awarded:* Baccalaureate, master's, doctorate.

Accreditation: *Regional:* NEASC. *Professional* chemistry, engineering, nursing

Institutional Structure: *Governing board:* The Board of Trustees of Norwich University. Extrainstitutional representation: 35 trustees, institutional representation: 1 administrator; 5 alumni. All voting. *Composition of institution:* Administrators 58. Academic affairs headed by vice president for academic affairs. Management/business/finances directed by treasurer. Full-time instructional faculty 146. Academic governance body, The Academic Board, meets an average of 9 times per year.

Calendar: Semesters. Academic year Sept. to May. Freshmen admitted Sept., Jan., June, July. Degrees conferred May, Sept. Formal commencement May. Summer session from early June to early Aug.

Characteristics of Freshmen: 2,962 applicants (female 767, male 2,195). 86% of applicants accepted. 40% of accepted applicants enrolled fuil-time.

57% of entering freshmen expected to graduate within 5 years. Freshmen from 39 states and 14 foreign countries.

Admission: Rolling admissions plan. For fall acceptance, apply as early as July 10 of previous year, but not later than Aug. 30 of year of enrollment. Apply by Nov. 15 for early decision; applications must be limited to Norwich University. Early acceptance plan available. *Requirements:* Either graduation from secondary school with 16 units or GED. Additional requirements vary with intended major. Physical examination required. *Entrance tests:* College Board SAT or ACT. *For transfer students:* 2.0 minimum GPA; 60 credit hours maximum transfer credit.

College credit and advanced placement for postsecondary-level work completed in secondary school. College credit for extrainstitutional learning on basis of portfolio and faculty assessments; personal interviews.

Tutoring available. Remedial courses offered in summer sessions and regular academic year; nondegree credit given.

Degree Requirements: 36–39 courses; 2.0 GPA; last 4 semesters in residence; 2 physical education courses; 2 semesters English composition; 1 semester history; for Corps of Cadets members, military training 3 hours per week for 2 years; for some programs, comprehensives in individual fields of study.

Fulfillment of some degree requirements and exemption from some beginning courses possible by passing departmental examinations, College Board CLEP, AP. *Grading system:* A–F; withdraw (carries time limit); pass-grade.

Distinctive Educational Programs: *For undergraduates:* Internships. Double degree program leading to baccalaureate of arts and baccalaureate of science. Dual-degree program leading to baccalaureate and master's in business administration with Clarkson College of Technology (NY). Special facilities for using telecommunications in the classroom. Interdisciplinary programs in computer science, humanities. Facilities and programs for independent research, including honors program in history and government, tutorials. Study abroad in France and by individual arrangement. *Available to all students:* Russian School summer immersion program providing introductory and advanced instruction. Radiation Laboratory providing facilities for study of atomic and nuclear physics, radioisotope techniques. *Other distinctive programs:* Continuing education. The University's Division of Alternative Education offers limited residency baccalaureate and graduate programs for nontraditional students.

ROTC: Army, Air Force, Navy.

Degrees Conferred: 389 *baccalaureate*; 163 *master's*. Bachelor's degrees awarded in top five disciplines: security and protective services 41; engineering 37; business, management, marketing, and related support services 35; health professions and related clinical sciences 32; history 24. Master's degrees awarded: various disciplines 163.

Fees and Other Expenses: *Full-time tuition per academic year 2008–09* $26,064. *Books and supplies:* $1,000. *Room and board per academic year:* $9,032. *Other expenses:* $800.

Financial Aid: Aid from institutionally generated funds is provided on the basis of academic merit, financial need.

Financial aid to full-time, first-time undergraduate students: 98% received some form of aid. Average amount of aid received: federal grants $5,566; Pell grants $2,900; other federal aid $2,914; state/local grants $2,003; institutional grants $12,171.

Departments and Teaching Staff: *Total instructional faculty:* 185. Degrees held by full-time faculty: doctorate 61%, master's 95%, baccalaureate 100%, professional 3%. 64% hold terminal degrees.

Enrollment: Total enrollment 3,309. Undergraduate 1,997 (full-time 96%; female 29%, male 71%). Graduate 1,312 (full-time 96%). Transfer-in student 196.

Characteristics of Student Body: *Ethnic/racial makeup:* Black non-Hispanic: 3%; Asian or Pacific Islander: 2%; Hispanic: 5%; White non-Hispanic: 81%; unknown: 8%.

International Students: 44 undergraduate nonresident aliens enrolled fall 2008. Programs available to aid students whose native language is not English: English as a Second Language Program. No financial aid specifically designated for international students.

Student Life: *Intercollegiate athletics:* male: baseball, basketball, football, hockey, lacrosse, soccer, wrestling; female: basketball, softball; both sexes: rifle, skiing, soccer, swimming, track and cross-country. *Special services:* Learning Resources Center, medical services, hourly bus service between main and north campuses. *Student publications: Chameleon*, an annual literary magazine.

Publications: *Norwich Record* (alumni news); *The American Journal of Art Therapy.*

Library Collections: 260,000 volumes. 905 serial subscriptions. 1,500 audiovisual materials. Online catalog. Students have access to online information retrieval services and the Internet.

Chief Executive Officer: Dr. Richard W. Schneider, President.

Address admission inquiries to Karen McGarth, Dean of Enrollment Management.

Norwich University - Military College of Vermont

Northfield, Vermont 05663
Tel: (802) 485-2001 **E-mail:** nuadm@norwich.edu
Fax: (802) 485-2580 **Internet:** www.norwich.edu

Institution Description: The Military College of Vermont is a unit of Norwich University. *Degrees awarded:* Baccalaureate.

Accreditation: *See* Norwich University.

Institutional Structure: *See* Norwich University.

Degree Requirements: 36–39 courses; 2.0 GPA; 2 physical education courses; 2 semesters English composition; 1 semester history; 45 of last 60 semester hours (and a minimum of 60 hours total) must be completed on campus; all students in the Military College must complete 4 years ROTC.

Fulfillment of some degree requirements and exemption from some beginning courses possible by passing departmental examinations, College Board CLEP, AP. *Grading system:* A–F; withdraw (carries time limit); pass-grade.

ROTC: Army, Air Force, Navy.

Degrees Conferred: Included with Norwich University.

Fees and Other Expenses: *See* Norwich University.

Enrollment: Included with Norwich University.

Characteristics of Student Body: *Age distribution:* 17–21: 85%, 22–24: 13%; 25–29: 1%; 30–34: .05%; 35–39: .05%.

International Students: Programs available to aid students whose native language is not English: English as a Second Language Program.

Student Life: All students required to be members of the Corps of Cadets. On-campus residence halls house 100% of the Corps of Cadets. Dormitories are co-ed. *Special regulations:* Cars permitted for all but freshmen. Uniform required for members of the Corps of Cadets. Quiet hours. *Student publications: Guidon*, a monthly newspaper; *War Whoop*, a yearbook; the *Chameleon*, a literary magazine. Radio station WNUB-FM broadcasts 125 hours per week. *Surrounding community:* Northfield, population 4,200. Boston (MA) and Montreal, Canada, are the nearest metropolitan areas; both are 150 miles from campus.

NORWICH UNIVERSITY - MILITARY COLLEGE OF VERMONT—*cont'd*

Served by a small airport 17 miles from campus, and a large airport 65 miles from campus; passenger rail service 10 miles from campus.

Library Collections: *See* Norwich University.

Buildings and Grounds: *See* Norwich University.

Saint Michael's College

One Winooski Park
Colchester, Vermont 05439-0001
Tel: (802) 654-3000 **E-mail:** admission@smcvt.edu
Fax: (802) 654-2906 **Internet:** www.smcvt.edu

Institution Description: Saint Michael's College is a private, independent, nonprofit college affiliated with the Society of St. Edmund and Roman Catholic Church. *Enrollment:* 2,460. *Degrees awarded:* Baccalaureate, master's. Certificates also awarded.

Accreditation: *Regional:* NEASC.

History: The college was opened in 1904 by members of the Society of Saint Edmund, a religious congregation of Priests and Brothers organized in France in 1843, and active in Catholic higher education at Mont-St-Michel since 1875. The Edmundites came to the United States in the late nineteenth century when the laws of association forced the community out of France. Because of the early work of the Edmundites in higher education, they established a 'college', which included a high school in the beginning. In 1931, the high school was discontinued. During these years, the College grew slowly, and by the time of World War II had reached an enrollment of 250 students. After the war, the College expanded rapidly towards its present enrollment. In 1954 the College opened a Center for International Programs that currently teaches English as a second language at basic, intermediate, and advanced levels. In 1970, the College became co-educational. The program of studies, devised by men steeped in the classic traditions of liberal education as practiced in France, was modified from time to time to meet the needs and requirements of a changing society without, however, losing its firm grasp of educational essentials.

Institutional Structure: *Governing board:* Saint Michael's Board of Trustees, with no more than 33members, including the Superior General of the Society of St. Edmund, 1 alumnus, college president. One-third of board to be members of the Society of St. Edmund. All voting. *Composition of institution:* Administrators 40. Vice presidents head Academic Affairs, Student Affairs, Administration and Business, Institutional Advancement, and Financial Planning. A Faculty Council and Department Chairs meet regularly to coordinate the efforts of a full-time undergraduate faculty of 141. A Graduate Council composed of the directors of the graduate programs (i.e., Administration and Management, Education, Teaching English as a Second Language, Clinical Psychology, and Theology and Pastoral Ministry) coordinates a graduate faculty of 154.

Calendar: Semesters. Academic year Aug. to May. Freshmen admitted Aug., Jan. Degrees conferred May, June, Aug., Dec. Formal commencement May. Summer session of 2 terms from May to Aug.

Characteristics of Freshmen: 3,618 applicants (female 1,809, male 1,809). 73% of applicants admitted. 27% of applicants admitted and enrolled.

96% (559 students) submitted SAT scores; 20% (115 students) submitted ACT scores. *25th percentile*: SAT Critical Reading 500, SAT Math 510, SAT Writing 510; ACT Composite 21, ACT English 21, ACT Math 19. *75th percentile*: SAT Critical Reading 600, SAT Math 610, SAT Writing 600; ACT Composite 26; ACT English 26; ACT Math 26.

76% of entering freshmen expected to graduate within 5 years. 17% of freshmen from Vermont. Freshmen from 20 states and 4 foreign countries.

Admission: Successful applicants to Saint Michael's typically rank in the top 25% of their high school class and have a strong college-preparatory background. Students should have completed 16 units of courses in English, mathematics, sciences, modern language, and social sciences. Candidates must also submit SAT scores. (The range of SAT scores for typical students at Saint Michael's is 1038–1210). In addition, students should submit a counselor recommendation and any teacher recommendations they choose. An interview is not required but is highly recommended. Alumni interviews are available in some locations. Transfer applicants must submit transcripts of all college work along with the appropriate catalog in addition to the information required of freshmen applicants. The application deadline is Feb. 1. Candidates for the fall semester are notified of the admission decision on or before April 1. A limited number of students may be admitted to the spring semester and should have their applications in by Nov. 1. The college adheres to the Candidates Reply Date of May 1 for the fall semester.

Degree Requirements: To earn a degree of Bachelor of Arts or the degree of Bachelor of Science a student must (1) complete a minimum of 124 credit hours; (2) complete the degree requirements of one of the established majors; (3) complete the core general education requirements; (4) achieve a minimum cumulative quality point average of 2.0 and a minimum of a 2.0 average in courses taken in the major; (5) complete a minimum of 8 of the last 10 courses at Saint Michael's. *Transfer students:* must be in residence for at least 1 academic year immediately preceding their graduation and must earn a minimum of 30 credits at Saint Michael's.

Grading system: A–F; pass-fail; withdraw.

Distinctive Educational Programs: *Available to all students:* Interdepartmental program in American studies, interdisciplinary program in environmental science. Freshman honors program. 3+2 engineering program with University of Vermont. Engineering program in cooperation with Clarkson University. Numerous for-credit internships opportunities available. Facilities and programs for independent research, including honors programs, individual majors. Flexible meeting places and schedules for graduate students, weekend and evening classes. Study abroad opportunities in Europe, Asia, Australia, Africa, South America, Mexico.

ROTC: Cross-town agreements with Norwich University (Air Force). Army in cooperation with University of Vermont.

Degrees Conferred: 441 *baccalaureate*; 119 *master's*. Bachelor's degrees awarded in top five disciplines: business, management, marketing, and related support services 123; social sciences and history 69; psychology 56; English 49; communications/communications technologies 42. Master's degrees awarded: various disciplines 119.

Fees and Other Expenses: *Full-time tuition per academic year 2008–09:* undergraduate $31,940; contact the college for graduate tuition/fees. *Required fees:* $235. *Room and board per academic year:* $7,960. *Books and supplies:* $1,200. *Other expenses:* $900.

Financial Aid: Aid from institutionally generated funds is provided on the basis of academic merit, financial need, athletic ability, and other criteria.

Financial aid to full-time, first-time undergraduate students: 89% received some form of aid. Average amount of aid received: federal grants $5,652; Pell grants $3,174; other federal aid $2,524; state/local grants $2,450; institutional grants $10,890.

Departments and Teaching Staff: *Total instructional faculty:* 249 (full-time 154, part-time 95). Total faculty with doctorate, first-professional, or other terminal degree: 169. Student/faculty ratio: 13:1. . Degrees held by full-time faculty: baccalaureate 100%, master's 100%, doctorate 72%. 75% hold terminal degrees.

Enrollment: Total enrollment 2,460. Undergraduate 2,008 (full-time 98%; female 53%, male 47%). Graduate 452 (full-time 13%). Transfer-in students 32.

Characteristics of Student Body: *Ethnic/racial makeup:* Black non-Hispanic: 1%; Asian or Pacific Islander: 1%; Hispanic: 1%; White non-Hispanic: 94%; unknown: 1%; nonresident alien 2%. *Age distribution:* number under 18: 1; 18–19: 704; 20–21: 887; 22–24: 356; 25–29: 16; 30–34: 6; 35–39: 2; 40–49: 6; 50–64: 5. 10% of student body attend summer sessions.

International Students: 50 nonresident aliens enrolled fall 2008. Students from Europe, Asia, Latin America, Africa, Canada, Middle East. Programs available to aid students whose native language is not English: social, cultural. English as a Second Language Program. Financial aid specifically designated for international students.

Student Life: On-campus residence halls house 93% of student body. Residence halls for males constitute 53% of such space while 47% are on-campus suites and apartments. *Intercollegiate athletics:* male: lacrosse, baseball, basketball, cross-country, golf, hockey, skiing, soccer, swimming, tennis; female: basketball, cross-country, field hockey, lacrosse, soccer, softball, skiing, swimming, tennis, volleyball. *Special regulations:* Registered cars with stickers permitted on campus; fee charged for some parking areas. Quiet hours during examination periods. Dormitory visitation from 9am to 1am Sun.–Thurs., 9am to 2am Fri. and Sat. *Special services:* Student Resource Center, health services, campus shuttle bus service. *Student publications, radio: The Defender*, a weekly newspaper; *The Onion River Review*, an annual literary magazine. Radio station WWPV. *Surrounding community:* Winooski, population 7,000, is in Burlington metropolitan area, 200 miles from Boston, MA. Served by mass transit bus system; airport and passenger rail service, each 5 miles from campus.

Library Collections: 260,000 volumes. 134,000 microforms; 9,000 audiovisual materials; 33,500 periodicals including via electronic access. Online catalog. Computer work stations available. Students have access to online information retrieval services.

Most important holdings include the Vermont Collection; Archives of the Society of Saint Edmund.

Buildings and Grounds: Campus area 430 acres.

Chief Executive Officer: Dr. Marc A. VanderHeyden, President.

Undergraduates address admission inquiries to Jacqueline Murphy, Director of Admissions; graduate inquiries to Director of Graduate Admissions.

School for International Training

Kipling Road
Box 676
Brattleboro, Vermont 05302-0676
Tel: (802) 251-7751 **E-mail:** admissions@sit.edu
Fax: (802) 258-3500 **Internet:** www.sit.edu

Institution Description: The School for International Training is a private, independent, nonprofit upper division college and graduate school founded by The Experiment in International Living. *Enrollment:* 654. *Degrees awarded:* Baccalaureate, master's.

Accreditation: *Regional:* NEASC.

History: Established and offered first instruction at postsecondary level 1964; awarded first degree (master's) 1970.

Institutional Structure: *Governing board:* The Board of Trustees of The Experiment in International Living, Inc. Representation: 37 trustees including president of The Experiment in International Living, Inc., 1 honorary member, 2 alumni. 2 ex officio. 35 voting. *Composition of institution:* Administrators 56. Academic affairs headed by director. Management/business/finances directed by vice president for finance. Total instructional faculty 69. Academic governance body, Academic Policies Committee, meets an average of 26 times per year.

Calendar: Academic year Sept. to June. World Issues/World Studies/MAT (Academic Year Program) Sept. to June. Program in Intercultural Management Sept. to Feb.; Mar. to Aug. Summer MAT June to Aug. College Semester abroad: fall, Sept. to Dec.; spring Feb. to May. Degrees conferred as earned. Formal undergraduate commencement June.

Admission: Rolling admissions plan. *Requirements:* 60 semester hours of college work or equivalent for undergraduate programs; B.A. or equivalent for graduate programs.

Degree Requirements: *For all baccalaureate degrees:* 120 credit hours; 1 year in residence; core curriculum; 6-month internships with international agency. *Grading system:* Pass-fail.

Distinctive Educational Programs: Four programs are offered: *For undergraduates:* (1) College Semester Abroad offers the opportunity for a semester abroad to add global context to a student's educational experience. Students live with a family in another culture which provides the basis for 5 components of the program: cross-cultural orientation, intensive language study, life and culture seminar, methods and techniques of field study, and an independent study project. 43 sites are offered, many in the developing countries of the Third World. (2) The World Issues Program, a 2-year junior/senior program also leading to the Bachelor of International Studies, with an 8-month internship overseas. *For graduate students:* (3) The Master of Arts in Teaching Program for language teachers, offering degrees in French, Spanish, and English to speakers of other languages. This program has 2 formats—a summer schedule for working teachers who complete an 8-week session each of 2 consecutive summers while completing their internship requirements at their regular jobs, and an academic year schedule which allows students to complete program coursework in 1 academic year. (4) The Program in Intercultural Management, a 14-month program leading to the Master of International Administration degree. Programs begin in Sept. and March, and feature an 8-month internship. Areas of concentration include development management, training, and foreign student advising.

Degrees Conferred: 175 *master's:* education 16; social sciences 99.

Fees and Other Expenses: *Full-time tuition per academic year 2008–09:* $28,893. undergraduate; contact the school for current graduate tuition/fees.

Financial Aid: Aid from institutionally generated funds is provided on the basis of academic merit, financial need. Institution has a Program Participation Agreement with the U.S. Department of Education for eligible students to receive Pell Grants and, depending upon the agreement, other federal aid.

Departments and Teaching Staff: Faculty members are unranked. Master of Arts in Teaching 11, International Management 8, World Issues 7, College Semester Abroad 43.

Total instructional faculty: 69.

Enrollment: Total enrollment 654 (female 75.2%, male 24.8%)

Characteristics of Student Body: *Ethnic/racial makeup:* Black non-Hispanic: 4%; American Indian or Alaska Native: 3%; Asian or Pacific Islander: 4%; White non-Hispanic: 51%; unknown: 21%.

International Students: 122 nonresident aliens enrolled fall 2008. Programs available to aid students whose native language is not English: English as a Second Language Program.

Student Life: On-campus residence halls house 55% of student body. *Special regulations:* Cars permitted without restrictions. Quiet hours from 11pm to 7am Sun.–Thurs., midnight to 7am Fri. and Sat. *Special services:* Medical services. *Student publications, radio: Kipling's Folly*, a weekly newsletter. *Surrounding community:* Brattleboro population 12,000. Boston, 110 miles from campus, is nearest metropolitan area. Served by passenger rail service 3 miles from campus.

Library Collections: 38,000 volumes. 8000 microforms; 500 audiovisual materials; 450 current periodical subscriptions.

Most important holdings include Peace Studies collection (with materials dealing with disarmament and the Middle East conflict); International Development collection (relating to social and economic development of Third-World countries); Languages and Linguistics collection (consisting primarily of language instruction methodology materials.)

Buildings and Grounds: Campus area 200 acres.

Chief Executive Officer: Dr. James A. Cramer, President.

Address admission inquiries to Admissions Department.

Southern Vermont College

982 Mansion Drive
Bennington, Vermont 05201
Tel: (802) 442-5427 **E-mail:** admis@svc.edu
Fax: (802) 442-5529 **Internet:** www.svc.edu

Institution Description: Southern Vermont College is a private, nonprofit college. *Enrollment:* 456. *Degrees awarded:* Associate, baccalaureate.

Accreditation: *Regional:* NEASC.

History: Established as St. Joseph College and offered first instruction at postsecondary level 1926; incorporated and awarded first degree (associate) 1964; adopted present name 1974.

Institutional Structure: *Governing board:* Board of Trustees. Extrainstitutional representation: 18 trustees; institutional representation: president of the college, 1 full-time instructional faculty member, 1 student; 1 alumnus. 4 ex officio. All voting. *Composition of institution:* Administrators 26. Academic affairs headed by dean of academics. Management/business/finances directed by comptroller. Full-time instructional faculty 27. Academic governance body, Academic Council, meets an average of 10 times per year.

Calendar: Semesters. Academic year Sept. to May. Freshmen admitted Sept., Jan., June. Degrees conferred and formal commencement May.

Characteristics of Freshmen: 454 applicants (female 296, male 198). 73% of applicants admitted. 27% of applicants admitted and enrolled.

79% (82 students) submitted SAT scores; 7% (7 students) submitted ACT scores. *25th percentile*: SAT Verbal 429, SAT Math 400; ACT Composite 15, ACT English 16, ACT Math 17. *75th percentile*: SAT Verbal 510, SAT Math 550; ACT Composite 22, ACT English 23, ACT Math 18.

41% of freshmen from Vermont. Freshmen from 22 states and 6 foreign countries.

Admission: Rolling admissions plan. Early acceptance available. *Requirements:* Either graduation from accredited secondary school or GED. *Entrance tests:* For foreign students TOEFL. *For transfer students:* 2.0 minimum GPA; 90 hours maximum transfer credit.

Degree Requirements: *For all associate degrees:* 60 credit hours; 15 credits in residence. *For all baccalaureate degrees:* 120 credit hours; 30 credits in residence. *For all degrees:* 2.0 GPA; core requirements.

Fulfillment of some degree requirements and exemption from some beginning courses possible by passing College Board CLEP. *Grading system:* A–F; withdraw (carries time limit).

Distinctive Educational Programs: Most degrees are interdisciplinary with a common liberal arts core. Students can combine a major with a minor option. Internship programs, work study programs, honors program, There is a Learning Disabilities Program. Special services provide tutoring, a writing center and other academic supports. Small class size (student-t0-faculty ratio 18:1) promotes an ideal learning environment.

Degrees Conferred: 29 *associate;* 74 *baccalaureate*: business/marketing 17; communications/communications technologies 5; English 4; health professions 10; law/legal studies 1; liberal arts/general studies 6; natural resources/environmental science 5; protective services/public administration 12; psychology 7; social sciences and history 7.

Fees and Other Expenses: *Full-time tuition per academic year 2008=09:* $18,160. *Books and supplies:* $1,000. *Room and board per academic year:* $8,500. *Other expenses:* $1,500.

Financial Aid: Aid from institutionally generated funds is provided on the basis of financial need.

Financial aid to full-time, first-time undergraduate students: 88% received some form of aid. Need-based scholarships/grants totaling $2,212,056, self-help $1,631,867, parent loans $149,153, tuition waivers $1,830; non-need-based scholarships/grants totaling $208,517, self-help $438,389, parent loans $311,141, tuition waivers $1,590.

SOUTHERN VERMONT COLLEGE—*cont'd*

Departments and Teaching Staff: *Total instructional faculty:* 56. Degrees held by full-time faculty: baccalaureate 100%, master's 100%, doctorate 15%. 18% hold terminal degrees.

Enrollment: Total enrollment 456. Undergraduate 456 (full-time 85%; female 61%, male 39%). Transfer-in students 50.

Characteristics of Student Body: *Ethnic/racial makeup:* Black non-Hispanic: 6%; Asian or Pacific Islander: 1%; Hispanic: 4%; White non-Hispanic: 79%; unknown: 8%; nonresident alien 2%. *Age distribution:* number under 18: 2; 18–19: 132; 20–21: 120; 22–24: 71; 25–29: 45; 30–34: 18; 35–39: 16; 40–49: 42; 50–64: 11.

International Students: 19 nonresident alien enrolled fall 2008. No programs available to aid students whose native language is not English. No financial aid specifically designated for international students.

Student Life: On-campus residence halls house 56% of full-time student body. *Intercollegiate athletics:* male: baseball, basketball, cross-country, soccer, volleyball; female: basketball, cross-country, soccer, softball, volleyball. *Special regulations:* Cars with registration with stickers permitted. *Special services:* Learning Resources Center; learning differences specialist; tutorial center; reading, writing, and math specialists. *Student publications: Mountain Musing*, a student weekly newspaper. *Surrounding community:* Bennington population16,500. Albany (NY), 40 miles from campus, is nearest metropolitan area. Served by airport 40 miles from campus; passenger rail service 40 miles from campus.

Library Collections: 26,000 volumes. 88 current periodical subscriptions (11,000 via electronic access). Students have access to online information retrieval services and the Internet.

Most important holdings include collections on criminal justice, environmental studies, and social studies.

Buildings and Grounds: Campus area 371 acres.

Chief Executive Officer: Dr. Barbara Pickard Sirvis, President.

Address admission inquiries to Kathleen James, Director of Admissions.

University of Vermont

85 South Prospect Street
Burlington, Vermont 05405-0160
Tel: (802) 656-3131 **E-mail:** admissions@uvm.edu
Fax: (802) 656-8611 **Internet:** www.uvm.edu

Institution Description: University of Vermont is a public university and is a land-grant and sea-grant college. *Enrollment:* 12,800. *Degrees awarded:* Baccalaureate, first-professional (medicine), master's, doctorate.

Accreditation: *Regional:* NEASC. *Professional*: athletic training, business, chemistry, counseling, dietetics, engineering, medical laboratory technology, medicine, nuclear medicine technology, nursing, physical therapy, psychology internship, radiation therapy, social work, speech-language pathology, teacher education

History: Established and chartered 1791; offered first instruction at postsecondary level 1800; awarded first degree (baccalaureate) 1804; merged with Vermont Agricultural College, chartered under present official name, University of Vermont and State Agricultural College 1865; became a state institution 1956. *See* Julian I. Lindsay, *Tradition Looks Forward* (Burlington: University of Vermont, 1954) for further information.

Institutional Structure: *Governing board:* Board of Trustees made up of 9 trustees elected by state legislature, 3 appointed by governor of Vermont, 9 self-perpetuating trustees elected by the board, 2 student trustees. The governor of Vermont and university president are ex-officio board members. *Composition of institution:* Administrators 86. Academic affairs and finances directed by provost. Finances, management/operation/facilities by vice president for finance and administration. Full-time instructional faculty 1,017. Academic governance body, faculty senate, meets several times per year.

Calendar: Semesters. Academic year Aug. to May. Freshmen admitted Sept., Jan. Degrees conferred May, Oct., Feb. Formal commencement May. Summer sessions from late May through mid-Aug.

Characteristics of Freshmen: 21,062 applicants (female 11,521, male 9,541). 65% of applicants admitted. 19% of applicants admitted and enrolled.

92% (2,024 students) submitted SAT scores; 24% (523 students) submitted ACT scores. *25th percentile*: SAT Critical Reading 530, SAT Math 540; ACT Composite 22. *75th percentile*: SAT Critical Reading 630, SAT Math 640; ACT Composite 27.

69% of entering freshmen expected to graduate within 5 years. 25% of freshmen from Vermont. Freshmen from 35 states and 6 foreign countries.

Admission: For fall acceptance, apply no later than Jan. 15. Students are notified of acceptance by Mar. 31. Apply by Nov. 1 of previous year for both early action/notification and early decision. Apr. 1 deadline for transfer applications; notification on a rolling basis. *Requirements:* Either graduation from accredited secondary school with 16 academic units which must include 4 English, 2 in a foreign language, 3 mathematics (2 algebra, 1 geometry), 3 social science, 2 natural or physical science (1 must be a lab science); or GED. Additional requirements for some programs. *Entrance tests:* Either SAT or ACT each with writing component.

College credit and advanced placement for postsecondary-level work completed in secondary school.

Tutoring and developmental services available.

Degree Requirements: All or most undergraduates are required to complete some coursework prior to graduation in arts/fine arts, English, humanities, mathematics, sciences (biological or physical), social science, and race and cultural awareness. Baccalaureate degree requires minimum of 122 credit hours (2.0 GPA); at least 30 of last 45 credit hours in residence.

Exemption from some beginning courses possible by passing College Board CLEP and other standardized tests. *Grading system:* A–F; withdraw (deadline after which pass-fail is appended to withdraw).

Distinctive Educational Programs: Special study options; cooperative (work-study) program; distance learning; double major; dual enrollment; exchange student program; honors college; independent study; internships; liberal arts/career combination; student-designed major; study abroad; teacher certification program; limited English s a Second Language; evening university option in several programs.

ROTC: Army.

Degrees Conferred: 2,003 *baccalaureate*; 360 *master's*; 68 *doctorate*; 97 *first-professional*. Bachelor's degrees awarded in top five disciplines: social sciences and history 347; business, management, marketing, and related support services 175; English 135; natural resources/environmental science 130; health professions and related clinical sciences 92. Master's degrees awarded: various disciplines 360. Doctorates awarded: various disciplines 68. First-professional degrees awarded: medicine 97.

Fees and Other Expenses: *Full-time tuition per academic year 2008–09:* $12,844 undergradaute; contact the university for graduate and medical school tuition/fees. *Room and board per academic year:* $8,354. *Books and supplies:* $990. *Other expenses:* $1,202.

Financial Aid: Aid from institutionally generated funds is provided on the basis of academic merit, financial need, athletic ability.

Financial aid to full-time, first-time undergraduate students: 92% received some form of aid. Average amount of aid received: federal grants $4,831; Pell grants $2,743; other federal aid $2,300; state/local grants $2,648; institutional grants $7,389.

Departments and Teaching Staff: *Total instructional faculty:* 767 (full-time 569, part-time 198). Total faculty with doctorate, first-professional, or other terminal degree: 560. Student/faculty ratio: 15:1. Degrees held by full-time faculty: baccalaureate 1%, master's 11%, doctorate 65%, professional 24%. 91% hold terminal degrees.

Enrollment: Total enrollment 12,800. Undergraduate 10,937 (full-time 89%; female 56%, male 44%). Graduate 1,863 (full-time 60%). Undergraduate transfer-in students 460.

Characteristics of Student Body: *Ethnic/racial makeup:* Black non-Hispanic: 15; Asian or Pacific Islander: 2%; Hispanic: 25; White non-Hispanic: 92%; unknown: 2%; nonresident alien 1%. *Age distribution:* number under 18: 201; 18–19: 3,511; 20–21: 3,138; 22–24: 891; 25–29: 198; 30–34: 85; 35–39: 42; 40–49: 54; 50–64: 17; 65 and over: 5. 21% of student body attend summer sessions.

International Students: 128 nonresident aliens enrolled fall 2008. Students from Europe, Asia, Latin America, Africa, Canada, Middle East. Programs available to aid students whose native language is not English: social, cultural, financial. English as a Second Language Program. Limited financial aid specifically designated for international students. '\260 Thirty-six residence halls on campus, all for both sexes, house 52% undergraduate student body. First-year students and sophomores are required to live in residence halls. *Intercollegiate athletics:* male: baseball, basketball, golf, hockey, lacrosse, skiing, soccer, track/cross-country; sports for females include basketball, field hockey, hockey, lacrosse, skiing, soccer, softball, swimming, track/cross-country. All sports are NCAA Division 1. *Special regulations:* Cars allowed with permits. *Special services:* Learning Resources Center, medical services. *Student publications, radio: Cynic*, a weekly newspaper. Radio station WRUV-FM. *Surrounding community:* Burlington population 40,000. Montreal, Quebec, 90 miles from campus, is nearest metropolitan area. Served by mass transit bus system; airport 3 miles from campus; passenger rail service 8 miles from campus; bus service for campus. .

Library Collections: 2,587,000 volumes including bound books, serial backfiles, electronic documents, and government documents not in separate collections. Online catalog. 2,102,000 microforms; 49,000 audiovisual materials; 21,000 periodicals including via electronic access. Students have access to the

Internet. Access to online information retrieval services (some charges applied). Computer work stations available.

Most important holdings include the Wilbur Collection (Vermont books, periodicals, documents, etc.); Ovid Collection; personal and business papers of Vermont public figures including former U.S. Senator George Aiken; Dana History of Medicine Collection.

Buildings and Grounds: Campus area 460 acres.

Chief Executive Officer: Dr. Daniel M. Fogel, President.

Address undergraduate admission inquiries to Susan Wertheimer, Dean of Admissions; graduate inquiries Ralph M. Swenson, Director of Graduate Admissions.

College of Agriculture and Life Sciences

Degree Programs Offered: *Baccalaureate* in animal sciences, biochemical science, biological science, botany/agriculture, community development and applied economics, dietetics, environmental science, family and consumer science education, microbiology, molecular genetics, nutritional food sciences, plant and soil science, self-designed, urban forestry and landscape horticulture; *master's* in agricultural biochemistry, animal and food sciences, botany, cell and molecular biology, community development and applied economics, family and consumer sciences education, microbiology and molecular genetics, nutritional food sciences, plant and soil science; *doctorate* in agricultural biochemistry, animal and food sciences, botany, cell and molecular biology, microbiology and molecular genetics, plant and soil science.

Admission: General university requirements.

Degree Requirements: General university requirements plus college course distribution requirements and specific major requirements.

College of Arts and Sciences

Degree Programs Offered: *Baccalaureate* in anthropology, art history, biology, botany, chemistry, classical civilization, communication science, computer science, economics, English, environmental science, French, geography, geology, German, Greek, history, individually designed, international studies (Asian studies, Canadian studies, European studies, Latin America, Russia/Eastern Europe), Latin, mathematics, music, philosophy, physics, psychology, religion, Russian, sociology, Spanish, studio art, theater, women's studies; *master's* in chemistry, communication sciences, English, French, geography, geology, German, Greek and Latin, historic preservation, history, physics, psychology, public administration; *doctorate* in biology, chemistry, psychology.

Admission: General requirements; 4th year of mathematics (trigonometry) recommended.

Degree Requirements: Minimum of 122 credit hours including 96 hours in programs with approved Arts and Sciences majors. Student must fulfill Arts and Sciences course distribution and complete requirements of both a declared major and a declared minor field of study.

Distinctive Educational Programs: Interdisciplinary programs in environmental science, environmental studies, women's studies, and African/Latino/Asian/Native American (ALANA) studies. First-year seminars and first-year interdisciplinary programs.

School of Business Administration

Degree Programs Offered: *Baccalaureate* in business administration; *master's* in business administration.

Admission: Must have college preparatory program covering all general university course requirements. Additional requirement of a 4th year of mathematics. Additional science year recommended.

Degree Requirements: Minimum of 122 credit hours with at least 58 hours not in business administration or upper level economics. Course distribution requirements.

College of Education and Social Services

Degree Programs Offered: *Baccalaureate* in art education, early childhood preschool, elementary education, environmental study/education, human development and family studies, individually designed, music education, physical education, secondary education, social work; *master's* in counseling, curriculum and instruction, educational studies, higher education and student affairs administration, interdisciplinary, reading and language, social work, special education; *certificates:* fifth year certificate; sixty year certificate, counseling, integrated studies; *doctorate* in educational leadership and policy study.

Admission: General university requirements; one year of biology recommended.

Degree Requirements: General university requirements; grade point average of 2.50 in major field and professional education courses required prior to student teaching or social work field experience; 3.0 GPA required for licensure. Course distribution requirements.

College of Engineering and Mathematics

Degree Programs Offered: *Baccalaureate* in civil engineering, computer science and information system, electrical engineering, engineering management, mathematical sciences, mechanical engineering, statistics; *master's* in biomedical engineering, biostatistics, civil engineering, computer science, electrical engineering, engineering physics, materials science, mathematical sciences, mathematics, mechanical engineering, statistics; *doctorate* in electrical engineering, materials science, mechanical engineering.

Admission: Must meet general university requirements; have 4 years of math including trigonometry; must include chemistry and physics. Chemistry required for engineering majors, recommended for others.

Degree Requirements: Must have cumulative GPA of 2.00 at end of sophomore year to be admitted to upper level. Other requirements depending upon chosen major.

Distinctive Educational Programs: Joint master's program in biomedical engineering with College of Medicine.

School of Environment and Natural Resources

Degree Programs Offered: *Baccalaureate* in environmental studies, forestry, natural resources, recreation management, resource economics, wildlife biology; *master's* in forestry, natural resource planning, water resources, wildlife and fisheries biology; *doctorate* in natural resources.

Admission: General university requirements.

Degree Requirements: Course distribution requirements within natural resources. Other requirements depending upon major.

College of Medicine

Degree Programs Offered: *Master's* in biochemistry, cell and molecular biology, microbiology and molecular genetics, pathology, pharmacology; *doctorate* in anatomy and neurobiology, biochemistry, cell and molecular biology, microbiology and molecular genetics, pharmacology, molecular physiology and biophysics; *first-professional* in medicine.

Admission: 3 years undergraduate study at accredited college or university which must include 1 year biology, 1 general or inorganic chemistry, 1 organic chemistry (including lab), 1 physics (including lab); MCAT. Recommend 2 years behavioral sciences, 2 English, 2 humanities, 2 mathematics.

Degree Requirements: 4 years in residence, grade of pass on all courses, core curriculum.

Distinctive Educational Programs: Combined MD-Ph.D. program.

College of Nursing and Health Science

Degree Programs Offered: *Baccalaureate, masters* in nursing.

Admission: General course requirements must include one year each of chemistry and biology. Additional science year recommended.

Degree Requirements: 127 credits for baccalaureate degree, with specific grade requirements for specified courses. Course distribution requirements.

Vermont Law School

Chelsea Street
P.O. Box 96
South Royalton, Vermont 05068-0096
Tel: (802) 763-8303 **E-mail:** admiss@vermontlaw.edu
Fax: (802) 763-2663 **Internet:** www.vermontlaw.edu

Institution Description: Vermont Law School is a private institution offering training leading to the law degree (first-professional, master's). *Enrollment:* 595. *Degrees awarded:* First-professional, master's.

Accreditation: *Regional:* NEASC. *Professional*: law

History: Founded 1972.

Institutional Structure: Independent free-standing law school. Independent Board of Trustees hires the president and dean to administer the day-to-day operations and academic program. Full-time instructional faculty 48.

Calendar: Semesters. Academic year Aug. to May. Summer session.

Admission: *Requirements:* Bachelor's degree from an accredited college or university; 2 written recommendations; narrative sketch; personal interview recommended. *Entrance tests:* LSAT.

Degree Requirements: *J.D.:* 6 semesters of full-time attendance; completion of a minimum of 87 semester hour credits with a cumulative academic average

VERMONT LAW SCHOOL—*cont'd*

of 2.0; completion of required first-year curriculum and specific advanced courses.

Distinctive Educational Programs: Master of Studies in Law (M.S.E.L.) in Environmental Law and Policy Planning; General Practice Program; Joint J.D./ M.S.L. Degree Program. Exchange program with McGill University in Montreal, Canada; exchange program with University of Trento, Italy; dual degree program with Yale School of Forestry and Environmental Studies; dual degree program with l'universite de Cergy-Pontoise (France).

Degrees Conferred: 175 *first-professional:* law; 95 *master's:* law. 2 *honorary degrees awarded:* Doctor of Laws,

Fees and Other Expenses: *Full-time tuition per academic year 2008–09:* $29,730. *Other Fees:* $225. No on-campus housing.

Financial Aid: Aid from institutionally generated funds is provided on the basis of academic merit, financial need.

Graduate aid: 575 students received $11,294,442 in federal and state-funded fellowships/grants; 250 received $677,333 in federal and state-funded loans; 330 received other fellowships/grants totaling $2,159,628.

Departments and Teaching Staff: *Total instructional faculty:* 90 (full-time 48, part-time 12). Total faculty with doctorate, first-professional, or other terminal degree: 88. Student/faculty ratio: 17.5:1.

Enrollment: Total enrollment 585.

Characteristics of Student Body: *Ethnic/racial makeup:* Black non-Hispanic: 1%; American Indian or Alaska Native: 2%; Asian or Pacific Islander: 1%; Hispanic: 1%; White non-Hispanic: 94%; unknown: 1%; nonresident alien 1%. *Age distribution:* number 22–24: 76; 30–34: 100; 35–39: 31; 40–49: 21; 50–64: 7.

International Students: 16 nonresident aliens enrolled fall 2008. No programs available to aid students whose native language is not English. No financial aid specifically designated for international students.

Student Life: Over 40 student organizations and clubs. On-campus child day care available. Athletic fields available adjacent to campus. Many recreational activities nearby (skiing, hiking, biking, canoeing, fishing, hunting).

Publications: *Vermont Law Review* and *Vermont Journal of Environmental Law Journal.*

Library Collections: 125,000 volumes including bound books, serial backfiles, electronic documents, and government documents not in separate collections. Online and card catalogs. Current serial subscriptions: 1,856 paper, 1,369 via electronic access. 874 audio/videotapes. Computer work stations available. Students have access to the Internet at no charge.

Most important special holdings include collections on American law, environmental law and historic preservation, and alternative dispute resolution.

Chief Executive Officer: Geoffrey B. Shields, President and Dean.

Address admission inquiries to Kathy Hartman, Associate Dean for Enrollment Management.

Vermont Technical College

P.O. Box 500

Randolph Center, Vermont 05061-0500

Tel: (802) 728-1000 **E-mail:** admissions@vtc.edu

Fax: (802) 728-1390 **Internet:** www.vtc.edu

Institution Description: Vermont Technical College is a public institution and is one of five schools that make up the Vermont State Colleges system. *Enrollment:* 1,649. *Degrees awarded:* Associate, baccalaureate.

Accreditation: *Regional:* NEASC. *Professional*: engineering, engineering technology, nursing

History: The college was established by the Vermont legislature in 1866 as Randolph State Normal School, the first public school in Vermont devoted to the education of teachers. It became Vermont School of Agriculture in 1910; adopted the name Vermont Agricultural and Technical Institute 1961; became Vermont Technical College and part of the Vermont State Colleges system 1962; baccalaureate degree program added 1993; nursing program began 1994.

Institutional Structure: *Governing board:* Vermont State Colleges Board of Trustees. *Composition of institution:* Faculty members are grouped under five divisions, subdivided by departments, each of which has a chair reporting to the dean of academic affairs. Faculty Assembly meets monthly. Administrative, student affairs, and public affairs functions are headed by the dean of administration, dean of the college, and dean of institutional advancement, all of whom report to the president.

Calendar: Semesters. Academic year Aug. to May.

Characteristics of Freshmen: 886 applicants (female 548, male 538). 78% (239 students) submitted SAT scores. 13% (38 students) submitted ACT scores.

25th percentile: SAT Critical Reading 410, SAT Math 460. *75th percentile:* SAT Critical reading 530, SAT math 570.

Admission: *Requirements:* High school graduation from an accredited school or GED.

Degree Requirements: *For all degrees:* Completion of all coursework listed in the catalog for specific majors; 50% of coursework must be completed in Vermont Technical College courses; 2.0 GPA. All academic programs have a general education component. *For associate degree:* 65–72 credits. *For baccalaureate degree:* 130–139 credits.

Some credit may be granted for nontraditional learning experiences such as military training, CLEP-type examinations, ACE evaluations, or through equivalency exams administered by individual Vermont Technical College departments.

Distinctive Educational Programs: Programs are two-plus-two formats that build on two-year associate degree programs.

Degrees Conferred: 385 *associate;* 59 *baccalaureate:* architecture 9; business/marketing 13; engineering technologies 37.

Fees and Other Expenses: *Full-time tuition per academic year 2008–09:* resident $9,984, nonresident $18,419. *Required fees:* $330. *Room and board per academic year:* $7,509. *Books and supplies:* $1,000. *Other expenses:* $1,650.

Financial Aid: The college offers a direct lending program. Aid from institutionally generated funds is provided on the basis of academic merit, financial need.

Financial aid to full-time, first-time undergraduate students: 84% received some form of aid. Average amount of aid received: federal grants $3,181; Pell grants $2,690; other federl aid $1,096; state/local grants $1,870; institutional grants $3,072.

Departments and Teaching Staff: *Total instructional faculty:* 139 (full-time 73, part-time 66). Total faculty with doctorate, first-professional, or other terminal degree: 32. Student/faculty ratio: 13:1. Degrees held by full-time faculty: doctorate 12%, master's 66%, baccalaureate 100%, professional 12%. 28% hold terminal degrees.

Enrollment: Total enrollment 1,649. Undergraduate 1,649 (full-time 71%; female 41%, male 59%). Transfer-in students 321.

Characteristics of Student Body: *Ethnic/racial makeup:* Black non-Hispanic: 1%; American Indian or Alaska Native: 1%; Asian or Pacific Islander: 2%; Hispanic: 1%; White non-Hispanic: 945; unknown: 1%; nonresident alien 1%. *Age distribution:* number under 18: 95; 18–19: 375; 20–21: 22; 22–24: 157; 25–29: 136; 30–34: 115; 35–39: 75; 40–49: 130; 50–64: 27.

International Students: 17 nonresident aliens from Europe enrolled fall 2008. Programs available to aid students whose native language is not English: English as a Second Language Program. No financial aid specifically designated for international students.

Student Life: *Student publications, radio:* WVTX-FM is the campus radio station offering live Internet streaming. *The Roundtable,* yearbook; *Knight Life,* student newsletter published weekly.

Library Collections: 60,000 volumes including bound books, serial backfiles, electronic documents, and government documents not in separate collections. Online catalog. Current serial subscriptions: 350; 6,000 microforms; 4,000 audiovisual materials. Computer work stations available.

Most important special collections include science and technology books and periodicals; science fiction.

Buildings and Grounds: Campus area 544 acres.

Chief Executive Officer: Dr. Ty Handy,, President.

<Address admission inquiries to Dwight Cross, Dean of Enrollment.

Virginia

Averett University

420 West Main Street
Danville, Virginia 24541
Tel: (434) 791-5600 **E-mail:** admit@averett.edu
Fax: (434) 797-2784 **Internet:** www.averett.edu

Institution Description: Averett University is a private institution. *Enrollment:* 842. *Degrees awarded:* Associate, baccalaureate, master's.

Accreditation: *Regional:* SACS-Comm. on Coll.

History: Established as Danville Female Institute 1854; changed name to Baptist Female Seminary 1858; chartered as Union Female College and offered first instruction at postsecondary level 1859; changed name to Trustees of Roanoke Female College 1893; awarded first degree (baccalaureate) 1898; changed name to Roanoke College 1904, Roanoke Institute 1910, Averett Junior College 1917; became Averett College 1968; became coeducational 1969 and Averett University 2001.

Institutional Structure: *Governing board:* Board of Trustees of Averett University. Extrainstitutional representation: 35 trustees; institutional representation: 1 administrator. All voting. *Composition of institution:* Administrators 13. Academic affairs headed by dean of arts and sciences. Management/business/finances directed by vice president for administration and finance. Full-time instructional faculty 62. Academic governance body, the faculty, meets an average of 7 times per year.

Calendar: Semesters (4-4 plan). Academic year Aug. to Apr. Degrees conferred and formal commencement Dec., Apr. Summer session from May to July.

Characteristics of Freshmen: 1,214 applicants (female 454, male 760). 85% of applicants admitted. 19% of applicants admitted and enrolled.

91% (146 students) submitted SAT scores; 31% (50 students) submitted ACT scores. *25th percentile*: SAT Critical Reading 430, SAT Math 440; ACT Composite 17. *75th percentile*: SAT Critical Reading 540, SAT Math 550; ACT Composite 21.

49% of entering freshmen expected to graduate within 5 years. 61% of freshmen from Virginia. Freshmen from 23 states and 13 foreign countries.

Admission: Rolling admissions plan. For fall acceptance, apply as early as Sept. of previous year, but not later than Aug. of year of enrollment. *Requirements:* Either graduation from accredited secondary school with 15 academic units or GED. 4 units of English, 2 history or social science, 5 mathematics and sciences. Minimum GPA 2.0. All in top 50% of class selected. *Entrance tests:* College Board SAT and/or ACT Composite. *For transfer students:* 2.0 minimum GPA. Grade C or higher earned from regionally accredited institutions for any course that may be transferred for credit.

College credit for postsecondary-level work completed in secondary school and for extrainstitutional learning on basis of portfolio assessment.

Tutoring available. Noncredit developmental courses offered during regular academic year.

Degree Requirements: *For all associate degrees:* 60 credit hours. *For all baccalaureate degrees:* 123 credit hours. *For all undergraduate degrees:* 2.0 GPA; 2 terms in residence.

Fulfillment of some degree requirements possible by passing College College Board CLEP. *Grading system:* A–F; pass-fail; withdraw (carries penalty, time limit, and deadline after which pass-fail is appended to withdraw).

Distinctive Educational Programs: *For undergraduates:* Graduate and Professional Studies (GPS) for working adults at sites throughout Virginia. Individually Developed Education for Adult Learners (IDEAL) for adult students who cannot enroll in a structured curriculum and tailored to their own schedules and backgrounds. Accelerated degree programs and dual enrollment; special studies; independent study; tutorials. Study abroad at Lahti Polytechnic Institution in Finland; Hong Kong Baptist University.

Degrees Conferred: 147 *baccalaureate*; 24 *master's*. Bachelor's degrees awarded in top five disciplines: business, management, marketing, and related support services 335; education 21; parks and recreation 17; protective services/public administration 13; health professions and related clinical sciences 13. *Master's:* education 24.

Fees and Other Expenses: *Full-time tuition per academic year 2008–09:* $21,300 undergraduate; graduate study charged per credit hour. *Room and board per academic year:* $7,990. *Books and supples:* $900. *Other expenses:* $900.

Financial Aid: Aid from institutionally generated funds is provided on the basis of academic merit, financial need.

Financial aid to full-time, first-time undergraduate students: 96% received some form of aid. Average amount of aid received: federal grants $3,165; Pell grants 42,619; other federal aid $658; state/local grants $3,193; institutional grants $6,803.

Departments and Teaching Staff: *Total instructional faculty:* 228 (full-time 62, part-time 166). Total faculty with doctorate, first-professional, or other terminal degree: 132. Student/faculty ratio: 14:1. Degrees held by full-time faculty: doctorate 5%, master's 27%, baccalaureate 68%. 79% hold terminal degrees.

Enrollment: Total enrollment 842. Undergraduate 792 (full-time 95%; female 46%, male 54%). Graduate 50 (full-time 8%). Transfer-in students 73.

Characteristics of Student Body: *Ethnic/racial makeup::* Black non-Hispanic: 29%; American Indian or Alaska Native: 1%; Asian or Pacific Islander: 1%; Hispanic: 3%; White non-Hispanic: 62%; nonresident alien 4%. *Age distribution:* number under 18: 16; 18–19: 323; 20–21: 347; 22–24: 288; 25–29: 232; 30–34: 263; 35–39: 360; 40–49: 190; 50–64: 52.

International Students: 32 nonresident aliens enrolled fall 2008. Students from Europe, Asia, Latin America, Africa, Canada. No programs available to aid students whose native language is not English. No financial aid specifically designated for international students.

Student Life: On-campus residence halls house 58% of student body. Residence halls for males constitute 52%, for females 48%. *Intercollegiate athletics:* male: baseball, basketball, cheerleading, cross-country, equestrian, football, golf, soccer, tennis; females: basketball, cheerleading, cross-country, equestrian, lacrosse, soccer, softball, tennis, volleyball. *Special regulations:* Cars permitted without restrictions. Quiet hours from 7pm to 10am Sun.–Thurs., 12am to 10am Fir.-Sat. *Student publications: Chanticleer*, a monthly newspaper; *Ember*, an annual literary magazine. *Surrounding community:* Danville population 48,000. Greensboro (NC), 42 miles from campus, is nearest metropolitan area. Served by mass transit system; airport 3.5 miles from campus; passenger rail service 1.5 miles from campus.

Publications: *Columns* alumni newspaper.

Library Collections: 171,000 volumes. 63,000 microforms; 420 serial subscriptions. Online catalog. Students have access to online information retrieval services.

Most important special collections include papers and library of Honorable W.C. Daniel (U.S. Representative); papers and library of Honorable Harry Wooding, Danville Mayor 1892–1938; library of William Rickman, local historian.

Buildings and Grounds: Campus area 169 acres. Campus DVD available.

Chief Executive Officer: Dr. Richard A. Pfau, President.

Address admission inquiries to Kathie Tune, Director of Admissions.

Baptist Theological Seminary at Richmond

3400 Brook Road
Richmond, Virginia 23227
Tel: (804) 355-8135 **E-mail:** btsr@btsr.edu
Fax: (804) 355-8182 **Internet:** www.btsr.edu

Institution Description: Baptist Theological Seminary at Richmond is a graduate institution for religious study with a Baptist identity, operating in an ecumenical consortium. *Enrollment:* 214. *Degrees offered:* Master's, first-professional, doctoral.

Accreditation: *National:* ATS. *Professional*: theology

History: The seminary was begun by the Alliance of Baptists in 1989. It opened for classes in 1991 with an initial class of 31 students. It operates in partnership with two other theological institutions in the Richmond Theological Consortium: Union Theological Seminary in Virginia and Presbyterian School of Christian Education, and the School of Theology of Virginia Union University.

BAPTIST THEOLOGICAL SEMINARY AT RICHMOND—*cont'd*

Institutional Structure: The seminary is a free-standing school with a self-perpetuating board of trustees.

Calendar: Semesters. Academic year July to May.

Admission: Admission to the master of divinity program requires a bachelor's degree from a regionally accredited college or university. Admission to the doctor of ministry program requires a master of divinity degree or equivalent plus three years of post-master of divinity ministry experience.

Degree Requirements: The master of divinity degree program is a 30-credit (90 hour) program, requiring coursework in Biblical studies, historical/theological studies and ministries studies areas. The doctor of ministry is a 12-credit (36 hour) program, requiring 4 seminars, 2 credits in an area of concentration, 4 credits of electives, and a ministry project.

Distinctive Educational Programs: Study abroad program at Oxford University (Regent's Park College).

Degrees Conferred: 27 *first-professional:* master of divinity; 8 *doctorate:* theology.

Fees and Other Expenses: *Full-time tuition per academic year 2008–09:* $6,590. *Other fees:* $60. *Room and board per academic year:* $4,570.

Financial Aid: Aid from institutionally generated funds is provided on the basis of academic merit, financial need.

Institution has a Program Participation Agreement with the U.S. Department of Education for eligible students to receive Pell Grants and, depending upon the agreement, other federal aid. *Graduate aid:* 26 students received $280,343 in federal and state-funded loans; 117 received $149,589 in other fellowships/grants.

Departments and Teaching Staff: *Total instructional faculty:* 23 (full-time 13, pat-time 10;). Student/faculty ratio: 15:1. Degrees held by full-time faculty: doctorate 100%.

Enrollment: Total enrollment 212.

Characteristics of Student Body: *Ethnic/racial makeup:* number of Black non-Hispanic: 8; White non-Hispanic: 203.

International Students: 7 nonresident aliens from Asia enrolled fall 2008. Programs available to aid students whose native language is not English: social, cultural. Financial aid specifically designated for international students: scholarships available annually;.

Library Collections: 40,000 volumes including bound books, serial backfiles, electronic documents, and government documents not in separate collections. Online catalog. Current serial subscriptions: 1,000 paper; 500 via electronic access. 35,000 recordings. Computer work stations available. Students have access to the Internet at no charge.

Chief Executive Officer: Dr. Thomas H. Graves, President.

Address admissions inquiries to Robert Fox, Director of Admissions.

Bluefield College

3000 College Drive
Bluefield, Virginia 24605
Tel: (276) 326-3682 **E-mail:** admissions@bluefield.edu
Fax: (276) 326-4288 **Internet:** www.bluefield.edu

Institution Description: Bluefield College is a private institution affiliated with the Baptist General Association of Virginia. *Enrollment:* 736. *Degrees awarded:* Baccalaureate.

Accreditation: *Regional:* SACS-Comm. on Coll.

History: Chartered 1920; established and offered first instruction at postsecondary level 1922; awarded first degree (associate) 1924.

Institutional Structure: *Governing board:* Board of Trustees of Bluefield College. Representation: 30 trustees. All voting. *Composition of institution:* Administrators 8. Academic affairs headed by academic dean. Management/business/finances directed by business manager. Full-time instructional faculty 45. Academic governance body, the faculty, meets an average of 9 times per year.

Calendar: Semesters. Academic year Aug. to May. Freshmen admitted Sept., Jan., Feb., June. Degrees conferred and formal commencement Dec. and May. Summer session from June to mid-Aug.

Characteristics of Freshmen: 471 applicants (female 273, male 204). 93% of applicants accepted. 36% of accepted applicants enrolled.

78% of applicants submitted SAT scores; 34% ACT scores. *25th percentile:* SAT Critical Reading 430, SAT Math 420; ACT Composite 16, ACT English 16, ACT Math 16. *75th percentile:* SAT Critical Reading 520, SAT Math 510; ACT Composite 21, ACT English 21, ACT Math 20. 66% of entering freshmen expected to graduate within 5 years. 54% of freshmen from Virginia. Freshmen from 16 states and 4 foreign countries.

Admission: Rolling admissions plan. *Requirements:* Either graduation from accredited secondary school with 4 units in English, 2 college preparatory mathematics, 2 social studies, 1 science (except for associate degree programs), 5 electives; or GED. Additional requirements for some programs. *Entrance tests:* College Board SAT or ACT composite. *For transfer students:* From 4-year accredited institution 2.0 minimum GPA, maximum transfer credit limited only by residence requirement; from 2-year accredited institution 2.0 minimum GPA, 64–68 hours.

College credit and advanced placement for postsecondary-level work completed in secondary school and for extrainstitutional learning.

Tutoring available. Noncredit remedial courses offered regular academic year.

Degree Requirements: *For all associate degrees:* 64 credit hours; 1 health and 3 activity courses. *For all baccalaureate degrees:* 126 credit hours; 1 health and 3 activity courses. *For all degrees* 2 semesters in residence; general education requirements.

Fulfillment of some degree requirements and exemption from some beginning courses possible by passing departmental examination, College Board CLEP, AP. *Grading system:* A–F; withdraw (deadline after which pass-fail is appended to withdraw).

Distinctive Educational Programs: Work-experience programs. Evening programs. Interdepartmental programs in business, education, fine arts, health, physical education and recreation, humanities, science, and social sciences. Facilities and programs for individual research. Study abroad program at Imperial College, London, England.

Degrees Conferred: 277 *baccalaureate*. Bachelor's degrees awarded in top five disciplines: business, management, marketing, and related support services 111; protective services/public administration 12; psychology 12; parks and recreation 11; philosophy/religion/theology 5.

Fees and Other Expenses: *Full-time tuition per academic year 2008–09:* $15,640. *Books and supplies:* $1,200. *Room and board per academic year:* $6,580. *Other expenses:* $2,700.

Financial Aid: Aid from institutionally generated funds is provided on the basis of academic merit, financial need, athletic ability, other criteria.

Financial aid to full-time, first-time undergraduate students: 96% received aid. Need-based scholarships/grants totaling $2,877,942, self-help $2,752,765, parent loans $127,152, tuition waivers $74,694, athletic awards $269,194; non-need-based scholarships/grants totaling $644,388, self-help $1,247,299, parent loans $342,656, tuition waivers $57,401, athletic awards $112,285.

Departments and Teaching Staff: *Total instructional faculty:* 96. Student/faculty ratio: 14:1. Degrees held by full-time faculty: doctorate 60%, master's 100%. 60% hold terminal degrees.

Enrollment: Total enrollment 736. Undergraduate 736 (full-time 81%; female 60%, male 40%).

Characteristics of Student Body: *Ethnic/racial makeup:* Black non-Hispanic: 18%; Asian or Pacific Islander: 1%; Hispanic: 5%; White non-Hispanic: 75%; unknown 1%. *Age distribution:* number under 18: 19; 18–19: 190; 20–21: 157; 22–24: 80; 25–29: 65; 30–34: 73; 35–39: 76; 40–49: 111; 50–64: 42; 65 and over: 1.

International Students: 6 nonresident aliens enrolled fall 2008. No programs available to aid students whose native language is not English. No financial aid specifically designated for international students.

Student Life: On-campus residence halls house 55% of student body. Residence halls for males constitute 56% of such space, for females 44%. 50% of married students request institutional housing; 12% are so housed. *Intercollegiate athletics:* male: baseball, basketball, golf, soccer, tennis; female: basketball, softball, tennis, volleyball. *Special regulations:* Cars must be registered. Quiet hours. Residence hall visitation limited to lobby areas. *Surrounding community:* Bluefield population 18,000. Roanoke (VA), 80 miles from campus, is nearest metropolitan area. Served by airport 8 miles from campus.

Library Collections: 75,000 volumes. 14,000 current periodical subscriptions. 900 audiovisual materials. Students have access to online information retrieval services and the Internet.

Buildings and Grounds: Campus area 85 acres. Campus DVD available.

Chief Executive Officer: Dr. Charles A. Warren, President.

Address admission inquiries to Director of Admissions.

Bridgewater College

402 East College Street
Bridgewater, Virginia 22812-1599
Tel: (540) 828-8000 **E-mail:** admissions@bridgewater.edu
Fax: (540) 828-5479 **Internet:** www.bridgewater.edu

Institution Description: Bridgewater College is a private, independent, non-profit college affiliated with the Church of the Brethren. *Enrollment:* 1,514. *Degrees awarded:* Baccalaureate.

Member of Online Computer Library Center (OCLC) and Southeastern Library Network.

Accreditation: *Regional:* SACS-Comm. on Coll.

History: Established as Spring Creek Normal School and Collegiate institute and offered first instruction at postsecondary level 1880; chartered and adopted present name 1889; awarded first degree (baccalaureate) 1891.

Institutional Structure: *Governing board:* Bridgewater College Board of Trustees. Extrainstitutional representation: 32 trustee including 24 alumni. institutional representation: 1 administrator. 1 ex officio. *Composition of institution:* Administrators 51. Academic affairs headed by vice president and dean of the college. Management/business/finances directed by vice president for finance and treasurer. Full-time instructional faculty 95. Academic governance body, the faculty, meets an average of 8 times per year.

Calendar: 4-1-4 plan. Academic year Aug. to May. Freshmen admitted Aug., Jan. Degrees conferred and formal commencement May. Summer session of 2 terms from May to July.

Characteristics of Freshmen: 2,169 applicants (female 1,605, male 1,164). 85% of applicants admitted. 31% of applicants admitted and enrolled.

96% (406 students) submitted SAT scores; 21% (90 students) submitted ACT scores. *25th percentile*: SAT Critical Reading 450, SAT Math 450; ACT Composite 18;ACT English 16, ACT Math 16. *75th percentile*: SAT Critical Reading 550, SAT Math 560; ACT Composite 24, ACT English 24, ACT Math 24.

64% of entering freshmen expected to graduate within 5 years. 78% of freshmen from Virginia. Freshmen from 26 states and 8 foreign countries.

Admission: Rolling admissions plan. It is recommended that applications be submitted between completion of the junior year and March of the year of enrollment. Early acceptance available. *Requirements:* either graduation from accredited secondary school with 16 units which must include 4 English,, 3 college-preparatory mathematics, 2 social studies and history, 2 science, and 4 academic electives; or GED. *Entrance tests:* SAT or ACT required; achievements in composition and advanced mathematics recommended. *For transfer students:* 2.0 minimum GPA; no maximum transfer credit hours from 4-year institutions; 27 of the last 30 credits and 9 credits of the major must be earned in residence at the college; from 2-year accredited institution 68 hours.

Advanced placement for postsecondary-level work completed in secondary school.

Tutoring available.

Degree Requirements: 123 credit hours; 2.0 GPA; 27 of the last 30 credits must be earned in residence; general education requirements and senior comprehensive examination over the major field.

Exemption from some courses possible by passing College Board AP. *Grading system:* plus/minus A–F; withdraw pass, withdraw fail (carries time limit).

Distinctive Educational Programs: Double major, honors program, independent study, internships. Liberal arts/career combination and teacher certification program. Various programs with other universities; preprofessional programs in dentistry, engineering, law, medicine, ministry, nursing, occupational therapy, pharmacy, physical therapy, and veterinary science. Interdepartmental majors in environmental science, nutrition and fellness. Personal Development Portfolio (PDP) program. Study with Brethren Colleges Abroad (BCA) in Australia, Belgium, China, Ecuador, England, France, Germany, Greece, Ireland, Japan, Mexico, New Zealand, Spain.

Degrees Conferred: 377 *baccalaureate*, Bachelor's degrees awarded in top five disciplines: business/marketing 60; education 39; biological sciences 37; parks and recreation 35; psychology 27.

Fees and Other Expenses: *Full-time tuition per academic year 2008–09:* $23,090. *Room and board per academic year:* $9,900. *Books and supplies:* $1,050. *Other expenses:* $1,760.

Financial Aid: Aid from institutionally generated funds is provided on the basis of academic merit, financial need, other criteria.

Financial aid to full-time, first-time undergraduate students: 100% received aid. Need-based scholarships/grants totaling $13,954,984, self-help $5,945,554, parent loans $2,114,930, tuition waivers $254,830; non-need-based scholarships/grants totaling $4,572,555, self-help $2,405,576, parent loans $605,911, tuition waivers $248,210.

Departments and Teaching Staff: *Total instructional faculty:* 129 (full-time 95, part-time 34). Total faculty with doctorate, first-professional, or other terminal degree: 85. Student/faculty ratio: 14:1. Degrees held by full-time faculty: master's 31%, doctorate 69%. 73% hold terminal degrees.

Enrollment: Total enrollment 1,514. Undergraduate 1,514 (full-time 99%; female 58%, male 42%).

Characteristics of Student Body: *Ethnic/racial makeup:* Black non-Hispanic: 7%; American Indian or Alaska Native: 1%; Asian or Pacific Islander: 1%; Hispanic: 2%; White non-Hispanic: 80%; unknown: 10%; nonresident alien 1%. *Age distribution:* number under 18: 17; 18–19: 801; 20–21: 582; 22–24: 112; 25–29: 15; 30–34: 2; 35–39: 2; 50–64: 1.

International Students: 15 nonresident aliens enrolled fall 2008. Students from Europe, Latin America, Africa, Canada, Middle East. No programs available to aid students whose native language is not English. *Financial aid specifically designated for international students:* scholarships available annually; 11 totaling $171,860 awarded 2008–09.

Student Life: On-campus residence halls house 83% of student body. *Intercollegiate athletics:* male: baseball, basketball, cross-country, football, golf, soccer, tennis, track and field; female: basketball, cross-country, field hockey, lacrosse, soccer, softball, tennis, track and field, volleyball; coeducational: equestrian. *Special regulations:* Cars permitted if registered with college. Residence hall visitation 10am to 12 midnight Sun. through Thurs.; from 10am until 2am Fri. and Sat. *Special services:* Health services; academic, personal, and religious counseling services; writing center. *Student publications, radio: Philomathean*, a literary magazine; *Ripples*, a yearbook; *The Veritas*, a weekly newspaper. Student radio programming (WGMB) broadcasts 18 hours a week on internal cable network. *Surrounding community:* Bridgewater population 5,203. Washington, D.C., 125 miles from campus, is nearest metropolitan area. Served by airport 15 miles from campus; passenger rail service 25 miles from campus.

Library Collections: 189,000 volumes including bound books, serial backfiles, electronic documents, and government documents not in separate collections. Online catalog. 412,000 microforms; 1,000 audiovisual materials; 400 current serial subscriptions. Computer work stations available. Students have access to the Internet at no charge.

Most important special holdings include collections on Church of the Brethren; Virginiana; genealogy and local history.

Buildings and Grounds: Campus area 40 acres.

Chief Executive Officer: Dr. Phillip C. Stone, President.

Address admission inquiries to Linda F. Stout, Director of Admissions.

Christopher Newport University

One University Place
Newport News, Virginia 23606-2998

Tel: (757) 594-7100 **E-mail:** admit@cnu.edu
Fax: (757) 594-7333 **Internet:** www.cnu.edu

Institution Description: Christopher Newport University is a 4-year comprehensive state-supported coeducational college offering undergraduate and graduate educational programs designed to serve the large metropolitan area of Newport News, Hampton, and several surrounding *Degrees awarded:* Baccalaureate, master's.

Accreditation: *Regional:* SACS-Comm. on Coll.

History: Established as a 2-year branch to the College of William and Mary in 1960; offered first instruction at postsecondary level 1961; became 4-year, baccalaureate institution 1971; became totally independent of the College of William and Mary 1977; offered first master's program in 1991; acquired university status 1997.

Institutional Structure: *Governing board:* Board of Visitors. Representation: 14 visitors. *Composition of institution:* Administrators 88. Academic affairs headed by provost. Management/finances directed by vice president for administration. Development and alumni relations directed by vice president for university advancement. Student affairs headed by the dean of student services.

Calendar: Semesters. Academic year Aug. to May. Formal commencement in May. Summer session of 3 terms from June to Aug.

Characteristics of Freshmen: 7,174 applicants (female 4,114, male 3,060). 61% of applicants accepted. 34% of accepted applicants enrolled.

Average secondary school rank of freshmen in top half of high school graduating class. Mean SAT scores 528 verbal, 510 mathematical; mean ACT Composite 18.

68% of entering freshmen expected to graduate within five years. 95% of freshmen from Virginia. Freshmen from 26 states and 31 foreign countries.

Admission: Rolling admissions plan. For fall acceptance, apply no later than Mar. 15. Apply by end of first semester of senior year of secondary school for early decision. Early acceptance for high ability students Dec. 1. *Requirements:* Either graduation from secondary school or GED. Recommend 4 units English, 2 in a foreign language, 3 mathematics, 2 history, 2 science. Recommend additional unit in mathematics, 1 laboratory science. Minimum grade average C. *Entrance tests:* College Board SAT or ACT. For foreign students TOEFL.

College credit and advanced placement for postsecondary-level work completed in secondary school.

Degree Requirements: *For all baccalaureate degrees:* 120 semester hours and 2 semesters of physical education activities courses, with a GPA of 2.00 are required for graduation. At least 30 of the last 36 credits, including the last 12 credits, must be taken in residence. *For all graduate degrees:* A minimum of 30 semester hour credits is required for a master's degrees. At least 24 of these credits must be taken in residence, with an overall GPA of 3.00. Also required is the completion of a comprehensive examination and presentation of a thesis.

CHRISTOPHER NEWPORT UNIVERSITY—*cont'd*

Fulfillment of some degree requirements and exemption from some beginning courses possible by passing institutional examinations, College Board CLEP, AP. *Grading system:* A–F; pass-fail; pass; withdraw (carries time limit).

Distinctive Educational Programs: The following degrees are offered by cooperating institutions: the Master of Forestry degree by Duke University and the Master of Business and Administration degree by the College of William and Mary. *Other distinctive programs:* Continuing education and an elder learning program for senior citizens. Servicemembers Opportunity College. Reduced tuition for senior citizens.

ROTC: Army in cooperation with the College of William and Mary.

Degrees Conferred: 837 *baccalaureate*; 67 *master's*. Bachelor's degrees awarded in top five disciplines: business, management, marketing, and related support services 133; English language and literature/letters 106; psychology 99; public administration 85; parks and recreation 83. Master's degrees awarded: various disciplines 67.

Fees and Other Expenses: *Full-time tuition per academic year 2008–09:* $7,550 resident; 14.990 nonresident. *Books and supplies:* $988. *Room and board per academic year:* $8,900. *Other expenses:* $3,189.

Financial Aid: Aid from institutionally generated funds is provided on the basis of academic merit, financial need, other criteria.

Institution has a Program Participation Agreement with the U.S. Department of Education for eligible students to receive Pell Grants and, depending upon the agreement, other federal aid.

Financial aid to full-time, first-time undergraduate students: 59% received some form of aid. Average amount of aid received: federal grants $3,314; Pell grants $2,668; other federal aid $791; state/local grants $3,938; institutional grants $1,292.

Departments and Teaching Staff: *Total instructional faculty:* 212. Student/faculty ratio: 17:1. Degrees held by full-time faculty: master's 16%, doctorate 84%. 84% hold terminal degrees.

Enrollment: Total enrollment 4,904. Undergraduate 4,763 (full-time 96%; female 55%, male 45%). Graduate 147 (full-time 51%). Transfer-in students 141.

Characteristics of Student Body: *Ethnic/racial makeup:* Black non-Hispanic: 8%; American Indian or Alaska Native: 1%; Asian or Pacific Islander: 3%; Hispanic: 8%; White non-Hispanic: 83%; unknown: 3%.

International Students: 14 nonresident aliens enrolled fall 2008. Programs available to aid students whose native language is not English: English as a Second Language Program. No financial aid specifically designated for international students.

Student Life: *Intercollegiate athletics:* male: basketball, cross-country, golf, soccer, tennis, track; female: basketball, tennis, volleyball; both sexes: track. *Special regulations:* Registered cars permitted. *Student publications: The Captain's Log*, a newspaper; *Currents*, a literary magazine. *Surrounding community:* The college is located in suburban Newport News, midway between Williamsburg and Norfolk. The campus is accessible to residents in the cities of Newport News, Hampton, Williamsburg, Virginia Beach, Chesapeake, Portsmouth, Gloucester, and Poquoson. Newport News population 175,000.

Library Collections: 400,000 volumes including bound books, serial backfiles, electronic documents, and government documents not in separate collections. Online catalog. 199,000 microforms; 680 audiovisual materials; 900 serial subscriptions. Students have access to the Internet at no charge.

Most important special holdings include A. C. Brown Nautical Collection.

Buildings and Grounds: Campus area 125 acres.

Chief Executive Officer: Dr. Richard M. Summerville, Provost.

Address admission inquiries to Lisa D. Raines, Registrar.

College of William and Mary

P.O. Box 8795
Williamsburg, Virginia 23187-8795
Tel: (757) 221-4000 **E-mail:** admiss@wm.edu
Fax: (757) 221-1242 **Internet:** www.wm.edu

Institution Description: The College of William and Mary is a state college. It includes the School of Marine Sciences, partially funded by the Virginia Institute of Marine Science, a state agency. *Enrollment:* 7,892. *Degrees awarded:* Baccalaureate, first-professional (law), master's, educational specialist, doctorate.

Accreditation: *Regional:* SACS-Comm. on Coll. *Professional*: business, chemistry, clinical psychology, law, teacher education

History: Established and chartered 1693; offered first instruction at postsecondary level 1729; awarded first recorded degree 1772. *See* J. E. Morpurgo, *Their Majesties' Royal College* (Williamsburg: Endowment Association of the College of William and Mary, 1976) for further information.

Institutional Structure: *Governing board:* Board of Visitors, College of William and Mary. Representation: 17 members. All voting. *Composition of institution:* Academic affairs headed by provost. Administrative affairs directed by vice president of administration. Financial affairs directed by vice president of finance. Full-time instructional faculty 594. Academic governance bodies of all the separate faculties meet separately.

Calendar: Semesters. Academic year Aug. to May. Freshmen admitted Aug., Jan., June. Degrees conferred May, Aug., Dec. Formal commencement May. Summer session June to Aug.

Characteristics of Freshmen: 11,836 applicants (female 7,327, male 4,309). 32% of applicants admitted. 35% of applicants admitted and enrolled.

96% (1,299 students) submitted SAT scores; 4% (50 students) submitted ACT scores. *25th percentile*: SAT Critical Reading 620, SAT Math 620; ACT Composite 28, ACT English 29, ACT Math 26. *75th percentile*: SAT Critical Reading 730, SAT Math 710; ACT Composite 32; ACT English 34; ACT Math 31.

90% of entering freshmen expected to graduate within 4 years. 65% of freshmen from Virginia. Freshmen from 47 states and 55 foreign countries.

Admission: Regular admissions plan. For fall acceptance, apply as early as Sept. 1 of previous year, but not later than Jan 5 of year of enrollment. Apply by Nov. 1 for early decision (first choice plan). Early acceptance available. *Requirements:* Recommend graduation from accredited secondary school. *Entrance tests:* College Board SAT; 3 SAT II tests strongly recommended. *For transfer students:* 60 semester hours must be completed in residence.

College credit and advanced placement for postsecondary-level work completed in secondary school. Tutoring available.

Degree Requirements: *For all undergraduate degrees:* 120 semester hours; 240 quality points; 2.0 GPA required for graduation overall and in concentration; last 2 semesters in residence; no more than 4 semester credits in physical education; demonstrated proficiency in writing, a foreign language; general education requirements.

Exemption from some beginning courses possible by passing College Board AP, other standardized tests. *Grading system:* A–F; pass-fail; withdraw.

Distinctive Educational Programs: Honors Programs; internships; preprofessional programs; combined degree programs (engineering, forestry, environmental science); interdisciplinary studies; international studies. Faculties and programs for independent research; evening classes. Institute of Bill of Rights Law offers courses and special programs aimed at exploring issues in constitutional and media law. Study abroad opportunities available in Australia, Canada, China, Denmark, Egypt, France, Italy, Japan, Scotland, Spain, and in other countries through several affiliated programs. Summer Study Abroad opportunities in available in China, England, France, Germany, Italy, and other locations. Other study abroad opportunities in Australia, Canada, China, Denmark, Egypt,

ROTC: Army.

Degrees Conferred: 1,454 *baccalaureate*; 440 *master's*; 63 *doctorate*; 206 *first-professional*. Bachelor's degrees awarded in top five disciplines: social sciences and history 391; business, management, marketing, and related support services 197; psychology 153; English 127; biological/life sciences 109. Master's degrees awarded: various disciplines 63. First-professional degrees awarded: law 206.

Fees and Other Expenses: *Full-time tuition per academic year 2008–09:* $10,246 undergraduate resident, $29,326 nonresident; contact the university for current graduate and Law School tuition. *Room and board per academic year:* $7,910. *Books and supplies:* $1,000. *Other expenses: >RM<$1,650.*

Financial Aid: Aid from institutionally generated funds is provided on the basis of academic merit, financial need.

Financial aid to full-time, first-time undergraduate students: 59% received some form of aid. Average amount of aid received: federal grants $3,517; Pell grants $3,047; other federal aid $1,565; state/local grants $4,314; institutional grants $11,288.

Departments and Teaching Staff: *Total instructional faculty:* 758 (full-time 594, part-time 164). Total faculty with doctorate, first-professional, or other terminal degree: 610. Student/faculty ratio: 11:1. Degrees held by full-time faculty: baccalaureate 1%, master's 9%, doctorate 83%, professional 6%. 92% hold terminal degrees.

Enrollment: Total enrollment: 7,892. Undergraduate 5,858 (full-time 99%; female 55%, male 45%). Graduate 2,042 (full-time 77%). Undergraduate transfer-in students 209.

Characteristics of Student Body: *Ethnic/racial makeup:* Black non-Hispanic: 7%; American Indian or Alaska Native: 1%; Asian or Pacific Islander: 8%; Hispanic: 8%; White non-Hispanic: 59%; unknown: 18%; nonresident alien 2%. *Age distribution:* number under 18: 89; 18–19: 2,244; 20–21: 2,664; 22–24: 596; 25–29: 35; 30–34: 14; 35–39: 12; 40–49: 7; 50–64: 4; 65 and over: 7.

International Students: 158 nonresident aliens enrolled fall 2008. Students from Europe, Asia, Latin America, Africa, Canada, Australia. Programs available to aid students whose native language is not English: social, cultural. English as a Second Language Program. No financial aid specifically designated for international students.

Student Life: On-campus residence halls house 76% of student body. Residence halls for males constitute 11% of such space, for females 18%, for both sexes 71%. 22% of males join fraternities with 15% of them living in fraternity houses. 29% of the females join sororities with 5% of them living in sorority houses. Language houses are also available for housing. *Intercollegiate athletics:* male: badminton, baseball, basketball, boxing, crew, cross-country, diving, equestrian, fencing, football, golf, gymnastics, ice hockey, lacrosse, racquetball, rugby, sailing, soccer, swimming, synchronized swimming, tennis, track and field, volleyball, weight lifting; female: badminton, basketball, crew, cross-country, diving, equestrian, fencing, golf, gymnastics, lacrosse, racquetball, rugby, sailing, soccer, softball, swimming, synchronized swimming, tennis, track and field, volleyball, weight lifting. *Special regulations:* Cars permitted for juniors, seniors, and graduate students only. *Special services:* Learning Resources Center, medical/psychological services, campus bus services, career guidance, campus police. *Student publications, radio: Advocate* and *The Colonial Lawyer*, law school publications; *Colonial Echo*, the yearbook; *The Flat Hat*, a weekly newspaper; *Jump Magazine*; *William and Mary Review*, a biannual literary magazine. Radio station WCWM is on campus. *Surrounding community:* Williamsburg area population 66,000. Richmond 50 miles, Norfolk 45 miles, Hampton 25 miles, and Newport News 15 miles from campus, are the nearest metropolitan areas. Served by mass transit bus system; airport 18 miles from campus; passenger rail service.

Publications: *Business Review* (annually) first published 1977; *Law Review* (quarterly) first published 1957; *William and Mary Quarterly* first published 1944; *William and Mary Magazine, Summer/Winter* first published 1979.

Library Collections: 2,116,300 volumes including bound books, serial backfiles, electronic documents, and government documents not in separate collections. Online catalog. 2,366,200 microforms; 33,700 audiovisual materials; 36,900 periodicals including via electronic access. Computer work stations available. Students have access to the Internet at no charge.

Most important special holdings include Tucker-Coleman Papers; Early American and Virginia History Collection; Peter Chapin Collection of books on dogs.

Buildings and Grounds: Campus area 1,848 acres.

Chief Executive Officer: Dr. Gene R. Nichol, President.

Address undergraduate admission inquiries to Henry Broaddus, Dean of Admissions.

Faculty of Arts and Sciences

Degree Programs Offered: *Baccalaureate, master's, doctorate.*

Admission: Application deadlines vary by department/program.

Degree Requirements: Degree requirements vary by department/program.

School of Business Administration

Degree Programs Offered: *Baccalaureate, master's.*

Admission: For master's: baccalaureate from accredited college or university, GMAT, 3 reference letters, applicant's essay. For part-time master's coursework in accounting, economics, information technology and mathematics (calculus) required.

Degree Requirements: For full-time master's program (MBA): 65 credit hours, 2.75/4.00 GPA; for executive master's program (MBA): 46 credit hours, 2.75/4.00 GPA; for part-time master's program (MBA): 48 credit hours, 2.75/4.00 GPA.

William and Mary Law School

Degree Programs Offered: *First-professional, master's* in American legal system; *L.L.M.* in American legal system for international students. Joint programs: Law/Master of Business Administration; Law/Master of Public Policy; Law/Master of Arts in American Studies.

Admission: *For first-professional degree:* Baccalaureate from accredited college or university, LSAT, LSDAS; completed application, letters of recommendation, personal statement/writing sample.

Degree Requirements: *For first-professional degree:* 90 credit hours, 2.0 GPA, 90 weeks in residence.

Distinctive Educational Programs: Legal Skills Program, Institute of Bill of Rights Law, summer sessions in Australia, England, Spain.

School of Education

Degree Programs Offered: *Master's, educational specialist, doctorate*

Admission: October 1 and Feb. 15. Baccalaureate degree (for master's applicants), master's degree (for educational specialist applicants); GRE or MAT; references. For doctoral program, master's degree required. Specific admissions criteria may vary by degree level and program.

Degree Requirements: 3.0 GPA. Number of credit hours and other specific requirements vary by degree level and program.

Distinctive Educational Programs: Master's degree programs in curriculum and instruction, educational leadership, counselor education, school psychology. Educational specialist programs in school psychology; doctoral programs in educational policy/planning/leadership; counselor education.

School of Marine Science

Degree Programs Offered: *Master's, doctorate* in marine science with areas of study to include biological sciences, coastal and ocean policy, environmental sciences, fisheries science, physical sciences.

Admission: Closing date for applications is Feb. 1 for fall admission. Official transcripts; GRE scores; 3 letters of recommendation. Required: median GPA of 3.37 and GRE score of 1290.

Degree Requirements: M.S. degree requires 36 semester hours of graduate work completed with a grade of B or better. Ph.D. requires a minimum of 3 years of study beyond the baccalaureate and at least 42 semester hours of advanced work with a grade of B or better.

Distinctive Educational Programs: Joint master's degree program offered with Thomas Jefferson Program in Public Policy.

Eastern Mennonite University

1200 Park Road
Harrisonburg, Virginia 22802-2462
Tel: (540) 432-4000 **E-mail:** admiss@emu.edu
Fax: (540) 432-4444 **Internet:** www.emu.edu

Institution Description: Easter Mennonite University, formerly named Eastern Mennonite College and Seminary is a private, Christian institution operated by the Mennonite Church. *Enrollment:* 1,387. *Degrees awarded:* Associate, baccalaureate, first professional, master's. One-year certificates also awarded.

Accreditation: *Regional:* SACS-Comm. on Coll. *National:* ATS. *Professional*: clinical pastoral education, counseling, nursing, pastoral counseling, social work,teacher education

History: Established and incorporated as Eastern Mennonite School 1917; offered first instruction at postsecondary level 1918; adopted the name Eastern Mennonite College and Seminary and awarded first degree (baccalaureate) 1948; adopted present name 1994. *See* Hubert R. Pellman, *Eastern Mennonite University, 1917–1967* (Harrisonburg: Eastern Mennonite College, 1967) for further information.

Institutional Structure: *Governing board:* Board of Trustees, Eastern Mennonite University. Extrainstitutional representation: 16 trustees, institutional representation: president of the college, 7 administrators, 16 voting. *Composition of institution:* Administrators 108. Academic affairs headed by academic provost. Finances directed by vice president for finances. Full-time instructional faculty 107, Academic governance body, Academic Council, meets an average of 8 times per year.

Calendar: Early semester calendar. Academic year Aug. to Apr. Freshmen admitted Sept., Jan., May. Degrees conferred and formal commencement late Apr./early May. Summer session of 2 terms May and June.

Characteristics of Freshmen: 717 applicants (female 413, male 304). 67% of applicants admitted. 26% of applicants admitted and enrolled.

83% (170 students) submitted SAT scores; 29% (59 students) submitted ACT scores. *25th percentile*: SAT Critical Reading 450, SAT Math 450; ACT Composite 21, ACT English 21, ACT Math 20. *75th percentile*: SAT Critical Reading 580, SAT Math 600; ACT Composite 27, ACT English 29, ACT Math 26.

33% of freshmen expected to graduate within 5 years. 48% of freshmen from Virginia. Freshmen from 22 states and 7 foreign countries.

Admission: Rolling admissions plan. For fall acceptance, apply as early as 1 year prior to enrollment, but not later than 30 days before beginning of term. Early acceptance available. *Requirements:* Recommend college preparatory program including units in a foreign language. GED accepted. Minimum GPA 2.2. *Entrance tests:* College Board SAT or ACT composite. *For transfer students:* 2.0 minimum GPA, 65 credit hours maximum transfer credit.

College credit and advanced placement for postsecondary-level work completed in secondary school. College credit for extrainstitutional learning (life experience) on basis of voluntary service with Mennonite Church mission and service agencies.

Remedial courses offered during regular academic year; credit given.

Degree Requirements: *For all associate degrees:* 64 semester hours. *For all baccalaureate degrees:* 128 semester hours, senior interdisciplinary course. *For all undergraduate degrees:* Minimum 2.0 GPA and 32 hours in residence required for graduation (some majors require higher minimum GPA for gradu-

EASTERN MENNONITE UNIVERSITY—*cont'd*

ation); "Global Village" general education curriculum required of all students including 9 semester hours cross-cultural requirement. *For Master of Arts in Church Leadership:* 60 semester hours.

Fulfillment of some degree requirements and exemption from some beginning courses possible by passing departmental examinations, College Board CLEP, AP. *Grading system:* A–F; pass-fail; withdraw (carries time limit).

Distinctive Educational Programs: Work-experience programs. Independent study. Evening classes. Interdisciplinary programs in community development, peace and justice, missions. Interdisciplinary "Global Village" curriculum requires all students to earn at least 3 semester hours of credit by study in different culture. Institutionally sponsored study abroad in the Middle East, Europe, Latin America, Africa; summer seminars (3–9 weeks) in a variety of locations such as Austria, Costa Rica, China, Ireland, Lithuania, Lesotho. Study abroad also available through Brethren Colleges Abroad Programs and the Council for Christian Colleges and Universities Study Abroad Programs. *Other distinctive programs:* Extension courses. Adult Degree Completion Program. Master's programs in business administration, counseling, conflict transformation, and education.

Degrees Conferred: 17 *associate;* 279 *baccalaureate;* 104 *master's*. Bachelor's degrees awarded in top five disciplines: business/marketing 79; health professions and related clinical sciences 52; liberal arts/general studies 41; education 38; public administration and social services 15. Master's degrees awarded: business/marketing 4; education 39; interdisciplinary studies 42; psychology 19. *First-professional:* master of divinity 27.

Fees and Other Expenses: *Full-time tuition per academic year 2008–09:* $23,280 undergraduate; contact the university for current graduate and first-professional tuition and applicable fees. *Required fees:* $100. *Room and board per academic year:* $7,200. *Books and supplies:* $1,000. *Other expenses:* $1,420.

Financial Aid: Aid from institutionally generated funds is provided on the basis of academic merit, financial need, other criteria.

Financial aid to full-time, first-time undergraduate students: 100% received some form of aid. Average amount of aid received: federal grants $2,976; Pell grants $2,647; other federal aid $3,288; state/local grants $2,630; institutional grants $8,757.

Departments and Teaching Staff: *Total instructional faculty:* 163 (full-time 107, part-time 36). Total faculty with doctorate, first-professional, or other terminal degree: 96. Student/faculty ratio: 10.6::1. Degrees held by full-time faculty: doctorate 61%, master's 34%. 70% hold terminal degrees.

Enrollment: Total enrollment 1,387. Undergraduate 995. Graduate 392 (full-time 30%). Transfer-in students 115.

Characteristics of Student Body: *Ethnic/racial makeup:* Black non-Hispanic: 7%; Asian or Pacific Islander: 6%; Hispanic: 45; White non-Hispanic: 82%; unknown: 2%; nonresident alien 3%. *Age distribution:* number under 18: 24; 18–19: 317; 20–21: 376;22–24: 181; 25–29: 118; 30–34: 61; 35–39: 55; 40–49: 106; 50–64: 58; 65 and over: 1. 20% of student body attend summer sessions.

International Students: 42 nonresident aliens enrolled fall 2008. Students from Europe, Asia, Latin America, Africa, Canada, Middle East. Programs to aid students whose native language is not English: social, cultural. English as a Second Language Program. Financial aid specifically designated for international students: variable number of scholarships available annually; 26 totaling $176,321 7awarded 2008–09.

Student Life: On-campus residence halls house 61% of student body. Residence halls for males constitute 25% of such space, for females 36%. 3% of student body live in cooperative facilities. *Intercollegiate athletics:* male: baseball, basketball, cross-country, soccer, tennis, track, volleyball; female: basketball, field hockey, cross-country, soccer, softball, track, volleyball. *Special regulations:* Cars permitted. *Special services:* Learning Center, medical services, counseling services. *Student publications, radio: Phoenix*, an annual literary and art magazine; *Shenandoah*, a yearbook; *Weather Vane*, a weekly newspaper. Radio station WEMC broadcasts 130 hours per week. *Surrounding community:* Harrisonburg population 32,500. Roanoke, 110 miles from campus, is nearest metropolitan area. Served by mass transit bus system; airport 15 miles from campus; passenger rail service 25 miles from campus.

Library Collections: 170,000 volumes including bound books, serial backfiles, electronic documents, and government documents not in separate collections. Online catalog. 92,000 microforms; 4,000 audiovisual materials; 1,050 current serial subscriptions. Computer work stations available. Students have access to the Internet at no charge.

Most important special holdings include Mennonite history and thought; Shenandoah Valley items of interest and genealogy; religion; general history; 16th-century imprints.

Buildings and Grounds: Campus area 93 acres. Campus DVD available.

Chief Executive Officer: D. Loren Swartzendruber, President.

Address undergraduate admission inquiries to Stephanie C. Shafer, Director of Admissions; graduate inquiries to Don A. Yoder, Director of Seminary and Graduate Admissions.

Eastern Mennonite Seminary

Degree Programs Offered: *Master's:* Master of Divinity, Master of Arts in Religion, Master of Arts in Church Leadership; *Certificate:* Certificate in Biblical Studies, Certificate in Pastoral Studies.

Admission: Baccalaureate degree from an accredited institution, GPA 2.5, for admission to degree program. Admission to a Certificate program based on criteria of age and vocational experience.

Degree Requirements: *Master of Arts in Church Leadership* 60 semester hours; *Master of Arts in Religion* 60 semester hours; *Master of Divinity* 90 semester hours. *Certificate* 24 semester hours. *All degrees:* 2.5 GPA, 9 months in residence.

Departments and Teaching Staff: Biblical studies *professors* 1, *associate professors* 2, *assistant professors* 0, *instructors* 0, *part-time teachers* 1; historical and theological studies 1, 1, 0, 0, 3; church ministries 2, 1, 2, 0, 7.

Total instructional faculty: 23. Degrees held by full-time faculty: doctorate 80%, master's 20%.

Emory and Henry College

One Garnand Drive
P.O. Box 947
Emory, Virginia 24327-0947
Tel: (276) 944-4121 **E-mail:** ehadmiss@ehc.edu
Fax: (276) 944-6598 **Internet:** www.ehc.edu

Institution Description: Emory and Henry College is a private institution affiliated with the United Methodist Church. *Enrollment:* 1,015. *Degrees awarded:* Baccalaureate, master's.

Accreditation: *Regional:* SACS-Comm. on Coll.

History: Established 1836; offered first instruction at postsecondary level 1838; chartered 1839; awarded first degree (baccalaureate) 1843. *See* George J. Stevenson, *Increase in Excellence* (New York: Meredith Publishing, Co., 1963) for further information.

Institutional Structure: *Governing board:* Board of Trustees, Holston Conference Colleges, which delegates governance to Board of Governors of Emory and Henry College. Extrainstitutional representation: 37 trustees, including 4 ex officio; institutional representation: 1 full-time instructional faculty, 1 student, 1 ex officio. *Composition of institution:* Administrators 17. Academic affairs headed by dean of faculty/provost. Management/business/finances directed by treasurer. Full-time instructional faculty 75. Academic governance body, the faculty, meets an average of 9 times per year.

Calendar: Semesters. Academic year Aug. to July. Freshmen admitted Sept., Dec., Mar., June, July. Degrees conferred and formal commencement May. Summer session of 1 term from May to June, summer session 2 from June to July.

Characteristics of Freshmen: 1,131 applicants (female 521, male 610). 75% of applicants admitted. 22% of applicants admitted and enrolled.

75% (210 students) submitted SAT scores; 25% (11 students) submitted ACT scores. *25th percentile*: SAT Critical Reading 470, SAT Math 478; ACT Composite 20, ACT English 18, ACT Math 19. *75th percentile*: SAT Critical Reading 590, SAT Math 570; ACT Composite 28, ACT English 25. 58r<54% of entering freshmen expected to graduate within 5 years. 70% of freshmen from Virginia. Freshmen from 23 states and 3 foreign countries.

Admission: Rolling admissions plan. *Requirements:* 4 years of college preparatory English, 3 or more units of mathematics (at least through Algebra II), 2 or more units of laboratory science, at least 2 units of a single foreign language, and 2 or more units of social studies and history. Among electives, at least 1 course in the fine arts is strongly recommended. *Entrance tests:* College Board SAT or ACT composite. *For transfer students:* 2.0 minimum GPA; 62 maximum transfer credit.

Advanced placement for postsecondary-level work completed in secondary school.

Tutoring available.

Degree Requirements: 120 semester hours for B.A., 124 for B.S.; 2.0 GPA; last 33 hours in residence; distribution requirements; demonstrated proficiency in writing; Lyceum requirement.

Fulfillment of some degree requirements and exemption from some beginning courses possible by passing College Board CLEP and APP. *Grading system:* A–F; pass-fail; withdraw failing, withdraw passing.

Distinctive Educational Programs: Core curriculum with strong emphasis on writing, reasoning, and broad knowledge of literature and history. First year Western Tradition course. Great Books program for all sophomores. Upper-level requirements in global studies, ethical inquiry. Cooperative education and internship opportunities. Facilities and programs for independent research, including individualized majors and tutorials. Computer applications in sciences, business, and social sciences.

Degrees Conferred: 216 *baccalaureate*. Bachelor's degrees awarded in top five disciplines: social sciences 33; education 33, business, management, marketing, and related support services 23; psychology 20; history 17. Master's degrees awarded: education 4.

Fees and Other Expenses: *Full-time tuition per academic year 2008–09:* $23,860. undergraduate; graduate study charged per per credit hour (contact the college for current rate). *Room and board per academic year:* $7,980. *books and supplies:* $700. *Other expenses:* $2,200.

Financial Aid: Aid from institutionally generated funds is provided on the basis of academic merit, financial need.

Financial aid to full-time, first-time undergraduate students: 100% received aid. Need-based scholarships/grants totaling $10,544,104, self-help $3,584,709, parent loans $2,548,262, parent loans $2,548,262, tuition waivers $178,190; non-need-based scholarships/grants totaling $2,104,569, self-help $210,625, parent loans $579,905, tuition waivers $91,720.

Departments and Teaching Staff: *Total instructional faculty:* 120 (full-time 75, part-time 45). Total faculty with doctorate, first-professional, or other terminal degree: 72. Student/faculty ratio: 11:1. Degrees held by full-time faculty: master's 14%, doctorate 86%. 86% hold terminal degrees.

Enrollment: *Total enrollment:* 1,015. Undergraduate 975 (full-time 93%; female 48%, male 52%). Gradaute 40 (full-time 20%). Transfer-in students 57.

Characteristics of Student Body: *Ethnic/racial makeup:* Black non-Hispanic: 6%; American Indian or Alaska Native: 1%; Asian or Pacific Islander: 1%; Hispanic: 6%; White non-Hispanic: 86%; unknown: 5%; nonresident alien 1%.

International Students: 11 nonresident aliens enrolled fall 2008. Students from Europe, Asia, Latin America. No programs available to aid students whose native language is not English. No financial aid specifically designated for international students.

Student Life: On-campus residence halls house approximately 82% of student body. Residence halls for males constitute 51% of such space, for females 49%. *Intercollegiate athletics:* male: baseball, basketball, football, soccer, golf, tennis; female: basketball, tennis, cross-country, soccer, softball, volleyball. *Special services:* Learning Resources Center, medical services. *Student publications, radio: The Whitetopper*, a biweekly newspaper; *Ampersand*, a quarterly magazine; *The Sphinx*, a yearbook. Radio station WASP broadcasts 45–50 hours per week. *Surrounding community:* Emory (unincorporated). Tri-Cities (Bristol VA/TN), 30 minutes from campus, is nearest metropolitan area. Arlington (VA) is 10 minutes from campus.

Library Collections: 180,000 volumes including bound books, serial backfiles, electronic documents, and government documents not in separate collections. Online catalog. 42,000 microforms; 4,000 audiovisual materials; 650 current serial subscriptions. Computer work stations available. Students have access to the Internet at no charge.

Most important special holdings include Holston Conference Archives; Appalachian Oral History Collections; George Stevenson Collection.

Buildings and Grounds: Campus area 200 acres.

Chief Executive Officer: Dr. Rosalind Richard, President.

Address admission inquiries to Davod Howsey, Vice Preisident for Enrollment Management.

Ferrum College

215 Ferrum Mountain Road
Ferrum, Virginia 24088-9000
Tel: (540) 365-2121 **E-mail:** admissions@ferrum.edu
Fax: (540) 365-4203 **Internet:** www.ferrum.edu

Institution Description: Ferrum College is a private, independent, nonprofit college affiliated with the United Methodist Church. *Enrollment:* 1,397. *Degrees awarded:* Baccalaureate.

Accreditation: *Regional:* SACS-Comm. on Coll. *Professional*: recreation and leisure services, social work

History: Established as Ferrum Training School and chartered 1913; offered first instruction at postsecondary level 1926; awarded first degree (associate) 1927; adopted present name 1975; initiated baccalaureate program 1976. *See* Frank B. Hurt, *A History of Ferrum College* (Roanoke, VA: Stone Printing Co., 1977) for further information.

Institutional Structure: *Governing board:* Board of Trustees. Representation: 36 trustees, including alumni, church officials, business leaders. *Composition of institution:* Administrators 42. Academic affairs headed by senior vice president and dean of the college. Student life headed by vice president for student affairs. Management/business/finances directed by vice president for business affairs. Full-time instructional faculty 64. Academic governance body, Academic Council, meets an average of 24 times per year.

Calendar: Semesters. Academic year Sept. to May. Freshmen admitted Aug., Jan., May, July. Degrees conferred May, June, Aug., Dec. Formal commencement May. Summer session from late May to early Aug.

Characteristics of Freshmen: 2,608 applicants (female 1,281, male 1,327). 76% of applicants accepted. 33% of accepted applicants enrolled.

96% (311 student) submitted SAT scores; 18% (78 students) submitted ACT scores. *25th percentile*: SAT Critical Reading 390, SAT Math 411; ACT Composite 13. *75th percentile*: SAT Critical Reading 480, SAT Math 490; ACT Composite 18.

33% of entering freshmen expected to graduate within 5 years. 86% of freshmen from Virginia. Freshmen from 24 states and 5 foreign countries.

Admission: Rolling admissions plan. For fall acceptance, apply as early as 1 year prior to enrollment. *Requirements:* Either graduation from accredited secondary school or GED. *Entrance tests:* College Board SAT recommended; ACT accepted. *For transfer students:* Same procedure for recent high school graduates and official transcript of all college work.

College credit for extrainstitutional learning.

Tutoring available. Developmental courses offered in summer session and regular academic year; credit given.

Degree Requirements: *For all baccalaureate degrees:* 121 credit hours; comprehensives in some fields of study. *For all undergraduate degrees:* 2.0 GPA; 2 terms, or 32 hours, in residence; swimming test; distribution requirements.

Fulfillment of some degree requirements and exemption from some beginning courses possible by passing College Board CLEP, AP. Exemption from some courses also possible by passing departmental examinations. *Grading system:* A–F; pass-fail.

Distinctive Educational Programs: Internships. Flexible meeting places and schedules. Active academic clubs which combine practical and academic expe riences (i.e., Students in Free Enterprise). Internet-based online catalog with access to dozens of electronic databases and full text resources. The Bonner Scholar program provides students with a learning environment while performing community service. Facilities for independent student research. Off-campus study in the Virgin Islands. Private College Consortium for International Studies; Internships available through exchange program with Pskov, Russia. Some study abroad experiences available for outstanding French students in France. Blue Ridge Institute and Museum offering courses of study and activities celebrating the Blue Ridge area and its heritage.

Degrees Conferred: 138 *baccalaureate*. Bachelor's degrees awarded in top five disciplines: business, management, marketing, and related support services 26; liberal arts/general studies 18; security and protective services 15; natural resources/environmental science 12; biological/life sciences 11.

Fees and Other Expenses: *Full-time tuition per academic year 2008–09:* $22,545. *Books and supplies:* $800. *Room and board per academic year:* $7,300. *Other expenses:* $1,685.

Financial Aid: Aid from institutionally generated funds is provided on the basis of academic merit, financial need, other criteria.

Institution has a Program Participation Agreement with the U.S. Department of Education for eligible students to receive Pell Grants and, depending upon the agreement, other federal aid.

Financial aid to full-time, first-time undergraduate students: 99% received federal grants averaging $3,351; 78% state/local grants averaging $2,533; 99% institutional grants averaging $3,133; 78% received loans averaging $3,821.

Departments and Teaching Staff: *Total instructional faculty:* 94 (full-time 64, part-time 30;). Student/faculty ratio: 13:1. Degrees held by full-time faculty: doctorate 61%, master's 38%, baccalaureate 1%. 65% hold terminal degrees.

Enrollment: Total enrollment 1,397. Undergraduate1,397 (full-time 98%; female 47%, male 33%). Transfer-in students 52.

Characteristics of Student Body: *Ethnic/racial makeup:* Black non-Hispanic: 26%; Asian or Pacific Islander: 1%; Hispanic: 3%; White non-Hispanic: 53%; unknown 13%; nonresident alien 1%.

International Students: 14 nonresident aliens enrolled fall 2008. Programs available to aid students whose native language is not English: English as a Second Language Program. Financial aid specifically designated for international students: 8 scholarships totaling $99,200 awarded awarded 2008–09.

Student Life: On-campus residence halls house 80% of student body. Over 60 clubs and organizations and numerous intramural activities are available for student involvement. *Intercollegiate athletics:* male: baseball, basketball, cross-country, football, golf, soccer, tennis; female: basketball, cross-country, lacrosse, softball, soccer, tennis, volleyball. Coed cheerleading and equestrian teams. *Special regulations:* Cars permitted without restrictions. *Special services:* Learning Resources Center, medical services. *Student publications, radio: Beacon*, a yearbook; *Chrysalis*, an annual literary magazine; *Iron Blade*, a biweekly newspaper. Radio station WFJC broadcasts 40 hours per week. *Surrounding community:* Ferrum, unincorporated, located in Franklin County, pop-

FERRUM COLLEGE—*cont'd*

ulation 36,000. Richmond, 195 miles from campus, is nearest metropolitan area. Served by airport and passenger rail services, each 30 miles from campus.

Library Collections: 220,000 volumes. 7,500 microforms; 2,290 audiovisual materials; 21,000 periodicals including via electronic access. Online catalog. Students have access to online information retrieval services and the Internet.

Most important special collections include the Archives of the Virginia Conference United Methodist Women; the late Governor Thomas B. Stanley, Sr. Collection.

Buildings and Grounds: Campus area 754 acres.

Chief Executive Officer: Dr. Jennifer L. Braaten, President.

Address admission inquiries to Gilda Woods, Director of Admissions.

George Mason University

4400 University Drive
Fairfax, Virginia 22030-4444
Tel: (703) 993-1000 **E-mail:** admissions@gmu.edu
Fax: (703) 993-2392 **Internet:** www.gmu.edu

Institution Description: George Mason University is a state institution. *Enrollment:* 30,613. *Degrees awarded:* Baccalaureate, first-professional (law), master's, doctorate.

Degree program subject to approval by statewide coordinating body. Budget subject to approval by state governing board. Member of Consortium for Continuing Higher Education in Northern Virginia.

Accreditation: *Regional:* SACS-Comm. on Coll. *Professional*: business, chemistry, computer science, engineering, law, music, nursing, psychology internship, public administration, social work, teacher education

History: Established by the University of Virginia as extension center for higher education 1948; became 2-year branch college and changed name to University College 1957; changed name to George Mason College of the University of Virginia 1960; became 4-year institution 1966; awarded first degree (baccalaureate) 1968; added master's programs 1970; adopted present name and became independent institution 1972; added doctoral program 1980.

Institutional Structure: *Governing board:* Board of Visitors. Representation: 16 trustees, including 4 alumni. All voting. *Composition of institution:* Administrators 71. Academic affairs headed by vice president for academic affairs. Management/business/finances directed by vice president for business and affairs. Full-time instructional faculty 881. Academic governance body, Faculty Senate, meets an average of 9 times per year.

Calendar: Semesters (quarters for law school). Academic year Sept. to May. Freshmen admitted Aug., Jan., June. Degrees conferred and formal commencement May. Summer session of 4 terms from May to Aug.

Characteristics of Freshmen: 12,943 applicants (female 8,901, male 8,042). 69% of applicants admitted. 33% of applicants admitted and enrolled full-time.

95% (2,145 students) submitted SAT scores; 15% (333 students) submitted ACT scores. *25th percentile*: SAT Critical Reading 490, SAT Math 500; ACT Composite 20, ACT English 19, ACT Math 19. *75th percentile*: SAT Critical Reading 600, SAT Math 600; ACT Composite 25, ACT English 25, ACT Math 25.

46% of freshmen expected to graduate within five years. 41% of freshmen from Virginia. Freshmen from 40 states and 127 foreign countries.

Admission: Admission is competitive. Feb. 1 decision for fall applications; Apr. 1 notification. Apply by Jan. 1 for early decision (need 3.0 or higher GPA and 1000 or higher on SATs). Early admission available. *Requirements:* Graduation from accredited secondary school with academic program that includes 4 units of English, 2 units of foreign language, 3 college-preparatory mathematics (at least through algebra II), 1 laboratory science, plus electives and social sciences. (Engineering majors need 1 extra unit each of mathematics and science). Average SAT scores are 1043 total; average GPA is 3.0 (on a 4.0 scale). *Entrance tests:* SAT or ACT required. For foreign students TOEFL with score of 550 or higher. Interviews are recommended. *For transfer students:* 2.0 minimum GPA, 2.4 preferred.

College credit and advanced placement for postsecondary-level work completed in secondary school. Tutoring available.

Degree Requirements: 120 semester hours; maximum of 12 hours with grade of D (6 hours in major); 30 hours in residence; general education requirements, including 6 hours of English; demonstrated proficiency in English composition. Additional requirements for some programs.

Fulfillment of some degree requirements and exemption from some beginning courses possible by passing departmental examinations, College Board CLEP, APP. *Grading system:* A–F; A–C, no credit; satisfactory-no credit; withdraw (carries time limit).

Distinctive Educational Programs: *For undergraduates:* Bachelor of Individualized Study, an external degree program offered through consortium. Interdisciplinary programs in American studies, area studies, European studies, Latin American studies, Russian studies. Facilities and programs for independent research, including individual majors, tutorials. *For graduate students:* Weekend classes. Research opportunities in the Child/Youth Study Center, and the Psychological Clinic. *Available to all students:* Work-experience programs, including internships, cooperative education. Evening classes. Accelerated degree programs. Special facilities for using telecommunications in the classroom. *Other distinctive programs:* Public Management Institute provides research and independent study opportunities for graduate students in public administration and for Faculty. Center for Government, Society, and the Arts offers interdisciplinary research and coursework on the interrelationships of these areas; credit given. A program unique in Virginia, the Plan for Alternative General Education (PAGE) is a program that offers the option of completing general education requirements through a series of 18 interdisciplinary courses designed to help one understand the vital connections among the various disciplines. Additionally, the University offers the Bachelor of Arts/Sciences Integrated Curriculum program (BA/SIC) to freshmen and sophomore students who elect to use it. BA/SIC attempts to achieve an integrated and coherent approach to the mastery of general education requirements of the BA or BS degree. This goal is achieved through team-teaching efforts by the instructors; students in the BA/SIC program take many of their courses together. Summer Program in Budapest, Ghent, Madrid, Nice, Quebec, Vienna; Semester a Year in Reading, England; Tbilisi, Georgia; Vaxjo, Sweden; Wurzburg, Germany. GMU is also a member of the International Student Exchange Program.

ROTC: Army offered in cooperation with Georgetown University (DC); Air Force in cooperation with University of Maryland.

Degrees Conferred: 3,809 *baccalaureate*; 2,549 *master's*; 191 *doctorate*; 214 *first-professional*. Bachelor's degrees awarded in top five disciplines: computer and information sciences 478; business, management, marketing, and related support services 470; English 456; protective services/public administration 317; social sciences and history 293. Master's degrees awarded: various disciplines 2,549. Doctorates awarded; various disciplines 191. First-professional degrees awarded: law 214.

Fees and Other Expenses: *Full-time tuition per academic year 2008–09:* resident $7,512, nonresident $22,476; contact the university for current graduate and Law School tuition. *Room and board per academic year* $7,360. *Books and supplies:* $900. *Other expenses:* $2,704.

Financial Aid: Aid from institutionally generated funds is provided on the basis of academic merit, financial need, athletic ability.

Financial aid to full-time, first-time undergraduate students: 80% received some form of aid. Average amount of aid received: federal grants $3,089; Pell grants $1,989; other federal aid $1,012; state/local grants $3,596; institutional grants $7,343.

Departments and Teaching Staff: *Total full-time instructional faculty:* 974. Student/faculty ratio: 15.4:1. Degrees held by full-time faculty: 90.2% hold terminal degrees.

Enrollment: Total enrollment 30,613. Undergraduate 18,708 (full-time 76%; female 53%, male 47%). Graduate 11,905 (full-time 20%) Undergraduate transfer-in students 2,254.

Characteristics of Student Body: *Ethnic/racial makeup:* Black non-Hispanic: 7%; Asian or Pacific Islander: 16%; Hispanic: 7%; White non-Hispanic 43%.

International Students: 1,710 nonresident aliens enrolled fall 2008. Students from Asia, Latin America, Africa, Canada, Australia, New Zealand. Programs available to aid students whose native language is not English: English as a Second Language Program. No financial aid specifically designated for international students.

Student Life: On-campus residence halls house 11% of student body. 8% of males and 8% of females participate in Greek life. *Division I sports:* male: baseball, basketball, cross-country, golf, lacrosse, rowing, soccer, softball, tennis, track, volleyball, wrestling; female: basketball, cross-country, softball, soccer, tennis, track, volleyball. *Special regulations:* Cars permitted without restrictions. *Special services:* Learning Resources Center, Student Health Services, intra-campus bus service. *Student publications, radio: Broadside*, a weekly newspaper; *By George!* a yearbook; *Phoebe*, a quarterly literary magazine. Radio station WGMU broadcasts on campus 7 days a week, 6am to 12 midnight. *Surrounding community:* Fairfax County, population 670,000, is located in Washington (DC) metropolitan area. Served by 2 airports 12 and 15 miles from campus; passenger rail service 4 miles from campus.

Publications: *George Mason Magazine* (quarterly) first published 1975 (as *GMU Today*); *Journal of Labor Research* (biannually) first published 1980; *The Law Review* (annually) first published 1976; *Northern Virginia Heritage* (triennially) first published 1979; *The Virginia Geographer* (biannually) first published 1966.

Library Collections: 1,155,000 volumes including bound books, serial backfiles, electronic documents, and government documents not in separate collections. Online catalog. 3,100,000 microforms; 32,000 audiovisual materials;

11,570 periodicals including via electronic access. Students have access to the Internet at no charge.

Most important special holdings include Federal Theatre Project Collection of the Library of Congress; Planned Community Archives; US and Virginia government documents; documents of the European community.

Buildings and Grounds: Campus area 806 acres.

Chief Executive Officer: Dr. Alan G. Merten, President.

Address admission inquiries to Andrew Flagel, Dean of Admissions.

Hampden-Sydney College

College Road
P.O. Box 128
Hampden-Sydney, Virginia 23943
Tel: (434) 223-6000 **E-mail:** hscapp@hsc.edu
Fax: (434) 223-6350 **Internet:** www.hsc.edu

Institution Description: Hampden-Sydney College is a private, independent, nonprofit men's college affiliated with the Presbyterian Church (USA). *Enrollment:* 1,120. *Degrees awarded:* Baccalaureate.

Member of the consortium Seven College Student Exchange.

Accreditation: *Regional:* SACS-Comm. on Coll.

History: Established and offered first instruction at postsecondary level 1776; chartered 1783; awarded first degree (baccalaureate) 1786.

Institutional Structure: *Governing board:* President and Trustees of Hampden-Sydney College. Extrainstitutional representation: 36 trustees, including 29 alumni; institutional representation: president of the college. 1 ex officio. All voting. *Composition of institution:* Administrators 61. Academic affairs headed by dean of the faculty. Management/business/finances directed by vice president for finance. Full-time instructional faculty 93. Academic governance body, the faculty, meets an average of 9 times per year.

Calendar: Semesters. Academic year Aug. to May. Freshmen admitted Aug., Jan. Degrees conferred and formal commencement May. Summer session of 1 term from May to June.

Characteristics of Freshmen: 1,553 applicants (female 1,553). 69% of applicants admitted. 34% of applicants admitted and enrolled.

100% (345 students) submitted SAT scores; 18% (60 students) submitted ACT scores. *25th percentile*: SAT Critical Reading 500, SAT Math 510; ACT Composite 20; ACT English 18, ACT Math 20. *75th percentile*: SAT Critical Reading 600, SAT Math 620; ACT Composite 25, ACT English 26, ACT Math 25.

64% of entering freshmen expected to graduate within 5 years. 68% of freshmen from Virginia. Freshmen from 33 states and 17 foreign countries.

Admission: For fall acceptance, apply as early as fall of senior year of secondary school, but not later than March 1. Students are notified of acceptance beginning Mar. 1. Apply by Nov. 15 for early decision which is binding. Student may apply to other schools, but only file early decision at Hampden-Sydney. If accepted, student must withdraw all other applications. *Requirements:* Graduation from accredited secondary school with 4 units in English, 2 in a foreign language, 3 mathematics, 2 natural science (1 of which must be a laboratory), 1 social studies. Additional units in foreign language and mathematics recommended. Minimum 2.0 GPA. Lowest acceptable secondary school class standing 60%. *Entrance tests:* College Board SAT I; 3 SAT IIs. recommended. *For transfer students:* 3.0 minimum GPA; 60 semester hours maximum transfer credit.

College credit and advanced placement for postsecondary-level work completed in secondary school.

Degree Requirements: 120 semester hours; 2.0 GPA; 60 hours, including last 30, in residence; distribution requirements; demonstrated proficiency in rhetoric and a foreign language.

Fulfillment of some degree requirements and exemption from some beginning courses possible by passing College Board APP (score of 4). *Grading system:* A–F; withdraw (carries time limit).

Distinctive Educational Programs: Dual-degree program with University of Virginia in which a student earns a baccalaureate degree in science from Hampden-Sydney College and a master's degree in nuclear engineering, materials science, systems engineering, biomedical, civil (environmental or transportation) engineering or engineering physics in five years. Cooperative program in chemical engineering and applied chemistry with Virginia Polytechnic Institute and State University. Facilities and programs for independent research, including honors programs offered at other institutions. Study abroad in Europe, Central and South America, Southeast Asia, East Asia, Middle East. Washington International Studies Center (in Washington, DC and United Kingdom in the areas of government, international relations, and economics). Senior fellowships. Appalachian semester at The Union College (KY); Washington (DC) semester at American University. Exchange program through consortium. Students may take courses at Longwood College.

ROTC: Army in cooperation with Longwood University.

Degrees Conferred: 235 *baccalaureate*. Bachelor's degrees awarded in top five disciplines: social sciences 96; history 38; biological/life sciences 27; psychology 11; physical sciences 8.

Fees and Other Expenses: *Full-time tuition per academic year 2008–09:* $29,801. *Required fees:* $1,004. *Room and board per academic year:* $9,228. *Books and supplies:* $1,100. *Other expenses:* $720.

Financial Aid: Aid from institutionally generated funds is provided on the basis of academic merit, financial need.

Financial aid to full-time, first-time undergraduate students: 100% received some form of aid. Need-based scholarships/grants totaling $7,934,044, self-help $2,533,102, parent loans $1,301,130; non-need-based scholarships/grants totaling $5,484,140, self-help $2,712,193, parent loans $7,462,372.

Departments and Teaching Staff: *Total instructional faculty:* 112 (full-time 93, part-time 19). Total faculty with doctorate, first-professional, or other terminal degree: 87. Student/faculty ratio: 11:1. Degrees held by full-time faculty: master's 21.2%, doctorate 78.8%, baccalaureate 100%. 80.3% hold terminal degrees.

Enrollment: Total enrollment 1,120 (undergraduate).

Characteristics of Student Body: *Ethnic/racial makeup:* Black non-Hispanic: 4%; Asian or Pacific Islander: 1%; Hispanic: 1%; White non-Hispanic: 87%; unknown: 4%; nonresident alien 2%.

International Students: 22 nonresident aliens from enrolled fall 2008. Students from Europe, Asia, Latin America, Africa, Canada. Programs available to aid students whose native language is not English: social. No financial aid specifically designated for international students.

Student Life: On-campus residence halls house 96% of student body. 39% of males join and 17% live in fraternity housing. *Intercollegiate athletics:* male: baseball, basketball, cross-country, football, golf, lacrosse, rugby, skeet shooting, soccer, tennis, track, water polo, wrestling. *Special regulations:* Cars permitted without restrictions. *Special services:* Medical services. *Student publications: The Garnet*, an annual literary magazine; *Kaleidoscope*, a yearbook; *The Tiger*, a newspaper published 22 times a year. Radio station WWHS-FM broad casts 85 hours per week. *Surrounding community:* Hampden-Sydney, located in Prince Edward County, population 18,750. Richmond, 65 miles from campus, is nearest metropolitan area.

Library Collections: 260,000 volumes including bound books, serial backfiles, electronic documents, and government documents not in separate collections. Online catalog. Current serial subscriptions: 383 paper, 7,000 via electronic access. 2,700 recordings; 900 compact discs; 100 CD-ROMs. Computer work stations available. Students have access to the Internet at no charge.

Most important special holdings include John Peter Mettauer Collection (personal papers of one of the college's first students who later became teacher and physician; also includes medical journals dealing with his surgical techniques); Jones Rare Book Collection; Hampden-Sydney Collection.

Buildings and Grounds: Campus area 820 acres.

Chief Executive Officer: Walter M. Bortz III, President.

Address admission inquiries to Anita H. Garland, Dean of Admissions.

Hampton University

100 East Queen Street
Hampton, Virginia 23668
Tel: (757) 727-5000 **E-mail:** admissions@hamptonu.edu
Fax: (757) 727-5095 **Internet:** www.hamptonu.edu

Institution Description: Hampton University, formerly Hampton Institute, is a private, independent, nonprofit institution. *Enrollment:* 5,427. *Degrees awarded:* Baccalaureate, master's.

Member of Virginia Tidewater Consortium for Continuing Higher Education.

Accreditation: *Regional:* SACS-Comm. on Coll. *Professional*: architecture, computer science, music, nursing, speech-language pathology

History: Established as Hampton Normal and Agricultural Institute 1868; incorporated 1870; offered first instruction at postsecondary level 1922; awarded first degree (baccalaureate) 1926; added graduate program 1928; adopted present name 1930. *See* Francis G. Peabody, *Education for Life: The Story of Hampton Institute* (Garden City, NY: Doubleday, Page and Company, 1919) for further information.

Institutional Structure: *Governing board:* Board of Trustees. Representation: 28 trustees; 2 alumni; 3 students. 1 ex officio. 28 voting. *Composition of institution:* Administrators 41. Academic affairs headed by vice president for academic affairs. Management/business/finances directed by vice president for business affairs and treasurer. Full-time instructional faculty 106. Academic governance body, the faculty, meets an average of 10 times per year.

HAMPTON UNIVERSITY—*cont'd*

Calendar: Semesters. Academic year late Aug. to May. Freshmen admitted Aug., Jan., June. Degrees conferred and formal commencement May. Summer session from early June to late July.

Characteristics of Freshmen: 7,700 applicants (female 5,005, male 2,695). 45% of applicants accepted. 62% (684 students) submitted SAT scores; 38% (414 students) submitted ACT scores. *25th percentile*: SAT Critical Reading 481, SAT Math 464; ACT Composite 17, ACT English 17, ACT Math 18. *75th percentile*: SAT Critical Reading 552, SAT Math 606; ACT Composite 27, ACT English 25, ACT Math 26.

54% of entering freshmen expected to graduate within 5 years 21% of freshmen from Virginia. Freshmen from 30 states and 34 foreign countries.

Admission: Rolling admissions plan. Apply by June 30 of junior year of secondary school for early decision; need not limit application to Hampton. Early acceptance available. *Requirements:* Either graduation from accredited secondary school with 4 units in English, 2 mathematics (1 algebra), 2 science (1 chemistry), 2 social studies, 6 academic electives; or GED. Recommend 2 units in a foreign language. Minimum GPA 2.0. *Entrance tests:* College Board SAT or ACT composite. For foreign students TOEFL. *For transfer students:* 2.0 minimum GPA; maximum transfer credit limited only by residence requirement.

College credit for postsecondary-level work completed in secondary school and for extrainstitutional learning on basis of faculty assessment.

Tutoring available. Remedial courses offered in summer session and regular academic year; nondegree credit given.

Degree Requirements: 120 credit hours; 2.0 GPA; 30 semester hours in residence; 4 semester hours physical education; general education and curriculum requirements.

Fulfillment of some degree requirements and exemption from some beginning courses possible by College Board CLEP, APP. *Grading system:* A–E; pass-fail; withdraw (carries time limit).

Distinctive Educational Programs: *For undergraduates:* Dual-degree program in engineering with Old Dominion University. Interdisciplinary programs in ethnic studies, gerontology. Tutorials. *For graduate students:* Weekend classes. *Available to all students:* Work-experience programs, including field experience, internships, practicums. Evening classes. Honors programs. *Other distinctive programs:* Credit and noncredit continuing education.

ROTC: Army, Navy.

Degrees Conferred: 2 *associate*; 988 *baccalaureate*; 105 *master's*; 50 *doctorate*. Bachelor's degrees awarded in top five disciplines: business, management, marketing, and related support services 196; psychology 107; health professions and related clinical sciences 80; communication, journalism, and related programs 69; social sciences 61. Master's degrees awarded: various disciplines 105. First-professional: pharmacy 50.

Fees and Other Expenses: *Full-time tuition per academic year 2008–09:* undergraduate $16,392. *Required fees:* $1,460. *Room and board per academic year:* $7,440. Contact the university for current graduate and first-professional tuition/fees. *Books and supplies:* $1,150. *Other expenses:* $3,688.

Financial Aid: Aid from institutionally generated funds is provided on the basis of academic merit, financial need, athletic ability.

Financial aid to full-time, first-time undergraduate students: 89% received some form of aid. Average amount of aid received: federal grants $2,404; Pell grants $3,041; other federal aid $1,189; state/local grants $3,955; institutional grants $12,155.

Departments and Teaching Staff: *Total instructional faculty:* 469. (full-time 363, part-time 106). Student/faculty ratio: 16:1. Degrees held by full-time faculty: doctorate 42%, master's 49%, professional 3%. 42% hold terminal degrees.

Enrollment: Total enrollment 5,421. Undergraduate 4,700 (full-time 95%; female 64%, male 36%). Graduate 727 (full-time 67%).

Characteristics of Student Body: *Ethnic/racial makeup:* Black non-Hispanic: 96%; Hispanic 2%; White non-Hispanic: 2%; nonresident alien 1%. *Age distribution:* number under 18: 81; 18–19: 1,182; 20–21: 2,066; 22–24: 1,328; 25–29: 664.

International Students: 54 nonresident aliens enrolled fall 2008. Programs available to aid students whose native language is not English: English as a Second Language Program. Financial aid specifically designated for international students: scholarships available annually.

Student Life: On-campus residence halls house 71% of student body. Some students live off-campus in institutionally owned apartments. *Intercollegiate athletics:* male: basketball, football, tennis, track, wrestling; female: basketball, track, volleyball. *Special regulations:* Cars permitted for all but freshmen. Curfews. Quiet hours. Residence hall visitation from 1pm to midnight on weekends. *Special services:* Learning Resources Center, medical services, van service for student teachers and nursing students. *Student publications, radio, television: Hamptonian*, a yearbook; *The Hampton Script*, a monthly newspaper; *The New Voice*, a weekly newspaper for mass media students. Radio station WHOV broadcasts 47 hours per week. Cable TV station broadcasts 168 hours per week. *Surrounding community:* Hampton population 125,000. Norfolk, 10 miles from campus, is nearest metropolitan area. Served by mass transit bus system; airport 13 miles from campus; passenger rail service 8 miles from campus.

Publications: *Hampton Institute Journal of Ethnic Studies* (annually) first published in 1976.

Library Collections: 318,000 volumes. 32,000 government documents; 357,000 microforms; 678 audiovisual materials; 1,326 serial subscriptions. Online catalog. Students have access to online information retrieval services.

Most important special holdings include George Foster Peabody Collection of Materials By and About Blacks; Hampton University Archives (approximately 7,000,000 items); Educational Resources Information Center (ERIC); publications on microfiche (approximately 300,000 microfiche).

Buildings and Grounds: Campus area 205 acres.

Chief Executive Officer: Dr. William R. Harvey, President.

Address undergraduate admission inquiries to Leonard M. Jones, Jr., Director of Admissions; graduate inquiries to Dr. Donald Whitney, Director of Graduate College.

Hollins University

7916 Williamson Road, N.W.
Roanoke, Virginia 24020

Tel: (540) 362-6000 **E-mail:** huadm@hollins.edu
Fax: (540) 362-6642 **Internet:** www.hollins.edu

Institution Description: Hollins University is a private, independent, nonprofit college primarily for women. Men admitted as unclassified students to undergraduate program through consortium. Graduate school is coeducational. *Enrollment:* 1,058. *Degrees awarded:* Baccalaureate, master's. Certificates also awarded.

Member of the consortium Seven College Student Exchange.

Accreditation: *Regional:* SACS-Comm. on Coll.

History: Established as Valley Union Seminary 1842; chartered 1844; offered first instruction at postsecondary level 1846; changed name to Hollins Institute 1855; awarded first degree (baccalaureate) 1903; changed name to Hollins College 1911; rechartered under this name 1926; adopted present official name, Hollins University Corporation 1998. *See* Frances J. Niederer, *Hollins College: An Illustrated History* (Charlottesville, VA: University Press of Virginia, 1973) for further information.

Institutional Structure: *Governing board:* Board of Trustees. Extrainstitutional representation: 21 members, including 14 alumnae; institutional representation: president of the university. 22 voting members. *Composition of institution:* Administrators 79. Academic affairs headed by vice president for academic affairs. Management/business/finances directed by vice president for finance and administration. Full-time instructional faculty 62. Academic governance body, the faculty, meets an average of 9 times per year.

Calendar: 4-4-1 academic calendar. Academic year Sept. to May. Freshmen admitted Sept., Feb. Degrees conferred and formal commencement May. Summer session (graduate) June to July.

Characteristics of Freshmen: 718 applicants (female 718). 86% of applicants accepted. 38% of accepted applicants enrolled.

Mean SAT class scores 591 verbal, 543 mathematical. Mean ACT Composite score 24.

68% of entering freshmen expected to graduate within 5 years. 32% of freshmen from Virginia. Freshmen from 37 states and 1 foreign country.

Admission: Modified rolling admissions plan. For fall acceptance, apply no later than Feb. 15. Students are notified of acceptance beginning late Jan. Apply by Dec. 1 for early decision. Early acceptance available. *Requirements:* Either graduation from accredited secondary school with 16 units; or GED. Recommend 4 units English, 3 in 1 or 2 foreign languages, 3 mathematics, 3 science, 3 social studies. *Entrance tests:* College Board SAT or ACT composite. 3 Achievements recommended. AP score of 4 or 5. *For transfer students:* 2.5 recommended minimum GPA; maximum transfer credit limited only by residence requirement.

College credit for postsecondary-level work completed in secondary school, if credits not counted toward high school graduation credits.

Degree Requirements: 144 credit hours (128 academic credits plus 16 short-term credits). 2.0 GPA; 2 years, including senior year, in residence; freshman courses with writing emphasis; distribution requirements.

Automatic college credit granted for AP scores of 4 or 5. Exemption from some beginning courses possible with College Board APP score of 3. *Grading system:* A–F; high pass/pass-fail (for courses taken during short term); pass-fail.

Distinctive Educational Programs: *For undergraduates:* Internships. Dual-degree programs in engineering with Virginia Polytechnic Institute and State University, Washington University (MO). Interdepartmental programs in women's studies and international studies. Honors programs. Institutionally sponsored study abroad in London, Paris; exchange or affiliated programs in Greece, Ireland, Italy, Japan, Mexico. Off-campus study in the U.S., including United Nations semester at Drew University (NJ), Washington (DC) semester at American University, student exchange program through seven-college Virginia consortium. Individually-designed interdisciplinary majors. Facilities and programs for independent research and tutorials. Other distinctive programs; degree-seeking program for older nontraditional undergraduate women.

Degrees Conferred: 181 *baccalaureate*; 108 *master's*. Bachelor's degrees awarded in top five disciplines: English 42; visual and performing arts 35; social sciences 33; psychology 28; business/marketing 12. Master's degrees awarded: various disciplines 108.

Fees and Other Expenses: *Full-time tuition per academic year 2008–09:* undergraduate and graduate $27,055; some graduate programs charged per credit hour. *Books and supplies:* $1,000. *Room and board per academic year:* $9,650. *Other exepenses:* $1,800.

Financial Aid: The university offers a direct lending program. Aid from institutionally generated funds is provided on the basis of academic merit, financial need, other criteria.

Financial aid to full-time, first-time undergraduate students: 98% received some form of aid. Amounts received: federal grants averaging $3,448; 55% state/local grants averaging $2,145; 97% institutional grants averaging $8,586; 54% received loans averaging $3,042.

Departments and Teaching Staff: *Total instructional faculty:* 107 (full-time 68, part-time 40). Student/faculty ratio: 10:1. Degrees held by full-time faculty: master's 15%, doctorate 85%. 94% hold terminal degrees.

Enrollment: Total enrollment 1,058. Undergraduate 798.

Characteristics of Student Body: *Ethnic/racial makeup:* Black non-Hispanic: 8%; American Indian or Alaska Native: 2%; Asian or Pacific Islander: 1%; Hispanic: 3%; White non-Hispanic: 82%; nonresident alien 4%.

International Students: 4 nonresident aliens enrolled fall 2008. Students from Europe, Asia, Latin America. Programs available to aid students whose native language is not English: social, cultural. Financial aid specifically designated for international students: variable number of scholarships available annually for undergraduate students.

Student Life: On-campus residence halls house 835% of undergraduate student body. Residences for females constitute 100% of such space. *Intercollegiate athletics:* female: volleyball, field hockey, tennis, soccer, riding, fencing, golf, basketball, lacrosse, swimming. Club sport: softball. *Special regulations:* Cars permitted for a $50.00 fee. Students set quiet hours during community standards discussions in each hall. Freshman halls permit male visitation Sun.–Thurs. noon to 1am Fri. and Sat. noon to 2am. Upperclass halls select from various visitation options. *Special services:* Medical and personal counseling services, career counseling center and writing center. *Student publications: Cargoes,* an annual literary magazine; *Hollins Columns*, a biweekly newspaper; *The Spinster*, a yearbook; *Womazine,* published 4 times per year by Women's Collective; *The Album*, published 4 times per year by the Literary Society. *Surrounding community:* Roanoke metropolitan area population 225,000. Served by airport 5 miles from campus.

Publications: *Hollins*, an award-winning magazine, published 3 times yearly. *Hollins Critic*, first published in 1964, published 5 times per year.

Library Collections: 258,300 volumes including bound books, serial backfiles, electronic documents, and government documents not in separate collections. Online catalog. Current serial subscriptions: 826 paper, 19 microform, 15,246 via electronic access. 3,000 recordings.Computer work stations available. Students have access to the Internet at no charge.

Most important special holdings include McVitty collection of incunables, rare and private press books; college archives; Margaret Wise Brown Collection (papers of children's book authors); Hollin's Authors Collection.

Buildings and Grounds: Campus area 475 acres. Campus DVD available.

Chief Executive Officer: Dr. Nancy O. Gray, President.

Address admission inquiries to Rebecca Eckstein, Dean of Admissions.

James Madison University

800 South Main Street
Harrisonburg, Virginia 22807
Tel: (540) 568-6211 **E-mail:** admissions@jmu.edu
Fax: (540) 568-3332 **Internet:** www.jmu.edu

Institution Description: James Madison University (Madison College until 1977) is a state institution. *Enrollment:* 18,454. *Degrees awarded:* Baccalaureate, master's, doctorate. Educational specialist (Ed.S.) also awarded.

Academic offerings subject to approval by statewide coordinating bodies.Budget subject to approval by state governing boards.

Accreditation: *Regional:* SACS-Comm. on Coll. *Professional*: art, athletic training, business, chemistry, dance, dietetics, counseling, health services administration, interior design, music, nursing, occupational therapy, physician assisting, psychology internship, social work, speech-language pathology, teacher education, theatre

History: Established and chartered as State Normal and Industrial School for Women at Harrisonburg 1908; offered first instruction at postsecondary level 1909; changed name to State Normal School for Women at Harrisonburg 1914; awarded first degree (baccalaureate) 1919; changed name to State Teachers College at Harrisonburg 1924; changed name to Madison College 1938; became fully coeducational 1966; adopted present name 1977. *See* Raymond C. Dingledine, Jr., *Madison College—The First Fifty Years* (Harrisonburg: Madison College, 1959) for further information.

Institutional Structure: *Governing board:* Board of Visitors. Representation: 15 visitors, plus 1 student. Student does not vote. *Composition of institution:* Administrators 240. Academic affairs headed by provost and vice president for academic affairs. Management/business/finances directed by senior vice president for administration and finance. Full-time instructional faculty 831. Academic governance body, University Council, meets when needed.

Calendar: Semesters. Academic year Aug. to May. Formal commencement May, Dec. Summer session of 5 terms from May to July.

Characteristics of Freshmen: 18,352 applicants (female 11,021, male 7,325). 84% of applicants admitted. 33% of applicants admitted and enrolled.

99% (3,693 students) submitted SAT scores; 21% (787 students) submitted ACT scores. *25th percentile*: SAT Critical Reading 520, SAT Math 530; ACT Composite 21. *75th percentile*: SAT Critical Reading 610,SAT Math 620; ACT Composite 26.

78% of entering freshmen expected to graduate within 5 years. 70% of freshmen from Virginia. Freshmen from 37 states and 15 foreign countries.

Admission: For fall acceptance, apply as early by Jan. 15 of year of enrollment. Apply by Nov. 1 for early action; need not limit application to James Madison. *Requirements:* Graduation from accredited secondary school with solid achievement in four or five academic courses each year of the four years of high school. *Entrance tests:* College Board SAT or ACT. For foreign students TOEFL. *For transfer students:* 2.0 minimum GPA.

College credit and advanced placement for postsecondary-level work completed in secondary school and extrainstitutional learning on basis of *2006 Guide to the Evaluation of Educational Experiences in the Armed Services*.

Degree Requirements: 120 credit hours; 2.0 GPA; 2 semesters in residence; 2 hours physical education. All students must choose a general education program regardless of their major or professional program.

Fulfillment of some degree requirements and exemption from some beginning courses possible by passing departmental examinations, College Board CLEP (available only to students seeking a B.G.S. degree), AP. *Grading system:* A–F; credit-no credit; withdraw (carries time limit).

Distinctive Educational Programs: *For undergraduates:* Accelerated degree programs. Interdisciplinary programs including biochemistry, American studies, Asian studies, liberal studies, urban and regional studies. Facilities and programs for independent research, including honors programs, independent study. Study abroad semester in London (art history, English, history, international humanities, music, theatre); Antwerp (Belgium); Florence (art, English, Italian, music, political science, international liberal studies); Salamanca (art history, economics, Spanish, integrated science and technology, international humanities, political science). *For graduate students:* Off-campus centers at various locations. *Available to all students:* Evening classes. Special facilities for using telecommunications in the classroom. *Other distinctive programs:* Individualized, degree-completion program for adults; Degree and nondegree granting continuing education programs.

ROTC: Air Force in cooperation with University of Virginia/

Degrees Conferred: 3,504 *baccalaureate*: 801 *master's*; 13 *doctorate*. Bachelor's degrees awarded in top five disciplines: business, management, marketing, and related support services 752; social sciences 401; health professions and related clinical sciences 349; communication, journalism, and related programs 285; psychology 242. Master's degrees awarded: various disciplines 801. Doctorates awarded: psychology 10; health professions 3.

Fees and Other Expenses: *Full-time tuition per academic year 2008–09:* undergraduate resident $6,964, nonresident $18,458; contact the university for current graduate tuition and applicable fees. *Room per academic year:* $7,712. *Books and supplies:* $876. *Other expenses:* $3,670.

Financial Aid: Aid from institutionally generated funds is provided on the basis of academic merit, financial need, athletic ability, other criteria.

Financial aid to full-time, first-time undergraduate students: 56% received some form of aid. Average amount of aid received: federal grants $4,018; Pell grants $$2,762; other federal aid $1,853; state/local grants $4,895; institutional grants $5,325.

Departments and Teaching Staff: *Total instructional faculty:* 1,209 (full-time 831, part-time 378). Total faculty with doctorate, first-professional, or other terminal degree: 708. Student/faculty ratio: 16:1. Degrees held by full-time faculty: doctorate 75%, master's 23%, professional 2%. 83% hold terminal degrees.

JAMES MADISON UNIVERSITY—*cont'd*

Enrollment: Total enrollment 19,454. Undergraduate 16,916 (full-time 96%; female 60%, male 40%). Graduate 1,538 (full-time 58%). Undergraduate transfer-in students 651.

Characteristics of Student Body: *Ethnic/racial makeup:* Black non-Hispanic: 4%; Asian or Pacific Islander: 5%; Hispanic: 2%; White non-Hispanic: 82%; unknown: 6%; nonresident alien 1%. *Age distribution:* number under 18: 121; 18–19: 6,032; 20–21: 6,479; 22–24: 1,670; 25–29: 195; 30–34: 45; 35–39: 36; 40–49: 36; 50–64: 13. 34% of student body attend summer sessions.

International Students: 185 nonresident aliens enrolled fall 2008. Students from Europe, Asia, Latin America, Africa, Canada, Australia, Middle East. No programs available to aid students whose native language is not English. No financial aid specifically designated for international students.

Student Life: On-campus residence halls house 5,837 students. Residence halls are co-ed. 12% of males join fraternities; 10% of females join sororities. *Intercollegiate athletics:* male: archery, baseball, basketball, cross-country, diving, football, golf, gymnastics, soccer, swimming, tennis, track and field, wrestling; female: archery, basketball, cross-country, diving, fencing, field hockey, golf, gymnastics, lacrosse, soccer, softball, swimming, tennis, track and field, volleyball. *Special regulations:* Registered cars permitted for sophomores, juniors, seniors, and for freshmen on individual basis. Quiet hours and dormitory visitation hours vary according to dormitory. *Special services:* Learning Resources Center, medical services, bus transportation to and from off-campus housing. *Student publications: The Breeze*, a biweekly newspaper; *The Chrysalis*, a literary magazine; *The Bluestone*, a yearbook. *Surrounding community:* Harrisonburg population 40,000. Richmond (VA) and Washington (DC), each 120 miles from campus, are nearest metropolitan areas. Served by mass transit bus system, airport 13 miles from campus.

Library Collections: 636,000 volumes including bound books, serial backfiles, electronic documents. 573,052 government documents. 1,050,000 microform units. Current serial subscriptions: 1,402 paper; 244 microform; 10,032 via electronic access. Online catalog. Computer work stations available. Students have access to the Internet at no charge.

Most important special collections include the JMU Historical Collection; Shenandoah Valley local history collections; rare books and periodicals collection; Laird L. Conrad Law Library (private library containing law books and legal reference materials).

Buildings and Grounds: Campus area 614 acres.

Chief Executive Officer: Dr. Linwood H. Rose, President.

Undergraduates address admission inquiries to Michael D. Walsh, Director of Admissions; graduate inquiries to Dr. Reid Linn, Dean, College of Graduate and Outreach Programs.

Liberty University

1971 University Boulevard
Lynchburg, Virginia 24502-2269
Tel: (434) 582-2000 **E-mail:** admissions@liberty.edu
Fax: (434) 582-2304 **Internet:** www.liberty.edu

Institution Description: Liberty University (Liberty Baptist College until 1985) is a private college affiliated with the Thomas Road Baptist Church. *Enrollment:* 17,590. *Degrees awarded:* Associate, baccalaureate, master's., doctorate.

Accreditation: *Regional:* SACS-Comm. on Coll.

History: Established as Lynchburg Baptist College, chartered, incorporated, and offered first instruction at postsecondary level 1971; awarded first degree (baccalaureate) 1974; became Liberty Baptist College 1976; adopted present name 1985.

Institutional Structure: *Governing board:* Board of Trustees. Representation: 35 trustees. 35 voting. *Composition of institution:* Administrators: 63. Academic affairs, spiritual life, student development, enrollment management, treasurer, planning, and technology, directed by vice presidents with deans and/or directors supporting them. Full-time instructional faculty 354. Academic governance body, Faculty Senate, meets an average of 10 times per year.

Calendar: Semesters. Academic year July to June. Freshmen admitted Aug., Jan, June, July. Degrees conferred and formal commencement May. Summer session of 2 terms from May to June; one- and two-week modulars throughout the summer.

Characteristics of Freshmen: 7,123 applicants (female 3,621, male 3,502). 71% of applicants admitted. 30% of applicants admitted and enrolled.

78% (1,594 students) submitted SAT scores; 23% (480 students) submitted ACT scores. *25th percentile*: SAT Critical Reading 440, SAT Math 420; ACT Composite 18, ACT English 17, ACT Math 16. *75th percentile*: SAT Critical Reading 550, SAT Math 540; ACT Composite 24, ACT English 24, ACT Math 23.

42% of entering freshmen expected to graduate within 5 years. 40% of freshmen from Virginia. Freshmen from 48 states.

Admission: Rolling admissions plan. For fall acceptance, apply as early as end of junior year of secondary school, but not later than Aug. 10 of year of enrollment. Early decision and early acceptance available. *Requirements:* Either 16 units from recognized secondary school or GED. Autobiographical sketch including description of applicant's salvation experience. Minimum 2.0 GPA. *Entrance tests:* College Board SAT or ACT composite. For foreign students TOEFL. *For transfer students:* 2.0 minimum GPA; from 2-year and 4-year accredited institutions, maximum transfer credit limited only by residence requirement; correspondence/extension students 32 hours.

College credit and advanced placement for postsecondary-level work completed in secondary school. For extrainstitutional learning college credit on basis of portfolio; faculty assessment.

Tutoring available. Remedial courses offered during regular academic year; credit given.

Degree Requirements: *For all associate degrees:* minimum of 60 credit hours; minimum 60 credit hours in EDP; 15 semester hours in residence; 8 semester hours on campus for EDP students. *For all baccalaureate degrees:* minimum of 120 credit hours; 30 semester hours, including 50% of work in major and minor fields must be done with Liberty University. *For B.S. degree:* general education requirement of 56 hours; B.A. degree includes 12 hours in a foreign language. Christian/community service for 8 semesters. *For all degrees:* 2.0 GPA; convocation attendance 3 times per week.

Fulfillment of some degree requirements and exemption from some beginning courses possible by passing College Board CLEP, AP, other standardized tests. *Grading system:* A–F; incomplete; withdraw; withdraw failing.

Distinctive Educational Programs: Evening classes. Internships. Interdisciplinary program. Independent study. Distance learning program offers flexibility for the adult learner.

Degrees Conferred: 171 *associate*; 1,521 *baccalaureate*. Bachelor's degrees awarded in top five disciplines: psychology 214; business, management, marketing, and related support services 213; philosophy/religion/theology 188; interdisciplinary studies 157; communication, journalism, and related programs 104. Master's degrees awarded: various disciplines 306. Doctorates awarded: various disciplines 129. First-professional degrees awarded: master of divinity 26.

Fees and Other Expenses: *Full-time tuition per academic year 2008–09:* undergraduate $16,434; contact the university for current graduate and first-professional tuition/fees. *Required fees:* $850. *Room and board per academic year:* $5,800. *Books and supplies:* $1,400. *Other expenses:* $3,400.

Financial Aid: Aid from institutionally generated funds is provided on the basis of academic merit, athletic ability, other criteria.

Financial aid to full-time, first-time undergraduate students: 96% received some form of aid. Average amount of aid received: federal grants $3,555; Pell grants $2,961; other federal aid $1,577; state/local grants $3,014; institutional grants $6,152.

Departments and Teaching Staff: *Total instructional faculty:* 701 (full-time 354, part-time 347). Total faculty with doctorate, first-professional, or other terminal degree: 369. Student/faculty ratio: 20:1. Degrees held by full-time faculty: doctorate 58%, master's 41%, professional 1%. 60% hold terminal degrees.

Enrollment: Total enrollment 17,590.

Characteristics of Student Body: *Ethnic/racial makeup:* Black non-Hispanic: 12%; American Indian or Alaska 1%; Asian or Pacific Islander: 1%; Hispanic: 3%; White non-Hispanic: 67%; unknown 12%; nonresident alien 3%. *Age distribution:* number under 18: 174; 18–19: 3,313; 20–21: 2,615; 22–24: 818; 25–29: 691; 30–34: 691; 35–39: 628; 40–49: 770; 50–64: 224; 65 and over: 15. 32% of student body attend summer sessions.

International Students: 719 nonresident aliens enrolled fall 2008. Students from Europe, Asia, Latin America, Africa, Canada, Australia. Programs available to aid students whose native language is not English: English as a Second Language Program. Some financial aid specifically designated for undergraduate/graduate international students.

Student Life: On-campus residence halls house 63% of student body in traditional program. *Intercollegiate athletics:* male: baseball, basketball, cross-country, football, golf, soccer, tennis, track and field; female: basketball, cross-country, soccer, softball, tennis, track and field, volleyball. Football plays as an Independent in the NCAA I-AA. *Special regulations:* Dress code; curfew. *Special services:* Learning Resources Center. *Student radio:* WRVL and WWMC. *Student publications: School Yearbook, Liberty Champion*, student newspaper; *Mocean*, literary magazine, published yearly. *Surrounding community:* Lynchburg population 66,000. Washington (DC), 180 miles from campus, is nearest metropolitan area. Served by mass transit bus system, airport 4 miles from campus, passenger rail service 4 miles from campus.

Library Collections: 300,000 volumes including bound books, serial backfiles, electronic documents, and government documents not in separate collections. Online catalog. Current serial subscriptions: 831 paper; 17,855 via electronic access. Computer work stations available. Students have access to the Internet. Fee-based access to online information retrieval services.

Most important special holdings include Liberty University Archives; Curriculum Library (5,581 volumes).

Chief Executive Officer: Dr. Ronald S. Godwin, Executive Vice President/ Chief Operating Officer.

Undergraduates address admission inquiries to David Hart, Associate Director of Admissions; graduate study inquiries Scott Traylor, Director of Graduate Admissions.

Longwood University

201 High Street
Farmville, Virginia 23909
Tel: (434) 395-2000 **E-mail:** lcadmit@longwood.edu
Fax: (434) 395-2332 **Internet:** www.longwood.edu

Institution Description: Longwood University is a state-assisted, coeducational, comprehensive, primarily residential institution. *Enrollment:* 4,727. *Degrees awarded:* Baccalaureate, master's.

Academic offering subject to approval by statewide coordinating bodies. Budget subject to approval by state governing boards. Member of Central Virginia Consortium.

Accreditation: *Regional:* SACS-Comm. on Coll. *Professional*: business, music, social work, teacher education, theatre

History: Established as Farmville Female College 1839; changed name to State Female Normal School and offered first instruction at postsecondary level 1884; changed name to State Normal School for Women 1914; awarded first degree (baccalaureate) 1919; changed name to State Teachers College at Farmville 1924; adopted present name 1949; became coeducational 1976; achieved university status 2001.

Institutional Structure: *Governing board:* Board of visitors. 11 members; 5 alumni. All voting. *Composition of institution:* Administrators 11. Academic affairs headed by vice president for academic affairs. Management/business/ finances directed by vice president for administration and finance. Full-time instructional faculty 168. Academic governance body, Faculty Senate, meets an average of 8 times per year.

Calendar: Semesters. Academic year late Aug. to mid-May. Freshmen admitted Aug., Jan., June, July. Degrees conferred Aug., Dec., May. Formal commencement May, Dec. Summer session from late June to mid-Aug.

Characteristics of Freshmen: 4,199 applicants (female 2,617, male 1,582). 75% of applicants accepted. 38% of accepted applicants enrolled.

Mean SAT class scores 535 verbal, 525 mathematical.

61% of freshmen expected to graduate within 5 years. 90% of freshmen from Virginia. Freshmen from 15 states and 11 foreign countries.

Admission: Rolling admissions plan. *Requirements:* Either graduation from accredited secondary school with 4 units English, 3 college preparatory mathematics, 1 American government, 1 American history, 3 science (3 with laboratory), 2 units foreign language, 1 social science, 2 health/physical education, 1 fine art;. Minimum 2.5 GPA. *Entrance tests:* College Board SAT or ACT composite. *For transfer students:* 2.2 minimum GPA; from 4-year accredited institution 96 semester hours maximum transfer credit; from 2-year accredited institution 70 semester hours; transfer credit also available for correspondence/ extension students.

College credit for extrainstitutional learning.

Tutoring available. Developmental courses offered through local community college; no credit given.

Degree Requirements: 126–128 credit hours; 2.0 GPA; 2 semesters, including final semester, in residence; 3 units physical education; general education courses; 30 credits at upper level; 25% of degree must be earned at the college. For art degree, annual faculty evaluation. >p<Fulfillment of some degree requirements and exemption from some beginning courses possible by passing College Board CLEP, AP, and IB. *Grading system:* A–F; pass-fail; withdraw (carries time limit).

Distinctive Educational Programs: *For undergraduates:* Cooperative baccalaureate and dual degree programs in physics/engineering with Georgia Institute of Technology, Old Dominion University, and University of Virginia. Preprofessional medical programs in cooperation with Virginia Commonwealth University/Medical College of Virginia, University of Virginia Medical Center, and several hospitals. Honors programs. Study abroad in France, Spain, Germany, Russia, Venezuela, Austria, Martinique, Honduras, Japan, China, England, Czech Republic, Ghana, Ireland, Belgium. *For graduate students:* Flexible meeting places and schedules, including off-campus centers and evening classes.

ROTC: Army.

Degrees Conferred: 746 *baccalaureate*; 144 *master's*. Bachelor's degrees awarded in top five disciplines: business, management, marketing, and related support services 204; liberal arts/general studies 154; social sciences 72; visual and performing arts 51; communication, journalism, and related programs 45. Master's degrees awarded: various disciplines 144.

Fees and Other Expenses: *Full-time tuition per academic year 2006:* resident $8,449, nonresident $17,112. *Books and supplies:* $1,000. *Room and board per academic year:* $6,856. *Other exepenses:* $3,673.

Financial Aid: Aid from institutionally generated funds is provided on the basis of academic merit, financial need, athletic ability, other criteria.

Financial aid to full-time, first-time undergraduate students: 67% received some form of aid. Average amount of aid received: federal grants $3,433; Pell grants $2,575; other federal aid $1,635; state/local grants $3,166; institutional grants $4,470.

Departments and Teaching Staff: *Total instructional faculty:* 187. Degrees held by full-time faculty: doctorate 79.75%, master's 18,35%, baccalaureate 1,9%, professional 3,16%. 92.4% hold terminal degrees.

Enrollment: Total enrollment 4,727. Undergraduate 4,024 (full-time 95%; female 65%, male 35%). Graduate 702 (full-time 13%). Transfer-in students 102.

Characteristics of Student Body: *Ethnic/racial makeup:* Black non-Hispanic: 6%; American Indian or Alaska Native: '1%; Asian or Pacific Islander: 2%; Hispanic: 2%; White non-Hispanic: 86%; unknown 2%; nonresident alien 1%.

International Students: 47 nonresident aliens enrolled fall 2008. No programs available to aid students whose native language is not English. No financial aid specifically designated for international students.

Student Life: 79% of residential students live in residence halls (single sex, coed, single, double, and suites). Honors and special interest housing. *Intercollegiate athletics:* male: baseball, basketball, golf, soccer, tennis, wrestling; female: basketball, field hockey, golf, soccer, lacrosse, softball, tennis. *Special regulations:* Cars permitted (parking fee). Freshmen not permitted to have cars. Quiet hours from 7pm to 10am. *Special services:* Medical services, learning center, counseling, fellness, and career services. Over 125 clubs, organizations, and professional societies. 21 fraternities and sororities. *Student publications, radio: The Gyre*, an annual literary magazine; *The Rotunda*, a weekly newspaper, *The Virginian*, yearbook. Radio station WLCX broadcasts 100 hours a week. *Surrounding community:* Farmville population 6,000. Richmond, 55 miles from campus, is nearest metropolitan area.

Library Collections: 1,061,000 volumes. 6,300 government documents; 696,000 microforms; 39,000 audiovisual materials; 2,500 current periodical subscriptions. Online catalog. Students have access to online information retrieval services and the Internet.

Most important special collections include Virginia Documents Depository; Virginia Curriculum Materials Depository; Longwood College/Southside Virginia.

Buildings and Grounds: Campus area 54 acres.

Chief Executive Officer: Dr. Patricia P. Cormier, President.

Address admission inquiries to Robert J. Chonko, Director of Admissions and Enrollment; graduate inquiries to Jennifer Apperson, Dean of Graduate Programs.

Lynchburg College

1501 Lakeside Drive
Lynchburg, Virginia 24501-3199
Tel: (434) 544-8081 **E-mail:** admissions@lynchburg.edu
Fax: (434) 544-8220 **Internet:** www.lynchburg.edu

Institution Description: Lynchburg College is a private, independent, nonprofit college affiliated with the Christian Church (Disciples of Christ). *Enrollment:* 2,572. *Degrees awarded:* Baccalaureate, master's.

Accreditation: *Regional:* SACS-Comm. on Coll. *Professional*: athletic training, nursing

History: Established as Virginia Christian College, chartered, and offered first instruction at postsecondary level 1903; awarded first degree (baccalaureate) 1904; adopted present name 1919. *See* Clifton W. Potter, Jr., ed., *Lynchburg College Jubilee: 1903–1978* (Lynchburg: Lynchburg College, 1978) for further information.

Institutional Structure: *Governing board:* Board of Trustees of Lynchburg College. Representation: 34 trustees. All voting. *Composition of institution:* Administrators 23. Academic affairs headed by dean of the college. Management/business/finances directed by vice president for business. Full-time instructional faculty 159. Academic governance body, the faculty, meets an average of 9 times per year.

Calendar: Semesters. Academic year late Aug. to May. Freshmen admitted Aug., Jan., May, June, July. Degrees conferred May, Aug., Jan. Formal commencement May. Summer session from mid-May to mid-Aug.

LYNCHBURG COLLEGE—*cont'd*

Characteristics of Freshmen: 5,536 applicants (female 2,722, male 1,814). 69% of applicants accepted. 19% of accepted applicants enrolled.

97% (536 students) submitted SAT scores; 21% (116 students) submitted ACT scores. *25th percentile*: SAT Critical Reading 460, SAT Math 460; ACT Composite 18, ACT English 16, ACT Math 17. *75th percentile*: SAT Critical Reading 560, SAT Math 570; ACT Composite 22, ACT English 23, ACT Math 23.

56% of freshmen graduating within 5 years. 55% of freshmen from Virginia. Freshmen from 27 states and 2 foreign countries.

Admission: Rolling admissions plan. Early acceptance available. *Requirements:* Either graduation from accredited secondary school with 16 units which must include 4 English, 3 mathematics, 3 science, 2 social studies, and 2 foreign language, or GED. *Entrance tests:* College Board SAT and 3 Achievements or ACT composite. For foreign students SAT or TOEFL. *For transfer students:* 2.0 minimum GPA; from 4-year and 2-year accredited institutions maximum transfer credit 76 credits; correspondence/extension students 30 hours.

College credit for postsecondary-level work completed in secondary school. Tutoring available.

Degree Requirements: 124 credit hours; 2.0 GPA; 48 hours in residence; 2 hours wellness; general education requirements, including freshmen English, foreign language, and senior symposium.

Fulfillment of some degree requirements possible by passing College Board CLEP, AP (score of 3). *Grading system:* A–F; pass-fail; withdraw (carries time limit).

Distinctive Educational Programs: *For undergraduates:* Under special arrangements with the University of Virginia, as student may earn a B.S. degree, usually in physics or mathematics, from Lynchburg College and a master of engineering degree from the University of Virginia in 5 years. Preprofessional program in medicine. Study abroad through approved programs. Cross-registration with Randolph-Macon Woman's College and Sweet Briar College. *Available to all students:* Internships. Facilities and programs for independent research, including honors programs, individual majors, tutorials.

Degrees Conferred: 412 *baccalaureate:* biological/life sciences 28; business and management 62; communications 38; computer and information sciences 11; education 59; English 26; foreign languages 11; health professions and related sciences 27; mathematics 6; natural resources/environmental science 11; parks and recreation 23; physical sciences 3; psychology 16; social sciences and history 147; visual and performing arts 17. 141 master's degrees awarded: business/marketing 58; education 74, health professions 9.

Fees and Other Expenses: *Full-time tuition per academic year 2008–09:* undergraduate $28,105; graduate study charged per credit hour (contact the college for current rate). *Other fees:* $405. *Room and board per academic year:* $7,510. *Books and supplies:* $750. *Other expenses:* $800.

Financial Aid: Aid from institutionally generated funds is provided on the basis of academic merit, financial need.

Financial aid to full-time, first-time undergraduate students: 98% received some form of aid. Average amount of aid received: federal grants $3,937; Pell grants $2,818; other federal aid $1,213; state/local grants $1,213; institutional grants $12,177.

Departments and Teaching Staff: *Total instructional faculty:* 229 (full-time 159, part-time 70). Total faculty with doctorate, first-professional, or other terminal degree: 144. Student/faculty ratio: 12:1. Degrees held by full-time faculty: doctorate 75%, master's 100% 81% hold terminal degrees.

Enrollment: Total enrollment 2,572. Undergraduate 2,183 (full-time 92%; female 60%, male 40%). Graduate 369 (full-time 38%). Transfer-in students 112.

Characteristics of Student Body: *Ethnic/racial makeup:* Black non-Hispanic: 7%; American Indian or Alaska Native: 1%; Asian or Pacific Islander: 1%; Hispanic: 3%; White non-Hispanic: 77%; unknown 11%; nonresident alien 1%.

International Students: 26 nonresident aliens enrolled fall 2008. Students from Europe, Asia, Canada. No programs available to aid students whose native language is not English. No financial aid specifically designated for international students.

Student Life: On-campus residence halls house 72% of undergraduate student body. *Intercollegiate athletics:* male: baseball basketball, cross-country, golf, lacrosse, soccer, tennis, track (indoor and outdoor); female: basketball, cross-country, field hockey, lacrosse, soccer, softball, tennis, track (indoor and outdoor), volleyball; coed: cheerleading, equestrian. *Special regulations:* Cars permitted on campus for day and married students, students 21 years and older, qualified resident sophomores, juniors, seniors. Quiet hours in effect during examination periods. Residence hall visitation hours vary. *Special services:* Learning Resources Center, Student Health Center. *Student publications, radio:* *The Argonaut*, a yearbook; *Critograph*, a weekly newspaper; *The Prism*, literary magazine. *Surrounding community:* Lynchburg metropolitan population 220,000. Served by airport 7 miles from campus; passenger rail service 7 miles from campus.

Library Collections: 199,000 volumes including bound books, serial backfiles, electronic documents, and government documents not in separate collections. Online catalog. 440,000 microforms; 5,600 audiovisual materials; 580 current serial subscriptions: Students have access to the Internet at no charge.

Most important special holdings include Capron Collection; Lynchburg College Archives (over 150 cubic feet of archival materials).

Buildings and Grounds: Campus area 214 acres. Campus DVD available.

Chief Executive Officer: Dr. Kenneth Garren, President.

Address admission inquiries to Rita Detwiler, Vice President for Enrollment Management.

Mary Baldwin College

New and Frederick Streets
Staunton, Virginia 24401
Tel: (540) 887-7086 **E-mail:** admissions@mbc.edu
Fax: (540) 886-5561 **Internet:** www.mbc.edu

Institution Description: Mary Baldwin College is a private, nonprofit institution affiliated with the Presbyterian Church (USA). *Enrollment:* 1,738. Adult Degree Program admits males. *Degrees awarded:* Baccalaureate, master's.

Member of Seven College Consortium.

Accreditation: *Regional:* SACS-Comm. on Coll.

History: Established as Augusta Seminary 1842; chartered 1845; name changed to Mary Baldwin Seminary 1895; became junior college 1916; became 4-year college and adopted present name 1923. *See* Mary Watters, *The History of Mary Baldwin College, 1842–1942* (Staunton, VA: The McClure Company, 1942) for further information.

Institutional Structure: *Governing board:* Board of Trustees. Representation: 30 trustees, including 5 alumnae, 5 administrators, 4 full-time instructional faculty members, 4 students; president of the college. 1 ex officio. All voting. *Composition of institution:* Administrators 7. Academic affairs headed by dean of the college. Management/business/finances directed by treasurer-business manager. Full-time instructional faculty 80. Academic governance body, College Faculty Meeting, meets an average of 10 times per year.

Calendar: Semesters (4-4-1 plan). Academic year Aug. to May. Freshmen admitted Sept. Degrees conferred and formal commencement May. No summer sessions.

Characteristics of Freshmen: 1,784 applicants (female 1,784). 81% of applicants accepted. 42% of accepted applicants enrolled.

Mean SAT scores 515.94 verbal, 491.05 mathematical. Mean ACT Composite score 20.

55% of freshmen expected to graduate within 5 years. 65% of freshmen from Virginia. Freshmen from 31 states and 3 foreign countries.

Admission: Rolling admissions plan. For fall acceptance, apply as early as Sept. 1 of senior year, but not later than Mar. 14. Students are notified of acceptance beginning Jan. 1. Apply by Nov. 15 for early decision; need not limit application to Mary Baldwin. Early acceptance available. *Requirements:* Recommend minimum of 16 secondary school units, including 4 English, 2 foreign language, 3 history/social studies, 3 mathematics, 1 laboratory science. GED accepted. *Entrance tests:* College Board SAT. *For transfer students:* 2.0 minimum GPA; 18 course units maximum transfer credit.

College credit and advanced placement for postsecondary-level work completed in secondary school on basis of College Board AP.

Degree Requirements: 132 semester hours; 2.0 minimum GPA on a scale of 1.0–4.0. 66 hours in residence; distribution requirements; senior projects.

Fulfillment of some degree requirements and exemption from some beginning courses possible by passing College Board AP. *Grading system:* A–D, NC; pass/no credit; withdraw (carries penalty except in case of acceptable excuse).

Distinctive Educational Programs: Program for the Exceptionally Gifted for gifted 13–16 year-olds capable of succeeding in college. Virginia Women's Institute for Leadership. Work-experience programs. Evening classes. Accelerated degree programs. Special facilities for using telecommunications in the classroom. Interdisciplinary majors. Facilities and programs for independent research, including honors programs, individual majors. Summer study in Germany in cooperation with Goethe Institute, Munich. Semester or academic year abroad through programs offered by other institutions. Courses taught abroad in May term (Australia, England, France, Japan, Spain). Through consortium, off-campus study at Hampden-Sydney, Hollins, Randolph-Macon, Randolph-Macon Woman's, and Sweet Briar Colleges, and Washington and Lee University. Major in medical technology in cooperation with local hospitals. Teacher certification programs. Adult Degree Program offers baccalaureate for off-campus study based on individualized learning contracts.

ROTC: Army.

Degrees Conferred: 243 *baccalaureate*; 73 *master's*. Bachelor's degrees awarded in top five disciplines: social sciences 58; psychology 45; business, management, marketing, and related support services 35; history 27; visual and performing arts 27. Master's degrees: various disciplines 73.

Fees and Other Expenses: *Full-time tuition per academic year 2008–09:* $23,645 undergraduate; graduate study tuition charged per credit hour. *Books and supplies:* $900. *Room and board per academic year:* $6,730. *Other expenses:* $1,615.

Financial Aid: Aid from institutionally generated funds is provided on the basis of academic merit, financial need, other criteria.

Financial aid to full-time, first-time undergraduate students: 100% received some form of aid. Average amount of aid received: federal grants $4,856; Pell grants $6,730; other federal aid $2,068; state/local grants $3,788; institutional grants $9,910.

Departments and Teaching Staff: *Total instructional faculty:* 127. Student/faculty ratio: 11:1. Degrees held by full-time faculty: baccalaureate 100%, master's 25%, doctorate 75%. 90% hold terminal degrees.

Enrollment: Total enrollment 1,738. Undergraduate 1,537 (full-time 98%; female 95%, male 5%). Graduate 20 (full-time 48%).

Characteristics of Student Body: *Ethnic/racial makeup:* Black non-Hispanic: 18%; American Indian or Alaska Native: 1%; Asian or Pacific Islander: 2%; Hispanic: 4%; White non-Hispanic: 74%; nonresident alien 1%.

International Students: 17 nonresident aliens enrolled fall 2008. Student from Europe, Asia, Africa. Programs available to aid students whose native language is not English: social, cultural. English as a Second Language Program. Financial aid specifically designated for international students: scholarships available annually.

Student Life: On-campus residence halls house 96% of student body. Residence halls for females constitute 100% of such space. *Intercollegiate athletics:* basketball, fencing, riding, swimming, tennis. *Special regulations:* Cars permitted without restrictions. Quiet hours set by residents in each dormitory. Residents also select from among 4 dormitory visitation options, one of which is open hours. *Special services:* Learning Resources Center, medical services. *Student publications: Bluestocking*, an annual; *Campus Comments*, a bimonthly newspaper; *Miscellany*, an annual literary magazine; *Student Handbook*, an annual publication. *Surrounding community:* Staunton population 24,000. Washington (DC), 160 miles from campus, is nearest metropolitan area. Served by mass transit bus system; airport 5 miles from campus; passenger rail service 2 blocks from campus.

Publications: *Alumni Magazine*.

Library Collections: 175,000 volumes including bound books, serial backfiles, electronic documents, and government documents not in separate collections. Online catalog. Current serial subscriptions: 433 paper, 41 microform, 5,000 electronic. 5 compact discs; 25 CD-ROMs. Computer work stations available. Students have access to the Internet at no charge.

Most important special holdings include Mary Julia Baldwin Letters; Tennessee Williams manuscripts and first editions; College Archives.

Buildings and Grounds: Campus area 54 acres.

Chief Executive Officer: Dr. Pamela Fox, President.

Address admission inquiries to Lisa Branson, Vice President for Enrollment Management.

Marymount University

2807 North Glebe Road
Arlington, Virginia 22207-4299
Tel: (703) 522-5600 **E-mail:** admissions@marymount.edu
Fax: (703) 522-0349 **Internet:** www.marymount.edu

Institution Description: Marymount University (Marymount College of Virginia until 1986) is a private college founded by the Religious of the Sacred Heart of Mary, a Roman Catholic educational order. *Enrollment:* 3,548. *Degrees awarded:* Associate, baccalaureate, master's.

Member of the Consortium of Universities of Washington Metropolitan Area.

Accreditation: *Regional:* SACS-Comm. on Coll. *Professional*: interior design, nursing, teacher education

History: Opened as Marymount Junior College for women under sponsorship of Religious of the Sacred Heart of Mary 1950; chartered as independent Virginia college and changed name to Marymount College of Virginia 1965; added baccalaureate programs 1973; added coeducational master's degree programs 1979; became totally coeducational 1986; changed name to Marymount University 1986.

Institutional Structure: *Governing board:* Board of Trustees numbering more than 30 professional men and women. *Composition of institution:* Academic affairs headed by vice president for academic affairs. Management/business/finance directed by vice president for financial affairs. Full-time instructional faculty 143. Academic governance body, Faculty Council, meets an average of 4 times per year; standing committees of the university meet 8 times per year. *Faculty representation:* Faculty in three schools served by collective bargaining agent, Marymount University Faculty Association, affiliated with NEA.

Calendar: Semesters. Academic year Aug. to May. Freshmen admitted Aug., Jan., May. Degrees conferred and formal commencements May, July. Summer session from May to July.

Characteristics of Freshmen: 1,766 applicants (female 1,346, male 420). 78% of applicants accepted. 20% of accepted applicants enrolled.

93% (345 students) submitted SAT scores; 17% (63 students) submitted ACT scores. *25th percentile*: SAT Critical Reading 450, SAT Math 440; ACT Composite 19, ACT English 18, ACT Math 17. *75th percentile*: SAT Critical Reading 550, SAT Math 550; ACT Composite 23, ACT English 23, ACT Math 22.

47% of freshmen expected to graduate within 5 years. 45% of freshmen from Virginia. Freshmen from 28 states and 10 foreign countries.

Admission: Rolling admissions policy. For fall acceptance, apply as early as Sept. of previous year, but not later than April of year of enrollment. *Requirements:* Either graduation from accredited secondary school with 15 units which include 4 English, 3 foreign language, 3 mathematics, 2 science, 3 social science; or GED. Nursing school applicants are recommended to take a high school biology and chemistry courses. Minimum 2.5 GPA. *Entrance tests:* College Board SAT or ACT composite. For foreign students TOEFL. *For transfer students:* 2.0 minimum GPA; maximum transfer credit limited only by residence requirements.

College credit and advanced placement for postsecondary-level work completed in secondary school.

Tutoring available. Developmental courses offered during regular academic year; credit given.

Degree Requirements: *For all associate degrees:* 64 credit hours; 2.0 GPA; 1 physical education course. *For all baccalaureate degrees:* 120 credit hours 2.0 GPA. *For all degrees:* 24 credits in residence; distribution requirements.

Fulfillment of some degree requirements possible by passing College Board APP. *Grading system:* A–F; pass; withdraw (deadline after which pass-fail is appended to withdraw).

Distinctive Educational Programs: Internships. Study abroad in London program. Weekend and evening classes. Accelerated degree program. *Other distinctive programs:* Continuing education program for nondegree students. Baccalaureate completion program for registered nurses; Physical Therapy Scholars Program.

ROTC: Army.

Degrees Conferred: 5 *associate;*; 550 *baccalaureate*; 430 *master's*; 55 *doctorate*. Bachelor's degrees awarded in top five disciplines: business, management, marketing, and related support services 71; visual and performing arts 55; communication, journalism, and related programs 44; psychology 43; liberal arts/general studies 38.

Fees and Other Expenses: *Full-time tuition per academic year 2008–09:* $21,528 undergraduate; contact the university for current graduate tuition. *Books and supplies:* $800. *Required fees:* $151. *Room and board per academic year:* $9,190.

Financial Aid: Financial aid to full-time, first-time undergraduate students: need-based scholarships/grants totaling $6,089,559, self-help $3,603,144; 94% received some form of aid. Average amount of aid received: federal grants $4,213; Pell grants $3,012; other federal aid $1,412; state/local grants $3,110; institutional grants $8,862.

Departments and Teaching Staff: *Total instructional faculty:* 345 (full-time 143, part-time 202). Student/faculty ratio: 13:1. Degrees held by full-time faculty: doctorate 86%, master's 14%.

Enrollment: Total enrollment 3,548. Undergraduate 2,193 (full-time 85%; female 73%, male 27%). Graduate 1,355 (full-tikme 37%). Transfer-in student 218.

Characteristics of Student Body: *Ethnic/racial makeup:* Black non-Hispanic: 15%; Hispanic: 121%; White non-Hispanic: 44%; unknown: 12%; nonresident alien 7%.

International Students: 220 nonresident aliens enrolled fall 2008. Students from Europe, Asia, Latin America, Africa, Canada, Australia, Middle East. Programs available to aid students whose native language is not English: English as a Second Language Program. No financial aid specifically designated for international students.

Student Life: On-campus residence halls house 30% of student body. *Intercollegiate athletics:* both sexes: basketball, lacrosse, soccer, swimming; female: volleyball; men: golf. *Special services:* Learning Resources Center; Counseling and Career Development Center; Campus Ministry; Student Health Center with 24-hour infirmary. University operates free shuttle buses serving main campus, nearby Spout Run campus, and Washington Metro transit stations. *Student pub-*

MARYMOUNT UNIVERSITY—*cont'd*

lications: Blue Banner, newspaper; yearbook; literary magazine. *Surrounding community:* Metropolitan Washington (DC) population 3.5 million.

Library Collections: 231,000 volumes. 340,000 microforms; 2,300 audiovisual materials; 31,000 periodicals including via electronic access. Online catalog. Students have access to online information retrieval services.

Most important special holdings include Gertrude Hoyt Collection (economics books); English and American literature collection (books); management collection (books).

Buildings and Grounds: Campus area 21 acres. Campus DVD available.

Chief Executive Officer: Dr. James F. Bundschuh, President.

Address undergraduate admission inquiries to Chris E. Domes, Vice President for Enrollment; graduate inquiries to Francesca Reed, Director of Graduate Admissions.

Norfolk State University

2401 Campus Avenue
Norfolk, Virginia 23504
Tel: (757) 823-8600 **E-mail:** admissions@nsu.edu
Fax: (757) 683-2057 **Internet:** www.nsu.edu

Institution Description: Norfolk State University is a public institution. *Enrollment:* 6,325. *Degrees awarded:* Associate, baccalaureate, master's.

Academic offerings subject to approval by statewide coordinating bodies. Budget subject to approval by state governing boards. Member of Virginia Tidewater Consortium for Continuing Education.

Accreditation: *Regional:* SACS-Comm. on Coll. *Professional*: business, medical record administration, music, nursing, psychology internship, social work, teacher education

History: Established as Norfolk unit of Virginia Union University, a junior college, and offered first instruction at postsecondary level 1935; chartered as Norfolk Polytechnic College 1942; became Norfolk Division of Virginia State College 1944; became 4-year institution 1956; changed name to Norfolk State College 1969; adopted present name 1979.

Institutional Structure: *Governing board:* Board of Visitors. Representation: 13 members. All voting. *Composition of institution:* Cabinet administrators, divisions of academic affairs, development, finance and business, student affairs. Full-time instructional faculty 317. Academic governance body, Faculty Senate, meets an average of 10 times per year.

Calendar: Semesters. Academic year late Aug. to mid-May. Freshmen admitted Aug., Jan., June. Degrees conferred May, July, Dec. Formal commencement May. Summer session from mid-June to late July.

Characteristics of Freshmen: 4,748 applicants (female 2,909, male 1,839). 73% of applicants accepted. 32% of accepted applicants enrolled.

84% of applicants submitted SAT scores; 12% ACT scores. *25th percentile*: SAT Critical Reading 410, SAT Math 400; ACT Composite 17. *75th percentile*: SAT Critical Reading 490, SAT Math 490; ACT Composite 20.

Admission: Rolling admissions. For fall acceptance, apply no later than May 31. *Requirements:* Graduation from an accredited secondary school with a minimum of 22 units or GED. Recommend 4 units English, 3 mathematics, 3 social studies, 3 science, 9 or more units electives. Additional requirements for some programs. Minimum 2.0 GPA unless extenuating circumstances. *Entrance tests:* College Board SAT. *For transfer students:* 2.0 minimum GPA; no maximum for transfer credit although final 30 semester hours must be taken at Norfolk State University.

College credit for advanced placement and military class-work. Tutoring available. Developmental/remedial courses offered in summer session and regular academic year.

Degree Requirements: *For all associate degrees:* 60–90 semester hours. *For all baccalaureate degrees:* 126–127 semester hours; last 30 hours in residence. *For all undergraduate degrees:* 2.0 GPA; 2 semesters physical education courses. Additional requirements for some programs.

Fulfillment of some degree requirements and exemption from some beginning courses possible by passing College Board CLEP. *Grading system:* A–F; pass-fail; withdraw (carries time limit).

Distinctive Educational Programs: Cooperative education. Flexible meeting places and schedules, including off-campus centers (at Norfolk and Virginia Beach, both less than 30 miles away from main institution; Melfa, 50 miles away, and at other varying locations), evening classes. Cooperative baccalaureate in health education and special education, and cooperative master's in art and fine art with Old Dominion University. Special facilities for using telecommunications in the classroom. Interdisciplinary programs in general studies, music in media, urban affairs, and urban planning. Facilities and programs for independent research, including honors programs, tutorials. Students may enroll for classes at Hampton Institute, Christopher Newport College, Tidewater Community College, Thomas Nelson Community College. Cross-registration with Old Dominion University. *Other distinctive programs:* Evening college offers degree study for adults. Servicemembers Opportunity College. Social Service Research Center for study of human resources within the urban environment. Community outreach programs provide academic and other support services to economically and educationally disadvantaged and physically handicapped students from day care through college.

ROTC: Air Force, Navy.

Degrees Conferred: 54 *associate;*; 751 *baccalaureate*; 222 *master's*; 4 *doctorate*. Bachelor's degrees awarded in top five disciplines: interdisciplinary studies 167; business, management, marketing, and related support services 111; social sciences and history 94; communication, journalism, and related programs 53; protective services/public administration 45. Master's degrees awarded: various disciplins 222. Doctorates awarded: psychology 3, public administration 1.

Fees and Other Expenses: *Full-time tuition per academic year 2008–09:* resident undergraduate $5,560, nonresident $16,857; contact the university for current graduate resident/nonresident tuition. *Room and board per academic year:* $8,884. *Books and supplies:* $1,320. *Other expenses:* $3,084.

Financial Aid: Aid from institutionally generated funds is provided on the basis of academic merit, financial need, athletic ability.

Financial aid to full-time, first-time undergraduate students: 84% received some form of aid. Average amount of aid received: federal grants $3,950; Pell grant $3,456; other federal aid $1,802; state/local grants $3,560; institutional grants $4,161.

Departments and Teaching Staff: *Total instructional faculty:* 422 (full-time 285, part-time137). Total faculty with doctorate, first-professional, or other terminal degree: 200. Student/faculty ratio: 16:1. Degrees held by full-time faculty: doctorate 67%, master's 100%, baccalaureate 100%. 67% hold terminal degrees.

Enrollment: Total enrollment 6,325. Undergraduate 5,653 (full-time 83%; female 63%; male 37%). Graduate 672 (full-time 58%). Transfer-in students 366.

Characteristics of Student Body: *Ethnic/racial makeup:* Black non-Hispanic: 89%; Asian or Pacific Islander: 1%; Hispanic: 2%; White non-Hispanic: 4%; unknown: 4%; nonresident alien 1%. *Age distribution:* number under 18: 797; 18–19: 1,547; 20–21: 1,232; 22–24: 683; 25–29: 394; 30–34: 236; 35–39: 189; 40–49: 232; 50–64: 81; 65 and over: 7.

International Students: 63 nonresident aliens enrolled fall 2008. Programs available to aid students whose native language is not English: English as a Second Language Program. No financial aid specifically designated for international students.

Student Life: On-campus residence halls house 30% of student body. *Intercollegiate athletics:* male: baseball, basketball, football, track; women only: basketball, track, volleyball. *Special regulations:* Cars with decals permitted in designated areas only. Dormitory visitation Sat. from noon to midnight, Sun. from noon to 10pm. *Special services:* Learning Resources Center, medical services, transportation to and from Old Dominion University. *Student publications, radio:* weekly newspaper, a yearbook. Radio station WNSB broadcasts 84 hours per week. *Surrounding community:* Norfolk metropolitan area population 810,000. Served by mass transit bus system; airport 10 miles from campus; passenger rail service 30 miles from campus.

Library Collections: 395,000 volumes. 75,000 microforms; 1,426 periodical subscriptions. Online catalog. Students have access to online information retrieval services and the Internet.

Most important special collection is the Herbert Marshall Black Collection.

Buildings and Grounds: Campus area 134 acres.

Chief Executive Officer: Dr. Marie V. McDemmond, President.

Address admission inquiries to Michelle Marable, Director of Admissions.

Old Dominion University

5215 Hampton Boulevard
Norfolk, Virginia 23529-0050
Tel: (757) 683-3000 **E-mail:** admit@odu.edu
Fax: (757) 683-3255 **Internet:** www.odu.edu

Institution Description: Old Dominion University is a state institution. *Enrollment:* 23,086. *Degrees awarded:* Baccalaureate, master's, doctorate. Certificate of advanced study also awarded.

Academic offerings subject to approval by statewide coordinating bodies. Budget subject to approval by state governing boards. Member of Virginia Tidewater Consortium for Continuing Higher Education.

Accreditation: *Regional:* SACS-Comm. on Coll. *Professional*: athletic training, business, computer science, counseling, dental assisting, dental hygiene, engineering, music, nuclear medicine technology, nursing, physical therapy, psychology internship, recreation and leisure services, public administration, speech-language pathology, teacher education, theatre

History: Established as extension center of The College of William and Mary in Virginia and offered first instruction at postsecondary level 1919; established as Norfolk Division of The College of William and Mary in Virginia 1930; changed name to College of William and Mary in Norfolk and awarded first degree (baccalaureate) 1956; changed name to Norfolk College of William and Mary of the Colleges of William and Mary in Virginia 1960; separately chartered as Old Dominion College 1962; adopted present name 1969. *See* Bridges, Maggie, *Old Dominion University—From the Great Depression to the Millenium* (Norfolk: Old Dominion University Office of Institutional Advancement, 2000) for further information.

Institutional Structure: *Governing board:* Board of Visitors of Old Dominion University. Representation: 17 visitors, including 8 alumni; appointed by the governor to 4-year terms, allowed to serve 2 terms. All voting. *Composition of institution:* Administrators 109. Academic affairs headed by provost/vice president for academic affairs. Student services directed by vice president for student services. Personnel management/business/finances directed by vice president for finance. Institutional advancement directed by the vice president for university relations. Academic governance body, Faculty Senate, meets an average of 10 times per year.

Calendar: Semesters. Academic year Aug. to Aug. Freshmen admitted Aug., Jan., May. Degrees conferred May, Aug., Dec. Formal commencements Dec., May. Summer session of 7 sessions from mid-May to late Aug.

Characteristics of Freshmen: 9,487 applicants (female 4,960, male 4,521). 69% of applicants admitted. 43% of applicants admitted and enrolled.

83% (1,750 students) submitted SAT scores; 19% (408 students) submitted ACT scores. *25th percentile*: SAT Critical Reading 480, SAT Math 490, ACT Composite 18. *75th percentile*: SAT Critical Reading 570, SAT Math 580; ACT Composite 23.

19% of entering freshmen expected to graduate within 5 years. 89% of freshmen from Virginia. Freshmen from 50 states and 21 foreign countries.

Admission: Rolling admissions plan. For fall acceptance, apply as May 1 of year of enrollment. December application required early action and scholarship consideration. *Requirements:* Either graduation from secondary school with 16 academic units, or acceptable score on GED. Minimum GPA 2.0 in academic areas. Lowest acceptable secondary school class standing 50th percentile. *Entrance tests:* College Board SAT. *For transfer students:* 2.2 minimum GPA; 90 semester hours maximum transfer credit.

Degree Requirements: 120 hours; 2.0 GPA; 30 hours in residence; general education requirements; exit competency examination in writing. *Grading system:* A–F; pass-fail; withdraw (carries time limit).

Distinctive Educational Programs: Several off-campus degree programs. State-wide engineering television network. Telecourses. Teleconferences. Satellite graduate centers, Articulation and cooperative agreements with American University, Eastern Virginia Medical College, Catholic University of America, Christopher Newport College, Longwood College, Norfolk State University, Thomas Nelson Community College, Tidewater Community College, and College of William and Mary. Joint graduate programs with Norfolk State University, College of William and Mary, and Eastern Virginia Medical School. All undergraduates are guaranteed an internship/practicum related to their major through the Career Advantage Program.

ROTC: Army, Navy. 20 Army and 56 Navy commissions awarded 2006.

Degrees Conferred: 2,858 *baccalaureate*; 1,274 *master's*; 106 *doctorate*. Bachelor's degrees awarded in top five disciplines: business, management, marketing, and related support services 566; health professions and related clinical sciences 488; social sciences and history 298; engineering/engineering technologies 242; English 186. Master's degrees awarded: various disciplines 1,274. Doctorates awarded: various disciplines 106.

Fees and Other Expenses: *Full-time tuition per academic year 2008–09:* resident $5,574 nonresident $14,910; contact the university for current graduate tution. *Required fees:* $188. *Room and board per academic year:* $7,100. *Books and supplies:* $1,000. *Other expenses:* $2,875.

Financial Aid: Aid from institutionally generated funds is provided on the basis of academic merit, financial need, athletic ability, other criteria.

Financial aid to full-time, first-time undergraduate students: 74% received some form of aid. Average amount of aid received: federal grants $1,783; Pell grants $1,509; other federal aid $626; state/local grants $1,388; institutional grants $4,641.

Departments and Teaching Staff: *Total instructional faculty:* 1,075. Total faculty with doctorate, first-professional, or other terminal degree: 535. Student/faculty ratio: 17:1. Degrees held by full-time faculty: baccalaureate 1%, master's 25%, doctorate 73%, professional 1%. 85% hold terminal degrees.

Enrollment: Total enrollment 23,086. Undergraduate 17,330 (full-time 74%; female 55%, male 45%). Graduate 5,756 (full-time 26%). Transfer-in students 1,975.

Characteristics of Student Body: *Ethnic/racial makeup:* Black non-Hispanic: 23%; American Indian or Alaska Native: 1%; Asian or Pacific Islander: 6%; Hispanic: 4%; White non-Hispanic: 61%; unknown: 5%; nonresident alien 2%. *Age distribution:* number under 18: 101; 18–19: 3,498; 20–21: 3,467; 22–24: 2,925; 25–29: 1,740; 30–34: 935; 35–39: 559; 40–49: 916; 50–64: 241.

International Students: 460 nonresident aliens enrolled fall 2008. Students from Europe, Asia, Latin America, Africa, Canada, Australia. Programs available to aid students whose native language is not English: social, cultural. English as a Second Language Program. Financial aid specifically designated for international students: variable number of scholarships available annually.

Student Life: On-campus residence halls house 25% of full-time undergraduates. Traditional residence halls and on-campus apartments available. 49% of undergraduate students involved in Greek Letter organizations. *Intercollegiate athletics:* male: baseball, basketball, golf, soccer, swimming, tennis, cross-country running, wrestling; female: basketball, field hockey, lacrosse, swimming, tennis, cross-country running. *Special regulations:* Cars with decals permitted; fee charged. *Special services:* learning resources center, minority student services, international student and faculty services, student health center, counseling and advising services, student employment, women's center, academic advising, career development services, transfer student center, academic skills development, financial aid services. *Student publications: Dominion Review,* an annual national literary-art magazine; *Mace and Crown*, a weekly student newspaper; *The Laureate,* student yearbook. Radio station WODU. *Surrounding community:* Norfolk population 262,000. Served by mass transit bus system, airport 10 miles from campus.

Publications: University catalog, biyearly; *Alumnews*, 4 times a year; *The ODU Courier*, monthly.

Library Collections: 1,152,000 volumes government documents; 35,000 audiovisual materials. Online catalog. 2,074,200 microforms; 55,500 audiovisual materials; 16,820 periodicals including via electronic access. Computer work stations available. Students have access to online information retrieval services and the Internet.

Most important special holdings include George Gay Recording Collection; Moses Myers Collection.

Buildings and Grounds: Campus area 187 acres. Campus DVD available.

Chief Executive Officer: Dr. Roseann Runte, President.

Address admission inquiries to Alice McAdony, Director of Admissions.

College of Arts and Letters

Degree Programs Offered: *Baccalaureate* in art history, communication, criminal justice, English, fine arts, French, geography, German, history, interdisciplinary studies, international studies, music, music composition, music performance, music education, philosophy, political science, sociology, Spanish, studio art, theater and dance, women's studies; *master's* in applied linguistics, applied sociology, English, fine arts, history, humanities, international studies, visual studies; *doctorate* in international studies.

Distinctive Educational Programs: Academic honors college. BA/MBA 5-year program. Joint master's in applied sociology and in visual studies in cooperation with Norfolk State University. Naval War College Cooperative Program. Institute for the Study of Minority Issues. Institute of Asian Studies. Women's Studies. Interdisciplinary programs in humanities, international studies.

College of Business and Public Administration

Degree Programs Offered: *Baccalaureate* in accounting, decision sciences, economics, financial management, information systems, international business; management, marketing management, *master's* in accounting, business administration, economics, public administration, urban studies; *doctorate* in business administration, urban services (management concentration).

Distinctive Educational Programs: Doctorate program in business administration which emphasizes the international aspect of business and includes a foreign language module. Master's program in accounting is designed to incorporate new standards for CPA examinations. Cooperative Education Program designed to allow students to integrate relevant work experience with academic studies. Center for Economic Education, Bureau of Research, and the Institute of Management are closely affiliated with the graduate programs of the College. BA/MBA 5-year program. MBA concentrations in Maritime and Ports Management, Health Care Management, Management of Service Operations.

Darden College of Education

Degree Programs Offered: *Baccalaureate* in human services counseling, occupational and technical studies, physical education, recreation and leisure studies, speech-language pathology and audiology; *master's* in biology, business and distributive education, chemistry, counseling, early childhood education, educational administration, elementary education, English, general secon-

OLD DOMINION UNIVERSITY—*cont'd*

dary education, mathematics, physical education, reading, social studies education, special education, speech-language pathology; *certificate of advanced study* in educational administration and guidance and counseling; *doctorate* in urban services.

Distinctive Educational Programs: Child Study Center, Center for Reading and Literacy, Occupational and Technical Studies Program. Military Career Transition Program designed to provide M.S.Ed. and state licensure to former military personnel desiring to pursue a second career in teaching.

College of Engineering and Technology

Degree Programs Offered: *Baccalaureate* in civil engineering, computer engineering, computer engineering technology, electrical engineering, mechanical engineering, engineering technology with majors in civil, electrical, and mechanical engineering technology; *master's* in aerospace engineering, computer engineering, engineering management, environmental engineering, operations research and systems analysis; *doctorate* in aerospace engineering, civil engineering, electrical engineering, engineering management, engineering mechanics, environmental engineering, mechanical engineering.

Distinctive Educational Programs: Off-campus graduate and undergraduate courses and programs offered at the Peninsula Center (Hampton, VA), the Virginia Beach (VA) Graduate Center, and Tri-Cities Higher Education Center (Portsmouth, VA). Dual degree programs available with both 2- and 4-year colleges. A special dual degree program with the College of Arts and Letters, on campus, which includes a semester abroad. Two-plus-two engineering technology program with Virginia Western Community College in Roanoke (VA) whereby the final 2 years of the Old Dominion BSET degree is offered on the VWCC campus in Roanoke. Commonwealth graduate engineering programs offer courses statewide via interactive television network in cooperation with other state universities. The master's in engineering management is the only such program offered via this medium, in its entirety, statewide.

College of Sciences

Degree Programs Offered: *Baccalaureate* in biochemistry, biology, chemistry, computer science, geology, mathematics, physics, psychology; *master's* in biology, chemistry, computational and applied mathematics, computer science, geology, oceanography, physics, psychology; *doctorate* in applied physics, biomedical sciences, computational and applied mathematics, computer science, ecological sciences, industrial/organizational psychology, oceanography, clinical psychology.

Distinctive Educational Programs: Cooperative doctorate in biomedical sciences with Eastern Virginia Medical School; in clinical psychology with Eastern Virginia Medical School, Norfolk State University, and the College of William and Mary. Joint program in Medicine with Eastern Virginia Medical School guarantees qualified entering freshmen a medical school position upon completion of the BS course of study. The Applied Marine Research Laboratory provides a strong interdisciplinary environmental research program with particular emphasis on marine studies. The Center for Coastal Physical Oceanography is an academic research environment for graduate education in which modeling of coastal oceanographic processes with state-of-the-art computer visualization capabilities is available.

College of Health Sciences

Degree Programs Offered: *Baccalaureate* in dental hygiene, environmental health, health sciences, medical technology, nuclear medicine technology, nursing, environmental engineering; *master's* in community health, dental hygiene, nursing, physical therapy, public health; *doctorate* in urban services (health services).

Protestant Episcopal Theological Seminary in Virginia

3737 Seminary Road
Alexandria, Virginia 22304
Tel: (703) 370-6600 **E-mail:** admissions@vts.edu
Fax: (703) 370-6234 **Internet:** www.vts.edu

Institution Description: The Protestant Episcopal Theological Seminary in Virginia is a private seminary offering professional and graduate study. *Enrollment:* 250. *Degrees awarded:* First-professional, master's, doctorate.

Accreditation: *National:* ATS. *Professional*: theology

History: Established 1823.

Calendar: Semesters. Academic year Aug. to May.

Admission: *Requirements:* Bachelor's degree; personal interview. *Entrance tests:* GRE.

Degree Requirements: Completion of prescribed curriculum.

Degrees Conferred: 13 *master's:* theology; 4 *doctorate:* theology; 21 *first-professional:* master of divinity.

Fees and Other Expenses: *Full-time tuition per academic year 2008–09:* contact the seminary for current information regarding tuition, fees, and housing costs. $9,000.

Financial Aid: Aid from institutionally generated funds is provided on the basis of academic merit, financial need.

Institution has a Program Participation Agreement with the U.S. Department of Education for eligible students to receive Pell Grants and, depending upon the agreement, other federal aid.

Departments and Teaching Staff: *Total instructional faculty:* 39.

Enrollment: Total enrollment 250.

International Students: No programs to aid students whose native language is not English. No financial aid specifically designated for international students.

Chief Executive Officer: V. Rev. Martha J. Horne, Dean and President.

Address admission inquiries to Director of Admissions.

Radford University

East Main Street
P.O. Box 6890
Radford, Virginia 24142
Tel: (540) 831-5000 **E-mail:** ruadmiss@radford.edu
Fax: (540) 831-5038 **Internet:** www.radford.edu

Institution Description: Radford University is a coeducational comprehensive public university. *Enrollment:* 9,157. *Degrees awarded:* Baccalaureate, master's; post-master's.

Academic offerings subject to approval by statewide coordinating bodies. Budget subject to approval by state governing boards. Members of Western Region Consortium for Higher Education.

Accreditation: *Regional:* SACS-Comm. on Coll. *Professional*: business, computer science, counseling, dietetics, music, nursing, recreation and leisure services, social work, speech-language pathology, teacher education, theatre

History: Established as State Normal and Industrial School for Women at Radford 1910; chartered and offered first instruction at postsecondary level 1913; became 4-year institution 1916; awarded first degree (baccalaureate) 1921; changed name to State Teachers College 1924; became woman's division of Virginia Polytechnic Institute and changed name to Radford College 1944; became independent institution 1964; became coeducational 1972; granted university status and adopted present name 1979. *See* Lenora Geissler Lewis-Smith, *Radford College: A Sentimental Chronicle Through Its First Half-Century* (Radford: Radford College Alumnae Association, 1970) for further information.

Institutional Structure: *Governing board:* The Board of Visitors. Extrainstitutional representation: rector, vice-rector, 11 members. All voting. *Composition of institution:* Administrators 39. Academic affairs headed by vice president. Student affairs head by vice president for student affairs. Management/business/finances directed by vice president for business affairs. Full-time instructional faculty 383. Academic governance body, Faculty Senate, meets an average of 16 times per year.

Calendar: Semesters. Academic year Aug. to May. Summer session from May to Aug.

Characteristics of Freshmen: 7,819 applicants (female 4,850, male 3,169). 75% of applicants accepted. 39% of accepted applicants enrolled.

91% (1,582 students) submitted SAT scores. 9% (148 students) submitted ACT scores. *25th percentile*: SAT Critical Reading 450, SAT Math 450; ACT Composite 19. *75th percentile*: SAT Critical Reading 540, SAT Math 540; ACT Composite 23.

40% of entering freshmen expected to graduate within 5 years. 91% of freshmen from Virginia. Freshmen from 24 states and 6 foreign countries.

Admission: Rolling admissions plan. For fall acceptance, apply as early as Sept. 15 of previous year, but not later than Apr. 1 for students seeking dormitory accommodations, June 1 for commuters. Students are notified of acceptance beginning Dec. 15. Early acceptance available. *Requirements:* Graduation from secondary school; or GED. 13 units and following program of study required: 4 units English, 4 mathematics, 3 or 4 lab science, 4 social science, including American history, and 3 or 4 units of foreign language. Minimum 2.0 GPA required. Portfolio required of art program applicants. Biology and chemistry recommended of nursing program applicants. Audition required of dance, music, and theatre program applicants for placement. Application to upper division (junior year) required of education and nursing program students. *Entrance tests:* College Board SAT I required; ACT may be substituted. TOEFL recommended for international students. Campus visit recommended. Admissions interview recommended. Off-campus interviews not available.

College credit and advanced placement for postsecondary-level work completed in secondary school.

Tutoring available. Noncredit remedial courses offered during regular academic year.

Degree Requirements: 120 credit hours minimum; 2.0 GPA minimum; physical education courses; general education and distribution requirements.

Fulfillment of some degree requirements and exemption from some beginning courses possible by passing departmental examinations, College Board CLEP, APP. *Grading system:* A–F; pass-fail; withdraw (carries time limit).

Distinctive Educational Programs: *For undergraduates:* interdisciplinary programs in liberal studies and social sciences. Honors Academy. RU Connections freshman living/learning communities; experiential learning opportunities; Undergraduate/Graduate Forum showcasing student research and creative projects. *Available to all students:* Work-experience programs. Evening and weekend college at Virginia Western Community College, off-campus programs in Roanoke, Abingdon, and other southwestern Virginia locations. Baccalaureate programs in nursing, including advanced placement program for registered nurses. Special facilities for using telecommunications in the classroom. Study abroad in England and western Europe and by individual arrangement. Diverse programs for study in England, Belgium, Costa Rica, Spain, Austria, Russia, France, Germany, Scotland, Australia, Ecuador, Greece, Japan.

ROTC: Army.

Degrees Conferred: 1,825 *baccalaureate* (B), 426 *master's* (M): biological sciences 53 (B); business and management 322 (B), 37 (M); communications 137 (B), 16 (M); computer and information sciences 85 (B); education 51 (B), 128 (M); English 38 (B), 9 (M); foreign languages 13 (B); home economics 18 (B); interdisciplinary studies 154 (B); liberal arts 31 (B), mathematics 10 (B); parks and recreation 38 (B); philosophy/religion/theology 9 (B); physical sciences 27 (B), 10 (M); protective services/public administration 159 (B), 54 (M); psychology 91 (B), 38 (M); social sciences and history 159 (B), 1 (M); visual and performing arts 151 (B), 16 (M); other 76 (B), 32 (M).

Fees and Other Expenses: *Full-time tuition per academic year 2008–09:* undergraduate resident $6,536; graduate resident $15,8450, contact the university for current graduate tuition and applicable fees. *Room and board per academic year:* $6,822. *Books and supplies:* $877. *Other expenes:* $2,600.

Financial Aid: Aid from institutionally generated funds is provided on the basis of academic merit, financial need, athletic ability, other criteria.

Financial aid to full-time, first-time undergraduate students: 61% received some form of aid. Average amount of aid received: federal grants $3,473; Pell grants $2,866; other federal aid $983; state/local grants $4,837; institutional grants $3,513.

Departments and Teaching Staff: *Total instructional faculty:* 580 (full-time 383, part-time 197). Total faculty with doctorate, first-professional, or other terminal degree: 338. Student/faculty ratio: 19:1. Degrees held by full-time faculty: doctorate 85%, master's 14%, baccalaureate 1%. 85% hold terminal degrees.

Enrollment: Total enrollment 9,157. Undergraduate 8,155 (full-time 95%; female 57%, male 43%). Graduate 1,002 (full-time 43%). Transfer-in students 646.

Characteristics of Student Body: *Ethnic/racial makeup:* Black non-Hispanic: 6%; Asian or Pacific Islander: 2%; Hispanic: 3%; White non-Hispanic: 86%; unknown: 2%; nonresident alien 1%. *Age distribution:* number under 18: 106; 18–19: 3,259; 20–21: 3,112; 22–24: 1,322; 25–29: 74; 30–34: 110; 35–39: 68; 40–49: 91; 50–64: 33; 65 and over: 2. 10% of student body attend summer sessions.

International Students: 92 nonresident aliens enrolled fall 2008. Students from Europe, Asia, Latin America, Africa, Canada, Middle East. Programs available to aid students whose native language is not English: social, cultural. English as a Second Language Program. No financial aid specifically designated for international students.

Student Life: On-campus residence halls house 34% of student body. Residence halls for females constitute 4% of such space; for both sexes 93%. 10% of males join fraternities; 11% of females join sororities. *Intercollegiate athletics:* NCAA Division I member, currently participates in 16 varsity sports; nine for females and seven for males. *Special regulations:* Quiet hours and curfews vary according to residence hall. *Special services:* Learning Resources Center, new student programs/orientation, University 100, Orientation for International Students, Adult Student Services, Multicultural and International Student Services, Disability Resources, Health Center, Speech and Hearing Clinic, Writing Center, Information Technology Resources. *Student publications, radio: The Beehive*, a yearbook; *The Tartan*, school newspaper; *Exit 109,* literary magazine, *RU Magazine,* published for alumni, parents, and friends of Radford University; *Whim*, weekly online magazine. ROC TV broadcast weekly on RU Reslife Channel. Radio station WVRU broadcasts 60 hours per week. *Surrounding community:* Radford population 16,200. Richmond, 250 miles from campus, is nearest metropolitan area.

Library Collections: 432,000 volumes including bound books, serial backfiles, electronic documents, and government documents not in separate collections. Online catalog. Current serial subscriptions: 2,210 paper, 25 microform, 3,484 electronic. 10,188 audio/videotapes; 1,927 DVD discs; 260 CD-ROMs. 96 computer work stations. Students have access to the Internet at no charge.

Most important special holdings include the Virginia Collection; John Preston McConnell Papers and Memorabilia; Radford University Archives; Supreme Court Justice Arthur Goldberg Personal Working Library of Selected Speeches and Papers.

Buildings and Grounds: Campus area 117 acres. Campus DVD available.

Chief Executive Officer: Dr. Penelope W. Kyle, President.

Address admission inquiries to David Kraus, Director of Admissions.

Randolph-Macon College

206 Henry Street
Ashland, Virginia 23005-5005
Tel: (800) 888-1762 **E-mail:** admissions@rmc.edu
Fax: (804) 752-4707 **Internet:** www.rmc.edu

Institution Description: Randolph-Macon is a private college, affiliated with the United Methodist Church, Virginia Conference. *Enrollment:* 1,201. *Degrees awarded:* Baccalaureate.

Member of Richmond Area Film Cooperative, Seven College Consortium, Virginia Foundation for Independent Colleges.

Accreditation: *Regional:* SACS-Comm. on Coll.

History: Established and incorporated 1830; offered first instruction at postsecondary level 1832; awarded first degree (baccalaureate) 1836; admitted women 1971.

Institutional Structure: *Governing board:* Randolph-Macon Board of Trustees. 39 members. Extrainstitutional representation: 46-member Board of Associates. *Composition of institution:* President's cabinet, 9 members directed by the president of the college. Academic affairs headed by provost and dean of the college. Management/business/finances directed by treasurer. Full-time instructional faculty 88. Academic governance body, the faculty, meets on a monthly basis throughout the academic year.

Calendar: Semesters. Academic year Sept. to May. Degrees conferred and formal commencement May. Summer session of 1 term from June to July.

Characteristics of Freshmen: 3,502 applicants (female 2,014, male 1,488). 74% of applicants accepted. 26% of accepted applicants enrolled.

Mean SAT scores 551 verbal, 547 mathematical.

65% of entering freshmen expected to graduate within 5 years. 57% of freshmen from Virginia. Freshmen from 22 states and 3 foreign countries.

Admission: Modified rolling admissions plan after Mar. 1. For fall acceptance, apply as early as Sept. of previous year, but not later than Mar. 1. Apply by Dec. 1 for early decision; need not limit application to Randolph-Macon. Early acceptance available. *Requirements:* Graduation from accredited secondary school with 4 units English, 3 foreign language, 2 lab science, 3 mathematics, 2 social studies; or GED. Additional academic units recommended. *Entrance tests:* College Board SAT or ACT composite. *For transfer students:* 2.0 GPA on all college work required; maximum transfer credit 65 semester hours from 2-year college, 75 semester hours from 4-year college.

College credit and advanced placement for postsecondary-level work completed in secondary school. Tutoring available.

Degree Requirements: 110 credit hours; 2.0 GPA; 2 semesters physical education; distribution requirements; proficiency requirements in English composition and literature, foreign language, and mathematics.

Fulfillment of some degree requirements and exemption from some beginning courses possible by passing College Board AP and institutional examinations. *Grading system:* A–F.

Distinctive Educational Programs: Work-experience programs. Dual-degree programs in engineering with Columbia University (NY), Washington University (MO), and in forestry with Duke University (NC). Women's studies minor. Interdepartmental/interdisciplinary minor in Asian studies; interdisciplinary majors in environmental studies, international relations, and international studies. Facilities for independent research, including senior projects, tutorials, and honors program. Study abroad in Australia, Brazil, England, France, Germany, Greece, Ireland, Italy, Japan, Korea, Mexico, Northern Ireland, Spain. Off-campus study at Hampden-Sydney College, Hollins College, Randolph-Macon Women's College, Sweet Briar College, Mary Baldwin College, and Washington and Lee University.

Degrees Conferred: 242 *baccalaureate*. Bachelor's degrees awarded in top five disciplines: social sciences 109; psychology 24; history 30; English language/literature 14; biological/biomedical sciences 12.

RANDOLPH-MACON COLLEGE—*cont'd*

Fees and Other Expenses: *Full-time tuition per academic year 2008–09:* $28,555. *Books and supplies:* $1,000. *Room and board per academic year:* $8,610. *Other expenses:* $1,500.

Financial Aid: Aid from institutionally generated funds is provided on the basis of academic merit, financial need, other criteria.

Financial aid to full-time, first-time undergraduate students: 100% received some form of aid. Students received federal grants averaging $3,009; 63% state/local grants averaging $2,175; 83% institutional grants averaging $8,791; 19% received loans averaging $3,575.

Departments and Teaching Staff: *Total instructional faculty:* 146. Student/faculty ratio: 11:1. Degrees held by full-time faculty: baccalaureate 100%, master's 100%, doctorate 77%. 83% hold terminal degrees.

Enrollment: Total enrollment 1,201. Undergraduate 1,201 (full-time 98%; female 53%, male 47%). Transfer-in students 23.

Characteristics of Student Body: *Ethnic/racial makeup:* Black non-Hispanic: 11%; American Indian or Alaska Native: 1%; Asian or Pacific Islander: 1%; Hispanic: 3%; White non-Hispanic: 80%; unknown: 1%; nonresident alien 2%.

International Students: 12 nonresident aliens enrolled fall 2008. Students from Europe, Asia, Latin America. No programs available to aid students whose native language is not English. No financial aid specifically designated for international students.

Student Life: On-campus residence halls house 90% of student body. Housing is available for married students. There are 7 fraternities, all with houses, and 5 sororities, all with houses. Approximately 50% of the student body participate in the Greek Life. *Intercollegiate athletics:* The varsity intercollegiate program consists of 13 sports: men's teams in football, baseball, and golf; men's and women's teams in basketball, lacrosse, tennis, soccer; women's teams in field hockey, softball, and volleyball. *Special regulations:* Cars permitted without restrictions. Residence hall visitation rules: 24 hours, 7 days a week. *Special services:* Tutorials available, career counseling. *Student publications, radio: Fish Tales*, an annual handbook; *Stylus*, an annual literary magazine; *The Yellow Jacket Annual,* a yearbook; *The Yellow Jacket,* a biweekly newspaper. *Surrounding community:* Ashland population 6,000. Nearest metropolitan area Richmond, 15 miles away. Served by airport 25 miles from campus; passenger rail service 5 minutes from campus.

Library Collections: 190,000 volumes including bound books, serial backfiles, electronic documents, and government documents not in separate collections. Online catalog. 207,000 microforms; 5,300 audiovisual materials; 2,550 current serial subscriptions. Computer work stations available. Students have access to the Internet at no charge.

Most important special holdings include Methodist Collection (Virginia Conference of the Methodist Church); Intellectual Life of the Colonial South; Casnoviana Collection; Henry Miller Collection.

Chief Executive Officer: Dr. Robert R. Lindgren, President.

Address admission inquiries to Steven W. Nape, Dean of Admissions.

Randolph-Macon Woman's College

2500 Rivermont Avenue
Lynchburg, Virginia 24503-1526
Tel: (434) 947-8000 **E-mail:** admissions@rmwc.edu
Fax: (434) 947-8138 **Internet:** www.rmwc.edu

Institution Description: Randolph-Macon Woman's College is a private, independent, nonprofit college affiliated with the United Methodist Church. *Enrollment:* 568. *Degrees awarded:* Baccalaureate.

Member of the consortia Seven-College Exchange and Tri-College Center of Virginia.

Accreditation: *Regional:* SACS-Comm. on Coll. *Professional*: teacher education

History: Chartered 1890; established 1891; offered first instruction at postsecondary level 1893; awarded first degree (baccalaureate) 1894. *See* Roberta D. Cornelius, *The History of Randolph-Macon Woman's College from the Founding Through 1949–50* (Chapel Hill, NC: University of North Carolina Press, 1951) for further information.

Institutional Structure: *Governing board:* Trustees of Randolph-Macon Woman's College. 28 trustees including 19 alumnae. All voting. *Composition of institution:* Administrators 9. President has overall responsibility for all aspects of college administration. Academic affairs headed by Dean of the College. Management/business/finances directed by Vice President for Finance. Full-time instructional faculty 69. Academic governance body, Academic Program Committee, meets weekly during academic year.

Calendar: Semesters. Academic year late Aug. to early May. Freshmen admitted Sept., Jan. Degrees conferred and formal commencement May. Summer travel/study options.

Characteristics of Freshmen: 1,222 applicants (female 911, male 311). 84% of applicants accepted. 33% of accepted applicants enrolled.

Mean SAT scores 601 verbal, 558 mathematical. Mean ACT Composite score 26.

63% of freshmen expected to graduate within 5 years. 27% of freshmen from Virginia. Freshmen from 37 states and 11 foreign countries.

Admission: Modified rolling admissions plan. For fall enrollment, apply no later than Feb. 15 for preferential consideration. Students are notified of acceptance Jan. 1–Apr. 15. Apply by Nov. 15 for early decision; notification Dec. 15. Early admission available. *Recommended minimum distribution of high school courses:* 4 units in English, 3–4 in foreign language, 3 in mathematics, 2 in history, 2 in natural sciences with lab work, 1–2 units in other academic courses. *Entrance tests:* College Board SAT or ACT composite. *For transfer students:* 62 hours maximum transfer credit.

College credit for extrainstitutional learning (life experience) on basis of committee review for Prime Time students only.

Tutoring available.

Degree Requirements: 124 credit hours; 2.0 GPA; 2 years in residence; general education requirements; senior program. *Grading system:* A–F; pass-fail; withdraw (deadline after which pass-fail is appended to withdraw).

Distinctive Educational Programs: Work-experience programs. Accelerated degree program. 3+2 nursing program with Johns Hopkins University. Interdepartmental majors by individual arrangement. Facilities and programs for independent research, including honors programs and tutorials. Study abroad in England through Randolph-Macon Woman's College at the University of Reading which offers a year-long tutorial program in British culture staffed by University faculty. Other overseas study in Denmark, France, Greece, Italy, Japan, Mexico, and elsewhere by individual arrangement. Semester programs in government in Washington (DC). Other off-campus study in U.S. through Seven-College Exchange Program and by individual arrangement. Cross-registration through Tri-College Consortium of Virginia. *Other distinctive programs:* Degree program (Prime Time Program) for women resuming interrupted studies. American Culture Program at R-MWC: semester-long immersion into the study of American culture that is concentrated, interdisciplinary, and often offsite at key locations in and near Virginia. The program capitalizes on the college's central location in historic Virginia and its own outstanding collection of American art in an inclusive study of American society. The American Culture Program is open to men and women undergraduates who have successfully completed three semesters of full-time college study and whose applications will be considered on a competitive basis.

Degrees Conferred: 144 *baccalaureate*. Bachelor's degrees awarded in top five disciplines: social sciences 39; biomedical/biological sciences 22; communication, journalism, and related programs 18; foreign languages 17; psychology 16. Master's degrees awarded: education 5.

Fees and Other Expenses: *Full-time tuition per academic year 2008–09:* $27,380. *Books and supplies:* $800. *Room and board per academic year:* $9,350. *Other expenses:* $1,000.

Financial Aid: Aid from institutionally generated funds is provided on the basis of academic merit, financial need.

Financial aid to full-time, first-time undergraduate students: federal grants averaging $3,397; 35% state/local grants averaging $2,188; 98% institutional grants averaging $12,843; 65% received loans averaging $5,755.

Departments and Teaching Staff: *Total instructional faculty:* 91. Student/faculty ratio: 9:1. Degrees held by full-time faculty: baccalaureate 1%, master's 15%, doctorate 84%. 95% hold terminal degrees.

Enrollment: Total enrollment 568. Undergradaute 562 (full-time 98%; female 82%, male 18%). Graduate 6 (full-time 83%). Transfer-in student 19.

Characteristics of Student Body: *Ethnic/racial makeup:* Black non-Hispanic: 9%; American Indian or Alaska Native: 1%; Asian or Pacific Islander: 1%; Hispanic: 7%; White non-Hispanic: 66%; unknown: 1%; nonresident alien 12%.

International Students: 68 nonresident aliens enrolled fall 2000. Students from Europe, Asia, Latin America, Caribbean. Programs available to aid students whose native language is not English: social, cultural. English as a Second Language Program. Some financial aid designated for international students.

Student Life: On-campus residence halls house 85% of student body. *Intercollegiate athletics:* basketball, fencing, field hockey, lacrosse, riding, soccer, swimming, tennis, and volleyball. *Special services:* Medical services, counseling services, Career Planning and Placement Center, Learning Resources Center. *Student publications, radio: Helianthus*, a yearbook; *Sundial*, a biweekly paper. Radio station WWRM. *Surrounding community:* Lynchburg population 66,000. Roanoke (VA), 50 miles from Lynchburg; Richmond (VA), 120 miles from Lynchburg; and Washington (DC) 180 miles from Lynchburg, are the nearest metropolitan areas. Served by mass transit system; Amtrak, the Greyhound-Trailways bus company; Delta and U.S. Airway, and United Express airlines.

Library Collections: 198,000 volumes including bound books, serial back-files, electronic documents, and government documents not in separate collections. Online catalog. 187,000 microforms; 4,000 audiovisual materials; 620 current serial subscriptions. Computer work stations available. Students have access to the Internet at no charge.

Most important special holdings include collected writings of Virginia women; Pearl S. Buck Manuscript Collection; Herbert C. Lipscomb Rare Book Collection.

Buildings and Grounds: Campus area 100 acres.

Chief Executive Officer: Dr. Kathleen G. Bowman, President.

Address admission inquiries to Patricia N. LeDonne, Director of Admissions.

Regent University

1000 Regent University Drive
Virginia Beach, Virginia 23464-9801
Tel: (757) 579-4014 **E-mail:** admissions@regent.edu
Fax: (757) 579-4042 **Internet:** www.regent.edu

Institution Description: Regent University is a private, four-year institution, evangelical Christian in nature, but nondenominational. *Enrollment:* 4,278. *Degrees awarded:* Baccalaureate, master's, doctorate, first-professional. Specialist certificate also awarded.

Accreditation: *Regional:* SACS-Comm. on Coll. *National:* ATS. *Professional*: law, psychology, theology

History: Dr. M. G. "Pat" Robertson, founder and president of the Christian Broadcast Network (CBN) has an inspired vision of establishing a graduate institution that would train mature men and women for the challenge of representing Christian principles in their professions. Classes began in fall 1977; first degree (master's) awarded 1980.

Institutional Structure: *Governing board:* Board of Trustees. 21 trustees. *Administrative Cabinet:* president, vice presidents for academic affairs, student services, advancement, general counsel, information technology, deans of colleges.

Calendar: Semesters. Academic year Sept. to May. Formal commencement May. Summer session.

Characteristics of Freshmen: 287 applicants (female 162, male 125). 58% of applicants admitted. 64% of admitted applicants enrolled.

22% (52 students) submitted SAT scores; 12% (38 students) submitted ACT scores. *25th percentile*: SAT Critical Reading 470, SAT Math 430; ACT Composite 20, ACT English 19, ACT Math 17. *75th percentile*: SAT Critical Reading 580, SAT Math 550; ACT Composite 25, ACT English 25, ACT Math 24.

53% of freshmen from Virginia. Freshmen from 49 states and 4 foreign countries.

Admission: Criteria for admissions includes: minimum cumulative undergraduate grade point average of 2.75; submission of test scores (GRE, MAT, LSAT, or GMAT) depending on the school of interest; 2 admissions interviews; submission of a personal goals statement of professional and spiritual goals; recommendations from employer, faculty member, and clergyman; a writing sample.

Degree Requirements: Satisfactory completion of all courses and credit hours as specified on the student's Approved Degree Program form; completion of all requirements within 5 years from the date of the student's initial enrollment (academic petitions may be submitted four weeks in advance of the students 5-year expiration date); minimum 3.0 GPA (2.0 for J.D. and M. Div.); payment of all fees; attendance at commencement for the conferring of the degree (permission to graduate in absentia may be requested in writing).

Distinctive Educational Programs: *Master Teacher Program:* Enables currently employed teachers to complete the master's degree in one academic year by offering courses biweekly on Thursday and Friday evenings and in the daytime on Saturday throughout the academic year. Focuses on behavior and character development, teaching strategies and at-risk students. Opportunity to integrate learning into the teacher's own classroom. *Extended Learning:* Graduate level instruction is delivered through the Internet (doctorates in organization leadership, communications cognate in divinity, education).

Degrees Conferred: 205 *baccalaureate*; 546 *master's*; 163 *doctorate*; *first-professional*: 173. Bachelor's degrees awarded: business/marketing 42; communications/journalism 4; education 17; psychology 10; theology and religious vocations 21. Master's degrees awarded: business and management 100; communications/journalism 60; education 185; psychology 81; public administration and social services 31; theology 43; visual and performing arts 12. Doctorates awarded: business/marketing 69; communications/journalism 10; education 5; psychology 22; theology 7. First-professional degrees awarded: law 173.

Fees and Other Expenses: *Full-time tuition for academic year 2008–09:* \$10,492 undergraduate. \$445 to \$860 per credit hour depending upon program. *Required fees:* \$150. *Room and board per academic year:* \$8,667. *Books and supplies:* \$598. *Other expenses:* \$9,333.

Financial Aid: Aid from institutionally generated funds is provided on the basis of academic merit, financial need, other criteria. Institution has a Program Participation Agreement with the U.S. Department of Education for eligible students to receive Pell Grants and, depending upon the agreement, other federal aid.

Financial aid to full-time, first-time undergraduate students: 81% received some form of aid. Students received need-based scholarships/grants totaling \$993,516, self-help \$1,845,305; non-need-based scholarships/grants totaling \$1,449,188, self-help \$2,400,358.

Departments and Teaching Staff: *Total instructional faculty:* 633 (full-time 162, part-time 471). Degrees held by full-time faculty: master's 30%, doctorate 45%, baccalaureate 100%, professional 25%. 70% hold terminal degrees.

Enrollment: Total enrollment 4,278. Undergraduate 1,488 (full-time 54%; female 67%, male 33%). Graduate 2,780 (full-time 41%). Transfer-in students 425.

Characteristics of Student Body: *Ethnic/racial makeup:* Black non-Hispanic: 24%; American Indian or Native Alaskan: 1%; Asian or Pacific Islander: 25; Hispanic: 6%; White non-Hispanic: 59%. *Age distribution:* 22–24: 52%; 25–29: 40%; 30–34: 40%; 35–39: 10%; 40–49: 4%; 50–59: 1%.

International Students: 132 nonresident aliens enrolled fall 2008. Students from Europe, Asia, Latin America, Africa, Canada, New Zealand. Programs available to aid students whose native language is not English: English as a Second Language Program. Financial aid specifically designated for international students: scholarships available annually for qualifying graduate international students.

Student Life: At Regent University the graduate experience involves more than academics. Students are members of a community sharing a commitment to a full schedule of events, such as workshops, chapel services, Bible studies, and student organizations. *Student publications: Focus Magazine, Hampton Roads Christian*, newspaper, *The Journal of Christian Jurisprudence, Regent University Law Review.* Students in the School of Radio, Television and Film produce a weekly television news program which airs nationally on The Family Channel.

Library Collections: 276,078 (main library) volumes; 120,000 (law library) volumes; 581,559 microforms (main), 736,834 (law); 10,781 audiovisual materials (main), 448 (law). Online catalog. Students have access to online information retrieval services and the Internet.

Most important special holdings include Clark Hymnology Collection; Baptist Film Collection; Transylvania Law Collection.

Buildings and Grounds: The campus includes 2 administrative classroom buildings and a 3-story, 152,000 sq.ft. library building that also contains classrooms and faculty offices. Each building is of traditional Williamsburg architecture. A university-operated community of 112 2-bedroom apartments is located near the campus. These apartments are available for families and single students.

Chief Executive Officer: Dr. M. G. Robertson, President.

Address admission inquiries to Office of Admissions.

Roanoke College

221 College Lane
Salem, Virginia 24153-3794
Tel: (540) 375-2500 **E-mail:** admissions@roanoke.edu
Fax: (540) 375-2267 **Internet:** www.roanoke.edu

Institution Description: Roanoke College is a private college affiliated with the Evangelical *Degrees awarded:* Baccalaureate.

Member of the Western Region Consortium for Continuing Higher Education. *Enrollment:* 2,021.

Accreditation: *Regional:* SACS-Comm. on Coll. *Professional*: business, chemistry

History: Established in 1842 and chartered in 1845, Roanoke College adopted its present name in 1853 and awarded its first baccalaureate degree in 1855. Roanoke is the country's second oldest Lutheran college. It awarded its 10,000 baccalaureate degree in 1992, the year of its sesquicentennial. *See* William Edward Eisenberg, *The First Hundred Years, An Authentic History* (Strasburg, VA: Shenandoah Publishing House, 1942) and Mark F. Miller, *Dear Old Roanoke* (Macon, GA: Mercer University Press, 1991) for further information.

Institutional Structure: *Governing Board:* The Board of Trustees of Roanoke College; 32 members and 4 ex officio members, all voting. The college is administered by a president, who has 4 vice presidents, which represent the 5 administrative divisions (Academic Affairs, Admissions and Resource Development, Business Affairs, and Student Affairs), reporting to him. Professional

ROANOKE COLLEGE—*cont'd*

administrative staff 89. Instructional faculty: 100 full-time and 70 part-time. Academic governance body, the faculty, meets approximately 7 times a year.

Calendar: Early semester. Academic year Aug. to May. Freshmen admitted Aug., Jan., June. Degrees conferred May, Aug. Formal commencement May. Summer session of 2 four-week sessions and an eight-week concurrent session beginning in early June. A May travel option is available.

Characteristics of Freshmen: 3,519 applicants (female 2,038, male 1,541). 80% of applicants accepted. 25% of accepted applicants enrolled.

Mean SAT scores 562 verbal, 541 mathematical.

65% of entering freshmen expected to graduate within 5 years. 43% of freshmen from Virginia. Freshmen from 42 states and 15 foreign countries.

Admission: Competitive. Application deadline is Nov. 1 for early decision by Nov. 30. Jan. 15 for early notification. Applications accepted until March 1 for April 1 notification. *Requirements:* Strongly suggest a minimum of 18 academic courses including 4 in English, 2 in social studies, 4 in a foreign language, 2 lab sciences, and 3 in mathematics, including 2 in algebra (algebra I and II) and 1 in geometry. Graduation from secondary school or GED required. *Entrance tests:* SAT or ACT. *For transfer students:* 2.2 minimum GPA in transferable courses.

College credit and advanced placement for postsecondary-level work completed in secondary school.

Degree Requirements: 36½ units (courses); 2.0 GPA; 16 units in residence, including the final 9; core curriculum requirements; total units include 2 physical education activity courses.

Distinctive Educational Programs: Honors Program for selected students; interdisciplinary programs in international relations and criminal justice; extensive internship, independent study, and research practicum opportunities; Center for Community Research; Virginia at Oxford summer program; Center for Church and Society; May travel option for study abroad; pre-professional programs in law, medicine, dentistry, and ministry. World-wide study opportunities.

Degrees Conferred: 429 *baccalaureate*. Bachelor's degrees awarded in top five disciplines: business, management, marketing, and related support services 107; social sciences 61; English language/literature 47; psychology 40; history 21.

Fees and Other Expenses: *Full-time tuition per academic year 2008–09:* $27,935. *Books and supplies:* $850. *Room and board per academic year:* $9,285. *Other expenses:* $1,750.

Financial Aid: Aid from institutionally generated funds is provided on the basis of academic merit, financial need.

Financial aid to full-time, first-time undergraduate students: 97% received federal grants averaging $2,584; 55% state/local grants averaging $2,123; 97% institutional grants averaging $9,779; 65% received loans averaging $4,763.

Departments and Teaching Staff: *Total instructional faculty:* 143. Student/faculty ratio: 14:1. Degrees held by full-time faculty: master's 13%, doctorate 87%. 90% hold terminal degrees.

Enrollment: Total enrollment 2,021. Undergraduate 2,021 (full-time 95%; female 55%, male 45%). Transfer-in students 141.

Characteristics of Student Body: *Ethnic/racial makeup:* Black non-Hispanic: 3%; Asian or Pacific Islander: 1%; Hispanic: 3%; White non-Hispanic: 90%; nonresident alien 2%.

International Students: 40 nonresident aliens enrolled fall 2008. Students from Europe, Asia, Latin America, Africa, Canada, Australia, New Zealand. Programs available to aid students whose native language is not English: social, cultural. Financial aid specifically designated for international students: scholarships available annually.

Student Life: On-campus residence halls house 56% of student body. One-third of the student body holds membership in a national fraternity or sorority. *Intercollegiate athletics:* male: basketball, cross-country, golf, lacrosse, soccer, tennis, track; female: basketball, cross-country, field hockey, lacrosse, soccer, softball, tennis, track, volleyball. *Special regulations:* Cars permitted without restrictions. Freshman visitation; coed and single-sex residence halls available; 65 student-run organizations. *Special services:* Peer tutoring, study skills assistance, professional advising, and career planning and placement services available through the Learning Center; Student Health Center; Counseling Center. *Student publications: The Brackety-Ack,* a weekly newspaper; *On Concept's Edge,* a literary magazine; *The Rawenoch,* the college yearbook. *Surrounding community:* Roanoke Valley metropolitan area population 250,000. Served by airport 10 miles from campus.

Library Collections: 215,000 volumes. 337,000 microforms; 5,900 audiovisual materials; 3,800 current periodical subscriptions. Online catalog. Students have access to online information retrieval services and the Internet.

Most important special holdings include Henry H. Fowler Collection; college archives.

Buildings and Grounds: Campus area 68 acres.

Chief Executive Officer: Dr. Sabine U. O'Hara, President. Address admission inquiries to Vice President for College Relations.

Saint Paul's College

115 College Drive
Lawrenceville, Virginia 23868
Tel: (434) 848-3111 **E-mail:** admissions@saintpauls.edu
Fax: (434) 848-6407 **Internet:** www.saintpauls.edu

Institution Description: Saint Paul's College is a private college affiliated with the Protestant Episcopal Church in the United States of America. *Enrollment:* 644. *Degrees awarded:* Baccalaureate.

Accreditation: *Regional:* SACS-Comm. on Coll.

History: Established as Saint Paul's Normal and Industrial School 1888; incorporated 1890; offered first instruction at postsecondary level 1922; changed name to Saint Paul's Polytechnic Institute 1941; awarded first degree (baccalaureate) 1944; adopted present name 1957. *See* James Solomon Russell, *Adventure in Faith* (New York: Morehouse Publisher, 1936) for further information.

Institutional Structure: *Governing board:* Board of Trustees. Extrainstitutional representation: 35 trustees, including 2 alumni; institutional representation: president of the college, 2 students. 1 ex officio. 36 voting. *Composition of institution:* Administrators 7. Academic affairs headed by dean of the college. Management/business/finances directed by treasurer. Full-time instructional faculty 33. Academic governance body, the faculty, meets an average of 8 times per year.

Calendar: Semesters. Academic year Aug. to July. Freshmen admitted Aug., Jan., June. Degrees conferred and formal commencement May.

Characteristics of Freshmen: 513 applicants (female 219, male 294) 96% of applicatns accepted. 40% of accepted applicants enrolled full-time.

21% of entering freshmen expected to graduate within 5 years. 67% of freshmen from Virginia. Freshmen from 19 states and 6 foreign countries.

Admission: Rolling admissions plan. For fall acceptance, apply as early as July 1 of previous year but not later than Aug. 15 of year of enrollment. Early acceptance available. *Requirements:* Either graduation from secondary school with 16 units which normally include 4 units in English, 2 each in mathematics, science, social studies, 6 electives; or GED. *Entrance tests:* College Board SAT.

Advanced placement for postsecondary-level work completed in secondary school.

Tutoring available. Noncredit developmental courses offered during regular academic year.

Degree Requirements: 120 semester hours; 2.0 GPA; last 30 hours in residence; 2 physical education courses; distribution requirements.

Exemption from some beginning courses possible by passing standardized examinations. *Grading system:* A–F; withdraw (carries time limit).

Distinctive Educational Programs: Work-experience programs, including internships and cooperative education. Evening classes. Accelerated degree programs. Study abroad in various countries through cooperating institutions.

ROTC: Army in cooperation with Virginia State University.

Degrees Conferred: 124 *baccalaureate*. Bachelor's degrees awarded in top five disciplines: business, management, marketing, and related support services 71; social sciences 9; liberal arts/general studies8; security and protective services 6; education 4.

Fees and Other Expenses: *Full-time tuition per academic year 2008–09:* $12,545. *Books and supplies:* $1,400. *Room and board per academic year:* $6,640. *Other expenses:* $3,200.

Financial Aid: Aid from institutionally generated funds is provided on the basis of academic merit, financial need, athletic ability, other criteria.

Financial aid to full-time, first-time undergraduate students: 73% received federal grants averaging $3,360; 71% state/local grants averaging $2,110; 43% institutional grants averaging $2,672; 76% received loans averaging $5,516.

Departments and Teaching Staff: *Total instructional faculty:* 52. Student/faculty ratio: 20:1. Degrees held by full-time faculty: master's 47%, doctorate 44%, professional 10%. 44% hold terminal degrees.

Enrollment: Total enrollment 644. Undergraduate644 (full-time 97%; female 48%, male 52%). Transfer-in students 51.

Characteristics of Student Body: *Ethnic/racial makeup:* Black non-Hispanic: 97%; Asian or Pacific Islander: 1%; Hispanic 1%; White non-Hispanic: 2%.

International Students: 6 nonresident aliens enrolled fall 2008. No programs available to aid students whose native language is not English. No financial aid specifically designated for international students.

Student Life: On-campus residence halls house 85% of student body. Residence halls for males constitute 50% of such space, for females 50%. *Intercollegiate athletics:* male: baseball, basketball, cross-country, golf, tennis, track; female: basketball, golf, softball, tennis, volleyball. *Special regulations:* Cars permitted without restrictions. Curfews and quiet hours. Residence hall visitation from 12 noon to 11pm. *Special services:* Learning Resources Center, medical services. *Publications: Sainte Paulite;* freshmen newsletter. *Surrounding community:* Lawrenceville population 1,500. Richmond, 75 miles from campus, is nearest metropolitan area.

Library Collections: 92,000 volumes. 2,500 government documents; 33,000 microforms; 4,500 audiovisual materials; 225 current periodical subscriptions. 448 recordings. Computer work stations available. Online catalog. Students have access to online information retrieval services and the Internet.

Most important special holdings include African American History; History of Saint Paul's College; Short Collection (West Indies); James Solomon Russell Collection.

Buildings and Grounds: Campus area 75 acres.

Chief Executive Officer: Dr. John K. Waddell, President.

Address admission inquiries to Rosemary Lewis, Vice President for Student Affairs.

Shenandoah University

1460 University Drive
Winchester, Virginia 22601
Tel: (540) 665-4500 **E-mail:** admit@su.edu
Fax: (540) 665-4627 **Internet:** www.su.edu

Institution Description: Shenandoah University, formerly known as Shenandoah College and Conservatory of Music, is a private college affiliated with the United Methodist Church. *Enrollment:* 3,511. *Degrees awarded:* Associate, baccalaureate, master's, doctorate

Accreditation: *Regional:* SACS-Comm. on Coll. *Professional*: music, nursing, nursing-midwifery, occupational therapy, pharmacy, physical therapy, physician assisting, respiratory therapy, respiratory therapy technology

History: Established as Shenandoah Seminary 1875; offered first instruction at postsecondary level and changed name to Shenandoah Collegiate Institute and School of Music 1883; chartered 1884; accredited as junior college, changed name to Shenandoah College, separated from school of music, and awarded first degree (associate) 1924; school of music became 4-year institution and changed name to Shenandoah Conservatory of Music 1937; college and conservatory became single institution once again, became Shenandoah College and Conservatory of Music 1974; adopted present name 1991. *See* Clarence Howard Connor, *A Study of the Functions of Shenandoah College and Shenandoah Conservatory of Music* (Ann Arbor: University Microfilms, 1955) for further information.

Institutional Structure: *Governing board:* The Board of Trustees of Shenandoah University. Representation: 46 trustees. All voting. *Composition of institution:* Administrators 10. Academic affairs headed by academic dean. Management/business/finances directed by business manager. Full-time instructional faculty 116. Academic governance body, Dean's Staff, meets an average of 20 times per year.

Calendar: Semesters. Academic year Aug. to May. Freshmen admitted Aug., Jan., May, June, July. Degrees conferred and formal commencement May, Aug., Dec. Summer sessions early June to mid-Aug.

Characteristics of Freshmen: 1,256 applicants (female 674, male 586). 92% of applicants admitted. 33% of applicants admitted and enrolled.

97% (327 students) submitted SAT scores; 3% (9 students) submitted ACT scores. *25th percentile*: SAT Critical Reading 460, SAT Math 450; ACT Composite 20, ACT English 18, ACT Math 19. *75th percentile*: SAT Critical Reading 570, SAT Math 570; ACT Composite 26, ACT English 26, ACT Math 26.

41% of entering freshmen expected to graduate within 5 years. 56% of freshmen from Virginia. Freshmen from 21 states and 10 foreign countries.

Admission: Rolling admissions plan. For fall acceptance, apply as early as Sept. 15 of previous year, but not later than Aug. 15 of year of enrollment. Apply by Dec. 1 for early decision; need not limit application to Shenandoah University. Early acceptance available. *Requirements:* Either graduation from accredited secondary school with 15 units of college entrance credit; or GED. Audition for music students. Minimum GPA 2.0. *Entrance tests:* College Board SAT or ACT. *For transfer students:* 2.0 minimum GPA; from 4-year accredited institution 90 hours maximum transfer credit.

Advanced placement for postsecondary-level work completed in secondary school and for extrainstitutional learning.

Tutoring available. Noncredit remedial courses offered in the Academic Support Center. Noncredit remedial courses offered.

Degree Requirements: *For associate of science in respiratory care:* 63 credit hours. *For baccalaureate degrees:* minimum 120 credit hours; 2.0 GPA; 24 of last 30 credit hours in residence. Core curriculum required.

Fulfillment of some degree requirements and exemption from some beginning courses possible by passing departmental examinations, College Board CLEP, other standardized tests. *Grading system:* A–F; pass-fail; pass; withdraw (deadline after which pass-fail is appended to withdraw).

Distinctive Educational Programs: *For all undergraduates:* Work-experience programs. Associate degree program in respiratory care and baccalaureate in nursing. Interdisciplinary programs in music management, music theater, music therapy. *Available to all students:* Evening classes, accelerated degree programs. Facilities and programs for independent research, including individual majors, tutorials.

Degrees Conferred: 7 *associate*; 314 *baccalaureate* (B); 205 *master's* (M); 84 *doctorate* (D): biological/life sciences 10 (B); business/marketing 45 (B), 60 (M); communications/communication technologies 15 (B); education 28 (B), 129 (M), 5 (D); English 1 (B); health professions and related clinical sciences 37 (B), 38 (M); liberal arts/general studies 8 (B); mathematics 1 (B); natural resources/environmental science 4; parks and recreation 2 (M); philosophy/religion/theology 1 (B); protective services/public administration 10 (B); psychology 12 (B); social sciences and history 5 (B); visual and performing arts 69 (B), 21 (M), 3 (D). *First-professional:* pharmacy 109.

Fees and Other Expenses: *Full-time tuition per academic year 2008–09:* $23,040 undergraduate; contact the university for current graduate tuition/fees. *Required fees:* $150 (other fees may apply). *Room and board per academic year:* $8,350. *Books and supplies:* $1,000. *Other expenses:* $2,100.

Financial Aid: Financial aid to full-time, first-time undergraduate students: need-based scholarships/grants totaling $2,811,563, self-help $4,943,270, parent loans $3,245,046, non-need-based scholarships/grants totaling $7,475,749, self-help $2,930,826, parent loans $1,327,462, tuition waivers $524,120.

Departments and Teaching Staff: *Total instructional faculty:* 326 (full-time 175, part-time 150). Total faculty with doctorate, first-professional, or other terminal degree: 194. Student/faculty ratio: 10:1. Degrees held by full-time faculty: doctorate 60%, master's 36%, baccalaureate 4%. 31% hold terminal degrees.

Enrollment: Total enrollment 3,511. Undergraduate 1,720 (full-time 92%; female 56%, male 44%). Graduate 1,791 (full-time 42%). Transfer-in students 226.

Characteristics of Student Body: *Ethnic/racial makeup:* Black non-Hispanic: 10%; Asian or Pacific Islander: 3%; Hispanic: 2%; White non Hispanic: 47%; unknown 34%; nonresident alien 35. *Age distribution:* number under 18: 23; 18–19: 535; 20–21: 477; 22–24: 241; 25–29: 99; 30–34: 58; 35–39: 27; 40–49: 53; 50–64: 25.

International Students: 105 nonresident aliens enrolled fall 2008. Students from Europe, Asia, Latin America, Africa, Canada, Australia, New Zealand. Programs available to aid students whose native language is not English: English as a Second Language Program. Financial aid specifically designated for international students: Scholarships available annually for qualifying undergraduate students.

Student Life: On-campus residence halls house 44% of undergraduate student population. *Intercollegiate athletics:* male: baseball, basketball, cross-country, football, golf, lacrosse, soccer, tennis; female: basketball, cross-country, field hockey, lacrosse, soccer, softball, tennis, volleyball. *Special regulations:* Cars with decals permitted without restrictions. Quiet hours. Residence hall visitation 8am to 2am Sun.-Thurs; Fri. and Sat. visitations vary by occupant. *Special services:* Academic Support Center, medical services. *Student publications: New Writers*, a biannual literary magazine; *Zynodoa*, a yearbook. *Surrounding community:* Winchester/Frederick County population 80,000. Washington (DC), 70 miles from campus, is nearest metropolitan area. Served by mass transit bus system; regional airport 2 miles from campus.

Library Collections: 134,000 volumes. 134,000 microforms; 20,000 audiovisual materials; 25,600 periodicals including via electronic access. Online catalog. Computer work stations available. Students have access to online information retrieval services and the Internet.

Most important special collections include Evangelical United Brethren; Shenandoah Valley Archives; U.S. Civil War; Early 20th-Century Sheet Music; EUB-United Methodist Church History.

Buildings and Grounds: Campus area 100 acres.

Chief Executive Officer: Dr. James A. Davis, President.

Address admission inquiries to David Anthony, Dean of Admissions.

Sweet Briar College

Sweet Briar, Virginia 24595
Tel: (434) 381-6142 **E-mail:** admissions@sbc.edu
Fax: (434) 381-6152 **Internet:** www.sbc.edu

Institution Description: Sweet Briar College is a private, independent, nonprofit college for women. *Enrollment:* 828. *Degrees awarded:* Baccalaureate.

Member of the consortia Seven College Exchange and Tri-College Center of Virginia.

Accreditation: *Regional:* SACS-Comm. on Coll.

SWEET BRIAR COLLEGE—*cont'd*

History: Chartered in 1901; established under present official name, Sweet Briar College, and offered first instruction at postsecondary level 1906; first degree (baccalaureate) awarded 1910. *See* Martha Lou Lemmon Stohlman, *The Story of Sweet Briar College* (Princeton, New Jersey: Princeton University Press, 1956) for further information.

Institutional Structure: *Governing board:* Board of Directors and Overseers. Representation: 32 overseers, including 7 directors, 21 alumnae, 3 recent graduates, and president of college. 2 ex officio. 32 voting. *Composition of institution:* Administrators 8. Academic affairs headed by dean of the college. Management/business/finances directed by vice president for business. Full-time instructional faculty 69. Academic governance body, the faculty, meets an average of 9 times per year.

Calendar: Semesters (4-1-4 plan). Academic year Sept. to May. Freshmen admitted Aug., Jan. Degrees conferred and formal commencement May. No summer session.

Characteristics of Freshmen: 629 applicants (female 629). 79% of applicants admitted. 43% of applicants admitted and enrolled.

94% (159 students) submitted SAT scores; 26% (44 students) submitted ACT scores. *25th percentile*: SAT Critical Reading 530, SAT Math 500; ACT Composite 22. *75th percentile*: SAT Critical Reading 645, SAT Math 610; ACT Composite 26.

67% of entering freshmen expected to graduate within 5 years. 41% of freshmen from Virginia. Freshmen from 27 states and 2 foreign countries.

Admission: For fall acceptance, apply before Feb. 1. Students are notified of acceptance by Mar. 15. Apply by Dec. 1 for early decision. Early acceptance available. *Requirements:* Either graduation from secondary school with 16 academic units or GED. Recommend 4 units English, 4 foreign language, 4 math, 4 science, 4 social studies. *Entrance tests:* College Board SAT Reasoning or ACT. *For transfer students:* 2.0 minimum GPA; 60 hours maximum transfer credit.

Advanced placement for postsecondary-level work completed in secondary school.

Tutoring available. Noncredit developmental courses offered during regular academic year.

Degree Requirements: 120 credit hours; 2.0 GPA; 2 years in residence; comprehensives in individual fields of study; specific requirements, including modern language proficiency.

Fulfillment of some degree requirements and exemption from some beginning courses possible on basis of College Board Achievements and APP. *Grading system:* A–F; pass-fail; withdraw (deadline after which pass-fail is appended to withdraw).

Distinctive Educational Programs: Work-experience programs, including internship programs in January term. Accelerated degree programs. Dual-degree programs in engineering with Columbia University (NY), Washington University (MO), and Virginia Tech leading to bachelor's degrees from both institutions and with the University of Virginia leading to master's degrees. Interdisciplinary programs in American studies, Asian studies, environmental studies, and European civilization. Preprofessional programs in business, engineering, journalism, law, medicine, and religion. Facilities and programs for independent research, including honors programs, individual majors, tutorials; independent study and intensive courses during January term. Study in France, Spain, and England through Sweet Briar Junior Year Program; summer program in Germany and in Florence, Italy; elsewhere through approved semester- and year-programs offered by other institutions. Study tours available during January term and summer. Other off-campus study includes Washington (DC) Semester in cooperation with American University and semester or academic year at Hampden-Sidney College, Mary Baldwin College, Randolph-Macon College, Randolph-Macon Woman's College, or Washington and Lee University through Seven College Exchange. Cross-registration with Lynchburg College or Randolph-Macon Woman's College through Tri-College program.

Degrees Conferred: 130 *baccalaureate:* biological sciences 7; business/marketing 5; computer and information science 2; English 11; environmental science 7; foreign languages and literature 13; mathematics 7; physical sciences 4; psychology 11; religion 1; social sciences and history 41; visual and performing arts 21. Master's degrees awarded: education 10.

Fees and Other Expenses: *Full-time tuition per academic year 2008–09:* $28,995 undergraduate; contact the college for current graduate tuition/fees. *Required fees:* $200. *Room and board per academic year:* $10,160. *Books and supplies:* $900. *Other expenses:* $1,916.

Financial Aid: The college offers a direct lending program. Aid from institutionally generated funds is provided on the basis of academic merit, financial need, other criteria (talent, leadership).

Financial aid to full-time, first-time undergraduate students: need-based scholarships/grants totaling $3,901,813, self-help $982,681, parent loans $1,026,615, tuition waivers $145,173; non-need-based scholarships/grants totaling $2,785,303, self-help $95,180, parent loans $423,080, tuition waivers $68,080.

Departments and Teaching Staff: *Total instructional faculty:* 105 (full-time 69, part-time 36). Total faculty with doctorate, first-professional, or other terminal degree: 82. Student/faculty ratio: 7:1. Degrees held by full-time faculty: 97% hold terminal degrees.

Enrollment: Total enrollment 828. Undergraduate813 (full-time 94%; female 97%, male 3%). Graduate 15 (full-time 80%). Transfer-in students 29.

Characteristics of Student Body: *Ethnic/racial makeup:* Black non-Hispanic: 3%; American Indian or Alaska Native: 1%; Asian or Pacific Islander: 1%; Hispanic: 3%; White non-Hispanic: 86%; unknown: 3%; nonresident alien 3%. . *Age distribution:* number under 18: 3; 18–19: 153; 20–21: 119; 22–24: 208; 25–29: 13; 30–34: 6; 35–39: 4; 40–49: 13; 50–64: 8; 65 and over: 3.

International Students: 24 nonresident aliens enrolled fall 2008. No programs available to aid students whose native language is not English. Financial aid specifically designated for international students: variable number of scholarships awarded annually.

Student Life: On-campus residence halls house 95% of student body. *Intercollegiate athletics:* Equestrian, fencing, field hockey, lacrosse, soccer, softball, swimming, tennis, volleyball. *Special regulations:* Cars permitted without restrictions. Visitation hours vary according to residence hall. *Special services:* Learning Resources Center, medical services. *Student publications, radio: Red Clay,* an annual literary magazine; *The Briar Patch*, a yearbook; *Sweet Briar Voice*, a news publication. Radio station WUDZ broadcasts 36 hours per week. *Surrounding community:* Sweet Briar (unincorporated) is 1 mile south of Amherst and 12 miles north of Lynchburg, Virginia. Served by airport 20 miles from campus.

Library Collections: 297,000 volumes including bound books, serial backfiles, electronic documents, and government documents not in separate collections. Online catalog. 451,000 microforms; 11,000 audiovisual materials; 36,000 periodicals including via electronic access. Computer work stations available. Students have access to the Internet at no charge.

Most important special holdings include George Meredith, W.H. Auden, and Virginia Woolf collections.

Buildings and Grounds: Campus area 3,250 acres.

Chief Executive Officer: Dr. Elisabeth S. Muhlenfeld, President.

Address admission inquiries to Ken Huus, Dean of Admissions.

Union Theological Seminary and Presbyterian School of Christian Education

3401 Brook Road
Richmond, Virginia 23227
Tel: (804) 355-0671 **E-mail:** admissions@utsva.edu
Fax: (804) 355-3919 **Internet:** www.utsva.edu

Institution Description: Union Theological Seminary and Presbyterian School of Christian Education is a private institution affiliated with the Presbyterian Church (USA). *Enrollment:* 375. *Degrees awarded:* First-professional (master of divinity), master's, doctorate.

Member of the Richmond Theological Consortium and Washington Theological Consortium.

Accreditation: *Regional:* SACS-Comm. on Coll. *National:* ATS. *Professional*: theology

History: Established and offered first instruction at postsecondary level 1812; chartered 1868; awarded first degree (first-professional) 1900.

Institutional Structure: *Governing board:* Board of Trustees. Representation: 33 trustees, including president of the seminary; all voting. *Composition of institution:* Administrators 27. Academic affairs headed by president. Management/business/finances directed by vice president for administration. Full-time instructional faculty 32. Academic governance body, the faculty, meets an average of 9 times per year.

Calendar: Semesters. Academic year Sept. to May. Students admitted Sept., Feb., July. Degrees conferred Nov., May. Formal commencement May. Intensive summer language courses and courses for Doctor of Ministry students in Aug.

Characteristics of Freshmen: 75% of applicants accepted. 49.5% of accepted applicants enrolled. Entering students from 14 states and 3 foreign countries.

Admission: Rolling admissions plan. For fall acceptance, apply as early as Sept. 1 of previous year, but not later than Aug. 1 of year of enrollment. *Requirements:* For first-professional degree, baccalaureate degree from accredited college or university. Recommend courses in English, foreign languages, history, philosophy, natural sciences, religion, social sciences.

Degree Requirements: *For first-professional degree:* 32 units (96 semester hours) which includes 75 hours of prerequisites in Hebrew, Old Testament, New Testament, theology, ethics, church history, education, pastoral studies, field education; demonstrated proficiency in Greek and Hebrew. *Grading system:* Honors, credit, marginal credit, no credit.

Distinctive Educational Programs: Special facilities for using telecommunications in the classroom. Tutorials. Cross-registration and cooperative programs with member schools of Richmond Theological Consortium, Washington Theological Consortium, Virginia Commonwealth University, Queens University. Study abroad in France, Korea, Ghana, Middle East, Latin America, Switzerland. *Other distinctive programs:* Continuing education.

Degrees Conferred: 11 *doctorate:* theology; 34 *master's degrees:* Christian education, theological studies; 38 *first-professional:* master of divinity.

Fees and Other Expenses: *Full-time tuition per academic year 2008–09:* contact the seminary for current tuition, fees, housing, and other costs.

Financial Aid: Aid from institutionally generated funds is provided on the basis of academic merit and financial need. Institution has a Program Participation Agreement with the U.S. Department of Education for eligible students to receive Pell Grants and, depending upon the agreement, other federal aid.

Departments and Teaching Staff: *Total instructional faculty:* 32 (full-time 31, part-time 1).

Enrollment: Total enrollment 311. Undergraduate

International Students: 38 nonresident aliens enrolled fall 2008. Programs available to aid students whose native language is not English: English as a Second Language Program. Financial aid specifically designated for qualifying international students.

Student Life: On-campus housing (dormitories and apartments). Approximately 73% of male students and 75% of female students are in campus housing. *Special regulations:* Cars permitted without restrictions. *Special services:* Learning Resources Center, medical services. *Student publications, radio: In Medias Rex*, a monthly newspaper. *Surrounding community:* Richmond metropolitan area population 800,000. Served by airport 12 miles from campus; passenger rail service 3 miles from campus.

Publications: *Interpretation* first published 1946; *As I See It Today* (6 times per year) first published 1970. *Focus* (3 times annually); annual calendar includes art and meditations by members of the campus community.

Library Collections: 332,000 volumes. 32,827 microforms; 66,945 audiovisual materials; 1,276 current periodical subscriptions. Online and card catalog. Computer work stations available. Students have access to online information retrieval services and the Internet.

Most important special holdings include H.H. Rowley Old Testament collection (biblical study); church history collection (especially Presbyterian); theology collection (John Calvin and early Reformed theology; Thomas Torrance collection of 19th- and 20th-century German theology).

Buildings and Grounds: Campus area 59 acres.

Chief Executive Officer: Dr. Louis B. Weeks, President.

Address admission inquiries to Director of Admissions.

University of Mary Washington

1301 College Avenue
Fredericksburg, Virginia 22401-5358
Tel: (540) 654-1000 **E-mail:** admit@umc.edu
Fax: (540) 654-1076 **Internet:** www.umc.edu

Institution Description: University of Mary Washington, formerly Mary Washington College, is a state institution. *Enrollment:* 5,084. *Degrees awarded:* Baccalaureate, master's.

Academic offering subject to approval by statewide coordinating bodies Member of Central Virginia Consortium.

Accreditation: *Regional:* SACS-Comm. on Coll. *Professional*: music

History: Established and chartered as Fredericksburg Normal and Industrial School for women 1908; offered first instruction at postsecondary level 1911; changed name to State Teacher's College, Fredericksburg and awarded first degree (baccalaureate) 1924; changed name to Mary Washington College 1938, to Mary Washington College of the University of Virginia and readopted present name 1972. *See* Edward Alvey, Jr., *History of Mary Washington College 1908–1972* (Charlottesville, VA: University Press of Virginia, 1974) for further information.

Institutional Structure: *Governing board:* Rector and Visitors of Mary Washington College. Extrainstitutional representation: 12 members, including 6 alumni. All voting. *Composition of institution:* Senior administrative staff: 11. Academic affairs headed by vice president for academic affairs and dean. Management/business/finances directed by vice president for fiscal affairs. Full-time administrative faculty 55. Full-time instructional faculty 242. Academic governance body, Faculty of Mary Washington College, meets an average of 9 times per year.

Calendar: Semesters. Academic year Aug. to May. Freshmen admitted Aug. Degrees conferred and formal commencement May. Summer session of 2 terms.

Characteristics of Freshmen: 4,600 applicants (female 3,061, male 1,539). 56% of applicants accepted. 74% of accepted applicants enrolled.

Mean SAT class scores 612 verbal, 596 mathematical.

72% of entering freshmen expected to graduate within 5 years. 63% of freshmen from Virginia. Freshmen from 31 states and 9 foreign countries.

Admission: *Application filing dates:* Nov. 1 for Early Decision Freshman; Feb. 1 for Regular Decision Freshman; March 1 for Transfer. Notification by April 1. Reply date May 1. *Requirements:* Graduation from accredited secondary school or GED equivalent. Minimum recommended academic program includes 4 units English, 3 units social studies, 3 units mathematics, 3 units laboratory science, 3–4 units foreign language. The typical student admitted has a high school grade average of at least "B" and ranks in the top quarter of the graduating class. The College requires official results of the SAT and recommends that candidates take at least 2 Achievement Tests of the College Board. Also considered are extracurricular activities, recommendations, and writing samples. College credit is awarded on the basis of Advanced Placement exams.

Degree Requirements: *For all baccalaureate degrees:* 122 credit hours. *For master's degree:* 30 graduate credit hours. *For all degrees:* distribution requirements.

Fulfillment of some degree requirements possible by passing College Board APP. *Grading system:* A–F; pass-fail; withdraw (deadline after which pass-fail is appended to withdraw).

Distinctive Educational Programs: Center for Historic Preservation. Work-experience programs. Interdisciplinary programs in American studies, environmental earth sciences, historic preservation, international affairs, Russian studies. Preprofessional program in medicine. Bachelor of Professional Studies program. Facilities for independent research, including honors programs, individual majors. Study abroad in England, France. *Available to all students:* Evening classes. Interdisciplinary programs in general liberal arts and sciences, liberal studies. *Other distinctive programs:* Reduced tuition for senior citizens.

Degrees Conferred: 1,011 *baccalaureate*; 210 *master's*. Bachelor's degrees awarded in top five disciplines: social sciences 150; business, management, marketing, and related support services 27; English language/literature 97; liberal arts/general studies 95; multidisciplinary studies 90. Master's degrees awarded: various disciplines 210.

Fees and Other Expenses: *Full-time tuition per academic year 2008–09:* resident $6,774, nonresident $17,942; contact the university for current graduate tuition/fees. *Books and supplies:* $1,000. *Room and board per academic year:* $7,040. *Books and supplies:* $1,000. *Other expenses:* $2,786.

Financial Aid: Aid from institutionally generated funds is provided on the basis of academic merit, financial need.

Financial aid to full-time, first-time undergraduate students: 59% received some form of aid. Average amount of aid received: federal grants $3,447; Pell grants $2,706; Other federal aid $1,024; state/local grants $5,301; institutional grants $2,290.

Departments and Teaching Staff: *Total instructional faculty:* 359 (full-time 242, part-time 117). Student/faculty ratio: 15:1. Degrees held by full-time faculty: master's 10%, doctorate 79%. 86% hold terminal degrees.

Enrollment: Total enrollment 5,084. Undergraduate 4,231 (full-time 88%; female 66%, male 34%). Graduate 853 (full-time 17%). Transfer-in students 283.

Characteristics of Student Body: *Ethnic/racial makeup:* Black non-Hispanic: 4%; Asian or Pacific Islander: 4%; Hispanic: 45; White non-Hispanic: 64%; unknown 23%; nonresident alien 1%.

International Students: 51 nonresident aliens enrolled fall 2008. Students from Europe, Asia, Latin America, Africa. No programs available to aid students whose native language is not English. No financial aid specifically designated for international students.

Student Life: On-campus residence halls house 68% of undergraduate students. Most residence halls are for both males and females. *Intercollegiate athletics:* male: baseball, basketball, cross-country, horseback riding, lacrosse, soccer, swimming and diving, tennis, track and field; female: basketball, cross-country, field hockey, horseback riding, lacrosse, soccer, softball, swimming and diving, tennis, track and field, volleyball. *Special regulations:* Cars permitted; parking allocated according to class standing. *Special services:* Medical, psychological counseling, bookstore, career advising and placement, intramurals, post office. *Student publications, radio: Aubade*, an annual literary magazine; *The Battlefield*, a yearbook; *The Bullet*, a weekly newspaper. Radio station WMWC broadcasts 70 hours a week. *Surrounding community:* Fredericksburg population 19,000. Washington (DC), 55 miles from campus, is nearest metropolitan area. Served by mass transit bus system and passenger rail service 2 miles from campus.

Library Collections: 374,000 volumes including bound books, serial backfiles, electronic documents, and government documents not in separate collections. Online catalog. Current serial subscriptions: 5,601 paper, microform, and via electronic. access. 843 CD-ROMs. Computer work stations available. Students have access to the Internet at no charge.

UNIVERSITY OF MARY WASHINGTON—*cont'd*

Most important special holdings include federal and state depository for documents; collections on William Butler Yeats, Claude Bernard.

Buildings and Grounds: Campus area 176 acres.

Chief Executive Officer: Dr. William J. Frawley, President.

Address admission inquiries to Martin A. Wilder, Vice President for Enrollment Management; graduate study inquiries to Matthew Mejia, Assistant Dean for Admissions.

University of Richmond

28 Westhampton Way
Richmond, Virginia 23173
Tel: (800) 289-8000 **E-mail:** admissions@richmond.edu
Fax: (804) 287-6003 **Internet:** www.richmond.edu

Institution Description: University of Richmond is a private institution. *Enrollment:* 4,249. *Degrees awarded:* Associate, baccalaureate, first-professional (law), master's.

Accreditation: *Regional:* SACS-Comm. on Coll. *Professional*: accounting, business, law

History: Established as Dunlora Academy 1830; changed name to Virginia Baptist Seminary 1832; chartered as Richmond College, discontinued theological instruction, and offered first instruction at postsecondary level 1840; awarded first degree (baccalaureate) 1849; established law school 1870; Westhampton College, the women's division, added 1914; adopted present name 1920; offered first graduate program 1921; established business school 1949; established nation's first school of leadership studies 1992. *See* Reuben E. Alley, *History of the University of Richmond, 1830–1971* (Charlottesville: University Press of Virginia, 1977) for further information.

Institutional Structure: *Governing board:* Board of Trustees of the University of Richmond. Representation: 40 elected trustees plus president of the university (ex officio), 41 voting; 19 trustees emeriti, university counsel. 40 voting. *Composition of institution:* Academic affairs headed by five academic deans and special assistant to the president. Management/business/finances directed by vice president for business and finance. Full-time instructional faculty 214. Academic governance body, University Faculty and University Senate, meet an average of 4 times and once per year, respectively.

Calendar: Semesters. Academic year late Aug. to early May. First-year students admitted Aug., Jan. Degrees conferred May, Aug. (Dec. for Law School only). Formal commencement May. Summer session from mid-May to mid-Aug.

Characteristics of Freshmen: 7,910 applicants (female 4,627; male 3,343). 96% of applicants admitted. 30% of applicants admitted and enrolled.

86% (672 students) submitted SAT scores; 14% (105 students) submitted ACT scores. *25th percentile*: SAT Critical Reading 590, SAT Math 600; ACT Composite 27. *75th percentile*: SAT Critical Reading 670, SAT Math 680; ACT Composite 30. 11 National Merit Scholars.

83% of first-year students expected to graduate within 5 years. 17% of freshmen from Virginia. Freshmen from 39 states and 23 foreign countries.

Admission: Filing dates: Nov. 15 for fall early decision; notified by Dec. 15; Jan. 15, winter early decision notify by Feb. 15; Jan. 15 regular decision, notification date Apr. 1. *Requirements:* Either graduation from secondary school with 16 units which must include 4 English, 3 mathematics (inclusive of algebra I and II and geometry), 2 units each in history, laboratory science, and foreign language. *Entrance tests:* College Board SAT-I. It is strongly recommended that a classical or modern foreign language SAT II be submitted for placement or exemption purposes. ACT scores may be submitted in lieu of the SAT-I. *For transfer students:* 2.0 minimum GPA; 60 hours maximum transfer credit.

College credit and advanced placement for postsecondary-level work completed in secondary school.

Degree Requirements: *For all associate degrees:* 61 credit hours; 31 hours in residence; proficiency and basic knowledge requirements. *For all baccalaureate degrees:* 120 hours; 60 hours in residence; core curriculum requirements. *For all degrees:* 2.00 GPA.

Fulfillment of some degree requirements and exemption from some beginning courses possible by passing departmental examinations, College Board CLEP or AP tests. *Grading system:* A–F; pass-fail; withdraw (carries penalty, carries time limit, deadline after which pass-fail is appended to withdraw, deadline after which fee is charged).

Distinctive Educational Programs: Jepson School of Leadership Studies; Women Involved in Living and Learning; Honors Law Program; undergraduate research. Interdepartmental programs in American studies, humanities, interdisciplinary studies, international studies, urban studies, women's studies. Teacher licensure program. Facilities and programs for independent research, including honors programs, individual majors, tutorials, first-year colloquia, undergraduate research grants. Study abroad in Argentina, Australia, Austria, Canada, Chile, China, Czech Republic, Denmark, England, France, Germany, Greece, Honduras, Ireland, Italy, Japan, Korea, Mexico, the Netherlands, New Zealand, Poland, Russia, Spain, Sweden, Taiwan, Thailand, Turkey, Vietnam.

ROTC: Army. 9 commissions awarded 2006.

Degrees Conferred: 4 *associate*; 794 *baccalaureate*: area and ethnic studies 14; biological/life sciences 44; business/marketing 242; communications/communication technologies 18; computer and information sciences 14; English 51; foreign languages and literature 32; interdisciplinary studies 5; mathematics 115; natural resources/environmental science 61 philosophy/religion/theology 19; physical sciences 18; protective services/public administration 3; psychology 33; social sciences and history 142; visual and performing arts 28; other disciplines74. Master's degrees awarded: various disciplines 71. Doctorates awarded: various disciplines 16. First-professional degrees awarded: law 152.

Fees and Other Expenses: *Full-time tuition per academic year 2008–09:* undergraduate $38,850; contact the university for current graduate and Law School tuition and applicable fees that vary by program. *Room and board per academic year:* $8,200. *Books and supplies* $1,050. *Other expenses:* $990.

Financial Aid: The university offers a direct lending program. Aid from institutionally generated funds is provided on the basis of academic merit, financial need, athletic ability, other criteria.

Financial aid to full-time, first-time undergraduate students: 66% received some form of aid. Average amount of aid received: federal grants $7,716; Pell grants $2,931; other federal aid $5,923; state/local grants $2,762; institutional grants $27,508.

Departments and Teaching Staff: *Total instructional faculty:* 343 (full-time 274, part-time 69). Total faculty with doctorate, first-professional, or other terminal degree: 296. Student/faculty ratio: 10:1. Degrees held by full-time faculty: doctorate 73.7%, master's 11/4%, baccalaureate 1.3%, professional 13.5%. 87.2% hold terminal degrees.

Enrollment: Total enrollment 4,249. Undergraduate 3,328 (full-time 87%; female 53%, male 47%). Graduate 921 (full-time 62%). Transfer-in students 126.

Characteristics of Student Body: *Ethnic/racial makeup:* Black non-Hispanic: 3%; Asian or Pacific Islander: 3%; Hispanic: 3%; White non-Hispanic: 8%; unknown: 10%; nonresident alien 7%.

International Students: 297 nonresident aliens enrolled fall 2008. Students from Europe, Asia, Latin America, Africa, Canada, Australia, Middle East. Programs available to aid students whose native language is not English: social, cultural. English as a Second Language Program. Financial aid specifically designated for international students: scholarships available annually to qualifying students.

Student Life: On-campus residence halls house 92% of student body. *Intercollegiate athletics:* male: baseball, basketball, cross-country, football, golf, soccer, tennis, track; female: basketball, cross-country, field hockey, lacrosse, swimming and diving, tennis, track synchronized swimming. *Special regulations:* Parking in designated areas only. *Special services:* Media Resources Center, medical services, International Education Center, Speech Center, Writing Center. *Student publications: The Collegian*, a weekly newspaper; *Juris Publici*, an irregularly published law school newspaper; *The Messenger*, an annual literary magazine; *The T.C. Williams Law Review*, an annual publication; *The Web*, a yearbook. Radio station WDCE-FM broadcasts 100 hours per week. *Surrounding community:* Richmond metropolitan area population 700,000. Served by mass transit bus system, airport 20 miles from campus, passenger rail service 10 miles from campus.

Publications: *University of Richmond Magazine*, quarterly since 1936; *Developments*, a fundraising newsletter; *Richmond Law,* a semiannual magazine for Law School alumni; *Richmond Alumni Magazine,* a quarterly publication for alumni and friends of the university.

Library Collections: 1,082,803 volumes including bound books, serial backfiles, electronic documents, and government documents not in separate collections. Online catalog. Current serial subscriptions: 2,243 paper and microform; 18,588 via electronic access. 17,684 recordings; 8,742 compact discs; 374 CD-ROMs. Computer work stations available. Students have access to the Internet at no charge.

Most important special holdings include Meredith Collection of Confederate Imprints; Carl Vechten/Mark Lutz Literature Collections; Gresham Collection of 20th Century First Editions.

Buildings and Grounds: Campus area 365 acres. Campus DVD available.

Chief Executive Officer: Dr. William E. Cooper, President.

Address admission inquiries to Pamela W. Spence, Dean of Admissions.

T. C. Williams School of Law

Degree Programs Offered: *First-professional.*

Admission: Graduation from an approved college or university; minimum 18 years of age.

Degree Requirements: 2.0 GPA; 86 semester hours within 5 calendar years.

Departments and Teaching Staff: *Professors* 15, *associate professors* 4, *assistant professors* 4, *part-time faculty* 61. *Total full-time instructional faculty:* 23.

Distinctive Educational Programs: Joint J.D.-master's in social work and joint J.S. and master of urban planning with Virginia Commonwealth University; joint J.D.-master of health administration with the Medical College of Virginia; joint J.D. and master of business administration with the Richard S. Reynolds Graduate School of Business at the University of Richmond.

University of Virginia

University Station
P.O. Box 400224
Charlottesville, Virginia 22904-4224
Tel: (434) 982-3200 **E-mail:** undergrad-admission@virginia.edu
Fax: (434) 924-3587 **Internet:** www.virginia.edu

Institution Description: The University of Virginia is a state institution. The University also maintains the University of Virginia's College at Wise. *Enrollment:* 24,541. *Degrees awarded:* Baccalaureate, first-professional (law, medicine), master's, doctorate. Specialist certificates in education also awarded.

Academic offerings subject to approval by statewide coordinating bodies. Budget subject to approval by state governing boards. Member of Central Virginia Consortium and Oak Ridge Associated Universities.

Accreditation: *Regional:* SACS-Comm. on Coll. *Professional*: architecture, business, chemistry, cytotechnology, engineering, landscape architecture, law, medicine, music, nuclear medicine technology, nursing, radiation therapy, radiography, speech-language pathology, teacher education

History: Established and chartered under sponsorship of Thomas Jefferson 1819; offered first instruction at postsecondary level 1825; awarded first degree (first-professional) 1828. *See* Alexander Bruce, *A History of the University of Virginia 1819–1919* (New York: Macmillan and Company, 1921) for further information.

Institutional Structure: *Governing board:* The Rector and Visitors of the University. Representation: 15 Visitors (voting), 1 Rector (voting), 1 student (non-voting). The Rector and 13 Visitors are alumni. *Composition of institution:* Administrators 562. Academic affairs headed by vice president and provost. Management/business/finances directed by executive vice president and chief financial officer. Full-time instructional faculty 1,217. Academic governing body, Faculty Senate.

Calendar: Semesters. Academic year Sept. to May. Freshmen admitted Sept. Degrees conferred May, Aug., Jan. Formal commencement May. Summer session of 1 term from early June to early Aug.

Characteristics of Freshmen: 18,363 applicants (female 9,982; male 8,377). 37% of applicants admitted. 19% of applicants admitted and enrolled.

98% (3,029 students) submitted SAT scores; 15% (456 students) submitted ACT scores. *25th percentile*: SAT Critical Reading 600, SAT 620 620; ACT Composite 26, ACT English 26, ACT 2 th 26. *75th percentile*: SAT Critical Reading 710, SAT Math 720; ACT Composite 31, ACT English 32, ACT Math 32.

91% of entering freshmen expected to graduate within 5 years. 64% of freshmen from Virginia. Freshmen from 47 states and 66 foreign countries.

Admission: For baccalaureate, recommended application in fall of senior year; deadline Jan. 2. Students are notified of acceptance on April 1. *Requirements:* 16 secondary school units which must include 4 English, 4 math, 2 lab sciences, 2 same foreign language, 1 social studies. Additional units in foreign language, math, science and social studies are recommended. Additional requirements exist for some programs. *Entrance tests:* College Board SAT I (preferred) or ACT, and 2 tests of the student's choice. *For transfer students:* To be competitive, 3.0–3.5 GPA from 4-year or 2-year accredited institution is recommended. 66 hours maximum transfer credit. Additional requirements for some programs. Admissions information for graduate and first-professional programs vary by school.

College credit and advanced placement may be earned through Advanced Placement Test.

Degree Requirements: 120–132 semester hours; 2.0 GPA; 2 years in residence. Additional requirements vary.

Fulfillment of some degree requirements and exemption from some beginning courses possible by passing College Board APP. *Grading system:* A–F; pass-fail; withdraw (deadline after which pass-fail is appended to withdraw).

Distinctive Educational Programs: Flexible meeting places and schedules, including off-campus centers (at Charlottesville; Richmond, 70 miles away; Falls Church, 120 miles away; Hampton Roads, 150 miles away; Abingdon, 180 miles away), weekend and evening classes. Facilities and programs for independent research, including individual majors, tutorials. *Other distinctive programs:* School of Continuing and Professional Studies awards a Bachelor of Interdisciplinary Studies degree. Courses for credit and enrichment are also provided. Study abroad programs include University of Virginia/University of Valencia Program in Spain; Summer Intensive Arabic Program in Jordan; Special Relationship with Birkbeck College in London, England. Semester at Sea affiliation

ROTC: Army, Navy, Air Force.

Degrees Conferred: 3,526 *baccalaureate* (B), 1,836 *master's* (M), 327 *doctorate* (D): architecture 94 (B), 72 (M), 1 (D); area and ethnic studies 20 (B), 3 (M); biological sciences 132 (B), 3 (M), 41 (D); business and management 325 (B), 476 (M), 1 (D); computer and information sciences 57 (B), 21 (M), 5 (D); education 23 (B), 468 (M), 89 (D); engineering 368 (B), 150 (M), 50 (D); English 232 (B), 41 (M), 12 (D); foreign languages and literature 116 (B), 29 (M), 6 (D); health professions 129 (B), 73 (M), 5 (D); law/legal studies 34 (M), 3 (D); liberal arts 177 (B); mathematics 24 (B), 7 (M), 6 (D); natural resources/environmental sciences 51 (B), 10 (M), 7 (D); philosophy/religion 113 (B), 13 (M), 20 (D); physical sciences 138 (B), 26 (M), 28 (D); psychology 252 (B), 74 (M), 27 (D); social sciences and history 946 (B), 74 (M), 34 (D); visual and performing arts 125 (B), 33 (M), 4 (D). 513 *first-professional:* law 376; medicine 137.

Fees and Other Expenses: *Full-time tuition per academic year 2008–09:* undergraduate resident $9,300 nonresident $29,600; contact the university for current graduate and first-professional tuition and applicable fees that vary by program. *Room per and board academic year:* $7,820. *Books and supplies:* $1,150. *Other expenses:* $2,139.

Financial Aid: Aid from institutionally generated funds is provided on the basis of academic merit, financial need, athletic ability.

Financial aid to full-time, first-time undergraduate students: 545 received some form of aid. Average amount of aid received: federal grants $3,780; Pell grants $2,876; other federal aid $988; state/local grants $6,122; institutional grants $10,861.

Departments and Teaching Staff: *Total instructional faculty:* 1,296 (full-time 1,217, part-time 78). *Student/faculty ratio:* 15.3:1. Degrees held by full-time faculty: 93% hold terminal degrees.

Enrollment: Total enrollment 24,541. Undergraduate 15,208 (full-time 95%; female 56%, male 44%). Graduate 4,333 (full-time 67%). Transfer-in students 588.

Characteristics of Student Body: *Ethnic/racial makeup:* Black non-Hispanic: 8%; Asian or Pacific Islander: 11%; Hispanic: 4%; White non-Hispanic: 62%; unknown: 9%; nonresident alien 5%. *Age distribution:* number 17–21: 63%; 22–24: 14%; 25–29: 14%; 30–34: 5%; 35–39: 2%; 40–49: 2%.

International Students: 1,638 nonresident aliens enrolled fall 2008. Programs available to aid students whose native language is not English: social, cultural. English as a Second Language Program. No financial aid specifically designated for international students.

Student Life: On-campus residence halls house 27% of the student body including 44% of the undergraduate students. Males and females are separated by floors. No residence halls are totally comprised of a single sex. 30% of all undergraduate males join and 12% live in fraternity housing; 30% of all undergraduate females join and 6% live in sorority housing. *Intercollegiate athletics:* male: baseball, basketball, cross-country, football, golf, lacrosse, soccer, swimming, tennis, track, wrestling; female: basketball, cross-country, field hockey, golf, lacrosse, rowing, softball, swimming, tennis, track, volleyball, soccer. *Special regulations:* Cars not permitted for first semester freshmen. *Special services:* Medical services, bus service on campus. *Student publications, radio: The Cavalier Daily*, a five-day a week newspaper; *The Declaration*, a weekly newspaper; *Corks and Curls*, a yearbook; *Law Weekly*, a newspaper published 24 times per year; *Loki*, a biannual literary magazine; *Virginia Literary Review*, a literary magazine published 8 times per year; *Essays in History*, an annual literary magazine. Radio station WTJU-FM; WUV. *Surrounding community:* Charlottesville metropolitan area population 132,000. Washington (DC) 120 miles from campus. Richmond (VA) 65 miles away. Served by airport 9 miles from campus; passenger rail service 1 mile from campus and bus service 2 miles from campus.

Library Collections: 6,073,000 volumes including bound books, serial backfiles, electronic documents, and government documents not in separate collections. Online catalog. Current serial publications: 24,673 paper; 2,703 microform; 44,449 via electronic access. 89,076 recordings; 10,051 DVD discs; 10,982 CD-ROMs. Computer work stations throughout the campus. Students have access to the Internet at no charge.

Most important special holdings include Barrett Library of American Literature; McGregor Library of American History; Massey William Faulkner Collection.

Buildings and Grounds: Campus area 1,691 acres.

Chief Executive Officer: Dr. Leonard W. Sandridge, President.

Address admission inquiries to John A. Blackburn, Director of Admissions. graduate/professional school inquiries to appropriate school.

UNIVERSITY OF VIRGINIA—*cont'd*

Darden Graduate School of Business Administration

Degree Programs Offered: *Master's* and *doctorate*.

Degree Requirements: For the MBA/MA degrees, candidates must complete the usual 2-year MBA program and integrate 1-year requirements from the department chosen in the graduate school of arts and sciences at UVA.

Distinctive Educational Programs: Student research opportunities and assistance to area businesses provided through Center for International Banking Studies, Center for the Study of Applied Ethics, Tayloe Murphy Institute. Joint MBA/JD, MBA/MA in East Asian studies, government, or foreign affairs. Professional development programs in management for public and private sector. *See* School of Law and Graduate School of Arts and Sciences.

School of Nursing

Degree Programs Offered: *Baccalaureate, master's, doctorate.*

Degree Requirements: *For baccalaureate:* 120 semester hours, residence requirement; *for master's:* 30 semester hours; *for doctorate:* 90 semester hours (post-baccalaureate).

Distinctive Educational Programs: Baccalaureate nursing study begins at the sophomore level and students select a fourth year area of focus in either acute care nursing or health promotion/long term care nursing. Master's areas of concentration offered in medical-surgical, mental health-psychiatric, pediatric, and primary care nursing as well as tracks in home health and rural health care. Doctoral program, providing for post-baccalaureate and post-master's study, prepares scholars and researchers through a course of study in the nursing field, psychosocial or complex organization in nursing minor, research, a selected cognate area, and electives.

School of Law

Degree Programs Offered: *First-professional, master's*, and *doctorate*.

Admission: *For first-professional degree:* baccalaureate from accredited college or university; LSAT; transcript; personal statement; letters of recommendation; registration with LSDAS.

Degree Requirements: *For first-professional degree:* 86 credit hours, 2.0 GPA, 6 months in residence.

Distinctive Educational Programs: Joint J.D.-master's in economics, history, philosophy, sociology; J.D.-master's and J.D.-Ph.D. in government and foreign affairs with Graduate School of Arts and Sciences. Joint J.D.-M.B.A. with Graduate School of Business Administration. Research opportunities available through the Institute of Law, Psychiatry, and Public Policy.

Curry School of Education

Degree Programs Offered: *Baccalaureate* in health and physical education, speech pathology and audiology; *master's* in communication disorders; *master's* and *doctorate* in administration and supervision, counselor education, curriculum and instruction, education, educational psychology, health and physical education, special education, higher education; *doctorate* in clinical psychology. The Curry School also offers a 5-year integrated teacher education program which will culminate in a student receiving a B.A. degree and M.Ed. degree at the end of 5 years. This program is one of the most innovative in the country and complies with the recommendations of the Holmes Group and the Governor's Commission on Excellence in Education.

Distinctive Educational Programs: Study-travel in Eastern Europe in conjunction with seminar on comparative education. Research and community service centers include Bureau of Educational Research, Center for Physical Fitness, Center for the Study of Higher Education, Center for Youth and Family Studies, Child Development Center, Consultative Research Center, Evaluation Research Center, McGuffey Reading Center, Motor Development Clinic, Motor Learning and Sport Psychology Laboratory, Speech and Hearing Center.

College of Arts and Sciences/Graduate School of Arts and Sciences

Degree Programs Offered: *Baccalaureate* in Afro-American and African studies, anthropology, area studies, art, astronomy, biology, chemistry, classics, drama, economics, English, environmental sciences, foreign affairs, French, general and comparative literature, German, government, history, Italian, mathematics, music, philosophy, physics, psychology, religious studies, Slavic languages and literature, sociology, Spanish. *Master's* in Asian studies, creative writing, drama, Italian, linguistics, music, *master's* and *doctorate* in anthropology, astronomy, biology, chemistry, classics, economics, English, environmental sciences, French, foreign affairs, German, government, history, history of art, mathematics, philosophy, physics, psychology, religious studies, Slavic languages and literature, sociology, Spanish.

Distinctive Educational Programs: Accelerated degree programs. Interdisciplinary programs in Afro-American, African, Asian, Latin American, Russian area studies, physics-astronomy. Honors program. Independent study; funded independent research. Study abroad in Austria, Brazil, China, Denmark, England, France, Greece, Hong Kong, India, Ireland, Israel, Italy, Japan, Korea, Mexico, Portugal, Russia, Scotland, Spain, Sweden, Taiwan, Germany. Echols Scholars program offers individually designed course of study for outstanding students. Curriculum I program for students who take their first and second year classes together. Freshman seminars on selected topics.

School of Architecture

Degree Programs Offered: *Baccalaureate* and *master's* in architectural history, architecture, planning, landscape architecture; *doctorate* in architectural history.

Distinctive Educational Programs: Research centers, including the Center of Housing and Social Environment, the Center for Research and Innovations for Buildings. Study abroad in Italy.

School of Medicine

Degree Programs Offered: *Master's* in biological and physical sciences, health evaluation sciences; surgery; *doctorate* in biochemistry, biophysics, cell biology, microbiology, neuroscience, pharmacology, physiology; *certificate* in medical technology.

Admission: 90 semester hours from an accredited college or university; 2 years each of biology (with lab), general chemistry (with lab), physics. MCAT; credentials must be assembled by AMCAS.

Degree Requirements: Prescribed curriculum first 2 years; 12 months clinical clerkship; 8 months optional clinical clerkship.

McIntire School of Commerce

Degree Programs Offered: *Baccalaureate* in commerce with concentrations in accounting, finance, international business, management, management information systems and marketing; *master of science* in accounting and management information systems.

Distinctive Educational Programs: Study-travel in Europe through a summer program in international business. Programs for the liberal arts through the McIntire Business Institute and the Career Opportunities Institute for the Arts and Sciences. Research centers include the Center for Entrepreneurial Studies and the Center for Financial Services Studies. Service to the community through the Small Business Institute and the Volunteer Income Tax Assistance Program (VITA). Service to the financial services industry through the Graduate School of Retail Bank Management and the Virginia Bankers School of Bank Management. Marketing research projects through the McIntire Research Associates. Management educational programs offered for the business, financial, governmental and professional communities.

School of Engineering and Applied Science

Degree Programs Offered: *Baccalaureate* in aerospace engineering, engineering science, mechanical engineering; *baccalaureate* and *master's* in applied mathematics, chemical, civil, computer science, electrical engineering, systems engineering; *master's* in applied mechanics, biomedical engineering, engineering, engineering physics, materials science; *master's* and *doctorate* in biomedical engineering, mechanical and aerospace engineering; *doctorate* in applied mathematics, chemical engineering, civil engineering, computer science, electrical engineering, engineering physics, materials science, nuclear engineering, systems engineering.

Distinctive Educational Programs: Research laboratories with facilities which include 500 KV electron microscope, 200 KV ion accelerator, X-ray diffraction units, complete polymer science laboratory, 2-megawatt swimming pool reactor, Schladitz chemical vapor disposition facility. Center for the Application of Science and Engineering to Public Affairs. Virginia Highway and Transportation Research Council.

University of Virginia's College at Wise

One College Avenue
Wise, Virginia 24293
Tel: (276) 328-0100 **E-mail:** admissions@uvawise.edu
Fax: (276) 376-1012 **Internet:** www.uvawise.edu

Institution Description: University of Virginia's College at Wise, formerly Clinch Valley College, is a unit of the University of Virginia system. *Enrollment:* 1,953. *Degrees awarded:* Baccalaureate.

Member of the Western Region Consortium for Continuing Higher Education.

Accreditation: *Regional:* SACS-Comm. on Coll.

History: Established and chartered as 2-year institution, and offered first instruction at postsecondary level 1954; became 4-year institution 1968; awarded first degree (baccalaureate) 1970; became the University of Virginia's College at Wise 1999. *See* George H. Zehmer, *Clinch Valley College* (Charlottesville, VA: University of Virginia Press, 1965) for further information.

Institutional Structure: *Composition of institution:* Administrators 19. Academic affairs headed provost. Management/business/finances directed by associate vice chancellor for administration. Full-time instructional faculty 67. Academic governance body, the faculty, meets an average of 4 times per year.

Calendar: Semesters. Academic year late Aug. to mid-May. Freshmen admitted Aug., Jan., June, July. Formal commencement and degrees conferred May. Summer session from late May to mid-Aug.

Characteristics of Freshmen: 74% of applicants accepted. 40% of accepted applicants enrolled.

45% of entering freshmen expected to graduate within 5 years. 95% of freshmen from Virginia. Freshmen from 5 states.

Admission: Rolling admissions plan. For fall acceptance, apply as early as Oct. of senior year of secondary school, but not later than Aug. of year of enrollment. Early acceptance available. *Requirements:* Either graduation from accredited secondary school with 23 units (grades 8–12); or GED. Minimum 2.0 GPA. *Entrance tests:* College Board SAT and 1 Achievement or ACT composite. For foreign students TOEFL. *For transfer students:* 2.0 minimum GPA.

College credit and advanced placement for postsecondary-level work completed in secondary school.

Tutoring available. Noncredit developmental courses offered in summer session and regular academic year.

Degree Requirements: 120 credit hours; 2.2 GPA; 30 semester hours in residence; core requirements.

Fulfillment of some degree requirements and exemption from some beginning courses possible by passing departmental examinations, College Board AP. *Grading system:* A–F; pass-fail; withdraw.

Distinctive Educational Programs: Work-experience programs. Evening classes. Interdisciplinary programs in arts, sciences. Preprofessional programs in forestry, law, medicine, nursing, physical therapy. Facilities and programs for independent research, including individual majors, tutorials. Electronic Classroom. Study abroad by individual arrangement. *Other distinctive programs:* Continuing education. Tuition-free courses for senior citizens. Liberal arts program that makes extensive use of technology. Business program with an entrepreneurial emphasis.

Degrees Conferred: 267 *baccalaureate*. Bachelor's degrees awarded in top five disciplines: business, management, marketing, and related support services 81; social sciences 43; liberal arts/general studies 36; multidisciplinary studies 34; history 23.

Fees and Other Expenses: *Full-time tuition per academic year:* contact the university for current information regarding tuition, fees, housing, and other costs.

Financial Aid: Aid from institutionally generated funds is provided on the basis of academic merit, financial need, athletic ability, other criteria.

Financial aid to full-time, first-time undergraduate students: 49% received federal grants averaging $2,950; 45% state/local grants averaging $2,265; 45% institutional grants averaging $2,045; 50% received loans averaging $2,323.

Departments and Teaching Staff: *Total instructional faculty:* 97. Student/faculty ratio: 18:1. Degrees held by full-time faculty: doctorate 75%, master's 20%, professional 5%. 80% hold terminal degrees.

Enrollment: Total enrollment 1,953.

Characteristics of Student Body: *Ethnic/racial makeup:* Black non-Hispanic: 5%; American Indian or Alaska Native: 1%; Asian or Pacific Islander: 1%; Hispanic: 1%; White non-Hispanic: 93%.

International Students: 7 nonresident aliens enrolled fall 2008. No programs available to aid students whose native language is not English. Financial aid specifically designated for international students: 2 scholarships awarded annually.

Student Life: On-campus residence halls house 35% of student body. Residence halls for males constitute 11% of such space, for females 9%, for both sexes 80%. 11% of student body housed on campus in mobile home units. 1% of males live in fraternity housing. Housing available for married students. 47% of student body lives on campus. *Intercollegiate athletics:* male: baseball, basketball, golf, tennis; female: basketball, tennis. *Special regulations:* Cars with decals permitted. *Special services:* Learning Resources Center, medical services. *Student publications: Highland Cavalier*, a weekly newspaper; *The Outpost*, a yearbook. *Surrounding community:* Wise population 4,000. Greensboro-Winston-Salem-High Point, 150 miles from campus, is nearest metropolitan area. Served by airport 5 miles from campus.

Library Collections: 150,000 volumes including bound books, serial backfiles, electronic documents, and government documents not in separate collections. Online catalog. Current serial subscriptions: 584 paper, 167 microform, 23 electronic. 2,933 recordings; 837 compact 203 discs; CD-ROMs. Computer work stations available. Students have access to the Internet at no charge.

Most important special holdings include archives of Southwest Virginia Historical Society; Elihu Jasper Sutherland Papers; James Taylor Adams Papers; Emory Hamilton Collection.

Buildings and Grounds: Campus area 350 acres.

Chief Executive Officer: Dr. David J. Prior, Chancellor.

Address admission inquiries to Russell D. Necessary, Vice Chancellor for Enrollment Management.

Virginia Commonwealth University

901 West Franklin Street
P.O. Box 842512
Richmond, Virginia 23284-2512
Tel: (804) 828-0100 **E-mail:** ugrad@vcu.edu
Fax: (804) 828-1899 **Internet:** www.vcu.edu

Institution Description: Virginia Commonwealth University is a public institution. *Enrollment:* 32,044. *Degrees awarded:* Associate, baccalaureate, first-professional (dentistry, medicine, pharmacy), master's, doctorate. Certificates also awarded.

Academic offerings subject to approval by statewide coordinating bodies. Budget subject to approval by state governing boards. Member of Capital Consortium.

Accreditation: *Regional:* SACS-Comm. on Coll. *Professional*: art, athletic training, business, chemistry, clinical lab scientist, computer science, dance, dental hygiene, dentistry, health services administration, interior design, journalism, medical record administration, medicine, music, nuclear medicine technology, nursing, occupational therapy, pharmacy, physical therapy, psychology internship, planning, public administration, public health, radiation therapy technology, radiography, recreation and leisure services, rehabilitation counseling, social work, teacher education, theatre

History: Established by merger of The Medical College of Virginia (established 1937) and Richmond Professional Institute (established 1917) and awarded first degree (baccalaureate) 1968. *See* Wyndham B. Blanton, *Medicine in Virginia in the Nineteenth Century* (Richmond: Garrett and Massie, 1933) and RPT Foundation, *The History of Richmond Professional Institute* (Richmond: Whittet and Sheperson, 1971) for further information.

Institutional Structure: *Governing board:* Board of Visitors. Representation: 16 visitors. All voting. *Composition of institution:* Academic affairs headed by provost and vice president for academic affairs and vice-president for health sciences. Management/business/finances directed by senior vice president for finance and administration. Full-time instructional faculty 1,696. Academic governance body, Faculty Senate and University Council, meet an average of 9 times per year.

Calendar: Semesters. Academic year late Aug. to May. Freshmen admitted Aug., Jan. Degrees conferred May, Aug., Dec. Formal commencement May. Summer session from mid-may to mid-Aug.

Characteristics of Freshmen: 87% of applicants admitted. 46% of applicants admitted and enrolled.

95% (3,184 students) submitted SAT scores; 12% (420 students) submitted ACT scores. *25th percentile*: SAT Critical Reading 480, SAT Math 470; ACT Composite 19. *75th percentile*: SAT Critical Reading 590, SAT Math 580; ACT Composite 23.

37% of entering freshmen expected to graduate within 5 years. 90% of freshmen from Virginia. Freshmen from 27 states and 33 foreign countries.

Admission: Rolling admissions plan. Recommended deadline Feb. 1 for fall acceptance. Early acceptance available. *Requirements:* Either graduation from secondary school or GED. For applicants to School of Arts, completion of Arts Admissions Packet. For all other applicants, 4 units English, 3 mathematics (one of which must be algebra and one which must be geometry or algebra II), 2 science (including 1 laboratory science), 3 social science, 7 academic electives. Additional units in college preparatory mathematics and laboratory science recommended for some programs. *Entrance tests:* College Board SAT Reasoning or

VIRGINIA COMMONWEALTH UNIVERSITY—*cont'd*

ACT. SAT I not required for freshmen 22 or older. *For transfer students:* 2.0 minimum GPA; maximum transfer credit limited only by residence requirement.

College credit and advanced placement for postsecondary-level work completed in secondary school and for extrainstitutional learning on basis of portfolio assessment.

Tutoring available. Noncredit remedial courses offered in summer session and regular academic year.

Degree Requirements: *For all baccalaureate degrees:* minimum requirements are needed for completion of a major: at least 30 credits in the major area, at least half of which are at the 300 or 400 level; GPA 2.0 or higher in courses in the student's major presented for graduation unless the major specifies a higher GPA; any special conditions stipulated by the major.

Fulfillment of some degree requirements and exemption from some beginning courses possible by passing departmental examinations, College Board CLEP, AP. *Grading system:* A–F; withdraw (carries time limit).

Distinctive Educational Programs: Work-experience programs. Flexible meeting places and schedules, including off-campus courses at various locations in the Richmond metropolitan area and throughout the state, and evening classes. Accelerated degree programs. Special facilities for using telecommunications in the classroom. Interdepartmental/interdisciplinary programs in gerontology, interdisciplinary studies, social policy, and social work. Facilities and programs for independent research, including honors programs, individual majors, tutorials. Bachelor of general studies program offers flexible scheduling and individualized curricula for older students. *Other distinctive programs:* Credit and noncredit continuing education programs. Cooperative Education Program and International Studies.

ROTC: Army.

Degrees Conferred: 3,544 *baccalaureate;*; 1,281 *master's*; 146 *doctorate*. Bachelor's degrees awarded in top five disciplines: visual and performing arts 438; business, management, marketing, and related support services 392; health professions and related clinical sciences 257; psychology 248; social sciences and history 179. 335 *first-professional:* dentistry 72; medicine 171; pharmacy 92.

Fees and Other Expenses: *Full-time tuition per academic year 2008–09:* resident $6,799, nonresident $19,724; contact the university for current graduate and professional school resident and nonresident tuition and fees. *Room and board per academic year:* $9,430.

Financial Aid: Aid from institutionally generated funds is provided on the basis of academic merit, financial need, athletic ability, other criteria.

Financial aid to full-time, first-time undergraduate students: 70% received some form of aid. Average amount of aid received: federal grants $3,853; Pell grants $2,967; other federal aid $1,404; state/local grants $3,386; institutional grants $3,427.

Departments and Teaching Staff: *Total instructional faculty:* 3,261 (full-time 1,696, part-time 975). Student/faculty ratio: 14:1.

Enrollment: Total enrollment 32,044. Undergraduate 22,552 (full-time 81%; female 51%, male 43%). Graduate 9,452 (full-time 55%). Transfer-in students 1,891.

Characteristics of Student Body: *Ethnic/racial makeup:* Black non-Hispanic: 19%; American Indian or Alaska Native: 1%; Asian or Pacific Islander: 11%; Hispanic: 4%; White non-Hispanic: 52%; unknown: 10%; nonresident alien 4%. *Age distribution:* number under 18: 458; 18–19: 5,883, 20–21: 5,404; 22–24: 3,759; 25–29: 117; 30–34: 742; 35–39: 439; 40–49: 467; 50–64: 190; 65 and over: 9; unknown: 102.

International Students: 1,282 nonresident aliens enrolled fall 2008. Programs available to aid students whose native language is not English: English as a Second Language Program. No financial aid specifically designated for international students.

Student Life: On-campus residence halls house 4,068 students. Most residence halls accommodate both sexes with single-sex residence halls available on both campuses. *Intercollegiate athletics:* male: baseball, basketball, cheerleading, cross-country, golf, soccer, tennis, track and field; female: basketball, cheerleading, cross-country, field hockey, tennis, track and field, volleyball. *Special regulations:* Cars with parking permits allowed on campus during evening hours. *Special services:* Office of Academic Support, Office of Services for Students with Disabilities. medical services, university counseling services, alumni career network, Career Center. Campus bus service between academic campus and medical college campus. *Student publications, radio: Commonwealth Times*, student press published twice a week during the school year. *Millennium*, student magazine published once a year in the spring. The *Vine-Multi Ethnic Student News Magazine,* published six times per year. Radio station WVCW. *Surrounding community:* Richmond population 220,000. Served by mass transit bus system; airport 8 miles from campus; passenger rail service 12 miles from campus.

Library Collections: 2 million volumes. 3,186,000 microforms; 104,000 audiovisual materials; 17,500 print and electronic journal subscriptions; access to articles form over 20,000 electronic titles; over 4,500 linear feet of manuscripts. Online catalog. Students have access to online information retrieval services and the Internet.

Most important special holdings include James Branch Cabell Collection; Medical Artifacts Collection; Book Art Collection; Health Sciences Serials.

Buildings and Grounds: Campus area 152 acres.

Chief Executive Officer: Dr. Eugene P. Trani, President.

Address admission inquiries to Sybil C. Halloran, Director of Admissions.

Virginia Intermont College

1013 Moore Street
Bristol, Virginia 24201

Tel: (800) 451-1842 **E-mail:** viadmit@vic.edu
Fax: (276) 669-5763 **Internet:** www.vic.edu

Institution Description: Virginia Intermont College is a private college affiliated with the Baptist General Association of Virginia. *Enrollment:* 542. *Degrees awarded:* Associate, baccalaureate.

Accreditation: *Regional:* SACS-Comm. on Coll. *Professional*: social work

History: Established in Glade Spring as Southwest Virginia Institute and offered first instruction at postsecondary level 1884; awarded first degree (baccalaureate) 1890; moved to present locations and changed name to Virginia Institute 1891; chartered 1902; adopted present name 1910.

Institutional Structure: *Governing board:* Board of Trustees of Virginia Intermont College. Representation: 32 trustees. All voting. *Composition of institution:* Administrators 6. Academic affairs headed by provost. Management/business/finances directed by chief financial officer. Full-time instructional faculty 44. Academic governance body, Faculty of Virginia Intermont College, meets an average of 9 times per year.

Calendar: Semesters. Academic year Aug. to May. Freshmen admitted Aug., Jan. Formal commencement May, Dec. May Term and summer School available.

Characteristics of Freshmen: 902 applicants (female 708, male 194). 58% of applicants admitted. 25% of applicants admitted and enrolled.

75% (446 students) submitted SAT scores; 25% (148 students) submitted ACT scores. *25th percentile*: SAT Critical Reading 410, SAT Math 410; ACT Composite 17, ACT English 14, ACT Math 16. *75th percentile*: SAT Critical Reading 530, SAT Math 540; ACT Composite 25, ACT English 24,ACT Math 24.

19% of entering freshmen expected to graduate within 5 years. 38% of freshmen from Virginia. Freshmen from 22 states and 10 foreign countries.

Admission: Rolling admissions plan. For fall acceptance, apply as early as spring of previous year. Early acceptance available. *Requirements:* Either graduation from accredited secondary school with a program normally comprised of 15 units, or GED. Minimum GPA 2.0. *Entrance tests:* College Board SAT/ACT accepted. For foreign students TOEFL. *For transfer students:* 2.0 minimum GPA; 30 of final 36 semester hours must be earned in residence; at least half of the hours in the major area must be completed in residence; correspondence/extension students may apply 9 hours to program requirements.

College credit and advanced placement for postsecondary-level work completed in secondary school. College credit for extrainstitutional learning.

Tutoring available.

Degree Requirements: 48-hour B.A. and B.S.W. core curriculum; 49 hour B.S. core curriculum. 124 hours to receive baccalaureate degree.

Fulfillment of some degree requirements and exemption from some beginning courses possible by passing College Board CLEP, AP (score of 3). *Grading system:* A–F.

Distinctive Educational Programs: Many majors offer internships and field experiences. Equine studies; photography; criminal justice with a rehabilitative focus; visual and performing arts; youth ministry. Accelerated degree program for adults (baccalaureate) both on- and off-campus. Study abroad opportunities.

Degrees Conferred: 2 *associate;* 246 *baccalaureate:* agriculture 18; biological sciences 9; business and management 24; computer and information sciences 9; education 100; English 3; health professions and related clinical sciences 3; law/legal studies 8; parks and recreation 4; personal and culinary services 7; philosophy/religion 1; psychology 5; security and protective services 1; social sciences 14; visual and performing arts 20.

Fees and Other Expenses: *Full-time tuition per academic year 2008–09:* $23,210. *Required fees:* $950. *Room and board per academic year:* $6,820. *Books and supplies:* $800. *Other expenses:* $350.

Financial Aid: Aid from institutionally generated funds is provided on the basis of academic merit, financial need, athletic ability.

Financial aid to full-time, first-time undergraduate students: 96% received some form of aid.

Departments and Teaching Staff: *Total instructional faculty:* 84 (full-time 44, part-time 40). Total faculty with doctorate, first-professional, or other terminal 50. Student/faculty ratio: 12:1. Degrees held by full-time faculty: baccalaureate 7%, master's 44%, doctorate 49%. 67% hold terminal degrees.

Enrollment: Total enrollment 542. Undergraduate 542 (full-time 81%; female 74%, male 26%). Transfer-in students 74.

Characteristics of Student Body: *Ethnic/racial makeup:* Black non-Hispanic: 6%; Asian or Pacific Islander: 1%; Hispanic: 6%; White non-Hispanic: 89%; unknown: 2%; nonresident alien 1%.

International Students: 5 nonresident aliens enrolled fall 2008. Students from Europe, Asia, Latin America, Africa, Canada, Australia. Programs available to aid students whose native language is not English: social, cultural. English as a Second Language Program. No financial aid specifically designated for international students.

Student Life: On-campus residence halls house 48% of traditional student body. *Intercollegiate athletics:* male: baseball, golf; female: softball, volleyball; both men/women:basketball, cross-country, equestrian, soccer, tennis, track and field. *Special regulations:* Registered cars permitted. Visitation hours; late key privilege; junior/senior honors housing. *Special services:* Student Support Services Office; free tutoring and counseling. *Student publications: Moore Street Review,* a literary magazine; *The Intermont,* a yearbook; *The Cobra Crier,* a newspaper. *Surrounding community:* Bristol population approximately 50,000. Bristol is part of the Tri-Cities Tennessee/Virginia area. Tri-Cities Airport is 20 miles from campus.

Library Collections: 109,800 volumes including bound books, serial backfiles, electronic documents, and government documents not in separate collections. Online catalog. 9,200 microforms; 2,210 audiovisual matereals; 15,000 periodicals including via electronic access. Computer work stations available. Students have access to the Internet at no charge.

Most important special holdings include collections on paralegal studies, photography and art; equine studies.

Buildings and Grounds: Campus area 25 acres (riding center 129 acres).

Chief Executive Officer: Dr. Michael J. Puglisi, President.

Address admission inquiries to Roger Lowe, Dean of Admissions.

Virginia Military Institute

Smith Hall
Lexington, Virginia 24450
Tel: (540) 464-7230 **E-mail:** admissions@vmi.edu
Fax: (540) 464-7443 **Internet:** www.vmi.edu

Institution Description: Virginia Military Institute is a state institution. *Enrollment:* 1,428. Women were enrolled for the first time in 1997. *Degrees awarded:* Baccalaureate.

Degree programs subject to approval by statewide coordinating bodies. Budget subject to approval by state governing boards. Member of Valley of Virginia Consortium.

Accreditation: *Regional:* SACS-Comm. on Coll. *Professional*: chemistry, engineering

History: Established, chartered, and offered first instruction at postsecondary level 1839; first degree (baccalaureate) awarded 1842. *See* Henry A. Wise, *Drawing Out the Man*, (Charlottesville, University Press of Virginia, 1978) for further information.

Institutional Structure: *Governing board:* Board of Visitors. Extrainstitutional representation: 16 regents, including 13 alumni; governor of Virginia; adjutant general of Virginia. 1 ex officio. 17 voting. *Composition of institution:* Administrators 43. Academic affairs headed by dean of the faculty. Management/business/finances directed by business executive officer. Full-time instructional faculty 106. Academic governance body, Academic Board, meets an average of 10 times per year.

Calendar: Semesters. Academic year Aug. to May. Freshmen admitted Aug. Degrees conferred May, Sept., Dec., Jan. Formal commencement May. Summer session of 2 terms from May to Aug.

Characteristics of Freshmen: 1,721 applicants (female 169, male 1,552). 78% of applicants accepted. 51% of accepted applicants enrolled.

84% (366 students) submitted SAT scores. 31% (137 students) submitted ACT scores. *25th percentile:* 510 Critical Reading, SAT Math 520; ACT Composite 21. *75th percentile:* 610 Critical Reading, 610 SAT Math; ACT Composite 25.

78% of entering freshmen expected to graduate within 5 years. 56% of freshmen from Virginia. Freshmen from 30 states and 1 foreign country.

Admission: For early decision, apply by Nov. 15; decision by Dec. 15. Rolling admission for second semester. *Requirements:* Graduation from secondary school with 19–20 academic desirable: 4 English, 4 mathematics, 3 social studies, 3 lab science, 3–4 foreign language, 2 electives; 2 writing intensive courses. Applicants must meet ROTC physical requirements. Minimum 2.0 GPA. *Entrance tests:* College Board SAT. Achievement tests in English composition and mathematics recommended. ACT accepted. TOEFL may be required. *For transfer students:* 2.0 minimum GPA.

Advanced placement and college credit are available.

Degree Requirements: 136–144 credit hours; 2.0 GPA; 2 years in residence; 3 hours military classes per week for first 2 years, 4 hours per week for final 2 years; all cadets required to take 4 years of ROTC courses and 4 hours physical education.

Distinctive Educational Programs: Independent research, honors programs, teacher certification. Study abroad in England, France, Germany, Australia, Austria, Japan, Mexico, Scotland, Spain, Czech Republic.

ROTC: ROTC required for 4 years; commissioning in the Armed Forces is optional.

Degrees Conferred: 280 *baccalaureate*. Bachelor's degrees awarded in top five disciplines: biological and life sciences 23, engineering 65, English language and literature 12, physical science 9, social sciences and history 125.

Fees and Other Expenses: *Full-time tuition per academic year 2008–09:* $10,586 resident, $27,454 nonresident. *Books and supplies* $775. *Room and board per academic year:* $6,444. *Other expenses:* $1,900.

Financial Aid: Aid from institutionally generated funds is provided on the basis of academic merit, financial need, athletic ability.

Financial aid to full-time, first-time undergraduate students: need-based scholarships/grants totaling $2,808,080, self-help $1,336,599, tuition waivers $40,000, athletic awards $15,476; Pell grants 3,007; non-need-based scholarships/grants totaling $4,948,222, self-help $1,256,866, parent loans $1,784,489, tuition waivers $7,500; athletic awards $1,427,266.

Departments and Teaching Staff: *Total instructional faculty:* 128. Student/faculty ratio: 13:1. Degrees held by full-time faculty: doctorate 93%, master's 7%, 93% hold terminal degrees.

Enrollment: Total enrollment 1,428. Undergraduate 1,428 (full-time 100%; female 8%, male 92%). Transfer-in students 29.

Characteristics of Student Body: *Ethnic/racial makeup:* Black non-Hispanic: 6%; Asian or Pacific Islander: 4%; Hispanic: 4%; White non-Hispanic: 84%; unknown 9%; nonresident alien 2%.

International Students: 24 nonresident aliens enrolled fall 2008. Students from Europe, Asia, Africa. No programs available to aid students whose native language is not English. No financial aid specifically designated for international students.

Student Life: On-campus barracks for males and females house 100% of student body. *Intercollegiate athletics:* male: baseball, basketball, cross-country, football, golf, lacrosse, riflery, soccer, swimming, tennis, track, wrestling; female: cross-country, indoor and outdoor track, swimming. *Special regulations:* Cars permitted for seniors with restricted privileges for juniors. Curfew hours. All cadets wear military uniforms. *Special services:* Medical services. *Student publications: The Bomb*, a yearbook; *VMI Cadet*, a weekly newspaper; *Sounding Brass*, an annual literary magazine. *Surrounding community:* Lexington population 7,500. Roanoke, 50 miles from campus, is nearest metropolitan area.

Library Collections: 470,000 titles. 10,200 microforms; 4,260 audiovisual materials; 950 current periodical subscriptions. Online catalog. Students have access to online information retrieval services and the Internet.

Most important special holdings include Civil War collection; VMI Archives (official documents, diaries, papers of graduates since 1842); Stonewall Jackson Papers; Matthew Fontaine Maury Papers.

Buildings and Grounds: Campus area 140 acres. Campus DVD available.

Chief Executive Officer: General J.H. Binford Peay III, Superintendent.

Address admission inquiries to Col. Vernon L. Beitzel, Director of Admissions.

Virginia Polytechnic Institute and State University

129 Smyth Hall
Blacksburg, Virginia 24061-0433
Tel: (540) 231-6000 **E-mail:** vtadmiss@vt.edu
Fax: (540) 231-9263 **Internet:** www.vt.edu e

Institution Description: Virginia Polytechnic Institute and State University is a state institution and land-grant college. *Enrollment:* 30,739. *Degrees awarded:* Associate, baccalaureate, first-professional (veterinary medicine), master's, doctorate.

Academic offerings subject to approval by statewide coordinating bodies. Budget subject to approval by state governing boards. Member of the Central Virginia Consortium, Valley of Virginia Consortium for Higher Education, Vir-

VIRGINIA POLYTECHNIC INSTITUTE AND STATE UNIVERSITY—*cont'd*

ginia Tidewater Consortium for Continuing Higher Education, Western Region Consortium for Continuing Education.

Accreditation: *Regional:* SACS-Comm. on Coll. *Professional*: accounting, architecture, business, dietetics, engineering, family and consumer science, forestry, interior design, landscape architecture, planning, psychology internship, teacher education, veterinary medicine

History: Chartered as Virginia Agricultural and Mechanical College and offered first instruction at postsecondary level 1872; awarded first degree (baccalaureate) 1883; changed name to Virginia Agricultural and Mechanical College and Polytechnic Institute 1885, to Virginia Polytechnic Institute 1944; adopted present name 1970. *See* Duncan Lyle Kinnear, *The First 100 Years* (Blacksburg, VA: Virginia Polytechnic and State University, 1972) for further information.

Institutional Structure: *Governing board:* The Board of Visitors. Representation: 14 visitors, 13 if whom are appointed by the Governor and confirmed by the Senate of Virginia. 1 ex officio. 13 voting. *Composition of institution:* Administrators 247, Academic affairs headed by provost. Management/business/finances directed by vice presidents for finance and for administration. Full-time instructional faculty 1,410. Academic governance body, University Council, meets an average of 15 times per year.

Calendar: Semesters. Academic year Aug. to May. Freshmen admitted Aug., Jan., Mar., June, July. Degrees conferred and formal commencement June. Summer session from June to Aug.

Characteristics of Freshmen: 10,615 applicants (female 8,752, male 1,863). 65% of applicants accepted. 405 of accepted applicants enrolled full-time. Average secondary school rank of freshmen 79.7 percentile. Mean SAT scores 565 verbal, 585 mathematical.

74% of freshmen from Virginia. Freshmen from 41 states and 32 foreign countries.

Admission: For fall acceptance, apply as early as Sept. 1 of previous year, but not later than Jan. 1 of year of enrollment. Students are notified of acceptance Apr. 1. Apply by Nov. 1 for early decision; need not limit application to Virginia Tech. Early acceptance available. *Requirements:* Either graduation from accredited secondary school with 18 units which must include 4 English, 1 algebra, 1 geometry, 1 history, 1 laboratory science; or GED. Additional requirements for some programs. *Entrance tests:* College Board SAT. For foreign students TOEFL. *For transfer students:* 2.0 minimum GPA.

College credit and advanced placement for postsecondary-level work completed in secondary school.

Noncredit developmental courses offered during regular academic year.

Degree Requirements: Completion of prescribed curriculum. 2.0 GPA; senior year must be completed in residence; distribution requirements.

Fulfillment of some degree requirements and exemption from some beginning courses possible by passing departmental examinations, College Board CLEP, AP. *Grading system:* A–F; pass-fail.

Distinctive Educational Programs: Work-experience programs, including cooperative education, internships. Flexible meeting places and schedules, including off-campus centers (at Fairfax, 250 miles away from main institution) and evening classes. Special facilities for using telecommunications in the classroom. Interdisciplinary programs in integrated pest management, international studies, liberal arts and sciences, public administration, urban affairs. Facilities and programs for independent research, including honors programs, tutorials. Institutionally sponsored study abroad in United Kingdom, Spain, Switzerland. Other academic year programs are conducted through exchange networks and agreements with over 100 universities in 40 different countries.

ROTC: Army, Air Force, Navy.

Degrees Conferred: 33 *associate*; 5,049 *baccalaureate*; 290 *master's*; 290 *doctorate*. Bachelor's degrees awarded in top five disciplines: business, management, marketing, and related support services 1,168; engineering 861; family and consumer science 421; social sciences 305; biological/biomedical sciences 294. *First-professional:* veterinary medicine 93.

Fees and Other Expenses: *Full-time tuition per academic year 2008–09:* undergraduate resident $8,198, nonresident $20,815; contact the university for graduate and veterinary medicine school tuition and fees. *Books and supplies:* $1,080. *Room and board per academic year:* $6.580. *Other expenses:* $3,680.

Financial Aid: Aid from institutionally generated funds is provided on the basis of financial need.

Financial aid to full-time, first-time undergraduate students: 72% received some form of aid. Average amount of aid received: federal grants $3.839; Pell grants $2,903; other federal aid $1,149; state/local grants $3,726; institutional grants $4,168.

Departments and Teaching Staff: *Total instructional faculty:* 1,410. Student/faculty ratio: 18:1. Degrees held by full-time faculty: doctorate 84%, master's 11%, baccalaureate .4%, professional 4%, other .6%. 84% hold terminal degrees.

Enrollment: Total enrollment 30,379. Undergraduate 23,567 full-time 98%. Graduate 7,172 (full-time 62%). Transfer-in students 961.

Characteristics of Student Body: *Ethnic/racial makeup:* Black non-Hispanic: 4%; Asian or Pacific Islander: 8%; Hispanic: 3%; White non-Hispanic: 74%; unknown: 10%; nonresident alien 2%.

International Students: 615 nonresident aliens enrolled fall 2008. Programs available to aid students whose native language is not English: English as a Second Language.

Student Life: On-campus residence halls house 8,080 students. *Intercollegiate athletics:* male: baseball, basketball, football, golf, soccer, swimming, tennis, track, wrestling; women only: basketball, field hockey, swimming, tennis, track, volleyball. *Special regulations:* Cars permitted without restrictions. Residence hall visitation policies vary by residence hall. *Special services:* Learning Resources Center, medical services. *Student publications, radio: Bugle*, a yearbook; *Campus Quarterly*, a magazine; *Collegiate Times*, a biweekly newspaper. Radio station WUVT AM and FM broadcast 168 hours per week. *Surrounding community:* Blacksburg population 31,000. Roanoke, 40 miles from campus, is nearest metropolitan area. Served by airport 40 miles from campus.

Library Collections: 2,300,000 volumes. 399,525 government documents; 6.323.000 microforms; 37,570 audiovisual materials; 35,600 periodical including via electronic access. Online catalog. Students have access to online information retrieval services and the Internet.

Most important special holdings include J. Hoge Tyler Papers (governor of Virginia from 1898–1902); Southwest Virginia account book collection; Virginia Academy of Science Archives (1922 to present).

Buildings and Grounds: Campus area 600 acres. Campus DVD available.

Chief Executive Officer: Dr. Charles W. Steeger, President.

Address undergraduate admission inquiries to Director of Admissions; graduate inquiries to Associate Provost, Research and Graduate Studies.

College of Arts and Sciences

Degree Programs Offered: *Baccalaureate* in art, biochemistry, biology, chemistry, communication studies, computer science, economics, English, French, geology, geography, geophysics, German, history, international studies, liberal arts and sciences, mathematics, music, philosophy, physics, political science, psychology, religion, sociology, Spanish, statistics, theater arts, urban affairs; *master's* in English, geography, history, information systems, political science, theater arts; *master's, doctorate* in botany, chemistry, computer science, geology, geophysics, mathematics, microbiology, physics, psychology, sociology, statistics, zoology.

College of Agriculture and Life Sciences

Degree Programs Offered: *Baccalaureate* in agricultural economics, agronomy, animal science, biochemistry, dairy science, food science and technology, forestry and wildlife, horticulture, integrated pest management, poultry science; *master's* in dairy science, poultry science; *master's, doctorate* in agricultural economics, agronomy, animal science, biochemistry and nutrition, entomology, fisheries and wildlife, food science and technology, forestry and forest products, genetics, horticulture, plant pathology and physiology.

College of Architecture and Urban Studies

Degree Programs Offered: *Baccalaureate* in architecture, building construction, landscape architecture; *master's* in architecture, landscape architecture, urban affairs, urban and regional planning, urban affairs, urban design; *doctorate* in environmental design and planning.

Pamplin College of Business

Degree Programs Offered: *Baccalaureate* in accounting, economics, finance, general business, management, management science, marketing, public administration; *master's* in accounting, business administration, economics; *doctorate* in business, economics.

College of Education

Degree Programs Offered: *Baccalaureate* in elementary education, health education, marketing education, secondary education; *master's* in adult and continuing education, curriculum and instruction, educational administration, health and physical education, student personnel services, vocational technical education; *intermediate, doctorate* in administration and supervision of special education, adult and continuing education, curriculum and instruction, educational administration, junior and community college education, student personnel services, vocational technical education; *doctorate* also in educational research and evaluation. Certificates also given.

College of Engineering

Degree Programs Offered: *Baccalaureate, master's* in aerospace engineering, agricultural engineering, chemical engineering, civil engineering, electrical engineering, engineering science and mechanics, industrial engineering and operations research, materials engineering, mechanical engineering, mining engineering; *master's* also in engineering administration, environmental engineering, nuclear science, sanitary engineering, systems engineering; *doctorate* in aerospace engineering, chemical engineering, civil engineering, electrical engineering, engineering science and mechanics, environmental science and engineering, industrial engineering and operations research, mechanical engineering.

College of Human Resources

Degree Programs Offered: *Baccalaureate, master's, doctorate* in clothing and textiles; human nutrition and foods, housing, interior design, resource management, family development.

Virginia-Maryland Regional College of Veterinary Medicine

Degree Programs Offered: *First-professional.*

Admission: 2 full years from accredited college or university with 8 semester hours biological sciences with lab, 8 organic chemistry with lab, 8 physics with lab; scores from general and biology portions of GRE; interview; residence in Virginia or Maryland.

Degree Requirements: Four-year program; prescribed curriculum.

Virginia State University

1 Hayden Street
Petersburg, Virginia 23806
Tel: (804) 524-5000 **E-mail:** admissions@vsu.edu
Fax: (804) 524-6506 **Internet:** www.vsu.edu

Institution Description: Virginia State University (Virginia College until 1979) is a public institution. *Enrollment:* 5,042. *Degrees awarded:* Baccalaureate, master's.

Academic offers subject to approval by statewide coordinating bodies. Budget subject to approval by state governing boards. Member of Capital Consortium for Continuing Higher Education.

Accreditation: *Regional:* SACS-Comm. on Coll.*Professional*: art, dietetics, engineering, music, social work, teacher education

History: Established as Virginia Normal and Collegiate Institute, chartered, and incorporated 1882; offered first instruction at postsecondary level 1883; awarded first degree (baccalaureate) 1889; changed name to Virginia Normal and Industrial Institute 1902, to Virginia State College of Negroes 1930, to Virginia State College 1946; adopted present name 1979.

Institutional Structure: *Governing board:* Board of Trustees. Extrainstitutional representation: 11 trustees. All voting. *Composition of institution:* Administrators 12. Academic affairs headed by provost/vice president for academic affairs. Management/business/finances directed by vice president for administration/finance. Full-time instructional faculty 218. Academic governance body, Faculty Senate, meets three times per month during academic year.

Calendar: Semesters. Academic year Aug. to May. Freshmen admitted Aug., Jan., June. Degrees conferred and formal commencement De., May.

Characteristics of Freshmen: 4,484 applicants. 78% of applicants accepted. 29% of accepted applicants enrolled.

95% (1,001 students) submitted SAT scores; 4% (43 students) submitted ACT scores. *25th percentile*: SAT Critical Reading 380, SAT Math 370; ACT Composite 16. *75th percentile*: SAT Critical Reading 460, SAT Math 460; ACT Composite 19.

37% of entering freshmen expected to graduate within 5 years. 65% of freshmen from Virginia. Freshmen from 35 states and 1 foreign country.

Admission: Rolling admissions plan. For fall acceptance, apply as early as Sept. of senior year of secondary school, but not later than July. Early acceptance available. *Requirements:* Either graduation from accredited secondary school with academic units which must include 4 English, 2 in a foreign language, 3 college preparatory mathematics, 2 science, 2 social studies; or GED. 4 additional units recommended. *Entrance tests:* College Board SAT. For foreign students minimum TOEFL score 500. *For transfer students:* 2.0 minimum GPA; 60 semester hours maximum transfer credit.

College credit for postsecondary-level work completed in secondary school. College credit for extrainstitutional learning.

Tutoring available.

Degree Requirements: *For undergraduate degree:* 120 semester hours; 2.0 GPA; 27 hours in residence.

Fulfillment of some degree requirements and exemption from some beginning courses possible by passing departmental examinations. *Grading system:* A–F; withdraw (carries time limit); satisfactory.

Distinctive Educational Programs: *For undergraduates:* Cooperative education. Cluster colleges. Cooperative baccalaureate programs in engineering technology and nursing with other Virginia public colleges and universities, with degree awarded by Virginia State University. Honors programs, individualized majors using travel-study to fulfill some degree requirements. *For graduate students:* Flexible meeting places and schedules, including off-campus center (at Fort Lee, less than 30 miles away from main institution), weekend and evening classes. Accelerated degree program. Facilities and programs for independent research, including individual majors, tutorials. *Other distinctive programs:* Continuing education.

ROTC: Army.

Degrees Conferred: 542 *baccalaureate* (B); 119 *master's* (M): agriculture 11 (B); biological/life sciences 29 (B), 12 (M); business/marketing 137 (B); 3 (M); communications/communication technologies 23 (B); computer and information sciences 11 (B): education 72 (B), 92 (M); engineering and engineering technologies 7 (B); English 9 (B), 3 (M); home economics and vocational home economics 8 (B); interdisciplinary studies 41 (B); liberal arts/general studies 28 (B); mathematics 2 (B), 1 (M); physical sciences 3 (B); protective services/public administration 55 (B); psychology 33 (B), 6 (M); social sciences and history 49 (B), 2 (M); visual and performing arts 24 (B).

Fees and Other Expenses: *Full-time tuition per academic year 2008–09:* undergraduate resident $5,903, nonresident $14,018; contact the university for current graduate resident/nonresident tuition/fees. *Required fees:* $2,575. *Room and board per academic year:* $7,710. *Books and supplies:* $900. *Other expenses:* $1,675.

Financial Aid: Aid from institutionally generated funds is provided on the basis of academic merit, financial need, athletic ability.

Financial aid to full-time, first-time undergraduate students: 91% received some form of aid. Aveage amount of aid received: federal grants $3,252; Pell grants $2,990; other federal aid $1,169; state/local grants $2,898; institutional grants $1,961.

Departments and Teaching Staff: *Total instructional faculty:* 309 (full-time 218, part-time 91). Total faculty with doctorate, first-professional, or other terminal degree: 102. Student/faculty ratio: 18:1. Degrees held by full-time faculty: Doctorate 68%, master's 100%. 68% hold terminal degrees.

Enrollment: Total enrollment 5,042. Undergraduate 4,489 (full-time 92%; female 61%, male 39%). Graduate 553 (full-time 15%). Transfer-in students 194.

Characteristics of Student Body: *Ethnic/racial makeup:* Black non-Hispanic: 94%; White non-Hispanic: 2%; unknown 3%.

International Students: No programs available to aid students whose native language is not English. No financial aid specifically designated for international students.

Student Life: On-campus residence halls house 41% of student body; residence halls for males constitute 45% of such space, for females 55%. *Intercollegiate athletics:* male: basketball, football, golf, tennis, track; female: basketball, softball, tennis, track, volleyball. *Special regulations:* Registered cars permitted without restrictions. *Special services:* Learning Resources Center, medical services. *Student publications: Virginia Statesman*, a bimonthly newspaper. *Surrounding community:* Petersburg population 41,000. Richmond (VA) 25 miles from campus, is nearest metropolitan area. Served by mass transit bus system; airport 32 miles from campus; passenger rail service .5 mile from campus.

Library Collections: 304,000 volumes. 192,000 government documents; 642,000 microforms; 82,900 audiovisual materials; 598 serial subscriptions. Online catalog. Students have access to online information retrieval services and the Internet.

Most important special holdings include Luther Porter Jackson Papers (manuscripts, correspondence, and letters of the Virginia historian); papers of Virginia Teachers Association (agendas, correspondence, and minutes of the association, originally for Black teachers in the state); Colson Hill Family Papers; Prince Edward Country Free School Papers.

Buildings and Grounds: Campus area 236 acres and 416-acre research farm. Campus DVD available.

Chief Executive Officer: Dr. Eddie N. Moore, Jr., President.

Address admission inquiries to Irene Logan, Director of Admissions.

Virginia Union University

1500 North Lombardy Street
Richmond, Virginia 23220-1711
Tel: (804) 257-5630 **E-mail:** admissions@vuu.edu
Fax: (804) 257-5818 **Internet:** www.vuu.edu

Institution Description: Virginia Union University is a private institution affiliated with the American Baptist Church. *Enrollment:* 1,501. *Degrees awarded:* Baccalaureate, first-professional (master of divinity, doctor of ministry).

Accreditation: *Regional:* SACS-Comm. on Coll. *National:* ATS. *Professional*: business, social work, theology

History: Established and offered first instruction at postsecondary level 1865; awarded first degree (baccalaureate) and adopted present name 1899.

Institutional Structure: *Governing board:* Board of Trustees. Representation: 35 trustees, 1 alumnus, 1 administrator. 34 voting trustees, president of student government association invited to trustee meetings. *Composition of institution:* Administrators 8. vice presidents for student affairs, academic affairs, financial affairs, university relations, university services. Full-time instructional faculty 87. Academic governance body, the faculty, meets an average of 11 times per year.

Calendar: Semesters. Academic year Aug. to May. Freshmen admitted Aug. Degrees conferred May, Aug., Dec. Summer session of 1 term beginning June.

Characteristics of Freshmen: 83% of applicants accepted. 30% of accepted applicants enrolled. Mean SAT score 749.

23% of entering freshmen expected to graduate within 5 years. 52% of freshmen from Virginia. Freshmen from 27 states and 4 foreign counties.

Admission: Rolling admissions plan. For fall acceptance, apply as early as Sept. 1 of previous year but not later than Aug. 1 of year of enrollment. Early acceptance available. *Requirements:* Either graduation from accredited secondary school with 16 units, including 4 English, 3 mathematics, 2 natural science, 2 social science, 2 foreign language, 3 electives; or GED. Minimum 2.0 GPA. *Entrance tests:* College Board SAT and ACT. *For transfer students:* 2.0 minimum GPA; maximum transfer credit limited only by residence requirement.

Advanced placement for postsecondary-level work completed in secondary school.

Tutoring available. Noncredit developmental/remedial courses available.

Degree Requirements: Minimum 120 semester hours; 2.0 GPA; 30 semester hours in residence; 80 credits for attendance at university-sponsored events for cultural enrichment. *Grading system:* A–F; satisfactory-unsatisfactory; withdraw (carries time limit, deadline after which pass-fail is appended to withdraw).

Distinctive Educational Programs: Weekend and evening classes in School of Theology and Weekend College Licensure Program for teachers. Interdepartmental programs. Facilities and programs for independent research, including honors program, individual majors, MARC, MEAMP, and RS-RISE programs for student scientific/medical research; criminology program; business; social work; psychology, media arts.

ROTC: Army in cooperation with Virginia State University.

Degrees Conferred: 203 *baccalaureate*. Bachelor's degrees awarded in top five disciplines: business, management, marketing, and related support services 33; social sciences 27; psychology 22; public administration 12; biomedical/biological sciences 12. *First-professional:* master of divinity 109.

Fees and Other Expenses: *Full-time tuition per academic year 2008–09:* $13,662. Contact the university for graduate and School of Theology tuition and fees. *Books and supplies:* $1,080. *Room and board per academic year:* $8,328. *Other expenses:* $2,800.

Financial Aid: Aid from institutionally generated funds is provided on the basis of academic merit, financial need, athletic ability, other criteria.

Financial aid to full-time, first-time undergraduate students: 98% received federal grants averaging $3,598; 34% state/local grants averaging $2,505; Pell grants averaging $3,236; 4% institutional grants averaging $13,468; 66% received loans averaging $5,660.

Departments and Teaching Staff: *Total instructional faculty:* 74. Student/faculty ratio: 18:1. Degrees held by full-time faculty: doctorate 46%, master's 45%, professional 9%. 55% hold terminal degrees.

Enrollment: Total enrollment 1,501. Undergraduate 1,123. Graduate 378 (full-time 97%). Transfer-in students 50.

Characteristics of Student Body: *Ethnic/racial makeup:* Black non-Hispanic: 97%; Hispanic: 1%; unknown 2%.

International Students: 17 nonresident aliens enrolled fall 2008. Students from Europe, Africa, Canada. No programs available to aid students whose native language is not English. No financial aid specifically designated for international students.

Student Life: On-campus residence halls house 66% of student body. *Intercollegiate athletics:* baseball, basketball, football, softball, tennis, track, volleyball. *Special regulations:* Cars with parking stickers permitted on campus. *Special services:* Learning Resources Center, medical services. *Surrounding community:* Richmond population 220,000. Served by mass transit bus system; airport 9 miles from campus; passenger rail service 2 miles from campus.

Publications: *The Unionite*, alumni magazine; *The VUU Informer*, student newspaper.

Library Collections: 153,000 volumes. 75,600 microforms; 1,100 audiovisual materials; 300 current periodical subscriptions plus access to 18,000 electronic. Online catalog. Students have access to online information retrieval ' services and the Internet.

Most important special holdings include The Wilder Collection: Memorabilia of Governor L. Douglas Wilder (Virginia); University Archives; Dr. and Mrs. James E. Sellman African Art Collection.

Buildings and Grounds: Campus area 93 acres.

Chief Executive Officer: Dr. Belinda C. Anderson, President.

Address undergraduate admission inquiries to James Edwards, Admissions Director; graduate inquiries to Registrar, School of Theology.

Virginia Wesleyan College

1584 Wesleyan Drive
Norfolk, Virginia 23502-5599
Tel: (757) 455-3200 **E-mail:** admissions@vwc.edu
Fax: (757) 461-5238 **Internet:** www.vwc.edu

Institution Description: Virginia Wesleyan College is a private liberal arts college affiliated with the United Methodist Church. *Enrollment:* 1,381. *Degrees awarded:* Baccalaureate.

Accreditation: *Regional:* SACS-Comm. on Coll.

History: Established and chartered 1961; offered first instruction at postsecondary level 1966; first degree (baccalaureate) awarded 1970.

Institutional Structure: *Governing board:* Board of Trustees. Extrainstitutional representation: 36 trustees; institutional representation: president of the college; 3 alumni. 3 ex officio. *Composition of institution:* Administrative council 9 men / 4 women. Academic affairs headed by vice president for academic affairs and dean of the college. Management/business/finance directed by vice president for business affairs. Full-time instructional faculty 88. Academic governance body, faculty, meets an average of 7 times per year.

Calendar: Semesters (4-1-4 plan). Academic year Aug. to May. Freshmen admitted Sept., Jan. Degrees conferred May, Aug. Formal commencement May. 4 summer sessions from May to Aug.

Characteristics of Freshmen: 1,448 applicants (female 633, male 615). 84% of applicants admitted. 28% of applicants admitted and enrolled full-time.

95% (354 students) submitted SAT scores; 20% (74 students) submitted ACT scores. *25th percentile*: SAT Critical Reading 440, SAT Math 430; ACT Composite 17. *75th percentile*: SAT Critical Reading 530, SAT Math 540; ACT Composite 21.

41% of entering freshmen expected to graduate within 5 years. 70% of freshmen from Virginia. Freshmen from 25 states and 2 foreign countries.

Admission: Competitive admission plan. For fall acceptance, apply as early as Sept. of senior year of secondary school. Applicants notified on a rolling basis. *Requirements:* Graduation from secondary school or GED. *Recommendations:* 19 units in academic subjects, including 4 English, 3 foreign language, 2 lab science, 3 social studies/history. *Entrance tests:* College Board SAT I or ACT. *For transfer students:* 2.5 minimum GPA; from 4-year accredited institution, 90 hours maximum transfer credit; from 2-year accredited institution, 64 hours.

College credit for postsecondary-level work completed in secondary school. College credit for life experience learning based on portfolio assessment.

Tutoring available in all subjects. Developmental/remedial courses offered during regular academic year.

Degree Requirements: 120 credit hours; 2.0 GPA; last 30 credit hours in residence; exit competency examination in writing and foreign language.

Fulfillment of some degree requirements and exemption from some beginning courses possible by passing College Board CLEP. *Grading system:* A–F; pass-fail; withdraw (deadline after which pass-fail is appended to withdraw); credit-no credit (in January term).

Distinctive Educational Programs: Adult Studies Program. Honors Program. Internships. Interdepartmental/interdisciplinary programs in American studies, communication studies, human services, international studies, liberal arts management, recreation/leisure services. Individualized majors. Study abroad in France, Spain, Germany, England and Mexico.

ROTC: Army in cooperation with Old Dominion University.

Degrees Conferred: 294 *baccalaureate:* biological sciences 6; business and management 57; communications 33; computer and information sciences 5; English 6; foreign languages 8; health professions and related sciences 8; interdisciplinary studies 2; mathematics 2; natural resources 6; parks and recreation 8; philosophy/religion 8; psychology 14; social sciences and history 45; visual and performing arts 6.

Fees and Other Expenses: *Full-time tuition per academic year 2008–09:* $26,438. *Room and board per academic year:* $7,925. *Required fees:* $160. *Books and supplies:* $900. *Other expenses:* $3,600.

Financial Aid: Aid from institutionally generated funds is provided on the basis of academic merit, financial need.

Financial aid to full-time, first-time undergraduate students: 99% recieved some form of aid.

Departments and Teaching Staff: *Total instructional faculty:* 195 (full-time 88, part-time 97). Total faculty with doctorate, first-professional, or other terminal degree: 86. Student/faculty ratio: 10.4:1. Degrees held by full-time faculty: doctorate 73%, master's 27%. 82% hold terminal degrees.

Enrollment: Total enrollment 1,381. Undergraduate 1,381 (full-time 84%; female 62%, male 36%). Transfer-in students 102.

Characteristics of Student Body: *Ethnic/racial makeup:* Black non-Hispanic: 20%; Asian or Pacific Islander 2%; Hispanic 4%; White non-Hispanic 70%; unknown 4%; nonresident alien 1%. *Age distribution:* number under 18: 45; 18–19: 526; 20–21: 356; 22–24: 150; 25–29: 89; 30–34: 54; 35–39: 68; 40–49: 114; 50–64: 31; 65 and over: 3; unknown: 6. 21% of student body attend summer sessions.

International Students: 7 nonresident aliens enrolled fall 2008. Students from Europe, Canada, Middle East. Programs available to aid students whose native language is not English: social, cultural. No financial aid specifically designated for international students.

Student Life: On-campus residence halls house 53% of day program students. Residence halls for males constitute 41% of such space, for females 59%. *Intercollegiate athletics:* NCAA Division III, ODAC; male: cross-country, soccer, basketball, golf, tennis, lacrosse, baseball; female: basketball, cross-country, lacrosse, softball, tennis, soccer, field hockey, volleyball; male and female: indoor track and field; outdoor track and field. *Special regulations:* Cars must be registered and insured. *Special services:* Learning Center, medical services. *Student publications, radio: Marlin Chronicle,* a student newspaper; *Sandpiper,* yearbook; *Outlet,* literary magazine. *Surrounding community:* Hampton Roads area population over 1.5 million. Served by mass transit bus system; airport 3 miles from campus.

Library Collections: 239,600 volumes. Current periodical subscriptions: 600 paper; 15,900 microform; 20,000 via electronic access. 3,700 audio/videotapes; 300 DVD discs; 500 CD-ROMs. Computer work stations available. Online catalog. Students have access to online information retrieval services and the Internet.

Most important special collection on history of Princess Anne County.

Buildings and Grounds: Campus area 296 acres.

Chief Executive Officer: Dr. William T. Greer, Jr., President.

Address admission inquiries to Richard T. Hinshaw, Dean of Admissions.

Washington and Lee University

204 West Washington Street
Lexington, Virginia 24450

Tel: (540) 463-8400 **E-mail:** admissions@wlu.edu
Fax: (540) 463-8062 **Internet:** www.wlu.edu

Institution Description: Washington and Lee University is an independent, nonprofit coeducational institution. *Enrollment:* 2,155. *Degrees awarded:* Baccalaureate, first-professional (law).

Accreditation: *Regional:* SACS-Comm. on Coll. *Professional*: business, journalism, law

History: Established as Augusta Academy 1749; offered first instruction at postsecondary level and changed name to Liberty Hall 1776; chartered and changed name to Liberty Hall Academy 1782; awarded first degree (baccalaureate) 1784; changed name to Washington Academy 1798, to Washington College 1812; affiliated with Lexington Law School under presidency of General Robert E. Lee 1870; adopted present name 1871. *See* Ollinger Crenshaw, *General Lee's College* (New York: Random House, 1969) for further information.

Institutional Structure: *Governing board:* Board of Trustees. Representation: 34 members. All voting. *Composition of institution:* Administrators 13. Provost of the college is the chief academic officer. Vice president for finance and treasurer is chief financial officer. Full-time instructional faculty 113. Academic governance body, the faculty, meets an average of 10 times per year.

Calendar: 2 twelve-week terms followed by a six-week term. Academic year Sept. to May. Freshmen admitted Sept. Degrees conferred May, June, Oct., Dec. Formal commencement May or June. No summer session.

Characteristics of Freshmen: 6,381 applicants (female 3,424, male 2,963). 27% of applicants admitted. 10% of applicants admitted and enrolled.

77% (346 students) submitted SAT scores; 21% (93 students) submitted ACT scores. *25th percentile*: SAT Critical Reading 650, SAT Math 650; ACT Composite 28. *75th percentile*: SAT Critical Reading 740, SAT Math 730; ACT Composite 31.

87% of entering freshmen expected to graduate within 5 years. 14 of freshmen from Virginia. Freshmen from 38 states and 19 foreign countries.

Admission: For fall acceptance, apply as early as Sept. of senior year of secondary school, but no later than Jan. 15th of year of enrollment. Applicants notified in early April. Apply by Dec. 1 for early decision; notification by Dec. 20. If accepted, all other applications must be withdrawn. *Requirements:* Graduation from secondary school with 17 units in academic subjects, including 4 English, 3 foreign language, 3 mathematics, 1 history, 1 natural science, and 4 additional electives from among English, foreign languages, history, mathematics, natural sciences, or social studies. *Entrance tests:* College Board SAT Reasoning or ACT in addition to 2 SAT IIs. *For transfer students:* 3.0 minimum GPA; from 2-year and 4-year accredited institutions 87 hours maximum transfer credit; 2-year full-time residence.

College credit and advanced placement for postsecondary-level work completed in secondary school.

Degree Requirements: 115 credit hours; 1.9 GPA; 2 years in residence; 4 physical education courses; fundamental and distribution requirements; for some programs, exit competency examinations (comprehensives in individual fields of study). *Grading system:* A–F; pass-fail.

Distinctive Educational Programs: Facilities and programs for academic year and summer collaborative research with faculty members; honors programs; individual majors; and tutorials. Students can take part in the Shepherd Program for the interdisciplinary Study of Poverty and Human Capability. Internships in politics, sociology, and journalism. Study abroad in England, France, Germany, Greece, Italy, Japan, Spain, Taiwan, Peoples Republic of China, Russia, Central America. Exchange programs with Chung Chi College of the Chinese University of Hong Kong; Rikkyo University in Tokyo; Kansai University of Foreign Studies near Kyoto; University College (Oxford); 6-week summer exchange program with St. Anne's College, Oxford.

ROTC: Army available through cooperative program with Virginia Military Institute.

Degrees Conferred: 533 *baccalaureate:* area and ethnic studies 5; biological/life sciences 34; business, management, marketing, and related support services 73; communications 22; engineering 4; English language and literature 34; foreign languages 42; interdisciplinary studies 3; mathematics 16; philosophy/religion/theology 22; physical sciences 13; psychology 30; social sciences and history 161; visual an performing arts 6; other 4. *Master's:* law/legal studies 2. *First-professional:* law 128.

Fees and Other Expenses: *Full-time tuition per academic year 2008–09:* undergraduate $31,412; contact the university for current graduate and first-professional tuition/fees. *Required fees:* $700. *Room and board per academic year:* $8,920. *Books and supplies:* $1,650. *Other expenses:* $1,778.

Financial Aid: Aid from institutionally generated funds is provided on the basis of academic merit, financial need, other considerations.

Financial aid to full-time, first-time undergraduate students: 62% received some form of aid. Average amount of aid received: federal grants $5,795; Pell grants $2,931; other federal aid $4,295; state/local grants $3,010; institutional grants $20,960.

Departments and Teaching Staff: *Total instructional faculty:* 214 (full-time 212, part-time 4). Total faculty with doctorate, first-professional, or other terminal degree: 189. Student/faculty ratio: 10: 1. Degrees held by full-time faculty: 96% hold terminal degrees.

Enrollment: Total enrollment 2,155. Undergraduate 1,752 (full-time 100%; female 50%, male 50%). Graduate 403 (full-time 100%). Transfer-in students 5.

Characteristics of Student Body: *Ethnic/racial makeup:* Black non-Hispanic: 4%; Asian or Pacific Islander: 3%; Hispanic: 2%; White non-Hispanic: 85%; unknown: 1%; nonresident alien 4%. *Age distribution:* number under 18: 21; 18–19: 806; 20–21: 822; 22–24: 110; 25–29: 1.

International Students: 88 nonresident aliens enrolled fall 2008. Students from Europe, Asia, Latin America, Africa, Canada, New Zealand, Middle East. Programs available to aid students whose native language is not English: social, cultural. Financial aid designated for international students: variable number awarded annually.

Student Life: On-campus residence halls house 46% of student body. 100% of freshmen and sophomores are required to live on campus. 40% of freshmen are housed in singles with the remaining in double occupancy rooms. *Intercollegiate athletics:* male: baseball, basketball, cross-country, football, golf, lacrosse, swimming, tennis, track and field, wrestling; female: basketball, cross-

WASHINGTON AND LEE UNIVERSITY—*cont'd*

country, field hockey, lacrosse, riding, swimming, tennis, track and field, volleyball. *Special regulations:* Honor system. Parking restrictions. *Special services:* Student medical services. *Student publications, radio, television:Ariel*, a literary magazine; *Calyx* yearbook; *The Ring-tum Phi,* student newspaper; *The Trident*, independent student-run weekly newspaper. Radio station WLUR-FM broadcasts 133 hours per week. TV station Cable Channel 18 student run. *Surrounding community:* Lexington population 7,000. Washington (DC), 230 miles from campus, is nearest metropolitan area.

Publications: *Journal of Science*, dedicated to the discussion of current scientific, psychological, sociological, medical, and bioethical issues.

Library Collections: 908,000 volumes. 106,200 government documents; 1,024,300 microforms; 16,080 audiovisual materials; 8,030 serial subscriptions. Online catalog. Students have access to online information retrieval services and the Internet.

Most important special holdings include Robert E. Lee Collection (manuscripts, letters, and other personal papers dating mostly from 1865–1870, while Lee was president of the institution); Valley of Virginia manuscripts (collections relating to area pioneer colonial families); books from 19th century literary debating societies (Franklin Society, Graham Society, Washington Society); Jessie Ball DuPont and Alfred I. DuPont Papers.

Buildings and Grounds: Campus area 250 acres. Campus DVD available.

Chief Executive Officer: Dr. Kenneth P. Ruscio, President.

Undergraduates address admission inquiries to William M. Hartog, Dean of Admissions; School of Law inquiries to Sarah Nichols, Assistant Director of Law School Admissions.

School of Commerce, Economics, and Politics

Degree Programs Offered: *Baccalaureate.*

Distinctive Educational Programs: Washington Term internships. Students intern in U.S. senator's office for 6 weeks and do supervised research under a faculty member. Spring term course in Europe studying European Monetary Union, supervised by 2 faculty members. Management internships: summer internships on New York Stock Exchange, manufacturing companies, and financial organizations. Accounting internships are available with 'Big Six' firms. Executive-in-Residence program brings top corporate executives into frequent contact with students.

School of Law

Degree Programs Offered: *First-professional.*

Distinctive Educational Programs: Participation in several Moot Court competitions. The Community Legal Practice Center (CLPC) provides free legal services to qualified residents of the Rockbridge area community. Leg Practice Clinic enables second and third year students to provide legal services to clients through the Legal Aid Society and Western State Hospital, and the Black Lung Benefits Program. Programs with U.S. Attorney and Public Defender allow courtroom experience, as do clerkships with trial judges in the region.

Washington

Bastyr University

14500 Juanita Drive N.E.
Kenmore, Washington 98028-4966
Tel: (425) 602-3000 **E-mail:** admissions@bastyr.edu
Fax: (425) 823-6222 **Internet:** www.bastyr.edu

Institution Description: Bastyr is a private, nonprofit, independent university offering junior, senior, and graduate level programs. *Enrollment:* 988. *Degrees awarded:* Baccalaureate, master's, doctorate.

Accreditation: *Regional:* NWCCU. *Professional*: acupuncture, dietetics, naturopathic medicine

History: The university was founded in 1978 as John Bastyr College of Naturapathic Medicine; awarded first degree in 1982; adopted present name 1994.

Institutional Structure: *Governing board:* Bastyr University Board of Trustees meets quarterly. 20 members, including president, student and faculty representatives; all voting. Chief operating officer is executive vice president. Academic affairs headed by vice president for academic affairs; finance/administration headed by vice president for finance and administration. Full-time instructional faculty 51.

Calendar: Quarters. Academic year Sept. to June. Degrees conferred quarterly; commencements June, Dec. Summers session July through Aug.

Admission: Rolling admissions. For fall acceptance, priority deadline Feb. 1 for naturapathic medical program; Mar. 15 for natural health sciences programs; rolling for master of arts programs. *Undergraduate requirements:* completion of 2 years (90 credits) prior to matriculation; 2.25 cumulative GPA with a grade of C or better in all required courses. General education requirements include 12 quarter credits of natural sciences and math; 15 of arts and humanities; 15 of social sciences; 17 elective credits in addition to the specific prerequisites. *Graduate requirements: Acupuncture:* bachelor's degree plus courses in college-level algebra, general chemistry, biology with lab, and general psychology. *Nutrition:* chemistry, organic chemistry, nutrition, plus one course each in chemistry of foods, food science, biology with lab, microbiology, biochemistry, introductory psychology, developmental psychology, algebra, and statistics. *Professional requirements:* For *Naturopathic Medicine:* 135 quarter credits, including 2 quantitative skills courses, 2 courses in English and humanities, 2 courses in psychology, 4 courses in chemistry (general and organic), 1 year of biology, and 1 course in physics.

Degree Requirements: *For bachelor's degrees in nutrition and behavioral sciences:* 180 quarter credits; *for bachelor of science in oriental medicine:* 185 quarter credits; *for master of science in nutrition:* 65 quarter credits; *for master of science in acupuncture:* 176 quarter credits; *for master of science in acupuncture and oriental medicine:* 229 quarter credits; *for doctor of naturopathic medicine:* 327 quarter credits.

Distinctive Educational Programs: Certificate programs in midwifery; traditional Chinese herbal medicine; homeopathy. AOM program has China internship option. Applied behavioral sciences programs offer schedules for working professions.

Degrees Conferred: 75 *baccalaureate:* health professions and related clinical sciences 27; interdisciplinary studies 24; psychology 24; 156 *master's*: health professions 71; interdisciplinary studies 63; psychology 43; *first-professional:* naturapathic medicine 101.

Fees and Other Expenses: *Full-time tuition per academic year 2008=09:* contact the university for current tuition, fees, housing, and other costs.

Financial Aid: Aid from institutionally generated funds is provided on the basis of academic merit, financial need, community service.

Financial aid to full-time, first-time undergraduate students: need-based scholarships/grants totaling $1,065,991, self-help $7,092,300.

Graduate aid: 850 students received $15,852,081 in federal and state-funded fellowships/grants; 295 received $493,467 for work-study jobs.

Departments and Teaching Staff: *Total instructional faculty:* 142 (full-time 51, part-time 91).

Enrollment: Total enrollment 988. Undergraduate 220 (full-time 77; female 84%, male 16%). Graduate 783 (full-time 85%).

Characteristics of Student Body: *Ethnic/racial makeup:* Black non-Hispanic: 1%; Asian or Pacific Islander 55; White non-Hispanic 66%; unknown: 16%; nonresident alien 5%.

International Students: 50 nonresident aliens enrolled fall 2008. No programs available to aid students whose native language is not English. Financial aid specifically designated for international graduate students: scholarships awarded annually to qualifying students.

Student Life: On-campus residence hall houses 39 students. No intercollegiate athletics. Students have teams to enter local leagues in softball, soccer, and frisbee. *Student services:* Health services through the university's Natural Health Clinic; Counseling and Wellness Center. Student Council and other student organizations.

Publications: *The Pulse* is published during the academic year. *Alumni Pulse* is published quarterly. *The Source* is published by the Development Office on a quarterly basis.

Library Collections: 20,000 volumes. 1,000 audiovisual materials; 275 current periodical subscriptions. 860 recordings; 15 compact discs, 35 CD-ROMs. Computer work stations available. Students have access to online information retrieval services and the Internet.

Most important special holdings include naturapathic medicine; oriental medicine; nutrition.

Buildings and Grounds: Campus area 50 acres.

Chief Executive Officer: Dr. Dan Church, President.

Address admissions inquiries to Ted Olson, Director of Admissions.

Central Washington University

400 East 8th Avenue
Ellensburg, Washington 98926-7501
Tel: (509) 963-1111 **E-mail:** cwuadmis@cwu.edu
Fax: (509) 963-3022 **Internet:** www.cwu.edu

Institution Description: Central Washington University is a state institution with six satellite campuses (three in the Puget Sound, Yakima, Wenatchee, and Moses Lake). *Enrollment:* 10,662. *Degrees awarded:* Baccalaureate, master's.

Budget subject to approval by state governing boards. Member of the consortium Northwest Interinstitutional Council on Study Abroad.

Accreditation: *Regional:* NWCCU. *Professional*: clinical lab scientist, music, teacher education

History: Established as Washington State Normal School and chartered 1890; offered first instruction at postsecondary level 1891; awarded first degree (baccalaureate) 1933; changed name to Central Washington State College 1961; adopted present name 1977. *See* Samuel R. Mohler, *The First 75 Years* (Ellensburg: Central Washington State College, 1967) for further information.

Institutional Structure: *Governing board:* Central Washington University Board of Trustees. Extrainstitutional representation: 8 trustees. All voting. *Composition of institution:* Administrators 81. Academic affairs headed by provost and vice president for academic affairs. 8 deans including dean of admissions and records. Management/business/finances directed by vice president of business and financial affairs. Full-time instructional faculty 315. Academic governance body, Faculty Senate, meets an average of 12 times per year.

Calendar: Trimester. Academic year Sept. to Aug. Freshmen admitted Sept., Jan., Mar., June. Degrees conferred June, Aug., Dec., Mar. Formal commencement June. Summer session of 3 terms from June to Aug.

Characteristics of Freshmen: 5,013 applicants (female 2,660, male 2,353). 83% of applicants admitted. 33% of applicants admitted and enrolled.

89% (1,237 students) submitted SAT scores; 27% (379 students) submitted ACT scores. *25th percentile*: SAT Verbal 440, SAT Math 440; ACT Composite 17, ACT English 16, ACT Math 17. *75th percentile*: SAT Verbal 550, SAT Math 550; ACT Composite 22, ACT English 22, ACT Math 23.

47% of entering freshmen expected to graduate within five years. 97% if freshmen from Washington. Freshmen from 9 states and 3 foreign countries.

CENTRAL WASHINGTON UNIVERSITY—*cont'd*

Admission: Rolling admissions plan using an admissions index based on high school GPA and standardized test scores. For fall matriculation, apply as early as June of the previous year. Students are notified of acceptance beginning Dec. 1. *Requirements:* Graduation from an accredited high school (or GED) with a minimum core pattern of 4 years English, 3 social studies, 3 mathematics, 2 science, 2 foreign language, 1 fine or performing arts or other elective. *Entrance tests:* ACT or SAT required. For foreign students TOEFL score of 525. *For transfer students:* First priority to holders of Associate of Arts transfer degree from Washington community colleges. Other transfer requirements are a GPA 2.3 for automatic admission. Advanced placement credits awarded for many College Board AP Tests with scores of 3 or above at discretion of departments. A maximum of 30 lower division credits may be granted for military schooling as recommended by the American Council of Education. Students admitted to the Vocational Trade and Industrial major may earn up to 45 credits for industrial experience. International Baccalaureate credits granted on a case-by-case basis at the discretion of the University. CLEP awarded on a case-by-case basis.

Tutoring available. Noncredit developmental courses offered.

Degree Requirements: Minimum of 60 upper division credits; 2.0 GPA; 3 quarters in residence; general education requirements. Additional requirements for education majors.

Fulfillment of some degree requirements and exemption from some beginning courses possible by passing College Board AP. *Grading system:* A–F; pass-fail; withdraw (carries time limit).

Distinctive Educational Programs: *For undergraduates:* Work-experience programs, including cooperative education, internships. Interdisciplinary programs. Douglas Honors College. Diverse major offerings, e.g., flight technology, music, special education, business and accounting, food science and nutrition. The office of international programs coordinates bilateral and consortia exchange programs with more than 100 universities in 38 countries abroad. Member of the National Student Exchange program permitting students to attend colleges and universities in over 100 institutions in the U.S. and abroad. Students need only pay in-state Washington tuition or in-state tuition of the institution they will attend. The University cooperates with several other Pacific Northwest institutions in the operation of study abroad sites. *For graduate students:* Interdisciplinary programs in resource management and organizational development. *Available to all students:* Flexible meeting places and schedules. *Other distinctive programs:* Off-campus continuing education. Access Programs provide support services for students lacking traditional academic background for college admission.

ROTC: Army, Air Force.

Degrees Conferred: 1,879 *baccalaureate* (B), 159 *master's* (M): biological and life sciences 55 (B), 3 (M); business 404 (B), 14 (M); computer and information sciences 20 (B); education 487 (B), 89 (M); engineering 61 (B); foreign languages 19 (B); health professions and related sciences 61 (B); home economics 61 (B), 2 (M); library science 3 (M); mathematics 7 (B); parks and recreation 55 (B); physical sciences 30 (B), 3 (M); protective services and public administration 147 (B); psychology 63 (B), 13 (M); social sciences and history 182 (B), 3 (M); visual and performing arts 55 (B), 19 (M); other 71 (B), 159 (M).

Fees and Other Expenses: *Full-time tuition per academic year 2008–09:* undergraduate resident $5,724, nonresident $15,596; contact the university for current graduate tuition. *Room and board per academic year:* $,8052. *Books and supplies:* $944. *Other expenses:* $3,114.

Financial Aid: Aid from institutionally generated funds is provided on the basis of academic merit, financial need, other criteria.

Financial aid to full-time, first-time undergraduate students: 76% received some form of aid. Average amount of aid received: federal grants $2,402; Pell grants $2,830; other federal aid $794; state/local grants $3,352; institutional grants $2,729.

Departments and Teaching Staff: *Total instructional faculty:* 935 (full-time 364, part-time 171). Total faculty with doctorate, first-professional, or other terminal degree: 376. Student/faculty ratio: 23:1. Degrees held by full-time faculty: 94% hold terminal degrees.

Enrollment: Total enrollment 10,662. Undergraduate 10,181 (full-time 88%; female 52%, male 48%). Graduate 481 (full-time 55%). Transfer-in students 1,317.

Characteristics of Student Body: *Ethnic/racial makeup:* Black non-Hispanic: 2%; American Indian or Alaska Native: 1%; Asian or Pacific Islander: 4%; Hispanic: 7%; White non-Hispanic: 73%; unknown: 7%; nonresident alien 2%.

International Students: 214 nonresident aliens enrolled fall 2008. Students from Europe, Asia, Latin America, Africa, Canada, Australia, New Zealand. Programs available to aid students whose native language is not English: social, cultural, financial. English as a Second Language Program.

Student Life: On-campus residence halls house 32% of student body. 9% of student body live on campus in married student housing. *Intercollegiate athletics:* male: baseball, basketball, cross-country, football, golf, soccer, swimming, tennis, track, wrestling; female: basketball, cross-country, soccer, swimming, tennis, track, volleyball. *Special regulations:* Registered cars permitted without restrictions. *Special services:* Learning Resources Center, medical services. *Student publications, radio, television: The Observer*, a weekly newspaper; occasional literary publications. Radio station KCAT broadcasts 84 hours per week. T.V. station KCWU broadcasts 24 hours a day, 7 days a week. *Surrounding community:* Ellensburg population 12,500. Seattle, 107 miles from campus, is nearest metropolitan area.

Library Collections: 2,100,000 volumes including bound books, serial backfiles, electronic documents, and government documents not in separate collections. Online catalog. Current serial subscriptions: 1,667 paper and microform, 3 electronic. 9,119 recordings. Computer work stations available throughout the university's campuses. Students have access to the Internet at no charge.

Buildings and Grounds: Campus area 300 acres.

Chief Executive Officer: Dr. Jerilyn S. McIntyre, President.

Address admission inquiries to Lisa Garcia-Hanson, Director of Admissions.

City University

11900 NE First Street
Bellevue, Washington 98005

Tel: (425) 637-1010 **E-mail:** info@cityu.edu
Fax: (425) 637-9689 **Internet:** www.cityu.edu

Institution Description: City University is a private, nonprofit institution that provides educational opportunities for those segments of the population not being fully served through traditional processes. It provides instruction in communities throughout the state of Washington, as well as sites in Oregon, California, British Columbia, Germany, Switzerland, Slovakia, and Denmark. It has developed an extensive distance learning center to service individuals throughout the United States, Canada, and overseas. *Enrollment:* 3,184. *Degrees awarded:* Associate, baccalaureate, master's. Certificates are also awarded.

Accreditation: *Regional:* NWCCU.

History: Established in Seattle as City College 1973; offered first instruction at postsecondary level 1973; awarded first degree (baccalaureate) 1974; adopted present name 1982.

Institutional Structure: *Governing board:* Board of Governors. Extrainstitutional representation: 9 directors and president of the university. All voting. *Composition of institution:* Administrators 10. Various vice presidents; 4 academic deans; directors. Full-time instructional faculty 57. Academic governance body, Curriculum Committee, meets monthly.

Calendar: Quarters. Academic year July to June. Degrees conferred each quarter. Formal commencement June.

Admission: Rolling admission; prospective student should contact an academic advisor; application form and fee must be received prior to registration; course registration must occur by the first week of the quarter; transfer credits must be documented by receipt of 'official transcripts' from previously attended schools.

Degree Requirements: *For all baccalaureate degrees:* 180 quarter hours of which 45 must be earned at City University; minimum 2.0 cumulative GPA; general education requirements. *For master's degree:* 45–70 quarter hours depending on program; minimum 3.0 cumulative GPA. *Undergraduate and graduate certificates:* 75% of required course work must be earned at City University.

Exemption from some courses possible by the following means: passing the CLEP exam; receiving credit for PLE; other standardized tests. The student must have fulfilled all financial obligations in order to receive a degree. *Grading system:* Decimal; pass/fail; withdrawal.

Distinctive Educational Programs: Weekend and evening classes; Fast Track; Distance Learning; Inside Track (advanced level high school courses which also earn college credit); Continuing Education; QUEST courses (experientially-based, short courses designed for continuing professional education programs).

Degrees Conferred: 86 *associate*; 602 *baccalaureate*; 1,228 *master's*. Bachelor's degrees awarded in top five disciplines: business, management, marketing, and related support services 179; education 90; computer and information sciences 86; liberal arts/general studies; psychology 21. Master's degrees awarded: various disciplines: 1,088.

Fees and Other Expenses: *Full-time tuition per academic year 2008–09:* $12,960. *Books and supplies:* $1,232. *Off-campus room and board:* $10,736. *Other expenses:* $4,052.

Financial Aid: Aid from institutionally generated funds is provided on the basis of academic merit, financial need. Institution has a Program Participation

Agreement with the U.S. Department of Education for eligible students to receive Pell Grants and, depending upon the agreement, other federal aid.

Departments and Teaching Staff: *Total instructional faculty:* 1,225. Degrees held faculty: doctorate 35%, master's 95%, baccalaureate 100%. 35% hold terminal degrees.

Enrollment: Total enrollment 3,184. Undergraduate 1,285 (full-time 57%; female 63%, male 37%). Gradaute 1,899 (full-time 83%). Transfer-in students 318.

Characteristics of Student Body: *Ethnic/racial makeup:* Black non-Hispanic: 6%; American Indian or Alaska Native: 1%; Asian or Pacific Islander: 5%; Hispanic: 3%; White non-Hispanic: 59%; unknown: 22%; nonresident alien 5%.

International Students: 153 undergraduate nonresident aliens enrolled fall 2008. Programs available to aid students whose native language is not English: English as a Second Language. No financial aid specifically designated for international students.

Student Life: No on-campus housing.

Library Collections: 38,000 volumes. 600 microform serial subscriptions; 500 current current periodical subscriptions. Computer work stations available. Online catalog. City University delivers library services to its students and faculty through a program of support for collection development by cooperating libraries located near its instructional sites and by the direct provision of reference assistance (including remote database searching), document delivery, interlibrary loan facilitation, and instruction in library-based and computer-based information access for its faculty and students.

Most important special collections include teacher education; business.

Buildings and Grounds: Urban campus.

Chief Executive Officer: Dr. Edward L. Gorsuch, II, President.

Address admission inquiries to Office of Admissions and Student Affairs.

Cornish College of the Arts

710 East Roy Street
Seattle, Washington 98102
Tel: (206) 726-5016 **E-mail:** admissions@cornish.edu
Fax: (206) 720-1011 **Internet:** www.cornish.edu

Institution Description: Cornish College of the Arts is a private, independent, nonprofit institution. *Enrollment:* 815. *Degrees awarded:* Baccalaureate.

Accreditation: *Regional:* NWCCU. *Professional*: art, interior design

History: Established 1914 as Cornish School; changed name to Cornish Institute 1976; became Cornish College of the Arts 1986.

Institutional Structure: *Governing board:* Trustees of Cornish. Representation: 30 trustees. All voting. *Composition of institution:* Management/business/finances directed by director of finance and administration. Full-time instructional faculty 55.

Calendar: Semesters. Academic year Sept. to May.

Characteristics of Freshmen: 62% of applicants accepted. 44% of accepted applicants enrolled.

45% of entering freshmen expected to graduate within 5 years. 63% of freshmen from Washington. Freshmen from 165 states and 4 foreign countries.

Admission: Rolling admissions plan. *Requirements:* Either graduation from secondary school or GED; portfolio or audition. *Entrance tests:* none required.

Degree Requirements: 120 credit hours minimum (each department has specific requirements varying from 120 to 130 credit hours); final year in residence. *Grading system:* A–F; pass-fail; withdraw.

Distinctive Educational Programs: Bachelor of Fine Arts degrees in art, dance, design, music, performance production, theater. Bachelor of Applied Arts in art.

Degrees Conferred: 144 *baccalaureate:* visual and performing arts.

Fees and Other Expenses: *Full-time tuition per academic year 2008–09:* $25,600. *Books and supplies:* $1,800. *Off-campus room and board per academic year:* $6,500. *Other expenses:* $2,800.

Financial Aid: Aid from institutionally generated funds is provided on the basis of academic merit, financial need.

Departments and Teaching Staff: *Total instructional faculty:* 148 (full-time 55, part-time 93). Student/faculty ratio: 8:1. Degrees held by faculty: master's 72%, baccalaureate 19%, professional 9%. 52% hold terminal degrees.

Enrollment: Total enrollment 815 (undergraduate).

Characteristics of Student Body: *Ethnic/racial makeup:* number of Black non-Hispanic: 19; American Indian or Alaska Native: 7; Asian or Pacific Islander: 25; Hispanic: 36; White non-Hispanic: 470; unknown: 185.

International Students: 24 nonresident aliens enrolled fall 2008. Students from Europe, Asia, Latin America, Africa, Canada. No programs available to aid students whose native language is not English. No financial aid specifically designated for international students.

Student Life: No on-campus housing. *Surrounding community:* Seattle population 500,000.

Library Collections: 25,000 volumes. 14,000 audiovisual materials; 140 current periodical subscriptions.

Most important special holdings include collections on the arts (dance, theater, music, fine arts, design).

Chief Executive Officer: Sergei Tschernisch, President.

Address admission inquiries to Jane Buckman, Dean of Enrollment Services.

Eastern Washington University

526 Fifth Street
Cheney, Washington 99004-2496
Tel: (509) 359-6200 **E-mail:** admissions@ewu.edu
Fax: (509) 359-6692 **Internet:** www.ewu.edu

Institution Description: Eastern Washington University (Eastern Washington State College until 1977) is a state institution. *Enrollment:* 10,809. *Degrees awarded:* Baccalaureate, master's.

Academic offerings subject to approval by statewide coordinating bodies. Budget subject to approval by state governing boards. Member of the consortium Intercollegiate Center for Nursing Education.

Accreditation: *Regional:* NWCCU. *Professional*: business, computer science, counseling, dental hygiene, engineering technology, music, nursing, physical therapy, planning, recreation and leisure services, social work, speech-language pathology, teacher education

History: Established as State Normal School at Cheney and offered first instruction at postsecondary level 1890; awarded first degree (baccalaureate) 1933; changed name to Eastern Washington College of Education 1939, Eastern Washington State College 1961; adopted present name 1977. *See* Cecil Dryden, *Light for an Empire* (Cheney: Eastern Washington State University, 1965) for further information.

Institutional Structure: *Governing board:* Board of trustees. Representation: 8 members (includes 1 student). All voting. *Composition of institution:* Administrators 10. Academic affairs headed by provost and vice president of academic affairs. Management/business/finances directed by vice president for business and finance. Full-time instructional faculty 364. Academic governance body, Academic Senate, meets an average of 30 times per year.

Calendar: Quarters. Academic year Aug. to June. Freshmen admitted Sept., Jan., Mar., June. Degrees conferred and formal commencement June. Summer session from June to Aug.

Characteristics of Freshmen: 3,624 applicants (female 2,066, male 1,558). 88% of applicants accepted. 46% of accepted applicants enrolled.

81% of entering freshmen were in top 50% of their high school graduating class. Mean SAT scores 493 verbal, 495 mathematical. Mean ACT Composite score 21.

37% of entering freshmen expected to graduate within 5 years. 86% of freshmen from Washington. Freshmen from 15 states and 5 foreign countries.

Admission: Rolling admissions plan. *Requirements:* Graduation from accredited secondary school or GED (minimum score of 50) and core courses in high school. Minimum GPA 2.0. SAT or ACT. For foreign students minimum TOEFL score of 525 and 2.75 GPA from schools outside the U.S. *For transfer students:* 2.0 minimum GPA or transferable associate degree from a Washington community college. 4-year accredited institution maximum transfer credit unlimited; from 2-year accredited institution 90 quarter credits; correspondence/extension students 45 credits.

College credit may be granted for advanced placement for postsecondary-level work completed in secondary school. College credit for USAFI-Dantes and CLEP while taken in the military is awarded on the basis of portfolio and faculty assessments.

Tutoring available. Developmental courses offered during regular academic year.

Degree Requirements: 180 quarter credits; 2.0 GPA; 45 credits in residence; general education and core curriculum requirements.

Fulfillment of some degree requirements and exemption from some beginning courses possible by passing departmental examinations, College Board AP. *Grading system:* Numerical system based on 4.0 scale; pass.

Distinctive Educational Programs: Cooperative education. Flexible meeting places and schedules, including off-campus centers, weekend and evening classes. Dual-degree programs. Special facilities for using telecommunications in the classroom. Interdisciplinary programs in earth science, nutrition education, occupational safety and health, women's studies. Preprofessional programs in dental hygiene, dentistry, law, medicine, veterinary medicine. Facilities and programs for independent research, including honors programs, individual majors, tutorials. Institutionally sponsored study abroad.

EASTERN WASHINGTON UNIVERSITY—*cont'd*

ROTC: Army.

Degrees Conferred: 2,014 *baccalaureate*; 522 *master's*; 29 *first-professional*. Bachelor's degrees awarded in top five disciplines: education 579; business, management, marketing, and related support services 312; health professions and related clinical sciences 144; multidisciplinary studies 92; communication, journalism, and related programs 91.

Fees and Other Expenses: *Full-time tuition per academic year 2008–09:* undergraduate resident $5,223, nonresident $14,325; contact the university for current graduate tuition and fees. *Books and supplies:* $1,050. *Room and board per academic year:* $6,782. *Other expenses:* $3,077.

Financial Aid: Aid from institutionally generated funds is provided on the basis of academic merit, financial need, athletic ability.

Financial aid to full-time, first-time undergraduate students: 75% received some form of aid. Average amount of aid received: federal grants $3,862; Pell grants $3,118; other federal aid $1,011; state/local grants $3,362; institutional grants $3,172.

Departments and Teaching Staff: *Total instructional faculty:* 506. Student/faculty ratio: 19:1. Degrees held by full-time faculty: 55% hold terminal degrees.

Enrollment: Total enrollment 10,809. Undergraduate 9,485 (full-time 87%; female 56%, male 44%). Graduate 1,324 (full-time 88%). Transfer-in students 1,022.

Characteristics of Student Body: *Ethnic/racial makeup:* Black non-Hispanic: 8%; American Indian or Alaska Native: 2%; Asian or Pacific Islander: 4%; Hispanic: 4%; White non-Hispanic: 63%; unknown: 17%; nonresident alien 2%.

International Students: 216 undergraduate nonresident aliens enrolled fall 2008. Programs available to aid students whose native language is not English: English as a Second Language Program. Financial aid specifically designated for international students: scholarships available annually to qualifying students;

Student Life: On-campus residence halls house 18% of student body. Housing available for married students. *Intercollegiate athletics:* male: basketball, cross-country, football, golf, swimming, tennis,track and field, female: basketball, cross-country, golf, tennis, track and field, volleyball. *Special regulations:* Registered cars with decals permitted. *Special services:* Learning Resources Center, medical services. *Student publications, radio: Easterner*, a weekly newspaper. Radio stations KEWC-AM and KEWC-FM each broadcasts 126 hours per week. *Surrounding community:* Cheney population 8,000. Spokane, 16 miles from campus, is nearest metropolitan area. Served by mass transit bus system; airport 12 miles from campus; passenger rail service 17 miles from campus.

Publications: *Pacific Northwest Forum* (quarterly) first published 1977; *View Point* (annually) first published 1980; *Willow Springs Magazine* (biannually) first published 1978.

Library Collections: 1,900,000 volumes including bound books, serial backfiles, electronic documents, and government documents not in separate collections. Online catalog. 4,800 current serial subscriptions (paper and microform). 27,595 audiovisual materials. Computer work stations available. Students have access to the Internet at no charge.

Buildings and Grounds: Campus area 174 acres.

Chief Executive Officer: Dr. Stephen M. Jordan, President.

Address undergraduate admission inquiries to Director of Admissions; graduate inquiries to Lawrence Briggs, Director of Graduate Programs.

Evergreen State College

2700 Evergreen Parkway N.W.
Olympia, Washington 98505-0005
Tel: (360) 866-6000 **E-mail:** admissions@evergreen.edu
Fax: (360) 866-6576 **Internet:** www.evergreen.edu

Institution Description: The Evergreen State College is a public institution. *Enrollment:* 4,676. *Degrees awarded:* Baccalaureate, master's.

Academic offerings subject to approval by statewide coordinating bodies. Budget subject to approval by state governing boards.

Accreditation: *Regional:* NWCCU.

History: Established 1967; offered first instruction at postsecondary level 1971; awarded first degree (baccalaureate) 1972; initiated graduate program 1980.

Institutional Structure: *Governing board:* Board of Trustees. Extrainstitutional representation: 7 trustees; institutional representation: 1 administrator, 1 full-time instructional faculty member, 1 student; 1 alumnus. 4 ex officio. 5 voting. *Composition of institution:* Administrators 495. Academic affairs headed by academic vice president-provost. Management/business/finances directed by vice president for finance and administration. Full-time instructional faculty 158. Academic governance bodies, faculty meetings and dean's group meetings, meet an average of 9 and 36 times per year, respectively.

Calendar: Quarters. Academic year Sept. to June. Freshmen admitted throughout the year. Degrees conferred June, Sept., Dec., Mar. Formal commencement June. Summer session from June to Sept.

Characteristics of Freshmen: 1,967 applicants (female 1,156, male 853). 95% of applicants admitted. 38% of applicants admitted and enrolled.

82% (479 students) submitted SAT scores; 27% (160 students) submitted ACT scores. *25th percentile*: SAT Critical Reading 520, SAT Math 470; ACT Composite 21. *75th percentile*: SAT Critical Reading 650, SAT Math 590; ACT Composite 27.

53% of entering freshmen expected to graduate within 5 years. 58% of freshmen from Washington. Freshmen from 40 state and 3 foreign countries.

Admission: Deadlines for freshmen and transfer students: Mar. 1 for fall quarter, Oct. 1 for winter quarter, Dec. 1 for spring quarter. The college reserves the right to accept late applications on a space available basis. High school transcript, official test scores from the ACT or SAT, transcripts from any colleges attended. College preparatory program in high school: 4 years of English, 3 social studies, 2 in a single foreign language, 3 mathematics, 2 science (1 must be a lab science), 1 year of fine, visual, or performing arts or other college prep elective form other subject areas mentioned above. Eligible applicants ranked by means of formulas that combine academic factor, i.e. GPA and/or test c=scores, and diversity factors. *Transfer students:* 2.0 minimum GPA; from 4-year accredited institution 135 quarter hours maximum transfer credit; from 2-year accredited institution 90 quarter hours.

College credit and advanced placement for postsecondary-level work completed in secondary school. College credit earned through CLEP.

Tutoring available through the Learning Resources Center.

Degree Requirements: 180 quarter hours for B.A. degree with 45 of last 90 credits in residence; 180 quarter hours for B.S. with 72 credits of science, math, or computer science for which 48 are upper division. 225 credits for a Bachelor of Arts and Science degree.

Fulfillment of some degree requirements and exemption from some beginning courses possible by passing College Board CLEP, AP. *Grading system:* Narrative evaluations instead of grades.

Distinctive Educational Programs: *For undergraduates:* All programs are interdisciplinary and developed through faculty-student collaboration; classes are run on a block basis. Students ordinarily enroll in one single, coherent academic program at a time rather than several non-related courses. These programs are the equivalent of 16 quarter hours. Flexible meeting places and schedules. Teacher certification program in cooperation with Western Washington University. Individually arranged study abroad. *Available to all students:* Work-experience programs. Weekend and evening classes. Special facilities for using telecommunications in the classroom. Facilities and programs for independent research. Study abroad programs in Chile, Japan, Ecuador, Russia.

Degrees Conferred: 1,077 *baccalaureate*: liberal arts and general studies; 97 *master's*: education 344; environmental science 25; public administration 28.

Fees and Other Expenses: *Full-time tuition per academic year 2008–09:* undergraduate resident $5,343, nonresident $18,203; contact the university for graduate tuition /fees which vary by program. *Required fees:* $490. *Room and board per academic year:* $8,052. *Books and supplies:* $924. *Other expenses:* $3,264.

Financial Aid: Aid from institutionally generated funds is provided on the basis of academic merit, financial need, other considerations.

Financial aid to full-time, first-time undergraduate students: 72% received some form of aid. Average amount of aid received: federal grants $3,569; Pell grants $2,894; other federal aid $1,101; state/local grants $3,101; instituional grants $3,809.

Departments and Teaching Staff: *Total instructional faculty:* 221 (full-time 158, part-time 63). Total faculty with doctorate, first-professional, or other terminal degree: 164. Student/faculty ratio: 21:1.

Enrollment: Total enrollment 4,696. Undergraduate 4,364 (full-time 90%; female 55%, male 45%). Graduate 332 (full-time 52%). Transfer-in students 802.

Characteristics of Student Body: *Ethnic/racial makeup:* Black non-Hispanic: 45; American Indian or Alaska Native: 3%; Asian or Pacific Islander: 3%; Hispanic: 5%; White non-Hispanic: 70%; unknown: 11%; nonresident alien 1%. *Age distribution:* number under 18: 15; 18–19: 757; 20–21: 957; 22–24: 890; 25–29: 30–34: 275; 35–39: 164; 40–49: 289; 50–64: 66; 65 and over: 11.

International Students: 47 nonresident aliens enrolled fall 2008. Students from Europe, Asia, Canada, Australia, Middle East. No programs available to aid students whose native language is not English. No financial aid specifically designated for international students.

Student Life: On-campus residence halls house 22% of student body. Residence halls for both sexes constitute 100% of such space. Residence halls are built as individual apartments (i.e., most have their own private bath and kitchen facilities). *Intercollegiate athletics:* male and female: basketball, cross-country, soccer, track and field, volleyball. *Special regulations:* Cars permitted without restrictions. *Special services:* Learning Resources Center with Writing Center and Quantitative and Symbolic Reasoning Center. *Student publications, radio: Cooper Point Journal*, a weekly newspaper. Radio station KAOS broadcasts to the local community. *Surrounding community:* Olympia population 42,500. Seattle, 60 miles from campus, is nearest metropolitan area. Served by mass transit bus system; airport 60 miles from campus; passenger rail service 15 miles from campus.

Library Collections: 472,000 volumes. Online and card catalogs. Current serial subscriptions: paper 361; microform 92; via electronic access 12,126. 13,277 audio/videotapes; 2,958 DVD discs; 7,172 CD-ROMs. 45 computer work stations available. *Most important special collections:* Miniature Press Collection; Fine Arts Press (limited editions); Chicano and Latino Culture of the Pacific Northwest.

Buildings and Grounds: Campus area 1,000 acres.

Chief Executive Officer: Dr. Thomas Purce, President.

Address admission inquiries to Douglas Scrima, Director of Admissions.

Gonzaga University

East 502 Boone Avenue
Spokane, Washington 99258-0001
Tel: (509) 328-4220 **E-mail:** admissions@gonzaga.edu
Fax: (509) 324-5718 **Internet:** www.gonzaga.edu

Institution Description: Gonzaga University is a private institution sponsored by the Roman Catholic Church (Society of Jesus). *Enrollment:* 7,272. *Degrees awarded:* Baccalaureate, first-professional (law), master's, doctorate. Licentiate in philosophy also awarded.

Accreditation: *Regional:* NWCCU. *Professional*: business, chemistry, engineering, nursing, law, teacher education

History: Established as Gonzaga College 1887; offered first instruction at postsecondary level 1890; incorporated and awarded first degree (baccalaureate) 1894; adopted present name 1912. *See* Wilfred P. Schoenberg, S.J., *Gonzaga University. Seventy-five Years, 1887–1962* (Spokane: Gonzaga University, 1963) for further information.

Institutional Structure: *Governing board:* Board of Trustees. Extrainstitutional representation: 25 trustees; institutional representation: 1 administrator (president ex officio) and 6 other representatives of the Society of Jesus. All voting. *Composition of institution:* Administrators 78. Vice presidents: academic, administration and planning, finance, student life, university relations. Academic governance body, Academic Council, meets an average of 6 times per year. Full-time instructional faculty 247.

Calendar: Semesters. Academic year Aug. to May. Freshmen admitted Aug., Jan., June. Degrees conferred May, July, Dec. Formal commencement May. Summer session of 2 terms from May to July.

Characteristics of Freshmen: 5,744 applicants (female 3,057, male 2,737). 87% of applicants accepted. 39% of accepted applicants enrolled.

Mean SAT scores 571 verbal, 573 mathematical. Mean ACT Composite score 25.4. 3 National Merit Scholars.

60% of entering freshmen expected to graduate within five years. 50% of freshmen from Washington. Freshmen from 28 states and 21 foreign countries.

Admission: Deadline for freshmen applicants is Apr. 1. Students are accepted after that only on a space available basis. For fall acceptance, apply as early as end of junior year of secondary school. Early acceptance available. *Requirements:* Graduation from secondary school with 4 units English, 2 in foreign language, 3 mathematics (including 2 algebra), 1 civics, 1 history, 1 lab science, and 6 electives. Students presenting a GED will be evaluated on an individual basis. Minimum 2.5 GPA. *Entrance tests:* College Board SAT, or ACT. *See* specific school for additional requirements. *For transfer students:* 2.0 minimum GPA; 98 hours maximum transfer credit; from 2-year accredited institution 64 hours; correspondence/extension students 6 hours.

College credit and advanced placement for postsecondary-level work completed in secondary school. College credit for College Board CLEP, PEP, departmental examinations, and for extrainstitutional learning.

Tutoring available. Remedial courses offered during regular academic year; elective credit given.

Degree Requirements: 128 semester credits; 2.0 minimum GPA; senior year in residence; distribution requirements; either senior thesis or comprehensive examination, depending on department. *See* specific school for additional requirements.

Fulfillment of some degree requirements and exemption from some beginning courses possible by passing departmental examinations, College Board CLEP, APP, PEP. *Grading system:* A–F; pass-fail; X (official withdrawal for which there is no penalty); V (unofficial withdrawal which counts as F).

Distinctive Educational Programs: *For undergraduates:* Work-experience programs. Major in interdisciplinary studies. Individual majors, honors program involving special core curriculum. Study abroad at Gonzaga-in-Florence, Italy; Japan; London, England; Salamanca, Spain; Paris, France; Guadalajara, Mexico; field studies in West Indies, Australia, Baja Mexico, Northwest Canada, Costa Rica, Kenya. *For graduate students:* Weekend classes. Accelerated degree programs. *Available to all students:* Evening classes. See specific school for other available programs.

ROTC: Army.

Degrees Conferred: 994 *baccalaureate*; 652 *master's*; 182 *doctorate*. Bachelor's degrees awarded in top five disciplines: business, management, marketing, and related support services 165; social sciences 97; engineering 75; communication, journalism, and related programs 62; psychology 56. Master's degrees awarded: various disciplines 652. First-professional degrees awarded: law 182.

Fees and Other Expenses: *Full-time tuition per academic year 2008–09:* undergraduate $26,322; contact the university for current graduate/first-professional tuition and fees. *Room and board per academic year:* $7,860. *Books and supplies:* $900. *Other expenses:* $2,900.

Financial Aid: Aid from institutionally generated funds is provided on the basis of academic merit, financial need, athletic ability, other criteria.

Financial aid to full-time, first-time undergraduate students: 98% received some form of aid. Average amount of aid received: federal grants $4,801; Pell grants $3,074; other federal aid $2,552; state/local grants $5,278; institutional grants $11,768.

Departments and Teaching Staff: *Total instructional faculty:* 454. Student/faculty ratio: 12:1. Degrees held by full-time instructional faculty: doctorates 84%, master's 6%, professional 10%. 94% hold terminal degrees.

Enrollment: *Total enrollment:* 7,272. Undergraduate 4,517. Graduate 2,785 (full-time 29%). Transfer-in students 170.

Characteristics of Student Body: *Ethnic/racial makeup:* Black non-Hispanic: 1%; American Indian or Alaska Native: 1%; Asian or Pacific Islander: 5%; Hispanic: 4%; White non-Hispanic: 77%; unknown: 9%; nonresident alien 2%. .

International Students: 144 nonresident aliens enrolled fall 2008. Programs available to aid students whose native language is not English: social, cultural, financial. English as a Second Language Program.

Student Life: On-campus residence halls house 50% of the undergraduate population. Residence halls are single sex and coed. Freshman and sophomore students under age 21 are required to live on campus. Residence hall visitation is from 10am to midnight. Quiet hours are daily from 7pm to 10am. *Intercollegiate athletics:* male: baseball, lacrosse, hockey; female: volleyball; both men and women: basketball, cross-country, golf, soccer, tennis, track, crew, rugby, skiing. *Special services:* health center; counseling and career assessment center; career resources center; campus ministry. *Student publications, radio: Charter* and *Reflections*, annual literary magazines; *Bulletin*, weekly student newspaper; *Spires*, a yearbook. Radio station KZAG broadcasts 102 hours per week. *Surrounding community:* Spokane population 175,000 (metropolitan area population 360,000). Seattle is 270 miles west from campus. Served by mass transit bus system; airport 10 miles from campus; passenger rail service 2 miles from campus.

Publications: Sources of information about Gonzaga include *Signum*, an institutional newspaper sent 8 times a year to alumni, parents, and friends of the university.

Library Collections: 595,000 volumes. 10,500 government documents; 50,000 microforms; 6,000 audiovisual materials; 4,760 periodical subscriptions. Online catalog. Computer work stations available. Students have access to online information retrieval services and the Internet.

Most important special collections include the Gerard Manley Hopkins Poetry Collection; Bing Crosby Memorabilia; rare book collection.

Buildings and Grounds: Campus area 83 acres. Campus DVD available.

Chief Executive Officer: Rev. Robert J. Spitzer, S.J., President.

Address admission inquiries to Julie A. McCulloh, Dean of Admissions; Graduate School inquiries to Leonard Doohan, Dean of Graduate School; Law School inquiries to John Clute, Dean of Law School.

College of Arts and Sciences

Degree Programs Offered: *Baccalaureate* in art, biology, broadcasting, chemistry, classical civilization, classics, communication disorders, criminal justice, drama, economics, English, French, history, Italian studies, Latin, literary studies, mathematics, mathematics-computer science, mathematics-quantitative, medical technology, music, nursing, philosophy, physics, political science, print journalism, psychology, religious studies, Spanish, speech, sociology. *See* Graduate School for advanced degrees.

Admission: *See* general requirements.

Degree Requirements: *See* general requirements. Minimum of 104 credits in field of arts and sciences. For degree candidates from St. Michael's Institute, 1 hour comprehensive oral examination in philosophy.

GONZAGA UNIVERSITY—*cont'd*

Distinctive Educational Programs: Classical baccalaureate for students completing 12 semester hours Latin beyond intermediate level and 6 semester hours Greek or courses in a modern language to at least intermediate level. Honors baccalaureate for students who participate in interdisciplinary seminars in fulfillment of general education requirements. Interdepartment and interdisciplinary majors, including criminal justice and literary studies. Business-communications, business-quantitative, and economics-accounting are offered in cooperation with the School of Business Administration Pre-professional programs in dentistry, law, medicine, nursing; a multi-disciplinary program in women's studies.

School of Business Administration

Degree Programs Offered: *Baccalaureate* in accounting, economics, finance, marketing, management, and operation and information systems. *See* Graduate School for advanced degrees.

Admission: *See* general requirements.

Degree Requirements: In addition to general requirements, core requirements in business subjects.

Distinctive Educational Programs: Interdisciplinary programs in business-communications, business-quantitative, economics-accounting in cooperation with College of Arts and Sciences; secondary major is offered in international business.

School of Education

Degree Programs Offered: *Baccalaureate* in physical education, special education (awarded by College of Arts and Sciences). *See* Graduate School for advanced degrees.

Admission: *See* general requirements.

Degree Requirements: *See* general requirements.

Distinctive Educational Programs: Certification programs for undergraduates and fifth-year students. Fifth-year programs in counseling and principalship. Research Center provides research experience for doctoral students.

School of Engineering

Degree Programs Offered: *Bachelor of Science* (Honors and General) in civil, electrical, and mechanical engineering. *See* Graduate School for advanced degrees.

Admission: In addition to general requirements, 1 further unit mathematics.

Degree Requirements: 135–138 credit hours for baccalaureate degrees; 30 credit hours for master's degrees.

Distinctive Educational Programs: 5-year engineering-master's in business administration program offered in cooperation with School of Business Administration.

St. Michael's Institute, Jesuit School of Philosophy and Letters

Degree Programs Offered: St. Michael's Institute, a liberal arts college and seminary that consists of Novitiate and Collegiate Divisions, provides the first 6 years of the religious and academic formation of Jesuit scholastics who are candidates for the priesthood. *Baccalaureate, licentiate in philosophy* (awarded by College of Arts and Sciences), *master's* in philosophy (awarded by Graduate School).

Admission: *See* general requirements. *For Collegiate Division*, completion of novitiate.

Degree Requirements: *See* general requirements and requirements for College of Arts and Sciences.

Gonzaga University School of Law

Degree Programs Offered: *First-professional* (Juris Doctor).

Admission: Baccalaureate degree; minimum 3.0 GPA; upper 50th percentile on LSAT.

Degree Requirements: 90 credit hours; 2.2 GPA; 90 weeks in residence.

Distinctive Educational Programs: 3-year full-time and 5-year part-time programs available. Clinical program available for third-year students. *Gonzaga Law Review* edited by students with faculty cooperation.

Graduate School

Degree Programs Offered: *Master's* in business administration, accountancy, counseling psychology, administration and curriculum, computer education, education in teaching, special education, administration of physical education and athletics, anesthesiology education, electrical engineering, mechanical engineering, organizational leadership, nursing, English, philosophy, pastoral ministry, religious studies. Doctorate in educational leadership.

Admission: *For master's:* 3.0 minimum GPA in upper-level work; GRE, MAT, or GMAT, depending on program. Other requirements vary with program. *For doctorate:* requirements include master's; 3.5 minimum GPA; GRE, MAT.

Degree Requirements: Requirements vary according to program.

Distinctive Educational Programs: Combined master's program in anesthesiology education in cooperation with Sacred Heart Medical Center School of Anesthesia. Dual-degree programs in business administration and law.

School of Professional Studies

Degree Programs Offered: *Baccalaureate* in general studies; Bachelor of Science in nursing. (*See* Graduate School for advanced degrees.)

Admission: Associate degree or its equivalent.

Degree Requirements: 128 credit hours, including associate degree credits; 40 credits in residence; 21 hours in area of concentration; 2 hours in religious studies; 2 hours in philosophy.

Distinctive Educational Programs: Off-campus and videotape programs at various locations.

Heritage University

3240 Fort Road
Toppenish, Washington 98948

Tel: (509) 865-8500 **E-mail:** admissions@heritage.edu
Fax: (509) 865-4469 **Internet:** www.heritage.edu

Institution Description: Heritage University is a nonprofit, independent, nondenominational institution of higher education offering undergraduate and graduate education. *Enrollment:* 1,081. *Degrees awarded:* Associate, baccalaureate, master's.

Accreditation: *Regional:* NWCCU.

History: The university is unique in its origin. Both old and new, it is a transformation of Spokane's Fort Wright College (formerly Holy Names College), founded in 1907. Through a change in name, location of administrative offices, and ownership/sponsorship, a new institution was born in 1981.

Calendar: Semesters. Academic year Sept. to May.

Admission: Students who have graduated from an accredited high school with satisfactory academic grade point averages or have successfully completed the GED test are eligible for admission.

Degree Requirements: *Baccalaureate:* completion of a minimum of 126 semester credits including 48 upper division credits, 32 credits earned at Heritage College, general college requirements, and completion of major requirements.

Distinctive Educational Programs: Strong professional and career-oriented programs to enrich the quality of life for students and their communities. Multicultural emphasis in courses. Cooperative agreements with local school districts.

Degrees Conferred: 13 *associate*; 94 *baccalaureate* 160 *master's*. Bachelor's degrees awarded in top five disciplines: education 29; public administration 16; psychology 13; business, management, marketing, and related support services 10; English language/literature 5. Master's degrees awarded: education 160.

Fees and Other Expenses: *Full-time tuition per academic year 2008–09:* $9,775; contact the university for graduate tuition./fees. *Books and supplies:* $924. *Room and board per academic year:* $8,052. *Other expenses:* $3,780.

Financial Aid: Aid from institutionally generated funds is provided on the basis of academic merit, financial need, other considerations.

Institution has a Program Participation Agreement with the U.S. Department of Education for eligible students to receive Pell Grants and, depending upon the agreement, other federal aid.

Financial aid to full-time, first-time undergraduate students: 77% received federal grants averaging $3,914; 80% Pell grants averaging $3,454; 68% state/local grants averaging $3,816; 81% institutional grants averaging $1,432; 49 % received loans averaging $3,374.

Departments and Teaching Staff: *Total instructional faculty:* 183. Degrees held by faculty: doctorates 60%, master's 40%. 40% hold terminal degrees.

Enrollment: Total enrollment 1,081. Undergraduate 758 (full-time 70%; female 76%; male 24%). Graduate 329 (full-time 10%). Transfer-in students 79.

Characteristics of Student Body: *Ethnic/racial makeup:* Black non-Hispanic: 1%; American Indian or Alaska Native: 54%; Asian or Pacific Islander: 1%; Hispanic: 12%; White non-Hispanic: 32%.

International Students: 5 nonresident aliens enrolled fall 2008. No programs available to aid students whose native language is not English. No financial aid specifically designated for international students.

Student Life: All students are commuters. The college is located in a rural area five miles from Toppenish, population 7,000. Public transportation is not available.

Library Collections: 40,000 volumes. 57,000 microforms; 165 audiovisual materials; 244 current periodical subscriptions. Students have access to online information retrieval services.

Most important special collections include education and social work.

Buildings and Grounds: Campus area 11.5 acres.

Chief Executive Officer: Dr. Kathleen A. Ross, President.

Address admission inquiries to Norberto Espindola, Director of Admissions.

Northwest University

5520 108th Avenue N.E.
P.O. Box 579
Kirkland, Washington 98033
Tel: (425) 822-8266 **E-mail:** admissions@northwest.edu
Fax: (425) 827-0148 **Internet:** www.northwest.edu

Institution Description: Northwest University, formerly named Northwest College of the Assemblies of God, is a private institution. *Enrollment:* 1,246. *Degrees awarded:* Associate, baccalaureate, master's. Diplomas also awarded.

Accreditation: *Regional:* NWCCU.

History: Established and chartered as Northwest Bible Institute, and offered first instruction at postsecondary level 1934; awarded first degree (baccalaureate) 1948; changed name to Northwest Bible College 1949; became Northwest College of the Assemblies of God 1962; adopted present name 2005.

Institutional Structure: *Governing board:* Board of Directors. Extrainstitutional representation: 30 directors; institutional representation: president of the college; 1 alumnus. All voting. *Composition of institution:* Academic affairs headed by vice president for academic affairs. Management/business/finances directed by vice president for administrative services. Full-time instructional faculty 47. Academic governance body, the faculty, meets an average of 12 times per year.

Calendar: Semesters. Academic year Aug. to May. Freshmen admitted Aug., Jan., May. Degrees conferred and formal commencement May. Summer session May to June.

Characteristics of Freshmen: 477 applicants (female 330, male 147). 85% of applicants admitted. 41% of applicants admitted and enrolled.

79% of applicants submitted SAT scores; 50% ACT scores.

45% of entering freshmen expected to graduate within five year. 85% of freshmen from Washington. Freshmen from 13 states and 3 foreign countries.

Admission: Rolling admissions plan. For fall acceptance, apply as early as 1 year prior to enrollment, but no later than Aug. 1 of year of enrollment. Early acceptance available. *Requirements:* Either graduation from secondary school with 16 units, or GED. Recommend 4 units English, 2 foreign language, 3 mathematics, 2 social studies, 2 science, 3 electives. Minimum 2.3 GPA. *Entrance tests:* ACT Composite; SAT. *For transfer students:* 2.3 minimum GPA; maximum transfer credit limited only by residence requirement except a limit of 30 credits from non-accredited schools. *For international students:* TOEFL.

College credit and advanced placement for postsecondary-level work completed in secondary school.

Degree Requirements: *For all associate degrees:* 60 semester hours. *For all baccalaureate degrees:* 125 semester hours. *For all degrees:* 2.0 GPA; 2 semesters in residence; chapel attendance; general education requirements.

Fulfillment of some degree requirements possible by passing College Board CLEP, AP. *Grading system:* A–F; withdraw (carries time limit).

Distinctive Educational Programs: Evening classes. Independent study. Ministerial training program leading to baccalaureate in theology can be pursued concurrently with or upon completion of first baccalaureate degree. Elementary education major; psychology major. Business administration major. Nursing; Master of Arts in counseling psychology, Master of Arts in business administration. Teaching of English as a Second Language Certification; adult degree completion program. Study abroad in China, Costa Rica, Egypt, England, and Russia available through Counsel for Christian Colleges and Universities.

ROTC: Army in cooperation with University of Washington.

Degrees Conferred: 20 *associate;* 250 *baccalaureate:* business/marketing 71; communications/communication technologies 9; education 41; English 9; health professions and related clinical sciences 38; interdisciplinary studies 3; natural resources/environmental science 1; philosophy,religion/theology 43; psychology 21; social sciences and history 1; visual and performing arts 15. *Master's:* philosophy/religion/theology 53.

Fees and Other Expenses: *Full-time tuition per academic year 2008–09:* $20,520. *Required fees:* $650. *Room and board per academic year:* $6,578. *Books and supplies:* $1,000. *Other expenses:* $2,050.

Financial Aid: Aid from institutionally generated funds is provided on the basis of academic merit, financial need, athletic ability, other criteria.

Financial aid to full-time, first-time undergraduate students: need-based scholarships/grants totaling $3,971,753, self-help $4,732,987, parent loans $511,198, tuition waivers $631,887, athletic awards $320,305; non-need-based scholarships/grants totaling $625,065, self-help $1,850,963, parent loans $669,420, tuition waivers $176,987, athletic awards $204,707.

Departments and Teaching Staff: *Total instuctional faculty:* 67. Total faculty with doctorate, first-professional, or other terminal degree: 33. Student/faculty ratio: 15:1. Degrees held by full-time faculty: doctorate 39%, master's 100%. 47.5% hold terminal degrees.

Enrollment: Total enrollment 1,246. Undergraduate 1,070 (full-time 88%; female 62%, male 38%). Graduate 176 (full-time 80%). Transfer-in students 130.

Characteristics of Student Body: *Ethnic/racial makeup:* Black non-Hispanic: 4%; American Indian or Alaska Native: 1%; Asian or Pacific Islander: 6%; Hispanic: 45; White non-Hispanic: 73%; unknown: 8%; nonresident alien 2%. *Age distribution:* number under 18: 10; 18–19: 269; 20–21: 300; 22–24: 208; 25–29: 93; 30–34: 53; 35–39: 33; 40–49: 71; 50–64: 31.

International Students: 24 nonresident aliens enrolled fall 2008. Students from Asia, Africa, Canada. Programs available to aid students whose native language is not English: social, cultural. English as a Second Language Program. Financial aid specifically designated for international students: variable number of scholarships available annually to qualifying students.

Student Life: On-campus residence halls house 52% of student body. Residence halls for males constitute 40% of such space, for females 60%; 15% live in married student housing. *Intercollegiate athletics:* male: basketball, cross-country, soccer, track and field; female: basketball, cross-country, track and field, volleyball. Member of MAIA and NCCAA. *Special regulations:* Cars must be registered. Curfew begins 2am. Quiet hours from 9pm to 8am. Residence hall visitation from 9am to 12pm in lounge areas only. *Special services:* Medical services; counseling services. *Student publications, radio: Karisma*, a yearbook. *Surrounding community:* Kirkland population 41,000. Located in Seattle metropolitan area. Served by mass transit system, airport 20 miles from campus; passenger rail service 12 miles from campus.

Library Collections: 174,000 volumes including bound books, serial backfiles, electronic documents, and government documents not in separate collections. Online catalog. Current serial subscriptions: 604 paper, 140 microform, 1,779 electronic. 1,775 recordings; 13 CD-ROMs. Computer work stations available. Students have access to the Internet at no charge.

Most important special collections include Pentecostal Movement Collection; Pacific Rim Centre Collection; Ness Collection (Bibles); Teacher Education Curriculum Library.

Buildings and Grounds: Campus area 56 acres.

Chief Executive Officer: Dr. Don Argue, President.

Address admission inquiries to Myles Corrigan, Vice President for Admissions.

Pacific Lutheran University

12180 Park Avenue South
Tacoma, Washington 98447-0003
Tel: (253) 535-6900 **E-mail:** admission@plu.edu
Fax: (253) 535-5068 **Internet:** www.plu.edu

Institution Description: Pacific Lutheran University is a private institution affiliated with the American Lutheran Church. *Enrollment:* 3,652. *Degrees awarded:* Baccalaureate, master's.

Member of Independent Liberal Arts Colleges Abroad (ILACA) and Pacific Northwest International Intercultural Educational Consortium.

Accreditation: *Regional:* NWCCU. *Professional*: business, chemistry, computer science, marriage and family therapy, music, nursing, social work, teacher education

History: Established and chartered as Pacific Lutheran University 1890; changed name to Pacific Lutheran Academy 1894; became junior college 1921; became 3-year normal school 1931; became college of education 1939; became 4-year institution, changed name to Pacific Lutheran College, and awarded first degree (baccalaureate) 1940; reorganized and readopted present name 1960. *See* Dr. Walter Schnackenberg, *The Lamp and the Cross* (Tacoma, WA: Pacific Lutheran University Press, 1965) for further information.

Institutional Structure: *Governing board:* Board of Regents. Extrainstitutional representation: 37 regents; institutional representation: 7 administrators, 3 full-time instructional faculty members, 3 students; 3 alumni, 4 church officials. 16 ex officio. 33 voting. *Composition of institution:* Administrators 200. Academic affairs headed by provost. Management/business/finances directed by vice president-finance and operations. Full-time instructional faculty 233. Aca-

PACIFIC LUTHERAN UNIVERSITY—*cont'd*

demic governance body, Faculty Assembly, meets an average of 10 times per year.

Calendar: Semesters (4-1-4 plan). Academic year Sept. to May. Freshmen admitted Sept., Jan., Feb., June. Degrees conferred May, Aug., Dec., Jan. Formal commencements May, Aug., Dec. Summer session from June to Aug.

Characteristics of Freshmen: 2,555 applicants (female 1,515, male 1,040). 93% of applicants accepted. 43% of accepted applicants enrolled.

83% (551 students) submitted SAT scores; 17% (111 students) submitted ACT scores. *25th percentile*: SAT Critical Reading 460, SAT Math 490; ACT Composite 21. *75th percentile*: SAT Critical Reading 610, SAT Math 610; ACT Composite 28.

63% of entering freshmen expected to graduate within 5 years. 74% of freshmen from Washington. Freshmen from 23 states and 3 foreign countries.

Admission: Modified rolling admissions plan. For fall acceptance, apply as early as summer following junior year in secondary school, but not later than summer following senior year. Students are notified of acceptance beginning in Dec. Apply by Nov. 15 for early decision; need not limit application to Pacific Lutheran. Early acceptance available. *Requirements:* Either graduation from secondary school or GED. Recommend 4 units English, 2 in a foreign language, 2 laboratory science, 2 mathematics (preferably algebra and geometry), 2 social studies, 3 electives. Additional units in mathematics and foreign language recommended for some programs. Minimum 2.5 GPA. Lowest acceptable secondary school class standing 50th percentile. *Entrance tests:* College Board SAT or ACT composite. *For transfer students:* 2.5 minimum GPA; from 4-year accredited institution 96 semester hours maximum transfer credit; from 2-year accredited institution 64 semester hours.

College credit and advanced placement for postsecondary-level work completed in secondary school. College credit for extrainstitutional learning on basis of portfolio and faculty assessments; personal interviews. Advanced placement on basis of institutional assessment, including testing.

Tutoring available.

Degree Requirements: 128 credit hours; 2.0 GPA (2.5 for Schools of Business and Education); 2 terms in residence; 4 hours physical education; 4 hours writing; 4 hours critical conversation; 4 hours J-term course; distribution requirements; 4 hours each in cross cultural perspectives and alternative perspectives courses.

Fulfillment of some degree requirements and exemption from some beginning courses possible by passing departmental examinations, College Board CLEP or APP. *Grading system:* A–F; high pass-pass-fail; incomplete; withdraw (carries time limit).

Distinctive Educational Programs: *For undergraduates:* Dual-degree programs in engineering with Columbia University (NY) and Washington University (MO). Interdepartmental/interdisciplinary programs, including Integrated Studies, a group of courses dealing with a particular theme; Scandinavian and World Area Studies; programs in classics, environmental studies, lay church staff work, legal studies, public affairs. Preprofessional programs in health studies and theology. Honors programs. Study abroad in England through ILACA, through programs offered by other institutions; and by individual arrangement. Service and cooperative education programs and study tours abroad also available. *Available to all students:* Evening classes. Special facilities for using telecommunications in the classroom. Individual majors.

ROTC: Army.

Degrees Conferred: 797 *baccalaureate;* 125 *master's.*

Fees and Other Expenses: *Full-time tuition per academic year 2008–09:* $26,800 undergraduate; contact the university for current graduate tuition. *Room and board per academic year:* $8,200. *Books and supplies:* $924. *Other expenses:* $2,467.

Financial Aid: Aid from institutionally generated funds is provided on the basis of academic merit, financial need, other criteria.

Financial assistance is available in the form of Pell Grants, College Work-Study, Veterans Administration Benefits, National Direct Student Loans, Supplemental Education Opportunity Grants (SEOG), Stafford Loans, other federal aid programs.

Financial aid to full-time, first-time undergraduate students: 93% received some form of aid. Average amount of aid received: federal grants $3,687; Pell grants $3,019; other federal aid $1,141; state/local grants $4,776; institutional grants $13,579.

Departments and Teaching Staff: *Total instructional faculty:* 267 (full-time 233, part-time 34). Student/faculty ratio: 14:1. Degrees held by full-time faculty: doctorate 82.3%, master's 17.7%. *Faculty development:* 23 faculty members awarded sabbaticals 2008–09.

Enrollment: Total enrollment 3,652. Undergraduate 3,334 (full-time 94%; female 62%, male 38%). Graduate 318 (full-time 67%). Transfer-in students 222.

Characteristics of Student Body: *Ethnic/racial makeup:* Black non-Hispanic: 2%; American Indian or Alaska Native: 1%; Asian or Pacific Islander: 6%; Hispanic: 2%; White non-Hispanic: 69%; unknown: 12%; nonresident alien 7%. *Age distribution:* 17–21: 66.3%; 22–24: 15.3%; 25–29: 7.1%; 30–34: 3.3%; 35–39: 2.5%; 40–49: 3.9%; 50–59: 1.5%; over 60: 6.1%.

International Students: 169 undergraduate nonresident aliens enrolled fall 2008. Students from Europe, Asia, Latin America, Africa, Canada, Middle East. Programs available to aid students whose native language is not English: English as a Second Language Program. No financial aid specifically designated for international students.

Student Life: On-campus residence halls house 51% of student body. One all-female residence hall; 9 co-ed. Housing available for married students. *Intercollegiate athletics:* male: baseball, basketball, cross-country, football, golf, soccer, skiing, swimming, tennis, track; female: basketball, cross-country, soccer, field hockey, skiing, swimming, tennis, track, volleyball. *Special regulations:* Cars permitted to park on campus. Residence hall visitation 8am to 2am daily. *Special services:* Academic Advising and Assistance; Health Center. *Student publications, radio, television:* KCCR radio, KCNS6 television, *The Mast*, a weekly newspaper; *Saxifrage*, a biannual literary magazine. National Public Radio Station KPLU-FM broadcasts jazz. Closed circuit TV station broadcasts sports and educational programs. *Surrounding community:* Tacoma population 186,000. Seattle 40 miles from campus. Served by mass transit bus system, airport 30 miles from campus, passenger rail service 7 miles from campus.

Library Collections: 610,000 volumes. 237,000 microforms; 14,000 audiovisual materials; 4,470 current periodical subscriptions. Online catalog. Students have access to computerized information retrieval services and the Internet.

Most important special holdings include Scandinavian Immigrant Experience Collection; Grace Blomquist Juvenile Literature Collection; Regional Archives of the Evangelical Lutheran Church in America.

Buildings and Grounds: Campus area 126 acres.

Chief Executive Officer: Dr. Loren Anderson, President.

Address admission inquiries to Jennifer Olsen Krengel, Director of Admissions.

Puget Sound Christian College

7011 226th Place, S.W.
Edmonds, Washington 98043-2333
Tel: (425) 257-4090 **E-mail:** admissions@pscc.edu
Fax: (425) 258-1488 **Internet:** www.pscc.edu

Institution Description: Puget Sound Christian College is a private, independent, nonprofit college affiliated with Christian Churches and Churches of Christ. *Enrollment:* 130. *Degrees awarded:* Associate, baccalaureate. Bible certificates also awarded.

Accreditation: *National:* ABHE.

History: Established and chartered 1950 as Puget Sound College of the Bible; adopted present name 1985.

Institutional Structure: *Governing board:* 18 trustees and one administrator ex-officio officer (non-voting). *Composition of institution:* Administrative committee composed of 5 officers. Academic departments for divisions of Biblical Studies, General Studies, and Practical Ministries. Full-time instructional faculty 10. Academic governance body is the Academic Committee. Faculty meetings twice per month.

Calendar: Semesters. Academic year Aug. to May. Freshmen admitted Sept, Jan, Mar. Degrees conferred and formal commencement June. No summer session. Degree-completion program operates year-round.

Characteristics of Freshmen: 80% of applicants accepted. 71% of accepted applicants enrolled.

Mean SAT scores 470 verbal, 490 mathematical. Mean ACT Composite score 21.

35% of entering freshmen expected to graduate within 5 years. 35% of entering freshmen expected to graduate within five years. 43% of freshmen from Washington. Freshmen from 6 states.

Admission: *Requirements:* 2 references required; high school and college transcript. *Entrance tests:* SAT or ACT.

Degree Requirements: *For baccalaureate degree:* 130 semester credits. *For associate degree:* 64 semester credits. *For certificate:* 32 semester credits. *Grading system:* A–F; I (incomplete); W (withdrawal).

Distinctive Educational Programs: Preaching, Family Education, World Mission, Biblical Research, Social Science, Music Ministry, Christian Ministry, Degree Completion Program.

Degrees Conferred: 3 *associate;* 24 *baccalaureate:* theology.

Fees and Other Expenses: *Full-time tuition per academic year 2008–09:* $10,870. *Required fees:* $175. *Room and board per academic year:* $6,000.

Financial Aid: Aid from institutionally generated funds provided on the basis of academic merit, financial need, other criteria (parent in ministry; faculty/staff family grants).

Institution has a Program Participation Agreement with the U.S. Department of Education for eligible students to receive Pell Grants and, depending upon the agreement, other federal aid.

Departments and Teaching Staff: *Total instructional faculty* 41. Student/faculty ratio: 12:1. Degrees held by full-time faculty: master's 100%, doctorate 30%.

Enrollment: Total enrollment 130.

Characteristics of Student Body: *Ethnic/racial makeup:* Black non-Hispanic: 7; American Indian or Native Alaskan: 1; Asian or Pacific Islander: 6; White non-Hispanic 286. *Age distribution:* 17–21: 50%; 22–24: 12%; 25–29: 6%; 30–34: 5%; 35–39: 5%; 40–49: 12%; 50–59: 6%; 60–up 3%. 23% of student body attend summer sessions.

International Students: No programs available to aid students whose native language is not English. No financial aid specifically designated for international students.

Student Life: On-campus residence halls. *Intercollegiate athletics:* varsity basketball for males; volleyball for females. *Special regulations:* Attendance at church and chapel services required. Use of alcoholic beverages, narcotics, or tobacco is expressly prohibited. *Student publications:* weekly newsletter. *Surrounding community:* Edmonds, population 33,000, is a suburban area of Seattle. Served by all major transportation.

Library Collections: 40,000 volumes. 1,100 microforms; 1,900 audiovisual materials; 130 current periodical subscriptions. Online and card catalogs. Computer work stations available. Students have access to online information retrieval services and the Internet.

Most important special collections include the Restoration Movement Church History; Missions - Christian Church and Churches of Christ.

Buildings and Grounds: Campus area 4 acres.

Chief Executive Officer: Dr. Randy J. Bridges, President.

Address admission inquiries to Admissions Counselor.

Saint Martin's University

5300 Pacific Avenue S.E.
Lacey, Washington 98503
Tel: (360) 491-4700 **E-mail:** admissions@stmartin.edu
Fax: (360) 459-4124 **Internet:** www.stmartin.edu

Institution Description: Saint Martin's University is a private institution founded by the monks of the Order of Saint Benedict, the oldest Roman Catholic religious order in western civilization. *Enrollment:* 1,659. *Degrees awarded:* Associate, baccalaureate, master's.

Accreditation: *Regional:* NWCCU. *Professional*: engineering

History: Established and chartered as junior college 1895; offered first instruction at postsecondary level 1900; added baccalaureate program 1937; awarded first degree (baccalaureate) 1940. *See* Meinrad J. Gaul, *Between the Years 1895–1945* (Lacey: Saint Martin's College, 1945) for further information.

Institutional Structure: *Governing board:* Board of Trustees. Representation: 21 trustees, including 5 church officials, president of the college. 3 ex officio. All voting. *Composition of institution:* Administrators 7. Academic affairs headed by vice president for academic affairs. Management/business/finances directed by business manager. Full-time instructional faculty 40. Academic governance body, the faculty, meets an average of 9 times per year.

Calendar: Semesters. Academic year Aug. to May. Freshmen admitted Nov. 1, Jan. 1, or Mar. 1. Degrees conferred May, Dec. Formal commencement May.

Characteristics of Freshmen: 699 applicants (female 431, male 268). 94% of applicants accepted. 33.9% of accepted applicants enrolled.

Average secondary school rank of freshmen top 34th percentile. Mean SAT scores 520 verbal, 515 mathematical. Mean ACT Composite score 22.

71% of entering freshmen expected to graduate within 5 years. 90% of freshmen from Washington. Freshmen from 7 states and 2 foreign countries.

Admission: Three admissions dates. For fall acceptance, apply as early as Nov. 1, Jan. 1, or Mar. 1. Early acceptance available. *Requirements:* Either graduation from secondary school, or for those 18 years of age or older, GED. Recommend 4 units English, 2 mathematics, 2 history or social science, 1-2 foreign language, 9 academic electives. Minimum 2.0 GPA. *Entrance tests:* College Board SAT, ACT Composite, or Washington Pre-College Test. *For transfer students:* 2.0 minimum GPA; from 4-year accredited institution 90 semester hours or 135 quarter hours maximum transfer credit; from 2-year accredited institution 60 semester hours or 90 quarter hours; correspondence/extension students 30 semester hours or 45 quarter hours.

College credit and advanced placement for postsecondary-level work completed in secondary school. College credit for USAF/DANTES and for extrainstitutional learning.

Tutoring available. Developmental courses offered in summer session and regular academic year; credit given.

Degree Requirements: *For all associate degrees:* 60 credit hours; 15 hours in residence. *For all baccalaureate degrees:* 120 credit hours; senior year in residence. *For all undergraduate degrees:* 2.0 GPA; 2 hours physical education; distribution requirements.

Fulfillment of some degree requirements and exemption from some beginning courses possible by passing College Board CLEP, AP. *Grading system:* A–F; withdraw (carries time limit); incomplete (carries time limit).

Distinctive Educational Programs: *For undergraduates:* Flexible meeting places and schedules, including off-campus center (at Fort Lewis McChord Air Force Base, less than 30 miles away from main institution); weekend and evening classes. Interdisciplinary program in humane studies. Preprofessional programs in medicine, law, dentistry, veterinary science, pharmacy, nursing, optometry. Facilities and programs for independent research, including individual majors, tutorials. Computers in Education program for teachers K–12.

ROTC: Army and Air Force offered in cooperation with Pacific Lutheran University.

Degrees Conferred: 299 *baccalaureate*: 85 *master's*. Bachelor's degrees awarded in top five disciplines: business, management, marketing, and related support services 95; psychology 48; Engineering 28; education 21; security and protective services 16. Master's degrees awarded: various disciplines 85.

Fees and Other Expenses: *Full-time tuition per academic year 2008 09:* undergraduate $24.112; contact the college for current graduate tuition/fees. *Books and supplies:* $1,200. *Room and board per academic year:* $8,630. *Other expenses:* $3,500.

Financial Aid: Aid from institutionally generated funds is provided on the basis of academic merit, financial need, athletic ability, other criteria.

Financial aid to full-time, first-time undergraduate students: 43% received federal grants averaging $3,310; 37% state/local grants averaging $3,243; 97% institutional grants averaging $8,559; 94% received loans averaging $4,146.

Departments and Teaching Staff: *Total instructional faculty:* 41. Degrees held by full-time faculty: doctorate 60%, master's 34%, professional 6%. 66% hold terminal degrees.

Enrollment: Total enrollment 1,659. Undergraduate 1,387 (full-time 76%; female 55%, male 45%). Graduate 272 (full-time 27%). Transfer-in students 213.

Characteristics of Student Body: *Ethnic/racial makeup:* Black non-Hispanic: 7%; American Indian or Alaska Native: 2%; Asian or Pacific Islander: 10%; Hispanic: 5%; White non-Hispanic: 60%; unknown: 7%; nonresident alien 7%.

International Students: 50 nonresident aliens enrolled fall 2008. Programs available to aid students whose native language is not English: English as a Second Language Program. Financial aid specifically designated for international students: scholarships awarded annually.

Student Life: On-campus residence halls house 20% of student body. Residence halls for both sexes constitute 100% of such space. *Intercollegiate athletics:* NCAA Division II basketball (male and female) baseball; female cross-country, fast pitch softball, volleyball; male and female: golf. *Special regulations:* Cars permitted to park on campus perimeter only. Dormitory visitation 8am to 2am daily. *Special services:* Learning Resources Center, medical services. *Student publications, radio: The Bell Tower*, a biweekly newspaper; *Samarco*, a yearbook. *Surrounding community:* Lacey, population 30,000, is adjacent to the state capital of Olympia. Water sports 5 minutes away; hiking, skiing, 1 hour. Major collection of Northwestern art on campus; theatre, sports, major arts events short distances from college.

Publications: Quarterly Alumni publication *Insight.*

Library Collections: 132,000 volumes. 18,000 microforms; audiovisual materials; 450 current periodical subscriptions. Online catalog. Students have access to online information retrieval services and the Internet.

Most important special holdings include collections on theology, children's literature, Northwest history.

Buildings and Grounds: Campus area 480 acres.

Chief Executive Officer: Dr. Neal G. Roth, President.

Address admission inquiries to Todd Abbott, Director of Admissions.

Seattle Pacific University

3307 3rd Avenue West
Seattle, Washington 98119-1997
Tel: (206) 281-2021 **E-mail:** admissions@spu.edu
Fax: (206) 281-2188 **Internet:** www.spu.edu

Institution Description: Seattle Pacific University is a private institution affiliated with the Free Methodist Church of North America. *Enrollment:* 3,873. *Degrees awarded:* Baccalaureate, master's. Certificates also awarded.

Member of Christian College Consortium.

Accreditation: *Regional:* NWCCU. *Professional*: engineering, music, nursing, teacher education

History: Established as Seattle Seminary, an academy, and incorporated 1891; offered first instruction at postsecondary level 1910; awarded first degree (baccalaureate) and changed name to Seattle Pacific College 1915; adopted present name 1976.

Institutional Structure: *Governing board:* Seattle Pacific University Board of Trustees. Representation: 27 trustees, including 2 alumni; 2 honorary members. 27 voting. *Composition of institution:* Administrators 13. Academic affairs headed by vice president for academic affairs. Management/business/finances directed by vice president for finance and planning. Full-time instructional faculty 159. Academic governance body, Faculty Senate, meets an average of 15 times per year.

Calendar: Quarters. Academic year Sept. to May. Freshmen admitted Sept., Jan., Mar., June. Degrees conferred June, Aug., Dec., Mar. Formal commencement June. Summer session of 2 terms from June to Aug.

Characteristics of Freshmen: 88% of applicants accepted. 40% admitted full-time.

93% (588 students) submitted SAT scores; 31% (195 students) submitted ACT scores. *25th percentile*: SAT Verbal 510, SAT Math 510; ACT Composite 21, ACT English 21, ACT Math 20. *75th percentile*: SAT Verbal 620, SAT Math 620; ACT Composite 27, ACT English 28, ACT Math 27.

35% of entering freshmen expected to graduate within 5 years. 57% of freshmen from Washington.

Admission: Modified rolling admissions plan. For fall acceptance, apply no later than Sept. 1 of year of enrollment. Students are notified of acceptance from Oct. to Sept. *Requirements:* Graduation from secondary school or GED. Recommend college preparatory curriculum. Minimum 2.5 GPA. *Entrance tests:* College Board SAT or ACT composite. For foreign students TOEFL. *For transfer students:* 2.0 minimum GPA; from 4-year accredited institution 135 quarter hours maximum transfer credit; from 2-year accredited institution 90 quarter hours; correspondence/extension students 30 quarter hours.

College credit and advanced placement for postsecondary-level work completed in secondary school.

Tutoring available. Remedial courses offered during regular academic year; credit given.

Degree Requirements: 180 credit hours; 2.0 GPA; 45 hours, including last 15, in residence; 8 credits of courses which offer a substantial component of writing; chapel attendance; general education and core requirements.

Fulfillment of some degree requirements and exemption from some beginning courses possible by passing departmental examinations, College Board CLEP, AP. *Grading system:* A–F; pass-no credit; withdraw; incomplete.

Distinctive Educational Programs: *For undergraduates:* Interdisciplinary programs in American studies, environmental studies, European studies, general studies, liberal studies. Preprofessional programs in allied health sciences, engineering, ministry. Honors program. *For graduate students:* Cooperative master's in theology with Fuller Theological Seminary (CA). *Available to all students:* Wilderness field station on Blakeley Island. Outdoor education campuses on Whidbey Island. Work-experience programs. Evening classes. Special facilities for using telecommunications in the classroom. Individual majors. Cooperative programs through consortium. Study abroad: European quarter; study tours to Singapore; quarter of Transcultural Nursing in Costa Rica; SPRINT mission teams to various locations; various desert and marine biology study strips.

ROTC: Available by a cross-town agreements with the University of Washington and Seattle University.

Degrees Conferred: 657 *baccalaureate*; 226 *master's*; 24 *doctorate*. Bachelor's degrees awarded in top five disciplines: business, management, marketing, and related support services 121; health professions and related clinical sciences 76; psychology 68; social sciences 57; family and consumer sciences 52.

Fees and Other Expenses: *Full-time tuition per academic year 2008–09:* $23,391. *Books and supplies:* $800. *Room and board per academic year:* $8,000.

Financial Aid: Aid from institutionally generated funds is provided on the basis of academic merit, financial need, athletic ability, other criteria.

Institution has a Program Participation Agreement with the U.S. Department of Education for eligible students to receive Pell Grants and, depending upon the agreement, other federal aid.

Financial aid to full-time, first-time undergraduate students: 17% received federal grants averaging $4,297; 42% state/local grants averaging $2,487; 85% institutional grants averaging $6,207; 60% received loans averaging $5,625.

Departments and Teaching Staff: *Total instructional faculty:* 208. Degrees held by full-time faculty: doctorate 73%, master's 25%, baccalaureate 1%. 74% hold terminal degrees.

Enrollment: Total enrollment 3,873.

Characteristics of Student Body: *Ethnic/racial makeup:* number of Black non-Hispanic: 25; American Indian or Alaska Native: .8%; Asian or Pacific Islander: 5.8%; Hispanic: 1.9%; White non-Hispanic: 83.9%; unknown: 4.7%.

International Students: 30 undergraduate nonresident aliens enrolled fall 2008. Students from Europe, Asia, Latin America, Africa, Middle East, Canada, Australia, New Zealand. Programs available to aid students whose native language is not English: social, cultural, financial. English as a Second Language Program. Financial aid specifically designated for international students: scholarships available annually for qualifying students.

Student Life: On-campus residence halls and apartments house 50% of the undergraduate population. The ratio of females to males living on campus is 60/40. Residence halls are co-ed by floor. Housing available for married students. 30% of married students request institutional housing and are so housed. *Intercollegiate athletics:* male: basketball, crew, cross-country, soccer, tennis, track; female: basketball, crew, gymnastics, soccer, tennis, track, volleyball. A variety of intramural sports activities are available also. *Special regulations:* Residence hall visitation from noon to 11pm Sun.–Thurs., noon to midnight Fri. and Sat. Attendance at chapel services is required 3 times a week. Cars permitted in designated areas only; fee charged. *Special services:* Learning Resources Center, media center, medical services. *Student publications: The Falcon*, a weekly newspaper; *Tawahsi*, a yearbook. *Surrounding community:* Seattle population 500,000. Served by mass transit bus system. International airport 12 miles from campus, passenger rail service 5 miles from campus. 4-hour drive to the Pacific Ocean coast and 1-hour drive to the Cascade Mountains.

Publications: *Response*, primary means of communication between the University and its constituent groups.

Library Collections: 189,700 volumes. 487,665 microforms; 2,594 audiovisual materials; 1,309 current serial subscriptions. Access to Western Library Network, OCLC, other online information retrieval services. Students have access to the Internet.

Most important special holdings include collections on Protestant theology; Wesleyan studies.

Buildings and Grounds: Main campus area 35 acres.

Chief Executive Officer: Dr. Philip Eaton, President. Address admission inquiries to Admissions Office.

Seattle University

900 Broadway
Seattle, Washington 98122-4340
Tel: (206) 296-6000 **E-mail:** admissions@seattleu.edu
Fax: (206) 296-5656 **Internet:** www.seattleu.edu

Institution Description: Seattle University is a private institution affiliated with the Society of Jesus, Roman Catholic Church. *Enrollment:* 7,560. *Degrees awarded:* Baccalaureate, master's, doctorate.

Accreditation: *Regional:* NWCCU. *Professional*: business, chemistry, diagnostic medical sonography, engineering, nursing, teacher education

History: Established as School of the Immaculate Conception, an academy for men, 1891; changed name to Seattle College and incorporated 1898; offered first instruction at postsecondary level 1900; awarded first degree (baccalaureate) 1909; became coeducational 1933; adopted present name 1948.

Institutional Structure: *Governing board:* Board of Trustees. Extrainstitutional representation: 12 trustees; institutional representation: president of the university, 3 full-time instructional faculty members. 1 ex officio. All voting. *Composition of institution:* Administrators 45. Academic affairs headed by provost. Management/business/finances directed by vice president for finance, and treasurer. Full-time instructional faculty 310. Academic governance body, Academic Council, meets an average of 8 times per year.

Calendar: Quarters. Academic year Sept. to Sept. Freshmen admitted Sept., Jan., Mar., June. Degrees conferred June, Aug., Dec., Mar. Formal commencement June. Summer session from June to Aug.

Characteristics of Freshmen: 4,999 applicants (female 3,126, male 1,873). 82% of applicants accepted. 22% of accepted applicants enrolled.

Average school rank of freshmen men 74th percentile. Mean SAT scores 563 verbal, 558 mathematical. Mean ACT Composite score 25.

55% of entering freshmen expected to graduate within 5 years. 50% of freshmen from Washington. Freshmen from 34 states and 20 foreign countries.

Admission: Rolling admissions plan. For fall acceptance, apply as early as Oct. of previous year, but not later than 30 days prior to beginning of term. Apply by Nov. for early decision; need not limit application to Seattle University. Financial aid/scholarship priority deadline Feb. 1. FAFSA required. Essay/personal statement required. Early acceptance available. *Requirements:* Either graduation from secondary school with 4 units English, 3 history/social science, 2 foreign language, 2 lab science, 3 mathematics, 2 electives; or GED. Minimum 2.5 GPA. Lowest acceptable secondary school class standing 50th percentile. *Entrance tests:* College Board SAT, ACT composite, or Washington Pre-College Test. For foreign students TOEFL. *For transfer students:* 2.0 minimum GPA; from 4-year accredited institution 135 quarter hours maximum transfer credit; from 2-year accredited institution 90 quarter hours.

College credit and advanced placement for postsecondary-level work completed in secondary school and for extrainstitutional learning on basis of faculty assessment.

Tutoring available. Developmental courses offered during regular academic year; credit given.

Degree Requirements: 180 quarter hours; 2.0 GPA; 45 credits in residence; general education and distribution requirements.

Fulfillment of some degree requirements and exemption from some beginning courses possible by passing departmental examinations, College Board CLEP, AP, International Baccalaureate. *Grading system:* A–F; pass; withdraw (carries time limit).

Distinctive Educational Programs: Evening classes. Accelerated degree programs. Preprofessional programs in dentistry, medicine. Facilities and programs for independent research, including honors programs, individual majors. Institutionally sponsored study abroad in France, Italy, Japan, Mexico. *Other distinctive programs:* Matteo Ricci College provides a six-year accelerated program of secondary school work and baccalaureate studies. Institute of Public Service provides professional development conferences, seminars, research, and technical assistance.

ROTC: Army. Air Force and Navy available through the University of Washington.

Degrees Conferred: 2,228 *baccalaureate*; 664 *master's*; 333 *doctorate*; 351 *first-professional*. Bachelor's degrees awarded in top five disciplines: business, management, marketing, and related support services 232; health professions and related clinical sciences 111; engineering 75; psychology 66; communication/communication] technologies 49. Master's degrees awarded: various disciplines 333. First-professional degrees awarded: law 351.

Fees and Other Expenses: *Full-time tuition per academic year:* $28,260; contact the university for current graduate and first-professional tuition and applicable fees that vary by program. *Books and supplies:* $1,350. *Room and board per academic year:* $8,340. *Other expenses:* $3,738.

Financial Aid: The university offers a direct lending program. Aid from institutionally generated funds is provided on the basis of academic merit, financial need, athletic ability, other criteria.

Financial aid to full-time, first-time undergraduate students: 87% feceived some form of aid. Average amount of aid received: federal grants $5,432; Pell grants $3,119; other federal aid $2,595; state/local grants $5,012; institutional grants $10,830.

Departments and Teaching Staff: *Total instructional faculty:* 474. Student/faculty ratio: 14:1. Degrees held by full-time faculty: doctorate 72%, master's 12%, baccalaureate 1%, professional 15%. 74% hold terminal degrees.

Enrollment: Total enrollment 7,560. Undergraduate 4,206 (full-time 94%; female 61%, male 39%). Graduate 3,354 (full-time 45%). Transfer-in students 354.

Characteristics of Student Body: *Ethnic/racial makeup:* Black non-Hispanic: 5%; American Indian or Alaska Native: 1%; Asian or Pacific Islander: 19%; Hispanic: 8%; White non-Hispanic: 52%; unknown 6%; nonresident alien 8%.

International Students: 340 nonresident aliens enrolled fall 2008. Programs available to aid students whose native language is not English: social, cultural. English as a Second Language Program. No financial aid specifically designated for international students.

Student Life: On-campus residence halls house 24% of student body. All residence halls are co-ed. *Intercollegiate athletics:* NCAA Div. II males and females: basketball, cross-country, soccer, tennis; female: softball, volleyball. Club sports include baseball, crew, golf, hockey, sailing, skiing, water polo. *Special regulations:* Cars with permits allowed in designated parking lot; fee charged. Quiet hours. Residence hall visitation from 11am to midnight Sun.–Thurs., 11am to 1am Fri. and Sat. *Special services:* Learning Resources Center, medical services. *Student publications: Fragments*, an annual literary magazine; *The Spectator*, a weekly newspaper; an annual student handbook. *Surrounding community:* Seattle population 500,000. Served by mass transit bus system; airport 18 miles from campus; passenger rail service 1 mile from campus.

Library Collections: 235,000 volumes. 397,000 microforms; 283 audiovisual materials; 2,694 current periodicals. Online and card catalogs. Student have access to online information retrieval services and the Internet.

Most important special holdings include collections on computer software engineering, theology, and business administration.

Buildings and Grounds: Campus area 52 acres.

Chief Executive Officer: Fr. Stephen V. Sundborg, S.J., President.

Address undergraduate admission inquiries to Michael K. Mickeon, Dean of Admissions; Law School inquiries to Carol Cochran, Director of Admissions; Graduate School inquiries to Janet Shandley, Associate Dean of Graduate Admissions.

Trinity Lutheran College

4221 228th Avenue S.E.
Issaquah, Washington 98029-9299
Tel: (425) 392-0400 **E-mail:** admission@tlc.edu
Fax: (425) 392-0404 **Internet:** www.tlc.edu

Institution Description: Trinity Lutheran College, formerly known as the Lutheran Bible Institute of Seattle, is a private and independent Lutheran college. *Enrollment:* 117. *Degrees awarded:* Associate, baccalaureate. Certificate of Professional Studies also awarded.

Accreditation: *Regional:* NWCCU.

History: The Lutheran Bible Institute o Seattle began in 1944 as an extension school of the Lutheran Bible Institute in Minneapolis. The institute became an independent college in 1959. The college moved from its original campus in Seattle to the present location in Issaquah in 1979. The present name was adopted in 1999.

Institutional Structure: *Governing board:* Board of Directors. Representation: 24 directors. *Composition of institution:* Administrative cabinet under the direction of the president. Academic dean, chief administrative officer, chief financial officer, dean of students, development director, admission director. Full-time instructional faculty 10. Academic governance body, the faculty, meets semimonthly.

Calendar: Quarters. Academic year Sept. to June. New students admitted Sept., Jan., Mar. Degrees conferred and formal commencement June.

Characteristics of Freshmen: 80% of applicants admitted. 42% of applicants admitted and enrolled.

21% (6 students) submitted SAT scores. *25th percentile*: SAT Verbal 490, SAT Math 540. *75th percentile*: SAT Verbal 600, SAT Math 610.

35% of entering freshmen expected to graduate within 5 years. 65% of freshmen from Washington. Freshmen from 5 states.

Admission: For fall acceptance, apply as early as after junior year of high school. All applicants are encouraged to complete the application process by Mar. 1 in the year of their enrollment. All accepted students are then eligible for merit scholarships. Applications are accepted up to two weeks before classes begin. *Requirements:* Either high school diploma or GED. *Entrance tests:* SAT or ACT scores must accompany the high school transcript. *For transfer students:* 45 quarter credits (30 semester credits) may be accepted from a regionally accredited college or university.

Degree Requirements: 180 credits; 60 upper division credits; 2.0 GPA; completion of major; last 9 credits must be form Trinity; at least 45 Trinity credits, of which at least 6 must be in Bible; 3 discovery modules (two-week accelerated terms); 3 cross-cultural courses; demonstrated proficiency in writing; general education requirement; participation in Trinity Student Ministries.

Fulfillment of some degree requirements and exemption from some beginning courses possible by passing College Board CLEP, AP. *Grading system:* 4.0–0.0; pass/unsatisfactory/fail.

Distinctive Educational Programs: Study abroad in Israel at the Jerusalem Center for Biblical Studies; language and culture acquisition in Mazatlan, Mexico.

Degrees Conferred: 5 *associate;* 24 *baccalaureate:* education 8; philosophy/religion/theology 5; other 11.

Fees and Other Expenses: *Full-time tuition per academic year:* $13,032. *Books and supplies:* $700. *Other fees:* $150. *Room and board per academic year:* $6,000.

Financial Aid: Aid from institutionally generated funds is provided on the basis of academic merit, financial need, other considerations.

Financial aid to full-time, first-time undergraduate students: need-based scholarships/grants totaling $261,497, self-help $549,270; non-need-based scholarships/grants totaling $109,205.

Total instructional faculty: 17 (full-time 8, part-time 9; women 5, men 12; members of minority groups 1). Student/faculty ratio: 7:1. Degrees held by full-time faculty: doctorate 33%, master's 66%, baccalaureate 100%. 100% hold terminal degrees.

TRINITY LUTHERAN COLLEGE—*cont'd*

Enrollment: Total enrollment 117. Undergraduate full-time 45 men / 50 women, part-time 6m / 16w. Transfer-in students 6.

Characteristics of Student Body: *Ethnic/racial makeup:* number of American Indian or Alaska Native: 1; Asian or Pacific Islander: 2; White non-Hispanic: 97; unknown: 14. *Age distribution:* number under 18: 1; 18–19: 25; 20–21: 32; 22–24: 17; 25–29: 14; 30–34: 3; 35–39: 8; 40–49: 8; 50–64: 8.

International Students: 3 nonresident aliens enrolled fall 2008. Programs available to aid students whose native language is not English: English as a Second Language. Financial aid specifically designated for international students: scholarships available annually.

Student Life: On-campus residence halls house 70% of student body. Limited housing available for married students. *Intramural athletics:* men and women: basketball, club sports, football, roller hockey, volleyball. *Special regulations:* Cars permitted with permit. *Special services:* Learning Resources Center, Health Center, Disabled Student Services. *Fitness Center:* Operated by local YMCA and free to all students. *Student activities:* Student Government Association; yearbook; ministries; drama and music groups (choir).

Publications: *Advance*, newsletter.

Library Collections: 40,000 volumes. 500 full-text journals (electronic); 140 current periodical subscriptions. Online and card catalogs. 15 computer work stations. Students have access to online information retrieval services and the Internet.

Most important special collections on religion; anthropology and ethnology; West Coast Indians.

Buildings and Grounds: Campus area 37 acres.

Chief Executive Officer: Dr. John M. Stamm, President.

Address admission inquiries to Sigrid Olsen, Director of Admissions.

University of Puget Sound

1500 North Warner Street
Tacoma, Washington 98416
Tel: (253) 879-3211 **E-mail:** admission@ups.edu
Fax: (253) 879-3993 **Internet:** www.ups.edu

Institution Description: University of Puget Sound is a private, independent, nonprofit institution. *Enrollment:* 2,844. *Degrees awarded:* Baccalaureate, master's, doctorate.

Accreditation: *Regional:* NWCCU. *Professional*: chemistry, music, occupational therapy, physical therapy, teacher education

History: Established as Puget Sound University by Puget Sound Conference of Methodist Episcopal Church (now United Methodist); incorporated, and offered first instruction at postsecondary level 1888; awarded first degree (baccalaureate) 1891; reincorporated as University of Puget Sound 1903; later named College of Puget Sound; became 4-year institution 1904; renamed University of Puget Sound 1960.

Institutional Structure: *Governing board:* Board of Trustees. Representation: 32 trustees, including president of the university. All voting. *Composition of institution:* President, five vice presidents: academic and dean; enrollment; finance and administration; student affairs and dean of students; university relations. Administrators 117. Academic affairs headed by dean of the university. Management/business/finances directed by financial vice president. Full-time instructional faculty 223. Academic governance body, the faculty, meets an average of 6 times per year.

Calendar: Semesters. Academic year Aug. to Aug. Freshmen admitted Aug., Jan. Degrees conferred May, Aug., Dec. Formal commencement May. Summer session of 2 terms from May to Aug.

Characteristics of Freshmen: 5,580 applicants (female 3,250, male 2,330). 65% of applicants admitted. 20% of applicants admitted and enrolled.

90% (607 students) submitted SAT scores; 45% (306 students) submitted ACT scores. *25th percentile*: SAT Critical Reading 575, SAT Math 570; ACT Composite 25, ACT English 25, ACT Math 24. *75th percentile*: SAT Critical Reading 690, SAT Math 660; ACT Composite 29, ACT English 30, ACT Math 29.

75% of freshmen expected to graduate within 5 years. 26% of freshmen from Washington. Freshmen from 34 states and 6 foreign countries.

Admission: Notification by Mar. 1. For fall acceptance, apply as early as Sept. 15 of previous year, but not later than Feb. 1 of year of enrollment. Early decision available. *Requirements:* Graduation from secondary school. *Entrance tests:* College Board SAT, ACT. For foreign students TOEFL. *For transfer students:* 2.5 minimum GPA; from 4-year accredited institution 16 units maximum transfer credit; from 2-year accredited institution 16 units maximum.

College credit and advanced placement for postsecondary-level work completed in secondary school.

Tutoring available. Noncredit refresher courses offered during regular academic year.

Degree Requirements: 32 units; 2.0 GPA; two years (16 units) in residence; core curriculum. Fulfillment of some degree requirements and exemption from some beginning courses possible by passing subject exams, AP, International Baccalaureate. *Grading system:* A–F; pass-fail; withdraw (deadline after which fail may be appended to withdraw).

Distinctive Educational Programs: *For undergraduates:* Interdisciplinary Programs in African American Studies, Asian Studies, Classics, Environmental Studies, Foreign Languages, International Affairs, Honors, International Political Economy, Latin American Studies, Women Studies. Dual degree programs in engineering and business leadership. Institutionally sponsored study abroad programs in various countries in Europe, Asia, Latin America, Pacific Rim/Asia Study/Travel Program. Distinctive traditional liberal arts major in twenty departments. *For graduates:* Master of Arts in Teaching; Master of Occupational Therapy and Doctor of Physical Therapy.

ROTC: Army in cooperation with Pacific Lutheran University.

Degrees Conferred: 663 *baccalaureate:* area studies 8; biological sciences 39; business and management 85; communications 16; computer and information sciences 11; education 3; English 46; foreign languages 31; health professions 7; interdisciplinary studies 27; mathematics 13; parks and recreation 22; philosophy/religion/theology 12; physical sciences 26; psychology 56; social sciences 128; visual and performing arts 48. *Master's*: education 72; health professions 15. *Doctorate*: health professions 46.

Fees and Other Expenses: *Full-time tuition per academic year 2008–09:* $33,975; contact the university for current graduate tutition/fees. *Required fees:* $190. *Room and board per academic year:* $8.760. *Books and supplies:* $1,000. *Other expenses:* $2,300.

Financial Aid: Aid from institutionally generated funds is provided on the basis of academic merit, financial need, other criteria.

Financial aid to full-time undergraduate students: 86% feceived some form of aid. Average amount of aid received: federal grants $4,263; Pell grants $2,788; other federal aid $2,202; state/local grants $5,213; institutional grants $14,508.

Departments and Teaching Staff: *Total instructional faculty:* 274 (full-time 223, part-time 51). Degrees held by full-time faculty: doctorate 81%, master's 18%, baccalaureate 1%. 84% hold terminal degrees.

Enrollment: *Total enrollment:* 2,844. Undergraduate 2,582 (full-time 98%; female 58%, male 42%). Graduate 262 (full-time 79%). Transfer-in students 72.

Characteristics of Student Body: *Ethnic/racial makeup:* Black non-Hispanic: 3%; American Indian or Alaska Native: 1%; Asian or Pacific Islander: 9%; Hispanic: 4%; White non-Hispanic: 73%; unknown: 8%. *Age distribution:* number under 18: 26; 18–19: 1,147; 20–21: 1,143; 22–24: 235; 25–29: 28; 30–34: 9; 35–39: 2; 40–49: 2; 50–64: 2.

International Students: 12 nonresident aliens enrolled fall 2008. Students from Europe, Asia, Latin America, Africa, Canada. No programs available to aid students whose native language is not English. Financial aid specifically designated for undergraduate international students: variable number of scholarships available annually.

Student Life: On-campus residence hall, fraternity and sorority housing, also special programs housing available. *Intercollegiate athletics:* male: baseball, basketball, crew, cross-country, football, golf, soccer, swimming, tennis, track; female: basketball, crew, cross-country, golf, lacrosse, soccer, softball, swimming, tennis, track, volleyball. *Special regulations:* Registered cars permitted without restrictions. *Special services:* Academic Advising, Career Development, Writing and Learning Center, Counseling and Health Services, Campus Ministry Center, Minority Programs, Student Diversity Center, off-campus student services, orientation. Student activities with 60 clubs and organizations. Community Involvement and Action Center; wilderness consciousness excursions. *Student publications, radio: Crosscurrents*, an annual literary magazine; *Tamanawas*, a yearbook; *The Trail*, a weekly newspaper. Radio station KUPS broadcasts 118 hours per week. *Surrounding community:* Tacoma population 196,800. Seattle, 35 miles from campus, is nearest metropolitan area. Served by mass transit bus system; airport 20 miles from campus; passenger rail service 3 miles from campus.

Library Collections: 546,000 volumes including bound books, serial backfiles, electronic documents, and government documents not in separate collections. Online catalog. Current serial subscriptions: 1,729 paper; 835 microform. 17,949 via electronic access. 6,634 recordings. Computer work stations available. Students have access to the Internet at no charge.

Most important special holdings include the Lionel Pries Rare Books Collection (25 volumes, including 16th- and 17th-century atlases, 1577 first edition of Holinshed's *Chronicles of England, Scotland, and Ireland*); Homer T. Bone Papers (correspondence, manuscripts, and personal papers of mid-20th century U.S. Senator and circuit judge); Abby Hill Digital Collection (45 painting); extensive humanities/fine arts book collection.

Buildings and Grounds: Campus area 97 acres.

Chief Executive Officer: Dr. Ronald R. Thomas, President.

Address admission inquiries to George H. Mills, Jr., Vice President for Enrollment.

University of Washington

Box 255840
Seattle, Washington 98195-4550
Tel: (206) 543-2100 **E-mail:** askuwadm@u.washington.edu
Fax: (206) 543-9686 **Internet:** www.washington.edu

Institution Description: The University of Washington is a state institution and sea-grant college. *Enrollment:* 39,675. *Degrees awarded:* Baccalaureate, first-professional, master's, doctorate.

Accreditation: *Regional:* NWCCU. *Professional*: accounting, architecture, art, business, construction education, cytotechnology, dentistry, EMT-paramedic, engineering, forestry, health services administration, journalism, landscape architecture, law, librarianship, medicine, music, nursing, occupational therapy, pharmacy, physical therapy, physician assisting, psychology internship, planning, public health, social work, speech-language pathology, teacher education

History: Established as Territorial University of Washington and offered first instruction at postsecondary level 1861; awarded first degree (baccalaureate) 1876; adopted present name 1889; designated a sea-grant college 1968.

Institutional Structure: *Governing board:* Board of Regents. Representation: 9 regents. All voting. *Composition of institution:* President, provost, 5 vice presidents, 16 college deans. Full-time instructional faculty 3,005. Academic governance body, Faculty Senate, meets an average of 6 times per academic year.

Calendar: Quarters. Academic year Sept. to June. Freshmen admitted Sept., Jan., Mar., June. Degrees conferred and formal commencement June. Freshman Convocation held each fall. Summer session from June to Aug.

Characteristics of Freshmen: 19,906 applicants (female 10,568, male 9,338). 69% of applicants accepted. 32% of accepted applicants enrolled.

Mid-50% range SAT scores 500–620 verbal, 520–640 mathematical.

61.6% of entering freshmen expected to graduate within 5 years.

Admission: For autumn quarter enrollment, apply beginning Nov. 1 of senior year, but no later than Jan. 31 for priority consideration. Transfer students apply beginning Jan. 1 for the following autumn; Apr. 15 priority closing date. *Requirements:* For freshmen and transfers, completion of core subjects (expressed in high school years): 4 units English, 3 social studies, 3 mathematics, 2 in a single foreign language, 2 science (including 1 year in lab science) 1/2 fine, visual, or performing arts, 1/2 academic electives. *Entrance tests:* SAT or ACT. Transfer students with A.A. from Washington community college, state residency, and 2.75 cumulative transfer GPA do not need test scores. Personal statement required. Admission based on Admission Index ranking (derived from GPA and test scores), academic awards and achievements, school and community service, leadership and work, educational/economic disadvantage, and cultural diversity.

College credit and advanced placement for postsecondary-level work completed in secondary school. Maximum of 90 credits from two-year accredited institutions; maximum of 90 credits for correspondence/extension course work. Educational Opportunity Program for under-represented minorities. Tutoring and noncredit developmental courses are provided for students. Limited noncredit general developmental courses available during summer quarter.

Degree Requirements: *For all undergraduate degrees:* 180 credit hours; 2.0 GPA; 45 credits in residence; general education requirements.

Fulfillment of some degree requirements and exemption from some beginning courses possible by passing departmental examinations, Advanced Placement varies by department. *Grading system:* A–E (failure or unofficial withdrawal) reported from 4.0 to 0.7 in 0.1 increments.

Distinctive Educational Programs: Work-experience programs, including cooperative education, internships. Evening classes. Special facilities for using telecommunications in the classroom. Interdepartmental programs. Honors programs. Individual majors. Henry Art Gallery includes European and American paintings and prints. Extensive collection of ethnic textiles and Western dress. Museum collection offers students first-hand contact with important works of art and research opportunities. Study abroad in Europe, Far East, Mexico, Middle East, and North Africa.

ROTC: Army, Navy, Marine Corps, Air Force.

Degrees Conferred: 6,952 *baccalaureate*; 2,631 *master's*; 636 *doctorate*. Bachelor's degrees awarded in top five disciplines: social sciences 1,313; business, management, marketing, and related support services 745; engineering 589; biomedical/biological sciences 585; visual and performing arts 528. Master's degrees awarded: various disciplinmes 636. First-professional: 488 (dentistry, pharmacy, law, medicine).

Fees and Other Expenses: *Full-time tuition per academic year:* undergraduate resident $6.802, nonresident $23,219; contact the university for current graduate and first-professional tuition and fees that vary by program. *Books and supplies:* $1,055. *Room and board per academic year:* $8,640. *Other expenses:* $2,661.

Financial Aid: Aid from institutionally generated funds is provided on the basis of academic merit, financial need, athletic ability, other considerations.

Institution has a Program Participation Agreement with the U.S. Department of Education for eligible students to receive Pell Grants and, depending upon the agreement, other federal aid.

Financial aid to full-time, first-time undergraduate students: 57% received some form of aid. Average amount of aid received: federal grants $4,389; Pell grants $3,095; other federal aid $1,522; state/local grants $5,308; institutional grants $4,933.

Departments and Teaching Staff: *Total instructional faculty:* 2,941. Student/faculty ratio: 9:1. Degrees held by full-time faculty: doctorate 99.6%.

Enrollment: Total enrollment 39,675. Undergraduate 29,397 (full-time 85%; female 52%, male 48%). Graduate 10,278. Transfer-in students 1,492.

Characteristics of Student Body: *Ethnic/racial makeup:* Black non-Hispanic: 3%; American Indian or Alaska Native: 1%; Asian or Pacific Islander: 26%; Hispanic: 3%; White non-Hispanic: 51%; unknown: 9%; nonresident alien 4%.

International Students: 915 nonresident aliens enrolled fall 2008. Programs available to aid students whose native language is not English: social, cultural. English as a Second Language Program. No financial aid specifically designated for international students.

Student Life: On-campus residence halls house 13% of student body. Family housing available for students. *Intercollegiate athletics:* male: baseball, football, soccer; female: gymnastics, tennis, volleyball; both sexes: basketball, crew, cross-country, golf, swimming, track and field. *Special services:* Campus transportation system, childcare services, disabled student services, Ethnic Cultural Center, Instructional Center, international student services, medical services, others. *Student publications, radio, television: The Daily*, a student newspaper published 5 times per week. Radio stations KCMU and KUOW each broadcast 168 hours a week. TV station KCTS broadcasts 133 hours per week. *Surrounding community:* Seattle population over 500,000. Served by mass transit bus system; airport 20 miles from campus; passenger rail service 5 miles from campus.

Publications: *Publisher:* University of Washington Press.

Library Collections: 7,000,000 000 volumes. 6,500,000 microform units; 1,400,000 audiovisual materials; 50,250 serial subscriptions. Online catalog. Students have access to online information retrieval services and the Internet.

Most important special holdings include the Pacific Northwest Collection (47,000 book and periodical volumes, 370,600 historical photographs, and 27,000 architectural drawings); East Asia Library (304,000 volumes); Congressional Papers (includes the papers of Senators Henry M. Jackson and Warren G. Magnuson); oceanography/fisheries;forest resources.

Buildings and Grounds: Campus area 703 acres.

Chief Executive Officer: Dr. Mark A. Emmert, President.

Address admission inquiries to Director of Admissions.

Walla Walla University

204 South College Avenue
College Place, Washington 99324-1198
Tel: (509) 527-2327 **E-mail:** info@wwc.edu
Fax: (509) 527-2397 **Internet:** www.wwc.edu

Institution Description: Walla Walla University is a private institution affiliated with the Seventh-day Adventist Church. *Enrollment:* 1,800. *Degrees awarded:* Associate, baccalaureate, master's.

Accreditation: *Regional:* NWCCU. *Professional*: business, engineering, music, nursing, social work

History: Established and offered first instruction at postsecondary level 1892; awarded first degree (baccalaureate) 1909; achieved university status 2007. *See* for further information, *Bold Ventures: A History of Walla Walla College* (College Press, Walla Walla College, 1992).

Institutional Structure: *Governing board:* Walla Walla University Board of Trustees. Extrainstitutional representation: 25 trustees (including 12 alumni, 12 church officials); institutional representation: 2 administrators, president of the college. 11 ex officio. 28 voting. *Composition of institution:* Administrators 56. Academic affairs headed by vice president for academic administration. Management/business/finances directed by vice president for financial administration. Full-time instructional faculty 114. Academic governance bodies, Academic Standards Committee and Curriculum Committee, each meet weekly. Graduate Council and Graduate Standards Committee meets biweekly.

Calendar: Quarters. Academic year Sept. to June. Freshmen admitted Sept., Jan., Mar., June. Degrees conferred June, Aug., Dec., Mar. Formal commencement June. Summer session from June to Aug.

WALLA WALLA UNIVERSITY—*cont'd*

Characteristics of Freshmen: 505 applicants (female 264, male 241). 78% of applicants admitted. 67% of applicants admitted and enrolled.

57% submitted SAT scores. 53% submitted ACT Scores. *25th percentile*: SAT Critical Rending 630; ACT Composite 19.5, ACT English 19.4, ACT Math 17.7. *75th percentile*: SAT Critical Rending 460; ACT Composite 26.2, ACT English 26.4, ACT Math 26.

64% of entering freshmen expected to graduate within 5 years. 35% of freshmen from Washington. Freshmen from 27 states and 3 foreign countries.

Admission: Rolling admissions plan. For fall acceptance, apply no later than Sept. 15. Early acceptance available. *Requirements:* Either graduation from secondary school with 3 units English, 1 history, 1 mathematics, 1 science; or GED. Additional units in a foreign language, mathematics, science recommended. *Entrance tests:* ACT composite. For foreign students TOEFL or other standardized test of English as a foreign language. *For transfer students:* 2.0 minimum GPA; from 4-year accredited institution maximum transfer credit limited only by resident requirement; from 2-year accredited institution 96 quarter hours; correspondence/extension students 24 quarter hours.

College credit and advanced placement for postsecondary-level work completed in secondary school. College credit for extrainstitutional learning.

Tutoring available. Developmental and remedial courses offered in summer session and regular academic year; credit given.

Degree Requirements: *For all associate degrees:* 96 quarter hours; 2 quarters in residence. *For all baccalaureate degrees:* 192 quarter hours; 3 quarters in residence; 2 quarter credits in physical education; comprehensives in individual fields of study. *For all undergraduate degrees:* 2.0 GPA; weekly chapel attendance; general education requirements.

Fulfillment of some degree requirements and exemption from some beginning courses possible by passing departmental examinations, College Board CLEP, AP. *Grading system:* A–F; withdraw (carries time limit).

Distinctive Educational Programs: Evening classes. Honors programs. Institutionally sponsored study abroad in Argentina, Austria, Brazil, England, France, Germany, Greece, Hong Kong, Italy, Mexico, Spain, Ukraine.

Degrees Conferred: 283 *baccalaureate* (B); 143 *master's* (M): biological and life sciences 13 (B), 3 (M); business 48 (B); computer and information sciences 2 (B); education 36 (B), 7 (M); engineering 11 (B); English 7 (B); foreign languages and literature 14 (B); health professions and related sciences 50 (B); liberal arts/general studies 3 (B); mathematics 8 (B); philosophy/religion/theology 21 (B); physical sciences 3 (B); public administration 12 (B), 130 (M); psychology 2 (B), 1 (M); social sciences and history 4 (B); trade and industry 7 (B); visual and performing arts 4 (B).

Fees and Other Expenses: *Full-time tuition per academic year 2008–09:* undergraduate $21,936; graduate study charged quarter credit (contact the college for current rate). *Required fees:* $192. *Room and board per academic year:* $4,320. *Books and supplies:* $1,014. *Other expenses:* $2,946.

Financial Aid: Aid from institutionally generated funds is provided on the basis of academic merit, financial need.

Financial aid to full-time, first-time undergraduate students: need-based scholarships/grants totaling $9,665,432, self-help $9,091,561, parent loans $579,098; non-need-based scholarships/grants totaling $2,098,177, self-help $1,005,646, parent loans $891,428.

Departments and Teaching Staff: *Total instructional faculty:* 181 (full-time 114, part-time 67). Total faculty with doctorate, first-professional, or other terminal degree: 92. Student/faculty ratio: 13:1.

Enrollment: Total enrollment 1,800. Undergraduate 1,563 (full-time 94%; female 48%, male 52%). Graduate 237 (full-time 91%). Transfer-in students 146.

Characteristics of Student Body: *Ethnic/racial makeup:* Black non-Hispanic: 3%; American Indian or Alaska Native: 1%; Asian or Pacific Islander: 6%; Hispanic: 10%; White non-Hispanic: 78%; unknown: 1%; nonresident alien 1%. *Age distribution:* number under 18: 34, 18–19: 529, 20–21: 566, 22–24: 318; 25–29: 134; 30–34: 38; 35–39: 22; 40–49: 28; 50–64: 12. 35% of student body attend summer sessions.

International Students: 18 nonresident aliens enrolled fall 2008 Students from Europe, Asia, Latin America, Canada. Programs available to aid students whose native language is not English: social, cultural, financial. English as a Second Language Program. No financial aid specifically designated for international students.

Student Life: On-campus residence halls house 70% of student body. Residence halls for males constitute 50% of such space, for females 50%. 78% students live on campus. *Special regulations:* Student dress should be appropriate to the occasion. Curfews. *Special services:* Learning Resources Center, medical services. *Student publications, radio: The Collegian*, a weekly newspaper; *Mt. Ash*, a yearbook; *The Mask*, student photo directory. Radio station KGTS broadcasts continuously. *Surrounding community:* College Place population 8,700. Portland (OR), 240 miles from campus, is nearest metropolitan area. Served by airport 10 miles from campus.

Publications: *Westwind*, Alumni journal.

Library Collections: 282,000 volumes. 4,600 government documents; 28,300 microforms; 17,500 audiovisual materials; 1,320 current periodical subscriptions. Computer work stations available. Online catalog. Students have access to online information retrieval services and the Internet. special holdings include collections on Seventh Day Adventist history, religion, biology.

Buildings and Grounds: Campus area 55 acres. Campus DVD available.

Chief Executive Officer: Dr. John K. McVry, President.

Address admission inquiries to Dallas Weis, Director of Admissions.

Washington State University

2580 N.E. Grimes Way
Pullman, Washington 99164-1046
Tel: (509) 335-3564 **E-mail:** admiss2@wsu.edu
Fax: (509) 335-3421 **Internet:** www.wsu.edu

Institution Description: Washington State University is a public institution and a land grant college. *Enrollment:* 25,352. *Degrees awarded:* Baccalaureate, first-professional (veterinary medicine), master's, doctorate.

Accreditation: *Regional:* NWCCU. *Professional*: architecture, business, chemistry, dietetics, engineering, forestry, interior design, landscape architecture, music, nursing, pharmacy, psychology internship, speech-language pathology, teacher education, veterinary medicine

History: Established and chartered as Washington State Agricultural College and School of Science 1890; changed name to Agricultural College, Experiment Station, and School of Science of the State of Washington 1891; offered first instruction at postsecondary level 1892; awarded first degree (baccalaureate) 1897; changed name to State College of Washington 1905; adopted present name 1959.

Institutional Structure: *Governing board:* Board of Regents. Extrainstitutional representation: 9 regents; institutional representation: president of the university, 1 ex officio. 9 voting. *Composition of institution:* Administrators 34. Academic affairs headed by executive vice president and provost. Management/business/finances directed by vice president for business and finance. Total instructional faculty 1,073. Academic governance body, Faculty Senate, meets 12 times per year.

Calendar: Semesters. Academic year Aug. to May. Freshmen admitted Aug., Jan., May. Degrees conferred May, Aug., Dec. Formal commencement June. Summer session of 1 term from May to August.

Characteristics of Freshmen: 11,326 applicants (female 5,946, male 5,380). 77% of applicants admitted. 40% of applicants admitted and enrolled.

95% (2,564 students) submitted SAT scores. *25th percentile*: SAT Critical Reading 480, SAT Math 500. *75th percentile*: SAT Critical Reading 590, SAT Math 610.

60.2% of entering freshmen expected to graduate within 5 years. 89% of freshmen from Washington. Freshmen from 25 states and 82 foreign countries.

Admission: Rolling admissions plan. For fall acceptance, apply as early as Dec. 1 of previous year, but not later than June 1 of year of enrollment. *Requirements:* Either graduation from accredited secondary school with academic units which normally include 4 English, 2 in a foreign language, 3 mathematics, 2 social science, 1 history, fine or performing arts 1 or additional academic elective; or GED. Additional requirements for some programs. *Entrance tests:* SAT or ACT. Washington students are required to take the Washington Pre-College Test. *For transfer students:* 2.0 minimum GPA; from 4-year accredited institution 90 semester hours maximum transfer credit; from 2-year accredited institution 60 hours; correspondence/extension students 30 hours.

College credit and advanced placement for postsecondary-level work completed in secondary school. For extrainstitutional learning, college credit on basis of portfolio and faculty assessments.

Tutoring available. Developmental courses offered in summer session and regular academic year; credit given.

Degree Requirements: 120 semester hours; 2.0 GPA; 1 year in residence; general education requirements.

Fulfillment of some degree requirements and exemption from some beginning courses possible by passing College Board CLEP, AP. *Grading system:* A–F; pass; withdraw (carries penalty).

Distinctive Educational Programs: Programs in business, broadcasting, hotel and restaurant administration, sociology, and honors program; agriculture and veterinary medicine. Off-campus programs include the Intercollegiate Nursing Center in Spokane, Hotel and Restaurant Administration Center in Seattle, graduate professional courses in fields such as business, education, and engineering taught through branch campuses in Spokane, the Tri-Cities and Vancouver. Washington Higher Education Telecommunication System links five cities.

Extension offices in all 39 counties and 8 agricultural research centers around the state. Research centers include the Institute for Biological Chemistry, the Social and Economics Research Center, Nuclear Radiation Center, the Wood Products Research Laboratory, Archaeological Research Center. Tri-state program in veterinary medical education; four-state program in human medical education. Work-experience programs; study abroad opportunities including Denmark, France, Germany, Japan, Spain, Sweden, Taiwan. Credit and noncredit continuing education and correspondence programs.

ROTC: Army, Air Force. Navy offered in association with University of Idaho.

Degrees Conferred: 4,818 *baccalaureate*; 724 *master's*; 217 *doctorate*; 160 *first-professional.* Bachelor's degrees awarded in top five disciplines: business, management, marketing, and related support services 850; social sciences and history 615; communications/communication technologies 369; engineering/engineering technologies 302; education 289. Master's degrees awarded: various disciplines 724. *First-professional:* 160 (pharmacy 74; veterinary medicine 93).

Fees and Other Expenses: *Full-time tuition per academic year 2008–09:* undergraduate resident $7,564, nonresident $18,600; contact the university for current graduate and first-professional tuition/fees. *Required fees:* $1,015. *Room and board per academic year:* $8,452. *Books and supplies:* $936. *Other expenses:* $3,542.

Financial Aid: Aid from institutionally generated funds is provided on the basis of academic merit, financial need.

Financial aid to full-time, first-time undergraduate students: 81% received some form of aid. Average amount of aid received: federal grants $3,738; Pell grants $2,819; other federal aid $1,145; state/federal grants $4,871; institutional grants $3,724.

Departments and Teaching Staff: *Total instructional faculty:* 1,337 (full-time 1,073, part-time 264). Total faculty with doctorate, first-professional, or other terminal degree: 1,142. Student/faculty ratio: 15:1. Degrees held by full-time faculty: baccalaureate .8%, master's

Enrollment: Total enrollment 25,352. Undergraduate 21,149 (full-time 85%; female 52%; male 48%). Graduate 4,203 (full-time 89%). Transfer-in students 2,664.

Characteristics of Student Body: *Ethnic/racial makeup:* Black non-Hispanic: 2%; American Indian or Alaska Native: 1%; Asian or Pacific Islander: 6%; Hispanic: 55; White non-Hispanic: 74%; unknown: 6%; nonresident alien 3%. *Age distribution:* number under 18: 121; 18–19: 4,168;20–21: 5,761; 22–24: 4,928; 25–29: 1,848; 30–34: 874; 35–39: 483; 40–49: 773; 50–64: 320; 65 and over: 5. 33% of student body attend summer sessions.

International Students: 1,130 nonresident aliens enrolled fall 2008. Students from Europe, Asia, Latin America, Africa, Canada, Australia, New Zealand, Programs available to aid students whose native language is not English: social, cultural. English as a Second Language Program. No financial aid specifically designated for international students.

Student Life: On-campus residence halls house 24% of student body. Residence halls for males constitute 10% of such space, for females 18%, for co-ed halls 71%. 89% of student body housed in university-owned apartments. 6.3% of undergraduate men join fraternities; 6.9% of women join sororities. 7.8% live in fraternity/sorority houses. Housing available for singles and families. 31% of student body live on campus. *Intercollegiate athletics:* male: baseball, basketball, cross-country, football, golf, track and field; female: basketball, cross-country, golf, rowing, soccer, swimming, tennis, track and field, volleyball. *Club sports:* bowling, cricket, cycling, equestrian, gymnastics, fencing, ice hockey, judo, lacrosse, logger sports, polo, rowing, tennis, wrestling.. *Special regulations:* Cars permitted; limited parking. All halls have quiet hours Sun. through Thurs 9pm to 9am and Fri. and Sat. midnight to 10am. *Special services:* Learning Resources Center, medical services. *Student publications: Chinook*, a yearbook; *Daily Evergreen*, a newspaper. *Surrounding community:* Pullman population 26,590. Seattle, 300 miles from campus, is nearest metropolitan area. Served by mass transit bus system; airport 3 miles from campus.

Publications: *ESQ* (quarterly) first published 1972; *Northwest Science* (quarterly) first published 1926; *Poe Studies* (twice yearly) first published 1970; *Western Journal of Black Studies* (quarterly) first published 1976; *Northwest Theatre Review* (annually) first published 1993; *Frontiers: A Journal of women's Studies* (three times annually) first published 1975; *International Education Forum* (twice yearly) first published 1985; *Communication Reports* (twice yearly) first published 1988.

Library Collections: 2,200,000 volumes. 4,300,000 microforms; 427,000 audiovisual materials; 30,100 peridicals including via electronic access. Computer work stations available. Online catalog. Student have access to online information retrieval services and the Internet.

Most important special holdings include Leonard and Virginia Woolf Library; Pacific Northwest History; Veterinary History Collection; American Popular Culture Collection; Bloomsbury Collection; L. V. McWhorter Papers.

Buildings and Grounds: Campus area 3,600 acres.

Chief Executive Officer: Dr. V. Lane Rawlins, President.

Address undergraduate admission inquiries to Wendy Peterson, Director of Admissions; graduate inquiries to the Graduate School.

College of Liberal Arts

Degree Programs Offered: *Baccalaureate, master's,* in American studies, anthropology, Asian studies, communication, comparative ethnic studies, criminal justice, digital technology and culture, English, fine arts, foreign languages and cultures, general studies, history, liberal arts, music, philosophy, social studies, sociology, speech and hearing sciences, theatre arts and drama, women studies.

College of Sciences

Degree Programs Offered: *Baccalaureate, master's* in biochemistry, biology, chemistry, environmental science, general studies, genetics and cell biology, geology, mathematics, microbiology, physics, zoology. *Doctorate* in various fields.

College of Agriculture, Human and Natural Resource Sciences

Degree Programs Offered: *Baccalaureate* in agricultural economics, agricultural education, agricultural engineering, agricultural mechanization, agronomy, animal sciences, entomology, environmental science, food science and technology, forest management, general agriculture, horticulture, landscape architecture, plant pathology, range management, soils; *master's, doctorate* in various fields.

College of Business and Economics

Degree Programs Offered: *Baccalaureate* in business administration, economics, hotel administration; *master's* in business administration, economics; *doctorate* in business administration, economics.

College of Education

Degree Programs Offered: *Baccalaureate, master's, doctorate.*

College of Engineering and Architecture

Degree Programs Offered: *Baccalaureate, master's, doctorate.*

Intercollegiate Center for Nursing Education

Degree Programs Offered: *Baccalaureate, master's.*

Distinctive Educational Programs: The Center, located in Spokane, is a school of nursing shared in cooperation with Eastern Washington University and Whitworth College. Students receive degrees from the participating institution in which they are enrolled.

College of Pharmacy

Degree Programs Offered: *Baccalaureate, master's, doctorate.*

Distinctive Educational Programs: Interdisciplinary graduate programs in cooperation with College of Veterinary Medicine. Clinical pharmacy training programs at hospitals in Spokane and Seattle.

College of Veterinary Medicine

Degree Programs Offered: *Baccalaureate, first-professional, master's, doctorate.*

Admission: *For first-professional degree:* 75 semester hours preveterinary curriculum at accredited college or university, 3.2 GPA, significant prior contact with a veterinarian. Preference given to residents of Washington, Oregon and Idaho.

Degree Requirements: *For first-professional:* 145 credit hours, 2.0 GPA.

Distinctive Educational Programs: Washington-Oregon-Idaho Regional Program offers a cooperative veterinary medicine curriculum with Oregon State University and the University of Idaho; the program is available to members of the Western Interstate Commission for Higher Education Compact.

Western Washington University

516 High Street
Bellingham, Washington 98225
Tel: (360) 650-3000 **E-mail:** admit@ca.wwu.edu
Fax: (360) 650-3022 **Internet:** www.wwu.edu

Institution Description: Western Washington University (Western Washington State College until 1977) is a public institution. *Enrollment:* 14,620. *Degrees awarded:* Baccalaureate, master's. Certificates also awarded.

Accreditation: *Regional:* NWCCU. *Professional*: business, chemistry, computer science, counseling, music, recreation and leisure services, speech-language pathology, teacher education

History: Established as New Whatcom State Normal School 1893; offered first instruction at postsecondary level 1899; awarded first degree (baccalaureate) 1933; changed name to Western Washington College of Education 1937, to Western Washington State College 1961; adopted present name 1977. See *Western Washington University: 100 Years* (Harmony House Publishers, 1999) and *Perspectives on Excellence: A Century of Teaching and Learning at Western Washington University* (Center for Pacific Northwest Studies, 2000) for further information.

Institutional Structure: *Governing board:* Board of Trustees of Western Washington University. Representation: 8 trustees (including student trustee). *Composition of institution:* Administrators 114. Student affairs headed by vice president for student affairs/dean for academic support services. Management/business/finances directed by vice president for business and financial affairs. Full-time instructional faculty 530. Faculty Senate meets 15 times a year.

Calendar: Quarters. Academic year Sept. to June. Freshmen admitted Sept., Jan., Mar., June. Degrees conferred June, Aug., Dec., Mar. Formal commencement Mar., June, Aug., Dec. summer session of 2 terms from June to Aug.

Characteristics of Freshmen: 9,519 applicants (female 5,487, male 4,032). 75% of applicants admitted. 31% of applicants admitted and enrolled.

95% (2,333 students) submitted SAT scores; 25% (609 students) submitted ACT scores. *25th percentile*: SAT Verbal 500, SAT Math 510; ACT Composite 21, ACT English 20, ACT Math 19. *75th percentile*: SAT Verbal 610, SAT Math 610; ACT Composite 26.

565 of freshmen expected to graduate within 5 years. 10% of freshmen from Washington. Freshmen from 30 states and 6 foreign countries.

Admission: Rolling admissions plan. For fall acceptance, apply as early as Mar. 1. *Requirements:* Graduation from secondary school with 4 units English, 2 in a foreign language, 3 social studies, 3 mathematics including two years of algebra beyond pre-algebra; 2 science including 1 year of either chemistry or physics; 1 unit fine and performing arts. Specific requirements for some programs. Minimum 2.5 GPA. Admissions Index of 13 (combination of high school GPA and standardized test scores through a formula determined by the Higher Education Coordinating Board of the State of Washington). *Entrance tests:* College Board SAT or ACT composite for out-of-state students; Washington Pre-College Test for in-state residents. *For transfer students:* 2.0 minimum GPA; from 4-year accredited institution 135 quarter hours maximum transfer credit; from 2-year accredited institution 90 quarter hours; correspondence/extension students 45 quarter hours.

College credit and advanced placement for postsecondary-level work completed in secondary school. For extrainstitutional learning (life experience) on basis of faculty assessment.

Tutoring available. Developmental courses offered during regular academic year.

Degree Requirements: 180 quarter hours; 2.0 GPA (2.75 in teacher education program); 1 year, including final quarter, in residence; general education requirements.

Fulfillment of some degree requirements and exemption from some beginning courses possible by passing departmental examinations, College Board CLEP, AP, other standardized tests. *Grading system:* A–F; pass-fail; withdraw (carries time limit) written student-faculty evaluations.

Distinctive Educational Programs: *For undergraduates:* Cluster colleges. Facilities and programs for independent research, including honors programs, individual majors, tutorials. Study abroad through the consortium in France, Germany, Great Britain, Greece, Mexico. *Available to all students:* Internships. Free University. Flexible meeting places and schedules, including off-campus center (at Seattle, 90 miles away from main institution) and evening classes. Special facilities for using telecommunications in the classroom. College of Arts and Sciences offers interdisciplinary programs in American studies, aquatic studies. Canadian-American studies, East Asian studies, Ethnic studies, gerontology, industrial design, Latin American studies, women's studies. Research opportunities at Sundquist marine Laboratory and at Vehicle Research Institute. Fairhaven College, an undergraduate division of Western Washington, offers 3-stage core curriculum, descriptive reports in place of letter grades, student-designed interdisciplinary concentrations as options to traditional majors, emphasis on independent studies. At Huxley College of Environmental Studies, another undergraduate division of Western Washington, the Problem Series, an individual or groups research project for a minimum of 10 credit hours, is required of all students. Huxley College also sponsors exchange programs with College of the Atlantic (ME) and with University of Waterloo (Ontario). The College of Business and Economics offers interdisciplinary programs, research opportunities through the Center for Business and Economic Research, a computer-based data system. The School of Education offers a master's in student personnel administration. The College of Fine and Performing Arts offers an interdisciplinary arts program, a jazz program, and a student-faculty designed major in the arts. Study abroad in France, Germany, Greece, Mexico, Italy, Spain, United Kingdom, Japan, China. Year-long exchanges with 60 universities in 25 countries. *Other distinctive programs:* Continuing education.

Degrees Conferred: 3,067 *baccalaureate* (B), 341 *master's* (M): *baccalaureate* (B), 341 *master's* (M): area and ethnic studies 110 (B); biological sciences 101 (B), 15 (M); business and management 368 (B), 18 (M); communications 98 (B), 26 (M); computer and information sciences 53 (B), 2 (M); education 349 (B), 89 (M); engineering technology 69 (B), 4 (M); English 140 (B), 17 (M); fine and applied arts 6 (B); foreign languages and literature 63 (B); health professions 103 (B), 5 (M); mathematics 25 (B), 8 (M); natural resources/environmental science 115 (B); parks and recreation 44 (B); physical sciences 58 (B), 7 (M); protective services/public administration 219 (B); psychology 128 (B), 14 (M); social sciences and history 207 (B), 27 (M); visual and performing arts 144 (B), 11 (M); other 123 (B).

Fees and Other Expenses: *Full-time tuition per academic year 2008–09:* \$5,535 undergraduate resident, \$17,166 nonresident; contact the university for current graduate tuition/fees. *Books and supplies:* \$969. *Room and board per academic year:* \$7,712. *Other expenses:* \$2,913.

Financial Aid: Aid from institutionally generated funds is provided on the basis of academic merit, financial need, other criteria (artistic or athletic ability); multicultural experience.

Institution has a Program Participation Agreement with the U.S. Department of Education for eligible students to receive Pell Grants and, depending upon the agreement, other federal aid.

Financial aid to full-time, first-time undergraduate students: 60% received some form of aid. Average amount of aid received: federal grants \$3,645; Pell grants \$2,758; other federal aid \$1,082; state/local grants \$3,431; institutional grants \$2,249.

Departments and Teaching Staff: *Total instructional faculty:* 651 (full-time 485, part-time 166). Total faculty with doctorate, first-professional, or other terminal degree: 459. Student/faculty ratio: 19.4:1. Degrees held by full-time faculty: doctorate 80%, master's 18%, baccalaureate 2%, 86.5% hold terminal degrees.

Enrollment: Total enrollment 14,620. Undergraduate 13,406 (full-time 91%; female 55%, male 45%). Graduate 1,214 (full-time 57%). Transfer-in student 972.

Characteristics of Student Body: *Ethnic/racial makeup:* Black non-Hispanic: 3%; American Indian or Alaska Native: 2%; Asian or Pacific Islander 9%; Hispanic: 45; White non-Hispanic: 76%; unknown: 4%; nonresident alien 1%.

International Students: 146 nonresident aliens enrolled fall 2008. Students from Europe, Asia, Latin America, Africa, Canada, Australia, New Zealand. Programs available to aid students whose native language is not English: social, cultural, financial. English as a Second Language Program. Financial aid specifically designated for international students: scholarships available annually for qualifying students.

Student Life: On-campus residence halls house 34% of student body. All residence halls co-ed. Approximately 5% of student body housed in university-owned apartments. Housing available for married students. *Intercollegiate athletics:* male: basketball, crew, cross-country, football, golf, soccer, tennis, track; female: basketball, crew, cross-country, soccer, softball, tennis, track, volleyball. *Special regulations:* Cars permitted. *Special services:* Learning Resources Center, disabled student services; Ethnic Student Center; math, tutoring, and writing centers; multicultural support and retention services; medical services; Lifestyle Advisors (peer wellness counselors). *Student publications, radio: Jeopardy*, an annual literary journal; *Klipsun*, a quarterly magazine; *The Planet*, environmental quarterly; *Western Front*, biweekly newspaper. Radio station KUGS broadcasts 92 hours per week. *Surrounding community:* Bellingham population 62,000. Seattle, 90 miles from campus, is nearest metropolitan area. Served by mass transit bus system; airport 7 miles from campus.

Publications: *Annals of Regional Science* (triennially) first published in 1967; *Journal of English Linguistics* (annually) first published 1967; *Journal of Ethnic Studies* (quarterly) first published 1972; occasional papers published by the Center for Pacific Northwest Studies and the Center for East Asian Studies.

Library Collections: 1,500,000 volumes including bound books, serial backfiles, electronic documents, and government documents not in separate collections. Online catalog. Current serial subscriptions: 4,516 paper; 1,841 via electronic access. 32,817 recordings. Computer work stations available. Students have access to the Internet at no charge.

Most important special collections include Mongolian and East Asian Collection; U.S. Document Depository; State and Canadian Document Depository.

Buildings and Grounds: Campus area 189 acres.

Chief Executive Officer: Dr. Karen W. Morse, President.

Address admission inquiries to Karen Copetas, Director of Admissions; graduate admission inquiries to Moheb Ghali, Dean, Graduate School.

Whitman College

345 Boyer Avenue
Walla Walla, Washington 99362
Tel: (509) 527-5111 **E-mail:** admission@whitman.edu
Fax: (509) 527-4967 **Internet:** www.whitman.edu

Institution Description: Whitman College is a private, independent, nonprofit college. *Enrollment:* 1,458. *Degrees awarded:* Baccalaureate.

Accreditation: *Regional:* NWCCU.

History: Established as Whitman Seminary 1859; offered first instruction at postsecondary level 1882; chartered and adopted present name 1883; awarded first degree (baccalaureate) 1886.

Institutional Structure: *Governing board:* The Board of Trustees of Whitman College. Extrainstitutional representation: 9 trustees. 3 ex officio. 9 voting. *Composition of institution:* Administrators 33. Academic affairs headed by president. Management/business/finances directed by treasurer. Full-time instructional faculty 119. women. Academic governance body, the faculty, meets an average of 11 times per year.

Calendar: Semesters. Academic year Sept. to May. Freshmen admitted Sept., Jan. Degrees conferred May, Dec. Formal commencement May.

Characteristics of Freshmen: 47% of applicants admitted. 28% of applicants admitted and enrolled.

81 (295 students) submitted SAT scores; 19% (715 students) submitted ACT scores. *25th percentile*: SAT Critical Reading 610, SAT math 620; ACT Composite 28. *75th percentile*: SAT Critical Reading 720, SAT Math 690; ACT Composite 32.

86% of entering freshmen expected to graduate within 5 years. 41 of freshmen from Washington. Freshmen from 43 states and 25 foreign countries.

Admission: For fall acceptance, apply as early as Oct. 1 of previous year, but not later than Jan. 15 of year of enrollment. Notification of acceptance by Mar. 15. Apply by Nov. 15 or Jan. 1 for early decision; must limit application to Whitman. Early acceptance available. *Requirements:* Either graduation from secondary school with a recommended program of 4 units English, 4 mathematics, 2 in a foreign language, 2 in laboratory science, 2 history and social studies, 2 electives; or GED. *Entrance tests:* College Board SAT I; ACT composite. *For transfer students:* 90 hours maximum transfer credit; from 2-year accredited institution 62 hours.

College credit for postsecondary-level work completed in secondary school. Tutoring available.

Degree Requirements: 124 credit hours; 2.0 GPA; 2 terms in residence; comprehensives in individual fields of study; completion of general studies program; completion of major study requirements.

Fulfillment of some degree requirements and exemption from some beginning courses possible by passing departmental examinations, College Board APP. *Grading system:* A–F; pass-D-fail; credit-no credit; withdraw (carries time limit); incomplete (carries time limit).

Distinctive Educational Programs: Evening classes. Dual-degree programs in engineering with California Institute of Technology, Columbia University (NY); in forestry and environmental science with Duke University (NC). Interdepartmental/interdisciplinary programs in environmental studies. Facilities and programs for independent research, including honors programs and individually designed majors. Study abroad in Austria, England, France, Spain, Germany through Institute of European Studies; and Japan through Associated Kyoto Program. Whitman in China program. Off-campus study programs in U.S.

Degrees Conferred: 449 *baccalaureate:* area and ethnic studies 15; biological/life sciences 52; communications/journalism 8; English 35; interdisciplinary studies 2; mathematics 25; philosophy and religious studies 31; physical sciences 40; psychology 33; social sciences 107; visual and performing arts 41.

Fees and Other Expenses: *Full-time tuition per academic year 2008–09:* $35,192. *Required fees:* $276. *Room and board per academic year:* $8,820. *Books and supplies:* $1,400. *Other expenses:* $800.

Financial Aid: Aid from institutionally generated funds is provided on the basis of academic merit, financial need.

Financial aid to full-time, first-time undergraduate students: need-based scholarships/grants totaling $11,857,800, self-help $3,380,650; non-need-based scholarships/grants totaling $5,411.15-. self-help $1,410,650, parent loans $1,701,925, tuition waivers $188,090.

Departments and Teaching Staff: *Total instructional faculty:* 191 (full-time 119, part-time 72). Total faculty with doctorate, first-professional, or other terminal degree : 158. Student/faculty ratio: 10:1. Degrees held by full-time faculty: doctorate 87%, master's 11%, baccalaureate 2%. 92% hold terminal degrees.

Enrollment: Total enrollment 1,458 (undergraduate).

Characteristics of Student Body: *Ethnic/racial makeup:* number of Black non-Hispanic: 32; American Indian or Alaska Native: 18; Asian or Pacific Islander: 142; Hispanic: 69; White non-Hispanic: 934; unknown: 212/ *Age distribution:* number under 18: 8; 18–19: 610; 20–21: 673; 22–24: 174; 25–29: 8; 30–34: 2; 40–49: 1.

International Students: 48 nonresident aliens enrolled fall 2008. Students from Europe, Asia, Latin America, Africa, Canada. Programs available to aid students whose native language is not English: social, cultural. Financial aid specifically designated for international students: scholarships available annually to qualifying students.

Student Life: On-campus residence halls house 62% of student body. One residence hall designated for sororities constitute 17% of such space; co-ed residence halls 83%. 31% of males join and 16% live in fraternity houses; 35% of females join and 19% live in sorority houses. *Intercollegiate athletics:* male: baseball; female: volleyball; male and female: basketball, cross-country, soccer, swimming, tennis, track, golf. *Special services:* Learning Resources Center, medical services. *Student publications, radio: The Whitman College Pioneer*, a weekly newspaper. Radio station KWCW broadcasts 126 hours per week. *Surrounding community:* Walla Walla population 30,000. Seattle, 275 miles from campus, is nearest metropolitan area. Served by mass transit bus system; airport 5 miles from campus.

Library Collections: 399,500 volumes. 500,000 government documents; 13,000 reels on microform; 1,500 videotapes; 2,140 current periodical subscriptions. Online catalog. Students have access to online information retrieval services and the Internet.

Most important special holdings include Pacific Northwest Collection; archives of early missionary materials and local and regional history; collection of Napoleonic literature and artifacts displayed in the Stuart Room; environmental studies.

Buildings and Grounds: Campus area 55 acres. Campus DVD available.

Chief Executive Officer: Dr. George S. Bridges, President.

Address admission inquiries to Dean of Admission and Financial Aid.

Whitworth College

300 West Hawthorne Road
Spokane, Washington 99251-0002
Tel: (509) 777-1000 **E-mail:** admissions@whitworth.edu
Fax: (509) 777-3773 **Internet:** www.whitworth.edu

Institution Description: Whitworth College is a private college affiliated with the Presbyterian Church (USA). *Enrollment:* 2,441. *Degrees awarded:* Baccalaureate, master's.

Member of the consortium Intercollegiate Center for Nursing Education.

Accreditation: *Regional:* NWCCU. *Professional*: music, teacher education

History: Established, incorporated, and offered first instruction at postsecondary level 1890; awarded first degree (baccalaureate) 1891. *See* Alfred O. Gray, *Not by Might* (Spokane: Whitworth College, 1965) for further information.

Institutional Structure: *Governing board:* Board of Trustees. Extrainstitutional representation: 43 trustees; institutional representation: president of the college, 6 administrators, 6 full-time instructional faculty members, 1 student, 6 alumni, 16 ex officio. 43 voting. *Composition of institution:* Administrators 29. Academic affairs headed by vice president for academic affairs. Management/business/finances directed by vice president for business affairs. Full-time instructional faculty 65 men / 28 women. Academic governance body, Academic Affairs Council, meets an average of 16 times per year.

Calendar: Semesters (4-1-4 plan). Academic year Sept. to May. Freshmen admitted Sept., Jan., Feb., May, June, Aug. Degrees conferred May, Aug., Jan. Formal commencement May. Summer session from May to Aug.

Characteristics of Freshmen: Mean SAT scores 460 verbal, 500 mathematical.

59% of freshmen from Washington. Freshmen from 38 states and 3 foreign countries.

Admission: Rolling admissions plan. For fall acceptance, apply as early as Dec. 1, but not later than Aug. 1. Apply by Dec. 1 for early action if Whitworth is first choice. *Requirements:* Either graduation from secondary school or GED. Recommend 3 units English, 2 foreign language, 2 mathematics, 2 science. Minimum 2.5 GPA (exceptions possible). *Entrance tests:* College Board SAT, ACT composite, or Washington Pre-College Test. For foreign students TOEFL. *For*

WHITWORTH COLLEGE—*cont'd*

transfer students: 2.7 minimum GPA; from 4-year accredited institution 135 quarter hours maximum transfer credit; from 2-year accredited institution 90 quarter hours.

College credit and advanced placement for postsecondary-level work completed in secondary school and for extrainstitutional learning on basis of faculty assessment.

Tutoring available. Developmental and remedial courses offered during regular academic year; credit given.

Degree Requirements: 130 semester hour; 2.0 GPA; 32 hours in residence; 3 physical education activities; distribution requirements.

Fulfillment of some degree requirements and exemption from some beginning courses possible by passing departmental examinations, College Board CLEP, AP (minimum score of 3). *Grading system:* A–F; pass-no credit; credit-no credit (with written evaluations); withdraw (may carry penalty); incomplete (carries time limit).

Distinctive Educational Programs: *For undergraduates:* Interdepartmental programs, including American studies, arts administration, international business communication, international studies. Institutionally sponsored study abroad in British Isles, Central America, Germany, France, Israel. Field courses in San Francisco, Honolulu, Washington (DC). Student exchanges with partner universities in Mexico, Japan, Korea, China, Hong Kong. *For graduate students:* Programs in education fields. *Available to all students:* Internships. Evening classes. Cooperative transfer agreement with the Institute of Holy Land Studies, Jerusalem and Christian College Coalition, Washington (DC). *Other distinctive programs:* Graduate and undergraduate continuing education.

Degrees Conferred: 473 *baccalaureate.* Bachelor's degrees awarded in top five disciplines: business, management, marketing, and related support services 80; education 77; visual and performing arts 43; social sciences 36; liberal arts/general studies 32. *Master's*: various disciplines 96.

Fees and Other Expenses: *Full-time tuition per academic year 2008–09:* $24,154; contact the university for current graduate tuition. *Books and supplies:* $800. *Room and board per academic year:* $9,000.

Financial Aid: Aid from institutionally generated funds is provided on the basis of academic merit, financial need, other criteria.

Institution has a Program Participation Agreement with the U.S. Department of Education for eligible students to receive Pell Grants and, depending upon the agreement, other federal aid.

Financial aid to full-time, first-time undergraduate students: 22% received federal grants averaging $2,945; 29% state/local grants averaging $2,308; 94% institutional grants averaging $9,332; 64 % received loans $4,345.

Departments and Teaching Staff: *Total instructional faculty:* 97. Student/faculty ratio: 16:1. Degrees held by full-time faculty: doctorate 71%, master's 29%. 71% hold terminal degrees.

Enrollment: Total enrollment 2,441 (undergraduate).

Characteristics of Student Body: *Ethnic/racial makeup:* Black non-Hispanic: 2%; American Indian or Alaska Native: 1%; Asian or Pacific Islander: 5%; Hispanic: 2%; White non-Hispanic: 86%; unknown: 3%.

International Students: 40 nonresident aliens enrolled fall 2008. Students from Europe, Asia, Latin America, Africa, Australia. Programs available to aid students whose native language is not English: Financial. Scholarships awarded to qualifying undergraduate international students.

Student Life: On-campus residence halls house 57% of student body. Residence halls for males constitute 9% of such space, for females 11.5%, for both sexes 79%. *Intercollegiate athletics:* male: baseball, basketball, cross-country, football, soccer, swimming, tennis, track; female: basketball, cross-country, soccer, swimming, tennis, track, volleyball. *Special regulations:* Registered cars permitted. *Special services:* Medical services, career guidance, handicapped and personal counseling. *Student publications, radio: Natsihi*, a yearbook; *Whitworthian*, a weekly publication. Radio station KWRS programming includes new music, Christian and rock programming. *Surrounding community:* Spokane population 188,000. Served by mass transit bus system; airport 10 miles from campus; passenger rail service 8 miles from campus.

Library Collections: 186000 volumes. 48,000 microforms; 7,000 audiovisual materials; 725 current periodical subscriptions. Online catalog. Students have access to online information retrieval services and the Internet.

Most important special holdings include Presbyterian Church, Synod of Alaska-Northwest collection (including some rare books); Early American Imprints through 1800 (microcard); 20th-century music (Moldenhauer Collection); Floyd Daniel Photography Collection; Whitworth College Archives.

Buildings and Grounds: Campus area 200 acres.

Chief Executive Officer: Dr. William P. Robinson, President.

Undergraduates address admission inquiries to Fred Plursch, Dean of Enrollment Services.

West Virginia

Alderson-Broaddus College

College Hill
Philippi, West Virginia 26416
Tel: (304) 457-1700 **E-mail:** admissions@ab.edu
Fax: (304) 457-6239 **Internet:** www.ab.edu

Institution Description: Alderson-Broaddus College is a private institution affiliated with the American Baptist Churches, U.S.A. *Enrollment:* 738. *Degrees awarded:* Associate, baccalaureate, master's.

Member of the consortium Mountain State Association of Colleges.

Accreditation: *Regional:* NCA. *Professional*: athletic training, nursing, physician assisting, teacher education

History: Established in Virginia as Winchester Female Institute 1871; chartered as Broaddus Female College 1875; moved to Clarksburg, West Virginia and changed name to Broaddus Academy 1876; moved to Philippi, West Virginia 1909; offered first instruction at postsecondary level 1917; first degree (baccalaureate) awarded 1927; merged with Alderson Junior College and chartered as Alderson-Broaddus College 1932.

Institutional Structure: *Governing board:* Extrainstitutional representation: Board of Trustees of Alderson Broaddus College, Inc. 1 ex officio. 37 voting. *Composition of institution:* Administrators 29. Academic affairs headed by provost, vice president for academic affairs. Full-time instructional faculty 58. Academic governance body, faculty-staff, meets an average of 9 times per year.

Calendar: Semesters. Academic year Aug. to May. Freshmen admitted Aug., Jan. Degrees conferred Dec., May, Aug. Formal commencement May. Certain 5-week courses May to June, June to July.

Characteristics of Freshmen: 637 applicants (female 493, male 144). 95% of applicants admitted. 25% of applicants admitted and enrolled.

21% (30 students) submitted SAT scores; 91% (127 students) submitted ACT scores. *25th percentile*: SAT Critical Reading 430, SAT Math 400; ACT Composite 18. *75th percentile*: SAT Critical Reading 520, SAT Math 520; ACT Composite 23.

50% entering students expected to graduate within five years. 81% of freshmen from West Virginia. Freshmen from 8 states.

Admission: Rolling admissions decision format. For fall semester acceptance, apply as early as Sept. of junior year, but not later than Aug. 1 of year of enrollment. Apply during junior year for early acceptance decision (requires at least 10, preferably 15, secondary school unites distributed among college preparatory subjects) and results from an ACT/SAT test. Regular admission requires completed application for admission, high school transcripts or GED scores, and ACT or SAT scores. Transfer students must also submit official transcripts from each college attended. Refer to college catalog for specific admissions requirements.

Advanced placement and CLEP opportunities available to students.

Degree Requirements: *For all baccalaureate degrees:* 128 credit hours; last 32 hours in residence; 2.0 GPA; comprehensive exams or research paper in field of study. Credit allowed for CLEP or locally prepared examinations (up to 60 hours). *For associate degrees:* 63–65 semester hours, 2.0 GPA. *Grading system:* A–F; honor, satisfactory, unsatisfactory, withdraw (carries time limit); audit.

Distinctive Educational Programs: Independent research opportunities in each department. Individually designed interdisciplinary major in liberal arts. Majors include digital arts, ophthalmic medical technology, physician assistant (B.S. and M.S.), athletic training, sports medicine, visual arts. Study abroad in Austria.

Degrees Conferred: 13 *associate*; 130 *baccalaureate:* business/marketing 10; communications/communication technologies 3; computer and information sciences 5; education 20; health professions and related sciences 49; home economics and vocational home economics 4; mathematics 2; parks and recreation 3; philosophy/religion/theology 5; physical sciences 2; psychology 4; social sciences and history 4; visual and performing arts 9; other 10. *Master's*: education 57.

Fees and Other Expenses: *Full-time tuition per academic year 2008–09:* $21,020. *Required fees:* $200. *Room and board per academic year:* $6,798. *Books and supplies:* $800. *Other expenses:* 2,320.

Financial Aid: Aid from institutionally generated funds is provided on the basis of academic merit, financial need, athletic ability, other criteria.

Financial aid to full-time, first-time undergraduate and graduate students: 100% received some form of aid.

Departments and Teaching Staff: *Total instructional faculty:* 86 (full-time 55, part-time 31). Total faculty with doctorate, first-professional, or other terminal degree: 27. Student/faculty ratio: 10:1. Degrees held by full-time faculty: doctorate 40%, master's 60%. 40% hold terminal degrees.

Enrollment: Total enrollment 738. Undergraduate 609 (full-time 93%; female 67%, male 33%). Graduate 129 (full-time 84%). Transfer-in students 51.

Characteristics of Student Body: *Ethnic/racial makeup:* Black non-Hispanic: 4%; Asian or Pacific Islander 1%; Hispanic 2%; White non-Hispanic: 87%; unknwond 2%; nonresident alien 2%.

International Students: 14 nonresident aliens enrolled fall 2008. Students from Europe, Asia, Canada. Programs available to aid students whose native language is not English: social, cultural, financial. Financial aid specifically designated for international students: scholarships available annually; 8 totaling $13,725 awarded 2008–09.

Student Life: On-campus residence halls house 50% of student body. Residence halls for males constitute 40% of such space, for females 60%. *Intercollegiate athletics:* male: baseball, basketball, cross-country, soccer; female: cross-country, basketball, volleyball. *Special regulations:* Alcohol is not permitted on campus or at college-sponsored activities. *Student publications, radio:* yearbook, monthly newspaper. WQAB-FM broadcasts 90 hours per week. *Surrounding community:* Philippi population 4,000. Pittsburgh (PA), 150 miles from campus, is nearest metropolitan area. Served by airport 26 miles from campus; bus service 24 miles from campus.

Publications: Sources of information about Alderson-Broaddus College include *A-B Times,* published four times yearly; *Annual Report* published once a year.

Library Collections: 100,000 volumes including bound books, serial backfiles, electronic documents, and government documents not in separate collections. Online catalog. Current serial subscriptions: 108 paper, 107 microform, 1,082 electronic. Computer work stations available. Students have access to the Internet at no charge.

Most important special holdings include C. Shirley Donnelly Civil War Collection; Baptist Church History Collection; Alderson-Broaddus College Archives.

Buildings and Grounds: Campus area 170 acres. Campus DVD available.

Chief Executive Officer: Dr. Stephen E. Markwood, President.

Address undergraduate admission inquiries to Kimberly Klaus, Director of Admissions; master's program to William Childers, Director of Master's Degree Program.

Appalachian Bible College

5701 Robert C. Byrd Drive
P.O. Box ABC
Bradley, West Virginia 25818-1353
Tel: (304) 877-6428 **E-mail:** admissions@appbibco.edu
Fax: (304) 877-5082 **Internet:** www.appbibco.edu

Institution Description: Appalachian Bible College is a private, independent, church-related (nondenominational) institution. *Enrollment:* 320. *Degrees awarded:* Associate, baccalaureate.

Accreditation: *Regional:* NCA. *National:* ABHE.

History: Established 1950; moved to present campus 1956; accredited 1967; offered baccalaureate 1973.

Institutional Structure: *Governing board:* Board of Directors. Extrainstitutional representation: 19 members; institutional representation: 1 administrator. 1 ex officio. All voting. affairs headed by academic dean. Management/business/

APPALACHIAN BIBLE COLLEGE—*cont'd*

finances directed by chief business officer. Public relations/alumni/fund raising directed by director of development. Student affairs directed by dean of students. Full-time instructional faculty 14. Academic governance body, the faculty, meets 2 times each month.

Calendar: Semesters. Academic year Sept. to May. Freshmen admitted Aug., Jan. Degrees conferred May. No summer sessions.

Characteristics of Freshmen: 73% of applicants admitted. 56% of applicants admitted and enrolled.

37% (23 students) submitted SAT scores; 63% (39 students) submitted ACT scores. *25th percentile*: SAT Critical Reading 420, SAT Math 430; ACT Composite 18, ACT English 18, ACT Math 16. *75th percentile*: SAT Critical Reading 590, SAT Math 560; ACT Composite 25, ACT English 28, ACT Math 23.

100% of entering freshmen expected to graduate within 5 years. 34% of freshmen from West Virginia. Freshmen from 17 states and 1 foreign country.

Distinctive Educational Programs: Adult learning seminars throughout the year.

Degrees Conferred: 6 *associate;* 40 *baccalaureate:* theology.

Fees and Other Expenses: *Full-time tuition per academic year:* $8,820. *Room and board per academic year:* $5,500.

Financial Aid: Aid from institutionally generated funds is provided on the basis of academic merit, financial need, other criteria.

Financial aid to full-time, first-time undergraduate students: need-based scholarships/grants totaling $944,922; self-help $278,000, parent loans $32,500.

Departments and Teaching Staff: *Total instructional faculty:* 15 (full-time 10, part-time 5). Total faculty with doctorate, first-professional, or other terminal degree: 4. Degrees held by full-time faculty: master's 87.5%, baccalaureate 100%.

Enrollment: Total enrollment 320 (undergraduate).

Characteristics of Student Body: *Ethnic/racial makeup:* number of: Black non-Hispanic: 6; Asian or Pacific Islander: 3; Hispanic: 1; White non-Hispanic: 288.

International Students: 6 nonresident aliens enrolled fall 2008. Programs available to aid students whose native language is not English: social, cultural. Financial aid specifically designated for international students: scholarships available annually to qualifying students.

Student Life: On-campus residence halls house 62% of student body. Residence halls for males constitute 46% of such space, for females 56%, for both sexes 62%. Married student housing: 24 duplexes. *Intercollegiate athletics:* male: basketball, soccer; female: basketball, volleyball. *Special services:* Medical services. *Surrounding community:* Beckley population 21,000. Charleston, 55 miles from campus, is nearest metropolitan area. Served by mass transit bus system; airport 15 miles from campus; passenger rail service 40 miles from campus.

Publications: *Introspect*, a biannual bulletin.

Library Collections: 42,500 volumes including bound books, serial backfiles, electronic documents, and government documents not in separate collections. Card catalog. Current serial subscriptions: 362 paper. 3,004 recordings; 34 compact discs. 73 CD-ROMs. Computer work stations available. Students have access to the Internet at no charge.

Most important special holdings include Judaica Collection; Antique Reference; Christian Counterfeit Library (Cults).

Buildings and Grounds: Campus area 110 acres.

Chief Executive Officer: Dr. Daniel L. Anderson, President.

Address admission inquiries to Angela Harding, Director of Admissions.

Bethany College

Bethany, West Virginia 26032

Tel: (304) 829-7611 **E-mail:** admission@bethanywv.edu
Fax: (304) 829-7142 **Internet:** www.bethanywv.edu

Institution Description: Bethany College is a private college affiliated with the Christian Church (Disciples of Christ). *Enrollment:* 825. *Degrees awarded:* Baccalaureate.

Member of East Central College Consortium.

Accreditation: *Regional:* NCA. *Professional*: social work, teacher education

History: Established, chartered, and offered first instruction at postsecondary level 1840; first degree (baccalaureate) awarded 1844. *See* William Kirk Woolery, *Bethany Years* (Huntington, W.Va.: Standard Printing and Publishing Company, 1941) for further information.

Institutional Structure: *Governing board:* Board of Trustees of Bethany College. Extrainstitutional representation: 30 trustees; institutional representation: president of college. 1 ex officio. 30 voting. *Composition of institution:* Administrators 29. Academic affairs headed by vice president and dean of faculty. Management/business/finances directed by treasurer and business manager. Full-time instructional faculty 53. The Faculty of Bethany College meets an average of 9 times per year.

Calendar: Semesters. Academic year Aug. to May. Freshmen admitted Sept., Jan., Feb., June. Degrees conferred and formal commencement May. Summer session from June to Aug.

Characteristics of Freshmen: 1,237 applicants (female 925, male 712). 63% of applicants accepted. 15% of accepted applicants enrolled.

67% (137 students) submitted SAT scores; 46% (95 students) submitted ACT scores. *25th percentile*: SAT Critical Reading 430, SAT Math 440; ACT Composite 19. *75th percentile*: SAT Critical Reading 550, SAT Math 550; ACT Composite 23.

67% of entering freshmen expected to graduate within 5 years. 46% of freshmen from West Virginia. Freshmen from 19 states.

Admission: Rolling admissions plan. For fall acceptance, apply as early as Aug. of previous year, but not later than Aug. of year of enrollment. Early acceptance available. *Requirements:* Either graduation from accredited secondary school with 15 college preparatory units, including 4 in English; or GED. *Entrance tests:* College Board SAT or ACT Composite. *For transfer students:* 2.0 minimum GPA; from 4-year accredited institution 96 hours maximum transfer credit; from 2-year accredited institution unlimited transfer credit with degree.

College credit and advanced placement for postsecondary level work completed in secondary school and for extrainstitutional learning (life experience) on basis of consortium and faculty assessments.

Tutoring available. Noncredit developmental courses offered on an individual basis.

Degree Requirements: 128 credit hours; 2.0 GPA; last 2 terms in residence; exit competency examinations in writing and comprehensives in individual fields of study; distribution requirements; completion of 4 practicums; senior project. *Grading system:* A–F; credit-no credit; withdraw (deadline after which failure may be appended to withdraw); incomplete (carries time limit).

Distinctive Educational Programs: Internships. Dual-degree programs in engineering with Case Western Reserve University (OH), Columbia University (NY); Georgia Institute of Technology, Washington University (MO). Special facilities for using telecommunications in the classroom. Interdisciplinary seminars for freshmen; individually designed interdisciplinary study programs. Facilities and programs for individual research, including individual majors, tutorials. Institutionally sponsored study abroad in England at Oxford University; in Paris at the Sorbonne; at the University of Navara in Pamplona, Spain; and in Germany at the University of Tubingen. Other programs include the Beaver College London semester; study at the American University in Beirut, Lebanon; at the University of Glasgow, Scotland. Off-campus study in the U.S. through Washington (DC) Semester in cooperation with American University. Academic Common Market, an interstate agreement among southern states, allows qualified Bethany students to get in-state tuition rates in graduate programs of out-of-state member schools. *Other distinctive programs:* Nondegree, nontraditional continuing education program. Leadership Center offers business and management training seminars.

Degrees Conferred: 78 *baccalaureate:* biological/life sciences 18; business 15; communications 28; computer and information science 4; English education 33; English 9; foreign languages 7; history 11; law/legal studies 8; 9l mathematics 8; public administration and social services 19; social sciences 7; philosophy/religion 2; visual and performing arts 6.

Fees and Other Expenses: *Full-time tuition per academic year 2008–09:* $19,565. *Required fees:* $825. *Room and board per academic year:* $7,770. *Books and supplies:* $800. *Other expenses:* $2,310.

Financial Aid: The college offers a direct lending program. Aid from institutionally generated funds is provided on the basis of financial need.

Financial aid to full-time, first-time undergraduate students: need-based scholarships/grants totaling $3,586,821, self-help $2,658,584; non-need-based scholarships/grants totaling $5,116,068, self-help $1,142,725, parent loans $1,899,774, tuition waivers $260,000.

Departments and Teaching Staff: *Total instructional faculty:* 92 (full-time 53, part-time 39). Student/faculty ratio: 13:1. . Degrees held by full-time faculty: doctorate 78%, master's 100%. 78% hold terminal degrees.

Enrollment: Total enrollment 825 (undergraduate).

Characteristics of Student Body: *Ethnic/racial makeup:* Black non-Hispanic: 6%; Asian or Pacific Islander: 1%; Hispanic: 3%; White non-Hispanic: 90%;

International Students: 30 nonresident aliens enrolled fall 2008. Students from Europe, Asia, Africa, Canada. Programs available to aid students whose native language is not English: social, cultural, financial. English as a Second Language Program. No financial aid specifically designated for international students.

Student Life: On-campus residence halls and fraternity-owned residences house 90% of student body. 55% of males join fraternities and approximately

50% live in college- or fraternity-owned houses. 54% of females join sororities and approximately 90% live in college-owned sorority houses. 1% of student body live in married student housing. *Intercollegiate athletics:* male: baseball, basketball, football, golf, soccer, tennis, track and cross-country; female basketball, field hockey, softball, tennis, volleyball; both sexes: swimming. *Special regulations:* Registered cars permitted in designated areas only. Residence hall visitation noon to midnight. *Special services:* Learning Resources Center, medical services. *Student publications, radio, television: The Bethanian*, a yearbook; *The Folio*, a biannual magazine; *The Harbinger*, an annual literary magazine; *The Tower*, a weekly newspaper. Radio station WVBC broadcasts 133 hours per week. Television station TV-3 broadcasts 10 hours per week. *Surrounding community:* Bethany population 9,950. Pittsburgh (PA), 50 miles from campus, is nearest metropolitan area. Served by airport 50 miles from campus.

Library Collections: 131,000 volumes including bound books, serial backfiles, electronic documents, and government documents not in separate collections. Online catalog. Current serial subscriptions: 91 paper; 74 microform; 10,345 via electronic access. 2,594 audio/videotapes; 306 DVD discs; 315 CD-ROMs. Computer work stations available. Students have access to the Internet at no charge.

Most important special holdings include Campbell Collection (personal library of Alexander Campbell, founder of Bethany; Campbell family letters; 19th-century periodicals published by individuals affiliated with the Disciples of Christ); Bethany College Archives; Upper Ohio Valley Collection.

Buildings and Grounds: Campus area 1,600 acres.

Chief Executive Officer: Dr. G.T. Smith, President.

Address admission inquiries to Wray Blair, Director of Admissions.

Bluefield State College

219 Rock Street
Bluefield, West Virginia 24701
Tel: (304) 327-4000 **E-mail:** admit@bluefieldstate.edu
Fax: (304) 327-7747 **Internet:** www.bluefieldstate.edu

Institution Description: Bluefield State College is a public institution. *Enrollment:* 1,568. *Degrees awarded:* Associate, baccalaureate. Certificates are also awarded.

Academic offerings subject to approval by statewide coordinating bodies. Budget subject to approval by state governing boards.

Accreditation: *Regional:* NCA. *Professional*: engineering technology, nursing, respiratory therapy, teacher education

History: Established as Bluefield Colored Institute 1895; offered first instruction at postsecondary level and changed name to Bluefield State Teachers College 1931; awarded first degree (baccalaureate) 1932; adopted present name 1943.

Institutional Structure: *Governing board:* West Virginia Board of Regents. Representation: 9 regents, state superintendent of schools, 1 faculty representative, 1 student representative. 3 ex officio. 11 voting. *Composition of institution:* Administrators 10. Academic affairs headed by academic vice president. Management/business/finances directed by vice president for finance and administration. Full-time instructional faculty 83. Academic governance body, Faculty Senate, meets an average of 10 times per year.

Calendar: Semesters. Academic year Aug. to May. Freshmen admitted Aug., Jan., June. Degrees conferred May, Aug., Dec. Formal commencement May. Summer session from June to Aug.

Characteristics of Freshmen: 445 applicants (female 260, male 185). 65% of applicants accepted. 75% of accepted applicants enrolled.

Mean ACT Composite score 18.6.

34% of entering freshmen expected to graduate within 5 years. 92% of freshmen from West Virginia.

Admission: Rolling admissions plan. For fall acceptance, apply as early as 1 year prior to enrollment, but not later than week of registration. *Requirements:* Open admissions for secondary school graduates and candidates 18 years of age or older; GED accepted. *Entrance tests:* ACT Composite. For foreign students TOEFL. *For transfer students:* Good standing at institution previously attended; from 2-year accredited institutions 72 hours maximum transfer credit; correspondence/extension students 32 hours.

College credit and advanced placement for postsecondary-level work completed in secondary school and for extrainstitutional learning on basis of faculty assessment.

Tutoring available. Developmental courses offered during regular academic year; credit given.

Degree Requirements: *For all associate degrees:* 64 credit hours. *For all baccalaureate degrees:* 128 credit hours; 2 physical education credits. *For all undergraduate degrees:* 2.0 GPA; 32 semester hours in residence; distribution requirements.

Fulfillment of some degree requirements and exemption from some beginning courses possible by passing departmental examinations, College Board CLEP. *Grading system:* A–F; withdraw (carries time limit).

Distinctive Educational Programs: Evening classes. Special facilities for using telecommunications in the classroom. Facilities and programs for independent research, including individual majors, tutorials. *Other distinctive programs:* Degree and nondegree granting continuing education program. Associate of Arts degree can be earned totally by distance education.

Degrees Conferred: 85 *associate*; 219 *baccalaureate*. Bachelor's degrees awarded in top five disciplines: engineering 40; education 39; business, management, marketing, and related support services 35; liberal arts/general studies 32; health professions and related clinical sciences 19.

Fees and Other Expenses: *Full-time tuition per academic year 2008–09:* resident $4,272, nonresident $8,568. *Books and supplies:* $1,600. *Off-campus room and board per academic year:* $6,400. *Other expenses* $3,100.

Financial Aid: The college offers a direct lending program. Aid from institutionally generated funds is provided on the basis of academic merit, financial need, athletic ability. Institution has a Program Participation Agreement with the U.S. Department of Education for eligible students to receive Pell Grants and, depending upon the agreement, other federal aid.

Financial aid to full-time, first-time undergraduate students: 85% received some form of aid. Average amount of aid received: federal grants $3,142; Pell grants $3,230; other federal aid $2,013; state/local grants $2,760; institutional grants $1,330.

Departments and Teaching Staff: *Total instructional faculty:* 82. Student/faculty ratio: 16:1. Degrees held by full-time instructional faculty: doctorate 34.1%, master's 52.5%, baccalaureate 12.2%. 34.1% hold terminal degrees.

Enrollment: Total enrollment 1,568. Undergraduate 1,568 (full-time 81%; female 60%; male 40%). Transfer-in students 270.

Characteristics of Student Body: *Ethnic/racial makeup:* Black non-Hispanic: 12%; Hispanic: 1%; White non-Hispanic: 84%; nonresident alien 3%.

International Students: 48 nonresident aliens enrolled fall 2008. Students from Europe, Asia, Canada, Middle East. No programs available to aid students whose native language is not English. No financial aid specifically designated for international students.

Student Life: No on-campus housing. *Intercollegiate athletics:* male: baseball, basketball, cross-country, golf, tennis; female: basketball, cross-country, tennis. *Special regulations:* Registered cars permitted without restrictions. *Special services:* Learning Resources Center, medical services. *Student publications: The Bluefieldian*, a weekly newspaper. *Surrounding community:* Bluefield population 16,000. Charleston, 100 miles from campus, is nearest metropolitan area. Served by airport 3 miles from campus.

Library Collections: 80,000 volumes including bound books, serial backfiles, electronic documents, and government documents not in separate collections. Online catalog. Current serial subscriptions: 325 paper. 19,159 microforms. Computer work stations available. Students have access to the Internet at no charge.

Buildings and Grounds: Campus area 40 acres.

Chief Executive Officer: Dr., Albert L. Walker, President.

Address admission inquiries to John C. Cardwell, Vice President for Enrollment Management.

Concord University

P.O. Box 1000
Athens, West Virginia 24712-1000
Tel: (304) 384-3115 **E-mail:** admissions@concord.edu
Fax: (304) 384-9044 **Internet:** www.concord.edu

Institution Description: Concord University is under the supervision of the West Virginia Higher Education Policy Commission. *Enrollment:* 2,812. *Degrees awarded:* Associate, baccalaureate, master's.

Academic offerings subject to approval by statewide coordinating bodies. Budget subject to approval by state governing boards.

Accreditation: *Regional:* NCA. *Professional*: social work, teacher education

History: Established and chartered as Concord State Normal School 1872; offered first instruction at postsecondary level 1919; awarded first degree (baccalaureate) 1923.

Institutional Structure: *Governing board:* Concord University Board of Governors. Extrainstitutional representation: 9 regents, state superintendent of schools, 1 faculty representative, 1 student representative. 3 ex officio. 11 voting. *Composition of institution:* Administrators 13. Academic affairs headed by vice president and academic dean. Management/business/finances directed by business manager. Full-time instructional faculty 95. Academic governance body, Faculty Senate, meets an average of 30 times per year.

CONCORD UNIVERSITY—*cont'd*

Calendar: Semesters. Academic year Aug. to May. Freshmen admitted Aug., Jan., June, July. Degrees conferred May, Dec. Formal commencement May, Dec. Summer session from mid-June to mid-Aug.

Characteristics of Freshmen: 2,489 applicants (female 1,433, male 1,056). 85% of applicants accepted. 74% of accepted applicants enrolled.

Average secondary school rank men 60th percentile, women 75th percentile. Mean ACT Composite score 18.

58% of entering freshmen expected to graduate within 5 years. 87% of freshmen from West Virginia. Freshmen from 15 states and 10 foreign countries.

Admission: Rolling admissions plan. For fall acceptance, apply as early as Sept. 1 of previous year, but not later than Aug. 15 of year of enrollment. Early acceptance available. *Requirements:* Either graduation from accredited secondary school with 17 units which must include 4 English, 3 social studies, 2 mathematics, 2 science, 1 health and physical education; or GED. First 2 years of secondary school in college preparatory program. Minimum GPA 3.0. Secondary school class rank in top three-fourths or minimum ACT Composite score 14. *Entrance tests:* College Board SAT or ACT Composite. *For transfer students:* 2.0 minimum GPA; from 4-year accredited institution hours maximum transfer credit limited only by residence requirement; from 2-year accredited institution 72 hours.

College credit and advanced placement for postsecondary-level work completed in secondary school. College credit for extrainstitutional learning on basis of faculty assessment.

Tutoring available. Remedial courses offered during regular academic year; credit given.

Degree Requirements: 128 credit hours; 2.0 GPA; 2 semesters in residence; 2 hours physical education; general studies program.

Fulfillment of some degree requirements and exemption from some beginning courses possible by passing departmental examinations, College Board CLEP, AP. *Grading system:* A–F; pass-fail; withdraw (carries time limit); incomplete (carries time limit).

Distinctive Educational Programs: Work-experience programs. Flexible meeting places and schedules, including off-campus centers (at Beckley, 35 miles away from main institution, and at varying locations), evening classes. Cooperative baccalaureate program in business administration with Beckley College. Special facilities for using telecommunications in the classroom. Facilities for independent research, including honors programs, individual majors. Institutionally sponsored study abroad in England, Virgin Islands; Caribbean Study at Sea. *Other distinctive programs:* Board of Regents Bachelor of Arts Degree (degree completion program).

Degrees Conferred: 366 *baccalaureate*; 27 *master's*. Bachelor's degrees awarded in top five disciplines: education 90; business, management, marketing, and related support services 70; social sciences and history 50; biological/life sciences 28; psychology 25. Master's degrees awarded: education 27.

Fees and Other Expenses: *Full-time tuition per academic year 2008–09:* resident undergraduate $4,578, nonresident $10,170; contact the university for current graduate tuition. *Room and board per academic year:* $6,530. *Books and supplies:* $1,060. *Other expenses:* $2,876.

Financial Aid: Aid from institutionally generated funds is provided on the basis of academic merit, financial need, other criteria. Institution has a Program Participation Agreement with the U.S. Department of Education for eligible students to receive Pell Grants and, depending upon the agreement, other federal aid.

Financial aid to first-time, full-time undergraduate students: 95% received some for of aid.

Departments and Teaching Staff: *Total instructional faculty:* 195. Student/faculty ratio: 22:1.

Enrollment: Total enrollment 2,872. Undergraduate 2,719 (full-time 88%; female 58%, male 42%). Graduate 93 (full-time 16%). Transfer-in students 147.

Characteristics of Student Body: *Ethnic/racial makeup:* Black non-Hispanic: 6%; Asian or Pacific Islander: 2%; Hispanic: 1%; White non-Hispanic: 92%. *Age distribution:* number under 18: 150; 18–19: 1,050; 20–21: 970; 22–24: 500; 25–29: 50; 30–34: 50; 35–39: 50; 40–49: 20; 50–64: 18.

International Students: 95 nonresident aliens enrolled fall 2008. No programs available to aid students whose native language is not English. No financial aid specifically designated for international students.

Student Life: On-campus residence halls house 50% of student body. Residence halls for males constitute 46% of such space, for females 47%, for both sexes 7%. Housing available for married students. *Intercollegiate athletics:* male: baseball, basketball, bowling, football, golf, soccer, tennis, track; female: basketball, tennis, volleyball. *Special regulations:* Cars permitted without restrictions. Dormitory visitation hours vary according to residence hall. *Special services:* Learning Resources Center, medical services. *Student publications, radio: The Concordian*, a weekly newspaper; *The Pines*, a yearbook; *Reflexes*, a biannual literary magazine. Radio station WXTC broadcasts 90 hours per week. *Surrounding community:* Athens population 1,100. Served by mass transit bus system; airport 12 miles from campus; passenger rail service 20 miles from campus.

Library Collections: 143,000 volumes. 35,000 government documents; 10,200 microforms; 3,000 audiovisual materials; 645 current periodical subscriptions.

Most important holdings include West Virginia Collection (approximately 1,500 items on West Virginia history and culture).

Buildings and Grounds: Campus area 123 acres.

Chief Executive Officer: Dr. Jerry L. Beasley, President.

Address all admission inquiries to Kent Gamble, Director of Admissions.

Davis and Elkins College

100 Campus Drive
Elkins, West Virginia 26241

Tel: (304) 637-1230 **E-mail:** admiss@davisandelkins.edu
Fax: (304) 637-1800 **Internet:** www.davisandelkins.edu

Institution Description: Davis and Elkins College is a private, independent, nonprofit college affiliated with the Presbyterian Church (USA). *Enrollment:* 580. *Degrees awarded:* Associate, baccalaureate.

Member of the consortium Mountain State Association of Colleges.

Accreditation: *Regional:* NCA. *Professional*: business, nursing, theatre

History: Established, incorporated and offered first instruction at postsecondary level 1904; awarded first degree (baccalaureate) 1910. *See* Thomas Richard Ross, *Davis and Elkins College: One Hundred Years Honoring Our Traditions, Celebrating Our Future* (Cedar Rapids, Iowa, WDC Communications Inc., 2004) for further information.

Institutional Structure: *Governing board:* The Board of Trustees of Davis and Elkins College. Representation: 33 trustees, including 16 alumni, president of the college and ex officio. All voting. *Composition of institution:* Administrators 7. Academic affairs headed by vice president and dean of the faculty. Management/business/finances directed by vice president for finance and administration. Full-time instructional faculty 45. Academic governance body, The Faculty Assembly, meets an average of 8 times per year.

Calendar: Semesters (4-1-4 plan). Academic year Aug. to May. Degrees conferred July, Dec., Jan. and formal commencement May. Summer session of 3 terms from May to July.

Characteristics of Freshmen: 430 applicants (female 249, male 181). 80% of applicants accepted. 32% of accepted applicants enrolled.

Average secondary school rank of freshmen 50th percentile. Mean SAT score 480 verbal, 450 mathematical. Mean ACT Composite score 20.

31% of entering freshmen expected to graduate within 5 years. 51% of freshmen from West Virginia. Freshmen from 15 states and 4 foreign countries.

Admission: Rolling admissions plan. For fall acceptance, apply as early as completion of junior year of secondary school, but not later than Sept. 1 of year of enrollment. Early acceptance available. *Requirements:* Either graduation from accredited secondary school with 14 credits. including 4 English, 3 social science, 3 math (including algebra I, geometry, and 1 additional math), 3 natural science (including 1 lab), 1 foreign language; or GED. Minimum TOEFL score of 500 for international students. Minimum 2.0 GPA for transfer students. *Entrance tests:* College Board SAT or ACT Composite.

College credit and advanced placement for postsecondary-level work completed in secondary school and for extrainstitutional learning (life experience).

Tutoring available. Remedial courses offered during regular academic year; nondegree credit given.

Degree Requirements: *For all associate degrees:* minimum of 62 semester hours. *For all baccalaureate degrees:* minimum of 124 semester hours. *For all degrees:* 2.0 GPA; 28 hours in residence; 2 hours physical education; exit assessment examination in general education subjects.

Fulfillment of some degree requirements and exemption from some beginning courses possible by passing departmental examinations, College Board CLEP, AP. *Grading system:* A–F; pass-fail; withdraw (carries time limit).

Distinctive Educational Programs: Internships, including at the Washington Center (DC). Dual-degree programs in forestry with Syracuse University (NY). Contract degree program. Winter Term (3 weeks in January) with experiential courses, many including off-campus domestic and international travel. Student Legislative Program at West Virginia Legislature. *Other distinctive programs:* On-campus English Language and culture program for foreign students through International Language Institute of Washington (DC). Servicemembers Opportunity College.

Degrees Conferred: 60 *associate*;; 107 *baccalaureate*. Bachelor's degrees awarded in top five disciplines: business, management, marketing, and related support services 39; education 18; psychology 11; parks and recreation 9; visual and performing arts 7.

Fees and Other Expenses: *Full-time tuition per academic year 2008–09:* $20,640. *Books and supplies:* $800. *Room and board per academic year:* $6,700. *Other expenses:* $1,500.

Financial Aid: Aid from institutionally generated funds is provided on the basis of academic merit, financial need, athletic ability, other criteria.

Financial aid to full-time, first-time undergraduate students: 95% received some form of aid.

Departments and Teaching Staff: *Total instructional faculty:* 80. Student/faculty ratio: 10:1. Degrees held by full-time faculty: doctorate 64.4%, master's 33.3%. 82% hold terminal degrees.

Enrollment: Total enrollment 580 (undergraduate).

Characteristics of Student Body: *Ethnic/racial makeup:* Black non-Hispanic: 5%; American Indian or Alaska Native: 1%; Asian or Pacific Islander: 1%; Hispanic: 1%; White non-Hispanic: 69%; unknown 18%; nonresident alien 6%.

International Students: 36 nonresident aliens enrolled fall 2008. Programs available to aid students whose native language is not English: English as a Second Language Program. Financial aid specifically designated for international students: scholarships available annually for qualifying students.

Student Life: On-campus residence halls house 47% of student body. Residence halls for males constitute 45% of such space, for females 35%, for both sexes 20%. *Intercollegiate athletics:* male: baseball, basketball, cross-country, golf, skiing, soccer, tennis; female: basketball, cross-country, skiing, soccer, softball, tennis, volleyball. *Special regulations:* Cars permitted without restrictions. *Special services:* Career, Academic, Personal Services Center; writing center; seven open and departmental computer labs; medical services. *Student publications, radio: The Senator*, a weekly newspaper; *The Senatus*, a yearbook; a yearly student literary magazine. Radio station WCDE broadcasts 75 hours per week. *Surrounding community:* Elkins population 8,500. Pittsburgh (PA), 150 miles from campus, is nearest metropolitan area. Served by airport 2 miles from campus.

Library Collections: 225,000 volumes. 300,000 microforms; 14,000 audiovisual materials; 410 current periodical subscriptions. Online catalog. Students have access to the Internet at no charge.

Most important special holdings include Appalachian Region Collection (2,300 books and records); Don Marion Wolfe Collection of 150 books by and about John Milton; Pearl S. Buck Collection; Comstock Collection; Augusta Collection; local history.

Buildings and Grounds: Campus area 170 acres.

Chief Executive Officer: Dr. G. Thomas Mann, President.

Address admission inquiries to Renee T. Heckel, Director of Enrollment Management.

Fairmont State University

1201 Locust Avenue
Fairmont, West Virginia 26554-2470
Tel: (304) 367-4000 **E-mail:** admit@fscwv.edu
Fax: (304) 367-4789 **Internet:** www.fscwv.edu

Institution Description: Fairmont State University is a public institution. *Enrollment:* 4,547. *Degrees awarded:* Associate, baccalaureate. Certificates also awarded.

Academic offerings subject to approval by statewide coordinating bodies. Budget subject to approval by state governing boards.

Accreditation: *Regional:* NCA. *Professional*: medical record technology, nursing, teacher education

History: Established as The Regency of West Virginia Normal School at Fairmont 1865; chartered as Fairmont State Normal School 1867; offered first instruction at postsecondary level 1912; awarded first degree (baccalaureate) 1924; changed name to Fairmont State Teachers College 1931; achieved university status 2005.

Institutional Structure: *Governing board:* West Virginia Board of Directors. Representation: 9 regents, state superintendent of schools, 1 faculty representative. 3 ex officio. 11 voting. *Composition of institution:* Administrators 8. Academic affairs headed by academic vice president. Management/business/finances directed by vice president for finance and facilities. Student affairs directed by vice president for student affairs. Full-time instructional faculty 196. Academic governance body, Faculty Senate, meets an average of 10 times per year.

Calendar: Semesters. Academic year Aug. to May. Freshmen admitted Aug., Jan., June, July. Degrees conferred Aug., Dec., May. Formal commencement May. Summer session of 2 terms from May to July.

Characteristics of Freshmen: 2,811 applicants (female 1,464, male 1,147). 99% of applicants accepted. 59% of accepted applicants enrolled.

Mean ACT Composite scores 18.8.

36% of entering freshmen expected to graduate within 5 years. 94% of freshmen from West Virginia. Freshmen from 14 states and 6 foreign countries.

Admission: Rolling admissions plan. Early acceptance available. *Requirements:* Either graduation from accredited secondary school or GED. *Entrance tests:* College Board SAT or ACT Composite. For foreign students TOEFL. *For transfer students:* 2.0 minimum GPA; from 4-year accredited institution maximum transfer credit limited only by residence requirement; from 2-year accredited institution 72 semester hours.

College credit and advanced placement for postsecondary-level work completed in secondary school.

Tutoring available. Developmental courses offered in summer session and regular academic year; credit given.

Degree Requirements: *For all associate degrees:* 64 credit hours; 16 semester hours in residence. *For all baccalaureate degrees:* 128 credit hours; 32 semester hours in residence; 1 physical education course; distribution requirements. *For all degrees:* 2.0 GPA.

Fulfillment of some degree requirements and exemption from some beginning courses possible by passing departmental examinations, College Board CLEP, AP. *Grading system:* A–F; pass-fail (option); withdraw (carries time limit).

Distinctive Educational Programs: The university operates a separate community and technical college component. Internships. Weekend College. Evening classes. Individual majors. Unique programs include sign language interpreter; physical therapy assistant; B.S. program in nursing.

ROTC: Army.

Degrees Conferred: 672 *baccalaureate*. Bachelor's degrees awarded in top five disciplines: education 179; business, management, marketing, and related support services 142; security and protective services 56; liberal arts/general studies 55; engineering 52. Master's degrees awarded: various disciplines 65.

Fees and Other Expenses: *Full-time tuition per academic year 2008–09:* resident $5,024, nonresident $10,590. *Books and supplies:* $1,000. *Room and board per academic year:* $6,652. *Other expenses:* $2,000.

Financial Aid: Aid from institutionally generated funds is provided on the basis of academic merit, financial need, athletic ability, other criteria. Institution has a Program Participation Agreement with the U.S. Department of Education for eligible students to receive Pell Grants and, depending upon the agreement, other federal aid.

Financial aid to full-time, first-time undergraduate students: 93% received fome form of aid. Average amount of aid received: federal grants averaging $2,783; 51% state/local grants averaging $2,739; 19% institutional grants averaging $762; 19% received loans averaging $2,029.

Departments and Teaching Staff: *Total instructional faculty:* 276. Student/faculty ratio: 17.5:1. Degrees held by full-time faculty: doctorate 45%, master's 49%, baccalaureate 3%, professional 3%. 45% hold terminal degrees.

Enrollment: Total enrollment 4,547. Undergraduate 4,115 (full-time 86%; female 55%, male 45%). Graduate 432 (full-time 35%). Transfer-in students 457.

Characteristics of Student Body: *Ethnic/racial makeup:* Black non-Hispanic: 4%; Asian or Pacific Islander: 2%; Hispanic: 1%; White non-Hispanic: 92%.

International Students: 88 nonresident aliens enrolled fall 2008. Programs available to aid students whose native language is not English: social, cultural. English as a Second Language Program. Financial aid specifically designated for international students: scholarships available annually.

Student Life: On-campus residence halls house 7% of student body. *Intercollegiate athletics:* male: baseball, basketball, swimming, tennis, track; female: basketball, swimming, tennis, track, volleyball. *Special regulations:* Cars permitted without restrictions. Curfews. *Special services:* Learning Resources Center, medical services. *Student publications: The Columns*, a weekly newspaper; *The Mound*, a yearbook. *Surrounding community:* Fairmont population 24,000. Pittsburgh (PA), 75 miles from campus, is nearest metropolitan area. Served by mass transit bus system; airport 15 miles from campus.

Library Collections: 235,000 volumes including bound books, serial backfiles, electronic documents, and government documents not in separate collections. Online catalog. Current serial subscriptions: 848 paper. 34,982 microforms. Computer work stations available. Students have access to the Internet; fee-based access to online information retrieval services.

Most important special collections include English and American literature; education; social studies.

Buildings and Grounds: Campus area 80 acres.

Chief Executive Officer: Dr. Daniel J. Bradley, President.

Address admission inquiries to Director of Admissions.

Glenville State College

200 High Street
Glenville, West Virginia 26351
Tel: (304) 462-7361 **E-mail:** admissions@glenville.edu
Fax: (304) 462-8619 **Internet:** www.glenville.wvnet.edu

Institution Description: Glenville State College is a public institution. *Enrollment:* 1,443. *Degrees awarded:* Associate, baccalaureate.

Academic offerings subject to approval by statewide coordinating bodies. Budget subject to approval by state governing boards.

Accreditation: *Regional:* NCA. *Professional*: teacher education

History: Established and chartered as Glenville Branch of State Normal School 1872; changed name to Glenville State Normal School 1898; changed name to Glenville State Teachers College and offered first instruction at postsecondary level 1930; awarded first degree (baccalaureate) 1931; present name adopted 1943.

Institutional Structure: *Governing board:* West Virginia Higher Education Policy Commission. Representation: 9 regents, state superintendent of schools, 1 faculty representative appointed by Governor, 1 student representative appointed by Governor. 3 ex officio. 11 voting. *Composition of institution:* Administrators 17. Academic affairs headed by vice president for academic affairs. Management/business/finances directed by vice president for finance and administration. Full-time instructional faculty 52. Academic governance body, Faculty Administrative Organization, meets an average of 9 times per year.

Calendar: Semesters. Academic year Aug. to May. Freshmen admitted Aug., Jan., June. Degrees conferred May, July, Dec. Formal commencement May. Summer session May to July.

Characteristics of Freshmen: 1,043 applicants (femlae 423, male 620). 100% of applicants admitted. 34% of applicants admitted and enrolled.

13% (34 students) submitted SAT scores; 87% (235 students) submitted ACT scores. *25th percentile*: SAT Critical Reading 380, SAT Math 380; ACT Composite 16. *75th percentile*: SAT Critical Reading 490, SAT Math 480; ACT Composite 21.

17% of entering freshmen expected to graduate within 5 years. 84% of freshmen from West Virginia. Freshmen from 11 states and 1 foreign country.

Admission: Early acceptance available. *Requirements:* Either graduation from approved secondary school with at least a 2.0 average; completion of 4 units of English, 3 social studies including U.S. history, 2 higher mathematics, 2 laboratory science; ACT or SAT; measles immunization record (if born after 1/57). Out-of-state students must have a 2.0 average on high school work or a 17 Composite of the ACT (760 on the SAT). Consult the college catalog for details. *Entrance tests:* College Board SAT or ACT. *For transfer students:* From 4-year accredited institution 90 hours maximum transfer credit; from 2-year accredited institution 72 hours; good standing at institution previously attended. *For international students:* TOEFL score of at least 550.

College credit and advanced placement for postsecondary level work completed in secondary school. For students in Regents B.A. Program, college credit for extrainstitutional learning.

Developmental courses offered in summer session and regular academic year; nondegree credit given.

Degree Requirements: *For all associate degrees:* 64 credit hours. *For all baccalaureate degrees:* 128 credit hours; 4 hours physical education. *For all degrees:* 2.0 GPA (teacher education requires 2.25); 32 hours in residence, including 16 of last 32; demonstrated proficiency in English.

Fulfillment of some degree requirements and exemption from some beginning courses possible by passing College Board CLEP. *Grading system:* A–F; credit-no credit; audit; withdraw; incomplete (carries time limit).

Distinctive Educational Programs: Work-experience programs. Evening classes. Professional program in dentistry, forestry, medicine, teacher education, pharmacy. International Business study abroad program during spring semester (10 days in Europe).

Degrees Conferred: 38 *associate*; 188 *baccalaureate:* biological/life sciences 17; business/marketing 39; education 68; English 6; health professions and related clinical sciences 10 interdisciplinary studies 3; liberal arts/general studies 18; natural resources 11; physical sciences 3; social sciences 35.

Fees and Other Expenses: *Full-time tuition per academic year 2008–09:* resident $4,486, nonresident $10,758. *Books and supplies:* $1,000. *Room and board per academic year:* $6,150. *Other expenses:* $4,392.

Financial Aid: Aid from institutionally generated funds is provided on the basis of academic merit, financial need, athletic ability.

Financial aid to full-time, first-time undergraduate students: 83% received some form of aid. Need-based scholarships/grants totaling $3,195,888, self-help $3,880,924, parent loans $375,890; non-need-based scholarships/grants totaling $1,160,678, self-help $1,448,278, athletic awards $310,314.

Departments and Teaching Staff: *Total instructional faculty:* 78 (full-time 52, part-time 26). Student/faculty ratio: 18:1. Degrees held by full-time faculty: doctorate 30%, master's 100%. 34% hold terminal degrees.

Enrollment: Total enrollment 1,443. Undergraduate 1,443 (full-time 78%; female 44%, male 56%). Transfer-in students 90.

Characteristics of Student Body: *Ethnic/racial makeup:* Black non-Hispanic: 18%; Hispanic: 1%; White non-Hispanic: 80%; unkown 1%. *Age distribution:* number under 18: 67; 18–19: 422; 20–21: 345; 22–24: 240; 25–29: 105; 30–34: 44; 35–39: 30; 40–49: 46; 50–64: 12; 65 and over: 2.

International Students: 13 nonresident aliens enrolled fall 2008. Students from Europe, Asia; Canada. Programs available to aid students whose native language is not English: English as a Second Language Program. No financial aid specifically designated for international students.

Student Life: On-campus residence halls have a capacity to house 596 students. All unmarried students who have earned less than 58 credit hours are required to reside on campus. Organizations and clubs are available for student participation and membership. *Intercollegiate athletics:* male: basketball, football, track, cross-country, golf; female: basketball, volleyball, track, cross-country. *Special regulations:* Automobiles are permitted on campus for all students with purchase of a parking permit. Resident Assistants are employed to assist students in residence hall living and to help observe regulations such as noise restrictions. *Special services:* Career planning and placement, CLEP testing, medical services, residence hall security guards, police protection, and foundation studies courses. *Student publications: Kanawachan*, a yearbook; *Mercury*, a weekly newspaper; student congress *New Student Guide*, an annual orientation publication; *Trillium*, an annual literary magazine; *The Phoenix*, a campus newsletter. The drama department produces several plays annually. *Surrounding community:* Glenville population 2,000. Charleston, 90 miles from campus, is nearest metropolitan area.

Library Collections: 120,500 volumes. 395,500 microforms; 10,500 audiovisual materials. Current serial subscriptions. paper 133; via electronic access 13,702. 2,685 audio/videotapes; 104 DVD discs; 163 CD-ROMs. Online catalog. Computer work stations available. Students have access to online information retrieval services and the Internet.

Most important special holdings include W. W. Baron Collection (papers of former state governor, 1960–64); Bender Collection (3,411 art gallery catalogs, 1950–72); Almira Sexton Letters (family correspondence detailing life in 19th-century West Virginia); Kidd Law Collection; West Virginia Collection; Arbuckle Juvenile Collection.

Buildings and Grounds: Campus area 378 acres.

Chief Executive Officer: Dr. Peter B. Borr, President.

Address admission inquiries to Michelle L. Wicks, Director of Admissions.

Marshall University

400 Hal Greer Boulevard
Huntington, West Virginia 25755
Tel: (304) 696-3160 **E-mail:** admissions@marshall.edu
Fax: (304) 696-3135 **Internet:** www.marshall.edu

Institution Description: Marshall University is a public institution and a unit of the West Virginia University System. *Enrollment:* 13,573. *Degrees awarded:* Baccalaureate, first-professional (medicine), master's. Certificates also awarded. Associate degrees awarded by Community College of Marshall University.

Academic offering subject to approval by statewide coordinating bodies. Budget subject to approval by state governing boards.

Accreditation: *Regional:* NCA. *Professional*: business, chemistry, engineering, health information administration, journalism, medicine, music, nursing, recreation and leisure services, social work, speech-language pathology, teacher education

History: Established as Marshall Academy 1837; incorporated 1838; reincorporated as Marshall College under West Virginia conference of Methodist Episcopal Church, South, and offered first instruction at postsecondary level 1858; closed 1861; reopened and incorporated as West Virginia State Normal School 1867; awarded first degree (baccalaureate) 1921; adopted present name 1961; opened School of Medicine 1978. *See* Charles H. Moffat, *Marshall University, An Institution Comes of Age* (State College, PA: Josten's, 1981) for further information.

Institutional Structure: *Governing board:* West Virginia Board of Regents. Representation: 9 regents, state superintendent of schools, 1 faculty representative, 1 student representative. 3 ex officio. All voting. *Composition of institution:* Administrators 20. Academic affairs headed by provost. Management/business/finances directed by vice president for administration. Full-time instructional faculty 539. Academic governance body, University Council, meets an average of 9 times per year.

Calendar: Semesters. Academic year Aug. to May. Freshmen admitted Sept., Jan., June, July. Degrees conferred May, July, Aug., Dec. Formal commencement May. Summer session of 2 terms from June to Aug.

Characteristics of Freshmen: 2,405 applicants (female 1,303, male 1,102). 82% of applicants accepted. 49% of accepted applicants enrolled.

30% (172 students) submitted SAT scores; 88% (1,581 students) submitted ACT scores. *25th percentile*: SAT Critical Reading 450, SAT Math 450;; ACT Composite 20, ACT English 20, ACT Math 18. *75th percentile*: SAT Critical Reading 570, SAT Math 570; ACT Composite 25, ACT English 26, ACT Math 24.

40% of entering freshmen expected to graduate within 6 years. 84% of freshmen from West Virginia. Freshmen from 41 states 34 foreign countries.

Admission: Rolling admissions plan. For fall acceptance, apply as early as Sept. 15 of previous year, but not later than Aug. 15 of year of enrollment. Early acceptance available. *Requirements:* Either graduation from accredited secondary school or GED. Minimum 2.0 GPA. *Entrance tests:* ACT Composite for placement. For foreign students TOEFL. *For transfer students:* 2.0 minimum GPA; from 4-year accredited institution maximum transfer credit limited only by residence requirement; from 2-year accredited institution 72 semester hours; correspondence/extension students 24 semester hours.

College credit and advanced placement for postsecondary-level work completed in secondary school. College credit for extrainstitutional learning.

Tutoring available. Developmental courses offered in summer session and regular academic year; credit given.

Degree Requirements: *For all associate degrees:* 64–72 semester hours. *For all baccalaureate degrees:* 128–134 semester hours. *For all undergraduate degrees:* 2.0 GPA; 24 hours in residence; distribution requirements.

Fulfillment of some degree requirements and exemption from some beginning courses possible by College Board CLEP, AP. *Grading system:* A–F; withdraw.

Distinctive Educational Programs: Work-experience programs, including internships, cooperative education. Flexible meeting places and schedules, including off-campus centers (at West Virginia Community College, with branch campuses at Logan and Williamson, each 60 miles away from main institution, as well as 10 other extension locations throughout the state) and evening classes. Accelerated degree program. Special facilities for using telecommunications in the classroom. Interdisciplinary programs in communication arts. Facilities and programs for independent research, including honors programs, individual majors, tutorials. Regents Bachelor of Arts program awards credit for experiential learning, and permits unrestricted credit transfer throughout West Virginia state university system.

ROTC: Army.

Degrees Conferred: 100 *associate*; 1,450 *baccalaureate*; 872 *master's*; 13 *doctorate*; 46 *first-professional*. Bachelor's degrees awarded in top five disciplines: business, management, marketing, and related support services 315; education 255; liberal arts/general studies 202; health professions and related clinical sciences 105; biological/biomedical sciences 85. Master's degrees awraded: various disciplines 872. Doctorates awarded: education 13. First-professional degrees awarded: medicine 46.

Fees and Other Expenses: *Full-time tuition per academic year 2008–09:* undergraduate resident $4,748, nonresident $11,832; contact the university for current graduate and first-professional tuition and fees that vary by program. *Books and supplies:* $1,000. *Room and board per academic year:* $7,800. *Othe expenses:* $2,688.

Financial Aid: Aid from institutionally generated funds is provided on the basis of academic merit, financial need, athletic ability, other criteria.

Financial aid to full-time, first-time undergraduate students: 89% received some form of aid. Average amount of aid receifed: federal grants $3,092; Pell grants $3,035; other federal aid $1,027; state/local grants $4,123; institutional grants $2,270.

Departments and Teaching Staff: *Total instructional faculty:* 749 (full-time 458, part-time 281). Student/faculty ratio: 19:1. Degrees held by full-time faculty: doctorate 61.04%, master's 21.89%, baccalaureate .37%, professional 16.7%. 79.78% hold terminal degrees.

Enrollment: Total enrollment 13,573. Undergraduate 9,310 (full-time 83%; female 56%, male 44%). Graduate 4,263 (full-time 47%). Transfer-in students 538.

Characteristics of Student Body: *Ethnic/racial makeup:* Black non-Hispanic: 5%; Asian or Pacific Islander: 1%; Hispanic: 1%; White non-Hispanic: 86%; unknown: 5%; nonresident alien 1%.

International Students: 136 nonresident aliens enrolled fall 2008. Students from Europe, Asia, Latin America, Africa, Canada. Programs available to aid students whose native language is not English: English as a Second Language Program. No financial aid specifically designated for international students.

Student Life: On-campus residence halls house 15% of student body. Residence halls for males constitute 40% of such space, for females 50%, for both sexes 10%. 9% of males join and 5% live in fraternity housing; 11% of females join and 6% live in sorority houses. Housing available for married students. *Intercollegiate athletics:* male: baseball, basketball, cross-country, golf, rifle, soccer, tennis, track, wrestling; female: basketball, cross-country, golf, softball, tennis, track, volleyball; both sexes: swimming. *Special regulations:* Cars permitted without restrictions. Quiet hours. Residence hall visitation from 1pm to 11pm Sun.–Thurs., 1pm to 1am Fri. and Sat. *Special services:* Learning Resources Center, medical services. *Student publications, radio: Chief Justice*, a yearbook; *Et Cetera*, a quarterly literary magazine; *The Parthenon*, a newspaper published 4 days per week. Radio station WMUL-FM broadcasts 133 hours per week. *Surrounding community:* Huntington population 65,000. Columbus (OH), 150 miles from campus, is nearest metropolitan area. Served by mass transit bus system, airport 10 miles from campus, passenger rail service 1 mile from campus.

Library Collections: 428,000 volumes. 952,000 government documents; 199,000 microforms; 18,950 audiovisual materials. Current serial subscriptions: 4,165 paper; 973,255 microform; 16,337 via electronic access. Online catalog. Students have access to online information retrieval services and the Internet.

Most important special collections include the Rosanna Blake Library of Confederate History; Hoffman History of Medicine Library; West Virginia and Appalachian Materials.

Buildings and Grounds: Campus area 70 acres.

Chief Executive Officer: Dr. Stephen J. Kapp, President.

Address admission inquiries to Craig Grooms, Director of Admissions.

Graduate College Campus

100 Angus Peyton Drive
South Charleston, West Virginia 25303-1600
Tel: (800) 642-9842

Degree Programs Offered: Marshall University Graduate College was created in 1997 upon the merger of West Virginia Graduate College into Marshall University. The university is a unit of the West Virginia University System.

Mountain State University

609 South Kanawha Street
Beckley, West Virginia 25802
Tel: (866) 367-6781 **E-mail:** admissions@cwv.edu
Fax: (304) 253-3463 **Internet:** www.cwv.edu

Institution Description: The Mountain State University, formerly The College of West Virginia, provides baccalaureate and graduate education. It is is a private institution located in southern West Virginia. Branch campuses are located in Martinsburg (WV), Center Township (PA), and Orlando (FL). *Enrollment:* 5,108. *Degrees offered:* Associate, baccalaureate, master's.

Accreditation: *Regional:* NCA. *Professional*: business, diagnostic medical sonography, nursing, occupational therapy, physician assisting, respiratory therapy, surgeon assisting, social work

History: Founded 1933 as Beckley College; renamed College of West Virginia and adopted its present name upon joining the West Virginia State University System in 2000.

Calendar: Semesters. Academic year Aug. to May.

Characteristics of Freshmen: 100% of applicants accepted. 29% of accepted applicants enrolled. 2.6% (11 students) submitted SAT scores; 14.5% (61 students) submitted ACT scores. *25th percentile*: SAT Critical Reading 390, SAT Math 340; ACT Composite 16; *75th percentile*: SAT Critical Reading 450, SAT Math 460; ACT Composite 21.

18% of freshmen expected to graduate within 5 years. 74% of freshmen from West Virginia. Freshmen from 29 states and 11 foreign countries.

Admission: Open admission. Early entrance. *Requirements:* School transcript, ACT. TOEFL for international students. Test scores used for admission and counseling/placement. *For transfer students:* College transcript; interview.

College credit and advanced placement for postsecondary-level work completed in secondary school and for extrainstitutional learning.

Developmental/remedial courses offered in summer session and regular academic year.

Degree Requirements: *For all associate degrees:* 64 semester hours (18 at MSI). *For baccalaureate degrees:* 128 semester hours (30 at MSU). General education requirements; 2.0 cumulative GPA; C or better in all core requirements. Additional requirements vary by program. *Grading system:* A–F.

Distinctive Educational Programs: Culinary arts, nurse anesthesia, criminal justice, forensics.

Degrees Conferred: 160 *associate*; 707 *baccalaureate*; 259 *master's*. Bachelor's degrees awarded in top five disciplines: business, management, marketing, and related support services 133; health professions and related clinical sciences 79; multidisciplinary studies 73; security and protective services 48; public administration 29. Master's degrees awarded: various disciplines 259.

MOUNTAIN STATE UNIVERSITY—*cont'd*

Fees and Other Expenses: *Full-time tuition per academic year 2008–09:* undergraduate $6,720. Graduate school charged per credit hour; contact the university for current tuition/fees. *Books and supplies:* $1,530. *Room and board per academic year:* $6,116. *Other expenses:* $1,000.

Financial Aid: Aid from institutionally generated funds is provided on the basis of academic merit, financial need, athletic ability.

Institution has a Program Participation Agreement with the U.S. Department of Education for eligible students to receive Pell Grants and, depending upon the agreement, other federal aid.

Financial aid to full-time, first-time undergraduate students: 62% received some form of aid. Average amount of aid received: federal grants $3,374; Pell grants $3,164; other federal aid $280; state/local grants $3,048; institutional grants $3,731.

Departments and Teaching Staff: *Total instructional faculty:* 368 (full-time 87, part-time 281). Student/faculty ratio: 20:1. Degrees held by full-time faculty: doctorate 39%, master's 42%, baccalaureate 19%. 96 hold terminal degrees.

Enrollment: Total enrollment 5,108. Undergraduate 4,378 (full-time 73%; female 66%, male 34%). Graduate 730 (full-time 93%). Transfer-in students 619.

Characteristics of Student Body: *Ethnic/racial makeup:* Black non-Hispanic: 11%; Asian or Pacific Islander: 1%; Hispanic: 2%; White non-Hispanic: 85%; unknown: 11%; nonresident alien 8%.

International Students: 409 nonresident aliens enrolled fall 2008. Students from Europe, Asia, Latin America, Africa, Canada. Programs available to aid students whose native language is not English: English as a Second Language Program. No financial aid specifically designated for international students.

Student Life: *Student services:* Counseling. Various student activities.

Library Collections: 114,000 volumes including bound books, serial backfiles, electronic documents, and government documents not in separate collections. Online catalog. 2,000 microforms; 4,000 audiovisual materials; 178 current serial subscriptions. Computer work stations avaialble. Students have access to the Internet at no charge.

Most important special collections include: medical books for physician assistant program; art; West Virginia Collection.

Buildings and Grounds: Campus area 4 acres.

Chief Executive Officer: Dr. Charles H. Polk, President.

Address admissions inquiries to Tony England, Director of Recruiting Services.

Ohio Valley University

1 Campus View Drive
Vienna, West Virginia 26105
Tel: (304) 865-6000 **E-mail:** admissions@ovu.edu
Fax: (304) 865-6001 **Internet:** www.ovu.edu

Institution Description: Ohio Valley University is a private, independent institution affiliated with Churches of Christ. *Enrollment:* 515. *Degrees awarded:* Associate, baccalaureate.

Accreditation: *Regional:* NCA.

History: Established and chartered 1958; offered first instruction 1960; awarded first associate degree 1962 and first baccalaureate degree 1983; consolidated with Northeastern Christian Junior College 1993; achieved university status 2001.

Institutional Structure: *Governing board:* 26 member Board of Trustees. *Composition of institution:* Administrators 10. Academic affairs headed by provost. Business/finance and auxiliary enterprises directed by vice president for finance. Full-time instructional faculty 25.

Calendar: Semesters. Academic year Aug. to May. Degrees conferred May. Summer mini-session in May.

Characteristics of Freshmen: 559 applicants (female 320, male 239). 55% of applicants accepted. 38% of accepted applicants enrolled.

25th percentile: SAT Critical Reading 510, SAT Math 480; ACT Composite 17. *75th percentile*: SAT Critical Reading 590, SAT Math 540; ACT Composite 23, ACT English 24, ACT Math 24.

30% of entering freshmen graduating within 5 years. 27% of freshmen from West Virginia. Freshmen from 14 states and 2 foreign countries.

Admission: Rolling admissions plan. *Requirements:* Either graduation from accredited secondary school with 15 units, 12 of which are in academic subjects; or GED. *Entrance tests:* College Board SAT or ACT Composite. Entry level program designed to prepare academically under prepared students for college work. 1st year students who score below 18 on their ACT in English, math, or reading will be enrolled in an entry-level course for that area.

Degree Requirements: *For all associate degrees:* Candidates must complete 64 hours with minimum GPA of 2.0; 32 hours must be taken in residence and at least 20 of the last 32 hours must be taken on campus. *For all baccalaureate degrees:* Candidates must complete 128 hours, 40 of which must be upper level; minimum 2.0 GPA; 32 hours must be taken on campus and 24 of last 32 hours must be taken on campus.

Distinctive Educational Programs: Personal and Academic Skill Development class for students whose ACT Composite scores are below 18 in order to better prepare them for college work. Counseling Center available for students on a walk-in basis. Computer Center with 24 work stations. On campus satellite television network. International studies program during summer.

Degrees Conferred: 14 *associate;* 109 *baccalaureate:* business and management 57; education 22; liberal arts 6; philosophy/religion/theology 11; psychology 13.

Fees and Other Expenses: *Full-time tuition per academic year 2008–09:* $18,990. *Required fees:* $1,272. *Room and board per academic year:* $6,324. *Books and supplies:* $1,000. *Other expenses:* $2,000.

Financial Aid: Aid from institutionally generated funds is provided on the basis of academic merit, financial need, athletic ability, other criteria.

Financial aid to full-time, first-time undergraduate students: 87% received some form of aid. Need-based scholarships/grants totaling $1,9997,539, self-help $1,866,498; non-need-based scholarships/grants totaling $334,021, self-help $502,356, parent loans $1,891,850, athletic awards $596,749.

Departments and Teaching Staff: *Total instructional faculty:* 59 (full-time 26, part-time 33). Total faculty with doctorate, first-professional, or other terminal degree: 15. Student/faculty ratio: 12:1. Degrees held by full-time faculty: doctorate 63%, master's 37%. 63% hold terminal degrees.

Enrollment: Total enrollment 515 (undergraduate).

Characteristics of Student Body: *Ethnic/racial makeup:* Black non-Hispanic: 4%; Hispanic: 3%; White non-Hispanic: 83%; nonresident alien 9%.

International Students: 45 nonresident aliens enrolled fall 2008. Students from Europe, Asia, Latin America, Africa, Canada. Programs available to aid students whose native language is not English: English as a Second Language Program. No financial aid specifically designated for international students.

Student Life: Residence students comprise 55% of the student body. *Intercollegiate athletics (NCWA 2nd division):* male: basketball, baseball, soccer; female: basketball, soccer, softball, volleyball. *Student publications: Highlander*, a student newspaper; *Vallerian*, a student yearbook. *Surrounding community:* Parkersburg area population 60,000.

Publications: *Horizon*, a quarterly newspaper, is the college's main publication for constituents.

Library Collections: 35,000 volumes. 52,000 microform; 3,000 audiovisual materials; 165 current periodical subscriptions. Online catalog. Computer work stations available. Students have access to the Internet; online information retrieval services available.

Buildings and Grounds: South campus area 126 acres; north campus area 134 acres.

Chief Executive Officer: Dr. James A. Johnson, President.

Address admission inquiries to Robert Dudley, Director of Admissions.

Salem International University

223 West Main Street
P.O. Box 500
Salem, West Virginia 26426-0500
Tel: (304) 782-5389 **E-mail:** admiss@salemiu.edu
Fax: (304) 782-5395 **Internet:** www.salemiu.edu

Institution Description: Salem International University, formerly Salem-Teikyo University, is a private, independent, nonprofit college. *Enrollment:* 574. *Degrees awarded:* Baccalaureate, master's.

Member of Mountain State Association of Colleges.

Accreditation: *Regional:* NCA.

History: Established and incorporated as Salem Academy 1888; offered first instruction at postsecondary level and adopted present name 1890; awarded first degree (baccalaureate) 1894; added graduate program 1979; adopted present name 2002.

Institutional Structure: *Governing board:* Salem International University Board of Trustees. Extrainstitutional representation: university president and 8 extrainstitutional representative. All voting. Board of Directors with university president and 14 extrainstitutional representatives. All voting. *Composition of institution:* Administrators 6. Academic affairs headed by vice president for academic affairs/provost. Management/business/finances directed by vice president for finance, admissions, and auxiliary services. Full-time instructional faculty 50. Academic governance body, the faculty, meets an average of 8 times per year.

Calendar: 18-day module. 12 modules per year. Academic year July to June. Freshmen admitted year round. Degrees conferred May, Aug., Dec. Formal commencement May.

Characteristics of Freshmen: 49% of entering freshmen expected to graduate within 5 years.

Mean SAT scores 515 verbal, 502 mathematical. Mean ACT Composite score 22.

28% of freshmen from West Virginia. Freshmen from 24 states and 4 foreign countries.

Admission: Rolling admissions plan. For fall acceptance, apply as early as June of previous year, but not later than Aug. of year of enrollment. Early acceptance available. *Requirements:* Either graduation from accredited secondary school with 16 units (11 in academic subjects) which are recommended to include 4 English, 1 history, 1 mathematics; or GED. Minimum 2.0 GPA. *Entrance tests:* ACT Composite preferred; College Board SAT accepted. *For transfer students:* 2.0 minimum GPA; from 4-year and 2-year accredited institutions maximum transfer credit limited only by residence requirement; correspondence/extension students 32 hours.

College credit and advanced placement for postsecondary level work completed in secondary school and for USAFI.

Tutoring available. Developmental courses offered in summer session and regular academic year; credit given.

Degree Requirements: *For all associate degrees:* 64–66 credit hours. *For all baccalaureate degrees:* 128 credit hours. *For all degrees:* 2.0 GPA; 32 hours, including last 16 in residence; general education requirements.

Fulfillment of some degree requirements and exemption from some beginning courses possible by passing College Board CLEP, AP. *Grading system:* A–F; pass-fail.

Distinctive Educational Programs: Undergraduate/graduate programs in molecular biology/biotechnology in equine careers in industry and management (grad-level education specialization); undergraduate programs in Japanese studies and aviation management. Study abroad. International internships.

Degrees Conferred: 46 *baccalaureate.* Bachelor's degrees awarded in top five disciplines: business, management, marketing, and related support services 11; security and protective services 8; biomedical/biological sciences 7; education 6; communication, journalism, and related programs 5. Master's degrees awarded: various disciplines 158.

Fees and Other Expenses: *Full-time tuition per academic year 2008–09:* undergraduate $14,000. Graduate tuition charged by the credit hour; contact the university for current rate. *Books and supplies:* $1,700. *Room and board per academic year:* $6,400. *Other expenses:* $2,500.

Financial Aid: Aid from institutionally generated funds is provided on the basis of academic merit, financial need, athletic ability. Institution has a Program Participation Agreement with the U.S. Department of Education for eligible students to receive Pell Grants and, depending upon the agreement, other federal aid.

Financial aid to full-time, first-time undergraduate students: 100 received some form of aid.

Departments and Teaching Staff: *Total instructional faculty:* 51. Student/faculty ratio: 15:1. Degrees held by full-time faculty: doctorate 76%, master's 24%. 76% hold terminal degrees.

Enrollment: Total enrollment 574. Undergraduate 312 (full-time 100%; female 49%, male 51%). Gradaute 262. Transfer-in students 71.

Characteristics of Student Body: *Ethnic/racial makeup:* Black non-Hispanic: 15%; American Indian or Alaska Native: 1%; Hispanic: 4%; White non-Hispanic: 49%; unknown: 17%; nonresident alien 13%.

International Students: 280 nonresident aliens enrolled fall 2008. Students from Europe, Asia, Latin America, Canada, Australia. Programs available to aid students whose native language is not English: social, cultural. English as a Second Language Program. No financial aid specifically designated for international students.

Student Life: On-campus residence halls house 70% of student body. Residence halls for males constitute 40% of such space, for females 30%, for both sexes 30%. 10% of males join fraternities; 20% of females join sororities. *Intercollegiate athletics:* male: basketball, tennis, swimming, cheerleading, equestrian; female: softball, volleyball; men only: baseball, soccer, rugby, golf. *Special regulations:* Registered cars permitted on campus in designated parking areas. Quiet hours from 11pm to 11am. *Special services:* Learning Resources Center, medical services, free peer tutoring. *Student publications, radio, television: Dirigo*, a yearbook; *Green and White*, a newspaper. On-campus: closed circuit radio and tv. *Surrounding community:* Salem population 3,000. Pittsburgh (PA), 100 miles from campus, is nearest metropolitan area. Served by mass transit bus system, airport 15 miles from campus.

Library Collections: 180,000 volumes. 7,300 government documents; 285,000 microforms; 1,000 audiovisual materials; 94 serial subscriptions. Online catalog. Students have access to online information retrieval services and the Internet.

Most important special holdings include collections on aviation; equestrian; Japanese collection.

Buildings and Grounds: Campus area 130 acres.

Chief Executive Officer: Dr. R. John Reynolds, President.

Address admission inquiries to Christine E. Howerton, Director of Admissions.

Shepherd University

P.O. Box 3210

Shepherdstown, West Virginia 25443-3210

Tel: (304) 876-5000 **E-mail:** admissions@shepherd.edu

Fax: (304) 876-3101 **Internet:** www.shepherd.edu

Institution Description: Shepherd University is a public institution. *Enrollment:* 4,185. *Degrees awarded:* Baccalaureate, master's. Academic offers subject to approval by statewide coordinating bodies. Budget subject to approval by state governing boards.

Accreditation: *Regional:* NCA. *Professional*: music, nursing, social work, teacher education

History: Established, chartered, incorporated, and offered first instruction at postsecondary level as Shepherd College 1871; changed name to Shepherd State Normal School 1872; awarded first degree (baccalaureate) 1879; readopted name Shepherd College 1948; achieved university status 2006.

Institutional Structure: *Governing board:* Board of Governors. *Composition of institution:* Administrators 7. Academic affairs headed by vice president. Management/business/finances directed by vice president for administration and finance. Full-time instructional faculty 120. Academic governance body, Faculty Senate, meets an average of 18 times per year.

Calendar: Semesters. Academic year Aug. to May. Freshmen admitted Aug., Jan., May, July. Degrees conferred May, Dec. formal commencement May. Summer session of 2 terms from May to Aug.

Characteristics of Freshmen: 1,611 applicants (female 848, male 763). 83% of applicants admitted. 45% of applicants admitted and enrolled.

48% (337 students) submitted SAT scores; 49% (341 students) submitted ACT scores. *25th percentile*: SAT Critical Reading 480, SAT Math 460; ACT Composite 19, ACT English 17, ACT Math 19. *75th percentile*: SAT Critical Reading 570, SAT Math 550; ACT Composite 24, ACT English 23, ACT Math 25.

38% of entering freshmen expected to graduate within 5 years. 55% of freshmen from West Virginia. Freshmen from 13 states and 6 foreign countries.

Admission: Rolling admissions plan. Apply by Nov. 15 for early admission. Early acceptance available. *Requirements:* Either graduation from accredited secondary school with 4 units English, 3 mathematics, 3 science, 3 social studies, 1 physical education, 7 electives; or GED. Additional units in foreign language and mathematics recommended. Minimum 2.0 GPA. *Entrance tests:* ACT Composite or SAT. *For transfer students:* 2.0 minimum GPA.

Advanced placement and international baccalaureate accepted. For students in Regents BA program, college credit and advanced placement for extrainstitutional learning (life experience) on basis of West Virginia Board of Regents guidelines.

Degree Requirements: *For all baccalaureate degrees:* 128 credit hours; 2 hours physical education; 2.0 GPA; 32 hours in residence; distribution requirements; 2.50 GPA for education majors.

Fulfillment of some degree requirements and exemption from some beginning courses possible by passing departmental examinations, College Board CLEP, AP. *Grading system:* A–F; pass-fail; withdraw; incomplete (carries time limit).

Distinctive Educational Programs: Work-experience programs. Evening classes. Accelerated degree programs. Special facilities for using telecommunications in the classroom. Preprofessional programs including pharmacy, physical therapy, theology. Credit transfer agreement with 24 community and 2-year colleges in West Virginia, Maryland, and Virginia. Regents Bachelor of Arts Program, a degree-program for mature students. Servicemembers Opportunity College.

Degrees Conferred: 65 *associate;* 553 *baccalaureate:* biological sciences 14; business and management 89; communications 20; computer and information sciences 37; education 91; English 7; health professions 43; home economics 6; liberal arts 74; mathematics 3; natural resources 9; parts and recreation 42; physical sciences 7; public administration 13; psychology 19; social sciences and history 50; visual and performing arts 38. Master's degrees awarded: business/marketing 26, education 22.

Fees and Other Expenses: *Full-time tuition per academic year 2008–09:* undergraduate resident $4,898, nonresident $12,812; contact the university for current graduate tuition. *Room and board per academic year:* $8,938. *books and supplies:* $1,000. *Other expenses:* $2,000.

SHEPHERD UNIVERSITY—*cont'd*

Financial Aid: The college offers a direct lending program. Aid from institutionally generated funds is provided on the basis of academic merit, financial need, athletic ability, other criteria.

Financial aid to full-time, first-time undergraduate students: 77% received some form of aid. Average amount of aid received: federal grants $3,220; Pell grants $2,782; other fedeal aid $915; state/local grants $3,948; institutional grants $3,220.

Departments and Teaching Staff: *Total instructional faculty:* 288 (full-time 116, part-time 172). Total faculty with doctorate, first-professional, or other terminal degree: 136. Student/faculty ratio: 19:1. Degrees held by full-time faculty: doctorate 59%, master's 37%, baccalaureate 1%, professional 3%. 66% hold terminal degrees.

Enrollment: Total enrollment 4,185. Undergraduate 4,044 (full-time 78%; female 57%, male 43%). Graduate 141 (full-time 28%). Transfer-in students 335.

Characteristics of Student Body: *Ethnic/racial makeup:* Black non-Hispanic: 5%; American Indian or Alaska Native: 1%; Asian or Pacific Islander: 2%; Hispanic: 2%; White non-Hispanic: 87%; unknown: 3%. *Age distribution:* number under 18: 150; 18–19: 1,134; 20–21: 1,034; 22–24: 855; 25–29: 492; 30–34: 351; 35–39: 266; 40–49: 519; 50–64: 335; 65 and over: 15. 10% of student body attend summer sessions.

International Students: 26 nonresident aliens enrolled fall 2008. Students from Europe, Asia, Latin America, Africa, Canada. No programs available to aid students whose native language is not English. No financial aid specifically designated for international students.

Student Life: On-campus residence halls house 33% of student body. All residence halls are co-ed by wing. *Intercollegiate athletics:* male: baseball, basketball, football, soccer, tennis; female: basketball, softball, tennis, volleyball; male and female: golf, cross-country. *Special regulations:* Registered cars permitted without restrictions. *Special services:* Learning Resources Center, medical services, disability support services, counseling center. *Student publications, radio: Picket*, a monthly newspaper; *Sans Merci*, an annual literary magazine. Radio station WSHC broadcasts 80 hours per week. *Surrounding community:* Shepherdstown population 2,500. Washington (D.C.), 65 miles from campus, is nearest metropolitan area. Served by passenger rail service 8 miles from campus.

Library Collections: 168,630 volumes. 132,919 government documents; 137,765 microforms; 11,556 audiovisual materials. Current periodical subscriptions: 516 paper; 8 microform; 8,986 via electronic access. Computer work stations available. Online catalog. Students have access to the Internet at no charge; online information retrieval services available.

Most important special holdings include West Virginia Collection; Folk Collection (regional history); Educational Curriculum Library.

Buildings and Grounds: Campus area 325 acres.

Chief Executive Officer: Dr. David L. Dunlop, President. Address admission inquiries to Kimberly Scranage, Director of Admissions; graduate inquiries to Michael Austin, Dean of Graduate Studies.

University of Charleston

2300 MacCorkle Avenue
Charleston, West Virginia 25304
Tel: (304) 357-4750 **E-mail:** gouc@ucwv.edu
Fax: (304) 357-4781 **Internet:** www.ucwv.edu

Institution Description: The University of Charleston is a private, independent, nonprofit institution. *Enrollment:* 1,435. *Degrees awarded:* Associate, baccalaureate, master's.

Accreditation: *Regional:* NCA. *Professional*: athletic training, nursing, radiography, respiratory therapy, teacher education

History: Established as Barboursville Seminary and offered first instruction at postsecondary level 1888; incorporated under West Virginia Conference of the Methodist Church, South and changed name to Barboursville College 1889; awarded first degree (baccalaureate) 1891; changed name to Morris Harvey College 1901; became independent 1941; revised charter and adopted present name 1979. *See* Frank Krebs, *Where There Is Faith: The MHC Story* (Charleston: Morris Harvey College Press, 1974) for further information.

Institutional Structure: *Governing board:* Board of Trustees. Representation: 37 trustees, including president of the university ex officio. All voting. *Composition of institution:* Administrators 6. Academic affairs headed by dean. Management/business/finances directed by vice president for administration and finance. Full-time instructional faculty 71. Academic governance body, the faculty, meets an average of 10 times per year.

Calendar: Semesters. Academic year Aug. to May. Freshmen admitted Aug., Jan., May. Degrees conferred Aug., Dec., May. Formal commencement May and Dec. Summer session from May to Aug.

Characteristics of Freshmen: 1,647 applicants (female 1,006, male 641). 72% of applicants admitted. 45% of applicants admitted and enrolled.

30% (96 students) submitted SAT scores; 82% (256 students) submitted ACT scores. *25th percentile*: SAT Critical Reading 430, SAT Math 420; ACT Composite 19, ACT English 19, ACT Math 18. *75th percentile*: SAT Critical Reading 540, SAT Math 560; ACT Composite 25, ACT English 25, ACT Math 24.

43% of entering freshmen expected to graduate within 5 years. 63% of freshmen from West Virginia. Freshmen from 19 states and 9 foreign countries.

Admission: Rolling admissions plan. For fall acceptance, apply as early as Aug. 30 of previous year. Apply by Jan. 1 for early decision; must limit application to Charleston. Early acceptance available. *Requirements:* Either graduation from accredited secondary school with 15 academic units, GPA 2.25, or GED. Recommend distribution from among English, mathematics, natural sciences, social studies. *Entrance tests:* College Board SAT or ACT Composite. For foreign students TOEFL or other demonstrated proficiency in English. *For transfer students:* 2.0 minimum GPA; from 4-year accredited institution 96 semester hours maximum transfer credit; from 2-year accredited institution 64 hours.

College credit and advanced placement for postsecondary-level work completed in secondary school. College credit for extrainstitutional learning on basis of portfolio and faculty assessment, USAFI, Federal Aviation Administration coursework by certified air controller specialists, coursework from West Virginia State Police Academy.

Tutoring available. Remedial courses offered during regular academic year; credit given.

Degree Requirements: *For all associate degrees:* 60 semester hours; 20 hours in residence. *For all baccalaureate degrees:* 120 hours; 32 hours in residence, 2 credit hours of health; distribution requirements; comprehensives in individual fields of study. *For all undergraduate degrees:* 2.0 GPA; general education requirements.

Fulfillment of some degree requirements and exemption from some beginning courses possible by passing departmental examinations, College Board CLEP, AP. *Grading system:* A–F; pass-fail; withdraw (deadline after which pass-fail is appended to withdraw).

Distinctive Educational Programs: Programs emphasizing leadership and service. Integrated, interdisciplinary curriculum. Online courses. Work-experience programs, including cooperative education and internships. Special facilities for using telecommunications in the classroom. Facilities and programs for independent research, individualized majors. *Other distinctive programs:* Environmental science, interior design, sports medicine, information technology.

Degrees Conferred: 26 *associate;* 119 *baccalaureate:* biological/life sciences 8; business, management, marketing, and related support services 30; communications/journalism 6; computer and information sciences 9; education 4; health professions and related clinical sciences 27; liberal arts/general studies 3; natural resources 2; parks and recreation 13; psychology 7; ; social sciences 2; visual and performing arts 8. Master's degrees awarded: business/marketing 42.

Fees and Other Expenses: *Full-time tuition per academic year 2008–09:* $23,150 undergraduate; contact the university for current graduate tuition. *Room and board per academic year:* $8,325. *Books and supplies:* $1,200. *Other expenses:* $750.

Financial Aid: Aid from institutionally generated funds is provided on the basis of academic merit, financial need, athletic ability, other criteria.

Financial aid to full-time, first-time undergraduate students: 75% received some form of aid. Need-based scholarships/grants totaling $2,400,000, self-help $5,000,000; parent loans $539,508, tuition waivers $510,645, athletic awards $1,895,894.

Departments and Teaching Staff: *Total instructional faculty:* 76 (full-time 71, part-time 5). Student/faculty ratio: 11.5:1. Degrees held by full-time instructional faculty: doctorate 37%, master's 89%, baccalaureate 100%, professional 9%. 72% hold terminal degrees.

Enrollment: Total enrollment 1,435. Undergraduate 1,122 (full-time 96%; female 58%, male 42%). Graduate 313 (full-time 97%). Trransfer-in student 76.

Characteristics of Student Body: *Ethnic/racial makeup:* Black non-Hispanic: 7%; Asian or Pacific Islander: 1%; Hispanic: 1%; White non-Hispanic: 58%; unknown: 23%; nonresident alien 10%. *Age distribution:* number under 18: 57; 18–19: 311; 20–21: 213; 22–24: 150; 25–29: 68; 30–34: 31; 35–39: 28; 40–49: 31; 50–64: 8; 65 and over: 2.

International Students: 14 nonresident aliens enrolled fall 2008. Students from Europe, Asia, Latin America, Africa, Canada, Middle East. Programs available to aid students whose native language is not English: social, cultural. English as a Second Language Program. Some financial aid specifically designated for international students.

Student Life: On-campus residence halls house 20% of on-campus student body. *Intercollegiate athletics:* male: basketball, crew, cross-country, soccer, swimming, tennis, golf, baseball; female: basketball, crew, cross-country, soccer, softball, swimming, tennis, volleyball. *Special regulations:* Cars permitted without restrictions. Freshmen required to live on campus or with parents. *Special services:* Learning Resources Center, freshmen monitoring program, free on-campus counseling, free weekend shuttle van, Computer Center/Apple Lab, Sports Medicine Clinic, indoor pool. *Student publications:* Weekly newspaper, annual literary magazine, yearbook. *Surrounding community:* Charleston population 65,000. Columbus (OH), 200 miles from campus, is nearest metropolitan area. Served by mass transit bus system; airport 10 miles from campus; Amtrak passenger rail service 1 mile from campus.

Library Collections: 170,458 volumes. 121,500 microforms; 1,656 audiovisual materials; Current periodical subscriptions: paper 238; via electronic access 14,500. Online catalog. Computer work stations available. Students have access to online information retrieval services and the Internet. Total 2008–09 budget for books and materials: $60,000.

Most important holdings include Gorman Civil War Collection; Kendall Vintoroux Political Cartoons; James David Barber Collection on Political Biography.

Buildings and Grounds: Campus area 39 acres. Campus DVD available.

Chief Executive Officer: Dr. Edwin H. Welch, President.

Address admission inquiries to Brad Parrish, Vice President for Enrollment and Student Life.

West Liberty State College

P.O. Box 295

West Liberty, West Virginia 26074-0295

Tel: (304) 336-5000 **E-mail:** wladmsn1@wlsc.edu

Fax: (304) 336-8540 **Internet:** www.wlsc.edu

Institution Description: West Liberty State College is a public institution. *Enrollment:* 2,513. *Degrees awarded:* Associate, baccalaureate.

Academic offerings subject to approval by statewide coordinating bodies. Budget subject to approval by state governing board.

Accreditation: *Regional:* NCA. *Professional*: dental hygiene, music, nursing, teacher education

History: Chartered as West Liberty Academy 1837; changed name to West Liberty State Normal School and offered first instruction at postsecondary level 1870; changed name to West Liberty State Teachers College and awarded first degree (baccalaureate) 1931; adopted present name 1943. *See* Frank T. Reuter, *West Liberty State College: The First 125 Years* (Wheeling, WV: Boyd Press, 1963) for further information.

Institutional Structure: *Governing board:* West Virginia Central Office of Higher Education: Board of Directors. The West Virginia State College System is governed by a 17-member Board of Directors consisting of 12 citizens appointed by the governor, the Chancellor of the University of West Virginia System and the State Superintendent of Schools (who serve ex officio), and an elected representative from each of the advisory councils of students, staff, and faculty. The chancellor serves as the chief executive officer for the system; a president as the chief executive officer for each institution. The president reports to the Board through the Chancellor. *Composition of institution:* Administrators 24. Academic affairs headed by the provost and vice president for academic affairs; Management/business/finances directed by vice president of administration and finance. Full-time instructional faculty 108. Academic governance body, Faculty Senate, meets monthly.

Calendar: Semesters. Academic year Aug. to May. Freshmen admitted Aug., Jan., June, July. Degrees conferred May, Aug., Dec. Formal commencements May, Dec. Summer session of 3 terms.

Characteristics of Freshmen: 1,809 applicants (female 1,004, male 805). 98% of applicants accepted. 45% of accepted applicants enrolled.

13.4% (62 students) submitted SAT scores; 86.6% (401 students) submitted ACT scores. *25th percentile*: SAT Critical Reading 400, SAT Math 390; ACT Composite 17. ACT English 17,ACT Math 15. *75th p percentile*: SAT Critical Reading 500, SAT Math 490; ACT Composite 22m ACT English 22, ACT Math 20.

78% of entering freshmen expected to graduate within 5 years. 70% of freshmen from West Virginia. Freshmen from 13 states.

Admission: All admission credentials must be received at least two weeks prior to the opening of the semester or summer term. *Requirements:* Graduation from accredited secondary school with a cumulative GPA of at least 2.0 or make a composite standard score of at least 17 on the Enhanced American College Test (ACT) or a minimum combined verbal/math score of 810 on the SAT. Applications should be submitted during the first semester of the senior year in high school. In addition to the above, freshmen must have completed 4 units English, 3 social studies, 2 mathematics, 2 laboratory science; strongly recommended: 2 foreign language. *Entrance tests:* ACT or SAT. *For transfer students:* 2.0 minimum GPA; from 4-year accredited institution 92 hours maximum transfer credit; from 2-year accredited institution 72 hours. Transfer credit available for correspondence/extension students.

College credit for postsecondary-level work completed in secondary school. For students in Regents BA Program college credit for extrainstitutional learning (life experience) on basis of faculty assessment.

Tutoring available. Developmental courses offered during regular academic year; credit given.

Degree Requirements: *For all associate degrees:* 64 credit hours; 32 hours in residence. *For all baccalaureate degrees:* 128 credit hours; 36 hours in residence; general education requirements. *For all degrees:* 2.0 GPA.

Fulfillment of some degree requirements and exemption from some beginning courses possible by passing departmental examinations, College Board CLEP, APP (score of 3). *Grading system:* A–F; pass-fail; withdraw (carries time limit).

Distinctive Educational Programs: Evening classes. Accelerated degree programs. Cooperative baccalaureate program in medical technology with Ohio Valley Medical Center. Special facilities for using telecommunications in the classroom. Interdisciplinary program in communications. Preprofessional programs including engineering, optometry, pharmacy. Facilities for independent research, including honors programs, individual majors. *Other distinctive programs:* Early entrance program for qualified high school students. Regents Bachelor of Arts, a nontraditional degree program for adults. Academic Common Market allows West Virginia residents reduced graduate school tuition at participating out-of-state institutions. Contract programs provide similar opportunities for students in architecture, optometry, podiatry, veterinary medicine. Cooperative baccalaureate program in nursing with Ohio Valley Medical Center, Inc.

Degrees Conferred: 31 *associate;* 436 *baccalaureate:* biological sciences 12, business and management 104, communications 15, education 89, English 1, fine and applied arts 1, health professions 81, liberal arts 23, parks and recreation 11, physical sciences 3, protective services/public administration 57, psychology 16, social sciences and history 13, other 9.

Fees and Other Expenses: *Full-time tuition per academic year 2008–09:* resident $4,464, nonresident $10,896. *Room and board per academic year:* $8,282. *Books and supplies:* $1,200. *Other expenses:* $3,250.

Financial Aid: The college offers a direct lending program. Aid from institutionally generated funds is provided on the basis of academic merit, financial need, athletic ability, other criteria.

Financial aid to full-time, first-time undergraduate students: 99% received some form of aid. Average amount of aid received: federal grants $2,005; Pell grants $2,837; other federal aid $343; state/local grants #3,557; institutional grants $3,896.

Departments and Teaching Staff: *Total full-time instructional faculty:* 156. Student/faculty ratio: 18:1. Degrees held by full-time faculty: doctorate 44%, master's 56%. 44% hold terminal degrees.

Enrollment: Total enrollment 2,523. Undergraduate 2,495 (full-time 84%; female 57%; male 43%). Graduate 18 (full-time 100%). Transfer-in students 236.

Characteristics of Student Body: *Ethnic/racial makeup:* Black non-Hispanic: 4%; Asian or Pacific Islander: 1%; Hispanic: 1%; White non-Hispanic: 93%; unknown 1%.

International Students: 12 nonresident aliens enrolled fall 2008. Students from Europe, Asia, Africa, Canada, Australia. No programs available to aid students whose native language is not English. No financial aid specifically designated for international students.

Student Life: On-campus residence halls house 43% of student body. Residence halls for males constitute 50% of such space, for females 50%. *Intercollegiate athletics:* male: baseball, basketball, cross-country, football, golf, tennis, track; female: basketball, cross-country, golf, softball, tennis, track, volleyball. *Special regulations:* Registered cars permitted without restrictions. *Special services:* Learning Resources Center, medical services. *Student publications: The Trumpet*, a weekly newspaper. *Surrounding community:* West Liberty population 1,000. Pittsburgh (PA), 40 miles from campus, is nearest metropolitan area.

Library Collections: 196,000 volumes including bound books, serial backfiles, electronic documents, and government documents not in separate collections. Online catalog. 131,000 microforms; 480 current serial subscriptions. Computer work stations available. Students have access to the Internet at no charge.

Most important special holdings include archives; Nelle Krise Rare Book Collection; Henry Lash Sheet Music; College Archives.

Buildings and Grounds: Campus area 291 acres.

Chief Executive Officer: Dr. John F.. McCullough, President.

Address admission inquiries to Brenda King, Director of Admissions.

West Virginia School of Osteopathic Medicine

400 North Lee Street
Lewisburg, West Virginia 24901
Tel: (800) 356-7836 **E-mail:** admissions@wvsom.edu
Fax: (304) 645-4859 **Internet:** www.wvsom.edu

Institution Description: The West Virginia School of Osteopathic Medicine is a self-standing, public, professional college offering a four-year osteopathic medical education. It is unit of the West Virginia University System. The curricular emphasis is on rural, primary care medicine. *Enrollment:* 363. *Degrees awarded:* First-professional.

Accreditation: *Professional*: osteopathy

History: Established 1972 as private Greenbrier College of Osteopathic Medicine; accepted first students 1974; brought into West Virginia public system of higher education 1976; awarded first degree (first-professional) 1978.

Institutional Structure: *Internal governing body:* President, dean for academic affairs, dean for service and research. Institutional Board of Advisors: 7 lay members, 4 institutional representatives. Full-time instructional faculty 23.

Calendar: 4-year curriculum consists of 10-month first year, 11-month second, third, and fourth year program. Semesters.

Admission: Deadline for application through American Association of Colleges of Osteopathic Medicine application service: Feb. 15. *Requirements:* 90 semester hours or three-fourths of the credits required for a baccalaureate degree from an accredited college or university; minimum course requirements include a complete course (6-8 semester hours or equivalent) in each of English, biology (general biology or zoology), physics, inorganic chemistry, organic chemistry.

Degree Requirements: *For first-professional degree:* 21 years of age; in residence for 4 academic years at an accredited college of osteopathic medicine or equivalent, the last two of which must have been at WVSOM; successful completion of all academic preclinical and clinical work; has taken Part I of the National Board of Examiners for Osteopathic Physicians and Surgeons; has demonstrated ethical, personal, and professional qualities deemed necessary for the continued successful study and practice of Osteopathic Medicine; attends in person the ceremony at which the degree is to be conferred; satisfactorily discharged all financial obligations to the School.

Degrees Conferred: 72 *first-professional:* osteopathic medicine.

Fees and Other Expenses: *Full-time tuition per academic year:* contact the institution for current information regarding tuition, fees, housing, and other applicable costs. No campus housing provided; active housing referral is available.

Departments and Teaching Staff: *Total instructional faculty:* 136 (full-time 41, part-time 95).

Enrollment: Total enrollment 363.

Characteristics of Student Body: *Ethnic/racial makeup:* Black non-Hispanic: 16%; Asian or Pacific Islander: 1%; Hispanic: 1%; White non-Hispanic: 14%; unknown 8%. *Age distribution:* average age of student body 27.

Student Life: No campus housing. *Special services:* Learning Resources Center, health center, student center. *Student publications: Appalachian Focus*, a biannual magazine; *News Briefs*, a monthly campus newsletter. *Surrounding community:* Lewisburg, population 5,000, is located in historic Greenbrier Valley in southeastern West Virginia.

Library Collections: 20,000 volumes. 700 current periodical subscriptions. Online catalog.

Buildings and Grounds: Campus area 43 acres.

Chief Executive Officer: Dr. Olen E. Jones, Jr., President.

Address admission inquiries to Donna Varney, Director of Admissions.

West Virginia State University

P.O. Box 1000
Institute, West Virginia 25112-1000
Tel: (304) 766-3033 **E-mail:** admissions@wvsc.edu
Fax: (304) 766-5182 **Internet:** www.wvsc.edu

Institution Description: West Virginia State University is a public institution. *Enrollment:* 3,005. *Degrees awarded:* Baccalaureate, master's. Certificates offered through Community College component.

Academic offering subject to approval by statewide coordinating bodies. Budget subject to approval by state governing boards.

Accreditation: *Regional:* NCA. *Professional*: chemistry, social work, teacher education

History: Established as West Virginia Colored Institute and chartered 1891; offered first instruction at postsecondary level and changed name to West Virginia Collegiate Institute 1915; awarded first degree 1919; became West Virginia State College 1929; became West Virginia State University 2006. *See* John Harlon, *A History of West Virginia State College* (Dubuque, IA: William C. Brown, 1968) for further information.

Institutional Structure: *Governing board:* West Virginia Board of Directors. Representation: 9 regents, state superintendent of schools, 1 faculty representative, 1 student representative. 3 ex officio. 11 voting. *Composition of institution:* Administrators 13. Academic affairs headed by vice president. Finances directed by vice president for administration. Full-time instructional faculty 124. Academic governance body, Faculty Senate, meets an average of 9 times per year.

Calendar: Semesters. Academic year Aug. to May. Freshmen admitted Aug., Jan., June, July. Degrees conferred May, Aug., and Dec. Formal commencements May and Dec. Summer session of 2 terms from June to Aug.

Characteristics of Freshmen: 1,719 applicants (female 894, male 825). 100% of applicants admitted. 26% of applicants admitted and enrolled.

14% (58 students) submitted SAT scores; 80% (332 students) submitted ACT scores. *25th percentile*: ACT Composite 16, ACT English 15, ACT Math 15. *75th percentile*: ACT Composite 21, ACT English 22, ACT Math 19.

14% of entering freshmen expected to graduate within 5 yeas. 91% of freshmen from West Virginia. Freshmen from 21 states.

Admission: Rolling admissions plan. Apply no later than Aug. 15. Early acceptance available. *Requirements:* Either graduation from accredited secondary school with 17 units which must include 4 English, 3 social studies (1 U.S. history), 2 mathematics (1 algebra), 3 lab science (1 biology); or GED. 2 additional units in foreign languages; 1 physical education recommended. Minimum recommended GPA 2.0. *Entrance tests:* College Board SAT or ACT Composite. *For transfer students:* 2.0 minimum GPA.

College credit and advanced placement for postsecondary level work completed in secondary school.

Tutoring available. Developmental courses offered in summer session and regular academic year; credit given.

Degree Requirements: *For all associate degrees:* 61–69 credit hours. *For all baccalaureate degrees:* 121–128 credit hours; core curriculum; for teacher education students, National Teacher Examinations. *For all degrees:* 2.0 GPA; last 2 terms in residence; Undergraduate Record Examination.

Fulfillment of some degree requirements and exemption from some beginning courses possible by passing departmental examinations, College Board CLEP, AP. *Grading system:* A–F; pass-fail; withdraw (carries time limit).

Distinctive Educational Programs: Board of Regents baccalaureate degree program offers nontraditional course of study. Through Academic Common Market, reduced graduate tuition for West Virginia residents in participating out-of-state schools.

ROTC: Army.

Degrees Conferred: 403 *baccalaureate*; 9 *master's*. Bachelor's degrees awarded: biological/life sciences 14; business/marketing 71; communications/communication technologies 24; education 64; English 6; health professions and related clinical sciences 11; liberal arts and sciences, general studies, and humanities 110; mathematics 3; parks and recreation 10; physical sciences 5; public administration 38; psychology 20; social sciences and history 43; visual and performing arts 13. Master's degrees awarded: biological/life sciences 5; communications/journalism 4.

Fees and Other Expenses: *Full-time tuition per academic year 2008–09:* undergraduate resident4,058, nonresident $9,980; contact the university for current graduate tuition/fees. *Room and board per academic year:* $5,739. *Books and supplies:* $1,125. *Other expenses:* $3,270.

Financial Aid: Aid from institutionally generated funds is provided on the basis of academic merit, financial need, athletic ability.

Financial aid to full-time, first-time undergraduate students: 835 received some form of aid. Average amount of aid received: federal grants $3,132; Pell grants $2,902; other federal aid $1,305; state/local grants $3,549; institutional grants $4,188.

Departments and Teaching Staff: *Total instructional faculty:* 196 (full-time 124, part-time 72). Total faculty with doctorate, first-professional, or other terminal degree: 70. Student/faculty ratio: 17:1. Degrees held by full-time faculty: doctorate 30%, master's 62%, baccalaureate 5%, professional 3%. 30% hold terminal degrees.

Enrollment: Total enrollment 3,003. Undergraduate 2,961. Graduate 42 (full-time 86%). Transfer-in students 82.

Characteristics of Student Body: *Ethnic/racial makeup:* Black non-Hispanic: 16%; Asian or Pacific Islander: 1%; Hispanic: 1%; White non-Hispanic: 74%; unknown 8%. *Age distribution:* number under 18: 126; 18–19: 579; 20–21: 627; 12–24: 735; 25–29: 530; 30–34: 256; 35–39: 163; 40–49: 216; 50–64: 77; 65 and over: 9. 20% of student body attend summer sessions.

International Students: 9 nonresident aliens enrolled fall 2008. No programs available to aid students whose native language is not English. No financial aid specifically designated for international students.

Student Life: On-campus residence halls. Married student housing also available. *Intercollegiate athletics:* meale: baseball, basketball, cross-country, football, track; female: basketball, tennis, track. *Special regulations:* Registered cars permitted without restrictions. *Special services:* Learning Resources Center, medical services. *Student publications: ARCH*, a yearbook; *Kanawha Review*, an annual literary magazine; *Yellow Jacket*, a monthly newspaper. *Surrounding community:* Institute population 3,000. Charleston, 8 miles from campus, is nearest metropolitan area. Served by mass transit bus system, airport 15 miles from campus, passenger rail service 10 miles from campus.

Library Collections: 220,677 volumes including bound books, serial backfiles, electronic documents, and government documents not in separate collections. Online catalog. Current serial subscriptions: 287 paper, 130 microform; 17 via electronic access. 1,846 video recordings; 370 compact discs. Computer work stations available. Students have access to the Internet at no charge.

Most important special holdings include the West Virginia State University Archives.

Buildings and Grounds: Campus area 90 acres.

Chief Executive Officer: Dr. Hazo W. Carter, Jr., President.

Address admission inquiries to Tryreno Sowell, Director of Admissions.

West Virginia University

P.O. Box 6201
Morgantown, West Virginia 26506-6201
Tel: (304) 293-0111 **E-mail:** admissions@wvu.edu
Fax: (304) 293-3080 **Internet:** www.wvu.edu

Institution Description: West Virginia University is a public institution and land-grant college with regional campuses that include Potomac State College, West Virginia - Parkersburg, and West Virginia University Institute of Technology. *Enrollment:* 28,840. *Degrees awarded:* Associate, baccalaureate, first-professional (dentistry, law, medicine, pharmacy), master's, doctorate.

Academic offerings subject to approval by statewide coordinating bodies. Budget subject to approval by state governing boards.

Accreditation: *Regional:* NCA. *Professional*: art, business, dental hygiene, dentistry, diagnostic medical sonography, engineering, forestry, journalism, landscape architecture, law, medicine, music, nuclear medicine technology, nursing, pharmacy, physical therapy, psychology internship, public administration, radiation therapy, radiography, recreation and leisure services, rehabilitation counseling, social work, speech-language pathology, teacher education

History: Established as Agricultural College of West Virginia, incorporated, and offered first instruction at postsecondary level 1867; adopted present name and awarded first degree (baccalaureate) 1870. *See* Charles H. Ambler, *History of Education in West Virginia* (Huntington, WV: Standard Printing and Publishing Co., 1951) and William T. Doherty, Jr. and Festus P. Summers, *West Virginia University: Symbol of Unity in a Sectionalized State* (Morgantown: West Virginia University Press, 1982) for further information.

Institutional Structure: *Governing board:* Central Policy Commissions coordinating Board of Governors for each member institution. *Composition of institution:* Administrators 40. Academic affairs headed by vice president and provost for academic affairs. Management/business/finances directed by vice president for administration and finance. Full-time instructional faculty 1,293. Academic governance body, Senate, meets an average of 12 times per year.

Calendar: Semesters. Academic year Aug. to May. Freshmen admitted Aug., Jan., May, July. Degrees conferred May, Aug., Dec. Formal commencement May. Summer session from May to Aug.

Characteristics of Freshmen: 13,634 applicants (female 6,167, male 7,444). 94% of applicants accepted. 47% of accepted applicants enrolled.

Mean ACT Composite score mid-50% range 19–24; Mean SAT mid-50% range verbal 460–560, mathematical 460–570.

49% of entering freshmen expected to graduate within 5 years. 55% of freshmen from West Virginia. Freshmen from 38 states and 25 foreign countries.

Admission: Admission based on high school record and ACT or SAT scores. High school coursework should include 4 units English, 3 units college preparatory math, 1 unit history, 3 units social studies, 2 units laboratory science. West Virginia residents must have at least a 2.0 GPA and minimum ACT Composite score of 19 or SAT combined score of 912. Nonresidents must have a 2.25 GPA and a minimum ACT Composite score of 18 or SAT combined score of 950. Students not meeting one of these requirements will be considered on an individual basis.

College credit and advanced placement for postsecondary level work completed in secondary school and for extrainstitutional learning (life experience), awarded through the Regents baccalaureate program on basis of faculty assessment.

Degree Requirements: 128–145 credit hours; 2.0–2.5 GPA; 90 hours in residence; 2 semesters English; 1 semester mathematics; liberal studies requirements.

Fulfillment of some degree requirements and exemption from some beginning courses possible by passing College Board CLEP, AP. *Grading system:* A–F; pass-fail; withdraw.

Distinctive Educational Programs: Off-campus centers for graduate students at 5 locations throughout the state. Evening classes. Accelerated degree programs. Special facilities for using telecommunications in the classrooms. Interdepartmental programs by individual arrangements. Facilities and programs for independent research, including honors programs, individual majors. West Virginia Consortium for Faculty and Course Development in International Studies with 8 host countries: Austria, France, Spain, England, Japan, China, Germany, Sweden.

ROTC: Army, Air Force.

Degrees Conferred: 3,790 *baccalaureate*; 1,527 *master's*: 221 *doctorate*. Bachelor's degrees awarded in top five disciplines: business, management, marketing, and related support services 358; engineering 316; liberal arts/general studies 308; communication, journalism, and related programs 294; social sciences 220. Master's degrees awarded: various disciplines 1,527. Doctorate awarded: various disciplines 221. First-professional degrees awarded: 338 (dentistry, law, medicine, pharmacy).

Fees and Other Expenses: *Full-time tuition per academic year 2008–09:* $5,100 resident, $15,770 nonresident. Contact the university for graduate and first-professional tuition/fees. *Books and supplies:* $1,160. *Room and board per academic year:* $7,201. *Other expenses:* $1,960.

Financial Aid: Aid from institutionally generated funds is provided on the basis of academic merit, financial need, athletic ability, other criteria.

Financial aid to full-time, first-time undergraduate students: 78% received some form of aid. Average amount of aid received: federal grants $3,167; Pell grants $2,754; other federal aid $1,088; state/local grants $3,710; institutional grants $2,310.

Departments and Teaching Staff: *Total instructional faculty:* 1,579. Student/faculty ratio: 19:1. Degrees held by full-time faculty: doctorate 63%, master's 12%, baccalaureate 1%, professional 24%. 87% hold terminal degrees.

Enrollment: Total enrollment 28,840. Undergraduate 21,930 (full time 94%; female 45%, male 55%). Graduate 6,910 (full-time 64%). Transfer-in students 1,033.

Characteristics of Student Body: *Ethnic/racial makeup:* Black non-Hispanic: 3%; Asian or Pacific Islander: 2%; Hispanic: 2%; White non-Hispanic: 89%; unknown: 1%; nonresident alien 2%.

International Students: 596 undergraduate nonresident aliens enrolled fall 2008. Programs to aid students whose native language is not English: social, cultural, financial. English as a Second Language Program.

Student Life: On-campus residence halls house 22% of undergraduate student body. Residence halls for males constitute 54% of such space, for females 46%. 9% of undergraduate males join and 7% live in fraternity housing; 11% of undergraduate females join and 5% live in sorority houses. Housing available for married students. *Intercollegiate athletics:* male: baseball, basketball, cross-country, football, soccer, swimming, tennis, track, wrestling; female: basketball, cross-country, gymnastics, swimming, tennis, track, volleyball; coed: rifle. Intramural sports include badminton, basketball, bowling, broomball hockey, flag football, indoor and outdoor soccer, riflery, racquetball, softball, swimming and diving, tennis, track and field, volleyball, and wrestling. Sport clubs include equestrian, fencing, fold dance, frisbee, grotto, ice hockey, isshinryu karate, judo, lacrosse, outings, racquetball, rowing, rugby, scuba, skiing, volleyball, whitewater rafting. *Special services:* Medical services, campus transportation system. *Student publications: Daily Athenaeum*, a daily newspaper; *Monticola*, the yearbook. Radio station WWVU-FM broadcasts 24 hours per day. *Surrounding community:* Morgantown population 30,000. Pittsburgh (PA), 70 miles from campus, is nearest metropolitan area. Served by airport 4 miles from campus.

Publications: *Monograph Series for the Rural Sociological Society* published annually, *Victorian Poetry* (first published 1963) quarterly. University Press published 6 titles in 1986 on such varying subjects as hospital ethics, East African history, the hero in the modern Spanish novel, and medieval women. The press also released *The Edden Hammons Collection*, a recording of old-time fiddling music.

Library Collections: 1,610,000 volumes. 2,352,000 microforms; 33,750 audiovisual materials; 34,400 periodicals including via electronic access. Online catalog. Students have access to online information retrieval services and the Internet.

Most important special holdings include the West Virginia and Regional History Collection; the African Collection; The Coal and Other Energy Resources Collection.

Buildings and Grounds: Campus area 673 acres.

Chief Executive Officer: Dr. David C. Hardesty, Jr., President.

Undergraduate and graduate students address admission inquiries to Craig H. Khoo, Director of Admissions and Records; medical students to Dean of the

WEST VIRGINIA UNIVERSITY—*cont'd*

School of Medicine; dental students to Dean of the School of Dentistry; law students to Dean of the College of Law.

College of Arts and Sciences

Degree Programs Offered: *Baccalaureate* in biology, chemistry, communication studies, computer science, economics, English, foreign languages, geography, geology, history, interdepartmental studies, mathematics, philosophy, physics, political science, psychology, sociology and anthropology, statistics; *master's* in biology, chemistry, communication studies, computer science, English, foreign languages, geography, geology, history, mathematics, physics, political science, psychology, public administration, sociology and anthropology, statistics; *doctorate* in biology, chemistry, English, geology, history, physics, political science, psychology.

Distinctive Educational Programs: Interdepartmental studies programs and Board of Regents baccalaureate for continuing education.

College of Agriculture, Forestry, and Consumer Science

Degree Programs Offered: *Baccalaureate* in agricultural education, animal and veterinary sciences, forest resources management, landscape architecture, plant and soil sciences, recreation and parks management, resource management, wildlife resources, wood industries; *master's* in agricultural biochemistry, agricultural economics, agricultural education, agricultural microbiology, agriculture, agronomy, animal and veterinary sciences, entomology, forestry, horticulture, plant pathology, recreation and parks management, wildlife management; *doctorate* in agricultural biochemistry, agricultural microbiology, agronomy, animal nutrition, forest resources sciences, plant pathology.

College of Business and Economics

Degree Programs Offered: *Baccalaureate* in accounting, business administration, business management, economics, finance, marketing; *master's* in business administration, economics, industrial relations, professional accountancy; *doctorate* in economics.

College of Creative Arts

Degree Programs Offered: *Baccalaureate* in art, music, theatre, visual art; *master's* in art, music, theatre, visual art; *doctorate* in music.

College of Engineering and Mineral Resources

Degree Programs Offered: *Baccalaureate* in aerospace engineering, chemical engineering, civil engineering, computer engineering, electrical engineering, industrial engineering, mechanical engineering; *master's* in engineering, aerospace engineering, chemical engineering, civil engineering, electrical engineering, industrial engineering, mechanical engineering, occupational health and safety engineering; *doctorate* in engineering.

College of Human Resources and Education

Degree Programs Offered: *Baccalaureate* in elementary education, family resources, secondary education, speech pathology and audiology; *master's* in counseling, education administration, educational psychology, elementary education, family resources, reading, rehabilitation counseling, secondary education, special education, speech pathology and audiology, technology education; *doctorate* in education.

Perly Isaac Reed School of Journalism

Degree Programs Offered: *Baccalaureate, master's.*

School of Nursing

Degree Programs Offered: *Baccalaureate, master's.*

School of Physical Education

Degree Programs Offered: *Baccalaureate* in physical education, sport and exercise studies; *master's* in community health education, physical education, safety studies; *doctorate* in education.

Distinctive Educational Programs: Interdisciplinary programs in physical education.

School of Dentistry

Degree Programs Offered: *Baccalaureate* in dental hygiene; *master's* in orthodontics, endodontics; *doctorate* in dentistry.

Degree Requirements: Completion of prescribed curriculum.

School of Law

Degree Programs Offered: *First-professional.*

Admission: Baccalaureate from an accredited institution, LSAT.

Degree Requirements: Prescribed curriculum; overall average of 60 on a scale of 80; 12 months in residence.

School of Medicine

Degree Programs Offered: *Baccalaureate* in medical technology, physical therapy; *master's* in anatomy, biochemistry (medical), medical technology, microbiology (medical), pharmacology and toxicology, physiology (medical); *doctorate* in anatomy, biochemistry (medical), biomedical sciences, microbiology (medical), pharmacology and toxicology, physiology (medical); *first-professional* in medicine.

Admission: *For first-professional degree:* 3 or more years of liberal arts study from an accredited institution which must include 6 hours each of English, biology, inorganic chemistry, organic chemistry, physics (all sciences with laboratory), social or behavioral sciences; MCAT; interview.

Degree Requirements: Completion of prescribed curriculum.

School of Pharmacy

Degree Programs Offered: *Master's, doctorate, first-professional.*

Admission: *For first-professional degree:* 68 hours from accredited institution with 6 hours English composition; 3 each algebra, trigonometry; 8 each biology, general chemistry, organic chemistry, physics; 6 economics; 18 hours in electives.

Degree Requirements: Completion of prescribed curriculum; 27 months in residence.

West Virginia University Institute of Technology

405 Fayette Pike
Montgomery, West Virginia 25136
Tel: (304) 442-3071 **E-mail:** admissions@wvutech.edu
Fax: (304) 442-3097 **Internet:** www.wvutech.edu

Institution Description: West Virginia University Institute of Technology, formerly named West Virginia Institute of Technology, is a public institution. *Enrollment:* 1,224. *Degrees awarded:* Associate, baccalaureate, master's.

Academic offerings subject to approval by statewide coordinating bodies. Budget subject to approval by state governing boards.

Accreditation: *Regional:* NCA. *Professional*: dental hygiene, engineering, engineering technology, teacher education

History: Established as Montgomery Preparatory School 1895; changed name to New River State School and offered first instruction at postsecondary level 1921; changed name to New River State College and awarded first degree (baccalaureate) 1931; became West Virginia Institute of Technology 1941; adopted present name 1996.

Institutional Structure: *Governing board:* West Virginia Board of Regents. Representation: 9 regents, state superintendent of schools, 1 faculty representative, 1 student representative. 3 ex officio. 11 voting. *Composition of institution:* Administrators 13. Academic affairs headed by president. Management/business/finances directed by administrative vice president. Full-time instructional faculty 122. Academic governance body, Faculty Assembly, meets an average of 9 times per year.

Calendar: Semesters. Academic year Aug. to May. Freshmen admitted Aug., Jan., May. Degrees conferred May, June, Aug., Dec. Formal commencement May. Summer session from May to Aug.

Characteristics of Freshmen: 1,143 applicants (female 367, male 775). 46% of applicants accepted. 45% of accepted applicants enrolled full-time. Mean SAT scores 462 verbal, 496 mathematical. Mean ACT Composite score 20.

Admission: Rolling admissions plan. For fall acceptance, apply as early as Sept. 1 of previous year, but not later than Aug. 15 year of enrollment. Early acceptance available. *Requirements:* Either graduation from accredited secondary school with 4 units in English, 3 social studies, 2 mathematics, 2 science; or GED. Additional requirements for some programs. Minimum GPA 2.0. *Entrance tests:* ACT Composite. For foreign students TOEFL strongly recommended. *For transfer students:* 98 hours maximum transfer credit; in-state residents 1.7 minimum GPA, out-of-state students 2.0.

College credit and advanced placement for postsecondary-level work completed in secondary school. College credit for extrainstitutional learning on basis of portfolio assessment for students in Board of Regents baccalaureate degree program.

Tutoring available. Developmental / remedial courses offered in summer session and regular academic year; credit given.

Degree Requirements: *For all associate degrees:* 64 semester hours. *For all baccalaureate degrees:* 128–136 hours; 2 hours physical education; 40 hours in upper division courses; additional requirements for some programs. *For all undergraduate degrees:* 2.0 GPA; core curriculum.

Fulfillment of some degree requirements and exemption from some beginning courses possible by passing departmental examinations, College Board CLEP, AP. *Grading system:* A–F; withdraw (carries time limit).

Distinctive Educational Programs: *For undergraduates:* Off-campus centers. Special facilities for using telecommunications in the classroom. Interdisciplinary programs. *Available to all students:* Work-experience programs, including cooperative education, and internships. Evening classes. Tutorials. *Other distinctive programs:* Continuing education. Board of Regents baccalaureate degree program offering nontraditional course of study to students who have been out of secondary school for at least 4 years.

ROTC: Army.

Degrees Conferred: 151 *associate*; 206 *baccalaureate*; 1 *master's*. Bachelor's degrees awarded in top five disciplines: engineering 56; health professions and related clinical sciences 39; business, management, marketing, and related support services 33; liberal arts/general studies 27; communication, journalism, and related programs 9. Master's degrees awarded: engineering 1.

Fees and Other Expenses: *Full-time tuition per academic year 2008–09:* undergraduate resident $4,964, nonresident $12,748. *Books and supplies:* $1,800. *Room and board per academic year:* $5,944. *Other expenses:* $3,000.

Financial Aid: Aid from institutionally generated funds is provided on the basis of academic merit, financial need, athletic ability.

Institution has a Program Participation Agreement with the U.S. Department of Education for eligible students to receive Pell Grants and, depending upon the agreement, other federal aid.

Financial aid to full-time, first-time undergraduate students: 92% received some form of aid.

Departments and Teaching Staff: *Total instructional faculty:* 177. Total tenured faculty: 84. Student/faculty ratio: 16:1. Degrees held by full-time faculty: doctorate 49%, master's 46%, baccalaureate 5%.

Enrollment: Total enrollment 1,224 (undergraduate).

Characteristics of Student Body: *Ethnic/racial makeup:* Black non-Hispanic: 9%; Asian or Pacific Islander: 1%; Hispanic: 1%; White non-Hispanic: 85%; nonresident alien 3%.

International Students: 36 nonresident aliens enrolled fall 2008. No programs available to aid students whose native language is not English. No financial aid specifically designated for international students.

Student Life: On-campus residence halls house 33% of student body. Residence halls for males constitute 59% of such space, for females 41%. *Intercollegiate athletics:* male: baseball, basketball, football, golf, tennis; female: basketball, softball, tennis, volleyball. *Special regulations:* Cars permitted on campus in designated areas. Quite hours in residence halls determined by students. Visitation from noon to 11pm Sun.–Thurs., noon to 2am Fri. and Sat. *Special services:* Learning Resources Center, medical services. *Student publications: Bear Tracks*, a yearbook; *The Collegian*, an irregularly published newspaper. *Surrounding community:* Montgomery population 3,500. Columbus (OH), 250 miles from campus, is nearest metropolitan area. Served by mass transit bus system, airport and passenger rail service, each 28 miles from campus.

Library Collections: 167,000 volumes including bound books, serial backfiles, electronic documents, and government documents not in separate collections. Online catalog. 438,000 microforms; 510 current serial subscriptions. Computer work stations available. Students have access to the Internet at no charge.

Buildings and Grounds: Campus area 200 acres.

Chief Executive Officer: Dr. Glenn Janeksela, President.

Address admission inquiries to Director of Admissions.

West Virginia Wesleyan College

59 College Avenue
Buckhannon, West Virginia 26201-2994
Tel: (304) 473-8000 **E-mail:** admissions@wvwc.edu
Fax: (304) 473-8108 **Internet:** www.wvwc.edu

Institution Description: West Virginia Wesleyan College is a coeducational, residential, liberal arts college affiliated with the United Methodist Church. *Enrollment:* 1,317. *Degrees awarded:* Baccalaureate, master's.

Accreditation: *Regional:* NCA. *Professional*: music, nursing, teacher education

History: Established as West Virginia Conference Seminary 1890; offered first instruction at postsecondary level 1901; changed name to Wesleyan University of West Virginia 1904; awarded first degree (baccalaureate) 1905; adopted present name 1906; incorporated 1919. *See* Kenneth M. Plummer, *A History of West Virginia Wesleyan College* (Nashville: Parthenon Press, 1965) for further information.

Institutional Structure: *Governing board:* Board of Trustees of West Virginia Wesleyan College. Extrainstitutional representation: 36 trustees; institutional representation: president of the college. 2 ex officio. All voting. *Composition of institution:* Administrators 11. Academic affairs headed by dean of college. Management/business/finances directed by treasurer. Full-time instructional faculty 76. Academic governance body, Faculty Assembly, meets an average of 9 times per year.

Calendar: Semesters (4-1-4 plan). Academic year Sept. to May. Freshmen admitted Sept., Jan., May, June, July. Degrees conferred May, June, July, Aug., Dec., Jan. Formal commencement May. Summer session of 3 terms from May to July.

Characteristics of Freshmen: 1,428 applicants (female 715, male 713). 85% of applicants accepted. 28% of accepted applicants enrolled.

Average secondary school rank of freshmen top 50th percentile. Mean SAT scores 527 verbal, 521 mathematical. Mean ACT Composite score 23.

53% of freshmen expected to graduate within 5 years. 55% of freshmen from West Virginia. Freshmen from 33 states and 27 foreign countries.

Admission: Rolling admissions plan. Early acceptance available. *Requirements:* Either graduation from accredited secondary school with 16 units or GED. Minimum 2.5 GPA. *Entrance tests:* College Board SAT or ACT Composite. *For transfer students:* 2.0 minimum GPA; from 2-year accredited institution 68 hours maximum transfer credit.

College credit and advanced placement for postsecondary level work completed in secondary school. College credit for extrainstitutional learning on basis of portfolio assessment.

Tutoring available. Developmental courses offered in summer session and regular academic year; credit given.

Degree Requirements: *For all baccalaureate degrees:* 128 credit hours. *For all degrees:* 2.0 GPA; 2 terms in residence; distribution requirements.

Fulfillment of some degree requirements and exemption from some beginning courses possible by passing departmental examinations, College Board CLEP subject examinations, APP. *Grading system:* A–F; pass-fail; withdraw (deadline after which pass-fail is appended to withdraw).

Distinctive Educational Programs: Laptop computers are provided to all entering students. Honors Program. Internships. Study abroad programs. Wesleyan has exchange agreements with institutes in South Korea, Bulgaria, and Norway.

Degrees Conferred: 228 *baccalaureate*; 30 *master's*. Bachelor's degrees awarded in top five disciplines: business, management, marketing, and related support services 39; education 29; social sciences 21; visual and performing arts 21; psychology 21. Master's degrees awarded: business/management 26; education 4.

Fees and Other Expenses: *Full-time tuition per academic year 2008–09:* undergraduate $22,880; graduate tuition charged per credit hour; contact the college for current rate. *Books and supplies:* $2,500. *Room and board per academic year:* $6,470. *Other expenses:* $3,500.

Financial Aid: Aid from institutionally generated funds is provided on the basis of academic merit, financial need, athletic ability, other criteria.

Financial aid to full-time, first-time undergraduate students: 99% received some form of aid. Federal grants averaging $3,927; 29% state/local grants averaging $3,084; 96% institutional grants averaging $11,298; 69% received loans averaging $3,776.

Departments and Teaching Staff: *Total instructional faculty:* 130. Total tenured faculty: 47. Student/faculty ratio: 14:1. Degrees held by full-time faculty: doctorate 67%, master's 100%, baccalaureate 100%. 71% hold terminal degrees.

Enrollment: Total enrollment 1,317. Undergraduate 1,274 (full-time 97%; female 55%, male 45%). Graduate 43 (full-time 845). Transfer-in students 39.

WEST VIRGINIA WESLEYAN COLLEGE—*cont'd*

Characteristics of Student Body: *Ethnic/racial makeup:* Black non-Hispanic: 5%; Hispanic: 1%; White non-Hispanic: 61%; unknown: 29%; nonresident alien 5%.

International Students: 64 nonresident aliens enrolled fall 2008. No programs available to aid students whose native language is not English. Financial aid specifically designated for international students: some financial aid available for qualifying students.

Student Life: On-campus residence halls guarantee housing for all Wesleyan students. Options include double and single rooms, suites, apartments, and quality living (substance free) areas. Over 80% of Wesleyan's students live on-campus. *Intercollegiate athletics:* male: baseball, basketball, cross-country, football, golf, soccer, swimming, tennis, track and field; female: basketball, cross-country, soccer, softball, swimming, tennis, track and field, volleyball. *Special regulations:* Registered cars permitted. Quiet hours. Residence hall visitation from 10am to 12pm. Sun.–Thurs., 10am to 2am Fri. and Sat. *Special services:* Special Support Services Program, Barnhart Memorial Health Center, Advising and Career Center, Benedum Campus Center. More than 70 clubs and organizations plus student government, fraternities and sororities, intramurals, Christian Life Council, extensive volunteer service opportunities; Campus Activities Board. *Student publications, radio: Pharos*, a newspaper; *Murmurmontis* (yearbook); *The Rickshaw* (literary magazine); *Wesleyan Business Journal*. Radio station C-92 FM. *Surrounding community:* Buckhannon population 7,500. Pittsburgh, 135 miles north of campus, is nearest metropolitan area. Served by airport 30 miles from campus.

Publications: *Laurel Review* (biannually) first published 1962.

Library Collections: 116,500 volumes. 59,000 microforms; 6,000 audiovisual materials; 14,000 periodicals including via electronic access. Online catalog. Students have access to online information retrieval services and the Internet.

Most important special holdings include C.A. Jones Lincoln Collection; Methodist history; Pearl S. Buck Collection (manuscripts).

Buildings and Grounds: Campus area 80 acres.

Chief Executive Officer: Dr. Pamela Balch, President. Address admission inquiries to Director of Admissions.

Wheeling Jesuit University

316 Washington Avenue
Wheeling, West Virginia 26003
Tel: (800) 624-6992 **E-mail:** admiss@wju.edu
Fax: (304) 243-4496 **Internet:** www.wju.edu

Institution Description: Wheeling Jesuit University (formerly Wheeling Jesuit College) is a private coeducational college within the Jesuit tradition. The college integrates career programs with traditional liberal arts and sciences. *Enrollment:* 1,319. *Degrees awarded:* Baccalaureate, master's.

Accreditation: *Regional:* NCA. *Professional*: nuclear medicine technology, nursing, nursing education, physical therapy, respiratory therapy

History: Established and incorporated 1954; offered first instruction at postsecondary level 1955; awarded first degree (baccalaureate) 1959; achieved university status 1996.

Institutional Structure: *Governing board:* Board of Directors. Representation: 20 directors, including president of the college. 1 ex officio. 19 voting. *Composition of institution:* Administrators 61. Academic affairs headed by academic dean. Management/business/finances directed by vice president of financial administration. Full-time instructional faculty 64. Academic governance body, Faculty Meeting, meets an average of 8 times per year.

Calendar: Semesters. Academic year Aug. to May. Freshmen admitted Sept., Jan. Degrees conferred May, Aug., Dec. Formal commencement May. Summer session of 2 terms from May to Aug.

Characteristics of Freshmen: 1,188 applicants (female 645, male 543). 75% of applicants admitted. 33% of applicants admitted and enrolled.

56% (159 students) submitted SAT scores; 77% (220 students) submitted ACT scores. *25th percentile*: SAT Critical Reading 480, SAT Math 470; ACT Composite 19, ACT English 19, ACT Math 18. *75th percentile*: SAT Critical Reading 580, SAT Math 580; ACT Composite 24, ACT English 26, ACT Math 25.

58% of entering freshmen expected to graduate within 5 years. 41% of freshmen from West Virginia. Freshmen from 13 states and 10 foreign countries.

Admission: For fall acceptance, apply as early as June prior to senior year, but not later than Aug. 1 of year of enrollment. Early acceptance available. *Requirements:* Either graduation from accredited secondary school with 15 college preparatory units which must include 4 English, 2 history or social studies, 2 mathematics, 2 science (including chemistry for nursing students), 5 academic electives; or GED. 2 units in a foreign language recommended. Entrants to Physical Therapy program will be required to take more science and mathematics. Minimum 2.5 GPA. *Entrance tests:* College Board SAT or ACT Composite. For foreign students TOEFL. *For transfer students:* 2.0 minimum GPA; courses will be accepted for transfer from colleges accredited by an association recognized by Wheeling Jesuit College; some core curriculum required.

College credit and advanced placement for postsecondary level work completed in secondary school.

Tutoring available. Developmental courses offered in summer session and regular academic year; credit given.

Degree Requirements: 120 credit hours; 2.0 GPA; 32 credit hours in residence; 16 core courses as specified in English, mathematics, modern language, humanities; exit competency examination in philosophy; comprehensives in some fields of study.

Fulfillment of some degree requirements and exemption from some beginning courses possible by passing departmental examinations, College Board CLEP. Exemption from some beginning courses also possible by passing College Board APP. *Grading system:* A–F; credit-no credit; withdraw (carries time limit); incomplete (for independent study and senior seminar courses).

Distinctive Educational Programs: *For undergraduates:* Work-experience programs, including cooperative education and internships. Weekend classes. Interdepartmental/interdisciplinary programs in Appalachian studies, fine arts management, public administration. Preprofessional program in engineering leading to baccalaureate awarded by University of Detroit (MI) or West Virginia University. Industrial Engineering Program in cooperation with Belmont Technical College; 3/2 engineering programs with Case Western Reserve University (OH) (leading to baccalaureate from each college). Teacher Preparation Program (5-12) in which students major in a discipline and also participate in experience-oriented teacher preparation program. Facilities and programs for independent research, including honors program, individual majors, tutorials; independent study courses for juniors and seniors. Study abroad through Wheeling Jesuit University program in home and by individual arrangement. Off-campus study in the U.S. through exchange program with other Jesuit colleges and universities by individual arrangement. Honors program for exceptional students. *Available to all students:* Evening classes. *Other distinctive programs:* Evening division degree program for adult learners.

Degrees Conferred: 274 *baccalaureate* (B); 54 *master's* (M): biological/life sciences 12 (B); business/marketing 12 (B), 23 (M); computer and information sciences 7 (B); education 5 (M); English 14 (B); foreign languages and literature 1 (B); health professions and related sciences 33 (B), 20 (M); interdisciplinary studies 8 (B); liberal arts/general studies 29 (B); mathematics 1 (B); natural resources 2 (B); parks and recreation 3 (B); philosophy/religion/theology 1 (B), 6 (M); physical sciences 10 (B); protective services/public administration 14 (B); psychology 22 (B); social sciences and history 16 (B). Doctorates awarded: health professions 30.

Fees and Other Expenses: *Full-time tuition per academic year 2008–09:* $24,390. *Required fees:* $410. *Room and board per academic year:* $8,640. *Books and supplies:* $800. *Other expenses:* $1,200.

Financial Aid: Aid from institutionally generated funds is provided on the basis of academic merit, financial need, athletic ability, choral ability.

Financial aid to full-time, first-time undergraduate students: 995 received some form of aid. Need-based scholarships/grants totaling $3,003,617, self-help $3,323,798; non-need-based scholarships/grants totaling $7,681,075, self-help $2,871,511, parent loans $1,062,398, tuition waivers $850,690, athletic awards $601,460.

Departments and Teaching Staff: *Total instructional faculty:* 142. Student/faculty ratio: 14:1. Degrees held by full-time faculty: doctorate 63%, master's 17.7%, baccalaureate 1%. 63% hold terminal degrees.

Enrollment: Total enrollment 1,319. Undergraduate 1,077 (full-time 81%; female 62%, male 38%). Graduate 244 (full-time 43%). Transfer-in student 64.

Characteristics of Student Body: *Ethnic/racial makeup:* Black non-Hispanic: 2%; Asian or Pacific Islander: 1%; Hispanic: 2%; White non-Hispanic: 85%; unknown:'10%. *Age distribution:* number under 18: 25; 18–19: 458; 20–21: 397; 22–24: 90; 25–29: 56; 30–34: 37; 35–39: 44; 40–49: 88; 50–64: 34; 65 and over: 3.

International Students: 45 nonresident aliens enrolled fall 2008. Students from Europe, Asia, Latin America, Africa, Canada. Programs available to aid students whose native language is not English: English as a Second Language Program. No financial aid available specifically designated for international students.

Student Life: On-campus residence halls house 70% of student body. Residence halls single sex or by floors. NCAA, Division II and NAIA teams for men and women in cross country, basketball, soccer, golf. *Intercollegiate athletics:* male: basketball, hockey, lacrosse, rugby, soccer, tennis; female: volleyball. Club sports include rugby, lacrosse, ice hockey, basketball, volleyball. *Special regulations:* Cars with parking permits allowed without restrictions; fee charged. Quiet hours from midnight to 11am. Residence hall visitation from noon to midnight Sun.–Thurs., noon to 2am Fri. and Sat. Visitors must be identified after

8pm. *Special services:* Learning Resources Center, medical services. *Student publications, radio: Jewelweed*, an annual literary magazine; *Manifest*, a yearbook; *The Voice,* a biannual newsletter; *Spokesman*, a student newspaper. *Surrounding community:* Wheeling population 45,000. Pittsburgh (PA), 60 miles from campus, is nearest metropolitan area. Served by mass transit bus system, international airport 60 miles from campus.

Library Collections: 192,000 volumes. 131,000 microforms; 1,235 audiovisual materials. 380 current serial subscriptions. Online catalog. Students have access to online information retrieval systems.

Most important special holdings include Jule Hearne Mark Twain Collection; theology and religious books; Wheeling Archives (West Virginia history).

Buildings and Grounds: Campus area 55 acres.

Chief Executive Officer: Fr. Joseph Hacala, S.J., President.

Address admission inquiries to Carol Deskak, Admissions Director.

Wisconsin

Alverno College

3400 South 43rd Street
P.O. Box 343922
Milwaukee, Wisconsin 53234-3922
Tel: (414) 382-6000 **E-mail:** admissions@alverno.edu
Fax: (414) 382-6354 **Internet:** www.alverno.edu

Institution Description: Alverno College is a private, Catholic, independent, nonprofit college. *Enrollment:* 2,782. Men are admitted as unclassified students and into the Master of Education program. *Degrees awarded:* Associate, baccalaureate, master's.

Member of the consortium Council for the Advancement of Experiential Learning.

Accreditation: *Regional:* NCA. *Professional*: music, nursing, teacher education

History: Established as St. Joseph Normal School 1887; changed name to Alverno Teachers College and offered first instruction at postsecondary level 1936; awarded first degree (baccalaureate) 1940; adopted present name 1946. *See* Alverno College Faculty, *Ability-based Learning Outcomes: Teaching and Assessment at Alverno College* (6th ed., 2005, Milwaukee WI and Alverno Institute).

Institutional Structure: *Governing board:* Board of Trustees of Alverno College. Representation: 33 trustees, including 5 School Sisters of St. Francis, 2 ex officio members (President of Alumnae Association and the President of Alverno College). *Composition of institution:* Administrators 4 at vice president level and above. Academic affairs headed by vice president for academic affairs. Management/business/finances directed by vice president for finance and management services. Development headed by vice president for college advancement. Full-time instructional faculty 107. The Educational Policies Committee and the Faculty Senate meet an average of 10 times per year.

Calendar: Semesters. Academic year Aug. to May. Freshmen admitted Aug., Jan. Degrees conferred May, Dec. Formal commencements May, Dec. Summer session.

Characteristics of Freshmen: 560 applicants (female 560). 59% of applicants accepted. 31% of accepted applicants enrolled. full-time.

22% (4 students) submitted SAT scores. 96% (238 students) submitted ACT scores. *25th percentile:* ACT Composite 17. *75th percentile*: ACT Composite 22.

35% of entering freshmen expected to graduate within 5 years. 96% of freshmen from Wisconsin. Freshmen from 6 states and 3 foreign countries.

Admission: Rolling admissions plan. For fall acceptance, apply as early as Sept. of previous year, but not later than Aug. 1 of year of enrollment. Early acceptance available. *Requirements:* Either graduation from accredited secondary school with 17 units which include 4 English, 3 mathematics, 3 science, 3 social studies, or GED. Additional requirements for some programs. *Entrance tests:* ACT composite required. *For transfer students:* 2.0 minimum GPA; maximum transfer credit limited only by residence requirements which vary according to department.

College credit and advanced placement for postsecondary level work completed in secondary school. College credit for extrainstitutional learning (life experience) on basis of college assessment.

Tutoring available. Noncredit developmental courses offered in summer session and regular academic year.

Degree Requirements: All students must demonstrate 4 successive levels of ability in each of 8 areas: communicating effectively, analyzing, problem solving, decision making, demonstrating effective social interaction, taking on global perspectives, developing effective citizenship, demonstrating aesthetic responsiveness. Baccalaureate students demonstrate advanced levels of abilities in 2 or 3 areas. All students must fulfill course requirements of their major and support areas of study.

Fulfillment of some degree requirements and exemption from some beginning courses possible by passing departmental examinations, College Board CLEP, AP. *Grading system:* Descriptive reports that list courses successfully completed and ability levels demonstrated. The graduation transcript includes a narrative statement of evaluation and the faculty's judgment regarding the quality of the student's academic work.

Distinctive Educational Programs: Experiential learning programs provide directed internships for students in every field. Weekend and evening classes. Special facilities for using telecommunications in the classroom. Interdisciplinary programs in art therapy, humanities, social science. Associate and baccalaureate degrees and major equivalency programs offered. A master of arts degree] focused on learning and human development, designed for adaptive education, administrative leadership, alternative schools, director of instruction, professional development, and human resource development specialists in business, government, and not-for-profit agencies. Student exchange programs: United Kingdom, Japan, Mexico. Alverno also offers courses that include an international travel component and arranges other programs through a worldwide consortium of facilities.

ROTC: Air Force and Army through cross-registration with Marquette University.

Degrees Conferred: 4 *associate;* 277 *baccalaureate:* biological sciences 14; business and management 94; communications 45; education 39; English 11; health professions 57; mathematics 4; philosophy and religion 4; physical sciences 10; public administration 6; psychology 17; social sciences and history 8; visual and performing arts 2. *Master's*: various disciplines 62.

Fees and Other Expenses: *Full-time tuition per academic year 2008–09:* undergraduate $18,161; contact the college for current graduate tuition/fees. *Books and supplies:* $1,050. *Required fees:* $350. *Room and board per academic year:* $6,436.

Financial Aid: Aid from institutionally generated funds is provided on the basis of academic merit, financial need.

Financial aid to full-time, first-time undergraduate students: 100% received some form of aid. Average amount of aid received: federal grants $3,573; Pell grants $3,015; other federal aid $601; state/local grants $3,265; institutional grants $5,839.

Departments and Teaching Staff: *Total instructional faculty:* 226 (full-time 107, part-time 119). Total faculty with doctorate, first-professional, or other terminal degree: 159. Student-to-faculty ratio: 12:1. Degrees held by full-time faculty: master's 49%, doctorate 51%. 89% hold terminal degrees.

Enrollment: Total enrollment 2,782. Undergraduate 2,371 (full-time 72%; female 100%) Graduate 417 (full-time 58%). Transfer-in students 268.

Characteristics of Student Body: *Ethnic/racial makeup:* Black non-Hispanic: 16%; American Indian or Alaska Native: 1%; Asian or Pacific Islander: 5%; Hispanic: 12%; 226; White non-Hispanic: 64%; nonresident alien 1%.

International Students: 29 nonresident aliens enrolled fall 2008. Students from Europe, Asia, Latin America, Africa. Programs available to aid students whose native language is not English: social, cultural. English as a Second Language Program. No financial aid specifically designated for international students.

Student Life: Two residence halls for females constitute 100% of housing space. *Special regulations:* Cars permitted without restrictions. *Special services:* Learning Resources Center, Health Services. Fitness Center available to students. Many opportunities to connect with colleges in the area through organized social events. *Student publications: Real Life Magazine, Inside-Out*, a student literary magazine published once a year; *Alpha* and *Campus NewsNet*, the student newsletter. *Surrounding community:* Milwaukee population 625,000. Served by mass transit bus system, airport and passenger rail service both 5 miles from campus.

Publications: *The Alverno Magazine*published three times a year and *Alverno Today* , a newspaper published two times per year.

Library Collections: 120,000 volumes including bound books, serial backfiles, electronic documents, and government documents not in separate collections. Online catalog. 249,000 micoroforms; 5,000 audiovisual materials; 550 current serial subscriptions. Computer work stations available. Students have access to the Internet at no charge.

Most important special holdings include collections on women's studies/feminism; education (preschool, elementary, secondary, college); fine arts (recorded music and art slides).

Buildings and Grounds: Campus area 46 acres. Campus DVD available.

Chief Executive Officer: Dr. Mary Jane Meehan, President.

Address admission inquiries to Kim Wankowski, Director of Admissions.

Bellin College of Nursing

725 South Webster Avenue
Green Bay, Wisconsin 54305-3400
Tel: (920) 433-3560 **E-mail:** admission@bcon.edu
Fax: (920) 433-7416 **Internet:** www.bcon.edu

Institution Description: The Bellin College of Nursing is a private professional school. *Enrollment:* 294. *Degrees awarded:* Baccalaureate, master's.

Accreditation: *Regional:* NCA. *Professional*: nursing

Calendar: Semesters. 4-1-4 plan. Academic year Aug. to May.

Characteristics of Freshmen: 81 applicants (female 79, male 2). 70% of applicants accepted. 37% of accepted applicants enrolled.

100% of applicants submitted ACT scores. *25th percentile*: ACT Composite 22, ACT English 21, ACT Math 21. *75th percentile*: ACT Composite 25, ACT English 27, ACT Math 26.

50% of entering freshmen expected to graduate within 5 years. 100% of freshmen from Wisconsin.

Admission: *Requirements:* High school graduation with 3.25 GPA or higher; ACT Composite of 23 or higher; or GED.

Degree Requirements: *For baccalaureate degree:* 128 credit hours; *master of science in nursing:* 38 credit hours.

ROTC: Army in cooperation with University of Wisconsin-Greenbay and St. Norbert College.

Degrees Conferred: 69 *baccalaureate:* nursing; 7 *master's:* health professions 7.

Fees and Other Expenses: *Full-time tuition per academic year 2008–09:* $17,939. *Required fees:* $339. *Books and supplies:* $1,517. *Off-campus room and board per academic year:* $6,300. *Other expenses:* $3,075.

Financial Aid: Aid from institutionally generated funds is provided on the basis of academic merit, financial need.

Financial aid to full-time, first-time undergraduate students: need-based scholarships/grants totaling $541,399, self-help $851,239, parent loans $152,655; non-need-based scholarships/grants totaling $26,408, self-help $392,553, parent loans $143,997. *Graduate aid:* 16 students received $202,545 in federal and state-funded loans.

Departments and Teaching Staff: *Total instructional faculty:* 21 (full-time 17, part-time 4). Degrees held by full-time faculty: doctorate 1%, master's 100%.

Enrollment: Total enrollment 294. Undergraduate 258 (full-time 76%; female 95%, male 5%). Graduate 36 (full-time 100%). Transfer-in students 18.

Characteristics of Student Body: *Ethnic/racial makeup:* Black non-Hispanic 2%; Asian or Pacific Islander: 3%; Hispanic 1%; White non-Hispanic: 94%;. *Age distribution:* number 18–19: 53; 20–21: 75; 22–24: 42; 25–29: 25; 30–34: 10; 35–39: 7; 40–49: 4. 3% of student body attend summer sessions.

International Students: No programs available to aid students whose native language is not English. No financial aid specifically designated for international students.

Library Collections: 6,000 volumes. Online catalog. 195 current periodicals. Computer work stations available. Students have access to the Internet at no charge.

Chief Executive Officer: Dr. V. Jane Muhl, President.

Address admission inquiries to Director of Admissions.

Beloit College

700 College Street
Beloit, Wisconsin 535115595
Tel: (608) 363-2000 **E-mail:** admiss@beloit.edu
Fax: (608) 363-2717 **Internet:** www.beloit.edu

Institution Description: Beloit College is a private, independent, nonprofit, liberal arts college that is nonsectarian but historically related to Congregationalism. *Enrollment:* 1,388. *Degrees awarded:* Baccalaureate.

Charter member of Associated Colleges of the Midwest.

Accreditation: *Regional:* NCA. *Professional*: chemistry

History: Established, chartered, and incorporated 1846; offered first instruction at postsecondary level 1847; awarded first degree (baccalaureate) 1851. *See* Edward Dwight Eaton, *Historical Sketches of Beloit College* (New York: A.S. Barnes and Company, 1928) for further information.

Institutional Structure: *Governing board:* The Board of Trustees of Beloit College. Extrainstitutional representation: 30 trustees. All voting. *Composition of institution:* Administrators 75. Academic affairs headed by vice president for academic affairs. Management/business/finances directed by vice president for administration. Full-time instructional faculty 86. Academic governance body, Senate of Beloit College meets an average of 10 times per year.

Calendar: Semesters. Academic year Aug. to May. Freshmen admitted Aug., Jan. Degrees conferred and formal commencement May. Summer programs in foreign language, science, anthropology, and other areas.

Characteristics of Freshmen: 2,248 applicants (female 1,238, male 1,010). 67% of applicants accepted. 30% of accepted applicants enrolled.

Mean SAT scores 640 critical reading, 610 mathematical. Mean ACT Composite score 27.

65% of freshmen expected to graduate within 5 years. Freshmen from 49 states and 50 countries.

Admission: Rolling admissions plan. For fall acceptance, apply as early as Oct. 1 of previous year, but not later than Aug. 1 of year of enrollment. Early acceptance and deferred admission available. *Requirements:* Either graduation from accredited secondary school with 4 units English, 2 in a foreign language, 3 in mathematics, 3 in laboratory science, 2 social studies; or GED. 2 additional academic units recommended. Recommendation letters required; essay required. *Entrance tests:* College Board SAT or ACT composite. Interview recommended. *For transfer students:* 2.0 minimum GPA; 64 semester hours maximum transfer credit.

College credit and advanced placement for postsecondary level work completed in secondary school.

Tutoring available.

Degree Requirements: 124 credit hours(31 units); 2.0 GPA; 60 hours in residence; writing requirement; comprehensives in individual fields of study in some departments; courses in natural sciences, social sciences, and arts and humanities; submission of a comprehensive academic plan, completion of a major.

Fulfillment of some degree requirements and exemption from some beginning courses possible by passing departmental examinations, College Board CLEP or AP. *Grading system:* A–F; credit-no credit.

Distinctive Educational Programs: The college provides extensive opportunities to study abroad through programs designed and administered by the World Affairs Center. Students can study in Europe, Latin America, the Middle East, and Africa. Exchange programs take students to Brazil, China, Hong Kong, Hungary, Japan, Russia, Senegal, and Turkey. Programs are also offered through the Associated Colleges of the Midwest. The college offers language instruction in 10 languages at the Center for Language Studies. The Interdisciplinary Studies Program sponsors courses and individual study programs. 'Field Experience' programs at Beloit provide opportunities for students to gain practical experience in a specific field of interest through internships and field terms at the Wilderness Field Station in northern Minnesota, the Chicago Semester in the Arts, the Newberry Library Seminars, and the Urban Education Program.

Degrees Conferred: 310 *baccalaureate*. Bachelor's degrees awarded in top five disciplines: social sciences 72; visual and performing arts 38; English language/literature 26; psychology 24; foreign languages 14.

Fees and Other Expenses: *Full-time tuition per academic year 2008–09:* $31,540. *Books and supplies:* $600. *Room and board per academic year:* $6,696. *Other expenses:* $900.

Financial Aid: Aid from institutionally generated funds is provided on the basis of academic merit, financial need.

Institution has a Program Participation Agreement with the U.S. Department of Education for eligible students to receive Pell Grants and, depending upon the agreement, other federal aid.

Financial aid to full-time, first-time undergraduate students: 89% received some form of aid. 15% received federal grants averaging $3,181; 12% state/local grants averaging $2,035; 85% institutional grants averaging $13,680; 63% received loans averaging $4,128.

Departments and Teaching Staff: *Total instructional faculty:* 119 (full-time 99, part-time 20). Student-to-faculty ratio: 11:1. Degrees held by full-time faculty: doctorate 93%, master's 2%, professional 5%. 98% hold terminal degrees.

Enrollment: Total enrollment 1,388. Undergraduate 1,388 (full-time 95%; female 57%, male 43%). Transfer-in students 25.

Characteristics of Student Body: *Ethnic/racial makeup:* Black non-Hispanic: 4%; American Indian or Alaska Native: 1%; Asian or Pacific Islander: 3%; Hispanic: 4%; White non-Hispanic: 76%; unknown: 6; nonresident alien 6%.

International Students: 83 nonresident aliens enrolled fall 2008. Students from Europe, Asia, Latin America, Africa, Canada, Australia, New Zealand. Programs available to aid students whose native language is not English: social, cultural. English as a Second Language Program. Financial aid specifically designated for international students: variable number of scholarships available annually.

BELOIT COLLEGE—*cont'd*

Student Life: On-campus residence halls, fraternities, and sororities house 94% of student body. Residence halls for both males and females constitute 85% of such space. 25% of males join and 15% live in fraternity housing; 15% of females join and 5% live in sorority housing. 6% of student body live off campus in college- or privately-owned facilities. *Intercollegiate athletics:* male: basketball, baseball, cross-country, football, golf, hockey, soccer, swimming, tennis, track; female: basketball, cross-country, soccer, softball, swimming, tennis, track, volleyball. Club sports include fencing and lacrosse for males and females. *Special regulations:* Cars permitted with parking permit. Quiet hours established by each residence hall. *Special services:* Career counseling and placement; academic and personal counseling services; medical services. *Student publications, radio: Avatar*, a biannual literary magazine; *Hippopotamus*, academic journal of student research papers; *The Gold*, yearbook; *The Round Table*, a weekly newspaper. Radio station WBCR-FM broadcasts 141 hours per week. Beloit operates the public and governmental access channel for local cable TV. *Surrounding community:* Beloit population 35,000. Milwaukee (70 miles from campus), Madison (50 miles), Rockford (second largest city in Illinois—17 miles), and Chicago (90 miles) are nearest metropolitan centers. Served by O'Hare International Airport 90 miles from campus and express bus service from airport; also Milwaukee airport.

Publications: *Logan Museum of Anthropology Reports* (published irregularly), first appearing in 1928; *Beloit Magazine* (published 3 times/year to alumni and friends of the College); *Beloit Fiction Journal* (published 2 times/year by subscription).

Library Collections: 245,000 volumes. 160,000 microforms; 5,500 audiovisual materials; 275,000 government documents; 940 current periodical subscriptions. Computer work stations available. Online catalogs Students have access to online information retrieval services and the Internet.

Most important special holdings include Martin Luther King Collection on nonviolence, including materials collected in India on Gandhi and nonviolence; Horace White Collection of Lincoln materials including old and rare volumes and Civil War notes; Beloit Poetry Journal collection; Kohler Science Collection.

Buildings and Grounds: Campus area 65 acres.

Chief Executive Officer: Dr. John E. Burris, President.

Address admission inquiries to James S. Zielenski, Director of Admissions.

Cardinal Stritch University

6801 North Yates Road
Milwaukee, Wisconsin 53217-3985
Tel: (414) 410-4040 **E-mail:** admityou@stritch.edu
Fax: (414) 410-4049 **Internet:** www.stritch.edu

Institution Description: Cardinal Stritch University is an independent, 4-year liberal arts institution sponsored by the Sisters of St. Francis of Assisi, Roman Catholic Church. *Enrollment:* 6,471. *Degrees awarded:* Associate, baccalaureate, master's.

Accreditation: *Regional:* NCA. *Professional*: nursing, teacher education

History: Established as St. Clare College, a women's institution 1937; chartered, offered first instruction at postsecondary level, and awarded first degree (baccalaureate) 1937; adopted present name 1946; moved to present location 1956; became coeducational 1970.

Institutional Structure: *Governing board:* Board of Trustees. Representation: 21 trustees, including president of college (ex officio) and 3 OSF Sisters. All voting. *Composition of institution:* Chancellor of the College, President, Senior Vice President, Vice President for Business and Finance, Vice President for Student Development/Dean of Students, Vice President for Academic Affairs/Dean of Faculty, Vice President for Development, Vice President for Planning and Enrollment Management. Full-time instructional faculty 65. Academic governance body, Curriculum and Academic Affairs Committee, meets an average of 9 times per year.

Calendar: Semesters. Academic year Aug. to May. Freshmen admitted Sept., Jan., June. Degrees conferred Aug., Dec., May. Formal commencement May. Summer session of six weeks.

Characteristics of Freshmen: 80% of applicants accepted. 48.8% of accepted applicants enrolled.

55% of entering freshmen expected to graduate within 5 years. 80% of freshmen from Wisconsin. Freshmen from 9 states.

Admission: Rolling admissions plan. *Requirements:* Either graduation from accredited secondary school with 4 units in English, 2 history, 2 mathematics, 2 science, 6 academic electives; or GED. Minimum 2.0 GPA. Recommended high school class rank 50th percentile. *Entrance tests:* College Board SAT or ACT composite. For foreign students TOEFL. *For transfer students:* 2.0 minimum GPA; maximum transfer credit limited only by residence requirement. Noncredit remedial courses offered during academic year. Graduate Division: Bachelor's degree from accredited institution; 2.5 GPA; Miller Analogy Test. For foreign students TOEFL.

College credit and advanced placement for postsecondary-level work completed in secondary school. For extrainstitutional learning (life experience) on basis of faculty assessment; personal interviews; portfolio assessment and/or other documentation.

Noncredit remedial courses offered during regular academic year.

Degree Requirements: *For all associate degrees:* 60–66 credit hours. *For all baccalaureate degrees:* 128 credit hours; senior research paper or project; exit competency examination in writing. *For all undergraduate degrees:* 2.0 GPA; last 2 semesters at Stritch; general education requirements. *Graduate Division:* For M.A. and M.E. degrees: 30 credit hours minimum; 3.0 GPA minimum; comprehensive exam, thesis or field experience, internship equivalent or software project. For MS degree: 36 credits; 3.0 GPA minimum; thesis or comprehensive exam. MBA degree requires 42 credit hours.

Fulfillment of some degree requirements and exemption from some beginning courses possible by passing College Board CLEP. Exemption from some courses also possible by passing departmental examinations, College AP, Credit for Prior Learning. *Grading system:* A–F; pass-fail; withdraw (carries time limit); incomplete (carries time limit).

Distinctive Educational Programs: *For undergraduates:* B.F.A. in art; education/special education, international business, math/computer studies, nursing, youth ministry; management and business administration programs for working adults. Field experience: clinical placements, student teaching, and others. *For graduate students:* M.A. in reading and special education; M.E. in educational computing, teaching, youth ministry; M.E/Ph.D. in professional development; M.S. in educational leadership, management, health services administration; M.B.A.

Degrees Conferred: 208 *associate*; 916 *master's*; 14 *doctorate*. Bachelor's degrees awarded in top five disciplines: business, management, marketing, and related support services 462; education 41; health professions and related clinical sciences 21; visual and performing arts 15; communication, journalism, and related programs 12.

Fees and Other Expenses: *Full-time tuition per academic year 2008–09:* $17,500 undergraduate; contact the university for current graduate tuition/fees. *Books and supplies:* $600. *Room and board per academic year:* $6,000.

Financial Aid: Aid from institutionally generated funds is provided on the basis of academic merit, financial need, other criteria.

Institution has a Program Participation Agreement with the U.S. Department of Education for eligible students to receive Pell Grants and, depending upon the agreement, other federal aid.

Financial aid to full-time, first-time undergraduate students: 30% received federal grants averaging $2,463; 31% state/local grants averaging $2,030; 60% institutional grants averaging $6,730; 77% received loans averaging $4,617.

Departments and Teaching Staff: *Total instructional faculty:* 676. Degrees held by full-time faculty: baccalaureate 100%, master's 99%, doctorate 50%. 55% hold terminal degrees.

Enrollment: Total enrollment 6,471.

Characteristics of Student Body: *Ethnic/racial makeup:* Black non-Hispanic: 14%; American Indian or Alaska Native: 1%; Asian or Pacific Islander: 2%; Hispanic: 4%; White non-Hispanic: 69%; unknown: 4%.

International Students: 64 nonresident aliens enrolled fall 2008. No programs available to aid students whose native language is not English. No financial aid specifically designated for international students.

Student Life: On-campus residence halls house 30% of full-time undergraduate students. Residence halls for males constitute 30% of such space, for females 70%. *Intercollegiate athletics:* male: baseball, basketball, cross-country, soccer; female: basketball, cross-country, soccer, softball, volleyball. Intramural sports program. *Special regulations:* Free parking for registered vehicles. Established hours for residence hall visitation. *Special services:* Academic advising, campus ministry, career/placement counseling, health services, personal counseling, recreation program, study skills center, car pools for commuters. *Student publications: Commentary,* a newspaper; *Future Concerns,* yearbook. *Surrounding community:* Metropolitan Milwaukee population 1 million plus. Served by mass transit bus system. Located one half mile from major freeway, 22 miles from airport, and 12 miles from passenger rail and interstate bus service.

Library Collections: 125,000 volumes. 150,000 microforms; 70 CD-ROMs; 1,100 current periodical subscriptions. Online catalog. Students have access to online information retrieval services and the Internet.

Most important special holdings include collections on education, special education, business.

Buildings and Grounds: Campus area 40 acres.

Chief Executive Officer: Sr. Mary Lea Schneider, O.S.F., President.

Undergraduates address admission inquiries to David Wegener, Director of Admissions; graduate inquiries to Registrar, Graduate Admissions.

Carroll College

100 North East Avenue
Waukesha, Wisconsin 53186
Tel: (262) 547-1211 **E-mail:** ccinfo@cc.edu
Fax: (262) 524-7139 **Internet:** www.cc.edu

Institution Description: Carroll College is a private, nonprofit college affiliated with the Presbyterian Church, U.S.A. *Enrollment:* 3,292. *Degrees awarded:* Baccalaureate, master's (education, physical therapy).

Accreditation: *Regional:* NCA. *Professional*: accounting, athletic training, chemistry, nursing, physical therapy, teacher education

History: Established as Prairieville Academy (a men's school) 1841; chartered as Carroll College and offered first instruction at postsecondary level 1846; awarded first degree (baccalaureate) 1857; became coeducational 1863. *See* Ellen Langhill, *Carroll College: The First Century 1846–1946* (Waukesha, WI: Carroll College Press, 1980) for further information.

Institutional Structure: *Governing board:* The Board of Trustees of Carroll College. Representation: 22 active members; 5 honorary life members. *Composition of institution:* president, senior vice president, 3 vice presidents. Full-time instructional faculty 111. Academic governance body, College Assembly, meets an average of 4 times per year.

Calendar: Semesters (4-1-4 plan). Academic year Sept. to May. Freshmen admitted Sept., Jan., Feb., May, July. Degrees conferred May, Aug., Dec. Formal commencement May. Summer session from May to Aug.

Characteristics of Freshmen: 75% of applicants accepted. 33% of accepted applicants enrolled.

31% (971 students) submitted SAT scores; 20% (653 students) submitted ACT scores. *25th percentile*: ACT Composite 19. *75th percentile*: ACT Composite 24.

60% of entering freshmen expected to graduate within 5 years. 70% of freshmen from Wisconsin. Freshmen from 9 states and 4 foreign countries.

Admission: Rolling admissions plan. *Requirements:* Either graduation from accredited secondary school or GED. *Entrance tests:* College Board SAT or ACT composite. *For transfer students:* 2.0 GPA; maximum transfer credit limited only by residence requirement.

College credit and advanced placement for postsecondary-level work completed in secondary school, for College Board CLEP and AP, and for extrainstitutional learning (life experience) on basis of faculty assessment.

Tutoring available.

Degree Requirements: 128 credit hours; 2.0 GPA; final 32 credits in residence; earned points points for confrontation program; competency in computer science and mathematics; competence in language other than English through the fourth semester college level; English 150 during first year in residence; 1 Religious Studies course.

Fulfillment of some degree requirements possible by passing achievement tests. *Grading system:* A–F; pass-fail; incomplete (carries time limit).

Distinctive Educational Programs: Work-experience programs. Evening classes. Interdepartmental/interdisciplinary programs in international relations and environmental science. For upper division students, study abroad in Europe, Asia, Africa, Latin America and Australia.

Degrees Conferred: 464 *baccalaureate*; 74 *master's*. Bachelor's degrees awarded in top five disciplines: education 97; business, management, marketing, and related support services 87; psychology 57; health professions and related clinical sciences 49; visual and performing arts 38.

Fees and Other Expenses: *Full-time tuition per academic year 2008–09:* $19,500. *Books and supplies:* $850. *Room and board per academic year:* $6,070.

Financial Aid: Aid from institutionally generated funds is provided on the basis of academic merit, financial need, talent.

Institution has a Program Participation Agreement with the U.S. Department of Education for eligible students to receive Pell Grants and, depending upon the agreement, other federal aid.

Financial aid to full-time, first-time undergraduate students: 22% received federal grants averaging $1,517; 36% state/local grants averaging $1,257; 97% institutional grants averaging $9,278; 73% received loans averaging $2,419.

Departments and Teaching Staff: *Total instructional faculty:* 194. Student-to-faculty ratio: 20:1. Degrees held by full-time faculty: master's 11%, doctorate 73%, professional 16%. 89% hold terminal degrees.

Enrollment: Total enrollment 3,507. Undedrgraduate 2,411.

Characteristics of Student Body: *Ethnic/racial makeup:* number of Black non-Hispanic: 66; American Indian or Alaska Native: 13; Asian or Pacific Islander:35; Hispanic: 81; White non-Hispanic: 2,617; unknown: 137.

International Students: 47 undergraduate nonresident aliens enrolled fall 2008. No programs available to aid students whose native language is not English. Financial aid specifically designated for international students: variable number of scholarships available annually to qualifying students.

Student Life: On-campus residence halls house 50% of student body. Residence halls for females constitute 11% of such space, for both sexes 81%. 13% of males join and live in fraternity houses. *Intercollegiate athletics:* male: baseball, basketball, cross-country, football, golf, soccer, swimming, tennis, track, wrestling; female: basketball, cross-country, soccer, swimming, tennis, track, volleyball. *Special services:* Learning Resource Center, career/placement counseling, health services, personal counseling. *Student publications, radio: Century*, an annual literary magazine; *Perspective*, a biweekly newspaper. Radio station WCCX broadcasts 91 hours per week. *Surrounding community:* Waukesha population approximately 65,324. Milwaukee, 20 miles from campus, is nearest metropolitan area.

Library Collections: 198,000 volumes. 22,000 microforms; 1,400 audiovisual materials; 14,000 periodicals including via electronic access. Online catalog. Students have access to online information retrieval services and the Internet.

Most important holdings include Carroll College Archives; W. Norman Fitzgerald Civil War Collection; Welsh Collection.

Buildings and Grounds: Campus area 26 acres.

Chief Executive Officer: Dr. Douglas N. Hastad, President.

Address undergraduate inquiries to James Wiseman, Vice President of Enrollment.

Carthage College

2001 Alford Park Drive
Kenosha, Wisconsin 53140
Tel: (262) 551-6000 **E-mail:** admissions@carthage.edu
Fax: (262) 551-5762 **Internet:** www.carthage.edu

Institution Description: Carthage College is a private college affiliated with the Evangelical Lutheran Church of America. *Enrollment:* 2,972. *Degrees awarded:* Baccalaureate, master's.

Accreditation: *Regional:* NCA. *Professional*: chemistry, music, social work

History: Established and chartered in Hillsboro, Illinois, as the Literary and Theological Institute of the Lutheran Church in the Far West, changed name to Hillsboro College,and offered first instruction at postsecondary level 1847; moved to Springfield, Illinois, changed name to Illinois State University 1852; adopted present name 1869; moved to Carthage, Illinois, 1870; awarded first degree (baccalaureate) 1875; moved to Kenosha, Wisconsin 1962. *See* Harold Lentz, *The Miracle of Carthage* (Lima, OH: C.S.S. Publishing Co., 1975) for further information.

Institutional Structure: *Governing board:* Carthage College Board of Trustees. 40 members. Extrainstitutional representation: 23 trustees; institutional representation: 13 alumni. 4 ex officio. 27 voting. *Composition of institution:* Administrators 20. Academic affairs headed by dean of the college. Management/business/finances directed by vice president for business and finance. Full-time instructional faculty 126. Academic governance body, the faculty, meets an average of 9 times per year.

Calendar: Semesters (4-1-4 plan). Academic year Sept. to Aug. Freshmen admitted Sept., Feb., June, July. Degrees conferred and formal commencement May. Summer terms from June to Aug.

Characteristics of Freshmen: 5,496 applicants (female 2,928, male 2,568). 77% of applicants accepted. 20% of accepted applicants enrolled.

8% (55 students) submitted SAT scores; 97% (634 students) submitted ACT scores. *25th percentile*: SAT Critical Reading 460, SAT Math 480; ACT Composite 21. *75th percentile*: SAT Critical Rending 630, SAT Math 620; ACT Composite 26.

56% of entering freshmen expected to graduate within 5 years. 27% of freshmen from Wisconsin. Freshmen from 17 states and 2 foreign countries.

Admission: Rolling admissions plan. For fall acceptance, apply as early as end of junior year, but not later than registration day. Early acceptance available. *Requirements:* Evidence of ability to do college work. GED accepted. Recommend 16 secondary school units, with 4 English, 2 in a foreign language, 3 mathematics, 3 social sciences, 2 sciences and 2 academic electives. *Entrance tests:* ACT composite preferred; College Board SAT accepted. *For transfer students:* 2.0 minimum GPA; from 4-year accredited institution 106 hours maximum transfer credit; from 2-year accredited institution 69 hours; correspondence/extension students 28 hours.

College credit and advanced placement for postsecondary-level work completed in secondary school.

Tutoring available.

Degree Requirements: 138 credit hours; 2.0 GPA; last 32 credits in residence; physical education activities.

CARTHAGE COLLEGE—*cont'd*

Fulfillment of some degree requirements and exemption from some beginning courses possible by passing College Board CLEP or AP. *Grading system:* A–F; pass-fail; satisfactory/unsatisfactory (s/u); withdraw.

Distinctive Educational Programs: *For undergraduates:* Entrepreneurial studies in the natural sciences; Great Ideas: Intellectual Foundations of the West; Women's/Gender Studies. Study abroad opportunities available.

ROTC: Air Force and Army by arrangement with Marquette University.

Degrees Conferred: 488 *baccalaureate* biological and life sciences 14; business 102; communications 3; education 36; foreign languages 8; mathematics 11; parks and recreation 1; personal and miscellaneous services 9; philosophy/religion 10; physical sciences 10; public administration 10; psychology 25; social sciences and history 33; visual and performing arts 43. *Master's*: education 28.

Fees and Other Expenses: *Full-time tuition per academic year 2008–09:* $26,500. *Room and board per academic year:* $7,500. *Books and supplies:* $1,200. *Other expenses:* $2,500.

Financial Aid: Aid from institutionally generated funds is provided on the basis of academic merit, financial need, other criteria.

Institution has a Program Participation Agreement with the U.S. Department of Education for eligible students to receive Pell Grants and, depending upon the agreement, other federal aid.

Financial aid to full-time, first-time undergraduate students: 97% received some form of aid. Average amount of aid received: need-based scholarships/grants totaling $16,380,421, self-help $8,600,042, parent loans $1,882,449; non-need-based scholarships/grants totaling $6,532,287, self-help $4,018,506, parent loans $2,851,730.

Departments and Teaching Staff: *Total instructional faculty:* 196 (full-time 126, part-time 70). Student-to-faculty ratio: 16:1. Degrees held by full-time faculty: master's 11%, doctorate 89%. 89% hold terminal degrees.

Enrollment: Total enrollment 2,972. Undergraduate 2,865 (full-time 83%; female 51%, male 43%). Graduate 107 (part-time 100%). Transfer-in students 299.

Characteristics of Student Body: *Ethnic/racial makeup:* Black non-Hispanic: 4%; Asian or Pacific Islander: 2%; Hispanic: 5%; White non-Hispanic: 77%; unknown: 12%; nonresident alien 1%. *Age distribution:* number under 18: 19; 18–19: 892; 20–21: 875; 22–24: 307; 25–29: 117; 30–34: 91; 35–39: 74; 40–49: 127; 50–64: 43; 65 and over: 1; unknown 14. 27% of student body attend summer sessions.

International Students: 30 nonresident aliens enrolled fall 2008. Students from Europe, Asia, Latin America, Africa. No programs available to aid students whose native language is not English. No financial aid specifically designated for international students.

Student Life: On-campus residence halls house 65% of student body. Residence halls for males constitute 43% of such space; for females 46%. *Intercollegiate athletics:* male: baseball, basketball, cross-country, football, golf, soccer, swimming, tennis, track, volleyball; female: basketball, cross-country, golf, soccer, softball, swimming, tennis, track, water polo, volleyball. *Special regulations:* Cars permitted without restrictions. Residence hall visitation from 8am to midnight Sunday through Thursday; 8am to 1am Friday and Saturday. *Special services:* Medical services. *Student publications: The Current,* a weekly newspaper; *Centrique*, an annual literary magazine; *Driftwood*, a yearbook. *Surrounding community:* Kenosha population 80,000. Milwaukee, 30 miles from campus, is nearest metropolitan area. Served by passenger rail service 2 miles from campus.

Library Collections: 140,000 volumes including bound books, serial backfiles, electronic documents, and government documents not in separate collections. Online catalog. 9,000 microforms; 1,300 audiovisual materials; 450 current serial subscriptions. Computer work stations available. Students have access to the Internet at no charge. Total 2008–09 budget for books and materials: $119,600.

Most important special holdings include Palumbo Collection on the Civil War; Dawe Collection on English and American Literature (1890–1950); Wilde Historiography Collection.

Buildings and Grounds: Campus area 95 acres.

Chief Executive Officer: Dr. F. Gregory Campbell, President.

Undergraduates address admission inquiries to Thomas V. Augustine, Director of Admissions; graduate inquiries to James Igleheart, Dean of Professional Studies.

Concordia University Wisconsin

12800 North Lake Shore Drive
Mequon, Wisconsin 53097-2402
Tel: (262) 243-5700 **E-mail:** admissions@cuw.edu
Fax: (262) 243-4351 **Internet:** www.cuw.edu

Institution Description: Concordia University Wisconsin is a private school owned and operated by The Lutheran Church-Missouri Synod. *Enrollment:* 6,549. *Degrees awarded:* Associate, baccalaureate, master's, doctorate (physical therapy). Certificates also awarded.

Accreditation: *Regional:* NCA.

History: Established as a Lutheran training school for men and offered first instruction at postsecondary level 1881; chartered 1886; became junior college 1891; awarded first degree (associate) 1892; added lay training institute 1961; admitted women 1965; added baccalaureate program 1978; moved to new campus in Mequon 1983. *See* Faculty of Concordia College, *Concordia College, Milwaukee, Wisconsin - 1881–1931* (Milwaukee: Northwestern Publishing House, 1931) for further information.

Institutional Structure: *Governing board:* Foundation Board of 15 members. Extrainstitutional representation: 11 trustees including 2 pastors of congregations, 1 alumnus; institutional representation: president of the university. 1 ex officio. 8 voting. *Composition of institution:* Administrators 11. Academic affairs headed by Vice President of Academics. Management/business/finances directed by Vice President of Business and Finance. Full-time instructional faculty 88. Academic governance body, Academic Council, meets an average of 12 times per year.

Calendar: Semesters (4-1-4 plan). Academic year Aug. to May. Freshmen admitted Aug. or Sept., Jan., Feb., June. Degrees conferred May, Dec. Formal commencement May. Summer session of 3 terms from May to Aug.

Characteristics of Freshmen: 2,278 applicants (female 1,312, male 966). 77% of applicants accepted. 30% of accepted applicants enrolled.

100% of applicants submitted ACT scores. *25th percentile*: ACT Composite 14, ACT English 14, ACT Math 19. *75th percentile*: ACT Composite 26, ACT English 26, ACT Math 26.

50% entering freshmen expected to graduate within 5 years. 75% of freshmen from Wisconsin. Freshmen from 19 states and 25 foreign countries.

Admission: Rolling admissions plan. For fall acceptance, apply as early as Sept. 1 of previous year, but not later than Aug. 25 of year of enrollment. *Requirements:* Either graduation from accredited secondary school with 16 units which normally include 3 English, 2 in a foreign language or in fine arts, 2 natural science, 2 social studies (including 1 history), 1 algebra, 1 geometry, 5 academic electives; or GED. Minimum 2.25 GPA. *Entrance tests:* College Board SAT or ACT composite. *For transfer students:* 2.0 minimum GPA; from 4-year accredited institution 72 hours maximum transfer credit; from 2-year accredited institution and correspondence/extension students 70 hours.

College credit and advanced placement for postsecondary-level work completed in secondary school and for extrainstitutional learning on basis of portfolio and faculty assessment.

Tutoring available. Developmental courses offered during regular academic year; credit given.

Degree Requirements: *For all associate degrees:* 63 credit hours; 18 credits, including last term, in residence; 2 credits physical education. *For all baccalaureate degrees:* 126 credit hours; 36 credits, including last 2 terms in residence; 3 credits physical education. *For all degrees:* 2.0 GPA; distribution requirements.

Fulfillment of some degree requirements and exemption from some beginning courses possible by passing departmental examinations, College Board CLEP, APP. *Grading system:* A–F; pass-no credit; withdraw (carries time limit); incomplete (carries time limit).

Distinctive Educational Programs: Work-experience programs. Evening classes. Pre-ministerial and Lay Ministry programs. Doctor of Physical Therapy. Teacher certification program. Facilities and programs for independent research, including individual majors, tutorials. Students may take courses at the University of Wisconsin-Milwaukee. Study abroad programs predominantly in Central and Latin American countries, although several winterim offerings travel to Europe.

Degrees Conferred: 12 *associate;* 583 *baccalaureate;* 348 *master's*; 24 *doctorate.*

Fees and Other Expenses: *Full-time tuition per academic year:* $19,990; contact the university for current graduate tuition /fees. *Required fees:* $60. *Room and board per academic year:* $7,700. *Books and supplies:* $1,156. *Other expenses:* $2,046.

Financial Aid: Aid from institutionally generated funds is provided on the basis of academic merit, financial need, other criteria.

Financial aid to full-time, first-time undergraduate students: 98% received some form of aid. Average amount of aid received: federal grants $3,501; Pell

grants $2,544; other federal aid $1,335; state/local grants $2,716; institutional grants $9,451.

Departments and Teaching Staff: *Total instructional faculty:* 204 (full-time 88, part-time 116). Total faculty with doctorate, first-professional, or other terminal degree: 81. Student-to-faculty ratio: 14:1. Degrees held by full-time faculty: 60% hold terminal degrees.

Enrollment: Total enrollment 6,549. Undergraduate 3,786 (full-time 52%; female 63%, male 37%). Graduate 2,763 (full-time 70%). Transfer-in students 593.

Characteristics of Student Body: *Ethnic/racial makeup:* Black non-Hispanic: 12%; American Indian or Alaska Native: 1%; Asian or Pacific Islander: 1%; Hispanic: 2%; White non-Hispanic: 53%; unknown: 30%; nonresident alien 1%.

International Students: 66 nonresident aliens enrolled fall 2008. Programs available to aid students whose native language is not English: social, cultural, financial. English as a Second Language Program. Financial aid specifically designated for international students: scholarships available annually for undergraduate international students.

Student Life: On-campus residence halls house 80% of student body. Residence halls for males constitute 54% of such space, for females 47%. *Intercollegiate athletics:* male: baseball, basketball, golf, soccer; female: basketball, softball, tennis, volleyball. *Special regulations:* Cars must have parking permits; fee charged. Quiet hours set by residence hall. Visitation in lounges 6pm to midnight. *Special services:* Medical services. *Surrounding community:* Milwaukee population 635,000. Served by mass transit bus system; airport 10 miles from campus; passenger rail service 3 miles from campus.

Publications: *The Concordian,* a Concordia magazine sent three times per year to various constituents; *Camera,* a bulletin insert, to same public.

Library Collections: 577 000 volumes. 271,000 microforms; 4,200 audiovisual materials. 37,000 periodicals including via electronic access. Online catalog. Computer work stations available. Students have access to online information retrieval services and the Internet.

Most important special holdings include collections of Lutheran theology books (16th to 20th century); 19th-century hymnals (primarily Protestant); 19th century bronzes.

Buildings and Grounds: Campus area 125 acres.

Chief Executive Officer: Rev. Dr. Patrick Ferry, President.

Address admission inquiries to Kenneth K. Gaschk, Director of Admissions.

Edgewood College

855 Woodrow Street
Madison, Wisconsin 53711

Tel: (608) 663-4861 **E-mail:** admissions@edgewood.edu
Fax: (608) 663-3291 **Internet:** www.edgewood

Institution Description: Edgewood College is a private college affiliated with the Roman Catholic Church. *Enrollment:* 2,544. *Degrees awarded:* Associate, baccalaureate, master's, doctorate.

Accreditation: *Regional:* NCA. *Professional*: nursing, teacher education

History: Chartered as St. Regina Academy 1881; established as junior college and offered first instruction at postsecondary level 1927; awarded first degree (associate) 1929; became senior college and adopted present name 1941. *See* Sister Barbara Beyenka, *Edgewood College, 1927–1977: A Jubilee History* (Madison, WI: Edgewood College, 1977) for further information.

Institutional Structure: *Governing board:* Edgewood College Board of Trustees. Extrainstitutional representation: 31 trustees; institutional representation: 3 instructional faculty members, president of the college. 1 ex officio. 26 voting. *Composition of institution:* Administrators 7. Academic affairs headed by academic dean and assistant academic dean. Management/business/finances directed by business officer. Full-time instructional faculty 74. Academic governance body, Faculty Association, meets an average of 8 times per year.

Calendar: Semesters (4-1-4 plan). Academic year Sept. to May. Freshmen admitted Sept., Jan., June. Degrees conferred and formal commencement May. Summer session of 1 term from late May to early Aug.

Characteristics of Freshmen: 80% of applicants accepted. 37.8% of accepted applicants enrolled.

Average ACT score 22. Average high school GPA 3.27.

46% of entering freshmen expected to graduate within 5 hears. 90% of freshmen from Wisconsin. Freshmen from 5 states and 3 foreign countries.

Admission: Rolling admissions plan. Early acceptance available. *Requirements:* 12 units in high school from natural science, social science, foreign language, English, mathematics, and 3 units of electives. Minimum 2.0 GPA. *Entrance tests:* ACT composite. *For transfer students:* 2.0 minimum GPA; maximum transfer credit limited only by residence requirements.

College credit for postsecondary-level work completed in secondary school. College credit and advanced placement for USAFI and for extrainstitutional learning on basis of portfolio and faculty assessments.

Developmental courses offered during regular academic year; credit given.

Degree Requirements: *For all associate degrees:* 60 credit hours. *For all baccalaureate degrees:* 120 credit hours (some majors require additional credit hours). *For all degrees:* 2.0 GPA; 32 hours in residence required; liberal arts foundation requirements. For nursing degree, additional requirements.

Fulfillment of some degree requirements and exemption from some beginning courses possible by passing departmental examinations; College Board CLEP, ACT-PEP. *Grading system:* A–F; pass-fail; withdraw (carries time limit); incomplete (deadline after which A–F is assigned).

Distinctive Educational Programs: Interdisciplinary programs in natural science and mathematics, social studies. Individual majors. Limited cross-registration with University of Wisconsin-Madison. Baccalaureate completion program for registered nurses in majors other than nursing. *Other distinctive programs:* master's programs in nursing administration, marriage and family therapy. Baccalaureate program in art therapy. Cooperative study abroad programs with many institutions. Baccalaureate accelerated degree program (evening courses). Doctoral program in educational leadership; human issues program; environmental studies minor; ethnic studies minor; women's studies minor.

ROTC: Air Force offered in cooperation with University of Wisconsin-Madison.

Degrees Conferred: 380 *baccalaureate;* 112 *graduate degrees.*

Fees and Other Expenses: *Full-time tuition per academic year:* $20,040. *Room and board per academic year:* $8,828. *Books and supplies:* $800. *Other expenses:* $2,735.

Financial Aid: Aid from institutionally generated funds is provided on the basis of academic merit, financial need.

Institutional funding for undergraduates: 678 scholarships and grants totaling $1,863,000; 280 college-assigned jobs totaling $354,000.

Federal and state funding for undergraduates: 465 scholarships and grants totaling $1,339,257; 896 loans totaling $4,765,851; 148 work-study jobs totaling $121,600. *For graduate students:* 69 loans totaling $679,490.

Departments and Teaching Staff: *Total instructional faculty:* 157. Student-to-faculty ratio: 13:1. Degrees held by full-time faculty: master's 20%, doctorate 70%. 76% hold terminal degrees.

Enrollment: Total enrollment 2,544. Undergraduate 1,989 (full-time 80%; female 70%, male 30%). Graduate 553. Transfer-in students 200.

Characteristics of Student Body: *Ethnic/racial makeup:* Black non-Hispanic: 3%; Asian or Pacific Islander: 2%; Hispanic: 3%; White non-Hispanic: 84%; unknown: 5%; nonresident alien 2%.

International Students: 52 nonresident aliens enrolled fall 2008. Students from Europe, Asia, Latin America, Africa. Programs available to aid students whose native language is not English: English as a Second Language Program. No financial aid specifically designated for international students.

Student Life: 20% of student body live on campus. 26% of residents are male. *Intercollegiate athletics:* male: basketball, cross-country, tennis, golf, soccer, baseball; female: basketball, cross-country, tennis, volleyball, softball, golf, soccer. *Special regulations:* Permits required for cars. Residence hall visitation and quiet hours set according to Sun.–Thurs. and Fri.–Sat. schedule. *Special services:* limited on-campus health care. *Student publications: On the Edge,* a bimonthly newspaper; *Cerebral Cafe,* a literary magazine published twice a year; yearbook. *Surrounding community:* Madison population approximately 191,000. Milwaukee, 95 miles from Madison. Served by mass transit bus system; airport 4 miles from campus.

Library Collections: 89,000 volumes including bound books, serial backfiles, electronic documents, and government documents not in separate collections. Online catalog. 94,000 microforms; 4,000 audiovisual materials; 490 current serial subscriptions. Computer work stations available. Students have access to the Internet at no charge.

Most important special holdings include collections on religion, education and curriculum, and liberal arts.

Buildings and Grounds: Campus area 55 acres.

Chief Executive Officer: Dr. Daniel Carey, President. >p<Address admission inquiries to Christien Benedict, Director of Admissions.

Lakeland College

W3718 South Drive, CTHM
Plymouth, Wisconsin 53073
Tel: (920) 565-2111 **E-mail:** admissions@lakeland.edu
Fax: (920) 565-1206 **Internet:** www.lakeland.edu

Institution Description: Lakeland College is a private institution affiliated with the United Church of Christ. *Enrollment:* 4,013. *Degrees awarded:* Baccalaureate, master's.

Accreditation: *Regional:* NCA.

History: Established as Mission House, an academy, college, and seminary, and offered first instruction at postsecondary level 1862; awarded first degree (baccalaureate) 1866; adopted present name 1956.

Institutional Structure: *Governing board:* Board of Trustees. Extrainstitutional representation: 36 trustees; institutional representation: president of the college, college attorney. *Composition of institution:* Administrators 12. Academic affairs headed by dean of the college. Business/finances directed by treasurer of the college.

Calendar: Semesters (4-1-4 plan). Academic year Sept. to May. Formal commencement May. Summer session of 1 term from May to Aug.

Characteristics of Freshmen: 68% of applicants accepted. 35% of accepted applicants enrolled.

Average secondary school rank of freshmen 59th percentile. Mean ACT Composite score 20.

79% of freshmen from Wisconsin. Freshmen from 5 states and 3 foreign countries.

Admission: Rolling admissions plan. Early acceptance available. *Requirements:* Either graduation from accredited secondary school or GED. GPA 2.0; ACT composite 19; rank top 50% of class. *Entrance tests:* College Board SAT or ACT composite.

College credit and advanced placement for postsecondary-level work completed in secondary school.

Degree Requirements: *For baccalaureate degrees:* 136 credit hours; 2.0 GPA in major area; final 40 hours in residence; general studies proficiency requirements.

Fulfillment of some degree requirements and exemption from some beginning courses possible by passing College Board CLEP, AP. *Grading system:* A–F; withdraw (carries time limit).

Distinctive Educational Programs: Credit received for courses taken during January term at other 4-year accredited schools. Study abroad in Germany. Semester in Washington (DC). Placement services. Study in Japan.

Degrees Conferred: 712 *baccalaureate*; 80 *master's*. Bachelor's degrees awarded in top five disciplines: business, management, marketing, and related support services 415; computer and information sciences 151; education 76; social sciences 15; psychology 13.

Fees and Other Expenses: *Full-time tuition per academic year 2008–09:* $16,795. *Books and supplies:* $600. *Room and board per academic year:* $6,195.

Financial Aid: Aid from institutionally generated fund is provided on the basis of academic merit, financial need.

Institution has a Program Participation Agreement with the U.S. Department of Education for eligible students to receive Pell Grants and, depending upon the agreement, other federal aid.

Financial aid to full-time, first-time undergraduate students: 40% received federal grants averaging $3,086; 50% state/local grants averaging $2,378; 55% institutional grants averaging $6,301; 82% received loans averaging $4,472.

Departments and Teaching Staff: *Total instructional faculty:* 55. Degrees held by full-time faculty: doctorate 30.9%, master's 58.2%, baccalaureate 10.9%. 36.4% hold terminal degrees.

Enrollment: Total enrollment 4,013. Undergraduate 3,443.

Characteristics of Student Body: *Ethnic/racial makeup:* Black non-Hispanic: 6%; American Indian or Alaska Native: 1%; Asian or Pacific Islander: 3%; Hispanic: 2%; White non-Hispanic: 74%; unknown: 10%.

International Students: 162 nonresident aliens enrolled fall 2008. Programs available to aid students whose native language is not English: English as a Second Language Program. No financial aid specifically designated for international students.

Student Life: On-campus residence halls. *Intercollegiate athletics:* male: baseball, basketball, football, soccer, tennis, track and field, cross-country; female: basketball, cross-country, softball, tennis, track and field, volleyball. *Student activities:* Greek fraternities and sororities, Circle K, Student Government, Activities Board, multicultural organizations. *Student publications, radio:* *Mirror*, a weekly newspaper; *Spectrum*, a yearbook. Radio station WVLC. *Surrounding community:* Sheboygan population 50,000. Milwaukee and Green Bay, both 60 miles from campus, are the nearest metropolitan areas.

Library Collections: 120,000 volumes. 25,500 units in microform; 590 audiovisual materials; 298 current periodical subscriptions.

Most important special interests are the Jewish Holocaust and modern American poetry.

Buildings and Grounds: Campus area 145 acres.

Chief Executive Officer: Dr. Stephen Gould, President.

Address admission inquiries to Nathan D. Dehne, Director of Admissions.

Lawrence University

115 South Drew Street
P.O. Box 599
Appleton, Wisconsin 54912
Tel: (920) 832-6500 **E-mail:** excel@lawrence.edu
Fax: (920) 832-6782 **Internet:** www.lawrence.edu

Institution Description: Lawrence University is a private, independent, nonprofit institution. *Enrollment:* 1,496. *Degrees awarded:* Baccalaureate.

Member of the consortium Associated Colleges of the Midwest (ACM).

Accreditation: *Regional:* NCA. *Professional*: chemistry, music

History: Established as Lawrence Institute, chartered, and offered first instruction at postsecondary level 1847; changed name to Lawrence University 1849; awarded first degree (baccalaureate) 1857; changed name to Lawrence College 1913; merged with Milwaukee Downer College and adopted present name 1964.

Institutional Structure: *Governing board:* Board of Trustees of Lawrence University of Wisconsin. Extrainstitutional representation: 31 trustees; institutional representation: president of the college. 1 ex officio. All voting. *Composition of institution:* Administrators 87 including 8 division heads and the president. Academic affairs headed by dean of the faculty. Dean of students assisted by 3 associate deans (for academic advising, activities, and residential life, respectively). Management/business/finances directed by vice president for business affairs and treasurer. Full-time instructional faculty 149. Academic governance body, the faculty, meets an average of 9 times per year.

Calendar: 3 ten-week terms. Academic year Sept. to June. Freshmen admitted Sept. Degrees conferred June, Dec. Formal commencement June. No summer session.

Characteristics of Freshmen: 2,618 applicants (female 1,48, male 1,132). 650% of applicants admitted. 29% of applicants admitted and enrolled.

38% (143 students) submitted SAT scores; 52% (194 students) submitted ACT scores. *25th percentile*: SAT Critical Reading 590, SAT Math 620; ACT Composite 26. *75th percentile*: SAT Critical Reading 720, SAT Math 690; ACT Composite 31. 19 National Merit Scholars.

75% of entering freshmen expected to graduate within 5 years. 38% of freshmen from Wisconsin. Freshmen from 43 states and 42 foreign countries.

Admission: Two early decision plans: option 1 deadline Nov. 15; option 2 deadline Dec. 1. Regular application deadline Jan. 15. Early admission available. *Requirements:* Graduation from accredited secondary school with 16 academic units (recommended), normally including English, a foreign language, history, mathematics, science, and social studies. Minimum of B average (recommended). *Entrance tests:* College Board SAT or ACT composite optional. . *For transfer students:* 3.0 minimum GPA; maximum transfer credits limited only by residence requirement.

College credit and advanced placement for postsecondary-level work completed in secondary school. Advanced placement for departmental examination.

Degree Requirements: 36 courses; 2.0 GPA; 6 terms in residence; general education and major course requirements; departmental examination (when required by the department).

Fulfillment of some degree requirements and exemption from some beginning courses possible by passing College Board AP test(s). Exemption from courses also possible by passing departmental examination and on the basis of faculty assessment. *Grading system:* A–F; withdraw (carries penalty if failing at time of withdrawal; also carries time limit); incomplete (deadline after which F is assigned); satisfactory-unsatisfactory.

Distinctive Educational Programs: 5-year double degree program through the Lawrence Conservatory of Music. Dual-degree programs in allied health sciences with Rush University; in engineering with Columbia University (NY), Washington University (MO), and Rensselaer Polytechnic Institute; in forestry and environmental studies with Duke University (NC); and in social service administration with University of Chicago. Cooperative program in nursing and medical technology with Rush-Saint Luke's Presbyterian Medical Center. Facilities for using telecommunications in the classroom. Interdisciplinary programs in computer studies, environmental studies, international studies, linguistics, neuroscience, public policy analysis, social thought, and (through the ACM)

Latin American culture and society. Extensive opportunities for independent research, including honors programs, student-designed courses and majors, tutorials, writing-for-credit, and the Scholar of the University program. Institutionally sponsored study abroad at the London Center, in Eastern Europe, in France (at both Tours and Paris), in Munich, and in a Spanish-speaking country. Through the ACM, the Great Lakes Colleges Association (GLCA), and various other organizations, additional opportunities for study abroad at the Chinese University of Hong Kong; in Florence; at the University of Poona in India; at the Intercollegiate Center for Classical Studies in Rome; at Waseda University in Tokyo; in Costa Rica (tropical field research); and at the University of Zagreb in Yugoslavia. Institutionally sponsored programs for off-campus study in U.S. include academic internships, field trips for geology and marine biology, and the Washington (DC) Semester for political science and American studies. Additional programs for off-campus study in U.S. (through ACM) in urban education and urban studies (Chicago, IL) and in wilderness studies (at the ACM Wilderness Field Station in Minnesota); and through ACM and GLCA joint sponsorship, in the humanities at the Newberry Library in Chicago and in scientific research at the Oak Ridge National Laboratory near Knoxville, Tennessee.

Degrees Conferred: 295 *baccalaureate:* degrees awarded in top five disciplines include biological and life sciences 36, foreign languages 18, physical sciences 15, social science and history 52, visual and performing arts 54.

Fees and Other Expenses: *Full-time tuition per academic year 2008–09:* $33,264. *Required fees:* $222. *Room and board per academic year:* $6,957. *Books and supplies:* $675. *Other expenses:* $1,405.

Financial Aid: Aid from institutionally generated funds is provided on the basis of academic merit, financial need.

Financial aid to full-time, first-time undergraduate students: 945 received some form of aid. Need-based scholarships/grants totaling $6,175,298, self-help $1,927,524; non-need-based scholarships/grants totaling $1,381,299, self-help $273,974, parent loans $2,318,808.

Departments and Teaching Staff: *Total instructional faculty:* 181 (full-time 149, part-time 32). Total faculty with doctorate, first-professional, or other terminal degree: 157. Student-to-faculty ratio: 9:1. Degrees held by full-time faculty: doctorate 75%, master's 22%, baccalaureate 3%. 96% hold terminal degrees.

Enrollment: Total enrollment 1,496. Undergraduate1,496 (full-time 96%; female 54%, male 48%). Transfer-in students 34.

Characteristics of Student Body: *Ethnic/racial makeup:* Black non-Hispanic: 2%; American Indian or Alaska Native: 3%; Hispanic: 2%; White non-Hispanic: 72%; unknown: 13%; nonresident alien 6%. *Age distribution:* number under 18: 78; 18–19: 624; 20–21: 551; 22–24: 102; 25–29: 18; 30–34: 5; 35–39: 1; 40–49: 1.

International Students: 90 nonresident aliens enrolled fall 2008. Students from Europe, Asia, Latin America, Africa, Canada, Middle East. Programs available to aid students whose native language is not English: social, cultural. Financial aid specifically designated for international students.

Student Life: Over 90% of the students live on campus in 8 coeducational residence halls, 30% belong to 6 fraternities and 3 sororities. *Intercollegiate athletics:* males and females participate in 26 varsity and 6 club sports. *Special regulations:* Cars maintained on-campus must be registered. *Special services:* Office of Career Planning and Placement, Writing Lab, Health Center, Counseling Center, campus store. *Student publications, radio: Lawrentian*, student newspaper; *Tropos*, literary magazine; *Ariel*, yearbook. WLFM student-run radio station and part of Wisconsin Public Radio network. *Surrounding community:* Situated in Appleton (population 60,000). Fox Valley and surrounding communities population 150,000. Campus overlooks the Fox River and is located near the city's downtown area. Appleton is accessible by car, bus, and plane.

Library Collections: 404,000 volumes. 296,000 government documents; 102,000 microforms; 22,000 audiovisual materials; 1,900 current periodical subscriptions. Online catalog. Students have access to online information retrieval services and the Internet.

Most important special holdings include Human Relations Area File; Evans Early American Imprints; 19th century novels in serial form; Lincoln Collection; Alice G. Chapman Memorial Library (rare books and manuscripts); Music Collection.

Buildings and Grounds: Campus area 84 acres.

Chief Executive Officer: Dr. Jill Beck, President.

Address admission inquiries to Steven T. Syverson, Dean of Admissions and Financial Aid.

Maranatha Baptist Bible College

745 West Main Street
Watertown, Wisconsin 53094
Tel: (920) 261-9300 **E-mail:** admissions@mbbc.edu
Fax: (920) 261-9109 **Internet:** www.mbbc.edu

Institution Description: Maranatha Baptist Bible College is a comprehensive, coeducation institution. *Enrollment:* 857. *Degrees offered:* Associate, baccalaureate, master's.

Accreditation: *Regional:* NCA. *National:* ATS. *Professional*: theology

History: Founded 1968.

Calendar: Semesters. Academic year Aug. to May.

Characteristics of Freshmen: 361 applicants (female 183, male 178). 58% of applicants accepted. 48% of accepted applicants enrolled.

Average secondary school rank of freshmen 34th percentile.

6% (13 students) submitted SAT scores; 94% (199 students) submitted ACT scores. *25th percentile*: ACT Composite 20. *75th percentile*: ACT Composite 25.

51% of entering freshmen expected to graduate within 5 years. 22% of freshmen from Wisconsin. Freshmen from 27 states and 3 foreign countries.

Admission: *Requirements:* High school graduation or GED. *For transfer students:* TOEFL.

College credit and advanced placement for postsecondary-level work completed in secondary school and for extrainstitutional learning.

Developmental/remedial courses offered in summer session and regular academic year; credit given.

Degree Requirements: *For all associate degrees:* 64 semester hours. *For all baccalaureate degrees:* 128 semester hours; 6 hours of mathematics or completion of math proficiency test; computer course for business, math education majors; internship (some majors). *Grading system:* A–F.

Degrees Conferred: 13 *associate* ; 120 *baccalaureate:* business and management 10; education 55; health professions 3; liberal arts 12; theology 36; visual and performing arts 6. *Master's:* theology 8.

Fees and Other Expenses: *Full-time tuition per academic year 2008–09:* undergraduate $10,560; contact the college for current graduate tuition. *Required fees:* 870. *Room and board per academic year:* $5,800. *Books and supplies:* $900. *Other expenses:* $3,200.

Financial Aid: Aid from institutionally generated funds is provided on the basis of academic merit, financial need, other criteria.

Institution has a Program Participation Agreement with the U.S. Department of Education for eligible students to receive Pell Grants and, depending upon the agreement, other federal aid.

Financial aid to full-time, first-time undergraduate students: 76% received some form of aid. Need-based scholarships/grants totaling $1,245,847, self-help $2,877,733, parent loans $871,616, tuition waivers $287,766; non-need-based scholarships/grants totaling $90,200, self-help $1,032,683, parent loans $131,857, tuition waivers $38,430.

Departments and Teaching Staff: *Total instructional faculty:* 72 (full-time 45, part-time 27). Total faculty with doctorate, first-professional, or other terminal degree: 16. Student-to-faculty ratio: 57:1. Degrees held by full-time faculty: doctorate 31%, master's 66%, professional 3%. 31% hold terminal degrees.

Enrollment: Total enrollment 857. Undergraduate 816 (full-time 94%; female 55%, male 45%). Graduate 41 (full-time 46%). Transfer-in students 42.

Characteristics of Student Body: *Ethnic/racial makeup:* Black non-Hispanic: 1%; Hispanic: 2%; White non-Hispanic: 92%; nonresident alien 1%.

International Students: 9 nonresident aliena enrolled fall 2008. No programs available to aid students whose native language is not English. No financial aid specifically designated for international students.

Student Life: On-campus residence required through senior year. *Intercollegiate athletics:* participation for males and females available: baseball, basketball, cross-country, soccer, softball, volleyball.

Library Collections: 125,000 volumes including bound books, serial backfiles, electronic documents, and government documents not in separate collections. Online catalog. Current serial subscriptions: 500 paper, 75,000 microform; 1 electronic. 500 recordings; 400 compact discs; 75 CD-ROMs. Computer work stations available. Students have fee-based access to online information retrieval services.

Most important special collections include Weeks Collection; Weniger Collection; Early British Baptist Microform Collection.

Buildings and Grounds: Campus area 60 acres.

Chief Executive Officer: Dr. Larry Oats, President.

Address admissions inquiries to Dr. James Harrison, Vice President for Institutional Advancement.

Marian College of Fond du Lac

45 South National Avenue
Fond du Lac, Wisconsin 54935
Tel: (800) 262-7426 **E-mail:** admissions@mariancollege.edu
Fax: (920) 923-7154 **Internet:** www.mariancollege.edu

Institution Description: Marian College of Fond du Lac is a private, nonprofit institution affiliated with the Congregation of the Sisters of St. Agnes, Roman Catholic Church. *Enrollment:* 3,040. *Degrees awarded:* Baccalaureate, master's, doctorate

Accreditation: *Regional:* NCA. *Professional*: nursing, social work, teacher education

History: Established 1936; awarded first degree (baccalaureate) 1941.

Institutional Structure: *Governing board:* Marian College Board of Trustees. Representation: 22 trustees. All voting. *Composition of institution:* Administrators 31. Academic affairs headed by Vice President of Academic Affairs. Management/business/finance directed by Vice President of Business and Finance. Full-time instructional faculty 81. Academic governance body, Curriculum and Educational Standards Committee, meets once per month.

Calendar: Semesters. Academic year Aug. to May. Freshmen admitted Aug., Jan., June. Degrees conferred May, Aug., Dec. Formal commencement May. Summer session: May to July.

Characteristics of Freshmen: 85% of applicants admitted. 32% of applicants admitted and enrolled.

25th percentile: ACT Composite 18, ACT English 16, ACT Math 17. *75th percentile*: ACT Composite 22, ACT English 22, ACT Math 23.

93% of freshmen from Wisconsin. Freshmen from 4 states and 1 foreign country.

Admission: Rolling admissions plan. Apply no later than first week of classes. *Requirements:* Either graduation from accredited secondary school with 16 units which must include 3 English, 1 history, 1 laboratory science, 2 mathematics; or GED. Additional units in science for nursing program. *Entrance tests:* College Board SAT or ACT composite; all admitted freshmen are required to take the ACT. For foreign students TOEFL. *For transfer students:* 2.0 minimum GPA; from 4-year accredited institution 96 hours maximum transfer credit. Maximum transfer credit from 2-year accredited institutions and for correspondence/extension students varies.

Advanced placement for postsecondary-level work completed in secondary school. College credit and advanced placement for extrainstitutional learning (life experience) on basis of faculty assessment.

Developmental/remedial courses offered during regular academic year; credit given.

Degree Requirements: 128 credit hours; 2.0 GPA; 32 hours in residence; general education requirements.

Fulfillment of some degree requirements and exemption from some beginning courses possible by passing College Board CLEP; exemption from some beginning courses possible by passing College Board AP. *Grading system:* A–F; withdraw; incomplete.

Distinctive Educational Programs: Traditional programs at the baccalaureate level in nursing, business, education, social sciences, liberal arts, mathematics, and natural sciences. Non-traditional evening/weekend programs in business, nursing, radiologic technology, operations management, and administration of justice. Master of Arts and Ph.D. in education. Community Service program, cooperative education program. Study abroad in England, Spain, and other locations.

ROTC: Army.

Degrees Conferred: 361 *baccalaureate:* biological sciences 8; business and management 127; communications 13; computer and information sciences 11 education 26l English 1; foreign languages 1; health professions 82; history 2; interdisciplinary studies 2; liberal arts 1; mathematics 1; parks and recreation 8; psychology 9; public administration 22; security and protective services 38; social sciences 6; visual and performing arts 3. 250 *master's:* business 39; education 200; health professions 16.

Fees and Other Expenses: *Full-time tuition per academic year 2008–09:* undergraduate $17,630; graduate tuition charges per credit. *Required fees:* $330. *Room and board per academic year:* $5,50.

Financial Aid: Aid from institutionally generated funds is provided on the basis of academic merit, financial need.

Financial aid to full-time, first-time undergraduate students: need-based scholarships/grants totaling $10,638,708, self-help $8,221,048, parent loans $779,598, tuition waivers $104,967; non-need-based scholarships/grants totaling $1,041,845,, self-help $,715,374, parent loans $403,631, tuition waivers $218,419.

Departments and Teaching Staff: *Total instructional faculty:* 278 (full-time 81, part-time 197). Total faculty with doctorate, first-professional, or other terminal degree: 77. Student-to-faculty ratio: 12.3:1. Degrees held by full-time faculty: doctorate 42%, master's 58%. 42% hold terminal degrees.

Enrollment: Total enrollment 3,040. Undergraduate 1,424.

Characteristics of Student Body: *Ethnic/racial makeup:* Black non-Hispanic: 74, American Indian or Alaska Native: 17; Asian or Pacific Islander: 27; Hispanic: 35; White non-Hispanic: 1,911; unknown: 49. *Age distribution:* number under 18: 409; 18–19: 448; 20–21: 273; 22–24: 170; 25–29: 222; 30–34: 175; 35–39: 152; 40–49: 212; 50–64: 45; 65 and over: 3; unknown: 17.

International Students: 14 nonresident aliens enrolled fall 2008. Students from Europe, Asia, Latin America, Canada. Programs to aid students whose native language is not English: social, cultural, financial. Financial aid available annually for undergraduate international students.

Student Life: On-campus residence halls house 34% of student body. *Intercollegiate athletics:* male: baseball, golf, ice hockey, basketball, soccer, cross-country, tennis; female: golf, volleyball, basketball, soccer, cross-country, tennis. *Special regulations:* Cars permitted for all students with proper registration. Students from outside Fond du Lac area required to live on campus in residence facilities freshman and sophomore years. *Special services:* Academic Support Services, personal counseling, cooperative education, safety and security. Career Services: 87% placement rate following graduation. Part-time Health Services Director. Full-time Campus Ministry and Music Ministry operation with full-time Chaplain. *Student publications:* newspaper, yearbook, literary publications. *Surrounding community:* Fond du Lac population 45,000. Milwaukee, 60 miles from campus, is nearest metropolitan area. Served by airport 6 miles from campus.

Library Collections: 98,000 volumes including bound books, serial backfiles, electronic documents, and government documents not in separate collections. Online catalog. 12,000 microforms; 2,000 audiovisual materials; 1,000 current serial subscriptions. Computer work stations available. Students have access to the Internet at no charge.

Most important holdings include collections on curriculum materials; English and American literature; American history.

Buildings and Grounds: Campus area 97 acres. Campus DVD available.

Chief Executive Officer: Dr. Josefina Baltodano, President.

Address admission inquiries to Eric Peterson, Dean of Admissions.

Marquette University

615 North Eleventh Street
Milwaukee, Wisconsin 53201
Tel: (414) 288-7710 **E-mail:** go2marquette@marquette.edu
Fax: (414) 288-7197 **Internet:** www.marquette.edu

Institution Description: Marquette University is an independent, coeducational institution affiliated with the Society of Jesus, Roman Catholic Church. *Enrollment:* 11,633. *Degrees awarded:* Associate, baccalaureate, first-professional (dentistry, law), master's, doctorate.

Accreditation: *Regional:* NCA. *Professional*: accounting, business, chemistry, clinical lab scientist, dental hygiene, dentistry, endodontics, engineering, journalism, law, nursing, nursing education, physical therapy, physician assisting, speech-language pathology, surgeon assisting, teacher education

History: Marquette began as Marquette College 1881 by the Society of Jesus (Jesuits), a Catholic religious order that has sponsored academically rigorous education rooted in faith and values since its founding in 1540 by St. Ignatius Loyola. Marquette was a small, liberal arts college for men until 1907. That year its leaders obtained a university charter from the state of Wisconsin and between 1907 and 1913, it expanded to include divisions of medicine, dentistry, nursing, pharmacy, law, business, engineering, music, and journalism. Marquette was the first Jesuit university in the world to admit women students (1909). In the 1960s and 70s, Marquette introduced doctoral programs in various fields. *See* Rev. Raphael N. Hamilton, S.J., *The Story of Marquette University* (Milwaukee: Marquette University Press, 1953) for further information.

Institutional Structure: *Governing board:* Trustees of the University. Extrainstitutional representation: 30 trustees, including 7 Jesuits (3 ex officio administrators). *Composition of institution:* Administrators 414. Academic affairs headed by vice president for academic affairs. Management/business/finances directed by vice president for administrative affairs and financial affairs. Full-time instructional faculty 600. Academic governance body, Academic Senate, meets an average of 8 times per year.

Calendar: Semesters. Academic year Aug. to May. Freshmen admitted Aug., Jan. Degrees conferred Dec., May, Aug. Formal commencements Dec., May. Summer session of 2 terms from May to Aug.

Characteristics of Freshmen: 1,593 applicants (female 8,124, male 7,069). 16% of accepted applicants enrolled full-time

18% (296 students) submitted SAT scores; 89% (1,556 students) submitted ACT scores. *25th percentile*: SAT Critical Reading 540, SAT Math 550; ACT Composite 24, ACT English 24. ACT Math 23. *75th percentile*: SAT Critical Reading 640, SAT Math 650; ACT Composite 29, ACT English 30, ACT Math 30.

785 of entering freshmen expected to graduate within 5 years. 40% of freshmen from Wisconsin. Freshmen from 50 states and 10 foreign countries.

Admission: Rolling admissions plan. *Requirements:* Either graduation from accredited secondary school with 16 academic units from a 4-year school or 12 units from a 3-year school, including coursework in English, foreign language, mathematics, natural science, social studies; or GED. *Entrance tests:* College Board SAT or ACT composite. *For transfer students:* 2.0 minimum GPA; from 4-year accredited institution hours maximum transfer credit limited only by resident requirement; from 2-year accredited institution 64 semester hours; correspondence/extension students 16 semester hours.

College credit and advanced placement for postsecondary level work completed in secondary school.

Tutoring available. Freshman Frontier Program, an academic support program for selected entering freshmen who do not meet regular admission requirements but show potential for success. Educational Opportunity Program, provides opportunity for first-generation students from minority groups and low-income families to attend Marquette.

Degree Requirements: *For all associate degrees:* 65 credit hours. *For all baccalaureate degrees:* 128 credit hours. *For all degrees:* 2.0 GPA.

Fulfillment of some degree requirements and exemption from some beginning courses possible by passing departmental examinations, College Board CLEP. *Grading system:* A–F; pass-fail; withdraw.

Distinctive Educational Programs: A six-year BS/MS program in physical therapy; five-year BS/MS program in physician assistant studies; executive MBA program; Saturday degree program; Les Aspin Center for Government semester in Washington, D.C. Study abroad opportunities in Australia, Austria, Belgium, Canada, Denmark, England, France, Ireland, Japan, Mexico, Russia, Spain.

ROTC: Air Force, Army, Navy.

Degrees Conferred: 1,766 *baccalaureate*; 574 *master's*; 85 *doctorate*. Bachelor's degrees awarded in top five disciplines: business, management, marketing, and related support services 336; health professions and related clinical sciences 254; communication, journalism, and related programs 247; engineering 184; social sciences 90. First-professional degrees awarded: law 235; dentistry 77.

Fees and Other Expenses: *Full-time tuition per academic semester 2008–09:* undergraduate $28,128. Graduate and professional school tuition and fees vary; contact the university for current information. *Books and supplies:* $900. *Room and board per academic year:* $9,200. *Other expenses:* $1,350.

Financial Aid: The university offers a direct lending program. Aid from institutionally generated funds is provided on the basis of academic merit, financial need, athletic ability, other criteria.

Institution has a Program Participation Agreement with the U.S. Department of Education for eligible students to receive Pell Grants and, depending upon the agreement, other federal aid.

Financial aid to full-time, first-time undergraduate students: 84% received some form of aid. Average amount of aid received: federal grants $6,074; Pell grants $3,130; other federal aid $3,234; state/local grants $2,977; institutional grants $10,990.

Departments and Teaching Staff: *Total instructional faculty:* 1,054 (full-time 600, part-time 454). Student-to-faculty ratio: 15:1. Degrees held by full-time faculty: master's 8.5%, doctorate 78.5%, professional 12.2%. 94.1% hold terminal degrees.

Enrollment: Total enrollment 11,633. Undergraduate 8,012 (full-time 95%; female 53%, male 47%). Graduate 3,621 (full-time 57%). Transfer-in students 176.

Characteristics of Student Body: *Ethnic/racial makeup:* Black non-Hispanic: 5%; American Indian or Alaska Native: 4%; Hispanic: 6%; White non-Hispanic: 82%; unknown 1%; nonresident alien 2%.

International Students: 233 nonresident aliens enrolled fall 2008. Students from Europe, Asia, Latin America, Africa, Canada, Australia. Programs available to aid students whose native language is not English: social, cultural, financial. English as a Second Language Program.

Student Life: On-campus residence halls house over one-third of the student body. One-third live in privately-owned apartment buildings within walking distance of campus. *Intercollegiate athletics:* male: basketball, cross-country, indoor and outdoor track, soccer, wrestling, tennis, and golf; female: basketball, volleyball, tennis, cross-country, indoor and outdoor track. *Special regulations:* All freshmen and sophomores must live in residence halls unless they commute from home. *Special services:* Student Life, Counseling Center, Campus Ministry, Health Services, Physical Recreation and Intercollegiate Athletics, student government; over 160 student organizations including college councils, service and community groups, fraternities and sororities, ethnic and cultural organizations, club sports, religious organizations, campus media, and performing arts groups. *Student publications, radio, television: The Marquette Tribune*, published twice weekly. Radio station WMUR and television station MUTV. *Surrounding community:* Milwaukee metropolitan area population 1.5 million. Served by mass transit. The campus is 7 miles from the airport, 1 mile from the train station, and less than 1 mile from 2 bus depots. Marquette is within walking distance of Lake Michigan.

Publications: *Marquette Magazine, Marquette Journal, Marquette Tribune, Marquette Sports Law Journal, Pere Marquette Lecture Series, Renascence, Thomas Aquinas Lecture Series.*

Library Collections: 1,320,000 volumes including bound books, serial backfiles, electronic documents, and government documents not in separate collections. Online catalog. 1,455,000 microforms; 12,000 audiovisual materials: 16,000 periodicals including via electronic access. Computer work stations available. Students have access to the Internet at no charge.

Most important special holdings include J.R.R. Tolkien Manuscripts; Dorothy Day-Catholic Worker Collection; Bureau of Catholic Indian Missions Records.

Buildings and Grounds: Campus area 80 acres.

Chief Executive Officer: Rev. Robert A. Wild, S.J., President.

Undergraduates address admission inquiries to Robert Blust, Director of Admissions; graduate inquiries to Admissions Officer, Graduate School; Law School inquiries to Admissions Officer, Law School.

College of Arts and Sciences

Degree Programs Offered: *Baccalaureate* in African-American studies, anthropology, biology, biochemistry and molecular biology, chemistry, computer science, economics, English, French, German, Latin, Spanish, history, mathematics, computer science, philosophy, physics, political science, psychology, anthropology, criminology and law studies, social work, sociology, theology.

Admission: Graduation from an accredited high school or the equivalent with 16 academic units. Algebra, geometry, and intermediate algebra required. Pre-medical/dental and science majors should complete 3 units of science (preferably biology, chemistry, physics; where physics is unavailable, another senior level science or math course should be substituted).

Degree Requirements: 128 credit hours and a minimum 256 quality points (2.000 quality point average).

Distinctive Educational Programs: Interdisciplinary major in international affairs, Latin American studies, human development.

College of Business Administration

Degree Programs Offered: *Baccalaureate* in accounting, business economics, business administration (with specialization in finance, human resources, information systems, international business, organizational management, and marketing); *master's* in business administration and applied economics through Graduate School.

Admission: Graduation from an accredited high school or the equivalent with 16 academic units. Algebra, geometry and intermediate algebra required. Fourth year of mathematics recommended. Students interested in International Business are strongly urged to complete 4 units of a single foreign language.

Degree Requirements: In business administration (non-accounting), 129 semester hours (includes one 1-credit pass/fail course) and 256 quality points (2.000 quality point average) are required. In addition, a candidate must achieve a 2.000 quality point average in all courses in the College of Business Administration. A candidate in accounting must earn 129 semester hours with a 2.500 average in all courses taken in the College.

Distinctive Educational Programs: Cooperative education.

School of Dentistry

Degree Programs Offered: *First-professional. Master's* through Graduate School.

Admission: 90 credit hours coursework from accredited college or university which must include 6 semester hours English, 8 hours general chemistry, 8 hours organic chemistry, 8 hours biology, 8 hours physics, DAT.

Degree Requirements: 150 credit hours, 2.0 GPA, 40 months in residence.

Fees and Other Expenses: Contact the school for current information.

School of Education

Degree Programs Offered: *Master's and doctorate* in administration and supervision, curriculum and instruction, educational foundations, educational psychology, educational policy and leadership, and counseling. *Specialist certificate* in administration and supervision, counseling, curriculum and instruction, and educational foundations.

MARQUETTE UNIVERSITY—*cont'd*

Admission: Students interested in the Teacher Education Program must apply for admission into the School of Education through the Office of Teacher Education. The admission and retention requirements at Marquette University meet requirements established by Wisconsin's Department of Public Instruction.

College of Engineering

Degree Programs Offered: *Baccalaureate* in biomedical engineering, civil engineering, electrical engineering, industrial engineering, mechanical engineering; *master's, doctorate* offered through Graduate School.

Admission: Graduation from an accredited high school with 16 academic units earned in a 4-year high school. Includes 4 units of mathematics, 1 unit each of chemistry and physics, 4 units of English.

Degree Requirements: 133 semester hours for a baccalaureate degree.

Distinctive Educational Programs: Cooperative education.

Graduate School

Degree Programs Offered: *Doctorate* in biology, biomedical engineering, chemistry, civil and environmental engineering, education, electrical and computer engineering, English, history, mathematics, mechanical and industrial engineering, philosophy, and theology; *master's* in biology, biomedical engineering, business administration, chemistry, civil and environmental engineering, advertising, broadcast and electronic communication, communication and rhetorical studies, journalism, speech pathology and audiology, theatre arts, dentistry, economics, education, electrical and computer engineering, English, French, Spanish, history, mathematics, mechanical and industrial engineering, nursing, philosophy, physical therapy, physics, political science, psychology, sociology, theatre arts, theology.

Admission: All applicants for admission to the Graduate School must hold a baccalaureate degree or its academic equivalent from a college or university of recognized standing and must have an undergraduate background appropriate for the proposed graduate study. Generally, applicants must have a "B" average in their undergraduate coursework.

Distinctive Educational Programs: Cooperative 3-year, 6-semester advanced program in engineering administered by Marquette University and the General Electric Company. Dispute resolution certificate program.

College of Communication

Degree Programs Offered: *Baccalaureate* with majors in advertising, broadcast and electronic communication, communication studies, journalism, public relations, theatre, teaching major in communication and rhetorical studies, journalism and theatre; *master's* through Graduate School.

Admission: Graduation from an accredited high school with 16 academic units earned in a 4-year high school. Basic typing skills are also required.

Degree Requirements: 128 credit hours and a minimum of 256 quality points (2.000 quality point average).

Marquette University Law School

Degree Programs Offered: *First-professional.*

Admission: Baccalaureate from accredited college or university; LSAT.

Degree Requirements: 90 credit hours. 76 GPA (on numerical grading system of 0-100).

Fees and Other Expenses: Contact the school for current information.

College of Nursing

Degree Programs Offered: *Baccalaureate; master's* with specialties in nursing administration, advanced practice nursing: nurse-midwifery, neonatal, children, adults, gerontology.

Admission: Graduation from accredited high school or the equivalent with 16 academic units earned in a 4-year high school. Biology and chemistry required.

Degree Requirements: 129 credit hours and a minimum of 258 quality points (2.000 quality point average).

College of Health Sciences

Degree Programs Offered: *Baccalaureate* in physician assisting, physical therapy.

Admission: The college is a merger of various departments into one college. Contact the university for information regarding the various programs offered.

College of Professional Studies

Degree Programs Offered: *Baccalaureate* in organization and leadership, criminology, law studies, professional communication, psychology, and liberal studies.

Admission: All new students, freshman or advanced standing, applying to the college must submit a completed application, writing sample, official transcripts from high school or institution granting GED; if appropriate official transcripts from all postsecondary institutions.

Degree Requirements: 126 semester hours including 30–34 credit hours in major; 51 credit hours in liberal arts core; 18–21 credit hours in a minor; 18–24 credit hours of electives. Grade of C or better in all coursework. Minimum of 36 semester hours in upper division courses must be completed and presented by candidates for degree.

Departments and Teaching Staff: The college has a faculty comprised of full-time, part-time, and adjuncts drawn from the various departments at Marquette University.

Medical College of Wisconsin

8701 Watertown Plank Road
Milwaukee, Wisconsin 53226

Tel: (414) 456-8296 **E-mail:** admissions@mcw.edu
Fax: (414) 456-6560 **Internet:** www.mcw.edu

Institution Description: The Medical College of Wisconsin is a private, independent, nonprofit, state-assisted institution. *Enrollment:* 1,293. *Degrees awarded:* First-professional (medicine), master's, doctorate.

Accreditation: *Regional:* NCA. *Professional*: community health, community health/preventive medicine, medicine, oral and maxillofacial surgery, radiation therapy technology

History: Wisconsin College of Physicians and Surgeons (established 1893) and Milwaukee Medical College (established 1894) acquired by Marquette University and operated as School of Medicine 1913; incorporated as Marquette University School of Medicine 1918; reorganized as independent corporation and changed name to Marquette School of Medicine 1967; adopted present name 1970.

Institutional Structure: *Governing board:* Medical College of Wisconsin Board of Directors. Extrainstitutional representation: 24 directors. All voting. *Composition of institution:* Administrators 24. Academic affairs headed by dean and academic vice president. Management/business/finances directed by vice president for finance and controller. Full-time instructional faculty 614. Academic governance body, Executive Committee of the Faculty, meets an average of 12 times per year.

Calendar: Semesters. Academic year Aug. to May. Entering students admitted Aug. Degrees conferred and formal commencement May. No summer session.

Admission: Rolling admissions plan. For fall acceptance, apply as early as January, but not later than April 15. *Requirements:* Vary by program. *Entrance tests:* GRE; TOEFL for foreign students. Students applying for the Doctor of Medicine (first-professional) program must take the Medical College Admission Test (MCAT).

Tutoring available. Noncredit remedial courses offered during regular academic year.

Degree Requirements: *For first-professional degrees:* core curriculum; Steps 1 and 2 of the United States Medical Licensing Examination (USMLE). *Grading system:* for first-professional degree: honors/pass/fail; for graduate school: A, B, C, F.

Distinctive Educational Programs: *For first-professional students:* Interdepartmental/interdisciplinary programs in nutrition, oncology. On-campus and off-campus resident training available at local centers and area hospitals. Member of the Milwaukee Regional Medical Center. Summer Bridging Program to help minority students prepare for medical school. *For graduate students:* Interdepartmental/interdisciplinary program in biophysics. Study abroad may be individually arranged. *Available to all students:* Interdepartmental/interdisciplinary programs in biomedical engineering, immunology.

Degrees Conferred: 73 *master's:* health professions; 29 *doctorate:* biological sciences; 188 *first-professional:* medicine.

Fees and Other Expenses: *Full-time tuition per academic year 2008–09:* contact the school for current information regarding tuition, fees, and other expenses.

Financial Aid: Aid from institutionally generated funds is provided on the basis of academic merit, financial need.

Institution has a Program Participation Agreement with the U.S. Department of Education for eligible students to receive Pell Grants and, depending upon the agreement, other federal aid.

Departments and Teaching Staff: *Total instructional faculty:* 810. Degrees held by full-time faculty: master's 0.6%, doctorate 99.4%. 99.4% hold terminal degrees.

Enrollment: Total enrollment 1,293. Undergraduate

Characteristics of Student Body: *Ethnic/racial makeup:* Black non-Hispanic: 1.9%; American Indian or Alaska Native: .5%; Asian or Pacific Islander: 10.1%; Hispanic: 2.8%; White non-Hispanic: 76%; unknown: 1%.

International Students: 94 nonresident aliens enrolled fall 2008. No programs available to aid students whose native language is not English. No financial aid specifically designated for international students.

Student Life: No on-campus housing. *Special regulations:* Cars permitted without restrictions. *Special services:* Learning Resources Center, medical services. *Student publications: MCW Dissector*, an annual magazine. *Surrounding community:* Milwaukee population 625,000. Served by mass transit bus system; airport 15 miles from campus; passenger rail service 10 miles from campus.

Publications: Sources of information about The Medical College of Wisconsin include the medical school and graduate studies bulletins, director of graduate medical education programs, the *Annual Report, Horizons, Trends,* and the *Physician's Guide to the Faculty of The Medical College of Wisconsin.*

Library Collections: 190,000 volumes. 19,500 government documents; 4,600 microforms; 648 audiovisual materials; 2,243 current periodical subscriptions. Students have access to online information retrieval services and the Internet.

Most important special holdings include Milwaukee Academy of Medicine History of Medicine Collection; Medical College of Wisconsin History of Medicine Collection; Medical College of Wisconsin Archives.

Buildings and Grounds: Campus area 8 acres.

Chief Executive Officer: T. Michael Bolger, J.D., President and Chief Executive Officer.

First-professional students address admission inquiries to Director of Admissions and Registrar; graduate students to Admissions Coordinator.

Milwaukee Institute of Art and Design

273 East Erie Street
Milwaukee, Wisconsin 53202
Tel: (414) 276-7889 **E-mail:** miadadm@miad.edu
Fax: (414) 291-8077 **Internet:** www.miad.edu

Institution Description: The Milwaukee Institute of Art and Design is a four-year professional art school. *Enrollment:* 669. *Degrees awarded:* Baccalaureate. Diplomas also awarded.

Accreditation: *Regional:* NCA. *Professional*: art, interior design

History: Founded 1974; occupied its permanent home in 1992.

Institutional Structure: *Governing board:* Board of Trustees. 24 trustees. Institutional representation: 1 student representative; 1 instructional faculty representative. Full-time instructional faculty 24.

Calendar: Semesters. Academic year Aug. to May. New/transfer students admitted for fall and spring semesters. Degrees conferred May, Aug., Dec.

Characteristics of Freshmen: 548 applicants (female 349, male 199). 75% of applicants accepted. 43% of accepted applicants enrolled full-time.

Admission: Applications are accepted at any time; due to class size limitations, students are encouraged to apply as early as possible after Sept. 1 of the year preceding the anticipated enrollment. *Requirements:* Either graduation from accredited secondary school or GED; portfolio and interview.

Students may be granted credit for experience and/or work of exceptional quality that has been acquired through nontraditional, educational, or occupation experience; review by Academic Policy and Procedure Committee.

Degree Requirements: *For Bachelor of Fine Arts degree:* 123 credits (81 studio credits, 15 art history credits, 15 humanities and sciences electives, 12 English and advanced writing credits). *Grading system:* A–F.

Distinctive Educational Programs: Internships for Communication Design, Illustration, and fine arts majors. Internship-cooperative programs are available for Industrial Design and Interior Architecture and Design majors. Opportunities to expand educational experiences through travel and international exchange programs, a cross-registration program with Marquette University, the New York Studio Program, the AICAD Mobility Program, and others.

Degrees Conferred: 123 *baccalaureate:* architecture and environmental design 13, fine and applied arts 110.

Fees and Other Expenses: *Full-time tuition per academic year 2008–09:* $25,164. *Books and supplies:* $1,828. *Room and board per academic year:* $7,400. *Other expenses:* $1,796.

Financial Aid: Aid from institutionally generated funds is provided on the basis of academic merit, financial need.

Financial aid to full-time, first-time undergraduate students: 87% received some form of aid. 49% received federal grants averaging $3,324; 50% state/local grants averaging $2,331; 87% institutional grants averaging $7,065; 78% received loans averaging $4,656.

Departments and Teaching Staff: *Total instructional faculty:* 101. Student-to-faculty ratio: 11:1. Degrees held by full-time faculty: baccalaureate 19.23%, master's 19.23%, doctorate 57.69%.

Enrollment: Total enrollment 669. Undergraduate 669 (full-time 79%; female 55%, male 45%). Transfer-in students 59.

Characteristics of Student Body: *Ethnic/racial makeup:* Black non-Hispanic: 4%; American Indian or Alaska Native: 2%; Asian or Pacific Islander: 1%; Hispanic: 7%; White non-Hispanic: 76%; unknown 6%; nonresident alien 3%.

International Students: 21 nonresident aliens enrolled fall 2008. No programs available to aid students whose native language is not English. No financial aid specifically designated for international students.

Student Life: Student housing accommodations are in three uniquely and comfortably renovated floors of an historic building at 222 E. Chicago Street, two blocks from classroom and studio spaces. Milwaukee area population over 1.5 million. Served by mass transit bus system; airport 15 miles from campus.

Library Collections: 32,000 volumes; 900 audiovisual titles; 130 current periodical subscriptions. Students have access to online information retrieval services.

Most important special holdings include collections on industrial design, graphic design, and art exhibition catalogs.

Buildings and Grounds: Campus DVD available.

Chief Executive Officer: Mary C. Schopp, President.

Address admission inquiries to Mark Fetherston, Direcotr of Admissions.

Milwaukee School of Engineering

1025 North Broadway
Milwaukee, Wisconsin 53202-3109
Tel: (800) 332-6763 **E-mail:** explore@msoe.edu
Fax: (414) 277-7475 **Internet:** www.msoe.edu

Institution Description: Milwaukee School of Engineering is a private, independent, nonprofit institution. *Enrollment:* 2,621. *Degrees awarded:* Baccalaureate, master's.

Member of the consortium Wisconsin Association of Independent Colleges and Universities.

Accreditation: *Regional:* NCA. *Professional*: construction education, engineering, engineering technology, nursing education

History: Established as a School of Engineering of Milwaukee 1903; offered first instruction at postsecondary level 1916; chartered 1917; awarded first degree (baccalaureate) 1919; adopted present name 1932. *See* Harry F. Bolton, ed., *Pioneer in Progress—A 75-Year History of the Milwaukee School of Engineering* (Milwaukee: Milwaukee School of Engineering, 1979) for further information.

Institutional Structure: *Governing board:* Milwaukee School of Engineering Board of Regents. Extrainstitutional representation: 49 regents; institutional representation: president of the school, 2 administrators. All voting. *Composition of institution:* Administrators 12. Academic affairs headed by vice president of academics. Management/business/finances directed by vice president of finance and treasurer. Full-time instructional faculty 122. Academic governance body, Executive Educational Council, meets an average of 40 times per year.

Calendar: Quarters. Academic year Sept. to May. Freshmen admitted Sept., Dec., Feb., June. Degrees conferred and formal commencement May, Aug., Nov., Mar. Summer session of 1 term from June to Aug.

Characteristics of Freshmen: 2,279 applicants (female 593, male 1,686). 71% of applicants admitted. 36% of applicants admitted and enrolled.

6% (35students) submitted SAT scores; 98% (560 students) submitted ACT scores. *25th percentile*: SAT Critical Reading 550, SAT Math 590; ACT Composite 23, ACT English 22, ACT Math 24. *75th percentile*: SAT Critical Reading 650, SAT Math 690; ACT Composite 28, ACT English 27, ACT Math 29.

53% of entering students expected to graduate within 5 years. 70% of freshmen from Wisconsin. Freshmen from 16 states and 3 foreign countries.

Admission: Rolling admissions plan. For fall acceptance, apply as early as 1 year prior to enrollment, but not later than 30 days prior to beginning of classes. *Requirements:* Either graduation from accredited secondary school with 16 units, including 4 English, 2 algebra, 1 plane geometry, ½ unit trigonometry, 2 science. Chemistry and physics recommended. *Entrance tests:* ACT preferred; SAT accepted. *For transfer students:* 2.0 minimum GPA; maximum transfer credit 50% of degree requirements.

College credit and advanced placement for postsecondary-level work completed in secondary school and for extrainstitutional learning. portfolio and faculty assessments, personal interviews.

MILWAUKEE SCHOOL OF ENGINEERING—*cont'd*

Tutoring available. Noncrédit developmental/remedial courses offered in summer session and regular academic year.

Degree Requirements: *For all baccalaureate degrees:* 194–197 quarter hours; 2.0 GPA; prescribed curriculum; general studies requirements; must complete ½ of degree requirements in residence.

Fulfillment of some degree requirements and exemption from some beginning courses possible by passing departmental examinations, College Board CLEP. *Grading system:* A–F; pass-fail; withdraw (deadline after which fail is appended to withdraw); incomplete (carries time limit).

Distinctive Educational Programs: Off-campus centers at varying locations. Weekend and evening classes. Special facilities for using telecommunications in the classroom. Facilities and programs for independent research, including tutorials, independent study. Part-time evening degree program. *Other distinctive programs:* Continuing education employee training programs. Applied Technology Center serves as an experimental station and provides training for industrial engineering and scientists. Fluid Power Institute offers academic and company-sponsored research; sponsors seminars on fluid power technology.

ROTC: Air Force, Army in cooperation with Marquette University.

Degrees Conferred: 372 *baccalaureate* (B), 53 *master's* (M): business, management, marketing, and related support services 68 (B), 39 (M); communications/communication technologies 2 (B); engineering and engineering technologies 277 (B), 15 (M); health professions 10 (B), 6 (M).

Fees and Other Expenses: *Full-time tuition per academic year 2997–08:* undergraduate $27,300; contact the school for current graduate tuition/fees. *Room and board per academic year:* $6,825. *Books and supplies:* $2,640. *Other expenses:* $4,000.

Financial Aid: Aid from institutionally generated funds is provided on the basis of academic merit, financial need.

Financial aid to full-time, first-time undergraduate students: 99% recieved some form of aid. Average amount of aid received: federal grants $3,982; Pell grants $2,789; other federal aid $1,316; state/local grants $2,102; institutional grants $11,911.

Departments and Teaching Staff: *Total instructional faculty:* 222 (full-time 122, part-time 100). Total faculty with doctorate, first-professional, or other terminal degree: 156. Student-to-faculty ratio: 12:1. Degrees held by full-time faculty: master's 100%, doctorate 48% hold terminal degrees.

Enrollment: Total enrollment 2,621. Undergraduate 2,417 (full-time 90%; female 14%, male 82%). Graduate 204 (full-time 6%). Transfer-in students 129.

Characteristics of Student Body: *Ethnic/racial makeup:* Black non-Hispanic: 4%; American Indian or Alaska Native: 3%; Hispanic 2%; White non-Hispanic: 82%; unknown: 6%; nonresident alien 2%. *Age distribution:* number under 18: 2; 18–19: 345; 20–21: 703; 22–24: 551; 25–29: 132; 30–34: 38; 35–39: 22; 40–49: 11; 50–64: 3.

International Students: 52 nonresident aliens enrolled fall 2008. Students from Europe, Asia, Latin America, Africa, Middle East. Programs available to aid students whose native language is not English: social, cultural, financial. English as a Second Language Program.

Student Life: On-campus residence halls house 45% of student body. *Intercollegiate athletics:* male: baseball, basketball, hockey, golf, wrestling, soccer, volleyball; female: basketball, softball, volleyball; coed: dance team, pep band, stunt team, various intramurals and club sports. *Special regulations:* Cars permitted without restrictions. *Special services:* Career counseling, academic advising, tutoring, gymnasium, athletic club passes. *Student publications, radio: ingenium*, a monthly newspaper; *Ink Waves*, annual literary magazine; *Brain Waves*, annual mathematics magazine. Radio station WMSE broadcasts 126 hours per week. *Surrounding community:* Milwaukee population 650,000. Served by mass transit system; airport 8 miles from campus; passenger rail service 2 miles from campus.

Library Collections: 57,000 volumes including bound books, serial backfiles, electronic documents, and government documents not in separate collections. Online catalog. 81,000 microforms; 2,000 audiovisual materials; 500 current serial subscriptions. All students are required to have a laptop computer. Students have access to the Internet at no charge.

Most important special holdings include collections on fluid power, automated manufacturing, engineering resources, computer science.

Buildings and Grounds: Campus area 15 acres.

Chief Executive Officer: Dr. Hermann Viets, President.

Address admission inquiries to Paul Borens, Director of Admissions.

Mount Mary College

2900 North Menomonee River Parkway
Milwaukee, Wisconsin 53222-4597
Tel: (414) 258-4810 **E-mail:** admiss@mtmary.edu
Fax: (414) 256-0182 **Internet:** www.mtmary.edu

Institution Description: Mount Mary College is a private college for women affiliated with the Roman Catholic Church. *Enrollment:* 1,862. *Degrees awarded:* Baccalaureate, master's (dietetics).

Accreditation: *Regional:* NCA. *Professional*: dietetics, occupational therapy, social work, teacher education

History: Established 1877 as Saint Mary's Institute in Prairie du Chien; changed name to Saint Mary's College, chartered, and offered first instruction at postsecondary level 1913; awarded first degree (baccalaureate) 1916; moved to Milwaukee and adopted present name 1929. *See* Edward Fitzpatrick, *The Autobiography of a College* (Milwaukee: Bruce, 1939) for further information.

Institutional Structure: *Governing board:* Board of Trustees. Extrainstitutional representation: 26 trustees, including 5 alumnae; institutional representation: president of the college. All voting. *Composition of institution:* Administrators 5. Academic affairs headed by academic vice president. Management/business/finances directed by business officer. Full-time instructional faculty 77. Academic governance body, the faculty, meets an average of 9 times per year.

Calendar: Semesters. Academic year Aug. to May. Freshmen admitted Aug., Jan., June. Degrees conferred Dec., May, July. Formal commencements Dec., May. Summer session from June to July.

Characteristics of Freshmen: 83% of applicants accepted. 47% of accepted applicants enrolled.

Average secondary school rank 64th percentile. ACT Composite score 23.

57% of entering freshmen expected to graduate within 5 years. 81% of freshmen from Wisconsin. Freshmen from 8 states and 1 foreign country.

Admission: Rolling admissions plan. For fall acceptance, apply as early as Sept. of previous year, but not later than Aug. 15 of year of enrollment. Early acceptance available. *Requirements:* Graduation from accredited secondary school with 4 units in English; 2 in a foreign language, 2 history, 2 science; 2 mathematics; 4 academic electives. GED accepted. Minimum 2.0 GPA. Consideration will be given to students who do not meet normal requirements. *Entrance tests:* College Board SAT or ACT composite. For foreign students TOEFL. *For transfer students:* 2.0 minimum GPA; from 4-year accredited institution 92 hours maximum transfer credit; from 2-year accredited institution 64 hours; correspondence/extension students 8 hours. Additional requirements for some programs.

College credit and advanced placement for postsecondary-level work completed in secondary school. College credit for extrainstitutional learning (life experience) on basis of portfolio and faculty assessment.

Tutoring available. Developmental English and mathematics courses offered during regular academic year; credit given.

Degree Requirements: 128 credit hours; 2.0 GPA; core curriculum requirement; major; last 32 credits in residence.

Fulfillment of some degree requirements and exemption from some beginning courses possible by passing departmental examinations, College Board CLEP, AP exams, international baccalaureate. *Grading system:* A–D; pass-fail; withdraw; incomplete.

Distinctive Educational Programs: Work-experience programs. Evening classes. Semester exchange with College of Notre Dame of Maryland. Interdepartmental/interdisciplinary programs in fashion, public relations, science, occupational therapy. Facilities and programs for independent research, including honors program, individual majors, tutorials. Double majors. Some graduate-level courses. Noncredit continuing education courses. Encore program (special admission procedures and counseling for women whose college education has been postponed or interrupted). Master of Science in Dietetics and Master of Arts in Art Therapy and Education. Accelerated Business Administration Program entitled 'Business Advantage.'

Degrees Conferred: 220 *baccalaureate*; 45 *master's*. Bachelor's degrees awarded in top five disciplines: business, management, marketing, and related support services 94; visual and performing arts 31; health professions and related clinical sciences 20; English language/literature 9; education 9. Master's degrees awarded: various disciplines 45.

Fees and Other Expenses: *Full-time tuition per academic year 2008–09:* undergraduate $20,550; contact the college for current graduate tuition/fees. *Books and supplies:* $1,100. *Room and board per academic year:* $8,542. *Other expenses:* $2,156.

Financial Aid: Aid from institutionally generated funds is provided on the basis of academic merit, financial need.

Financial aid to full-time, first-time undergraduate students: 50% received federal grants averaging $2,869; 57% state/local grants averaging $2,568; 80% institutional grants averaging $4,272; 66% received loans averaging $4,527.

Departments and Teaching Staff: *Total instructional faculty:* 104. Student-to-faculty ratio: 8:1. Degrees held by full-time faculty: doctorate 39%, master's 57%, baccalaureate 4%. 51% hold terminal degrees.

Enrollment: Total enrollment 1,862. Undergraduate 1,428 (full-time 61%; female 97%, male 3%). Graduate 434 (full-time 65%). Transfer-in stuedents 165.

Characteristics of Student Body: *Ethnic/racial makeup:* Black non-Hispanic: 7%; American Indian or Alaska Native: 4%; Hispanic: 1%; White non-Hispanic: 82%; unknown: 8%; nonresident alien 1%.

International Students: 2 nonresident aliens enrolled fall 2008. No programs available to aid students whose native language is not English. No financial aid specifically designated for international students.

Student Life: On-campus residence halls house 20% of student body. *Intercollegiate athletics:* basketball, volleyball. *Special regulations:* Cars permitted without restrictions. Midnight curfew for freshmen Mon.–Fri. Quiet hours begin 7:30pm Mon.–Fri. Men may visit residence halls on weekends. *Special services:* Learning Resources Center, medical services. *Student publications: Arches*, a monthly newspaper; *Exit*, a yearbook; *Kwhyet*, a quarterly literary magazine. *Surrounding community:* Milwaukee area population over 1.5 million. Served by mass transit bus system; airport 12 miles from campus; passenger rail service 7 miles from campus.

Library Collections: 140,080 volumes including bound books, serial backfiles, electronic documents, and government documents not in separate collections. Online catalog. Current serial subscriptions: 1,452 paper, 47 microform, 18 electronic. 434 recordings; 210 compact discs; 22 CD-ROMs. Computer work stations available. Students have access to the Internet at no charge.

Most important special holdings include Age Collection (complete contents of a Milwaukee gerontology library, donated in 1986); Alfred Lunt Cookbook Collection; Kennedy materials.

Buildings and Grounds: Campus area 80 acres. Campus DVD available.

Chief Executive Officer: Dr. Patricia O'Donoghue, President.

Address undergraduate admission inquiries to Brooke Konopacki, Dean of Enrollment Management; graduate inquiries to Sr. Jane Forni, Associate Academic Dean for Graduate and Nontraditional Programs.

Nashotah House

2777 Mission Road
Nashotah, Wisconsin 53058-9793
Tel: (414) 646-3371 **E-mail:** admissions@nashotah.edu
Fax: (414) 646-6504 **Internet:** www.nashotah.edu

Institution Description: Nashotah House is a privately supported graduate theological seminary of the Episcopal Church. *Enrollment:* 69. *Degrees awarded:* First-professional, master's.

Accreditation: *National:* ATS. *Professional*: theology

History: Founded 1842.

Calendar: Trimesters. Academic year Aug. to May.

Admission: *Requirements:* Bachelor of Arts degree or equivalent from an accredited college or university; applicant must be a postulant or candidate for Holy Orders. *Entrance tests:* GRE.

Degree Requirements: Completion of prescribed curriculum.

Degrees Conferred: 1 *master's;* 4 *first-professional:* master of divinity.

Fees and Other Expenses: *Full-time tuition per academic year 2008–09;* contact the school for current information regarding tuition, fees, and housing costs.

Departments and Teaching Staff: *Total instructional faculty:* 7. Degrees held by full-time faculty: 86% hold terminal degrees.

Enrollment: Total enrollment 69.

Characteristics of Student Body: *Ethnic/racial makeup:* Black non-Hispanic: 3%; White non-Hispanic: 92%; unknown: 4%.

International Students: 2 nonresident aliens enrolled fall 2008. No programs available for students whose native language is not English. No financial aid specifically designated for international students.

Library Collections: 80,000 volumes. 300 current periodical subscriptions. Most important special collections include theological materials.

Chief Executive Officer: V. Rev. Robert S. Monday, Dean and President.

Address admission inquiries to Director of Admissions.

Northland College

1411 Ellis Avenue
Ashland, Wisconsin 54806
Tel: (715) 682-1846 **E-mail:** admissions@northland.edu
Fax: (715) 682-1692 **Internet:** www.northland.edu

Institution Description: Northland College is a private, independent, nonprofit college affiliated with the United Church of Christ. *Enrollment:* 677. *Degrees awarded:* Baccalaureate.

Member of Spring Term Consortium.

Accreditation: *Regional:* NCA.

History: Established as North Wisconsin Academy 1892; chartered, offered first instruction at postsecondary level, and adopted present name 1906; awarded first degree (baccalaureate) 1912. *See* Nathaniel B. Dexter, *Northland College: A History* (Ashland: Privately printed, 1968) for further information.

Institutional Structure: *Governing board:* Northland College Board of Trustees. Extrainstitutional representation: 38 trustees, 6 trustees emeriti; institutional representation: president of the college, 1 student; 1 alumnus. 7 ex officio. *Composition of institution:* Administrators 8. Academic affairs headed by dean of academic affairs. Management/business/finances directed by vice president of business affairs. Full-time instructional faculty 45. Academic governance body, Faculty Senate, meets an average of 9 times per year.

Calendar: Semesters (4-4-1). Academic year Sept. to May. Freshmen admitted Sept., Jan. Degrees conferred May, Sept., Dec. Formal commencement May. Summer session from June to July.

Characteristics of Freshmen: 634 applicants (female 553, male 281). 90% of applicants accepted. 50% of accepted applicants enrolled.

25th percentile: SAT Critical Reading 510, SAT Math 490; ACT Composite 22. *75th percentile*: SAT Critical Reading 590, SAT Math 570; ACT Composite 26.

82% entering freshmen expected to graduate within 5 years. 40% of freshmen from Wisconsin. Freshmen from 22 states and 2 foreign countries.

Admission: Modified rolling admissions plan. For fall acceptance, apply as early as fall of senior year of secondary school. Students are notified of acceptance beginning Jan. Apply by Nov. 22 for early decision; need not limit application to Northland. Early acceptance available. *Requirements:* Either graduation from accredited secondary school with academic units in English, mathematics, natural sciences, social studies; or GED. *Entrance tests:* College Board SAT or ACT composite. For foreign student TOEFL. *For transfer students:* 2.0 minimum GPA; from 4-year accredited institution 90 hours maximum transfer credit; from 2-year accredited institution 62 hours.

College credit and advanced placement for postsecondary-level work completed in secondary school. For extrainstitutional learning credit and advanced placement on basis of portfolio and faculty assessments; personal interview.

Tutoring available. Remedial courses offered during regular academic year; credit given.

Degree Requirements: 124 semester hours; 2.0 GPA overall, and in major field; 20 of last 30 hours in residence; 2 physical education courses; distribution requirements.

Fulfillment of some degree requirements and exemption from some beginning courses possible by passing departmental examinations, College Board CLEP. *Grading system:* A–F; pass-fail; withdraw (deadline after which pass-fail is appended to withdraw).

Distinctive Educational Programs: Work-experience programs, including internships, cooperative education. Flexible meeting places and schedules, including off-campus centers (at Ironwood, MI, 40 miles away from main institution; at the following Indian reservations: Bad River, less than 30 miles away, Red Cliff, 30 miles away, Lac-Courte Oreilles, 40 miles away, and Lac De Flambeau, 70 miles away). Evening classes. Dual-degree programs in forestry and in engineering with Michigan Technological University, and in natural resources with University of Michigan. Interdisciplinary programs for independent research, including individual majors, tutorials. Study abroad by individual arrangement. *Other distinctive programs:* Workshops and conferences on environmental issues sponsored by Sigurd Olson Institute of Environmental Studies.

Degrees Conferred: 132 *baccalaureate:* degrees awarded in top five disciplines include biological and live sciences 26, business and management 20, education 39, conservation and renewable natural resources 31, psychology 12.

Fees and Other Expenses: *Full-time tuition per academic year 2008–09:* $23,101. *Required fees:* $580. *Room and board per academic year:* $6,440. *Books and supplies:* $800. *Other expenses:* $1,600.

Financial Aid: Aid from institutionally generated funds is provided on the basis of academic merit, financial need, other criteria.

Financial aid to full-time, first-time undergraduate students: 100% received some form of aid. Need-based scholarships/grants totaling $5,977,499, self-help $3,008,855, parent loans $1,099,012, tuition waivers $2,468,878; non-need-

NORTHLAND COLLEGE—*cont'd*

based scholarships/grants totaling $196,300, self-help $1,416,494, parent loans $223,207; tuition waivers $54,405.

Departments and Teaching Staff: *Total instructional faculty:* 82 (full-time 45, part-time 37). Total faculty with doctorate, first-professional, or other terminal degree: 47. Student-to-faculty ratio: 15:1.

Enrollment: Total enrollment 677. Undergraduate 660 (full-time 92%; female 53%, male 47%). Graduate 17 (part-time 100%). Transfer-in students 58.

Characteristics of Student Body: *Ethnic/racial makeup:* Black non-Hispanic: 2%; American Indian or Alaska Native: 1%; Asian or Pacific Islander: 3%; Hispanic: 2%; White non-Hispanic: 82%; unknown: 7%; nonresident alien 3%. *Age distribution:* number under 18: 11; 18–19: 215; 20–21: 22–24: 117; 25–29: 28; 30–34: 15; 35–39: 13; 40–49: 16; 50–64: 4;.

International Students: 24 nonresident aliens enrolled fall 2008. No programs available to aid students whose native language is not English. No financial aid specifically designated for international students.

Student Life: On-campus residence halls house 60% of student body. Residence halls for for both sexes. 65% of student body housed on campus in cooperative facilities. *Intercollegiate athletics:* male: baseball, basketball, soccer; female: basketball, volleyball. *Special regulations:* Cars permitted without restrictions. Quiet hours set by dormitory residents. *Special services:* Learning Resources Center, medical services. *Student publications: Drifts*, a monthly newspaper; *The Mosaic*, a quarterly literary publication; *The Wedge*, a yearbook. *Surrounding community:* Ashland population 9,500. Duluth (MN)-Superior (WI), 66 miles from campus, is nearest metropolitan area. Served by airport 3 miles from campus.

Library Collections: 78,000 volumes. 10,000 microforms; 350 current periodical subscriptions. Online catalog. Students have access to online information retrieval services and theInternet.

Most important holdings include ethnic heritage collection (cassette tapes and field notes of oral histories of northern Wisconsin and the upper peninsula of Michigan).

Buildings and Grounds: Campus area 60 acres. Campus DVD available.

Chief Executive Officer: Dr. Karen Halbersleben, President.

Address admission inquiries to Jason Turley, Director of Admissions.

Ripon College

300 Seward Street
P.O. Box 248
Ripon, Wisconsin 54971-0248

Tel: (920) 748-8115 **E-mail:** adminfo@ripon.edu
Fax: (920) 748-9262 **Internet:** www.ripon.edu

Institution Description: Ripon College is a private, independent, liberal arts, nonprofit college. *Enrollment:* 1,057. *Degrees awarded:* Baccalaureate.

Member of the consortium Associated Colleges of the Midwest.

Accreditation: *Regional:* NCA. *Professional*: chemistry

History: Established and chartered as Ripon Lyceum 1851; offered first instruction at postsecondary level and adopted present name 1863; awarded first degree (baccalaureate) 1867. *See* Robert Ashley and George Miller, *Ripon College: A History* , 1990, for further information.

Institutional Structure: *Governing board:* Ripon College Board of Trustees. Extrainstitutional representation: 36 trustees; institutional representation: president of the college; 3 alumni, 1 special graduate trustee. All voting. *Composition of institution:* Administrators 117. Academic affairs headed by dean of faculty. Management/business/finances directed by vice president for finance. Full-time instructional faculty 53. Academic governance body, the faculty, meets an average of 10 times per year.

Calendar: Semesters. Academic year Aug. to May. Freshmen admitted Aug., Jan. Degrees conferred May, Jan. Formal commencement May. No summer session.

Characteristics of Freshmen: 1,081 applicants (femlae 559, male 522). 83% of applicants admitted. 33% of applicants admitted and enrolled.

16% of applicants submitted SAT scores; 84% ACT scores. *25th percentile*: SAT Critical Reading 500, SAT Math 490; ACT Composite 20. *75th percentile*: SAT Critical Reading 590, SAT Math 610; ACT Composite 27.

71% of freshmen expected to graduate within 5 years. 76% of freshmen from Wisconsin. Freshmen from 18 states and 1 foreign country.

Admission: Rolling admissions plan. Early acceptance available. *Requirements:* Either graduation from accredited secondary school with 15 units which normally include 4 units English, 1 algebra, 1 geometry, and 9 additional units chosen from foreign languages, mathematics, science, social studies; or GED. Upper 40% of secondary class preferred. *Entrance tests:* College Board SAT or ACT composite recommended. *For transfer students:* 2.0 minimum GPA; 92 hours maximum transfer credit.

College credit and advanced placement for postsecondary-level work completed in secondary school. College credit for extrainstitutional learning.

Tutoring available.

Degree Requirements: 124 credit hours; 2.0 GPA; senior year and half of courses required for major must be completed in residence; 2 credits physical education; distribution requirements; one-person exhibition for studio art majors.

Fulfillment of some degree requirements and exemption from some beginning courses possible by College Board AP (score of 3). Exemption from courses also possible by passing Achievements (score of 550) or departmental examinations. *Grading system:* A–F; pass-fail; satisfactory-unsatisfactory; withdraw (deadline after which pass-fail is appended to withdraw).

Distinctive Educational Programs: Work-experience programs. Evening classes. Accelerated degree programs. Dual-degree programs in engineering with Rensselaer Polytechnic Institute (NY), University of Madison (WI), and Washington University (M); in forestry and environmental studies with Duke University (NC); and in social welfare with University of Chicago (IL). Cooperative baccalaureate degree program in medical technology, nursing, and physical therapy with Rush University (IL). Interdepartmental/interdisciplinary programs in business management, chemistry-biology, Latin American studies, psychobiology, global studies, environmental studies. Facilities for independent research, including honors programs, individual majors, tutorials. Study abroad through Ripon College programs in England, France, Germany, Spain, Tanzania; through the consortium, in Florence, Hong Kong at Chinese University, India at University of Poona, Japan at Waseda University, Russia at Krasnodar, Yugoslavia at University of Zagreb, Zimbabwe and in Costa Rica. Through the consortium, off-campus study in U.S., including geology in the Rocky Mountains (CO), Newberry Library Humanities Program in Chicago, Oakridge (TN) science semester, urban education and urban studies programs in Chicago, Wilderness Field Station (MN) program, Washington (DC) semesters in cooperation with American University. Other off-campus programs, as approved by Ripon, may be individually designed.

Degrees Conferred: 187 *baccalaureate.*

Fees and Other Expenses: *Full-time tuition per academic year 2008–09:* $24,425. *Required fees:* $250. *Room and board per academic year:* $6,770. *Books and supplies:* $1,000. *Other expenses:* $1,300.

Financial Aid: Aid from institutionally generated funds is provided on the basis of academic merit, financial need, other criteria.

Financial aid to full-time, first-time undergraduate students: 99% received some form of aid. Need-based scholarships/grants totaling $9,385,750; self-help $3,011,586, parent loans $40,899, tuition waivers $316,083; non-need-based scholarships/grants totaling $2,292,422, self-help $2,183,816, parent loans $619,544, tuition waivers $87,521.

Departments and Teaching Staff: *Total instructional faculty:* 88 (full-time 52, part-time 36). Total faculty with doctorate, first-professional, or other terminal degree: 67. Student-to-faculty ratio: 13.5:1.

Enrollment: Total enrollment 1,057. Undergraduate 1,057 (full-time 99%; female 52%, male 48%). Transfer-in students 31.

Characteristics of Student Body: *Ethnic/racial makeup:* Black non-Hispanic: 2%; American Indian or Alaska Native: 1%; Asian or Pacific Islander: 1%; Hispanic: 3%; White non-Hispanic: 84%; unknown: 7%; nonresident alien 2%.

International Students: 22 nonresident aliens enrolled fall 2008. Students from Europe, Asia, Africa, other. No programs available to aid students whose native language is not English. No financial aid specifically designated for international students.

Student Life: On-campus residence halls, including fraternities and sororities, house 94% of student body. Residence halls for males constitute 26% of such space, for females 35%, for both sexes 39%. *Intercollegiate athletics:* male: baseball, basketball, cross-country, football, golf, soccer, swimming, tennis, track; female: basketball, cross-country, soccer, softball, swimming, tennis, track, volleyball. *Special regulations:* Cars permitted without restrictions. *Special services:* Learning Resources Center, medical services. *Student publications, radio: College Days*, a weekly newspaper; *Crimson*, a yearbook; *Parallax*, an annual literary magazine. Radio station WRPN-FM broadcasts approximately 120 hours per week. *Surrounding community:* Ripon population 7,500. Milwaukee, 80 miles from campus, is nearest metropolitan area. Served by airport 20 miles from campus (Oshkosh).

Publications: Sources of information about Ripon College: *Ripon Magazine*, distributed to alumni, parents, and friends, 4 issues yearly.

Library Collections: 194,000 volumes including bound books, serial backfiles, electronic documents, and government documents not in separate collections. Online catalog. 26,000 microforms; 600 audiovisual materials; 800 current serial subscriptions. Computer work stations available. Students have access to the Internet at no charge.

Most important special holdings include local history collection (Samuel Pedrick Collection); military history; Lincolniana; Ripon College Archives.

Buildings and Grounds: Campus area 252 acres.

Chief Executive Officer: Dr. David Joyce, President.

Address admission inquiries to Office of Admissions.

Sacred Heart School of Theology

7335 South Highway 100
P.O. Box 429
Hales Corners, Wisconsin 53130-0429
Tel: (414) 425-8300 **E-mail:** admissions@shst.edu
Fax: (414) 529-6999 **Internet:** www.shst.edu

Institution Description: Sacred Heart School of Theology is a Roman Catholic Seminary preparing candidates for the priesthood. *Enrollment:* 120. *Degrees awarded:* First-professional, master's.

Accreditation: *Regional:* NCA. *National:* ATS. *Professional*: theology

Calendar: Semesters. Academic year Aug. to May.

Admission: *Requirements:* Minimum of 2 years of liberal arts study at an accredited college or university; undergraduate degree preferred; background in philosophy required.

Degree Requirements: Completion of prescribed curriculum.

Degrees Conferred: 14 *first-professional:* master of divinity.

Fees and Other Expenses: *Full-time tuition per academic year 2008*+09:* contact the school for current information regarding tuition, fees, and housing costs.

Financial Aid: Aid from institutionally generated funds is provided on the basis of financial need. *Graduate aid:* 8 students received $60,245 in federal and state-funded loans.

Departments and Teaching Staff: *Total instructional faculty:* 31 (full-time 14, part-time 17).

Enrollment: Total enrollment 120.

International Students: 23 nonresident aliens enrolled fall 2008. Programs available to aid students whose native language is not English: English as a Second Language Program available. No financial aid specifically designated for international students.

Library Collections: 96,000 volumes. 9,700 microforms; 16,600 audiovisual materials; 120 current periodical subscriptions. Students have access to online information retrieval services.

Most important special collections include Sacred Heart Collection; Catechetical Curriculum Collection; Canon Law.

Chief Executive Officer: V. Rev. Thomas P. Cassidy, S.C.J., President-Rector.

Address admission inquiries to Rev. Thomas Knoebel, Vice-Rector, Director of Recruitment/Admissions.

Saint Francis Seminary

3257 South Lake Drive
Milwaukee, Wisconsin 53235-3795
Tel: (414) 747-6400 **E-mail:** admissions@sfs.edu
Fax: (414) 747-6442 **Internet:** www.sfs.edu

Institution Description: Saint Francis Seminary, School of Pastoral Ministry is a private institution owned by the Archdiocese of Milwaukee, Roman Catholic Church. *Enrollment:* 100. *Degrees awarded:* First-professional (master of divinity), master's.

Accreditation: *Regional:* NCA. *National:* ATS. *Professional*: theology

History: Established as Saint Francis Seminary, a secondary school and 4-year seminary, and offered first instruction at postsecondary level 1845; awarded first degree (baccalaureate) 1920; became graduate seminary and adopted present name 1970. *See* Msgr. Peter L. Johnson, *Halcyon Days* (Milwaukee: Bruce Publishing Co., 1956) for further information.

Institutional Structure: *Governing board:* The Board of Trustees. Representation: 20 members, including Rector of the institution, 1 ex officio, all voting. *Composition of institution:* Academic affairs headed by academic dean; business/finances directed treasurer/business director. Full-time instructional faculty 13. Academic governance body, Faculty Council, meets an average of 14 times per year.

Calendar: Semesters. Academic year Aug. to May. Entering students admitted Aug., Jan. Degrees conferred in May. Formal commencement May. Summer session from June to July.

Admission: For fall acceptance, apply as early as 1 year prior to enrollment, but not later than July 15 of year of enrollment. *Requirements:* For first-professional program, baccalaureate from accredited college or university; humanities background with recommended 12 credits philosophy. Requirements for master's program include 2 units ethical studies, 2 scriptural studies, 2 systematic studies. *Entrance tests:* Standardized personality test and concept mastery or intelligence test.

Degree Requirements: *For first-professional degree:* 112 semester hours. *For master's degree:* 42 semester hours; formation program. *For all degrees:* 2.6 GPA; core and elective requirements; field education; exit interdisciplinary comprehensive. *Grading system:* A–F; withdraw (carries time limit).

Distinctive Educational Programs: All programs include spiritual formation and emphasis on relationship between theology and behavioral science. Individual evaluations. Continuing education through Church Leadership Institute and general program. Sabbatical study for clergy.

Degrees Conferred: 8 *master's:* theology; 5 *first-professional:* master of divinity.

Fees and Other Expenses: *Full-time tuition per academic year 2008–09:* contact the seminary for current tuition, fees, and housing costs.

Financial Aid: Aid from institutionally generated funds is provided on the basis of academic merit, financial need, other criteria.

Departments and Teaching Staff: *Total instructional faculty:* 20. Degrees held by faculty: doctorates 61%, master's 39%. 61% hold terminal degrees.

Enrollment: Total enrollment 100.

Characteristics of Student Body: *Ethnic/racial makeup:* Black non-Hispanic: 1.5%; Hispanic: 1.5%; White non-Hispanic: 89.6%.

International Students: 5 nonresident aliens enrolled fall 2008. Programs available to aid students whose native language is not English: English as a Second Language Program. No financial aid specifically designated for international students.

Student Life: Candidates for the priesthood, except religious order students, are expected to live on campus. On-campus residence halls for men only house 29% of student body. *Special regulations:* Cars with decals permitted on campus in designated areas only; fee charged. *Surrounding community:* Milwaukee area population over 1.5 million. Served by mass transit bus system; airport 3 miles from campus; passenger rail service 7 miles from campus.

Library Collections: 85,000 volumes including bound books, serial backfiles, electronic documents, and government documents not in separate collections. Online catalog. Current serial subscriptions: 457 paper. Computer work stations available. Students have access to the Internet at no charge.

Most important holdings include Rembert Weakland Collection; 14th-century Papal letters; early canon law.

Buildings and Grounds: Campus area 168 acres.

Chief Executive Officer: V. Rev. Michael E. Michalski, Rector.

Address admission inquiries to Mary Karr, Director of Admissions.

St. Norbert College

100 Grant Street
De Pere, Wisconsin 54115-2099
Tel: (800) 236-4878 **E-mail:** admit@snc.edu
Fax: (920) 403-4072 **Internet:** www.snc.edu

Institution Description: St. Norbert College is a private college affiliated with the Norbertine Order, Roman Catholic Church. *Enrollment:* 2,137. *Degrees awarded:* Baccalaureate, master's.

Accreditation: *Regional:* NCA.

History: Established as St. Norbert College 1898; awarded first degree (baccalaureate) 1902.

Institutional Structure: *Governing board:* Board of Trustees. Extrainstitutional representation: 45 trustees including 28 alumni. All voting. *Composition of institution:* Administrators 7. Academic affairs headed by dean of the college. Management/business/finances directed by vice president for business and finance. Full-time instructional faculty 109. Academic governance body, Faculty Assembly, meets an average of 8 times per year.

Calendar: Semesters. Academic year Aug. to May. Freshmen admitted Aug., Jan., June. Degrees conferred May, July, Dec. Formal commencement May. Summer session from June to July.

Characteristics of Freshmen: 2,116 applicants (female 1,014, male 1,042). 88% of applicants admitted. 37% of applicants admitted and enrolled.

9% (53 students) submitted SAT scores; 96% (532 students) submitted ACT scores. *25th percentile*: ACT Composite 22, ACT English 21, ACT Math 20. *75th percentile*: ACT Composite 26, ACT English 27; ACT Math 27.

72% of entering freshmen expected to graduate within 5 years. 75% of freshmen from Wisconsin. Freshmen from 23 states and 27 foreign countries.

Admission: Rolling admissions plan. For fall acceptance, apply as early as June of previous year, but not later than June of year of enrollment. Early decision available. *Requirements:* Either graduation from accredited secondary

ST. NORBERT COLLEGE—*cont'd*

school with 16 units which normally include 4 English, 3 mathematics, 3 science (each of which must be a lab science); 2 foreign language, 2 social studies, 2 history; or GED score in the 55% range. *Entrance tests:* College Board SAT or ACT Composite. For foreign students TOEFL. *For transfer students:* 2.5 minimum GPA, 96 semester hours maximum transfer credit.

Advanced placement for postsecondary-level work completed in secondary school.

Tutoring available.

Degree Requirements: 128 semester hours; 2.0 GPA; last 2 terms in residence; distribution requirements.

Fulfillment of some degree requirements and exemption from some beginning courses possible by passing College Board CLEP, AP (score of 3). *Grading system:* A, AB, B, BC, C, CD, D, F; W (withdraw; carries time limit); I (incomplete); DE (deferred); CT (continuing course); AU (audit).

Distinctive Educational Programs: Inter-divisional programs: international business language area studies. Facilities and programs for independent research (including individual majors, tutorials, independent study) and for student/faculty research. Institutionally sponsored study abroad in Australia, Chile, Ecuador, Egypt, England, France, Germany, Hungary, Ireland, Israel, Italy, Japan, Mexico, the Netherlands, New Zealand, Philippines, Scotland, Spain, Wales. The school also sues agencies in 34 more countries. SNC has 89 sites to offer its students. Philippines, Russia, Spain, Ukraine.

ROTC: Army.

Degrees Conferred: 440 *baccalaureate:* area and ethnic studies 8; biological sciences 25; business and management 102; communications 59; computer and information sciences 4; education 79; English 26; foreign languages 21; interdisciplinary studies 8; liberal arts/general studies 1; mathematics 14; natural resources 3; philosophy/religion 9; physical sciences 14; psychology 25; social sciences and history 99; visual and performing arts 30. Master's degrees awarded: education 18.

Fees and Other Expenses: *Full-time tuition per academic year 2008–09:* $25,926 undergraduate; graduate tuition charged per credit hour (contact the college for current rate). *Required fees:* $400. *Room and board per academic year:* $6,781. *books and supplies:* $900. *Other expenses* $1,100.

Financial Aid: The college offers a direct lending program. Aid from institutionally generated funds is provided on the basis of academic merit, financial need.

Financial aid to full-time, first-time undergraduate students: 96% received some form of aid. Average amount of aid received: federal grants $3,445; Pell grants $2,451; other federal aid $1,158 state/local grants $2,822; institutional grants $11,079.

Departments and Teaching Staff: *Total instructional faculty:* 179 (full-time 109, part-time 70). Total faculty with doctorate, first-professional, or other terminal degree: 110. Student-to-faculty ratio: 14:1. Degrees held by full-time faculty: doctorate 88%, master's 100%. 92% hold terminal degrees.

Enrollment: Total enrollment 2,137. Undergraduate 2,084 (full-time 96%; female 56%; male 44%). Graduate 53 (full-time 100%). Transfer-in students 58.

Characteristics of Student Body: *Ethnic/racial makeup:* Black non-Hispanic: 1%; American Indian or Alaska Native: 1%; Asian or Pacific Islander: 1%; Hispanic: 2%; White non-Hispanic: 90%; unknown: 2%; nonresident alien 4%.

International Students: 84 nonresident alien enrolled fall 2008. Students from Europe, Asia, Latin America, Africa, Canada. Programs available to aid students whose native language is not English: English as a Second Language Program. Financial aid specifically designated for international students.

Student Life: On-campus residence halls and apartments house 76% of student body. 11% for females; 89% for both males and females. *Intercollegiate athletics:* meale: baseball, football, hockey; female: softball, swimming, volleyball; both sexes: basketball, cross-country, golf, soccer, tennis, track. . *Special regulations:* Registered cars permitted in designated areas only. Dormitory visitation from 9am to midnight Sun.–Thurs., 9am to 2am Fri. and Sat. *Student publications, radio: ALPS,* a biannual literary magazine; *Graphos,* biennial literary magazine; *SNC Times*, a weekly newspaper. Radio station WSNC broadcasts 21 hours per week. *Surrounding community:* De Pere population 22,679. Green Bay, 5 miles from campus, is nearest metropolitan area. Served by airport 6 miles from campus.

Library Collections: 227,000 volumes including documents, and government documents not in separate collections. Online catalog. 30,000 microforms; 7,000 audiovisual materials; 750 current serial subscriptions. Computer work stations available. Students have access to the Internet at no charge.

Most important holdings include a collection of limited edition classics; Menomenee Indian Archives (personal papers of tribal chief from the 1940s); John P. Bennett Papers; theology and philosophy.

Buildings and Grounds: Campus area 93 acres.

Chief Executive Officer: Dr. William J. Hynes, President.

Address admission inquiries to Bridget K. O'Connor, Vice Preident for Enrollment Management. Admissions.

Silver Lake College

2406 South Alverno Road
Manitowoc, Wisconsin 54220-9319
Tel: (920) 684-6100 **E-mail:** admslc@sl.edu
Fax: (920) 684-7082 **Internet:** www.sl.edu

Institution Description: Silver Lake College is a private college affiliated with the Roman Catholic Church. *Enrollment:* 853. *Degrees awarded:* Associate, baccalaureate, master's.

Accreditation: *Regional:* NCA. *Professional*: teacher education

History: Established and chartered as Holy Family College and offered first instruction at postsecondary level 1935; awarded first degree (baccalaureate) 1939; became coeducational 1969; incorporated and adopted present name 1972. Off-campus program of study (management) begun in 1986.

Institutional Structure: *Governing board:* Board of Directors of Silver Lake College. Extrainstitutional representation: 14 directors; institutional representation: president of the college; 4 alumni. 1 ex officio. All voting. *Composition of institution:* Administrators 7. Academic affairs headed by academic dean. Management/business/finances directed by business officer. Full-time instructional faculty 44. Academic governance body, the faculty, meets an average of 9 times per year.

Calendar: Semesters. Academic year Aug. to May. Freshmen admitted Aug., June. Degrees conferred May, Jan. formal commencement May. Summer session of 1 term from June to July.

Characteristics of Freshmen: 243 applicants (female 157, male 86). 76% of applicants admitted. 31% of applicants admitted and enrolled.

<74% (23 students) submitted ACT scores. *25th percentile*: ACT Composite 16, ACT English 16, ACT Math 166. *75th percentile*: ACT Composite 21, ACT English 21, ACT Math 20.

52% of freshmen expected to graduate within 5 years. 90% of freshmen from Wisconsin. Freshmen from 3 states.

Admission: Rolling admissions plan. For fall acceptance, apply as early as summer following junior year of secondary school, but not later than Aug. 1 of year of enrollment. Early acceptance available. *Requirements:* Either graduation from accredited secondary school with 16 units which must include 3 English, 2 history/social studies, 2 mathematics, 1 laboratory science; or GED. Minimum GPA 2.00. *Entrance tests:* College Board SAT or ACT composite. For foreign students TOEFL. *For transfer students:* 2.0 minimum GPA, maximum transfer credit limited only by residence requirement.

Advanced placement for postsecondary-level work completed in secondary school. College credit for College Board CLEP.

Tutoring available. Remedial study skills courses offered during regular academic year; credit given.

Degree Requirements: *For all associate degrees:* 60 credit hours minimum. *For all baccalaureate degrees:* 120 credit hours; 2.00 GPA. Additional requirements for some programs. *For all degrees:* 30 hours in residence; distribution requirements.

Fulfillment of some degree requirements and exemption from some beginning courses possible by passing College Board CLEP. *Grading system:* A–F; pass-no credit; withdraw (deadline after which F is assigned); incomplete (deadline after which A–F is assigned).

Distinctive Educational Programs: Work-experience programs. Evening classes. Interdepartmental seminars and workshops. *Other distinctive programs:* student designed major; accelerated delivery; degree completion; cooperative arrangements with University of Nebraska - Omaha, Webster University (St. Louis MO); Bellin College of Nursing (Green Bay WI). Pre-natal and early childhood music programs as well. Special education clinical program.

Degrees Conferred: 119 *baccalaureate:* biological/life sciences 5; business and management 56; computer and information sciences 4; education 21; engineering 10; English 2; philosophy/religion/theology 2; protective services/public administration 2; psychology 18; social sciences and history 1; visual and performing arts 1. *M<aster's*: business and management 39; education 47. Master's degrees awarded: various disciplines 56.

Fees and Other Expenses: *Full-time tuition per academic year 2008–09:* undergraduate $19,194; contact the college for current graduate tuition. No campus housing. *Room and board off-campus per academic year:* $6,700. *books and supplies:* $1,050. *Other expenses:* $2,500.

Financial Aid: Aid from institutionally generated funds is provided on the basis of academic merit, financial need, athletic ability, other criteria.

Financial aid to full-time, first-time undergraduate students: 100% received some form of aid. Need-based scholarships/grants totaling $1,286,400, self-help $1,559,155, parent loans $24,674; athletic awards $34,312; non-need-based scholarships/grants totaling $137,623, self-help $304,924, parent loans $96,897, tuition waivers $33,600, athletic awards $16,688.

Departments and Teaching Staff: *Total instructional faculty:* 138 (full-time 44, part-time 94). Total faculty with doctorate, first-professional, or other terminal degree 56. Student-to-faculty ratio: 8:1. Degrees held by full-time faculty: baccalaureate .02%, master's 62.08%, doctorate 37%. 42% hold terminal degrees.

Enrollment: Total enrollment 853. Undergraduate 592 (full-time 35%; female 70%, male 30%). Graduate 261 (full-time 7%). Transfer-in students 74.

Characteristics of Student Body: *Ethnic/racial makeup:* Black non-Hispanic: 1%; American Indian or Alaska Native: 1%; Asian or Pacific Islander: 4%; Hispanic: 1%; White non-Hispanic: 73%; unknown 19%; nonresident alien 1%. *Age distribution:* number 18–19: 30; 20–21: 90; 22–24: 77; 25–29: 136; 30–34: 90; 35–39: 106; 40–49: 174; 50–64: 45; 65 and over: 8. 12% of student body attend summer sessions.

International Students: 9 nonresident aliens enrolled fall 2008. Students from Asia, Africa. Programs available to aid students whose native language is not English: English as a Second Language Program. No financial aid specifically designated for international students.

Student Life: No on-campus housing. 21 females and 10 males housed off campus in controlled housing. *Intercollegiate athletics:* female: basketball, volleyball. *Special regulations:* Cars permitted on campus in designated areas only. *Special services:* Learning Resources Center, art gallery and studios, greenhouse/herbarium, computer-equipped library and academic departments, 2 computer laboratories, closed circuit TV studio, clothing design areas, music listening room and fine arts theater. *Student publications: Perspective*, a monthly newspaper; *Quiddity*, an annual literary journal. *Surrounding community:* Manitowoc population 35,000. Milwaukee, 80 miles from campus, is nearest metropolitan area. Served by airport 5 miles from campus.

Publications: *Update*, a weekly campus newsletter; *Directions*, a seasonal, alumni/constituent publication.

Library Collections: 62,000 volumes including bound books, serial backfiles, electronic documents, and government documents not in separate collections. Online catalog. Current serial subscriptions: 283 paper, 2,154 microform, 8 via electronic access. 13,000 audiovisual materials; 92 DVD discs; 23 CD-ROMs. Computer work stations available. Students have access to the Internet at no charge.

Most important special holdings include Kodaly Music Theory publications; Rare Book Collection (European and Colonial American); business, education, children's literature.

Buildings and Grounds: Campus area 27.5 acres.

Chief Executive Officer: Dr. George Arnold, President.

Address admission inquiries to Dr. jane Bishop, Dean of Enrollment Management.

University of Wisconsin - Eau Claire

105 Garfield Avenue
Eau Claire, Wisconsin 54702-4004

Tel: (715) 836-2637 **E-mail:** admission@uwec.edu
Fax: (715) 836-2380 **Internet:** www.uwec.edu

Institution Description: *Enrollment:* 11,140. *Degrees awarded:* Associate, baccalaureate, master's. Specialist certificates in education also awarded.

Member of West Central Wisconsin Consortium.

Accreditation: *Regional:* NCA. *Professional*: business, chemistry, computer science, counseling, environmental health, journalism, music, nursing, social work, speech-language pathology, teacher education

History: Established as Eau Claire State Normal School and offered first instruction at postsecondary level 1916; awarded first degree (baccalaureate) and changed name to Eau Claire State Teachers College 1927; changed name to Wisconsin State College at Eau Claire 1951, to Wisconsin State University - Eau Claire 1964; adopted present name 1971. *See* Hilda Carter Richardson, *Fifty Years of Higher Education at Eau Claire* (River Falls, WI: River Falls University Press, 1976) for further information.

Institutional Structure: *Composition of institution:* Administrators 20. Academic affairs headed by provost and vice chancellor. Business and student services directed by vice chancellor. Information and technology directed by associate vice chancellor. assistant chancellors. Academic governance structure, University Senate, meets approximately 18 times per year.

Calendar: Semesters. Academic year Aug. to May. Freshmen admitted Aug., Jan., May. Degrees conferred and formal commencement Aug., Dec., May. Summer session of 1 term from late May to early Aug.

Characteristics of Freshmen: 7,024 applicants (female 4,365, male 2,659). 69% of applicants admitted. 40% of applicants admitted and enrolled.

33% (57 students) submitted SAT scores; 97% (1,993 students) submitted ACT scores. *25th percentile*: SAT Critical Reading 500, SAT Math 530; ACT Composite 22, ACT English 21, ACT Math 21. *75th percentile*: SAT Critical Reading 650, SAT Math 650; ACT Composite 26, ACT English 26, ACT Math 26.

32% of freshmen expected to graduate within 5 years. 77% of freshmen from Wisconsin. Freshmen from 9 states and 4 foreign countries. 6 National Merit Scholars.

Admission: Applicants must rank in at least the top 25% of their graduating class and present an ACT Composite score of at least 22 or SAT score of 250 or higher; or applicants must rank in at least the top 50% of their graduating class and present an ACT Composite score of at least 23 or SAT of at least 1090. .For fall acceptance, apply as early as Sept. 15 of previous year. *Requirements:* Graduation from recognized high school with 17 units as follows: 4 English, 3 mathematics, 3 natural science, 3 social science, 2 foreign language, 2 other electives. For foreign students TOEFL. *For transfer students:* 2.0 minimum GPA; from 4-year accredited institution 90 semester hours maximum transfer credit; from 2-year accredited institution and for correspondence/extension students 72 hours; from county teachers college 64 hours.

College credit for postsecondary-level work completed in secondary school.

Tutoring available. Noncredit remedial courses offered in summer session and regular academic year.

Degree Requirements: *For all associate degrees:* 60 semester hours; last 15 credits in residence; 1 credit physical education. *For all baccalaureate degrees:* 120 hours; 30 credits in residence. *For all undergraduate degrees:* 2.0 GPA; 4–5 credits in English composition; general education requirement.

Fulfillment of some degree requirements and exemption from some beginning courses possible by passing departmental examinations, College Board CLEP. *Grading system:* A–F; pass-fail; withdraw (deadline after which pass/fail is appended to withdraw).

Distinctive Educational Programs: Work-experience programs. Evening classes. Special facilities for using telecommunications in the classroom. Interdepartmental/interdisciplinary programs in chemistry-business, communicative diseases, criminal justice, environmental and public health, health care administration, music therapy, public administration, social work. Honors programs. Study abroad in Australia, Austria, China, Costa Rica, Denmark, England, France, Germany, Ireland, Japan, Latvia, Mexico, South Africa, Spain, Sweden, Thailand.

Degrees Conferred: 6 *associate;* 652 *baccalaureate* (B), 80 *masters* (M): area studies 2 (B); biological sciences 99 (B), 1 (M); business and management 299 (B), 23 (M); communications 133 (B); computer and information sciences 28 (B); education 183 (B), 47 (M); English 74 (B), 6 (M); foreign languages 24 (B); health professions 156 (B), 38 (M); mathematics 32 (B); parks and recreation 73 (B); philosophy/religion 12 (B); physical sciences 49 (B); public affairs and services 91 (B); psychology 85 (B), 13 (M); social sciences and history 153 (B), 6 (M); visual and performing arts 121 (B).

Fees and Other Expenses: *Full-time tuition per academic 2008–09:* undergraduate resident $6,199, nonresident $13,772; contact the university for current graduate tuition/fees. *Room and board per academic year:* $4,960. *Books and supplies:* $460. *Other expenses:* $2,890.

Financial Aid: The university offers a direct lending program. Aid from institutionally generated funds is provided on the basis of academic merit, financial need, other criteria.

Financial aid to full-time, first-time undergraduate students: 89% received some form of aid. Average amount of aid received: federal grants $4,050; Pell grants $2,711; other federal aid $1,518; state/local grants $2,198; institutional grants $1,425.

Departments and Teaching Staff: *Total instructional faculty:* 518 (full-time 412, part-time 106). Total faculty with doctorate, first-professional, or other terminal degree 385. Degrees held by full-time faculty: doctorate 73%, master's 12%, professional 15%. 88% hold terminal degrees.

Enrollment: Total enrollment 11,140. Undergraduate 10,454 (full-time 93%; female 58%, male 42%). Graduate 683 (full-time 17%). Transfer-in students 599.

Characteristics of Student Body: *Ethnic/racial makeup:* American Indian or Alaska Native: 3%; Asian or Pacific Islander: 1%; Hispanic: 1%; White non-Hispanic: 92%; unknown: 2%; nonresident alien 1%. *Age distribution:* number under 18: 67; 18–19: 3,582; 20–21: 3,552; 22–24: 2,022; 25–29: 186; 30–34: 136; 35–39: 95; 40–49: 138; 50–64: 56.

International Students: 111 nonresident aliens enrolled fall 2008. Students from Europe, Asia, Latin America, Africa, Canada, Middle East. Programs available to aid students whose native language is not English: social, cultural. English as a Second Language Program. Financial aid specifically designated for international students: scholarships available annually for undergraduate students.

Student Life: On-campus residence halls house 37% of student body. Resident halls for males constitute 6% of such space, for females 9%, for both sexes

UNIVERSITY OF WISCONSIN - EAU CLAIRE—*cont'd*

85%. 1% of males join and some live in fraternity housing; 1% of females join and some live in sorority housing. *Intercollegiate athletics:* male: basketball, cross-country, football, golf, hockey, swimming, tennis, track, wrestling; female: basketball, cross-country, golf, gymnastics, hockey, soccer, softball, swimming, tennis, track, volleyball. *Special regulations:* Cars with parking permits allowed on campus; fee charged. Residence hall visitation Sat.–Sun.; additional hours set by residents in individual halls. *Special services:* Learning Resources Center, medical services. *Student publications, radio, television: NOTA*, a quarterly literary publication; *The Spectator*, a biweekly newspaper. Radio station WUEC broadcasts 125 hours per week. TV station WIS CATV. *Surrounding community:* Eau Claire population 63,000. Minneapolis-St. Paul, 90 miles from campus, is nearest metropolitan area. Served by mass transit bus system; airport 5 miles from campus.

Publications: *Wisconsin Dialogue* (annually) first published 1980.

Library Collections: 765,000 volumes including bound books, serial backfiles, electronic documents, and government documents not in separate collections. Online catalog. 1,400,000 microforms; 18,000 audiovisual materials; 2,500 current serial subscriptions. Computer work stations available. Students have access to the Internet at no charge.

Most important special holdings include land and lumbering industry records of northwest Wisconsin; federal government depository publications; Area Research Center Collections; University Archives.

Buildings and Grounds: Campus area 310 acres.

Chief Executive Officer: Dr. Brian Levin-Stankeevich, Chancellor.

Address admission inquiries to Kristina Anderson, Director of Enrollment Services and Admissions.

University of Wisconsin - Green Bay

2420 Nicolet Drive

Green Bay, Wisconsin 54311-7001

Tel: (920) 465-2000 **E-mail:** admissions@uwgb.edu
Fax: (920) 465-5754 **Internet:** www.uwgb.edu

Institution Description: *Enrollment:* 6,286. *Degrees awarded:* Associate, baccalaureate, master's.

Member of the Urban Corridor Consortium.

Accreditation: *Regional:* NCA. *Professional*: dietetics, music, nursing, social work

History: Established 1965; offered first instruction at postsecondary level 1968; awarded first degree (baccalaureate) 1970; added graduate program 1974.

Institutional Structure: *Composition of institution:* Administrators 26. Academic affairs headed by vice chancellor for academic affairs. Management/business/finances directed by assistant chancellor for fiscal and administrative services; other activities by associate chancellor. Full-time instructional faculty 177. Academic governance body, Faculty Senate, meets about 30 times per year.

Calendar: Semesters. Academic year Sept. to May. Freshmen admitted Sept., Jan., Dec., June. Degrees conferred May, Aug., Dec. Formal commencements May, Dec. Summer session June to Aug.

Characteristics of Freshmen: 2,761 applicants (female 1,724, male 1,051). 70% of applicants accepted. 45% of accepted applicants enrolled.

Average secondary school rank 74th percentile. Mean ACT Composite score5.

40% of entering freshmen expected to graduate within 5 years. 93% of freshmen from Wisconsin. Freshmen from 11 states and 11 foreign countries.

Admission: Rolling admissions plan. For fall acceptance, apply as early as Oct. 1 of previous year, but not later than Sept. 1 of year of enrollment. Early acceptance available. *Requirements:* Either graduation from accredited secondary school with 17 college preparatory credits including 4 English, 3 mathematics, 3 social science,/history, 3 natural science, 4 academic electives; or GED. Provisional admission on individual basis. *Entrance tests:* For foreign students TOEFL. *For transfer students:* 2.0 minimum GPA; from 4-year accredited institution 93 hours maximum transfer credit; from 2-year accredited institution 72 hours.

College credit for postsecondary-level work completed in secondary school and for extrainstitutional learning on basis of portfolio and faculty assessments; personal interviews.

Tutoring available. Developmental courses offered in summer session, regular academic year, and interim period; nondegree credit given.

Degree Requirements: *For all associate degrees:* 62 credit hours; 15 credits in residence. *For all baccalaureate degrees:* 120 credit hours; 31 credits in residence; liberal education curriculum; demonstrated proficiency in writing. *For all undergraduate degrees:* 2.0 GPA; 2.0 GPA in major.

Fulfillment of some degree requirements and exemption from some beginning courses possible by passing College Board CLEP. *Grading system:* A–F; pass-fail.

Distinctive Educational Programs: Work-experience programs. Flexible meeting places and schedules, including weekend and evening classes. Cooperative baccalaureate in nursing with University of Wisconsin system, Bellin College of Nursing. Special facilities for using telecommunications in the classroom. Interdisciplinary programs. Facilities and programs for independent research, including honors programs, individual majors. Institutionally sponsored month-long study abroad opportunities in many parts of the world, including England, France, Germany, and Mexico. Semester and year-long programs available in Denmark, France, Germany, Spain, Mexico, and Russia. Student exchange program for qualified students. *Other distinctive programs:* Extended degree program offers baccalaureate to adults in nontraditional setting.

ROTC: Army in cooperation with St. Norbert College.

Degrees Conferred: 995 *baccalaureate*; 49 *master's*. Bachelor's degrees awarded in top five disciplines: business, management, marketing, and related support services 199; psychology 119; biomedical/biological sciences 99; education 70; visual and performing arts 63. Master's degrees awarded: various disciplines 49.

Fees and Other Expenses: *Full-time tuition per academic year 2008–09:* undergraduate resident $6,308, nonresident $13,881; contact the university for current graduate tuition/fees. *Books and supplies:* $800. *Required fees:* $1,148. *Room and board per academic year:* $4,700. *Books and supplies:* $800. *Other expenses:* $2,820.

Financial Aid: Aid from institutionally generated funds is provided on the basis of academic merit, financial need, athletic ability.

Financial aid to full-time, first-time undergraduate students: 77% received some form of aid. Average amount of aid received: federal grants $3,685; Pell grants $2,342; other federal aid $1,391; state/local grants $2,089; institutional grants $3,783.

Departments and Teaching Staff: *Total instructional faculty:* 285 (full-time 177, part-time 108). Student-to-faculty ratio: 23.6:1. Degrees held by full-time faculty: baccalaureate 3%, master's 8%, doctorate 88%, professional 1%. 89% hold terminal degrees.

Enrollment: Total enrollment 6,286. Undergraduate 6,088 (full-time 77%; female 64%, male 38%). Graduate 196 (full-time 21%). Transfer-in students 587.

Characteristics of Student Body: *Ethnic/racial makeup:* Black non-Hispanic: 1%; American Indian or Alaska Native: 3%; Asian or Pacific Islander: 2%; Hispanic: 2%; White non-Hispanic: 90%; unknown 1%; nonresident alien 1%.

International Students: 63 nonresident aliens enrolled fall 2008. Students from Europe, Asia, Latin America, Africa, Canada. Programs available to aid students whose native language is not English: social, cultural. English as a Second Language Program. Financial aid specifically designated for international students: scholarships available annually for qualifying undergraduate students.

Student Life: 33% of student body housed on campus in apartments and residence halls. *Intercollegiate athletics:* male: basketball, cross-country, soccer, wrestling, golf, tennis; female: basketball, cross-country, golf, volleyball, softball, tennis; both sexes: sailing, swimming-diving. *Special regulations:* Cars permitted without restriction. Quiet hours. *Special services:* Learning Resources Center, medical services, American Intercultural Center, tutoring center. *Student publications, radio: Fourth Estate*, a weekly (during school year) newspaper; *Sheepshead Review*, an annual literary magazine. Radio station WGBW broadcasts 113 hours per week. *Surrounding community:* Green Bay metropolitan population 100,000. Milwaukee, 115 miles from campus, is nearest metropolitan area. Served by mass transit bus system; airport 13 miles from campus.

Publications: *Inside UWGB* (semiannual since 1972) for employees, friends, and graduates.

Library Collections: 339,000 volumes including bound books, serial backfiles, electronic documents, and government documents not in separate collections. Online catalog. 734,000 microforms; 48,000 audiovisual materials; 5,300 current serial subscriptions including via electronic access. Computer work stations available campus-wide. Students have access to the Internet at no charge.

Most important special holdings include Leon Kramer Collection of Socialist Materials; Eleazer Williams (personal papers); Brown County and Northeast Wisconsin Historical Records.

Buildings and Grounds: Campus area 700 acres. Campus DVD available.

Chief Executive Officer: Dr. Bruce Shepard, Chancellor.

Address undergraduate admission inquiries Pam Harvey Jacobs, Director of Admissions; graduate inquiries to Dean for Graduate Studies.

University of Wisconsin - La Crosse

1725 State Street
La Crosse, Wisconsin 54601
Tel: (608) 785-8000 **E-mail:** admissions@uwlax.edu
Fax: (608) 785-6695 **Internet:** www.uwlax.edu

Institution Description: *Enrollment:* 9,880. *Degrees awarded:* Associate, baccalaureate, master's.

Budget subject to approval by state governing boards. Member of West Central Wisconsin Consortium.

Accreditation: *Regional:* NCA. *Professional*: athletic training, business, clinical lab scientist, music, nurse anesthesia education, occupational therapy, physical therapy, physician assisting, public health, radiation therapy, recreation and leisure services, teacher education

History: Chartered as State Normal School 1905; established and offered first instruction at postsecondary level 1909; changed name to State Teachers College and awarded first degree (baccalaureate) 1926; changed name to Wisconsin State College—La Crosse 1951, to Wisconsin State University—La Crosse 1964; adopted present name 1971. *See* George R. Gilkey, *The First Seventy Years* (La Crosse: La Crosse Foundation, University of Wisconsin, 1981) for further information.

Institutional Structure: *Composition of institution:* Administrators 62. Academic affairs headed by vice chancellor. Management/business/finances directed by 2 assistant chancellors. Full-time instructional faculty 343. Academic governance body, Faculty Senate, meets an average of 18-20 times per year. Academic Staff Council meets an average of 16 times per year.

Calendar: Semesters. Academic year Aug. to May. Freshmen admitted Sept., Jan., June. Degrees conferred May, Aug., Dec. Summer session May to Aug.

Characteristics of Freshmen: 6,751 applicants (female 4,138, male 2,621). 64% of applicants admitted. 25% of applicants admitted and enrolled.

2% (42 students) submitted SAT scores; 99% (1,719 students) submitted ACT scores. *25th percentile*: SAT Critical Reading 490, SAT math 520; ACT Composite 23, ACT English 21, ACT Math 22. *75th percentile*: SAT Critical Reading 622.5, SAT Math 630; ACT Composite 26, ACT English 27, ACT Math 27. 54% of entering freshmen expected to graduate in 5 years. 82% of freshmen from Wisconsin. Freshmen from 12 states and 41 foreign countries.

Admission: Rolling admissions plan. For fall acceptance, priority date is Jan. 1; those dated after Jan. 1 will be reviewed on a space available basis. *Requirements:* Graduation in top 35% of high school class and ACT score of 22 or greater, or top 40% and ACT of 26 or greater. 17 specific high school courses are required. *Entrance tests:* ACT or SAT. For foreign students TOEFL. *For transfer students:* minimum 2.75 GPA. Admission on space available basis with GPA of 2.00–2.74.

College credit and advanced placement CLEP, International Baccalaureate.

Degree Requirements: *For all associate degrees:* 64 credit hours. *For all baccalaureate degrees:* 120 hours; distribution requirements. *For all undergraduate degrees:* Minimum GPA 2.0.; GPA for some programs will be considerably higher. 2 terms in residence; general education curriculum.

Fulfillment of some degree requirements and exemption from some beginning courses possible by passing departmental examinations. *Grading system:* A–F; pass-fail; withdraw.

Distinctive Educational Programs: Cooperative education and internship programs. Flexible meeting places and schedules, including evening and weekend classes. Special facilities for using telecommunications in the classroom. Interdisciplinary programs, including minority studies, various regional studies, women's studies. Preprofessional programs in architecture, chiropractic, dentistry, engineering, forestry (natural resources, conservation, wildlife management), law, medicine, nursing, optometry, osteopathy, pharmacy, social work, and veterinary medicine. Facilities and programs for independent research, including honors programs, various majors, tutorials. Cross-registration with Viterbo College. Academic Success Institute (ASI) for multicultural students. Summer programs at Pigeon Lake field station. Summer archaeology field study programs. Study abroad. The university offers a full range of academic programs throughout the world via exchange agreements, institutional affiliations and foreign study centers. International studies programs in Australia, China, Denmark, France, Germany, Israel, Japan, Mexico, Russia, Spain, United Kingdom. *Other distinctive programs:* La Crosse Exercise and Health Program in adult fitness and cardiopulmonary rehabilitation. Community extension programs. Free tuition for senior citizens to audit classes. Distance education; 3+3 chiropractic dual degree; 3+2 engineering dual degree.

ROTC: Army

Degrees Conferred: 1,690 *baccalaureate* (B), 545 *master's* (M): biological sciences 149 (B), 10 (M); business and marketing 307 (B), 19 (M); communications 88 (B); computer and information sciences 14 (B); education 139 (B), 357 (M); engineering 1 (M); English 39 (B); foreign languages and literature 48 (B); health professions and related sciences 117 (B), 42 (M); history 34 (B); mathematics 18 (B), parks and recreation 206 (B), 98 (M); philosophy/religion 13 (B); psychology 18 (M); social sciences 169 (B); visual and performing arts 49 (B).

Fees and Other Expenses: *Full-time tuition per academic year 2008–09:* undergraduate resident $6,648, nonresident $14,221; contact the university for current graduate tuition/fees. *Room and board per academic year:* $5,420. *Books and supplies:* $300. *Other expenses:* $2,715.

Financial Aid: Aid from institutionally generated funds is provided on the basis of academic merit, financial need.

Financial aid to full-time, first-time undergraduate students: 59% received some form of aid. Average amount of aid redeived: federal grants $4,075; Pell grants $2,906; other federal aid $1,241; state/local grants $2,207; institutional grants $1,208.

Departments and Teaching Staff: *Total instructional faculty:* 443 (full-time 343, part-time 100). Total faculty with doctorate, first-professional, or other terminal degree 280. Student-to-faculty ratio: 24:1. Degrees held by full-time faculty: baccalaureate 1%, master's 18%, doctorate 81%. 82% hold terminal degrees.

Enrollment: Total enrollment 9,880. Undergraduate 8,641 (full-time 95%; female 58%, male 42%). Graduate 1,239 (full-time 36%). Transfer-in students 298.

Characteristics of Student Body: *Ethnic/racial makeup:* Black non-Hispanic: 1%; American Indian or Alaska Native: 4%; Asian or Pacific Islander: 1%; Hispanic: 1%; White non-Hispanic: 89%; unknown: 25; nonresident alien 3%. *Age distribution:* number under 18: 41; 18–19: 2,828; 20–21: 2,836; 22–24: 1,511; 25–29: 220; 30–34: 61; 35–39: 34; 40–49: 34; 50–64: 14.

International Students: 296 nonresident aliens enrolled fall 2008. Students from Europe, Asia, Latin America, Africa, Canada, Australia, Middle East. Programs available to aid students whose native language is not English: English as a Second Language Program. Financial aid specifically designated for international students: scholarships available annually for both undergraduate and graduate international students.

Student Life: On-campus residence halls house about 36% of student body. Men only, substance-free, international student, disabled student, and first-year experience housing available. *Intercollegiate athletics:* male: baseball, basketball, cross-country, football, golf, swimming, tennis, track and field, wrestling; female: basketball, cross-country, gymnastics, softball, swimming, tennis, track and field, volleyball. *Special regulations:* Cars permitted without restrictions. *Special services:* Medical services; Multicultural Student Services; academic discovery lab; Counseling and Testing Center; legal aid, writing laboratory, and career services. *Student publications, television: Racquet*, a weekly newspaper; *Focus*, twice-yearly magazine. TV station WMCM-TV broadcasts approximately 6 hours per week. *Surrounding community:* La Crosse population 50,000. Minneapolis-St. Paul, 160 miles from campus, is nearest metropolitan area. Served by mass transit bus system; airport 7 miles from campus; passenger rail service 5 miles from campus.

Library Collections: 667,000 volumes. 194,176 government documents; 1,223,000 microforms; 2,000 audiovisual materials; 1,600 current periodical subscriptions. Online catalog. Computer work stations available. Students have access to the Internet at no charge.

Most important special holdings include Inland Riverboat Steamboat Collection; regional history books (Wisconsiana) and photos; Skeeters Collection (gothic, fantasy, and science fiction).

Buildings and Grounds: Campus area 120 acres.

Chief Executive Officer: Dr. Joseph Gow, Chancellor.

Address undergraduate admission inquiries to Timothy R. Lewis, Director of Admissions; graduate inquiries to Dean of Graduate Studies.

University of Wisconsin - Madison

500 Lincoln Drive
Madison, Wisconsin 53706
Tel: (608) 262-1234 **E-mail:** onwisconsin@wisc.edu
Fax: (608) 262-1429 **Internet:** www.wisc.edu

Institution Description: *Enrollment:* 41,620. *Degrees awarded:* Baccalaureate, first-professional (law, medicine, pharmacy, veterinary medicine), master's, doctorate. Certificates also awarded.

Accreditation: *Regional:* NCA. *Professional*: accounting, art, athletic training, audiology, business, clinical psychology, counseling psychology, diagnostic medical sonography, dietetics, engineering, forestry, health services administration, interior design, journalism, landscape architecture, law, librarianship, medicine, music, nursing, nursing education, occupational therapy, pharmacy, physical therapy, physician assisting, psychology internship, planning, public administration, rehabilitation counseling, social work, speech-language pathology, surgeon assisting, theatre, veterinary medicine

UNIVERSITY OF WISCONSIN - MADISON—*cont'd*

History: Chartered as University of Wisconsin 1848; established and offered first instruction at postsecondary level 1849; awarded first degree (baccalaureate) 1854; became part of University of Wisconsin system and adopted present name 1973. *See* Carstensen and Curti, *The University of Wisconsin* (Madison: University of Wisconsin Press, 1974) for further information.

Institutional Structure: *Composition of institution:* Academic affairs headed by vice chancellor-academic affairs. Management/business/finances directed by vice chancellor-administration. Full-time instructional faculty 2.365. Academic governance body, Faculty Senate, meets an average of 8 times per year.

Calendar: Semesters. Academic year Sept. to May. Degrees conferred June, Aug., Dec. Formal commencements May, Dec. Summer session from May to Aug.

Characteristics of Freshmen: 22,289 applicants (female 11,804, male 10,685). 68% of applicants admitted. 42% of applicants admitted and enrolled.

21% (1,923 students) submitted SAT scores; 83% (5,080 students) submitted ACT scores. *25th percentile*: SAT Critical Reading 560, SAT Math 600; ACT Composite 26. ACT *75th percentile*: SAT Critical Reading 670, SAT Math 700; ACT Composite 30.

45% of entering freshmen expected to graduate within 5 years. 29% of freshmen from Wisconsin. Freshmen from 50 states and 130 foreign countries.

Admission: Rolling admissions for well qualified applicants; remaining qualified students may be placed on a waiting list for selection if space permits. Applications should be received by priority date, postmark not accepted: Fall semester, Feb. 1; Spring semester, Nov. 15; Summer session, Feb. 1. Early application is advised, but not before Sept. 15. *Requirements:* High school graduation or equivalent (GED or Wisconsin High School Equivalency Examination); GED or WHSEE applicants must have completed 2 years of a foreign language, plus one year each of high school algebra and plane geometry and a third year of math. Completion of required college prep courses in high school, total of 17 units including 4 units English (with emphasis on literature, composition, or speech); 3 units mathematics (1 algebra, 1 college-track geometry, 1 in any of the following: advanced algebra, trigonometry, analytic geometry, calculus); 3 units history and social studies; 2 units of a single foreign language; 2 units from any of previous, or fine arts, communication arts, computer science or statistics. *Entrance tests:* Applicants may submit either ACT or SAT scores. *For transfer students:* Transfer students must have completed one year each of high school algebra and plane geometry, and a third year of math; and two years of a single foreign language; must have sophomore or higher standing, minimum of 24 transferable semester credits. Transfers from 2-year institutions may transfer up to half the total credits required for graduation, to a maximum of 72 credits, depending upon the admissions and residency regulations of the admitting college/school. Students are selected for transfer admission on the basis of their qualification for academic success at the University of Wisconsin-Madison. Because there are more qualified applicants than can be offered admission, students with the best qualifications are selected. There can be no assurance of admission based on grade point average.

College credit and advanced placement for postsecondary-level work completed in secondary school.

Degree Requirements: Vary by program. Generally, 120–158 credit hours; 2.0–2.75 GPA; 9–22 months in residence.

Fulfillment of some degree requirements and exemption from some beginning courses possible by passing departmental examinations. Some College Board CLEP, APP are accepted. *Grading system:* A–F; pass-fail, withdraw (carries time limit), credit-no credit.

Distinctive Educational Programs: Evening classes and summer sessions offer a wide array of courses. Office of Continuing Education Services for returning adults. Tutorial program available in most fields. About 60 foreign languages are taught, 40 in any one semester. Biology core curriculum offers broad-based preparation in the biological sciences; Integrated Liberal Studies courses may be taken to gain an interdisciplinary overview of Western civilization. Coordinative and internship programs combining work and study are available or required in several fields. Facilities and programs for independent research, including honors programs, numerous research laboratories, institutes, and centers. Individual majors for qualified undergraduate and graduate students. Programs in Letters and Science, Engineering, Agriculture, Business, Human Ecology, and other areas can be arranged to incorporate international study. Various study abroad programs are available in numerous countries, including Brazil, England, Germany, France, Hungary, India, Israel, Italy, Nepal, Spain, Thailand, Siera Leone, Russia, West Indies, Denmark, Ecuador, Holland, Japan, Norway, Sweden, Mexico, Canada, Togo, People's Republic of China, and Indonesia. A variety of special opportunities in graduate and professional programs is available for undergraduate student participation if qualified.

ROTC: Air Force, Army, Navy.

Degrees Conferred: 6,477 *baccalaureate* (B); 1,666 *master's* (M), 654 *doctorate* (D): agriculture and natural resources 96 (B), 19 (M), 47 (D); architecture and environmental design 22 (B), 1 (M), 20 (D); area studies 753 (B), 5 (M), 23 (D); biological sciences 661 (B), 108 (M), 87 (D); business and management 601 (B), 8 (M), 295 (D); communications 393 (B), 17 (M), 22 (D); computer and information sciences 116 (B), 10(M), 50 (D); education 209 (B), 91 (M), 162 (D); engineering 612 (B), 99 (M), 162 (D); foreign languages 219 (B), 27 (M), 56 (D); health professions 257 (B), 27 (M), 95 (D); home economics 310 (B), 5 (M), 11 (D); law 97 (B), 28 (D); library science 4 (M), 84 (D); mathematics 73 (B), 15 (M), 35 (D); natural resources 36 (B), 12 (M), 52 (D); parks and recreation 64 (B), 1 (M), 4 (D); philosophy/religion/theology 77 (B), 5 (M), 10 (10); physical sciences 98 (B), 65 (M), 34 (D); protective services/public administration 56 (B), 3 (M), 136 (D); psychology 305 (B), 13 (M), 40 (D); social sciences and history 1,159 (B), 70 (M), 124 (D); visual and performing arts 296 (B), 24 (M), 106 (D). 654 *first-professional:* law 273, medicine 148; pharmacy 127, veterinary medicine 74.

Fees and Other Expenses: *Full-time tuition per academic year 2008–09:* undergraduate in-state $7,564, out-of-state $21,814; contact the university for current tuition for graduate and professional schools. *Room and board per academic year:* $6,909. *Books and supplies:* $990. *Other expenses:* $3,510.

Financial Aid: Aid from institutionally generated funds is provided on the basis of academic merit, financial need, athletic ability, other criteria.

Financial aid to full-time, first-time undergraduate students: 89% recieved some form of aid. Average amount of aid received: federal grants $4,938, Pell grants $2,644; other federal aid $2,344; state/local grants $2,463; institutional grants $1,998.

Departments and Teaching Staff: *Total instructional faculty:* 2.975 (full-time 2,365, part-time 610). Total faculty with doctorate, first-professional, or other terminal degree 2,515. Student-to-faculty ratio: 13:1. Degrees held by full-time faculty: 97% hold terminal degrees.

Enrollment: Total enrollment 41,620. Undergraduate 30,362 (full-time 91%; female 52%, male 48%). Graduate 11,258 (full-time 93%). Transfer-in student 1,238.

Characteristics of Student Body: *Ethnic/racial makeup:* Black non-Hispanic: 3%; American Indian or Alaska Native: 1%; Asian or Pacific Islander: 3%; Hispanic: 3%; White non-Hispanic: 78%; nonresident alien 5%. *Age distribution:* number under 18: 318; 18–19: 10,746; 20–21: 11,530; 22–24: 4,282; 25–29: 783; 30–34: 246; 35–39: 121; 40–49: 133; 50–64: 86; 65 and over: 1.

International Students: 2,081 nonresident aliens enrolled fall 2008. Students from Europe, Asia, Latin America, Africa, Canada, Australia, New Zealand. Programs available to aid students whose native language is not English: Social, cultural. English as a Second Language Program. No financial aid specifically designated for international students.

Student Life: Approximately 24% of student body live on campus. *Intercollegiate athletics:* male: basketball, crew, cross-country, football, golf, hockey, soccer, swimming, tennis, track, wrestling; female: basketball, crew, cross-country, golf, hockey, soccer, softball, swimming, tennis, track, volleyball. *Special regulations:* Cars permitted; parking limited. Quiet hours and residence hall visitation hours vary according to residence hall. *Special services:* residential learning communities, medical services, campus bus system. *Student daily newspapers: Badger Herald, Daily Cardinal.* Radio stations WHA 970 KHz, 4340 watts, 88.7 MHz, 25,000 watts; television station WHA-TV Ch. 21, 60 mile radius. *Surrounding community:* Madison population 250,000. Milwaukee, 77 miles from campus, is nearest metropolitan area. Served by mass transit bus system; airport 6 miles from campus.

Publications: Scholarly journals published by the University of Wisconsin Press include: *American Orthoptic Journal, Arctic Anthropology, Contemporary Literature, Journal of Human Resources, Land Economics, Landscape Journal, Luso-Brazilian Review, Monatshefte, Sub-Stance, Ecological Restoration.*

Library Collections: 7,900,000 volumes. Current serial subscriptions: 33,499 paper; 6,196,602 microforms; 21,697 via electronic access. 240,000 audiovisual materials, 284,148 recordings. Online catalog. Computer work stations available. Students have access to online information retrieval services and the Internet.

Most important special holdings include collections on German and Scandinavian studies; history of science; little magazines (special literary publication); Cairns Collection of American Women Writers.

Buildings and Grounds: Campus area 900 acres. *New buildings:* Health Sciences Learning Center completed 2006; Newell J. Smith Residence Hall 2006.

Chief Executive Officer: Dr. John Wiley, Chancellor.

Undergraduates address admission inquiries to Director of Admissions; graduate inquiries to Assistant Dean of the Graduate School; first-professional, law students to Admissions Office, Law School; medicine to Admissions Office, Medical School; veterinary medicine to Admissions Office, School of Veterinary Medicine; special and guest students to Summer Sessions and Inter-College Programs.

College of Agricultural and Life Sciences

Degree Programs Offered: *Baccalaureate* in agricultural business management; agricultural and applied economics; agricultural education; agricultural biological systems engineering; agricultural journalism; agronomy; bacteriology; biochemistry; dairy science; dietetics; entomology; food science; forest science, genetics; horticulture, landscape architecture; animal science; nutritional sciences; plant pathology; poultry science; recreation resources management; rural sociology; soil science; wildlife ecology. *Master's* and *doctorate* in various fields.

Admission: Admissions requirements vary by program. Contact the college for current information.

Degree Requirements: 124 credits and 248 grade points minimum required; 2.00 cumulative GPA; residency, as defined; requirements for majors vary by department.

Distinctive Educational Programs: Honors degree program. Coordinative internship program. Special facilities for research, including agricultural experiment station, experimental farms and several special centers. Interdisciplinary majors, particularly at the graduate level, in such areas as: biometry, environmental studies, plant breeding and plant genetics, development, endocrinology-reproductive physiology, mass communications and molecular biology. Pre-professional veterinary medicine and pre-medicine study programs can be completed concurrently with 15 majors within the Natural Science option. Two-year certificate in agriculture, and short course program in farm and industry.

School of Business

Degree Programs Offered: *Baccalaureate* in accounting; actuarial sciences; finance, investment and banking; information systems; management and human resources; marketing; international business, real estate and urban land economics; risk management and insurance; transportation and public utilities. *Master's* in baccalaureate fields as well as arts administration, health services administration, rational business, supply chain management. *Doctorate* in business.

Admission: By application. Spring: 15 Sept., on campus; 15 Nov. off-campus; Fall: Feb. 1, on campus; Mar. 1, off campus.

Degree Requirements: Degree requirements vary by program. Contact the school for current information.

School of Education

Degree Programs Offered: *Baccalaureate* in art or graduate-level training. counseling psychology and counselor education, curriculum and instruction (curriculum theory, elementary education, instructional media, instructional theory, reading, teacher education, and the academic teaching fields of art, communication arts, English, foreign languages, health education, mathematics, music, safety education, science, and social studies), educational leadership and policy analysis, educational policy studies (history of education, social sciences of education, philosophy of education, comparative education, and public policy and educational institutions), educational psychology (human development, human learning, quantitative methods, school psychology, classroom learning and individual differences, and education of the gifted, talented, and creative), physical education and dance (physical education/teacher education, exercise physiology, motor development, biomechanics/kinesiology, measurement/assessment, perceptual motor learning, curriculum, teaching and administration, sport psychology, and dance, including choreography/performance and teacher certification), and rehabilitation psychology and special education (rehabilitation counseling psychology, rehabilitation facilities administration, individualized master's program, special education/clinical, and special education/postsecondary teaching and research), occupational therapy,

Admission: Requirements vary by program.

Degree Requirements: Requirements vary by program.

Distinctive Educational Programs: Special facilities for research, including Wisconsin Research and Development Center for Individualized Schooling, Wisconsin Vocational Studies Center, Biodynamics Laboratory, Guidance Institute for Talented Students, Waisman Center on Mental Retardation and Human Development. Special services and programs include Cooperative Children's Book Center, Coordinative Services for Multicultural Programs, Instructional Media Development Center, International Programs in Education, Laboratory for Experimental Design, Minority Students Programs, Office of Field Experiences for Educational Personnel, Psycho-Educational Clinic, Wisconsin Center for Education Research.

Gaylord Nelson Institute for Environmental Studies

Degree Programs Offered: *Undergraduate certificate* in environmental studies; *master's* in conservation biology and sustainable development, water resources management; *master's* and *doctorate* in land resources; *master's certificate* in energy analysis and policy.

Admission: *Environmental Studies Certificate Program for Undergraduates:* open to UW-Madison undergraduates. *Graduate Program:* undergraduate degree required for admission, with training in the fields of botany, biology, forestry, wildlife ecology and zoology.

Degree Requirements: Degree requirements vary by program.

School of Human Ecology

Degree Programs Offered: *Baccalaureate* in consumer science, family and consumer education, family and consumer journalism, human ecology, human development and family studies, interior design, textile and apparel design, retailing. *Master's* and *doctorate* in human ecology.

Admission: Contact the school for current information.

Distinctive Educational Programs: Internships. Cooperative programs in apparel design and textile design with Fashion Institute of Technology (NY). Research opportunities through Helen Allen Textile Collection. Joint degree program in preschool and kindergarten education with School of Education. Internships and field-experience for juniors and seniors in retailing, interior design, consumer science, and family and consumer journalism.

Graduate School

Degree Programs Offered: *Master's* in 172 fields, *doctorate* in 125 fields.

Departments and Teaching Staff: Faculty drawn from other schools in the university.

Law School

Degree Programs Offered: *First-professional, master's and doctorate* in law; *master's* of legal institutions (for foreign law graduates).

Admission: *For first-professional students:* Baccalaureate degree from accredited institution, LSAT, LSDAS.

Degree Requirements: *For first-professional degree:* 90 credit hours; 6 semesters in residence; 77.00 weighted average on 100 point scale.

Distinctive Educational Programs: Joint degree programs with the LaFollette Institute, the Library School, and the Philosophy Department. Clinical programs with state and federal agencies, state and federal courts. Legal Research Institute. Criminal Justice Administration Programs include Legal Assistance to Institutionalized Persons (LAIP), Legal Defense Project (for indigent defendants), Prosecutor Internship Program. Clinical Programs include Judicial Internship Program (clerkship with judges), Center for Public Representation (Administrative Advocacy) for traditionally under represented groups (elderly, disabled, women and women with health care needs, consumers), Labor Law Clinical Program, NAACP Legal Defense and Education Fund Summer Internships Program, Public Intervenor's Program in environmental law and practice.

College of Letters and Science

Degree Programs Offered: *Baccalaureate* in African languages and literature; Afro-American studies; anthropology; applied mathematics, engineering and physics; Asian studies; art history; astronomy-physics; bacteriology; behavioral science and law; biochemistry; biological aspects of conservation; biology, botany; cartography and geographic information systems; chemistry; chemistry course; Chinese; classical humanities; classics; communication arts; communicative disorders; comparative literature; computer sciences; economics; English; French; geography; geology; geophysics; geophysics; German; Hebrew; history; history of science; history of culture; international studies; Italian; Japanese; Jewish studies; journalism; Latin; Latin American and Iberian studies; linguistics; mathematics; medical microbiology and immunology; medical science; atmospheric and oceanic sciences; molecular biology; music, applied; music; music education; philosophy; physics; Polish; political science; Portuguese; psychology; religious studies; Russian; Scandinavian studies; social welfare; social work; sociology; South Asian studies; Spanish; statistics; theater and drama; women's studies; zoology. *Master's* and *doctorate* in various fields. Certificates also awarded.

Admission: For specific information, contact the college.

Degree Requirements: Requirements vary according to program.

Distinctive Educational Programs: Interdisciplinary majors in African languages and literature; Asian studies; behavioral science and law; cartography; history of science; Latin American and Iberian studies; Scandinavian studies; South Asian studies. Interdisciplinary programs in Afro-American studies; applied mathematics, engineering, and physics; biological aspects of conservation; French area studies; international studies; medieval studies; molecular biology; Russian area studies; Southeast Asian studies; Western European studies; women's studies. Study abroad in Brazil, England, France, Germany, India, Israel, Italy, Nepal, Spain. Special facilities for research, including Center for Communication Research, Wisconsin Center for Film and Theatre Research, Mass Communication History Center, Cartographic Laboratory and Map

UNIVERSITY OF WISCONSIN - MADISON—*cont'd*

Library, Laboratory for Recorded Instruction (foreign language), and several other research centers.

School of Pharmacy

Degree Programs Offered: *Baccalaureate* in pharmacology and toxicology; *master's* and *doctorate* in related fields; *first-professional* in pharmacy.

Admission: Admissions requirements vary by program. Contact the school for current information.

Degree Requirements: Degree requirements vary by program.

Distinctive Educational Programs: Courses in team approach to emergency medical care.

Division of Continuing Education

Degree Programs Offered: This unit offers provides summer sessions courses, continuing education programs for professionals and people of all ages, student services, and precollege programs.

Departments and Teaching Staff: Continuing education *professors* 2, *assistant professors* 1.

School of Veterinary Medicine

Degree Programs Offered: *First-professional.*

Admission: 60 semester credits of required coursework from an accredited institution; GRE.

Degree Requirements: Successful completion of prescribed 4-year program.

Fees and Other Expenses: Contact the school for current tuition.

Departments and Teaching Staff: Master's and doctorate are also offered.

School of Medicine and Public Health

Degree Programs Offered: *Baccalaureate* in clinical laboratory science and physician assistant. *First-professional* medicine; *master's* and *doctorate* in anatomy, environmental toxicology, human cancer biology (human oncology), medical genetics, medical microbiology, medical physics, neurosciences, oncology, pathology, pharmacology (medical), physiological chemistry, physiology; *master's* in public health, physical therapy.

Admission: *For first-professional degree:* 90 semester hours prescribed curriculum from accredited institution; MCAT. Recommended baccalaureate degree. AMCAS application must be completed and sent to Admissions Office, Medical School.

Degree Requirements: Successful completion of prescribed 4-year program.

Fees and Other Expenses: Contact the school for current tuition.

Distinctive Educational Programs: Opportunities for research available to medical students in individually arranged programs leading to master's and doctorate or by non-degree arrangements. Conditional admission of up to 20 qualified resident secondary school seniors through the Medical Scholars Program. Completion of most basic science requirements on self-paced schedule available to a limited number of students through the Independent Study Program.

School of Nursing

Degree Programs Offered: *Baccalaureate, master's, doctorate.*

Admission: *For baccalaureate:* Minimum 2.25 GPA or minimum of 24 college credits. *For master's:* Baccalaureate in nursing with a minimum 2.75 GPA, GRE, 1 year nursing experience, statistics course. *For doctorate:* baccalaureate in nursing with minimum 3.0 GPA, GRE verbal and quantitative sum score of at least 1200, 2 original papers, academic references.

Degree Requirements: *For baccalaureate:* 120 credits; 49 in nursing. *For master's:* 36 credits, including thesis or project. *For doctorate:* MS in nursing, 9 credits in clinical nursing research, 15–19 credits in psychology, 9 credits in research methods and statistics, 6 seminars, preliminary, dissertation, oral exam.

Distinctive Educational Programs: Accelerated degree program for registered nurses. Geriatric and pediatric nurse practitioner programs. Early-entry Ph.D. Distance education program.

College of Engineering

Degree Programs Offered: *Baccalaureate* in chemical engineering, civil and environmental engineering, electrical and computer engineering, engineering mechanics and astronautics, geological engineering, industrial engineering, material science and engineering, mechanical engineering, nuclear engineering and engineering physics. *Master's* in all baccalaureate degree programs plus manufacturing systems engineering, water chemistry. *Doctorate* in all baccalaureate degree programs plus materials science, water chemistry.

Admission: *Students without college credit:* eligible for admission as pre-engineering students with an EGR classification; non-residents must be in the top percentage of high school class, foreign students admitted on a highly selective process as space is available. *For admission to a degree-granting classification in Engineering:* satisfied college English requirement; minimum of 24 degree credits; minimum of 17 credits in and GPA of at least 2.5 for courses in calculus, statistics, chemistry, computer science, statics and physics courses required; must include Math 222; GPA of at least 2.0 for all other degree credits earned.

Degree Requirements: For graduation from any curriculum in engineering, a student must: have fulfilled the published graduation requirements of that curriculum with all substitutions formally approved.

Distinctive Educational Programs: Full-time study is interspersed with full-time engineering employment in the Engineering Cooperative Education Program; study abroad programs in Germany, France, Scotland, Norway, Spain and Japan; summer international work experience programs through the International Association for Exchange of Students for Technical Experience and the American Scandinavian Foundation. Programs can be arranged for cross-disciplinary preparation in architecture, business and medicine.

University of Wisconsin - Milwaukee

P.O. Box 413
Milwaukee, Wisconsin 53201
Tel: (414) 229-1122 **E-mail:** uwmlook@@uwm.edu
Fax: (414) 229-6940 **Internet:** www.uwm.edu

Institution Description: *Enrollment:* 29,215. *Degrees awarded:* Baccalaureate, master's, doctorate.

Member of Urban Corridor Consortium; Urban Thirteen, Committee on Institutional Cooperation.

Accreditation: *Regional:* NCA. *Professional*: architecture, business, chemistry, engineering, journalism, librarianship, medical record administration, music, nursing, occupational therapy, rehabilitation counseling, social work, speech-language pathology, teacher education

History: Formed by merger of Wisconsin State College, Milwaukee and the University of Wisconsin's Milwaukee Extension Center, chartered, and awarded first degree (baccalaureate) 1956. *See* J. Martin Klotsche, *The UWM - An Urban University* (Milwaukee: University of Wisconsin, 1972) for further information.

Institutional Structure: *Composition of institution:* Academic affairs headed by provost. Management/business/finances directed by assistant chancellor for administrative affairs. Faculty/instructional staff 1,351, Academic governance body, Faculty Senate, meets an average of 9 times per year.

Calendar: Semesters. Academic year Sept. to May. Freshmen admitted Sept., Jan., May. Degrees conferred May, Aug., Dec. Formal commencement May, Dec. Summer session of 9 sessions from May to Aug.

Characteristics of Freshmen: 11,136 applicants (female 5,782, male 5,354). 81% of applicants accepted. 45% of accepted applicants enrolled.

3% (151 students) submitted SAT scores; 97% (4,223 students) submitted ACT scores. *25th percentile*: SAT Critical Reading 470, SAT Math 480; ACT Composite 20, ACT English 18, ACT Math 19. *75th percentile*: SAT Critical Reading 519, SAT Math 600; ACT Composite 24, ACT English 24, ACT Math 25.

25% of freshmen expected to graduate within 5 years. 94% of freshmen from Wisconsin. Freshmen from 19 states and 11 foreign countries.

Admission: *Freshmen:* June 30 application priority date. Early acceptance available. *Requirements:* Graduation from accredited high school; high school rank at or above 50th percentile; total of at least 16 high school units including 3 years English, 1 each of algebra and geometry, at least 11 other units of which no more than 4 may be nonacademic electives. Adequate ACT (Wisconsin residents)/SAT (non-residents) scores may be accepted in lieu of rank in the upper 50%. GED also accepted. *For transfer students:* 2.0 minimum GPA; 90 semester hours maximum transfer credit (72 hours from 2-year colleges) from accredited postsecondary institutions. Auditions required for admission to Fine Arts programs.

Advanced placement for postsecondary-level work completed in secondary school.

Tutoring available. Noncredit remedial courses offered in summer session and regular academic year.

Degree Requirements: *For baccalaureate degrees:* 120–128 semester hours; 2.0–2.5 GPA; 30–40 hours in residence. Competency examinations in writing and mathematics required.

Fulfillment of some degree requirements possible by passing departmental examinations, College Board CLEP, AP. *Grading system:* A–F; credit-no credit.

Distinctive Educational Programs: Work-experience programs. Flexible meeting places and schedules, including off-campus centers, weekend and evening classes. Accelerated degree programs. Special facilities for using telecommunications in the classroom. Facilities and programs for independent research, including honors programs, individual majors, tutorials. Semester or year programs in England, France, Germany, Italy, Mexico; also study tours to China, Commonwealth of Independent States, Denmark, Poland.

Degrees Conferred: 3,612 *baccalaureate:* degrees awarded in top five disciplines include business and management, education, health professions and related sciences, social sciences and history, visual and performing arts. Master's degrees awared: various disciplines 1,237. Doctorates awarded: various disciplines 115.

Fees and Other Expenses: *Full-time tuition per academic year 2008–09:* undergraduate resident $7,305, nonresident $17,633; contact the university for graduate tuition and fees. *Books and supplies:* $800. *Room and board per academic year:* $8,500. *Books and supplies:* $800. *Other expenses:* $3,640.

Financial Aid: Aid from institutionally generated funds is provided on the basis of academic merit, athletic ability, other criteria.

Institution has a Program Participation Agreement with the U.S. Department of Education for eligible students to receive Pell Grants and, depending upon the agreement, other federal aid.

Financial aid for first-timem full-time undergraduate: 68% received some form of aid. Average amount of aid received: federal grants $3,881; Pell grants $2,819; other federal aid $1,628; state/local grants $2,260; institutional grants $2,588.

Departments and Teaching Staff: *Total instructional faculty:* 1,399 (full-time 1,046, part-time 353). Total faculty with doctorate, first-professional, or other terminal degree 917. Student-to-faculty ratio: 20:1. Degrees held by full-time faculty: 87% hold terminal degrees.

Enrollment: Total enrollment 29,215. Undergraduate 24,299 (full-time 83%; female 52%, male 48%). Graduate 1,916 (full-time 47%). Transfer-in students 1,517.

Characteristics of Student Body: *Ethnic/racial makeup:* Black non-Hispanic: 7%; American Indian or Alaska Native: 5%; Asian or Pacific Islander: 1%; Hispanic: 4%; White non-Hispanic: 80%, unknown 2%; nonresident alien 1%.

International Students: 292 nonresident aliens enrolled fall 2008. Students from Europe, Asia, Latin America, Africa, Canada, Australia. Programs available to aid students whose native language is not English: English as a Second Language Program. No financial aid specifically designated for international students.

Student Life: On-campus residence halls house 9% of student body. Residence halls for both males and females constitute 100% of such space. *Intercollegiate athletics:* male: baseball, basketball, cross-country, soccer, swimming, tennis, track; female: basketball, cross-country, soccer, swimming, tennis, track, volleyball. *Special regulations:* Limited parking space available; fee charged. *Special services:* Tutoring and Learning Center, medical services. *Student publications, radio, television: UWM Post, UWM Times.* Radio station WUWM-FM 89.7 broadcasts 24 hours a day, 7 days a week. *Surrounding community:* Milwaukee area population over 1.5 million. Served by mass transit system; airport 10 miles from campus; passenger rail service 4 miles from campus.

Publications: *Current Geographical Publications* (10 times a year) first published in 1938, now published by UWM Golda Meir Library in cooperation with the American Geographical Society; *Metropolitan Education* (3 times a year) first published in Spring 1986, published by UWM School of Education; *Economic Development Quarterly* (4 times a year) first published in Feb. 1987, edited by UWM Urban Research Center.

Library Collections: 1,900,000 volumes. 131,500 government documents collections; 1,700,000 microforms; 39,000 audiovisual materials; 8,760 periodical subscriptions including via electronic access. Online catalog. Students have access to online information retrieval services and the Internet.

Most important special holdings include American Geographical Society Collection; Kwasniewski Collection; Hohlweck Civil War Collection.

Buildings and Grounds: Campus area 90 acres.

Chief Executive Officer: Dr. Carlos Santiago, Chancellor.

Undergraduates address admission inquiries to Beth L. Weckmueller, Director of Undergraduate Admissions; graduate inquiries to Dean of Graduate School.

College of Letters and Science

Degree Programs Offered: *Baccalaureate* in Afro-American studies, anthropology, applied mathematics and physics, art and criticism, biological aspects of conservation, biological science, chemistry, classics, communication, comparative literature, economics, English, film, French, geography, geological sciences, German, Hebrew studies, history, international relations, Italian, Latino studies, law studies, linguistics, mass communications, mathematics, medical science, philosophy, physics, political science, psychology, Russian, sociology, Spanish; *master's* in industrial and labor relations, mathematics, philosophy, physics, political science, psychology, public administration, Russian, urban affairs, zoology; *doctorate* in anthropology, biological sciences, chemistry, economics, English, geography, geosciences, mathematics, physics, political science, psychology, urban social institutions. Certificates also given.

Distinctive Educational Programs: Internships available in Washington, D.C. Foreign study program in England, France, Germany, Mexico, and Poland. Interdisciplinary programs in ethnic studies, native American studies, women's studies. Individually designed committee interdisciplinary major. Preprofessional programs in dentistry, forestry, medicine, pharmacy, physical therapy. Dual-degree program in medicine with the Medical College of Wisconsin. University-wide honors program administered by the College of Letters and Science. Research facilities include multidisciplinary research in humanistic studies of contemporary cultures through Center for Twentieth Century Studies, cartographic services laboratory, environmental science field station, geological museum, Great Lakes Studies research center, herbarium. *Other distinctive programs:* Off-campus instructional program offers nontraditional college-level study opportunities.

School of Allied Health Professions

Degree Programs Offered: *Baccalaureate* in allied health, kinesiology, health information administration, medical technology, occupational therapy, recreation, speech pathology and audiology; *master's* in human kinetics, medical technology, communication sciences and disorders.

School of Architecture and Urban Planning

Degree Programs Offered: *Baccalaureate* in architectural studies; *master's* in architecture, urban planning; *doctorate* in architecture.

Distinctive Educational Programs: Interdisciplinary programs in urban planning and urban social institutions. Preprofessional program in architecture.

School of Business Administration

Degree Programs Offered: *Baccalaureate, master's* in business administration, finance, human resource management, marketing, real estate and urban development, accounting, management information; *master's* in management; *doctorate* in management science.

School of Education

Degree Programs Offered: *Baccalaureate* in community education, education, educational studies, exceptional education; *master's* in administrative leadership and supervision in education, curriculum and instruction, educational psychology, education rehabilitation counseling, exceptional education, cultural foundations of education; *doctorate* in urban education.

Distinctive Educational Programs: Center for Behavioral Studies and Day Care Center serve as training, service, and research facilities for students.

College of Engineering and Applied Science

Degree Programs Offered: *Baccalaureate* in civil engineering, computer science, electrical engineering, engineering science, industrial and manufacturing engineering, materials engineering, mechanical engineering; *master's* in computer science, engineering; *doctorate* in engineering.

Distinctive Educational Programs: Gateway to Engineering, Science, and Technology provides a precollege enrichment program for minority secondary school students.

School of Fine Arts

Degree Programs Offered: *Baccalaureate* in art, art education, film, music, music education, theater; *master's* in art, art education, music, performing arts.

Distinctive Educational Programs: Institute of Chamber Music provides advanced professional training for chamber music ensembles. Professional Theatre Training Program offers intensive professional training for actors.

School of Nursing

Degree Programs Offered: *Baccalaureate, master's, doctorate.*

Admission: *For doctorate:* baccalaureate and master's with major in nursing from NLN-accredited programs; GPA 3.2 on 4.0 scale; satisfactory GRE on aptitude portion within last 5 years; current nursing registration; 3 professional references.

Degree Requirements: *For doctorate:* course completion with GPA of 3.0 on 4.0 scale; satisfactory completion of Comprehensive Preliminary Examina-

UNIVERSITY OF WISCONSIN - MILWAUKEE—*cont'd*

tions; successful oral defense of dissertation; completion of UMW Graduate School requirements, including residence and minor requirements.

School of Social Welfare

Degree Programs Offered: *Baccalaureate, master's* in criminal justice, social work.

Distinctive Educational Programs: MSW/MFT certificate program designed to meet requirements for both the MSW degree and associate membership in the American Association of Marriage and Family Therapists. Corrections concentration in MSW program and MS in criminal justice program.

School of Library and Information Science

Degree Programs Offered: *Master's.* Certificate of advanced study and opportunities for multidisciplinary doctoral studies with other programs.

University of Wisconsin - Oshkosh

800 Algoma Boulevard
Oshkosh, Wisconsin 54901-8601
Tel: (920) 424-1234 **E-mail:** oshadmuw@uwosh.edu
Fax: (920) 424-7317 **Internet:** www.uwosh.edu

Institution Description: *Enrollment:* 12,753. *Degrees awarded:* Associate, baccalaureate, master's.

Member of Urban Corridor Consortium.

Accreditation: *Regional:* NCA. *Professional*: business, chemistry, journalism, music, nursing, social work, teacher education

History: Established as Oshkosh Normal School and offered first instruction at postsecondary level 1871; awarded first degree (baccalaureate) 1924; changed name to Oshkosh Teachers Colleges 1925, Wisconsin State College—Oshkosh 1949, Wisconsin State University—Oshkosh 1964; adopted present name 1971.

Institutional Structure: *Composition of institution:* Administrators 101. Academic affairs headed by vice chancellor. Management/business/finances directed by executive director, financial services/budgets. Full-time instructional faculty 381. Academic governance body, Faculty senate, meets weekly.

Calendar: Semesters (courses are offered in 7-week, 14-week, and 3-week modules). Academic year Sept. to June. Freshmen admitted Sept., Feb., June, July, or at beginning of any module. Degrees conferred June, Aug., Jan. Formal commencement May, Aug., Dec. Summer session of 2 terms from mid-June to early Aug.

Characteristics of Freshmen: 5,006 applicants (female 2,998, male 2,008). 80% of applicants accepted. 44% of accepted applicants enrolled full-time. Average secondary rank of freshmen 66.8 percentile. Mean ACT Composite 21.9.

96% freshmen from Wisconsin. Freshmen from 32 states and 33 foreign countries.

Admission: Rolling admissions plan. For fall acceptance, apply as early as Oct. 1 of previous year, but not later than 5th day of classes. Early acceptance available. *Requirements:* Graduation from accredited secondary school with 4 units of English, 2 mathematics (algebra and/or geometry), 2 units natural science, 2 units social studies (including U.S. history), and 5 units electives; or completion of high school equivalency. *Entrance tests:* College Board SAT or ACT composite must be submitted prior to registration. *For transfer students:* 2.0 minimum GPA required, but 2.4 given preference; from 4-year accredited institution hours maximum transfer credit limited only by residence requirement; from 2-year accredited institution 72 hours; correspondence/extension students 15 hours.

College credit and advanced placement for postsecondary level work completed in secondary school. For extrainstitutional learning (life experience), college credit and advanced placement on basis of portfolio and faculty assessments.

Tutoring available. Developmental courses offered in summer session and regular academic year; credit given.

Degree Requirements: *For all associate degrees:* 64 credit hours; 2 terms in residence. *For all baccalaureate degrees:* a minimum of 120 credits; 30 credits (including 16 in senior year) in residence. *For all undergraduate degrees:* GPA required varies with program, but no lower than 2.00; 2 credits physical activity courses; demonstrated proficiency in English composition; general education requirements.

Fulfillment of some degree requirements and exemption from some beginning courses possible by passing departmental examinations, College Board CLEP, AP, and other standardized tests. *Grading system:* A–F; pass-fail; withdraw.

Distinctive Educational Programs: Work-experience programs. Weekend and evening classes. Accelerated degree programs. Special facilities for using telecommunications in the classroom. Facilities and programs for independent research, including honors programs, individual majors, tutorials. *Other distinctive programs:* Multicultural Education Center serves as a minority student and resource center and works with area minority groups. Credit and noncredit continuing education. Weekend liberal studies degree program. Project Success (for learning disabled students); Bachelor of Liberal Studies (evening/weekend liberal arts program); University Learning Community; University Scholars; new 5-year Liberal Arts/MBA program. Study abroad in England, France, Japan, Mexico, Spain.

ROTC: Army.

Degrees Conferred: 1,787 *baccalaureate*; 264 *master's*. Bachelor's degrees awarded in top five disciplines: business, management, marketing, and related support services 327' education 267; health professions and related clinical sciences 187; communication, journalism, and related programs 137; social sciences 115. Master's degrees awarded: various disciplines 264.

Fees and Other Expenses: *Full-time tuition per academic year 2008–09:* undergraduate resident $6,037, nonresident $15,028; contact the university for graduate rates. *Books and supplies* $1,000. *Room and board per academic year:* $5,720. *Other expenses:* $2,700.

Financial Aid: Aid from institutionally generated funds is provided on the basis of academic merit, financial need.

Financial aid to full-time, first-time undergraduate students: 68% recieved some form of aid. Average amount of aid received: federal grants $3,812; Pell grants $2,713; other federal aid $1,147; state/federal aid $2,172; institutional grants $1,459.

Departments and Teaching Staff: *Total instructional faculty:* 536. Degrees held by full-time faculty: master's 23%, doctorate 77%. 82% hold terminal degrees.

Enrollment: Total enrollment 12,753. Undergraduate 11,393 (full-time 77%; female 60%, male 40%). Graduate 1,360 (full-time 12%). Transfer-in students 920.

International Students: 127 nonresident aliens enrolled fall 2008. Programs available to aid students whose native language is not English: social, cultural. Financial aid specifically designated for international students: scholarships available annually for undergraduate students.

Student Life: On-campus residence halls house 33% of student body. *Intercollegiate athletics:* male: baseball, basketball, football, swimming, soccer, track, cross-country, golf, tennis, wrestling, gymnastics; female: volleyball, track, cross-country, basketball, swimming, tennis, gymnastics, softball. *Special regulations:* Cars permitted without restrictions. *Special services:* Learning Resources Center, medical services. *Student publications, radio:* Weekly newspaper, quarterly literary magazine. Radio station WRST-FM broadcasts 24 hours a day, 365 days a year. *Surrounding community:* Oshkosh population 55,000. Milwaukee, 80 miles from campus, is nearest metropolitan area. Served by mass transit bus system; airport 4 miles from campus.

Publications: *Context* (annual) first published 1976.

Library Collections: 487,000 volumes. 626,000 government documents; 1,275,000 microforms; 7,000 audiovisual materials; 1,850 current periodical subscriptions. Online catalog. Students have access to online information retrieval services.

Most important special holdings include Pare Lorentz Collection; WI Area Research Center Collection; Buckstaff Collection.

Buildings and Grounds: Campus area 116 acres. Campus DVD available.

Chief Executive Officer: Dr. Richard H. Wells, Chancellor.

Address admission inquiries to Jill Endries, Director of Admissions.

College of Letters and Science

Degree Programs Offered: *Baccalaureate* in anthropology, art, biology, chemistry, computer science, criminal justice, economics, English, foreign language, geography, geology, history, international studies, journalism, library science, mathematics, medical technology, microbiology and public health, music, philosophy, physics, physical education, political science, psychology, radio-television-film, religion, social work, sociology, speech, urban and regional studies. Certificates also given.

Distinctive Educational Programs: Cooperative baccalaureate in medical technology with affiliated hospitals. Interdisciplinary programs in African studies; Afro-American studies; Asian studies; European studies; Latin American studies; operations research; microbiology and public health; music merchandising; biology, chemistry, and geology, all with environmental emphases; urban and regional studies; criminal justice; radio-television-film; international studies. Preprofessional programs in architecture, dentistry, engineering, medicine, pharmacy, veterinary medicine. Observatory. Limnology laboratory. Aeromagnetic survey plan and laboratory. Commercial art facilities.

College of Business Administration

Degree Programs Offered: *Baccalaureate* in accounting, administrative management, finance, human resources management, management information systems, marketing, operations management.

Admission: Cumulative GPA of 2.30.

College of Nursing

Degree Programs Offered: *Baccalaureate*.

Distinctive Educational Programs: Degree completion program for registered nurses, offering flexible scheduling, competency assessment, self-pacing. Interdisciplinary courses, including politics, ethics. Continuing education, including overseas courses.

College of Education and Human Services

Degree Programs Offered: *Baccalaureate* in art education, education, human services, music education; *master's* in curriculum and supervision, elementary education, guidance, reading, special education.

Admission: Requirements vary with degree sought.

University of Wisconsin - Parkside

900 Wood Road
P.O. Box 2000
Kenosha, Wisconsin 53141-2000
Tel: (262) 595-2573 **E-mail:** admit@uwp.edu
Fax: (262) 595-2630 **Internet:** www.uwp.edu

Institution Description: *Enrollment:* 5,167. *Degrees awarded:* Baccalaureate, master's.

Member of Urban Corridor Consortium.

Accreditation: *Regional:* NCA. *Professional*: business

History: Established 1968; offered first instruction at postsecondary level 1968; awarded first degree (baccalaureate) 1969; adopted present name 1967.

Institutional Structure: *Composition of institution:* Administrators 7. Academic affairs headed by provost/vice chancellor. University relations headed by assistant chancellor for university relations. Management/business/finances directed by assistant chancellor for administration and fiscal affairs. Student services headed by assistant chancellor. Academic governance body, Faculty Senate, meets an average of 6 times per year.

Calendar: Semesters. Academic year Sept. to May. Freshmen admitted Sept., Jan., June; year round for module classes. Degrees conferred May, Aug., Dec. Formal commencement May. Summer session of 1 term from June to Aug.

Characteristics of Freshmen: 2,054 applicants (female 1,124, male 930). 93% of applicants accepted. 62% of accepted applicants enrolled.

Average secondary school rank of freshmen 59th percentile. Mean ACT Composite score 20.5.

20% of entering freshmen expected to graduate within 5 years. 90% of freshmen from Wisconsin. Freshmen from 9 states and 3 foreign countries.

Admission: Rolling admissions plan. For fall acceptance, apply as early as one year prior to enrollment, but not later than registration period. Early acceptance available. *Requirements:* Either graduation from accredited secondary school with 13 units from among English, mathematics, natural science, social science; or GED. *For transfer students:* Minimum GPA varies according to number of credits being transferred; from 4-year accredited institution 90 hours maximum transfer credit; from 2-year accredited institution 72 hours; transfer credit also accepted for correspondence/extension courses.

College credit and advanced placement for postsecondary-level work completed in secondary school.

Tutoring available. Developmental/remedial courses offered in summer session and regular academic year, and between semesters; credit given.

Degree Requirements: *For baccalaureate degrees:* 120 credit hours; 2.0 GPA; 30 credits, including 15 of last 30, in residence; distribution requirement; demonstrated proficiency in library skills, reading and writing, mathematics, and foreign language.

Fulfillment of some degree requirements and exemption from some beginning courses possible by passing institutional examinations, College Board CLEP, AP. *Grading system:* A–F.

Distinctive Educational Programs: Work-experience programs. Weekend and evening classes. Accelerated degree programs. Cooperative baccalaureate program in nursing and cooperative master's program in education with University of Wisconsin - Milwaukee. Special facilities for using telecommunications in the classroom. Interdisciplinary programs for undergraduates in communications, interdisciplinary studies, humanities, international studies, graduate program in public services and administration. Facilities for independent research, including honors programs, independent study seminars. *Other distinctive programs:* Credit and noncredit continuing education. Center for Teaching Excellence. Business Outreach Program.

Degrees Conferred: 656 *baccalaureate*; 23 *master's*. Bachelor's degrees awarded in top five disciplines: business, management, marketing, and related support services 147; social sciences 86; security and protective services 60; visual and performing arts 47; biomedical and biological sciences 45. Master's degrees awarded: business/management 28; communications 8.

Fees and Other Expenses: *Full-time tuition per academic year:* undergraduate resident $6,088, nonresident $14,694; contact the university for graduate tuition and fees. *Books and supplies:* $872. *Room and board per academic year:* $5,570. *Other expenses:* $3,328.

Financial Aid: Aid from institutionally generated funds is provided on the basis of academic merit, financial need, athletic ability.

Financial aid to full-time, first-time undergraduate students: 71% received some form of aid. Average amount of aid received: federal grants $3,806; Pell grants $3,018; other federal aid $1,157; state/local grants $2,456; institutional grants $2,847.

Departments and Teaching Staff: *Total instructional faculty:* 271 (full-time 162, part-time 109). Student-to-faculty ratio: 20:1. Degrees held by full-time faculty: baccalaureate 1.8%, master's 23.8%, doctorate 74.4%. 74.4% hold terminal degrees.

Enrollment: Total enrollment 5,167. Undergraduate 5,045 (full-time 73%; female 55%, male 45%).

Characteristics of Student Body: *Ethnic/racial makeup:* Black non-Hispanic: 10%; American Indian or Alaska Native: 3%; Hispanic: 8%; White non-Hispanic: 74%; unknown 2%; nonresident alien 1%.

International Students: 52 nonresident aliens enrolled fall 2008. Students from Europe, Asia, Africa, Canada. No programs available to aid students whose native language is not English. No financial aid specifically designated for international students.

Student Life: Residence halls accommodate 800 students. *Intercollegiate athletics:* male: baseball, basketball, cross-country, golf, soccer, track, wrestling; female: basketball, cross-country, soccer, track, volleyball. *Special regulations:* Cars with parking permits allowed. *Special services:* Academic Resource Center, medical services, counseling services, university bus service between the cities of Racine and Kenosha. *Student publications: Ranger*, a weekly student newspaper. *Surrounding community:* Kenosha population 85,000. Milwaukee, 30 miles from campus, is nearest metropolitan area. Served by mass transit bus system, airport 30 miles from campus, passenger rail service 5 miles from campus.

Publications: *Journal of Geological Education* (5 times per year) first published 1951.

Library Collections: 395,000 volumes. 919,034 microforms; 18,000 audiovisual materials; 1,694 current periodical subscriptions. Online catalog. Students have access to online information retrieval services.

Most important special holdings include Kenosha and Racine government and public records; personal papers of Kenosha and Racine business and civic leaders; Irving Wallace Collection.

Buildings and Grounds: Campus area 751 acres.

Chief Executive Officer: Dr. John P. Keating, Chancellor.

Address admission inquiries to Director of Admissions.

University of Wisconsin - Platteville

One University Plaza
Platteville, Wisconsin 53818-3099
Tel: (608) 342-1421 **E-mail:** admit@uwplatt.edu
Fax: (608) 342-1122 **Internet:** www.uwplatt.edu

Institution Description: *Enrollment:* 7,512. *Degrees awarded:* Associate, baccalaureate, master's.

Accreditation: *Regional:* NCA. *Professional*: engineering, music, teacher education

History: Established as Platteville Normal School, chartered, and offered first instruction at postsecondary level 1886; awarded first degree (baccalaureate) and changed name to Platteville State Teachers College 1927; changed name to Wisconsin State College, Platteville 1951, to Wisconsin State College and Institute of Technology, Platteville 1959, to Wisconsin State University—Platteville 1964; adopted present name 1971. *See* Richard D. Gamble, *From Academy to University* (Platteville: University of Wisconsin - Platteville Foundation, 1966) for further information.

Institutional Structure: *Composition of institution:* Administrators 59. Academic affairs headed by chancellor. Management/business/finances directed by assistant chancellor for business affairs. Full-time instructional faculty 263. Academic governance body, Faculty Senate, meets an average of 18 times per year.

UNIVERSITY OF WISCONSIN - PLATTEVILLE—*cont'd*

Calendar: Semesters. Academic year Aug. to May. Freshmen admitted Aug., Jan., June. Degrees conferred May, Dec. Summer session of 1 term from June to July.

Characteristics of Freshmen: 3,156 applicants (female 1,017, male 2,019). 84% of applicants accepted. 42% of accepted applicants enrolled.

100% (1,384 students) submitted ACT scores.. *25th percentile*: ACT Composite 19, ACT English 18, ACT Math 19. *75th percentile*: ACT Composite 24, ACT English 23, ACT Math 26.

41% of entering freshmen expected to graduate within 5 years. 81% of freshmen from Wisconsin. Freshmen from 5 states and 1 foreign country.

Admission: Rolling admissions plan. Apply as early as Oct. of year prior to enrollment, but not later than first day of classes. Early acceptance available. *Requirements:* Graduation from accredited secondary school with college preparatory program; or GED. *Entrance tests:* ACT required. *For transfer students:* 2.0 minimum GPA; from 4-year accredited institution maximum transfer credit limited only by residence requirement; from 2-year accredited 72 hours. Transfer credit for some correspondence/extension courses.

College credit and advanced placement for postsecondary-level work completed in secondary school and for extrainstitutional learning.

Tutoring available.

Degree Requirements: *For all associate degrees:* 64 credit hours; 30 credits, including last 15, in residence. *For all baccalaureate degrees:* 128 credit hours; 32 credits, and 23 of last 32, in residence. *For all undergraduate degrees:* 2.0 GPA; 2 credits in physical education; distribution requirements.

Fulfillment of some degree requirements possible by passing departmental examinations, College Board CLEP, AP. *Grading system:* A–F.

Distinctive Educational Programs: Work-experience programs. Flexible meeting places and schedules including weekend and evening classes. Accelerated degree programs. Special facilities for using telecommunications in the classroom. External degree programs through business and administration department. Preprofessional programs in veterinary medicine, medicine, dentistry. Interdisciplinary programs in environmental studies, general science, geosciences, international studies, reclamation (mining), women's studies. Facilities and programs for independent research, including honors programs, individual majors, tutorials. Study abroad in London, England; Seville, Spain; Aix-en-Provence, Avignon, Strasbourg, and Toulon, France; Puebla, Mexico; Dublin, Ireland; Lisbon, Portugal; Lund, Sweden.

ROTC: Army.

Degrees Conferred: 956 *baccalaureate*; 200 *master's*. Bachelor's degrees awarded in top five disciplines: engineering 235; education 123; business, management, marketing, and related support services 118; engineering technologies 78; security and protective services 60. Master's degrees awarded: various disciplines 200.

Fees and Other Expenses: *Full-time tuition per academic year 2008–09:* $6,147 resident, $13,720 nonresident; contact the university for current graduate tuition/fees. *Books and supplies:* $320. *Required fees:* $882. *Room and board per academic year:* $4,009. *Other expenses:* $2,750.

Financial Aid: Aid from institutionally generated funds is provided on the basis of academic merit, financial need, other criteria.

Financial aid to full-time, first-time undergraduate students: 73% received some form of aid. Average amount of aid rece3ived: federal grants $3,601; Pell grants $2,662; other federal aid $1,055; state/local grants $1,944; institutional grants $981.

Departments and Teaching Staff: *Total instructional faculty:* 356 (full-time 263, part-time 93). Student-to-faculty ratio: 20:1. Degrees held by full-time faculty: doctorate 60%, master's 40%. 60% hold terminal degrees.

Enrollment: Total enrollment 7,512. Undergraduate 6,612 (full-time 90%; female 36%; male 64%). Graduate 900 (full-time 16%). Transfer-in students 334.

Characteristics of Student Body: *Ethnic/racial makeup:* Black non-Hispanic: 2%; American Indian or Alaska Naitve 1%; Asian or Pacific Islander: 1%; Hispanic: 1%; White non-Hispanic: 93%; unknown: 2%; nonresident alien 1%.

International Students: 75 nonresident aliens enrolled fall 2008. Programs available to aid students whose native language is not English: social, cultural. No financial aid specifically designated for international students.

Student Life: On-campus residence halls house 47% of student body. Residence halls for males constitute 44% of such space, for females 12%, for both sexes 44%. 4% of males join and 3% live in fraternity housing; 4% of females join and 3% live in sorority housing. *Intercollegiate athletics:* male: baseball, basketball, cross-country, football, golf, gymnastics, soccer, swimming, tennis, track, volleyball, wrestling; female: basketball, field hockey, gymnastics, softball, track. *Special regulations:* Cars permitted without restrictions. *Special services:* Medical services. *Student publications, radio, television: Exponent*, a weekly newspaper; *Geode*, a monthly engineering magazine; *Pioneer,* a yearbook; *Sweetwater Review*, a biennial literary booklet. Radio station WSUP broadcasts 140 hours per week. TV station WSUP-TV broadcasts 25 hours per week. *Surrounding community:* Platteville population 10,000. Milwaukee, 150 miles from campus, is nearest metropolitan area. Served by mass transit bus system, airport 25 miles from campus.

Library Collections: 274,000 volumes. 1,000,000 microforms; 11,000 audiovisual materials; 1,082 current periodical subscriptions. Online catalog. Students have access to online information retrieval services and the Internet.

Most important special holdings include Southwest Wisconsin Collection; Area Research Center of Wisconsin materials; State Historical Center materials.

Buildings and Grounds: Campus area 300 acres. DVD available.

Chief Executive Officer: Dr. David J. Markee, Chancellor.

Address admission inquiries to Angela M. Udelhofen, Director of Admissions.

University of Wisconsin - River Falls

410 3rd Street
River Falls, Wisconsin 54022-5001

Tel: (715) 425-3911 **E-mail:** admit@uwrf.edu
Fax: (715) 425-3304 **Internet:** www.uwrf.edu

Institution Description: *Enrollment:* 6,555. *Degrees awarded:* Associate, baccalaureate, master's.

Member of West Central Wisconsin Consortium.

Accreditation: *Regional:* NCA. *Professional*: business, journalism, music, social work, speech-language pathology, teacher education

History: Established as River Falls Normal School, chartered, and offered first instruction at postsecondary level 1875; changed name to River Falls State Teachers College 1926; awarded first degree (baccalaureate) 1928; changed name to Wisconsin State College at River Falls 1951, to Wisconsin State University—River Falls 1964; adopted present name 1971. *See* James T. King and Walker D. Wyman, *Centennial History: The University of Wisconsin—River Falls* (River Falls: University of Wisconsin—River Falls Press, 1975) for further information.

Institutional Structure: *Composition of institution:* Administrators 22/ Academic affairs headed by vice chancellor. Management/business/finances directed by assistant chancellor for business/finance. Full-time instructional faculty 223. Academic governance body, Faculty Senate, meets an average of 12 times per year.

Calendar: Semesters. Academic year Sept. to May. Freshmen admitted Sept., Jan., June. Degrees conferred Dec., May, Aug. Formal commencements May, Dec. Summer session of four 3-week terms from May to Aug.

Characteristics of Freshmen: 2,886 applicants (female 1,662, male 2,886). 85% of applicants admitted. 43% of applicants admitted and enrolled.

1% of applicants SAT scores; 99% ACT scores. *25th percentile*: SAT Critical Reading 430, SAT Math 470; ACT Composite 19, ACT English 18, ACT Math 18. *75th percentile*: SAT Critical Reading 530, SAT math 540; ACT Composite 24, ACT English 24, ACT Math 24.

51% of entering freshmen expected to graduate in 5 years. 52% of freshmen from Wisconsin. Freshmen from 10 states and 10 foreign countries.

Admission: Rolling admissions plan. Deadline dates established each semester based on volume of applications. *Freshmen admission requirements:* Graduation from a recognized or accredited secondary school with 17 units (4 units of English, 3 units of math, 3 units of science, 3 units of social sciences, 4 units academic elective); high school equivalency diploma or GED. Students with high school equivalency diploma or GED may not be considered until 2 years beyond the date their high school class would have graduated. High school graduates must have an ACT composite score of at least 22 or rank in the top 40% of their graduating class with an ACT score of 18 or higher. Students in top 70% of class, but not in top 40%, with ACT less than 22, are considered on space available basis. *Transfer admission requirements:* Priority given to students with GPA of 2.6 or higher. Students with GPA of 2.0, but less than 2.6, admitted on space available basis. Higher standards may be set in specific programs, if necessary to limit enrollment. Maximum of 72 semester credits accepted in total from accredited 2-year colleges.

College credit for postsecondary-level work completed in secondary school and for extrainstitutional learning on basis of Advanced Placement Program, CLEP, faculty assessment.

Tutoring available. Limited number of credit and noncredit developmental courses offered in summer session and regular academic year.

Degree Requirements: *For all baccalaureate degrees:* 120 semester hours; basic studies. *For all undergraduate degrees:* 2.0 GPA; 2 terms in residence; 3 physical education courses.

Fulfillment of some degree requirements and exemption from some beginning courses possible by passing College Board CLEP. *Grading system:* A–F; pass-fail; withdraw (deadline after which pass-fail is appended to withdraw).

Distinctive Educational Programs: Internship programs for most majors. Pre-professional programs in dentistry, engineering, forestry, home economics, law, medicine, mortuary science, music therapy, nursing, optometry, pharmacy, police science, veterinary medicine. Honors program. Credit by examination program. Tutorials. Study abroad in Europe, Mexico, and Republic of China. Wisconsin in Scotland Program through West Central Wisconsin Consortium.

Degrees Conferred: 1,012 *baccalaureate* (B), 147 *master's* (M): agriculture 161 (B); biological/life sciences 53 (B); business and management 143 (B), 13 (M); communications 116 (B); computer and information sciences 34 (B); education 166 (B), 84 (M); English 33 (B); foreign languages 16 (B); health professions and related science 22 (B), 15 (M); interdisciplinary studies 15 (B); mathematics 13 (B); natural resources/environmental science 30 (B); physical sciences 21 (B); protective services/public administration 14 (B); psychology 68 (B), 20 (M); social sciences and history 94 (B); visual and performing arts 34 (B).

Fees and Other Expenses: *Full-time tuition per academic year 2008–09:* undergraduate resident $6,110, nonresident $13,793; contact the unviersity for current graduate tuition/fees. *Room and board per academic year:* $5,106. *Books and supplies:* $330. *Other expenses:* $2,450.

Financial Aid: Aid from institutionally generated funds is provided on the basis of academic merit, financial need.

Institution has a Program Participation Agreement with the U.S. Department of Education for eligible students to receive Pell Grants and, depending upon the agreement, other federal aid.

Departments and Teaching Staff: *Total instructional faculty:* 363 (full-time 223, part-time 140). Student/faculty ratio: 16:1. Degrees held by full-time faculty: master's 21.6%, doctorate 78.4%. 82% hold terminal degrees.

Enrollment: Total enrollment 6,555. Undergraduate 6,050. Gradute 505 (full-time 74%). Transfer-in students 399.

Characteristics of Student Body: *Ethnic/racial makeup:* Black non-Hispanic: 1%; American Indian or Alaska Native: 1%; Hispanic: 1%; White non-Hispanic: 91%; unknown: 2%; nonresident alien 1%.

International Students: 7 nonresident aliena enrolled fall 2008. No programs available to aid students whose native language is not English. No financial aid specifically designated for international students.

Student Life: On-campus residence halls house 40% of student body. Residence halls for males constitute 20% of such space, for females 22%, for both sexes 58%. *Intercollegiate athletics:* male: baseball, basketball, football, hockey, swimming, tennis, track; female: basketball, field hockey, gymnastics, swimming, tennis, track, volleyball. *Special regulations:* Students living in residence halls must purchase parking permits. *Special services:* Learning Resources Center, Adult Student Center, medical services. *Student publications, radio, television: The Student Voice*, a weekly newspaper; *Prologue*, an annual literary publication. Radio station WRFW; Television Services Channel 20. *Surrounding community:* River Falls population 10,000. Minneapolis-St. Paul, 30 miles from campus, is nearest metropolitan area. Served by airport 40 miles from campus; passenger rail service 30 miles from campus.

Publications: University of Wisconsin-River Falls Bulletins: undergraduate, graduate. Class schedules: undergraduate, graduate. Student Service Publications: *On Campus; Residence Life Information.* UW—River Falls Foundation: *Falcon Features* (alumni magazine); UW—River Falls Press.

Library Collections: 314,000 volumes. 103,000 government documents; 726,000 microforms; 9,000 audiovisual materials; 1,320 current periodical subscriptions. Students have access to online information retrieval services and the Internet.

Most important special holdings include collections on local history (Pierce County) and agricultural books; census records for Wisconsin 1836–1920; newspapers for northwestern Wisconsin mid-1800s to present.

Buildings and Grounds: Campus area 729 acres.

Chief Executive Officer: Dr. Donald Betz, Chancellor.

Address undergraduate admission inquiries to Dr. Alan Tuchtenhagen, Admissions Director; graduate inquiries to Dean of the Graduate College.

University of Wisconsin - Stevens Point

2100 Main Street
Stevens Point, Wisconsin 54481-3897

Tel: (715) 346-0123 **E-mail:** admiss@uwsp.edu
Fax: (715) 346-2561 **Internet:** www.uwsp.edu

Institution Description: *Enrollment:* 9,163. *Degrees awarded:* Associate, baccalaureate, master's, clinical doctorate (audiology).

Accreditation: *Regional:* NCA. *Professional*: art, audiology, clinical lab scientist, dance, forestry, interior design, music, speech-language pathology, theatre

History: Chartered 1893; established as Stevens Point Normal School and offered first instruction at postsecondary level 1894; awarded first degree (baccalaureate) and changed name to Stevens Point State Teachers College 1926; changed name to Wisconsin State College; Stevens Point 1951, to Wisconsin State University at Stevens Point 1964; adopted present name 1971.

Institutional Structure: *Composition of institution:* Administrators 60. Academic affairs headed by vice chancellor/provost. Management/business/finances directed by assistant chancellor for business affairs. Full-time instructional faculty 355. Academic governance body, Faculty Senate, meets an average of 14 times per year.

Calendar: Semesters. Academic year Sept. to May. Freshmen admitted Sept., Jan., June. Degrees conferred and formal commencements May, Dec. Summer session of 2 terms from June to Aug.

Characteristics of Freshmen: 4,719 applicants (feamle 2,674, male 2,045). 79% of applicants admitted. 34% of applicants admitted and enrolled.

2% (24 students) submitted SAT scores; 97% (1,593 students) submitted ACT scores. *25th percentile*: ACT Composite 20, ACT English 21, ACT Math 19. *75th percentile*: ACT Composite 25, ACT English 25, ACT Math 25. 53% of entering freshmen expected to graduate within 5 years. 91% of freshmen from Wisconsin. Freshmen from 17 states and 9 foreign countries.

Admission: Rolling admissions plan. For fall acceptance, apply as early as Sept. 15 of previous year. *Requirements:* Graduation from a recognized secondary school in top 25% or above or cumulative high school GPA of 3.25 (on 4.0 scale) or above with an ACT composite score of 21 (SAT 990) or above, or an ACT score of 21 (SAT 990) or above with high school rank of 50% or above; 4 units English, 3 units social science/history, 3 units mathematics, 3 units natural science, and 4 units electives (2 must be chosen from core college preparatory areas, foreign language, fine arts or computer science and 2 may be from any academic or vocational area). *For transfer students:* 2.0 or higher minimum GPA (on a 4.0 point scale), depending on enrollment restrictions.

For extrainstitutional learning, college credit and advanced placement on basis of faculty assessment; personal interviews.

Tutoring available. Credit and noncredit developmental courses offered in summer session and regular academic year.

Degree Requirements: *For all associate degrees:* 62 semester hours. *For all baccalaureate degrees:* 120 semester hours; basic studies. *For all undergraduate degrees:* 2.0 GPA; 30 semester hours in residence.

Fulfillment of some degree requirements and exemption from some beginning courses possible by passing College Board CLEP. *Grading system:* A–F (+/-); pass-fail; withdraw.

Distinctive Educational Programs: Cooperative education. Evening classes. Special facilities for using telecommunications within the classroom. Writing across the curriculum; information technology, including computer network and labs; natural resources, including forestry and environmental education; exceptional education; and wellness and health promotion. Interdisciplinary programs in international studies, women's studies. Facilities and programs for independent research, individual majors. Semester study abroad in Australia, France, Germany, Greece, Hungary, Ireland, New Zealand, Poland, Spain, United Kingdom; various summer and interim credit bearing trips.

ROTC: Army.

Degrees Conferred: 14 *associate;* 1,702 *baccalaureate*. area and ethnic studies 2; biological/life sciences 138; business and management 159; communications 121; computer and information sciences 48; education 173; engineering 19; English 55; foreign languages 33; health professions 36; home economics 34, interdisciplinary studies 1; mathematics 311 natural resources/environmental science 236; parks and recreation 61; philosophy/religion 16; physical sciences 15; psychology 85; social sciences and history 179; visual and performing arts 143. Master's degrees awarded: various disciplines 131. Doctorates awarded: health professions 3.

Fees and Other Expenses: *Full-time tuition per academic year 2008–09:* undergraduate resident $6,196, nonresident $13,769; contact the university for current graduate tuition/fees. *Required fees:* 891. *Room and board per academic year:* $5,780. *Books and supplies:* $450. *Other expenses:* $2,204.

Financial Aid: Aid from institutionally generated funds is provided on the basis of academic merit, financial need.

Financial aid to full-time, first-time undergraduate students: 74% received some form of aid. Average amount of aid received: federal grants $4,013; Pell grants $2,781; other federal aid $1,397; state/local grants $2,106; institutional grants $1,264.

Departments and Teaching Staff: *Total instructional faculty:* 439 (full-time 355 part-time 84). Total faculty with doctorate, first-professional, or other terminal degree: 342. Student-to-faculty ratio: 22:1. Degrees held by full-time faculty: master's 25%, doctorate 73%, baccalaureate 2%. 79% hold terminal degrees.

UNIVERSITY OF WISCONSIN - STEVENS POINT—*cont'd*

Enrollment: Total enrollment 9,163. Undergraduate 8,717 (full-time 93%; female 53%, male 47%). Graduate 446 (full-time 25%). Transfer-in students 630.

Characteristics of Student Body: *Ethnic/racial makeup:* Black non-Hispanic: 1%; American Indian or Alaska Native: 2%; Asian or Pacific lander: 1%; Hispanic: 1%; White non-Hispanic: 91%; unknown: 1%; nonresident alien 2%. *Age distribution:* number under 18: 26; 18–19: 2,130; 22–24: 2,917; 30–34: 176; 35–39: 96; 40–49: 180; 50–64: 62; 65 and over: 8%.

International Students: 184 nonresident aliens enrolled fall 2008. 5students from Europe, Asia, Latin America, Africa, Canada. Programs available to aid students whose native language is not English: social, cultural, Financial. English as a Second Language Program. Financial aid specifically designated for international students: a total of $548,710 awarded to qualifying student 2005–06.

Student Life: On-campus residence halls house 36% of student body; 5% males, 5% females, 90% coeducational. Numerous lifestyle options available. *Intercollegiate athletics:* male: basketball, baseball, cross-country, football, golf, swimming, track, wrestling, ice hockey; female: basketball, cross-country, ice hockey, soccer, softball, swimming, tennis, track, volleyball. *Special regulations:* Residence hall visitation varies according to individual halls. *Special services:* Learning Resource Center, medical services. *Student publications, radio, television: Barney Street*, a literary-art magazine; *The Pointer*, a weekly newspaper; *Pointer Alumnus*, a tabloid. Radio station WWSP-FM90 broadcasts 168 hours per week. Cable TV system. *Surrounding community:* Stevens Point population 24,000. Milwaukee, 160 miles from campus, is nearest metropolitan area. Served by mass transit bus system. Regional airport 15 miles from campus.

Library Collections: 1,100,000 volumes including bound books, serial backfiles, electronic documents, and government documents not in separate collections. Online catalog. 650,000 microforms; 13,000 audiovisual materials; 1,320 current serial subscriptions. Computer work stations available campus-wide. Students have access to the Internet at no charge.

Most important special holdings include collections on natural resources, communications disorders, Kennedy assassination.

Buildings and Grounds: Campus area 324 acres.

Chief Executive Officer: Dr. Linda Bunnell, Chancellor.

Address admission inquiries to Catherine Glennon, Director of Admissions.

College of Letters and Science

Degree Programs Offered: *Associate* in general studies; *baccalaureate* in anthropology, biology, business administration, chemistry, CIS, economics, English, French, German, geography, history, international studies, managerial accounting, mathematics, natural science, philosophy, physics, political science, psychology, public administration and policy analysis, Spanish, social science, sociology, web and digital media development; *master's* in biology, English, history.

College of Fine Arts and Communication

Degree Programs Offered: *Baccalaureate* in communication, theatre arts, arts management, studio arts or design, drama, dance, musical theatre, music (with options in jazz, applied music, theory, communication, music literature and music education); *master's* in communication, music education.

Admission: Admission to the BFA and BM program requires audition or portfolio and interview.

Degree Requirements: Students in the BFA and BM programs take 65% of the total credits needed in their major area. Senior public performance recitals and exhibitions are required.

College of Natural Resources

Degree Programs Offered: *Baccalaureate* in forestry, resource management, soil, and water resources, wildlife management and paper science; *master's* in natural resources.

College of Professional Studies

Degree Programs Offered: *Baccalaureate* in athletic training, communicative disorders, dietetics, health promotion, education, interior architecture, health science, family and consumer science, physical education; *master's* in communicative disorders, education, human and community resources, nontraditional sciences; *clinical doctorate* in audiology.

University of Wisconsin - Stout

1 Clock Tower Plaza
Menomonie, Wisconsin 54751-0790
Tel: (715) 232-1411 **E-mail:** admissions@uwstout.edu
Fax: (715) 232-1667 **Internet:** www.uwstout.edu

Institution Description: *Enrollment:* 8,839. *Degrees awarded:* Baccalaureate, master's, education specialist.

Academic offering subject to approval by statewide coordinating bodies. Budget subject to approval by state governing boards.

Accreditation: *Regional:* NCA. *Professional*: construction education, dietetics, industrial technology, interior design, marriage and family therapy, rehabilitation counseling

History: Established as Stout Manual Training and Domestic Science School and offered first instruction at postsecondary level 1893; chartered 1899; awarded first degree (baccalaureate) 1900; changed name to Stout Institute 1908; to Stout State College 1955, to Stout State University 1964; adopted present name 1972.

Institutional Structure: *Composition of institution:* Administrators 44. Academic affairs headed by provost/vice chancellor of academic student affairs. Management/finances directed by vice chancellor of administrative and student life services. Total instructional faculty 397. Academic governance body, Faculty Senate, meets an average of 20 times per year.

Calendar: Semesters. Academic year Aug. to May. Freshmen admitted Aug., Jan., June. Degrees conferred and formal commencements May, Aug., Dec. Summer session of 1 term from June to Aug.

Characteristics of Freshmen: 3,650 applicants (female 1,901, male 1,749). 62% of applicants accepted. 48% of accepted applicants enrolled.

1% (13 students) submitted SAT scores; 95% (1,214 students) submitted ACT scores. *25th percentile*: ACT Composite 19, ACT English 18, ACT Math 18. *75th percentile*: ACT Composite 23, ACT English 23, ACT Math 24.

40% of entering freshmen expected to graduate within 5 years. 72% of freshmen from Wisconsin. Freshmen from 16 states and 12 foreign countries.

Admission: Rolling admissions plan. For fall acceptance, apply as early as Sept. 15 of previous year. Early acceptance available. *Requirements:* Either graduation from secondary school or GED. Lowest acceptable secondary school class standing 50th percentile. *For transfer students:* 2.0 minimum GPA; 72 semester hours maximum transfer credit.

College credit and advanced placement for postsecondary-level work completed in secondary school and for extrainstitutional learning (life experience) on basis of faculty assessment.

Tutoring available. Noncredit remedial courses offered during regular academic year.

Degree Requirements: 124–137 semester hours; 2.0 GPA; last 32 hours in residence; distribution requirements.

Fulfillment of some degree requirements and exemption from some beginning courses possible by passing departmental examinations, College Board CLEP, AP, International Baccalaureate. *Grading system:* A–F; pass-fail; withdraw (deadline after which pass-fail is appended to withdraw); incomplete; in-progress; satisfactory-unsatisfactory.

Distinctive Educational Programs: Work-experience programs. Evening classes. Special facilities for using telecommunications in the classroom. Facilities and programs for independent research. Semester at Fashion Institute of Technology (NY). Summer in Pigeon Lake Field Station. Continuing education. Study abroad programs in United Kingdom, Sweden, Mexico. Art and Design Department Exchange Programs in England and Germany. Apparel, Textiles, and Design Department Program.

Degrees Conferred: 1,208 *baccalaureate* (B), 268 *master's* (M): business and management 332 (B), 49 (M); education 165 (B), 106 (M); engineering 225 (B), 17 (M); health professions 59 (B), 14 (M); home economics 110 (B), 19 (M); mathematics 28 (B); psychology 56 (B), 28 (M); visual and performing arts 75 (B).

Fees and Other Expenses: *Full-time tuition per academic year 2008–09:* undergraduate resident $7,584, nonresident $16,925; contact the university for current graduate tuition/fees. *required fees:* $1,807. *Room and board per academic year:* $5,170. *Books and supplies:* $343. *Other expenses:* $2,780.

Financial Aid: Aid from institutionally generated funds is provided on the basis of academic merit, financial need.

Financial aid to full-time, first-time undergraduate students: 80% received some form of aid. Average amount of aid received: federal grants $2,658; Pell grants $2,706; other federal aid $1,040; state/local grants $2,177; institutional grants $974.

Departments and Teaching Staff: *Total instructional faculty:* 397 (full-time 291, part-time 106). *Student-to-faculty ratio:* 20:1. Degrees held by full-time faculty: 76% hold terminal degrees.

Enrollment: Total enrollment 8,839. Undergraduate 7,769 (full-time 88%; female 48%, male 52%). Graduate 1,070 (full-time 29%). Transfer-in students 598.

Characteristics of Student Body: *Ethnic/racial makeup:* Black non-Hispanic: 1%; American Indian or Alaska Native: 3%; Asian or Pacific Islander: 1%; Hispanic: 1%; White non-Hispanic: 92%; unknown: 1%; nonresident alien 1%.

International Students: 88 nonresident aliens enrolled fall 2008. Students from Europe, Asia, Latin America, Africa, Canada, Australia. Programs available to aid students whose native language is not English: social, cultural. English as a Second as Language Program. Financial aid specifically designated for international students: scholarships available annually for both undergraduate and graduate students.

Student Life: On-campus residence halls house 35% of student body. No university housing available for married students. *Intercollegiate athletics:* male: baseball, basketball, cross-country, football, hockey, track, wrestling; female: basketball, cross-country, gymnastics, soccer, softball, tennis, track, volleyball. Many intramural sports for males and females. *Special regulations:* Cars permitted without restrictions. *Special services:* Learning Resources Center, medical services. *Student publications, radio: Stoutonia*, a weekly newspaper. Radio station WVSS-FM broadcasts 56 hours per week. *Surrounding community:* Menomonie population 14,000. Minneapolis-St. Paul (MN), 65 miles from campus, is nearest metropolitan area.

Library Collections: 226,000 volumes including bound books, serial backfiles, electronic documents, and government documents not in separate collections. Online catalog. 1,214,000 microforms; 14,500 audiovisual materials; 1,000 current serial subscriptions.Computer work stations available campus-wide. Students have access to the Internet at no charge.

Most important special holdings include collections on hospitality/tourism; industrial technology; home economics.

Buildings and Grounds: Campus area 120 acres. Campus DVD available.

Chief Executive Officer: Dr. Charles Sorensen, Chancellor.

Address admission inquiries to Cindy Jenkins, Director of Admissions.

University of Wisconsin - Superior

Belknap and Catlin
P.O. Box 2000
Superior, Wisconsin 54880-4500
Tel: (715) 394-8101 **E-mail:** admissions@uwsuper.edu
Fax: (715) 394-8407 **Internet:** www.uwsuper.edu

Institution Description: *Enrollment:* 2,689. *Degrees awarded:* Associate, baccalaureate, master's. Specialist certificates in education also awarded.

Member of the Council of Public Liberal Arts Colleges.

Accreditation: *Regional:* NCA. *Professional*: chemistry, counseling, music, social work, teacher education

History: Established as Superior Normal School 1893; offered first instruction at postsecondary level 1896; changed name to State Teachers College—Superior 1925; awarded first degree (baccalaureate) 1927; changed name to Wisconsin State College—Superior 1952; changed name to Wisconsin State University—Superior 1964; adopted present name 1971.

Institutional Structure: *Composition of institution:* Administrators 23. Academic affairs headed by provost. Management/business/finances directed by director of business affairs and controller. Full-time instructional faculty 118.. Academic governance body, University of Wisconsin—Superior Senate, meets an average of 12 times per year.

Calendar: Semesters. Academic year Sept. to May. Freshmen admitted Aug., Nov., Mar., June. Degrees conferred May, Aug., Dec. Formal commencement May. Summer sessions May to Aug.

Characteristics of Freshmen: 897 applicants (female 508, male 389). 74% of applicants admitted. 38% of applicants admitted and enrolled.

5% (17students) submitted SAT scores; 91% (314 students) submitted ACT scores. *25th percentile*: SAT Critical Reading 485, SAT Math 500; ACT Composite 20, ACT English 19, ACT Math 18. *75th percentile*: SAT Critical Reading 505, SAT Math 625; ACT Composite 24, ACT English 24, ACT Math 24.5.

41% of freshmen expected to graduate within 5 years. 56% of freshmen from Wisconsin. Freshmen from 15 states and 12 foreign countries.

Admission: Rolling admissions plan. Apply no later than day of registration. Early acceptance available. *Requirements:* Graduation from accredited secondary school with 17 units including 4 English, 3 math, 3 social science, 3 science, 4 electives. Students must rank in upper 50% of secondary school class and have ACT 21 *or* lower rank with ACT 23 *or* rank in top third of graduating class. GED accepted. *For transfer students:* 2.0 minimum GPA; from 4-year accredited institution 144 hours maximum transfer credit; from 2-year accredited institution 108 hours; correspondence/extension students 60 hours.

Advanced placement for postsecondary-level work completed in secondary school. College credit and advanced placement for extrainstitutional learning on basis of portfolio and faculty assessments.

Tutoring available. Developmental/remedial courses offered in summer session and regular academic year; credit given.

Degree Requirements: *For all associate degrees:* 60 semester hours. *For all baccalaureate degrees:* 120 semester hours; liberal education requirements.

Fulfillment of some degree requirements and exemption from some beginning courses possible by passing College Board CLEP. *Grading system:* A–F; pass-fail; withdraw (carries time limit).

Distinctive Educational Programs: Work-experience programs. Flexible meeting places and schedules, including off-campus centers, weekend and evening classes. Dual-degree program in engineering with Michigan Technological University and University of Wisconsin - Madison. Strong liberal arts emphasis. Special facilities for using telecommunications in the classroom. Interdisciplinary programs, including criminal justice, ethnic studies, science, social science, women's studies. New majors in legal studies and transportation/logistics management.Individual majors. Student teaching in Europe through consortium. Lake Superior field research center. *Other distinctive programs:* Credit and noncredit continuing education and extension programs. Distance learning program; study abroad programs; individualized majors; online courses. Center for Lake Superior Environmental Studies. Center for Advancement of Science Education.

ROTC: Air Force.

Degrees Conferred: 447 *baccalaureate* (B),100 114 *master's* (M): biological/life sciences 28 (B); business and management 56 (B); communications 27 (B), 7 (M); computer and information sciences 10 (B); education 81 (B), 93 (M); English 11 (B); interdisciplinary studies 28 (B); law/legal studies 7 (B); mathematics 8 (B); physical sciences 4; protective services/public administration18 (B); psychology 29 (B); social sciences and history 64 (B); visual and performing arts 24 (B), 14 (M).

Fees and Other Expenses: *Full-time tuition per academic year 2008–09:* undergraduate resident $6,359, nonresident $13,932; contact the university for current graduate tuition/fees. *Room and board per academic year:* $4,954. *Books and supplies:* $358. *Other expenses:* $1,595.

Financial Aid: Aid from institutionally generated funds is provided on the basis of academic merit, financial need.

Financial aid to full-time, first-time undergraduate students: 85% received some form of aid. Average amount of aid received: federal grants $3,721; Pell grants $3,045; other federal aid $942; state/local grants $2,443; institutional grants $3,285.

Departments and Teaching Staff: *Total instructional faculty:* 170 (full-time 118, part-time 52). Total faculty with doctorate, first-professional, or other terminal degree: 97. *Student-to-faculty ratio:* 18:1. Degrees held by full-time faculty: master's 29%, doctorate 71%. 82% hold terminal degrees.

Enrollment: Total enrollment 2,689. Undergraduate 2,448 (full-time 80%; female 58%, male 42%). Graduate 249 (full-time 31%). Transfer-in students 365.

Characteristics of Student Body: *Ethnic/racial makeup:* Black non-Hispanic: 1%; American Indian or Alaska Native: 1%; Asian or Pacific Islander: 3%; Hispanic: 1%; White non-Hispanic: 87%; unknown 2%; nonresident alien 5%.

International Students: 134 undergraduate nonresident aliens enrolled fall 2008. Students from Europe, Asia, Latin America, Africa, Canada, Australia. Programs available to aid students whose native language is not English: social, cultural. English as a Second Language Program. Financial aid specifically designated for international students: scholarships available annually.

Student Life: On-campus housing for 600 students. *Intercollegiate athletics:* male: baseball, basketball, cross-country, hockey, soccer, track; female: basketball, cross-country, golf, hockey, soccer, track, volleyball. *Special regulations:* Cars permitted without restrictions. *Special services:* Learning Resources Center, medical services. *Student publications, radio: Promethean*, a bimonthly newspaper. Radio station KUWS broadcasts 105 hours per week. *Surrounding community:* Superior/Duluth population 240,000. Minneapolis (MN), 160 miles from campus, is nearest metropolitan area. Served by mass transit bus system; airport 7 miles from campus.

Library Collections: 605,800 volumes including bound books, serial backfiles, electronic documents, and government documents not in separate collections. Online catalog. 106,000 microforms; 6,000 audiovisual materials; 750 current serial subscriptions. Computer work stations available. Students have access to the Internet at no charge.

Most important special holdings include Bee Croft Collection; personal papers; Literary Guild Collection.

Buildings and Grounds: Campus area 230 acres.

UNIVERSITY OF WISCONSIN - SUPERIOR—*cont'd*

Chief Executive Officer: Dr. Julius Erlenback, Chancellor.

Undergraduates address admission inquiries to James Miller, Admissions Director; graduate inquiries to Dr. David Prior, Dean of Graduate Studies.

University of Wisconsin - Whitewater

800 West Main Street
Whitewater, Wisconsin 53190-1790
Tel: (262) 472-1440 **E-mail:** uwwadmit@uww.edu
Fax: (262) 472-1515 **Internet:** www.uww.edu

Institution Description: *Enrollment:* 10,962. *Degrees awarded:* Baccalaureate, master's.

Accreditation: *Regional:* NCA. *Professional*: business, chemistry, counseling, music, social work, theatre, teacher education

History: Established as Whitewater Normal School, chartered, and offered first instruction at postsecondary level 1868; awarded first degree (baccalaureate) 1927; changed name to Whitewater State Teachers College 1925; adopted present name 1971. *See* M. Janette Bohi, *A History of Wisconsin State University—Whitewater 1868–1968* (Whitewater: State University Foundation, Inc., 1967) for further information.

Institutional Structure: *Composition of institution:* Administrators 27. Academic affairs headed by vice chancellor and dean of faculties. Management/business/finances directed by assistant chancellor for administrative services. Full-time instructional faculty 392. Academic governance body, Faculty Senate, meets an average of 18 times per year.

Calendar: Semesters. Academic year Sept. to May. Freshmen admitted Aug., Jan., June. Degrees conferred and formal commencement May, Aug., Dec. Winterim Term 3 weeks in Jan. Summer session of 1 term from June to Aug.

Characteristics of Freshmen: 5,428 applicants (female 2,775, male 2,653). 76% of applicants admitted. 32% of applicants admitted and enrolled.

3% (51 students) submitted SAT scores; 98% (1,764 students) submitted ACT scores. *25th percentile*: SAT Critical Reading 470, SAT Math 480; ACT Composite 20, ACT English 19, ACT Math 19. *75th percentile*: SAT Critical Reading 610, SAT Math 600; ACT Composite 24, ACT English 24, ACT Math 25. 2 National Merit Scholars.

45% of entering freshmen expected to graduate within 5 years. 93% of freshmen from Wisconsin. Freshmen from 9 and 5 foreign countries.

Admission: Rolling admissions plan. For fall acceptance, apply as early as 1 year prior to enrollment, but not later than beginning of classes. Early acceptance available. *Requirements:* Either graduation from recognized secondary school with 18 units from among English, mathematics, lab sciences, and social sciences; or GED. Students graduating in bottom 60% of secondary school class must meet class rank/test score requirement. *Entrance tests:* ACT composite accepted; College Board SAT accepted. *For transfer students:* From 4-year accredited institution 90 hours maximum transfer credit; from 2-year accredited institution 72 hours.

College credit and advanced placement for postsecondary-level work completed in secondary school. College credit for extrainstitutional learning (life experience) on basis of faculty assessment.

Tutoring available. Developmental courses offered in summer session and regular academic year; credit given.

Degree Requirements: 120 credit hours; 2.0 GPA (higher for some programs); 30 credits in residence; 1 credit in physical education; liberal studies requirement; demonstrated proficiency in English, mathematics, speech.

Fulfillment of some degree requirements and exemption from some beginning courses possible by passing departmental examinations, College Board CLEP, AP. *Grading system:* A–F; pass-fail; withdraw (carries time limit).

Distinctive Educational Programs: Internships. Off-campus centers. Evening classes. Cooperative master's programs in public administration with the University of Wisconsin—Oshkosh and in school administration with the University of Wisconsin—Madison. Online MBA completion available (*see* www.uww.ed/onlinemba). Special facilities for using telecommunications in the classroom. Interdisciplinary programs in American studies, ethnic studies, management computer systems, school business management, women's studies. Facilities and programs for independent research, including honors programs, individual majors, tutorials. Study abroad in varying countries. Noncredit and credit continuing education. Courses available via the Internet.

ROTC: Army.

Degrees Conferred: 1,635 *baccalaureate* (B), 424 *master's* (M): biological sciences 36 (B); business and management 459 (B), 219 (M); communications 184 (B), 9 (M); computer and information sciences 107 (B), 5 (M); education 286 (B), 206 (M); English 36 (B); foreign languages 21 (B); health professions 8 (B); liberal arts/general studies 16 (B); mathematics 25 (B); physical sciences 5 (B); public administration 16 (B); psychology 72 (B); social sciences and history 222 (B); visual and performing arts 103 (B).

Fees and Other Expenses: *Full-time tuition per academic year 2008–09:* undergraduate resident $6,162, nonresident $13,735; contact the university for current graduate tuition/fees. *Room and board per academic year:* $4,790. *Books and supplies:* $640. *Other expenses:* $2,350.

Financial Aid: The university offers a direct lending program. Aid from institutionally generated funds is provided on the basis of academic merit, financial need.

Financial aid to full-time, first-time undergraduate students: 73% received some form of aid. Average amount of aid received: federal grants $3,773; Pell grants $2,671; other federal aid $1,351; state/local grants $2,116; institutional grants $1,221.

Departments and Teaching Staff: *Total instructional faculty:* 502 (full-time 392, part-time 110). Total faculty with doctorate, first-professional, or other terminal degree: 373. Student-to-faculty ratio: 22:1. Degrees held by full-time faculty: 94% hold terminal degrees.

Enrollment: Total enrollment 10,962. Undergraduate 9,621 (full-time 93%; female 49%, male 51%). Graduate 1,341 (full-time 27%). Transfer-in student 620.

Characteristics of Student Body: *Ethnic/racial makeup:* Black non-Hispanic: 4%; American Indian or Alaska Native: 2%; Hispanic: 2%; White non-Hispanic: 89%. *Age distribution:* number under 18: 38; 18–19: 3,130; 20–21: 3,355; 22–24: 2,050; 25–29: 448; 30–34: 170; 35–39: 112; 40–49: 176; 50–64: 50; 65 and over: 4.

International Students: 109 nonresident aliens enrolled fall 2008. Students from Europe, Asia, Latin America, Africa, Canada, Australia, Middle East. Programs available to aid students whose native language is not English: social, cultural. English as a Second Language Program. Financial aid specifically designated for international students: scholarships available annually to qualifying students.

Student Life: On-campus residence halls house 40% of student body. 9% of student body housed on campus in privately owned and operated residence halls. Some students live in fraternitiy and sorority housing. *Intercollegiate athletics:* male: baseball, football, wrestling; female: bowling, gymnastics, golf, softball, volleyball; both sexes: basketball, cross-country, soccer, swimming and diving, indoor track, tennis, track and field. *Special regulations:* Cars must be registered. Quiet hours in all residence halls. *Special services:* Learning Resources Center, Center for Students with Disabilities, medical services. *Student publications, radio: Royal Purple*, a weekly newspaper. Radio station WSUW broadcasts 80 hours per week. Residence hall movie channel (RHMC) broadcasts 4 movies per day, 7 days a week. UW-Whitewater cable 19 broadcasts campus news and events. *Surrounding community:* Whitewater population 11,500. Milwaukee, 50 miles from campus, is nearest metropolitan area. Served by airport 17 miles from campus.

Library Collections: 676,000 volumes including bound books, serial backfiles, electronic documents, and government documents not in separate collections. Online catalog. 993,000 microforms; 8,000 audiovisual materials; 5,000 periodicals including via electronic access. Computer work stations available. Students have access to the Internet at no charge. Students have fee-based access to online information retrieval services.

Most important special holdings include Arts Media Center Collection; reference collection; Wisconsin Instructional Technology Resource Center (WITRIC).

Buildings and Grounds: Campus area 385 acres. Campus DVD available.

Chief Executive Officer: Dr. Martha Saunders, Chancellor.

Undergraduates address admission inquiries to Stephen McKellips, Director of Admissions; graduate inquiries to John Stone, Associate Dean, School of Graduate Studies.

Viterbo University

900 Viterbo Drive
La Crosse, Wisconsin 54601
Tel: (608) 796-3000 **E-mail:** admission@viterbo.edu
Fax: (608) 796-3020 **Internet:** www.viterbo.edu

Institution Description: Viterbo University, formerly Viterbo College, is a private, independent, nonprofit college founded by the Franciscan Sisters of Perpetual Adoration of La Crosse, Roman Catholic Church. *Enrollment:* 2,944. *Degrees awarded:* Baccalaureate, master's.

Accreditation: *Regional:* NCA. *Professional*: business, chemistry, dietetics, music, nursing, teacher education

History: Established as St. Rose Normal School 1890; adopted present name 1937; became 4-year institution 1939; awarded first degree (baccalaureate)

1940; incorporated 1960; became coeducational 1970. Master of Arts program in education instituted in 1988; Master of Science in nursing began 1998.

Institutional Structure: *Governing board:* Board of Directors of Viterbo College, Inc. Extrainstitutional representation: 30 directors. All voting. *Composition of institution:* Administrators 7. Academic affairs headed by academic vice president. Management/business/finances directed by vice president for finance and administration. Full-time instructional faculty 111. Academic governance body, administrative assembly, faculty assembly, student assembly, staff assembly.

Calendar: Semesters. Academic year Aug. to May. Freshmen admitted Aug., Jan., June. Degrees conferred May, July, Dec. Formal commencement May, July, Dec. Summer session of 2 terms from May to July.

Characteristics of Freshmen: 1,374 applicants (female 991, male 383). 89% of applicants admitted. 32% of applicants admitted and enrolled.

94% (292 students) submitted ACT scores. *25th percentile*: ACT Composite 19, ACT English 18, ACT Math 18. *75th percentile*: ACT Composite 24, ACT English 24, ACT Math 24.

49% of applicants expected to graduate within 5 years. 74% of freshmen from Wisconsin. Freshmen from 11 states and 1 foreign country.

Admission: Rolling admissions plan. For fall acceptance, apply as early as Sept. 1 of previous year, but not later than Aug. 15 of year of enrollment. *Requirements:* Either graduation from accredited secondary school with 16 units or GED. Recommend 3–4 units English, 2 in a foreign language, 2 history and social studies, 2 mathematics, 2 natural science, and 4–5 electives. Chemistry required for dietetics, medical technology, and nursing students. *Entrance tests:* ACT preferred. College Board SAT accepted. *For transfer students:* 2.0 minimum GPA; 98 hours maximum transfer credit.

College credit and advanced placement for postsecondary-level work completed in secondary school and for College Board CLEP.

Tutoring available.

Degree Requirements: *For associate arts/science degree:* fulfill general education requirements; earn a minimum of 64 semester hours; minimum GPA 2.0. *For baccalaureate degree:* fulfill all general education requirements; complete all courses required for the major; minimum 128 credit hours; earn a minimum of 43 semester hours of upper division credit; achieve a minimum GPA 2.0; complete a minimum of 30 consecutive semester hours in residence, including alternative credits; foreign language required for the BA degree. *For master's degree:* varies with program (education, servant leadership, nursing, business administration).

Fulfillment of some degree requirements and exemption from some beginning courses possible by passing departmental examinations, College Board CLEP or APP. *Grading system:* A–F; credit-no credit; withdraw (carries time limit).

Distinctive Educational Programs: Cooperative education program. Evening classes. Special credit transfer system for students holding associate degree from noncollege parallel technical institutions. Undergraduate Honors Program. Cross-registration with University of Wisconsin—La Crosse. Extensive use of computers in coursework. Facilities in fine arts programs; music, theatre, music theatre, and art. Majors in personnel management, ministry, art in business, music theatre, health care administration, community medical dietetics. Interdisciplinary majors in biology/chemistry, liberal studies; interdisciplinary courses may be individually designed. Preprofessional programs in dentistry, medicine, optometry, pharmacy, veterinary medicine. Facilities and programs for independent research, including individual majors, tutorials. Study abroad by individual arrangement. Higher Education Consortium for Urban Affairs (HECUA). Short interim field trips for credit offered. Full- and part-time evening school degree program. Degree completion program for registered nurses. *Other distinctive programs:* Continuing education; limited tuition-free program for adults and senior citizens.

ROTC: Army offered in cooperation with University of Wisconsin-La Crosse.

Degrees Conferred: 376 *baccalaureate* (B), 507 *master's* (M): biological/life sciences 13 (B); business and management 65 (B); computer and information sciences 8 (B); education 46 (B), 409 (M); English 5 (B); foreign languages 54 (B); health professions 99 (B), 12 (M); interdisciplinary studies 24; liberal arts/general studies 14 (B); philosophy/religion 1 (B), 17 (M); physical sciences 4 (B); public administration 18 (B); psychology 18; social sciences and history 6; visual and performing arts 28.

Fees and Other Expenses: *Full-time tuition per academic year 2008–09:* undergraduate $19,490; contact the university for current graduate tuition/fees. *Required fees:* $420. *Room and board per academic year:* $6,380. *books and supplies:* $850. *Other expenses:* $2,500.

Financial Aid: Aid from institutionally generated funds is provided on the basis of academic merit, financial need, athletic ability, other criteria.

Institution has a Program Participation Agreement with the U.S. Department of Education for eligible students to receive Pell Grants and, depending upon the agreement, other federal aid.

Financial aid to first-time, full-time undergraduate students; 99% received some form of aid. Average amount of aid received: federal grants $5,111; Pell grants $2,518; other federal aid $3,140; state/local grants $2,725; institutional grants $7,986.

Departments and Teaching Staff: *Total instructional faculty:* 168 (full-time 104, part-time 64). Total faculty with doctorate, first-professional, or other terminal degree: 67. Student-to-faculty ratio: 13:1. Degrees held by full-time faculty: doctorate 48%, master's 39%, baccalaureate 4%. 50% hold terminal degrees.

Enrollment: Total enrollment: 2,944. Undergraduate 2,093 (full-time 73%; female 71%, male 29%). Graduate 851 (full-time 34%). Transfer-in students 300.

Characteristics of Student Body: *Ethnic/racial makeup:* Black non-Hispanic: 1%; American Indian or Alaska Native: 2%; Asian or Pacific Islander: 1%; Hispanic: 1%; White non-Hispanic: 92%; unknown: 1%; nonresident alien 1%. *Age distribution:* number under 18: 52; 18–19: 514; 20–21: 490; 22–24: 319; 25–29: 165; 30–34: 115; 35–39: 72; 40–49: 146; 50–64: 47; unknown: 2.

International Students: 29 nonresident aliens enrolled fall 2008. Students from Europe, Asia, Latin America, Africa, Canada, Australia, Middle East. Programs available to aid students whose native language is not English: social, cultural. Financial aid specifically designated for international students.

Student Life: On-campus housing for 561 students. 25 clubs and organizations. *Intercollegiate athletics:* male: baseball, basketball, soccer; femlae: basketball, soccer, softball, volleyball. *Special regulations:* Cars permitted with restrictions. *Special services:* Learning Resources Center, medical/counseling services, religious services. *Student publications: Lumen*, a biweekly newspaper; *Touchstone*, a annual literary magazine. *Surrounding community:* La Crosse population 55,000. Minneapolis-St. Paul (MN), 150 miles from campus, is nearest metropolitan area. Served by mass transit bus system, airport 6 miles from campus, passenger rail service 3 miles from campus.

Library Collections: 92,000 volumes including bound books, serial backfiles, electronic documents, and government documents not in separate collections. Online catalog. Current serial subscriptions: 698 paper; 16,900 via electronic access. 2.347 recordings; 192 DVD discs; 924 compact discs. Computer work stations available. Students have access to the Internet at no charge.

Most important special holdings include collections on religious studies, business and nursing, children's and curriculum materials.

Buildings and Grounds: Campus area 5 square blocks. Campus DVD available.

Chief Executive Officer: Dr. Richard Artman, President.

Address undergraduate admission inquiries to Roland Nelson, Vice President for Enrollment; graduate inquiries to Jack Havertape, Vice President for Academic Affairs.

Wisconsin Lutheran College

8800 West Bluemond Road
Milwaukee, Wisconsin 53226-4699
Tel: (414) 443-8800 **E-mail:** admissions@wlc.edu
Fax: (414) 443-8514 **Internet:** www.wlc.edu

Institution Description: Wisconsin Lutheran College is a private liberal arts college affiliated with the Wisconsin Evangelical Lutheran Synod. *Enrollment:* 753. *Degrees awarded:* Baccalaureate.

Accreditation: *Regional:* NCA.

History: Founded 1973.

Institutional Structure: *Governing board:* Board of Regents. Academic affairs headed by vice president for academic affairs. Management/business/finances headed by director of fiscal affairs. Full-time instructional faculty 35.

Calendar: Semesters. Academic year Aug. to May. Freshmen admitted Aug. Degrees conferred and formal commencement May. Summer session May to July.

Characteristics of Freshmen: 75% of applicants accepted. 50% of accepted applicants enrolled.

Average secondary school rank of freshmen 73rd percentile. Mean ACT Composite score 24.

53% of freshmen expected to graduate within 5 years. 70% of freshmen from Wisconsin. Freshmen from 11 states and 2 foreign countries.

Admission: *Requirements:* High school graduation in upper 50% of class; minimum GPA 2.5; Spiritual Advisor's Reference Form completed by the pastor of the applicant.

Degree Requirements: *For baccalaureate degree:* 128 credits distributed among 4 basic skill ares and a 7-part core curriculum. Special requirements include convocation series.

Degrees Conferred: 153 *baccalaureate*. Bachelor's degrees awarded in top five disciplines: communication, journalism, and related programs 31; psychol-

WISCONSIN LUTHERAN COLLEGE—*cont'd*

ogy 25; business, management, marketing, and related support services 20; education 16; visual and performing arts 13.

Fees and Other Expenses: *Full-time tuition per academic year* $20,560. *Books and supplies:* $700. *Room and board per academic year:* $7,120. *Other expenses:* $1,740.

Financial Aid: Aid from institutionally generated funds is provided on the basis of academic merit, financial need.

Financial aid to full-time, first-time undergraduate students: 100% received some form of aid. 36% received federal grants averaging $2,084; 40% state/local grants averaging $2,365; 100% institutional grants averaging $7,591; 62% received loans averaging $3,120.

Departments and Teaching Staff: *Total instructional faculty:* 75. Student/faculty ratio: 8:1. Degrees held by full-time faculty: doctorate 63%, master's 100%, professional 2%. 74% hold terminal degrees.

Enrollment: Total 753.

Characteristics of Student Body: *Ethnic/racial makeup:* Black non-Hispanic: 4%; Americn Indian or Alaskan Native 2%; Hispanic: 25; White non-Hispanic: 86%; unknown: 3%; nonresident alien 2%.

International Students: 16 nonresident aliens enrolled fall 2008. Students from Europe, Asia, Latin America, Africa. No programs available to aid students whose native language is not English. No financial aid specifically designated for international students.

Student Life: Single-sex housing and apartments. Drug-free campus. Intramural and intercollegiate sports activities. College choirs, instrumental ensembles, art society, theater productions, student clubs.

Library Collections: 75,000 volumes. 8,300 microforms; 3,150 audiovisual materials; 585 current periodical subscriptions. Online catalog. Students have access to online information retrieval services and the Internet.

Most important special collections include Lutheran Practical Theology; Bible Studies.

Chief Executive Officer: Dr. Timothy J. Kriewall, President.

Address admission inquiries to Craig Swionteck, Director of Admissions.

Wyoming

University of Wyoming

1000 East University Avenue
Laramie, Wyoming 82071
Tel: (307) 766-5160 **E-mail:** why-wyo@uwyo.edu
Fax: (307) 766-4042 **Internet:** www.uwyo.edu

Institution Description: University of Wyoming is a state institution and land-grant university. *Enrollment:* 13,303. *Degrees awarded:* Baccalaureate, first-professional (law), master's, doctorate.

Budget subject to approval by state governing boards.

Accreditation: *Regional:* NCA. *Professional*: business, engineering, law, music, nursing, pharmacy, psychology internship, social work, speech-language pathology, teacher education

History: Established and chartered as University of Wyoming 1886; offered first instruction at postsecondary level 1887; awarded first degree (baccalaureate) 1891; established graduate school 1945. *See* Wilson O. Clough, *A History of the University of Wyoming, 1887–1964,* rev. ed. (Laramie: University of Wyoming, 1965) for further information.

Institutional Structure: *Governing board:* The Trustees of the University of Wyoming. Extrainstitutional representation: 12 trustees, governor of Wyoming, state superintendent of public instruction, institutional representation: president of the university, 1 student. 4 ex officio. 12 voting. *Composition of institution:* Administrators 25. Academic affairs headed by the Provost and Vice President for Academic and Student Affairs. Management/business/finances directed by the Vice President for Administration and Finance. Full-time instructional faculty 635. Academic governance body, Faculty Senate, meets an average of 9 times per year.

Calendar: Semesters. Academic year Sept. to May. Freshmen admitted Sept., Jan., June. Degrees conferred May, Aug., Dec. Formal commencement May. Summer session of 1 term from June to Aug.

Characteristics of Freshmen: 96% of applicants accepted. 50% of accepted applicants enrolled.

23% (360 students) submitted SAT scores; 89% (1,400 students) submitted ACT scores. *25th percentile*: SAT Critical Reading 480, SAT Math 490; ACT Composite 21, ACT English 19, ACT Math 19. *75th percentile*: SAT Critical Reading 600, SAT Math 610; ACT Composite 26. ACT English 26. ACT Math 26.

20% of entering freshmen expected to graduate within 5 years. 62% of freshmen from Wyoming. Freshmen from 42 states and 17 foreign countries.

Admission: Rolling admissions plan. Apply as early as 12 months, but not later than 30 days, prior to registration. *Requirements:* University of Wyoming admits all first-time college students who graduated from an accredited Wyoming High School. Out-of-state high school graduates must have a minimum 2.5 or higher cumulative high school GPA and acceptable ACT or SAT scores. Foreign students minimum TOEFL score 525. Higher for selected majors. *Entrance tests:* ACT or SAT required for new freshmen under 21 years of age. *Transfer students:* 2.3 minimum cumulative GPA in transferable courses. No maximum on acceptable credit from 4-year colleges. Maximum of 70 semester credit hours accepted toward a University of Wyoming degree from 2-year colleges.

Credit awarded for acceptable CLEP and AP test scores. Limited credit for experiential learning available. ACE *2006 Guide to the Evaluation of Educational Experiences in the Armed Services* used to determine specific military training.

Academic Enrichment Center provides tutoring. Non-credit preparatory English, reading, and math courses available.

Degree Requirements: *For undergraduate degrees:* 120–164 credit hours; 2.0 GPA; 30 hours in residence; University Studies and 1 physical education requirements; college and major requirements.

Fulfillment of some degree requirements possible by passing institutional examinations. *Grading system:* A–F; pass-fail; withdraw (carries time limit).

Distinctive Educational Programs: Work-experience programs, including internships, cooperative education. Flexible meeting places and schedules, including off-campus courses offered in all counties throughout the state in 61 communities, weekend and evening classes. Degree programs are offered in association with University of Wyoming departments and the School of Extended Studies and Public Service through the state community colleges. Special facilities for using telecommunications in the classroom. Preprofessional programs offered are dentistry, forestry, law, medicine, occupational therapy, optometry, physical therapy, veterinary medicine. Facilities and programs for independent research, including honors programs, individual majors, tutorials. Student exchange with professional education programs through Western Interstate Commission for Higher Education. Institutionally sponsored study abroad programs. *Other distinctive programs:* Upward Bound for low income secondary school students. Educational Talent Search Program identifies economically and educationally deprived students for programs in higher education.

ROTC: Air Force, Army.

Degrees Conferred: 1,706 *baccalaureate* (B), 439 *master's* (M), 59 *doctorate:* (D): agriculture and natural resources 109 (B), 17 (M), 5 (D); architecture 2 (M); area studies 5 (B), 10 (M); biological sciences 87 (B), 26 (M), 11 (D); business 236 (B), 38 (M); communications 72 (B), 5 (M); computer and information sciences 32 (B), 15 (M); education 338 (B), 95 (M); 8 (D); engineering 169 (B,)32 (M), 10 (D); English 23 (B), 10 (M); foreign languages 17 (B), 5 (M); health professions 111 (B), 31 (M); home economics 37 (B), 3 (M); mathematics 26 (B), 16 (M), 7 (D); natural resources/environmental science 24 (B); parks and recreation 47 (B), 3 (M); physical sciences 31 (B), 17 (M), 15 (D); protective services/public administration 115 (B), 32 (M); psychology 91 (B), 1 (M), 6 (D); social sciences and history 155 (B), 36 (M); visual and performing arts 50 (B), 3 (M); other 9 (B), 1, (M), 1 (D). 116 *first-professional:* law 73; pharmacy 43.

Fees and Other Expenses: *Full-time tuition per academic year 2008–09:* undergraduate in-district resident $3,429, out-of-state $10,660; contact the university for current gradAute and first-professional (law, pharmacy) tuition/fees. *Required fees:* $800. *Room and board per academic year:* $8,000. *Books and supples:* $1,200.

Financial Aid: Aid from institutionally generated funds is provided on the basis of academic merit, financial need, athletic ability.

Institution has a Program Participation Agreement with the U.S. Department of Education for eligible students to receive Pell Grants and, depending upon the agreement, other federal aid.

Financial aid to full-time, first-time undergraduate students: need-based scholarships/grants totaling $7,554,844, self-help $14,003,606; non-need-based scholarships/grants totaling $16,294,078, self-help $9,746,664, parent loans $2,850,098, tuition waivers $6,817,231, athletic awards $2,781,490.

Departments and Teaching Staff: *Total instructional faculty:* 720 (full-time 666, part-time 54). Student/faculty ratio: 15:1. Degrees held by full-time faculty: baccalaureate 1%, master's 7.5%, doctorate 82%, professional .5%, other 1%. 90% hold terminal degrees.

Enrollment: Total enrollment 13,203. Undergraduate 9,468 (full-time 7,713, part-time 1,755).

Characteristics of Student Body: *Ethnic/racial makeup:* number of Black non-Hispanic: 129; American Indian or Alaska Native: 137; Asian or Pacific Islander: 150; Hispanic: 394; White non-Hispanic 10,645; unknown: 1,310.

International Students: 438 nonresident aliens enrolled fall 2008. Students from Europe, Asia, Latin America, Africa, Canada, Australia. Programs available to aid students whose native language is not English: English as a Second Language Program. No financial aid specifically designated for international students.

Student Life: On-campus residence halls house 17% of student body. All dormitories are co-ed. 10–12% of the student body join fraternities and sororities. Apartments available, student families given priority. *Intercollegiate athletics:* male: baseball, basketball, football, golf, skiing, swimming, track, wrestling; female: basketball, skiing, swimming, track, volleyball, golf. *Special regulations:* Registered cars with decals permitted in designated areas. *Special services:* Programs available to help minority, physically and learning disabled, first generation, low income, women, or adult students; counseling services; drug education resource center; career planning and placement services; legal services; academic advising; computer access; medical services; shuttle bus service. *Student publications, radio: Branding Iron*, a newspaper published four days per week; *Owen Wister Review*, a biannual literary magazine; *Frontiers* a

UNIVERSITY OF WYOMING—*cont'd*

biannually published magazine. Radio station KUWR-FM broadcasts 133 hours per week. *Surrounding community:* Laramie population 28,000. Served by airport 5 miles from campus; passenger rail service 1 mile from campus. Denver (CO), 139 miles from campus, is nearest metropolitan area.

Library Collections: 2,500,000 volumes. 931,000 government documents; 2,953,200 microforms; 10,000 audiovisual materials; 11,700 periodicals including via electronic access. Computer work stations available campus-wide. Online catalog. Students have access to online information retrieval services and the Internet.

Most important special holdings include Hebard Collection of Wyoming; Rocky Mountain Herbarium Collection; Beuf/Gallatin Collection of Italian Renaissance.

Buildings and Grounds: Campus area 750 acres.

Chief Executive Officer: Dr. Thomas Buchanan, President.

Address admission inquiries to Noah A. Buckley, Director of Admissions.

College of Agriculture

Degree Programs Offered: *Baccalaureate* in agricultural business, agricultural communications, animal science, crop science, entomology, farm and ranch management, food science, general agriculture, home economics, international agriculture, molecular biology, range management, soil science, vocational agriculture; *master's* in agricultural economics, agricultural economics/water resources, agronomy, agronomy/water resources, animal science, entomology, food science and human nutrition, home economics, molecular biology, pathobiology, plant pathology, range management, range management/water resources, reproductive biology; *doctorate* in agronomy, animal science, entomology, molecular biology, range management, reproductive biology.

College of Arts and Sciences

Degree Programs Offered: *Baccalaureate* in administration of justice, American studies, anthropology, applied mathematics, art, astronomy/astrophysics, biology, botany, broadcasting, chemistry, communication, computer science, computer science/statistics, economics, economics/mathematics, English, English/theater, French, geography, geology, geophysics, German, history, humanities/fine arts, international studies, journalism, management information systems, mathematics, mathematics/statistics, music, music education, music-performance, music theory and composition, natural science/mathematics, philosophy, physics, political economy, political science, psychology, Russian, social science, sociology, Spanish, statistics, theater and dance, wildlife and fisheries biology management, zoology and physiology; *master's* in American studies, anthropology, art, botany, botany/water resources, chemistry, communication, computer science, English, French, geography, geology, geology/water resources, geophysics, German, history, international studies, journalism, mathematics, music, natural science, philosophy, physics, planning, political science, psychology, public administration, recreation and park administration, reproductive biology, sociology, Spanish, statistics, zoology and physiology, zoology and physiology/water resources; *doctorate* in botany, chemistry, computer science, geology, geophysics, history, mathematics, mathematics and computer science, physics, psychology, reproductive biology, statistics, zoology and physiology.

College of Business

Degree Programs Offered: *Baccalaureate* in accounting, business administration, economics, finance, management, marketing, small business management; *master's* in business administration, economics, economics/water resources, finance; *doctorate* in economics.

College of Education

Degree Programs Offered: *Baccalaureate* in business education, distributive education, elementary education, elementary and special education, industrial arts education, secondary education, special education, trades and industrial education, vocational agriculture, vocational homemaking; *master's* in adult education, business education, counselor education, curriculum and instruction, educational administration, education foundations, elementary education, instructional technology, special education, vocational education; *specialist* in adult education, counselor education, curriculum and instruction, educational administration, special education, vocational education; *doctorate* in counselor education, curriculum and instruction, educational administration, education.

College of Engineering

Degree Programs Offered: *Baccalaureate* in architectural engineering, chemical engineering, civil engineering, electrical engineering, mechanical engineering, petroleum engineering; *master's* in atmospheric science, bioengineering, chemical engineering, civil engineering, civil engineering/water resources, electrical engineering, mechanical engineering, mineral engineering, petroleum engineering, water resources; *doctorate* in atmospheric science, chemical engineering, civil engineering, electrical engineering, mechanical engineering, petroleum engineering.

College of Health Sciences

Degree Programs Offered: *Baccalaureate* in dental hygiene, health education, medical technology, nursing, pharmacy, physical education, physical education non-teaching, social work, speech, language and hearing sciences; *master's* in audiology, nursing, physical education, speech-language pathology.

College of Law

Degree Programs Offered: *First-professional*

Admission: Baccalaureate from accredited institution, LSAT, LSDAS.

Degree Requirements: 88 credit hours, 2.0 GPA, 58 hours in residence.

U.S. Trust Territories

University of Guam

303 University Drive
UOG Station
Mangliao, Guam 96923
Tel: (671) 735-2990 **E-mail:** www.uog.edu
Fax: (671) 735-2296 **Internet:** admitme@uog.edu

Institution Description: The University of Guam is a territorial institution and land-grant college. *Enrollment:* 3,387. *Degrees awarded:* baccalaureate, master's.

Accreditation: *Regional:* WASC.

History: Established as Territorial College of Guam and offered first instruction at potsecondary level 1952; awarded first degree (associate) 1953; changed name to College of Guam 1960; adopted present name 1968.

Institutional Structure: *Governing board:* Board of Regents. Extrainstitutional representation: 8 regents; institutional representation: 1 student. Composition of institution: full-time instructional faculty 201. A Faculty Council established 1985. Academic government bodies: University Academic Affairs Committee; University Registration and Admissions Committee; Graduate Council. Faculty representation: faculty served by collective bargaining agent, Guam American Federation of Teachers, affiliated with AFT.

Calendar: Semesters. Academic year Aug. to May. Freshmen admitted Aug., Jan., June. Degrees conferred and formal commencement May. Summer session June to July.

Characteristics of Freshmen: 97% of applicants accepted. 51% of accepted applicants enrolled. 41% of entering freshmen expected to graduate within 5 years.

Admission: Rolling admission plan. For fall admission, apply no later than Aug. 8; spring term no later than Dec. 30; summer term no later than Apr. 30. International students apply no later than June 27 for fall semester; Nov. 7 for spring term; Apr. 7 for summer session. Early acceptance available. Requirements: 12 years formal education or GED. For transfer students: 2.0 minimum GPA; maximum transfer credit limited only by residence requirement. Remedial/developmental courses offered fall, spring, summer; non-degree credit given. from 2-year colleges.

Degree Requirements: *For all associate degrees:* 60 credit hours; 16 credits in residence. *For all baccalaureate degrees:* 124 credit hous; 32 credits in residence. *For all undergraduate degrees:* 2.0 GPA in all courses including majro; general education requirements.

Fulfillment of some degree requirements from some beginng courses possible by passing College Board CLEP. Grading system: A-F, pass, fail; no credit; withdraw (deadline after which pass-fail is appended to withdraw).

Distinctive Educational Programs: Interdisciplinary course "People and Their Society" taught in close conjunction with developmental reading and English composition course. "Offering of Individual Degree Program" plans for in-service teachers through the Agricultural Experiment Station, Marine Laboratory, Micronesian Area Research Center, and Water and Energy Research Institution. Guam English Langauge Institute offered annually in the summer. Center for Contnuing Education and Outreach Program Micronesia.

ROTC: Army.

Degrees Conferred: 302 *baccalaureate*; 67 *master's*. Bachelor's degrees awarded in top five disciplines: education 79; business/management 45; public administration 24; security and protective services 24; health professions and related clinical sciences 18. Master's degrees awarded: various disciplines 67.

Fees and Other Expenses: *Full-time tuition per academic year 2008–09:* territory resident $5,342 nonresident $14,890; contact the university for graduate tuition. *Room and board per academic year:*$8,277. *Books and supplies:* $3,808.

Financial Aid: Aid from institutionally generated funds is provided on the basis of academic merit, financial need, athletic ability.

Departments and Teaching Staff: *Total instructional faculty:* 236. 75% hold terminal degrees.

Enrollment: Total enrollment 3,387. Undergraduate full-time 3,094; graduate full-time 293. Transfer-in students: 98.

Characteristics of Student Body: *Ethnic/racial makeup:* number of Black non-Hispanic 24; American Indian or Alaska Native 6; Asian or Pacific Islander 2,429; Hispanic 20; White non-Hispanic 153. *Age distribution:* number under 18: 18; 18–19: 823; 20–21: 586; 22–24: 472; 25–29: 326; 30–34: 177; 35–39: 127; 40–49: 113; 50–64: 34; 65 and over: 2.

International Students: 40 nonresident aliens enrolled fall 2008. Students from Asia, Canada, Australia. Programs available to aid students whose native language is not English: English as a Second Language Program. No financial aid specifically designated for international students.

Student Life: Two on-campus residence halls house 6% of student body. 20 student organizations serve the campus. Special regulations: Cars permitted without restrictions. Special services: medical services. Surrounding community: Guam population 125,000. Served by Guam public transprotation.

Publications: *Micronesia* (biannual) first published in 1964.

Library Collections: 120,000 volumes. 3,900 government documents; 980,000 microforms; 11,000 audiovisual materials. Students have acess to online information retrieval services and the Internet. Computer work stations available.

Most important special holdings include Pacific Collection of the Micronesian Area Research Center; federal grovernment documents; East Asian Collection.

Buildings and Grounds: Campus area 120 acres.

Chief Executive Officer: Dr. Harold Allen, President. Address admission inquiries to Admissions Office.

University of the Virgin Islands

2 John Brewer's Bay
St. Thomas, Virgin Islands 00802
Tel: (340) 776-9200 **E-mail:** www.uvi.edu
Fax: (340) 776-2399 **Internet:** admissions@uvi.edu

Institution Description: The University of the Virgin Islands is a territorial institution with a two-year branch at St. Croix. *Enrollment:* 2,393. *Degrees awarded:* associate, baccalaureate, master's.

Accreditation: *Regional:* WASC. *Professional*: teacher education

History: Established and chartgered 1962; offered and offered first instruction at potsecondary level 1963; awarded first degree (associate) 1965; became a four-year institution 1968; initiated master's program 1972.

Institutional Structure: *Governing board:* Board of Trustees. Extrainstitutional representation: 14 turstees; institutional representation: president of the university. 3 ex officio. All voting. Composition of institution: administrators 23. Academic affairs headed by dean of instruction. Management/business/finances directted by director of business and financial affairs. Full-time instructional faculty: 99. Academic governance body, Divisional Council, meets on the average of 10 times per year.

Calendar: Semesters. Academic year Aug. to May. Freshmen admitted Aug. Degrees conferred and formal commencement May. Summer session of one term from June to July.

Characteristics of Freshmen: 1,256 applicants 87% of applicants accepted. 71% of accepted applicants enrolled. *25th percentile:* SAT Critical Reading 300, SAT Math 520. *75th percentile:* SAT Critical Reading 550, SAT Math 600.

93% of freshmen from the Virgin Islands.

Admission: Rolling admission plan. For fall accepance, apply as early as beginning of senior year of secondary school, but not later than Apr. 15 year of enrollment. Early acceptance available. Requirements: Either graduation from accredited secondary school with 4 units English, 2 mathematics, or GED. Recommnend 2 in a foreign language. Foreign students from British-oriented systems must submit 5 G.C.E. O-levels, including 1 English at C grade or higher. Minimum 2.0 GPA; maximum transfer credits limited only by residence requirement.

UNIVERSITY OF THE VIRGIN ISLANDS—*cont'd*

College credit and advanced placement for postsecondary-level work completed in secondary school. Tutoring available. Noncredit remedial courses offered in summer session and regular academic year.

Degree Requirements: *For all associate degrees:* 62 credit hours. *For all baccalaureate degrees:* 120 credit hours; 2.0 GPA; final year in residence; 2 credits physical education; general education requirements; exit competency examination in English.

Distinctive Educational Programs: Liberal arts, pre-engineering, mathematics, basic sciences. Upon completion and recommendation by the faculty, students spend two years to complete the engineering course requirements for their specialization at the cooperative university; completion of this program leads to a baccalaureate degree.

Degrees Conferred: 69 *associate*: 93 *baccalaureate* (B); 53 *master's* (M): biological sciences 16 (B); business/marketing 99 (B), 12 (M); computer and information sciences 4 (B); education 24 (B), 39 (M); English 2 (B); liberal arts 1 (B); physical sciences 2 (B); public administration 3 (B), 12 (M); psychology 24 (B); social sciences and history 4 (B).

Fees and Other Expenses: *Full-time tuition per academic year 2008–09:* resident $8,394, nonresident $10,895. *Room and board per academic year:* $7,662. *Books and supplies:* $1,500. *Other expenses:* $2,900.

Financial Aid: Aid from institutionally generated funds is provided on the basis of academic merit, financial need, athletic ability. 80% of first-time, full-time students received some form of financial aid.

Departments and Teaching Staff: *Total instructional faculty:* 262. 93 hold terminal degrees.

Enrollment: Total enrollment 2,393. Undergraduate 2,212; graduate 181. Transfer-in students 113.

Characteristics of Student Body: *Ethnic/racial makeup:* number of Black non-Hispanic 1,931; American Indian or Alaska Native 4; Asian or Pacific Islander 22; Hispanic 154; White non-Hispanic 129; unknown 151. *Age distribution:* number under 18: 118; 18–19: 466; 20–21: 423; 25–29: 310; 30–34: 229; 35–39: 207; 40–49: 279; 50–64: 114; 65 and over: 12.

International Students: 170 nonresident aliens enrolled fall 2008. Programs available to aid students whose native language is not English: English as a Second Language Program. No financial aid specifically designated for international students.

Student Life: On-campus residence halls house 10% of student body. Cars permitted without restrictions. Quiet hours and residence hall visitation hours specified. *Special services:* Learning Resources Center; medical services. *Student publications: Passages*, an annual literary magazine; *Viewpoint*, a monthly newspaper. *Surrounding community:* St. Thomas population 50,000. San Juan (Puerto Rico) 75 miles from campus, is nearest metropolitan areas. Served by mass transet bus system; airport 1/4 mile from campus.

Publications: *Journal of the College of the Virgin islands* (annual) first published in 1975.

Library Collections: 120,000 volumes. 157,000 government documents; 1,200,000 microforms; 11,000 audiovisual materials; 940 current periodical subscriptions. Online catalog. Students have acess to online information retrieval services and the Internet. Computer work stations available.

Most important special holdings include Melchior Recent History (Virgin Islands); Caribbean Collection (books and periodicals); collection of material relating to Black Americans.

Buildings and Grounds: St. Thomas campus 175 acres; St. Croix campus 130 acres.

Chief Executive Officer: Dr. Laverne E. Ragster, President.

Address admission inquiries Carolyn Cook-Roberts, Director of Enrollment Management.

III

Indexes

Institution Index

A

B

C

D

E

F

G

H

I

J

K

L

M

N

O

P

Q

R

S

T

U

V

W

X

Y

Subject Accreditation Index

BUSINESS *(Cont'd)*

BUSINESS *(Cont'd)*

CLINICAL PSYCHOLOGY *(Cont'd)*

CONSTRUCTION EDUCATION *(Cont'd)*

CONSTRUCTION TECHNOLOGY

COUNSELING

DENTAL ASSISTING

DENTAL HYGIENE

ENGINEERING *(Cont'd)*

ENGINEERING *(Cont'd)*

ENGINEERING TECHNOLOGY

ENGINEERING TECHNOLOGY *(Cont'd)*

ENGLISH LANGUAGE EDUCATION

ENGLISH LANGUAGE EDUCATION *(Cont'd)*

ENVIRONMENTAL HEALTH

FAMILY AND CONSUMER SCIENCE

HEALTH INFORMATION ADMINISTRATION *(Cont'd)*

HEALTH INFORMATION TECHNICIAN

HEALTH SERVICES ADMINISTRATION

HEALTH SERVICES ADMINISTRATION *(Cont'd)*

HISTOLOGIC TECHNOLOGY

INDUSTRIAL TECHNOLOGY

INTERIOR DESIGN

INTERIOR DESIGN *(Cont'd)*

JOURNALISM *(Cont'd)*

KINESIOTHERAPY

LANDSCAPE ARCHITECTURE

MEDICINE

MUSIC *(Cont'd)*

MUSIC *(Cont'd)*

NURSING *(Cont'd)*

NURSING *(Cont'd)*

PHYSICIAN ASSISTING *(Cont'd)*

PLANNING

PSYCHOLOGY INTERNSHIP *(Cont'd)*

PUBLIC ADMINISTRATION

REHABILITATION COUNSELING *(Cont'd)*

RESPIRATORY THERAPY

SOCIAL WORK *(Cont'd)*

SOCIAL WORK *(Cont'd)*

SPEECH-LANGUAGE PATHOLOGY *(Cont'd)*

SPEECH-LANGUAGE PATHOLOGY *(Cont'd)*

SURGEON ASSISTING

TEACHER EDUCATION *(Cont'd)*

TEACHER EDUCATION *(Cont'd)*

TEACHER EDUCATION *(Cont'd)*

TEACHER EDUCATION *(Cont'd)*

Levels of Degrees Offered

ALABAMA

Alabama Agricultural and Mechanical University, **(B, M, D)**, 25
Alabama State University, **(A, B, M, D, C)**, 25
Ambridge University, **(B, M, D, C)**, 26
Athens State University, **(B)**, 27
Auburn University, **(B, M, D, P)**, 27
Auburn University at Montgomery, **(B, M)**, 28
Birmingham-Southern College, **(B, M)**, 29
Concordia College Selma, **(B)**, 30
Faulkner University, **(A, B)**, 30
Heritage Christian University, **(A, B)**, 30
Huntingdon College, **(A, B)**, 31
Jacksonville State University, **(B, M)**, 32
Judson College, **(B)**, 32
Miles College, **(B)**, 33
Oakwood College, **(A, B)**, 33
Samford University, **(A, B, M, D, P, C)**, 34
Southeastern Bible College, **(A, B)**, 36
Spring Hill College, **(A, B, M)**, 36
Stillman College, **(B)**, 37
Talladega College, **(B)**, 37
Troy University, **(A, B, M, C)**, 38
Troy University Dothan, **(A, B, M, C)**, 39
Troy University Montgomery, **(A, B, M)**, 39
Tuskegee University, **(B, M, P, C)**, 40
United States Sports Academy, **(B, M, D)**, 40
University of Alabama, **(B, M, D, P, C)**, 41
University of Alabama at Birmingham, **(B, M, D, P)**, 42
University of Alabama in Huntsville, **(B, M, D, C)**, 43
University of Mobile, **(A, B, M)**, 44
University of Montevallo, **(B, M, C)**, 45
University of North Alabama, **(B, M, C)**, 45
University of South Alabama, **(B, M, D, P, C)**, 46
University of West Alabama, **(A, B, M)**, 47

ALASKA

Alaska Bible College, **(A, B, C)**, 49
Alaska Pacific University, **(A, B, M, C)**, 49
Sheldon Jackson College, **(A, B)**, 50
University of Alaska Anchorage, **(B, M)**, 50
University of Alaska Fairbanks, **(B, M, D)**, 51
University of Alaska Southeast, **(A, B, M, C)**, 52

ARIZONA

American Indian College of the Assemblies of God, **(A, B)**, 53
Arizona State University, **(B, M, D, P)**, 53
Arizona State University at the West Campus, **(B, A)**, 56
DeVry University-Arizona, **(A, B, M)**, 56
Embry Riddle Aeronautical University, **(A, B)**, 56
Grand Canyon University, **(B, M)**, 57
Northern Arizona University, **(A, B, M, D, C)**, 57
Prescott College, **(B, M)**, 58
Southwestern College, **(A, B)**, 59
Thunderbird School of Global Management, **(M, C)**, 59
University of Advancing Technology, **(A, B, M)**, 60
University of Arizona, **(B, M, D, P)**, 61
University of Phoenix, **(B, M, D)**, 62
Western International University, **(A, B, M)**, 63

ARKANSAS

Arkansas Baptist College, **(B)**, 64
Arkansas State University, **(A, B, M, D, C)**, 64
Arkansas Tech University, **(A, B, M)**, 65
Central Baptist College, **(A, B)**, 66
Harding University, **(B, M, D)**, 66
Henderson State University, **(A, B, M)**, 67
Hendrix College, **(B)**, 68
John Brown University, **(B, M)**, 69
Lyon College, **(B)**, 70
Ouachita Baptist University, **(A, B)**, 70
Philander Smith College, **(B)**, 71
Southern Arkansas University, **(A, B, M)**, 71
University of Arkansas at Fayetteville, **(B, M, D, P)**, 72
University of Arkansas at Fort Smith, **(A, B, C)**, 74
University of Arkansas at Little Rock, **(A, B, M, P, C)**, 74
University of Arkansas at Monticello, **(A, B, M)**, 75
University of Arkansas at Pine Bluff, **(A, B, M)**, 76
University of Arkansas for Medical Sciences, **(A, B, M, D, P)**, 77
University of Central Arkansas, **(A, B, M, C)**, 77
University of the Ozarks, **(A, B, M)**, 78
Williams Baptist College, **(A, B)**, 78

CALIFORNIA

Academy of Art University, **(A, B, M)**, 80
Alliant International University - Fresno, **(M, D)**, 80
Alliant International University - Los Angeles, **(M, D)**, 81
Alliant International University - San Diego, **(B, M, D, C)**, 81
Alliant International University - San Francisco, **(M, D)**, 81
American Baptist Seminary of the West, **(M, D, P)**, 82
American Conservatory Theater, **(M, C)**, 82
American Film Institute Conservatory, **(M, C)**, 82
American Jewish University, **(B, M, D, P)**, 83
Antioch University - Los Angeles, **(B, M)**, 83
Antioch University - Santa Barbara, **(B, M)**, 84
Art Center College of Design, **(B, M)**, 84
Art Institute of California - Los Angeles, **(A, B)**, 85
Art Institute of California - San Diego, **(A, B)**, 85
Art Institute of California - San Francisco, **(A, B)**, 85
Azusa Pacific University, **(A, B, M, D)**, 86
Bethany University, **(A, B, M, C)**, 87
Biola University, **(B, M, D, P)**, 87

A=Associate; **B**=Baccalaureate; **M**=Master's; **D**=Doctorate; **P**=First Professional; **C**=Certificate

CALIFORNIA *(Cont'd)*

CALIFORNIA *(Cont'd)*

University of San Diego, **(B, M, D, P, C)**, 164
University of San Francisco, **(B, M, D, P)**, 165
University of Southern California, **(B, M, D, P)**, 166
University of the Pacific, **(B, M, D, P, C)**, 164
University of West Los Angeles, **(B, P)**, 169
Vanguard University of Southern California, **(B, M)**, 169
Western State University College of Law, **(P)**, 170
Western University of Health Sciences, **(M, D, P, C)**, 170
Westminster Seminary California, **(M, P)**, 171
Westmont College, **(B)**, 171
Whittier College, **(B, M, P)**, 172
William Jessup University, **(A, B, C)**, 173
Woodbury University, **(B, M)**, 173
Wright Institute, **(M, D)**, 174

COLORADO

Adams State College, **(A, B, M)**, 175
Colorado Christian University, **(A, B, M)**, 176
Colorado College, **(B, M)**, 176
Colorado School of Mines, **(B, M, D)**, 177
Colorado State University, **(B, M, D, P)**, 178
Colorado State University - Pueblo, **(B, M)**, 179
Colorado Technical University, **(A, B, M, D)**, 180
Denver Seminary, **(M, D, P, C)**, 180
Fort Lewis College, **(A, B)**, 181
Iliff School of Theology, **(M, D, P)**, 182
ITT Technical Institute, **(A, B)**, 182
Mesa State College, **(A, B, M, C)**, 183
Metropolitan State College of Denver, **(B)**, 183
Naropa University, **(B, M)**, 184
National Theatre Conservatory, **(M)**, 185
Nazarene Bible College, **(B)**, 185
Regis University, **(B, M)**, 186
United States Air Force Academy, **(B)**, 186
University of Colorado at Boulder, **(B, M, D, P)**, 187
University of Colorado at Colorado Springs, **(B, M, D)**, 188
University of Colorado at Denver and Health Sciences Center-Downtown Denver Campus, **(B, M, D)**, 189
University of Colorado at Denver and Health Sciences Center-Health Sciences Program, **(B, M, D, P)**, 190
University of Denver, **(B, M, D, P, C)**, 191
University of Northern Colorado, **(B, M, D, C)**, 191
Western State College of Colorado, **(B)**, 192

CONNECTICUT

Albertus Magnus College, **(A, B, M)**, 194
Central Connecticut State University, **(B, M, D, C)**, 194
Charter Oak State College, **(A, B)**, 195
Connecticut College, **(B, M)**, 196
Eastern Connecticut State University, **(A, B, M)**, 196
Fairfield University, **(B, M)**, 197
Hartford Seminary, **(M, D)**, 198
Holy Apostles College and Seminary, **(A, B, P, C)**, 199
Lyme Academy College of Fine Arts, **(B, C)**, 199
Mitchell College, **(A, B)**, 200
Paier College of Art, **(B, C)**, 200
Post University, **(A, B, C)**, 200
Quinnipiac College, **(B, M, P, C)**, 201
Rensselaer at Hartford, **(M)**, 202
Sacred Heart University, **(A, B, M, C)**, 202
Saint Joseph College, **(B, M, C)**, 203
Southern Connecticut State University, **(A, B, M, D)**, 204
Trinity College, **(B, M)**, 205
United States Coast Guard Academy, **(B)**, 205
University of Bridgeport, **(A, B, M, D, P)**, 206
University of Connecticut, **(B, M, D, P, C)**, 207
University of Hartford, **(A, B, M, D, C)**, 209
University of New Haven, **(A, B, M, D)**, 210
Wesleyan University, **(B, M, D)**, 211
Western Connecticut State University, **(A, B, M)**, 212
Yale University, **(B, M, D, P)**, 212

DELAWARE

Delaware State University, **(B, M)**, 215
Goldey-Beacom College, **(A, B, C)**, 215
University of Delaware, **(A, B, M, D)**, 216
Wesley College, **(A, B, M)**, 218
Widener University - Delaware Campus, **(A, B, D, P)**, 218
Wilmington University, **(A, B, M)**, 219

DISTRICT OF COLUMBIA

American University, **(A, B, M, D, P)**, 220
Catholic University of America,
Corcoran College of Art and Design, **(B, M, C)**, 222
Dominican House of Studies, **(P)**, 223
Gallaudet University, **(A, B, M, D)**, 224
George Washington University, **(A, B, M, D, P, C)**, 224
Georgetown University, **(B, M, D, P)**, 226
Howard University, **(B, M, D, P)**, 228
Joint Military Intelligence College, **(B, M, C)**, 230
Potomac College, **(B)**, 230
Southeastern University, **(A, B, M, C)**, 230
Strayer College, **(A, B, M, C)**, 231
Trinity University, **(B, M)**, 232
University of the District of Columbia, **(A, B, M)**, 232
Washington Theological Union, **(M, P)**, 233
Wesley Theological Seminary, **(M, D, P)**, 234

FLORIDA

Baptist College of Florida, **(A, B)**, 235
Barry University, **(B, M, D)**, 235
Bethune-Cookman University, **(B)**, 236
Clearwater Christian College, **(A, B)**, 237
Eckerd College, **(B)**, 237
Edward Waters College, **(B)**, 238
Embry-Riddle Aeronautical University, **(A, B, M)**, 239
Flagler College, **(B)**, 240
Florida Agricultural and Mechanical University, **(A, B, M, D, P)**, 240
Florida Atlantic University, **(A, B, M, D)**, 241
Florida Christian College, **(A, B)**, 242
Florida College, **(A, B)**, 242
Florida Gulf Coast University, **(B, M)**, 242
Florida Institute of Technology, **(A, B, M, D)**, 243
Florida International University, **(B, M, D, C)**, 244
Florida Memorial College, **(B)**, 244
Florida Metropolitan College, **(A, B, M)**, 245
Florida Southern College, **(B, M)**, 246
Florida State University, **(A, B, M, D, P)**, 246

FLORIDA *(Cont'd)*

Hobe Sound Bible College, **(A, B)**, 249
Hodges University, **(A, B, M)**, 249
International Academy of Design and Technology, **(A, B)**, 250
Jacksonville University, **(B, M)**, 250
Jones College, **(A, B, C)**, 251
Lynn University, **(B, M)**, 251
Nova Southeastern University, **(B, M, D, P)**, 252
Palm Beach Atlantic University, **(A, B, M, D)**, 253
Ringling School of Art and Design, **(B)**, 253
Rollins College, **(B, M)**, 254
St. John Vianney College Seminary, **(B)**, 255
Saint Leo University, **(A, B, M)**, 255
St. Petersburg College, **(A, B)**, 257
St. Thomas University, **(B, M, P)**, 256
St. Vincent de Paul Regional Seminary, **(M, P)**, 257
Schiller International University, **(B, M)**, 257
Southeastern University, **(B, M)**, 258
Stetson University, **(B, M, P)**, 258
University of Central Florida, **(A, B, M, D, C)**, 259
University of Florida, **(A, B, M, D, P, C)**, 260
University of Miami, **(B, M, D, P)**, 263
University of North Florida, **(B, M, D)**, 265
University of South Florida, **(A, B, M, D)**, 266
University of Tampa, **(A, B, M)**, 267
University of West Florida, **(A, B, M, D)**, 268
Warner University, **(A, B)**, 269
Webber International University, **(A, B, M)**, 270

GEORGIA

Agnes Scott College, **(B, M)**, 271
Albany State University, **(B, M)**, 271
American Intercontinental University, **(A, B, M)**, 272
Armstrong Atlantic State University, **(A, B, M, D, C)**, 273
Art Institute of Atlanta, **(A, B)**, 273
Atlanta Christian College, **(A, B)**, 274
Atlanta College of Art, **(B)**, 274
Augusta State University, **(A, B, M, C)**, 275
Berry College, **(B, M, C)**, 276
Beulah Heights University, **(A, B, M)**, 277
Brenau University, **(B, M)**, 277
Brewton-Parker College, **(A, B)**, 278
Clark Atlanta University, **(B, M, D)**, 278
Clayton State University, **(A, B)**, 279
Columbia Theological Seminary, **(M, D, P)**, 280
Columbus State University, **(A, B, M)**, 280
Covenant College, **(A, B, M)**, 281
Emmanuel College, **(A, B)**, 282
Emory University, **(B, M, D, P)**, 282
Fort Valley State University, **(A, B, M)**, 283
Georgia College and State University, **(B, M)**, 284
Georgia Institute of Technology, **(B, M, D)**, 285
Georgia Southern University, **(B, M, D, C)**, 286
Georgia Southwestern State University, **(A, B, M, C)**, 287
Georgia State University, **(A, B, M, D)**, 288
Interdenominational Theological Center, **(M, D, P)**, 289
Kennesaw State University, **(B, M)**, 289
LaGrange College, **(A, B, M)**, 290
Life University, **(B, M, P)**, 291
Macon State College, **(A, B)**, 291
Medical College of Georgia, **(A, B, M, D, P)**, 292
Mercer University, **(B, M, D, P)**, 292
Morehouse College, **(B)**, 293
Morehouse School of Medicine, **(M, D, P)**, 294
North Georgia College and State University, **(A, B, M, C)**, 294
Oglethorpe University, **(B, M)**, 295
Paine College, **(B)**, 296
Piedmont College, **(B, M)**, 296
Reinhardt College, **(A, B)**, 297
Savannah College of Art and Design, **(B, M)**, 297
Savannah State University, **(B, M)**, 298
Shorter College, **(B, M)**, 299
South University, **(A, B, M, P)**, 299
Southern Polytechnic State University, **(A, B, M)**, 300
Spelman College, **(B)**, 300
Thomas University, **(A, B)**, 301
Toccoa Falls College, **(A, B)**, 302
University of Georgia, **(B, M, D, P, C)**, 302
University of West Georgia, **(B, M, D, C)**, 303
Valdosta State University, **(A, B, M, D, C)**, 304
Wesleyan College, **(B, M)**, 305

GUAM

University of Guam,

HAWAII

Brigham Young University - Hawaii Campus, **(A, B, C)**, 306
Chaminade University of Honolulu, **(A, B, M)**, 306
Hawaii Pacific University, **(A, B, M)**, 307
University of Hawaii at Hilo, **(B, M)**, 308
University of Hawaii at Manoa, **(A, B, M, D, P, C)**, 309
University of Hawaii at West Oahu, **(B)**, 311

IDAHO

Boise Bible College, **(A, B)**, 312
Boise State University, **(A, B, M, D)**, 312
College of Idaho, **(B, M)**, 313
Idaho State University, **(A, B, M, D)**, 314
Lewis-Clark State College, **(A, B)**, 315
New Saint Andrews College, **(A, B)**, 316
Northwest Nazarene University, **(A, B, M)**, 316
University of Idaho, **(B, M, D, P)**, 317

ILLINOIS

Adler School of Professional Psychology, **(M, D)**, 319
Augustana College, **(B)**, 319
Aurora University, **(B, M, D)**, 320
Benedictine University, **(B, M)**, 321
Blackburn College, **(B, M)**, 321
Bradley University, **(B, M, D)**, 322
Chicago School of Professional Psychology, **(D)**, 323
Chicago State University, **(B, M)**, 323
Chicago Theological Seminary, **(M, D, P)**, 324
Columbia College Chicago, **(B, M)**, 324
Concordia University River Forest, **(B, M, D)**, 325
DePaul University, **(B, M, D, P, C)**, 326
DeVry University, **(B, M)**, 327
Dominican University, **(B, M)**, 327
Dr. William M. Scholl College of Podiatric Medicine, **(B, P)**, 327
Eastern Illinois University, **(B, M)**, 329

ILLINOIS *(Cont'd)*

East-West University, **(A, B)**, 329
Elmhurst College, **(B, M)**, 330
Erikson Institute, **(D)**, 331
Eureka College, **(B)**, 331
Garrett-Evangelical Theological Seminary, **(M, D, P)**, 331
Governors State University, **(B, M)**, 332
Greenville College, **(B, M)**, 333
Harrington College of Design, **(A, B)**, 334
Illinois College, **(B)**, 334
Illinois College of Optometry, **(B, P)**, 335
Illinois Institute of Technology, **(B, M, D, P, C)**, 335
Illinois State University, **(B, M, D)**, 336
Illinois Wesleyan University, **(B)**, 337
John Marshall Law School, **(M, P)**, 338
Judson University, **(B, M)**, 338
Keller Graduate School of Management of DeVry University, **(M)**, 339
Kendall College, **(A, B)**, 339
Knox College, **(B)**, 340
Lake Forest College, **(B, M)**, 341
Lake Forest Graduate School of Management, **(M)**, 342
Lewis University, **(A, B, M, C)**, 342
Lincoln Christian College, **(A, B, M, P)**, 343
Loyola University Chicago, **(B, M, D, P)**, 343
Lutheran School of Theology at Chicago, **(M, D, P)**, 345
MacMurray College, **(A, B)**, 346
McCormick Theological Seminary, **(M, D, P, C)**, 345
McKendree University, **(B, M)**, 346
Meadville-Lombard Theological School, **(M, D, P)**, 347
Mennonite College of Nursing,
Midstate College, **(A, B, C)**, 348
Midwestern University, **(B, M, P)**, 348
Millikin University, **(B, M)**, 348
Monmouth College, **(B)**, 350
Moody Bible Institute, **(A, B, M)**, 350
NAES College, **(B)**, 351
National University of Health Sciences, **(B, P)**, 351
National-Louis University, **(B, M, D, C)**, 352
North Central College, **(B, M)**, 352
North Park University, **(B, M, D, P)**, 353
Northeastern Illinois University, **(B, M)**, 354
Northern Illinois University, **(B, M, D, P, C)**, 355
Northern Seminary, **(M, D, P)**, 356
Northwestern University, **(B, M, D, P, C)**, 356
Olivet Nazarene University, **(A, B, M)**, 358
Principia College, **(B)**, 359
Quincy University, **(A, B, M)**, 359
Robert Morris College, **(A, B)**, 360
Rockford College, **(B, M)**, 361
Roosevelt University, **(B, M, D, C)**, 361
Rosalind Franklin University of Medicine and Science, **(B, M, D, P)**, 363
Rush University, **(B, M, D, P)**, 363
Saint Anthony College of Nursing, **(B)**, 364
Saint Francis Medical Center College of Nursing, **(B, M)**, 364
St. John's College, **(B)**, 365
Saint Xavier University, **(B, M)**, 365
School of the Art Institute of Chicago, **(B, M, C)**, 366
Seabury-Western Theological Seminary, **(M, P, C)**, 366
Southern Illinois University Carbondale, **(A, B, M, D, P)**, 367
Southern Illinois University Edwardsville, **(B, M, P, C)**, 368
Spertus College, **(M, D)**, 369
Telshe Yeshiva-Chicago, **(P)**, 369
Trinity Christian College, **(B)**, 370
Trinity International University, **(B, M, D)**, 370
University of Chicago, **(B, M, D, P)**, 371
University of Illinois at Chicago, **(B, M, D, P)**, 372
University of Illinois at Springfield, **(B, M)**, 374
University of Illinois at Urbana-Champaign, **(B, M, D, P, C)**, 375
University of St. Francis, **(B, M)**, 377
University of St. Mary of the Lake - Mundelein Seminary, **(M, D, P)**, 378
VanderCook College of Music, **(B, M)**, 378
Western Illinois University, **(B. M, D, C)**, 379
Wheaton College, **(B, M, D)**, 380

INDIANA

Anderson University, **(A, B, M, D, P)**, 382
Associated Mennonite Biblical Seminary, **(M, P)**, 383
Ball State University, **(A, B, M, D)**, 383
Bethany Theological Seminary, **(M, P)**, 384
Bethel College, **(A, B, M)**, 384
Butler University, **(A, B, M, P, C)**, 385
Calumet College of Saint Joseph, **(A, B, M, C)**, 386
Christian Theological Seminary, **(M, D, P)**, 386
Concordia Theological Seminary, **(M, D, P)**, 387
DePauw University, **(B)**, 387
Earlham College, **(B, M P)**, 388
Franklin College, **(B)**, 389
Goshen College, **(B)**, 390
Grace College and Theological Seminary, **(A, B, M, P, C)**, 391
Hanover College, **(B)**, 391
Huntington University, **(B)**, 392
Indiana Institute of Technology, **(A, B, M)**, 393
Indiana State University, **(A, B, M, D, C)**, 394
Indiana University Bloomington, **(A, B, M, D, P, C)**, 396
Indiana University East, **(A, B, C)**, 397
Indiana University Kokomo, **(A, B, M)**, 398
Indiana University Northwest, **(A, B, M)**, 399
Indiana University - Purdue University Fort Wayne, **(A, B, M)**, 399
Indiana University - Purdue University Indianapolis, **(A, B, M, D, P)**, 400
Indiana University South Bend, **(A, B, M)**, 402
Indiana University Southeast, **(A, B, M)**, 402
Indiana Wesleyan University, **(A, B, M, D)**, 403
Indiana University, **(A, B, M, D, P, C)**, 395
ITT Technical Institute, **(A, B, M)**, 404
Manchester College, **(A, B)**, 404
Marian College, **(A, B)**, 405
Martin University, **(B, M)**, 406
Oakland City University, **(A, B. M, D, P)**, 406
Purdue University, **(A, B, M, D, P)**, 407
Purdue University Calumet, **(A, B, M)**, 409
Purdue University North Central, **(A, B)**, 409
Rose-Hulman Institute of Technology, **(B, M, C)**, 410
Saint Joseph's College, **(A, B, M)**, 410
Saint Mary-of-the-Woods College, **(A, B, M)**, 411
Saint Mary's College, **(B)**, 412
Saint Meinrad School of Theology, **(M, P)**, 413
Taylor University, **(A, B)**, 413

INDIANA *(Cont'd)*

Trine University, **(A, B)**, 414
University of Evansville, **(A, B, M)**, 415
University of Indianapolis, **(A, B, M, D)**, 416
University of Notre Dame, **(B, M, D, P)**, 417
University of Saint Francis, **(A, B, M)**, 418
University of Southern Indiana, **(A, B, M)**, 419
Valparaiso University, **(A, B, M, P, C)**, 420
Wabash College, **(B)**, 421

IOWA

Allen College, **(A, B, M)**, 423
Ashford University, **(B, M)**, 423
Briar Cliff University, **(A, B, M)**, 424
Buena Vista University, **(B, M)**, 425
Central College, **(B)**, 425
Clarke College, **(A, B, M)**, 426
Coe College, **(B, M)**, 427
Cornell College, **(B)**, 428
Des Monies University - Osteopathic Medical Center, **(M, P)**, 429
Divine Word College, **(A, B)**, 429
Dordt College, **(A, B, M, C)**, 430
Drake University, **(B, M, D, P)**, 430
Emmaus Bible College, **(B)**, 431
Faith Baptist Bible College and Theological Seminary, **(A, B, M, C)**, 432
Graceland University, **(B, M, C)**, 432
Grand View College, **(A, B)**, 433
Grinnell College, **(B)**, 434
Iowa State University of Science and Technology, **(B, M, D, P, C)**, 435
Iowa Wesleyan College, **(B)**, 436
Kaplan University, **(A, B)**, 437
Loras College, **(A, B, M)**, 437
Luther College, **(B)**, 438
Maharishi University of Management, **(B, M, D)**, 439
Mercy College of Health Sciences, **(A, B)**, 439
Morningside College, **(A, B, M)**, 440
Mount Mercy College, **(B)**, 440
Northwestern College, **(A, B)**, 441
Palmer College of Chiropractic, **(A, B, M, P)**, 442
St. Ambrose University, **(B, M, D)**, 442
Simpson College, **(B, M)**, 443
University of Dubuque, **(A, B, M, P)**, 444
University of Iowa, **(B, M, D, P, C)**, 445
University of Northern Iowa, **(B, M, D, C)**, 446
Upper Iowa University, **(B, M)**, 446
Vennard College, **(A, B)**, 447
Waldorf College, **(B)**, 448
Wartburg College, **(B)**, 448
Wartburg Theological Seminary, **(P)**, 449
William Penn University, **(B)**, 449

KANSAS

Baker University, **(B, M)**, 451
Barclay College, **(A, B)**, 451
Benedictine College, **(A, B, M)**, 452
Bethany College, **(B)**, 453
Bethel College, **(B)**, 453
Central Baptist Theological Seminary, **(M, P)**, 454
Central Christian College of Kansas, **(A, B)**, 455
Emporia State University, **(B, M, D, C)**, 455
Fort Hays State University, **(A, B, M, C)**, 456
Friends University, **(A, B, M)**, 457
Kansas State University, **(A, B, M, D, P)**, 457
Kansas Wesleyan University, **(A, B)**, 459
Manhattan Christian College, **(A, B)**, 460
McPherson College, **(A, B)**, 460
MidAmerica Nazarene College, **(A, B, M)**, 461
Newman University, **(A, B, M)**, 462
Ottawa University, **(B)**, 463
Pittsburg State University, **(A, B, M, C)**, 463
Southwestern College, **(B, M)**, 464
Sterling College, **(B)**, 465
Tabor College, **(A, B, M)**, 466
United States Army Command and General Staff College, **(M, C)**, 467
University of Kansas, **(B, M, D, P, C)**, 467
University of Saint Mary, **(A, B, M)**, 469
Washburn University, **(A, B, M, P)**, 470
Wichita State University, **(A, B, M, D, C)**, 471

KENTUCKY

Alice Lloyd College, **(A, B)**, 473
Asbury College, **(B, M)**, 473
Asbury Theological Seminary, **(M, D, P)**, 474
Bellarmine University, **(A, B, M, C)**, 474
Berea College, **(B)**, 475
Brescia University, **(A, B, M, C)**, 476
Campbellsville University, **(A, B, M, C)**, 477
Centre College, **(B)**, 477
Clear Creek Baptist Bible College, **(B)**, 478
Eastern Kentucky University, **(A, B, M, C)**, 479
Georgetown College, **(B, M)**, 480
Kentucky Christian College, **(A, B)**, 480
Kentucky Mountain Bible College, **(A, B)**, 481
Kentucky State University, **(A, B, M)**, 481
Kentucky Wesleyan College, **(B)**, 482
Lexington Theological Seminary, **(M, D)**, 483
Lindsey Wilson College, **(A, B, M)**, 483
Louisville Presbyterian Theological Seminary, **(M, D, P)**, 484
Mid-Continent University, **(B)**, 485
Midway College, **(A, B)**, 485
Morehead State University, **(A, B, M, D, C)**, 486
Murray State University, **(A, B, M, D, C)**, 487
Northern Kentucky University, **(A, B, M, P)**, 487
Pikeville College, **(A, B, P C)**, 488
Southern Baptist Theological Seminary, **(M, D, P)**, 489
Spalding University, **(B, M, D, C)**, 490
Sullivan University, **(A, B, M)**, 490
Thomas More College, **(A, B, M, C)**, 491
Transylvania University, **(B)**, 492
Union College, **(A, B, M, C)**, 492
University of Kentucky, **(B, M, D, P, C)**, 494
University of Louisville, **(A, B, M, D, P, C)**, 496
University of the Cumberlands, **(B, M)**, 493
Western Kentucky University, **(A, B, M, C)**, 497

LOUISIANA

Centenary College of Louisiana, **(B, M)**, 499

LOUISIANA *(Cont'd)*

Dillard University, **(B)**, 500
Grambling State University, **(A, B, M, D)**, 500
Louisiana College, **(B)**, 501
Louisiana State University and Agricultural and Mechanical College, **(B, M, D, P, C)**, 502
Louisiana State University Health Sciences Center at New Orleans, **(A, B, M, D, P)**, 504
Louisiana State University in Shreveport, **(B, M, C)**, 505
Louisiana Tech University, **(A, B, M, D)**, 506
Loyola University New Orleans, **(B, M, P)**, 507
McNeese State University, **(A, B, M, C)**, 508
New Orleans Baptist Theological Seminary, **(A, M, D, P)**, 508
Nicholls State University, **(A, B, M, C)**, 509
Northwestern State University of Louisiana, **(A, B, M)**, 510
Notre Dame Seminary Graduate School of Theology, **(M, P)**, 510
Our Lady of the Holy Cross College, **(A, B, M)**, 511
Our Lady of the Lake College, **(A, B, M)**, 511
St. Joseph Seminary College, **(B)**, 512
Southeastern Louisiana University, **(A, B, M)**, 513
Southern University and A&M College, **(A, B, M, D, P, C)**, 514
Southern University at New Orleans, **(A, B, M)**, 515
Tulane University, **(B, M, D, P)**, 515
University of Louisiana at Lafayette, **(A, B, M, D)**, 517
University of Louisiana at Monroe, **(A, B, M, D, C)**, 518
University of New Orleans, **(A, B, M, D)**, 519
Xavier University of Louisiana, **(B, M, P)**, 520

MAINE

Bangor Theological Seminary, **(M, D, P)**, 521
Bates College, **(B)**, 521
Bowdoin College, **(B)**, 522
Colby College, **(B)**, 523
College of the Atlantic, **(B, M)**, 524
Husson College, **(A, B, M, D)**, 525
Maine College of Art, **(B)**, 525
Maine Maritime Academy, **(A, B, M)**, 526
Saint Joseph's College, **(B)**, 527
Thomas College, **(A, B, M)**, 527
Unity College, **(A, B)**, 528
University of Maine, **(B, M, D, C)**, 529
University of Maine at Augusta, **(A, B)**, 530
University of Maine at Farmington, **(B)**, 530
University of Maine at Fort Kent, **(A, B)**, 531
University of Maine at Machias, **(B)**, 532
University of Maine at Presque Isle, **(A, B, C)**, 532
University of New England, **(A, B, M, P)**, 533
University of Southern Maine, **(A, B, M, P)**, 534

MARYLAND

Baltimore Hebrew University, **(B, M, D)**, 536
Baltimore International College, **(B)**, 536
Bowie State University, **(B, M, D, C)**, 536
Capitol College, **(A, B, M)**, 537
College of Notre Dame of Maryland, **(B, M)**, 538
Columbia Union College, **(A, B, M, C)**, 539
Coppin State University, **(B, M)**, 539
Frostburg State University, **(B, M)**, 540
Goucher College, **(B)**, 541
Hood College, **(B, M)**, 542
Johns Hopkins University, **(A, B, M, D, P)**, 542
Loyola College in Maryland, **(B, M, D)**, 544
Maryland Institute College of Art, **(B, M)**, 545
McDaniel College, **(B, M)**, 545
Morgan State University, **(B, M, D)**, 546
Mount Saint Mary's University, **(B, M, P)**, 547
St. John's College, **(B, M)**, 547
St. Mary's College of Maryland, **(B)**, 548
St. Mary's Seminary and University, **(B, M. D, P)**, 549
Salisbury University, **(B, M)**, 549
Sojourner-Douglass College, **(B)**, 550
Stevenson University, **(A, B, M)**, 551
Towson University, **(B, M, D, C)**, 551
Uniformed Services University of the Health Sciences, **(M, D, P)**, 552
United States Naval Academy, **(B)**, 553
University of Baltimore, **(B, M, D, P, C)**, 553
University of Maryland Baltimore, **(B, M, D, P)**, 554
University of Maryland Baltimore County, **(B, M, D)**, 555
University of Maryland College Park, **(B, M, D, P, C)**, 556
University of Maryland Eastern Shore, **(B, M, D)**, 557
University of Maryland University College, **(A, B, M, D)**, 557
Washington Bible College - Capital Bible Seminary, **(A, B, M, P)**, 558
Washington College, **(B, M)**, 558

MASSACHUSETTS

American International College, **(A, B, M, C)**, 560
Amherst College, **(B)**, 561
Andover Newton Theological School, **(M, D, P)**, 561
Anna Maria College, **(A, B, M)**, 562
Assumption College, **(A, B, M)**, 563
Atlantic Union College, **(A, B, M)**, 563
Babson College, **(B, M)**, 564
Bay Path College, **(A, B)**, 565
Bentley College, **(B, M)**, 566
Berklee College of Music, **(B)**, 566
Blessed John XXIII National Seminary, **(M, P)**, 567
Boston Architectural College, **(B, M)**, 567
Boston College, **(B, M, D, P)**, 568
Boston Conservatory, **(B, M, C)**, 569
Boston University, **(A, B, M, D, P, C)**, 570
Brandeis University, **(B, M, D)**, 571
Bridgewater State College, **(B, M)**, 572
Cambridge College, **(B, M)**, 572
Clark University, **(B, M, D)**, 573
College of Our Lady of the Elms, **(A, B, M)**, 575
College of the Holy Cross, **(B)**, 574
Curry College, **(B)**, 575
Eastern Nazarene College, **(A, B, M)**, 576
Emerson College, **(B, M, D)**, 577
Emmanuel College, **(B, M)**, 578
Endicott College, **(A, B, M)**, 578
Episcopal Divinity School, **(M, D, P)**, 579
Fisher College, **(A, B, C)**, 579
Fitchburg State College,
Framingham State College, **(B, M)**, 580
Gordon College, **(B, M)**, 581
Gordon-Conwell Theological Seminary, **(M, D, P)**, 582
Hampshire College, **(B)**, 582
Harvard University, **(A, B, M, D, P, C)**, 583

A=Associate; **B**=Baccalaureate; **M**=Master's; **D**=Doctorate; **P**=First Professional; **C**=Certificate

MASSACHUSETTS *(Cont'd)*

Hebrew College, **(B, M)**, 585
Hellenic College/Holy Cross Greek Orthodox School of Theology, **(B, M, P)**, 585
Hult International Business School, **(M)**, 585
Lasell College, **(B, M)**, 586
Lesley University, **(A, B, M, D, C)**, 586
Massachusetts College of Art and Design, **(B, M, C)**, 587
Massachusetts College of Liberal Arts, **(B, M)**, 588
Massachusetts College of Pharmacy and Health Sciences, **(B, M, D, P, C)**, 589
Massachusetts Institute of Technology, **(B, M, D)**, 589
Massachusetts Maritime Academy, **(B,)**, 590
Merrimack College, **(A, B, M)**, 591
MGH Institute of Health Professions, **(M, D, C)**, 592
Montserrat College of Art, **(B, C)**, 592
Mount Holyoke College, **(B)**, 593
Mount Ida College, **(A, B)**, 593
New England College of Optometry, **(B, P)**, 594
New England Conservatory of Music, **(B, M, D)**, 594
Nichols College, **(A, B, M)**, 595
Northeastern University, **(B, M, D, P)**, 596
Pine Manor College, **(A, B)**, 597
Regis College, **(A, B, M, C)**, 597
Saint John's Seminary, **(M, P)**, 598
Salem State College, **(B, M)**, 599
School of the Museum of Fine Arts, Boston, **(B, M, C)**, 599
Simmons College, **(B, M, D, C)**, 600
Simon's Rock College of Bard, **(A, B)**, 601
Smith College, **(B, M, D)**, 602
Southern New England School of Law, **(P)**, 602
Springfield College, **(B, M, D)**, 603
Stonehill College, **(B, M)**, 604
Suffolk University, **(A, B, M, D, P)**, 604
Tufts University, **(B, M, D, P)**, 605
University of Massachusetts Amherst, **(A, B, M, D)**, 607
University of Massachusetts Boston, **(B, M, D, C)**, 608
University of Massachusetts Dartmouth, **(B, M, D)**, 609
University of Massachusetts Lowell, **(A, B, M, D)**, 610
University of Massachusetts Medical School, **(M, D, P)**, 611
Wellesley College, **(B)**, 611
Wentworth Institute of Technology, **(A, B, C)**, 612
Western New England College, **(A, B, M, P)**, 613
Westfield State College, **(B, M)**, 613
Weston Jesuit School of Theology, **(M, P)**, 614
Wheaton College, **(B)**, 614
Wheelock College, **(B, M, C)**, 615
Williams College, **(B, M)**, 616
Worcester Polytechnic Institute, **(B, M, D)**, 617
Worcester State College, **(B, M)**, 618

MICHIGAN

Adrian College, **(A, B)**, 619
Albion College, **(B)**, 619
Alma College, **(B)**, 620
Andrews University, **(A, B, M, D, P, C)**, 621
Aquinas College, **(B, M)**, 622
Calvin College, **(B, M)**, 623
Calvin Theological Seminary, **(M, D, P)**, 624
Central Michigan University, **(B, M, D, C)**, 624
Cleary University, **(A, B, M)**, 625
College for Creative Studies, **(B)**, 625
Concordia University, Ann Arbor, **(B, M)**, 626
Cornerstone University, **(A, B, M, P)**, 626
Cranbrook Academy of Art,
Davenport University, **(A, B, M)**, 627
Eastern Michigan University, **(B, M, D, C)**, 628
Ferris State University, **(A, B, M, P, C)**, 629
Grace Bible College, **(A, B)**, 630
Grand Valley State University, **(B, M)**, 630
Great Lakes Christian College, **(A, B)**, 631
Hillsdale College, **(B)**, 631
Hope College, **(B)**, 632
Kalamazoo College, **(B)**, 633
Kettering University, **(B, M)**, 634
Kuyper College, **(A, B)**, 634
Lake Superior State University, **(A, B, M)**, 635
Lawrence Technological University, **(A, B, M)**, 636
Madonna University, **(A, B, M)**, 636
Marygrove College, **(A, B, M)**, 637
Michigan State University, **(B, M, D, P, C)**, 638
Michigan Technological University, **(A, B, M, D, C)**, 640
Northern Michigan University, **(A, B)**, 641
Northwood University, **(A, B, C)**, 642
Oakland University, **(B, M, D, C)**, 643
Olivet College, **(B, M)**, 644
Rochester College, **(A, B)**, 645
Sacred Heart Major Seminary, **(B, M, P)**, 646
Saginaw Valley State University, **(B, M)**, 646
Siena Heights University, **(A, B, M)**, 647
Spring Arbor University, **(A, B, M)**, 648
University of Detroit Mercy, **(A, B, M, D, P, C)**, 649
University of Michigan - Ann Arbor, **(B, M, D, P, C)**, 649
University of Michigan - Dearborn, **(B, M)**, 652
University of Michigan - Flint, **(B, M, D)**, 653
Walsh College of Accountancy and Business Administration, **(B, M)**, 654
Wayne State University, **(B, M, D, P)**, 654
Western Michigan University,
Western Theological Seminary, **(M, D, P)**, 657

MINNESOTA

Augsburg College, **(B, M, C)**, 659
Bemidji State University, **(A, B, M)**, 659
Bethany Lutheran College, **(B)**, 660
Bethel University, **(A, B, M, D)**, 661
Carleton College, **(B)**, 662
College of Saint Benedict, **(B)**, 663
College of St. Catherine, **(A, B, M, D)**, 663
College of St. Scholastica, **(B, M, P)**, 664
College of Visual Arts, **(B, C.)**, 665
Concordia College - Moorhead, **(B, M)**, 665
Concordia University - St. Paul, **(A, B, M)**, 666
Crossroads College, **(A, B)**, 667
Crown College, **(A, B, M, C)**, 667
Gustavus Adolphus College, **(B)**, 668
Hamline University, **(B, M, D, P)**, 669
Luther Seminary, **(M, D, P)**, 670
Macalester College, **(B)**, 670
Metropolitan State University, **(B, M)**, 671

MINNESOTA *(Cont'd)*

Minneapolis College of Art and Design, **(B, M)**, 672
Minnesota State University - Mankato, **(A, B, M, C)**, 672
Minnesota State University - Moorhead, **(A, B, M)**, 673
North Central University, **(A, B)**, 674
Northwestern College, **(A, B, C)**, 674
Northwestern Health Sciences University, **(B, P)**, 675
Oak Hills Christian College, **(A, B)**, 676
St. Cloud State University, **(A, B, M, C)**, 676
Saint John's University, **(B, M, P)**, 677
Saint Mary's University of Minnesota, **(B, M, D)**, 678
St. Olaf College, **(B)**, 679
Southwest Minnesota State University, **(A, B)**, 680
United Theological Seminary of the Twin Cities, **(M, D, P)**, 681
University of Minnesota - Crookston, **(A, B)**, 681
University of Minnesota - Duluth, **(B, M)**, 682
University of Minnesota - Morris, **(B)**, 682
University of Minnesota - Twin Cities, **(B, M, D, P, C)**, 683
University of St. Thomas, **(B, M, D, P)**, 685
Walden University, **(B, M, D)**, 686
William Mitchell College of Law, **(P)**, 687
Winona State University, **(A, B, M)**, 687

MISSISSIPPI

Alcorn State University, **(A, B, M)**, 689
Belhaven College, **(A, B, M)**, 689
Blue Mountain College, **(B, M)**, 690
Delta State University, **(B, M, D, C)**, 691
Jackson State University, **(B, M, D, C)**, 691
Magnolia Bible College, **(B)**, 692
Millsaps College, **(B, M)**, 693
Mississippi College, **(B, M, D, P, C)**, 694
Mississippi State University, **(B, M, D, P, C)**, 694
Mississippi University for Women, **(A, B, M)**, 696
Mississippi Valley State University, **(B, M, C)**, 697
Reformed Theological Seminary, **(M, D, P, C)**, 697
Rust College, **(A, B)**, 698
Southeastern Baptist College, **(A, B)**, 698
Tougaloo College, **(A, B)**, 699
University of Mississippi, **(B, M, D, P)**, 699
University of Mississippi Medical Center, **(M, D, P, C)**, 700
University of Southern Mississippi, **(B, M, D)**, 701
Wesley College, **(B)**, 702
William Carey University, **(B, M)**, 702

MISSOURI

Aquinas Institute of Theology, **(M, D, P)**, 704
Assemblies of God Theological Seminary, **(M, D, P)**, 705
A.T. Still University of Health Science/Kirksville College of Osteopathic Medicine, **(P)**, 704
Avila University, **(B, M)**, 705
Calvary Bible College and Theological Seminary, **(A, B, M)**, 706
Central Bible College, **(A, B)**, 706
Central Christian College of the Bible, **(A, B)**, 707
Central Methodist University, **(A, B, M)**, 707
Cleveland Chiropractic College, **(P)**, 708
College of the Ozarks, **(B)**, 708
Columbia College, **(A, B, M)**, 709
Conception Seminary College, **(B)**, 710
Concordia Seminary, **(M, D, P)**, 711
Covenant Theological Seminary, **(M, D, P)**, 711
Culver-Stockton College, **(B)**, 712
Drury University,
Eden Theological Seminary, **(M, D, P)**, 713
Evangel University, **(A, B, M)**, 714
Fontbonne University, **(B, M)**, 714
Hannibal-LaGrange College, **(A, B, C)**, 715
Harris-Stowe State College, **(B)**, 716
Kansas City Art Institute, **(B)**, 716
Kansas City University of Medicine and Biosciences, **(M, P)**, 717
Kenrick-Glennon Seminary, **(M, P)**, 717
Lincoln University, **(A, B, M)**, 718
Lindenwood University, **(B, M)**, 718
Logan College of Chiropractic, **(B, M, P)**, 719
Maryville University of Saint Louis, **(B, M)**, 720
Midwestern Baptist Theological Seminary, **(M, D, P, C)**, 720
Missouri Baptist University, **(A, B)**, 721
Missouri Southern State University, **(A, B, M)**, 721
Missouri State University, **(A, B, M, C)**, 722
Missouri University of Science and Technology, **(B, M, D)**, 723
Missouri Valley College, **(A, B)**, 724
Missouri Western State University, **(A, B, C)**, 725
Nazarene Theological Seminary, **(M, D, P)**, 725
Northwest Missouri State University, **(B, M, C)**, 726
Ozark Christian College, **(A, B)**, 727
Park University, **(A, B, M)**, 727
Research College of Nursing, **(B, M)**, 728
Rockhurst University, **(B, M, D)**, 728
Saint Louis Christian College, **(A, B)**, 729
Saint Louis College of Pharmacy, **(M, P)**, 730
Saint Louis University, **(A, B, M, D, P, C)**, 730
Saint Luke's College, **(B)**, 731
Saint Paul School of Theology, **(M, D, P)**, 731
Southeast Missouri State University, **(A, B, M, C)**, 732
Southwest Baptist University, **(A, B, M, D, C)**, 733
Stephens College, **(A, B, M)**, 734
Truman State University, **(B, M)**, 734
University of Central Missouri, **(A, B, M, C)**, 735
University of Missouri - Columbia, **(B, M, D, P, C)**, 736
University of Missouri - Kansas City, **(B, M, D, P, C)**, 738
University of Missouri - St. Louis, **(B, M, D, P, C)**, 740
Washington University in St. Louis, **(B, M, D, P)**, 741
Webster University, **(B, M, D)**, 742
Westminster College, **(B)**, 742
William Jewell College, **(B)**, 743
William Woods University, **(B, M, C)**, 744

MONTANA

Carroll College, **(A, B)**, 746
Montana State University, **(B, M, D)**, 746
Montana State University - Billings, **(A, B, M)**, 747
Montana State University - Northern, **(A, B, M, C)**, 748
Montana Tech of the University of Montana, **(A, B, M)**, 749
Rocky Mountain College, **(A, B, M)**, 749
University of Great Falls, **(A, B, M)**, 750
University of Montana, **(A, B, M, D, P)**, 751
University of Montana - Western, **(A, B)**, 753

NEBRASKA

Bellevue University, **(B, M)**, 754

NEBRASKA *(Cont'd)*

Chadron State College, **(B, M, C)**, 754
Clarkson College, **(A, B, M)**, 755
College of Saint Mary, **(A, B, M)**, 756
Concordia University, **(B, M)**, 756
Creighton University, **(A, B, M, D, P)**, 757
Dana College, **(B)**, 759
Doane College, **(B, M)**, 759
Grace University, **(A, B, M)**, 760
Hastings College, **(B, M)**, 761
Midland Lutheran College, **(A, B)**, 761
Nebraska Christian College, **(B, M)**, 762
Nebraska Wesleyan University, **(B, M)**, 763
Peru State College, **(B, M)**, 763
Union College, **(A, B)**, 764
University of Nebraska at Kearney, **(B, M, C)**, 767
University of Nebraska at Omaha, **(B, M, D, C)**, 768
University of Nebraska - Lincoln, **(A, B, M, D, P, C)**, 765
University of Nebraska Medical Center, **(B, M, D, P, C)**, 769
Wayne State College, **(B, M, C)**, 770
York College, **(A, B)**, 771

NEVADA

Morrison University, **(A, B, C)**, 772
Sierra Nevada College, **(B, M)**, 772
University of Nevada, Las Vegas, **(A, B, M, D, C)**, 773
University of Nevada, Reno, **(B, M, D, P, C)**, 774

NEW HAMPSHIRE

Colby-Sawyer College, **(A, B)**, 776
Daniel Webster College, **(A, B)**, 776
Dartmouth College, **(B, M, D, P)**, 777
Franklin Pierce Law Center, **(M, P)**, 778
Franklin Pierce University, **(A, B, M, D)**, 779
Granite State College, **(A, B)**, 780
Keene State College, **(A, B, M)**, 780
New England College, **(B, M)**, 781
Plymouth State University, **(A, B, M)**, 782
Rivier College, **(A, B, M, C)**, 783
Saint Anselm College, **(A, B)**, 783
Southern New Hampshire University, **(A, B, M, C)**, 784
Thomas More College of Liberal Arts, **(B)**, 785
University of New Hampshire, **(A, B, M, D, C)**, 785

NEW JERSEY

Bloomfield College, **(B, C)**, 788
Caldwell College, **(B, M, C)**, 788
Centenary College, **(A, B, M)**, 789
College of New Jersey, **(B, M)**, 790
College of Saint Elizabeth, **(B, M)**, 791
Drew University, **(B, M, D, P)**, 792
Fairleigh Dickinson University, **(A, B, D)**, 792
Felician College, **(A, B, M)**, 793
Georgian Court University, **(B, M)**, 794
Immaculate Conception Seminary, **(M, P)**, 795
Kean University, **(B, M, C)**, 795
Monmouth University, **(B, M, C)**, 796
Montclair State University, **(B, M, C)**, 797
New Brunswick Theological Seminary, **(M, P)**, 798
New Jersey City University, **(B, M)**, 798
New Jersey Institute of Technology, **(B, M, D)**, 799
Princeton Theological Seminary, **(M, D, P)**, 800
Princeton University, **(B, M, D)**, 800
Ramapo College of New Jersey, **(B, M)**, 801
Richard Stockton College of New Jersey, **(B, M)**, 802
Rider University, **(A, B, M)**, 802
Rowan University, **(B, M, D, C)**, 803
Rutgers, The State University of New Jersey, **(B, M, D, P, C)**, 804
Saint Peter's College, **(A, B, M)**, 808
Seton Hall University, **(B, M, D, P, C)**, 809
Stevens Institute of Technology, **(B, M, D)**, 810
Thomas Edison State College, **(A, B, M)**, 811
University of Medicine and Dentistry of New Jersey, **(A, B, M, D, C)**, 812
William Paterson University of New Jersey, **(B, M)**, 813

NEW MEXICO

College of Santa Fe, **(A, B)**, 814
Eastern New Mexico University, **(A, B, M, C)**, 814
New Mexico Highlands University, **(A, B, M)**, 815
New Mexico Institute of Mining and Technology, **(A, B, M, D)**, 816
New Mexico State University, **(A, B, M, D, C)**, 817
St. John's College, **(B, M)**, 818
Southwestern College, **(M)**, 818
University of New Mexico, **(A, B, M, D, P)**, 819
University of the Southwest, **(B, M)**, 821
Western New Mexico University, **(A, B, M)**, 822

NEW YORK

Adelphi University, **(A, B, M, D, C)**, 827
Albany College of Pharmacy, **(B, P)**, 828
Albany Law School of Union University, **(P)**, 828
Albany Medical College, **(M, D, P)**, 829
Alfred University, **(B, M, D)**, 829
Bank Street College of Education, **(M, C)**, 830
Bard College, **(B, M)**, 831
Barnard College, **(B)**, 831
Bernard M. Baruch College / CUNY, **(B, M)**, 832
Boricua College, **(A, B, M)**, 833
Brooklyn College / CUNY, **(B, M, C)**, 833
Brooklyn Law School, **(P)**, 834
Canisius College, **(A, B, M, C)**, 835
Cazenovia College, **(A, B)**, 836
Christ the King Seminary, **(M, P)**, 836
City College / CUNY, **(B, M)**, 837
City University of New York, **(B, M, D, P)**, 838
Clarkson University, **(B, M, D)**, 838
Colgate Rochester Crozer Divinity School, **(M, D, P)**, 839
Colgate University, **(B, M)**, 840
College of Mount Saint Vincent, **(A, B, M)**, 841
College of New Rochelle, **(B, M)**, 841
College of Saint Rose, **(B, M)**, 842
College of Staten Island / CUNY, **(A, B, M, D)**, 843
Columbia University, **(B, M, D, P)**, 844
Concordia College, **(A, B)**, 846
Cooper Union for the Advancement of Science and Art, **(B, M)**, 847
Cornell University, **(B, M, D, P)**, 847
Culinary Institute of America, **(A, B)**, 850
Daemen College, **(B, M, C)**, 851
Davis College, **(A, B)**, 852

NEW YORK *(Cont'd)*

Dominican College of Blauvelt, **(A, B, M, D, C)**, 852
Dowling College, **(B, M, D)**, 853
D'Youville College, **(B, M)**, 853
Elmira College, **(A, B, M)**, 854
Excelsior College, **(A, B, M)**, 855
Farmingdale State University of New York, **(A, B)**, 855
Fashion Institute of Technology, **(A, B, M)**, 856
Five Towns College, **(A, B, M, D)**, 856
Fordham University, **(B, M, D, P, C)**, 857
General Theological Seminary, **(M, D, P)**, 859
Graduate School and University Center / CUNY, **(B, M, D)**, 859
Hamilton College, **(B)**, 860
Hartwick College, **(B)**, 861
Hebrew Union College - Jewish Institute of Religion, **(M, D, P)**, 862
Hilbert College, **(A, B)**, 862
Hobart and William Smith Colleges, **(B, M)**, 863
Hofstra University, **(A, B, M, D, P, C)**, 863
Houghton College, **(A, B, M)**, 864
Hunter College / CUNY, **(B, M)**, 865
Iona College, **(A, B, M)**, 866
Ithaca College, **(B, M, D, C)**, 867
Jewish Theological Seminary of America, **(B, M, D, P, C)**, 868
John Jay College of Criminal Justice / CUNY, **(A, B, M)**, 869
Keuka College, **(B, M)**, 869
Laboratory Institute of Merchandising, **(A, B)**, 870
Le Moyne College, **(B, M)**, 871
Lehman College / CUNY, **(B, M)**, 871
Long Island University - Brooklyn Campus, **(A, B, M, D, P)**, 872
Long Island University - C. W. Post Campus, **(A, B, M, P)**, 873
Manhattan College, **(A, B, M)**, 873
Manhattan School of Music, **(B, M, D, C)**, 875
Manhattanville College, **(B, M)**, 875
Marist College, **(B, M)**, 876
Marymount College of Fordham University, **(A, B)**, 877
Marymount Manhattan College, **(A, B)**, 878
Medaille College, **(A, B, M)**, 878
Medgar Evers College / CUNY, **(A, B)**, 879
Mercy College, **(A, B, M)**, 880
Molloy College, **(A, B, M)**, 880
Morrisville State College, **(A, B)**, 881
Mount Saint Mary College, **(B, M)**, 882
Mount Sinai School of Medicine, **(D, P)**, 882
Nazareth College of Rochester, **(B)**, 883
New School, **(A, B, M, D, C)**, 883
New York Chiropractic College, **(P)**, 885
New York City College of Technology / CUNY, **(A, B, C)**, 885
New York College of Podiatric Medicine, **(P)**, 886
New York Institute of Technology, **(A, B, M, P)**, 886
New York Law School, **(M, P)**, 887
New York Medical College, **(M, D, P)**, 887
New York School of Interior Design, **(A, B, M, C)**, 888
New York Theological Seminary, **(M, D, P)**, 888
New York University, **(A, B, M, D, P)**, 888
Niagara University, **(A, B, M)**, 891
Nyack College, **(A, B, M, P)**, 892
Pace University, **(A, B, M, D, P, C)**, 892
Polytechnic University, **(B, M, D)**, 893
Pratt Institute, **(A, B, M, P)**, 894
Queens College / CUNY, **(B, M, P)**, 895
Rensselaer Polytechnic Institute, **(B, M, D)**, 895
Roberts Wesleyan College, **(A, B,)**, 896
Rochester Institute of Technology, **(A, B, M, D)**, 897
Russell Sage College, **(B, M)**, 898
Sage College of Albany, **(A, B. M)**, 899
St. Bonaventure University, **(B, M)**, 900
St. Francis College, **(A, B)**, 901
St. John Fisher College, **(B, M)**, 901
St. John's University, **(A, B, M, D, P, C)**, 902
St. Joseph's College, **(B)**, 903
St. Joseph's Seminary, **(M, P, C)**, 904
St. Lawrence University, **(B, M)**, 904
Saint Thomas Aquinas College, **(A, B, M)**, 905
St. Vladimir's Orthodox Theological Seminary, **(M, P)**, 906
Sarah Lawrence College, **(B, M)**, 906
School of Visual Arts, **(B, M)**, 907
Seminary of the Immaculate Conception, **(M, D, P)**, 907
Siena College, **(B, M, C)**, 908
Skidmore College, **(B, M)**, 909
State University College of Technology at Canton, **(A, B)**, 925
State University College of Technology at Delhi, **(A, B)**, 926
State University of New York at Albany, **(B, M, D)**, 909
State University of New York at Binghamton, **(B, M, D, C)**, 910
State University of New York at Buffalo, **(A, B, M, D, P, C)**, 911
State University of New York at New Paltz, **(B, M, C)**, 913
State University of New York at Purchase College, **(B, M)**, 922
State University of New York at Stony Brook, **(B, M, D, P, C)**, 914
State University of New York College at Brockport, **(B, M, C)**, 915
State University of New York College at Buffalo, **(B, M)**, 916
State University of New York College at Cortland, **(B, M, C)**, 916
State University of New York College at Fredonia, **(B, M. C)**, 917
State University of New York College at Geneseo, **(B, M)**, 918
State University of New York College at Old Westbury, **(B, M)**, 919
State University of New York College at Oneonta, **(B, M, C)**, 919
State University of New York College at Oswego, **(B, M, C)**, 920
State University of New York College at Plattsburgh, **(B, M)**, 921
State University of New York College at Potsdam, **(B, M)**, 922
State University of New York College of Agriculture and Technology at Cobleskill, **(A, B)**, 923
State University of New York College of Environmental Science and Forestry, **(A, B, M, D)**, 924
State University of New York College of Optometry, **(M, D, P)**, 924
State University of New York College of Technology at Alfred, **(A, B, C)**, 925
State University of New York Empire State College, **(A, B, M)**, 926
State University of New York Health Science Center at Brooklyn, **(B, M, D, P, C)**, 927
State University of New York Health Science Center at Syracuse, **(B, M, D, P)**, 927
State University of New York Institute of Technology at Utica/Rome, **(B, M)**, 928
State University of New York Maritime College, **(A, B, M)**, 928
Syracuse University, **(B, M, D, P, C)**, 929
Teachers College at Columbia University, **(M, D)**, 931
Touro College, **(A, B, M, P)**, 931
Unification Theological Seminary, **(M, D, P)**, 932
Union College, **(B)**, 932
Union Theological Seminary, **(M, D, P)**, 933
United States Merchant Marine Academy, **(B)**, 933
United States Military Academy, **(B)**, 934

A=Associate; **B**=Baccalaureate; **M**=Master's; **D**=Doctorate; **P**=First Professional; **C**=Certificate

NEW YORK *(Cont'd)*

University of Rochester, **(B, M, D, P)**, 934
Utica College, **(B, M, P)**, 936
Vassar College, **(B)**, 937
Vaughn College of Aeronautics and Technology, **(A, B)**, 938
Wagner College, **(B, M)**, 938
Webb Institute, **(B)**, 939
Wells College, **(B)**, 939
Yeshiva University, **(A, B, M, D, P)**, 940
York College / CUNY, **(B)**, 942

NORTH CAROLINA

Appalachian State University, **(B, M)**, 944
Barber-Scotia College, **(B)**, 945
Barton College, **(B)**, 945
Belmont Abbey College, **(B)**, 946
Bennett College for Women, **(B)**, 946
Cabarrus College of Health Sciences, **(A, B)**, 947
Campbell University, **(A, B, M, P)**, 948
Catawba College, **(B, M)**, 949
Chowan University, **(A, B)**, 950
Davidson College, **(B)**, 950
Duke University, **(B, M, D, P)**, 951
East Carolina University, **(B, M, D, P, C)**, 952
Elizabeth City State University, **(B, M)**, 953
Elon University, **(B, M)**, 954
Fayetteville State University, **(A, B, M, D)**, 955
Gardner-Webb University, **(A, B, M)**, 955
Greensboro College, **(B, M)**, 956
Guilford College, **(B)**, 957
High Point University, **(B, M)**, 958
John Wesley College, **(B)**, 958
Johnson C. Smith University, **(B)**, 959
Lees-McRae College, **(B)**, 959
Lenoir-Rhyne College, **(B, M, C)**, 960
Livingstone College, **(B, M, P)**, 961
Mars Hill College, **(B)**, 961
Meredith College, **(B, M)**, 962
Methodist University, **(A, B, M)**, 963
Montreat College, **(A, B, M)**, 964
Mount Olive College, **(A, B)**, 964
North Carolina Agricultural and Technical State University, **(B, M)**, 965
North Carolina Central University, **(B, M, P)**, 966
North Carolina School of the Arts, **(B, M, C)**, 967
North Carolina State University at Raleigh, **(A, B, M, D, P)**, 967
North Carolina Wesleyan College, **(B)**, 969
Pfeiffer University, **(B, M)**, 970
Piedmont Baptist College, **(A, B, M)**, 971
Queens University of Charlotte, **(B, M)**, 971
Roanoke Bible College, **(A, B)**, 972
St. Andrews Presbyterian College, **(B)**, 973
Saint Augustine's College, **(B)**, 973
Salem College, **(B, M)**, 974
Shaw University, **(A, B)**, 975
Southeastern Baptist Theological Seminary, **(A, M, D, P)**, 975
University of North Carolina at Asheville, **(B, M)**, 976
University of North Carolina at Chapel Hill, **(B, M, D, P, C)**, 977
University of North Carolina at Charlotte, **(B, M, D, C)**, 978
University of North Carolina at Greensboro, **(B, M, D, C)**, 980
University of North Carolina at Pembroke, **(B, M)**, 981
University of North Carolina at Wilmington, **(B, M, D)**, 982
Wake Forest University, **(B, M, D, P)**, 983
Warren Wilson College, **(B, M)**, 984
Western Carolina University, **(B, M, D, C)**, 984
Wingate University, **(B, M)**, 985
Winston-Salem State University, **(B, M)**, 986

NORTH DAKOTA

Dickinson State University, **(A, B)**, 988
Jamestown College, **(B)**, 988
Mayville State University, **(A, B)**, 989
Minot State University, **(A, B, M, C)**, 990
North Dakota State University of Agriculture and Applied Science, **(A, B, M, D, P)**, 991
Trinity Bible College, **(A, B)**, 991
University of Mary, **(A, B, M, D)**, 992
University of North Dakota, **(B, M, D, P, C)**, 992
Valley City State University, **(B, C)**, 994

OHIO

Air Force Institute of Technology, **(M, D)**, 996
Antioch University, **(B, M, D)**, 996
Antioch University - Antioch College, **(B)**, 997
Antioch University - McGregor, **(B, M)**, 997
Art Academy of Cincinnati, **(A, B, M)**, 997
Ashland University, **(A, B, M, D, P)**, 998
Athenaeum of Ohio, **(B, M, P)**, 999
Baldwin-Wallace College, **(B, M, C)**, 999
Bluffton University, **(B, M, C)**, 1000
Bowling Green State University, **(B, M, D, C)**, 1001
Capital University, **(B, M, P)**, 1002
Case Western Reserve University, **(B, M, D, P)**, 1003
Cedarville University, **(A, B, M)**, 1004
Central State University, **(B, M)**, 1005
Chancellor University, **(A, B, M)**, 1006
Cincinnati College of Mortuary Science, **(A, B)**, 1006
Cleveland Institute of Art, **(B)**, 1007
Cleveland Institute of Music, **(B, M, D)**, 1007
Cleveland State University, **(B, M, D, C)**, 1008
College of Mount St. Joseph, **(A, B, M, D)**, 1009
College of Wooster, **(B)**, 1010
Columbus College of Art and Design, **(B)**, 1011
Defiance College, **(A, B, M)**, 1011
Denison University, **(B)**, 1012
Franciscan University of Steubenville, **(A, B, M)**, 1013
Franklin University, **(A, B, M)**, 1014
Hebrew Union College - Jewish Institute of Religion, **(M, D, P)**, 1014
Heidelberg College, **(B, M)**, 1015
Hiram College, **(B, M)**, 1016
John Carroll University, **(B, M)**, 1017
Kent State University, **(A, B, M, D,)**, 1017
Kenyon College, **(B)**, 1019
Lake Erie College, **(B, M)**, 1019
Laura and Alvin Siegal College of Judaic Studies, **(B, M)**, 1020
Lourdes College, **(A, B, M)**, 1020
Malone College, **(B, M)**, 1021
Marietta College, **(B, M, C)**, 1022
Medical College of Ohio at Toledo, **(M, D, P)**, 1022
Methodist Theological School in Ohio, **(M, P)**, 1023

OHIO *(Cont'd)*

Miami University, **(A, B, M, D, C)**, 1023
Mount Union College, **(B)**, 1025
Mount Vernon Nazarene University, **(A, B, M)**, 1026
Muskingum College, **(B, M)**, 1026
Northeastern Ohio Universities College of Medicine and Pharmacy, **(P)**, 1027
Notre Dame College of Ohio, **(A, B, M)**, 1028
Oberlin College, **(B, C)**, 1028
Ohio Christian University, **(A, B)**, 1030
Ohio College of Podiatric Medicine, **(P)**, 1030
Ohio Dominican University, **(A, B, M, C)**, 1030
Ohio Northern University, **(B, P)**, 1031
The Ohio State University, **(A, B, M, D, P, C)**, 1033
The Ohio State University at Lima, **(A, B, M)**, 1035
The Ohio State University at Mansfield, **(A, B, M)**, 1036
The Ohio State University at Marion, **(A, B, M)**, 1036
The Ohio State University at Newark, **(A, B, M)**, 1036
Ohio University, **(A, B, M, D, P)**, 1037
Ohio Wesleyan University, **(B)**, 1038
Otterbein College, **(A, B)**, 1038
Pontifical College Josephinum, **(B, M, P)**, 1039
Saint Mary Seminary and Graduate School of Theology, **(M, D, P)**, 1040
Shawnee State University, **(A, B, M)**, 1040
Tiffin University, **(A, B, M)**, 1041
Trinity Lutheran Seminary, **(M, P)**, 1041
Union Institute, **(B, M, D)**, 1042
United Theological Seminary, **(M, D, P)**, 1043
University of Akron, **(A, B, M, P, C)**, 1043
University of Cincinnati, **(A, B, M, D, P, C)**, 1045
University of Dayton, **(B, M, D, P)**, 1048
The University of Findlay, **(A, B, M)**, 1048
University of Toledo, **(A, B, M, D, C)**, 1049
Urbana University, **(A, B, M)**, 1050
Ursuline College, **(B, M, C)**, 1051
Walsh University, **(A, B, M)**, 1052
Wilberforce University, **(B, M)**, 1053
Wilmington College, **(B, M)**, 1053
Winebrenner Theological Seminary, **(M, P)**, 1054
Wittenberg University, **(B, M)**, 1054
Wright State University, **(B, M, D, P)**, 1055
Xavier University, **(A, B, M, D)**, 1056
Youngstown State University, **(A, B, M, D)**, 1057

OKLAHOMA

Bacone College, **(A, B)**, 1059
Cameron University, **(A, B, M)**, 1059
East Central University, **(B, M)**, 1060
Langston University, **(A, B, M, D)**, 1060
Mid-America Christian University, **(A, B)**, 1061
Northeastern State University, **(B, M, D, P)**, 1062
Northwestern Oklahoma State University, **(B, M)**, 1063
Oklahoma Baptist University, **(A, B)**, 1064
Oklahoma Christian University, **(B, M)**, 1064
Oklahoma City University, **(B, M, P)**, 1065
Oklahoma Panhandle State University, **(A, B, C)**, 1066
Oklahoma State University, **(A, B, M, D, P)**, 1066
Oklahoma Wesleyan University, **(A, B)**, 1067
Oral Roberts University, **(B, M, D, P)**, 1068
Rogers State University, **(A, B)**, 1069
St. Gregory's University, **(A, B, M)**, 1069
Southeastern Oklahoma State University, **(B, M)**, 1070
Southern Nazarene University, **(A, B, M)**, 1071
Southwestern Christian University, **(A, B, M, D)**, 1071
Southwestern Oklahoma State University, **(B, M, P)**, 1072
University of Central Oklahoma, **(B, M, C)**, 1072
University of Oklahoma, **(B, M, D, P, C)**, 1073
University of Oklahoma Health Sciences Center, **(B, M, D, P)**, 1075
University of Science and Arts of Oklahoma, **(B)**, 1076
University of Tulsa, **(B, M, D, P)**, 1077

OREGON

Art Institute of Portland, **(A, B)**, 1079
Concordia University, **(B, M)**, 1079
Corban College, **(A, B, M)**, 1080
Eastern Oregon University, **(B, M)**, 1080
Eugene Bible College, **(B)**, 1081
George Fox University, **(B, M, D)**, 1081
Lewis and Clark College, **(B, M, P)**, 1082
Linfield College, **(B, M)**, 1083
Marylhurst University, **(B, M)**, 1084
Multnomah University, **(B, M, D)**, 1085
Northwest Christian University,
Oregon Health and Science University, **(A, B, M, D, P)**, 1086
Oregon Institute of Technology, **(B, M)**, 1087
Oregon State University, **(B, M, D, P, C)**, 1087
Pacific Northwest College of Art, **(B)**, 1089
Pacific University, **(B, M, D, P)**, 1089
Portland State University, **(B, M, D, C)**, 1090
Reed College, **(B, M)**, 1091
Southern Oregon University, **(B, M)**, 1092
University of Oregon, **(B, M, D, P)**, 1093
University of Portland, **(B, C)**, 1094
Warner Pacific College, **(A, B, M)**, 1095
Western Oregon University, **(A, B, M)**, 1096
Western Seminary, **(M, D, P)**, 1097
Western States Chiropractic College, **(B, P)**, 1097
Willamette University, **(B, M, P)**, 1098

PENNSYLVANIA

Albright College, **(B, M)**, 1099
Allegheny College, **(B)**, 1100
Alvernia College, **(A, B, M)**, 1100
The American College, **(M)**, 1101
Arcadia University, **(B, M, D, C)**, 1101
Baptist Bible College and Seminary, **(A, B, C)**, 1102
Bloomsburg University of Pennsylvania, **(A, B, M)**, 1103
Bryn Athyn College of the New Church, **(A, B, M, P)**, 1104
Bryn Mawr College, **(B, M, D)**, 1104
Bucknell University, **(B, M)**, 1105
Cabrini College, **(B, M)**, 1106
California University of Pennsylvania, **(A, B, M)**, 1107
Carlow University, **(B, M, C)**, 1108
Carnegie Mellon University, **(B, M, D)**, 1108
Cedar Crest College, **(B)**, 1109
Chatham University, **(B, M, D)**, 1110
Chestnut Hill College, **(A, B, M, D)**, 1111
Cheyney University of Pennsylvania, **(B, M, C)**, 1112
Clarion University of Pennsylvania, **(A, B, M, C)**, 1112

A=Associate; **B**=Baccalaureate; **M**=Master's; **D**=Doctorate; **P**=First Professional; **C**=Certificate

PENNSYLVANIA *(Cont'd)*

Curtis Institute of Music, **(A, B, M)**, 1113
Delaware Valley College, **(A, B, M)**, 1113
DeSales University, **(B, M, C)**, 1114
Dickinson College, **(B)**, 1115
Dickinson School of Law, **(P)**, 1116
Drexel University, **(B, M, D, P, C)**, 1116
Duquesne University, **(B, M, D, P)**, 1118
East Stroudsburg University, **(A, B, M)**, 1119
Eastern Baptist Theological Seminary, **(D, P)**, 1120
Eastern University, **(B, M)**, 1121
Edinboro University of Pennsylvania, **(A, B, M, C)**, 1121
Elizabethtown College, **(A, B, M)**, 1122
Evangelical School of Theology, **(M, P)**, 1123
Franklin and Marshall College, **(B)**, 1124
Gannon University, **(A, B, M, C)**, 1124
Geneva College, **(A, B, M)**, 1125
Gettysburg College, **(B)**, 1126
Gratz College, **(B, M, C)**, 1127
Grove City College, **(B)**, 1127
Gwynedd-Mercy College, **(A, B, M)**, 1128
Haverford College, **(B)**, 1129
Holy Family University, **(A, B, M, C)**, 1129
Immaculata University, **(A, B, M, D)**, 1130
Indiana University of Pennsylvania, **(A, B, M, D)**, 1131
Juniata College, **(B)**, 1132
King's College, **(A, B, M, C)**, 1133
Kutztown University of Pennsylvania, **(B. M)**, 1134
La Roche College, **(A, B, M)**, 1134
La Salle University, **(A, B, M)**, 1135
Lafayette College, **(B)**, 1136
Lancaster Bible College, **(A, B, M)**, 1137
Lebanon Valley College, **(A, B, M, D)**, 1137
Lehigh University, **(A, B, M, D)**, 1138
Lincoln University, **(B, M)**, 1139
Lock Haven University of Pennsylvania, **(A, B, M)**, 1140
Lutheran Theological Seminary at Gettysburg, **(M, P)**, 1140
Lutheran Theological Seminary at Philadelphia, **(M, D, P)**, 1141
Lycoming College, **(B)**, 1142
Mansfield University of Pennsylvania, **(A, B, M)**, 1143
Marywood University, **(A, B, M, D, C)**, 1143
Mercyhurst College, **(A, B, M)**, 1144
Messiah College, **(B)**, 1145
Millersville University of Pennsylvania, **(A, B, M, C)**, 1146
Misericordia University, **(B, M, D)**, 1146
Moore College of Art and Design, **(B)**, 1147
Moravian College and Theological Seminary, **(B, M, D, P)**, 1148
Mount Aloysius College, **(A, B, M)**, 1149
Muhlenberg College, **(A, B, M)**, 1149
Neumann College, **(A, B, N)**, 1150
The Pennsylvania State University - Harrisburg Capital College, **(B, M, D)**, 1151
The Pennsylvania State University - Milton S. Hershey Medical Center, **(A, M, D, P, C)**, 1152
The Pennsylvania State University - University Park Campus, **(A, B, M, D)**, 1151
Philadelphia Biblical University, **(A, B, M)**, 1153
Philadelphia College of Osteopathic Medicine, **(M, D, P)**, 1153
Philadelphia University, **(A, B, M)**, 1154
Pittsburgh Theological Seminary, **(M, D, P)**, 1154
Point Park University, **(A, B, M)**, 1155
Robert Morris University, **(A, B, M, D, C)**, 1156
Rosemont College, **(B, M)**, 1156
Saint Charles Borromeo Seminary, **(B, M, P)**, 1157
Saint Francis University, **(A, B, M)**, 1158
Saint Joseph's University, **(A, B, M, C)**, 1159
Saint Vincent College and Seminary, **(B)**, 1160
Seton Hill University, **(B, M)**, 1160
Shippensburg University of Pennsylvania, **(B, M)**, 1161
Slippery Rock University of Pennsylvania, **(B, M, D)**, 1162
Susquehanna University, **(A, B)**, 1163
Swarthmore College, **(B, M)**, 1164
Temple University, **(A, B, M, D, P)**, 1164
Temple University School of Podiatric Medicine, **(P)**, 1166
Thiel College, **(A, B)**, 1166
Thomas Jefferson University, **(A, B, M, D. P)**, 1167
Trinity Episcopal School for Ministry, **(M, P)**, 1168
University of Pennsylvania, **(A, B, M, D, P)**, 1169
University of Pittsburgh, **(B, M, D, P, C)**, 1171
University of Pittsburgh at Bradford, **(A, B)**, 1173
University of Pittsburgh at Greensburg, **(B,C)**, 1174
University of Pittsburgh at Johnstown, **(A, B)**, 1174
University of Scranton, **(A, B, M)**, 1176
University of the Arts, **(A, B, M, C)**, 1168
University of the Sciences in Philadelphia, **(B, M, D, P)**, 1175
Ursinus College, **(A, B)**, 1177
Valley Forge Christian College, **(A, B, C)**, 1177
Washington and Jefferson College, **(A, B, M)**, 1178
Waynesburg University, **(A, B)**, 1179
West Chester University of Pennsylvania, **(A, B, M, C)**, 1179
Westminster College, **(B, M)**, 1180
Westminster Theological Seminary, **(P)**, 1181
Widener University, **(A, B, M, D, P)**, 1182
Wilkes University, **(B, M, P)**, 1183
Wilson College, **(A, B, M)**, 1183
York College of Pennsylvania, **(A, B, M, C)**, 1184

PUERTO RICO

American University of Puerto Rico, **(A, B, C)**, 1186
Bayamon Central University, **(A, B)**, 1186
Caribbean University, **(A, B, M)**, 1187
Carlos Albizu University, **(B, M, D)**, 1187
Columbia Century Universitario, **(A, B, C)**, 1188
Conservatory of Music of Puerto Rico, **(B)**, 1188
Electronic Data Processing College, **(A, B, M, C)**, 1188
Escuela de Artes Plasticas de Puerto Rico, **(B)**, 1188
Evangelical Seminary of Puerto Rico, **(M, P)**, 1189
Inter American University of Puerto Rico, Arecibo University College, **(A, B)**, 1189
Inter American University of Puerto Rico, Bayamon Campus, **(B)**, 1190
Inter American University of Puerto Rico, Fajardo Campus, **(A, B)**, 1190
Inter American University of Puerto Rico, Metropolitan Campus, **(A, B, M, D, P)**, 1190
Inter American University of Puerto Rico, Ponce Campus, **(A, B)**, 1191
Inter American University of Puerto Rico, San German Campus, **(A, B, M, D)**, 1191
Inter American University of Puerto Rico, School of Law, **(P)**, 1192
University of Puerto Rico, **(A, B, M, D, P)**, 1195

PUERTO RICO *(Cont'd)*

Pontifical Catholic University of Puerto Rico, **(A, B, M, P)**, 1192
Universidad Adventista de las Antillas, **(A, B)**, 1193
Universidad Central del Caribe, **(A, M, P)**, 1193
Universidad del Este, **(A, B)**, 1194
Universidad del Turabo, **(A, B, M)**, 1194
Universidad Metropolitana, **(B, M)**, 1194
Universidad Politecnica de Puerto Rico, **(B, M)**, 1195
University of Puerto Rico, Arecibo Technological University College, **(A, B)**, 1196
University of Puerto Rico, Cayey University College, **(B)**, 1196
University of Puerto Rico, Humacao University College, **(A, B)**, 1197
University of Puerto Rico, Mayaguez Campus, **(A, B, M, D, C)**, 1197
University of Puerto Rico, Medical Sciences Campus, **(A, B, M, D, P, C)**, 1198
University of Puerto Rico, Rio Piedras Campus, **(A, B, M, D, P)**, 1198
University of the Sacred Heart, **(A, B, M, C)**, 1199

RHODE ISLAND

Brown University, **(B, M, D, P)**, 1200
Bryant University, **(B, M)**, 1201
Johnson and Wales University, **(A, B, M, D)**, 1201
Providence College, **(A, B, M, D)**, 1202
Rhode Island College, **(B, M)**, 1203
Rhode Island School of Design, **(B, M)**, 1203
Roger Williams University, **(A, B, P)**, 1204
Salve Regina University, **(A, B, M, D)**, 1205
University of Rhode Island, **(A, B, M, D, P)**, 1205

SOUTH CAROLINA

Allen University, **(B)**, 1208
Anderson College, **(B)**, 1208
Benedict College, **(B)**, 1209
Charleston Southern University, **(A, B, M)**, 1209
Citadel Military College of South Carolina, **(B, M)**, 1210
Claflin University, **(B, M)**, 1210
Clemson University, **(B, M, D)**, 1211
Coastal Carolina University, **(B, M)**, 1213
Coker College, **(B)**, 1213
College of Charleston, **(B, M)**, 1214
Columbia College, **(B, M)**, 1215
Columbia International University, **(A, B)**, 1216
Converse College, **(B, M)**, 1217
Erskine College and Theological Seminary, **(B, D, P)**, 1217
Francis Marion University, **(B, M)**, 1218
Furman University, **(B, M)**, 1219
Lander University, **(B, M)**, 1220
Limestone College, **(A, B)**, 1220
Lutheran Theological Southern Seminary, **(M, P)**, 1221
Medical University of South Carolina, **(B, M, D, P)**, 1222
Morris College, **(B)**, 1223
Newberry College, **(B)**, 1224
North Greenville University, **(A, B)**, 1224
Presbyterian College, **(B)**, 1225
South Carolina State University, **(B, M, D, C)**, 1226
Southern Wesleyan University, **(A, B, M)**, 1226
University of South Carolina - Aiken, **(A, B, M)**, 1227
University of South Carolina - Columbia, **(B, M, D, P)**, 1228
University of South Carolina - Upstate, **(B, M)**, 1230
Voorhees College, **(A, B)**, 1230
Winthrop University, **(B, M)**, 1231
Wofford College, **(B)**, 1232

SOUTH DAKOTA

Augustana College, **(B, M)**, 1234
Black Hills State University, **(A, B, M)**, 1235
Dakota State University, **(A, B)**, 1235
Dakota Wesleyan University, **(nursing, social work)**, 1236
Mount Marty College, **(A, B, M, C)**, 1237
National American University, **(A, B, C)**, 1238
Northern State University, **(A, B, M)**, 1238
Oglala Lakota College, **(A, B, M)**, 1239
Presentation College, **(A, B)**, 1239
Sinte Gleska College, **(A, B, M)**, 1240
Sioux Falls Seminary, **(M, D, P)**, 1240
South Dakota School of Mines and Technology, **(B, M, D)**, 1240
South Dakota State University, **(A, B,M, D)**, 1241
University of Sioux Falls, **(A, B, M)**, 1242
University of South Dakota, **(A, B, M, D, P)**, 1243

TENNESSEE

American Baptist College, **(B)**, 1245
Aquinas College, **(A, B)**, 1245
Austin Peay State University, **(A, B, M, C)**, 1246
Belmont University, **(B, M, D)**, 1247
Bethel College, **(B, M)**, 1247
Bryan College, **(A, B, M)**, 1248
Carson-Newman College, **(A, B, M)**, 1249
Christian Brothers University, **(B, M)**, 1249
Crichton College, **(B)**, 1250
Cumberland University, **(A, B, M)**, 1251
East Tennessee State University, **(B, M, D, P)**, 1251
Fisk University, **(B, M)**, 1252
Free Will Baptist Bible College, **(A, B, M)**, 1253
Freed-Hardeman University, **(B, M)**, 1254
Harding University Graduate School of Religion, **(M, D, P)**, 1255
Johnson Bible College, **(A, B, M)**, 1255
King College, **(B, M)**, 1256
Lambuth University, **(B)**, 1256
Lane College, **(B)**, 1257
Lee University, **(B,)**, 1258
LeMoyne-Owen College, **(B)**, 1258
Lincoln Memorial University, **(A, B, M, C)**, 1259
Lipscomb University, **(B, M)**, 1260
Martin Methodist College, **(A, B)**, 1261
Maryville College, **(B)**, 1261
Meharry Medical College, **(M, D, P)**, 1262
Memphis College of Art, **(B, M)**, 1262
Memphis Theological Seminary, **(M, D, P)**, 1263
Mid-America Baptist Theological Seminary, **(M, D, P,)**, 1263
Middle Tennessee State University, **(A, B, M, D)**, 1264
Milligan College, **(B, M)**, 1265
O'More College of Design, **(A, B)**, 1265
Rhodes College, **(B, M)**, 1266
Southern Adventist University, **(A, B, M)**, 1266
Southern College of Optometry, **(B, P)**, 1267
Tennessee State University, **(A, B, M, D)**, 1268
Tennessee Technological University, **(A, B, M, D, C)**, 1269

A=Associate; **B**=Baccalaureate; **M**=Master's; **D**=Doctorate; **P**=First Professional; **C**=Certificate

TENNESSEE *(Cont'd)*

Tennessee Temple University, **(A, B, M)**, 1270
Tennessee Wesleyan College, **(B)**, 1270
Trevecca Nazarene University, **(A, B, M, D)**, 1271
Tusculum College, **(B, M)**, 1272
Union University, **(A, B, M)**, 1273
University of Memphis, **(B, M, D, P, C)**, 1273
University of Tennessee at Chattanooga, **(B, M, D, C)**, 1276
University of Tennessee at Knoxville, **(B, M, D, P)**, 1277
University of Tennessee at Martin, **(B, M)**, 1279
University of Tennessee Health Science Center, **(B, M, D, P)**, 1279
University of the South, **(B, M, D, P)**, 1275
Vanderbilt University, **(B, M, D, P, S)**, 1280

TEXAS

Abilene Christian University, **(A, B, M, D, P)**, 1283
Amberton University, **(B, M)**, 1284
Angelo State University, **(A, B, M)**, 1284
Arlington Baptist College, **(B)**, 1285
Austin College, **(B, M)**, 1285
Austin Graduate School of Theology, **(B, M)**, 1286
Austin Presbyterian Theological Seminary, **(M, D, P)**, 1286
Baptist Missionary Association Theological Seminary, **(A, B, M, P)**, 1287
Baylor College of Medicine, **(B, D, P, C)**, 1287
Baylor University, **(B, M, D, P)**, 1288
Concordia University at Austin, **(A, B)**, 1289
Criswell College, **(A, B, M, P)**, 1290
Dallas Baptist University, **(A, B, M)**, 1290
Dallas Christian College, **(A, B)**, 1291
Dallas Theological Seminary, **(M, D, C)**, 1291
East Texas Baptist University, **(A, B)**, 1292
Episcopal Theological Seminary of the Southwest, **(M, P, C)**, 1293
Hardin-Simmons University, **(B, M)**, 1293
Houston Baptist University, **(A, B)**, 1294
Howard Payne University, **(A, B, MB)**, 1294
Huston-Tillotson University, **(B)**, 1295
Jarvis Christian College, **(B)**, 1296
Lamar University, **(A, B, M, D)**, 1296
LeTourneau University,
Lubbock Christian University, **(B, M)**, 1298
McMurry University, **(B)**, 1299
Midwestern State University, **(B, M)**, 1300
Oblate School of Theology, **(M, D, P, C)**, 1301
Our Lady of the Lake University, **(B, M, D)**, 1301
Paul Quinn College, **(B)**, 1302
Prairie View A & M University, **(A, B, M)**, 1302
Rice University, **(B, M, D, P)**, 1303
St. Edward's University, **(B, M)**, 1304
St. Mary's University, **(B, M, P)**, 1305
Sam Houston State University, **(B, M, D)**, 1305
Schreiner University, **(A, B, C)**, 1306
South Texas College of Law, **(P, C)**, 1307
Southern Methodist University, **(B, M, D, P)**, 1308
Southwestern Adventist University, **(A, B, M)**, 1309
Southwestern Assemblies of God University, **(A, B)**, 1310
Southwestern Baptist Theological Seminary, **(M, D, P, C)**, 1307
Southwestern Baptist Theological Seminary, **(M, D, P, C)**, 1310
Southwestern Christian College, **(A, B)**, 1311
Southwestern University, **(B)**, 1311
Stephen F. Austin State University, **(B, M, D)**, 1312
Sul Ross State University, **(B, M, C)**, 1313
Tarleton State University, **(A, B, M)**, 1314
Texas A & M International University, **(B, M, D)**, 1314
Texas A & M University, **(B, M, D, P)**, 1315
Texas A & M University - Baylor College of Dentistry, **(B, P)**, 1316
Texas A & M University - Commerce, **(B, M, D)**, 1316
Texas A & M University - Corpus Christi, **(B, M, D)**, 1317
Texas A & M University - Galveston, **(B)**, 1318
Texas A & M University - Kingsville, **(B, M, D)**, 1318
Texas A & M University - Texarkana, **(B, M, C)**, 1319
Texas Chiropractic College, **(P)**, 1320
Texas Christian University, **(B, M, D, P, C)**, 1320
Texas College, **(A, B)**, 1321
Texas Lutheran University, **(B)**, 1321
Texas Southern University, **(B, M, D, P, C)**, 1322
Texas State University - San Marcos, **(B, M, D)**, 1323
Texas Tech University, **(B, M, D, P)**, 1324
Texas Tech University Health Science Center, **(B, M, D, P)**, 1325
Texas Wesleyan University, **(B, M, P)**, 1326
Texas Woman's University, **(B, M, D)**, 1326
Trinity University, **(B, M)**, 1327
University of Dallas, **(B, M, D)**, 1328
University of Houston - Clear Lake, **(B, M, C)**, 1329
University of Houston - Downtown, **(B, M)**, 1329
University of Houston - University Park, **(B, M, D, P)**, 1330
University of Houston - Victoria, **(B, M)**, 1331
University of Mary Hardin-Baylor, **(B, M)**, 1333
University of North Texas, **(B, M, D)**, 1334
University of North Texas Health Science Center at Fort Worth, **(B, M, D, P)**, 1335
University of St. Thomas, **(B, M, D, P)**, 1335
University of Texas at Arlington, **(B, M, D)**, 1336
University of Texas at Austin, **(B, M, D, P)**, 1337
University of Texas at Brownsville, **(B, M)**, 1338
University of Texas at Dallas, **(B, M, D)**, 1338
University of Texas at El Paso, **(B, M, D)**, 1339
University of Texas at San Antonio, **(B, M, D)**, 1341
University of Texas at Tyler, **(B, M)**, 1341
University of Texas Health Science Center at Houston, **(B, M, D, P, C)**, 1342
University of Texas Health Science Center at San Antonio, **(B, P, C)**, 1343
University of Texas Medical Branch at Galveston, **(B, M, D, P)**, 1344
University of Texas of the Permian Basin, **(B, M)**, 1346
University of Texas - Pan American, **(A, B, M, D)**, 1345
University of Texas Southwestern Medical Center at Dallas, **(B, M, D, P, C)**, 1346
University of the Incarnate Word, **(B, M, D)**, 1332
Wayland Baptist University, **(B, M)**, 1347
West Texas A & M University, **(B, M, C)**, 1348
Wiley College, **(A, B)**, 1348

UTAH

Brigham Young University, **(B, M, D, P)**, 1350
Dixie State College of Utah, **(B)**, 1351
ITT Technical Institute, **(A, B)**, 1352
Southern Utah University, **(A, B, M, C)**, 1352
University of Utah, **(B, M, D, P)**, 1353
Utah State University, **(B, M, D, C)**, 1354

UTAH *(Cont'd)*

Utah Valley University, **(A, B, C)**, 1354
Weber State University, **(A, B, M, C)**, 1355
Westminster College of Salt Lake City, **(B, M)**, 1356

VERMONT

Bennington College, **(B, M)**, 1358
Burlington College, **(A, B)**, 1358
Castleton State College, **(A, B, M, C)**, 1359
Champlain College, **(A, B, M)**, 1360
College of St. Joseph, **(A, B, M)**, 1360
Goddard College, **(B, M)**, 1361
Green Mountain College, **(A, B)**, 1361
Johnson State College, **(A, B, M)**, 1362
Lyndon State College, **(A, B, M)**, 1363
Marlboro College, **(B)**, 1363
Middlebury College, **(B, M, D)**, 1364
Norwich University, **(B, M, D)**, 1365
Norwich University - Military College of Vermont, **(B)**, 1365
Saint Michael's College, **(B, M, C)**, 1366
School for International Training, **(B, M)**, 1367
Southern Vermont College, **(A, B)**, 1367
University of Vermont, **(B, M, D, P)**, 1368
Vermont Law School, **(M, P)**, 1369
Vermont Technical College, **(A, B)**, 1370

VIRGIN ISLANDS

University of the Virgin Islands,

VIRGINIA

Averett University, **(A, B, M)**, 1371
Baptist Theological Seminary at Richmond, **(M, D, P)**, 1371
Bluefield College, **(B)**, 1372
Bridgewater College, **(B)**, 1372
Christopher Newport University, **(B, M)**, 1373
College of William and Mary, **(B, M, D, P, C)**, 1374
Eastern Mennonite University,
Emory and Henry College, **(B, M)**, 1376
Ferrum College, **(B)**, 1377
George Mason University, **(B, M, D, P)**, 1378
Hampden-Sydney College, **(B)**, 1379
Hampton University, **(B, M)**, 1379
Hollins University, **(B, M, C)**, 1380
James Madison University, **(B, M, D, C)**, 1381
Liberty University, **(A, B, M, D)**, 1382
Longwood University, **(B, M)**, 1383
Lynchburg College, **(B, M)**, 1383
Mary Baldwin College, **(B, M)**, 1384
Marymount University, **(A, B, M)**, 1385
Norfolk State University, **(A, B, M)**, 1386
Old Dominion University, **(B, M, D,C)**, 1386
Protestant Episcopal Theological Seminary in Virginia, **(M, D, P)**, 1388
Radford University, **(B, M)**, 1388
Randolph-Macon College, **(B)**, 1389
Randolph-Macon Woman's College, **(B)**, 1390
Regent University, **(B, M, D, P, C)**, 1391
Roanoke College, **(B)**, 1391
Saint Paul's College, **(B)**, 1392
Shenandoah University, **(A, B, M, D.)**, 1393
Sweet Briar College,
Union Theological Seminary and Presbyterian School of Christian Education, **(M, D, P)**, 1394
University of Mary Washington, **(B, M)**, 1395
University of Richmond, **(A, B, M, P, C)**, 1396
University of Virginia, **(B, M, D, P, C)**, 1397
University of Virginia's College at Wise, **(B)**, 1399
Virginia Commonwealth University, **(A, B, M, D, P, C)**, 1399
Virginia Intermont College, **(A, B)**, 1400
Virginia Military Institute, **(B)**, 1401
Virginia Polytechnic Institute and State University, **(A, B, M, D, P)**, 1401
Virginia State University,
Virginia Union University, **(B, M, D, P)**, 1404
Virginia Wesleyan College, **(B)**, 1404
Washington and Lee University, **(B, P)**, 1405

WASHINGTON

Bastyr University, **(B, M, D)**, 1407
Central Washington University, **(B, M)**, 1407
City University, **(A, B, M, C)**, 1408
Cornish College of the Arts, **(B)**, 1409
Eastern Washington University, **(B, M)**, 1409
Evergreen State College, **(B, M)**, 1410
Gonzaga University, **(B, M, D, P)**, 1411
Heritage University, **(A, B, M)**, 1412
Northwest University, **(A, B, M, C)**, 1413
Pacific Lutheran University, **(B, M)**, 1413
Puget Sound Christian College, **(A, B, C)**, 1414
Saint Martin's University, **(A, B, M)**, 1415
Seattle Pacific University, **(B, M, C)**, 1416
Seattle University, **(B, M, D)**, 1416
Trinity Lutheran College, **(A, B, C)**, 1417
University of Puget Sound, **(B, M, D)**, 1418
University of Washington, **(B, M, D, P)**, 1419
Walla Walla University, **(A, B, M)**, 1419
Washington State University, **(B, M, D, P)**, 1420
Western Washington University, **(B, M, C)**, 1422
Whitman College, **(B)**, 1423
Whitworth College, **(B, M)**, 1423

WEST VIRGINIA

Alderson-Broaddus College, **(A, B, M)**, 1425
Appalachian Bible College, **(A, B)**, 1425
Bethany College, **(B)**, 1426
Bluefield State College, **(A, B, C)**, 1427
Concord University, **(A, B, M)**, 1427
Davis and Elkins College, **(A, B)**, 1428
Fairmont State University, **(A, B, C)**, 1429
Glenville State College, **(A, B)**, 1430
Marshall University, **(B, M, P, C)**, 1430
Mountain State University, **(A, B, M)**, 1431
Ohio Valley University, **(A, B)**, 1432
Salem International University, **(B, M)**, 1432
Shepherd University, **(B, M)**, 1433
University of Charleston, **(A, B, M)**, 1434
West Liberty State College, **(A, B)**, 1435
West Virginia School of Osteopathic Medicine, **(P)**, 1436
West Virginia State University, **(B, M)**, 1436
West Virginia University, **(A, B, M, D, P)**, 1437
West Virginia University Institute of Technology, **(A, B, M)**, 1438

WEST VIRGINIA *(Cont'd)*

West Virginia Wesleyan College, **(B, M)**, 1439
Wheeling Jesuit University, **(B, M)**, 1440

WISCONSIN

Alverno College, **(A, B, M)**, 1442
Bellin College of Nursing, **(B, M)**, 1443
Beloit College, **(B)**, 1443
Cardinal Stritch University, **(A, B, M)**, 1444
Carroll College, **(B, M)**, 1445
Carthage College, **(B, M)**, 1445
Concordia University Wisconsin, **(A, B, M, D, C)**, 1446
Edgewood College, **(A, B, M)**, 1447
Lakeland College, **(B, M)**, 1448
Lawrence University, **(B)**, 1448
Maranatha Baptist Bible College, **(A, B, M)**, 1449
Marian College of Fond du Lac, **(B, M)**, 1450
Marquette University, **(A, B, M, D)**, 1450
Medical College of Wisconsin, **(M, D, P)**, 1452
Milwaukee Institute of Art and Design, **(B, C)**, 1453
Milwaukee School of Engineering, **(B, M)**, 1453
Mount Mary College, **(B, M)**, 1454
Nashotah House, **(M, P)**, 1455
Northland College, **(B)**, 1455
Ripon College, **(B)**, 1456
Sacred Heart School of Theology, **(M, P)**, 1457
Saint Francis Seminary, **(M, P)**, 1457
St. Norbert College, **(B, M)**, 1457
Silver Lake College, **(A, B, M)**, 1458
University of Wisconsin - Eau Claire, **(A, B, M, C0)**, 1459
University of Wisconsin - Green Bay, **(A, B, M)**, 1460
University of Wisconsin - La Crosse, **(A, B, M)**, 1461
University of Wisconsin - Madison, **(B, M, D, P, C)**, 1461
University of Wisconsin - Milwaukee, **(B, M, D)**, 1464
University of Wisconsin - Oshkosh, **(A, B, M)**, 1466
University of Wisconsin - Parkside, **(B, M)**, 1467
University of Wisconsin - Platteville, **(A, B, M)**, 1467
University of Wisconsin - River Falls, **(A, B, M)**, 1468
University of Wisconsin - Stevens Point, **(A, B, M)**, 1469
University of Wisconsin - Stout, **(B, M, C)**, 1470
University of Wisconsin - Superior, **(A, B, M, C)**, 1471
University of Wisconsin - Whitewater, **(B, M)**, 1472
Viterbo University, **(B, M)**, 1472
Wisconsin Lutheran College, **(B)**, 1473

WYOMING

University of Wyoming, **(B, M, D, P)**, 1475

Summary Data by State for Institutions Appearing in Part II*

State and Institution	Highest Degree	Control: Public	Control: Private: Indep.	Control: Private: Rel.	Total Enrollment 2008-2009	Full-Time Undergraduate Enrollment 2008-2009: Male	Full-Time Undergraduate Enrollment 2008-2009: Female	Total Foreign Students 2008-2009	Teaching Staff 2008-2009	% with terminal degrees	Associate	Baccalaureate	First-professional	Master's	Doctorate
ALABAMA															
Alabama Agricultural and Mechanical University	D	X			5,706	2,217	2,499	114	150	70		631	2	256	25
Alabama State University	M	X			5,608	1,873	2,774	56	238	62		487	15	184	21
Ambridge University	D		X	X	720	274	297	-	50	63		128	8	35	3
Athens State University	B	X			3,072	1,005	2,067	-	141	66		756			
Auburn University	D	X			24,137	10,104	9,708	241	998	88		3,763	197	849	220
Auburn University at Montgomery	M	X			5,138	1,572	2,796	-	180	82		678		244	
Birmingham-Southern College	M				1,389	619	720	2	101	94		290		16	
Concordia College Selma	B		X	X	565	282	283	28	17	47	18	47			
Faulkner University	P		X	X	2,918	991	1,487	75	75	57	19	591	43	109	64
Heritage Christian University	B		X	X	76	64	12	5	15	75	3	12		2	
Huntingdon College	B		X	X	954	636	318	10	45	78		194			
Jacksonville State University	M	X			7,485	3,136	4,349	182	320	70		1,052		434	
Judson College	B		X	X	311	0	300	3	20	74		50			
Miles College	B		X	X	1,210	537	673		92	38		220			
Oakwood College	B		X	X	1,824	766	1,058	255	96	54	5	267			
Samford University	D		X	X	4,485	1,107	1,783	45	192	84	5	607	329	150	342
Southeastern Bible College	B		X	X	220	133	87	2	33	66		46			
Spring Hill College	M		X	X	1,338	439	879	15	147	85		232		61	
Stillman College	B		X	X	915	411	504	40	52	70		106			
Talladega College	B		X	X	350	106	244	-	40	60		29			
Troy University	P	X			28,955	10,757	10,541	579	496	56	422	2,376		2,278	
Troy University Dothan	D	X			1,998	231	521		116	50		254		95	18
Troy University Montgomery	M	X			4,255	1,155	2,106		44		30	294		209	
Tuskegee University	P		X		2,936	1,049	1,466	29	230	70		335		44	52
United States Sports Academy	D		X		822	77	20	-	-	-		6		189	
University of Alabama	D	X			25,544	9,587	11,494	255	700	90		3,398		1,237	345
University of Alabama at Birmingham	D	X			16,246	4,286	6,510	216	880	87		1,907		1,098	442
University of Alabama in Huntsville	D	X			7,264	2,782	2,969	218	290	91		889		322	37
University of Mobile	M		X	X	1,541	458	888	30	85	70	37	311		70	
University of Montevallo	M	X			2,949	322	2,191	61	247	49		411		154	
University of North Alabama	M	X			7,097	2,526	3,242	710	234	76		845		463	
University of South Alabama	D	X			13,779	4,287	6,403	551	720	75		1,559		719	137
University of West Alabama	M	X			4,011	778	1,049	49	88	65	49	204		627	
ALASKA															
Alaska Bible College	B		X	X	41	20	21		10	20		7			
Alaska Pacific University	M		X	X	719	165	349		48	69	2	74		88	
Sheldon Jackson College	B		X	X	139	44	95	3	44	25	14	14			
University of Alaska Anchorage	M	X			16,463	3,040	12,548	323	637	57	666	871		289	
University of Alaska Fairbanks	D	X			8,618	3,107	4,452	172	288	75	238	494		199	29
University of Alaska Southeast	M	X			2,952	952	1,744	60	60	32	65	93		116	
ARIZONA															
American Indian College of the Assemblies of God	B		X	X	68	31	37	-	20	10	2	11			
Arizona State University	D	X			51,481	21,040	20,586	1,544	2,664	85		7,455	180	2,631	389

***Highest Degree** indicates the highest level of training offered; B—four or five-year baccalaureate; P—first-professional; M—master's; D—doctorate. **Control** of institution can either be public or private. Private institutions are designated as being independent of religious control, under religious control, or independent with religious affiliation. **Total Enrollment** includes all students attending the institution. **Full-Time Enrollment** includes only undergraduates. **Total Foreign Students** includes all full or part-time nonresident aliens enrolled in the institution. **Teaching Staff** is the full instructional faculty, including part and full-time teaching staff. Where data was provided as full-time equivalent (FTE), the number was rounded off. When available, percentage of staff with terminal degrees is indicated. A— indicates information was not available.

State and Institution	Highest Degree	Control: Public	Control: Private: Indep.	Control: Private: Rel.	Total Enrollment 2008-2009	Full-Time Undergraduate Enrollment 2008-2009: Male	Full-Time Undergraduate Enrollment 2008-2009: Female	Total Foreign Students 2008-2009	Teaching Staff 2008-2009	% with terminal degrees	Associate	Baccalaureate	First-professional	Master's	Doctorate
ARIZONA *(cont'd)*															
Arizona State University at the West Campus	M	X			7,734	2,317	4,303	397	301	84		1,550		236	
DeVry University-Arizona	M		X		1,608	935	313	12	-	-	35	232		116	
Embry Riddle Aeronautical University	M		X		1,674	1,216	418	64	101	66		327		11	
Grand Canyon University	M		X		13,415	1,389	3,433	134	744	32		621		3,609	
Northern Arizona University	D	X			21,347	6,289	9,217	310	1,460	76		2,873		1,763	87
Prescott College	M		X		1,007	278	393	10	77	59		214		96	
Southwestern College	B		X	X	361	191	170	7	28	33	2	68			
Thunderbird School of Global Management	M		X		1,194	858	336	230	91	57				56	
University of Advancing Technology	M		X		1,203	1,078	125		59	11		115		6	
University of Arizona	D	X			37,217	13,750	15,320	1,117	1,485	98		5,613	303	1,435	395
University of Phoenix	D		X		224,880	56,761	118,439		33,819	40	12,119	15,117		15,749	354
Western International University	M		X		8,909	2,225	5,954	27	85	55	3,309	398		182	
ARKANSAS															
Arkansas Baptist College	B		X	X	802	546	256		15	90	27	15			
Arkansas State University	D	X			11,130	3,678	5,368	111	619	67	197	1,362		421	9
Arkansas Tech University	M	X			6,842	2,569	2,796	205	367	68	100	834		233	
Central Baptist College	B		X	X	571	312	259	10	55	30	25	65			
Harding University	D		X	X	6,139	1,856	2,269	307	80	80		787		351	12
Henderson State University	M	X			3,503	1,506	1,619	72	218	69		447		129	
Hendrix College	M		X	X	1,195	541	650	12	123	97		192		4	
John Brown University	M		X		2,061	800	902	124	145	68	4	487		146	
Lyon College	B		X	X	497	233	264	10	45	90		98			
Ouachita Baptist University	B		X	X	1,448	656	792	43	115	76		263			
Philander Smith College	B		X	X	561	217	344	6	32	20		82			
Southern Arkansas University	M	X			3,147	1,139	1,667	157	138	58	97	427		77	
University of Arkansas at Fayetteville	D	X			18,648	6,646	6,437	559	824	88		2m343	146	963	274
University of Arkansas at Fort Smith	B	X			6,734	2,624	3,927	6	357	6		403			
University of Arkansas at Little Rock	D	X			12,135	3,160	5,734	121	841	45	179	1,038	139	473	146
University of Arkansas at Monticello	M	X			3,187	1,246	1,786	12	208	47	259	294		56	
University of Arkansas at Pine Bluff	B	X			3,200	1,348	1,791	23	171	57		365		21	
University of Arkansas for Medical Sciences	D	X			2,538	152	681	3	703	85	6	313	228	137	20
University of Central Arkansas	D	X			12,619	4,473	6,202	504	398	58	24	1,480		439	35
University of the Ozarks	B		X		643	290	353	116	69	80		98			
Williams Baptist College	B		X	X	619	276	343	6	28	50	8	115			
CALIFORNIA															
Academy of Art University	M		X		11,834	4,063	4,582	1,657	150	80	70	683		312	
Alliant International University - Fresno	D		X		351	-	-	-	21	100				54	47
Alliant International University - Los Angeles	D		X		645	142	503	-	39	100				59	80
Alliant International University - San Diego	D		X		3,704	68	109	809	168	100		55		477	361
Alliant International University - San Francisco	D		X		798	-	-	-	152	100				54	88
American Baptist Seminary of the West	D		X	X	58	26	32	12	15	100			11		
American Conservatory Theater	M		X		50	25	25	-	25	50				14	
American Film Institute Conservatory	M		X		347	228	113	90	42	100				107	
American Jewish University	P		X	X	223	59	47	-	67	100		39	3	25	
Antioch University - Los Angeles	M		X		676	66	129	7	92	50		47		174	
Antioch University - Santa Barbara	B		X		347	24	72	4	71	50		29		91	
Art Center College of Design	M		X		1,832	959	724	-	140	25		534		40	
Art Institute of California - Los Angeles	B		X		2,151	1,377	774	195	110	50	113	309			
Art Institute of California - San Diego	B		X		1,912	994	918	27	110	50	110	351			
Art Institute of California - San Francisco	B		X		1,581	838	743	63	108	50	16	288		4	
Azusa Pacific University	P		X		8,084	1,708	2,907	242	319	73		1,282	42	1,173	44
Bethany University	M		X	X	537	182	272	6	27	53		93		25	
Biola University	P		X	X	5,830	1,842	2,880	233	115	65		896	43	291	94
Brooks Institute of Photography	M		X		1,743	912	746	35	31	26	13	525		18	
California Baptist University	M		X	X	3,775	822	1,460	76	285	65		626		211	
California College of the Arts	M		X		1,613	334	983	113	136	64		233		98	
California Institute of Integral Studies	D		X		1,126	18	38	45	125	80		42		165	41
California Institute of Technology	D		X		2,133	630	283	192	284	100		208		128	185
California Institute of the Arts	M		X		1,324	147	380	54	165	75		187		205	
California Lutheran University	M		X	X	3,411	915	1,214	102	105	87		532		361	12
California Maritime Academy	B	X			859	713	146	18	49	50		161			

State and Institution	Highest Degree	Control: Public	Control: Private: Indep.	Control: Private: Rel.	Total Enrollment 2008-2009	Full-Time Undergraduate Enrollment 2008-2009: Male	Full-Time Undergraduate Enrollment 2008-2009: Female	Total Foreign Students 2008-2009	Teaching Staff 2008-2009	% with terminal degrees	Associate	Baccalaureate	First-professional	Master's	Doctorate
CALIFORNIA *(cont'd)*															
California Polytechnic State University, San Luis Obispo	M	X			19,777	10,744	8,105	198	788	75		3,617		444	
California State Polytechnic University, Pomona	M	X			21,477	11,296	8,522	1,288	604	76		3,724		348	
California State University, Bakersfield	M	X			7,700	2,077	4,033	154	478	50		1,350		280	
California State University, Channel Islands	M	X			3,599	1,303	2,039	-	222	50		756		45	
California State University, Chico	M	X			17,034	7,508	8,133	340	615	58		3,003		363	
California State University, Dominguez Hills	M	X			12,082	2,859	6,072	242	678	80		1,962		1,028	
California State University, East Bay	M	X			13,124	3,841	5,996	787	510	90		1,800		896	
California State University, Fresno	M	X			22,383	6,624	12,902	671	1,101	90		3,571		808	14
California State University, Fullerton	M	X			37,130	13,335	18,415	1,485	2,007	84		5,779		1,323	
California State University, Long Beach	M	X			36,868	12,298	18,448	1,843	1,846	80		6,567		1,721	
California State University, Los Angeles	M	X			21,051	6,338	9,708	1,263	1,184	50		2,681		1,030	
California State University, Monterey Bay	M	X			4,080	1,609	2,049	77	142	74		640		82	
California State University, Northridge	M	X			35,446	12,202	17,558	1,773	1,941	85		6,819		1,543	
California State University, Sacramento	M	X			28,829	10,036	14,100	288	1,617	50		4,593		976	
California State University, San Bernardino	M	X			17,066	4m746	8,813	512	633	76		3,779		1,061	
California State University, San Marcos	M	X			9,159	3,163	4,946	275	238	65		1,633		225	
California State University, Stanislaus	M	X			8,936	6,681	4,607	88	511	50		1,524		216	
California Western School of Law	P		X		871	-	-	15	99	100				24	255
Chapman University	P		X	X	5,908	1,596	2,277	118	581	90		923	100	380	221
Church Divinity School of the Pacific	P			X	114	-	-	6	11	90			30	2	1
Claremont McKenna College	B		X		1,153	619	534	58	146	100		281			
Claremont School of Theology	D		X	X	435	-	-	39	44	50				24	38
Cleveland Chiropractic College, Los Angeles	P		X		363	63	39	72	48	90		9	61	46	
Cogswell Polytechnical College	B		X		230	189	41	-	10	35		54			
Coleman University	M		X		488	391	86		36	20	185	81		14	
Columbia College Hollywood	B		X		312	225	87	25	36	5	1	71			
Concordia University	M		X	X	2,392	490	766	144	199	69		299		442	
Dominican School of Philosophy and Theology	P		X	X	89	7	3	10	27	95		7	4	12	
Dominican University of California	M		X	X	2,125	359	1,136	43	310	61		301		158	
Fielding Graduate University	D		X		1,588	-	-	22	106	100				157	106
Five Branches Institute	M		X		219	-	-	8	23	65				48	
Franciscan School of Theology	M		X	X	76	-	-	6	15	100			2	31	
Fresno Pacific University	M		X	X	2,391	520	1,057	96	93	62		448		140	
Fuller Theological Seminary	D		X	X	3,010	-	-	400	58	98			138	311	175
Golden Gate Baptist Theological Seminary	D		X	X	1,167	-	-	40	109	11			86	4	
Golden Gate University	D		X		3,550	207	285	433	841	83		148	270	701	7
Graduate Theological Union	D		X	X	382	-	-	97	104	100				65	26
Harvey Mudd College	B		X		735	492	243	29	91	100		179			
Hebrew Union College - Jewish Institute of Religion	P		X	X	105	-	-	7	30	85			14	34	
Holy Names University	M		X	X	1,114	184	413	44	123	90		105		135	
Hope International University	M			X	974	296	407	20	152	52	4	177		111	
Humboldt State University	M	X			7,773	3,253	3,669	78	551	73		1,317		176	
Humphreys College	P		X		756	94	575	18	39	2	40	95	10		
ITT Technical Institute, San Diego	B		X		1,043	866	177	95	30	32	155	69			
Jesuit School of Theology at Berkeley	P		X	X	194	-	-	56	24	100			21	17	
John F. Kennedy University	D		X		1,565	91	217	32	32	80		57	42	286	17
La Sierra University	D		X	X	1,749	597	860	210	420	86		205		48	8
Life Chiropractic College - West	P		X		451	-	-	54	99	32			118		
Life Pacific College	B		X	X	459	239	220	2	37	40		83			
Loma Linda University	D		X	X	3,854	251	841	40	1,911	76		208	280	378	128
Loyola Marymount University	P		X	X	8,477	1,822	3,944	180	419	66		1,477	403	664	3
The Master's College	M		X	X	1,511	556	557	60	186	81		286		87	9
Menlo College	B		X		680	401	279	68	67	58		140			
Mennonite Brethren Biblical Seminary	P		X	X	149	-	-	23	7	72			11	18	
Mills College	M		X		1,446	-	941	30	157	91		194		182	6
Monterey Institute of International Studies	M		X		783	3	10	2	64	95		9		348	34
Mount St. Mary's College	D		X	X	2,366	134	1,776	59	299	60	147	373		86	17
National University	D		X		26,363	4,254	3,163	263	3,160	86		1,029		3,462	1,998
Notre Dame de Namur University	D		X	X	1,491	247	502	45	157	96		202		182	109

State and Institution	Highest Degree	Control: Public	Control: Private: Indep.	Control: Private: Rel.	Total Enrollment 2008-2009	Full-Time Undergraduate Enrollment 2008-2009: Male	Full-Time Undergraduate Enrollment 2008-2009: Female	Total Foreign Students 2008-2009	Teaching Staff 2008-2009	% with terminal degrees	Associate	Baccalaureate	First-professional	Master's	Doctorate
CALIFORNIA *(cont'd)*															
Occidental College	M		X		1,877	820	1,043	38	156	97		474		7	
Otis College of Art and Design	M		X		1,177	359	762	153	237	25		197		16	
Pacific Graduate School of Psychology	D		X		349	-	-	17	50	75				51	42
Pacific Lutheran Theological Seminary	P		X	X	117	-	-	5	9	100		2	14		
Pacific Oaks College	M		X		1,064	12	227	-	125	75		105		149	23
Pacific School of Religion	D		X	X	214	-	-	16	22	100			37	10	6
Pacific Union College	M		X	X	1,363	626	734	27	102	56	99	211		2	
Pardee RAND Graduate School of Policy Studies	D		X		102	-	-	39	48	100				27	9
Patten University	B		X	X	758	425	284	50	58	75	18	43		8	11
Pepperdine University	D		X	X	7,582	1,529	1,869	531	743	90		809	211	1,400	91
Pitzer College	B		X		999	410	589	30	68	100		231			
Point Loma Nazarene University	M		X	X	3,480	915	1,431	20	168	65		552		320	1
Pomona College	B		X		1,547	779	778	46	215	100		385			
Saint Mary's College of California	D		X	X	3,801	1,660	1,017	76	589	93	32	651		241	10
St. Patrick's Seminary and University	P			X	88	-	-	-	25	64			33	31	
Samra University of Oriental Medicine	M		X		279	-	-	51	14	50				63	
Samuel Merritt University	D		X		1,278	56	413	-	162	50		278	23	166	69
San Diego Christian College	B			X	489	213	250	-	30	50		128			
San Diego State University	D	X			35,695	12,819	16,991	1,071	1,580	55		6,481		1,886	64
San Francisco Art Institute	M		X		655	194	202	33	35	58		79		98	
San Francisco Conservatory of Music	M		X		406	117	100	89	69	29		38		75	
San Francisco State University	D	X			30,125	8,556	14,578	1,808	1,499	85		5,471		1,368	23
San Francisco Theological Seminary	P		X	X	493	-	-	112	24	100			44	14	31
San Jose State University	M	X			31,906	11,951	12,439	2,552	1,925	84		4,862		2,396	
Santa Clara University	P		X	X	8,685	3,220	2,041	347	744	90		1,316	297	677	1
Saybrook Graduate School and Research Center	D		X		497	-	-	13	19	100				23	45
Scripps College	B		X		920	-	899	9	95	98		185			
Simpson University	M		X	X	1,076	294	596	11	104	68	2	227		51	
Sonoma State University	M	X			8,770	1,383	6,300	88	569	88		1,657		213	
Southern California College of Optometry	P	X			378	-	-	10	92	100			96		
Southern California University of Health Sciences	P		X		638	-	-	-	103	90			135	28	
Southwestern University School of Law	P		X		931	-	-	11	75	100			267	5	
Stanford University	P		X		19,783	3,424	3,160	1,646	1,031	99		1,646	217	1,974	727
Starr King School for the Ministry	P		X	X	79	-	-	-	28	100			111	2	
Thomas Aquinas College	B		X	X	360	184	186	22	38	61		80			
Thomas Jefferson School of Law	P		X		762	-	-	3	68	100			268		
United States Naval Postgraduate School	D	X			1,746	-	-	250	200	30			6	682	9
University of California, Berkeley	P	X			34,940	24,523	13,303	1,048	2,026	76		6,960	357	2,053	1,218
University of California, Davis	P	X			29,796	12,330	13,148	596	1,445	98		5,785	408	873	492
University of California, Hastings College of the Law	P	X			1,276	-	-	38	166	100			409	16	
University of California, Irvine	D	X			26,483	10,414	11,282	795	1,925	98		5,209	79	942	303
University of California, Los Angeles	D	X			37,476	12,768	13,160	1,259	7,227	98		7,889	563	2,571	798
University of California, Riverside	D	X			17,787	7,158	7,755	344	857	98		3,544		372	224
University of California, San Diego	D	X			27,020	10,363	11,685	811	1,569	99		5,328	186	894	457
University of California, San Francisco	D	X			2,863	-	-	-	1,584	95			366	213	128
University of California, Santa Barbara	D	X			21,410	8,287	10,128	214	1,033	100		4,977		578	346
University of California, Santa Cruz	D	X			15,825	6,625	7,178	158	759	98		3,450		270	131
University of La Verne	D		X		7,370	1,359	2,637	74	394	80		1,099	78	476	64
University of Redlands	M		X		4,188	1,213	1,544	84	326	86		637		404	
University of San Diego	D		X	X	7,504	2,071	2,261	150	724	97		1,137	324	626	22
University of San Francisco	D		X	X	8,714	1,998	3,402	610	837	94		1,281	227	927	36
University of Southern California	D		X		33,408	8,192	8,192	3,007	2,570	90		4,528	207	4,455	1,316
University of the Pacific	D		X		6,235	1,881	1,909	283	652	92		726	294	191	414
University of West Los Angeles	P		X		157	-	-	-	7	100			60		
Vanguard University of Southern California	M		X	X	2,254	704	1,251	23	204	80		471		74	
Western State University College of Law	P		X		497	-	-	-	49	100			111		
Western University of Health Sciences	P		X		2,130	-	-	55	132	92			277	131	
Westminster Seminary California	D		X	X	169	-	-	8	20	81			17	12	
Westmont College	B		X	X	1,337	462	869	11	150	90		305			
Whittier College	P		X		1,985	567	692	40	133	90		307	163	78	
William Jessup University	B			X	515	209	300	6	86	90	1	169			
Woodbury University	M		X		1,539	570	726	92	206	58		296		119	
Wright Institute	D		X		323	-	-	9	41	100				50	62

State and Institution	Highest Degree	Control: Public	Control: Private: Indep.	Control: Private: Rel.	Total Enrollment 2008-2009	Full-Time Undergraduate Enrollment 2008-2009: Male	Full-Time Undergraduate Enrollment 2008-2009: Female	Total Foreign Students 2008-2009	Teaching Staff 2008-2009	% with terminal degrees	Associate	Baccalaureate	First-professional	Master's	Doctorate
COLORADO															
Adams State College	M	X			2,830	955	1,216	2	193	35	25	345		226	
Colorado Christian University	M		X	X	2,151	749	1,172	22	48	85	19	332		1,44	
Colorado College	M		X		2,075	944	1,109	62	197	94		587		43	
Colorado School of Mines	D	X			4,560	2,611	757	274	296	90		626		247	35
Colorado State University	D	X			27,569	10,402	11,269	847	892	99		4,286	135	4,286	342
Colorado State University - Pueblo	M	X			5,908	2,017	2,786	118	301	70		742		58	
Colorado Technical University	D		X		1,904	241	222	-	92	53	37	240		276	10
Denver Seminary	D		X	X	858	-	-	37	60	100				113	48
Fort Lewis College	B	X			3,928	2,041	1,887	39	240	79		699			
Iliff School of Theology	D		X	X	199	-	-	6	58	100			18	42	
ITT Technical Institute	B		X		540	452	88	-	24	11	115	30			
Mesa State College	B	X			6,199	2,355	3,528	20	438	76	180	527		36	
Metropolitan State College of Denver	B	X			21,425	9,641	11,784	118	1,033	86		2,844			
Naropa University	M	X			1,104	215	263	22	206	45		111		173	
National Theatre Conservatory	M		X		24	14	10	-	11	50				8	
Nazarene Bible College	B		X	X	957	622	329	4	79	49		66			
Regis University	D		X	X	11,238	2,003	3,103	112	425	70		1,301		1,785	96
United States Air Force Academy	B	X			4,461	3,013	848	47	531	55		1,024			
University of Colorado at Boulder	D	X			31,796	14,012	12,336	318	1,849	92		5,790	165	996	331
University of Colorado at Colorado Springs	D	X			8,660	2,816	3,734	87	556	64		1,166		495	7
University of Colorado at Denver and Health Sciences Center-Downtown Denver Campus	D	X			21,658	5,032	6,670	434	496	72		1,718		1,656	534
University of Colorado at Denver and Health Sciences Center-Health Sciences Program	D	X			3,330	84	440	73	1,632	75		257	306	133	59
University of Denver	D		X		11,053	2,378	2,907	332	1,137	32		1,101	87	1,768	366
University of Northern Colorado	D	X			12,702	4,062	6,354	127	632	60		2,033		548	71
Western State College of Colorado	B	X			2,146	1,309	839		135	72		439			
CONNECTICUT															
Albertus Magnus College	B		X	X	2,034	674	1,012	30	192	70	114	395		192	
Central Connecticut State University	D	X			12,106	4,949	4,155	242	885	48		1,641		552	1
Charter Oak State College	B	X			1,577	946	631	1	97	50	52	429			
Connecticut College	M		X		1,869	773	1,114	75	214	91		440		10	
Eastern Connecticut State University	M	X			5,137	2,172	2,654	52	404	65		959		117	
Fairfield University	M		X	X	5,024	1,693	2,357	50	491	65	3	886		324	
Hartford Seminary	D		X	X	169	-	-	-	28	100				21	12
Holy Apostles College and Seminary	P		X	X	284	30	16	18	23	100		12	21	10	
Lyme Academy College of Fine Arts	B	X			139	59	79	-	24	55		14			
Mitchell College	B	X			894	438	456	89	24	55		115			
Paier College of Art	B		X		277	108	169	11	34	10	2	48			
Post University	B		X		1,271	486	778	13	127	20	25	205		2	
Quinnipiac College	P		X		7,216	2,191	3,574	72	678	78		1,327	125	431	
Rensselaer at Hartford	M		X		743	25	75	15	54	65				287	
Sacred Heart University	M		X	X	5,801	1,648	2,578	580	169	80	23	852		442	21
Saint Joseph College	M		X	X	1,803	3	736	1	212	65		227		155	
Southern Connecticut State University	D	X			11,930	3,235	5,280	113	674	83	1	1,426		826	5
Trinity College	M		X		2,526	1,145	1,192	76	243	76		542		47	
United States Coast Guard Academy	B	X			963	703	260	10	134	55		223			
University of Bridgeport	D		X		4,752	215	1,576	250	380	95	41	269		755	65
University of Connecticut	D	X			23,692	8,011	8,337	236	1,234	94	35	4,591	188	1,437	368
University of Hartford	D		X		7,290	3,018	2,619	292	787	38	171	957		396	14
University of New Haven	M		X		4,774	1,566	1,445	96	323	90	57	568		802	8
Wesleyan University	D		X	X	3,222	1,409	1,408	193	364	92		732		93	12
Western Connecticut State University	M	X			5,907	2,286	2,909	416	496	35		731		239	
Yale University	D		X		11,454	1,709	2,602	422	3,330	85		1,319	367	1,3898	379
DELAWARE															
Delaware State University	D	X			3,756	2,058	1,316	223	335	53		455		159	4
Goldey-Beacom College	M		X	X	1,197	730	467	-	65	20	27	166		130	
University of Delaware	D	X			20,342	7,914	9,023	203	1,421	75	188	3,500		695	208
Wesley College	M		X	X	2,320	1,360	799	10	149	60	27	260		73	
Widener University - Delaware Campus	P		X		1,170	29	150	-	-	-		18	320	26	4
Wilmington University	D		X		8,353	1,800	3,885	-	555	57	38	929		1,239	48
DISTRICT OF COLUMBIA															
American University	D		X	X	11,449	2,296	3,745	687	941	91		1,483	479	1,387	54

State and Institution	Highest Degree	Control: Public	Control: Private: Indep.	Control: Private: Rel.	Total Enrollment 2008-2009	Full-Time Undergraduate Enrollment 2008-2009: Male	Full-Time Undergraduate Enrollment 2008-2009: Female	Total Foreign Students 2008-2009	Teaching Staff 2008-2009	% with terminal degrees	Associate	Baccalaureate	First-professional	Master's	Doctorate
DISTRICT OF COLUMBIA															
Catholic University of America	D		X	X	6,440	1,422	1,904	193	452	96		599	272	449	89
Corcoran College of Art and Design	M		X		975	230	591	59	178	65	7	67		22	
Dominican House of Studies	D			X	85	-	-	23	21	90			6		1
Gallaudet University	D		X		1,423	582	458	114	267	60		198		115	15
George Washington University	D		X		25,078	4,815	5,886	1,003	2,660	93		2,485	529	3,461	427
Georgetown University	D		X	X	14,826	3,229	3,801	1,186	1,215	75		1,730	760	1,887	281
Howard University	D		X		10,125	2,379	4,619	304	1,915	77		1,400	154	384	386
Joint Military Intelligence College	M	X			532	-	-	-	129	-		32		154	
Potomac College	P		X	X	318	112	206	-	-	-	2			85	
Southeastern University	M		X		787	144	420	71	124	70	45	82		90	
Strayer College	M		X		27,309	7,738	12,625	570	117	55	497	2,132		1,508	
Trinity University	M		X	X	1,630	-	1,012	17	140	94	3	139		253	
University of the District of Columbia	M	X			5,371	2,106	3,031	791	342	52	152	318	74	52	
Washington Theological Union	P		X	X	240	-	-	12	25	100			11	40	
Wesley Theological Seminary	D		X	X	487	-	-	-	45	100			14		27
FLORIDA															
Baptist College of Florida	B		X	X	564	203	361	-	63	83	8	121			
Barry University	D		X	X	8,733	611	4,477	349	845	80		1,352	352	935	241
Bethune-Cookman University	B		X	X	3,434	1,392	2,003	35	163	54		383		9	
Clearwater Christian College	B		X		594	297	297	6	51	77	2	103			
Eckerd College	B		X	X	2,544	992	1,552	51	167	80		381			
Edward Waters College	B		X	X	811	399	412	8	44	40		126			
Embry-Riddle Aeronautical University	M		X		4,584	3,851	735	448	245	68		844		110	
Flagler College	B		X		2,537	989	1,548	25	158	62		589			
Florida Agricultural and Mechanical University	D	X			11,562	2,847	6,643	116	786	50	96	1,430	122	238	154
Florida Atlantic University	X				26,193	8,921	12,837	706	1,065	86	159	4,481		1,114	83
Florida Christian College	B		X	X	226	136	90	-	38	30	6	54			
Florida College	B		X		524	241	283	5	35	30	133	27			
Florida Gulf Coast University	M	X			9,339	3,280	4,919	93	490	77	184	1,214		247	
Florida Institute of Technology	D		X		5,118	1,816	772	1,074	416	89		429		786	37
Florida International University	D	X			28,102	13,838	17,485	1,524	1,352	77	50	5,497	90	2,147	122
Florida Memorial College	M		X	X	1,750	634	1,035	158	80	60		184		52	
Florida Metropolitan College	M		X		1,436	359	969	53	88	50	202	87		55	
Florida Southern College	M		X		2,295	809	1,378	69	178	84		564		34	
Florida State University	D	X			40,555	13,902	17,693	1,293	1,654	92	131	7,613	305	2,075	425
Hobe Sound Bible College	B		X	X	135	59	76	11	24	20	3	15			
Hodges University	B		X		1,699	476	1,011	-	111	66	135	362		82	
International Academy of Design and Technology	B		X		1,209	242	967	-	171	18	20	180			
Jacksonville University	M		X	X	3,212	1,147	1,650	64	114	68		618		127	
Jones College	B		X		537	113	424	11	84	10	26	95			
Lynn University	D		X		2,549	1,133	1,050	331	238	80		446		134	24
Nova Southeastern University	D		X		27,518	1,465	4,170	1,376	1,553	82	14	1,390	253	3,078	1,519
Palm Beach Atlantic University	B		X		3,291	1,202	2,009	50	274	75		496		144	65
Ringling School of Art and Design	B		X		1,199	552	647	60	124	51		241			
Rollins College	M		X		3,453	1,107	1,592	138	233	75	4	676		275	
St. John Vianney College Seminary	B			X	67	64	3		15	33		17			
Saint Leo University	M		X	X	13,788	4,815	7,223	276	129	86	939	2,468		589	
St. Petersburg College	B		X		25,450	9,416	15,361	609	-	-	2,812	504			
St. Thomas University	M		X		2,407	494	656	209	303	76		287	207	249	
St. Vincent de Paul Regional Seminary	P			X	88	-	-	7	22	85			17	4	
Schiller International University	M		X		471	53	55	208	-	-	1	16		87	
Southeastern University	B		X	X	3,069	1,231	1,700	69	138	60		462		33	
Stetson University	P		X	X	3,721	928	1336	37	259	90		510	300	251	
University of Central Florida	D	X			46,398	19,066	22,382	1,459	1,599	80	247	9,001		1,882	134
University of Florida	D	X			51,725	15,690	16,199	517	4,126	85	393	8,137	488	3,337	1,810
University of Miami	D		X		15,449	4,666	5,713	1,881	1,292	98		2,445	478	989	225
University of North Florida	M	X			16,406	6,249	8,283	164	696	95	470	2,751		575	10
University of South Florida	D	X			44,870	16,900	17,798	896	1,802	96	254	7,631	92	2,252	371
University of Tampa	M		X		5,628	2,016	2,902	450	435	85		1,000		240	
University of West Florida	D	X			10,358	3,480	5,220	208	575	80	139	1,733		408	31
Warner University	M		X	X	1,181	406	635	24	50	39	44	313		45	
Webber International University	B		X		601	330	241	84	47	70	10	112		19	
GEORGIA															
Agnes Scott College	M		X	X	892	7	885	50	106	100		191		7	12

State and Institution	Highest Degree	Control: Public	Control: Private: Indep.	Control: Private: Rel.	Total Enrollment 2008-2009	Full-Time Undergraduate Enrollment 2008-2009: Male	Full-Time Undergraduate Enrollment 2008-2009: Female	Total Foreign Students 2008-2009	Teaching Staff 2008-2009	% with terminal degrees	Associate	Baccalaureate	First-professional	Master's	Doctorate
GEORGIA *(cont'd)*															
Albany State University	M	X			4,033	1,154	2,452	40	180	76	3	505		110	
American Intercontinental University	M		X		981	322	624	-	115	18	30	190		20	
Armstrong Atlantic State University	D	X			6,848	1,942	4,128	137	372	76	77	835		201	
Art Institute of Atlanta	B		X		2,646	1,455	1,191	52	165	60	198	270			
Atlanta Christian College	B			X	395	201	194	32	25	60	1	61			
Atlanta College of Art	B		X		324	162	162	19	79	100		66			
Augusta State University	M	X			6,588	2,098	3,730	66	359	70	71	572		245	
Berry College	M		X		1,858	591	1,146	38	193	77		382		45	
Beulah Heights University	M			X	1,303	503	724	52	34	35	28	52		1	
Brenau University	M		X		2,577	171	1,733	104	219	75	5	410		276	
Brewton-Parker College	B		X	X	1,034	393	641	10	189	64	20	182			
Clark Atlanta University	D		X	X	4,271	3,274	2,579	43	246	78		573		175	36
Clayton State University	B	X			6,043	1,732	4,242	120	299	50	126	542			
Columbia Theological Seminary	P			X	298	-	-	21	27	80				63	39
Columbus State University	M	X			7,593	2,554	3,994	76	390	75	27	836		279	
Covenant College	M		X	X	1,343	541	746	13	65	75		347		10	
Emmanuel College	B			X	658	303	355	7	60	50	8	77			
Emory University	D		X	X	12,570	2,289	3,830	880	1,459	100	314	1,513	245	1,037	490
Fort Valley State University	M	X			2,562	1,110	1,357	26	135	76		268		22	
Georgia College and State University	M	X			6,249	2,128	3,191	126	405	50		913		297	
Georgia Institute of Technology	D	X			18,742	3,909	8,656	937	859	96		2,582		1,429	396
Georgia Southern University	D	X			16,841	7,576	7,278	168	738	75		2,383		459	69
Georgia Southwestern State University	M	X			2,405	777	1,444	48	143	72	1	362		85	
Georgia State University	D	X	X		27,134	7,757	12,132	814	1,514	90		3,630	181	1,690	204
Interdenominational Theological Center	D			X	442	-	-	18	21	100			80	11	7
Kennesaw State University	M	X			20,607	7,126	11,146	618	872	76		2,854		960	
LaGrange College	M		X	X	1,071	449	549	22	141	80	1	226		63	
Life University	P		X		1,427	185	267	56	115			60	166	1	
Macon State College	B		X		6,464	2,068	4,396	-	-	-	341	363			
Medical College of Georgia	D	X			2,392	88	538	147	738	97		277	215	107	108
Mercer University	D		X	X	7,307	1,340	2,982	219	591	88		1,084	402	306	8
Morehouse College	B		X		2,810	2,810	-	84	176	74		521			
Morehouse School of Medicine	P		X		300	-	-	-	204	86			38	13	3
North Georgia College and State University	M	X			5,227	1,813	2,719	105	330	75	125	163		169	
Oglethorpe University	M	X			1,020	374	584	51	113	96		197		30	
Paine College	B			X	917	303	614	46	109	45		100			
Piedmont College	M		X		2,283	348	708	28	217	85		226		361	
Reinhardt College	B		X		1,028	423	585	10	73	71	11	158			
Savannah College of Art and Design	M		X		8,966	3,384	4,135	448	508	78		1,359		467	
Savannah State University	M	X			3,169	1,308	1,733	32	176	68		300		45	
Shorter College	M			X	1,035	538	537	53	122	70		136			
South University	B		X		4,883	940	3,334	10	291	28	53	98		71	
Southern Polytechnic State University	M	X			4,460	3,228	709	268	226	64		550		145	
Spelman College	B		X		2,343	-	2,343	69	249	84		483			
Thomas University	M		X		725	167	428	22	78	50	2	79		13	
Toccoa Falls College	B		X	X	969	462	507	10	79	55		130			
University of Georgia	D	X			33,831	10,641	14,694	1,295	2,159	80		6,414	454	1,554	378
University of West Georgia	M	X			10,677	2,737	5,305	107	490	80		1,222		346	8
Valdosta State University	M	X			11,280	3,988	5,740	113	491	78	53	1,588		388	15
Wesleyan College	M			X	691	-	592	78	55	80		76		35	
GUAM															
University of Guam	M	X			3,387	727	2,367	40	236	90		302		67	63
HAWAII															
Brigham Young University - Hawaii Campus	B		X	X	2,397	1,044	1,342	1,079	187	60		340			
Chaminade University of Honolulu	M		X	X	2,685	721	1,283	27	139	60	125	342		234	
Hawaii Pacific University	M		X		7,943	2,605	4,072	953	590	65	194	1,088		356	
University of Hawaii at Hilo	B	X			3,573	1,306	1,959	286	197	83		522		28	
University of Hawaii at Manoa	D	X			20,051	6,222	7,605	1,207	1,563	88		2,994	165	1,141	204
University of Hawaii at West Oahu	B	X			940	339	601	9	20	100		180			
IDAHO															
Boise Bible College	B		X	X	172	86	86	4	12	18	14	14			
Boise State University	D	X			19,540	8,408	9,552	195	1,232	78	296	1,840		311	1
College of Idaho	M		X		840	322	504	25	100	50		146		11	
Idaho State University	D	X			13,208	4,820	6,204	264	763	55	307	1,045	63	316	67

State and Institution	Highest Degree	Control: Public	Control: Private: Indep.	Control: Private: Rel.	Total Enrollment 2008-2009	Full-Time Undergraduate Enrollment 2008-2009: Male	Full-Time Undergraduate Enrollment 2008-2009: Female	Total Foreign Students 2008-2009	Teaching Staff 2008-2009	% with terminal degrees	Associate	Baccalaureate	First-professional	Master's	Doctorate
IDAHO *(cont'd)*															
Lewis-Clark State College	B	X			3,612	1,445	2,167	144	155	72	124	387			
New Saint Andrews College	B			X	157	63	82	11	15	25	11	21			
Northwest Nazarene University	M		X	X	1,836	499	748	18	98	69		251		156	
University of Idaho	P	X			11,636	4,610	4,348	232	590	75		1,782	102	560	62
ILLINOIS															
Adler School of Professional Psychology	D		X		455	109	371	-	51	100				78	23
Augustana College	B		X	X	2,537	1,091	1,446	25	259	96		521			
Aurora University	M		X	X	3,946	249	1,826	6	293	80		497		712	12
Benedictine University	M			X	4,573	1,287	1,706	46	130	90	41	596		492	6
Blackburn College	M		X	X	617	278	339	4	75	79		101			
Bradley University	D		X		6,053	3,147	2,069	61	541	82		1,186		270	16
Chicago School of Professional Psychology	D		X		1,327	-	-	-	53	100				250	52
Chicago State University	M	X			6,810	1,461	3,756	36	376	75		630		343	
Chicago Theological Seminary	D		X	X	236	-	-	30	12	100			20	18	16
Columbia College Chicago	M		X		12,021	5,569	5,797	120	1,477	45		1,859		200	
Concordia University River Forest	M		X	X	4,126	426	695	-	208	65		189		1,269	3
DePaul University	D		X	X	23,401	6,611	8,413	795	1,697	88		2,910	307	2,417	25
DeVry University	M		X		49,000	-	-	-	-	-		-		-	
Dominican University	M		X	X	3,338	479	1,119	204	315	85		339		722	
Dr. William M. Scholl College of Podiatric Medicine	P		X		270	-	-	-	26	54		88	102		
Eastern Illinois University	M	X			12,179	4,529	5,881	122	770	66		2,374		568	
East-West University	P		X		1,144	400	744	125	11	9	48	85			
Elmhurst College	M		X		3,184	1,030	1,848	32	276	85		736		128	
Erikson Institute	D		X		233	-	-	-	25	80				66	
Eureka College	B		X	X	672	296	376	9	44	85		122			
Garrett-Evangelical Theological Seminary	D		X	X	350	165	185	-	25	95			39	24	12
Governors State University	M	X			5,692	755	1,621	14	335	81		878		1,033	
Greenville College	B		X	X	1,528	632	742	15	147	66		357		66	
Harrington College of Design	B		X		1,418	29	1,177	-	40	50	127	209			
Illinois College	B			X	1,014	487	527	20	99	76		216			
Illinois College of Optometry	P		X		614	-	-	92	81	94		4	150		
Illinois Institute of Technology	D		X		7,277	1,880	696	1,164	647	97		465	316	1,140	66
Illinois State University	D	X			20,214	7,612	9,029	202	1,113	82		4,186		663	56
Illinois Wesleyan University	B		X	X	2,094	879	1,275	63	224	78		466			
John Marshall Law School	P	X			1,682	-	-	48	187	100			337	79	
Judson University	B		X	X	1,236	417	699	58	111	65		317		28	
Keller Graduate School of Management of DeVry University	M		X		1,856	-	-	-	73	76				346	
Kendall College	B		X		1,448	44	1,014	38	84	18	91	112			
Knox College	B		X		1,371	636	795	84	127	91		289			
Lake Forest College	M		X	X	1,456	589	847	116	156	98		286		3	
Lake Forest Graduate School of Management	M		X		750	-	-	-	153	20				262	
Lewis University	M		X	X	5,347	1,509	2,359	160	169	58	1	856		468	
Lincoln Christian College	B		X	X	1,039	368	340	42	41	76	20	123		21	
Loyola University Chicago	D		X	X	14,545	3,482	6,458	155	804	97		2,089	230	1,417	269
Lutheran School of Theology at Chicago	D		X	X	383	-	-	56	28	98			39	23	12
MacMurray College	B		X	X	648	207	441	42	75	60		126			
McCormick Theological Seminary	D		X	X	251	-	-	15	437	90			18	8	28
McKendree University	M		X		3,312	1,090	1,332	66	325	70		587		300	
Meadville-Lombard Theological School	D		X	X	121	-	-	-	13	76			13	2	2
Midstate College	B		X		641	122	519	-	62	10	79	37 nil58			
Midwestern University	P		X		1,970	12	15	20	570	90		29	368	92	32
Millikin University	M		X	X	2,376	911	1,424	24	200	89		544		32	
Monmouth College	B		X	X	1,343	604	739	27	105	78		261			
Moody Bible Institute	M		X		3,356	890	513	81	80	51		322		68	
NAES College	B		X		80	-	-	-	3	55		14			
National University of Health Sciences	P		X		651	139	69	10	84	95		43	66		
National-Louis University	D		X		7,405	538	1,803	-	156	65		645		1m996	6
North Central College	M		X	X	2,559	960	1,272	26	225	80		550		106	
North Park University	B		X	X	3,200	828	1,410	96	130	77		371		187	30
Northeastern Illinois University	M	X			12,814	4,114	6,171	256	508	78		1,503		562	
Northern Illinois University	D	X			25,254	9,080	9,837	253	1,193	83		3,979	111	1,606	106
Northern Seminary	D		X	X	233	-	-	-	30	100			24	8	8
Northwestern University	D		X		19,005	4,353	4,908	950	2,538	100		2,031	414	2,805	462

State and Institution	Highest Degree	Control: Public	Control: Private: Indep.	Control: Private: Rel.	Total Enrollment 2008-2009	Full-Time Undergraduate Enrollment 2008-2009: Male	Full-Time Undergraduate Enrollment 2008-2009: Female	Total Foreign Students 2008-2009	Teaching Staff 2008-2009	% with terminal degrees	Associate	Baccalaureate	First-professional	Master's	Doctorate
ILLINOIS *(cont'd)*															
Olivet Nazarene University	M		X	X	4,636	1,212	1,978	46	113	34	35	628		728	
Principia College	B		X	X	525	246	278	66	71	68		111			
Quincy University	M		X	X	1,323	528	550	13	120	76		215		74	
Robert Morris College	M		X		4,824	1,734	2,829	48	343	50	1,033	801		92	
Rockford College	M		X		1.566	326	556	17	101	70		214		226	
Roosevelt University	D		X		7,163	1,351	2,622	216	649	80		958		990	11
Rosalind Franklin University of Medicine and Science	P	X			1,729	-	-	-	731	100		175	244	40	2
Rush University	D		X		1,596	31	209	48	524	85		151		174	175
Saint Anthony College of Nursing	B			X	182	11	152		11	100		66			
Saint Francis Medical Center College of Nursing	M			X	454	33	296	-	28	30		158		13	
St. John's College	B		X	X	69	1	68	1	14	20		69			
Saint Xavier University	M		X	X	5,675	2,006	2,334	57	160	76		819		955	
School of the Art Institute of Chicago	M		X		3,006	865	1,539	541	466	86		478		223	
Seabury-Western Theological Seminary	D		X	X	198	-	-	7	29	100			9	2	9
Southern Illinois University Carbondale	D	X			20,963	9,230	6,963	1,133	1,098	84		4,262	107	895	212
Southern Illinois University Edwardsville	D	X			13,398	5,023	5,897	355	815	82		2,078	48	721	
Spertus College	M		X	X	288	-	-	-	35	10				42	
Telshe Yeshiva-Chicago	P		X	X	77	58	-	-	-	-		2			
Trinity Christian College	B		X	X	1,367	150	1,217	12	148	64		307			
Trinity International University	D		X	X	2,783	468	595	56	381	83		205	133	166	
University of Chicago	D		X		14,538	2,463	2,463	1,163	1,404	75		1,185	214	2,599	504
University of Illinois at Chicago	D	X			25,147	5,836	9,836	583	2,613	74		3,323	643	230	311
University of Illinois at Springfield	M	X			4,855	1,260	1,603	49	191	71		684		840	
University of Illinois at Urbana-Champaign	D	X			42,326	16,374	14,521	2,340	2,051	92		7,314	211	2,635	856
University of St. Francis	M		X	X	3,503	502	1,428	36	206	64		189		806	
University of St. Mary of the Lake - Mundelein Seminary	D		X	X	241	-	-	98	22	100			45		5
VanderCook College of Music	M		X		320	82	92	3	36	70		20		76	
Western Illinois University	M	X			13,441	5,908	5,239	133	745	70		2,518		643	
Wheaton College	M		X	X	2,895	1,167	1,214	29	295	70		633		214	19
INDIANA															
Anderson University	P		X	X	2,707	918	1,218	54	250	66		478	8	134	11
Associated Mennonite Biblical Seminary	P			X	166	-	-	39	16	85			16	6	
Ball State University	D	X			19,849	8,013	8,681	-	1,148	76	428	3m321		956	71
Bethany Theological Seminary	P		X	X	82	37	45	-	18	100			8	3	
Bethel College	M		X		2,097	651	1,265	42	153	74	86	305		35	
Butler University	P		X		4,479	1,378	2,239	135	435	85		693	156	187	
Calumet College of Saint Joseph	M			X	1,238	477	583	6	24	50	16	297		109	
Christian Theological Seminary	D		X	X	304	-	-	6	39	76			36	22	
Concordia Theological Seminary	D		X	X	390	-	-	12	36	80			55	5	5
DePauw University	B		X	X	2,398	1,055	1,343	72	209	93		609			
Earlham College	P		X	X	1,365	537	657	150	112	96		285	9	33	
Franklin College	B		X	X	1,130	576	554	5	115	52		171			
Goshen College	B		X	X	971	382	573	68	132	60		237			
Grace College and Theological Seminary	D		X	X	1,404	625	601	11	125	64	60	193	6	33	
Hanover College	B		X	X	929	427	502	36	102	99		271			
Huntington University	M		X	X	1,148	477	583	33	55	76	10	189		14	
Indiana Institute of Technology	M		X	X	3,294	1,394	1,573	47	261	48	144	414		101	
Indiana State University	D	X			10,543	4,162	4,331	165	663	85	132	1,430		503	72
Indiana University Bloomington	D	X			38,990	14,883	115,491	1,950	2,233	82	45	5,770	215	1,745	480
Indiana University East	B	X			2,266	734	1,490	2	187	53	75	229			
Indiana University Kokomo	M	X			2,835	809	1,887	-	174	65	201	282		30	
Indiana University Northwest	M	X			4,790	1,286	2,864	10	367	72	190	380		92	
Indiana University - Purdue University Fort Wayne	M	X			11,943	4,816	6,205	119	766	86	453	994		192	
Indiana University - Purdue University Indianapolis	D	X			29,854	8,693	12,509	597	3,091	82	405	2,906	289	1,871	431
Indiana University South Bend	M	X			7,517	2,447	3,993	156	551	75	143	554		195	
Indiana University Southeast	M	X			6,241	2,065	3,369	16	415	73	98	664		235	
Indiana Wesleyan University	D		X	X	14,156	3,373	6,548	16	121	54	728	2,328		1,873	4
ITT Technical Institute	M		X		3,270	1,846	1,231	-	32	3	187	173		80	
Manchester College	B		X	X	1,035	517	518	51	90	93		180			
Marian College	B		X	X	2,043	634	1,348	18	132	52	111	303		20	
Martin University	B		X		618	134	404	6	36	36		75		34	
Oakland City University	M		X	X	2,007	785	959	20	37	71	136	339	2	158	16

State and Institution	Highest Degree	Control: Public	Control: Private: Indep.	Control: Private: Rel.	Total Enrollment 2008-2009	Full-Time Undergraduate Enrollment 2008-2009: Male	Full-Time Undergraduate Enrollment 2008-2009: Female	Total Foreign Students 2008-2009	Teaching Staff 2008-2009	% with terminal degrees	Associate	Baccalaureate	First-professional	Master's	Doctorate
INDIANA *(cont'd)*															
Purdue University	D	X			40,534	13,370	19,240	2,432	2,347	84	575	6,034	219	1,326	621
Purdue University Calumet	M		X		9,607	3,823	4,763	288	303	59	251	854		273	
Purdue University North Central	B		X		3,904	1,564	2,251	70	239	60	183	319		20	
Rose-Hulman Institute of Technology	M		X		1,936	1,495	384	39	158	98		417		38	
Saint Joseph's College	M		X	X	1,010	464	606	11	90	81	1	184		7	
Saint Mary-of-the-Woods College	M		X	X	1,677	61	1,458	32	66	70	7	174		35	
Saint Mary's College	B		X	X	1,604	-	1,604	10	201	96		330			
Saint Meinrad School of Theology	P		X	X	176	-	-	2	24	90			11	34	
Taylor University	B		X		1,879	846	1,033	20	193	74	3	400			
Trine University	M	X			1,351	903	425	14	98	72	26	204		4	
University of Evansville	M		X	X	2,852	1,123	1,615	171	239	86	9	531		36	
University of Indianapolis	M		X	X	4,706	1m181	2,398	192	445	60	74	569		291	90
University of Notre Dame	D		X	X	11,733	4,437	3,934	352	964	88		2,887	186	901	195
University of Saint Francis	M		X	X	2,135	570	1,270	7	192	46	162	209		84	
University of Southern Indiana	M	X			9,939	3,782	5,443	199	576	62	123	1,216		257	
Valparaiso University	P		X	X	3,872	1,399	1,516	116	378	84	21	665	151	174	
Wabash College	B		X		917	917	-	40	88	98		204			
IOWA															
Allen College	M		X		462	15	362	-	27	24	14	96		10	
Ashford University	M		X	X	10,568	2,268	7,597	-	268	30		1,089		237	
Briar Cliff University	M		X	X	1,138	486	594	2	64	60		226		2	
Buena Vista University	M		X	X	2,548	859	1,595	25	115	58		768		41	
Central College	B			X	1,605	750	867	32	137	92		344			
Clarke College	D		X	X	1,230	296	726	12	133	57	1	245		52	38
Coe College	M		X	X	1,316	584	714	26	148	92		277		10	
Cornell College	B		X	X	1,083	531	552	33	92	80		242			
Des Monies University - Osteopathic Medical Center	P	X			1,615	-	-	16	137	98			229	150	
Divine Word College	B		X	X	59	50	9	12	13	76	3	3			
Dordt College	M		X	X	1,300	650	650	120	75	85		263		4	
Drake University	D		X	X	5,617	1,944	1,497	449	396	70		735	263	418	118
Emmaus Bible College	B		X	X	244	102	142	25	26	33	7	41			
Faith Baptist Bible College and Theological Seminary	M			X	389	156	170	16	27	50	15	73		21	
Graceland University	M		X	X	2,462	643	1,050	246	94	47		417		376	
Grand View College	B		X	X	1,748	559	1,189	17	174	48	1	411			
Grinnell College	B		X		1,652	777	877	182	203	70		408			
Iowa State University of Science and Technology	D	X			26,160	11,972	9,032	1,046	1,040	88		5,514	106	893	281
Iowa Wesleyan College	B		X	X	834	356	578	83	50	57		162			
Kaplan University	P		X		32,734	9,082	23,652	-	-	-	1,866	1,943	50		
Loras College	M		X	X	1,591	786	635	48	166	90		335		22	
Luther College	B		X	X	2,476	1,065	1,411	73	241	73		546			
Maharishi University of Management	D		X		948	116	88	64	49	100		59		182	2
Mercy College of Health Sciences	B		X	X	880	79	801	-	36	40	199	55			
Morningside College	M		X		1,798	546	667	18	154	73		217		148	
Mount Mercy College	B			X	1,506	422	1,084	15	147	62		429			
Northwestern College	M			X	1,315	513	802	39	140	89		271			
Palmer College of Chiropractic	P		X		2,184	34	36	2	128	83	12	90	558		
St. Ambrose University	M		X	X	3,870	1,070	1,823	39	142	75		589		337	50
Simpson College	B		X	X	2,039	847	1,170	20	226	90		394			
University of Dubuque	D		X	X	1,560	675	610	16	135	88		265	29	49	12
University of Iowa	D	X			29,117	9,826	11,881	1,403	1,649	98		4,488	473	1,361	926
University of Northern Iowa	D	X			12,692	4,751	6,299	381	810	70		2,221		483	16
Upper Iowa University	M		X		5,143	1,890	2,955	28	36	75	41	1,002		100	
Vennard College	B		X	X	83	43	40	2	13	50	4	9			
Waldorf College	B		X	X	630	315	315	36	41	50	14	121			
Wartburg College	B		X	X	1,810	869	941	90	178	94		350			
Wartburg Theological Seminary	P		X	X	184	-	-	8	25	86			30	5	
William Penn University	B		X	X	1,949	858	1,091	19	43	40	48	373			
KANSAS															
Baker University	M		X	X	3,959	714	1,263	40	118	92	90	411		858	14
Barclay College	B		X	X	129	66	63	3	15	25	2	15			
Benedictine College	M		X	X	1,829	822	927	72	112	55		214		50	
Bethany College	B		X	X	537	274	263	15	89	52		98			
Bethel College	B		X	X	541	270	271	57	68	59		129			
Central Baptist Theological Seminary	P		X	X	102	-	-	2	12	100			19		

State and Institution	Highest Degree	Control: Public	Control: Private: Indep.	Control: Private: Rel.	Total Enrollment 2008-2009	Full-Time Undergraduate Enrollment 2008-2009: Male	Full-Time Undergraduate Enrollment 2008-2009: Female	Total Foreign Students 2008-2009	Teaching Staff 2008-2009	% with terminal degrees	Associate	Baccalaureate	First-professional	Master's	Doctorate
KANSAS *(cont'd)*															
Central Christian College of Kansas	B		X	X	364	197	167	12	37	20	23	62			
Emporia State University	D	X			6,354	1,642	2,678	381	279	84		687		521	5
Fort Hays State University	M	X			7,784	3,249	3,924	-	347	48	59	1,646		263	
Friends University	M		X		2,826	934	1,291	22	50	59	37	658		287	
Kansas State University	D	X			23,332	9,643	8,902	1,046	1,047	85	63	3,450	116	687	149
Kansas Wesleyan University	M		X	X	864	345	457	18	32	59		167		67	
Manhattan Christian College	B		X	X	388	213	175	12	32	30	5	84			
McPherson College	B		X	X	544	321	223	5	46	72		132			
MidAmerica Nazarene College	M		X	X	1,779	651	706	19	172	74	47	346		236	
Newman University	M		X	X	2,166	577	983	88	247	53	45	252		141	
Ottawa University	B		X	X	489	225	264	5	22	54		80			
Pittsburg State University	M	X			7,087	2,723	2,527	425	359	70	18	1,058		411	
Southwestern College	M		X	X		727	819	17	181	50		436		102	
Sterling College	B		X	X	603	338	265	6	57	30		57			
Tabor College	B		X	X	574	281	293	6	57	70		134		1	
United States Army Command and General Staff College	M	X			1,000	-	-	-	-	-				182	
University of Kansas	D	X			28,589	10,414	10,414	565	1,322	96		3,997	326	1,429	455
University of Saint Mary	B		X	X	882	225	368	12	102	62	1	115		150	
Washburn University	P		X		6,901	2,348	3,672	138	536	67	143	816	160	144	
Wichita State University	D	X			14,236	5,022	6,139	854	520	78	78	1,692		753	60
KENTUCKY															
Alice Lloyd College	B		X	X	621	298	323	-	44	55		110			
Asbury College	B		X	X	1,396	572	758	12	146	51		222		25	
Asbury Theological Seminary	D		X	X	1,569	-	-	131	53	89			164	92	32
Bellarmine University	D		X	X	3,001	887	1,488	90	307	75		461		234	36
Berea College	B		X		1,582	613	919	111	128	88		312			
Brescia University	M		X	X	573	330	306	42	80	70	5	88		13	
Campbellsville University	M		X	X	2,560	959	1,221	103	230	64	35	220		196	
Centre College	B		X		1,189	535	654	24	102	98		281			
Clear Creek Baptist Bible College	B		X	X	191	151	40	2	23	2	7	30			
Eastern Kentucky University	M	X			15,839	5,600	8,059	158	957	66	189	2,030		613	
Georgetown College	M		X	X	1,903	588	780	19	154	93		261		209	
Kentucky Christian College	M		X	X	632	300	313	18	34	58		107		7	
Kentucky Mountain Bible College	B		X	X	66	36	30	11	16	76	6	8			
Kentucky State University	M	X			2,696	1,054	1,456	81	152	67	37	231		47	
Kentucky Wesleyan College	B		X	X	956	507	449	10	96	52		144			
Lexington Theological Seminary	D		X	X	105	-	-	1	14	100			180	6	2
Lindsey Wilson College	M		X	X	1,893	211	1,410	95	112	48	28	271		82	
Louisville Presbyterian Theological Seminary	D		X	X	210	-	-	6	42	100			32	14	3
Mid-Continent University	B		X	X	1,540	755	785	48	71	30	169	300			
Midway College	B		X	X	1.422	270	1,152	8	55	42	69	271			
Morehead State University	M	X			8,897	2,902	4,549	52	527	68	149	973		380	
Murray State University	M	X			10,778	3,773	5,210	216	580	90	17	1,632		537	
Northern Kentucky University	P	X			14,785	5,335	7,368	148	1,089	82	226	1,706	150	466	
Pikeville College	P		X	X	1,100	356	438	11	69	52	19	100	306		
Southern Baptist Theological Seminary	D		X	X	3,190	193	474	-	68	76	12	96	287	119	84
Spalding University	D		X	X	1,695	772	244	19	76	62	6	180		209	40
Sullivan University	B	X			4,538	1,652	2,664	-	85	24	569	268		95	
Thomas More College	M		X	X	1,645	739	800	16	127	72	67	261		66	
Transylvania University	B		X	X	1,153	450	703	1	99	85		264			
Union College	M		X	X	1,368	351	299	70	45	69		121		217	
University of Kentucky	D	X			25,856	8,904	9,267	259	1,695	94		3,519	378	1,350	256
University of Louisville	D	X			20,592	6,912	7,780	410	1,335	68	51	2,253	327	1,368	144
University of the Cumberlands	M		X	X	2,245	866	866	69	92	70		234		85	
Western Kentucky University	M	X			19,258	6,930	9,571	385	621	84	240	2,391		835	
LOUISIANA															
Centenary College of Louisiana	M		X	X	938	359	495	28	113	74		195		39	
Dillard University	B		X	X	956	295	661	10	199	80		176			
Grambling State University	D	X			5,161	2,044	2,710	361	263	60	36	537		93	3
Louisiana College	B		X	X	1,056	507	549	11	92	55		128			
Louisiana State University and Agricultural and Mechanical College	D	X			28,628	11,209	12,186	1,526	1,515	78		4,600	191	977	314
Louisiana State University Health Sciences Center at New Orleans	D	X			2,234	97	552	-	1,276	76	5	244	241	171	
Louisiana State University in Shreveport	M	X			3,948	1,278	2,271	80	245	55		521		103	

State and Institution	Highest Degree	Control: Public	Control: Private: Indep.	Control: Private: Rel.	Total Enrollment 2008-2009	Full-Time Undergraduate Enrollment 2008-2009: Male	Full-Time Undergraduate Enrollment 2008-2009: Female	Total Foreign Students 2008-2009	Teaching Staff 2008-2009	% with terminal degrees	Associate	Baccalaureate	First-professional	Master's	Doctorate
LOUISIANA *(cont'd)*															
Louisiana Tech University	D	X			10,564	4,345	4,011	212	371	79	90	1,382		443	35
Loyola University New Orleans	P		X	X	4,360	1,084	1,561	132	399	64		653	248	211	
McNeese State University	M	X			8,095	2,767	4,328	241	264	66	148	1,055		262	
New Orleans Baptist Theological Seminary	D		X	X	2,036	789	185	8	89		25	53	92	67	44
Nicholls State University	M	X			6,864	2,353	3,839	693	283	56	146	738		164	
Northwestern State University of Louisiana	M	X			9,037	2,534	5,383	90	610	52	238	1,098		263	
Notre Dame Seminary Graduate School of Theology	P		X	X	109	-	-	-	32	71			15	4	
Our Lady of the Holy Cross College	M		X	X	1,298	205	925	-	145	61		141		26	
Our Lady of the Lake College	M		X	X	2,103	357	1,746	-	145	32	326	84		51	
St. Joseph Seminary College	B		X	X	171	135	36		26	50		9			
Southeastern Louisiana University	M	X			14,744	5,093	8,213	147	653	50	76	1,765		355	
Southern University and A&M College	D	X			8,298	3,658	5,316	520	493	65	4	940		305	9
Southern University at New Orleans	M	X			2,648	516	1,557	-	235	76		229		143	
Tulane University	D		X		10,125	2,938	3,449	204	1,271	90	29	1,483	243	981	290
University of Louisiana at Lafayette	D	X			16,345	6,271	8,660	326	693	79	2	2,142		284	39
University of Louisiana at Monroe	D	X			8,541	4,067	4,586	85	467	70	50	931		234	122
University of New Orleans	D	X			11,363	4,067	4,586	341	494	67		1,260	75	570	62
Xavier University of Louisiana	P		X	X	3,088	650	1,672	93	289	91		343	152	31	
MAINE															
Bangor Theological Seminary	P		X	X	140	-	-	-	36	80			17		
Bates College	B		X		1,660	797	863	83	193	100		440			
Bowdoin College	B		X		1,716	824	892	51	200	96		451			
Colby College	B		X		1,867	840	1,027	112	160	96		521			
College of the Atlantic	M		X		349	123	218	45	26	90		68		4	
Husson College	D		X		2,414	879	1,264	25	66	100	36	356		102	19
Maine College of Art	M		X		379	109	233	44	40	81		78		15	
Maine Maritime Academy	M	X			901	742	141	-	69	37	4	166		9	
Saint Joseph's College	M		X	X	2,847	629	1,338	1	122	98	9	302		150	
Thomas College	M		X		975	390	375	-	83	26	12	91		34	
Unity College	B		X		555	327	228	3	44	64		124			
University of Maine	D	X			11,912	4,302	4,694	765	740	64		1,622		465	50
University of Maine at Augusta	B	X			5,101	1,209	3,809	4	259	26	258	289			
University of Maine at Farmington	B	X			2,351	795	1,556	24	168	89		445			
University of Maine at Fort Kent	B	X			1,269	419	850	279	82	70	46	246			
University of Maine at Machias	B	X			1,093	306	787	22	92	71		77			
University of Maine at Presque Isle	B	X			1,533	491	1,042	122	80	80	16	285			
University of New England	D		X		3,792	570	1,562	35	271	55	99	293	126	403	
University of Southern Maine	P	X			10,453	3,416	4,717	-	402	61	12	1,208	72	390	
MARYLAND															
Baltimore Hebrew University	D		X	X	109	18	18	4	10	100		2		13	1
Baltimore International College	B		X		492	249	221	5	29	38	95	24			
Bowie State University	D	X			5,464	1,585	2,100	55	300	60		616		353	9
Capitol College	M	X			696	260	49	10	41	29		51		175	
College of Notre Dame of Maryland	D		X	X	3,402	89	1,387	34	91	68		437		422	5
Columbia Union College	M		X	X	1,068	377	615	41	53	40	9	176		47	
Coppin State University	M	X			3,932	681	2,561	121	191	55		293		97	
Frostburg State University	M	X			4,993	2,124	2,211	50	344	85		790		241	
Goucher College	M		X		2,360	191	1,280	127	206	60		318		136	
Hood College	M		X	X	2,522	420	1,028	50	238	55		345		193	
Johns Hopkins University	D		X		18,682	2,968	2,682	1,181	3,160	99		1,548	102	4,002	547
Loyola College in Maryland	D		X	X	6,028	1,504	2,076	61	567	91		819		803	17
Maryland Institute College of Art	M		X		2,213	1,278	1,335	88	282	82		388		111	
McDaniel College	M		X		3,637	762	969	17	139	98		356		391	
Morgan State University	D	X			7,208	2,858	3,493	360	402	80		813		130	42
Mount Saint Mary's University	P		X	X	2,157	672	1,009	22	186	75		358	36	126	
St. John's College	M		X		563	226	255	28	67	78		106		42	
St. Mary's College of Maryland	B	X			2,002	871	1,109	40	285	75		426		33	
St. Mary's Seminary and University	D			X	217	10	-	-	10	83		5	8	21	
Salisbury University	M	X			7,381	2,923	3,818	76	489	82		1,563		222	
Sojourner-Douglass College	B		X		1,151	216	862	-	50	76		141		20	
Stevenson University	M		X		3,304	908	2,118	32	349	65	1	605		85	
Towson University	D	X			19,750	6,488	9,731	593	1,238	46		3,204		924	14
Uniformed Services University of the Health Sciences	D	X			854	-	-		2,745	98			159	45	10

State and Institution	Highest Degree	Control: Public	Control: Private: Indep.	Control: Private: Rel.	Total Enrollment 2008-2009	Full-Time Undergraduate Enrollment 2008-2009: Male	Full-Time Undergraduate Enrollment 2008-2009: Female	Total Foreign Students 2008-2009	Teaching Staff 2008-2009	% with terminal degrees	Associate	Baccalaureate	First-professional	Master's	Doctorate
MARYLAND *(cont'd)*															
United States Naval Academy	B	X			4,411	3,508	933	44	525	64		1,051			
University of Baltimore	P	X			5,421	1,161	1,257	153	322	92		517	292	426	2
University of Maryland Baltimore	D	X			5,884	113	697	294	1,094	94		350	268	701	503
University of Maryland Baltimore County	D	X			12,041	2,053	2,411	482	752	80		1,844		449	93
University of Maryland College Park	D	X			36,014	13,446	12,411	3,025	2,157	84		6,301		2,059	683
University of Maryland Eastern Shore	M	X			4,086	1,410	2,205	123	111	64		448		74	13
University of Maryland University College	D	X			32,540	9,178	12,675	651	1,590	82	191	2,793		2,089	14
Washington Bible College - Capital Bible Seminary	P		X	X	816	137	117	24	44	50	1	32	9	34	
Washington College	M		X		1,289	477	745	39	149	75		243		15	
MASSACHUSETTS															
American International College	D		X		2,678	696	1,089	54	91	70	1	251		191	6
Amherst College	B		X		1,648	830	818	117	207	94		430			
Andover Newton Theological School	P			X	350	-	-	4	52	73			45	9	7
Anna Maria College	M		X		1,244	403	512	2	187	50	8	145		104	
Assumption College	M		X	X	2,872	948	1,482	29	125	70	14	543		150	
Atlantic Union College	M		X	X	562	184	347	-	64	42	34	87		6	
Babson College	M		X		3,434	1,061	738	618	174	88		457		649	
Bay Path College	M		X		1,603	-	1,322	23	36	54	49	264		66	
Bentley College	M		X		5,636	1,898	2,539	395	453	84	4	1,065		521	
Berklee College of Music	B		X		4,090	2,945	1,145	864	489	16		732			
Blessed John XXIII National Seminary	P		X	X	56	-	-	-	16	56			16		
Boston Architectural College	M		X		1,338	486	352	-	275	80		21		49	
Boston College	D		X	X	14,521	4,827	5,033	439	982	95		2,319	273	1,260	158
Boston Conservatory	M		X		630	417	266	43	139	95		69		69	
Boston University	P		X		32,053	6,881	11,052	2,885	3,326	80		4,777	601	3,624	589
Brandeis University	D		X		5,333	1,423	1,810	373	456	96		826		596	84
Bridgewater State College	M	X			9,934	3,346	4,614	99	329	77		1,413		413	
Cambridge College	D		X		5,353	445	946	211	30	82		175		1,273	11
Clark University	D		X		3,210	928	1,392	657	278	60		493		333	34
College of Our Lady of the Elms	M		X		1,258	238	846	3	69	70		239		42	
College of the Holy Cross	B		X	X	2,847	1,253	1,594	28	299	93		670			
Curry College	M		X		3,182	1,189	1,643	32	405	57		591		139	
Eastern Nazarene College	M		X		1,075	371	536	22	146	65		155		69	
Emerson College	M		X		4,380	1,529	1,947	88	374	60		840	270	132	
Emmanuel College	M		X		2,467	616	1,666	25	271	65		456		70	
Endicott College	M		X		3,710	798	1,149	37	75	41		376		185	
Episcopal Divinity School	P		X	X	108	-	-	5	31	100			20	5	6
Fisher College	B		X		1,225	318	907	12	22	30	125	47			
Fitchburg State College	M	X			6,692	1,726	2,109	75	259	75		628		370	
Framingham State College	M	X			5,903	1,378	2,450	59	193	75		831		462	
Gordon College	M		X		1,648	566	963	33	149	72		325		50	
Gordon-Conwell Theological Seminary	P		X	X	2,134	-	-	171	41	100			136	189	62
Hampshire College	B		X		1,431	615	816	54	149	86		289			
Harvard University	D		X		25,690	4,831	5,028	1,798	2,035	98	7	1,755	845	3,622	623
Hebrew College	M			-	201	-	-	6	40	100		3		49	
Hellenic College/Holy Cross Greek Orthodox School of Theology	P		X	X	186	49	23	20	16	100		37	18	24	
Hult International Business School	M		X		50	-	-	46	29	50				44	
Lasell College	M		X		1,403	410	911	28	150	50		269		23	
Lesley University	M		X		7,003	401	1,345	140	212	70		362		2,456	6
Massachusetts College of Art and Design	M	X			2,312	725	1,432	46	98	70		274		50	
Massachusetts College of Liberal Arts	M	X			1,841	620	030	-	154	64		299		37	
Massachusetts College of Pharmacy and Health Sciences	P		X		3,626	314	76	36	192	84		217	468	70	3
Massachusetts Institute of Technology	D		X		10,220	2,795	1,877	818	1,669	90		1,217		1,509	599
Massachusetts Maritime Academy	M	X			1,135	978	97	6	59	3		190		23	
Merrimack College	M		X	X	2,098	1,001	1,042	21	215	77	2	431		17	
MGH Institute of Health Professions	D		X		864	-	-	14	66	72				136	123
Montserrat College of Art	B		X		285	91	194	2	61	16		49			
Mount Holyoke College	M		X		2,204	2,201	3	353	241	91		548		3	
Mount Ida College	B		X		1,429	472	951	-	170	21		180			
New England College of Optometry	P		X		464	135	329	-	81	97		4	119	2	
New England Conservatory of Music	D		X		787	224	169	173	212	15		106		165	5
Nichols College	M		X		1,246	748	498	8	76	59		192		88	
Northeastern University	D	X			24,454	8,802	9,162	1,222	1,245	88	60	3,326	198	1,314	316

State and Institution	Highest Degree	Control: Public	Control: Private: Indep.	Control: Private: Rel.	Total Enrollment 2008-2009	Full-Time Undergraduate Enrollment 2008-2009: Male	Full-Time Undergraduate Enrollment 2008-2009: Female	Total Foreign Students 2008-2009	Teaching Staff 2008-2009	% with terminal degrees	Associate	Baccalaureate	First-professional	Master's	Doctorate
MASSACHUSETTS *(cont'd)*															
Pine Manor College	B		X		472	-	450	20	71	56		47			
Regis College	M		X	X	1,511	75	859	15	108	77	139	180		82	
Saint John's Seminary	P		X	X	118	118	-	3	36	87		6	6	13	
Salem State College	M	X			10,085	2,891	4,116	400	409	77		1,213		649	
School of the Museum of Fine Arts, Boston	M		X		797	220	490	48	158	53		155		44	
Simmons College	D		X		4,733	-	2,072	79	410	94		482		1,032	72
Simon's Rock College of Bard	B		X		394	165	229	9	46	97		40			
Smith College	D		X		3,065	-	2,596	215	313	98		708		166	7
Southern New England School of Law	P		X		256	-	-	6	39	99			60		
Springfield College	D		X		4,755	1,398	1,930	43	625	62		971		658	2
Stonehill College	B		X	X	2m450	972	1,468	7	266	81		588			
Suffolk University	P		X		9,103	2,352	3,117	728	980	95	3	1,041	472	680	15
Tufts University	D		X		9,758	2,467	2,568	585	1,207	99		1,407	343	835	190
University of Massachusetts Amherst	D	X			25,073	10,057	10,057	259	1,316	93	73	4,431		1,215	291
University of Massachusetts Boston	D	X			13,433	4,304	5,104	403	815	75		1,505		792	30
University of Massachusetts Dartmouth	M	X			9,080	3,084	4,043	337	575	55		1,140		295	2
University of Massachusetts Lowell	D	X			11,635	5,327	3,552	116	624	89	23	1,358		586	67
University of Massachusetts Medical School	P	X			1,008	-	-	-	1,871	9			93	28	24
Wellesley College	B		X		2.380	71	2,309	119	333	96		604			
Wentworth Institute of Technology	B		X		3,728	2,982	254	111	269	22	52	603			
Western New England College	P		X		3,657	1,633	1,142	57	153	69	1	652	139	112	
Westfield State College	M	X			5,392	2,162	2,537	8	248	81		919		131	
Weston Jesuit School of Theology	P			X	159	-	-	-	26	100			18	15	4
Wheaton College	B		X		1,657	640	1,011	51	163	85		296			
Wheelock College	M		X		1,086	76	`1,010	11	91	66		160		149	
Williams College	M		X		2,073	1,012	1,012	141	313	96		510		35	
Worcester Polytechnic Institute	D		X		4,158	2,253	784	333	306	75		676		328	18
Worcester State College	M	X			5,358	1,887	2,715	54	385	71		762		183	
MICHIGAN															
Adrian College	B		X	X	1,309	589	720	52	144	74		200			
Albion College	B		X	X	1,938	969	969	19	170	92		442			
Alma College	B		X	X	1,355	583	772	13	110	80		230			
Andrews University	D		X	X	3,221	782	995	451	165	65		330	103	177	83
Aquinas College	M		X	X	2,107	658	1,169	11	229	50	5	311		128	
Calvin College	M		X	X	4,224	1,918	2,251	296	412	75		823		15	
Calvin Theological Seminary	D		X	X	305	-	-	97	29	90			29	36	
Central Michigan University	D	X			26,611	8,834	11,244	532	1,119	86		3,493		2,022	98
Cleary University	B		X		691	181	221	5	128	16	43	172		13	
College for Creative Studies	B		X		1,291	750	541	50	43	78		227			
Concordia University, Ann Arbor	M		X	X	1,075	240	281	11	86	60		76		102	
Cornerstone University	P		X	X	2,466	755	1,086	25	138	60	45	366	10	211	
Cranbrook Academy of Art	M		X		144	-	-	33	10	100				77	
Davenport University	M		X		11,606	2,921	7,896	192	1,207	32	656	1,034		171	
Eastern Michigan University	D	X			22,837	7,544	10,418	812	1,242	50	42	2,963		1,268	15
Ferris State University	P	X			13,087	6,275	5,564	131	834	35		1,470	147	134	
Grace Bible College	B			X	160	93	67	1	28	50	13	20			
Grand Valley State University	M	X			23,464	7,922	11,884	234	1,404	50		3,623		975	35
Great Lakes Christian College	B		X	X	260	133	127	3	16	56	6	22			
Hillsdale College	B		X		1,250	620	630	16	95	82		242			
Hope College	B		X	X	3,226	1,323	1,903	32	322	77		699			
Kalamazoo College	B		X	X	1,340	563	777	39	114	90		266			
Kettering University	M		X		2,809	1,941	349	51	145	75		424		185	
Kuyper College	B			X	300	149	149	27	32	55	5	47			
Lake Superior State University	M	X			2,819	1,316	1,483	182	114	49	109	456			
Lawrence Technological University	M	X			4,570	2,388	547	46	397	62	38	425		472	15
Madonna University	M		X	X	4,019	765	2,295	116	325	56	22	592		186	
Marygrove College	M		X	X	2,756	173	615	28	64	48	6	97		935	
Michigan State University	D	X			46,045	16,986	19,086	2,342	2,950	95		7,941	305	1,817	465
Michigan Technological University	D	X			6,744	4,491	1,341	337	374	88	28	1,146		196	54
Northern Michigan University	M	X			9,358	4,144	4,490	94	338	80	122	1,208		150	
Northwood University	B		X		4,095	2,089	1,641	205	57	30	433	1,088		103	
Oakland University	D	X			18,081	5,334	8,735	434	906	72		2,241		915	94
Olivet College	B		X	X	1,049	592	412	21	96	35		173		12	
Rochester College	B			X	977	367	600	10	144	29	14	263			
Sacred Heart Major Seminary	P		X	X	448	50	6	23	50	75		13	5	19	

State and Institution	Highest Degree	Control: Public	Control: Private: Indep.	Control: Private: Rel.	Total Enrollment 2008-2009	Full-Time Undergraduate Enrollment 2008-2009: Male	Full-Time Undergraduate Enrollment 2008-2009: Female	Total Foreign Students 2008-2009	Teaching Staff 2008-2009	% with terminal degrees	Associate	Baccalaureate	First-professional	Master's	Doctorate
MICHIGAN *(cont'd)*															
Saginaw Valley State University	M	X			9,662	3,273	4,711	386	570	55		1,159		461	
Siena Heights University	M		X		2,161	789	1,062	22	110	65	18	668		78	
Spring Arbor University	M		X	X	3,965	873	1,856	40	143	50		666		383	
University of Detroit Mercy	D		X	X	5,552	1,133	2,105	94	566	81			153	431	5
University of Michigan - Ann Arbor	D	X			41,042	13,042	12,041	2,052	2,987	75		5,122	751	3,613	725
University of Michigan - Dearborn	M	X			8,336	3,095	6,447	83	517	84		1,147		581	
University of Michigan - Flint	M	X			6,883	2,213	3,611	69	439	55		915		291	33
Walsh College of Accountancy and Business Administration	M		X		3,195	492	555	148	187	34		396		620	
Wayne State University	D	X			32,380	8,669	12,476	1,619	1,925	85		2,781	516	2,271	214
Western Michigan University	D	X			24,433	9,859	9,859	489	1,057	91		4,046		1,339	111
Western Theological Seminary	D			X	232	-	-	11	23	100			37		5
MINNESOTA															
Augsburg College	M		X	X	3,793	1,254	1,732	71	355	48		589		94	
Bemidji State University	M	X			4,571	2,036	2,119	229	184	68		763		45	
Bethany Lutheran College	B		X	X	611	237	354	14	78	20		92			
Bethel University	D		X	X	4,280	1,297	2,117	10	291	72	10	766		215	5
Carleton College	B		X		1,994	1,236	758	120	225	80		461			
College of Saint Benedict	B		X	X	2,086	2,086	-	100	178	86		441			
College of St. Catherine	D		X	X	5,238	3,697	114	165	443	60		518		254	25
College of St. Scholastica	P		X	X	3,239	761	1,777	132	241	60		680		172	31
College of Visual Arts	B		X		178	75	103	5	45	20		32			
Concordia College - Moorhead	M		X	X	2,811	1,102	1,709	84	244	64		611			
Concordia University - St. Paul	M		X	X	2,260	651	916	23	433	77	2	458		132	
Crossroads College	B		X	X	184	88	96	4	25	67	10	31			
Crown College	M		X	X	1,270	433	706	2	52	50	36	203		6	
Gustavus Adolphus College	B		X	X	2,625	1,129	1,496	26	267	70		666			
Hamline University	P		X	X	4,803	861	1,239	192	399	98		452	204	338	8
Luther Seminary	P		X	X	720	-	-	24	38	95			74	50	12
Macalester College	B		X		1,920	806	1,114	230	217	93		446			
Metropolitan State University	M	X			6,802	2,555	3,616	141	504	74		1,309		151	
Minneapolis College of Art and Design	B		X		789	345	390	-	121	75		148		24	
Minnesota State University - Mankato	M	X			14,515	6,152	6,664	437	716	59	45	2,128		461	
Minnesota State University - Moorhead	M	X			7,494	3,027	4,013	300	318	75	43	1,273		82	
North Central University	B		X	X	1,220	537	683	86	64	20	4	197			
Northwestern College	B		X		3,026	1,208	1,738	9	173	67	18	494			
Northwestern Health Sciences University	P		X		931	26	87	39	123	91		49	190	34	
Oak Hills Christian College	B		X	X	169	91	78	2	19	22	11	31			
St. Cloud State University	M	X			16,940	6,931	8,842	847	862	70	100	2,412		424	
Saint John's University	P		X	X	2,080	1,952	-	105	164	86		441	9	26	
Saint Mary's University of Minnesota	D		X	X	5,960	960	1,082	120	561	86		427		1,280	24
St. Olaf College	B		X		3,040	1,368	1,672	30	324	86		722			
Southwest Minnesota State University	M	X			6,073	2,403	3,318	183	195	77	4	443		169	
United Theological Seminary of the Twin Cities	P		X	X	186	-	-	-	25	100			156	8	2
University of Minnesota - Crookston	B	X			2,346	1,173	1,173	92	100	38	20	209			
University of Minnesota - Duluth	M	X			11,184	5,233	4,831	112	523	81		1,769		238	
University of Minnesota - Morris	B	X			1,686	708	978	51	204	82		356			
University of Minnesota - Twin Cities	D	X			50,883	15,178	17,116	1,018	1,526	92		6,650	785	3,180	776
University of St. Thomas	D		X	X	10,984	3,099	2,977	110	745	82		1,213	127	1,066	178
Walden University	D	X			29,455	531	871	-	1,260	-		199		6,488	219
William Mitchell College of Law	P		X		1,114	-	-	-	237	100			322		
Winona State University	M	X			8,334	2,997	4,688	333	624	73	23	1,385		125	
MISSISSIPPI															
Alcorn State University	M	X			3,668	1,022	1,940	64	206	48	48	442		143	
Belhaven College	B		X	X	2,483	688	1,277	25	287	80		412		154	
Blue Mountain College	B		X	X	451	89	183	1	43	55		83		16	
Delta State University	D	X			4,091	1,158	1,673	36	277	57		635		191	5
Jackson State University	D	X			8,698	2,464	4,196	87	324	73		915		370	33
Magnolia Bible College	B		X	X	35	16	2	-	7	75		9			
Millsaps College	M		X	X	1,151	553	532	12	97	91		246		59	
Mississippi College	D		X	X	4,467	908	1,348	180	394	73		537	129	341	
Mississippi State University	D	X			17,039	5,905	5,304	586	1,032	75		2,354	59	7898	185
Mississippi University for Women	M	X			2,379	340	1,784	24	179	59	40	356		73	
Mississippi Valley State University	M	X			3,009	842	1,870	-	168	41		375		88	
Reformed Theological Seminary	D		X	X	216	127	20	-	17	100			26	24	

State and Institution	Highest Degree	Control: Public	Control: Private: Indep.	Control: Private: Rel.	Total Enrollment 2008-2009	Full-Time Undergraduate Enrollment 2008-2009: Male	Full-Time Undergraduate Enrollment 2008-2009: Female	Total Foreign Students 2008-2009	Teaching Staff 2008-2009	% with terminal degrees	Associate	Baccalaureate	First-professional	Master's	Doctorate
MISSISSIPPI *(cont'd)*															
Rust College	B		X	X	979	289	690	50	67	55	5	85			
Southeastern Baptist College	B		X	X	83	59	24	-	15	25	11	6			
Tougaloo College	B		X	X	856	103	753	-	91	63	4	127			
University of Mississippi	D	X			15,129	5,172	5,693	151	988	83		2,450	218	506	97
University of Mississippi Medical Center	D	X			1,702	89	468	-	1,107	100		225	17	107	26
University of Southern Mississippi	D	X			14,592	4,248	6,479	517	824	90		2,165		750	120
Wesley College	B		X	X	145	50	95	-	18	90		10			
William Carey University	M		X	X	2,678	451	1,105	81	125	70		449		456	
MISSOURI															
Aquinas Institute of Theology	P		X	X	245	-	-	8	32	95				42	8
Assemblies of God Theological Seminary	D		X	X	463	-	-	-	27	73			24	76	13
A.T. Still University of Health Science/ Kirksville College of Osteopathic Medicine	P		X		2,880	-	-	-	89	94			349	300	349
Avila University	M		X	X	1,831	105	87	128	147	75		229		161	
Calvary Bible College and Theological Seminary	M		X	X	313	124	134	3	24	30	3	70		13	
Central Bible College	B		X	X	741	408	333	7	66	29	5	131			
Central Christian College of the Bible	B		X	X	451	253	198	6	27	22	26	70			
Central Methodist University	B		X	X	954	476	458	9	63	46	2	153			
Cleveland Chiropractic College	P		X		483	52	21	12	47	100		43	116		
College of the Ozarks	B		X	X	1,364	600	764	14	128	61		291			
Columbia College	B		X		12,954	4,896	7,658	1,295	94	60	953	2,183		105	
Conception Seminary College	B		X	X	89	75	2	11	26	75		27			
Concordia Seminary	D		X	X	660	620	40	-	35	69			105	31	9
Covenant Theological Seminary	D		X	X	194	-	-	19	24	85			59	74	4
Culver-Stockton College	B		X	X	849	340	509	8	52	70		188			
Drury University	M		X		4,978	1,578	2,931	100	163	90	138	657		150	
Eden Theological Seminary	D		X	X	213	-	-	14	13	100			23	7	
Evangel University	M		X	X	1,647	614	920	5	128	74	5	324		25	
Fontbonne University	M		X	X	2,969	623	1,455	30	339	73		468		344	
Hannibal-LaGrange College	B		X	X	1,184	391	759	4	99	34		196			
Harris-Stowe State College	B	X			1,882	1,117	583	19	76	65		106			
Kansas City Art Institute	B		X		676	304	372	7	81	10		119			
Kansas City University of Medicine and Biosciences	P		X		1,000	-	-	10	54	98			243		
Kenrick-Glennon Seminary	P		X	X	70	-	-	7	17	100			23		
Lincoln University	M	X			3,126	1,181	1,771	96	199	45	82	245		70	
Lindenwood University	M		X	X	9,633	2,535	3,360	866	453	55		1,144		1,420	2
Logan College of Chiropractic	P		X		1,133	100	21	22	85	100		239	217	6	
Maryville University of Saint Louis	M		X		3,422	644	2,157	14	355	63		546		223	35
Midwestern Baptist Theological Seminary	D		X	X	735	182	46	7	44	84		21	54	34	
Missouri Baptist University	B		X	X	4,598	1,362	2,044	90	60	53	3	294		223	
Missouri Southern State University	M	X			5,593	2,225	3,338	112	284	62	125	673		6	
Missouri State University	D	X			19,348	7,152	9,103	387	714	85		2,795		793	31
Missouri University of Science and Technology	D	X			6,166	3,707	1,045	185	399	98		910		430	63
Missouri Valley College	B		X	X	1,682	976	786	163	204	58	1	215			
Missouri Western State University	B	X			5,342	2,226	3,075	11	323	70	52	587			
Nazarene Theological Seminary	P		X	X	293	-	-	5	27	89			37	23	10
Northwest Missouri State University	M	X			6,511	2,4991	3,170	132	274	60	37	854		195	
Ozark Christian College	B		X	X	669	341	272	21	72	15	36	123			
Park University	M		X	X	13,259	6,467	5,614	265	60	60	63	2,554		198	
Research College of Nursing	M		X	X	383	21	273	3	29	22		46		17	
Rockhurst University	D		X	X	3,124	927	1,391	31	226	55		403		287	30
Saint Louis Christian College	B		X	X	321	196	125	6	22	14	17	29			
Saint Louis College of Pharmacy	P		X		1,156	292	356	3	101	96		1	158	1	
Saint Louis University	D		X		15,539	4,427	6,371	311	1,004	95		1,538	394	736	169
Saint Luke's College	B		X		113	11	102	-	17	100		47			
Saint Paul School of Theology	D		X	X	303	-	-	-	29	70				47	5
Southeast Missouri State University	M	X			10,624	3,667	5,501	212	579	91	10	1,469		199	
Southwest Baptist University	M		X	X	3,539	963	1,789	35	246	54	151	367		182	40
Stephens College	M		X		1,050	27	863	4	91	61	1	140		23	
Truman State University	M	X			5,920	2,411	3,197	237	363	82		1,104		160	
University of Central Missouri	M	X			10,918	4,014	4,905	328	273	83	1	810		257	
University of Missouri - Columbia	D	X			28,405	10,361	11,225	1,115	1,126	75		4,779	232	1,421	377

State and Institution	Highest Degree	Control: Public	Control: Private: Indep.	Control: Private: Rel.	Total Enrollment 2008-2009	Full-Time Undergraduate Enrollment 2008-2009: Male	Full-Time Undergraduate Enrollment 2008-2009: Female	Total Foreign Students 2008-2009	Teaching Staff 2008-2009	% with terminal degrees	Associate	Baccalaureate	First-professional	Master's	Doctorate
MISSOURI *(cont'd)*															
University of Missouri - Kansas City	D	X			14,442	3,819	5,275	748	1,101	70		1,289	418	852	49
University of Missouri - St. Louis	D	X			15,527	5,097	7,335	311	811	51		2,016	34	729	66
Washington University in St. Louis	D		X		13,382	3,554	3,699	535	1,076	80		1,760	267	1,304	470
Webster University	D		X		19,398	1,829	2,345	1,618	1,767	76		1,197		5,230	5
Westminster College	B		X		972	544	428	69	78	75		168			
William Jewell College	B		X	X	1,329	532	797	9	154	45		316			
William Woods University	M		X	X	2,189	264	712	66	56	75	24	249		821	
MONTANA															
Carroll College	B		X	X	1,382	567	815	14	142	63		272			
Montana State University	D	X			11,932	5,622	4,746	239	827	79		1,809		434	40
Montana State University - Billings	M	X			3,752	1,043	2,122	38	286	81	29	502		121	
Montana State University - Northern	M	X			1,215	621	594	36	111	43	97	170		13	
Montana Tech of the University of Montana	M	X			1,900	700	1,096	97	149	50	28	263		30	
Rocky Mountain College	M		X	X	899	407	440	36	120	35		168		31	
University of Great Falls	M	X			722	230	409	14	41	65	11	119		26	
University of Montana	D	X			13,628	5,209	6,115	409	672	78	206	1,712	136	459	68
University of Montana - Western	M	X			1,148	528	620	11	49	46	25	148			
NEBRASKA															
Bellevue University	M		X		7,792	3,007	2,667	390	361	60		1,838		493	
Chadron State College	M	X			2,660	976	1,283	27	115	67		358		44	
Clarkson College	M		X	X	788	72	587	18	41	37	46	100		22	
College of Saint Mary	M		X	X	973	-	818	10	70	32	78	109		32	3
Concordia University	M		X	X	1,279	486	593	21	65	59		225		63	
Creighton University	D		X		6,992	1,642	2,462	70	657	75	2	887	521	193	92
Dana College	B		X	X	634	336	298	40	76	51		136			
Doane College	M		X	X	921	433	488	9	96	70		188			
Grace University	B		X	X	431	160	203	9	52	55	3	71		13	
Hastings College	M		X	X	1,138	589	502	11	115	55		225		11	
Midland Lutheran College	B		X	X	827	356	471	-	62	50		170			
Nebraska Christian College	B		X	X	101	38	63	-	18	20	7	10			
Nebraska Wesleyan University	B		X	X	2,107	687	1,201	21	217	81		408		71	
Peru State College	M	X			2,307	945	946	4	101	51		276		170	
Union College	B		X	X	1,009	413	525	81	87	98	8	163		27	
University of Nebraska at Kearney	M	X			6,478	2,436	2,747	583	321	72		917		281	
University of Nebraska at Omaha	D	X			14,156	5,439	5,892	471	865	87		1,768		145	21
University of Nebraska - Lincoln	D	X			22,973	9,749	8,304	1,311	1,060	95	12	3,246	123	802	259
University of Nebraska Medical Center	D	X			3,128	99	730	163	946	90		370	229	124	296
Wayne State College	M	X			3,527	1,289	1,513	35	204	71		466		219	
York College	B		X	X	404	198	206	8	65	49	12	75			
NEVADA															
Morrison University	M		X		134	44	61	1	32	41	8	21		13	
Sierra Nevada College	M		X		833	116	86	16	76	74		44		20	
University of Nevada, Las Vegas	D	X			27,960	9,669	12,306	1,118	1,677	92		3,966	135	1,374	155
University of Nevada, Reno	D	X			16,681	4,806	6,399	500	1,144	55		2,119	54	606	97
NEW HAMPSHIRE															
Colby-Sawyer College	B		X		950	332	618	20	121	75		189			
Daniel Webster College	B		X		957	641	202	-	72	45	17	136		48	
Dartmouth College	D		X		5,849	2,082	2,082	409	600	96		1,084	56	496	143
Franklin Pierce Law Center	P		X		456	-	-	69	42	100			115	45	
Franklin Pierce University	D		X		2,615	1,052	1,186	52	156	74	37	428		72	32
Granite State College	B	X			1,550	301	1,027	14	700	22	90	256			
Keene State College	M	X			5,602	2,709	3,193	23	405	80	48	999		62	
New England College	M		X		1,460	564	501	90	107	63		162		120	
Plymouth State University	M	X			6,501	2,259	2,004	65	431	60	1	806		278	
Rivier College	M		X	X	2,177	285	1,139	-	180	47	125	196		192	
Saint Anselm College	B		X	X	1,968	846	1,122	20	176	89		426			
Southern New Hampshire University	M		X		6,439	1,952	2,586	130	380	63	165	1,032		819	5
Thomas More College of Liberal Arts	B		X	X	98	49	49	4	7	100		18			
University of New Hampshire	D	X			15,005	5,300	6,745	150	948	75	143	2,377		807	48
NEW JERSEY															
Bloomfield College	B		X	X	2,054	699	1,357	42	244	35		277			
Caldwell College	M		X	X	2,306	546	1,160	115	152	80		249		137	
Centenary College	B		X	X	3,028	758	1,478	120	97	62	80	371		396	

State and Institution	Highest Degree	Control: Public	Control: Private: Indep.	Control: Private: Rel.	Total Enrollment 2008-2009	Full-Time Undergraduate Enrollment 2008-2009: Male	Full-Time Undergraduate Enrollment 2008-2009: Female	Total Foreign Students 2008-2009	Teaching Staff 2008-2009	% with terminal degrees	Associate	Baccalaureate	First-professional	Master's	Doctorate
NEW JERSEY *(cont'd)*															
College of New Jersey	M	X			6,934	2,483	3,396	22	703	65		1,344		401	
College of Saint Elizabeth	B		X	X	2,044	83	1,107	152	197	75		251		219	
Drew University	D		X	X	2,630	666	1,000	52	241	75		354		29	96
Fairleigh Dickinson University	D		X	X	8,658	2,892	3,132	346	667	79	45	802		959	11
Felician College	M		X	X	2,403	434	1,655	-	67	59	17	293		51	
Georgian Court University	M		X	X	3,045	156	1,799	30	282	48		408		233	
Immaculate Conception Seminary	P		X	X	225	-	-	-	-	-			10	65	
Kean University	M	X			13,394	3,923	6,578	268	1,222	88		1,908		671	
Monmouth University	M		X		6,494	1,992	2,752	137	459	50	10	960		551	
Montclair State University	M	X			16,736	5,366	7,451	837	1,197	65		2,632		837	8
New Brunswick Theological Seminary	P		X	X	204	-	-	8	32	88			18	7	1
New Jersey City University	M	X			8,437	2,388	3,897	600	636	74		1,023		474	
New Jersey Institute of Technology	D	X			8,288	4,342	1,086	414	633	60		880		983	58
Princeton Theological Seminary	D		X	X	653	-	-	-	72	100			131	54	25
Princeton University	D		X		7,261	2,568	2,227	726	1,025	85		1,137		436	307
Ramapo College of New Jersey	M	X			5,702	2,157	3,236	110	430	55		1,234		116	
Richard Stockton College of New Jersey	M	X			7,355	2,774	3,993	260	287	19		1,723		110	20
Rider University	M	X			5,963	1,886	2,829	92	512	88	5	895		317	
Rowan University	D	X			10,091	4,189	4,723	-	1,064	40		2,034		180	28
Rutgers, The State University of New Jersey	D	X			49,760	15,750	16,631	2,191	3,219	98		7,904	629	2,430	434
Saint Peter's College	M		X	X	3,081	1,042	1,324	93	353	78	21	457		317	
Seton Hall University	D		X	X	9,374	2,386	2,801	282	495	89		1,033	377	699	83
Stevens Institute of Technology	D		X		5m241	1,513	531	210	328	75		370		964	25
Thomas Edison State College	M	X			16,423	9,897	6,066	492	318	82	492	1,915		80	
University of Medicine and Dentistry of New Jersey	D	X			5,617	180	720	169	2,566	83	198	218	477	352	146
William Paterson University of New Jersey	M	X			10,443	3,885	4,945	104	366	85		1,597		305	
NEW MEXICO															
College of Santa Fe	M		X		672	343	329	8	268	73		139			
Eastern New Mexico University	M	X			4,173	1,584	1,859	84	276	50	14	481		107	
New Mexico Highlands University	M	X			3,457	818	1,228	70	77	70	2	657		534	
New Mexico Institute of Mining and Technology	D	X			1,710	890	438	34	103	95	4	194		90	15
New Mexico State University	D	X			16,722	5,872	7,473	167	968	80	21	2,255		836	72
St. John's College	M		X		535	261	174	6	65	75		89		64	
Southwestern College	M		X		138	18	120	66	36	75				59	
University of New Mexico	D	X			25,672	8,563	11,350	847	1,411	88	41	3,052	227	1,110	345
University of the Southwest	B		X	X	552	164	235	41	66	38		205		40	
Western New Mexico University	M	X			2,697	821	1,398	27	135	60	106	192		112	
NEW YORK															
Adelphi University	D		X		8,308	1,210	2,935	267	908	40	8	1,139		1,111	24
Albany College of Pharmacy	D		X		1,423	386	503	73	43	84		5	193		
Albany Law School of Union University	P		X		710	-	-	14	53	100			212	12	
Albany Medical College	P		X		762	-	-	43	372	26			142	55	9
Alfred University	D		X		2,235	980	081	24	172	96		416		111	11
Bank Street College of Education	M		X		1,032	-	-	10	68	53				323	
Bard College	M		X		2,109	764	1,700	132	161	97	117	324		115	2
Barnard College	B		X		2,297	2,297	-	71	324	80		600			
Bernard M. Baruch College / CUNY	M	X			16,097	5,180	7,064	1,374	921	75		2,506		1,262	
Boricua College	B		X		1,058	207	684	-	119	35	161	146		5	
Brooklyn College / CUNY	M	X			16,087	3,243	4,666	963	1,134	55		2,154		1,008	
Brooklyn Law School	P		X		1,496	-	-	15	71	100			470		
Canisius College	M		X	X	4,984	1,403	1,777	200	532	90	4	811		653	
Cazenovia College	B		X		1,084	271	813	2	141	25	6	176			
Christ the King Seminary	P		X	X	92	-	-	-	20	80			4	16	
City College / CUNY	M	X			14,392	4,803	4,615	1,234	857	97		1,463		112	
Clarkson University	D		X		2,949	1,885	646	90	197	85		609		111	37
Colgate Rochester Crozer Divinity School	D		X	X	156	-	-	8	20	90			17	20	5
Colgate University	M		X		2,841	1,159	1,472	142	322	75		675		2	
College of Mount Saint Vincent	M		X	X	1,810	347	1,180	15	82	72	2	281		79	
College of New Rochelle	M		X	X	6,226	895	4,953	21	90	65		976		409	
College of Saint Rose	M		X	X	4,949	831	2,247	49	204	80		693		745	
College of Staten Island / CUNY	D	X			12,442	4,518	6,612	501	851	74	766	1,060		309	
Columbia University	D		X		23,196	3,806	3,513	1,472	2,240	90		1,824	721	5,401	497

State and Institution	Highest Degree	Control: Public	Control: Private: Indep.	Control: Private: Rel.	Total Enrollment 2008-2009	Full-Time Undergraduate Enrollment 2008-2009: Male	Full-Time Undergraduate Enrollment 2008-2009: Female	Total Foreign Students 2008-2009	Teaching Staff 2008-2009	% with terminal degrees	Associate	Baccalaureate	First-professional	Master's	Doctorate
NEW YORK *(cont'd)*															
Concordia College	B		X	X	707	362	347	55	46	79	5	123			
Cooper Union for the Advancement of Science and Art	M		X		957	571	348	153	211	65		215		12	
Cornell University	D		X		19,800	6,881	6,744	1,584	1,869	95		3,431	287	1,751	465
Culinary Institute of America	B		X		2,812	1,737	1,020	141	190	76	1,085	266			
Daemen College	M		X		2,716	329	987	315	269	42		263		355	50
Davis College	B		X	X	325	94	93	14	17	25	9	38			
Dominican College of Blauvelt	D		X	X	1,977	387	700	-	170	46		304		39	16
Dowling College	M		X		5,706	928	1,280	267	407	96		590		873	20
D'Youville College	M		X	X	2,943	345	526	166	166	67		290		449	25
Elmira College	M		X		1,639	450	1,108	67	74	98	3	300		49	
Excelsior College	M	X			33,453	12,118	15,290	325	-	-	2,481	2,714		72	
Farmingdale State University of New York	B	X			6,850	3,231	3,230	45	318	76	523	544			
Fashion Institute of Technology	M	X			10,065	1,632	8,567	775	939	76	1,707	1,196		60	
Five Towns College	B	X			1,173	633	465	-	125	76	8	281		21	
Fordham University	D		X	X	14,666	3,086	4,142	98	1,068	98		1,865	485	1,868	126
General Theological Seminary	P		X	X	146	-	-	2	22	99			41	2	
Graduate School and University Center / CUNY	D	X			5,468	1,651	1,822	786	391	99		195		55	358
Hamilton College	B		X		1,872	905	904	96	205	94		442			
Hartwick College	B		X		1,493	806	657	59	154	91		297			
Hebrew Union College - Jewish Institute of Religion	D		X	X	182	-	-	7	19	100			24		26
Hilbert College	B		X	X	996	334	479	1	119	56	31	221			
Hobart and William Smith Colleges	B		X		2,078	900	1,028	32	188	96		399		9	
Hofstra University	D		X		12,333	3,623	4,139	238	1,206	93		1,750	300	903	84
Houghton College	M		X	X	1,415	468	867	47	115	82	7	355		8	
Hunter College / CUNY	M	X			21,258	5,002	10,629	1,031	1,961	80		2,511		1,566	
Iona College	M		X		4,375	1,467	1,767	71	382	80		787		255	
Ithaca College	D		X		6,448	2,676	3,241	176	656	91		1,340		246	63
Jewish Theological Seminary of America	D		X	X	544	67	121	1	121	95		32	28	63	6
John Jay College of Criminal Justice / CUNY	D	X			14,844	4,374	8,062	460	913	78	186	1,717		526	
Keuka College	M		X	X	1,526	388	348	4	63	62		362		57	
Laboratory Institute of Merchandising	B		X		1,295	51	899	14	119	20	27	212			
Le Moyne College	M		X	X	3,479	889	1,362	23	338	75		526		300	
Lehman College / CUNY	M	X			11,860	1,014	3,903	489	898	40		1,383		654	
Long Island University - Brooklyn Campus	D		X		8,051	1,272	3,134	295	320	80	26	580	200	815	26
Long Island University - C. W. Post Campus	P		X		8,421	1,587	2,549	301	328	77	2	1,011		1,527	28
Manhattan College	M		X	X	3,441	1,513	1,513	30	176	91		658		121	
Manhattan School of Music	D		X		967	188	181	273	380	25		95		135	10
Manhattanville College	M		X		2,823	572	1,133	150	288	95		394		375	
Marist College	M		X	X	5,929	2,105	2,191	147	265	78		1,155		320	
Marymount College of Fordham University	B		X	X	949	95	854	10	156	98	1	218			
Marymount Manhattan College	B		X	X	1,,988	462	1,545	50	317	65	5	375			
Medaille College	M		X		2,883	647	950	23	411	74	94	318		280	
Medgar Evers College / CUNY	B	X			6,036	1,251	3,360	646	339	65	390	225			
Mercy College	M		X		9,043	1,634	4,002	90	219	76	95	1,037		1,603	14
Molloy College	M		X		3,879	484	1,515	3	493	52	44	572		221	
Morrisville State College	B	X			3,338	1,606	1,161	38	260	25	453	132			
Mount Saint Mary College	M		X		2,629	445	1,247	-	215	73		431		179	
Mount Sinai School of Medicine	D		X		902	-	-	70	1,478	76			111	9	11
Nazareth College of Rochester	M		X		3,259	494	1,563	10	294	97		516		413	
New School	D		X		9,825	1,803	3,885	189	1,769	75	413	1,014		880	63
New York Chiropractic College	P		X		842	-	-	100	79	100			164		
New York City College of Technology / CUNY	B	X			14,268	6,220	6,129	1,604	304	65	875	559			
New York College of Podiatric Medicine	P		X		344	-	-	8	62	`100			60		
New York Institute of Technology	P		X		9,073	2,548	1,604	1,475	849	90	11	639	46	985	30
New York Law School	P		X		1,655	-	-	27	135	100			407	40	
New York Medical College	D		X		1,414	-	-	68	1,689	100			192	119	10
New York School of Interior Design	M		X		628	58	666	52	79	61	78	32		9	
New York Theological Seminary	D		X	X	342	-	-	49	40	96			37	26	6
New York University	D		X		42,189	7,512	11,970	4,305	5,005	55	454	5,086	906	5,563	415
Niagara University	M		X		4,254	1,125	1,701	157	341	88		683		448	
Nyack College	P		X	X	3,041	792	1,238	99	288	50	12	516	35	185	

State and Institution	Highest Degree	Control: Public	Control: Private: Indep.	Control: Private: Rel.	Total Enrollment 2008-2009	Full-Time Undergraduate Enrollment 2008-2009: Male	Full-Time Undergraduate Enrollment 2008-2009: Female	Total Foreign Students 2008-2009	Teaching Staff 2008-2009	% with terminal degrees	Associate	Baccalaureate	First-professional	Master's	Doctorate
NEW YORK *(cont'd)*															
Pace University	D		X		12,704	3,482	5,446	285	1,384	60	99	1,635	219	1,495	27
Polytechnic University	D		X		3,983	1,122	281	165	273	84		259		540	29
Pratt Institute	M		X		4,946	1,304	1,955	310	473	80	49	686		701	
Queens College / CUNY	M	X			19,572	3,490	5,326	1,206	1,260	70		2,433		1,238	
Rensselaer Polytechnic Institute	D		X		6,777	3,868	1,291	682	481	95		1,144		384	158
Roberts Wesleyan College	M		X	X	1,902	436	972	34	101	60		390		270	
Rochester Institute of Technology	D		X		15,055	8,089	3,569	1,213	1,230	75	172	2,266		829	19
Russell Sage College	M		X		699	-	699	16	98	74		197			
Sage College of Albany	M		X		2,070	299	732	2	162	60	71	201		332	
St. Bonaventure University	M		X	X	2,406	1,092	1,049	39	174	85		463		271	
St. Francis College	B		X		2,425	1,075	1,261	203	211	71	18	443		8	
St. John Fisher College	M		X		3,7832	1,075	1,486	-	345	91		695		344	
St. John's University	D		X	X	20,109	5,257	6,628	1,066	1,486	55	46	2,117	528	1,115	72
St. Joseph's College	M		X		5,350	939	2,629	168	334	91		1,197		139	
St. Joseph's Seminary	P		X	X	115	-	-	11	30	90			21		
St. Lawrence University	M		X		2,715	1,309	1,148	109	189	92		303		131	
Saint Thomas Aquinas College	M		X		2,100	894	1,092	22	79	94	8	294		76	
St. Vladimir's Orthodox Theological Seminary	P		X	X	88	-	-	10	20	80			2	22	2
Sarah Lawrence College	M		X		1,715	349	969	49	236	98		303		131	
School of Visual Arts	M		X		3,988	1,405	1,578	586	830	36		674		187	
Seminary of the Immaculate Conception	P		X	X	150	-	-	-	25	90			6	30	7
Siena College	B		X	X	3,305	1,312	1,669	18	307	75		769			
Skidmore College	M		X		2,777	1,043	1,530	34	329	85		638		13	
State University College of Technology at Canton	B	X			2,970	1,045	1,115	20	168	30	467	85			
State University College of Technology at Delhi	B	X			2,971	1,406	1,151	51	117	25	460	111			
State University of New York at Albany	D	X			18,204	5,570	5,641	912	1,161	95		2,734		1,362	151
State University of New York at Binghamton	D	X			14,882	1,765	5,302	1,643	889	95		2,821		636	116
State University of New York at Buffalo	D	X			28,192 27,220	9,809	8,356	1,290	1,746	98		3,966	552	1,973	353
State University of New York at New Paltz	M	X			8,205	1,780	1,732	399	703	84		1,592		230	
State University of New York at Purchase College	M	X			4,251	1,653	2,020	51	263	100		743		46	
State University of New York at Stony Brook	D	X			23,991	6,835	6,901	2,345	1,389	98		3,671	650	1,716	307
State University of New York College at Brockport	M	X			8,275,	2,558	3,347	77	615	90		1,610		437	
State University of New York College at Buffalo	M	X			11m234	3,205	4,858	49	715	75		1,767		757	
State University of New York College at Cortland	M	X			7,234	2,525	3,444	36	481	87		1,275		379	
State University of New York College at Fredonia	M	X			5,573	2,124	2,717	88	444	98		1,124		199	
State University of New York College at Geneseo	M	X			5,585	2,150	3,080	139	329	87		1,132		87	
State University of New York College at Old Westbury	M	X			3,505	1,098	1,698	66	264	45		630		13	
State University of New York College at Oneonta	M	X			5,757	2,296	3,169	102	475	71		1,315		52	
State University of New York College at Oswego	M	X			8,909	2,884	3,265	143	507	73		1,440		347	
State University of New York College at Plattsburgh	M	X			6,358	2,251	2,982	363	487	55		1,103		277	
State University of New York College at Potsdam	M	X			4,319	1,520	2,099	123	327	75		679		420	
State University of New York College of Agriculture and Technology at Cobleskill	B	X			2,615	1,338	1,140	64	146	35	361	203			
State University of New York College of Environmental Science and Forestry	D	X			2,523	1,278	320	18	140	92	38	265		97	22
State University of New York College of Optometry	D	X			303	-	-	23	123	100			80	3	
State University of New York College of Technology at Alfred	B	X			3,276	2,181	1,123	46	132	76	691	186			
State University of New York Empire State College	M	X			13,614	1,295	2,841	747	1,118	32	618	2,181		123	
State University of New York Health Science Center at Brooklyn	P	X			1,613	62	283	5	134	76		189	198	125	16
State University of New York Health Science Center at Syracuse	D	X			1,374	68	175	8	773	30		94	157	33	40

State and Institution	Highest Degree	Control: Public	Control: Private: Indep.	Control: Private: Rel.	Total Enrollment 2008-2009	Full-Time Undergraduate Enrollment 2008-2009: Male	Full-Time Undergraduate Enrollment 2008-2009: Female	Total Foreign Students 2008-2009	Teaching Staff 2008-2009	% with terminal degrees	Associate	Baccalaureate	First-professional	Master's	Doctorate
NEW YORK *(cont'd)*															
State University of New York Institute of Technology at Utica/Rome	M	X			2,590	1,030	989	20	157	70		425		147	
State University of New York Maritime College	M	X			1,630	1,024	126	40	82	76	4	218		46	
Syracuse University	D		X		19,366	5,367	6,777	1,813	1,191	56	7	2,886	309	1,648	812
Teachers College at Columbia University	D		X		5,040	-	-	534	139	80				1,565	214
Touro College	P		X		17,327	4,628	7,552	-	810	76	795	1,526	389	2,341	46
Unification Theological Seminary	D		X	X	173	-	-	53	39	50			9	25	
Union College	B		X		2,240	1,143	1,011	47	223	52		473			
Union Theological Seminary	D		X	X	245	-	-	10	43	100			58	24	4
United States Merchant Marine Academy	B	X			986	828	126	18	85	45		211			
United States Military Academy	B	X			4,448	3,543	905	46	119	33		960			
University of Rochester	D		X		9,735	2,360	2,243	630	1,542	99		1,232	99	913	221
Utica College	M		X		3,082	802	1,184	48	290	59		487		145	49
Vassar College	B		X		2,389	960	1,122	131	318	60		638			
Vaughn College of Aeronautics and Technology	B		X		1,097	731	366	34	65	30	117	114			
Wagner College	M		X	X	2,294	682	1,194	11	231	85		384		165	
Webb Institute	B		X		90	59	31	-	14	60		34			
Wells College	B		X		481	74	395	8	69	80		89			
Yeshiva University	D		X		6,292	1,129	1,202	140	227	71	292	646	536	412	113
York College / CUNY	B	X			7,157	1,803	3,940	431	378	70		746		17	
NORTH CAROLINA															
Appalachian State University	D	X			16,610	6,389	6,121	166	998	85		2,634		652	15
Barber-Scotia College	B		X	X	488	219	269	2	28	50		36			
Barton College	B		X		1,155	290	599	24	111	73		210			
Belmont Abbey College	B		X	X	1,497	448	563	60	84	49		155			
Bennett College for Women	B		X	X	689	-	689	7	70	58		108			
Cabarrus College of Health Sciences	B		X		372	37	287	17	46	10	93	13			
Campbell University	D		X		8,033	2,082	2.542	241	434	89	122	888	214	181	
Catawba College	M		X	X	1,261	588	606	24	100	67		281		5	
Chowan University	B		X	X	952	463	393	6	73	55	9	93			
Davidson College	B		X	X	1,688	836	831	68	172	98		432			
Duke University	D		X		14,060	3,228	3,102	316	1,579	97		1,505	434	1,423	271
East Carolina University	D	X			22,767	6,430	9,306	201	1,290	78		3,237	68	1,359	121
Elizabeth City State University	B	M			3,104	1,006	1,614	31	105	76		389		22	
Elon University	M		X	X	5,628	2,337	2,572	112	335	75		1,104		66	33
Fayetteville State University	D	X			6,217	1,674	3,725	-	200	53		775		160	13
Gardner-Webb University	M		X	X	4,070	757	1,468	63	127	76	65	689	15	334	
Greensboro College	M		X		1,2279	544	664	-	125	82		151		16	
Guilford College	B		X	X	2,641	902	1,323	23	205	89		521			
High Point University	M		X	X	3,409	910	1,480	86	267	55		479		102	
John Wesley College	B		X	X	102	71	31	-	21	55		39			
Johnson C. Smith University	B		X		1,571	594	841	-	132	80		213			
Lees-McRae College	B		X	X	889	356	533	27	51	77		134			
Lenoir-Rhyne College	M	X		X	1,540	534	909	-	135	80		284		36	
Livingstone College	B		X	X	994	505	383	10	53	64		118			
Mars Hill College	B		X	X	1,245	509	655	34	83	65		214			
Meredith College	M		X		2,250	8	1,981	20	262	79		349		37	80
Methodist University	M		X	X	2,190	1,086	910	85	118	50	15	324		48	
Montreat College	M		X	X	1,113	377	532	19	49	67	45	151		33	
Mount Olive College	B		X	X	3,390	1,208	1,947	-	199	65	206	627			
North Carolina Agricultural and Technical State University	M	X			10,388	4,563	5,124	52	374	61		1,172		437	32
North Carolina Central University	D	X			8,035	2,295	4,319	30	467	75		854	141	390	
North Carolina School of the Arts	M	X			879	463	325	31	139	51		119		39	
North Carolina State University at Raleigh	D	X			32,872	11,392	8,650	1,891	1,845	90	132	4,535	75	1,307	369
North Carolina Wesleyan College	B		X	X	1,506	788	964	88	177	49		386			
Pfeiffer University	M		X		2,019	438	597	46	157	73		234		407	
Piedmont Baptist College	M		X	X	393	170	121	3	39	35	7	46		4	
Queens University of Charlotte	M		X	X	2,302	374	1,294	83	81	83	124	255		155	
Roanoke Bible College	B		X	X	153	67	55	2	28	21	6	19			
St. Andrews Presbyterian College	B		X	X	625	284	443	25	84	88		171			
Saint Augustine's College	B		X	X	1,451	682	565	62	114	47		168			
Salem College	M		X	X	939	15	663	96	103	92		157		44	
Shaw University	B		X		2,882	950	1,719	27	265	50	7	435	27	6	

State and Institution	Highest Degree	Control: Public	Control: Private: Indep.	Control: Private: Rel.	Total Enrollment 2008-2009	Full-Time Undergraduate Enrollment 2008-2009: Male	Full-Time Undergraduate Enrollment 2008-2009: Female	Total Foreign Students 2008-2009	Teaching Staff 2008-2009	% with terminal degrees	Associate	Baccalaureate	First-professional	Master's	Doctorate
NORTH CAROLINA *(cont'd)*															
Southeastern Baptist Theological Seminary	D		X	X	2,109	361	164	25	33	100	10	78	142	36	11
University of North Carolina at Asheville	M	X			3,629	1,229	1,695	39	304	75		704		11	
University of North Carolina at Chapel Hill	D	X			28,587	6.721	9,598	211	1,467	88		3,733	608	1,414	490
University of North Carolina at Charlotte	D	X			23,000	6,818	7,422	815	1,245	88		3,375		1,058	45
University of North Carolina at Greensboro	D	X			19,976	3,565	7,482	297	989	75		2,388		967	93
University of North Carolina at Pembroke	M	X			5,827	1,550	2,332	70	355	78		555		110	
University of North Carolina at Wilmington	D	X			12,643	4,138	5,621	39	784	75		2,451		398	1
Wake Forest University	D		X	X	6,062	2,136	2,196	64	428	85		1,028	288	531	56
Warren Wilson College	M		X		1,002	412	429	25	73	76		177		32	
Western Carolina University	D	X			9,050	3,423	3,723	71	608	65		1,525		471	15
Wingate University	M		X	X	2,128	643	710	33	162	80		278		61	
Winston-Salem State University	M	X			6,442	1,420	3,279	16	400	50		867		131	
NORTH DAKOTA															
Dickinson State University	B	X			2,730	768	961	167	175	35	48	386			
Jamestown College	B		X	X	1,025	423	488	51	77	40		166			
Mayville State University	B	X			789	489	300	31	74	15	2	106			
Minot State University	M	X			3,432	928	1,510	283	264	64	1	477		90	
North Dakota State University of Agriculture and Applied Science	D	X			13,230	5,233	4,270	674	630	70		1,770	65	390	59
Trinity Bible College	B		X	X	296	158	138	-	24	29	8	34			
University of Mary	M		X	X	2,862	769	1,164	49	212	37		540		461	25
University of North Dakota	D	X			12,748	4,895	4,226	332	825	70		1,836	397	110	117
Valley City State University	B	X			1,019	362	352	58	91	36		156		18	
OHIO															
Air Force Institute of Technology	D	X			773	-	-	21	136	93				371	26
Antioch University	D		X		3,464	-	-	58	642	-		344		590	11
Antioch University - Antioch College	B		X		300	118	182	-	54	75		95			
Antioch University - McGregor	M		X		630	16	40	-	63	55		46		240	
Art Academy of Cincinnati	M		X		167	97	121	2	52	80		30		6	
Ashland University	D		X	X	6,200	1,067	1,326	124	200	81	9	564	43	1,001	25
Athenaeum of Ohio	P		X	X	253	88	36	37	26	50		24	4	16	
Baldwin-Wallace College	M		X	X	4,274	1,462	2,147	44	360	72		850		311	
Bluffton University	M		X	X	1,149	447	533	24	114	60		253		55	
Bowling Green State University	D	X			17,874	6,783	8,245	659	1,012	80		3,310		974	86
Capital University	P		X	X	3,632	917	1,399	36	419	80		570	181	100	
Case Western Reserve University	D		X		9,814	2,274	1,584	1,076	863	85		793	438	951	243
Cedarville University	M		X	X	3,066	1,291	1,610	31	262	63		617		6	
Central State University	M	X			1,766	877	870	160	91	77		166		5	
Chancellor University	M		X		942	286	759	-	150	24	22	137		34	
Cincinnati College of Mortuary Science	B		X		134	-	-	2	7	86	35	87			
Cleveland Institute of Art	B		X		503	264	258	15	101	40		74			
Cleveland Institute of Music	D		X		462	101	134	31	112	70		40		74	
Cleveland State University	D	X			15,139	3,002	3,724	523	963	60		1,695	220	1,373	43
College of Mount St. Joseph	M		X	X	2,133	619	1,297	-	225	27	9	392		165	
College of Wooster	B		X	X	1,884	891	928	94	184	75		398			
Columbus College of Art and Design	B		X		1,558	590	721	94	170	78		265			
Defiance College	B		X	X	1,001	360	275	1	103	25	7	179		36	
Denison University	B		X		2,220	956	1,278	110	196	90		541			
Franciscan University of Steubenville	M		X	X	2,449	727	1,255	25	137	62	43	425		116	
Franklin University	M		X		7,416	2,875	3,781	199	199	69	63	1,235		532	
Hebrew Union College - Jewish Institute of Religion	D		X	X	292	-	-	10	26	100			8	8	4
Heidelberg College	M		X	X	1,546	528	531	45	159	50		246		60	
Hiram College	B		X	X	1,360	396	715	42	119	70		232			
John Carroll University	M		X	X	3,826	1,416	1,596	33	365	70		677		239	
Kent State University	D	X			22,944	6,230	9,143	458	1,512	55		3,841		1,198	177
Kenyon College	B		X	X	1,644	787	844	64	182	92		429			
Lake Erie College	M		X		1,051	164	432	11	89	50		152		56	
Laura and Alvin Siegal College of Judaic Studies	M		X	X	135	4	7	-	31	75		1		14	
Lourdes College	M		X	X	2,066	139	743	3	178	20	33	247		50	
Malone College	M		X	X	2,296	768	1,192	30	195	58		477		87	
Marietta College	M		X		1,606	664	572	124	145	74		306		46	

State and Institution	Highest Degree	Control: Public	Control: Private: Indep.	Control: Private: Rel.	Total Enrollment 2008-2009	Full-Time Undergraduate Enrollment 2008-2009: Male	Full-Time Undergraduate Enrollment 2008-2009: Female	Total Foreign Students 2008-2009	Teaching Staff 2008-2009	% with terminal degrees	Associate	Baccalaureate	First-professional	Master's	Doctorate
OHIO *(cont'd)*															
Medical College of Ohio at Toledo	D	X			1,086	-	-	61	390	87			128	84	18
Methodist Theological School in Ohio	D		X	X	222	-	-	-	38	90			32	17	
Miami University	D	X			17,191	7,028	7,529	342	1,161	81	281	3,632		468	50
Mount Union College	B		X	X	2,204	1,067	1,137	66	226	65		446			
Mount Vernon Nazarene University	M		X	X	2,558	783	1,147	26	244	65	10	545		255	
Muskingum College	M		X	X	2,135	817	859	21	132	85		299		110	
Northeastern Ohio Universities College of Medicine and Pharmacy	P	X			602	-	-	-	46	100			101		
Notre Dame College of Ohio	M		X	X	1,637	416	824	16	79	91	8	97		26	
Oberlin College	M		X		2,841	1,262	1,587	170	288	92		695		6	
Ohio Christian University	B		X	X	730	194	217	7	38	40	5	104			
Ohio College of Podiatric Medicine	P		X		386	-	-	20	26	99			77		
Ohio Dominican University	M		X	X	2,854	740	1,085	31	217	65	77	451		254	
Ohio Northern University	P		X	X	3,721	1,331	1,166	41	317	75		448	277	8	
The Ohio State University	D	X			53,715	18,539	16,443	3,638	4,031	75	342	8,721	726	2,576	885
The Ohio State University at Lima	M	X			1,409	498	683	2	31	-	33	110			
The Ohio State University at Mansfield	M	X			1,545	557	1,002	2	62	70		115		87	
The Ohio State University at Marion	M	X			1,673	599	841	4	54	95	150	96			
The Ohio State University at Newark	M	X			2,472	858	1,180	2	29	-	137	117		-	
Ohio University	D		X	X	21,369	7,793	8,174	1,066	1,182	80	52	4,025	106	956	147
Ohio Wesleyan University	B		X	X	1,959	928	989	1,031	182	85		380			
Otterbein College	M		X	X	3,131	982	1,822	55	124	60		544		93	
Pontifical College Josephinum	P		X	X	184	115	-	15	53	75		17	9	4	
Saint Mary Seminary and Graduate School of Theology	P		X	X	130	-	-	3	21	98			6	13	1
Shawnee State University	B	X			3,976	1,335	1,887	40	304	25		270		1	
Tiffin University	M		X		2,674	1,437	677	134	117	52	3	271		196	
Trinity Lutheran Seminary	P		X	X	146	-	-	3	25	95			47		
Union Institute	D	X			2,051	331	662	-	125	98		444		246	55
United Theological Seminary	D		X	X	228	-	-	5	36	83			17	7	54
University of Akron	D	X			24,119	7,072	7,307	771	1,590	82	365	2,219	152	954	110
University of Cincinnati	D	X			29,617	8,509	7.841	2,961	1,263	76	174	3,546	278	2,032	408
University of Dayton	D		X	X	10,290	3,464	3,461	204	914	60		1,584	163	735	146
The University of Findlay	M		X	X	5,761	1,122	1,729	288	299	33	68	540		524	
University of Toledo	D	X			22,336	8,162	7,305	670	1,154	80	118	2,480	116	854	332
Urbana University	M		X	X	1,354	708	512	14	120	50	59	208		33	
Ursuline College	M		X	X	1,639	42	746	9	213	52		215		79	
Walsh University	M		X	X	2,738	620	1,046	27	217	45	4	366		123	5
Wilberforce University	M		X	X	785	348	437	79	63	31		172		3	
Wilmington College	M		X	X	1,542	753	887	15	129	40		248		5	
Winebrenner Theological Seminary	P		X	X	99	-	-	-	19	85			12	5	4
Wittenberg University	M		X	X	1,976	885	1,091	40	202	75		452		2	
Wright State University	D	X			16,676	4,562	5,823	590	756	76		2,287	91	1,199	55
Xavier University	M		X	X	6,884	1,475	1,818	201	600	50	18	927		892	17
Youngstown State University	D	X			13,704	4,259	5,113	137	989	80	226	1,478		308	2
OKLAHOMA															
Bacone College	B		X	X	958	413	495	-	84	35	75	58			
Cameron University	M	X			5,449	1,312	2,078	275	313	45	191	527		102	
East Central University	M	X			4,361	1,596	2,250	132	203	60		654		268	
Langston University	D	X			2,754	885	1,197	27	162	75	14	320		41	7
Mid-America Christian University	B		X	X	771	376	333	-	28	47	1	158			
Northeastern State University	P	X			8,771	2,597	3,812	263	459	76		1,525	27	261	
Northwestern Oklahoma State University	M	X			2,074	596	739	21	156	35		320		62	
Oklahoma Baptist University	B		X	X	1,769	564	541	70	152	56		257			
Oklahoma Christian University	B		X	X	2,060	897	712	-	183	67		246		122	
Oklahoma City University	P		X		3,884	619	1,054	980	278	75		461	170	386	
Oklahoma Panhandle State University	B	X			1,223	476	747	23	81	46	22	183			
Oklahoma State University	D	X			23,461	8,054	8,077	756	1,184	91		3,698	68	904	177
Oklahoma Wesleyan University	B		X	X	1,021	397	624	11	33	16	29	218		39	
Oral Roberts University	D		X		3,244	1,145	1,613	140	185	51		532	39	91	38
Rogers State University	B		X	X	3,913	802	3,111	4	204	35		159			
St. Gregory's University	B		X	X	745	191	510	60	46	35		91			
Southeastern Oklahoma State University	M	X			3,866	1,286	1,505	39	229	52		616		106	
Southern Nazarene University	M		X	X	2,069	805	809	42	140	65		538		214	
Southwestern Christian University	M		X	X	291	107	96	9	23	50	3	37		22	7
Southwestern Oklahoma State University	M	X			3,866	2,189	1,245	39	198	69		616	78	186	
University of Central Oklahoma	M	X			15,724	5,995	8,314	907	802	40		2,184		406	

State and Institution	Highest Degree	Control: Public	Control: Private: Indep.	Control: Private: Rel.	Total Enrollment 2008-2009	Full-Time Undergraduate Enrollment 2008-2009: Male	Full-Time Undergraduate Enrollment 2008-2009: Female	Total Foreign Students 2008-2009	Teaching Staff 2008-2009	% with terminal degrees	Associate	Baccalaureate	First-professional	Master's	Doctorate
OKLAHOMA *(cont'd)*															
University of Oklahoma	D	X			26,140	8,704	9,163	592	1,719	75		3,877	468	1,476	337
University of Oklahoma Health Sciences Center	D	X			3,790	121	872	20	801	69		430	299	333	25
University of Science and Arts of Oklahoma	B	X			1,174	385	789	10	89	75		217			
University of Tulsa	D		X	X	4,192	1,582	1,320	459	376	96		561	212	203	20
OREGON															
Art Institute of Portland	B		X		1,621	549	593	15	104	35		160			
Concordia University	M		X	X	1,709	377	786	17	138	15		251		238	
Corban College	M		X	X	1,031	338	509	-	53	37	4	191		6	
Eastern Oregon University	M	X			3,666	797	1,148	37	115	96		625		76	
Eugene Bible College	B		X	X	129	99	30	2	22	52		51			
George Fox University	D		X	X	3,383	617	1,005	136	324	69		513		416	54
Lewis and Clark College	P		X		3,565	774	1,088	119	379	94		464	238	246	
Linfield College	M		X	X	1,720	841	819	85	274	62		619			
Marylhurst University	M		X			235	620	90	223	76		141		142	
Multnomah University	M		X	X	840	235	296	8	62	60		113		58	
Northwest Christian University	M		X	X	534	131	209	1	80	34	8	118		40	
Oregon Health and Science University	D	X			2,424	226	1,351	24	563	88		209	162	204	52
Oregon Institute of Technology	M	X			3,515	1,608	1,526	35	152	26	81	434		4	
Oregon State University	D	X			20,305	8,452	7,376	406	1,554	85		3,267	118	874	173
Pacific Northwest College of Art	B		X		507	129	207	-	49	100		96			
Pacific University	D		X	X	3,167	390	425	-	278	84		236	88	340	65
Portland State University	D	X			26,382	5,165	5,183	1,432	1,260	55		3,289		1,500	45
Reed College	M		X		1,471	618	824	122	132	85		299		5	
Southern Oregon University	M	X			5,079	1,454	2,602	102	272	91		663		260	
University of Oregon	D	X			21,452	7,064	7,924	1,207	1,129	85		3,836	182	856	151
University of Portland	P		X	X	3,661	1,038	1,776	74	309	95		702		214	
Warner Pacific College	M		X	X	973	231	643	6	40	50	19	190		14	
Western Oregon University	M	X			4,885	1,707	2,476	84	279	88	1	805		107	
Western Seminary	D		X	X	748	-	-	22	116	88			21	75	4
Western States Chiropractic College	P		X		449	9	3	-	41	92		14	124		
Willamette University	P		X	X	2,721	1,075	1,273	117	237	93		451	110	158	
PENNSYLVANIA															
Albright College	M		X		2,305	871	1,223	93	156	55		491		4	
Allegheny College	B		X		2,125	942	1,183	25	167	93		434			
Alvernia College	M		X		2,809	501	1,056	28	273	40	17	451		175	
The American College	M		X		540	-	-	-	35	70				61	
Arcadia University	M		X	X	3,868	507	1,385	78	393	60		445		429	56
Baptist Bible College and Seminary	P		X	X	910	269	366	20	44	33	8	102	7	35	7
Bloomsburg University of Pennsylvania	M	X			8,855	2,985	4,353	88	412	75		1,545		335	10
Bryn Athyn College of the New Church	P		X	X	164	58	71	25	49	76		15	3	4	
Bryn Mawr College	D		X		1,799	31	1,296	83	146	99		311		128	18
Bucknell University	M		X		3,759	1,724	1,805	113	321	75		896		34	
Cabrini College	M		X	X	3,580	529	1,091	4	224	79		316		185	
California University of Pennsylvania	M	X			7,720	2,607	2,848	63	319	72	37	1,130		546	
Carlow University	M		X	X	2,128	125	1,320	-	108	51		341		208	
Carnegie Mellon University	D		X		10,875	3,351	2,178	719	856	98		1,295		1,621	258
Cedar Crest College	B		X		1,872	17	990	19	145	70		327		28	
Chatham University	D		X		2,184	50	755	88	94	97		134		258	74
Chestnut Hill College	D		X	X	2,085	282	625	21	265	45		235		185	18
Cheyney University of Pennsylvania	M	X			1,488	467	571	15	97	55		147		49	
Clarion University of Pennsylvania	M	X			7,100	2,266	3,589	71	375	64	130	822		268	
Curtis Institute of Music	M		X		162	73	67	62	86	100		23		4	
Delaware Valley College	M		X		2,029	927	936	-	109	53	6	319		13	
DeSales University	M		X	X	3,162	710	931	10	172	72		420		242	
Dickinson College	B		X		2,388	1,042	1,346	144	208	75		528			
Dickinson School of Law	P		X		620	-	-	11	88	100			2090		
Drexel University	D		X		19,860	6,026	3,818	1,034	1,247	97		2,314	238	1,286	141
Duquesne University	D		X	X	10,106	2,223	3,089	202	875	55		1,184	270	865	144
East Stroudsburg University	M	X			7,234	2,223	3,186	-	258	76		1,230		312	
Eastern Baptist Theological Seminary	D		X	X	443	-	-		16	76			39	39	18
Eastern University	M		X		4,364	786	1,513	88	71	38	83	537	249	353	17
Edinboro University of Pennsylvania	M	X			7,671	2,465	3,137	77	401	65	83	1,049		358	
Elizabethtown College	M		X		2,311	721	1,369	46	152	71	21	516		18	
Evangelical School of Theology	P		X	X	177	-	-	1	20	100		14	11		

State and Institution	Highest Degree	Control: Public	Control: Private: Indep.	Control: Private: Rel.	Total Enrollment 2008-2009	Full-Time Undergraduate Enrollment 2008-2009: Male	Full-Time Undergraduate Enrollment 2008-2009: Female	Total Foreign Students 2008-2009	Teaching Staff 2008-2009	% with terminal degrees	Associate	Baccalaureate	First-professional	Master's	Doctorate
PENNSYLVANIA *(cont'd)*															
Franklin and Marshall College	B		X		2,164	1,035	1,129	198	207	95		440			
Gannon University	M		X		4,197	930	1,324	212	312	85	44	442		449	30
Geneva College	M		X	X	1,951	758	1,057	20	148	70	11	424		141	
Gettysburg College	B		X	X	2,480	1,128	1,352	48	186	90		645			
Gratz College	P		X		323	4	8	2	41	90				275	
Grove City College	B		X		2,499	1,260	1,239	25	189	75		568			
Gwynedd-Mercy College	M		X	X	2,548	1,075	1,473	25	280	40	227	391		153	
Haverford College	B		X		1,189	547	642	43	117	85		301			
Holy Family University	M		X	X	3,471	500	1,573	69	134	69	23	342		265	
Immaculata University	D		X	X	3,853	231	698	23	297	65	11	463		109 655 46	
Indiana University of Pennsylvania	D	X			14,310	4,994	6,063	551	795	83	13	2,099		720	79
Juniata College	B		X		1,526	654	872	120	130	91		328			
King's College	M		X	X	2,673	1,001	835	5	197	85	2	436		79	
Kutztown University of Pennsylvania	M	X			10,393	3,474	4,798	103	501	72		1,652		256	
La Roche College	M		X	X	1,425	521	963	136	84	91	22	236		71	
La Salle University	M		X	X	6,176	1,456	1,798	62	371	35	40	890		506	18
Lafayette College	B		X	X	2,382	1,092	1,290	143	183	100		599			
Lancaster Bible College	B			X	931	276	284	10	91	52		126		22	
Lebanon Valley College	D		X	X	1,965	782	893	-	66	49	1	398		22	8
Lehigh University	D		X		6,994	2,677	1,848	210	393	99		1,092		526	98
Lincoln University	M		X		2,524	689	1,047	50	116	75		227		213	
Lock Haven University of Pennsylvania	M	X			5,266	1,916	2,529	106	256	58	76	837		83	
Lutheran Theological Seminary at Gettysburg	D		X	X	299	-	-	5	26	100			37	8	
Lutheran Theological Seminary at Philadelphia	D			X	423	-	-	14	20	100			39	20	6
Lycoming College	B		X		1328	595	739	13	132	81		331			
Mansfield University of Pennsylvania	M	X			3,422	1,213	1,914	34	157	68	29	508		152	
Marywood University	M		X	X	3,378	475	1,259	68	123	90		355		363	14
Mercyhurst College	M		X	X	4,326	1,325	1,961	172	237	52	194	590		85	
Messiah College	B		X	X	2,802	1,018	1,784	84	310	77		617			
Millersville University of Pennsylvania	M	X			8,320	2,811	3,719	83	433	81	4	1,426		235	
Misericordia University	M		X	X	2,501	930	1,009	2	256	56		188		104	36
Moore College of Art and Design	B		X		546	-	524	12	112	12		86			
Moravian College and Theological Seminary	P		X	X	2,040	703	1,113	20	147	76		383	13	26	
Mount Aloysius College	M		X	X	1,644	321	782	16	160	30	189	159			
Muhlenberg College	B		X	X	2,500	945	1,366	5	267	80	189	329		16	
Neumann College	M		X	X	3,037	687	1,194	60	218	63	27	407		196	33
The Pennsylvania State University - Harrisburg Capital College	D	X			3,936	1,186	773	44	138	77	4	598		498	8
The Pennsylvania State University - Milton S. Hershey Medical Center	D	X			791	-	-	79	345	76			123	11	20
The Pennsylvania State University - University Park Campus	D	X			44,406	19,050	15,587	1,332	2,543	88	102	9,442		1,267	643
Philadelphia Biblical University	M		X	X	1,335	448	526	26	128	54	15	276		82	
Philadelphia College of Osteopathic Medicine	P		X		1,605	-	-	2	185	100			413	135	281
Philadelphia University	M		X		3,360	832	1,915	78	428	85	11	561		224	
Pittsburgh Theological Seminary	D			X	318	-	-	12	22	100			39	12	21
Point Park University	M		X		3,784	958	1,425	38	431 54 4635 7			610		216	
Robert Morris University	D		X		4,815	1,777	1,336	96	364	66	70	835		403	15
Rosemont College	M		X	X	995	138	440	12	162	80		131		152	
Saint Charles Borromeo Seminary	P		X	X	243	96	29	7	27	90		10	16	28	
Saint Francis University	M		X	X	2,210	544	845	28	187	75	4	328		226	17
Saint Joseph's University	M		X	X	7,900	2,006	2,106	158	569	93	11	1,103		799	4
Saint Vincent College and Seminary	P		X	X	2,021	756	802	20	187	65		302		50	
Seton Hill University	M		X	X	2,087	495	775	42	192	67		264		127	
Shippensburg University of Pennsylvania	M	X			7,942	2,953	3,143	27	378	75		1,269		349	
Slippery Rock University of Pennsylvania	D	X			8,458	3,162	4,040	85	442	73		1,506		193	51
Susquehanna University	B		X		2,137	914	1,223	21	122	96	7	455			
Swarthmore College	M		X		1,498	705	793	89	205	85		372			
Temple University	D	X			35,490	8,684	11,499	1,593	3,783	87	9	4,979	822	1,273	383
Temple University School of Podiatric Medicine	P		X		288	-	-	22	122	93			99		
Thiel College	B		X	X	1,137	636	501	55	113	49		182			
Thomas Jefferson University	D		X		3,202	136	772	32	407	76	88	325	217	149	18
Trinity Episcopal School for Ministry	P		X	X	286	-	-	6	19	60			31	10	
University of Pennsylvania	D		X		24,107	4,679	4,688	2,410	5,869	77		2,766	666	3,019	496

State and Institution	Highest Degree	Control: Public	Control: Private: Indep.	Control: Private: Rel.	Total Enrollment 2008-2009	Full-Time Undergraduate Enrollment 2008-2009: Male	Full-Time Undergraduate Enrollment 2008-2009: Female	Total Foreign Students 2008-2009	Teaching Staff 2008-2009	% with terminal degrees	Associate	Baccalaureate	First-professional	Master's	Doctorate
PENNSYLVANIA *(cont'd)*															
University of Pittsburgh	D	X		x	37,562	7,590	7,832	2,756	4,243	90		3,913	914	2,006	412
University of Pittsburgh at Bradford	B	X			1,504	502	1002	9	124	40	34	191			
University of Pittsburgh at Greensburg	B	X			1,826	757	1,069	-	140	60		225			
University of Pittsburgh at Johnstown	B	X			3,032	578	1,454	-	133	77	21	533			
University of Scranton	M		X	X	5,651	1,618	2,180	57	509	47	6	8693		616	36
University of the Arts	M		X		2,401	898	1,128	96	83	55		452		88	
University of the Sciences in Philadelphia	D		X		3,000	974	597	60	250	75		170	218	850	9
Ursinus College	B		X		1,680	706	974	17	95	92		365			
Valley Forge Christian College	B		X	X	1,201	400	544	12	34	22	6	109			
Washington and Jefferson College	B		X		1,519	696	823	8	145	87		366			
Waynesburg University	M		X		2,549	661	476	-	110	62	5	413		233	
West Chester University of Pennsylvania	M	X			13,619	3,715	6,008	76	806	78		2,114		575	
Westminster College	M		X		1,516	587	844	-	104	82		306		47	
Westminster Theological Seminary	D		X	X	808	-	-	63	32	85			51	59	14
Widener University	D		X		4,861	1,142	1,331	98	587	70	12	590	475	399	170
Wilkes University	M		X		4,687	974	1,056	98	315	88		423	73	224	
Wilson College	B			X	770	14	350	25	77	56	55	81			
York College of Pennsylvania	M		X		5,627	2,051	2,539	23	427	35	38	983		78	
PUERTO RICO															
American University of Puerto Rico	B		X		1,528	849	615	-	68	66	13	181		5	
Bayamon Central University	M		X	X	2,382	943	1,449	-	113	28	8	280		126	
Caribbean University	M		X		2,009	807	911	-	98	100	13	105		106	
Carlos Albizu University	M	X			826	98	456	-	16	100		16		29	38
Columbia Century Universitario	B		X		1,142	-	-	-	30	77	176	144			
Conservatory of Music of Puerto Rico	B	X			237	161	76	74	30	77		29			
Electronic Data Processing College	M		X		512	220	292	-	28	66		63			
Escuela de Artes Plasticas de Puerto Rico	B	X			461	103	105	-	77	26		11			
Evangelical Seminary of Puerto Rico	P			X	175	-	-	5	17	100			22	11	
Inter American University of Puerto Rico, Arecibo University College	B		X		5,800	1,102	2,254	-	249	100	62	422		142	
Inter American University of Puerto Rico, Bayamon Campus	B		X		5,337	2,474	1,900	11	298	33		372			
Inter American University of Puerto Rico, Fajardo Campus	P		X		2,252	491	1732	-	151	80	16	252		17	
Inter American University of Puerto Rico, Metropolitan Campus	D		X		10,613	3,197	3,754	-	274	33	58	782		649	61
Inter American University of Puerto Rico, Ponce Campus	M		X		5,963	1,423	1,886	-	199	21	88	381		49	
Inter American University of Puerto Rico, San German Campus	M		X		5,712	1,994	2,365	43	355	90	40	460		207	4
Inter American University of Puerto Rico, School of Law	P		X		782	-	-	-	57	100			174		
Pontifical Catholic University of Puerto Rico	P		X	X	7,413	1,622	3,157	50	360	85	10	707	174	178	46
Universidad Adventista de las Antillas	B		X	X	950	262	444	50	63	20	23	101		9	
Universidad Central del Caribe	P		X		357	-	-	-	282	87	28	4	58	9	
Universidad del Este	M		X		9,735	1,205	2,418	-	292	15	207	247			
Universidad del Turabo	M		X		16,296	5,213	7,819	-	364	66	85	838		238	5
Universidad Metropolitana	M		X		12,369	3,233	6,563	-	151	36	70	734		526	
Universidad Politecnica de Puerto Rico	M		X		5,800	1,999	659	-	340	25		326		146	
University of Puerto Rico, Arecibo Technological University College	B	X			4,599	1,167	2,899	-	245	15	28	408			
University of Puerto Rico, Cayey University College	B	X			3,658	923	2,356	-	197	35	21	401			
University of Puerto Rico, Humacao University College	B	X			4,744	1,045	3,699	-	269	35	123	532			
University of Puerto Rico, Mayaguez Campus	D	X			13,325	5,101	4,909	-	650	70		1,461		179	19
University of Puerto Rico, Medical Sciences Campus	D	X			2,334	56	348	29	733	70		182	160	194	7
University of Puerto Rico, Rio Piedras Campus	D	X			18,653	4,693	10,438	111	1,357	46		2,405	111	364	196
University of the Sacred Heart	M		X	X	4,978	-	-	-	336	100	10	533		39	
RHODE ISLAND															
Brown University	D		X		8,318	2,778	2,964	915	823	90		1,542	89	348	186
Bryant University	B		X		3,800	1,795	1,295	152	283	65		724		167	
Johnson and Wales University	D		X		10,488	3,979	4,323	629	398	76	1,455	1,523		409	37
Providence College	D		X	X	5,085	1,757	2,824	31	379	86	6	984		208	

State and Institution	Highest Degree	Control: Public	Control: Private: Indep.	Control: Private: Rel.	Total Enrollment 2008-2009	Full-Time Undergraduate Enrollment 2008-2009: Male	Full-Time Undergraduate Enrollment 2008-2009: Female	Total Foreign Students 2008-2009	Teaching Staff 2008-2009	% with terminal degrees	Associate	Baccalaureate	First-professional	Master's	Doctorate
RHODE ISLAND *(cont'd)*															
Rhode Island College	M	X			9,095	1,779	3,501	36	657	90		1,246		249	7
Rhode Island School of Design	M		X		2,352	646	1,218	285	342	20		500		161	
Roger Williams University	P		X		4,609	1,852	1,888	92	465	65	14	871		80	
Salve Regina University	M		X	X	2,693	608	1,464	27	194	65		474		137	5
University of Rhode Island	D	X			15,904	4,506	5,704	32	706	91		2,201	87	481	68
SOUTH CAROLINA															
Allen University	B		X	X	725	357	368	17	50	30		50			
Anderson College	B		X	X	2,064	453	506	34	151	21		220		13	
Benedict College	B		X		2,883	1,356	1,175	-	143	50		343			
Charleston Southern University	M		X	X	3,200	970	1,512	-	71	68		437		130	
Citadel Military College of South Carolina	M	X			3,328	2,014	89	66	283	75		467		214	
Claflin University	M		X	X	1,773	574	1,124	54	133	63		274		31	
Clemson University	D	X			18,317	7,053	6,082	756	1,233	76		3,075		816	145
Coastal Carolina University	B	X			8,154	2,856	3,148	82	443	60		1,276		86	
Coker College	B		X		1,099	334	765	3	73	83		240			
College of Charleston	M	X			11,367	3,230	5,825	114	858	75		2,140		189	
Columbia College	M		X	X	1,445	4	1,441	29	154	70		220		210	
Columbia International University	D		X	X	923	188	292	18	82	50	4	118	19	111	10
Converse College	M		X		2,068	-	735	42	165	55		171		208	
Erskine College and Theological Seminary	D		X	X	864	268	323	16	68	75		117	28	11	10
Francis Marion University	M		X		4,020	1,145	2,324	40	213	78		581		104	
Furman University	M		X	X	2,977	1,154	1,494	60	274	94		651		71	
Lander University	M	X			2,614	796	1,886	78	183	45		404		41	
Limestone College	B		X		3,255	1,237	2,018	27	65	65	82	397			
Lutheran Theological Southern Seminary	P		X	X	146	-	-	3	19	100			21	8	
Medical University of South Carolina	D	X			2,521	57	295	1	916	90		166	239	229	30
Morris College	B		921	X	494	727		-	64	60		158			
Newberry College	B		X	X	973	502	471	40	70	77		134			
North Greenville University	B		X	X	1,944	734	1,112	28	147	76		262			
Presbyterian College	B		X	X	1,171	552	619	17	130	70		247			
South Carolina State University	D	X			4,888	1,558	1,970	107	267	75		554		98	13
Southern Wesleyan University	M		X	X	2,391	701	1,222	24	246	45		402		245	
University of South Carolina - Aiken	M	X			3,232	783	1,584	64	265	55	25	502		17	
University of South Carolina - Columbia	D	X			27,488	7,425	8,974	275	1,552	85	9	3,859	383	1,652	244
University of South Carolina - Upstate	M	X			5,063	1,293	2,508	102	352	45		927		12	
Voorhees College	B		X	X	568	277	291	12	40	60		189			
Winthrop University	M	X			6,249	1,424	3,197	126	453	65		930		262	
Wofford College	B		X	X	1,429	642	787	2	129	90		296			
SOUTH DAKOTA															
Augustana College	M		X	X	1,754	629	1,024	17	176	97		341		12	
Black Hills State University	M	X			4,016	1,444	2,225	40	105	66	32	394		35	
Dakota State University	M	X			2,675	964	1,101	27	64	58	44	194		46	
Dakota Wesleyan University	M		X	X	730	292	399	7	99	50	66	102		17	
Mount Marty College	M		X	X	1,180	171	528	-	54	60	26	169		44	
National American University	B		X		1,837	418	671	-	-	-	70	158		40	
Northern State University	M	X			2,927	744	928	24	93	78	14	263		81	
Oglala Lakota College	M	X			1,31	401	133	-	19	50	95	42		18	
Presentation College	B		X	X	733	95	544	1	31	19	33	131			
Sinte Gleska College	M		X		1,012	230	782	-	17	70	21	20		1	
Sioux Falls Seminary	D		X	X	100	-	-	-	16	100			15	10	2
South Dakota School of Mines and Technology	D	X			2,061	1,374	728	21	104	76	9	250		73	2
South Dakota State University	D	X			11,995	5,166	3,787	120	598	55	16	1,884	59	27	24
University of Sioux Falls	M		X		1,589	459	540	4	136	45		262		108	
University of South Dakota	D	X			9,291	1,906	2,978	144	335	86	284	819	126	448	49
TENNESSEE															
American Baptist College	B		X	X	106	68	35	-	15	80	1	19			
Aquinas College	B		X	X	847	157	690	-	69	17	101	78			
Austin Peay State University	M	X			9,401	2,369	4,027	52	494	94	108	1,159		215	
Belmont University	M		X	X	4,991	1,414	2,034	50	466	40		915		246	37
Bethel College	M		X	X	2,408	570	564	48	66	59		372		68	
Bryan College	B		X	X	1,079	487	519	22	54	87		247		11	
Carson-Newman College	M		X		2,032	755	977	60	192	68		401		69	
Christian Brothers University	M		X	X	1,869	550	635	38	144	75		208		144	

State and Institution	Highest Degree	Control			Total Enrollment 2008-2009	Full-Time Undergraduate Enrollment 2008-2009		Total Foreign Students 2008-2009	Teaching Staff 2008-2009	% with terminal degrees	Associate	Baccalaureate	First-professional	Master's	Doctorate
		Public	Private												
			Indep.	Rel.		Male	Female								
TENNESSEE *(cont'd)*															
Crichton College	B		X	X	1,016	307	709	20	79	54		167			
Cumberland University	B		X		1,351	403	652	52	84	55	2	193		240	
East Tennessee State University	D	X			13,646	3,371	4,617	136	760	70		1,694	58	506	30
Fisk University	M		X	X	726	219	464	29	71	70		107		16	
Free Will Baptist Bible College	M		X	X	317	156	161	6	42	37		66			
Freed-Hardeman University	M		X	X	2,061	627	780	30	136	70		252		117	14
Harding University Graduate School of Religion	D		X	X	221	-	-	3	14	100			15	9	3
Johnson Bible College	M		X		801	359	369	8	58	18		139		29	
King College	B		X	X	1,706	369	665	52	122	25		368		90	
Lambuth University	B		X		749	381	368	24	93	55		152			
Lane College	B		X	X	1,981	544	1,437	-	52	55		175			
Lee University	B		X	X	4,147	1,444	1,911	205	320	52		577		120	
LeMoyne-Owen College	B		X	X	893	215	678	-	72	41		100			
Lincoln Memorial University	M		X		3,365	255	1,174	132	159	75	139	140		216	
Lipscomb University	M		X		3,073	927	1,157	62	184	75		443		68	
Martin Methodist College	B		X	X	953	251	712	63	52	45	15	105			
Maryville College	B		X		1,114	649	650	11	58	87		214			
Meharry Medical College	D		X		730	-	-	-	214	77			102	11	10
Memphis College of Art	M		X		404	121	283	8	37	59		53		6	
Memphis Theological Seminary	P		X	X	280	-	-	4	13	77			45	11	6
Mid-America Baptist Theological Seminary	D		X	X	349	31	27	18	35	100	14	14	28	14	
Middle Tennessee State University	D	X			23,872	9,576	10,712	239	749	74	3	3,547		606	
Milligan College	M		X	X	1,018	278	521	20	99	48		170		91	
O'More College of Design	B		X		202	14	188	-	9	50		21			
Rhodes College	B		X		1,678	682	987	34	175	85		407		14	
Southern Adventist University	B		X	X	2,777	1,133	1,441	168	216	56	131	302		33	
Southern College of Optometry	P		X		483	-	-	5	44	100			125		
Tennessee State University	D	X			8,254	2,627	3,824	-	295	61	149	942		471	44
Tennessee Technological University	D	X			9,733	3,523	3,846	200	544	58		1,284		532	13
Tennessee Temple University	M		X	X	716	192	351	7	49	63		74		41	
Tennessee Wesleyan College	B		X	X	988	263	620		88	50		216			
Trevecca Nazarene University	M		X	X	2,366	439	772	24	219	45	2	351		385	24
Tusculum College	M		X	X	2,241	787	1,283	44	110	84		592		90	
Union University	M		X	X	2,910	635	992	60	151	68	7	399		312	22
University of Memphis	D	X			20,220	4,682	7,101	202	1,279	60		2,432	125	870	68
University of Tennessee at Chattanooga	M	X			9,807	2,726	3,754	98	637	55		1,258		355	27
University of Tennessee at Knoxville	D	X			30,410	9,482	0,686	1,199	1,625	87		3,655	556	1,556	319
University of Tennessee at Martin	M	X			7,574	2,272	2,833	150	446	52		998		142	
University of Tennessee Health Science Center	D	X			2,116	-	-	-	715	91		252	281	34	5
University of the South	D		X		1,562	662	723	32	140	95		346	26	2	7
Vanderbilt University	D		X		12,093	3,005	3.197	363	2,263	93		1,342	334	1,044	650
TEXAS															
Abilene Christian University	D		X	X	4,669	1,793	2,144	188	378	72	3	830	25	144	6
Amberton University	M		X	X	1,537	535	1,002	-	54	95		42	199		
Angelo State University	M	X			6,155	2,311	2,610	62	344	60	61	780		143	
Arlington Baptist College	B		X	X	140	73	56	8	21	10		33			
Austin College	M		X		1,298	568	695	26	132	96		336		17	
Austin Graduate School of Theology	B		X	X	66	44	22	-	11	100		9		7	
Austin Presbyterian Theological Seminary	D		X	X	275	-	-	6	25	85			48	9	5
Baptist Missionary Association Theological Seminary	P		X	X	140	24	33	-	14	75		11	1	11	
Baylor College of Medicine	D		X		1,385	-	-	267	1,353	94			170	49	45
Baylor University	D		X	X	14,541	4,675	6,879	291	928	78		2,445	226	538	108
Concordia University at Austin	B		X	X	2,260	428	623	-	50	69		142			
Criswell College	M		X	X	459	110	30	-	27	54	12	26	5	22	
Dallas Baptist University	M		X	X	5,297	917	1,252	404	488	40	1	811		262	1
Dallas Christian College	B			X	315	141	160	1	78	30	1	59			
Dallas Theological Seminary	D		X	X	1,937	-	-	148	71	83			121	158	18
East Texas Baptist University	B		X		1,210	556	654	12	102	64		258			
Episcopal Theological Seminary of the Southwest	M		X	X	75	-	-	1	47	50			27		
Hardin-Simmons University	M		X	X	2,387	789	944	24	184	75		380	13	100	26
Houston Baptist University	M		X	X	2,564	587	1,231	51	125	67	5	333		111	
Howard Payne University	B		X	X	1,388	571	800	2	147	45		247		3	

State and Institution	Highest Degree	Control: Public	Control: Private: Indep.	Control: Private: Rel.	Total Enrollment 2008-2009	Full-Time Undergraduate Enrollment 2008-2009: Male	Full-Time Undergraduate Enrollment 2008-2009: Female	Total Foreign Students 2008-2009	Teaching Staff 2008-2009	% with terminal degrees	Associate	Baccalaureate	First-professional	Master's	Doctorate
TEXAS *(cont'd)*															
Huston-Tillotson University	B		X	X	785	383	347	27	67	76		93			
Jarvis Christian College	B		X	X	728	304	424	-	41	55		86			
Lamar University	D	X			15,465	2,160	3,745	504	498	62	39	1,191		412	35
LeTourneau University	B		X	X	3,662	1,573	2,089	37	199	71	3	637		112	
Lubbock Christian University	M		X	X	1,868	596	788	19	149	42		360		59	
McMurry University	B		X	X	1,515	571	944	15	132	55		226			
Midwestern State University	M	X			6,093	1.640	2,235	345	314	52	38	974		122	
Oblate School of Theology	D			X	198	-	-	41	26	79			18	20	5
Our Lady of the Lake University	D		X	X	2,642	298	920	26	120	69		318		346	9
Paul Quinn College	B		X	X	445	216	229	35	48	76		132			
Prairie View A & M University	M	X			8,203	2,802	2,522	82	329	46		758		699	10
Rice University	D		X		5,351	1,516	1,448	378	701	92		792		512	186
St. Edward's University	M		X	X	5,348	1,276	1,955	108	472	70		921		306	53
St. Mary's University	M		X	X	4,110	945	1,344	118	177	81		473	179	242	9
Sam Houston State University	M	X			16,662	5,070	6,688	166	920	60		2,695		696	28
Schreiner University	B		X		974	404	559	7	84	67		137		12	
South Texas College of Law	P		X		1,262	-	-	-	90	100			382		
Southern Methodist University	D		X	X	10,765	2,693	3,194	658	889	74		1,541	332	1,261	61
Southwestern Adventist University	M		X	X	821	395	426	16	60	60	31	103		10	
Southwestern Assemblies of God University	B		X	X	1,659	741	759	18	45	56	77	270		42	
Southwestern Baptist Theological Seminary	D		X	X	2,588	-	-	104	158	90		10	220	450	36
Southwestern Baptist Theological Seminary	D		X	X	2,588	93	38	96	184	90		74	197	297	53
Southwestern Christian College	B		X	X	203	134	69	23	18	22	31	8			
Southwestern University	B		X	X	1,270	513	757	-	166	94		305			
Stephen F. Austin State University	D	X			12,000	3,587	5,231	120	627	75		1,783		454	16
Sul Ross State University	M	X			2,772	586	514	28	129	72	9	361		196	
Tarleton State University	M	X			9,653	2,735	3,342	96	528	55		1,706		437	12
Texas A & M International University	M	X			5,856	842	1,403	236	256	55		684		295	
Texas A & M University	D	X			48,039	17,234	16,335	3,554	2,320	84		8,152	125	1,430	622
Texas A & M University - Baylor College of Dentistry	P		X		537	-	-	-	220	93			351		
Texas A & M University - Commerce	D	X			8,725	3,184	5,352	425	317	81		1,280		948	38
Texas A & M University - Corpus Christi	M		X		654	162	492	122	69	21				175	
Texas A & M University - Galveston	M	X			1,812	885	692	18	45	70		257		5	
Texas A & M University - Kingsville	D	X			7,133	1,044	4,601	142	311	66		916		514	37
Texas A & M University - Texarkana	M	X			1,666	303	743	-	115	87		334		175	
Texas Chiropractic College	P		X		369	12	6	-	43	100		20	118		
Texas Christian University	D		X	X	8,696	2,801	4,056	435	803	85		1,564	25	482	28
Texas College	B		X	X	807	407	345	5	38	53		105			
Texas Lutheran University	B		X	X	1,429	630	704	11	114	143	2	290			
Texas Southern University	D	X			11,903	4,074	5,511	34	335	55		451	239	164	14
Texas State University - San Marcos	D	X			29,105	8,606	10,506	406	1,773	56		5,083		1,163	9
Texas Tech University	D	X			28,001	11,382	4,571	1,110	1,11	90		3,918	210	1,045	175
Texas Tech University Health Science Center	D	X			2,272	86	508	2	527	54		266	208	225	10
Texas Wesleyan University	M		X	X	3,202	361	1,347	106	238	81		263	153	161	27
Texas Woman's University	D	X			12,465	519	6,901	249169	482	69		1,446		1,390	67
Trinity University	M		X	X	2,703	1,125	1,320	135	280	90		544		105	
University of Dallas	D		X	X	2,977	454	616	60	233	90		221		504	2
University of Houston - Clear Lake	M	X			7,853	2,577	1,440	112	353	86		1,059		915	
University of Houston - Downtown	M		X		12,283	4,594	6,667	495	440	50		2,002		36	
University of Houston - University Park	D		X		36,104	9,468	10,134	1,124	1,823	87		4,759	466	1,448	343
University of Houston - Victoria	M	X			2,491	96	337	57	122	95		265		271	
University of Mary Hardin-Baylor	M		X	X	2,648	841	1,619	26	211	84		500		64	
University of North Texas	D	X			34,830	8,399	10,656	1,045	1,520	86		5,183		1,524	200
University of North Texas Health Science Center at Fort Worth	P	X			1,225	-	-	45	177	46			130	12	24
University of St. Thomas	D		X	X	3,165	498	1,180	156	275	41		346	17	351	
University of Texas at Arlington	D	X			25,084	6,419	7,289	1,003	1,081	83		2,835	44	1,665	142
University of Texas at Austin	D	X			49,984	16,174	17,714	1,999	2,271	76		8.669	597	2,975	862
University of Texas at Brownsville	M	X			11,560	4,527	6,356	353	197	76		661		157	
University of Texas at Dallas	D	X			14,913	3,447	2,925	597	627	95		2,384	146	1,395	121
University of Texas at El Paso	D	X			20,458	5,037	5,901	1,841	919	75		2,631		744	37
University of Texas at San Antonio	D	X			28,413	10,480	12,057	568	866	99		3,553		886	57
University of Texas at Tyler	M	X			6,117	1,518	2,111	61	378	90		1,028		28	

State and Institution	Highest Degree	Control: Public	Control: Private: Indep.	Control: Private: Rel.	Total Enrollment 2008-2009	Full-Time Undergraduate Enrollment 2008-2009: Male	Full-Time Undergraduate Enrollment 2008-2009: Female	Total Foreign Students 2008-2009	Teaching Staff 2008-2009	% with terminal degrees	Associate	Baccalaureate	First-professional	Master's	Doctorate
TEXAS *(cont'd)*															
University of Texas Health Science Center at Houston	D	X			3,587	46	335	7	1,046	75		152	250	337	98
University of Texas Health Science Center at San Antonio	D	X			2,781	799	167	11	935	91		318	281	131	34
University of Texas Medical Branch at Galveston	D	X			2,172	65	236	117	1,137	99		240	190	114	38
University of Texas of the Permian Basin	M	X			3,406	689	1,121	-	195	80		409		109	
University of Texas - Pan American	M	X			17,534	4,718	6,313	789	740	-		2,405		643	9
University of Texas Southwestern Medical Center at Dallas	D	X			2,350	30	64	474	1,703	99		61	204	84	62
University of the Incarnate Word	M		X	X	6,361	3,083	2,027	128	445	56	10	802		315	18
Wayland Baptist University	M		X	X	6,031	2,567	2,186	69	107	75	255	1,452		311	
West Texas A & M University	M	X			7,535	2,834	3,403	151	212	46		1,188		387	2
Wiley College	B		X	X	961	316	645	30	43	76		157			
UTAH															
Brigham Young University	D		X	X	34,244	12,441	12,507	685	1,744	82		6,834	163	1,079	67
Dixie State College of Utah	B			X	6,088	2,922	3,086	27	337	20		150			
ITT Technical Institute	B		X		706	619	87	-	34	21	95	17			
Southern Utah University	M	X			7,516	2,776	3,605	75	201	60	209	870		262	
University of Utah	D	X			28,211	11,839	9,681	2,532	1,687	90		4,882	277	1,611	590
Utah State University	D	X			21,388	5,418	5,310	1,200	870	76		1,677		1,881	195
Utah Valley University	B	X			26,696	6,787	4,781	534	1,256	223	1,716	1,532			
Weber State University	M	X			21,388	10,017	10,853	214	904	80	1,671	1,881		195	
Westminster College of Salt Lake City	M		X		2,859	938	1,193	59	246	110		397		203	
VERMONT															
Bennington College	M		X		759	178	340	32	89	48		145		60	
Burlington College	B		X		167	90	23	4	62	28	3	37			
Castleton State College	M	X			1,971	736	1,060	2	176	94		187			
Champlain College	B		X		2,891	1,542	1,182	10	256	52	405	99			
College of St. Joseph	M		X	X	120		130	-	30	62	16	59		64	
Goddard College	M		X		731	73	179	17	12	75		57		158	
Green Mountain College	B		X		867	352	353	10	78	55		131		9	
Johnson State College	M	X			1,898	721	898	4	177	40	12	270		92	
Lyndon State College	M	X				1,384	719	637	162	52	17	183		2	
Marlboro College	B		X		326	152	174	-	58	85		74			
Middlebury College	B		X		2,455	1,119	336	192	242	90		636		267	5
Norwich University	D		X		3,309	1,453	543	44	185	64		389		163	
Saint Michael's College	M		X	X	2,460	877	1,065	50	249	60		441		119	
School for International Training	M		X		654	162	492	122	69	21				175	
Southern Vermont College	B		X		456	332	124	19	56	18	29	56			
University of Vermont	D	X			12,800	4,000	4,908	262	767	91		2,003	97	360	68
Vermont Law School	P		X		595	-	-	13	90	99			159	95	
Vermont Technical College	B	X			1,649	973	676	17	139	28	385	59			
VIRGIN ISLANDS															
University of the Virgin Islands	M	X			2,393	922	1,471	170	236	90	69	193		53	
VIRGINIA															
Averett University	M		X	X	842	428	364	32	228	79		149		24	
Baptist Theological Seminary at Richmond	P		X	X	214	151	63	7	23	100		8	27		
Bluefield College	B		X	X	736	314	422	6	96	48		277			
Bridgewater College	B		X	X	1,514	636	878	13	129	73		377			
Christopher Newport University	B	X			4,904	2,036	2,644	14	212	84		857		67	
College of William and Mary	D	X			7,892	2,592	3,037	262	758	82		1,454	206	440	63
Eastern Mennonite University	P		X	X	1,387	369	612	42	163	70	17	279	27	104	
Emory and Henry College	B		X		1,015	430	468	11	120	70		216		4	
Ferrum College	B		X	X	1,397	608	709	14	94	50		138			
George Mason University	D	X			30,613	5,954	7,135	1,710	974	82		3,809	214	2,549	191
Hampden-Sydney College	B		X	X	1,120	1,120	-	22	112	90		235			
Hampton University	M		X		5,421	1,660	3,076	-	469	70	2	988	50	105	5
Hollins University	M		X		1,056	-	798	4	108	80		181		108	
James Madison University	M	X			18,454	5,903	9,356	186	1,209	76		3,504		801	13
Liberty University	M		X	X	17,590	4,527	5,372	719	701	60	171	1,521	26	306	129
Longwood University	M	X			4,727	1,271	2,468	47	187	93		746		144	
Lynchburg College	M		X	X	2,572	810	1,156	26	229	55		412		141	
Mary Baldwin College	M		X	X	1,738	124	1,400	17	127	90		243		73	
Marymount University	M		X	X	3,348	513	1,435	220	345	86	5	550		430	55

State and Institution	Highest Degree	Control: Public	Control: Private: Indep.	Control: Private: Rel.	Total Enrollment 2008-2009	Full-Time Undergraduate Enrollment 2008-2009: Male	Full-Time Undergraduate Enrollment 2008-2009: Female	Total Foreign Students 2008-2009	Teaching Staff 2008-2009	% with terminal degrees	Associate	Baccalaureate	First-professional	Master's	Doctorate
VIRGINIA *(cont'd)*															
Norfolk State University	M	X			6,325	1,707	2,762	63	422	60	54	737		222	4
Old Dominion University	D	X			23,086	4,580	6,248	782	1,075	52		2,858		1,274	106
Protestant Episcopal Theological Seminary in Virginia	D		X	X	250	-	-	12	39	-			21	13	4
Radford University	M	X			9,157	3,247	4,481	92	580	85		1,825		426	
Randolph-Macon College	B		X	X	1,201	528	673	12	146	83		242			
Randolph-Macon Woman's College	B		X	X	568	-	568	68	91	95		144		5	
Regent University	P		X	X	4,278	491	997	132	633	70			173	546	163
Roanoke College	B		X	X	2,021	909	1,112	40	143	90		429			
Saint Paul's College	B		X	X	644	301	343	6	52	44		124			
Shenandoah University	M		X	X	3,511	757	969	105	325	35	7	314	109	205	84
Sweet Briar College	B		X		828	24	789	24	105	85		130		10	
Union Theological Seminary and Presbyterian School of Christian Education	D			X	375	-	-	37	32	100			38	78	11
University of Mary Washington	M	X			5,084	1,222	2,372	51	205	86		1,011		210	
University of Richmond	D		X	X	4,249	1,371	1,433	297	343	87	4	794	146	16	
University of Virginia	D	X			24,541	6,210	7,679	1,638	1,245	91		3,526	533	1,836	327
University of Virginia's College at Wise	B	X			1,953	834	1,002	7	97	80		267			
Virginia Commonwealth University	D	X			32,044	6,041	9,059	1,282	2,671	91		3,544	335	1,281	146
Virginia Intermont College	B		X	X	542	141	401	5	84	50		227			
Virginia Military Institute	B	X			1,428	1,262	166	24	128	93		280			
Virginia Polytechnic Institute and State University	D	X			30,739	12,648	8,682	555	1,410	84	33	4,876	93	1,444	290
Virginia State University	M	X			5,042	1,589	2,290	-	309	68		542		119	
Virginia Union University	P		X	X	1,501	539	658	17	74	60		203	109		
Virginia Wesleyan College	B		X	X	1,381	497	884	7	185	82		294			
Washington and Lee University	P		X		2,155	883	864	88	214	96		533	128	2	
WASHINGTON															
Bastyr University	P		X		988	35	185	50	142	96		75	101	156	
Central Washington University	M	X			10,682	4,887	5,294	214	535	84		1,879		159	
City University	M		X		3,184	475	810	153	1,225	35	86	602		1,088	
Cornish College of the Arts	B		X		815	295	520	24	148	25		144			
Eastern Washington University	M	X			10,809	3,982	5,407	216	506	65		2,015		522	29
Evergreen State College	M	X			4,696	1,964	2,400	47	221	84		1,077		97	
Gonzaga University	D		X	X	7,272	1,809	2,185	144	454	94		994	182	652	
Heritage University	M		X		1,087	226	584	5	183	40	13	94		160	
Northwest University	B			X	1,246	364	619	24	67	106		250		53	
Pacific Lutheran University	M		X	X	3,652	1,127	1,980	169	267	90		797		125	
Puget Sound Christian College	B		X	X	130	99	89	-	41	30	3	24			
Saint Martin's University	M		X	X	1,659	624	763	50	41	66		299		85	
Seattle Pacific University	M		X	X	3,873	955	1,904	30	208	76		657		226	24
Seattle University	D		X	X	7,560	1,525	2,386	340	474	74		1,128	351	664	333
Trinity Lutheran College	B			X	117	45	50	3	17	100	5	24			
University of Puget Sound	P		X	X	2,844	1,048	1,455	12	274	84		663		82	46
University of Washington	D	X			39,675	13,478	14,254	915	2,941	97		6,952	488	2,556	503
Walla Walla University	M		X	X	1,800	790	717	18	181	60		283		143	
Washington State University	D	X			25,532	8,290	4,340	1,130	1,337	84		4,818	160	724	217
Western Washington University	M	X			14,620	5,281	6,560	22	617	87		3,067		341	
Whitman College	B		X	X	1,458	644	814	48	191	75		449			
Whitworth College	M		X	X	2,441	903	1,246	40	97	71		473		96	
WEST VIRGINIA															
Alderson-Broaddus College	M		X		738	180	429	14	86	40	13	130		57	
Appalachian Bible College	B			X	320	115	113	6	15	25		40			
Bethany College	B		X	X	825	390	435	30	92	55		78			
Bluefield State College	B	X			1,568	627	941	40	82	34	85	219			
Concord University	B	X			2,812	1,200	1,519	95	195	76		366		27	
Davis and Elkins College	B		X		586	237	349	36	60	79	60	107			
Fairmont State University	B	X			4,547	1,808	2,307	88	276	45	67	2 650 65			
Glenville State College	B	X			1,443	554	889	13	78	50	38	188			
Marshall University	P	X			13,573	3,562	5,718	136	711	60	100	1,450	46	81761	13
Mountain State University	B		X		5,108	1,369	3,009	409	368	37	160	707		259	
Ohio Valley University	B		X	X	515	237	278	30	59	25	14	109			
Salem International University	B		X		574	159	153	279	51	76		46		158	
Shepherd University	M	X			4,185	1,335	2,709	26	288	66	65	553		48	
University of Charleston	M		X		1,455	413	709	14	76	62	26	119		42	
West Liberty State College	B	X			2,513	1,073	1,422	12	156	44	31	436			

State and Institution	Highest Degree	Control: Public	Control: Private: Indep.	Control: Private: Rel.	Total Enrollment 2008-2009	Full-Time Undergraduate Enrollment 2008-2009: Male	Full-Time Undergraduate Enrollment 2008-2009: Female	Total Foreign Students 2008-2009	Teaching Staff 2008-2009	% with terminal degrees	Associate	Baccalaureate	First-professional	Master's	Doctorate
WEST VIRGINIA *(cont'd)*															
West Virginia School of Osteopathic Medicine	P	X			363	183	180	-	136	100			72		
West Virginia State University	B	X			3,003	1,049	1,912	9	196	52		403		9	
West Virginia University	D	X			28,840	9,961	8,392	317	1,579	87		3,798	338	1,527	221
West Virginia University Institute of Technology	M	X			1,224	759	465	36	177	49	151	206		1	
West Virginia Wesleyan College	M		X	X	1,317	690	584	64	130	71		228		30	
Wheeling Jesuit University	M		X		1,319	416	661	45	142	63		274		54	30
WISCONSIN															
Alverno College	B		X	X	2,782	-	2,371	29	226	89	4	277		62	
Bellin College of Nursing	M		X		294	13	215	-	1	21		69		7	
Beloit College	M		X		1,388	597	791	83	119	98		310			
Cardinal Stritch University	M		X	X	6,471	966	2,232	64	676	55	208	587		916	14
Carroll College	M		X	X	3,507	790	1,621	47	115	84		464		84	
Carthage College	M		X	X	2,972	1,232	1,633	30	196	89		439		28	
Concordia University Wisconsin	M		X	X	6,549	1,401	2,305	66	204	60	12	583		348	24
Edgewood College	M		X	X	2,544	597	1,392	52	157	76		380		112	
Lakeland College	M		X	X	4,013	1,353	2,090	162	55	36		712		80	
Lawrence University	B		X	X	1,496	634	862	90	181	90		295			
Maranatha Baptist Bible College	M		X	X	857	352	464	9	72	32	13	120		8	
Marian College of Fond du Lac	M		X	X	3,040	357	1,067	14	278	42		361		250	
Marquette University	D		X	X	11,633	3,452	4,417	233	1,054	64		1,766	312	574	85
Medical College of Wisconsin	D		X		1,293	-	-	94	810	99			188	73	29
Milwaukee Institute of Art and Design	B		X		669	299	370	28	76	58		123			
Milwaukee School of Engineering	M		X		2,621	1,588	829	52	222	52		372		53	
Mount Mary College	M		X	X	1,862	43	1,385	2	104	51		220		45	
Nashotah House	P		X	X	-	-	2	4	7	86			4		1
Northland College	B		X	X	677	282	378	24	82	55		132			
Ripon College	B		X		1,057	421	636	22	36	52		187			
Sacred Heart School of Theology	P		X	X	120	-	-	23	31	50			12	2	
Saint Francis Seminary	P			X	100	-	-	5	20	61			5	8	
St. Norbert College	M		X	X	2,137	851	1,233	84	179	80		440		18	
Silver Lake College	M		X	X	853	177	415	9	138	42		119		56	
University of Wisconsin - Eau Claire	M	X			11,140	3,918	6,536	111	518	80	6	1,652		80	
University of Wisconsin - Green Bay	M	X			6,286	1,638	4,420	63	285	89		999		49	
University of Wisconsin - La Crosse	M	X			9,880	3,256	5,385	296	443	82		1,690		545	
University of Wisconsin - Madison	D	X			41,620	12,728	17,634	3,154	2,975	94		6,477	654	1,666	654
University of Wisconsin - Milwaukee	D	X			29,215	8,830	10,026	292	1,399	87		3,612		1,237	115
University of Wisconsin - Oshkosh	M	X			12,753	4,027	7,366	128	536	82		1,787		264	
University of Wisconsin - Parkside	M	X			5,167	2,270	2,775	52	191	75		656		36	
University of Wisconsin - Platteville	M	X			7,512	4,232	2,380	75	356	60		956		200	
University of Wisconsin - River Falls	M	X			6,555	1,980	4,150	7	363	82		1,079		160	
University of Wisconsin - Stevens Point	M	X			9,163	3,709	5,008	184	439	79		1,702		131	3
University of Wisconsin - Stout	M	X			8,839	3,098	4,671	88	397	76		1,208		268	
University of Wisconsin - Superior	M	X			2,689	1,028	1,420	134	170	82		447		100	
University of Wisconsin - Whitewater	M	X			10,962	4,907	4,714	109	502	65		1,635		424	
Viterbo University	M		X	X	2,944	607	1,486	29	168	45		376		507	
Wisconsin Lutheran College	B		X	X	753	263	490	16	75	74		153			
WYOMING															
University of Wyoming	D	X			13,203	3,928	3,785	438	720	90		1,706	116	439	59